# FINITE ELEMENT HANDBOOK

# OTHER McGRAW-HILL REFERENCE BOOKS OF INTEREST

## Handbooks

*American Institute of Physics* • AMERICAN INSTITUTE OF PHYSICS HANDBOOK
*Avallone and Baumeister* • MARKS' STANDARD HANDBOOK FOR MECHANICAL ENGINEERS
*Brady and Clauser* • MATERIALS HANDBOOK
*Callender* • TIME-SAVER STANDARDS FOR ARCHITECTURAL DESIGN DATA
*Chopey and Hicks* • HANDBOOK OF CHEMICAL ENGINEERING CALCULATIONS
*Condon and Odishaw* • HANDBOOK OF PHYSICS
*Croft, Watt, and Summers* • AMERICAN ELECTRICIANS' HANDBOOK
*Dean* • LANGE'S HANDBOOK OF CHEMISTRY
*Fink and Beaty* • STANDARD HANDBOOK FOR ELECTRICAL ENGINEERS
*Fink and Christiansen* • ELECTRONICS ENGINEERS' HANDBOOK
*Gaylord and Gaylord* • STRUCTURAL ENGINEERING HANDBOOK
*Harris and Crede* • SHOCK AND VIBRATION HANDBOOK
*Hopp and Hennig* • HANDBOOK OF APPLIED CHEMISTRY
*Juran* • QUALITY CONTROL HANDBOOK
*Maynard* • INDUSTRIAL ENGINEERING HANDBOOK
*Merritt* • STANDARD HANDBOOK FOR CIVIL ENGINEERS
*Perry* • ENGINEERING MANUAL
*Perry and Green* • PERRY'S CHEMICAL ENGINEERS' HANDBOOK
*Rohsenow and Hartnett* • HANDBOOK OF HEAT TRANSFER FUNDAMENTALS
*Rohsenow and Hartnett* • HANDBOOK OF HEAT TRANSFER APPLICATIONS
*Rosaler and Rice* • STANDARD HANDBOOK OF PLANT ENGINEERING
*Seidman and Mahrous* • HANDBOOK OF ELECTRIC POWER CALCULATIONS
*Shigley and Mischke* • STANDARD HANDBOOK OF MACHINE DESIGN
*Tuma* • ENGINEERING MATHEMATICS HANDBOOK
*Tuma* • HANDBOOK OF PHYSICAL CALCULATIONS
*Tuma* • TECHNOLOGY MATHEMATICS HANDBOOK

## Encyclopedias

CONCISE ENCYCLOPEDIA OF SCIENCE AND TECHNOLOGY
ENCYCLOPEDIA OF ELECTRONICS AND COMPUTERS
ENCYCLOPEDIA OF ENERGY
ENCYCLOPEDIA OF ENGINEERING
ENCYCLOPEDIA OF PHYSICS

## Dictionaries

DICTIONARY OF SCIENTIFIC AND TECHNICAL TERMS
DICTIONARY OF MECHANICAL AND DESIGN ENGINEERING
DICTIONARY OF COMPUTERS

# FINITE ELEMENT HANDBOOK

**H. KARDESTUNCER**  *Editor-in-Chief*

**D. H. NORRIE**  *Project Editor*

*Part Editors*

F. BREZZI
S. N. ATLURI
D. H. NORRIE
W. D. PILKEY

*Honorary Editors*

J. H. ARGYRIS
J. T. ODEN
O. C. ZIENKIEWICZ

*Editorial Advisory Board*

| | | | |
|---|---|---|---|
| J. H. ARGYRIS | L. COLLATZ | J. NITSCHE | T. H. H. PIAN |
| I. BABUSKA | B. A. FINLAYSON | W. OLSZAK | G. STRANG |
| K. I. BABENKO | R. H. GALLAGHER | A. PHILLIPS | K. WASHIZU |
| P. G. CIARLET | | | J. R. WHITEMAN |

*Editorial Secretary*

Dr. A. E. KARDESTUNCER

McGRAW-HILL BOOK COMPANY

New York  St. Louis  San Francisco  Auckland  Bogotá
Hamburg  London  Madrid  Mexico  Milan
Montreal  New Delhi  Panama
Paris  São Paulo  Singapore
Sydney  Tokyo  Toronto

**Library of Congress Cataloging-in-Publication Data**

Finite element handbook.

  Includes bibliographies and index.
  1. Finite element method.   I. Kardestuncer,
Hayrettin.   II. Norrie, Douglas H.   III. Brezzi, F.
TA347.F5F578   1987        620′.001′515353        86-3051
ISBN 0-07-033305-X

1234567890   DOCDOC   893210987

ISBN 0-07-033305-X

*The editors for this book were Harold B. Crawford, Susan Thomas,*
*and Nancy Warren; the designers were Mark E. Safran*
*and Naomi Auerbach; the production supervisors were*
*Sara L. Fliess and Teresa F. Leaden. It was set in Times Roman*
*by J. W. Arrowsmith, Ltd.*

*Printed and bound by R. R. Donnelley & Sons Company.*

# CONTENTS

CONTENTS

# LIST OF CONTRIBUTORS

**Abel, J. F.** Professor of Civil Engineering, Department of Structural Engineering and Program of Computer Graphics, Cornell University, Ithaca, New York
(PART 4)   CHAPTER 4: *4.3 Interactive Computer Graphics for CAD/CAM*

**Akay, H. U.** Professor of Mechanical Engineering, Purdue University, School of Engineering and Technology at Indianapolis, Indianapolis, Indiana
(PART 3)   CHAPTER 4: *4.6 Transonic Flow and Shock Waves: Combined Shock Capturing and Shock Fitting*

**Allik, H.** BBN Laboratories Incorporated, New London, Connecticut
(PART 4)   CHAPTER 2: *2.3 Static Condensation and Substructuring*

**Astley, R. J.** Senior Lecturer in Mechanical Engineering, University of Canterbury, Christchurch, New Zealand
(PART 3)   CHAPTER 7: *7.4 Acoustics*

**Atluri, S. N.** Regents' Professor of Mechanics and Director, Center for the Advancement of Computational Mechanics, Georgia Institute of Technology, Atlanta, Georgia
(PART 2)   CHAPTER 2: *2.2 Properties of Materials*
Editor of PART 2, Editor of CHAPTERS 1, 2, and 6 in PART 2

**Baker, A. J.** Professor, Department of Engineering Sciences and Mechanics, The University of Tennessee, Knoxville, Tennessee
(PART 3)   CHAPTER 2: *2.8 Boundary-Layer Turbulent Flow*

**Bathe, K. J.** Professor, Department of Mechanical Engineering, Massachusetts Institute of Technology, Cambridge, Massachusetts
(PART 2)   CHAPTER 4: *4.7 Plate-Bending Elements*

**Bettess, P.** Professor, School of Marine Technology, University of Newcastle upon Tyne, Newcastle upon Tyne, England
(PART 3)   CHAPTER 2: *2.5 Coastal and Estuary Flow*

**Bramble, J. H.** Professor, Department of Mathematics, Cornell University, Ithaca, New York
(PART 1)   CHAPTER 5: *Finite-Element Methods for Elliptic Boundary-Value and Eigenvalue Problems*

**Brebbia, C.** Computational Mechanics Institute and University of Southampton, Southampton, England
(PART 3)   CHAPTER 5: *Coupled Systems*

**Brezzi, F.** Professor, Dipartimento di Meccanica Strutturale dell'Università & Istituto di Analisi Numerica del C.N.R., Pavia, Italy
(PART 1)   CHAPTER 1: *Functional Analysis*   CHAPTER 2: *Functional Spaces*   CHAPTER 3: *Partial Differential Equations*
Editor of PART 1

**Bristeau, M. O.** INRIA, Le Chesnay, France
(PART 3)  CHAPTER 4: *4.3 Transonic Flow and Shock Waves: Least-Squares and Conjugate-Gradient Methods*

**Byrne, P. M.** Professor, Department of Civil Engineering, University of British Columbia, Vancouver, British Columbia
(PART 3)  CHAPTER 3: *3.1 Static Finite-Element Analysis of Soil-Structure Systems*

**Chao, E. Y.** Director, Orthopedic Biomechanics Laboratory, Mayo Clinic, Rochester, Minnesota
(PART 3)  CHAPTER 6: *6.2 Orthopedic and Joint Mechanics*

**Chari, M. V. K.** Manager, Electromagnetics Program, Electromechanics Branch, Corporate Research and Development, General Electric Company, Schenectady, New York
(PART 3)  CHAPTER 7: *7.5 Finite Elements for Electric and Magnetic Fields*

**Chung, T. J.** Department of Mechanical Engineering, The University of Alabama, Huntsville, Alabama
(PART 3)  CHAPTER 4: *Introduction, 4.2 Compressible Viscous Flows, 4.4 Transonic Flow and Shock Waves: Discontinuous Functions*
Editor of CHAPTER 4 in PART 3

**Ciarlet, P. G.** Professor, Analyse Numérique, Université Pierre et Marie Curie, Paris, France
(PART 1)  CHAPTER 4: *Finite-Element Approximation Theory*

**Cook, R. D.** Professor, Department of Engineering Mechanics, University of Wisconsin, Madison, Wisconsin
(PART 2)  CHAPTER 4: *4.1 Theory and General Remarks, 4.2 Isoparametric Families of Elements*
Editor of CHAPTER 4 in PART 2

**Craig, R. G.** Chairman, Department of Biomaterials, School of Dentistry, University of Michigan, Ann Arbor, Michigan
(PART 3)  CHAPTER 6: *6.3 Dental Mechanics*

**Cullen, M. J. P.** Meteorological Office, Bracknell, Berkshire, England
(PART 3)  CHAPTER 4: *4.8 Convection and Diffusion in the Atmosphere*

**Dawe, D. J.** Reader, Department of Civil Engineering, The University of Birmingham, Birmingham, England
(PART 2)  CHAPTER 4: *4.4 Curved-Beam and Arch Elements, 4.5 Circular Cylindrical Shell Elements*

**Dietrich, D.** Manager of Professional Support, Swanson Analysis, Houston, Pennsylvania
(PART 4)  CHAPTER 3: *3.1 Modeling in Structural Mechanics*

**Dill, E. H.** Professor, Dean of Engineering, Rutgers University, Piscataway, New Jersey
(PART 2)  CHAPTER 2: *2.1 Nonlinear Mechanics of Materials*

**Eberle, A.** Dr.-Ing., Theoretical Aerodynamics, Messerschmitt-Bölkow-Blohm, Munich, West Germany
(PART 3)  CHAPTER 4: *4.5 Transonic Flow and Shock Waves: Artificial Compressibility and Successive-Line Overrelaxation*

**Ecer, A.** Professor of Mechanical Engineering, Purdue University School of Engineering and Technology at Indianapolis, Indianapolis, Indiana
(PART 3)  CHAPTER 4: *4.6 Transonic Flow and Shock Waves: Combined Shock Capturing and Shock Fitting*

**Eversman, W.**   Department of Mechanical and Aerospace Engineering, University of Missouri, Rolla, Missouri
(PART 3)   CHAPTER 7: *7.4 Acoustics*

**Everstine, G. C.**   Numerical Mechanics Division, David Taylor Naval Ship Research and Development Center, Bethesda, Maryland
(PART 4)   CHAPTER 3: *3.2 Grid-Point Sequencing, 3.3 Symmetry*

**Finlayson, B. A.**   Professor, Chemical Engineering Department, University of Washington, Seattle, Washington
(PART 2)   CHAPTER 1: *1.3 Variational Principles in Fluid Mechanics and Heat Transfer*   CHAPTER 6: *6.2 Collocation Finite-Element Method*   (PART 3)   CHAPTER 2: *2.6 Convection and Dispersion*   CHAPTER 7: *7.1 Chemical Reactions*

**Finn, W. D. L.**   Professor of Civil Engineering, Soil Dynamics Group, University of British Columbia, Vancouver, British Columbia
(PART 3)   CHAPTER 3: *Introduction, 3.2 Dynamic-Response Analysis of Soil Structures*
Editor of CHAPTER 3 in PART 3

**Fulton, R. E.**   Professor of Mechanical Engineering, Georgia Institute of Technology, Atlanta, Georgia
(PART 4)   CHAPTER 4: *4.1 Modern Computing Systems, 4.2 Algorithms and Software Development*

**Gallagher, R. H.**   Professor, Vice President, and Dean of Faculty, Worcester Polytechnic Institute, Worcester, Massachusetts
(PART 2)   CHAPTER 7: *Finite-element Method for Instability Analysis*

**Geradin, M.**   Professor, Institut de Mécanique, Université de Liège, Liège, Belgium
(PART 4)   CHAPTER 1: *1.1 Solution Algorithms for Static and Eigenvalue Problems, 1.3 Solving Systems of Nonlinear Equations, 1.4 Time Integration of Dynamic Equations*

**Gilardi, G.**   Dipartimento di Matematica, Università di Pavia, Pavia, Italy
(PART 1)   CHAPTER 1: *Functional Analysis*   CHAPTER 2: *Functional Spaces*   CHAPTER 3: *Partial Differential Equations*

**Glowinski, R.**   Laboratoire d'Analyse Numérique, Université Pierre et Marie Curie, Paris, France; Department of Mathematics, University of Houston, Houston, Texas
(PART 1)   CHAPTER 7: *Finite-Element Methods for Variational Inequalities*   (PART 3)   CHAPTER 4: *4.3 Transonic Flow and Shock Waves: Least-Squares and Conjugate-Gradient Methods*

**Gould, P. L.**   Harold D. Jolley Professor, Department of Civil Engineering, Washington University, St. Louis, Missouri
(PART 2)   CHAPTER 4: *4.6 Shells of Revolution*

**Gupta, R. P.**   National Research Council, Ottawa, Ontario
(PART 3)   CHAPTER 7: *7.3 Plasmas*

**Habashi, W. G.**   Professor, Department of Mechanical Engineering, Concordia University, Montreal, Quebec
(PART 3)   CHAPTER 2: *2.7 Analysis and Design of Subsonic and Supersonic Turbomachinery*   CHAPTER 4: *4.1 Compressible Inviscid Flows, 4.7 Transonic Shock Waves: Mixed-Type Algorithms*

**Hafez, M. M.**   Professor, Department of Mechanical Engineering, University of California, Davis, California
(PART 3)   CHAPTER 2: *2.7 Analysis and Design of Subsonic and Supersonic Turbo-*

*machinery* CHAPTER 4: *4.1 Compressible Inviscid Flows, 4.7 Transonic Shock Waves: Mixed-Type Algorithms*

**Hirai, I.** Department of Civil Engineering, Faculty of Engineering Kumamoto University, Kumamoto, Japan
(PART 4) CHAPTER 2: *2.1 Reanalysis, 2.2 Modal Synthesis*

**Hogge, M.** Associate Professor, Institut de Mécanique, Université de Liège, Liège, Belgium
(PART 4) CHAPTER 1: *1.3 Solving Systems of Nonlinear Equations, 1.4 Time Integration of Dynamic Equations*

**Hourani, M. C.** Department of Civil Engineering, Washington University, St. Louis, Missouri
(PART 2) CHAPTER 4: *4.6 Shells of Revolution*

**Hutton, A. G.** Central Electricity Generating Board, Berkeley Nuclear Laboratories, Berkeley, Gloucester, England
(PART 3) CHAPTER 2: *2.9 Turbulent Flow*

**Jay, A.** Pratt & Whitney, East Hartford, Connecticut
(PART 4) CHAPTER 3: *Introduction*
Editor of CHAPTER 3 in PART 4

**Kardestuncer, H.** School of Engineering, The University of Connecticut, Storrs, Connecticut
(PART 2) CHAPTER 3: *Basic Concepts of the Finite-Element Method* CHAPTER 4: *4.8 General Shell Elements* (PART 3) CHAPTER 1: *Introduction, 1.1 Classification of Problems in Solid Mechanics, 1.2 Finite-Element Analysis of Structures (1D Elements), 1.3 Finite-Element Analysis of 2D Solids, 1.4 Finite-Element Analysis of 3D Solids*
EDITOR IN CHIEF, Editor of CHAPTER 1 in PART 3

**Kawahara, M.** Department of Civil Engineering, Chuo University, Tokyo, Japan
(PART 3) CHAPTER 2: *2.4 Lake and Harbor Motion*

**Khalil, T.** Biomedical Sciences Department, General Motors Research Laboratories, Warren, Michigan
(PART 3) CHAPTER 6: *6.1 Crash-Injury Studies*

**Kikuchi, N.** Professor, Department of Mechanical Engineering, University of Michigan, Ann Arbor, Michigan
(PART 2) CHAPTER 9: *9.4 Problems with Constraints*

**King, A. I.** Professor and Director, Bioengineering Center, Wayne State University, Detroit, Michigan
(PART 3) CHAPTER 6: *6.1 Crash-Injury Studies*

**Kitis, L.** Department of Mechanical Engineering and Aerospace Sciences, University of Central Florida, Orlando, Florida
(PART 4) CHAPTER 2: *2.1 Reanalysis, 2.2 Modal Synthesis*

**Kotiuga, P. L.** Staff Engineer, Department of Aerodynamics, Pratt & Whitney Canada, Ltd., Longueuil, Quebec
(PART 3) CHAPTER 2: *2.7 Analysis and Design of Subsonic and Supersonic Turbomachinery*

**Lee, G. C.** Professor and Dean, Faculty of Engineering and Applied Sciences, State University of New York at Buffalo, New York
(PART 3) CHAPTER 6: *6.5 Lung-Parenchyma Analysis*

**Lee, J. K.**   Professor, Department of Engineering Mechanics, The Ohio State University, Columbus, Ohio
(PART 2)   CHAPTER 9: *9.5 Hybrid Finite-Element Methods*

**Levy, A.**   Staff Scientist, Grumman Corporate Research Center, Bethpage, New York
(PART 3)   CHAPTER 1: *1.8 Finite-Element Analysis of High-Temperature Inelastic Solids*   (PART 4)   CHAPTER 3: *3.1 Modeling in Structural Mechanics*

**Macagno, E. O.**   Professor of Fluid Mechanics, Institute of Hydraulic Research, University of Iowa, Iowa City, Iowa
(PART 3)   CHAPTER 6: *6.6 Intestinal Flow*

**Medwell, J. O.**   Department of Mechanical Engineering, University College of Swansea, Swansea, Wales
(PART 3)   CHAPTER 2: *2.11 Hydrodynamic Lubrication*

**Melosh, R. J.**   Department of Civil Engineering, Duke University, Durham, North Carolina
(PART 3)   CHAPTER 8: *8.1 Solution Errors in Finite-Element Analysis, 8.2 Principles for Design of Finite-Element Meshes*
Editor of CHAPTER 8 and Principal Author of Section 8.2 in PART 3

**Morgan, K.**   University College of Swansea, University of Wales, Swansea, Wales
(PART 3)   CHAPTER 2: *2.10 Turbulent Heat Transfer*

**Nagtegaal, J. C.**   MARC Analysis Research Corporation, Palo Alto, California
(PART 3)   CHAPTER 1: *1.6 Finite-Element Analysis of Fracture-Mechanics Problems*

**Nakazawa, S.**   MARC Analysis Research Corporation, Palo Alto, California
(PART 3)   CHAPTER 2: *2.3 Generalized Newtonian Flows*

**Noor, A. K.**   Professor, NASA Langley Research Center, The George Washington University, Hampton, Virginia
(PART 4)   CHAPTER 4: *4.1 Modern Computing Systems, 4.2 Algorithms and Software Development*   CHAPTER 5: *Survey of Some Finite-Element Software Systems*

**Norrie, D. H.**   Professor, Department of Mechanical Engineering, The University of Calgary, Calgary, Alberta
(PART 3)   CHAPTER 2: *2.1 Potential Flow*   CHAPTER 7: *Introduction*
PROJECT EDITOR, Editor of PART 3, Editor of CHAPTERS 1 and 7 in PART 3.

**Oden, J. T.**   Carol and Henry Groppe Professor of Engineering, Texas Institute for Computational Mechanics, University of Texas, Austin, Texas
(PART 2)   CHAPTER 9: *9.1 Introduction, 9.3 Some $L^{\infty}$-Estimates for Finite-Element Approximations in Plane Elasticity, 9.4 Problems with Constraints*
Editor of CHAPTER 9 in PART 2

**Olson, M. D.**   Professor, Department of Civil Engineering, University of British Columbia, Vancouver, British Columbia
(PART 3)   CHAPTER 2: *2.2 Laminar Viscous Flow*

**Palazzolo, A.**   Assistant Professor, Department of Mechanical Engineering, Texas A & M University, College Station, Texas
(PART 4)   CHAPTER 1: *1.2 Eigensolution Extraction Methods*

**Pao, Y. C.**   Professor of Engineering Mechanics, University of Nebraska, Lincoln, Nebraska
(PART 3)   CHAPTER 6: *Introduction, 6.4 Cardiomechanical Studies*
Editor of CHAPTER 6 in PART 3

**Peano, A. G.**   Head, Mathematical Modeling Department, Istituto Sperimentale di Modelli e Strutture (ISMES), Bergamo, Italy
(PART 2)   CHAPTER 6: *6.4 Hierarchic Finite Elements*   (PART 3)   (CHAPTER 1: *1.5 h- and p-Version of FEM Models in Solids*

**Periaux, J.**   Avions Marcel Dassault, St. Cloud, France
(PART 3)   CHAPTER 4: *4.3 Transonic Flow and Shock Waves: Least-Squares and Conjugate-Gradient Methods*

**Perrier, P.**   Avions Marcel Dassault, St. Cloud, France
(PART 3)   CHAPTER 4: *4.3 Transonic Flow and Shock Waves: Least-Squares and Conjugate-Gradient Methods*

**Pian, T. H. H.**   Professor, Department of Aeronautics and Astronautics, Massachusetts Institute, of Technology, Cambridge, Massachusetts
(PART 2)   CHAPTER 5: *Mixed and Hybrid Finite-Element Methods*

**Pifko, A. B.**   Research Department, Grumman Aerospace Corporation, Bethpage, New York
Editor of CHAPTER 4 in PART 4

**Pilkey, W. D.**   Frederick Tracy Morse Professor, Department of Mechanical and Aerospace Engineering School of Engineering and Applied Science, University of Virginia, Charlottesville, Virginia
(PART 4)   CHAPTER 1: *Introduction, 1.2 Eigensolution Extraction Methods*   CHAPTER 2: *2.1 Reanalysis, 2.2 Modal Synthesis*
Editor of PART 4, Editor of CHAPTERS 1 and 2 in PART 4

**Pinder, G. F.**   Professor and Chairman, Department of Civil Engineering and Operations Research, School of Engineering/Applied Science, Princeton University, Princeton, New Jersey
(PART 3)   CHAPTER 3: *3.3 Porous Media*

**Pironneau, O.**   Laboratoire d'Analyse Numérique, Université Pierre et Marie Curie, Paris, France
(PART 3)   CHAPTER 4: *4.3 Transonic Flow and Shock Waves: Least-Squares and Conjugate-Gradient Methods*

**Pittman, J. F. T.**   Department of Chemical Engineering, University College of Swansea, University of Wales, Swansea, Wales
(PART 3)   CHAPTER 2: *2.3 Generalized Newtonian Flows*

**Poirier, G.**   Avions Marcel Dassault, St. Cloud, France
(PART 3)   CHAPTER 4: *4.3 Transonic Flow and Shock Waves: Least-Squares and Conjugate-Gradient Methods*

**Reddy, J. N.**   Clifton C. Garvin Professor, Engineering Science and Mechanics Department, Virginia Polytechnic Institute and State University, Blacksburg, Virginia
(PART 2)   CHAPTER 6: *6.5 The Penalty–Finite-Element Method*   CHAPTER 9: *9.2 Standard Results for Linear-Elliptic Boundary-Value Problems*

**Reissner, E.**   Professor Emeritus, Department of Applied Mechanics and Engineering Sciences, University of California at San Diego, La Jolla, California
(PART 2)   CHAPTER 1: *1.1 Variational Principles in Elasticity*

**Robert, G.**   L.T.A.S., Institut de Mécanique, Université de Liège, Liège, Belgium
(PART 4)   CHAPTER 1: *1.4 Time Integration of Dynamic Equations*

**Schmidt, F. A. R.**   Institut für Kernenergetik, Universtät Stuttgart, Stuttgart, West Germany
(PART 3)   CHAPTER 7: *7.2 Neutron Flux*

**Schulz, J. C.**   Research Department, Naval Weapons Center, China Lake, California
(PART 3)   CHAPTER 1: *1.7 Finite-Element Analysis of Projectile Impact Response*

**Shephard, M. S.**   Professor, Associate Director, Center for Interactive Computer Graphics, Rensselaer Polytechnic Institute, Troy, New York
(PART 4)   CHAPTER 3: *3.4 Automatic Mesh Generation and Adaptive Analysis*   CHAPTER 4: *4.3 Interactive Computer Graphics for CAD/CAM*

**Skalak, R.**   Director, Bioengineering Institute, Department of Civil Engineering and Engineering Mechanics, Columbia University, New York, New York
(PART 3)   CHAPTER 6: *6.7 Blood Flow*

**Smith, R. M.**   Central Electricity Generating Board, Berkeley Nuclear Laboratories, Berkeley, Gloucestershire, England
(PART 3)   CHAPTER 2: *2.9 Turbulent Flow*

**Storaasli, O. O.**   Structures and Dynamics Division, NASA Langley Research Center, Hampton, Virginia
(PART 4)   CHAPTER 4: *4.1 Modern Computing Systems, 4.2 Algorithms and Software Development*

**Stronge, W. J.**   Lecturer, Engineering Department, University of Cambridge, Cambridge, England
(PART 3)   CHAPTER 1: *1.7 Finite-Element Analysis of Projectile Impact Response*

**Surana, K. S.**   Associate Professor, Department of Mechanical Engineering, The University of Kansas, Lawrence, Kansas
(PART 2)   CHAPTER 4: *4.3 Isoparametric Finite Elements*

**Szabo, B. A.**   Professor, Albert P. and Blanche Y. Greensfelder Professor of Mechanics, Director, Center for Computational Mechanics, Washington University, St. Louis, Missouri
(PART 2)   CHAPTER 6: *6.4 Hierarchic Finite Elements*   (PART 3)   CHAPTER 1: *1.5 h- and p-Version of FEM Models in Solids*

**Taylor, C.**   Professor, University College of Swansea, University of Wales, Swansea, Wales
(PART 3)   CHAPTER 2: *Introduction, 2.10 Turbulent Heat Transfer*
Editor of CHAPTER 2 in PART 3

**Thomas, C. E.**   University College of Swansea, University of Wales, Swansea, Wales
(PART 3)   CHAPTER 2: *2.10 Turbulent Heat Transfer*

**Thomée, V.**   Professor, Department of Mathematics, Chalmers University of Technology, Göteborg, Sweden
(PART 1)   CHAPTER 6: *Finite-Element Methods for Time-Dependent Problems*

**Tong, P.**   Chief, Structures and Dynamics Division, Transportation Systems Center, U.S. Department of Transportation, Cambridge, Massachusetts
(PART 2)   CHAPTER 5: *Mixed and Hybrid Finite-Element Methods*

**Utku, S.**   Professor of Civil Engineering and Professor of Computer Science, Duke University, Durham, North Carolina
(PART 3)   CHAPTER 8: *8.1 Solution Errors in Finite-Element Analysis, 8.2 Principles for Design of Finite-Element Meshes*
Editor of CHAPTER 8 and Principal Author of Section 8.1 in PART 3

**Wachspress, E. L.**   Professor, Department of Mathematics, The University of Tennessee, Knoxville, Tennessee
(PART 2)   CHAPTER 6: *6.3 Rational Finite Elements*

**Whiteman, J. R.**   Professor, Institute of Computational Mathematics, Brunel University, Uxbridge, Middlesex, England
(PART 2)   CHAPTER 6: *6.1 Finite-Element Method with Singularities*

**Wood, W. L.**   Department of Mathematics, University of Reading, Reading, England
(PART 2)   CHAPTER 8: *Transient Response Analysis*

**Zienkiewicz, O. C.**   Director, Institute for Numerical Methods in Engineering, University College of Swansea, University of Wales, Swansea, Wales
(PART 2)   CHAPTER 8: *Transient Response Analysis*

NOTE: The above listing includes all contributions—editorial, sole authorship, and joint authorship. The Contents list shows authorship of both individual and collaborative contributions under their respective PART, CHAPTER, or Section.

# PREFACE

The finite element method is one of the most important developments in computational methods to occur in this century. Within only a few decades, this technique has evolved from one with initial applications in structural engineering to a widely utilized and richly varied computational approach for many scientific and technological areas. By the early 1980s, there were over 20,000 finite-element users worldwide, who were estimated to spend about $500 million annually on finite-element analysis. Since that time, there has been continuing rapid expansion in both the number of users and the range of applications.

The purpose of this Handbook is to present the underlying mathematical principles, the fundamental formulations, and both commonly used and specialized applications of the finite-element method within a single volume. It represents the most comprehensive survey of finite-element theory and practice available at the date of publication.

There are four separate but interrelated parts to the *Finite Element Handbook*. The first part provides the modern mathematical background to the finite-element method. In the second part, the fundamentals of the method are explored, leading on to the third and largest part dealing with applications. The fourth part considers computational aspects of the method. The chapters within each part and the sections within each chapter were contributed by 96 invited authors from academia and industry, selected on the basis of their notable contributions to the field. The names and affiliations of the authors and their respective contributions are given (in alphabetical order by name) in the List of Contributors.

Part 1 of the Handbook begins by considering functional analysis, functional spaces, and partial differential equations, to establish the mathematical foundations for finite-element methods. Then follows the concise and elegant theory for affine-equivalent and almost-affine-equivalent finite elements. This theory has proved to be a highly valuable tool for numerical analysis in such areas as isoparametric and curved elements, singular and rational elements, composite elements, numerical integration, and nonconforming methods. The succeeding chapters deal with the finite-element methods for elliptic boundary-value and eigenvalue problems and for time-dependent problems. In the last chapter, finite-element methods for variational inequalities are examined.

In Part 2, variational principles and constitutive equations are first reviewed. Then, the fundamental steps in the variational finite-element method are presented—from initial discretization and choice of element through solution of the system matrix equation. This is followed by detailed treatments of finite elements based on displacement fields and by coverage of mixed and hybrid finite-element methods. Discussion then moves through other types of finite element method to a review of finite-element methods for instability analysis and transient-response analysis. The final chapter brings together important information on error estimates, convergence ratios, and stability.

Part 3 contains a wide-ranging consideration of finite-element applications within solid mechanics, fluid mechanics, geomechanics, aeromechanics, biomechanics, chemical reactions, nuclear reactors, plasmas, acoustics, and electromagnetics. Coupled systems variously involving fluids, structures, and soils are also studied. The last and very important chapter assesses errors in finite-element computation and considers the principles for selecting a mesh-design strategy.

Part 4 begins by reviewing techniques for solving the system matrix equations of finite-element analysis, and then considers reanalysis, nodal synthesis, static condensation, and substructuring. Next follow topics in modeling, and pre- and postprocessing. New directions in computer technology in the recent past and near future are then assessed and related to the anticipated development of finite-element hardware and software systems. The final chapter presents an overview of the current capabilities of finite-element software packages.

It is anticipated that the *Finite Element Handbook* will become a valuable reference and sourcebook for many occupational groups within science and technology. The practicing professional engineer will be able to turn to the Handbook for guidance and instruction on questions such as the following:

• Which problems can finite elements be used for?

• What formulation is suited to a particular type of problem?

• Which algorithm should be used for the system matrix equations?

• What kind of element is best suited for a given problem?

• What are the principles of good mesh design?

• To what extent are pre- and postprocessing desirable?

• Are there existing software packages which could satisfy a particular need?

Researchers from academia, industry, and government and those whose interests are more fundamental than applied, will find the Handbook a most useful sourcebook, with its wide coverage of theory as well as practice and with its extensive lists of references at the end of each chapter. The mathematical foundations of the finite-element method in the earlier chapters will be of interest to applied mathematicians and other theoretically oriented researchers. This Handbook not only brings together in one volume essential information on the finite-element method from many existing sources—texts, monographs, theses, research reports and papers, proceedings, and journal articles—but also includes original material not previously available.

While every care has been taken to eliminate errors in this work, it is inevitable that some will remain. It would be much appreciated if any errors noted could be communicated to the publisher, so that these can be removed in later printings. Address correspondence to Reprint Editor, Professional and Reference Division.

The publication of this volume is the culmination of a cooperative effort involving more than a hundred people from many places around the world. It is our sincere hope that this work will not only be of value to those whose interests lie within the field of finite elements but will also contribute, at least in some measure, to the welfare of the global human family.

D. H. NORRIE
*Project Editor*

# ACKNOWLEDGMENTS

This volume represents a monumental undertaking by a very large number of researchers and practitioners in Finite Elements and allied areas. The original objective was concisely to present the fundamentals of the finite element method, together with guidelines for its multifarious applications suitable for the practicing engineer or scientist. Given the nature of the task, it may not have been realistic to anticipate full achievement of this objective, but it is nonetheless true that here is a most valuable source and reference book in this ever-broadening subject. As the extensive lists of references indicate, the material has been brought together from many places, including texts, monographs, published and unpublished reports, corporate technical papers, theses, and conference proceedings. In addition, there is original material presented here which has not previously appeared in print or in the public domain. The total number of separate authors involved is 96, and to this number must be added all those who assisted in advisory, review, or publishing capacities. During all stages of preparation, there have been revisions incorporated wherever possible to update the material presented.

While it is impractical to list all of those whose work has made this volume possible, at least an attempt will be made here to acknowledge those whose contributions have been especially significant. First of all, there are the authors themselves, whose names are given in the List of Contributors on page xiii. It is their efforts, given unstintingly and under often difficult deadlines, which form the basis for the value of this work. The 14-member Editorial Advisory Board listed on the title page provided invaluable advice on the form and scope of the Handbook, as did the Honorary Editors, J. H. Argyris, J. T. Oden and O. C. Zienkiewicz. The Part Editors, F. Brezzi, S. N. Atluri, D. H. Norrie, W. D. Pilkey, carried the burden of integrating the source information within their Parts of the Handbook into a cohesive whole—a demanding task which extended over more than six years. Over this long period, Dr. Aino Kardestuncer played an essential organizational role as Editorial Secretary for the project. At the McGraw-Hill Book Company, Harold Crawford, as Editor-in-Chief of Technical Books has been responsible for overseeing this project from its inception. It is due to his foresight that this project was not only undertaken but carried through to successful completion. The Editing Supervisor, Susan Thomas, a true professional of her craft, directed much of the lengthy process by which the manuscript became transformed into a published volume. A debt is also owed to McGraw-Hill's highly competent staff in art, design, production, copy-editing, and related areas. Acknowledgment must be made of the high standards of the typesetters for the project: Arrowsmith of Bristol, England.

As Project Editor, it is my privilege to pay tribute to Dr. Hayrettin (Harry) Kardestuncer, the Editor in Chief whose vision brought this Handbook into existence. His determination and unsparing effort carried the project from conception to final manuscript. Sadly, illness prevented his participation in the concluding phase of publication, but the *Finite Element Handbook* has nonetheless been brought to completion in the form that he had envisaged. This reference work will stand in recognition of his notable contribution to the field. Those of us who worked with him closely on this project will treasure the remembrance of a gentleman and a scholar.

Douglas H. Norrie
*University of Calgary*

# FEM MATHEMATICS

# CHAPTER 1
# FUNCTIONAL ANALYSIS

## 1.1 INTRODUCTION

In this chapter we review some basic definitions and theorems of functional analysis. In particular, we first deal with linear spaces and then with Banach and Hilbert spaces. We present, at the same time, both the finite- and the infinite-dimensional cases to establish the mathematical foundation for the finite-element methods. The different physical problems which are examined elsewhere in this book are described by one or more differential equations whose solution lies in some functional space of infinite dimension. Yet, the finite-element approximation will have a solution described by means of a finite number of parameters, and hence will belong to a finite-dimensional space.

Further information on the topics considered in this chapter will be found in the sources listed in Sec. 1.5.

## 1.2 LINEAR SPACES

### 1.2A Definition and Basic Properties

**DEFINITION 1.1** A real linear space, or, simply, a linear space, consists of a set $V$ and two operations: $(u, v) \to u + v$ from $V \times V$ into $V$, and $(\alpha, v) \to \alpha v$ from $\mathbb{R} \times V$ into $V$, such that the following properties hold:

For every $u, v, w \in V$ and $\alpha, \beta \in \mathbb{R}$

$$(u+v)+w = u+(v+w) \qquad u+v = v+u$$

$$(\alpha+\beta)v = \alpha v + \beta v \qquad \alpha(u+v) = \alpha u + \alpha v \tag{1.1}$$

$$(\alpha\beta)v = \alpha(\beta v) \qquad 1v = v$$

There exists a unique element in $V$, denoted by 0, such that

$$v+0 = v \qquad \forall v \in V \tag{1.2}$$

For every $v \in V$ there exists a unique element in $V$, denoted by $-v$, such that

$$v+(-v) = 0 \tag{1.3}$$

Elements of $V$ and $\mathbb{R}$ are called *vectors* and *scalars*, respectively. The zero scalar and the zero vector will not be distinguished by symbols. A linear space $V$ is called *trivial* or *nontrivial* according to whether $V = \{0\}$ or not.

By (1.1), $u+v+w$, $\alpha\beta v$, $\alpha\beta\gamma v$, etc., make sense. Moreover, we write $u-v$ instead of $u+(-v)$.

**PROPOSITION 1.1**   Let $V$ be a linear space. Then, for any $u, v \in V$ and $\alpha, \beta \in \mathbb{R}$:

$$0v = 0 \qquad \alpha 0 = 0 \qquad -(\alpha v) = (-\alpha)v = \alpha(-v) \qquad (-1)v = -v$$

$$(\alpha-\beta)v = \alpha v - \beta v \qquad \alpha(u-v) = \alpha u - \alpha v$$

$$\alpha v = 0 \qquad \text{implies} \qquad \alpha = 0 \quad \text{or} \quad v = 0$$

## 1.2B   Examples of Linear Spaces

**EXAMPLE 1.1**   $V = \mathbb{R}$ is a linear space with the usual sums and products.

**EXAMPLE 1.2**   If $V_1, \ldots, V_n$ are linear spaces, then $V_1 \times \cdots \times V_n$ is a linear space with

$$(u_1, \ldots, u_n)+(v_1, \ldots, v_n) = (u_1+v_1, \ldots, u_n+v_n)$$

$$\alpha(v_1, \ldots, v_n) = (\alpha v_1, \ldots, \alpha v_n)$$

In particular, $\mathbb{R}^n$ is a linear space.

**EXAMPLE 1.3**   If $\Omega$ is a nonempty set, the set $\mathscr{F}(\Omega)$ of all real functions defined in $\Omega$ is a linear space with

$$(u+v)(x) = u(x)+v(x) \qquad \forall x \in \Omega$$

$$(\alpha v)(x) = \alpha v(x) \qquad \forall x \in \Omega$$

## 1.2C   Subspaces

**DEFINITION 1.2**   Let $V$ be a linear space. A subset $V_0 \subset V$ is called a *linear subspace* or a *subspace*, if $V_0 \neq \varnothing$ and

$$u, v \in V_0 \text{ and } \alpha \in \mathbb{R} \Rightarrow u+v \text{ and } \alpha v \in V_0$$

**REMARK 1.1**   A subspace $V_0$ of a linear subspace $V$ is itself a linear space when we restrict sums and products to elements of $V_0$.

**DEFINITION 1.3**   Let $V$ be a linear space. If $\{v_i\}$ is a finite subset of $V$, a *linear combination of $v_i$'s* is a vector of the form $\Sigma \alpha_i v_i$ with any scalars $\alpha_i$'s. If $E$ is any nonempty subset of $V$, we set

$$\operatorname{span} E = \{\Sigma \alpha_i v_i \,;\, \alpha_i \in \mathbb{R}, \, v_i \in E\} \tag{1.4}$$

where $\Sigma$ means any finite sum.

Elements of span $E$ are thus all linear combinations of arbitrary finite subsets of $E$.

It is clear that span $E$ is a subspace of $V$, namely, the smallest subspace containing $E$. Thus, span $E = E$ if and only if (iff) $E$ is a subspace.

**DEFINITION 1.4**   Let $V$ be a linear space and $V_0$ be a subspace of $V$. We say that a nonempty set $E \subset V_0$ *generates* $V_0$ iff span $E = V_0$. A *generating set* is a set which generates $V$.

**PROPOSITION 1.2**   The intersection of (possibly infinitely many) subspaces of a linear space is a subspace.

Analogous results for unions are not true. Hence, we have:

**DEFINITION 1.5**   If $V_1, \ldots, V_n$ are subspaces of a linear space $V$, we set

$$V_1 + \cdots + V_n = \operatorname{span}(V_1 \cup \cdots \cup V_n)$$

Moreover, we say that $V_1 + \cdots + V_n$ is a *direct sum* of $V_i$'s iff $(V_1 + \cdots + V_k) \cap V_{k+1} = \{0\}$ for $k = 1, \ldots, n-1$.

To signify that the above sum is direct we write

$$V_1 \oplus \cdots \oplus V_n \quad \text{or} \quad \bigoplus_{k=1}^{n} V_k \quad \text{instead of} \quad V_1 + \cdots + V_n$$

**THEOREM 1.1**   Let $V_1, \ldots, V_n$ be subspaces of a linear space $V$. Then $V_1 + \cdots + V_n$ is a direct sum iff every $v \in V_1 + \cdots + V_n$ can be written in exactly one way in the form

$$v = v_1 + \cdots + v_n \quad \text{with} \quad v_k \in V_k \text{ for } k = 1, \ldots, n \tag{1.5}$$

**DEFINITION 1.6**   Let $V_0 = V_1 \oplus \cdots \oplus V_n$ be a direct sum of subspaces of a linear space $V$. Then for $v \in V_0$ we define

$$P_k(v) = v_k \quad \text{for } k = 1, \ldots, n \quad \text{iff (1.5) holds}$$

The maps $P_k : V_0 \to V_k (k = 1, \ldots, n)$ thus defined are called the *projections* associated with the decomposition of $V_0$ in the direct sum of the subspaces $V_k$'s.

**REMARK 1.2**   In general, a subspace $V_0$ can be written as a direct sum in several ways. For each such decomposition the corresponding projections are defined.

## 1.2D Examples of Subspaces

**EXAMPLE 1.4**  *Continuous functions.* If $\Omega$ is an open subset of $\mathbb{R}^n$, the subset of all $v \in \mathscr{F}(\Omega)$ (Example 1.3) which are continuous is a subspace of $\mathscr{F}(\Omega)$ and is denoted by $C^0(\Omega)$.

**EXAMPLE 1.5**  *Polynomials.* If $V = C^0(\Omega)$, we consider polynomials in $n$ variables as elements of $V$. To introduce notations we define multi-index, which will be used later:

A *multi-index* is any element $\alpha = (\alpha_1, \ldots, \alpha_n) \in \mathbb{N}^n$, and its length is defined by $|\alpha| = \Sigma \alpha_i$.
For $x \in \Omega$ and $\alpha \in \mathbb{N}^n$, we set $x^\alpha = x_1^{\alpha_1} x_2^{\alpha_2} \cdots x_n^{\alpha_n}$. $\hspace{2cm}$ (1.6)

We define the sets of polynomials in $\Omega$ and of polynomials of degree $\leq k$, where $k \in \mathbb{N}$, as follows:

$$P^{(n)}(\Omega) = \text{span}\, \{x^\alpha : \alpha \in \mathbb{N}^n\}$$
$$P_k^{(n)}(\Omega) = \text{span}\, \{x^\alpha : \alpha \in \mathbb{N}^n \text{ and } |\alpha| \leq k\}$$
(1.7)

Another useful set is given by polynomials whose degree is $\leq k$ with respect to each variable and is defined by

$$Q_k^{(n)}(\Omega) = \text{span}\, \{x^\alpha : \alpha = (\alpha_1, \ldots, \alpha_n) \in \mathbb{N}^n \text{ and } \alpha_i \leq k \text{ for } i = 1, \ldots, n\} \quad (1.8)$$

We do not write $\Omega$ when $\Omega = \mathbb{R}^n$ and we omit $n$ when no confusion would result.
For instance, if $n = 2$, writing $x$ and $y$ instead of $x_1$ and $x_2$, we have

$$P_1^{(2)} = \text{span}\, \{1, x, y\} \hspace{1cm} P_2^{(2)} = \text{span}\, \{1, x, y, x^2, y^2, xy\}$$
$$Q_1^{(2)} = \text{span}\, \{1, x, y, xy\} \hspace{1cm} Q_2^{(2)} = \text{span}\, \{1, x, y, x^2, y^2, xy, xy^2, x^2y, x^2y^2\}$$

## 1.2E Linear Dependence; Dimensions

**DEFINITION 1.7**  Let $V$ be a linear space and $A$ be a nonempty subset of $V$. Then, $A$ is called:

*dependent* iff there exists a linear combination $\Sigma \alpha_i v_i$ of a finite number of distinct vectors $v_i \in A$ with some nonzero coefficient, such that $\Sigma \alpha_i v_i = 0$; $\hspace{1cm}$ (1.9)

*independent* otherwise; i.e., iff, for any linear combination $\Sigma \alpha_i v_i$ of a finite number of distinct vectors $v_i \in A$, $\Sigma \alpha_i v_i = 0$ implies $\alpha_i = 0 \,\forall\, i$; $\hspace{1cm}$ (1.10)

a *Hamel basis*, or, simply, a *basis*, iff $A$ is independent and generates $V$. $\hspace{1cm}$ (1.11)

**PROPOSITION 1.3**  If $A$ is a basis of a linear space $V$, then every $v \in V$ can be written as a finite combination $v = \Sigma \alpha_i v_i$ of elements $v_i \in A$ in exactly one way.

**THEOREM 1.2**  Let $V$ be a nontrivial linear space; then:

Every generating set contains some basis; $\hspace{1cm}$ (1.12)

every independent set is contained in some basis; $\hspace{1cm}$ (1.13) if $A$ and $B$ are, respectively, an independent set and a generating set, there exists a one-to-one map from $A$ into $B$.                                                    (1.14)

**REMARK 1.3**  Theorem 1.2 implies that whenever a finite generating set of a nontrivial linear space exists, all independent sets are finite and all bases have the same cardinality. Thus, we can give the following definition.

**DEFINITION 1.8**  We define a linear space $V$ to be finite- or infinite-dimensional according to whether a finite generating set exists or not, and define the dimension of $V$ by

dim $V = 0$, iff $V$ is trivial;                                                      (1.15)

dim $V = $ cardinality of any basis, iff $V$ is nontrivial and finite-dimensional;     (1.16)

dim $V = \infty$, iff $V$ is infinite-dimensional.                                    (1.17)

## 1.2F Examples of Dimensions

**EXAMPLE 1.6**  dim $(V_1 \times \cdots \times V_n) = $ dim $V_1 + \cdots + $ dim $V_n$, where dim $V_i = 0$ or $= \infty$ is allowed.

**EXAMPLE 1.7**  dim $\mathbb{R}^n = n$

**EXAMPLE 1.8**  dim $C^0(\Omega) = $ dim $P^{(n)} = \infty$

**EXAMPLE 1.9**  dim $P_k^{(1)} = k + 1$

**EXAMPLE 1.10**  dim $P_k^{(2)} = \frac{1}{2}(k+1)(k+2)$; dim $P_k^{(n)} = \dfrac{1}{n!}(k+1)\cdots(k+n)$

**EXAMPLE 1.11**  dim $Q_k^{(2)} = (k+1)^2$; dim $Q_k^{(n)} = (k+1)^n$

## 1.2G Convexity

**DEFINITION 1.9**  The *segment* joining two points, $v_0$ and $v_1$, of a linear space $V$ is defined by

$$\{\theta v_1 + (1-\theta)v_0 : 0 \leq \theta \leq 1\} \tag{1.18}$$

**DEFINITION 1.10**  A subset $K$ of a linear space $V$ is said to be *convex* if the segment joining any two points of $K$ is contained in $K$; i.e.,

$$v_0, v_1 \in K \quad \text{and} \quad 0 \leq \theta \leq 1 \quad \text{imply} \quad \theta v_1 + (1-\theta)v_0 \in K \tag{1.19}$$

**DEFINITION 1.11**  A function $f: K \rightarrow \mathbb{R} \cup \{+\infty\}$ is said to be *convex* iff $K$ is convex and

$$v_0, v_1 \in K \quad \text{and} \quad 0 < \theta < 1 \quad \text{imply}$$

$$f(\theta v_1 + (1-\theta)v_0) \leq \theta f(v_1) + (1-\theta)f(v_0) \tag{1.20}$$

$f$ is called *strictly convex* if, in addition, equality in (1.20) never holds for $v_0 \neq v_1$; a function $f$ is concave (respectively, strictly concave) iff $-f$ is convex (respectively, strictly convex).

**DEFINITION 1.12**   Let $V$ be a linear space. If $\{v_i\}$ is a finite subset of $V$, a *convex combination* of $v_i$'s is a vector of the form $\Sigma \alpha_i v_i$ with any nonnegative scalars, such that $\Sigma \alpha_i = 1$. If $E$ is any nonempty subset of $V$, we set

$$\text{co } E = \{\Sigma \alpha_i v_i : \alpha_i \geqslant 0, \Sigma \alpha_i = 1, v_i \in E\}$$

where $\Sigma$ means any finite sum.

Elements of co $E$ are thus all convex combinations of arbitrary finite subsets of $E$.

It is clear that co $E$ is a convex set, namely, the smallest convex set containing $E$. Thus co $E = E$ iff $E$ is convex.

**PROPOSITION 1.4**   Every subspace of a linear space is convex, and the intersection of (possibly infinitely many) convex sets is convex.

Important examples of convex sets will be given in Chap. 7 in Part 1. We conclude by introducing some notations.

**DEFINITION 1.13**   If $E_1$ and $E_2$ are nonempty subsets of a linear space $V$, $v_0 \in V$, and $\lambda \in \mathbb{R}$, we set

$$E_1 + E_2 = \{v_1 + v_2 : v_1 \in E_1, v_2 \in E_2\} \qquad v_0 + E_1 = \{v_0\} + E_1$$

$$\lambda E_1 = \{\lambda v_1 : v_1 \in E_1\} \qquad -E_1 = (-1)E_1 \qquad E_1 - E_2 = E_1 + (-E_2)$$

Notice that this definition of $E_1 + E_2$ agrees with Def. 1.5 (case $n = 2$) when $E_i$ are subspaces.

## 1.2H  Linear Operators and Functionals

**DEFINITION 1.14**   Let $V$ and $W$ be linear spaces. A map $L : V \to W$ is called *linear*, or a *linear operator* from $V$ into $W$, iff

$$L(v_1 + v_2) = L(v_1) + L(v_2) \qquad \forall v_1, v_2 \in V$$

$$L(\alpha v) = \alpha L(v) \qquad \forall \alpha \in \mathbb{R}, \forall v \in V$$

If $L$ is linear we also write $Lv$ instead of $L(v)$.

**DEFINITION 1.15**   A linear operator from $V$ into $\mathbb{R}$ is called a *linear functional* on $V$ or a *linear form* on $V$.

**PROPOSITION 1.5**   If $V_0$ and $W_0$ are subspaces of the linear space $V$ and $W$, respectively, and $L$ is a linear operator from $V$ into $W$, then

$$L(V_0) \text{ and } L^{-1}(W_0) \text{ are subspaces of } W \text{ and } V, \text{ respectively} \tag{1.21}$$

In particular, defining the *range* and the *kernel* of $L$ by

$$R(L) = L(V) \quad \text{and} \quad \ker L = L^{-1}\{0\} \tag{1.22}$$

*we have* $\qquad R(L)$ and $\ker L$ are subspaces of $W$ and $V$, respectively $\qquad$ (1.23)

**EXAMPLE 1.12**  If $V = \mathbb{R}^n$, $W = \mathbb{R}^m$, and $A$ is an $(n, m)$-matrix, setting $L_A(x) = Ax$ for $x$ column vector in $\mathbb{R}^n$, $L_A$ is a linear operator from $V$ into $W$. Moreover, $R(L)$ is the set of $y \in W$ for which the linear system $Ax = y$ can be solved and $\ker L$ is the set of solutions of the homogeneous system $Ax = 0$.

It is well known that for every linear operator $L$ from $\mathbb{R}^n$ into $\mathbb{R}^m$ there exists a unique matrix $A$ such that $L = L_A$. Therefore, linear operators generalize matrices in the case of arbitrary linear spaces. Recalling Def. 1.6, we have, for instance, that *projections are linear maps*.

## 1.2ı Bilinear Operators and Forms

**DEFINITION 1.16**  If $V_1$, $V_2$, and $W$ are linear spaces, a map $a : V_1 \times V_2 \to W$ is called a *bilinear operator* from $V_1 \times V_2$ into $W$ iff

$$\forall \bar{v}_1 \in V_1, \, v_2 \to a(\bar{v}_1, v_2) \text{ is linear on } V_2 \text{ and}$$

$$\forall \bar{v}_2 \in V_2, \, v_1 \to a(v_1, \bar{v}_2) \text{ is linear on } V_1$$

If, moreover, $W = \mathbb{R}$, then $a$ is called a *bilinear form* on $V_1 \times V_2$.

**DEFINITION 1.17**  Let $a$ be a bilinear operator from $V \times V$ into $W$; the *symmetric part $a_s$* of $a$ is defined by

$$a_s(u, v) = \tfrac{1}{2}(a(u, v) + a(v, u)) \tag{1.24}$$

$a$ is said to be *symmetric* iff $a \equiv a_s$.

**DEFINITION 1.18**  If $V$ is a linear space, a map $\phi : V \to \mathbb{R}$ is called a *quadratic form* on $V$ iff there exists a bilinear form $a$ on $V \times V$ such that $\phi(v) = a(v, v)$ $\forall v \in V$.

**PROPOSITION 1.6**  Let $\phi(v) = b(v, v)$ be a quadratic form on a linear space $V$. Then there exists exactly one symmetric bilinear form $a$ on $V \times V$ such that $a(v, v) = \phi(v)$ $\forall v \in V$. Moreover, $a$ is given by

$$a(u, v) = \tfrac{1}{2}[\phi(u+v) - \phi(u) - \phi(v)] = \tfrac{1}{2}[\phi(u) + \phi(v) - \phi(u-v)]$$

$$= \tfrac{1}{4}[\phi(u+v) - \phi(u-v)] = b_s(u, v)$$

Similarly, trilinear, $m$-linear $(m > 2)$ operators and forms, etc., can be defined.

## 1.2ᴊ Isomorphisms

**DEFINITION 1.19**  Let $V$ and $W$ be linear spaces. A map $L : V \to W$ is called an *algebraic isomorphism* from $V$ onto $W$, iff

$$L \text{ is linear} \tag{1.25}$$

$$\ker L = \{0\} \tag{1.26}$$

$$R(L) = W \tag{1.27}$$

Moreover, we say that $V$ and $W$ are *algebraically isomorphic* iff an algebraic isomorphism from $V$ onto $W$ exists.

**REMARK 1.4**   (1.26) and (1.27) mean, respectively, that $L$ is one-to-one and onto. When (1.25) and (1.26) hold, the *inverse map* $L^{-1}: R(L) \to V$ exists and is an algebraic isomorphism. If in addition (1.27) holds, $L^{-1}$ is an algebraic isomorphism from $W$ onto $V$. This justifies the symmetry in the last part of Def. 1.19.

All the properties that are relevant in the theory of linear spaces are preserved by algebraic isomorphisms, as shown in the next theorem; hence, algebraically isomorphic linear spaces could be identified.

**THEOREM 1.3**   Let $V$ and $W$ be linear spaces and let $L: V \to W$ be an algebraic isomorphism. Then $L$ maps independent sets (respectively, generating sets, bases, subspaces, convex sets) of $V$ onto independent sets (respectively, generating sets, bases, subspaces, convex sets) of $W$. In particular,

if $V$ and $W$ are algebraically isomorphic, then $\dim V = \dim W$

**REMARK 1.5**   By definition $P^{(1)}$ in Eq. (1.7) has a countable infinite basis. On the contrary, $\{\exp \lambda x: \lambda \in \mathbb{R}\}$ is independent in $C^0(\mathbb{R})$, so that any basis of $C^0(\mathbb{R})$ cannot be countably infinite, by (1.14). Thus Theorem 1.3 implies that $P^{(1)}$ and $C^0(\mathbb{R})$ are not algebraically isomorphic, even if $\dim P^{(1)} = \dim C^0(\mathbb{R})$ (Example 1.8). However, the following holds:

**THEOREM 1.4**   Let $A$ and $B$ be bases of the linear spaces $V$ and $W$ respectively. If $l: A \to B$ is one-to-one and onto, there exists exactly one linear map $L: V \to W$ such that $Lv = l(v)$, $\forall v \in A$. Moreover, $L$ is an algebraic isomorphism and is given by (recall Prop. 1.3)

$$L(\Sigma \alpha_i v_i) = \Sigma \alpha_i l(v_i)$$

for any finite sum with $v_i \in A$ and $\alpha_i \in \mathbb{R}$.

If two finite sets $A$ and $B$ have the same cardinality, a map $l$ as above certainly exists. Thus:

**COROLLARY 1.1**   Let $V$ and $W$ be finite-dimensional linear spaces. Then $\dim V = \dim W$ implies that $V$ and $W$ are algebraically isomorphic. In particular,

$\dim V = n$ implies that $V$ is algebraically isomorphic to $\mathbb{R}^n$

Algebraic isomorphisms can be used to state interesting formulae.

**THEOREM 1.5**   Let $V_1$ and $V_2$ be subspaces of a linear space $V$. Then $(V_1 + V_2) \times (V_1 \cap V_2)$ and $V_1 \times V_2$ are algebraically isomorphic. In particular (see Example 1.6),

$$\dim (V_1 + V_2) + \dim (V_1 \cap V_2) = \dim V_1 + \dim V_2$$

**PROPOSITION 1.7**   Let $V_0$ be a subspace of a linear space $V$. Then a subspace $V_1$ exists such that $V = V_0 \oplus V_1$. Moreover, $V_0 \oplus V_1 = V_0 \oplus V_2$ implies that $V_1$ and $V_2$ are algebraically isomorphic, so that dim $V_1$ depends only on $V_0$ and $V$.

**DEFINITION 1.20**   Let $V_0$ be a subspace of a linear space $V$. The *codimension of* $V_0$ (with respect to $V$) is defined by

$$\text{codim } V_0 = \dim V_1$$

where $V_1$ is any subspace such that $V = V_0 \oplus V_1$.

**PROPOSITION 1.8**   If $V_0$ is a subspace of a linear space $V$, then

$$\dim V_0 + \text{codim } V_0 = \dim V$$


## 1.3  BANACH  SPACES

### 1.3A  Normed Spaces

**DEFINITION 1.21**   Let $V$ be a linear space (Def. 1.1). A *seminorm* on $V$ is a map $v \to |v|$ from $V$ into $[0, \infty[$ such that

$$|u + v| \leqslant |u| + |v| \qquad \text{and} \qquad |\lambda u| = |\lambda| |u| \qquad \forall u, v \in V, \forall \lambda \in \mathbb{R} \tag{1.28}$$

A *norm* on $V$ is a seminorm on $V$ such that

$$|u| = 0 \text{ iff } u = 0 \tag{1.29}$$

A *normed space* is a linear space with a norm on it.

We denote seminorms and norms by $|\cdot|$ and $\|\cdot\|$, respectively, or by similar symbols. For any seminorm on $V$ we have

$$\big| |u| - |v| \big| \leqslant |u - v| \qquad \text{and} \qquad |u - v| = |v - u| \qquad \forall u, v \in V$$

If $\|\cdot\|$ is a norm, the real number $\|u - v\|$ is called the *distance* between $u$ and $v$. Using the norm one can generalize for normed spaces many of the results which hold in $\mathbb{R}^n$.

**DEFINITION 1.22**   Let $V$ be a normed space with the norm $\|\cdot\|$, $A$ a subset of $V$, $v_0 \in V$, and $\{v_m\}$ a sequence in $V$. We give the following definitions:

The *ball* of center $v_0 \in V$ and radius $r > 0$ is the set $B_r(v_0) = \{v \in V : \|v - v_0\| < r\}$; we set $B_r = B_r(0)$. \hfill (1.30)

$\{v_n\}$ *converges strongly* to $v_0$ (in $V$) (and we write $v_n \to v_0$) iff $\lim \|v_n - v_0\| = 0$. \hfill (1.31)

$\{v_n\}$ satisfies the *Cauchy condition* (in $V$) iff $\forall \varepsilon > 0 \exists n_\varepsilon : \forall n, m > n_\varepsilon \ \|v_n - v_m\| < \varepsilon$; a sequence that satisfies the Cauchy condition is called a *Cauchy sequence*. \hfill (1.32)

$A$ is *open* (in $V$) iff $\forall v \in A \exists r > 0 : B_r(v) \subset A$; \hfill (1.33)

$A$ is *closed* (in $V$) iff $v_n \in A$ and $v_n \to v$ imply $v \in A$; (1.34)

$A$ is *dense* (in $V$) iff for every $v \in V$ a sequence $\{v_n\}$ in $A$ exists such that $v_n \to v$; (1.35)

$A$ is *bounded* (in $V$) iff there exists a constant $M$ such that $\|v\| \leq M \; \forall v \in A$. (1.36)

The *closure* $\bar{A}$ of $A$ is the smallest closed set containing $A$; (1.37)

The *interior* $\mathring{A}$ of $A$ is the largest open set contained in $A$. (1.38)

Note that the above definitions accord with the usual ones when $V = \mathbb{R}^n$ and

$$\|(x_1, \ldots, x_n)\| = (\Sigma x_i^2)^{1/2} \tag{1.39}$$

Many results which hold in $\mathbb{R}^n$ also hold for a general normed space. In particular, every sequence that converges strongly is a Cauchy sequence. The converse (i.e., every Cauchy sequence converges strongly to something) holds in $\mathbb{R}^n$ but not in a general normed space.

## 1.3B  Definition of Banach Spaces

**DEFINITION 1.23**   A normed space $V$ is called *complete* or a *Banach space* iff every Cauchy sequence in $V$ has a strong limit in $V$.

**PROPOSITION 1.9**   A subspace of a Banach space is a Banach space iff it is closed.

**EXAMPLE 1.13**   $\mathbb{R}^n$ is a Banach space with the norm (1.39). More generally, if $V_i (i = 1, \ldots, n)$ are Banach spaces with norms $\|\cdot\|_{V_i}$, then $V = V_1 \times \cdots \times V_n$ is a Banach space with the norm $\|(v_1, \ldots, v_n)\| = (\Sigma \|v_i\|_{V_i}^2)^{1/2}$.

More interesting examples of Banach spaces are given in Chap. 2 of Part 1.

**DEFINITION 1.24**   A Banach space (or, more generally, a normed space) is called *separable* iff it contains a finite or countably infinite set $A$, such that span $A$ is dense.

Note that every finite-dimensional normed space is separable.

## 1.3C  Continuous and Linear Operators; Dual Spaces

**DEFINITION 1.25**   Let $V$ and $W$ be normed spaces and $f: A \to W$ a map defined on a subset $A$ of $V$. Then $f$ is called *continuous at a point* $v_0 \in A$ iff $v_n \in A$ and $v_n \to v_0$ in $V$ imply $f(v_n) \to f(v_0)$ in $W$; $f$ is called *continuous* (in $A$) iff it is continuous at every point (of $A$).

**REMARK 1.6**   Definition 1.25 makes use only of the concept of *limit*. Hence we may use the same formal definition of continuity for more general linear spaces $V$ and $W$ provided that the symbols $v_n \to v$ in $V$ and $w_n \to w$ in $W$ are defined.

**THEOREM 1.6**   Let $V$ and $W$ be normed spaces and $L$ be a linear operator (Def. 1.14) from $V$ into $W$; then $L$ is continuous iff there exists a constant $M$ such that

$$\|Lv\|_W \leq M \|v\|_V \qquad \forall v \in V \tag{1.40}$$

In particular, a linear functional $L$ (Def. 1.15) on $V$ is continuous iff there exists a constant $M$ such that

$$|Lv| \leq M\|v\| \qquad \forall v \in V$$

Moreover a seminorm $|\cdot|$ on $V$ is continuous iff there exists a constant $M$ such that

$$|v| \leq M\|v\| \qquad \forall v \in V$$

**DEFINITION 1.26** Let $V$ and $W$ be normed spaces; an operator $L$ from $V$ into $W$ is said to be *bounded* if it maps bounded sets of $V$ into bounded sets of $W$.

Note that Theorem 1.6 implies that *a linear operator is continuous iff it is bounded.*

**THEOREM 1.7** Let $V$ and $W$ be normed spaces. If $V$ is finite-dimensional, then every linear operator from $V$ into $W$ is continuous and every seminorm (in particular, a norm) on $V$ is continuous.

**DEFINITION 1.27** Let $V$ and $W$ be normed spaces.

$$\mathscr{L}(V; W) = \text{set of all continuous linear operators from } V \text{ into } W \tag{1.41}$$

$$\|L\|_{\mathscr{L}(V;W)} = \sup_{v \in V, v \neq 0} \frac{\|Lv\|_W}{\|v\|_V} \qquad \text{for } L \in \mathscr{L}(V; W) \tag{1.42}$$

As in Example 1.3, we can define the sum of operators or the product of operators and real numbers. Hence $\mathscr{L}(V; W)$ is a linear space.

**THEOREM 1.8** Let $V$ be a normed space and let $W$ be a Banach space; then $\mathscr{L}(V; W)$ is a Banach space with the norm (1.42).

If $V_1, V_2, V_3$ are normed spaces and if $L_{12} \in \mathscr{L}(V_1, V_2)$, $L_{23} \in \mathscr{L}(V_2, V_3)$, the product $L_{13} = L_{12}L_{23}$ is naturally defined by

$$L_{13}(v) = L_{23}(L_{12}(v)) \qquad \forall v \in V_1 \tag{1.43}$$

**PROPOSITION 1.10** Let $V_1, V_2, V_3$ be normed spaces and let $L_{12} \in \mathscr{L}(V_1, V_2)$, $L_{23} \in \mathscr{L}(V_2; V_3)$; then $L_{13}$ defined in (1.43) belongs to $\mathscr{L}(V_1; V_3)$ and we have

$$\|L_{13}\|_{\mathscr{L}(V_1;V_3)} \leq \|L_{12}\|_{\mathscr{L}(V_1;V_2)} \cdot \|L_{23}\|_{\mathscr{L}(V_2;V_3)} \tag{1.44}$$

The particular case $W = \mathbb{R}$ in (1.41) plays a crucial role.

**DEFINITION 1.28** If $V$ is a normed space, the space $\mathscr{L}(V; \mathbb{R})$ is called the *dual space of $V$* and noted $V'$.

Theorem 1.8 yields the following fundamental result.

**COROLLARY 1.2**  If $V$ is a normed space, then $V'$ is a Banach space with the norm

$$\|L\|_{V'} = \sup_{v \in V, v \neq 0} \frac{|Lv|}{\|v\|_V} \quad \text{for } L \in V' \tag{1.45}$$

where sup is used as the standard abbreviation for supremum.

If $v \in V$ and $L \in V'$, we set

$$_{V'}\langle L, v \rangle_V = Lv \tag{1.46}$$

and simply write $\langle L, v \rangle$ when no confusion would result.

**DEFINITION 1.29**  Let $V$ be a normed space. The dual space of $V'$ is called the *second dual space* of $V$ and denoted by $V''$. $V''$ is a Banach space with the norm

$$\|L\|_{V''} = \sup_{l \in V', l \neq 0} \frac{|_{V''}\langle L, l \rangle_{V'}|}{\|l\|_{V'}} \tag{1.47}$$

## 1.3D  Dual Operators

**DEFINITION 1.30**  Let $V$, $W$ be normed spaces, let $V_0$ be a dense subspace of $V$, and let $T$ be a linear operator $V_0 \to W$. We define $D(T')$ as the set of all $g \in W'$ such that there exists a constant $c$ (depending on $g$) verifying

$$|_{W'}\langle g, Tv \rangle_W| \leq c \|v\|_V \, \forall v \in V_0$$

**PROPOSITION 1.11**  On the above assumptions, for $g \in D(T')$, there exists a unique linear continuous mapping $f: V \to \mathbb{R}$ such that

$$f(v) = {}_{W'}\langle g, Tv \rangle_W \, \forall v \in V_0 \tag{1.48}$$

**DEFINITION 1.31**  With the assumptions and notations of Def. 1.30 and Prop. 1.11, we define the mapping $T': D(T') \to V'$ which maps every $g \in D(T')$ into the element $f \in V'$ defined by (1.48). $T'$ is called the *dual operator* of $T$. Hence we have

$$_{V'}\langle T'g, v \rangle_V = {}_{W'}\langle g, Tv \rangle_W \quad \forall v \in V_0, \forall g \in D(T') \tag{1.49}$$

**REMARK 1.7**  In finite-dimensional spaces, if $T$ is associated with a matrix $M$, $T'$ will be associated with the transposed matrix of $M$ (usually denoted by $M'$ or $M^T$).

**THEOREM 1.9**  Let $V$ and $W$ be normed spaces. If $T \in \mathcal{L}(V; W)$, then $T' \in \mathcal{L}(W'; V')$ and [see (1.45)]

$$\|T\|_{\mathcal{L}(V;W)} = \|T'\|_{\mathcal{L}(W';V')} \tag{1.50}$$

## 1.3E  Isomorphisms

**DEFINITION 1.32**  Let $V$ and $W$ be normed spaces. A map $L: V \to W$ is called an *isomorphism* from $V$ onto $W$ iff

$$L \text{ is an algebraic isomorphism (Def. 1.19) from } V \text{ onto } W \tag{1.51}$$

$$L \text{ and } L^{-1} \text{ (Remark 1.4) are continuous} \tag{1.52}$$

An isomorphism from $V$ onto $W$ is called *isometric* iff

$$\|Lv\|_W = \|v\|_V \ \forall v \in V \tag{1.53}$$

**DEFINITION 1.33** Two norms, $\|\cdot\|_1$ and $\|\cdot\|_2$, on $V$ are called *equivalent* iff constants $M_1$ and $M_2$ exist such that

$$\|v\|_2 \leqslant M_1\|v\|_1 \quad\text{and}\quad \|v\|_1 \leqslant M_2\|v\|_2 \quad \forall v \in V \tag{1.54}$$

By Theorem 1.6, the above definition means that the identity map is an isomorphism between $V$ with $\|\cdot\|_1$ and $V$ with $\|\cdot\|_2$. Equivalent seminorms are defined in a similar way.

**REMARK 1.8** Isomorphisms preserve everything which is important from the point of view of the theory of normed spaces; i.e., they map open, closed, and dense sets, strongly convergent sequences, etc., onto sets and sequences of the same type. If a norm of a normed space $V$ is replaced by an equivalent one, the set $V'$ does not change and its norm is changed into an equivalent one.

From Corollary 1.1 and Theorem 1.7, we have:

**THEOREM 1.10** Let $V$ and $W$ be finite-dimensional normed spaces. If dim $V =$ dim $W$, then $V$ and $W$ are isomorphic. In particular:

dim $V = n$ implies that $V$ is isomorphic to $\mathbb{R}^n$ and thus complete; $\tag{1.55}$

all norms in $V$ are equivalent to each other. $\tag{1.56}$

## 1.3F  $m$-Linear Operators and Forms

Let $V_1$, $V_2$, and $W$ be Banach spaces. Recalling Sec. 1.2I, Def. 1.25, and Example 1.13, we define the following set:

$$\mathscr{L}_2(V_1, V_2; W) = \text{set of all continuous bilinear operators from } V_1 \times V_2 \text{ into } W \tag{1.57}$$

which is a linear space with obvious definitions of operations. Now let $a \in \mathscr{L}(V_1, V_2; W)$ be given. For every $v_1 \in V_1$, consider the map $A_{v_1}: V_2 \to W$ defined by $v_2 \to a(v_1, v_2)$. It is easy to see that $A_{v_1} \in \mathscr{L}(V_2; W)$. One can also show that the map $A: v_1 \to A_{v_1}$ is linear and continuous from $V_1$ into $\mathscr{L}(V_2; W)$ and thus belongs to $\mathscr{L}(V_1; \mathscr{L}(V_2; W))$. Hence, we obtain a map

$$a \to A \text{ from } \mathscr{L}_2(V_1, V_2; W) \text{ into } \mathscr{L}(V_1; \mathscr{L}(V_2; W)) \tag{1.58}$$

**THEOREM 1.11** The map (1.58) is an algebraic isomorphism (Def. 1.19) from $\mathscr{L}_2(V_1, V_2; W)$ onto $\mathscr{L}(V_1; \mathscr{L}(V_2; W))$.

**REMARK 1.9** The norm of $A$ in $\mathscr{L}(V_1; \mathscr{L}(V_2; W))$ can be expressed in terms of the corresponding $a$ as follows:

$$\|A\|_{\mathscr{L}(V_1; \mathscr{L}(V_2; W))} = \sup_{v_1 \in V_1, v \neq 0} \frac{\|A_{v_1}\|_{\mathscr{L}(V_2; W)}}{\|v_1\|_{V_1}}$$

$$= \sup_{v_1 \in V_1 - \{0\}} \sup_{v_2 \in V_2 - \{0\}} \frac{\|a(v_1, v_2)\|_W}{\|v_1\|_{V_1}\|v_2\|_{V_2}} \tag{1.59}$$

Taking (1.59) as a norm in $\mathscr{L}_2(V_1, V_2; W)$, we obtain a Banach space and (1.58) becomes an isometric isomorphism.

**REMARK 1.10**   The results of Theorem 1.11 and of Rem. 1.9 obviously can be extended to $m$-linear operators and forms for $m > 2$.

**REMARK 1.11**   The results stated above for linear operators extend naturally to $m$-linear operators and forms (as, for instance, Theorems 1.6 and 1.7). Note that, in particular (Theorem 1.6), a bilinear form $a(v_1, v_2)$ is continuous iff $\exists M > 0$, such that

$$|a(v_1, v_2)| \leqslant M \|v_1\|_{V_1} \|v_2\|_{V_2} \qquad \forall v_1 \in V_1, \forall v_2 \in V_2 \tag{1.60}$$

## 1.3G Weak and Weak* Convergence

**DEFINITION 1.34**   Let $V$ be a normed space. A sequence $\{v_n\}$ in $V$ is called *weakly convergent to* $v_0 \in V$ (and we write $v_n \rightharpoonup v_0$) iff

$$\lim \langle L, v_n \rangle = \langle L, v_0 \rangle \qquad \forall L \in V' \tag{1.61}$$

**THEOREM 1.12**   If the weak limit exists, it is unique.

**THEOREM 1.13**   If $v_n \to v_0$ in $V$, then $v_n \rightharpoonup v_0$ in $V$.

Note that the converse of Theorem 1.13 is not true unless $V$ is finite-dimensional. In particular, finite-dimensional normed spaces can be characterized as the normed spaces where weak convergence implies strong convergence.

**THEOREM 1.14**   If $L \in \mathscr{L}(V; W)$ and $v_n \rightharpoonup v_0$ in $V$, then $Lv_n \rightharpoonup Lv_0$ in $W$.

It is clear that *not every* Banach space can be presented as the dual space of some space (we will see some examples in Chap. 2 of Part 1). In *dual spaces* a third kind of limit (besides strong and weak) can be defined.

**DEFINITION 1.35**   Let $V'$ be the dual space of a normed space $V$. A sequence $\{l_n\}$ in $V'$ is called *weakly\* convergent* to $l \in V'$ (and we write $l_n \overset{*}{\rightharpoonup} l$) iff

$$\lim {}_{V'}\langle l_n, v \rangle_V = {}_{V'}\langle l, v \rangle_V \ \forall v \in V \tag{1.62}$$

**THEOREM 1.15**   If the weak\* limit exists, it is unique.

**THEOREM 1.16**   If $l_n \rightharpoonup l$ in $V'$, then $l_n \overset{*}{\rightharpoonup} l$ in $V'$.

## 1.3H Reflexive Banach Spaces

Let $V$ be a normed space. For every $v \in V$ we can define the map $L_v : V' \to \mathbb{R}$ by

$$L_v(l) = {}_{V'}\langle l, v \rangle_V \qquad \forall l \in V' \tag{1.63}$$

Clearly, $L_v \in V''$; it can be proved that the map $v \to L_v$, (from $V$ into $V''$) is an isometric isomorphism between $V$ and a subspace of $V''$.

**DEFINITION 1.36**   A normed space $V$ is called *reflexive* iff the map $v \to L_v$ defined by (1.63) is *onto* $V''$; i.e., iff

$$\forall L \in V'' \, \exists v \in V : \forall l \in V' \qquad {}_{V''}\langle L, l \rangle_{V'} = {}_{V'}\langle l, v \rangle_V \tag{1.64}$$

It follows that every reflexive normed space $V$ is isometrically isomorphic to its second dual space $V''$. From Cor. 1.2 and Rem. 1.8 we have, therefore, the following results.

**THEOREM 1.17**   Every reflexive normed space is a Banach space.

Moreover, we have:

**THEOREM 1.18**   If $V$ is complete, then $V$ is reflexive iff $V'$ is reflexive.

**THEOREM 1.19**   If $V$ is reflexive, weak and weak* convergence in $V'$ coincide.

## 1.3ɪ Completions

**DEFINITION 1.37**   Let $V$ be a normed space. A Banach space $W$ is said to be a *completion* of $V$ iff there exists an isomorphism from $V$ onto a dense subspace of $W$.

**THEOREM 1.20**   Let $V$ be a normed space. Then there exists at least one completion of $V$; moreover, any two completions of $V$ are isomorphic.

It can be proved that, in particular, the closure in $V''$ of the subspace $\{L_v; v \in V\}$ [with the notation (1.63)] is a completion of $V$.

## 1.3ᴊ Compactness

**DEFINITION 1.38**   Let $V$ and $W$ be normed spaces. A linear operator $L: V \to W$ is called *compact* iff

$$v_n \rightharpoonup v \text{ in } V \text{ implies } Lv_n \to Lv \text{ in } W \tag{1.65}$$

**THEOREM 1.21**   Every compact operator is continuous. Moreover, the product of continuous linear operators (1.43) is compact whenever one of them is compact.

## 1.3ᴋ Continuous and Compact Inclusions

Given two linear spaces $V$ and $W$ such that $V$ is a subset of $W$, we write

$$V \subset W \text{ iff } V \text{ is a subspace of } W \tag{1.66}$$

If, in addition, $V$ and $W$ are normed spaces, we write

$$V \hookrightarrow W \text{ iff } v_n \to v \text{ in } V \text{ implies } v_n \to v \text{ in } W \tag{1.67}$$

Notice that (1.67) can also be written

$$V \hookrightarrow W \text{ iff } \exists c: \forall v \in V \quad \|v\|_W \le c\|v\|_V \tag{1.68}$$

Moreover, as in Rem. 1.6, we have that:

The same formal definition (1.67) holds for more general linear spaces $v$ and $w$ with $v \subset w$, when the symbols $v_n \to v$ in $v$ and $w_n \to w$ in $w$ are defined. $\tag{1.69}$

Finally, if $V$ and $W$ are normed spaces with $V \subset W$, we write

$$V \hookrightarrow\hookrightarrow W \text{ iff } v_n \rightharpoonup v \text{ in } V \text{ implies } v_n \to v \text{ in } W \tag{1.70}$$

Notice that $V \hookrightarrow\hookrightarrow W$ implies $V \hookrightarrow W$ by Theorem 1.13. Properties (1.66), (1.67), and (1.70) mean, respectively, that the identity map $v \to v$ is linear, continuous, or compact from $V$ into $W$; hence, we say that the inclusion of $V$ in $W$ is algebraic, continuous, or compact, respectively.

### 1.3L Identifications

Sometimes we write $V \subset W$, $V \hookrightarrow W$, or $V \hookrightarrow\hookrightarrow W$ in a generalized sense. We now explain when this is allowed. Assume, to begin, that $V$ and $W$ are linear spaces and $L: V \to W$ is linear and injective. Hence, $L(V) = R(L)$ is a subspace of $W$ by (1.23), and we can write

$$V \leftrightarrow L(V) \subset W \tag{1.71}$$

If in addition $V$ and $W$ are normed spaces and $L$ is continuous, we may *define* for sequences $\{w_n\}$ and elements $w$ in $L(V)$

$$w_n \to w \text{ in } L(V) \text{ iff } L^{-1}w_n \to L^{-1}w \text{ in } V \tag{1.72}$$

which is allowed since $L^{-1}$ is well defined in $L(V)$. Hence we can write

$$V \leftrightarrow L(V) \hookrightarrow W \tag{1.73}$$

The same can be done for more general linear spaces $V$ and $W$ when convergences are defined.

Notice that, for normed spaces, (1.72) amounts to $\|w\|_{L(V)} = \|L^{-1}w\|_V$ for $w \in L(V)$. Obviously, if in addition $L$ is compact, we have

$$V \leftrightarrow L(V) \hookrightarrow\hookrightarrow W \tag{1.74}$$

Since, in each one of cases (1.71), (1.73), and (1.74), $L$ is a one-to-one map $V \to L(V)$ which preserves the *structure* of $V$, we are allowed to *identify* $V$ with $L(V)$ and write $V \subset W$, $V \hookrightarrow W$, and $V \hookrightarrow\hookrightarrow W$, respectively. Obviously, the map $L$ must be specified, in each particular case, before the identification is made. We shall see some interesting applications to functional spaces in Chap. 2 of Part 1. An application to an abstract (but general) situation can be given as follows.

Assume that $V$ and $W$ are Banach spaces with

$$V \hookrightarrow W \quad V \text{ is a dense subset of } W \tag{1.75}$$

Consider for $u \in W'$ the restriction $u|_V$. Since for $v \in V$ $|_W\langle u, v\rangle_W| \leq \|u\|_{W'}\|v\|_W \leq c\|u\|_{W'}\|v\|_V$, $u|_V$ is an element of $V'$. Moreover, the map $u \to u|_V$ is linear, continuous, and one-to-one (since $V$ is dense in $W$) from $W'$ into $V'$. We, thus, have the previous situation (with $L: W' \to V'$ and $Lu = u|_V$) and write

> $W' \hookrightarrow V'$, with the following identification: $u \in W'$ is identified with $u|_V \in V'$; that is, $_V\langle u, v\rangle_V = {}_W\langle u, v\rangle_W$    $\forall u \in W', \forall v \in V$              (1.76)

## 1.3M The Graph Norm

Let $V$ and $W$ be Banach spaces and $v$ and $w$ be linear spaces. Assume convergences in $v$ and $w$ are defined and

$$V \hookrightarrow v \quad \text{and} \quad W \hookrightarrow w$$

Let $L: v \to w$ be linear and continuous (see Rem. 1.6). Consider the following subspace of $V$:

$$D(L; V; W) = \{v \in V: Lv \in W\} \tag{1.77}$$

and the following norm on it, called the *graph norm*:

$$\|v\|_{D(L;V;W)} = \|(v, Lv)\|_{V \times W} = (\|v\|_V^2 + \|Lv\|_W^2)^{1/2} \tag{1.78}$$

where the exponent 2 could be replaced with any $p \in [1, \infty[$ [the corresponding norm would be equivalent to (1.78)].

**THEOREM 1.22** On the the above assumptions, $D(L; V; W)$ defined in (1.77) is a Banach space with the norm (1.78). Moreover, if $V$ and $W$ are separable or reflexive, then $D(L; V; W)$ is separable or reflexive, respectively.

**DEFINITION 1.39** Let $v$ and $w$ be linear spaces and let $L$ be a linear mapping from a subspace $v_0 \subset v$ into $w$. We define graph $(L)$ as the following subspace of $v \times w$:

$$\text{graph}\,(L) = \{(v, w)\,|\,v \in v_0, w = Lv\} \tag{1.79}$$

**PROPOSITION 1.12** On the above assumptions, the map $v \to (v, Lv)$ is an isometric isomorphism from $D(L; V; W)$ onto graph $(L) \cap (V \times W)$ (equipped with the norm of $V \times W$).

**REMARK 1.12** In the particular case $v = w$ and $L = $ identity, we may define the intersection space $V \cap W$ as a normed space by

$$V \cap W = D(I; V; W) \tag{1.80}$$

## 1.3N Basic Theorems

We conclude this section with a list of basic theorems in Banach spaces. Note that several of the theorems stated above require, in their proof, some of the basic theorems stated below.

**THEOREM 1.23** *Uniform boundedness.* Let $V$ and $W$ be Banach spaces, let $\{L_n\}$ be a sequence of linear continuous mappings from $V$ into $W$, and let $S$ be the unit ball in $V$. If, for each $v \in V$, the sequence $\|L_n v\|_W$ is bounded (in $\mathbb{R}$), then there exists a $c \in \mathbb{R}$ such that $\|L_n v\|_W \leqslant c$ for all $n \in \mathbb{N}$ and for all $v \in S$.

**COROLLARY 1.3** Let $V$ be a Banach space. Then

$$v_n \rightharpoonup v \text{ in } V \text{ implies } \|v_n\|_V \text{ bounded} \tag{1.81}$$

$$L_n \overset{*}{\rightharpoonup} L \text{ in } V' \text{ implies } \|L_n\|_{V'} \text{ bounded} \tag{1.82}$$

**THEOREM 1.24** *Open mapping.* Let $V$, $W$ be Banach spaces and let $L$ be a linear one-to-one mapping from $V$ onto $W$. Then $L$ is continuous iff $L^{-1}$ is continuous.

**THEOREM 1.25** *Closed-graph theorem.* Let $V$, $W$ be Banach spaces and let $L$ be a linear mapping $V \to W$ such that

$$x_n \to x \text{ and } Lx_n \to y \text{ imply } y = Lx \tag{1.83}$$

[that is, graph $(L)$ is a closed subspace of $V \times W$]. Then $L$ is continuous.

**THEOREM 1.26** *Closed-range theorem.* Let $V$ and $W$ be Banach spaces, let $L \in \mathscr{L}(V; W)$, and let $L'$ be the dual operator of $L$. Then the four following statements are equivalent:

$$R(L) \text{ is closed in } W \tag{1.84}$$

$$R(L') \text{ is closed in } V' \tag{1.85}$$

$$R(L) = [\ker(L')]^0 = \{w \mid w \in W, \, {}_W\langle f, w\rangle_W = 0 \; \forall f \in \ker(L')\} \tag{1.86}$$

$$R(L') = [\ker(L)]^0 = \{l \mid l \in V', \, {}_V\langle l, v\rangle_V = 0 \; \forall v \in \ker(L)\} \tag{1.87}$$

**COROLLARY 1.4** Let $V$ and $W$ be Banach spaces and let $L \in \mathscr{L}(V; W)$; then

$$R(L) = W \text{ iff } \exists c_1 \colon \|L'g\|_{V'} \geqslant c_1 \|g\|_{W'} \qquad \forall g \in W' \tag{1.88}$$

and conversely $\qquad R(L') = V' \text{ iff } \exists c_2 \colon \|Lv\|_W \geqslant c_2 \|v\|_V \qquad \forall v \in V \tag{1.89}$

In particular, $L$ is an isomorphism iff both (1.88) and (1.89) hold.

**THEOREM 1.27** *Hahn–Banach theorem.* Let $V$ be a normed space, $V_0$ a subspace of $V$, and $L_0$ a linear mapping $V_0 \to \mathbb{R}$ such that $\exists M > 0$ with $|L_0 v| \leqslant M \|v\|_V \; \forall v \in V_0$; then there exists at least one $L \in V'$ such that $Lv = L_0 v \; \forall v \in V_0$ and $\|L\|_{V'} \leqslant M$.

**COROLLARY 1.5** Let $V$ be a normed space and $V_0$ a subspace of $V$; then $V_0$ is dense in $V$ iff

$$L \in V' \text{ and } Lv = 0 \; \forall v \in V_0 \text{ imply } L = 0 \tag{1.90}$$

**THEOREM 1.28** *Compactness theorem.* Let $V$ be a separable normed space. Then every sequence which is bounded in $V'$ contains a subsequence which converges weakly* in $V'$.

**THEOREM 1.29**  *Eberlein–Shmulyan theorem.* Let $V$ be a Banach space. Then $V$ is reflexive iff every sequence which is bounded in $V$ contains a subsequence which converges weakly in $V$.

**THEOREM 1.30**  *C. Neumann theorem.* Let $V$ be a Banach space and $L \in \mathscr{L}(V; V)$. If $\|I - L\|_{\mathscr{L}(V;V)} < 1$, then $L$ is an isomorphism and

$$\sum_{k=0}^{n} (I-L)^k v \to L^{-1}v, \forall v \in V \qquad \|L^{-1}\| \leq (1 - \|I-L\|)^{-1} \tag{1.91}$$

**THEOREM 1.31**  *Contraction theorem.* Let $V$ be a Banach space, $A$ a closed subset of $V$, and $f: A \to A$ a contraction (that is, $\exists \lambda \in [0, 1[: \|f(u) - f(v)\| \leq \lambda \|u - v\|, \forall u, v \in A$). Then $f$ has a unique fixed point $\bar{v} = f(\bar{v})$ in $A$. Moreover, if $v_0 \in A$ and $v_{n+1} = f(v_n)$ for $n \geq 0$, we have

$$\|v_n - \bar{v}\| \leq \lambda^n (1-\lambda)^{-1} \|v_1 - v_0\| \qquad \forall n$$

in particular, $v_n \to \bar{v}$ in $V$.

## 1.4 HILBERT SPACES

### 1.4A Definitions and Examples

**DEFINITION 1.40**  A Banach space $V$ is called a *Hilbert space* if the mapping

$$v \to \|v\|^2$$

is a quadratic form on $V$ (*see* Def. 1.18).

Following Prop. 1.6 in a Hilbert space there exists a unique symmetric bilinear form

$$u, v \to (u, v)_V \equiv \tfrac{1}{4}(\|u + v\|^2 - \|u - v\|^2) \tag{1.92}$$

such that $(v, v)_V = \|v\|^2$ for all $v$ in $V$.

**DEFINITION 1.41**  Let $V$ be a Hilbert space; the symmetric bilinear form (1.92) is called the *scalar product.* The scalar product $(u, v)_V$ is also noted by $(u, v)$ when there is no risk of confusion.

**EXAMPLE 1.14**  $\mathbb{R}^n$, with the euclidean norm (1.39), is a Hilbert space.

Note that on $\mathbb{R}^n$ the norm

$$\|x\|_1 = \Sigma |x_i| \tag{1.93}$$

is equivalent (see Def. 1.33 and Theorem 1.10) to the norm (1.39). However, $x \to \|x\|_1^2$ is not a quadratic form; hence, $\mathbb{R}^n$ with the norm (1.93) is a Banach space but not a Hilbert space.

**EXAMPLE 1.15**  If $V_1, \ldots, V_n$ are Hilbert spaces, then $V = V_1 \times \cdots \times V_n$ is a Hilbert space with the norm of Example 1.13. The corresponding scalar product is given by

$$(v, w)_V = \Sigma (v_i, w_i)_{V_i} \tag{1.94}$$

**REMARK 1.13**   One can prove that $v \to \|v\|^2$ is a quadratic form iff $\|u - v\|^2 + \|u + v\|^2 = 2\|u\|^2 + 2\|v\|^2$ for all $u, v \in V$; hence this may give an equivalent definition of Hilbert space.

## 1.4B  Basic Properties

We present here some basic results for Hilbert spaces. Note that the order in which they are presented does not reflect the "natural" order for proving them.

**THEOREM 1.32**   *Schwarz inequality.* Let $V$ be a Hilbert space; then

$$|(u, v)| \leqslant \|u\| \|v\| \qquad \forall u, v \in V \tag{1.95}$$

Moreover, equality holds iff $\alpha u + \beta v = 0$ for some $\alpha, \beta \in \mathbb{R}$ with $x^2 + \beta^2 \neq 0$.

**THEOREM 1.33**   *Riesz theorem.* Let $V$ be a Hilbert space, and consider, for each $u \in V$, the mapping $Ju: V \to \mathbb{R}$ defined by

$$Ju : v \to (u, v) \qquad \forall v \in V \tag{1.96}$$

Then the map $u \to Ju$ is an isometric isomorphism from $V$ onto $V'$.

**COROLLARY 1.6**   If $V$ is a Hilbert space, then $V'$ is a Hilbert space.

**COROLLARY 1.7**   If $V$ is a Hilbert space, then $\forall f \in V' \ \exists u (= J^{-1}f)$ such that

$$_V\langle f, v \rangle_V = (u, v)_V \qquad \forall v \in V \tag{1.97}$$

**COROLLARY 1.8**   Every Hilbert space is reflexive.

**REMARK 1.14**   Corollary 1.7 implies

$$v_n \rightharpoonup v_0 \qquad \text{iff} \qquad \lim_{n \to \infty} (v_n, v) = (v_0, v) \qquad \forall v \in V \tag{1.98}$$

Moreover, one can prove that, in a Hilbert space,

$$v_n \to v_0 \qquad \text{iff} \qquad v_n \rightharpoonup v_0 \quad \text{and} \quad \|v_n\| \to \|v_0\| \tag{1.99}$$

**THEOREM 1.34**   *Projection theorem.* Let $V_0$ be a closed subspace of Hilbert space $V$. Then for every $u \in V$ there exists a unique $u_0 \in V_0$ such that

$$\|u_0 - u\| \leqslant \|u - v\| \qquad \forall v \in V_0 \tag{1.100}$$

Moreover, $u_0$ can be characterized by

$$(u - u_0, v) = 0 \qquad \forall v \in V_0 \tag{1.101}$$

**DEFINITION 1.42**   Let $V_0$ be a closed subspace of a Hilbert space $V$. Then the mapping $u \to u_0$ defined by the projection theorem (Theorem 1.34) is called the *orthogonal projection* onto $V_0$ and noted by

$P_{V_0}$. Hence (1.101) becomes

$$(u - P_{V_0}u, v) = 0 \qquad \forall v \in V_0 \tag{1.102}$$

**THEOREM 1.35**  The operator $P = P_{V_0}$ defined in Def. 1.42 belongs to $\mathcal{L}(V; V)$ and satisfies

$$P = P^2 \tag{1.103}$$

$$(Pv, w) = (w, Pv) \qquad \forall v, w \in V \tag{1.104}$$

Conversely, for any $P \in \mathcal{L}(V; V)$ that satisfies (1.103) and (1.104) we have $P = P_{V_0}$, where $V_0 = R(P)$.

**DEFINITION 1.43**  Let $V_0$ be a closed subspace of a Hilbert space $V$. We set

$$V_0^\perp = \{v \in V: (v, v_0) = 0 \qquad \forall v_0 \in V_0\} \tag{1.105}$$

**THEOREM 1.36**  *Decomposition theorem.* Let $V_0$ be a closed subspace of a Hilbert space $V$. Then $V_0^\perp$, defined by (1.105), is a closed subspace of $V$ and

$$V = V_0 \oplus V_0^\perp \tag{1.106}$$

Moreover, we have $\qquad\qquad P_{V_0} + P_{V_0^\perp} = I (= \text{identity in } V) \tag{1.107}$

so that $P_{V_0}$ and $P_{V_0^\perp}$ are projections associated with the decomposition (1.106) of $V$ (Def. 1.42).

## 1.4c  Adjoint Operators

Now let $V$ be a Hilbert space, let $V_0$ be a dense subspace of $V$, and let $L$ be a linear operator from $V_0$ into $V$. Recalling Defs. 1.30 and 1.31, we may consider the dual operator $L'$ from $D(L') \subset V'$ into $V'$. Formula (1.49) now gives

$$_{V'}\langle L'g, v \rangle_V = {}_{V'}\langle g, Lv \rangle_V \qquad \forall v \in V_0 \qquad \forall g \in D(L')$$

Making use of the Riesz operator $J$ (1.96), we have for $g = Ju$

$$(J^{-1}L'Ju, v) = (u, Lv) \qquad \forall v \in V_0 \qquad \forall u \in J^{-1}(D(L')) \tag{1.108}$$

**DEFINITION 1.44**  The operator $J^{-1}L'J$ defined above is called the *adjoint operator* of $L$. Usual notations are $L^* = J^{-1}L'J$ and $D(L^*) = J^{-1}(D(L')) \subset V$.

Note that (1.108) now becomes

$$(L^*u, v) = (u, Lv) \qquad \forall v \in V_0 \qquad \forall u \in D(L^*) \tag{1.109}$$

**THEOREM 1.37**  If $L \in \mathcal{L}(V; V)$, then $L^* \in \mathcal{L}(V; V)$ and

$$\|L\|_{\mathcal{L}(V;V)} = \|L^*\|_{\mathcal{L}(V;V)} \tag{1.110}$$

**DEFINITION 1.45**  A linear operator $L$ from a dense subspace $V_0$ of a Hilbert space $V$ into $V$ itself is called *symmetric* if $V_0 \subset D(L^*)$ and $L^*v = Lv \ \forall v \in V_0$.

Note that the condition $v_0 \in D(L^*)$ means that there exists a $u_0 \in V$ such that

$$(Lv, v_0) = (v, u_0) \qquad \forall v \in V_0 \tag{1.111}$$

**DEFINITION 1.46**   A linear operator $L$ from a dense subspace $V_0$ of a Hilbert space $V$ into itself is called *self-adjoint* if $D(L^*) = V_0$ and $L^*v = Lv \; \forall v \in V_0$.

**REMARK 1.15**   Note that the relationship

$$(u, Lv) = (Lu, v) \qquad \forall u, v \in V_0 \tag{1.112}$$

implies that $L$ is symmetric but *not* that $L$ is self-adjoint (unless $V_0 \equiv V$).

**THEOREM 1.38**   If $L$ is symmetric and $V_0 = V$, then $L$ is bounded and self-adjoint.

**THEOREM 1.39**   If a self-adjoint operator $L$ admits an inverse $L^{-1}$, then $L^{-1}$ is also self-adjoint.

**THEOREM 1.40**   If $L \in \mathcal{L}(V; V)$ is self-adjoint, then

$$\|L\|_{\mathcal{L}(V;V)} = \sup_{\|v\| \leqslant 1} (Lv, v) \tag{1.113}$$

## 1.4D Orthogonality; Fourier Series

**DEFINITION 1.47**   Let $V$ be a Hilbert space, $v_1, v_2 \in V$, and $A \subset V$. We say that $v_1$ and $v_2$ are *orthogonal* (or that $v_1 \perp v_2$) if $(v_1, v_2) = 0$. We say that $A$ is an *orthogonal set* if $v_1 \perp v_2$ for each pair of distinct elements $v_1$ and $v_2$ of $A$. If, in addition, $\|v\| = 1$ for all $v \in A$, we say that $A$ is an *orthonormal set*.

**DEFINITION 1.48**   Let $V$ be a Hilbert space and $\{u_n\}$ be a (finite or countable infinite) orthonormal set. For any $v \in V$ we define the *Fourier coefficients* of $v$ with respect to $\{u_n\}$ by

$$v_n = (v, u_n) \in \mathbb{R} \tag{1.114}$$

**THEOREM 1.41**   *Bessel inequality.* With the notations of Def. 1.48, we have $\Sigma v_n^2 \leqslant \|v\|^2$ for all $v$ in $V$.

**DEFINITION 1.49**   An orthonormal set $A$ is said to be *complete* in $V$ if span $A$ is dense in $V$.

**THEOREM 1.42**   Let $\{u_n\}$ be a countable complete orthonormal set in a Hilbert space $V$. Let $v \in V$ and let $v_n \in \mathbb{R}$ be defined by (1.114); then

$$\Sigma v_n^2 = \|v\|^2 \qquad (\textit{Parseval relation}) \tag{1.115}$$

$$\lim_{k \to \infty} \sum_{n < k} v_n u_n = v \qquad \text{strongly in } V \tag{1.116}$$

**REMARK 1.16**   It can be proved that if $\{u_n\}$ is an orthonormal set, then (1.116) holds for every $v$ in $V$ iff $\{u_n\}$ is complete.

**REMARK 1.17**   Throughout this section, we have used orthonormal sets which are finite or countably infinite. Nevertheless, all the previous results hold for more general orthonormal sets; we simply wanted to avoid summations over an uncountable set of indices.

## 1.4E Schmidt's Procedure

The following theorem can be used in order to construct orthonormal sets.

**THEOREM 1.43**   Let $\{u_n\}$ be an independent set in a Hilbert space $V$. Define $\{w_n\}$ and $\{z_n\}$ inductively as follows

$$w_0 = u_0 \qquad\qquad z_0 = \frac{w_0}{\|w_0\|}$$

$$w_{n+1} = u_{n+1} - \sum_{k\leqslant n} (u_{n+1}, z_k) z_k \quad z_{n+1} = \frac{w_{n+1}}{\|w_{n+1}\|} \tag{1.117}$$

Then $\{z_n\}$ is an orthonormal set and span $\{z_k, k \leqslant n\} =$ span $\{u_k, k \leqslant n\}$ for every $n$.

**COROLLARY 1.9**   A Hilbert space $V$ is separable iff it has a countable complete orthonormal subset.

## 1.4F Isomorphisms

It is clear that if $V$ is a Hilbert space and $W$ is a normed space isomorphic to $V$, then $W$ is also a Hilbert space. Assume now that we are given two Hilbert spaces, $V$ and $W$. Are they isomorphic? Not in general. We have seen in Cor. 1.1 that two finite-dimensional linear spaces *with the same dimension* are always isomorphic. The same is true for Hilbert spaces.

**THEOREM 1.44**   Two finite-dimensional Hilbert spaces with the same dimension are isometrically isomorphic.

Moreover, for Hilbert spaces the result can be extended to the case of countably infinite dimension.

**THEOREM 1.45**   Two separable infinite-dimensional Hilbert spaces are isometrically isomorphic.

**REMARK 1.18**   In both cases an isometric isomorphism $L$ can be constructed from two complete orthonormal sets, $\{v_n\} \subset V$ and $\{w_n\} \subset W$, as follows:

$$Lv = \Sigma(v, v_n)w_n \qquad \forall v \in V \tag{1.118}$$

**REMARK 1.19**   It follows from Theorem 1.44 that every Hilbert space with dimension $n$ is isometrically isomorphic to $\mathbb{R}^n$ [with the norm (1.39)]. As a typical infinite-dimensional separable Hilbert space one can take

$$l^{(2)} = \{\{a_n\}, a_n \in \mathbb{R}\colon \Sigma a_n^2 < +\infty\} \tag{1.119}$$

with norm $\|\{a_n\}\| = (\Sigma a_n^2)^{1/2}$ and corresponding scalar product $(\{a_n\}, \{b_n\}) = \Sigma a_n b_n$.

## 1.4G Identifications; Hilbert Triplets

Let $V$ be a Banach space and $H$ a Hilbert space. Assume

$$V \hookrightarrow H, \ V \text{ dense in } H \tag{1.120}$$

Then, by (1.76), $H' \hookrightarrow V'$. We now use the Riesz map $J$ of the Hilbert space $H$ (Theorem 1.33) in order to identify $H$ and $H'$. This means that for every $u \in H$ we identify $u$ and $Ju$, writing

$$_H\langle u, v \rangle_H = (u, v)_H \qquad \forall u, v \in H \tag{1.121}$$

Now, combining (1.120), (1.76) and (1.121), we obtain

$$V \hookrightarrow H \equiv H' \hookrightarrow V' \tag{1.122}$$

where the inclusion $H \hookrightarrow V'$ now signifies that

$$_V\langle u, v \rangle_V = (u, v)_H \qquad \forall u \in H \qquad \forall v \in V \tag{1.123}$$

In the special case $V = $ Hilbert space, we call $(V, H, V')$ a *Hilbert triplet*. Hilbert triplets will be used, for instance, to study evolution equations.

An important remark should now be made. We made two identifications: $H' \hookrightarrow V'$ and $H = H'$; from these we *deduced* $H \hookrightarrow V'$ (1.123). This means that (1.123) is not a new (arbitrary) identification, but that (1.123) is *implied* by the previous identifications. The same is true for $V \hookrightarrow H'$, $V \hookrightarrow V'$, which also follow from (1.122). If $V$ is now a Hilbert space, one might be tempted to use the Riesz map again to identify $V$ and $V'$ (which are, indeed, isometrically isomorphic); this would mean setting

$$_V\langle u, v \rangle_V = (u, v)_V \qquad \forall u, v \in V \tag{1.124}$$

However, now (1.123), (1.124) would give

$$(u, v)_V = (u, v)_H \qquad \forall u, v \in V \tag{1.125}$$

and (1.120) and (1.125) imply $V = H$ with $\|\cdot\|_V = \|\cdot\|_H$! Hence, we have the following.

**Warning** Given a Hilbert triplet (1.122), one is *not allowed* to make the further identification $V \equiv V'$ unless $V = H$ with equal norms. More generally, any new identification must be compatible with the two identifications previously assumed in (1.122). The wiser policy, for the inexperienced, is simply not to attempt any new identification in a Hilbert triplet.

## 1.5 REFERENCES

1. Aubin, J. P., *Applied Functional Analysis*, Wiley, New York, 1979.
2. Courant, R., and D. Hilbert, *Methods of Mathematical Physics*, Interscience, New York, vol. I, 1953; vol. II, 1962.
3. Dunford, N., and J. T. Schwartz, *Linear Operators*, Interscience, New York, part I, 1958; part II, 1963.

4. Guelfand, I. M., and G. E. Chilov, *Les Distributions*, Dunod, Paris, tome I, 1963; tome II, 1964; tome III, 1965. (Russian ed., Nauka, Moscow, 1958.)

5. Hörmander, L., *Linear Partial Differential Operators*, 2d rev. ptg., Springer, Berlin, 1964.

6. Kato, T., *Perturbation Theory for Linear Operators*, Springer, Berlin, 1966.

7. Kolmogorov, A. N., and S. V. Fomin, *Elements of the Theory of Functions and Functional Analysis*, vol. I, Graylock, Rochester, 1957 (Russian ed., 1954); vol. II, Graylock, Baltimore, 1961 (Russian ed., 1960).

8. Nečas, J., *Les Méthodes Directes en Théorie des Equations Elliptiques*, Masson, Paris/Academia, Prague, 1967.

9. Riesz, F., and B. Sz.-Nagy, *Functional Analysis*, Frederick Ungar, New York, 1955.

10. Rudin, W., *Functional Analysis*, McGraw-Hill, New York, 1973.

11. Treves, G., *Topological Vector Spaces, Distributions and Kernels*, Academic Press, New York, 1967.

12. Yoshida, K., *Functional Analysis*, 3d ed., Springer, Berlin, 1971.

# CHAPTER 2
# FUNCTIONAL SPACES

## 2.1 INTRODUCTION

In this chapter we introduce some functional spaces which are important in boundary-value problems. Roughly speaking, we introduce two families: first, functional spaces noted to continuity, Hölder continuity, and differentiability in the classical sense; then, the so-called Sobolev spaces, whose construction uses Lebesgue integrals and the definition of a weak derivative, that is, a derivative in the sense of distributions. Hence, some background on distributions is given. At the end of this chapter we introduce analogous spaces, whose elements are functions valued in a Banach space, instead of real functions. These are used in studying equations of evolution.

All spaces of real functions that we introduce are constructed on open subsets $\Omega$ of $\mathbb{R}^n$. Even if some definitions and properties do not need any assumptions on $\Omega$, many results are true only for particular open sets. Therefore, for simplicity, we introduce all the assumptions at the outset.

For further information on the topics discussed in this Chapter, see the sources listed in Sec. 2.11.

## 2.2 ASSUMPTIONS ON $\Omega$

**DEFINITION 2.1**  An open subset $\Omega$ of $\mathbb{R}^n$ is called *smooth* (or a *smooth domain*) iff it is connected and bounded and satisfies the following condition:

For every $x_0 \in \partial\Omega$ there exist $r(x_0) > 0$ and a coordinate system $(\xi_1, \ldots, \xi_n)$ with origin at $x_0$ such that $\Omega \cap B_{r(x_0)}(x_0)$ and $\partial\Omega \cap B_{r(x_0)}(x_0)$ are described in new coordinates respectively by

$$\{(\xi_1, \ldots, \xi_n) \in B_{r(x_0)}: \xi_n > \zeta_{x_0}(\xi_1, \ldots, \xi_{n-1})\} \qquad \text{and}$$

$$\{(\xi_1, \ldots, \xi_n) \in B_{r(x_0)}: \xi_n = \zeta_{x_0}(\xi_1, \ldots, \xi_{n-1})\} \tag{2.1}$$

where $\zeta_{x_0}$ is a function defined on $\mathbb{R}^{n-1}$ continuous with all the derivatives of every order.

For instance, a ball $B_R(0)$ in $\mathbb{R}^2$ is smooth. Indeed, if $x_0 \in \partial B_R$ and $\zeta_{x_0}$ coincides on $[-R/2, R/2]$ with $\zeta_{x_0}(\xi_1) = R - (R^2 - \xi_1^2)^{1/2}$, (2.1) holds if $r(x_0) < R$ and the $\xi_1$-axis and the $\xi_2$-axis are tangential and orthogonal, respectively, to $\partial B_R$ at $x_0$.

**DEFINITION 2.2**   An open subset $\Omega$ of $\mathbb{R}^n$ is called a *convex polygon* iff it is bounded and there exists a finite number $m$ of scalars $c_i$ and linear maps $L_i : \mathbb{R}^n \to \mathbb{R}$ such that

$$\Omega = \{x \in \mathbb{R}^n: L_i x > c_i, i = 1, \ldots, m\}$$

Every such $\Omega$ is convex. Moreover, for $n = 2$ we obtain exactly all the convex polygons in the usual sense.

**DEFINITION 2.3**   An open subset $\Omega$ of $\mathbb{R}^n$ is called a *polygon* iff it is connected and there exists a finite number of convex polygons $\Omega_j$ such that $\Omega = $ interior of $\cup \bar{\Omega}_j$.

**ASSUMPTION 2.1**   We will always assume that one of the following conditions holds:

$$\Omega \text{ is smooth} \tag{2.2}$$

$$\Omega \text{ is a polygon} \tag{2.3}$$

$$\Omega \text{ is the half space } \mathbb{R}^n_+ = \{x \in \mathbb{R}^n: x_n > 0\} \text{ or } \mathbb{R}^n_- = \{x \in \mathbb{R}^n: x_n < 0\} \tag{2.4}$$

$$\Omega \text{ is the whole space } \mathbb{R}^n \tag{2.5}$$

For instance, "$\Omega$ bounded" will mean that either (2.2) or (2.3) holds; "any $\Omega$" will mean that one of (2.2) to (2.5) holds. However, it should be clear that more general domains could be considered, e.g., a *half ball* $B_1 \cap \mathbb{R}^n_+$, which behaves locally as either a smooth set or a polygon. We shall use such domains in the examples whenever this simplifies the exposition.

## 2.3 SPACES OF CONTINUOUS FUNCTIONS

### 2.3A The Space $C^0(\bar{\Omega})$

The space $C^0(\Omega)$ was defined in Example 1.4 of Part 1. We now set the following definition.

**DEFINITION 2.4**   $C^0(\bar{\Omega}) = \{v \in C^0(\Omega): v \text{ is bounded and uniformly continuous in } \Omega\}$ with the norm

$$\|v\|_{C^0(\bar{\Omega})} = \sup_{x \in \Omega} |v(x)| \tag{2.6}$$

REMARK 2.1   Notice that

$$v_n \to v \text{ in } C^0(\bar{\Omega}) \text{ iff } \lim v_n(x) = v(x) \text{ uniformly in } \Omega \tag{2.7}$$

REMARK 2.2   We recall that $v$ is uniformly continuous iff $\forall \varepsilon > 0 \; \exists \delta > 0: |x - y| < \delta$ implies that $|v(x) - v(y)| < \varepsilon$; we also recall that uniform continuity implies continuity, but the converse is not true. Thus, in particular, one has to distinguish between $C^0(\mathbb{R}^n)$ and $C^0(\overline{\mathbb{R}^n})$, even if $\mathbb{R}^n = \overline{\mathbb{R}^n}$. In this case the unusual notation $\overline{C^0}(\Omega)$, instead of $C^0(\bar{\Omega})$, would be clearer. The same remark has to be made for other spaces in this section.

REMARK 2.3   It is well known that a bounded and uniformly continuous function $v$ on $\Omega$ has a unique continuous extension on $\bar{\Omega}$, which is bounded and uniformly continuous and which we also denote by $v$, because of uniqueness. This fact justifies the notation $C^0(\bar{\Omega})$. In particular, *if $\Omega$ is bounded*, this implies that *our definition coincides with the more usual one*:

$$C^0(\bar{\Omega}) = \{\text{restrictions on } \Omega \text{ of functions which are continuous on } \bar{\Omega}\}$$

## 2.3B  The Spaces $C^k(\bar{\Omega})$

If $k \in \mathbb{N}$, $C^k(\Omega)$ is the set of functions $v \in C^0(\Omega)$ whose derivatives of order $\leq k$ exist and are continuous. For $v \in C^k(\Omega)$ the notation [see Eq. (1.16) in Part 1]

$$D^\alpha v = D_1^{\alpha_1} \cdots D_n^{\alpha_n} v \quad \text{where } D_j = \frac{\partial}{\partial x_j} \quad (D_j^0 = \text{identity}) \tag{2.8}$$

for $|\alpha| \leq k$ can be used because of the Schwarz theorem.

DEFINITION 2.5   We set

$$C^k(\bar{\Omega}) = \{v \in C^k(\Omega): D^\alpha v \in C^0(\bar{\Omega}) \text{ for } |\alpha| \leq k\} \tag{2.9}$$

Hence the derivatives of order $\leq k$ of functions $v \in C^k(\bar{\Omega})$ can be extended up to the boundary by Rem. 2.3. For $v \in C^k(\bar{\Omega})$ we define the following seminorm and norm:

$$|v|_{C^k(\bar{\Omega})} = \sum_{|\alpha| = k} \|D^\alpha v\|_{C^0(\bar{\Omega})} \tag{2.10}$$

$$\|v\|_{C^k(\bar{\Omega})} = \sum_{j=0}^{k} |v|_{C^j(\bar{\Omega})} = \sum_{|\alpha| \leq k} \|D^\alpha v\|_{C^0(\bar{\Omega})} \tag{2.11}$$

Notice that (2.11) is a graph norm (see Sec. 1.3M).

## 2.3c  The Spaces $C^{0,\lambda}(\bar{\Omega})$

DEFINITION 2.6   Assume $0 < \lambda \leq 1$. A function $v$ on $\Omega$ is called *$\lambda$-Hölder-continuous* (or *Hölder-continuous of order $\lambda$*) iff the function $|v(x) - v(y)| \cdot |x - y|^{-\lambda}$ is bounded on $\{(x, y) \in \Omega \times \Omega: x \neq y\}$.

In other words, $v(x)$ is $\lambda$-Hölder-continuous iff $\exists M > 0$ such that $|v(x) - v(y)| \leq M|x - y|^\lambda$ $\forall x, y \in \Omega$. Thus $\lambda$-Hölder continuity implies uniform continuity [take $\delta = (\varepsilon/M)^{1/\lambda}$], so that bounded $\lambda$-Hölder-continuous functions belong to $C^0(\bar{\Omega})$.

**DEFINITION 2.7**  We set for $0 < \lambda \leq 1$:

$$C^{0,\lambda}(\bar{\Omega}) = \{v \in C^0(\bar{\Omega}): v \text{ is } \lambda\text{-Hölder-continuous in } \Omega\} \qquad (2.12)$$

with the following seminorm and norm:

$$|v|_{C^{0,\lambda}(\bar{\Omega})} = \sup_{x,y \in \Omega, x \neq y} |v(x) - v(y)||x - y|^{-\lambda} \qquad (2.13)$$

$$\|v\|_{C^{0,\lambda}(\bar{\Omega})} = \|v\|_{C^0(\bar{\Omega})} + |v|_{C^{0,\lambda}(\bar{\Omega})} \qquad (2.14)$$

**REMARK 2.4**  In Defs. 2.6 and 2.7, we assumed $0 < \lambda \leq 1$, even if the definitions make sense for any $\lambda$. But $\lambda \leq 0$ and $\lambda > 1$ are trivial cases. Indeed, (2.13) is finite for every $v \in C^0(\bar{\Omega})$ if $\lambda < 0$ and $\Omega$ is bounded; if $\lambda < 0$ and $\Omega$ is unbounded, (2.13) is finite iff $v$ is a constant; the same is true for any $\Omega$ if $\lambda > 1$. Finally (2.13) is finite for any $v \in C^0(\bar{\Omega})$ if $\lambda = 0$ for any $\Omega$. This suggests the definition

$$C^{0,0}(\bar{\Omega}) = C^0(\bar{\Omega}) \qquad (2.15)$$

## 2.3D The Spaces $C^{k,\lambda}(\bar{\Omega})$ and $C^{k,\lambda}(\Omega)$

**DEFINITION 2.8**  For $k \in \mathbb{N}$ and $0 \leq \lambda \leq 1$ we set

$$C^{k,\lambda}(\bar{\Omega}) = \{v \in C^k(\bar{\Omega}): D^\alpha v \in C^{0,\lambda}(\bar{\Omega}) \text{ for } |\alpha| \leq k\} \qquad (2.16)$$

with the following seminorm and norm:

$$|v|_{C^{k,\lambda}(\bar{\Omega})} = \sum_{|\alpha|=k} |D^\alpha v|_{C^{0,\lambda}(\bar{\Omega})} \qquad (2.17)$$

$$\|v\|_{C^{k,\lambda}(\bar{\Omega})} = \sum_{|\alpha|\leq k} \|D^\alpha v\|_{C^{0,\lambda}(\bar{\Omega})} \qquad (2.18)$$

We introduce the following notation

$$\Omega_1 \subset\subset \Omega \qquad means \qquad \Omega_1 \text{ and } \Omega \text{ are open, } \Omega_1 \text{ is bounded,}$$

$$\text{and } \bar{\Omega}_1 \subset \Omega \qquad (2.19)$$

**DEFINITION 2.9**  We set, for $0 \leq \lambda \leq 1$ and $k \in \mathbb{N}$:

$$C^{k,\lambda}(\Omega) = \{v \in C^k(\Omega): v_{|\Omega_1} \in C^{k,\lambda}(\bar{\Omega}_1) \text{ for every } \Omega_1 \subset\subset \Omega\} \qquad (2.20)$$

Notice that $C^{k,0}(\Omega) = C^k(\Omega)$ by (2.15)

**REMARK 2.5**  For $0 < \lambda \leq 1$, elements of $C^{0,\lambda}(\Omega)$ are called locally $\lambda$-Hölder-continuous functions. In particular, for $\lambda = 1$, 1-Hölder-continuous and locally 1-Hölder-continuous functions are called *Lipschitz-continuous* and *locally Lipschitz-continuous functions*, respectively. Moreover, a function is called Hölder-continuous (*locally Hölder-continuous*) iff it is $\lambda$-Hölder-continuous (locally $\lambda$-Hölder-continuous) for some $\lambda \in ]0, 1]$.

## 2.3E The Spaces $C^\infty(\Omega)$, $C^\infty(\bar\Omega)$, and $C_0^\infty(\Omega)$

**DEFINITION 2.10**   We set

$$C^\infty(\Omega) = \{v \in C^0(\Omega): v \in C^k(\Omega) \ \forall k\} \tag{2.21}$$

$$C^\infty(\bar\Omega) = \{v \in C^0(\bar\Omega): v \in C^k(\bar\Omega) \ \forall k\} \tag{2.22}$$

If $V$ is any linear space (thus, in particular, if $V = \mathbb{R}$) and $\Omega$ is any open set in $\mathbb{R}^n$, we introduce the following notation:

A function $v: \Omega \to V$ is a *compact support function* iff there exists $\Omega_1 \subset\subset \Omega$ such that $v$ vanishes outside $\Omega_1$. $\tag{2.23}$

**DEFINITION 2.11**   We set

$$C_0^\infty(\Omega) = \{v \in C^\infty(\Omega): v \text{ is a compact support function}\} \tag{2.24}$$

**REMARK 2.6**   With suitable definitions of *compact* and *support*, a compact support function would be a function whose support is compact.

## 2.3F Miscellaneous Properties

In $C^k(\bar\Omega)$ and in $C^{k,\lambda}(\bar\Omega)$ we have defined norms. The choice we have made for them is strictly related to the corresponding spaces; that is, all the properties in the definitions of spaces are related to terms of the corresponding norms. More precisely, we used graph norms (cf. Sec. 1.3M in Part 1). That is essentially why the next theorem is true.

**THEOREM 2.1**   For $k \in \mathbb{N}$ and $0 \leq \lambda \leq 1$, $C^k(\bar\Omega)$ and $C^{k,\lambda}(\bar\Omega)$ are Banach spaces with (2.11) and (2.18), respectively. Moreover, they are separable iff $\Omega$ is bounded and $\lambda = 0$; none of them is reflexive.

It is clear that, for $0 < \lambda \leq 1$ the functions of the spaces $C^{k,\lambda}(\bar\Omega)$ have a regularity which is intermediate between $C^k(\bar\Omega)$ and $C^{k+1}(\bar\Omega)$. More generally, we have the following *inclusion* theorem.

**THEOREM 2.2**   For $k, l \in \mathbb{N}$ and $\lambda, \mu \in [0, 1]$ we have:

$l + \mu < k + \lambda$ implies $C^{k,\lambda}(\bar\Omega) \hookrightarrow C^{l,\mu}(\bar\Omega)$ $\tag{2.25}$

$k \geq 1$ implies $C^k(\bar\Omega) \hookrightarrow C^{k-1,1}(\bar\Omega)$ $\tag{2.26}$

Algebraic inclusions corresponding to (2.25) and (2.26) hold for $C^k(\Omega)$ and $C^{k,\lambda}(\Omega)$ $\tag{2.27}$

$C_0^\infty(\Omega) \subset C^\infty(\bar\Omega) \subset C^{k,\lambda}(\bar\Omega) \subset C^k(\bar\Omega)$, and $C^\infty(\bar\Omega) \subset C^\infty(\Omega)$ $\tag{2.28}$

Moreover,

The inclusion (2.25) is compact iff $\Omega$ is bounded; the inclusion (2.26) is never compact. $\tag{2.29}$

Regarding the *density* properties we have the following theorem.

**THEOREM 2.3**   For $k \in \mathbb{N}$ and $0 \leqslant \lambda \leqslant 1$, we have:

$$C^\infty(\bar{\Omega}) \text{ is dense in } C^{k,\lambda}(\bar{\Omega}) \text{ iff } \lambda = 0 \qquad (2.30)$$

$$C_0^\infty(\Omega) \text{ is not dense in } C^{k,\lambda}(\bar{\Omega}) \qquad (2.31)$$

**REMARK 2.7**   Theorem 2.3 implies that, for instance, $C^0(\bar{\Omega})$ is a completion (Sec. 1.3 of Part 1) of $C^\infty(\bar{\Omega})$ with the norm $\|\cdot\|_{C^0}$; hence *a fortiori*, of $C^1(\bar{\Omega})$ with the norm $\|\cdot\|_{C^0}$. Therefore $C^1(\bar{\Omega})$ with the norm $\|\cdot\|_{C^0}$ is not complete. This shows the importance of the use of the graph norm.

In many particular cases, *different norms* may be useful; some of them are given in the next theorem.

**THEOREM 2.4**   For $k \in \mathbb{N}$, $0 \leqslant \lambda \leqslant 1$, $\Omega$ bounded, $x_0 \in \Omega$ we have:

The norm $\|v\|_{C^k}$ is equivalent (*see* Def. 1.33 in Part 1) to both

$$\|v\|_{C^0} + |v|_{C^k} \qquad \text{and} \qquad \sum_{|\alpha| \leqslant k} |D^\alpha v(x_0)| + |v|_{C^k} \qquad (2.32)$$

The norm $\|v\|_{C^{k,\lambda}}$ is equivalent to both

$$\|v\|_{C^0} + |v|_{C^{k,\lambda}} \qquad \text{and} \qquad \sum_{|\alpha| \leqslant k} |D^\alpha v(x_0)| + |v|_{C^{k,\lambda}} \qquad (2.33)$$

## 2.3G  Examples

We give the following one-dimensional examples:

**EXAMPLE 2.1**   For $k \in \mathbb{N}$ and $0 < \lambda < 1$: $x^{k+\lambda} \in C^{k,\lambda}([0,1]) \cap C^\infty(]0,1[)$, but $x^{k+\lambda} \notin C^{k,\mu}([0,1])$ for $\mu > \lambda$.

**EXAMPLE 2.2**   $\sin x^{-1} \in C^\infty(]0,1[)$, but $\sin x^{-1} \notin C^0([0,1])$.

**EXAMPLE 2.3**   $1/(\ln x) \in C^0([0,\frac{1}{2}]) \cap C^\infty(]0,\frac{1}{2}[)$, but $1/(\ln x) \notin C^{0,\lambda}([0,\frac{1}{2}])$ for $\lambda > 0$; in fact, $1/(\ln x) \to 0$ and $x^{-\lambda}/(\ln x) \to \infty$ for $\lambda > 0$ as $x \to 0+$.

**EXAMPLE 2.4**   $n^{-1} \sin nx \to 0$ in $C^{0,\lambda}([0,1])$ $\forall \lambda \in [0,1[$, but not in $C^{0,1}([0,1])$.

**EXAMPLE 2.5**   $(x^2 + n^{-1})^{1/4} \to x^{1/2}$ in $C^0([0,1])$. Notice that $x^{1/2}$ is irregular even if $(x^2 + n^{-1})^{1/4} \in C^\infty([0,1])$.

**EXAMPLE 2.6**   In any dimension, consider a function $u$ which is $C^\infty$ for $x \neq 0$ and $\mu$-homogeneous, that is, $u(tx) = t^\mu u(x)$ $\forall x \in \mathbb{R}^n \backslash \{0\}$, $\forall t > 0$. If $u$ is not a polynomial, then $u \in C^{k,\lambda}(\bar{B}_1)$ iff $\mu \geqslant k + \lambda$ $0 < \lambda \leqslant 1$).

**EXAMPLE 2.7**   In particular, in two dimensions, using polar coordinates: $u = \rho^\mu \sin \mu\theta$, $0 < \theta < \pi$, is a polynomial iff $\mu \in \mathbb{N}$. Otherwise $u \in C^{k,\lambda}(\bar{B}_1 \cap \mathbb{R}_+^2)$ iff $\mu \geqslant k + \lambda$. The same is true with cos in place of sin.

## 2.4 THE $L^p$ SPACES

### 2.4A The Space $\mathcal{M}(\Omega)$ of Measurable Functions

We recall one of the possible definitions: a function $v \in \mathcal{F}(\Omega)$ (1.5) is called *measurable* iff
a sequence of functions $v_k \in C^0(\Omega)$ (1.15) exists such that $v_k \to v$ almost everywhere in $\Omega$
[i.e., the set where $v_k(x)$ does not converge to $v(x)$ as $k \to \infty$ has zero Lebesgue measure].
Now we identify two measurable functions $u$ and $v$ iff $u = v$ almost everywhere in $\Omega$ (i.e.,
iff the set where $u(x) \neq v(x)$ has zero Lebesgue measure). In this context, we can allow
functions to be defined only almost everywhere in $\Omega$ instead of everywhere. The reason for
such an identification will be clear in Sec. 2.4C. After this identification is made, we call
$\mathcal{M}(\Omega)$ the resulting set of measurable functions. Therefore the equality relation is not the
logical identity relation, since $u = v$ means $u = v$ almost everywhere in $\Omega$ (all these facts
could be made more rigorous by introducing an equivalence relation instead of an identification). Now we want to define some operations on $\mathcal{M}(\Omega)$. To do this we have to be
careful and pay attention to the following: not everything that makes sense for functions
[i.e., elements of $\mathcal{F}(\Omega)$ where $u = v$ means $u(x) = v(x) \, \forall x$] still makes sense for elements of
$\mathcal{M}(\Omega)$; we are now allowed to define only what is invariant under changing functions on sets
of zero Lebesgue measure. For instance, the value at one point, the restriction to a curve (if
$n \geq 2$), and the pointwise limits do not make sense. On the contrary, $u + v$, $uv$, $\alpha u$, $u < v, \ldots$,
make sense for $u, v \in \mathcal{M}(\Omega)$ and $\alpha \in \mathbb{R}$. Indeed, $u_1 = u_2$ and $v_1 = v_2$ almost everywhere implies
that $u_1 + v_1 = u_2 + v_2$ almost everywhere, and similarly $uv$, $\alpha u$, and so on. In particular, $\mathcal{M}(\Omega)$
becomes a linear space. The composition $f \circ u$ makes sense for $u \in \mathcal{M}(\Omega)$ and $f \in C^0(\mathbb{R})$, i.e.
$f \circ u$ is measurable [while if $f \notin C^0(\mathbb{R})$, $f \circ u$ need not be measurable], and $u_1 = u_2$ almost
everywhere implies that $f \circ u_1 = f \circ u_2$ almost everywhere. In particular, for $u \in \mathcal{M}(\Omega)$, we have
$u^+$, $u^-$, $|u|^p \in \mathcal{M}(\Omega)$ for $p > 0$. For positive measurable functions the Lebesgue integral is
always defined, and could be $= \infty$; we recall that

$$v \in \mathcal{M}(\Omega) \quad \text{and} \quad \int_\Omega |v|^p = 0 \quad \text{imply} \quad v = 0 \text{ almost everywhere} \quad (2.34)$$

In what follows all integrals will be Lebesgue integrals. Finally, we recall that $u_k \in \mathcal{M}(\Omega)$ and
$u(x) = \lim u_k(x)$ almost everywhere implies $u \in \mathcal{M}(\Omega)$; i.e., the limit almost everywhere makes
sense.

### 2.4B The Inclusion $C^0(\Omega) \subset \mathcal{M}(\Omega)$

By definition every continuous function is measurable. However, the identity relations in
$C^0(\Omega)$ and $\mathcal{M}(\Omega)$ are different, so that a continuous function can be considered as an element
of $\mathcal{M}(\Omega)$ only in the sense of Sec. 1.3L in Part 1. To be precise, for $u \in C^0(\Omega)$ consider,
besides $u$, all measurable $v$ such that $u = v$ almost everywhere: they give the same measurable
function. Hence, a natural map from $C^0(\Omega)$ into $\mathcal{M}(\Omega)$ is defined. Notice that it is linear
and injective, since $u, v \in C^0(\Omega)$ and $u = v$ almost everywhere implies $u(x) = v(x) \, \forall x$. According to Sec. 1.3L, we thus identify $C^0(\Omega)$ with a subspace of $\mathcal{M}(\Omega)$. In particular, all spaces
of Sec. 2.3 become subspaces of $\mathcal{M}(\Omega)$, since they are subspaces of $C^0(\Omega)$.

## 2.4c The Spaces $L^p(\Omega)$

**DEFINITION 2.12**   We set for $1 \leqslant p < \infty$:

$$L^p(\Omega) = \left\{ v \in \mathcal{M}(\Omega) : \int_\Omega |u|^p < \infty \right\} \tag{2.35}$$

The elementary inequality $|u + v|^p \leqslant 2^{p-1}(|u|^p + |v|^p)$ implies that $L^p(\Omega)$ *is a subspace of* $\mathcal{M}(\Omega)$.
For $v \in L^p(\Omega)$ define

$$\|v\|_{L^p(\Omega)} = \|v\|_{0,p,\Omega} = \left( \int_\Omega |u|^p \right)^{1/2} \tag{2.36}$$

where $\Omega$ is omitted when no confusion is possible. $\|\cdot\|_{0,p}$ *is a norm on* $L^p$: the triangle inequality (1.28) for $\|\cdot\|_{0,p}$ is obvious when $p = 1$. However, it still holds iff $p \geqslant 1$, and is called *Minkowsky's inequality*; $\|v\|_{0,p} = 0$ iff $v = 0$ almost everywhere, by (2.34) above. That is why we made the identification in Sec. 2.4A. The convergence in $L^p(\Omega)$ is related, but not equivalent, to the convergence almost everywhere. One can prove that

$$v_k \to v \text{ in } L^p \text{ implies } v_{k_j} \to v \text{ almost everywhere for some subsequence } \{v_{k_j}\} \tag{2.37}$$

$$v_k \to v \text{ almost everywhere and } |v_k| \leqslant u, \text{ for some fixed } u \in L^p, \text{ imply } v_k \to v \text{ in } L^p \tag{2.38}$$

Moreover, from $|\int u_k - \int u| \leqslant \|u_k - u\|_{0,1}$ we have

$$u_k \to u \text{ in } L^1 \text{ implies } \int u_k \to \int u \tag{2.39}$$

It is easy to see that, for $v \in \mathcal{M}(\Omega)$, sup $v$ and inf $v$ (where sup and inf are the standard abbreviations for supremum and infimum) do not make sense, since $u = v$ almost everywhere does not imply sup $u = $ sup $v$. Hence we introduce, for $v \in \mathcal{M}(\Omega)$,

$$\sup_{\Omega} \text{ess } v = \sup_{x \in \Omega} \text{ess } v(x)$$

$$= \inf \{M \in \,]{-\infty}, +\infty] : v(x) \leqslant M \text{ almost everywhere in } \Omega\} \tag{2.40}$$

and        $$\inf_{\Omega} \text{ess } v = \inf_{x \in \Omega} \text{ess } v(x)$$

$$= \sup \{M \in [-\infty, +\infty[\, : v(x) \geqslant M \text{ almost everywhere in } \Omega\} \tag{2.41}$$

When sup ess $v < +\infty$ (inf ess $v > -\infty$), $v$ is called *essentially bounded above* (resp. *below*) or, in short, *bounded above* (resp. *below*). $v$ is called *essentially bounded* (or *bounded*) iff both sup ess $v$ and inf ess $v$ are finite.

**DEFINITION 2.13**   We define

$$L^\infty(\Omega) = \{v \in \mathcal{M}(\Omega) : v \text{ is bounded}\} \tag{2.42}$$

For $v \in L^\infty(\Omega)$ we set

$$\|v\|_{L^\infty(\Omega)} = \|v\|_{0,\infty,\Omega} = \sup_{\Omega} \text{ess } |v| \tag{2.43}$$

and omit $\Omega$ when no confusion is possible. Moreover, sometimes one writes sup and inf instead of sup ess and inf ess. Clearly, (2.43) is a norm. The reason for these notations is the following:

$$\|v\|_{L^\infty} = \lim_{p\uparrow\infty} \|v\|_{L^p} \quad \text{for } v \in L^p \; \forall p \in [1, \infty] \tag{2.44}$$

Notice that for continuous $v$, $\sup v = \sup$ ess $v$, etc. Thus

$$C^0(\bar\Omega) \hookrightarrow L^\infty(\Omega) \quad \text{and} \quad \|v\|_{C^0} = \|v\|_{L^\infty} \quad \forall v \in C^0(\bar\Omega) \tag{2.45}$$

**THEOREM 2.5** For $1 \le p \le \infty$, $L^p(\Omega)$ is a Banach space. Moreover, $L^p(\Omega)$ is separable iff $1 \le p < \infty$ and it is a Hilbert space iff $p = 2$. The scalar product in $L^2(\Omega)$ is given by

$$(u, v)_{L^2(\Omega)} = (u, v)_{0,\Omega} = \int_\Omega uv \tag{2.46}$$

**THEOREM 2.6** Assume $p, p_1, \ldots, p_m \in [1, \infty]$ and $\Sigma p_i^{-1} = p^{-1}$ (with $\infty^{-1} = 0$). If $v_i \in L^{p_i}(\Omega)$ for $i = 1, \ldots, m$, then the function $\Pi v_i$ belongs to $L^p(\Omega)$ and

$$\|\Pi v_i\|_{0,p,\Omega} \le \Pi \|v_i\|_{0,p_i,\Omega} \quad (\text{Hölder's inequality}) \tag{2.47}$$

In particular, 
$$\left| \int_\Omega \Pi v_i \right| \le \Pi \|v_i\|_{0,p_i,\Omega} \quad \text{if} \quad \Sigma p_i^{-1} = 1 \tag{2.48}$$

i.e., the map $(v_1, \ldots, v_m) \to \int \Pi v_i$ is a continuous $m$-linear form on $L^{p_1}(\Omega) \times \cdots \times L^{p_m}(\Omega)$.

Defining $q'$ as follows, for $q \in [1, \infty]$:

$$\frac{1}{q} + \frac{1}{q'} = 1 \tag{2.49}$$

from (2.48) with $m = 2$ we have

$$\left| \int_\Omega uv \right| \le \|u\|_{0,q,\Omega} \|v\|_{0,q',\Omega} \quad \forall u \in L^q(\Omega) \quad \forall v \in L^{q'}(\Omega) \tag{2.50}$$

The number $q'$ given by (2.49) is called the *conjugate* of $q$. Notice that $(q')' = q$, $2' = 2$, $1' = \infty$, $\infty' = 1$. In particular, (2.50) becomes the *Schwarz inequality* when $q = 2$. When $\Omega$ is bounded and $\Sigma p_i^{-1} \le p^{-1}$, setting $r^{-1} = p^{-1} - \Sigma p_i^{-1}$, we have $r \ge 1$ and $1 \in L^r(\Omega)$, so that (2.47) gives

$$\|\Pi v_i\|_{0,p,\Omega} \le \|1\|_{0,r,\Omega} \cdot \Pi \|v_i\|_{0,p_i,\Omega} \tag{2.51}$$

**THEOREM 2.7** Assume $1 \le p \le q < \infty$. Then we have

$$L^p(\Omega) \cap L^q(\Omega) \hookrightarrow L^r(\Omega) \quad \forall r \in [p, q] \tag{2.52}$$

$$\|u\|_{0,r} \leqslant \|u\|_{0,p}^{\theta} \|u\|_{0,q}^{1-\theta}$$

with $\qquad\qquad \theta = \dfrac{[(q-r)p]}{[(q-p)r]} \qquad \forall r \in [p,q] \qquad \forall u \in L^p(\Omega) \cap L^q(\Omega)$ (2.53)

$$\text{if } \Omega \text{ is bounded, then } L^\infty(\Omega) \hookrightarrow L^q(\Omega) \hookrightarrow L^p(\Omega) \hookrightarrow L^1(\Omega)$$ (2.54)

**THEOREM 2.8** $C_0^\infty(\Omega)$ and $C^\infty(\bar{\Omega})$ are dense in $L^p(\Omega)$ iff $1 \leqslant p < \infty$.

## 2.4D The Dual Space $(L^p(\Omega))'$; Reflexivity

For $u \in L^{p'}(\Omega)$ [see (2.49)] consider the map $L(u): v \to \int uv$ defined for $v \in L^p(\Omega)$. By (2.50) $L(u)$ is continuous on $L^p(\Omega)$; that is, $L(u) \in (L^p(\Omega))'$. Moreover, the map $u \to L(u)$ is one-to-one, linear, and isometric from $L^{p'}(\Omega)$ into $(L^p(\Omega))'$. If, moreover, $p < \infty$ this map is *onto*. Therefore, if $p < \infty$ we *identify* $(L^p(\Omega))'$ with $L^{p'}(\Omega)$ and write

$$_{(L^p)}\langle u, v \rangle_{L^p} = {}_{0,p',\Omega}\langle u, v \rangle_{0,p,\Omega} = \int_\Omega uv\, dx \qquad \text{for } u \in L^{p'}(\Omega), \qquad v \in L^p(\Omega), \qquad 1 \leqslant p < \infty$$ (2.55)

In particular, $L^2(\Omega)$ is identified with its dual, and the identification we made agrees with our definitions in Sec. 1.4G in Part 1.

**THEOREM 2.9** The space $L^p(\Omega)$ is reflexive iff $1 < p < \infty$.

## 2.4E Weak and Weak* Convergence

By Sec. 2.4D, we have for $1 \leqslant p < \infty$

$$v_k \rightharpoonup v \text{ in } L^p(\Omega) \text{ iff } \int_\Omega uv_k \to \int_\Omega uv \qquad \forall u \in L^{p'}(\Omega)$$ (2.56)

If $1 < p \leqslant \infty$, then $1 \leqslant p' < \infty$, so that Sec. 2.4D applied to $p'$ gives $L^p(\Omega) = (L^{p'}(\Omega))'$. In particular, weak* convergence in $L^p(\Omega)$ makes sense for $1 < p \leqslant \infty$. Given Theorems 2.9 and 1.19 in Part 1, the only interesting case is $p = \infty$. We have

$$v_k \overset{*}{\rightharpoonup} v \text{ in } L^\infty(\Omega) \text{ iff } \int_\Omega uv_k \to \int_\Omega uv \qquad \forall u \in L^1(\Omega)$$ (2.57)

For instance, $\sin kx \overset{*}{\rightharpoonup} 0$ in $L^\infty(0,1)$.

## 2.4F The Spaces $L_{loc}^p(\Omega)$

Besides the spaces $L^p$ we introduce the spaces $L_{loc}^p$. The relations between $L^p$ and $L_{loc}^p$ and between $C^{k,\lambda}(\bar{\Omega})$ and $C^{k,\lambda}(\Omega)$ are very close. This idea will be generalized in Sec. 2.7F.

**DEFINITION 2.14** We set for $1 \leqslant p \leqslant \infty$

$$L_{loc}^p(\Omega) = \{v \in \mathcal{M}(\Omega): v_{|\Omega_1} \in L^p(\Omega_1) \; \forall \Omega_1 \subset\subset \Omega\}$$ (2.58)

We note that for any $\Omega$ and for $1 \leqslant p \leqslant q \leqslant \infty$ we have

$$L^p(\Omega) \subset L^p_{\text{loc}}(\Omega) \tag{2.59}$$

$$C^0(\Omega) \subset L^\infty_{\text{loc}}(\Omega) \subset L^q_{\text{loc}}(\Omega) \subset L^p_{\text{loc}}(\Omega) \subset L^1_{\text{loc}}(\Omega) \tag{2.60}$$

## 2.4G Examples

In one dimension we have the following examples.

**EXAMPLE 2.8**  $x^\lambda \in L^p(]0, 1[)$ iff $\lambda p > -1$; $x^\lambda \in L^p(]1, \infty[)$ iff $\lambda p < -1$.

**EXAMPLE 2.9**  $x^{-1/p}|\ln x|^\mu \in L^p(]0, \frac{1}{2}[)$ iff $\mu p < -1$; $x^{-1/p}(\ln x)^\mu \in L^p(]2, \infty[)$ iff $\mu p < -1$.

**EXAMPLE 2.10**  $\ln x \in L^p(]0, 1[)$ iff $p < \infty$; $\ln x \in L^p_{\text{loc}}(]0, \infty[)$ $\forall p$.

**EXAMPLE 2.11**  $x^{-1} \in L^1_{\text{loc}}(]0, \infty[)$, but $x^{-1} \notin L^1_{\text{loc}}(\mathbb{R})$.

In two dimensions, using polar coordinates, we have the following examples.

**EXAMPLE 2.12**  $\rho^\lambda \in L^p(B_1)$ iff $\lambda p > -2$; $\rho^\lambda \in L^p(\mathbb{R}^2 \backslash B_1)$ iff $\lambda p < -2$.

**EXAMPLE 2.13**  $\rho^{-2} \in L^1_{\text{loc}}(\mathbb{R}^2 \backslash \{0\})$, but $\rho^{-2} \notin L^1_{\text{loc}}(\mathbb{R}^2)$.

The following example shows that no property of the type (2.54) can hold for arbitrary $\Omega$.

**EXAMPLE 2.14**  The function $u(x) = (x-1)(\sqrt{x}(x+1) \ln x)^{-1}$ is smooth in $]0, \infty[$ (also at $x = 1$!), and $|u(x)|$ behaves like $(\sqrt{x}|\ln x|)^{-1}$ near 0 and $\infty$. Thus $u \in L^p(0, \infty)$ iff $p = 2$.

**REMARK 2.8**  From Theorems 2.9 and 1.29 in Part 1, we have, for $1 < p < \infty$, that for every sequence $\{v_n\}$ which is bounded in $L^p$, that is, $\|v_n\|_{0,p} \leqslant c$, there exists a subsequence $\{v_{n_k}\}$ and an element $v \in L^p$ such that $v_{n_k} \rightharpoonup v$ in $L^p$.

*Warning*  Remark 2.8 is not true for $p = 1$ and $p = \infty$. However, if $p = \infty$ one can apply (1.85) in Part 1, since $L^\infty = (L^1)'$ (Sec. 2.4D), and obtain $v_{n_k} \overset{*}{\rightharpoonup} v$ in $L^\infty$. On the contrary, nothing can be done if $p = 1$, since $L^1$ is *not* a dual space; for instance, take $v_n(x) = n$ for $x \in [0, 1/n]$ and $x = 0$ elsewhere in $\mathbb{R}$. Then $\|v_n\|_{0,1} = 1$ $\forall n$. We shall see later on (Example 2.19) that $\{v_n\}$ converges to the Dirac mass $\delta_0$ (in a very weak sense): since $\delta_0 \notin L^1$, this will imply that there cannot exist any kind of "convergence in $L^1$" for which $\{v_n\}$ converges. The passage to a subsequence would not be of any help. This is the main reason why we shall often have to distinguish between $1 < p < \infty$ and $p = 1$ or $p = \infty$ in the following.

## 2.5 DISTRIBUTIONS

### 2.5A Motivations

Even if distributions have applications in several fields, we are interested here in their applications to partial differential equations. Therefore we consider now the bad properties of derivatives.

**1.** Many functions exist that do not have derivatives.

**2.** The differentiation of a series of functions is not always permissible; it depends on the smoothness of the functions and on the kind of convergence.

**3.** Functions of several variables show some strange properties; for instance, $u(x, y) = |x|$ satisfies $(\partial/\partial x)(\partial u/\partial y) = 0$, but not $(\partial/\partial y)(\partial u/\partial x) = 0$, since $\partial u/\partial x$ does not exist; if $u(x, t) = f(x + t)$, then $u$ formally satisfies (for any $f$) the wave equation $\partial^2 u/\partial t^2 - \partial^2 u/\partial x^2 = 0$, but $u(x, t) = |x + t|$ does not have second derivatives.

**4.** Green's formulae (i.e., integration by parts) hold only for smooth functions.

**5.** The classical definition of a derivative cannot be applied to a measurable function, since the behavior of the differential quotients of $u$ and $v$ can be different, even if $u = v$ almost everywhere.

On the contrary, when derivatives are continuous, they have, in general, good properties.

Therefore we should like to change the definition of derivatives and get rid of the bad properties mentioned above, without changing the definition when the classical derivatives are continuous. To do this (in particular because of property 1), we have to introduce new objects, called *distributions*, besides functions.

### 2.5B Definition of Distributions

We start by considering property 4 above and noticing that Green's formula involves integrals of products. Hence we first try to generalize integrals of products as much as possible. Therefore consider the integral $\int uv$. We saw (2.55) that

$$\int uv = {}_{0,p}\langle u, v \rangle_{0,p} \qquad \text{for } u \in L^{p'} \text{ and } v \in L^{p}$$

Let us then follow the same idea and replace $\int uv$ by ${}_{V}\langle u, v \rangle_{V}$ with some space $V$. Since we are interested in a very general $u$, we need a very particular $v$; that is, $V$ has to be a small space. We take the smallest space that we have introduced, that is, $C_0^\infty(\Omega)$. Since we did not introduce any norm in $C_0^\infty(\Omega)$, we have to define at least a convergence in order to define continuity. We thus give the following definitions.

**DEFINITION 2.15** Given $v_k$, $v \in C_0^\infty(\Omega)$ (2.24), we say that $\{v_k\}$ *converges to $v$ in* $\mathscr{D}(\Omega)$ and write $v_k \to v$ in $\mathscr{D}(\Omega)$ iff:

> There exists a bounded closed set $K \subset \Omega$ such that $v_k$ vanishes outside $K$ for any $k$;  (2.61)

> for every $\alpha$, $D^\alpha v_k \to D^\alpha v$ uniformly in $\Omega$.  (2.62)

The space $C_0^\infty(\Omega)$ endowed with this convergence is denoted $\mathscr{D}(\Omega)$.

On $\mathscr{D}(\Omega)$ we do not define any norm, but only this convergence. Nevertheless it is possible to define *continuity* on $\mathscr{D}(\Omega)$, from Rem. 1.6 in Part 1.

**DEFINITION 2.16** A *distribution* on $\Omega$ is any linear functional $L$ on $\mathscr{D}(\Omega)$ which is continuous in the sense of Rem. 1.6 in Part 1; that is,

$$v_k \to v \text{ in } \mathscr{D}(\Omega) \text{ implies } L(v_k) \to L(v) \tag{2.63}$$

The set of all distributions on $\Omega$ is denoted by $\mathscr{D}'(\Omega)$.

The present definition is close to the definition of the dual space of a normed space, even if $\mathscr{D}(\Omega)$ is not a normed space. We thus use similar notations and define

$$_{\mathscr{D}'(\Omega)}\langle L, v \rangle_{\mathscr{D}(\Omega)} = L(v) \qquad \text{for } L \in \mathscr{D}'(\Omega) \text{ and } v \in \mathscr{D}(\Omega) \tag{2.64}$$

With standard definitions (as we did for functions in Example 1.3 and for linear operators after Def. 1.27 in Part 1), $\mathscr{D}'(\Omega)$ becomes a linear space.

## 2.5c Functions as Distributions

Take any $u \in L^1_{loc}(\Omega)$ (Sec. 2.4F) and consider the linear functional $L_u(v) = \int_\Omega uv$ on $\mathscr{D}(\Omega)$. One can see that $L_u$ is a distribution, so that we can write

$$_{\mathscr{D}'(\Omega)}\langle L_u, v \rangle_{\mathscr{D}(\Omega)} = \int_\Omega uv \qquad \text{for } u \in L^1_{loc}(\Omega) \text{ and } v \in \mathscr{D}(\Omega) \tag{2.65}$$

Since one can prove that the map $u \to L_u$ is linear and one-to-one from $L^1_{loc}(\Omega)$ into $\mathscr{D}'(\Omega)$, by Sec. 1.3L we can identify $u$ with $L_u$ and write instead of (2.65)

$$_{\mathscr{D}'(\Omega)}\langle u, v \rangle_{\mathscr{D}(\Omega)} = \int_\Omega uv \qquad \text{for } u \in L^1_{loc}(\Omega) \text{ and } v \in \mathscr{D}(\Omega) \tag{2.66}$$

We thus have $L^1_{loc}(\Omega) \subset \mathscr{D}'(\Omega)$. By (2.60) and (2.28), all functional spaces we introduced, *except* $\mathcal{M}(\Omega)$, are subspaces of $\mathscr{D}'(\Omega)$. Notice that $\int uv$ may not exist for $u \in \mathcal{M}(\Omega)$ and $v \in \mathscr{D}(\Omega)$. To be sure that we have actually generalized the integral of a product, we have to show that not every distribution is a function, where from now on *function* will mean *element of $L^1_{loc}$*. For any given $x_0 \in \Omega$ consider the map $v \to v(x_0)$ as a map $\mathscr{D}(\Omega) \to \mathbb{R}$; it is easy to see that this is a distribution, called the *Dirac distribution*, or *Dirac mass at $x_0$*. It is sometimes called the *Dirac function at $x_0$*, but it is not a function, since no $u \in L^1_{loc}$ could satisfy $v(x_0) = \int uv \ \forall v \in \mathscr{D}(\Omega)$. It is denoted by $\delta_{x_0}$, that is,

$$_{\mathscr{D}'(\Omega)}\langle \delta_{x_0}, v \rangle_{\mathscr{D}(\Omega)} = v(x_0) \qquad \text{for } v \in \mathscr{D}(\Omega) \tag{2.67}$$

## 2.5D Operations on Distributions

One can extend to distributions many operations, e.g., translations, product by a function. The idea is to start with $\int uv$ in defining them. For instance, if $u \in L^1_{loc}(\mathbb{R})$, $u(2x-3)$ satisfies

$$\int u(2x-3)v(x) = \tfrac{1}{2} \int u(x)v\left(\frac{x+3}{2}\right)$$

Hence, the "good definition" of $u(2x-3)$ for $u \in \mathscr{D}'(\mathbb{R})$ will be as follows: it is the map

$$v \to \tfrac{1}{2}\left\langle u, v\left(\frac{x+3}{2}\right)\right\rangle$$

If $u \in L^1_{\mathrm{loc}}(\Omega)$, the function $wu$ satisfies $\int (wu)v = \int u(wv)$, so that for $u \in \mathscr{D}'(\Omega)$, $wu$ will be defined by $_{\mathscr{D}'}\langle wu, v\rangle_{\mathscr{D}} = _{\mathscr{D}'}\langle u, wv\rangle_{\mathscr{D}}$. We have of course to *check* that we are defining new distributions. For instance, $wu$ is a well-defined distribution if $w \in C^\infty(\Omega)$; otherwise this is not generally true.

## 2.5E Derivatives of Distributions

To define derivatives we use the idea given in Sec. 2.5D and consider the case of functions. If $D_i = \partial/\partial x_i$, $u \in C^1(\Omega)$, and $v \in \mathscr{D}(\Omega)$, Green's formula gives

$$\int_\Omega D_i u \cdot v = -\int_\Omega u \cdot D_i v$$

Thus it is natural to *define*

$$_{\mathscr{D}'}\langle D_i u, v\rangle_{\mathscr{D}} = -_{\mathscr{D}'}\langle u, D_i v\rangle_{\mathscr{D}} \qquad \text{for } u \in \mathscr{D}' \text{ and } v \in \mathscr{D} \tag{2.68}$$

One can check that (2.68) actually defines a distribution $D_i u$, called the *derivative of $u$ with respect to $x_i$ in the sense of $\mathscr{D}'$*. Notice that, from (2.68), *any distribution $u \in \mathscr{D}'$ has a derivative, in the sense of $\mathscr{D}'$, which is itself a distribution*. Clearly, if $u \in C^1(\Omega)$ the new derivative coincides with the classical one. However, since the definition of $D_i u$ is Green's formula itself, we can hope that distributional derivatives lose the bad properties of classical derivatives of irregular functions.

Consider, for instance, the so-called unit step function on $\mathbb{R}$:

$$H(x) = 0 \text{ or } 1 \qquad \text{when } x < 0 \text{ or } x > 0, \text{ respectively} \tag{2.69}$$

For (2.69), the classical Green's formula does not hold. If $DH$ is the distributional derivative of $H$ (we can compute it since $H \in L^\infty \subset \mathscr{D}'$), we have $\forall v \in \mathscr{D}(\mathbb{R})$:

$$_{\mathscr{D}'}\langle DH, v\rangle_{\mathscr{D}} = -_{\mathscr{D}'}\langle H, v'\rangle_{\mathscr{D}} = -\int_{-\infty}^{+\infty} Hv' = -\int_0^\infty v' = v(0) = _{\mathscr{D}'}\langle \delta_0, v\rangle_{\mathscr{D}}$$

Thus, the derivative of the unit step function is not a function, but the Dirac mass at 0 (2.67). That is, for such a bad function $H$ we change the definition of derivative in order to preserve Green's formula.

It is easy to check that

$$D_i D_j u = D_j D_i u \qquad \text{for every } i, j \text{ and for } u \in \mathscr{D}'(\Omega) \tag{2.70}$$

We can therefore use the notation $D^\alpha u$ for higher-order derivatives. We have

$$_{\mathscr{D}'}\langle D^\alpha u, v\rangle_{\mathscr{D}} = (-1)^{|\alpha|}\,_{\mathscr{D}'}\langle u, D^\alpha v\rangle_{\mathscr{D}} \tag{2.71}$$

Standard properties of classical derivatives still hold; for instance,

$$D_i(wu) = (D_i w)u + w(D_i u) \qquad \text{for } u \in \mathscr{D}'(\Omega) \text{ and } w \in C^\infty(\Omega) \qquad (2.72)$$

## 2.5F Restriction of a Distribution

If $\Omega_1 \subset \Omega$ and $u \in \mathscr{D}'(\Omega)$, we define $u|_{\Omega_1}$ as follows. Assume first $u \in L^1_{\text{loc}}(\Omega)$. The distribution $u|_{\Omega_1} \in L^1_{\text{loc}}(\Omega_1) \subset \mathscr{D}'(\Omega_1)$ is the map defined on $\mathscr{D}(\Omega_1)$ by $v \to \int_{\Omega_1} uv = \int_\Omega u\tilde{v}$, where $\tilde{v}$ is the extension of $v$ by 0 to the whole of $\Omega$, so that $\tilde{v} \in \mathscr{D}(\Omega)$ and $\tilde{v} = 0$ in $\Omega \setminus \Omega_1$. This suggests the *definition of* $u|_{\Omega_1}$ with $u \in \mathscr{D}(\Omega)$.

$$_{\mathscr{D}'(\Omega_1)}\langle u|_{\Omega_1}, v \rangle_{\mathscr{D}(\Omega_1)} = {}_{\mathscr{D}'(\Omega)}\langle u, \tilde{v} \rangle_{\mathscr{D}(\Omega)} \qquad \text{for every } v \in \mathscr{D}(\Omega_1) \qquad (2.73)$$

One can easily check that in fact $u|_{\Omega_1} \in \mathscr{D}'(\Omega_1)$. For instance, the restriction of the Dirac mass at $x_0$ to the complement of $\{x_0\}$ is the function which is identically zero.

## 2.5G Convergence in $\mathscr{D}'(\Omega)$

Given $u_k, u \in \mathscr{D}'(\Omega)$, we say that the sequence $\{u_k\}$ is *converging to u in the sense of distributions*, and write $u_k \to u$ *in* $\mathscr{D}'(\Omega)$, iff

$$_{\mathscr{D}'}\langle u_k, v \rangle_{\mathscr{D}} \to {}_{\mathscr{D}'}\langle u, v \rangle_{\mathscr{D}} \qquad \forall v \in \mathscr{D}(\Omega) \qquad (2.74)$$

One can see that a distribution $u$ exists such that $u_k \to u$ in $\mathscr{D}'(\Omega)$, whenever $\lim {}_{\mathscr{D}'}\langle u_k, v \rangle_{\mathscr{D}}$ exists and is finite for every $v \in \mathscr{D}(\Omega)$.

Moreover:

All convergences (i.e. strong, weak, and weak*) that we introduced in $L^p(\Omega)$ imply the convergence in $\mathscr{D}'(\Omega)$. The same is true for strong and weak convergences in $C^k(\bar{\Omega})$ and $C^{k,\lambda}(\bar{\Omega})$. \hfill (2.75)

A good property of this kind of convergence is the following. Without any other assumption we have

$$u_k \to u \text{ in } \mathscr{D}'(\Omega) \text{ implies } D^\alpha u_k \to D^\alpha u \text{ in } \mathscr{D}'(\Omega) \text{ for every } \alpha \qquad (2.76)$$

In particular, $u_k \to u$ in $L^p(\Omega)$ implies $D^\alpha u_k \to D^\alpha u$ in $\mathscr{D}'(\Omega)$. For instance, if $\Omega = ]-1, 1[$, we see immediately that $u_k \to H$ (2.69) in $L^1$, where $u_k(x) = 0$, or $kx$, or 1, according to $x < 0$, or $0 < x < 1/k$, or $x > 1/k$. Hence $u_k' \to \delta_0$ in $\mathscr{D}'$.

## 2.5H Spaces of Distributions

Even though we have not defined any norm on $\mathscr{D}(\Omega)$ and $\mathscr{D}'(\Omega)$, continuous inclusions make sense from Def. 1.37 in Part 1. Namely, $\mathscr{D}(\Omega) \hookrightarrow V$ (where $V$ is a Banach space) means that $\mathscr{D}(\Omega) \subset V$ algebraically (1.66) and that $v_k \to v$ in $\mathscr{D}(\Omega)$ implies $v_k \to v$ in $V$. $V \hookrightarrow \mathscr{D}'(\Omega)$ has an analogous meaning. We say that $V$ is a *space of distributions* iff $V \hookrightarrow \mathscr{D}'(\Omega)$. (2.75) then gives

$$C^k(\bar{\Omega}), C^{k,\lambda}(\bar{\Omega}), L^p(\Omega) \text{ are spaces of distributions} \qquad (2.77)$$

Moreover, what is done in Eqs. (1.75) and (1.76) makes sense with $V = \mathscr{D}(\Omega)$ and a Banach space $W$. Hence:

$\mathscr{D}(\Omega) \hookrightarrow W$ and $\mathscr{D}(\Omega)$ dense in $W$ imply $W' \hookrightarrow \mathscr{D}'(\Omega)$; i.e., $W'$ is a space of distributions. (2.78)

**Warning** If $\mathscr{D}(\Omega)$ is not dense in $V$ (for example, $V = L^\infty$, $C^{k,\lambda}$), then $V'$ cannot be identified with a subspace of $\mathscr{D}'(\Omega)$. (2.79)

There are some general facts that we want to point out in this context. Assume that $V$ and $W$ are functional Banach spaces with

$$\mathscr{D}(\Omega) \hookrightarrow V \hookrightarrow W, \ \mathscr{D}(\Omega) \text{ dense in } V, V \text{ dense in } W \tag{2.80}$$

so that
$$W' \hookrightarrow V' \hookrightarrow \mathscr{D}'(\Omega) \tag{2.81}$$

If $\alpha$ is any multi-index and $\phi$ is any function on $\Omega$, we have:

If the map $v \to D^\alpha v$ is linear and continuous from $V$ into $W$, then it is linear and continuous from $W'$ into $V'$ and $_V\langle D^\alpha u, v\rangle_V = (-1)^{|\alpha|} \, _W\langle u, D^\alpha v\rangle_W \ \forall u \in W', \forall v \in V$. (2.82)

If the map $v \to \phi v$ is linear and continuous from $V$ into $W$, then it is linear and continuous from $W'$ into $V'$ and $_V\langle \phi u, v\rangle_V = {}_W\langle u, \phi v\rangle_W \ \forall u \in W', \forall v \in V$. (2.83)

Finally if $\Omega_1 \subset \Omega_2$, define for functions $v$ on $\Omega_1$ the *trivial extension* $\tilde{v}$ by

$$\tilde{v}(x) = v(x) \text{ or } = 0 \text{ according to } x \in \Omega_1 \text{ or } x \in \Omega_2 \backslash \Omega_1 \tag{2.84}$$

If $V(\Omega_1)$ and $W(\Omega_2)$ are functional Banach spaces with $\mathscr{D}(\Omega_1) \hookrightarrow V(\Omega_1)$, $\mathscr{D}(\Omega_1)$ dense in $V(\Omega_1)$, $\mathscr{D}(\Omega_2) \hookrightarrow W(\Omega_2)$, $\mathscr{D}(\Omega_2)$ dense in $W(\Omega_2)$, so that $V'(\Omega_1) \hookrightarrow \mathscr{D}'(\Omega_1)$ and $W'(\Omega_2) \hookrightarrow \mathscr{D}'(\Omega_2)$, we have:

If the trivial extension $v \to \tilde{v}$ is linear and continuous from $V(\Omega_1)$ into $W(\Omega_2)$, then the restriction $u \to u|_{\Omega_1}$ is linear and continuous from $W'(\Omega_2)$ into $V'(\Omega_1)$ and we have (2.85)

$$_{V'(\Omega_1)}\langle u|_{\Omega_1}, v\rangle_{V(\Omega_1)} = {}_{W'(\Omega_2)}\langle u, \tilde{v}\rangle_{W(\Omega_2)} \quad \forall u \in W'(\Omega_2), \forall v \in V(\Omega_1)$$

Basic examples of spaces of distributions are Sobolev spaces (see Sec. 2.6) to which the previous remarks apply.

## 2.5ı Examples

**EXAMPLE 2.15** Define $v(x) = \exp(|x|^2 - 1)^{-1}$, or $v(x) = 0$, according to $|x| < 1$, or $|x| \geq 1$. Then $v \in \mathscr{D}(\mathbb{R}^n)$.

**EXAMPLE 2.16** If $v \in \mathscr{D}(\mathbb{R}) \backslash \{0\}$, set $v_n(x) = n^{-1}v(x - n)$. Then $D^k v_n \to 0$, uniformly in $\mathbb{R}$, $\forall k$, but $v_n$ does not converge to 0 in $\mathscr{D}(\mathbb{R})$.

**EXAMPLE 2.17** Each one of the following sequences converges to $\frac{1}{2}\operatorname{sgn} x = H(x) - \frac{1}{2}$, where sgn is the sign function [see (2.69)], in $\mathscr{D}'(\mathbb{R})$: $\pi^{-1}\arctan nx$; $\frac{1}{2}\tanh nx$; $\pi^{-1/2}\int_0^{nx}\exp(-t^2)$. The reader could draw the corresponding graphs. For instance, if $\phi \in \mathscr{D}(R)$ and $\phi = 0$ outside $]-M, M[$, we have

$$\left| \int \frac{1}{\pi} \arctan nx \cdot \phi(x) - \int \frac{1}{2} \operatorname{sgn} x \cdot \phi(x) \right| \leq \|\phi\|_{C^0} \int_{-M}^{M} \left| \frac{1}{\pi} \arctan nx - \frac{1}{2} \operatorname{sgn} x \right| \to 0$$

From Example 2.17, we deduce (let the reader draw the corresponding graphs) the following examples.

**EXAMPLE 2.18**  $1/\pi(n/(1+n^2x^2))$, $n/2(\cosh/nx)^{-2}$, $n\pi^{-1/2} \exp(-n^2x^2)$ converge to $\delta_0$ in $\mathscr{D}'(\mathbb{R})$.

**EXAMPLE 2.19**  One can check directly that $n(H(x) - H(x-1/n)) \to \delta_0$ in $\mathscr{D}'(\mathbb{R})$.

**EXAMPLE 2.20**  If $u(x) = \ln |x|$ in $\mathbb{R}$ (notice the singularity only at $x = 0$), then

$$\langle u', v \rangle = \lim_{\varepsilon \to 0} \int_{|x| > \varepsilon} \frac{v(x)}{x} \, dx \qquad \forall v \in \mathscr{D}(\mathbb{R})$$

If $v = 0$ near $x = 0$, then

$$\langle u', v \rangle = \int \frac{v}{x} = \left\langle \frac{1}{x}, v \right\rangle \qquad \text{that is} \qquad u'_{|\mathbb{R} \setminus \{0\}} = \frac{1}{x}$$

**EXAMPLE 2.21**  If $\delta = \delta_0$ in $\mathbb{R}$, we have $x\delta = 0$. Thus, differentiating, $\delta + x\delta' = 0$.

**EXAMPLE 2.22**  If $\phi \in C^0(\mathbb{R})$ and $u(x, t) = \phi(x + t)$, then $\partial^2 u/\partial t^2 - \partial^2 u/\partial x^2 = 0$ in $\mathscr{D}'(\mathbb{R}^2)$.

**EXAMPLE 2.23**  $\omega_n = n\pi^{n/2}/\Gamma(1+n/2)$ is the area of the unit sphere in $\mathbb{R}^n$ ($\omega_1 = 2$, $\omega_2 = 2\pi$, $\omega_3 = 4\pi, \ldots$); setting $u(x) = |x|^{2-n}/(2-n)$ if $n \neq 2$ and $u(x) = \ln |x|$ if $n = 2$ [notice that $\ln |x| = \lim_{\lambda \to 2} |x|^{2-\lambda}/(2-\lambda)$], we have $\Sigma \partial^2 u/\partial x_i^2 = \omega_n \delta_0$ in $\mathscr{D}'(\mathbb{R}^n)$.

## 2.6 SOBOLEV SPACES WITH AN INTEGER INDEX

### 2.6A The Spaces $W^{k,p}(\Omega)$

In Sec. 2.3 we introduced spaces of smooth functions, i.e., those whose elements are differentiable functions in the classical sense. In Sec. 2.5 we introduced the derivatives of any distribution. It is thus natural to study those functions whose derivatives up to some order $k$ in the sense of distributions are actually functions, known also as *weak derivatives*. Spaces containing this kind of function are the so-called Sobolev spaces $W^{k,p}$ with an integer index $k$, which we deal with in this section.

Besides this, we introduce the spaces $W^{-k,p}$ of negative order $-k$, which essentially contain the derivatives up to the order $k$ of functions of $L^p$.

Moreover, in Sec. 2.3 we introduced, between $C^k$ and $C^{k+1}$, a whole family of spaces, the spaces $C^{k,\lambda}$. It is thus natural to introduce between $W^{k,p}$ and $W^{k+1,p}$ a family of spaces, the so-called Sobolev spaces of real index. This will be done in the next section.

But since many properties (completeness, reflexivity, etc.) of Sobolev spaces of both integer and real index are identical, most of them are contained in the next section, after the introduction of the whole family of Sobolev spaces. We thus introduce the spaces $W^{k,p}$. Of course, all derivatives are taken in the sense of distributions. Moreover, in the entire section we assume that

$$\Omega \text{ satisfies Assump. 2.1} \tag{2.86}$$

**DEFINITION 2.17**   For $k \in \mathbb{N}$ and $1 \le p \le \infty$ we define

$$W^{k,p}(\Omega) = \{ v \in L^p(\Omega) \colon D^\alpha v \in L^p(\Omega) \text{ for } |\alpha| \le k \} \tag{2.87}$$

For $1 \le p < \infty$ and $v \in W^{k,p}(\Omega)$ we define the following seminorm and norm:

$$|v|_{W^{k,p}(\Omega)} = |v|_{k,p,\Omega} = \left( \sum_{|\alpha|=k} \|D^\alpha v\|_{0,p,\Omega}^p \right)^{1/p} \tag{2.88}$$

$$\|v\|_{W^{k,p}(\Omega)} = \|v\|_{k,p,\Omega} = \left( \sum_{j=0}^k |v|_{j,p,\Omega}^p \right)^{1/p}$$

$$= \left( \sum_{|\alpha| \le k} \|D^\alpha v\|_{0,p,\Omega}^p \right)^{1/p} \tag{2.89}$$

and for $v \in W^{k,\infty}(\Omega)$ we define

$$|v|_{W^{k,\infty}(\Omega)} = |v|_{k,\infty,\Omega} = \max_{|\alpha|=k} \|D^\alpha v\|_{0,\infty,\Omega} \tag{2.90}$$

$$\|v\|_{W^{k,\infty}(\Omega)} = \|v\|_{k,\infty,\Omega} = \max_{0 \le j \le k} |v|_{j,\infty,\Omega} = \max_{|\alpha| \le k} \|D^\alpha v\|_{0,\infty,\Omega} \tag{2.91}$$

Notice that (2.89) and (2.91) are graph norms (see Sec. 1.3M in Part 1). The norm (2.89) is a *Hilbert* norm iff $p = 2$. In this case we set

$$H^k(\Omega) = W^{k,2}(\Omega) \qquad |\cdot|_{k,\Omega} = |\cdot|_{k,2,\Omega} \qquad \|\cdot\|_{k,\Omega} = \|\cdot\|_{k,2,\Omega} \tag{2.92}$$

The scalar product in $H^k(\Omega)$ is given by

$$(u, v)_{k,\Omega} = \sum_{|\alpha| \le k} \int_\Omega D^\alpha u \cdot D^\alpha v \tag{2.93}$$

**REMARK 2.9**   Notice that $W^{0,p}(\Omega) = L^p(\Omega)$ for $1 \le p \le \infty$ and all notations with $k = 0$ agree with Sec. 2.4. In particular, since $W^{k,p}(\Omega) \hookrightarrow L^p(\Omega)$, we have by Sec. 2.5:

$$W^{k,p}(\Omega) \text{ is a space of distributions, i.e., } W^{k,p}(\Omega) \hookrightarrow \mathscr{D}'(\Omega) \tag{2.94}$$

In fact, the case $p = \infty$ has already been analyzed, and we have the following theorem.

**THEOREM 2.10**   For $k \ge 1$ and $\Omega$ satisfying Assump. 2.1 $W^{k,\infty}(\Omega) = C^{k-1,1}(\Omega)$ with equivalent norms.

We explicitly observe that convergences in $W^{k,p}$ have the following meanings:

$$v_m \to v \text{ in } W^{k,p}(\Omega) \text{ iff } D^\alpha v_m \to D^\alpha v \text{ in } L^p(\Omega) \text{ for } |\alpha| \le k \tag{2.95}$$

$$v_m \rightharpoonup v \text{ in } W^{k,p}(\Omega) \text{ iff } D^\alpha v_m \rightharpoonup D^\alpha v \text{ in } L^p(\Omega) \text{ for } |\alpha| \le k \tag{2.96}$$

Moreover it is clear that

$$C^k(\bar{\Omega}) \hookrightarrow W^{k,p}(\Omega) \text{ for } k \geq 0, 1 \leq p \leq \infty, \text{ and bounded } \Omega \tag{2.97}$$

**THEOREM 2.11** Assume $k \in \mathbb{N}$ and $1 \leq p < \infty$. Then

$$C^\infty(\bar{\Omega}) \cap W^{k,p}(\Omega) \text{ is dense in } W^{k,p}(\Omega) \tag{2.98}$$

$$C_0^\infty(\Omega) \text{ is dense in } W^{k,p}(\Omega) \text{ iff } \Omega = \mathbb{R}^n \text{ or } k = 0 \tag{2.99}$$

## 2.6B The Spaces $W_0^{k,p}(\Omega)$

By (2.99), if $k > 0$ and $\Omega$ has a boundary (i.e., $\Omega \neq \mathbb{R}^n$), $C_0^\infty(\Omega)$ is not dense in $W^{k,p}(\Omega)$.

**DEFINITION 2.18** We define, for $k \in \mathbb{N}$ and $1 \leq p < \infty$,

$$W_0^{k,p}(\Omega) = \text{closure of } C_0^\infty(\Omega) \text{ in } W^{k,p}(\Omega) \qquad H_0^k(\Omega) = W_0^{k,2}(\Omega) \tag{2.100}$$

From Theorem 2.8 and (2.99) we have, for $k \geq 0$ and $1 \leq p < \infty$,

$$W_0^{0,p}(\Omega) = L^p(\Omega) \qquad W_0^{k,p}(\mathbb{R}^n) = W^{k,p}(\mathbb{R}^n)$$

$$W_0^{k,p}(\Omega) \neq W^{k,p}(\Omega) \qquad \text{if } k > 0 \text{ and } \Omega \neq \mathbb{R}^n \tag{2.101}$$

If $k > 0$ and $\Omega \neq \mathbb{R}^n$, the functions of $W^{k,p}(\Omega)$ can be characterized by their behavior at the boundary $\partial\Omega$. This will be done in Theorems 2.16 and 2.28.

## 2.6c The Spaces $W^{-k,p}(\Omega)$

**DEFINITION 2.19** For $k \in \mathbb{N}$ and $1 \leq p < \infty$, we define

$$W^{-k,p'}(\Omega) = \text{dual space of } W_0^{k,p}(\Omega) \qquad H^{-k}(\Omega) = W^{-k,2}(\Omega)$$

where

$$p' \text{ is the conjugate of } p: \frac{1}{p} + \frac{1}{p'} = 1 \tag{2.102}$$

We also introduce the following notations:

$$_{-k,p',\Omega}\langle \cdot, \cdot \rangle_{k,p,\Omega} = {}_{W^{-k,p'}(\Omega)}\langle \cdot, \cdot \rangle_{W_0^{k,p}(\Omega)}$$

$$_{-k,\Omega}\langle \cdot, \cdot \rangle_{k,\Omega} = {}_{-k,2,\Omega}\langle \cdot, \cdot \rangle_{k,2,\Omega} \tag{2.103}$$

For $k = 0$, we have $L^{p'}(\Omega) = W^{0,p'}(\Omega) = $ dual space of $W_0^{0,p}(\Omega)$, that is, of $L^p(\Omega)$, so that this definition is in agreement with the identification we made in Sec. 2.4D.

Since $\mathscr{D}(\Omega) \hookrightarrow W^{k,p}(\Omega)$ and $\mathscr{D}(\Omega) \subset W_0^{k,p}(\Omega)$, we have $\mathscr{D}(\Omega) \hookrightarrow W_0^{k,p}(\Omega)$. Moreover $\mathscr{D}(\Omega)$ is dense in $W_0^{k,p}(\Omega)$ by definition. Thus (2.78) gives

$$W^{-k,p'}(\Omega) \hookrightarrow \mathscr{D}'(\Omega) \qquad \text{i.e.} \qquad W^{-k,p'}(\Omega) \text{ is a space of distributions} \tag{2.104}$$

In particular, we can ask: Which distributions belong to $W^{-k,p'}(\Omega)$?

**THEOREM 2.12**   Let $v \in \mathscr{D}'(\Omega)$. Then $v \in W^{-k,p'}(\Omega)$ iff

$$v = \sum_{|\alpha| \leq k} D^\alpha v_\alpha \qquad \text{for some } v_\alpha \in L^{p'}(\Omega)$$

## 2.6D Examples

**EXAMPLE 2.24**   If $\Omega$ is split into subsets $\Omega_j$ by piecewise smooth hypersurfaces, $u \in C^{k-1}(\bar{\Omega})$, and $u|_{\Omega_j} \in C^k(\bar{\Omega}_j)$, then $u \in W^{k,p}(\Omega)$ for $k \geq 1$ and $1 \leq p \leq \infty$. This situation occurs if $\Omega$ is a polygon, $\{\Omega_j\}$ is a triangulation of $\Omega$, $u \in C^{k-1}(\bar{\Omega})$, and $u|_{\Omega_j}$ is a polynomial $\forall j$.

**EXAMPLE 2.25**   If $u \in C^k(\bar{\Omega})$, it is clear that $u \in W^{k,p}(\Omega)$. One sees that, for $k \geq 1$, $u \in W_0^{k,p}(\Omega)$ iff $D^\alpha u$ vanish on $\partial\Omega$ for $|\alpha| \leq k - 1$.

**EXAMPLE 2.26**   Since $\ln x \in L^p(0,1)$ $\forall p < \infty$, we have by Theorem 2.12 $x^{-1} \in W^{-1,p}(0,1)$, $1 < p < \infty$.

**EXAMPLE 2.27**   Since $H \in L^p(-1,1)$ (2.69), we have $\delta_0 \in W^{-1,p}(-1,1)$.

*Warning*   The dual space of $W^{k,p}(\Omega)$ *cannot* be identified with a subspace of $\mathscr{D}'(\Omega)$ (2.79), unless $k = 0$ or $\Omega = \mathbb{R}^n$ by (2.99).

## 2.7 SOBOLEV SPACES WITH A REAL INDEX

### 2.7A The Spaces $W^{s,p}(\Omega)$, $s \in \mathbb{R}_+$

We have seen that $W^{k,\infty}(\Omega) = C^{k-1,1}(\Omega)$. Moreover, $C^{k-1,\lambda}(\Omega)$ is between $C^{k-1,1}(\Omega)$ and $C^{k-2,1}(\Omega)$, and therefore between $W^{k,\infty}(\Omega)$ and $W^{k-1,\infty}(\Omega)$. Hence it is natural to introduce, also for $p < \infty$, some spaces between $W^{k,p}(\Omega)$ and $W^{k-1,p}(\Omega)$, that is, to define Sobolev spaces with real indices. In order to be able to define $W^{s,p}(\Omega)$ with real $s$, recall that the definition of $C^{k,\lambda}(\Omega)$ was related to the boundedness on $\Omega \times \Omega$ of some kind of differential quotient. Hence the spaces $W^{s,p}(\Omega)$ will have to be related to the $p$-integrability on $\Omega \times \Omega$ of some kind of differential quotient. The choice of the exponents in the definition is made in order to have good inclusion properties. We still assume that $\Omega \subset \mathbb{R}^n$ satisfies Assump. 2.1.

**DEFINITION 2.20**   For $0 < \sigma < 1$, $1 \leq p < \infty$ we define,

$$W^{\sigma,p}(\Omega) = \{v \in L^p(\Omega): |v(x) - v(y)| \cdot |x - y|^{-n/p - \sigma} \in L^p(\Omega \times \Omega)\} \tag{2.105}$$

$$H^\sigma(\Omega) = W^{\sigma,2}(\Omega) \tag{2.106}$$

On $W^{\sigma,p}(\Omega)$ we define the following seminorm and norm, for $p < \infty$:

$$|v|_{\sigma,p,\Omega} = \||v(x) - v(y)| \cdot |x - y|^{-n/p - \sigma}\|_{0,p,\Omega \times \Omega}$$

$$= \left( \int_\Omega \int_\Omega \frac{|v(x) - v(y)|^p}{|x - y|^{n + \sigma p}} \, dx \, dy \right)^{1/p} \tag{2.107}$$

$$\|v\|_{\sigma,p,\Omega} = (\|v\|_{0,p,\Omega}^p + |v|_{\sigma,p,\Omega}^p)^{1/p} \tag{2.108}$$

Usual modifications when $p = \infty$ (see Def. 2.17) give $W^{\sigma,\infty}(\Omega) = C^{0,\sigma}(\bar{\Omega})$ with equivalent norms.

Notice that (for $p < \infty$) the definition depends on $n$. This precise choice of the exponent gives, for instance, the following: if $\Omega \subset \mathbb{R}^n$, $\Omega_1 \subset \mathbb{R}^m$, and $u \in W^{\sigma,p}(\Omega)$, then the function $U$ defined on $\Omega \times \Omega_1$ by $U(x, \xi) = u(x)$, for $x \in \Omega$ and $\xi \in \Omega_1$, belongs to $W^{\sigma,p}(\Omega \times \Omega_1)$, and conversely, if $U \in W^{\sigma,p}(\Omega \times \Omega_1)$, then $u \in W^{\sigma,p}(\Omega)$.

**DEFINITION 2.21**   For $s > 0$ not an integer and $1 \leq p \leq \infty$, write $s = k + \sigma$ with $k \in \mathbb{N}$, and $0 < \sigma < 1$ (i.e, $k = [s]$ and $\sigma = s - k$) and define

$$W^{s,p}(\Omega) = \{v \in W^{k,p}(\Omega): D^\alpha v \in W^{\sigma,p}(\Omega) \text{ for } |\alpha| \leq k\} \tag{2.109}$$

In $W^{s,p}(\Omega)$ we introduce the following seminorm and norm, if $p < \infty$:

$$|v|_{s,p,\Omega} = \left( \sum_{|\alpha| = k} |D^\alpha v|^p_{\sigma,p,\Omega} \right)^{1/p} \tag{2.110}$$

$$\|v\|_{s,p,\Omega} = \left( \|v\|^p_{k,p,\Omega} + \sum_{j=0}^{k} |v|^p_{j+\sigma,p,\Omega} \right)^{1/p}$$

$$= \left( \sum_{|\alpha| \leq k} \|D^\alpha v\|^p_{\sigma,p,\Omega} \right)^{1/p} \tag{2.111}$$

Usual modifications if $p = \infty$ give $W^{s,\infty}(\Omega) = C^{k,\sigma}(\bar{\Omega})$ with equivalent norms.

Therefore we will only deal with the case $1 \leq p < \infty$. In the next theorem we summarize important properties of Sobolev spaces with both integer and real indices.

**THEOREM 2.13**   Assume $k \in \mathbb{N}$, $0 \leq \sigma < 1$, $s = k + \sigma$, $1 \leq p < \infty$. Then $W^{s,p}(\Omega)$ is a separable Banach space with the norm (2.89) or (2.111) according to whether $s = k$ or $s > k$. $W^{s,p}(\Omega)$ is reflexive iff $1 < p < \infty$ and a Hilbert space iff $p = 2$. The scalar product in $H^s(\Omega) = W^{s,2}(\Omega)$ is given by (2.93) if $s = k$, while, if $s > k$, it is given by

$$(u, v)_{s,\Omega} = \sum_{|\alpha| \leq k} \left\{ \int_\Omega D^\alpha u \cdot D^\alpha v + \int_\Omega \int_\Omega \frac{(D^\alpha u(x) - D^\alpha u(y))(D^\alpha v(x) - D^\alpha v(y))}{|x - y|^{n + 2\sigma}} \, dx \, dy \right\} \tag{2.112}$$

The following theorem generalizes Theorem 2.11.

**THEOREM 2.14**   *Density.* Let $k$, $\sigma$, $s$, $p$ be as in Theorem 2.13. Then

$$C^\infty(\bar{\Omega}) \cap W^{s,p}(\Omega) \text{ is dense in } W^{s,p}(\Omega) \tag{2.113}$$

$$C_0^\infty(\Omega) \text{ is dense in } W^{s,p}(\Omega) \text{ iff } \Omega = \mathbb{R}^n, \text{ or } 0 \leq s \leq \frac{1}{p} \text{ and } (s, p) \neq (1, 1) \tag{2.114}$$

In other words,

$W^{s,p}(\Omega)$ is the completion (Sec. 1.3I of Part 1) of $C^\infty(\bar{\Omega}) \cap W^{s,p}(\Omega)$ or $C_0^\infty(\Omega)$ [according to (2.113) or (2.114)] with respect to the norm $\|\cdot\|_{s,p,\Omega}$. $\tag{2.115}$

**THEOREM 2.15**   *Extension.* Assume $\Omega$ is smooth or a half space. Then for every $k_0 > 0$ there exists an operator $\mathscr{P}$ such that, for $0 \leq s \leq k_0$ and $1 \leq p < \infty$,

$$\mathscr{P} \in \mathscr{L}(W^{s,p}(\Omega); W^{s,p}(\mathbb{R}^n)) \qquad (\mathscr{P}v)|_\Omega = v \qquad \forall v \in W^{s,p}(\Omega)$$

## 2.7B The Spaces $W_0^{s,p}(\Omega)$

Also for real $s$, $C_0^\infty(\Omega)$ need not be dense in $W^{s,p}(\Omega)$, from Theorem 2.14. The following definition includes Def. 2.18.

**DEFINITION 2.22**  For $s \geq 0$ and $1 \leq p < \infty$ we define

$$W_0^{s,p}(\Omega) = \text{closure of } C_0^\infty(\Omega) \text{ in } W^{s,p}(\Omega) \qquad H_0^s(\Omega) = W_0^{s,2}(\Omega) \tag{2.116}$$

From (2.114) we have

$$W_0^{s,p}(\Omega) = W^{s,p}(\Omega) \text{ iff } \Omega = \mathbb{R}^n \text{ or } 0 \leq s \leq \frac{1}{p} \text{ and } (s,p) \neq (1,1) \tag{2.117}$$

By definition, $W_0^{s,p}(\Omega)$ is a closed subspace of $W^{s,p}(\Omega)$ and thus (Prop. 1.9 in Part 1) is a Banach space. Moreover, Theorem 2.13 holds completely if we replace $W^{s,p}(\Omega)$ by $W_0^{s,p}(\Omega)$.

In many cases it is convenient to use different norms for the spaces $W^{s,p}(\Omega)$ and $W_0^{s,p}(\Omega)$. In particular, we have, for $k \in \mathbb{N}$, $0 \leq \sigma < 1$, $s = k + \sigma$, $1 \leq p < \infty$, and $\Omega$ bounded,

$(\|\cdot\|_{0,p,\Omega}^p + |\cdot|_{s,p,\Omega}^p)^{1/p}$ is a norm on $W^{s,p}(\Omega)$ equivalent to (2.111) [or to (2.89) if $s = k$]. $\tag{2.118}$

$(|\cdot|_{k,p,\Omega}^p + |\cdot|_{s,p,\Omega}^p)^{1/p}$ is a norm on $W_0^{s,p}(\Omega)$ equivalent to (2.111) [or to (2.89) if $s = k$]. $\tag{2.119}$

Moreover, we can use $\|\cdot\|_{0,p,\Omega} + |\cdot|_{s,p,\Omega}$ instead of (2.118) (and similarly for all other norms) and obtain equivalent norms (note, however, that we do not obtain, in this way, a Hilbert norm even if $p = 2$). More generally, the notation $\|\cdot\|_{s,p,\Omega}$ will be used for any equivalent norm.

## 2.7C The Spaces $W^{-s,p'}(\Omega)$

**DEFINITION 2.23**  As for integer indices we set for $s \geq 0$, $1 \leq p < \infty$,

$W^{-s,p'}(\Omega) = $ dual space of $W_0^{s,p}(\Omega)$; $H^{-s}(\Omega) = W^{-s,2}(\Omega)$; where $p'$ is the conjugate of $p$: $1/p' + 1/p = 1$. $\tag{2.120}$

Notations (2.103) are also used, with $s$ instead of $k$. As in the case of an integer index we have

$$W^{-s,p'}(\Omega) \hookrightarrow \mathscr{D}'(\Omega); \text{ i.e., } W^{-s,p'}(\Omega) \text{ is a space of distributions.} \tag{2.121}$$

## 2.7D Different Characterizations of $W_0^{s,p}(\Omega)$; the Spaces $W_{00}^{s,p}(\Omega)$

Let $\rho(x)$ be a function $\Omega \to \mathbb{R}$ that satisfies the following conditions:

$$\text{If } \Omega \text{ is smooth, } \rho \in C^\infty(\bar\Omega), \rho(x) = \text{dist}(x, \partial\Omega) \text{ near } \partial\Omega \tag{2.122}$$

$$\text{If } \Omega \text{ is a half space, } \rho(x) = |x_n| \tag{2.123}$$

If $s \geq 0$, $1 < p < \infty$, and $\Omega$ is smooth or a half space, we introduce the following spaces:

$\{v \in W^{s,p}(\Omega): \rho^{-s}v \in L^p(\Omega)\}$ with the graph norm (Sec. 1.3M in Part 1), that is,

$$\|v\| = (\|v\|_{s,p}^p + \|\rho^{-s}v\|_{0,p}^p)^{1/p} \tag{2.124}$$

$\{v \in W^{s,p}(\Omega): \tilde{v} \in W^{s,p}(\mathbb{R}^n)\}(\tilde{v} = \text{extension of } v \text{ by } 0)$ with the norm (equivalent to the graph norm) $\|v\| = \|\tilde{v}\|_{s,p,\mathbb{R}^n}$ \hfill (2.125)

*Notice that in fact* (2.125) *makes sense for any* $\Omega$. if $\Omega$ is smooth or a half space, we have the following theorem.

**THEOREM 2.16** If $s - 1/p$ is not an integer, the spaces (2.124), (2.125), and $W_0^{s,p}(\Omega)$ coincide with equivalent norms.

By Theorem 2.16 it is natural to ask what happens when $s - 1/p$ is an integer. We thus have the following theorem.

**THEOREM 2.17** If $s > 0$, $1 < p < \infty$, and $s - 1/p$ is an integer, the spaces (2.124) and (2.125) coincide and have equivalent norms. Moreover they are dense subspaces of $W_0^{s,p}(\Omega)$ but different from it.

Theorem 2.17 naturally suggests the following definition.

**DEFINITION 2.24** If $s > 0$, $1 < p < \infty$, and $s - 1/p$ is an integer, the normed space (2.125) is denoted by $W_{00}^{s,p}(\Omega)$. Moreover we set $H_{00}^s(\Omega) = W_{00}^{s,2}(\Omega)$.

Notice that $W_{00}^{s,p}(\mathbb{R}^n) = W^{s,p}(\mathbb{R}^n)$. We have by Theorem 1.22:

$W_{00}^{s,p}(\Omega)$ is a separable reflexive Banach space. It is a Hilbert space iff $p = 2$; in this case its scalar product is $(u, v) = (\tilde{u}, \tilde{v})_{s,\mathbb{R}^n}$. \hfill (2.126)

Moreover:

$\mathcal{D}(\Omega) \hookrightarrow W_{00}^{s,p}(\Omega)$ and it is a dense subspace; hence $(W_{00}^{s,p}(\Omega))' \hookrightarrow \mathcal{D}'(\Omega)$. \hfill (2.127)

Theorem 2.17 and (1.76) in Part 1 imply $W^{-s,p'}(\Omega) \hookrightarrow (W_{00}^{s,p}(\Omega))'$; Example 2.31 will show that these spaces are different.

## 2.7E Some Fundamental Properties

**THEOREM 2.18** *Inclusions with fixed p.* Assume $k_j \in \mathbb{N}$, $s_j \geq 0$ $(j = 1, 2)$, $1 \leq p < \infty$. Then we have:

$$s_1 < s_2 \text{ implies } W^{s_2,p}(\Omega) \hookrightarrow W^{s_1,p}(\Omega), \ W_0^{s_2,p}(\Omega) \hookrightarrow W_0^{s_1,p}(\Omega) \tag{2.128}$$

$$k_1 < k_2 \text{ implies } W_{00}^{k_2+1/p,p}(\Omega) \hookrightarrow W_{00}^{k_1+1/p,p}(\Omega) \tag{2.129}$$

$$s_1 < k_2 + \frac{1}{p} \text{ implies } W_{00}^{k_2+1/p,p}(\Omega) \hookrightarrow W_0^{s_1,p}(\Omega) \tag{2.130}$$

$$k_1 + \frac{1}{p} < s_2 \text{ implies } W_0^{s_2,p}(\Omega) \hookrightarrow W_{00}^{k_1+1/p,p}(\Omega) \tag{2.131}$$

Moreover each left-hand side is *dense* in the corresponding right-hand side, so that using (2.76) we obtain inclusions between dual spaces for $p>1$. For instance, (2.130) gives $W^{-s_1,p'}(\Omega) \hookrightarrow (W_{00}^{k_2+1/p,p}(\Omega))'$. Finally, each of the above inclusions is *compact* if $\Omega$ is bounded.

**THEOREM 2.19**   *Sobolev inclusions.* Assume $0 \le r \le s$, $k \in \mathbb{N}$, and $\Omega \subset \mathbb{R}^n$.

If $1 < p \le q < \infty$ and $0 < \lambda < 1$, we have:

$$r - \frac{n}{q} \le s - \frac{n}{p} \qquad \text{implies} \qquad W^{s,p}(\Omega) \hookrightarrow W^{r,q}(\Omega) \tag{2.132}$$

$$k + \lambda \le s - \frac{n}{p} \qquad \text{implies} \qquad W^{s,p}(\Omega) \hookrightarrow C^{k,\lambda}(\bar{\Omega}) \tag{2.133}$$

If $1 \le p \le q \le \infty$, $0 \le \lambda \le 1$, and $\Omega$ is bounded, we have:

$$r - \frac{n}{q} < s - \frac{n}{p} \qquad \text{implies} \qquad W^{s,p}(\Omega) \hookrightarrow\hookrightarrow W^{r,q}(\Omega) \tag{2.134}$$

$$k + \lambda < s - \frac{n}{p} \qquad \text{implies} \qquad W^{s,p}(\Omega) \hookrightarrow\hookrightarrow C^{k,\lambda}(\Omega) \tag{2.135}$$

Moreover we have the following limit cases:

If $p = 1$ then $q = \infty$, and $\lambda = 0$ or $1$ are permissible in (2.132) and (2.133). $\qquad$ (2.136)

If $p = 1$ and $q < \infty$, (2.132) holds if either both $r$ and $s$ are integers, or $s$ is not an integer, or $s - r \ge 1$. $\qquad$ (2.137)

Finally, all previous statements hold with $W_0$ in place of $W$.

It must be pointed out that the previous results are *sharp*. Sharpness of some of them is shown in Sec. 2.7G. We also remark that no inclusion is compact if $\Omega$ is unbounded. Moreover, using (1.76) in Part 1 one can obtain results regarding Sobolev spaces with a negative index. An example is given in Sec. 2.7G.

In order to have a shorter statement for the next theorem (on interpolation) we introduce the following notations for $s \in \mathbb{R}$, $1 < p < \infty$:

If $s \ge 0$:

$$\mathcal{W}^{s,p} = W^{s,p}(\Omega)$$

$$\mathcal{W}_0^{s,p} = \begin{cases} W_0^{s,p}(\Omega) & \text{if } s - \dfrac{1}{p} \notin \mathbb{N} \\[2mm] W_{00}^{s,p}(\Omega) & \text{if } s - \dfrac{1}{p} \in \mathbb{N} \end{cases}$$

If $s < 0$:

$$\mathcal{W}^{s,p} = \mathcal{W}_0^{s,p} = \begin{cases} W^{s,p}(\Omega) & \text{if } s - \dfrac{1}{p} \notin \mathbb{Z} \\[2ex] (W_{00}^{-s,p'}(\Omega))' & \text{if } s - \dfrac{1}{p} \in \mathbb{Z} \end{cases}$$

$$= (\mathcal{W}_0^{-s,p'})' \tag{2.138}$$

**THEOREM 2.20** *Interpolation properties and the interpolation inequality.* Assume $r_j$, $s_j$, $r$, $s$ are real, $0 < \theta < 1$, $r = r_1 + \theta(r_2 - r_1)$, $s = s_1 + \theta(s_2 - s_1)$, $W$ is a Banach space, and $L$ is a linear operator. Then the following so-called interpolation properties hold:

If $L$ is continuous from $\mathcal{W}^{r_j,p}$ into $W$, with norm $\leq M_j$ for $j = 1, 2$, and either $p = 2$ or $r$ is not an integer, then $L$ is continuous from $\mathcal{W}^{r,p}$ into $W$ with norm $\leq c M_1^{1-\theta} M_2^{\theta}$, where $c$ does not depend on $L$. (2.139)

If $L$ is continuous from $W$ into $\mathcal{W}^{s_j,p}$, with norm $\leq M_j$ for $j = 1, 2$, and either $p = 2$ or $s$ is not an integer, then $L$ is continuous from $W$ into $\mathcal{W}^{s,p}$ with norm $\leq c M_1^{1-\theta} M_2^{\theta}$, where $c$ does not depend on $L$. (2.140)

If $L$ is continuous from $\mathcal{W}^{r_j,p}(\Omega_1)$ into $\mathcal{W}^{s_j,p}(\Omega_2)$, with norm $\leq M_j$ for $j = 1, 2$, and either $p = 2$ or both $r$ and $s$ are nonintegers, then $L$ is continuous from $\mathcal{W}^{r,p}(\Omega_1)$ into $\mathcal{W}^{s,p}(\Omega_2)$, with norm $\leq c M_1^{1-\theta} M_2^{\theta}$, where $c$ does not depend on $L$. (2.141)

Moreover the following interpolation inequality holds:

If $s_1 < s_2$ and either $p = 2$ or $s$ is not an integer, then $\|v\|_{\mathcal{W}^{s,p}} \leq c \|v\|_{\mathcal{W}^{s_1,p}}^{1-\theta} \|v\|_{\mathcal{W}^{s_2,p}}^{\theta}$ for $v \in \mathcal{W}^{s_2,p}$, where $c$ does not depend on $v$. (2.142)

Finally,

Statements (2.139) to (2.142) hold with $\mathcal{W}_0$ instead of $\mathcal{W}$. (2.143)

## 2.7F The Spaces $\mathcal{W}_{\text{loc}}(\Omega)$

We have defined $L_{\text{loc}}^p(\Omega)$ in Sec. 2.4F. The same idea can be used in other cases. We give a general definition. $W_{\text{loc}}^{s,p}(\Omega)$ is a particular case of this definition. Assume that $\mathcal{W}(\Omega)$ denotes a linear space defined for every $\Omega \subset \mathbb{R}^n$. If $\mathcal{W}(\Omega)$ is a space of distributions on $\Omega$ and $v \to v|_{\Omega_1}$ maps $\mathcal{W}(\Omega)$ into $\mathcal{W}(\Omega_1)$ for $\Omega_1 \subset \Omega$, we define

$$\mathcal{W}_{\text{loc}}(\Omega) = \{ v \in \mathcal{D}'(\Omega) : v|_{\Omega_1} \in \mathcal{W}(\Omega_1) \; \forall \Omega_1 \subset\subset \Omega \} \tag{2.144}$$

This agrees with (2.58) if $\mathcal{W} = L^p$. If $\mathcal{W}(\Omega) = C^k(\bar{\Omega})$, $C^{k,\lambda}(\bar{\Omega})$, or $C^{\infty}(\bar{\Omega})$, then $\mathcal{W}_{\text{loc}}(\Omega) = C^k(\Omega)$, $C^{k,\lambda}(\Omega)$, or $C^{\infty}(\Omega)$, respectively. In particular, we defined $W_{\text{loc}}^{s,p}(\Omega)$. It is clear that inclusion properties for $\mathcal{W}(\Omega)$ give analogous properties for $\mathcal{W}_{\text{loc}}(\Omega)$.

## 2.7G Applications and Examples

Let us give some applications of Sec. 2.5H and of Theorem 2.20. We use the notations (2.138).

Let $D$ be, for instance, any derivative of the first order. It is clear that $D \in \mathcal{L}(H^1(\Omega); L^2(\Omega))$; in particular, $D \in \mathcal{L}(H_0^1(\Omega); L^2(\Omega))$. Thus (2.82) gives $D \in \mathcal{L}(L^2(\Omega); H^{-1}(\Omega))$. Hence, for $0 < \sigma < 1$, we have from (2.141) $D \in \mathcal{L}(H^\sigma(\Omega); H^{\sigma-1}(\Omega))$ if $\sigma \neq \frac{1}{2}$ and $D \in \mathcal{L}(H^{1/2}(\Omega); (H_{00}^{1/2}(\Omega))')$. Example 2.31 shows that $u \in H^{1/2}(\Omega)$ does not imply $Du \in H^{-1/2}(\Omega)$.

More generally, we have:

If $|\alpha| = k$, $D^\alpha$ is continuous from $\mathcal{W}^{s,p}$ into $\mathcal{W}^{s-k,p}$ for every real $s$ and $1 < p < \infty$. $\qquad$ (2.145)

The same kind of argument [using (2.83) instead of (2.82)] gives:

If $\phi \in W^{k,\infty}(\Omega)$, the map $v \to \phi v$ is continuous from $\mathcal{W}^{s,p}$ into itself (and from $\mathcal{W}_0^{s,p}$ into itself) for $|s| \le k$ and $1 < p < \infty$. $\qquad$ (2.146)

Now we consider restrictions. $\Omega_1 \subset \Omega_2$ implies $\|v|_{\Omega_1}\|_{s,p,\Omega_1} \le \|v\|_{s,p,\Omega_2}$; that is, the map $v \to v|_{\Omega_1}$ is continuous from $W^{s,p}(\Omega_2)$ into $W^{s,p}(\Omega_1)$, for $s \ge 0$ and $1 < p < \infty$ (actually $1 \le p \le \infty$). For $k \in \mathbb{N}$ and $1 < p < \infty$, the map $v \to \tilde{v}$ is continuous from $W_0^{k,p'}(\Omega_1)$ into $W_0^{k,p'}(\Omega_2)$. Thus by (2.85) $v \to v|_{\Omega_1}$ is continuous from $W^{-k,p}(\Omega_2)$ into $W^{-k,p}(\Omega_1)$. Applying (2.141), we can see that the same is true with $W^{-k,p}$ replaced by $\mathcal{W}^{s,p}$, where $s < 0$ is not an integer. Combining them, we have:

If $\Omega_1 \subset \Omega_2$ and $\mathcal{W}^{s,p}$ is given by (2.138), the map $v \to v|_{\Omega_1}$ is continuous from $\mathcal{W}^{s,p}(\Omega_2)$ into $\mathcal{W}^{s,p}(\Omega_1)$ for real $s$ and $1 < p < \infty$. $\qquad$ (2.147)

**_Warning_** For $s < 0$ and $s - 1/p \in \mathbb{Z}$, (2.138) says that $v \to v|_{\Omega_1}$ is continuous from $(W_{00}^{-s,p'}(\Omega_2))'$ into $(W_{00}^{-s,p'}(\Omega_1))'$; since we have $W^{s,p}(\Omega_2) \hookrightarrow (W_{00}^{-s,p'}(\Omega_2))'$, this implies that $v \to v|_{\Omega_1}$ is continuous from $W^{s,p}(\Omega_2)$ into $(W_{00}^{-s,p'}(\Omega_2))'$. However, notice that $v \to v|_{\Omega_1}$ is *not* continuous from $W^{s,p}(\Omega_2)$ into $W^{s,p}(\Omega_1)$ (always for $s < 0$ and $s - 1/p \in \dot{\mathbb{Z}}$) unless $\Omega_2 = \Omega_1$. See also Example 2.31.

We end this section with several examples.

**EXAMPLE 2.28** In any dimension $n$, consider a function $u$ such that $u$ is $C^\infty$ for $x \neq 0$, $u$ is not a polynomial, and $u$ is $\lambda$-homogeneous, that is, $u(tx) = t^\lambda u(x) \; \forall x \neq 0, \; \forall t > 0$. Note that $u \in L^1(B_1)$ iff $\lambda > -n$. Assuming therefore $\lambda > -n$, $s \in \mathbb{R}$, $1 < p < \infty$ (or $1 \le p < \infty$ if $s \ge 0$), we have $u \in W^{s,p}(B_1)$ iff $\lambda > s - n/p$. The same is true for the half ball.

**EXAMPLE 2.29** In two dimensions, using polar coordinates, consider $u = \rho^\lambda \sin \lambda\theta$, $0 < \theta < \pi$ with $\lambda > -2$ and noninteger. If $s \in \mathbb{R}$ and $1 < p < \infty$ (or $1 \le p < \infty$ if $s \ge 0$), then $u \in W^{s,p}(B_1 \cap \mathbb{R}_+^2)$ iff $\lambda > s - 2/p$. The same is true with cosine instead of sine. This is indeed a particular case of the previous example.

**EXAMPLE 2.30** In two dimensions, define $u(x) = \ln|\ln|x||$, or 0, according to $|x| < 1/e$ or $|x| \ge 1/e$. One can easily check that $u \in H^1(\mathbb{R}^2)$ and $u \in L^q(\mathbb{R}^2) \; \forall q < \infty$ [according to (2.132)]. Nevertheless $u$ is unbounded. Hence $q = \infty$ is not permissible in (2.132).

**EXAMPLE 2.31** In one dimension, define $u(x) = \ln|\ln|x||$ or 0, according to $|x| < 1/e$ or $|x| \ge 1/e$. We shall see (Theorem 2.24) that the previous example implies $u \in H^{1/2}(\mathbb{R})$ and, thus [see (2.145)], $u' \in H^{-1/2}(\mathbb{R})$. (2.147) gives $u' \in (H_{00}^{1/2}(0, 1/e))'$. One could show that $u' \notin H^{-1/2}(0, 1/e)$, essentially for the following reason: $u'$ satisfies

$$\langle u', v \rangle = \lim_{\varepsilon \to 0} \int_{\varepsilon < |x| < 1/e} (x \ln |x|)^{-1} v(x) \, dx \qquad \text{for smooth } v$$

and the limit exists since $(x \ln |x|)^{-1}$ is an odd function. But

$$\lim_{\varepsilon \to 0} \int_{\varepsilon}^{1/e} (x \ln |x|)^{-1} v(x) \, dx \qquad \text{converges, for smooth } v, \text{ iff} \qquad v(0) = 0$$

Functions $v \in H_{00}^{1/2}(0, 1/e)$ have such a property in a generalized sense [that is, $\tilde{v} \in H^{1/2}(\mathbb{R})$], while elements of $H^{1/2}(0, 1/e)$ do not (e.g., $v \equiv 1$). This example shows that (2.145) and (2.147) are sharp.

**EXAMPLE 2.32**  Define $u(x) = x^{\lambda}$ in $]0, 1[$ and its left-side trivial extension $\tilde{u}$ on $]-\infty, 1[$ by $\tilde{u}(x) = x^{\lambda}$ or 0, according to $0 < x < 1$ or $x < 0$. By Example 2.28, $u \in W^{s,p}(-\infty, 1)$ iff $\lambda > s - 1/p$. Since $x^{\lambda - s} \in L^p(0, 1)$ iff $\lambda > s - 1/p$, we have $\tilde{u} \in W^{s,p}(-\infty, 1)$ iff $x^{-s} u \in L^p(0, 1)$, according to one-sided versions of Theorems 2.16 and 2.17.

**EXAMPLE 2.33**  Assume $r - n/q > s - n/p$ and choose $\lambda$, a noninteger, between them. By Example 2.28, $|x|^{\lambda} \in W^{s,p}(B_1)$ and $|x|^{\lambda} \notin W^{r,q}(B_1)$. Hence (2.132) is sharp.

**EXAMPLE 2.34**  Assume $k + \lambda > s - n/p$ and choose $\mu$, a noninteger, between them. By Examples 2.28 and 2.6, $|x|^{\mu} \in W^{s,p}(B_1)$ and $|x|^{\mu} \notin C^{k,\lambda}(B_1)$. Hence (2.133) is sharp.

**EXAMPLE 2.35**  Let $u \in C^{\infty}(\mathbb{R}^n)$ with $u(x) = |x|^{\lambda}$ for $|x| > 1$. Then $u \in W^{1,p}(\mathbb{R}^n)$ iff

$$\int_{|x| > 1} (|u|^p + |\nabla u|^p) < \infty \qquad \text{that is}$$

$$\int_1^{\infty} \rho^{n-1} (\rho^{\lambda p} + \rho^{(\lambda - 1)p}) \, d\rho < \infty \qquad \text{that is} \qquad \lambda < -n/p$$

Similarly, $u \in L^q(\mathbb{R}^n)$ iff $\lambda < -n/q$. If $q < p$, choose $\lambda \in ]-n/q, -n/p[$. We have $u \in W^{1,p}(\mathbb{R}^n)$ and $u \notin L^q(\mathbb{R}^n)$; that is, $q \geq p$ is necessary in (2.132). On the contrary, for bounded $\Omega$, $W^{1,p}(\Omega) \hookrightarrow L^q(\Omega)$ implies $W^{1,p}(\Omega) \hookrightarrow L^r(\Omega)$ for $1 \leq r \leq q$ by (2.54).

**EXAMPLE 2.36**  In three dimensions: $H_0^1 \hookrightarrow L^6$ and (1.76) in Part 1 give $L^{6/5} = L^{6'} \hookrightarrow H^{-1}$. Similarly, $W_0^{1,3/2} \hookrightarrow L^3$ implies $L^{3/2} \hookrightarrow W^{-1,3}$; since $W^{1,1} \hookrightarrow L^{3/2}$, we have $W^{1,1} \hookrightarrow W^{-1,3}$. Using this kind of argument one could show that (2.132) holds also for negative $r$ and $s$. If $W^{s,p} = W^{1,1}$ and $W^{-1,3} = W^{r,q}$, we have indeed $r - n/q = s - n/p$ (with $n = 3$).

**EXAMPLE 2.37**  Take $\Omega = ]-1, 1[$ and $u_n(x) = 0$, $= nx$ or $= 1$, according to $x \leq 0$, $0 \leq x \leq 1/n$, or $x \geq 1/n$, respectively. Assume that $r \geq 0$ and $q \in ]1, \infty[$ are such that $W^{1,1} \hookrightarrow W^{r,q}$. Since $\|u_n\|_{1,1} \leq \text{const.}$, we have $\|u_n\|_{r,q} \leq \text{const.}$ But $u_n \to H$ in $L^1$ [recall (2.69)]. Therefore (since $1 < q < \infty$) Cor. 2.62 gives $H \in W^{r,q}$. Then Example 2.28 (with $\lambda = 0$ and $n = 1$) gives $r < 1/q$. We have thus proved that $W^{1,1} \hookrightarrow W^{r,q}$, $r \geq 0$ and $1 < q < \infty$, implies $r < 1/q$, i.e., that (2.137) is sharp.

**EXAMPLE 2.38**   Assume $1<p<\infty$ and $u \in W^{1,p}(0,1)$. We have, for $0 \le y \le x \le 1$,

$$|u(x)-u(y)| = \left| \int_y^x u' \right| \le \left( \int_y^x |u'|^p \right)^{1/p} (x-y)^{1/p'}$$

by (2.51). Hence $|u|_{C^{0,\lambda}} \le |u|_{1,p}$ with $\lambda = 1/p' = 1 - 1/p$, that is, (2.133) in the simplest case.

**Warning**   From (2.114) and (2.79), for $s>0$, the dual space of $W^{s,p}(\Omega)$ *is not* a subspace of $\mathcal{D}'(\Omega)$ unless either $\Omega = \mathbb{R}^n$, or $s \le 1/p$ and $1<p<\infty$, or $s<1$ and $p=1$ [see also (2.99) for integer $s$]. For instance, the sequence $v_{n,\alpha}$ defined by $v_{n,\alpha}(x) = \alpha n$ for $0<x<1/n$ and $=0$ for $x>1/n$ converges to 0 in $\mathcal{D}'(0,\infty)\ \forall \alpha \in R$; but for $\phi \in H^1(0,\infty)$ we have $\int v_{n,\alpha}\phi \to \alpha\phi(0)$!

## 2.8 SOBOLEV SPACES ON THE BOUNDARY

### 2.8A Preliminaries

In this section we extend the definition and properties of Sobolev spaces to the case in which $\Omega$ is replaced by its boundary $\partial\Omega$ or by a subset of it. But since this theory is similar to that of the previous sections, we restrict ourselves to some brief comments. We consider only bounded sets in $\mathbb{R}^2$; however, the results for smooth sets apply to higher dimensions. On the contrary, the case of polygons in any dimension is much more delicate.

**ASSUMPTION 2.2**   *On $\Omega$ and $\Gamma_0$.* We assume that either (2.148) or (2.149) holds:

$\Omega$ is a smooth open set in $\mathbb{R}^2$ whose boundary is a simple curve $\Gamma$ of length $L$.     (2.148)

$\Omega$ is a polygon in $\mathbb{R}^2$ with vertices $V_1,\ldots,V_m$ and sides $l_1,\ldots,l_m$. Setting $V_{j+m}=V_j$, $j \ge 1$, for convenience, $V_j$ and $V_{j+1}$ are the endpoints of $l_j$ and $\alpha_j \in\ ]0,2\pi[$, $\alpha_j \ne \pi$, is the angle at $V_j$. $\Gamma = \partial\Omega$. $L_j$ is the length of $l_j$.     (2.149)

Whenever orientation is important we also assume that:

The orientation of $\Gamma$ is counterclockwise and $L$ is the length of $\Gamma$. Moreover $x=\phi_{x_0}(s)$, $0 \le s \le L$, is the parameterization of $\Gamma$ by arc length such that $\phi_{x_0}(0)=x_0$ and $\psi_{x_0}:\Gamma \to [0,L[$ is the inverse map of $\phi_{x_0}$. Thus $\psi_{x_0}(x_0)=0$. If $\Omega$ is a polygon we set $\phi_j=\phi_{V_j}$, $\psi_j=\psi_{V_j}$.     (2.150)

Moreover:

$\Gamma_0$ is an open arc of $\Gamma$ and $L_0$ is its length. If $\Omega$ is a polygon we assume either $l_j \subset \Gamma_0$ or $l_j \cap \Gamma_0 = \varnothing$ and suppose that $V_1$ and $V_{m_0}$ (with $1<m_0 \le m$) are the left and the right endpoints of $\Gamma_0$.     (2.151)

### 2.8B The Spaces $W^{s,p}(\Gamma)$ with $s \ge 0$ and Smooth $\Omega$

**DEFINITION 2.25**   Assume $s \ge 0$, $1 \le p \le \infty$, and that (2.148) holds. Using the notations of Def. 2.1 with $\xi, \eta$ instead of $\xi_1, \xi_2$ and denoting by $x = X_{x_0}(\xi,\eta)$ the relation between fixed coordinates $x=(x_1,x_2)$ and local coordinates $\xi, \eta$, take any function $v$ on $\Gamma$ and, for $x_0 \in \Gamma$, consider the function

$\xi \to v(X_{x_0}(\xi, \zeta_{x_0}(\xi)))$ defined on $]-r_{x_0}, r_{x_0}[$. We set

$$W^{s,p}(\Gamma) = \{v: v(X_{x_0}(\cdot, \zeta_{x_0}(\cdot))) \in W^{s,p}(-r_{x_0}, r_{x_0}) \,\forall x_0 \in \Gamma\} \tag{2.152}$$

Moreover, among the infinite set of intevals $]-r_{x_0}, r_{x_0}[$ choose a finite number of them, say, $]-r_{x_j}, r_{x_j}[$, $j = 1, \ldots, N$, such that:

$$\text{The graphs of } \zeta_{x_j} \ (j = 1, \ldots, N) \text{ cover } \Gamma \tag{2.153}$$

When this choice is made, we define on $W^{s,p}(\Gamma)$ the following seminorm and norm (for $p < \infty$, with the usual modifications when $p = \infty$):

$$|v|_{s,p,\Gamma} = \left( \sum_j |v(X_{x_0}(\cdot, \zeta_{x_j}(\cdot)))|^p_{s,p,]-r_{x_j},r_{x_j}[} \right)^{1/p} \tag{2.154}$$

$$\|v\|_{s,p,\Gamma} = \left( \sum_j \|v(X_{x_0}(\cdot, \xi_{x_j}(\cdot)))\|^p_{s,p,]-r_{x_j},r_{x_j}[} \right)^{1/p} \tag{2.155}$$

One can prove that (2.152) does not depend on the particular local coordinate systems used in Def. 2.1. On the contrary, (2.154) and (2.155) depend on the local coordinate systems and on the subfamily satisfying (2.153). But by changing them, one can see that the norm (2.155), as well as (2.154), changes into an equivalent one. The previous definitions apply to any dimension (with obvious modifications, for example, $B_r(x_0)$ instead of $]-r_{x_0}, r_{x_0}[$). With this definition we have the usual properties, i.e., completeness, reflexivity for $1 < p < \infty$, etc. In the Hilbert case where $p = 2$ we write as usual $|\cdot|_{s,\Gamma}$ and $\|\cdot\|_{s,\Gamma}$ instead of (2.154) and (2.155). Moreover we set $L^p(\Gamma) = W^{0,p}(\Gamma)$.

**PROPOSITION 2.1**  If $\Omega$ is smooth and $k \in \mathbb{N}$, the map $v \to v|_\Gamma$ is linear and continuous from $C^k(\bar{\Omega})$ into $W^{s,p}(\Gamma)$ for $0 \le s \le k$ and $1 \le p \le \infty$. In particular,

$$v \in C^\infty(\bar{\Omega}) \text{ implies } v|_\Gamma \in W^{s,p}(\Gamma) \text{ for any } s \ge 0 \text{ and } 1 \le p \le \infty \tag{2.156}$$

In the particular case for $n = 2$ which we are dealing with, the following property holds:

**THEOREM 2.21**  Assume (2.148) and (2.150), $s \ge 0$, and $1 \le p \le \infty$. Then $v \in W^{s,p}(\Gamma)$ iff for every $x_0 \in \Gamma$, $v \circ \phi_{x_0} \in W^{s,p}(0, L)$. Moreover, if $x_j$ $(j = 1, \ldots, N)$ satisfy (2.153), the norm

$$\|v\| = \left( \sum_j \|v \circ \phi_{x_j}\|^p_{s,p,]0,L[} \right)^{1/p}$$

is equivalent to (2.155).

## 2.8c The Spaces $W^{s,p}(\Gamma_0)$ with $s \ge 0$ and a Smooth Arc $\Gamma_0$

**DEFINITION 2.26**  Assume (2.148), (2.150), (2.151) and call $x_0$ the left endpoint of $\Gamma_0$. We define for $s \ge 0$ and $1 \le p \le \infty$

$$W^{s,p}(\Gamma_0) = \{v: v \circ \phi_{x_0} \in W^{s,p}(0, L_0)\}.$$

The natural seminorm and norm are (for $p < \infty$)

$$|v|_{s,p,\Gamma_0} = |v \circ \phi_{x_0}|_{s,p,]0,L_0[} \tag{2.157}$$

$$\|v\|_{s,p,\Gamma_0} = \|v \circ \phi_{x_0}\|_{s,p,]0,L_0[} \tag{2.158}$$

Let us consider an example. Take $\Omega = B_1$. If $x_0 = (\cos \theta_0, \sin \theta_0) \in \Gamma$, choose local coordinates $\xi$, $\eta$ as follows: the $\xi$- and $\eta$-axes are tangential and orthogonal to $\Gamma$ at $x_0$, the $\xi$-axis is oriented according to the counterclockwise orientation of $\Gamma$, and the $\eta$-axis has the direction of the inner normal. Thus the relationship between fixed and local coordinates is given by

$$(x_1, x_2) = X_{x_0}(\xi, \eta) = (\cos \theta_0 - \xi \sin \theta_0 - \eta \cos \theta_0, \sin \theta_0 + \xi \cos \theta_0 - \eta \sin \theta_0)$$

$\zeta_{x_0}$ is given by $\zeta_{x_0}(\xi) = 1 - (1 - \xi^2)^{1/2}$, and we can choose $r_{x_0} = \frac{3}{4}$. To satisfy (2.153) we can take $N = 4$ and the four points $(1,0)$, $(0,1)$, $(-1,0)$, $(0,-1)$. To check that $v \in W^{s,p}(\Gamma)$ we have to see whether $v(\cos \theta_0 - \xi \sin \theta_0 - \cos \theta_0 (1 - (1 - \xi^2)^{1/2})$, $\sin \theta_0 + \xi \cos \theta_0 - \sin \theta_0 (1 - (1 - \xi^2)^{1/2}))$ belongs to $W^{s,p}(-\frac{3}{4}, \frac{3}{4})$. The map $\phi_{x_0}$ of (2.150) is $\phi_{x_0}(s) = (\cos (\theta_0 + s), \sin (\theta_0 + s))$, $0 \leq s < 2\pi$, so that (from Theorem 2.21) an equivalent check is $v(\cos (\theta_0 + s), \sin (\theta_0 + s)) \in W^{s,p}(0, 2\pi)$ for every $\theta_0$. Take, for instance, $v(x) = x_1$. Previous functions are $v(X_{x_0}(\xi, \zeta_{x_0}(\xi))) = -\xi \sin \theta_0 + (1 - \xi^2)^{1/2} \cos \theta_0$ and $v(\phi_{x_0}(s)) = \cos (\theta_0 + s)$, which belong to $W^{s,p}(-\frac{3}{4}, \frac{3}{4})$ and $W^{s,p}(0, 2\pi)$, respectively. Thus $v \in W^{s,p}(\Gamma)$, according to Prop. 2.1.

## 2.8D The Spaces $W^{s,p}(\Gamma)$ and $W^{s,p}(\Gamma_0)$ with $s \geq 0$ and $\Omega$ a Polygon

To justify the definition of $W^{s,p}(\Gamma)$ when $\Omega$ is a polygon, consider the case $\Omega = ]0, 1[ \times ]0, 1[$ and the previous function $v(x) = x_1$. We would like Prop. 2.1 to hold even if $\Omega$ is a polygon. On the other hand, take, for instance, $x_0 = (0, 1)$ and consider $v \circ \phi_{x_0}$ near $s = 1$, which corresponds to the corner $(0, 0)$ of $\Omega$. We have $\phi_{x_0}(s) = (0, 1 - s)$ or $(s - 1, 0)$ according to $0 \leq s \leq 1$ or $1 \leq s \leq 2$. Hence $v(\phi_{x_0}(s)) = 0$ or $s - 1$ according to $0 \leq s \leq 1$ or $1 \leq s \leq 2$. Since $(v \circ \phi_{x_0})'$ has a jump, it is clear that, for high values of $s$, $v \circ \phi_{x_0} \notin W^{s,p}(0, 4)$, even if $v \in C^\infty(\bar{\Omega})$. More precisely Example 2.28 with $\lambda = 0$ gives $(v \circ \phi_{x_0})' \in W^{s,p}(0, 4)$ iff $s < 1/p$ (for $p < \infty$); thus $v \circ \phi_{x_0} \in W^{s,p}(0, 4)$ iff $s < 1 + 1/p$. Therefore, if we want to preserve (2.156), the definition will have to be such that Theorem 2.21 holds only for $s < 1 + 1/p$. Hence, for high values of $s$, the definition of $W^{s,p}$ will imply only continuity at the corners, while tangential derivatives will be allowed to have jumps.

Before stating the definition we give the following result [where $v(0\pm)$ make sense by (2.133)].

**THEOREM 2.22**    Assume $1 \leq p \leq \infty$ and $0 \leq s < 1 + 1/p$. Let $v$ be such that

$$v \in L^p(-1, 1) \qquad v|_{]-1,0[} \in W^{s,p}(-1, 0) \qquad v|_{]0,1[} \in W^{s,p}(0, 1) \tag{2.159}$$

Then:

$$\text{If } s < \frac{1}{p} \text{ (or } s = 0 \text{ and } p = \infty), v \in W^{s,p}(-1, 1) \tag{2.160}$$

If $s > \dfrac{1}{p}$ (or $s \geq 1$ and $p = 1$), $v \in W^{s,p}(-1, 1)$ iff $v(0-) = v(0+)$    (2.161)

If $s = \dfrac{1}{p}$ and $1 < p < \infty$, $v \in W^{s,p}(-1, 1)$ iff $\displaystyle\int_{-\delta}^{\delta} \dfrac{|v(t) - v(-t)|^p}{|t|}\, dt < \infty$ for some $\delta \leq 1$    (2.162)

**DEFINITION 2.27**   Assume (2.149) to (2.151), $s \geq 0$, $1 \leq p \leq \infty$; setting $\delta = \min L_j$ we define:

For $1 \leq p < \infty$ and $0 \leq s < \dfrac{1}{p}$, or $p = \infty$ and $s = 0$:

$$W^{s,p}(\Gamma) = \{v: v \circ \phi_1 \in W^{s,p}(0, L)\} \qquad L^p(\Gamma) = W^{0,p}(\Gamma)$$

$$W^{s,p}(\Gamma_0) = \{v: v \circ \phi_1 \in W^{s,p}(0, L_0)\} \qquad L^p(\Gamma_0) = W^{0,p}(\Gamma_0)$$

$$\|v\|_{s,p,\Gamma} = \|v \circ \phi_1\|_{s,p,]0,L[}$$

$$\|v\|_{s,p,\Gamma_0} = \|v \circ \phi_1\|_{s,p,]0,L_0[}$$

(2.163)

For $1 < p < \infty$:

$$W^{1/p,p}(\Gamma) = \left\{ v \in L^p(\Gamma) \colon v \circ \phi_j \in W^{1/p,p}(0, L_j) \qquad \text{and} \right.$$

$$\left. \int_{-\delta}^{\delta} \frac{|v(\phi_j(L_j + t)) - v(\phi_j(L_j - t))|^p}{|t|}\, dt < \infty \text{ for } j = 1, \ldots, m \right\}$$

$$W^{1/p,p}(\Gamma_0) = \left\{ v \in L^p(\Gamma_0) \colon v \circ \phi_j W^{1/p,p}(0, L_j) \qquad \text{and} \right.$$

$$\left. \int_{-\delta}^{\delta} \frac{|v(\phi_j(L_j + t)) - v(\phi_j(L_j - t))|^p}{|t|}\, dt < \infty \text{ for } j = 1, \ldots, m_0 - 1 \right\}$$

(2.164)

$$\|v\|_{1/p,p,\Gamma} = \left( \Sigma(\|v \circ \phi_j\|^p_{1/p,p,]0,L_j}) \right.$$

$$\left. + \int_{-\delta}^{\delta} \frac{|v(\phi_j(L_j + t)) - v(\phi_j(L_j - t))|^p}{|t|}\, dt \right)^{1/p} \qquad \text{and}$$

$$\|v\|_{1/p,p,\Gamma_0} \qquad \text{defined in a similar way}$$

For $1 < p \leq \infty$ and $s > 1/p$, or $p = 1$ and $s \geq 1$:

$$W^{s,p}(\Gamma) = \{v \in L^p(\Gamma) \colon v \circ \phi_j W^{s,p}(0, L_j) \text{ and } v(\phi_j(L_j -))$$

$$= v(\phi_j(L_j +)) \text{ for } j = 1, \ldots, m\}$$

$$W^{s,p}(\Gamma_0) = \{v \in L^p(\Gamma) \colon v \circ \phi_j W^{s,p}(0, L_j) \text{ and } v(\phi_j(L_j -))$$

$$= v(\phi_j(L_j +)) \text{ for } j = 1, \ldots, m_0 - 1\}$$

(2.165)

$$\|v\|_{s,p,\Gamma} = (\Sigma \|v \circ \phi_j\|^p_{s,p,]0,L_j[})^{1/p} \qquad \text{and}$$

$$\|v\|_{s,p,\Gamma} \qquad \text{defined in a similar way}$$

$H^s(\Gamma) = W^{s,2}(\Gamma)$, $H^s(\Gamma_0) = W^{s,2}(\Gamma_0)$, $\|\cdot\|_{s,\Gamma} = \|\cdot\|_{s,2,\Gamma}$, $\|\cdot\|_{s,\Gamma_0} = \|\cdot\|_{s,2,\Gamma_0}$, $(\cdot,\cdot)_{s,\Gamma}$, and $(\cdot,\cdot)_{s,\Gamma_0}$ are the scalar products in $H^s(\Gamma)$ and $H^s(\Gamma_0)$.                             (2.166)

The definitions of $W^{s,p}(\Gamma)$ are independent of the choice of the first vertex $V_1$ on $\Gamma$.

**THEOREM 2.23**   Assume (2.149) to (2.151), $1 \leqslant p < \infty$ and $0 \leqslant s < 1 + 1/p$, or $p = \infty$ and $0 \leqslant s \leqslant 1$. Then $v \in W^{s,p}(\Gamma)$ iff $v \circ \phi_j \in W^{s,p}(0, L)$ for $j = 1, \ldots, m$; $v \in W^{s,p}(\Gamma_0)$ iff $v \circ \phi_1 \in W^{s,p}(0, L_0)$.

## 2.8E The Spaces $W_0^{s,p}(\Gamma_0)$ and $W_{00}^{s,p}(\Gamma_0)$

**DEFINITION 2.28**   Let Assump. 2.2 hold; for $s \geqslant 0$ and $1 \leqslant p < \infty$ we define:

$$W_0^{s,p}(\Gamma_0) = \text{closure in } W^{s,p}(\Gamma_0) \text{ of the set } \{v|_\Gamma : v \in C^\infty(\bar{\Omega}), v \text{ vanishes in some neighborhood of } \Gamma \backslash \Gamma_0\}$$

For $s \geqslant 0$ and $1 < p < \infty$ such that $s - 1/p$ is an integer, we define:

$$W_{00}^{s,p}(\Gamma_0) = \{v \in W^{s,p}(\Gamma_0) : \tilde{v} \in W^{s,p}(\Gamma)\} \qquad \text{and}$$

$$\|v\|_{W_{00}^{s,p}(\Gamma_0)} = \|\tilde{v}\|_{s,p,\Gamma}$$

where $\tilde{v}$ is the trivial extension of $v$ defined on $\Gamma$. The usual notations hold if $p = 2$.

## 2.8F The Spaces $W^{-s,p'}(\Gamma)$ and $W^{-s,p'}(\Gamma_0)$

**DEFINITION 2.29**   We define for $s \geqslant 0$, $1 \leqslant p < \infty$

$$W^{-s,p'}(\Gamma_0) = \text{dual space of } W_0^{s,p}(\Gamma_0)$$

Moreover, since $\Gamma$ has no endpoints, a definition of $W_0^{s,p}(\Gamma)$ does not make sense. Therefore we define

$$W^{-s,p'}(\Gamma) = \text{dual space of } W^{s,p}(\Gamma)$$

At least when $\Gamma$ is smooth, we could define $\mathscr{D}'(\Gamma)$ and prove that $W^{-s,p'}(\Gamma) \hookrightarrow \mathscr{D}'(\Gamma)$.

## 2.8G Final Remarks

Many properties of $W^{s,p}(\Omega)$ can be proved for Sobolev spaces on the boundary. We point out very briefly that theorems 2.13, 2.18, and 2.20 extend to the present case. The extension of (2.132) and (2.133) is also true, with $n = 1$ in the formulae ($\Gamma$ and $\Gamma_0$ have one dimension!). Since we did not define $C^{k,\lambda}(\Gamma)$ [while $C^0(\Gamma)$ and $C^0(\Gamma_0)$ have obvious meanings], we only point out that $W^{s,p}(\Gamma) \subset C^0(\Gamma)$ and $W^{s,p}(\Gamma_0) \subset C^0(\bar{\Gamma}_0)$ for $s > 1/p$ ($1 \leqslant p \leqslant \infty$). Finally, (2.147) extends with $\Gamma_0$ and $\Gamma$ instead of $\Omega_1$ and $\Omega_2$.

Moreover, the whole section [with suitable changes, especially in the definitions of $W^{s,p}(\Gamma_0)$] extends to higher dimensions in the case of a smooth $\Omega$.

## 2.9 TRACE THEOREMS

### 2.9A Preliminaries

If $v \in C^0(\bar{\Omega})$ (2.9), $v$ can be extended by continuity up to the boundary, so that $v|_{\partial\Omega}$ has an obvious meaning. On the contrary, if $v \in \mathcal{M}(\Omega)$ (Sec. 2.4A) we are in trouble: the restriction of $v$ to $\partial\Omega$ does not make sense, for $\partial\Omega$ has zero measure and limits need not exist as we approach $\partial\Omega$. The same situation occurs for Sobolev spaces, since only for special values of $s$ and $p$ is $W^{s,p}$ made of continuous functions.

However, for some values of the indices, if $v \in W^{s,p}(\Omega)$, we shall define the *trace* of $v$, denoted by $\gamma_0 v$ or $v|_{\partial\Omega}$, which actually coincides with $v|_{\partial\Omega}$ whenever $v \in C^0(\bar{\Omega})$. Hence, we extend the map $v \to v|_{\partial\Omega}$, defined for smooth functions, to a more general $v$ and introduce trace operators which will behave like the classical restriction to $\partial\Omega$ and replace it when it is not defined. The assumption on $\Omega$ we need is as follows:

$$\text{Either Assump. 2.2 holds or } \Omega = \mathbb{R}^n_+ \text{ and } \Gamma = \mathbb{R}^{n-1} \times \{0\} = \mathbb{R}^{n-1} \tag{2.167}$$

### 2.9B First Trace Theorem

**THEOREM 2.24**   *First trace theorem.* Assume $1 \le p \le \infty$, $s > 1/p$, $s - 1/p$ a noninteger; then:

There exists a unique operator $\gamma_0 \in \mathcal{L}(W^{s,p}(\Omega); W^{s-1/p,p}(\Gamma))$ such that $\gamma_0 v = v|_\Gamma \ \forall v \in C^\infty(\bar{\Omega}) \cap W^{s,p}(\Omega)$. 

$$\tag{2.168}$$

There exists an operator $\mathcal{R} \in \mathcal{L}(W^{s-1/p,p}(\Gamma); W^{s,p}(\Omega))$ such that $\gamma_0 \mathcal{R} g = g \ \forall g \in W^{s-1/p,p}(\Gamma)$. 

$$\tag{2.169}$$

Moreover:

(2.168) also holds in the cases: $1 \le p \le 2$ and $s > 1/p$; $p = 1$ and $s \ge 1$; $p = \infty$ and $s > 0$; (2.170)

(2.169) also holds in the cases: $2 \le p \le \infty$ and $s > 1/p$; $p = 1$ and $s = 1$. (2.171)

Notice that $\gamma_0 \in \mathcal{L}(W^{s,p}(\Omega); W^{s-(1/p)-\varepsilon,p}(\Gamma)) \ \forall \varepsilon > 0$ if $p > 2$ and $s - 1/p$ is an integer $\ge 1$ (see (2.128)) (2.172)

**REMARK 2.10**   The operator $\gamma_0$ works in the following way: if $v \in W^{s,p}(\Omega)$ take $v_m \in C^\infty(\bar{\Omega}) \cap W^{s,p}(\Omega)$ with $v_m \to v$ in $W^{s,p}(\Omega)$ (2.113), then $v_{m|\Gamma} \to \gamma_0 v$ in $W^{s-1/p,p}(\Gamma)$. In particular, it is easy to see that $\gamma_0 v$ does not depend on the values of $s$ and $p$ for which $v \in W^{s,p}(\Omega)$. This "justifies" (2.171) and (2.172). Take, for instance, $g \in W^{2,3}(\Gamma)$; then $\mathcal{R} g \in W^{7/3,3}(\Omega)$. Now no trace operator from $W^{7/3,3}(\Omega)$ into $W^{2,3}(\Gamma)$ is defined by (2.168) and (2.170); however, $\mathcal{R} g \in W^{s,p}(\Omega)$ for other permissible values of $s$ and $p$, for example, $\mathcal{R} g \in W^{2,3}(\Omega)$, and $\gamma_0 \mathcal{R} g$ is defined.

In the following we extend $\gamma_0$ to much more general cases, and (2.171) can be improved (including, for example, $p = \infty$ and $s = 0$). For the new operator $\gamma_0$, $\gamma_0 v$ will coincide with the previous one whenever both of them are defined. The same will be true for other trace operators ($\gamma_j$, $\gamma$, $\gamma_A$), which we shall define below. Moreover the notation $v|_\Gamma$ instead of $\gamma_0 v$ (and similar ones for $\gamma_j$, $\gamma$, $\gamma_A$) will also be used.

## 2.9c Higher-Order Derivatives: Second Trace Theorem

Now we will deal with higher-order traces. If, for instance, $v \in H^2(\Omega)$, then $v$ and its first derivative have traces. However, a result such as (2.169) is impossible for the whole family $v|_\Gamma, D_1 v|_\Gamma, \dots, D_n v|_\Gamma$, because of compatibility conditions; indeed the tangential derivatives depend on $v|_\Gamma$. Therefore we choose particular derivatives.

**DEFINITION 2.30** *Normal derivatives.* If $\Omega$ is smooth or a half space, $\nu$ denotes the unit outer normal vector to $\partial\Omega$. If $\Omega$ is a polygon, $\nu$ is not defined everywhere on $\partial\Omega$. Wherever $\nu$ makes sense we define the $k^{\text{th}}$ normal derivative $D_\nu^k$ by

$$D_\nu^k = (\Sigma \nu_i D_i)^k \quad \text{if } k > 0; \qquad D_\nu^0 = \text{identity} \tag{2.173}$$

**THEOREM 2.25** *Second trace theorem.* Assume $\Omega$ is smooth or a half space, $1 \le p \le \infty$, $k \in \mathbb{N}$, $s > k + 1/p$, and $s - 1/p$ a noninteger. Then:

There exist unique operators $\gamma_j \in \mathscr{L}(W^{s,p}(\Omega); W^{s-j-1/p,p}(\Gamma))$, $j = 0, \dots, k$, such that $\gamma_j v = D_\nu^j v|_\Gamma \, \forall v \in W^{s,p}(\Omega) \cap C^\infty(\bar{\Omega})$. (2.174)

There exists an operator $\mathscr{R} \in \mathscr{L}(W^{s-1/p,p}(\Gamma) \times \cdots \times W^{s-k-1/p,p}(\Gamma); W^{s,p}(\Omega))$ such that $\gamma_j \mathscr{R}(g_0, \dots, g_k) = g_j \, \forall g_j \in W^{s-j-1/p,p}(\Gamma)$. (2.175)

Cases such as those in (2.170) and (2.171) are also permissible; in particular, $s - 1/p$ can be an integer if $p = 2$. (2.176)

**REMARK 2.11** The previous results are sharp. For instance, one cannot deal with $s = 1/p$: Example 2.30 and (2.169) give $\ln|\ln|x|| \in H^{1/2}(0, \frac{1}{2})$, which is unbounded at 0, so that its trace at 0 makes no sense (in one dimension a trace theorem coincides with a Sobolev inclusion of type $W^{s,p} \hookrightarrow C^k$). Moreover, exceptional values of $s$ are related to Theorem 2.20.

## 2.9D Traces of Normal Components: Third Trace Theorem

The next theorem deals with traces of irregular functions (i.e., belonging to $W^{s,p}$ with $s < 1/p$) satisfying further properties.

We define the *divergence* of a vector-valued function $w$ by

$$\text{div } w = \Sigma D_i w_i \qquad (w_i = \text{components of } w) \tag{2.177}$$

and consider the space (with the graph norm—Sec. 1.3M in Part 1)

$$L^p_{\text{div}}(\Omega) = \{ w \in (L^p(\Omega))^n : \text{div } w \in L^p(\Omega) \} \tag{2.178}$$

Notice that $L^p_{\text{div}}(\Omega) = (W^{1,p}(\Omega))^n$ iff $n = 1$, while in general $(W^{1,p})^n \subset L^p_{\text{div}}$ (see Example 2.40). For $w \in (W^{1,p})^n$ every component of $w$ has its trace; in the more general case $w \in L^p_{\text{div}}$, at least the *normal component* $w \cdot \nu$ has a trace. For simplicity we will not deal any longer with the "exceptional" values $p = 1$ and $p = \infty$.

**THEOREM 2.26**    *Third trace theorem.* Assume $1 < p < \infty$. Then:

There exists a unique operator $\gamma \in \mathscr{L}(L_{\text{div}}^p(\Omega); W^{-1/p,p}(\Gamma))$ such that $\gamma w = w \cdot \nu|_\Gamma \; \forall v \in$
$(C^\infty(\bar\Omega))^n \cap L_{\text{div}}^p(\Omega)$.                                                                                                            (2.179)

There exists an operator $\mathscr{R} \in \mathscr{L}(W^{-1/p,p}(\Gamma); L_{\text{div}}^p(\Omega))$ such that $\gamma \mathscr{R} g = g \; \forall g \in W^{-1/p,p}(\Gamma)$.    (2.180)

## 2.9E Fourth Trace Theorem (Using Elliptic Operators)

We start with an application of Theorem 2.26. Consider operators $A$ of the following type (in what follows they will be called *elliptic*):

$$Av = -\Sigma D_j(a_{ij}D_i v) + \Sigma b_i D_i v - \Sigma D_i(c_i v) + dv$$

$$a_{ij}, \; b_i, \; c_i, \; d \in C^\infty(\bar\Omega)$$

$\Sigma a_{ij}(x)\xi_i\xi_j \geq \alpha|\xi|^2$ for some $\alpha > 0$ and every $x \in \Omega$ and $\xi \in \mathbb{R}^n$, which means that
$(a_{ij})$ is a positive-definite matrix, uniformly in $x \in \Omega$.                                                          (2.181)

Assume $v \in W^{1,p}(\Omega)$ and $Av \in L^p(\Omega)$. Then the vector $w$, with components $w_j = \Sigma_i a_{ij} D_i v + c_j v$,
satisfies $w \in (L^p(\Omega))^n$ and div $w = \Sigma b_i D_i v + dv - Av \in L^p(\Omega)$; that is, $w \in L_{\text{div}}^p(\Omega)$. Thus
Theorem 2.26 gives $w \cdot \nu|_\Gamma$ (that is, $\gamma w) \in W^{-1/p,p}(\Gamma)$. For smooth $v$ we have $w \cdot \nu =$
$\Sigma a_{ij}\nu_j D_i v + \Sigma c_i \nu_i v$, so that we have given a generalized sense to

$$\frac{\partial v}{\partial \nu_A}\bigg|_\Gamma = (\Sigma a_{ij}\nu_j D_i v + \Sigma c_i \nu_i v)\bigg|_\Gamma \tag{2.182}$$

The first-order boundary operator (2.182) is called the *conormal derivative of $v$*: its first-order part is indeed the derivative of $v$ in the direction of the vector of components $\Sigma_j a_{ij}\nu_j$, called the *conormal direction*. Hence, for $v \in W^{1,p}$ with $Av \in L^p$, the conormal derivative of $v$ has a trace, even though other first derivatives might have no trace.

This result will be improved in Theorem 2.27 (which has even more general extensions; for example, $A$ could be replaced by a higher-order operator).

*Warning*    An operator $A$ can be written in the form (2.181) in several ways, and (2.182) depends on the particular choice of (2.181). Thus we have *several conormal directions related to the same operator*. Thus the usual notation $\partial u/\partial \nu_A$, which we have followed here, is *highly misleading*. The simplest example is the Laplace operator

$$\Delta v = \Sigma D_i^2 v \tag{2.183}$$

If we choose $(a_{ij}) = $ identity matrix and $b_i = c_i = d = 0$, $A$ and (2.182) become $-\Delta$ and $D_\nu$, respectively. On the contrary, the choice $a_{ij} = 1$ or $-1$ according to whether $i \leq j$ or $i > j$, and $b_i = c_i = d = 0$ gives $A = -\Delta$ again, but $\partial v/\partial \nu_A \neq D_\nu v$ (see also Example 2.44).

To state the generalization of Theorem 2.26 mentioned above, consider the following spaces (with the graph norm—see Sec. 1.3M in Part 1):

$$W_{A,j}^{s,p}(\Omega) = \{v \in W^{s,p}(\Omega), \; Av \in W^{-2+j+1/p,p}(\Omega)\} \qquad H_{A,j}^s = W_{A,j}^{s,2} \qquad j = 0, 1 \tag{2.184}$$

**THEOREM 2.27** *Fourth trace theorem.* Assume that $\Omega$ is smooth or a half space, $A$ satisfies (2.181), $s \in \mathbb{R}$, $1 < p < \infty$, and either $p = 2$ or $s - 1/p$ is not an integer. Then:

There exist unique operators $\gamma_0 \in \mathscr{L}(W_{A,0}^{s,p}(\Omega); \; W^{s-1/p,p}(\Gamma))$ and $\gamma_A \in \mathscr{L}(W_{A,1}^{s,p}(\Omega);$ $W^{s-1-1/p,p}(\Gamma))$ such that $\gamma_0 v = v|_\Gamma$ and $\gamma_A v = \partial v / \partial \nu_A|_\Gamma \; \forall v \in C^\infty(\bar{\Omega}) \cap W_{A,j}^{s,p}(\Omega).$ (2.185)

There exists an operator $\mathscr{R} \in \mathscr{L}(W^{s-1/p,p}(\Gamma) \times W^{s-1-1/p,p}(\Gamma); \; W_{A,1}^{s,p}(\Omega))$ such that $\gamma_0 \mathscr{R}(g_0, g_1) = g_0$ and $\gamma_A \mathscr{R}(g_0, g_1) = g_1 \; \forall g_j \in W^{s-j-1/p,p}(\Gamma) \; (j = 1, 2).$ (2.186)

**Warning** The result (2.185) implies the existence of a constant $c$ such that $\forall v \in W_{A,0}^{s,p}(\Omega)$

$$\|v|_\Gamma\|_{s-1/p,p,\Gamma} \leq c(\|v\|_{s,p,\Omega} + \|Av\|_{-2+1/p,p,\Omega})$$ (2.187)

For $s - 1/p > 0$ and a noninteger the simpler estimate

$$\|v|_\Gamma\|_{s-1/p,p,\Gamma} \leq c \|v\|_{s,p,\Omega}$$ (2.188)

holds for $v \in W^{s,p}(\Omega)$ from (2.168). One might wonder whether (2.188) holds for any $s$, provided more regularity assumptions are made on $v$, for example, $v \in C^\infty(\bar{\Omega}) \cap W^{s,p}(\Omega)$. *The answer is no.* Let us examine the case $s = 0$, $p = 2$, and $\Omega = ]0, 1[$. From Theorem 2.8 $v_n \in C_0^\infty(0, 1)$ exist such that $v_n \to 1$ in $L^2(0, 1)$. The application of (2.188) to $v_n - 1$ would give $\|1\| \to 0$! The same argument applies in general for $s \leq 1/p$ [using (2.114)].

**REMARK 2.12** As stated in Rem. 2.10, when traces are defined by two of the previous theorems, the definitions are in agreement. If, for instance, $v \in H^2$, then Theorems 2.25 and 2.27 give two definitions of $\partial v / \partial \nu|_\Gamma$ which actually define the same function on $\Gamma$, which moreover is the restriction of $\partial v / \partial \nu$ to $\Gamma$ if, in addition, $v \in C^1(\bar{\Omega})$. That is, the traces just defined coincide with the classical restrictions whenever the latter make sense.

**REMARK 2.13** It should be made clear that Theorem 2.26 defines $w \cdot \nu|_\Gamma$ globally; that is, we can not split $w \cdot \nu|_\Gamma$ into $\Sigma(w_i|_\Gamma)\nu_i$ since the single terms in the last sum are not defined for a general $w \in L^p_{\text{div}}$ (see Example 2.40). But $w \cdot \nu|_\Gamma = \Sigma(w_i|_\Gamma)\nu_i = w|_\Gamma \cdot \nu$ if in addition $w \in (W^{s,p})^n$ with $s > 1/p$.

**REMARK 2.14** In all the trace theorems, the *regularity index* $s$ (i.e., the "real number of derivatives") *loses* $1/p$ in addition to the natural loss of the order of the derivative (i.e., $j$ for $\gamma_j$). Example 2.39 helps in explaining why.

## 2.9F Traces on $\Gamma_0 \subset \Gamma$

One can also deal with traces on a part $\Gamma_0 \subset \Gamma$. This can be done in general using the same procedure which we adopted in order to define traces on $\Gamma$, or in the following simpler way. Whenever $v|_\Gamma$, or $\partial v / \partial \nu|_\Gamma$, etc., are defined (by previous theorems) we set

$$v|_{\Gamma_0} = (v|_\Gamma)|_{\Gamma_0}, \quad \frac{\partial v}{\partial \nu}\bigg|_{\Gamma_0} = \left(\frac{\partial v}{\partial \nu}\bigg|_\Gamma\right)\bigg|_{\Gamma_0}, \dots$$ (2.189)

where $\cdot |_\Gamma$ is understood in the sense of trace theorems, while $\cdot |_{\Gamma_0}$ on the right-hand side is the restriction on $\Gamma_0$ which actually makes sense as in (2.147) (see also Sec. 2.8F). For the convenience of the reader, we now give the list of spaces containing traces on $\Gamma_0$, by referring to theorems where the corresponding traces on $\Gamma$ are defined:

For Theorem 2.24 we have $v|_{\Gamma_0} \in W^{s-1/p,p}(\Gamma_0)$. $\hspace{2cm}$ (2.190)

For Theorem 2.25 we have $D_\nu^j|_{\Gamma_0} \in W^{s-j-1/p,p}(\Gamma_0)$. $\hspace{2cm}$ (2.191)

For Theorem 2.26 we have $w \cdot v|_{\Gamma_0} \in W^{-1/p,p}(\Gamma_0)$ or $(H_{00}^{1/2}(\Gamma_0))'$, depending on whether $p \neq 2$ or $p = 2$. $\hspace{2cm}$ (2.192)

For Theorem 2.27 we have $v|_{\Gamma_0} \in W^{s-1/p,p}(\Gamma_0)$ if $s \geq 1/p$ or $s - 2/p \notin \mathbb{Z}$; $v|_{\Gamma_0} \in (W_{00}^{-s+1/p,p'}(\Gamma_0))'$ if $s < 1/p$ and $s - 2/p \in \mathbb{Z}$; $\partial v/\partial \nu_A|_{\Gamma_0} \in W^{s-1-1/p,p}(\Gamma_0)$ if $s \geq 1 + 1/p$ or $s - 2/p \notin \mathbb{Z}$; $\partial v/\partial \nu_A|_{\Gamma_0} \in (W_{00}^{-s+1+1/p,p'}(\Gamma_0))'$ if $s < 1 + 1/p$ and $s - 2/p \in \mathbb{Z}$. $\hspace{2cm}$ (2.193)

A remark about (2.193) for $v|_{\Gamma_0}$ in the case $s < 1/p$. Applying the boundary version of (2.147), we have to distinguish whether $(s - 1/p) - 1/p$ is an integer or not, because of (2.138). Clearly $\partial v/\partial \nu_A|_{\Gamma_0}$ is considered in the same way. Finally, the same remark for (2.192), where $s = 0$, leads to the distinction between the cases in which $-2/p$ is an integer or not, that is, $p = 2$ or $p \neq 2$.

## 2.9G Traces on Lower-Dimensional Manifolds

For a function $v$ defined in $\Omega \subset \mathbb{R}^n$, by successive applications of restrictions and trace operators, one could define traces $v|_\Sigma$ where $\Sigma$ is an $r$-dimensional manifold, $0 \leq r < n$. For instance, if $\Omega = R^3$ and $\Sigma = \{x_2 = x_3 = 0\}$, we may take

$$R^3 \xrightarrow{\text{res}} \{x_3 > 0\} \xrightarrow{\text{tr}} \{x_3 = 0\} \xrightarrow{\text{res}} \{x_3 = 0, x_2 > 0\} \xrightarrow{\text{tr}} \{x_2 = x_3 = 0\} \quad (2.194)$$

Hence for $v \in H^s(\mathbb{R}^3)$, we have $v|_{x_1\text{-axis}} \in H^{s-1}(\mathbb{R})$ if $s > 1$. More generally, $v \in H^s(\Omega)$ implies $v|_\Sigma \in H^{s-(n-r)/2}(\Sigma)$ provided $s > (n-r)/2$. For $p \in \,]1, \infty[$ and $p \neq 2$, $v \in W^{s,p}(\Omega)$ implies $v|_\Sigma \in W^{s-(n-r)/p,p}(\Sigma)$, provided $s - (n-r)/p > 0$ and a noninteger. Pointwise value could be regarded as trace on a zero-dimensional manifold; thus $s > n/p$ is required, in agreement with (2.133).

## 2.9H Green's Formulae

Assume that $A$ satisfies (2.181) and define

$$a(u, v) = \int_\Omega (\Sigma a_{ij} D_i u D_j v + \Sigma b_i D_i u \cdot v + \Sigma c_i u D_i v + duv) \quad (2.195)$$

$A^*$ is obtained by $A$ replacing $a_{ij}$, $b_i$, $c_i$ by $a_{ji}$, $c_i$, $b_i$. $\hspace{2cm}$ (2.196)

The following statements then hold:

$$\int_\Omega w \cdot \nabla v = \int_\Omega v \, \text{div} \, w + {}_{-1/p,p,\Gamma}\langle w \cdot \nu|_\Gamma, v|_\Gamma\rangle_{1/p,p',\Gamma}$$

$$\text{for } w \in L_{\text{div}}^p(\Omega), v \in W^{1,p'}(\Omega), 1 < p < \infty \quad (2.197)$$

$$a(u, v) = \int_\Omega vAu + {}_{-1/p,p,\Gamma}\left\langle \left.\frac{\partial u}{\partial \nu_A}\right|_\Gamma , v|_\Gamma \right\rangle_{1/p,p',\Gamma}$$

$$\text{for } u \in W^{1,p}_{A,1}(\Omega), v \in W^{1,p'}(\Omega), 1 < p < \infty \qquad (2.198)$$

Assume $\Omega$ is smooth or a half space, $1 < p < \infty$, and either $p = 2$ or $s - 1/p$ a noninteger. Moreover assume either $s \le 0$, $u \in W^{s,p}_{A,1}(\Omega)$, $v \in W^{2-s,p'}(\Omega)$, and $A^*v \in W^{-s,p'}_0(\Omega)$; or $s \ge 2$, $u \in W^{s,p}(\Omega)$, $Au \in W^{s-2,p}_0(\Omega)$, and $v \in W^{2-s,p'}_{A^*,1}(\Omega)$; or $0 \le s \le 2$, $u \in W^{s,p}_{A,1}(\Omega)$, and $v \in W^{2-s,p'}_{A^*,1}(\Omega)$. Then

$$\int_\Omega uA^*v - \int_\Omega vAu = \int_\Gamma \gamma_A u \cdot \gamma_0 v - \int_\Gamma \gamma_0 u \cdot \gamma_{A^*}v \qquad (2.199)$$

where integrals may stand for scalar products according to:

$$\int_\Omega uA^*v = {}_{r,p}\langle u, A^*v \rangle_{-r,p'} \qquad \text{with } r = \min\left\{s, \frac{1}{p}\right\}$$

$$\int_\Omega vAu = {}_{2-r,p}\langle u, Au \rangle_{r-2,p} \qquad \text{with } r = \max\left\{s, 1 + \frac{1}{p}\right\}$$

$$\int_\Gamma \gamma_A u \gamma_0 v = {}_{s-1-1/p,p}\langle \gamma_A u, \gamma_0 v \rangle_{2-s-1/p',p'}$$

$$\int_\Gamma \gamma_0 u \gamma_{A^*}v = {}_{s-1/p,p}\langle \gamma_0 u, \gamma_{A^*}v \rangle_{1-s-1/p',p'},$$

where $\qquad {}_t\langle f, g \rangle_{-t} \qquad$ stands for $\qquad {}_{-t}\langle f, g \rangle_t \qquad$ if $t > 0$

## 2.9ı Characterization of $W^{s,p}_0(\Omega)$

**THEOREM 2.28**  Assume $1 < p < \infty$ and $s > 1/p$. Then

$$W^{s,p}_0(\Omega) = \left\{ v \in W^{s,p}(\Omega) : \gamma_j v = 0 \text{ for integer } j < s - \frac{1}{p} \right\} \qquad (2.200)$$

Moreover, for $s \ge 1$ and $p = 1$,

$$W^{s,1}_0(\Omega) = \{ v \in W^{s,1}(\Omega) : \gamma_j v = 0 \text{ for integer } j \le s - 1 \} \qquad (2.201)$$

**REMARK 2.15**  All smoothness assumptions on $\Omega$ and on the coefficients of the operator $A$ in (2.181) could be weakened in the trace theorems and Green's formulae. One could replace them with assumptions depending on $s$: the required smoothness increases with $|s|$; that is, very smooth domains and coefficients are needed when one deals with very regular (large $s > 0$) or very irregular ($s < 0$ and large $|s|$) cases.

We end this section with some examples.

**EXAMPLE 2.39**  Take $v(x) = |x|^\lambda$, with $\lambda \notin \mathbb{N}$, in the half ball $\Omega = B_1 \cap \mathbb{R}^2_+$. Its trace on the straight part of $\partial\Omega$ is $\gamma_0 v(x) = |x_1|^\lambda$, $-1 < x_1 < 1$. Examples 2.28 and 2.6 give the following: for $p < \infty$, $v \in W^{s,p}(\Omega)$ iff $s < \lambda + 2/p$ and $\gamma_0 v \in W^{r,p}(-1, 1)$ iff $r < \lambda + 1/p$; for $p = \infty$, $v \in C^{k,\mu}(\Omega)$ iff $k + \mu \le \lambda$ iff $\gamma_0 v \in C^{k,\mu}([-1, 1])$. That is, we lose exactly $1/p$ in the "number of derivatives." The same arguments give sharpness for $n > 2$ and in Sec. 2.9G.

**EXAMPLE 2.40** Take $w(x_1, x_2) = (\ln x_2, \ln x_1)$ in $\Omega = ]0, 1[ \times ]0, 1[$. We have $w \in L^p_{\mathrm{div}}(\Omega)$ $\forall p < \infty$. The trace on the bottom of $w \cdot \nu$ is $-\ln x_1$, $0 < x_1 < 1$, while the trace of the whole vector $w$ does not exist. More generally, consider $w(x_1, x_2) = (f_1(x_2), f_2(x_1))$.

**EXAMPLE 2.41** Applying (2.197) with $v = 1$, we get the generalized Gauss theorem, that is,

$$\int_\Omega \mathrm{div}\, w = {}_{-1/p,p,\Gamma}\langle w \cdot \nu|_\Gamma, 1\rangle_{1/p,p',\Gamma} \qquad \text{for } w \in L^p_{\mathrm{div}}(\Omega),\ 1 < p < \infty$$

**EXAMPLE 2.42** Take $\Omega = \mathbb{R}^2_+$ and $u(x) = \ln|x|$ in $\Omega$. Then $u \in W^{1,p}_{-\Delta}(\Omega)$ for $p < 2$ so that $\partial u/\partial \nu|_\Gamma \in W^{-1/p,p}(R)$ for $p < 2$. To compute it, take $\phi \in \mathscr{D}(\mathbb{R})$, $\psi \in \mathscr{D}(\mathbb{R})$ with $\psi(0) = 1$, $v(x_1, x_2) = \phi(x_1)\psi(x_2)$, $\Omega_n = \{x \in \mathbb{R}^2 : x_2 > 1/n\}$; (2.198) and Example 2.18 give

$$\left\langle \frac{\partial u}{\partial \nu}\Big|_\Gamma, \phi \right\rangle = \left\langle \frac{\partial u}{\partial \nu}\Big|_\Gamma, v|_\Gamma \right\rangle = \int_\Omega \nabla u \cdot \nabla v = \lim \int_{\Omega_n} \nabla u\, \nabla v$$

$$= \lim \int_{\partial\Omega_n} \frac{\partial u}{\partial \nu} v = -\lim \psi\left(\frac{1}{n}\right) \cdot \int_\mathbb{R} \frac{n}{1 + n^2 x_1^2} \phi(x_1)\, dx_1$$

$$= -\pi\phi(0) \qquad \text{that is} \qquad \frac{\partial u}{\partial \nu}\Big|_\Gamma = -\pi\delta$$

where $\delta$ is the Dirac mass at 0 in $\mathbb{R}$.

**EXAMPLE 2.43** Take $\Omega \subset \mathbb{R}^2$, $u \in W^{1,p}(\Omega)$, $w = (-D_2 u, D_1 u)$. Then $w \in L^p_{\mathrm{div}}(\Omega)$ and (2.197) applies with $v \in W^{1,p'}(\Omega)$. We get

$$\int_\Omega (D_1 u\, D_2 v - D_2 u\, D_1 v) = {}_{-1/p,p,\Gamma}\left\langle \frac{\partial u}{\partial \tau}\Big|_\Gamma, v|_\Gamma \right\rangle_{1/p,p',\Gamma}$$

where we set (as natural) $\partial u/\partial \tau|_\Gamma = w \cdot \nu|_\Gamma$ and $\tau$ is the unit tangent vector to $\partial\Omega$ in the counterclockwise orientation. If $\Omega$ is smooth, $\partial u/\partial \tau|_\Gamma$ is the derivative of $u|_\Gamma$ with respect to the arc length.

**EXAMPLE 2.44** Let $\Omega = \mathbb{R}^2_+$ and $\alpha(x_1) \in C^1(\bar{\mathbb{R}})$. Setting

$$a(u, v) = \int_\Omega (\nabla u \cdot \nabla v + \alpha D_1 u\, D_2 v - \alpha D_2 u\, D_1 v - \alpha' D_2 u \cdot v)$$

we have $Au = -\Delta u$. Thus for $u \in W^{1,p}_{-\Delta}$ and $v \in W^{1,p'}$ we have (2.198)

$$a(u, v) = \int_\Omega v(-\Delta u) + {}_{-1/p,p}\left\langle \left(\frac{\partial u}{\partial \nu} + \alpha(x_1)\frac{\partial u}{\partial \tau}\right)\Big|_\Gamma, v|_\Gamma \right\rangle_{1/p,p'}$$

that is, the conormal derivative is now any prescribed oblique derivative.

## 2.10 VECTOR-VALUED FUNCTIONS

### 2.10A Preliminaries

Consider a function $(x, t) \to v(x, t)$, defined for $x \in \Omega$ and $t \in ]0, T[$, and suppose $v \in L^2(\Omega \times ]0, T[)$. Fubini's theorem ensures that

For almost all $t \in ]0, T[$, the function $x \to v(x, t)$ is measurable and $\int_\Omega |v(x, t)|^2 \, dx < \infty$. (2.202)

Moreover

$$\int_0^T \left( \int_\Omega |v(x, t)|^2 \, dx \right) dt < \infty \qquad (2.203)$$

Actually

$$\int_0^T \left( \int_\Omega |v|^2 \, dx \right) dt = \iint_{\Omega \times ]0, T[} |v|^2 \, dx \, dt$$

Conversely, under suitable measurability assumptions, (2.202) and (2.203) imply $v \in L^2(\Omega \times ]0, T[)$. This shows that $L^2(\Omega \times ]0, T[)$ can be presented in a different way: its functions satisfy certain measurability conditions and the properties (2.202) and (2.203), which we can write in the following form:

For almost all $t \in ]0, T[$, $v(\cdot, t) \in L^2(\Omega)$ (2.204)

$$\int_0^T \|v(\cdot, t)\|_{L^2(\Omega)}^2 \, dt < \infty. \qquad (2.205)$$

That is, instead of the original function $(x, t) \to v(x, t)$, we are considering the map $t \to v(\cdot, t)$, whose values are elements of $L^2(\Omega)$ instead of numbers.

Using the same idea, one can show that $v \in C^0(\bar\Omega \times [0, T])$ iff (2.206) and (2.207) hold:

For every $t \in [0, T]$, $v(\cdot, t) \in C^0(\bar\Omega)$ (2.206)

For every $t$ and $\{t_n\}$ in $[0, T]$, $t_n \to t$ implies $v(\cdot, t_n) \to v(\cdot, t)$ in $C^0(\bar\Omega)$ (2.207)

These are, again, the properties of the map $t \to v(\cdot, t)$, whose values are now elements of $C^0(\bar\Omega)$.

In previous examples the common factor is as follows: the map $t \to v(\cdot, t)$ takes values in a Banach space, $L^2(\Omega)$ and $C^0(\bar\Omega)$, respectively. Moreover, (2.207) means that $t \to v(\cdot, t)$ is continuous from $[0, T]$ into $C^0(\Omega)$, according to Def. 1.25 in Part 1 with $V = \mathbb{R}$, $W = C^0(\bar\Omega)$, and $A = [0, T]$.

It is thus natural to read (2.205) as a square-integrability property of the map $t \to v(\cdot, t)$ from $]0, T[$ into $L^2(\Omega)$. Therefore, these examples lead us to consider continuity, integrability, etc., of functions $t \to v(t)$, valued in a Banach space, which we shall call simply *vector-valued functions*. We can obtain such functions starting from a different point of view. Consider a usual vector-valued function, i.e., an $n$-tuple $(v_1, \ldots, v_n)$ of scalar functions $t \to v_j(t)$. Denoting by $v(t)$ the euclidean vector $(v_1(t), \ldots, v_n(t))$, the above $n$-tuple is a function $t \to v(t)$ valued in $\mathbb{R}^n$. By replacing $\mathbb{R}^n$ with a general Banach space we obtain a general vector-valued function. In this section we extend the definition and the properties given in the previous sections to vector-valued functions; in this context we define continuity, integrals, classical and weak derivatives, etc., of vector-valued functions. Derivatives, for instance, will be the natural generalizations of both $n$-tuples of derivatives of scalar functions and partial derivatives of functions of several variables. That is:

$$v'(t) = (v_1'(t), \ldots, v_n'(t)) \text{ if } v(t) = (v_1(t), \ldots, v_n(t)) \text{ with scalar functions } t \to v_j(t), \quad (2.208)$$

and

$v'(t) = (\partial v/\partial t)(\cdot, t)$ if $v(t)$ denotes an element of a functional space (e.g., $L^2(\Omega)$ or $C^0(\bar{\Omega})$, as in the previous examples), which varies with respect to time $t$.　　(2.209)

It follows that different evolution equations can be seen as different models of the same abstract equation. For instance, a system of ordinary differential equations

$$v_i'(t) + \sum_j a_{ij} v(t) = f_i(t)$$

and the heat equation

$$\frac{\partial v}{\partial t}(x, t) - \Delta u(x, t) = f(x, t)$$

are models of the abstract first-order equation $v'(t) + Av(t) = f(t)$, if we read (1) $v(t) = (v_1(t), \ldots, v_n(t))$, $f(t) = (f_1(t), \ldots, f_n(t))$, $A = $ matrix of elements $a_{ij}$, and (2) $v(t) = v(\cdot, t)$, $f(t) = f(\cdot, t)$, $A = -\Delta$, respectively.

Therefore, spaces of vector-valued functions will be used to study time-dependent problems, while Sobolev spaces and the like, already introduced, have applications to stationary problems. We introduce now the $C^k$, $C^{k,\lambda}$, and $W^{s,p}$ families of spaces of functions valued in Banach spaces $V$, $W$, etc. All definitions and properties will be so similar to those in the previous sections that the reader should be able to guess almost all of them and read the next paragraphs simply to check the guesswork. Hence we shall proceed very briefly to point out only the important differences between the vector and scalar cases.

## 2.10B Spaces $C^k$, $C^{k,\lambda}$, $C^\infty$, $C_0^\infty$

Continuity for functions $v: ]0, T[ \to V$ was defined in Def. 1.25. The classical derivative is defined as follows:

$v'(t)$ is the strong limit in $V$ (if it exists):

$$\lim_{\tau \to t} \frac{v(\tau) - v(t)}{\tau - t}$$　　(2.210)

$$v'' = (v')', \ldots \qquad v^{(0)} = v$$

We recall now the definitions and some features of several spaces.

- $C^0(]0, T[; V)$ is the space of continuous functions $v: ]0, T[ \to V$.
- $C^0([0, T]; V)$ is the space of functions $v \in C^0(]0, T[; V)$ which have a continuous extension (still denoted by $v$) to $[0, T]$.
- For $0 < \lambda \leq 1$, $C^{0,\lambda}([0, T]; V)$ is the space of $v \in C^0([0, T]; V)$ such that $|t - \tau|^{-\lambda} \|v(t) - v(\tau)\|$ is bounded on the set $\{(t, \tau) \in [0, T] \times [0, T]: t \neq \tau\}$ where $\|\cdot\|$ denotes the norm in $V$.
- $C^{0,\lambda}(]0, T[; V)$ is the space of $v \in C^0(]0, T[; V)$, whose restriction to $[\varepsilon, T - \varepsilon]$ belongs to $C^{0,\lambda}([\varepsilon, T - \varepsilon]; V)$ for every $\varepsilon > 0$ (if $]0, T[$ is replaced by another interval, the previous spaces must of course be defined in a similar way).

- For $k = 1, 2, \ldots,$ $C^k(]0, T[; V)$ (respectively, $C^k([0, T]; V)$, $C^{k,\lambda}([0, T]; V)$, $C^{k,\lambda}(]0, T[; V))$ is the space of $v : ]0, T[ \to V$, whose $j^{\text{th}}$ derivative $v^{(j)}$ (exists and) belongs to $C^0(]0, T[; V)$ [respectively, $C^0([0, T]; V)$, $C^{0,\lambda}([0, T]; V)$, $C^{0,\lambda}(]0, T[; V)]$ for $0 \le j \le k$; $C^{k,0} \equiv C^k$.
- $C^\infty(]0, T[; V)$ (respectively, $C^\infty([0, T]; V)$) is the space of $v$ belonging to $C^k(]0, T[; V)$ (respectively, $C^k([0, T]; V)$) for every $k$.
- $C_0^\infty(]0, T[; V)$ is the space of $v \in C^\infty(]0, T[; V)$ which are compact-support functions (2.23) from $]0, T[$ into $V$.

Clearly the previous spaces are the natural generalization of spaces of Sec. 2.3. Almost the whole of Sec. 2.3 extends to the case of vector-valued functions. In particular, spaces on $[0, T]$ (except $C^\infty([0, T]; V)$) are Banach spaces with respect to their natural norms. For instance, the norm in $C^{0,\lambda}([0, T]; V)$ $(0 < \lambda \le 1)$ is

$$\|v\|_{C^{0,\lambda}([0,T];V)} = \sup_{0 \le t \le T} \|v(t)\| + \sup_{\substack{0 \le t \le T \\ 0 \le \tau \le T \\ t \ne \tau}} |t - \tau|^{-\lambda} \|v(t) - v(\tau)\| \qquad (2.211)$$

Compact inclusions (2.25) have to be replaced by continuous inclusions. For instance, $\ell < k$ implies $C^k([0, T]; V) \hookrightarrow C^\ell([0, T]; V)$. More generally, $\ell < k$ and $V \hookrightarrow W$ imply $C^k([0, T]; V) \hookrightarrow C^\ell([0, T]; W)$, and the inclusion is compact if in addition $V \hookrightarrow \hookrightarrow W$. In a similar way, one can generalize (2.26) to (2.29).

Let $\Omega$ be as usual, and set $Q = \Omega \times ]0, T[$. We have already noted (Sec. 2.10A) that

$$v \in C^0([0, T]; C^0(\bar\Omega)) \qquad \text{iff} \qquad v \in C^0(\bar Q) \qquad (2.212)$$

Similarly, we have

$$v \in C^0([0, T]; C^1(\bar\Omega)) \qquad \text{iff} \qquad v, \frac{\partial v}{\partial x_i} \in C^0(\bar Q) \qquad i = 1, \ldots, n \qquad (2.213)$$

$$v \in C^1([0, T]; C^0(\bar\Omega)) \qquad \text{iff} \qquad v, \frac{\partial v}{\partial t} \in C^0(\bar Q) \qquad (2.214)$$

It follows that $\qquad C^1(\bar Q) = C^0([0, T]; C^1(\bar\Omega)) \cap C^1([0, T]; C^0(\bar\Omega)) \qquad (2.215)$

Other relations between Sec. 1.3 of Part 1 and vector-valued functions could be easily found. Note that $v \in C^0([0, T]; L^p(\Omega))$ means $v(t) = v(\cdot, t) \in L^p(\Omega)$ for $0 \le t \le T$ and

$$t_n \to t \text{ implies } v(\cdot, t_n) \to v(\cdot, t) \text{ in } L^p(\Omega) \qquad (2.216)$$

For instance, if $T = 1$ and $\Omega = ]0, 1[$, the function $v$ defined by $v(x, t) = 0$ or $1$ depending on whether $x > t$ or $x \le t$, belongs to $C^0([0, T]; L^p(\Omega))$ $\forall p < \infty$. Indeed (2.216) holds, since

$$\|v(\cdot, t_n) - v(\cdot, t)\|_{0,p,\Omega} = \left( \int_0^1 |v(x, t_n) - v(x, t)|^p \, dx \right)^{1/p} = |t_n - t|^{1/p}$$

## 2.10c The Spaces $L^p$

If $0 < T \le \infty$, a function $v : ]0, T[ \to V$ (defined almost everywhere in $]0, T[$) is called *measurable* iff

$v_n \in C^0([0, T]; V)$ exist such that $v_n(t) \to v(t)$ (strongly in $V$) for almost all $t \in ]0, T[$. (2.217)

One can show that

If $t \to v(t)$ is measurable, then $t \to \|v(t)\|$ is measurable. (2.218)

In particular, the integral $\int_0^T \|v(t)\|^p\, dt$ is defined (it could be $=\infty$) for every measurable $v$ and $1 \leq p < \infty$. Hence the following definition makes sense:

$$L^p(0, T; V) = \left\{ v: ]0, T[ \to V: v \text{ is measurable and } \int_0^T \|v(t)\|^p\, dt < \infty \right\} \quad (2.219)$$

which is a Banach space with respect to its natural norm

$$\|v\|_{0,p;0,T;V} = \left( \int_0^T \|v(t)\|^p\, dt \right)^{1/p} \quad (2.220)$$

Moreover, $L^\infty(0, T; V)$ is the space of measurable functions $v$, such that $t \to \|v(t)\|$ is essentially bounded [i.e., belongs to $L^\infty(0, T)$], which is a Banach space with

$$\|v\|_{0,\infty;0,T;V} = \sup_{0<t<T} \text{ess } \|v(t)\| \quad (2.221)$$

It is important to note that:

If $V$ is a Hilbert space, $L^2(0, T; V)$ is a Hilbert space and its scalar product is

$$(u, v) = \int_0^T (u(t), v(t))_V\, dt \quad (2.222)$$

For $v \in L^1(0, T; V)$ one can define the integral $\int_0^T v(t)\, dt$, which is an element of $V$. These integrals have the usual properties; for instance,

$$\left\| \int_0^T v(t)\, dt \right\| \leq \int_0^T \|v(t)\|\, dt$$

$$_{V'}\left\langle u, \int_0^T v(t)\, dt \right\rangle_V = \int_0^T {}_{V'}\langle u, v(t)\rangle_V\, dt \quad \forall u \in V' \quad (2.223)$$

Observe that, if $V$ is a functional space $V(\Omega)$ and $v \in L^1(0, T; V(\Omega))$, then

$$\int_0^T v(t)\, dt = \int_0^T v(\cdot, t)\, dt$$

has the usual meaning; i.e., one integrates $v$ with respect to $t$ and obtains a function of $x$ on $\Omega$. If $1 \leq p < \infty$ and $V$ is separable, the *dual space* of $L^p(0, T; V)$ can be *identified* with

$L^{p'}(0, T; V')$ by

$$_{(L^p(V))'}\langle u, v \rangle_{L^p(V)} = \int_0^T {}_{V'}\langle u(t), v(t) \rangle_V \, dt \qquad \text{for}$$

$$u \in L^{p'}(0, T; V') \quad \text{and} \quad v \in L^p(0, T; V) \tag{2.224}$$

If in addition $p > 1$ and $V$ is *reflexive*, $L^p(0, T; V)$ is *reflexive*.

## 2.10D The Sobolev Spaces

We consider the case $T < \infty$. In a similar way, one deals with the case $T = \infty$. We could introduce first vector-valued distributions and then generalize Secs. 2.6 and 2.7. Since this leads to a complicated theory, we prefer another approach. Applying the definitions of this section with $V = \mathbb{R}$, one can again obtain the usual Sobolev spaces in one dimension presented from a different point of view. The starting points are Theorem 2.14 and Sec. 1.31 in Part 1. Since $p = \infty$ leads to the $C^{k,\lambda}$ family, we deal with the case $p < \infty$. Let then $p$, $k$, $\sigma$, $s$ be such that

$$1 \le p < \infty \qquad k \in \mathbb{N} \qquad 0 \le \sigma < 1 \qquad \text{and} \qquad s = k + \sigma \tag{2.225}$$

and define

$W^{s,p}(0, T; V)$ is the completion of $C^\infty([0, T]; V)$ with respect to the norm
$\| \cdot \|_{s,p;0,T;V}$ $\tag{2.226}$

The norm $\| \cdot \|_{s,p;0,T;V}$ is defined (of course) as follows:

$$\|v\|_{k,p;0,T;V} = \left( \sum_{j=0}^k \|v^{(j)}\|_{0,p;0,T;V}^p \right)^{1/p} \qquad \text{for } s = k \tag{2.227}$$

$$\|v\|_{s,p;0,T;V} = \left( \|v\|_{k,p;0,T;V}^p + \sum_{j=0}^k \int_0^T \int_0^T \frac{\|v^{(j)}(t) - v^{(j)}(\tau)\|^p}{|t - \tau|^{1+\sigma p}} \, dt \, d\tau \right)^{1/p} \qquad \text{if } \sigma > 0 \tag{2.228}$$

Hence, $W^{s,p}(0, T; V)$ are Banach spaces by definition (Hilbert spaces if $p = 2$ and $V$ is a Hilbert space). Moreover, we set

$$W_0^{s,p}(0, T; V) = \text{closure of } C_0^\infty(0, T; V) \text{ in } W^{s,p}(0, T; V) \tag{2.229}$$

If $V$ is a *separable* and *reflexive* Banach space and $1 < p < \infty$, we set moreover

$$W^{-s,p}(0, T; V) = \text{dual space of } W_0^{s,p'}(0, T; V') \tag{2.230}$$

The norm in $W^{-s,p}(V)$ is denoted by $\| \cdot \|_{-s,p;0,T;V}$.

One can similarly define $W^{s,p}$ spaces on any interval (e.g., $]-\infty, +\infty[$); we could thus consider the trivial extension and obtain similar results as for the scalar case. This leads to the definition of $W_{00}^{k+1/p,p}(0, T; V)$. But we will not deal any longer with such definitions, and we prefer to speak about weak derivatives and the like for vector-valued functions.

Assume that $\{v_m\}$ is a sequence of elements of $C^\infty([0, T]; V)$ which converges to a $v$ in $W^{s,p}(0, T; V)$. For $j$ an integer $\leq s$ we have

$$\|v_{m'}^{(j)} - v_{m''}^{(j)}\|_{0,p;V} \leq \|v_{m'} - v_{m''}\|_{s,p;V}$$

$$\leq \|v_{m'} - v\|_{s,p;V} + \|v - v_{m''}\|_{s,p;V}$$

so that the sequence $\{v_m^{(j)}\}$ is a Cauchy sequence in $L^p(0, T; V)$; thus $\{v_m^{(j)}\}$ is convergent in $L^p(0, T; V)$ to some element that we denote by $v^{(j)}$ and call the $j^{\text{th}}$ *weak derivative* of $v$. This definition makes sense, because $v^{(j)}$ actually depends only on $v$ and $j$, and not on the particular sequence $\{v_m\}$. Therefore:

$$\text{If } v \in W^{s,p}(0, T; V), \text{ then } v^{(j)} \in L^p(0, T; V) \qquad 0 \leq j \leq s \qquad (2.231)$$

One can be even more precise; that is, $v^{(j)} \in W^{\sigma,p}(0, T; V)$, $\sigma = s - j$. Since we did not define vector-valued distributions, for $u \in L^p(0, T; V)$, $u'$ does not make any sense yet, so we will have to define it.

Assume $u \in L^p(0, T; V)$ with $1 < p < \infty$ and consider the map

$$v \to L(v) = -\int_0^T {}_V\langle v'(t), u(t)\rangle_V \, dt$$

defined on $W_0^{1,p'}(0, T; V')$. We have

$$|L(v)| \leq \int_0^T |{}_V\langle v'(t), u(t)\rangle_V| \, dt$$

$$\leq \int_0^T \|v'(t)\|_{V'} \|u(t)\|_V \, dt$$

$$\leq \left(\int_0^T \|v'(t)\|^{p'} \, dt\right)^{1/p'} \left(\int_0^T \|u(t)\|_V^p \, dt\right)^{1/p}$$

$$\leq \|u\|_{0,p;V} \|v\|_{1,p';V'}$$

Hence

$$L \in (W_0^{1,p'}(0, T; V'))' = W^{-1,p}(0, T; V) \qquad \text{and} \qquad \|L\|_{-1,p;V} \leq \|u\|_{0,p;V}$$

It is thus natural to define $u' = L$. In a similar way, one defines higher derivatives. We have:

If $u \in L^p(0, T; V)$, then $u^{(k)} \in W^{-k,p}(0, T; V)$ for $1 < p < \infty$, $k = 0, 1, \ldots$, and the map $u \to u^{(k)}$ is linear and continuous. $\qquad (2.232)$

One could prove, using the reflexivity of $V$, which was assumed in the definition of $W^{-s,p}(V)$, that *every element of $W^{-k,p}(V)$ is the $k^{\text{th}}$ derivative of some element of $L^p(V)$.*

As in the previous sections one uses $H^s$ instead of $W^{s,2}$; moreover, seminorms in $W^{s,p}(V)$, with $s > 0$, are defined in the obvious way. All results regarding scalar Sobolev spaces extend to vector Sobolev spaces with some changes in Theorems 2.19 and 2.20. Indeed, compact inclusions (2.134) and (2.135) have to be replaced by continuous inclusions with $n = 1$ in the formulae. More generally, we have the same situation which we found for the $C^{k,\lambda}$-family. For instance, (2.132) and (2.135) may be replaced by the following:

$0 \leq r \leq s,\ k \in \mathbb{N},\ 1 < p \leq q < \infty,\ 0 < \lambda < 1,\ V \hookrightarrow W,$ and $r - 1/q \leq s - 1/p$ (respectively, $k + \lambda \leq s - 1/p$) imply $W^{s,p}(0, T; V) \hookrightarrow W^{r,q}(0, T; W)$ (respectively, $\hookrightarrow C^{k,\lambda}([0, T]; W))$. The inclusions are compact if in addition, $r - 1/q < s - 1/p$ (respectively, $k + \lambda < s - 1/p$) and $V \hookrightarrow\hookrightarrow W.$                                          (2.233)

Moreover, Theorem 2.20 holds if in (2.138) we replace $W^{s,p}(\Omega)$, $W_0^{s,p}(\Omega)$, $W_{00}^{s,p}(\Omega)$, and $(W_{00}^{|s|,p'}(\Omega))'$ with $W^{s,p}(0, T; W)$, $W_0^{s,p}(0, T; W)$, $W_{00}^{s,p}(0, T; W)$, and $(W^{|s|,p'}(0, T; W'))'$, respectively, where $W$ is a reflexive and separable Banach space.

As for the one-dimensional scalar case, the trace theorems follow from the Sobolev inclusions. We have, for instance, $W^{1,p}(0, T; V) \hookrightarrow C^0([0, T]; V)$, so that $v(0)$ makes sense for $v \in W^{1,p}(V)$. Moreover, all the characterizations (such as Theorems 2.16 and 2.28) of $W_0^{s,p}(V)$ extend to the present case. Green's formulae have suitable extensions. Since div $= d/dt$ and $\Delta = d^2/dt^2$ if $\Omega = ]0, T[$, we need only to extend formulae involving integrals of the type $\int uv'$. We have:

If $1 \leq p < \infty$, $u \in W^{1,p}(0, T; V)$, $v \in W^{1,p'}(0, T; V')$, and $\phi \in W^{1,p}(0, T)$, then:

$$\int_0^T {}_{V'}\langle v'(t), u(t)\rangle_V\, dt = -\int_0^T {}_{V'}\langle v(t), u'(t)\rangle_V\, dt + {}_{V'}\langle v(T), u(T)\rangle_V - {}_{V'}\langle v(0), u(0)\rangle_V$$

$$\int_0^T \phi(t)v'(t)\, dt = -\int_0^T \phi'(t)v(t)\, dt + \phi(T)v(T) - \phi(0)v(0) \qquad (2.234)$$

We think the following examples are useful; using the notation $Q = \Omega \times ]0, T[$, we have the following statements (where partial derivatives are weak derivatives in $Q$):

$$v \in L^p(0, T; W^{1,p}(\Omega)) \qquad \text{iff} \qquad v, \frac{\partial v}{\partial x_i} \in L^p(Q) \qquad i = 1, \ldots, n \qquad (2.235)$$

$$v \in W^{1,p}(0, T; L^p(\Omega)) \qquad \text{iff} \qquad v, \frac{\partial v}{\partial t} \in L^p(Q)$$

Moreover
$$v'(t) = \frac{\partial v}{\partial t}(\cdot, t) \qquad (2.236)$$

In particular, $\qquad W^{1,p}(Q) = L^p(0, T; W^{1,p}(\Omega)) \cap W^{1,p}(0, T; L^p(\Omega))$

If $V = L^p(\Omega)$, then ${}_{V'}\langle \cdot, \cdot \rangle_V$ is the integral (on $\Omega$) of the product. Hence (2.234) gives

$$\int_0^T \int_\Omega \frac{\partial v}{\partial t}(x, t)u(x, t)\, dx\, dt = -\int_0^T \int_\Omega v(x, t)\frac{\partial u}{\partial t}(x, t)\, dx\, dt + \int_\Omega v(x, T)u(x, T)\, dx$$

$$- \int_\Omega v(x, 0)u(x, 0)\, dx \qquad \text{for } u \in W^{1,p}(L^p(\Omega)),\ v \in W^{1,p'}(L^{p'}(\Omega))$$

$$(2.237)$$

which is a *usual Green's formula*.

We conclude with the following general remark. If $L \in \mathscr{L}(V; W)$, then we can consider the operator (still denoted by $L$) defined on $L^1(0, T; V)$ by

$$Lv \text{ is the function } t \to L(v(t)) \tag{2.238}$$

One can see that $L \in \mathscr{L}(W^{s,p}(0, T; V), W^{s,p}(0, T; W))$ for $s \geq 0$ and $1 \leq p < \infty$. The same is true with $C^k$ or $C^{k,\lambda}$ instead of $W^{s,p}$. For instance:

$\gamma_0 \in \mathscr{L}(H^1(\Omega); H^{1/2}(\Gamma))$ implies $\gamma_0 \in \mathscr{L}(L^2(H^1(\Omega)); L^2(H^{1/2}(\Gamma)))$, which is a *trace theorem* (not yet considered in the present and in the previous sections); (2.239)

$\partial/\partial x_i \in \mathscr{L}(L^2(\Omega); H^{-1}(\Omega))$ implies that $\partial/\partial x_i \in \mathscr{L}(L^2(Q) = L^2(L^2(\Omega)); L^2(H^{-1}(\Omega)))$, that is, that $L^2(0, T; H^{-1}(\Omega))$ contains space derivatives of functions of $L^2(Q)$, while their time derivative belongs to $H^{-1}(0, T; L^2(\Omega))$. (2.240)

As an application, if $u \in L^2(0, T; H^1(\Omega))$ satisfies the heat equation $u' - \Delta u = 0$, then $u'(=\partial u/\partial t) = \Delta u \in L^2(0, T; H^{-1}(\Omega))$; in particular, $u$, $u' \in L^2(0, T; H^{-1}(\Omega))$, so that $u \in H^1(0, T; H^{-1}(\Omega)) \hookrightarrow C^0([0, T]; H^{-1}(\Omega))$ and $u(\cdot, 0) = u(0)$ makes sense and is an element of $H^{-1}(\Omega)$. In general, $u(0) \notin H^1(\Omega)$, since $u$ need not belong to $C^0([0, T]; H^1(\Omega))$. However, one can show that $u(0) \in L^2(\Omega)$, as a particular case of the following result:

If $V \hookrightarrow H \hookrightarrow V'$ is a Hilbert triplet (Sec. 1.4G in Part 1), then $L^2(0, T; V) \cap H^1(0, T; V') \hookrightarrow C^0([0, T]; H)$. (2.241)

## 2.11 REFERENCES

1. Adams, R., *Sobolev Spaces*, Academic Press, New York, 1975.

2. Bergh, J., and J. Löfström, *Interpolation Spaces: An introduction*, Springer, Berlin, 1976.

3. Ladyženskaja, O. A., and N. N. Ural'ceva, *Equations aux Dérivées Partielles de Type Elliptique*, Dunod, Paris, 1968. (Russian ed., Nauka, Moscow, 1964.)

4. Lions, J. L., *Equations Différentielles Opérationnelles et Problèmes aux Limites*, Springer, Berlin, 1961.

5. Lions, J. L., and E. Magenes, *Non-Homogeneous Boundary Value Problems and Applications*, vols. I and II, Springer, Berlin, 1972. (French ed., Dunod, Paris, 1968.)

6. Nečas, J., *Les Méthodes Directes en Théorie des Equations Elliptiques*, Masson, Paris/Academia, Prague, 1967.

7. Nikol'skiĭ, S. M., *Approximation of Function of Several Variables and Imbedding Theorems*, Springer, Berlin, 1975. (Russian ed., Nauka, Moscow, 1969.)

8. Schwartz, L., *Théorie des Distributions*, 2d ed., Hermann, Paris, 1966.

9. Triebel, H., *Interpolation Theory, Function Spaces, Differential Operators*, North Holland, Amsterdam, 1978.

10. Kufner, A., O. John, and S. Fučik, *Function Spaces*, Academia, Prague/Noordhoff, Leyden, 1977.

# CHAPTER 3
# PARTIAL DIFFERENTIAL EQUATIONS

## 3.1 INTRODUCTION

In this chapter we present a few basic results on existence, uniqueness, and properties of the solution of boundary-value problems for partial differential equations. For the sake of simplicity we restrict ourselves to the case of second-order equations of elliptic, parabolic, and hyperbolic type. The chapter is divided into four sections. In the first section we deal with linear second-order elliptic problems: we give rather general regularity theorems in the spaces $W^{s,p}$ and $C^{k,\lambda}$ and discuss the problems of existence and uniqueness; the case of a polygonal domain is also considered. Moreover we analyze some basic properties of solutions, such as local regularity, the maximum principle, and the Hopf principle. In the second section we consider linear parabolic problems. The regularity of the solutions is discussed in a class of anisotropic Sobolev spaces that we introduce and study for $p=2$ or $\infty$ (for the sake of simplicity). Existence and uniqueness results are also presented, together with basic properties such as local regularity, the maximum principle, and asymptotic behavior. The case of linear hyperbolic problems is considered in the third section, where again we discuss existence, uniqueness, and regularity of the solutions. In this last case the regularity results are nonoptimal, but this is due to the "pathology" of hyperbolic equations, as shown in the examples which also illustrate the lack of other properties, such as local regularity or the maximum principle. Finally, in the fourth section we give some complements on weak and variational formulations and present some of the above results in a more abstract setting. The last part of the section is devoted to variational inequalities for linear operators. We give abstract existence and uniqueness theorems; some regularity results are also presented in particular cases.

No proofs are given; however, several examples illustrate the results and discuss their optimality.

Particular stress is laid on the regularity theorems; it is our belief that they are important and useful in studying the approximation of partial differential equations.

For background and other relevant information, see the sources listed in Sec. 3.6.


## 3.2 ELLIPTIC EQUATIONS

### 3.2A Introduction

In this section we shall consider problems of type

$$Au = f \quad \text{in } \Omega$$

$$\text{boundary condition} \tag{3.1}$$

where $A$ will be an elliptic operator in the sense of (2.181) in Part 1 and the boundary conditions will be mainly of the Dirichlet or Neumann type.

At an intuitive level it is clear that the regularity of the solution of (3.1) will depend on the regularity of the domain $\Omega$, the coefficients of $A$, the right-hand side $f$, and the boundary data. On the other hand, the existence, as well as the uniqueness, of the solution will depend on the numerical values of the above quantities.

For the sake of simplicity we shall list once and for all the assumptions that we make on the domain $\Omega$ and the coefficients. The following theorems will therefore state relations between the regularity of $f$ (and the boundary data) and $u$.

**ASSUMPTION 3.1**   *On* $\Omega$. In this section we assume that $\Omega \subset \mathbb{R}^n$ is smooth in the sense of Def. 2.1 in Part 1 and $\Gamma = \partial\Omega$.

Some results for a more general $\Omega$ will be quoted in Rems. 3.4, 3.5, 3.6 and Examples 3.5, 3.6.

We recall for convenience the assumptions on $A$ that we made in (2.181) in Part 1.

**ASSUMPTION 3.2**   *On A.* We assume that $A$ has the form

$$Au = -\Sigma D_j(a_{ij}D_i u) + \Sigma b_i D_i u - \Sigma D_i(c_i u) + du \tag{3.2}$$

with $$a_{ij}, b_i, c_i, d \in C^\infty(\bar{\Omega}) \quad (1 \le i, j \le n) \tag{3.3}$$

Moreover the (*uniform*) *ellipticity condition* is fulfilled; i.e., there exists $\alpha > 0$ such that

$$\Sigma a_{ij}(x)\xi_i\xi_j \ge \alpha|\xi|^2 \quad \forall x \in \bar{\Omega}, \forall \xi \in \mathbb{R}^n \tag{3.4}$$

**DEFINITION 3.1**   The adjoint operator $A^*$ is obtained from $A$ by replacing $a_{ij}, b_i, c_i$ with $a_{ji}, c_i, b_i$ in (3.2). The conormal derivative $\partial u/\partial\nu_A$ is defined by

$$\frac{\partial u}{\partial\nu_A} = \Sigma a_{ij}D_i u \cdot \nu_j + \Sigma c_i \nu_i u \tag{3.5}$$

where $\nu$ is the outer unit normal vector to $\partial\Omega$ (see also Sec. 2.9E in Part 1). $\partial u/\partial\nu_{A^*}$ is similarly defined.

## 3.2B Regularity Results

In the following regularity theorems we assume that $u$ is a distribution satisfying the equation

$$Au = f \quad \text{in } \Omega \tag{3.6}$$

and one of the following boundary conditions:

$$u|_{\Gamma} = g_0 \quad (Dirichlet\ boundary\ condition) \tag{3.7}$$

$$\left.\frac{\partial u}{\partial \nu_A}\right|_{\Gamma} = g_1 \quad (Neumann\ boundary\ condition) \tag{3.8}$$

It is understood that Eq. (3.6) holds in the sense of distributions [for a given $f \in \mathscr{D}'(\Omega)$, of course]. On the other hand, it has to be assumed that $u$ belongs to some better space than $\mathscr{D}'(\Omega)$ in order to give meaning to (3.7) or (3.8); for instance, we could suppose $u \in C^0(\bar{\Omega})$ [or $C^1(\bar{\Omega})$ for (3.8)] or, much more generally, that $u$ satisfies the assumptions of one of the trace theorems of Sec. 2.9 (Part 1).

**THEOREM 3.1**  $C^{k,\lambda}$-*regularity*. Assume $k \in \mathbb{N}$, $0 < \lambda < 1$, and $f \in C^{k,\lambda}(\bar{\Omega})$. If $g_0 \in C^{k+2,\lambda}(\Gamma)$, then any $u$ satisfying (3.6) and (3.7) belongs to $C^{k+2,\lambda}(\bar{\Omega})$; if $g_1 \in C^{k+1,\lambda}(\Gamma)$, then any $u$ satisfying (3.6) and (3.8) belongs to $C^{k+2,\lambda}(\bar{\Omega})$. In both cases, if the set of solutions is not empty, we have the estimate

$$\inf \|u\|_{C^{k+2,\lambda}(\bar{\Omega})} \leqslant c(\|f\|_{C^{k,\lambda}(\bar{\Omega})} + \|g_j\|_{C^{k+2-j,\lambda}(\Gamma)}) \tag{3.9}$$

for $j = 0$ or 1, where the infimum is taken over all solutions $u$, and $c$ does not depend on $f$ and $g_j$.

**THEOREM 3.2**  $W^{s,p}$-*regularity*. Assume $r$, $t$, $s \in \mathbb{R}$, $1 < p < \infty$, and either $p = 2$ or $s - 1/p$ is not an integer, and let $f \in W^{r,p}(\Omega)$. If $g_0 \in W^{t,p}(\Gamma)$, $r + 2 \geqslant 1/p$, and $s = \min\{r+2; t+1/p\}$, then any solution $u$ of (3.6) and (3.7) belongs to $W^{s,p}(\Omega)$. If $g_1 \in W^{t,p}(\Gamma)$, $r + 1 \geqslant 1/p$, and $s = \min\{r+2; t+1+1/p\}$, then any solution $u$ of (3.6) and (3.8) belongs to $W^{s,p}(\Omega)$. In both cases, if the set of solutions is not empty, we have the estimate:

$$\inf \|u\|_{s,p,\Omega} \leqslant c(\|f\|_{r,p,\Omega} + \|g_j\|_{t,p,\Gamma}) \tag{3.10}$$

for $j = 0$ or 1, where the infimum is taken over all solutions $u$, and $c$ does not depend on $f$ and $g_j$.

**REMARK 3.1**  The conditions $r \geqslant -2 + 1/p$ and $r \geqslant -1 + 1/p$, respectively, in Theorem 3.2 are unnecessarily restrictive. Indeed any $r$ is allowed provided the following (more general) condition holds: $f$ has the form $f = f_1 + f_2$ with $f_1 \in W^{r,p}(\Omega)$ and vanishing outside some $\Omega_1 \subset\subset \Omega$, and $f_2 \in W^{-2+1/p,p}(\Omega)$ or $W^{-1+1/p,p}(\Omega)$, respectively. In particular, any $r$ is allowed if $f$ itself vanishes near $\Gamma$.

*Warning 3.1*  It has to be pointed out that the estimate (3.10) *does not hold* for $r < -2 + 1/p$ (or $r < -1 + 1/p$, respectively), even for $f$ as in Rem. 3.1.

For instance, take $u_\lambda(x) = x$ or $x - 1$ according to $0 < x < \lambda$ or $\lambda < x < 1$. Then $u_\lambda$ is the unique solution of $-u''_\lambda = \delta'_\lambda$ and $u_\lambda(0) = u_\lambda(1) = 0$ (where $\delta'_\lambda$ is the derivative of the Dirac mass $\delta_\lambda$). A simple computation shows that $\|u_\lambda\|_0^2 = (\lambda^3 + (1-\lambda)^3)/3 \geqslant \frac{1}{12} \; \forall \lambda \in \,]0, 1[$. On the other hand, using (2.133) in Part 1, we have, for any $\phi \in H_0^2(0, 1)$,

$$|\langle \delta_\lambda', \phi \rangle| = |\phi'(\lambda)| = |\phi'(\lambda) - \phi'(0)| \leqslant |\phi'|_{C^{0,1/2}} \cdot \lambda^{1/2}$$

$$\leqslant c\lambda^{1/2}\|\phi'\|_1 \leqslant c\lambda^{1/2}\|\phi\|_2$$

where $c$ does not depend on $\lambda$. Hence

$$\|\delta_\lambda'\|_{-2} = \sup_{\phi \in H_0^2\setminus\{0\}} \frac{|\langle \delta_\lambda', \phi \rangle|}{\|\phi\|_2} \leqslant c\lambda^{1/2}$$

Thus (3.10) cannot hold with $r = -2$ and $j = 0$.

**REMARK 3.2** Independently of the smoothness of $\Omega$ and of the boundary conditions, one always has local regularity results: for *any* open sets $\Omega$, $\Omega_1$, $\Omega_2$ with $\Omega_2 \subset\subset \Omega_1 \subset \Omega$, and *any* $k \in \mathbb{R}$, $\lambda \in ]0, 1[$, $r \in \mathbb{R}$, and $p \in ]1, \infty[$, we have the following:

$$f|_{\Omega_1} \in C^{k,\lambda}(\bar\Omega_1) \text{ and (3.6)} \quad \text{imply} \quad u|_{\Omega_2} \in C^{k+2,\lambda}(\bar\Omega_2)$$

$$f|_{\Omega_1} \in W^{r,p}(\Omega_1) \text{ and (3.6)} \quad \text{imply} \quad u|_{\Omega_2} \in W^{r+2,p}(\Omega_2)$$

Local regularity results can also be obtained near the boundary. For instance, for the Dirichlet problem we have the following: if $B = B_R(x_0)$ is a ball with $x_0 \in \Gamma$ such that (1) $f|_{B \cap \Omega} \in W^{r,p}(B \cap \Omega)$, (2) $B \cap \Gamma$ is smooth, and (3) $g_0|_{B \cap \Gamma} \in W^{t,p}(B \cap \Gamma)$, then $u|_{B' \cap \Omega} \in W^{s,p}(B' \cap \Omega)$ for any smaller ball $B' = B_\rho(x_0)$, $\rho < R$, where $r$, $s$, $t$, $p$ are as in Theorem 3.2. Similar results hold for the $C^{k,\lambda}$-regularity and the Neumann problem.

*Warning 3.2* The assumptions $0 < \lambda < 1$ and $1 < p < \infty$ in Theorems 3.1 and 3.2 are crucial (see Examples 3.1 and 3.4). For instance, if we have $f \in C^{k,1}(\bar\Omega) = W^{k+1,\infty}(\Omega)$ and, for example, $g_0 = 0$, the solution of (3.6) and (3.7) satisfies only $u \in C^{k+2,\lambda}(\bar\Omega)$ and $W^{k+3,p}(\Omega)$ $\forall \lambda < 1$, $\forall p < \infty$. Nevertheless $p = \infty$ in Theorem 3.2 is allowed for nonintegral $s > 0$, being a particular case of Theorem 3.1, since $C^{k,\lambda}(\bar\Omega) = W^{k+\lambda,\infty}(\Omega)$. A few words are needed concerning $p = 1$. Consider, for instance, the Dirichlet problem with $f \in W^{1,1}(\Omega)$ and $g_0 = 0$. One cannot deduce $u \in W^{3,1}(\Omega)$, but only $u \in W^{3-\varepsilon,1}(\Omega)$ $\forall \varepsilon > 0$. Indeed $f \in W^{1-\varepsilon/2,1+\delta}(\Omega)$ for some $\delta = \delta(\varepsilon)$ by (2.134) in Part 1; thus, by Theorem 3.2, $u \in W^{3-\varepsilon/2,1+\delta}(\Omega) \hookrightarrow W^{3-\varepsilon,1}(\Omega)$ (using Hölder's inequality).

**REMARK 3.3** *Other boundary-conditions.* Consider, for instance, the mixed boundary condition of the Dirichlet–Neumann type:

$$u|_{\Gamma_0} = g_0 \quad \text{and} \quad \left.\frac{\partial u}{\partial \nu_A}\right|_{\Gamma_1} = g_1 \tag{3.11}$$

where $\Gamma$ is split into two parts, $\Gamma_0$ and $\Gamma_1$. It is clear that no problems arise when $\Sigma = \bar\Gamma_0 \cap \bar\Gamma_1 = \varnothing$, as, for instance, in the case $\Omega = B_2(0)\setminus\overline{B_1(0)}$, $\Gamma_0 = \partial B_1(0)$, and $\Gamma_1 = \partial B_2(0)$. The situation is completely different in the opposite case $\Sigma \neq \varnothing$ [for instance, $\Omega = B_1(0)$, $\Gamma_0 = \partial\Omega \cap \{x_1 > 0\}$, and $\Gamma_1 = \partial\Omega \cap \{x_1 < 0\}$]. Local regularity exists as in Rem. 3.2 only away from $\Sigma$.

Let us see what happens near $\Sigma$. Even for $C^\infty$ $f$ and $g_j$, there is an upper bound for the regularity of $u$; for instance, in two dimensions, $u$ will not in general belong to $W^{s,p}(\Omega)$ with $s \geqslant \frac{1}{2} + 2/p$, nor to $C^{0,\lambda}(\bar\Omega)$ for $\lambda > \frac{1}{2}$ (see Example 3.6).

**REMARK 3.4**  *Polygons.* A similar situation arises when $\Gamma$ contains corners, as in the case of polygons in $\mathbb{R}^2$. Away from them we have the same regularity as above (see Rem. 3.2), while near a corner we have the following upper bound for the regularity: $u$ does not in general belong to $W^{s,p}$ for $s \geq \pi/\alpha + 2/p$, nor to $C^{k,\lambda}$ for $k + \lambda > \pi/\alpha$ where $\alpha$ is the width of the angle, even for $f \in C^\infty$ and zero boundary conditions (see Example 3.5).

**REMARK 3.5**  In both the previous cases (mixed boundary conditions and polygons) sufficient conditions on data $f$ and $g_j$ can be given in order to overcome the bounds on regularity mentioned above: in general, they are compatibility conditions of the integral type which involve the values of $f$ and $g_j$ on the whole domain, and the integral kernels cannot be computed explicitly, except under fortunate circumstances. Moreover the number of such compatibility conditions increases with the required regularity (see Examples 3.5 and 3.6).

## 3.2c Examples

**EXAMPLE 3.1**  Set $\Omega_0 = ]-1, 1[ \times ]0, 1[$ and take $\Omega$ smooth such that $\Omega_0 \subset \Omega \subset \mathbb{R}^2_+$. If $u_\varepsilon(x) = (x_2 + \varepsilon)/(x_1^2 + (x_2 + \varepsilon)^2)$, explicit and easy computations give

$$\Delta u_\varepsilon = 0 \text{ in } \Omega \qquad \int_\Omega |D_1 u_\varepsilon| \geq \int_{\Omega_0} |D_1 u_\varepsilon| = -2 \ln \varepsilon + \phi(\varepsilon)$$

with $\phi$ bounded near $\varepsilon = 0$, and

$$\int_1^1 |u_\varepsilon(x_1, 0)| \, dx_1 \leq \pi$$

Moreover, if $\Gamma' \subset \Gamma$ is far from 0, it is clear that $\int_{\Gamma'} |u_\varepsilon| \, ds \leq c$. Thus $\|\gamma_0 u_\varepsilon\|_{0,1,\Gamma}$ is bounded, while $\|u_\varepsilon\|_{1,1,\Omega}$ is not. Since $u_\varepsilon$ is the unique harmonic function with its boundary values (by Theorem 3.3 and Example 3.9 below), this shows that (3.10) does not hold for $p = 1$. Notice that $u_\varepsilon \to u$, for example, in $L^1(\Omega)$, where $u(x) = x_2|x|^{-2}$ and $\gamma_0 u \notin L^1(\Gamma)$ since it "contains" a Dirac mass at 0. We were already prepared for trouble with the case $p = 1$.

**EXAMPLE 3.2**  In $\mathbb{R}^2_+$ define $u(x) = (3x_1^2 x_2 - x_2^3) \ln \rho + (x_1^3 - x_1 x_2^2)\theta = \text{Im}\,(z^3 \log z)$, where $z = x_1 + ix_2 = \rho(\cos\theta + i\sin\theta)$, $0 < \theta < \pi$. One can check that $\Delta u = 0$ in $\mathbb{R}^2_+$, $u(x_1, 0) = \pi x_1^3$ or $= 0$, according to $x_1 \leq 0$ or $x_1 \geq 0$, and $u(0, x_2) = -x_2^3 \ln x_2$. Thus $\Delta u \in C^\infty$, $u|_\Gamma \in C^{2,1} = W^{3,\infty}$, while $u \notin C^{2,1} = W^{3,\infty}$ near 0, since $D_2^3 u \notin L^\infty$. One has $u \in C^{2,\lambda}$ and $W^{3,p}$ $\forall \lambda < 1$, $\forall p < \infty$, according to Theorems 3.1 and 3.2.

**EXAMPLE 3.3**  In $B_{1/2} \subset \mathbb{R}^2$ consider $u(x) = |\ln |x||^{1/2}$. We have $\Delta u(x) = -\frac{1}{4}|x|^{-2}|\ln |x||^{-3/2} \in L^1(B_{1/2})$, while $D_1 D_2 u(x) = |x|^{-4} x_1 x_2 (|\ln |x||^{-1/2} - \frac{1}{4}|\ln |x||^{-3/2}) \notin L^1_{\text{loc}}(B_{1/2})$, because of the first logarithm. Hence, $u \notin W^{2,1}_{\text{loc}}(B_{1/2})$. Thus $p = 1$ is not allowed in Theorem 3.2.

**EXAMPLE 3.4**  The function on $\mathbb{R}^2$ given by

$$u(x) = \int_0^{x_1} \left( \int_0^{x_2} \ln |\xi| \, d\xi_2 \right) d\xi_1$$

satisfies       $\Delta u(x) = \dfrac{\pi}{2} x_1 x_2 |x_1 x_2|^{-1}$    and    $D_1 D_2 u(x) = \ln |x|$

Thus $\Delta u \in L^\infty(\mathbb{R}^2)$ and $u \notin W^{2,\infty}_{\text{loc}}(\mathbb{R}^2)$; that is, $p = \infty$ is not allowed even for local regularity in the interior.

**EXAMPLE 3.5**  In two dimensions, set

$$\Omega = B_1(0) \cap \{0 < \theta < \alpha\} \qquad \lambda_k = \frac{k\pi}{\alpha} \qquad u = \sum_{k \geq 1} c_k \rho^{\lambda_k} \sin(\lambda_k \theta)$$

$$g_0 = \sum_{k \geq 1} c_k \sin(\lambda_k \theta) \text{ on } \partial\Omega \cap \partial B_1(0) \qquad \text{and} \qquad g_0 = 0 \text{ elsewhere on } \Gamma$$

Then $u$ solves (3.6) and (3.7) with $A = -\Delta$ and $f = 0$ (provided the series converges, of course!). If $\pi/\alpha \in \mathbb{N}$ (lucky case!) $u$ is $C^\infty$ near 0, since $\lambda_k \in \mathbb{N}\ \forall k$. In the worst case, when $\pi/\alpha$ is not even rational, none of the $\lambda_k$'s is an integer and $u$ is $W^{s,p}$ (respectively, $C^{m,\lambda}$) iff $\lambda_k > s - 2/p$ (respectively, $\lambda_k \geq m + \lambda$) for all $k$ such that $c_k \neq 0$ (recall Examples 2.7 and 2.28 in Part 1). Therefore a high regularity of $u$ near 0 corresponds to a large set of conditions $c_k = 0$, which are of the global type, since $c_k$ are Fourier coefficients, namely,

$$c_k = \frac{2}{\alpha} \int_0^\alpha g_0(\cos\theta, \sin\theta) \sin(\lambda_k \theta)\, d\theta$$

The particular choice $g_0 = \sin(\pi\theta/\alpha)$, that is, $c_1 = 1$ and $c_k = 0$ for $k > 1$, gives $u = \rho^{\pi/\alpha} \sin(\pi\theta/\alpha)$, which does not belong to $W^{s,p}$, nor to $C^{m,\lambda}$, if $s \geq \pi/\alpha + 2/p$, or $m + \lambda > \pi/\alpha$, and $\pi/\alpha$ is not an integer.

**EXAMPLE 3.6**  In two dimensions, set $\Omega = B_1(0) \cap \{0 < \theta < \alpha\}$, $\Gamma_1 - \Gamma \cap \{\theta = \alpha\}$, $\Gamma_0 = \Gamma \backslash \bar{\Gamma}_1$, $\lambda_k - (k - \frac{1}{2})\pi/\alpha$,

$$u = \sum_{k \geq 1} c_k \rho^{\lambda_k} \sin(\lambda_k \theta)$$

$$g_1 = 0 \text{ on } \Gamma_1 \qquad g_0 = \sum_{k \geq 1} c_k \sin(\lambda_k \theta) \text{ on } \Gamma \cap \partial B_1(0) \qquad \text{and} \qquad g_0 = 0 \text{ elsewhere on } \Gamma_0$$

Then $u$ solves the mixed problem (3.6) and (3.11) with $A = -\Delta$, $\partial/\partial\nu_A = \partial/\partial\nu$, and $f = 0$. One can study the regularity of $u$ exactly as above. In particular, notice that for $\alpha = \pi$ the boundary is smooth near 0 and none of the $\lambda_k$'s is an integer; the choice $g_0 = \sin(\theta/2)$, that is, $c_1 = 1$ and $c_k = 0$ for $k > 1$, gives $u = \rho^{1/2} \sin(\theta/2)$, which does not belong to $W^{s,p}$ for $s \geq \frac{1}{2} + 2/p$, nor to $C^{0,\lambda}$ for $\lambda > \frac{1}{2}$, by Examples 2.7 and 2.28 in Part 1.

**EXAMPLE 3.7**  Recall first of all that the Dirac mass $\delta$ at 0 (see Sec. 2.5c in Part 1) belongs to $W^{s,p}(\mathbb{R}^n)$ for $s < -n/p'$, $1 < p < \infty$, by Example 2.38 in Part 1. Therefore, Rem. 3.2 and Example 2.23 in Part 1 give a sharp property of the so-called *fundamental solution* $u(x) = |x|^{2-n}/(2-n)$ if $n \neq 2$ or $u(x) = \ln|x|$ if $n = 2$ *of the Laplace equation*: $u \in W_{loc}^{s+2,p}(\mathbb{R}^n)$ for $s < -n/p'$, $1 < p < \infty$; in particular, $\ln|x| \in W_{loc}^{s+2,p}(\mathbb{R}^2)$ for $s < -2/p'$, that is, $\ln|x| \in W_{loc}^{r,p}(\mathbb{R}^2)\ \forall r < 2/p$, $\forall p \in\ ]1, \infty[$.

**EXAMPLE 3.8**  By Examples 2.23 and 2.42 in Part 1, $\ln|x|$ solves a Neumann problem for $\Delta u = 0$ on $\mathbb{R}_+^2$ with boundary condition $\partial u/\partial\nu = -\pi\delta \in W^{-1/p'-\varepsilon,p}(\mathbb{R})\ \forall\varepsilon > 0$ (see Example 3.7). Thus Rem. 3.3 gives $\ln|x| \in W^{1+1/p-1/p'-\varepsilon,p}(B_1(0) \cap \mathbb{R}_+^2)$, in agreement with the conclusion of Example 3.7.

### 3.2D  Uniqueness

Let us observe that the ellipticity condition (3.4) does not ensure in general the uniqueness of the solution. Indeed $u(x) = C \sin x$ is a solution of $-u'' - u = 0$ (check that this operator is elliptic!), with $u(0) = u(\pi) = 0$, for any real $C$.

We give now some sufficient conditions for uniqueness. As a general remark, the problem posed in (3.6) and (3.7) [or (3.8)] being linear, the solution will be unique iff the corresponding homogeneous problem [that is, $Au = 0$, $\gamma_0 u = 0$ (or $\partial u/\partial \nu_A = 0$)] possesses only the solution $u = 0$. Hence we can deal only with the homogeneous problem. Note that in this case Theorem 3.1 says that any solution must be $C^\infty$ up to the boundary. Hence we have the following theorem:

**THEOREM 3.3**   Let $A$ satisfy (3.2) to (3.4) and define for $u$, $v \in C^\infty(\bar{\Omega})$

$$a(u, v) = \int_\Omega (\Sigma a_{ij} D_i u D_j v + \Sigma b_i D_i u \cdot v + \Sigma c_i u D_i v + duv) \qquad (3.12)$$

Then the solution of (3.6) and (3.7) [respectively, (3.8)] is unique if

$$a(v, v) > 0 \qquad (3.13)$$

for every $v \in C^\infty(\bar{\Omega})$ satisfying $v|_\Gamma = 0$ (respectively, $\partial v/\partial \nu_A|_\Gamma = 0$) and not identically zero. Moreover this condition is fulfilled, provided $\inf_\Omega d$ is big enough.

**EXAMPLE 3.9**   If $a(u, v) = \int_\Omega (\nabla u \cdot \nabla v + duv)$ (which implies $Au = -\Delta u + du$ and $\partial/\partial \nu_A = \partial/\partial \nu$), let $\lambda_1$ be the first eigenvalue of $-\Delta$ in $\Omega$ with the Dirichlet (respectively, Neumann) boundary condition. Then it is easy to see that $\inf d > -\lambda_1$ implies (3.13). In particular, for the Neumann problem $\lambda_1 = 0$ (for any $\Omega$); for the Dirichlet problem $\lambda_1 > 0$ and depends on $\Omega$. In the case $\Omega = \,]0, L[$ one has $\lambda_1 = (\pi/L)^2$.

## 3.2E  Existence

Let us consider the simple example of the equation $-u'' + 2u' - 2u = f$ in $]0, L[$ with the boundary conditions $u(0) = u(L) = 0$. The general solution of the equation is given by

$$u(x) = e^x (c_1 \cos x + c_2 \sin x) - w(x)$$

where

$$w(x) = \int_0^x e^{x-t} \sin (x-t) f(t) \, dt$$

Moreover, $u(0) = 0$ means $c_1 = 0$. Consider first the case $L = \pi/2$. Then there is a unique solution given by $u(x) = C e^x \sin x - w(x)$, with $C = e^{-\pi/2} w(\pi/2)$.

Consider now the case $L = \pi$. Then $u(\pi) = 0$ iff $w(\pi) = 0$, that is, iff

$$\int_0^\pi e^{-t} \sin t \cdot f(t) \, dt = 0$$

Thus we have existence iff $f$ is orthogonal to $v(x) = e^{-x} \sin x$, which is a nontrivial solution of the *adjoint problem*: $-v'' - 2v' - 2v = 0$, $v(0) = v(L) = 0$, with $L = \pi$.

We can see now that, for $L = \pi/2$, the adjoint problem has only the trivial solution $v = 0$, which is obviously orthogonal to any $f$. Hence, for both $L = \pi/2$ and $L = \pi$, we have the following: a necessary and sufficient condition for the existence of a solution is that $f$ is orthogonal to every solution of the adjoint problem. This is a general fact, and the necessity of the above condition is easily seen; indeed, if $Au = f$, $u|_\Gamma = 0$, $A^*v = 0$, and $v|_\Gamma = 0$, one has, by Green's formula [(2.199) in Part 1]

$$\int_\Omega fv = \int_\Omega vAu = \int_\Omega uA^*v - \int_\Gamma \frac{\partial u}{\partial \nu_A} \cdot v + \int_\Gamma u \frac{\partial v}{\partial \nu_{A^*}} = 0$$

In the next theorem we state the general result, involving nonhomogeneous boundary conditions, for both the Dirichlet and the Neumann problems with suitable assumptions on the data, which, however, can be weakened as in Rem. 3.2.

**THEOREM 3.4**  Let $A$ satisfy (3.2) to (3.4) and consider the following problems:

$$(P) \qquad\qquad Au = f, \quad u|_\Gamma = g_0 \quad \left( \text{respectively,} \left. \frac{\partial u}{\partial \nu_A} \right|_\Gamma = g_1 \right)$$

$$(P^*) \qquad\qquad A^*v = 0, \quad v|_\Gamma = 0 \quad \left( \text{respectively,} \left. \frac{\partial v}{\partial \nu_{A^*}} \right|_\Gamma = 0 \right)$$

Assume $r, t \in \mathbb{R}$, $1 < p < \infty$, $f \in W^{r,p}(\Omega)$, and $g_j \in W^{t,p}(\Gamma)$ with $r + 2 \geq 1/p$ (respectively, $r + 1 \geq 1/p$ for the Neumann problem). Then we have:

   If $(P^*)$ has the unique solution $v = 0$, then $(P)$ has a unique solution.                     (3.14)

   If $(P^*)$ has nontrivial (i.e., $\neq 0$) solutions, then $(P)$ has a solution iff

$$\int_\Omega fv = \int_\Gamma g_0 \frac{\partial v}{\partial \nu_{A^*}} \quad \left( = -\int_\Gamma g_1 v, \text{ respectively} \right)$$

   for every solution $v$ of $(P^*)$. Moreover in this case the solution is never unique.         (3.15)

**EXAMPLE 3.10**  Consider the Neumann problem $-\Delta u = f$, $\partial u / \partial \nu|_\Gamma = g_1$ [that is, $a(u, v) = \int_\Omega \nabla u \cdot \nabla v$]. Then any constant solves $(P^*)$ and, conversely, any solution $v$ of $(P^*)$ is a constant, since

$$\int_\Omega |\nabla v|^2 = -\int_\Omega v \, \Delta v + \int_\Gamma v \frac{\partial v}{\partial \nu} = 0$$

Thus from Theorem 3.4, a solution $u$ exists iff

$$\int_\Omega f + \int_\Gamma g_1 = 0$$

(that is, $\langle f, 1 \rangle + \langle g_1, 1 \rangle = 0$ with suitable duality pairing if $f$ and $g$ are not smooth; the same remark has to be made for Theorem 3.4). Moreover the above argument shows that a solution is unique for the addition of a constant.

## 3.2F  Maximum Principle

Several theorems are known in the literature as maximum principles. Their general feature is the following: from the sign of $Au$ in $\Omega$ one deduces that $u$ takes its maximum (for $Au \leq 0$)

or its minimum (for $Au \geq 0$) on $\Gamma$; in particular both the maximum and the minimum are taken on $\Gamma$ if $Au = 0$. More generally, from the signs of $Au$ in $\Omega$ and of the boundary conditions one makes deductions on the sign of $u$ in $\Omega$. In order to state some of those theorems, we need a definition of "$w \geq 0$" for a general $w$ in a Sobolev space $W^{s,p}$; if $s \geq 0$ the meaning is obvious: $w(x) \geq 0$ almost everywhere.

**DEFINITION 3.2** Let $s < 0$ and $1 < p \leq \infty$. For $w \in W^{s,p}(\Omega)$ [respectively, $W^{s,p}(\Gamma)$], we say that $w \geq 0$ iff $_{s,p}\langle w, v \rangle_{|s|,p'} \geq 0$ for every nonnegative $v \in W_0^{|s|,p'}(\Omega)$ [respectively, $v \in W^{|s|,p'}(\Gamma)$]. For instance $\delta_{x_0} \geq 0$ by (2.67) in Part 1 for any $x_0$.

**THEOREM 3.5** *Maximum principle*. Assume that $A$ satisfies (3.2) to (3.4) and $a(v, v) > 0$ [with the notation (3.12)] for all $v \in H_0^1(\Omega)$ with $v \neq 0$. Assume $r, s \in \mathbb{R}$, $1 < p < \infty$, $r + 2 \geq 1/p$, $u \in W^{s,p}(\Omega)$, and $Au \in W^{r,p}(\Omega)$. Then

$$Au \geq 0 \quad \text{and} \quad u|_\Gamma \geq 0 \quad \text{imply} \quad u \geq 0 \tag{3.16}$$

If, in addition, $u \in C^0(\bar{\Omega})$, $u$ is not a constant, and $e = d - \Sigma D_i c_i$, then

$$Au \geq 0 \quad \text{and} \quad e \geq 0 \quad \text{imply} \quad u(x) > \min\left\{0, \min_\Gamma u\right\} \quad \forall x \in \Omega$$

$$Au \geq 0 \quad \text{and} \quad e \equiv 0 \quad \text{imply} \quad u(x) > \min_\Gamma u \quad \forall x \in \Omega$$

$$\tag{3.17}$$

Note that $e(x)$ [and not $d(x)$] is the true coefficient of $u$ in $Au$.

**THEOREM 3.6** *Hopf principle*. Assume that $\Gamma$ is split into two parts $\Gamma_0$ and $\Gamma_1$ with $\Gamma_0 \neq \emptyset$ and $A$ satisfies (3.2) to (3.4) and $a(v, v) > 0$ [with the notation (3.12)] for all $v \in H^1(\Omega)$ with $v \neq 0$ and $v|_{\Gamma_0} = 0$. Assume $u \in H^1(\Omega)$ and $Au \in H^{-1/2}(\Omega)$. Then

$$Au \geq 0, \quad u|_{\Gamma_0} \geq 0 \quad \text{and} \quad \left.\frac{\partial u}{\partial \nu_A}\right|_{\Gamma_1} \geq 0 \quad \text{imply} \quad u \geq 0 \tag{3.18}$$

If, in addition, $u \in C^0(\bar{\Omega})$ and $u$ is not a constant, setting $e = d - \Sigma D_i c_i$ and $\tilde{e} = \Sigma c_i \nu_i$, we have

$$Au \geq 0 \quad \left.\frac{\partial u}{\partial \nu_A}\right|_{\Gamma_1} \geq 0 \quad e \geq 0 \quad \text{and} \quad \tilde{e}|_{\Gamma_1} \geq 0 \quad \text{imply}$$

$$u(x) > \min\left\{0, \min_{\Gamma_0} u\right\} \quad \forall x \in \Omega \cup \Gamma_1$$

$$Au \geq 0 \quad \left.\frac{\partial u}{\partial \nu_A}\right|_{\Gamma_1} \geq 0 \quad e \equiv 0 \quad \text{and} \quad \tilde{e}|_{\Gamma_1} \geq 0 \quad \text{imply}$$

$$u(x) > \min_{\Gamma_0} u \quad \forall x \in \Omega \cup \Gamma_1$$

$$\tag{3.19}$$

If moreover $x_0 \in \Gamma_0$ is a minimum point for $u$, $u$ is $C^1$ near $x_0$, and $\nu'$ is any unit vector such that $\nu' \cdot \nu > 0$, then

$$Au \geq 0 \quad e \geq 0 \quad \text{and} \quad u(x_0) \leq 0 \quad \text{imply} \quad \frac{\partial u}{\partial \nu'} < 0 \text{ at } x_0$$

$$Au \geq 0 \quad \text{and} \quad e \equiv 0 \quad \text{imply} \quad \frac{\partial u}{\partial \nu'} < 0 \text{ at } x_0$$

$$\tag{3.20}$$

In Theorem 3.6, $\Gamma_1$ could be empty. In this case the only significant part is the last one.

**REMARK 3.6** Extensions of both Theorems 3.5 and 3.6 to a more general $\Omega$, e.g., a polygon, are possible, provided it is assumed that $u$ is smooth enough, for instance, $u \in H^1(\Omega)$ with $Au \in L^2(\Omega)$. If $u \in C^0(\bar{\Omega})$ and it is not a constant, (3.17) and (3.19) hold unchanged. The last part of Theorem 3.6 holds away from the corners. For $e \equiv 0$ (3.20) says that, if $Au \geqslant 0$, $u$ has a linear growth near any minimum point $x_0$ in the smooth part of the boundary. On the contrary, if $\Gamma$ is not smooth at $x_0$, the behavior of $u$ is different: $u$ might be irregular and $(u(x) - u(x_0))/|x - x_0|$ could be unbounded, or $u$ could have a faster decay in the smooth case, as shown in Example 3.11.

Previous theorems are the basic ones in order to obtain comparison results. Here is an application. Assume now $Au \geqslant 0$, $Av = 0$, and $u|_\Gamma = v|_\Gamma$. Then $A(u - v) \geqslant 0$ and $(u - v)|_\Gamma = 0$, so that either $u - v$ is a constant, thus $u = v$, or $u - v > 0$ in $\Omega$, that is, $u > v$ in $\Omega$. Hence a function $u$ with $Au \geqslant 0$ lies above the function $v$ with $Av = 0$ and the same boundary values as $u$. If $A = -\Delta$, such a $u$ is called *superharmonic*, since the solutions of the Laplace equation $-\Delta v = 0$ are called *harmonic* functions. Of course, $w$ *subharmonic* means $-\Delta w \leqslant 0$.

**EXAMPLE 3.11** In two dimensions, take $\Omega = B_1(0) \cap \{0 < \theta < \alpha\}$ and $u = \rho^{\pi/\alpha} \sin(\pi\theta/\alpha)$. Then $\Delta u = 0$ in $\Omega$ and both maximum and minimum are taken on $\Gamma$. In particular, the set of minimum points is $\Gamma \backslash \partial B_1(0)$. If $x_0 = (\rho_0, 0)$ with $0 < \rho_0 < 1$, then $\partial u/\partial \nu_A = \partial u/\partial \nu = -(1/\rho_0)\partial u/\partial \theta = -(\pi/\alpha)\rho_0^{-1+\pi/\alpha} < 0$ at $x_0$; that is, (3.20) holds. Consider now $x_0 = 0$: if $\alpha = \pi$, then $\Gamma$ is smooth at that point and $u$ is linear; if $\alpha > \pi$ (reentrant corner), then $\pi/\alpha < 1$ and $u/\rho$ is unbounded near 0; if $\alpha < \pi$, then $u$ is $C^1$ and behaves like $\rho^{\pi/\alpha}$ with $\pi/\alpha > 1$, that is, its decay is faster than linear.

## 3.3. PARABOLIC EQUATIONS

### 3.3A Introduction

The elliptic equations that we have studied in the previous section are a natural generalization of the Poisson equation $-\Delta u = f$. In this section we analyze some generalizations of the heat equation $\partial u/\partial t - \Delta u = f$, briefly $u' - \Delta u = f$ following the notation of (2.209) in Part 1. In particular, we study boundary-value problems for the equation $u' + Au = f$, where $A$ is an elliptic operator in the space variable $x$, whose coefficients may now depend on the time variable $t$. It is natural to assume that $x$ belongs, as usual, to some smooth domain $\Omega$ while $t$ varies in some interval $]0, T[$. Hence $(x, t)$ belongs to $Q = \Omega \times ]0, T[$.

**ASSUMPTION 3.3** *On Q.* We assume that $Q$ is of the type $Q = \Omega \times ]0, T[$, where $\Omega \subset \mathbb{R}^n$ is smooth in the sense of Def. 2.1 in Part 1 and $T \in ]0, \infty[$ is a fixed number. Moreover we shall use the following notation:

$$\Gamma = \partial\Omega \quad \text{and} \quad \Sigma = \Gamma \times ]0, T[ \tag{3.21}$$

**ASSUMPTION 3.4** *On A.* We assume that $A$ has the form

$$Au = -\Sigma D_j(a_{ij}D_i u) + \Sigma b_i D_i u - \Sigma D_i(c_i u) + du \tag{3.22}$$

with
$$a_{ij}, b_i, c_i, d \in C^\infty(\bar{Q}) \quad (1 \leqslant i, j \leqslant n) \tag{3.23}$$

Moreover the (*uniform*) *parabolicity condition* is fulfilled; i.e., there exists $\alpha > 0$ such that

$$\Sigma a_{ij}(x, t)\xi_i\xi_j \geq \alpha |\xi|^2 \qquad \forall (x, t) \in \bar{Q}, \forall \xi \in \mathbb{R}^n \tag{3.24}$$

The conormal derivative $\partial/\partial \nu_A$ is defined (as usual) by (3.5).

## 3.3ᴮ Unisotropic Sobolev Spaces $H^{r,s}(Q)$

Let us go back to the heat equation $u' - \Delta u = f$ and suppose that $f$ is a smooth function (e.g., $f = 0$). It is clear that $u'$ and $\Delta u$ have the same regularity. Assume, for instance, that they are in $L^p(Q) = L^p(0, T; L^p(\Omega))$ (see Sec. 2.10 in Part 1); then $-\Delta u(t) \in L^p(\Omega)$ (almost everywhere in $]0, T[$) and

$$\int_0^T \|-\Delta u(t)\|_{0,p,\Omega}^p \, dt < \infty$$

If $u$ satisfies "good" boundary conditions on $\Sigma$, for example $u|_\Sigma$ is smooth, (3.10) implies $u(t) \in W^{2,p}(\Omega)$ (almost everywhere in $]0, T[$) and

$$\int_0^T \|u(t)\|_{2,p,\Omega}^p \, dt \leq c \int_0^T (\|-\Delta u(t)\|_{0,p,\Omega}^p + \|u(t)_{|\Gamma}\|_{2-1/p,p,\Gamma}^p) \, dt < \infty$$

that is, $u \in L^p(0, T; W^{2,p}(\Omega))$, which means that all the space derivatives up to the order *2* are in $L^p(Q)$. On the other hand, we have assumed $u' \in L^p(Q)$, i.e., that all the time derivatives up to the order *1* are in $L^p(Q)$. Therefore $u$ has the following "unisotropic" regularity: second space derivatives and first time derivatives are in $L^p(Q)$. Hence we have to consider functional spaces involving different regularities in space and time, for instance,

$$W^{r,s;p}(Q) = L^p(0, T; W^{r,p}(\Omega)) \cap W^{s,p}(0, T; L^p(\Omega))$$

where the previous example corresponds to the simple case of $W^{2,1;p}(Q)$. However, we have seen that several exceptional cases were already present for $W^{s,p}$ if $p \neq 2$. Having now to deal with two indices $r$ and $s$, we prefer to lose in generality and restrict ourselves to the simplest case $p = 2$, where (as usual) we write $H$ instead of $W$, and to nonnegative $r$ and $s$.

**DEFINITION 3.3**   For real $r, s \geq 0$ we set

$$H^{r,s}(Q) = L^2(0, T; H^r(\Omega)) \cap H^s(0, T; L^2(\Omega)) \tag{3.25}$$

with its natural norm (see Rem. 1.12 in Part 1), which becomes

$$\|u\|_{H^{r,s}(Q)} = (\|u\|_{L^2(H^r)}^2 + \|u\|_{H^s(L^2)}^2)^{1/2} \tag{3.26}$$

**DEFINITION 3.4**   For real $r, s \geq 0$ we set

$$H^{r,s}(\Sigma) = L^2(0, T; H^r(\Gamma)) \cap H^s(0, T; L^2(\Gamma)) \tag{3.27}$$

with its natural norm.

By Secs. 2.10 and 1.3ᴍ in Part 1, $H^{r,s}(Q)$ and $H^{r,s}(\Sigma)$ are separable Hilbert spaces.

As in the previous chapter we use the notation $D^\alpha v$ and $v^{(k)}$ for derivatives with respect to space and time variables, respectively. The next theorem gives in particular a property of derivatives involving both space and time which is not explicitly stated in the definition of $H^{r,s}$.

**THEOREM 3.7**    Assume $r, s > 0$, $j, k \in \mathbb{N}$, $|\alpha| = j$, and

$$\frac{j}{r} + \frac{k}{s} \le 1 \tag{3.28}$$

and define

$$\rho = r\left(1 - \frac{j}{r} - \frac{k}{s}\right) \quad \text{and} \quad \sigma = s\left(1 - \frac{j}{r} - \frac{k}{s}\right) \tag{3.29}$$

Then $v \in H^{r,s}(Q)$ implies $D^\alpha v^{(k)} \in H^{\rho,\sigma}(Q)$ and

$$\|D^\alpha v^{(k)}\|_{H^{\rho,\sigma}} \le c\|v\|_{H^{r,s}}$$

where $c$ does not depend on $v$.

For instance, $v \in H^{1,2}(Q)$ means $v \in L^2(0, T; H^1(\Omega))$ and $v', v'' \in L^2(0, T; L^2(\Omega))$; Theorem 3.7 gives the additional information $v' \in H^{1/2,1}(Q)$, that is, $v' \in H^1(0, T; L^2(\Omega))$ (already known) and $v' \in L^2(0, T; H^{1/2}(\Omega))$. In the next theorem we generalize this property to derivatives of fractional order and list a set of inclusions which can be useful.

**THEOREM 3.8**    The following properties hold:

$$r, s \ge 0 \text{ and } 0 \le \theta \le 1 \quad \text{imply} \quad H^{r,s}(Q) \hookrightarrow H^{\theta s}(0, T; H^{(1-\theta)r}(\Omega)) \tag{3.30}$$

$$0 \le r_1 \le r_2 \text{ and } 0 \le s_1 \le s_2 \quad \text{imply} \quad H^{r_2,s_2}(Q) \hookrightarrow H^{r_1,s_1}(Q) \tag{3.31}$$

$$0 \le r_1 < r_2 \text{ and } 0 \le s_1 < s_2 \quad \text{imply} \quad H^{r_2,s_2}(Q) \hookrightarrow \hookrightarrow H^{r_1,s_1}(Q) \tag{3.32}$$

$$s \ge 0 \quad \text{implies} \quad H^{s,s}(Q) = H^s(Q) \tag{3.33}$$

$$r, s > 0 \text{ and } \frac{n}{r} + \frac{1}{s} < 2 \quad \text{imply} \quad H^{r,s}(Q) \hookrightarrow \hookrightarrow C^0(\bar{Q}) \tag{3.34}$$

Moreover, the same properties hold with $Q$ and $n$ replaced by $\Sigma$ and $n-1$, respectively.

**REMARK 3.7**    Note that (3.31) is obvious from the definition, and (3.33) is a simple consequence of Theorem 3.7 if $s$ is an integer. Finally $n/r + 1/s < 2$ implies the existence of $\theta$ with $0 < \theta < 1$, $\theta s > \frac{1}{2}$, and $(1 - \theta)r > n/2$, so that $H^{\theta s}(0, T; H^{(1-\theta)r}(\Omega)) \hookrightarrow \hookrightarrow C^0(]0, T[; C^0(\bar{\Omega})) = C^0(\bar{Q})$ [see (2.135) and (2.233) in Part 1]; thus (3.34) follows from (3.30).

**EXAMPLE 3.12**    If $Q \subset \mathbb{R}^2$, $v \in H^1(Q)$, and either $v_{xx}$, $v_{tt}$, or $v_{xt} \in L^2(Q)$, then $v \in C^0(Q)$. Indeed, we have, respectively, $v \in H^{2,1}(Q) \hookrightarrow C^0(Q)$, $v \in H^{1,2}(Q) \hookrightarrow C^0(Q)$ [both by (3.34)], $v \in H^1(0, T; H^1(\Omega)) \hookrightarrow C^0(]0, T[; C^0(\bar{\Omega})) = C^0(\bar{Q})$ [by (2.135) and (2.233) in Part 1].

Notice that now for $k \in \mathbb{N}$ and $s > k + \frac{1}{2}$, $v \in H^{0,s}(Q)$ implies $v^{(k)} \in H^{0,s-k}(Q) = H^{s-k}(0, T; L^2(\Omega)) \hookrightarrow C^0(]0, T[; L^2(\Omega))$ [by Theorem 3.7 and (2.233) in Part 1]. If, in addition,

$v \in H^{r,s}(Q)$, it is natural to hope that $v^{(k)} \in C^0(]0, T[; V)$ with some better space $V$ than $L^2(\Omega)$. This is the object of the following theorems.

**THEOREM 3.9**  Assume $k \in \mathbb{N}$, $r \geq 0$, $s > k + \frac{1}{2}$ and define

$$\tau_k = r - (k + \tfrac{1}{2})(r/s) \tag{3.35}$$

Then $v \in H^{r,s}(Q)$ implies $v^{(k)} \in C^0(]0, T[; H^{\tau_k}(\Omega))$ and

$$\|v^{(k)}(t)\|_{\tau_k, \Omega} \leq c \|v\|_{H^{r,s}(Q)} \qquad \forall t \in [0, T] \tag{3.36}$$

where $c$ does not depend on $v$ and $t$.

Moreover the same result holds if we replace $Q$ and $\Omega$ by $\Sigma$ and $\Gamma$, respectively.

The above theorem is very close to the trace theorem stated below.

**THEOREM 3.10**  *Trace theorem on* $\Omega$. Assume $k_* \in \mathbb{N}$, $r \geq 0$, and $s > k_* + \frac{1}{2}$. Then the map $v \to (v(0), v'(0), \ldots, v^{(k_*)}(0))$ defined for $v \in C^\infty(\bar{Q})$ can be extended in a unique way to a map (denoted with the same symbol) which is linear and continuous from $H^{r,s}(Q)$ into $H^{\tau_0}(\Omega) \cdots H^{\tau_{k_*}}(\Omega)$, with $\tau_k$ given by (3.35). Moreover there exists $\mathcal{R} \in \mathscr{L}(H^{\tau_0}(\Omega) \times \cdots \times H^{\tau_{k_*}}(\Omega); H^{r,s}(Q))$ such that $(\mathcal{R}(v_0, \ldots, v_{k_*}))^{(k)}(0) = v_k$ for $k = 0, \ldots, k_*$ and every $v_k \in H^{\tau_k}(\Omega)$. Finally the same result holds if we replace $Q$ and $\Omega$ with $\Sigma$ and $\Gamma$, respectively.

Note that for $s > k + \frac{1}{2}$ the value of $\tau_k$ for which $u^{(k)}(0) \in H^{\tau_k}(\Omega)$ [see (3.35)] and the value $\tilde{\tau}_k$ for which $u \in H^{k+1/2}(0, T; H^{\tau_k}(\Omega))$ [see (3.30)] coincide.

Let us go back to Theorem 3.7. For $j \in \mathbb{N}$, $|\alpha| = j$, and $r > j + \frac{1}{2}$, $v \in H^{r,0}(Q)$ implies $D^\alpha v \in H^{r-j,0}(Q) = L^2(0, T; H^{r-j}(\Omega))$, so that [using Theorem 2.24 and (2.239) in Part 1] $D^\alpha v|_\Sigma$ is defined and belongs to $L^2(0, T; H^{\rho_j}(\Gamma)) = H^{\rho_j, 0}(\Sigma)$, with $\rho_j = r - j - \frac{1}{2}$. Thus the same is true for $\gamma_j v = D^j_\nu v|_\Sigma$. If, in addition, $v \in H^{r,s}(Q)$, $\gamma_j v$ has to belong to a better space (with respect to time dependence), as stated below.

**THEOREM 3.11**  *Trace theorem on* $\Sigma$. Assume $j_* \in \mathbb{N}$, $r > j_* + \frac{1}{2}$, $s > 0$, and define

$$\rho_j = r - (j + \tfrac{1}{2}) \quad \text{and} \quad \sigma_j = \rho_j \frac{s}{r} \quad \text{for } j = 0, \ldots, j_* \tag{3.37}$$

Then there exist unique operators $\gamma_j \in \mathscr{L}(H^{r,s}(Q); H^{\rho_j, \sigma_j}(\Sigma))$ such that $\gamma_j v = D^j_\nu v|_\Sigma \ \forall v \in C^\infty(\bar{Q})$ and $j = 0, \ldots, j_*$. Moreover there exists an operator $\mathcal{R} \in \mathscr{L}(H^{\rho_0, \sigma_0}(\Sigma) \times \cdots \times H^{\rho_{j_*}, \sigma_{j_*}}(\Sigma); H^{r,s}(Q))$ such that $\gamma_j \mathcal{R}(g_0, \ldots, g_{j_*}) = g_j$ for $j = 0, \ldots, j_*$ and every $g_j \in H^{\rho_j, \sigma_j}(\Sigma)$.

**REMARK 3.8**  As usual we sometimes write $D^j_\nu v|_\Sigma$ instead of $\gamma_j v$. In the one-dimensional case $\Omega$ is an interval $]a, b[$ and traces on $\Sigma$ have to be replaced with the values of $v$ and its derivatives (with a suitable sign) at $x = a$ and $x = b$. In this case $H^{\rho_j, \sigma_j}(\Sigma)$ is replaced by $H^{\sigma_j}(0, T)$.

Note that the second parts of Theorems 3.10 and 3.11 say (in particular) the following: given $v_k \in H^{\tau_k}(\Omega)$ (for $k < s - \frac{1}{2}$) and $g_j \in H^{\rho_j, \sigma_j}(\Sigma)$ (for $j < r - \frac{1}{2}$), there exist *two* functions $v, w \in H^{r,s}(Q)$ such that $v^{(k)}(0) = v_k$ and $\gamma_j w = g_j$ for $k < s - \frac{1}{2}$ and $j < r - \frac{1}{2}$. Is it always possible to choose such functions so that $v = w$? The answer is *no*, in general. For instance, for sufficiently large $r$ and $s$, we have $H^{r,s}(Q) \hookrightarrow C^0(\bar{\Omega})$, so that $v = w$ would imply $v_0|_\Gamma = g_0(0)$. Thus *compatibility conditions* are needed on the families $\{v_k\}\{g_j\}$. We shall deal with this problem in discussing the regularity of the solutions of parabolic problems (see Rem. 3.11 below).

### 3.3c Existence, Uniqueness, and $H^{2s,s}$-regularity

We have seen at the beginning of Sec. 3.3B that if $u' - \Delta u = 0$ and $u' \in L^2(Q)$ then $u \in H^{2,1}(Q)$. Suppose now that $u'' \in L^2(Q)$: we have $\Delta^2 u = \Delta u' = (\Delta u)' = u'' \in L^2(Q)$. Thus, for good boundary conditions, $u \in H^{4,2}(Q)$. This kind of consideration shows that the regularity theory in the $H^{r,s}$-spaces will be simpler if we assume $r = 2s$; this will be done in what follows.

The following theorems will state existence, uniqueness, and regularity results for the problem

$$u' + Au = f \quad \text{in } Q \tag{3.38}$$

$$u(0) = u_0 \quad \text{in } \Omega \; (\textit{Cauchy condition}) \tag{3.39}$$

and one of the following boundary conditions:

$$u|_\Sigma = g_0 \quad (\textit{Dirichlet boundary condition}) \tag{3.40}$$

$$\left.\frac{\partial u}{\partial \nu_A}\right|_\Sigma = g_1 \quad (\textit{Neumann boundary condition}) \tag{3.41}$$

where $\partial u / \partial \nu_A$ is defined by (3.5) (see also Sec. 2.9E in Part 1). In order to give unified results we use the notation

$$\gamma_j u = g_j \quad \text{for } j = 0 \text{ or } j = 1 \tag{3.42}$$

instead of (3.40) or (3.41), respectively.

$Q$ and $A$ are assumed to satisfy Assumps. 3.3 and 3.4.

**THEOREM 3.12**  Assume $j = 0$ or $j = 1$, $s \geq 1$, $f \in H^{2s-2,s-1}(Q)$, $u_0 \in H^{2s-1}(\Omega)$, and $g_j \in H^{2s-j-1/2,s-j/2-1/4}(\Sigma)$. Then there exists a unique $u \in L^2(0, T; H^1(\Omega)) \cap C^0([0, T]; L^2(\Omega))$ satisfying (3.38), (3.39), and (3.42).

Moreover $u \in H^{2s,s}(Q)$ iff the following compatibility condition is fulfilled:

$$\exists w \in H^{2s,s}(Q): w(0) = u_0 \text{ (in } \Omega) \qquad \gamma_j w = g_j \qquad \text{and}$$
$$(w' + Aw - f)^\sim \in H^{2s-2,s-1}(Q^\sim) \tag{3.43}$$

where $Q^\sim = \Omega \times ]-T, T[$ and $\phi^\sim$ is the trivial extension of $\phi \in L^2(Q)$ to $Q^\sim$, that is, $\phi^\sim(x, t) = \phi(x, t)$ or $= 0$ according to $(x, t) \in Q$ or $\in Q^\sim \backslash Q$. Finally, if (3.43) holds, we have

$$\|u\|_{H^{2s,s}(Q)} \leq c(\|w\|_{H^{2s,s}(Q)} + \|(w' + Aw - f)^\sim\|_{H^{2s-2,s-1}(Q^\sim)}) \tag{3.44}$$

where $c$ does not depend on the data.

**THEOREM 3.13** Assume $j = 0$ or $j = 1$, $\frac{1}{2} + j/4 < s < 1$, $f = f_1 + f_2$ with $f_1 \in L^2(0, T; H^{2s-2}(\Omega))$ and $f_2 \in H^{s-1}(0, T; L^2(\Omega))$, $u_0 \in H^{2s-1}(\Omega)$, and $g_j \in H^{2s-j-1/2,s-j/2-1/4}(\Sigma)$. Then there exists a unique $u \in L^2(0, T; H^1(\Omega)) \cap C^0([0, T]; L^2(\Omega))$ satisfying (3.38), (3.39), and (3.42).

Moreover $u \in H^{2s,s}(Q)$ iff the following compatibility condition is fulfilled:

$$\exists w \in H^{2s,s}(Q): w(0) = u_0 \quad \text{and} \quad \gamma_j w = g_j \tag{3.45}$$

Finally, if (3.45) holds, we have

$$\|u\|_{H^{2s,s}(Q)} \leq c(\|w\|_{H^{2s,s}(Q)} + \|f_1\|_{L^2(H^{2s-2})} + \|f_2\|_{H^{s-1}(L^2)}) \tag{3.46}$$

where $c$ does not depend on the data.

**REMARK 3.9** If $s = \frac{3}{4}$ and $j = 0$, Theorem 3.13 holds even for $f_1 \in L^2(0, T; (H_{00}^{1/2}(\Omega))')$; if $s = \frac{1}{2}$ and $j = 0$, we still have existence and uniqueness, provided $f_2 = 0$. In such a case $u \in H^{1,1/2}(Q)$ and (3.45) must be omitted.

**REMARK 3.10** For $s \leq \frac{1}{2} + j/4$ it is possible to study existence, uniqueness, and regularity results by looking for $u \in H^{2s,s}(Q)$ if $s \geq 0$, or $u = u_1 + u_2$ with $u_1 \in L^2(0, T; H^{2s}(\Omega))$ and $u_2 \in H^s(0, T; L^2(\Omega))$ if $s < 0$; moreover, as in Sec. 2.9E in Part 1, we should require that $u' + Au$ is not too irregular. But a general theory is very complicated, much more than in the elliptic case. Indeed the basic difficulty arises in defining traces, since it is actually possible to give a meaning to a "trace" on the whole *parabolic boundary*

$$\partial_P Q = \{(x, t) \in \partial Q : t < T\} \tag{3.47}$$

but it is difficult afterward to split such a trace into a value on $\Sigma$ and a value for $t = 0$. Take, for instance, $u(x, t) = xt^{-3/2} \exp(-x^2 t^{-1})$; it satisfies $4u_t - u_{xx} = 0$ for $x > 0$ and $t > 0$, $u(x, 0) = 0$ for $x > 0$, $u(0, t) = 0$ for $t > 0$, and $\lim u(x, t) = 0$ as $x \to +\infty$ for $t > 0$. One would expect $u \equiv 0$! Is something happening at $(0, 0)$?

**REMARK 3.11** *Compatibility conditions.* In order to give the compatibility conditions (3.43) and (3.45) in terms of data $f$, $u_0$, and $g_j$, we start with the following observation: if the solution $u$ belongs to $C^\infty(\bar{Q})$, then we have

$$(\gamma_j u)^{(k)}(0) = \gamma_j(u^{(k)}(0)) \quad \text{on } \Gamma \tag{3.48}$$

for all $k \in \mathbb{N}$ and $j = 0$ or 1. Conditions (3.48) can be expressed as follows by means of data

$$g_j(0) = \gamma_j u_0$$

$$g_j'(0) = \gamma_j(u'(0)) = \gamma_j(f(0) - A(0)u_0)$$

$$g_j''(0) = \gamma_j(u''(0)) = \gamma_j((f - Au)'(0)) = \gamma_j(f'(0) - A'(0)u_0 - A(0)u'(0))$$

$$= \gamma_j(f'(0) - A'(0)u_0 - A(0)(f(0) - A(0)u_0))$$

and so on, with $A(0)$, $A'(0)$ having the obvious meaning. So we can consider (3.48) as conditions on the data. If $u$ is less regular, say $u \in H^{2s,s}(Q)$, conditions (3.48) make sense (and thus must be required) only for some value of $k$, namely,

$$(\gamma_j u)^{(k)}(0) = \gamma_j(u^{(k)}(0)) \quad \text{for integral } k, 0 \leq k < s - j/2 - \frac{3}{4} \tag{3.49}$$

It is possible to prove that *if $s - j/2 - \frac{3}{4}$ is not an integer*, then (3.49) is a necessary and sufficient condition for (3.43) or (3.45) (note that if $s - j/2 - \frac{3}{4} < 0$ no conditions are required) and (3.44) and (3.46) can be replaced, respectively, by

$$\|u\|_{H^{2s,s}} \leq c(\|f\|_{F(s)} + \|u_0\|_{2s-1,\Omega} + \|g_j\|_{G_j(s)}) \tag{3.50}$$

and
$$\|u\|_{H^{2s,s}} \leq c(\|f_1\|_{F_1(s)} + \|f_2\|_{F_2(s)} + \|u_0\|_{2s-1,\Omega} + \|g_j\|_{G_j(s)}) \tag{3.51}$$

where $F(s) = H^{2s-2,s-1}(Q)$, $F_1(s) = L^2(0, T; H^{2s-2}(\Omega))$, $F_2(s) = H^{s-1}(0, T; L^2(\Omega))$, and $G_j(s) = H^{2s-j-1/2,s-j/2-1/4}(\Sigma)$.

On the contrary, when $s - j/2 - \frac{3}{4}$ is an integer $\geq 0$, conditions (3.49) are only necessary; in order to have sufficient conditions one should add a relationship of the integral type which expresses (3.49) in a weaker form for $k = s - j/2 - \frac{3}{4}$. The integral involved in such a relationship should appear explicitly in (3.50) and (3.51), which would be *false otherwise* (see Example 3.19).

**REMARK 3.12** It is worthwhile noting that the existence and the uniqueness of the solution of (3.38), (3.39), and (3.42) are related only to the parabolicity condition (3.24), regardless of the eigenvalues of the whole operator $A$. As we have seen, the situation was completely different in the case of an elliptic problem. In order to understand the reasons for such a difference, consider the simple operator $Au = -\Delta u \quad \lambda u$, with $\lambda =$ eigenvalue of $-\Delta$. This would cause problems in the elliptic case. For the corresponding parabolic problem, instead, consider the change of the unknown function $u(x, t) = w(x, t) \exp((\lambda + 1)t)$; $w$ will satisfy $w' - \Delta w + w = f \exp(-(\lambda + 1)t)$ in $Q$, $w(0) = u_0$ in $\Omega$, and $\gamma_j w = g_j \exp(-(\lambda + 1)t)$ on $\Sigma$, and, as we know, the operator $-\Delta w + w$ is a very good one. However, the above example shows that the eigenvalues of $A$ can affect the behavior of $u$ for $t \to \infty$ (see Sec. 3.3E below).

### 3.3D Hölder Continuity

In this section we state a regularity theorem similar to Theorem 3.1 in spaces of type $C^{k,\lambda}$. For this we should introduce spaces $C^{2k,2\lambda;k,\lambda}(\bar{Q})$; to simplify the notation we prefer to call them $W^{2k+2\lambda,k+\lambda,\infty}(Q)$ [recalling that $C^{k,\lambda}(\bar{\Omega}) = W^{k+\lambda,\infty}(\Omega)$; see Def. 2.21 in Part 1].

**DEFINITION 3.5** For $r, s > 0$ we set

$$W^{r,s,\infty}(Q) = L^{\infty}(0, T; W^{r,\infty}(\Omega)) \cap W^{s,\infty}(0, T; L^{\infty}(\Omega))$$

with its natural norm (see Rem. 1.12 in Part 1). $W^{r,s,\infty}(\Sigma)$ is defined similarly.

**REMARK 3.13** Such spaces have properties similar to those of spaces $H^{r,s}(Q)$. In particular, Theorem 3.7 holds if we replace $H^{r,s}$ and $H^{\rho,\sigma}$ with $W^{r,s,\infty}$ and $W^{\rho,\sigma,\infty}$, respectively.

**THEOREM 3.14** Assume $j = 0$ or 1, $s > 1$, with $2s$ not an integer, $f \in W^{2s-2,s-1,\infty}(Q)$, $u_0 \in W^{2s,\infty}(\Omega)$, and $g_j \in W^{2s-j,s-j/2,\infty}(\Sigma)$. Then the solution $u$ (which exists in $H^{2,1}(Q)$ by Theorem 3.12) belongs to $W^{2s,s,\infty}(Q)$ iff there exists $w \in W^{2s,s,\infty}(Q)$ such that $w(0) = u_0$, $\gamma_j w = g_j$, and $(w' + Aw - f)^{(k)}(0) = 0$ for integral $k$, $0 \leq k < s - 1$.

**REMARK 3.14** The above condition on the existence of $w$ can be made explicit in terms of the data $f$, $u_0$, and $g_j$ as in Rem. 3.11; precisely, we need (3.49) for integral $k$, $0 \leqslant k < s - j/2$.

As in the case of elliptic problems (see Rem. 3.2) it is possible to prove local regularity results for parabolic problems. More precisely, away from the parabolic boundary [see (3.47)] the regularity of $u$ depends only on the regularity of $f$; near $\Sigma$, but away from $t = 0$, the regularity of $u$ depends only on $f$ and $g_j$; near $t = 0$, but away from $\Sigma$, the regularity of $u$ depends only on $f$ and $u_0$; finally, near $\Sigma$ and $t = 0$, the regularity of $u$ depends on the local regularity of all the data and on their compatibility (3.49). In particular, if $f$ and $g_j$ are smooth for $t > t_*$, then $u(x, t)$ is also smooth for $x \in \Omega$ and $t > t_*$ independently of the regularity for $t \leqslant t_*$. For instance, for $t_* = 0$ and assuming for simplicity that $f = 0$ and $g_j = 0$, one has $u(t) \in H^s(\Omega) \; \forall s \geqslant 0, \; \forall t \in \,]0, T]$, and

$$\|u(t)\|_{s,\Omega} \leqslant ct^{-s/2}\|u_0\|_{0,\Omega} \qquad 0 < t \leqslant T$$

where $c$ depends on $\Omega$, $T$, $s$, and $A$.

## 3.3E Asymptotic Behavior

In general, if $(A(t), f(t), g_j(t)) \to (A_\infty, f_\infty, g_{j\infty})$ as $t \to \infty$, it is interesting to compare $u(t)$ with the solution $u_\infty$ (if it exists!) of the limit stationary problem $A_\infty u_\infty = f_\infty$ in $\Omega$, $\gamma_j u_\infty = g_{j\infty}$ on $\Gamma$. For the sake of simplicity we consider here only the simplest case when $(A(t), f(t), g_j(t)) = (A, f, g_j)$ independent of $t$. In that case, if the problem

$$A u_\infty = f \quad \text{in } \Omega \qquad \gamma_j u_\infty = g_j \quad \text{on } \Gamma \tag{3.52}$$

has a solution, then the difference $w(t) = u(t) - u_\infty$ will satisfy

$$w' + A w = 0 \qquad \text{in } \Omega \times \,]0, \infty[ \tag{3.53}$$

$$\gamma_j w = 0 \qquad \text{on } \Gamma \times \,]0, \infty[ \qquad (\text{for } j = 0 \text{ or } 1) \tag{3.54}$$

$$w(0) = w_0 = u_0 - u_\infty \qquad \text{on } \Omega \tag{3.55}$$

As we have seen in Rem. 3.14, $w$ will be smooth for $t > 0$.

**THEOREM 3.15** Assume that the coefficients of $A$ do not depend on $t$ and $w_0 \in L^2(\Omega)$. Assume moreover there exists $\lambda > 0$ such that

$$(Av, v)_{0,\Omega} \geqslant \lambda \|v\|_{0,\Omega}^2 \tag{3.56}$$

for every $v \in C^\infty(\bar{\Omega})$ satisfying $\gamma_j v = 0$. Then the solution $w$ of (3.53) to (3.55) satisfies

$$\|w(t)\|_{s,\Omega} \leqslant c\|w_0\|_{0,\Omega} \cdot \exp(-\lambda t) \qquad \forall t > 1, s \in \mathbb{R} \tag{3.57}$$

where $c$ depends on $\Omega$, $A$, and $s$ (but $c = 1$ and $t \geqslant 0$ for $s = 0$).

**REMARK 3.15** Note that (3.56) implies (3.13) and hence the existence of a unique solution $u_\infty$ of (3.52), from Secs. 3.2D and 3.2E.

**REMARK 3.16**  The estimate (3.57) holds in more general cases. For instance, consider the case when $A$ is self-adjoint, i.e., $A = A^*$ (see Def. 3.1); then it is well known that all eigenvalues of $A$ (with the boundary condition $\gamma_j v = 0$, of course) form a real sequence $\lambda_1 \leqslant \lambda_2 \leqslant \lambda_3 \leqslant \cdots$. Note that (3.56) holds iff $\lambda_1 > 0$; in such a case $\lambda = \lambda_1$. On the contrary, if one of the $\lambda_n$'s is zero, the existence of a solution of (3.52) depends on compatibility conditions on $f$ and $g_j$, and uniqueness will fail (see Theorem 3.4). In any case, if a solution $u_\infty$ of (3.52) is given, the corresponding solution $w$ of (3.53) to (3.55) satisfies (3.57) with $\lambda =$ smallest positive eigenvalue, provided $(w_0, v_n)_{0,\Omega} = 0$ for all eigenfunctions $v_n$ corresponding to eigenvalues $\lambda_n \leqslant 0$. On the contrary, if such a condition is violated, we have the following: if $(w_0, v_n)_{0,\Omega} \neq 0$ for some $n$ for which $\lambda_n < 0$ (or if $u_\infty$ does not exist), then $\|u(t)\|_s \to \infty \; \forall s \in \mathbb{R}$; if $\lambda = 0$ is an eigenvalue, $u_\infty$ exists, and $(w_0, v_n)_{0,\Omega} = 0$ for all $n$ for which $\lambda_n < 0$, but $(w_0, v_n)_{0,\Omega} \neq 0$ for some $n$ with $\lambda_n = 0$, then $w(t)$ converges as $t \to +\infty$, but not to 0.

## 3.3F Maximum Principle

As for elliptic problems (see Sec. 3.2F) it is possible to prove a maximum principle for parabolic problems. The main differences are as follows: no further conditions on $a(v, v)$ are required besides the uniform parabolicity (3.24), and we need only prescribe a sign condition on the parabolic boundary $\partial_P Q$ (3.47) (instead of on the whole of $\partial Q$). For the sake of simplicity we state the next theorem under the assumption that the solution $u$ belongs to $H^{2,1}(Q)$, but the same result holds in more general cases; we could indeed assume that the data satisfy the assumptions of Theorem 3.13 [see also Rem. 3.9 and (3.34)]. In such cases "$f \geqslant 0$" is meant in the sense of Def. 3.2.

**THEOREM 3.16**  Let $u \in H^{2,1}(Q)$. Then

$$u' + Au \geqslant 0 \text{ in } Q \qquad \text{and} \qquad u \geqslant 0 \text{ on } \partial_P Q \qquad \text{imply} \qquad u \geqslant 0 \text{ in } Q \tag{3.58}$$

If, in addition, $u \in C^0(\bar{Q})$, setting $e = d - \Sigma D_i c_i$ and $M = \min_{\partial_P Q} u$, then

$$u' + Au \geqslant 0, e \geqslant 0, (x_0, t_0) \in Q, M \leqslant 0, \text{ and } u(x_0, t_0) = M \qquad \text{imply} \qquad u \equiv M \qquad \text{for } t \leqslant t_0$$
$$\tag{3.59}$$
$$u' + Au \geqslant 0, e \equiv 0, (x_0, t_0) \in Q, \text{ and } u(x_0, t_0) = M \qquad \text{imply} \qquad u \equiv M \qquad \text{for } t \leqslant t_0$$

Moreover assume that $(x_0, t_0) \in \Sigma$ is a strict [i.e., $u > M$ near $(x_0, t_0)$] minimum point for $u$, $u$ is $C^1$ near $(x_0, t_0)$, and let $\nu'$ be any unit vector in $\mathbb{R}^n$ with $\nu' \cdot \nu > 0$. Then

$$u' + Au \geqslant 0, e \geqslant 0, \text{ and } M \leqslant 0 \qquad \text{imply} \qquad \frac{\partial u}{\partial \nu'} < 0 \qquad \text{at } (x_0, t_0)$$
$$\tag{3.60}$$
$$u' + Au \geqslant 0 \text{ and } e \equiv 0 \qquad \text{imply} \qquad \frac{\partial u}{\partial \nu'} < 0 \qquad \text{at } (x_0, t_0)$$

## 3.3G Examples

**EXAMPLE 3.13**  If $u(x, t) = u_1(x) + u_2(t)$, then $u \in H^{r,s}(Q)$ iff $u_1 \in H^r(\Omega)$ and $u_2 \in H^s(0, T)$. The same is true for $u(x, t) = u_1(x) u_2(t)$ with $u_1 \neq 0$ and $u_2 \neq 0$.

**EXAMPLE 3.14**  Let $\Omega$ be the unit ball of $\mathbb{R}^n$ and $\alpha$, $\beta$, $\gamma$ be real numbers with $\gamma > 0$. Setting $u(x, t) = |x|^\alpha t^\beta \exp(-|x|^2 t^{-\gamma})$ and $\lambda = (2\alpha + n)/2 + (2\beta + 1)/\gamma$, we have, for $r, s \geqslant 0$:

$$\text{If } r < \lambda, 2s/\gamma < \lambda, \text{ and } r < (2\alpha + n)/2, \text{ then } u \in H^{r,s}(Q). \tag{3.61}$$

The conditions on $r$ and $s$ in (3.61) are also necessary, in order to have $u \in H^{r,s}(Q)$, provided that $\alpha$, $\beta$, and $\gamma$ do not belong to a "small" set of exceptional values. For instance, if $r < 1$ and $s < 1$, it is sufficient to exclude that $\alpha/2 \in \mathbb{N}$. Moreover (3.61) still holds for $u(x, t) = v(x)t^\beta \exp(-|x|^2 t^{-\gamma})$, where $v$ is $C^\infty$ for $x \neq 0$ and $\alpha$-homogeneous (see also Example 2.8 in Part 1).

Assuming now, for the sake of simplicity, that $\beta = -\frac{1}{2}$, (3.61) becomes:

$$\text{If } r < (2\alpha + n)/2 \text{ and } s < \gamma(2\alpha + n)/4, \text{ then } u \in H^{r,s}(Q). \tag{3.62}$$

Consider now the trace of $u$ on $Q' = \{(x, t) \in Q: x_n = 0\}$: it is given by $w(x', t) = |x'|^\alpha t^{-1/2} \exp(-|x'|^2 t^{-\gamma})$. Applying (3.62) to $w$ we have:

$$\text{If } r' < (2\alpha + n - 1)/2 \text{ and } s' < \gamma(2\alpha + n - 1)/4, \text{ then } w \in H^{r',s'}(Q'). \tag{3.63}$$

In particular, if $r$ and $s$ satisfy the bounds given in (3.62), then $w \in H^{r',s'}(Q')$ for $r' = r - \frac{1}{2}$ and $s' = s - \gamma/4$. On the other hand, Theorem 3.11 states that $w \in H^{\rho,\sigma}(Q')$ for $\rho = r - \frac{1}{2}$ and $\sigma = \rho s/r = s - s/2r$. In particular, $\rho = r'$. When $r$ and $s$ approach their bounds in (3.62), then $r/s$ approaches $\gamma/2$, $r' = \rho$ tends to $(2\alpha + n - 1)/2$, and both $s'$ and $\sigma$ tend to $\gamma(2\alpha - n - 1)/4$. This shows that Theorem 3.11 is optimal. Taking now $\alpha = 0$, $\beta = -n/2$, and $\gamma = 1$, we have $u(x, t) = t^{-n/2} \exp(-|x|^2/t)$, which clearly has the same regularity as the *fundamental solution* $U(x, t) = (4\pi t)^{-n/2} \exp(-|x|^2/4t)$ of the heat operator $L = \partial/\partial t - \Delta$. If $H^{r,s}$ with negative indices had been introduced, (3.61) would state $U \in H^{r,s}(Q)$ for $r < 1 - n/2$ and $s < (1 - n/2)/2$. On the other hand, it is possible to prove a trace theorem similar to Theorem 2.27 for functions $v$ in $H^{r,s}(Q)$ with $Lv = 0$, which would give $v(0) \in H^{\tau_0}(\Omega)$ with $\tau_0$ still given by (3.35). Since one can show that $U(\cdot, t) \to \delta$ as $t \to 0$, where $\delta$ is the Dirac mass at 0 [see (2.67) in Part 1 for the one-dimensional case], we have $\delta = U(\cdot, 0) \in H^\tau(\Omega)$ for $\tau < -n/2$, in agreement with (2.130) in Part 1.

**EXAMPLE 3.15**  Consider the Cauchy–Dirichlet problem [(3.38) to (3.40), i.e., (3.42) with $j = 0$]. If $\frac{1}{2} < s < \frac{3}{4}$, then (3.49) is an "empty condition"; that is, whenever $f$, $u_0$, and $g_0$ belong to the spaces given by Theorem 3.13, then $u \in H^{2s,s}(Q)$ and (3.51) holds. In particular, for smooth $f$, $u_0$, and $g_0$ the solution $u$ always belongs to $H^{2s,s}(Q)$ for $s < \frac{3}{4}$.

**EXAMPLE 3.16**  Consider the Cauchy–Neumann problem (i.e., $j = 1$) with $\frac{1}{2} < s < \frac{5}{4}$. We have the same as above. In particular, for smooth $f$, $u_0$, and $g_1$ the solution $u$ always belongs to $H^{2s,s}(Q)$ for $s < \frac{5}{4}$, and (3.50) and (3.51) hold for $1 \leq s < \frac{5}{4}$ and $\frac{1}{2} < s < 1$, respectively. In particular, $u \in H^{2,1}(Q)$ and $\|u\|_{H^{2,1}(Q)} \leq c(\|f\|_{L^2(Q)} + \|u_0\|_{H^1(\Omega)} + \|g_1\|_{H^{1/2,1/4}(\Sigma)})$.

**EXAMPLE 3.17**  For $j = 0$ and $\frac{3}{4} < s < \frac{7}{4}$ (3.49) becomes $g_0(0) = \gamma_0 u_0$, which means that $g_0(x, 0) = u_0(x) \ \forall x \in \Gamma$ when $g_0$ and $u_0$ are smooth. In particular, for smooth data $u$ belongs to $H^{2,1}(Q)$ iff $g_0(x, 0) = u_0(x) \ \forall x \in \Gamma$. If this is the case, we have (3.50), i.e. $\|u\|_{H^{2,1}(Q)} \leq c(\|f\|_{L^2(Q)} + \|u_0\|_{H^1(\Omega)} + \|g_0\|_{H^{3/2,3/4}(\Sigma)})$. The same compatibility conditions ensure that $u \in H^{3,3/2}(Q)$ (provided the data are smooth enough), which gives, in particular, $u \in L^2(0, T; H^3(\Omega))$; i.e., the third space derivatives belong to $L^2(Q)$, and $u' \in H^{1,1/2}(Q) \hookrightarrow L^2(0, T; H^1(\Omega))$ (by Theorem 3.7), that is, $\partial^2 u/\partial x_i \partial t \in L^2(Q)$.

**EXAMPLE 3.18**  For $j = 0$ and $\frac{7}{4} < s < \frac{11}{4}$, (3.49) becomes $g_0(0) = \gamma_0 u_0$ and $g_0'(0) = \gamma_0(f(0) - A(0)u_0)$. For the heat equation and smooth data these conditions state $g_0(x, 0) = u_0(x)$ and $(\partial g_0/\partial t)(x, 0) = f(x, 0) + \Delta u_0(x, 0) \ \forall x \in \Gamma$. In such a case $u$ satisfies, in particular, $u \in H^{5,5/2}(Q)$, and thus (by Theorem 3.7) $D^\alpha u \in L^2(Q)$ for $|\alpha| \leq 5$, $D^\alpha u' \in L^2(Q)$ for $|\alpha| \leq 3$, and $D^\alpha u'' \in L^2(Q)$ for $|\alpha| \leq 1$.

**EXAMPLE 3.19** *A limit case.* In Rem. 3.11 values of $s$ for which $s - j/2 - \frac{3}{4}$ is an integer were exceptional. We restrict ourselves to the Cauchy–Dirichlet problem (that is, $j = 0$) in the case $s = \frac{3}{4}$, i.e., the lower bound for the first compatibility condition $g_0(0) = \gamma_0 u_0$, which does not make sense now, because $g_0 \in H^{1,1/2}(\Sigma)$ and $u_0 \in H^{1/2}(\Omega)$. Consider the integral

$$\|u_0, g_0\|_{(\delta)}^2 = \int_\Gamma \int_0^\delta |u_0(x - \nu\xi) - g_0(x, \xi^2)|^2 \xi^{-1} \, d\xi \, d\Gamma$$

$$= \frac{1}{2} \int_\Gamma \int_0^{\delta^2} |u_0(x - \nu t^{1/2}) - g_0(x, t)|^2 t^{-1} \, dt \, d\Gamma \qquad (3.64)$$

where $\delta > 0$ is small such that the set $\Omega_\delta = \{x - \nu\xi : x \in \Gamma, 0 < \xi < \delta\}$ is a smooth ring near $\partial\Omega$. One can prove that, if the data have the regularity prescribed by Theorem 3.13 with $s = \frac{3}{4}$, then $u \in H^{3/2,3/4}(Q)$ iff

$$\|u_0, g_0\|_{(\delta)} < \infty \qquad (3.65)$$

Moreover the following estimate holds:

$$\|u\|_{H^{3/2,3/4}} \leq c(\|f_1\| + \|f_2\| + \|u_0\| + \|g_0\|) + c(\delta)\|u_0, g_0\|_{(\delta)} \qquad (3.66)$$

where the norms are as in (3.51) with $s = \frac{3}{4}$ now. One can also show that (3.65) does not depend on the choice of $\delta$ and that, for smoother data, it amounts to $g_0(0) = \gamma_0 u_0$. In the case $g_0 = 0$ (3.65) becomes (recall Sec. 2.7D in Part 1)

$$\int_\Gamma \int_0^\delta |u_0(x - \nu\xi)|^2 \xi^{-1} \, d\xi \, d\Gamma < \infty$$

that is

$$\int_{\Omega_\delta} u_0^2 \rho^{-1} < \infty$$

that is

$$u_0 \in H_{00}^{1/2}(\Omega)$$

In the case $u_0 = 0$ (3.65) becomes

$$\int_0^{\delta^2} t^{-1} \int_\Gamma g_0^2 \, d\Gamma \, dt < \infty \qquad \text{that is} \qquad \int_0^{\delta^2} \|g_0(t)\|_{0,\Gamma}^2 t^{-1} \, dt < \infty$$

i.e., an $H_{00}^{1/2}$-condition at $t = 0$.

In the following two examples we consider the one-dimensional case $\Omega = ]a, b[$; hence the integral on $\Gamma$ of (3.64) has to be replaced by the sum of the values at $x = a$ and $x = b$.

**EXAMPLE 3.20** Take $\Omega = ]0, 1[$ and $A = -\frac{1}{4} d^2/dx^2$. Then $u(x, t) = \text{erf}(xt^{-1/2})$, where

$$\text{erf } z = 2\pi^{-1/2} \int_0^z \exp(-y^2) \, dy$$

satisfies $u' + Au = 0$ in $Q$ (for any $T > 0$), $u(x, 0) = 1$, $u(0, t) = 0$, and $u(1, t) = \text{erf}(t^{1/2})$. Even though the data are smooth we have $u \notin H^{3/2,3/4}(Q)$ since (clearly!) (3.65) does not hold. One can see directly that $D_x u \notin L^2(0, T; H^{1/2}(\Omega))$ [while $u \in H^{3/2,3/4}$ would imply $D_x u \in L^2(H^{1/2})$ by Theorem 3.7]. Indeed

$$\int_0^T dt \int_0^1 \int_0^1 |x-y|^{-2} |D_x u(x, t) - D_x u(y, t)|^2 \, dx \, dy$$

$$= \int_0^T t^{-1} dt \int_0^{t^{-1/2}} \int_0^{t^{-1/2}} |\xi - \eta|^{-2} |\exp(-\xi^2) - \exp(-\eta^2)| \, d\xi \, d\eta$$

$$\geq c \int_0^{T/2} t^{-1} \, dt = \infty$$

where $c$ is the double integral in $\xi, \eta$ with $t = T/2$.

**EXAMPLE 3.21**  Notice first that for $\phi \in H^{1/2}(0, \infty)$ and $\phi_\varepsilon(x) = \phi(x/\varepsilon)$ we have

$$|\phi_\varepsilon|_{1/2, ]0, 1[} \leq |\phi_\varepsilon|_{1/2, ]0, \infty[} = |\phi|_{1/2, ]0, \infty[}$$

by computation. Take now $Q, A, u$ as in Example 3.20 and $u_\varepsilon(x, t) = u(x, t + \varepsilon^2)$, so that $u_\varepsilon \in C^\infty(\bar{Q})$ and satisfies a similar problem as $u$ (with data depending on $\varepsilon$ now). By the previous remark, with $\phi(x) = u(x, 0) - 1$, we see that $\|u_\varepsilon(0)\|_{1/2, \Omega} \leq c$; moreover, $u_{\varepsilon|\Sigma}$ is bounded in $H^{1/2}(0, T)$ and $u_\varepsilon' + Au_\varepsilon = 0$. Therefore (3.51) with $s = \frac{3}{4}$ would lead to a contradiction since $u_\varepsilon$ is unbounded in $H^{3/2,3/4}(Q)$ [use the argument of Example 3.20 or note that $u_\varepsilon \to u$ in $L^2(Q)$ and apply Cor. 1.6 from Part 1]. On the contrary, taking $\varepsilon \to 0$ in (3.66), we obtain (correctly!) $\infty \leq \infty$, since the integral (3.64) is also unbounded.

**EXAMPLE 3.22**  Take $k \in \mathbb{N}$ and $w \in W^{k+\lambda, \infty}(\Omega) \, \forall \lambda < 1$ such that $w \notin W^{k+1, \infty}(\bar{\Omega})$, $\Delta w = 0$, $w|_\Gamma \in W^{k+1, \infty}(\Gamma)$ (see Example 3.2). Then $u(x, t) = tw(x)$ satisfies $u - \Delta u = w \in W^{k+1,(k-1)/2, \infty}(Q)$, $u|_\Sigma = tw|_\Sigma \in W^{k+1,(k+1)/2, \infty}(\Sigma)$, and $u(0) = 0$. Nevertheless $u \notin W^{k+1,(k+1)/2, \infty}(Q)$, i.e., Theorem 3.14 actually does not hold when $2s$ is an integer.

**EXAMPLE 3.23**  Take $k \in \mathbb{N}$ and $w \in W^{k+\lambda, \infty}(\Omega) \, \forall \lambda < 1$ such that $w \notin W^{k+1, \infty}(\Omega)$, $w|_\Gamma \in C^\infty(\Gamma)$, $\Delta w \in W^{k-1, \infty}(\Omega)$ (see Example 3.4). Taking $u(x, t) = tw(x)$, we have the same conclusion as in Example 3.22.

**EXAMPLE 3.24**  Hölder continuity results can also be deduced using (3.30) and (2.233) in Part 1. For instance, taking $0 < \lambda \leq \frac{1}{2}$ and $\theta = \lambda + \frac{1}{2}$, we have

$$H^{2,1}(Q) \hookrightarrow H^{\lambda+1/2}(0, T; H^{1-2\lambda}(\Omega)) \hookrightarrow C^{0,\lambda}([0, T]; H^{1-2\lambda}(\Omega))$$

Thus $u \in H^{2,1}(Q)$ implies

$$\|u(t) - u(0)\|_{1-2\lambda, \Omega} \leq c(\lambda) t^\lambda \qquad 0 < \lambda \leq \frac{1}{2}$$

**EXAMPLE 3.25**  Take $\Omega = ]0, \pi[$, $Au = -d^2u/dx^2 - 2u$, and $u(x, t) = e^t \sin x$. Then $u' + Au = 0$ in $Q$, $u|_\Sigma = 0$, $u(x, 0) = \sin x$, and $\|u(t)\|_{s, \Omega} = c(s) e^t \to \infty$ and $t \to \infty$, in agreement with Rem. 3.16: the corresponding stationary problem has only the trivial solution, but $u(0)$ is an eigenfunction corresponding to the negative eigenvalue $\lambda = -1$ of $A$.

**EXAMPLE 3.26**  Take any $\Omega$ and $u(t) = t$. Then $u' - \Delta u = 1$, $\partial u/\partial \nu|_\Sigma = 0$, $u(0) = 0$, and $\|u(t)\|_{s, \Omega} = c(s) t \to \infty$, since the stationary problem has no solutions (from Example 3.10).

**EXAMPLE 3.27** Take $f$, $g$ smooth, independent of $t$, and such that

$$\int_\Omega f + \int_\Gamma g = 0$$

For any smooth $u_0$ the problem $u' - \Delta u = f$, $u(0) = u_0$, $\partial u / \partial \nu|_\Sigma = g$ has one solution $u$. On the other hand, the corresponding elliptic problem has infinitely many solutions of the form $u_{\infty,\mu} = u_{\infty,0} + \mu$ with $\mu \in \mathbb{R}$, by Example 3.10. Since $\lambda_1 = 0$ is the first eigenvalue for the Neumann problem (see also Example 3.9) and the eigenfunctions are all constants, Rem. 3.16 gives the following. The difference $w(t) = u(t) - u_{\infty,\mu}$ tends to 0 as $t \to \infty$ iff $(u_0 - u_{\infty,\mu}, 1)_{0,\Omega} = 0$, that is, $u(t)$ tends to the solution $u_\infty$ of the corresponding stationary problem which satisfies the supplementary condition

$$\int_\Omega u_\infty = \int_\Omega u_0$$

and we have $$\|u(t) - u_\infty\|_{s,\Omega} \leq c(s) \, e^{-\lambda_2 t} \|u_0\|_{0,\Omega} \qquad \text{for } t \geq 1$$

where $\lambda_2$ is the first positive eigenvalue.

## 3.4 HYPERBOLIC EQUATIONS

### 3.4A Introduction

We restrict ourselves to second-order equations, which are the natural generalization of the wave equation $u'' - \Delta u = f$ (where $u''$ means $\partial^2 u / \partial t^2$ as in Sec. 3.3; the notations of that section are followed here). Therefore we shall consider equations of the form $u'' + Au = f$, where $A$ is an elliptic operator in space variables whose coefficients depend also on $t$, as in the previous section.

**ASSUMPTION 3.5** We assume that $Q$ and $A$ satisfy Assumps. 3.3 and 3.4 and, in addition, the following symmetry condition:

$$a_{ij}(x, t) = a_{ji}(x, t) \qquad \forall (x, t) \in \bar{Q} \qquad i, j = 1, \ldots, n \tag{3.67}$$

i.e., the so-called *principal part* of $A$ is symmetric.

In the present case (3.24) will be called the (*uniform*) *hyperbolicity condition* for $u'' + Au$.

### 3.4B Existence, Uniqueness, and Regularity in the Sobolev Spaces

We deal now with existence, uniqueness, and regularity results for the problem

$$u'' + Au = f \qquad \text{in } Q \tag{3.68}$$

$$u(0) = u_0 \qquad \text{and} \qquad u'(0) = u_1 \qquad \text{in } \Omega \qquad (\textit{Cauchy conditions}) \tag{3.69}$$

and, with the notations (3.42),

$$\gamma_j u = g_j \qquad \text{on } \Sigma \qquad \text{for } j = 0 \text{ or } 1 \qquad (\textit{boundary condition}) \tag{3.70}$$

$Q$ and $A$ are assumed to satisfy Assump. 3.5. As we shall see in the examples (see Sec. 3.4C), the solutions of hyperbolic problems show regularity properties quite different from those of elliptic or parabolic problems. For instance, $u_0(x + t)$ satisfies the wave equation $u_{tt} - u_{xx} = 0$, with appropriate initial and boundary conditions. Even though $f \equiv 0$, $u$ does not have better regularity in the interior than for $t = 0$; indeed, if $u_0$ is, say, an $H^1$-function of one variable, $u$ is an $H^1$-function in $(x, t)$ and nothing better. However, the natural space of traces for $t = 0$ of functions in $H^1(Q)$ is $H^{1/2}(\Omega)$ (see Sec. 2.9 in Part 1). This simple example shows how difficult it would be to give *necessary and sufficient* conditions on the data in order that the solution have the prescribed regularity in Sobolev spaces. In view of these difficulties we choose to present here firstly a rather general result (not optimal) and then a list of particular cases which may be of special interest.

**THEOREM 3.17**   Assume that $\rho$, $\sigma$, $r$, $s$ are nonnegative real numbers with $1 \leq r \leq \rho + 2$, $s \leq \sigma + 2$, $r + s \leq \rho + \sigma + 1$, and $\rho - \frac{1}{2}$ and $r - \frac{1}{2}$ are not integers. Assume that $j = 0$ or 1, $f \in L^2(Q)$, $g_j \in L^2(\Sigma)$, $u_0 \in H^1(\Omega)$, and $u_1 \in L^2(\Omega)$ are given such that, setting $W = C^0([0, T]; H^1(\Omega)) \cap C^1([0, T]; L^2(\Omega)) \cap H^s(0, T; H^r(\Omega))$, we have:

There exists $w \in W$ such that

$$w'' + Aw - f \in H^\sigma(0, T; H_0^\rho(\Omega))$$

$$w(0) - u_0 \in H_0^r(\Omega) \qquad w'(0) - u_1 \in H^{r-1}(\Omega) \qquad \text{and} \qquad \gamma_j w = g_j \text{ on } \Sigma \tag{3.71}$$

Then the problem posed by (3.68) to (3.70) has a unique solution $u \in W$, and

$$\|u\|_W \leq c(\|w\|_W + \|w'' + Aw - f\|_{H^\sigma(H_0^\rho)} + \|w(0) - u_0\|_{r,\Omega} + \|w'(0) - u_1\|_{r-1,\Omega}) \tag{3.72}$$

where $c$ does not depend on $u$, $f$, $u_0$, $u_1$ and $w$.

When $\rho - \frac{1}{2}$ or $r - \frac{1}{2}$ is an integer, the same result holds, with the $H_{00}$-spaces in place of the corresponding $H_0$-spaces. Note, in particular, that if $g_j = 0$, we can take $w \equiv 0$ in (3.71), provided $u_0 \in H_0^r(\Omega)$, $u_1 \in H_0^{r-1}(\Omega)$, and $f \in H^\sigma(0, T; H_0^\rho(\Omega))$. These last conditions on the vanishing on $\Sigma$ (i.e., the $H_0$-conditions) are stronger than necessary, as we shall also see in the following particular cases, but it would be too complicated and difficult to state a general theorem. We thus list some additional results which may be of special interest.

**PROPOSITION 3.1**   Assume $j = 0$ and $g_0 = 0$. If $f = f_1 + f_2$ with $f_1 \in H^1(0, T; L^2(\Omega))$ and $f_2 \in L^2(0, T; H_0^1(\Omega))$, $u_0 \in H^2(\Omega) \cap H_0^1(\Omega)$, and $u_1 \in H_0^1(\Omega)$, then $u \in H^2(Q)$; moreover, $u \in C^1([0, T]; H_0^1(\Omega)) \cap C^0([0, T]; H^2(\Omega))$ and

$$\|u\|_{2,Q} + \|u\|_{C^1(H^1)} + \|u\|_{C^0(H^2)} \leq c(\|f_1\|_{H^1(L^2)} + \|f_2\|_{L^2(H^1)} + \|u_0\|_{2,\Omega} + \|u_1\|_{1,\Omega}) \tag{3.73}$$

If, in addition, $f_2 \in C^0([0, T]; L^2(\Omega))$, then $u \in C^2([0, T]; L^2(\Omega))$ and

$$\|u\|_{C^2(L^2)} \leq c(\|f_1\|_{H^1(L^2)} + \|f_2\|_{L^2(H^1)} + \|f_2\|_{C^0(L^2)} + \|u_0\|_{2,\Omega} + \|u_1\|_{1,\Omega}) \tag{3.74}$$

In both formulae $c$ depends only on $A$ and $Q$.

**PROPOSITION 3.2**   Assume $j = 1$ and $g_1 = 0$. If $f = f_1 + f_2$ with $f_1 \in H^1(0, T; L^2(\Omega))$ and $f_2 \in L^2(0, T; H^1(\Omega))$, $u_0 \in H^2(\Omega)$ with $\gamma_1 u_0 = 0$, and $u_1 \in H^1(\Omega)$, then $u \in H^2(Q)$; moreover, $u \in$

$C^1([0, T]; H^1(\Omega)) \cap C^0([0, T]; H^2(\Omega))$ and (3.73) holds. If, in addition, $f_2 \in C^0([0, T]; L^2(\Omega))$, then $u \in C^2([0, T]; L^2(\Omega))$ and (3.74) holds.

**PROPOSITION 3.3**   Assume $j = 0$ and $g_0 = 0$, $f \in C^0([0, T]; L^2(\Omega))$, $u_0$ and $u_1 \in H^2(\Omega) \cap H_0^1(\Omega)$, and the compatibility condition $f(0) - A(0)u_0 \in H_0^1(\Omega)$. Then we have

$$f \in H^2(0, T; L^2(\Omega)) \qquad \text{implies} \qquad u \in C^k([0, T]; H^{3-k}(\Omega)) \qquad \text{for } k = 1, 2, 3$$
(3.75)

and
$$\sum_{k=1}^{3} \|u\|_{C^k(H^{3-k})} \leq c(\|f\|_{H^2(L^2)} + \|u_0\|_{3,\Omega} + \|u_1\|_{2,\Omega})$$

$$f \in H^1(0, T; H_0^1(\Omega)) \qquad \text{implies} \qquad u \in C^k([0, T]; H^{3-k}(\Omega)) \qquad \text{for } k = 0, 1, 2; u \in H^3(Q) \quad (3.76)$$

and
$$\|u\|_{3,Q} + \sum_{k=0}^{2} \|u\|_{C^k(H^{3-k})} \leq c(\|f\|_{H^1(H^1)} + \|u_0\|_{3,\Omega} + \|u_1\|_{2,\Omega})$$

In both estimates $c$ depends only on $A$ and $Q$.

**REMARK 3.17**   Further regularity results of this type can be deduced by using Props. 3.1 and 3.2 and Eqs. (3.68) and (3.69); this is particularly easy when $A$ does not depend on $t$; for instance, (3.75) is nothing more than (3.69) applied to $v = u'$, noting that $v'' + Av = f'$, $v(0) = u_1$, $v'(0) = u''(0) = f(0) - Au(0) = f(0) - Au_0$.

**REMARK 3.18**   We see in Assump. 3.5 that no conditions are required on the eigenvalues of the whole operator $A$, as in the parabolic case (see Rem. 3.12), since the uniform hyperbolicity condition (3.70) involves only the principal part of $A$. However, it is less simple to check it here than it was in that case.

**REMARK 3.19**   It is clear that the local regularity results that hold for elliptic and parabolic problems (see Rem. 3.2 and Sec. 3.3B) cannot be true for the wave equation and for general hyperbolic operators. Indeed, a singularity for $t = 0$ propagates along characteristic lines for $t > 0$ (see examples below).

   Other important differences between hyperbolic and parabolic problems are the following: the solution of a hyperbolic problem does not, in general, tend to a stationary solution for $t \to \infty$; moreover it can change sign even though all the data keep their signs unchanged. This implies that no maximum principle can be expected.

**REMARK 3.20**   The following diagrams can be useful for illustrating the regularity results for the equations:

$$-\frac{\partial^2 u}{\partial t^2} - \frac{\partial^2 u}{\partial x^2} = f \qquad \text{(elliptic: } t \text{ is a space variable } here\text{)}$$
(3.77)

$$\frac{\partial u}{\partial t} - \frac{\partial^2 u}{\partial x^2} = f \qquad \text{(parabolic)}$$
(3.78)

$$\frac{\partial^2 u}{\partial t^2} - \frac{\partial^2 u}{\partial x^2} = f \qquad \text{(hyperbolic)}$$
(3.79)

To every function $v(x, t) \in L^2(Q)$ (say, $Q = ]0, 1[ \times ]0, 1[$) we associate a region $R(v)$ in the $r, s$-plane by the following rule:

$$(r, s) \in R(v) \qquad \text{iff} \qquad \frac{\partial^{r+s} v}{\partial x^r \, \partial t^s} \in L^2(Q) \tag{3.80}$$

Formula (3.80) is clear when $r$ and $s$ are integers and may be extended to the case of real $r$ and $s$.

Figure 3.1 shows the regularity regions corresponding to $v \in H^s(H^r)$ and $v \in H^{r,s}$, respectively. Note that the cases shown in Fig. 3.1 include $H^s = H^{s,s}$ [see (3.33)], $H^{r,0}$ (horizontal segment), and $H^{0,s}$ (vertical segment); moreover, $R(v)$ is always a convex set, essentially by (3.30).

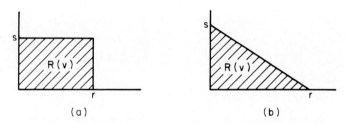

**FIG. 3.1**  (*a*) Regularity region for $v \in H^s(H^r)$. (*b*) Regularity region for $v \in H^{r,s}$.

Assume now that $f \in H^s(H^r)$ and no problems arise due to boundary and/or initial conditions; thus Fig. 3.2 represents $R(u)$ in the three cases (3.77) to (3.79).

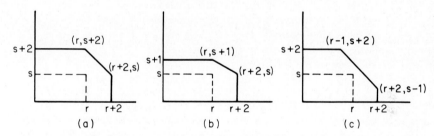

**FIG. 3.2**  Regularity region for three types of equation where $f \in H^s(H^r)$. (*a*) Elliptic. (*b*) Parabolic. (*c*) Hyperbolic.

If instead $f \in H^s$ or $H^{2s,s}$ or $H^s$, again the respective shapes of $R(u)$ are given in Fig. 3.3.

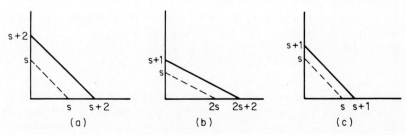

**FIG. 3.3**  Regularity region for three types of equation where $f \in H^s$ or $H^{2s,s}$. (*a*) Elliptic. (*b*) Parabolic. (*c*) Hyperbolic.

In order to deduce Fig. 3.3 from Fig. 3.2 note that, if $V$ and $W$ are spaces of the Sobolev type and if $R_V$ and $R_W$ are the corresponding regularity regions, then $R_{V \cap W} = \text{co}\,(R_V \cup R_W)$, where co is as explained in Def. 1.12 of Part 1.

It is worth noting that the diagrams can be used to prove further regularity for $u$. Take, for instance, the case (3.79). It is clear that if $\partial^2 u / \partial t^2$ and $f$ belong to $H^\sigma$ $(H^\rho)$, then $\partial^2 u / \partial x^2 \in H^\sigma$ $(H^\rho)$, which implies $u \in H^\sigma$ $(H^{\rho+2})$, provided no problems arise from boundary conditions; similarly, $\partial^2 u / \partial x^2$ and $f \in H^\sigma$ $(H^\rho)$ imply $u \in H^{\sigma+2}$ $(H^\rho)$ if $u_0$ and $u_1 \in H^\rho$.

In terms of regularity regions this can be summarized as follows: if $(r, s) \in R(u)$ and $(r, s-2) \in R(f)$, then $(r+2, s-2) \in R(u)$.

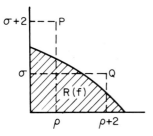

**FIG. 3.4**  Regularity region for $P \in R(u)$ iff $Q \in R(u)$.

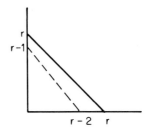

**FIG. 3.5** Regularity region for $f \in H^{r-2,r-1}(Q)$ [or $H^{r-1,r-2}(Q)$] and $u \in H^r(Q)$ $(r \geq 2)$.

In Fig. 3.4 we have that $P \in R(u)$ iff $Q \in R(u)$. Using this argument one can see (Fig. 3.5) that $f \in H^{r-2,r-1}(Q)$ [or $H^{r-1,r-2}(Q)$] gives $u \in H^r(Q)$ $(r \geq 2)$, provided as usual that the other data are smooth and compatible. More generally, for $f \in H^{\rho,\sigma}(Q)$ we have that $u$ is at least in $H^{r,s}(Q)$ for $r \leq \max\,(\rho+1, \min\,(\rho+2, \sigma+1))$ and $s \leq \max\,(\sigma+1, \min\,(\sigma+2, \rho+1))$.

In Fig. 3.6 $f \in H^{6,3}$ and $u \in H^{7,5} \cap H^4$ $(H^3)$.

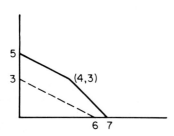

**FIG. 3.6**  Regularity region for $f \in H^{6,3}$ and $u \in H^{7,5} \cap H^4$ $(H^3)$.

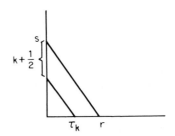

**FIG. 3.7**  $H^{\tau_k}$-regularity of $v^{(k)}(0)$.

The previous representations may also be useful in other situations. For instance, if $v \in H^{r,s}$, then the $H^{\tau_k}$-regularity of $v^{(k)}(0)$ (see Theorem 3.10) is shown in Fig. 3.7; on the other hand, the $H^{\rho,\sigma}$-regularity of $D^j v^{(k)}$ (see Theorem 3.7) is given in Fig. 3.8. Actually this representation holds in a space of any number of dimensions. For instance, if $v \in H^{r,s}$ $(\Omega \times ]0, T[)$, then $\gamma_j v \in H^{\rho,\sigma}(\Gamma \times ]0, T[)$ (see Theorem 3.11), with $\rho, \sigma$ as in Fig. 3.9.

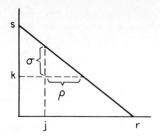
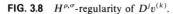
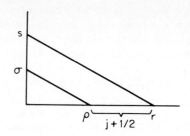

**FIG. 3.8** $H^{\rho,\sigma}$-regularity of $D^j v^{(k)}$.      **FIG. 3.9** $H^{\rho,\sigma}$-regularity of $\gamma_j v$.

**REMARK 3.21** In Theorem 3.17 the condition (3.71) on the existence of $w$ combines some kind of regularity and compatibility conditions of the data. Assume for simplicity that all the data are $C^\infty$; otherwise, the situation would be much more complicated and also conditions of integral type would have to be considered, as in Example 3.19. Starting from $u_0$ and $u_1$, define by induction

$$u_{k+2} = f^{(k)}(0) - \sum_{i=1}^{k} \binom{k}{i} A^{(k-i)}(0) u_i$$

If

$$g_j^{(k)}(0) = \gamma_j u_k \qquad \text{for } k = 0, \ldots, m \tag{3.81}$$

then for any $\varepsilon > 0$ we have

$$u \in H^{m+j+3/2-\varepsilon}(Q) \qquad \text{and} \qquad u^{(i)} \in C^0([0,T]; H^{m-i+j+3/2-\varepsilon}(\Omega)) \qquad i = 0, \ldots, m+2 \tag{3.82}$$

When no compatibility condition is satisfied, for $j = 1$ we still have $u \in H^{3/2-\varepsilon}(Q)$ and $u^{(i)} \in C^0([0,T]; H^{-i+3/2-\varepsilon}(\Omega))$ $(i = 0, 1)$; i.e., (3.82) holds with $m = -1$. In the case $j = 0$ we still have a "solution" $u \in H^{1/2-\varepsilon}(Q) \cap C^0([0,T]; H^{1/2-\varepsilon}(\Omega)) \cap C^1([0,T]; H^{-1/2-\varepsilon}(\Omega))$. However, since such a $u$ is too irregular, it can be accepted as a solution only in a generalized sense that we have not introduced here (see examples below).

## 3.4c Examples

**EXAMPLE 3.28** Let $\phi \in L^1_{\text{loc}}(\mathbb{R})$ and consider $u(x,t) = (\phi(x+ct) + \phi(x-ct))/2$. Then $u \in L^1_{\text{loc}}(\mathbb{R}^2_+)$ and $u_{tt} - c^2 u_{xx} = 0$ in the sense of distributions; moreover $u(\cdot, t) \to \phi(\cdot)$ and $u_t(\cdot, t) \to 0$ in $\mathscr{D}'(\mathbb{R})$ as $t \to 0$. This can be an example of a "solution" in a generalized sense for a Cauchy problem in $\mathbb{R}^2_+$. Assume now that we have $u_0 \in L^1(0, l)$; let $\phi \in L^1_{\text{loc}}(\mathbb{R})$ be the $2l$-periodic odd extension of $u_0$; that is, $\phi(x + 2kl) = u_0(|x|) \operatorname{sgn} x$ for $|x| < l$ and $k \in \mathbb{Z}$. One can check immediately that the corresponding $u$ also satisfies $u(0, t) = u(l, t) = 0$, for $t > 0$, i.e., a problem of type (3.68) to (3.70), again in a generalized sense. It is also easy to see that $u \in C^0([0,T]; H^1(0,l)) \cap C^1([0,T]; L^2(0,l))$ iff $u_0 \in H^1_0(0,l)$. If this is the case, $u$ is the solution given by Theorem 3.17 (take $w = 0$). Assume now $u_0 \in C^\infty([0,l])$, but $u_0(0) \neq 0$. Hence $\phi$ jumps at $x = 2kl \ \forall k \in \mathbb{Z}$ and $u$ is discontinuous along the characteristic lines $x \pm ct = 2kl$ [even on $x \pm ct = (2k+1)l$ if $u_0(l) \neq 0$]. In this case $u$ is not a solution in the sense of Theorem 3.17 even for smooth data; this is due to the failure of the first compatibility condition (3.81) since $g_0(0) \neq \gamma_0 u_0$. Let us go back to the case $u_0(0) = u_0(l) = 0$. Then $\phi \in C^{1,1}(\mathbb{R})$ and (3.82) holds with $m = 1$ (and not only with $m = 0!$); indeed (3.81) is now satisfied with $m = 1$ since $g_0'(0) = 0 = \gamma_0 u_1$. More generally $u$ has the same regularity as $\phi$, and a high regularity of $\phi$ is equivalent to the vanishing of a large number of derivatives of even order of $u_0$ at the boundary, in agreement with Rem. 3.21. In particular, $u$ is a classical solution [i.e., $u \in C^2(\bar{Q})$] iff $u_0$ and $u_0''$ vanish at $x = 0, l$. Notice that $u(x, t)$ does not have a limit as $t \to \infty$, unless $u_0 \equiv 0$; moreover, even for $u_0(x) > 0$ (or $< 0$), $u(x, t)$ changes sign (reflecting on $\Sigma$). All this in agreement with Rem. 3.19.

**EXAMPLE 3.29**   Let $F \in L^1_{\text{loc}}(\bar{\mathbb{R}}^2_+)$ [that is, $F \in L^1(B_R^+) \; \forall R > 0$] and $\phi, \psi \in L^1_{\text{loc}}(\mathbb{R})$. Then the function $u$ given by

$$u(x, t) = \frac{1}{2c} \int_0^t d\tau \int_{x-c(t-\tau)}^{x+c(t-\tau)} F(\xi, \tau) \, d\xi + \frac{1}{2}[\phi(x+ct) + \phi(x-ct)] + \frac{1}{2c} \int_{x-ct}^{x+ct} \psi(\xi) \, d\xi \qquad (3.83)$$

is the solution (in a generalized sense as in Example 3.28) of the Cauchy problem in $\mathbb{R}^2_+$: $u_{tt} - c^2 u_{xx} = F$, $u(\cdot, 0) = \phi$, $u_t(\cdot, 0) = \psi$. Assume now that we have given functions $f$ on $]0, l[ \times ]0, \infty[$ and $u_0, u_1$ on $]0, l[$. If $F, \phi, \psi$ are the $2l$-periodic odd extensions of $f, u_0, u_1$ with respect to $x$, one checks that the corresponding $u$ also satisfies the homogeneous Dirichlet conditions $u(0, t) = u(l, t) = 0$ for $t > 0$. If instead $F, \phi, \psi$ are the $2l$-periodic even extensions of $f, u_0, u_1$ with respect to $x$ [for example, $F(x+2kl, t) = f(|x|, t)$ for $|x| < l$, $t > 0$, and $k \in \mathbb{Z}$], the corresponding $u$ satisfies $u_x(0, t) = u_x(l, t) = 0$ and thus a problem of type (3.68) to (3.70) with $j = 1$, since the conormal derivative $\gamma_1 u$ is given now by $\gamma_1 u = -c^2 u_x$ at $x = 0$ and $\gamma_1 u = c^2 u_x$ at $x = l$.

Consider now the nonhomogeneous Dirichlet condition $\gamma_0 u = g_0$, which means $u(0, t) = g_{00}(t)$ and $u(l, t) = g_{0l}(t)$ for $t > 0$. Setting $w(x, t) = (1 - x/l)g_{00}(t) + (x/l)g_{0l}(t)$, we use the above procedure and solve the homogeneous Dirichlet problem $v_{tt} - c^2 v_{xx} = f - (w_{tt} - c^2 w_{xx})$, $v(0) = u_0 - w(0)$, $v'(0) = u_1 - w'(0)$, $\gamma_0 v = 0$. Then the solution $u$ we are looking for is given by $u = v + w$.

The case of the Neumann problem, that is, $\gamma_1 u = g_1$, which means now $-c^2 u_x(0, t) = g_{10}(t)$ and $c^2 u_x(l, t) = g_{1l}(t)$ for $t > 0$, is solved in exactly the same way with a proper choice of $w$, namely, $w(x, t) = x^2(g_{10}(t) + g_{1l}(t))/(2lc^2) - xg_{10}(t)/c^2$. Note, in particular, that the eigenvalue $\lambda = 0$ of the corresponding stationary problem does not cause any trouble in the hyperbolic case, as mentioned in Rem. 3.18.

**EXAMPLE 3.30**   Consider the particular case of Example 3.29 given by $j = 1$, $f \equiv 0$, $u_1 \equiv 0$, $g_1 \equiv 0$. Then $u(x, t) = (\phi(x+ct) + \phi(x-ct))/2$, where $\phi$ is the $2l$-periodic even extension of $u_0$. As in Example 3.28, the regularity of $u$ is given by the regularity of $\phi$. Assuming that $u_0$ is very smooth [for example, $u_0 \in C^\infty([0, l])$], we have $\phi \in C^{0,1}(\mathbb{R})$ and $u$ is Lipschitz-continuous too, i.e., the regularity of $u$ is higher than for the corresponding Dirichlet problem, in agreement with (3.82), which gives different regularity for $j = 0$ or 1. For further regularity we need the compatibility conditions (3.81), the first of which is now $u_0'(0) = u_0'(l) = 0$. In this case even the second derivative of $\phi$ is continuous and $u$ is a classical solution.

**EXAMPLE 3.31**   Let us go back to Example 3.29 in the case of the homogeneous Dirichlet problem, that is, $j = 0$ and $g_0 = 0$. Then the solution is given by (3.83) where $F, \phi, \psi$ are the $2l$-periodic odd extensions of data. We want to discuss the $H^2$-regularity of $u$ and split the discussion into three cases: (1) $u_1 = 0$ and $f = 0$, (2) $u_0 = 0$ and $f = 0$, (3) $u_0 = 0$ and $u_1 = 0$. The first case was treated in Example 3.28. In the second case it is clear that the second derivatives of $u$ involve the first derivative of $\psi$: for instance, $u_{tt} = (c/2)(\psi'(x+ct) - \psi'(x-ct))$; thus we need the $H^1$-regularity of $\psi$, that is, $u_1 \in H_0^1(0, l)$, in agreement with Prop. 3.1. Consider now the third case. The computation of the second derivatives of $u$ involves the space derivative of $F$; for instance,

$$u_{tt}(x, t) = F(x, t) + \frac{c}{2} \int_0^t (F_x(x+ct-c\tau, \tau) - F_x(x-ct+c\tau, \tau)) \, d\tau$$

Thus we need, say, the $H^{1,0}$-regularity of $F$, which means $f \in H^{1,0}(Q)$ and $f(0, t) \equiv f(l, t) \equiv 0$, that is, $f \in L^2(0, T; H_0^1(\Omega))$ and we are in the case $f_1 = 0$ and $f_2 = f$ of Prop. 3.1. However, Prop. 3.1 can be applied even with $f_1 = f$ and $f_2 = 0$, provided $f_t \in L^2(Q)$, regardless of any condition on the vanishing of $f$; but this is not a contradiction. Indeed, changing the order of integration in (3.83), we have

$$u(x, t) = \frac{1}{2c} \int_{x-ct}^{x+ct} d\xi \int_0^{t-|x-\xi|/c} F(\xi, \tau) \, d\tau$$

which shows that the second derivatives of $u$ involve the time derivative of $F$; for instance,

$$u_{tt}(x, t) = \tfrac{1}{2}(F(x+ct, 0) + F(x-ct, 0)) + (2c)^{-1} \int_{x-ct}^{x+ct} F_t(\xi, t-|x-\xi|/c) \, d\xi$$

Thus we need $F_t$, say, in $L^2$, which is true whenever $f_t \in L^2(Q)$, that is, $f \in H^1(0, T; L^2(0, l))$. In conclusion we can see directly that $u \in H^2(Q)$ if either $f$ is smooth in $t$ or $f$ is smooth in $x$ and vanishes at $x = 0, l$. Further regularity of $u$ can also be discussed directly.

**EXAMPLE 3.32**    Consider now the simple case $j = 0$, $g_0 = 0$, $u_0 = 0$, $u_1 = 0$ for the equation $u_{tt} - c^2 u_{xx} = f$ on $Q = ]0, l[ \times ]0, T[$, with a piecewise smooth $f$. If $f$ jumps only in space [for example, $f(x, t) = 0$ or 1 according to $x < l/2$ or $x > l/2$], then $f_t$ is smooth and $u$ is at least in $H^2(Q)$. If $f$ jumps only in time [for example, $f(x, t) = 0$ or $f(x, t) = x(l-x)$ according to $t < T/2$ or $t > T/2$], then $f_x$ is smooth and $u \in H^2(Q)$ if $f(0, t) = f(l, t) = 0$. All this follows from Prop. 3.1. When $f$ is less simple (e.g., $f$ jumps in space at a point which moves in time), then we can only apply Theorem 3.17 with small $\rho, \sigma, r, s$. For instance, if $f$ is the characteristic function of a "good" subset of $Q$, then $f \in H^{1/2-\varepsilon}(Q)$ and thus, by (3.30), or, in a simpler way, by comparing Fig. 3.1a and b, $f \in H^\sigma (H^\rho)$ with $\rho + \sigma < \frac{1}{2}$. Hence Theorem 3.17 (take $w = 0$ in our case) gives $u \in H^s (H^r)$ for $r + s < \frac{3}{2}$, which means $u \in H^{3/2-\varepsilon}(Q)$ (see Fig. 3.3c). The optimality of this result is shown by the following example: take $Q = ]0, 2[ \times ]0, 1[$, $u(x, t) = (t+x-1)^+(t-x+1)^+$, $f(x, t) = 4$ if $t > |x-1|$, and $f(x, t) = 0$ otherwise. Then $u_{tt} - u_{xx} = f$, $u(x, 0) = u_t(x, 0) = 0$, $u(0, t) = u(2, t) = 0$. In particular, the data are compatible, since (3.81) holds for every $m$. But $f$ is irregular, namely, $f \in H^{1/2-\varepsilon}(Q)$, and $u$ is irregular too. Indeed $u_x$ jumps along $t = |x-1|$, which implies $u_x(\cdot, t) \notin H^{1/2}(\Omega) \; \forall t \in ]0, 1[$; thus $u \notin L^2(0, T; H^{3/2}(\Omega))$ and, in particular, $u \notin H^{3/2}(Q)$.

## 3.5 COMPLEMENTS

### 3.5A Weak Formulations

Let us consider again the *model problem*

$$-\Delta u = f \qquad \text{in } \Omega \tag{3.84}$$

$$u = g_0 \qquad \text{on } \Gamma = \partial\Omega \tag{3.85}$$

If $v$ is a very smooth function on $\Omega$ [say, $v \in C^\infty(\bar{\Omega})$], (3.84) formally implies

$$\int_\Omega u(-\Delta v) = \int_\Omega fv + \int_\Gamma \frac{\partial u}{\partial \nu} v - \int_\Gamma u \frac{\partial v}{\partial \nu} \tag{3.86}$$

In particular, by (3.85),

$$\int_\Omega u(-\Delta v) = \int_\Omega fv - \int_\Gamma g_0 \frac{\partial v}{\partial \nu} \qquad \text{for every } v \in C^\infty(\Omega) \text{ vanishing on } \Gamma \qquad (3.87)$$

Assume now that one seeks a solution $u \in L^2(\Omega)$ (say, because $f$ is an "irregular" distribution). Then (3.84) still makes sense [in $\mathcal{D}'(\Omega)$], while (3.85) makes no sense at all. On the other hand, the formula in (3.87) can be written for very general $f$ and $u$; for instance, if $g_0$ is smooth and $f = \delta_{x_0}$, a Dirac mass at $x_0 \in \Omega$, it will be sufficient to write $\langle f, v \rangle$, that is, $v(x_0)$, in place of $\int fv$. However, notice that for $n \geqslant 4$ we have $\delta_{x_0} \notin H^{-2}(\Omega)$ (by Example 2.38), and thus it is impossible to find $u \in L^2(\Omega)$ satisfying (3.87). But, for $n \geqslant 4$, we could look for $u \in H^{2-n/2-\varepsilon}(\Omega)$, since $\delta_{x_0} \in H^{-n/2-\varepsilon}(\Omega)$; to do this we have to consider $\langle u, -\Delta v \rangle$ in place of $\int u(-\Delta v)$. However, this requires $-\Delta v \in H_0^{n/2-2+\varepsilon}(\Omega)$, and this, for a general $v \in C^\infty(\bar\Omega)$ vanishing on $\Gamma$, is true only for $n = 4$ by (2.117) in Part 1. Hence, for $n > 4$, we have to change the set of the admissible test functions $v$ in (3.87). For instance,

$$\langle u, -\Delta v \rangle = v(x_0) - \int_\Gamma g_0 \frac{\partial v}{\partial \nu} \qquad \forall v \in C^\infty(\bar\Omega)$$

$$(3.88)$$

with
$$v|_\Gamma = 0 \qquad \text{and} \qquad -\Delta v \in H_0^{n/2-2+\varepsilon}(\Omega)$$

where $u$ is sought in $H^{2-n/2-\varepsilon}(\Omega)$.

Similar modifications have to be done in (3.87) for more general $f$ and $g_0$ (note that in the previous particular case $f = \delta_{x_0}$, the local regularity of $f$ and $g_0$, and thus of $u$, away from $x_0$ could have been used to simplify the argument, but such a simplification does not extend to the general case).

At first sight one might think that a general remedy is to take only $v \in \mathcal{D}(\Omega)$ in (3.87): this works and gives back just (3.84) (by definition!), but the information in (3.85) is obviously completely lost now, while it was contained in the original (3.87). Indeed, for $\mathcal{D}(\Omega) \subset \mathcal{V} \subset C^\infty(\bar\Omega)$, consider formally

$$\int_\Omega u(-\Delta v) = \int_\Omega fv - \int_\Gamma g_0 \frac{\partial v}{\partial \nu} \qquad \forall v \in \mathcal{V} \text{ vanishing on } \Gamma \qquad (3.89)$$

Condition (3.89) always implies (3.84), and using (3.84), (3.86), and (3.89), we deduce

$$\int_\Gamma (u - g_0) \frac{\partial v}{\partial \nu} = 0 \qquad \forall v \in \mathcal{V} \text{ vanishing on } \Gamma \qquad (3.90)$$

which implies (3.85) provided $\partial v/\partial \nu|_\Gamma$ describes a space which is rich enough, e.g., containing $C^\infty(\Gamma)$. This is true when $\mathcal{V} = C^\infty(\bar\Omega)$, as in (3.87), and when $\mathcal{V} = \{v \in C^\infty(\Omega): -\Delta v \in H_0^s(\Omega)\}$ ($\forall s > 0$), as in (3.88), but not (obviously!) for $\mathcal{V} = \mathcal{D}(\Omega)$.

Similarly, one can consider a general elliptic operator $A$, as in Assump. 3.2, in place of $-\Delta$. The corresponding weak formulation of the problem (3.6) and (3.7) is

$$\int_\Omega uA^*v = \int_\Omega fv - \int_\Gamma g_0 \frac{\partial v}{\partial \nu_{A^*}} \qquad \forall v \in \mathcal{V} \text{ vanishing on } \Gamma \qquad (3.91)$$

where the choice of $\mathscr{V}$ has to be made, following the above criteria, according to the regularity of $f$ and $g_0$ and to the space where $u$ is sought. For instance, if $f \in H^{-3/2}(\Omega)$ and $g_0 \in H^{-4}(\Gamma)$, the expected regularity of $u$ should be $H^{-7/2}(\Omega)$, so that we choose $\mathscr{V} = \{v \in H_0^{3/2}(\Omega): A^*v \in H_0^{7/2}(\Omega), \ \partial v/\partial \nu_{A^*} \in H^4(\Gamma)\} = \{v \in H^{11/2}(\Omega) \cap H_0^{3/2}(\Omega): A^*v \in H_0^{7/2}(\Omega)\}$. Note that $f \in H^{-2}(\Omega)$ would compel us to choose $\mathscr{V} \subset H_0^2$, and (3.90) does not imply any boundary condition on $u$. Hence, for $f \in H^{-s}(\Omega)$ with $s > \frac{3}{2}$, the Dirichlet problem cannot be treated in such a way in the usual Sobolev spaces, unless $f$ is smoother near $\Gamma$. Similar considerations hold for $W^{s,p}$-spaces.

Let us now briefly consider the Neumann problem (3.6) and (3.8). The weak formulation is

$$\int_\Omega uA^*v = \int_\Omega fv + \int_\Gamma g_1 v \qquad \forall v \in \mathscr{V} \qquad \text{with} \qquad \frac{\partial v}{\partial \nu_{A^*}|_\Gamma} = 0 \qquad (3.92)$$

Again the choice of $\mathscr{V}$ depends on $f$, $g_1$, and on the expected regularity for $u$. For instance, if $f \in H^{-1/2}(\Omega)$ and $g_1 \in H^{-5}(\Gamma)$, one expects $u \in H^{-7/2}(\Omega)$ and thus chooses $\mathscr{V} = \{v \in H^{11/2}(\Omega): A^*v \in H_0^{7/2}(\Omega)\}$. Note that the case $f \in H^{-s}(\Omega)$ with $s > \frac{1}{2}$ cannot be treated, since it would require $\mathscr{V} \subset H_0^s(\Omega)$ [hence $v = 0$ on $\Gamma \ \forall v \in \mathscr{V}$ and any information on $g_1$ would be lost in (3.92)], unless $f$ is smoother near $\Gamma$.

**REMARK 3.22**  It appears that the *weak formulations* (3.91) and (3.92) are more general than the corresponding *strong formulations* (3.6), (3.7) and (3.6), (3.8), respectively. Indeed, writing the strong formulation for irregular data, one tackles the problem of giving sense to the boundary conditions; this problem is not present in the weak formulations. On the other hand, in Sec. 2.3B of Part 1 the problem was solved using very general trace theorems such as Theorem 2.27 in Part 1, which allowed us to deal with data which are as irregular as they are here. But for proving Theorem 2.27, one uses the weak formulations! Actually the true meaning of boundary conditions in Theorem 3.2 lies in the weak formulations.

In a similar way, one can introduce weak formulations of parabolic and hyperbolic problems. The idea is exactly the same. One formally multiplies the equation by a smooth test function $v \in \mathscr{V}$ and integrates over the domain $Q$; then one performs all the necessary integration by parts so that no derivatives are left on $u$. Many surface integrals (on $\Sigma$ and $\Omega$) appear; in some of them the contribution of $u$ can be replaced by data, using boundary conditions, and a selection of $v \in \mathscr{V}$ is made such that the other surface terms vanish identically.

In the case of the parabolic problems (3.38), (3.39), and (3.40) or (3.41) we have, respectively,

$$-\int_Q uv' + \int_Q uA^*v = \int_Q fv + \int_\Omega u_0 v(0) - \int_\Sigma g_0 \frac{\partial v}{\partial \nu_{A^*}}$$

$$\forall v \in \mathscr{V} \qquad \text{with} \qquad v(T) = 0 \text{ in } \Omega \qquad \text{and} \qquad v = 0 \text{ on } \Sigma \qquad (3.93)$$

$$-\int_Q uv' + \int_Q uA^*v = \int_Q fv + \int_\Omega u_0 v(0) + \int_\Sigma g_1 v$$

$$\forall v \in \mathscr{V} \qquad \text{with} \qquad v(T) = 0 \text{ in } \Omega \qquad \text{and} \qquad \frac{\partial v}{\partial \nu_{A^*}} = 0 \text{ on } \Sigma \qquad (3.94)$$

In the case of the hyperbolic problems (3.68) to (3.70) for $j = 0$ or $j = 1$ we have, respectively,

$$\int_Q uv'' + \int_Q uA^*v = \int_Q fv - \int_\Omega u_0 v'(0) + \int_\Omega u_1 v(0) - \int_\Sigma g_0 \frac{\partial v}{\partial \nu_{A^*}}$$

$$\forall v \in \mathcal{V} \quad \text{with} \quad v(T) = v'(T) = 0 \text{ in } \Omega \quad \text{and} \quad v = 0 \text{ on } \Sigma \qquad (3.95)$$

$$\int_Q uv'' + \int_Q uA^*v = \int_Q fv - \int_\Omega u_0 v'(0) + \int_\Omega u_1 v(0) + \int_\Sigma g_1 v$$

$$\forall v \in \mathcal{V} \quad \text{with} \quad v(T) = v'(T) = 0 \text{ in } \Omega \quad \text{and} \quad \frac{\partial v}{\partial \nu_{A^*}} = 0 \text{ on } \Sigma \qquad (3.96)$$

In all cases the choice of $\mathcal{V}$ is related to the regularity of data and to the expected regularity for $u$, as in the elliptic case. Obviously all the integrals have to be replaced, when necessary, by suitable duality pairing.

## 3.5B  Variational Formulations

We introduced the weak formulations in order to treat problems with irregular data. As a general fact in a weak formulation one looks for a solution $u$ in a very big space; that is, very few properties of $u$ are required a priori. Hence, still in general, it will be easier to prove an existence theorem, but for the same reason it will be more difficult to prove uniqueness. On the contrary, looking a priori for a more regular $u$, as in the strong formulations, it will be easier to prove uniqueness and more difficult to prove existence, which could even fail. Therefore it is interesting to investigate whether there are situations where we assume a priori an intermediate regularity of $u$ so that both existence and uniqueness are easy to prove. Looking back at the weak formulations of Sec. 3.5A, we see that for dealing with more and more irregular $u$ we had to assume more and more properties on the test functions $v$. The idea is thus to look for cases where the assumed regularities of $u$ and $v$ are as close as possible. *Variational formulations* can be seen as an answer to this kind of question.

Let us analyze first the case of elliptic problems and consider the problem (3.6) and (3.7) with $g_0 = 0$. Taking $V_0 = H_0^1(\Omega)$, it is easy to see that a function $u \in H^1(\Omega)$ satisfies (3.6) and (3.7) with $g_0 = 0$ iff

$$u \in V_0 \quad \text{and} \quad a(u, v) = \int_\Omega fv \quad \forall v \in V_0 \qquad (3.97)$$

where $a(u, v)$ is given in (3.12).

The variational formulation of (3.6) and (3.8) can be obtained, setting $V_1 = H^1(\Omega)$. A function $u \in H^1(\Omega)$ is a solution of (3.6) and (3.8) iff

$$u \in V_1 \quad \text{and} \quad a(u, v) = \int_\Omega fv + \int_\Gamma g_1 v \quad \forall v \in V_1 \qquad (3.98)$$

Of course, the regularity of $f$ in (3.97) and of $f$ and $g_1$ in (3.98) must allow us to write the corresponding right-hand sides, if not as integrals, at least as duality pairings. More precisely, one needs $f \in H^{-1}(\Omega)$ in (3.97) and $f \in H^{-1/2}(\Omega)$, $g_1 \in H^{-1/2}(\Gamma)$ in (3.98). Assuming such regularity for the data, one can even prove existence and uniqueness by means of the following theorem.

**THEOREM 3.18** *Lax–Milgram.* Let $V$ be a Hilbert space and $a(\,\cdot\,,\,\cdot\,)$ be a continuous bilinear form on $V \times V$ (see Sec. 1.3F in Part 1). Assume that the so-called *V-ellipticity condition*

$$\exists \alpha_* > 0 : a(v, v) \geqslant \alpha_* \|v\|_V^2 \qquad \forall v \in V \tag{3.99}$$

is satisfied. Then for every $L \in V'$ there exists a unique $u$ such that

$$u \in V \qquad \text{and} \qquad a(u, v) = L(v) \qquad \forall v \in V \tag{3.100}$$

Moreover,
$$\|u\|_V \leqslant \frac{1}{\alpha_*} \|L\|_{V'} \tag{3.101}$$

Let us briefly discuss the applicability of Theorem 3.18 to (3.97) and (3.98). We need first that $a(u, v)$ be a continuous bilinear form on $V$. For this it is sufficient to assume very little regularity of the coefficients; for instance, the assumptions $a_{ij}$, $b_i$, $c_i$, and $d \in L^\infty(\Omega)$ work in both cases. We then have to check (3.99). In the simplest case $b_i = c_i = 0$ it is clear that (3.99) is implied by the uniform ellipticity condition (3.4) and by $d(x) \geqslant d_0$ in $\Omega$, with $d_0 = 0$ or $d_0 > 0$ for (3.97) or (3.98), respectively [using (2.129) in Part 1 for (3.97)]. In the general case, (3.4) gives

$$a(v, v) \geqslant \alpha \int |\nabla v|^2 + \int d v^2 - M|v|_{1,\Omega}|v|_{0,\Omega}$$

and thus (3.99) holds for $d(x) \geqslant d_0$ with $d_0$ large enough. Finally one needs $L \in V'$. It is easy to check that the above conditions on $f$ and $f$, $g_1$ work.

**REMARK 3.23** In the case $V = H^1(\Omega)$, Theorem 3.18 ensures that we can take, as the right-hand side, any $L \in V' = (H^1(\Omega))'$ and obtain a solution of (3.100). On the other hand, we said that in (3.98) we were not allowed to choose $f \notin H^{-1/2}(\Omega)$, while $f \in H^{-1}(\Omega)$ was permitted in (3.97). Let us see in detail what really happens. It is easy to see that, for $f_0 \in L^2(\Omega)$ and $F \in (L^2(\Omega))^n$, the functional $L : v \to \int (f_0 v + F \cdot \nabla v)$ is linear and continuous on $H^1(\Omega)$; moreover one can show that every $L \in (H^1(\Omega))'$ can be written in this form. The corresponding unique solution $u$ of (3.100) satisfies $Au = f_0 - \operatorname{div} F$. Let $w(u) \in (L^2(\Omega))^n$ be defined by $w_j(u) = \Sigma_i a_{ij} D_i u + c_j u$ and $z(u) = \Sigma_i b_i D_i u + du$; one has $\operatorname{div}(w(u) - F) = z(u) - f_0 \in L^2(\Omega)$. Hence $w(u) - F \in L^2_{\operatorname{div}}(\Omega)$ (see Sec. 2.9D in Part 1) and $(w(u) - F) \cdot v|_\Gamma = 0$ (by Green's formula) in the sense of Theorem 2.26 in Part 1. Note that, in general, one cannot write $(\partial u / \partial v_A|_\Gamma \equiv) w(u) \cdot v|_\Gamma = F \cdot v|_\Gamma$ (see also Rem. 2.13 in Part 1), since neither of the two sides has a meaning (see Example 3.35). Thus (3.6) holds with $f = f_0 - \operatorname{div} F$, but (3.8) does not make sense.

On the other hand, every $v \in H^1(\Omega)$ can be split up in a unique way as $v = v_0 + v_1$ with $v_0 \in H^1_0(\Omega)$ and $-\Delta v_1 = 0$. Therefore, having $f \in H^{-1}(\Omega)$ and $g \in H^{-1/2}(\Gamma)$, one could consider $L(v) = \langle f, v_0 \rangle + \langle g, v_1|_\Gamma \rangle = \langle f, v_0 \rangle + \langle g, v|_\Gamma \rangle$. Again, one can show that every $L \in (H^1(\Omega))'$ can be written in this new form, whose relationship with the previous one is given by $f_0 = \phi$ and $F = \nabla(\phi + \psi)$, where $\phi$ and $\psi$ solve $\phi \in H^1(\Omega)$, $-\Delta\phi + \phi = 0$, $\partial\phi/\partial v|_\Gamma = g$; $\psi \in H^1_0(\Omega)$, $-\Delta\psi = f$. One has now $Au = f$ and $(w(u) - \nabla(\phi + \psi)) \cdot v|_\Gamma = 0$, that is, $(w(u) - \nabla\phi) \cdot v|_\Gamma = g$. Now the left-hand side can be split up as $\partial u / \partial v_A - \partial\psi/\partial v$ provided $\partial\psi/\partial v$ makes sense, and this is the case when (see Theorem 2.27) $-\Delta\psi \in H^{-1/2}(\Omega)$, that is, $f \in H^{-1/2}(\Omega)$.

<u>REMARK 3.24</u>  We have briefly seen some applications of Theorem 3.18 to Dirichlet and Neumann problems for a second-order elliptic equation. Actually its range of applicability is much wider, involving mixed boundary conditions, higher-order equations, systems of partial differential equations, and even numerical cases where $V$ is finite-dimensional (see examples below).

Consider now the parabolic case. The corresponding variational formulations are as follows. For (3.38) to (3.40) with $g_0 = 0$ [see (2.241) in Part 1],

$$u \in L^2(0, T; H_0^1(\Omega)) \cap H^1(0, T; H^{-1}(\Omega)) \qquad u(0) = u_0$$

$$\int_\Omega u'(t)v + a(t, u(t), v) = \int_\Omega f(t)v \qquad \forall v \in H_0^1(\Omega), \text{almost everywhere in } ]0, T[ \quad (3.102)$$

For (3.38), (3.39), and (3.41) with $g_1 = 0$,

$$u \in L^2(0, T; H^1(\Omega)) \cap H^1(0, T; H^{-1/2}(\Omega)) \qquad u(0) = u_0$$

$$\int_\Omega u'(t)v + a(t, u(t), v) = \int_\Omega f(t)v \qquad \forall v \in H^1(\Omega), \text{amost everywhere in } ]0, T[ \quad (3.103)$$

Of course, the integrals have to be interpreted as duality pairings and assumptions on the data have to be made: $f \in L^2(0, T; H^{-1}(\Omega))$ for (3.102) and $f \in L^2(0, T; H^{-1/2}(\Omega))$ for (3.103).

A general abstract result can also be applied to show existence and uniqueness for (3.102) and (3.103).

<u>THEOREM 3.19</u>  Let $V \hookrightarrow H \hookrightarrow V'$ be a Hilbert triplet (see Sec. 1.4G in Part 1) and $a(t, \cdot, \cdot)$ a family of continuous bilinear forms on $V \times V$ such that:

$$\text{The map } (t, u, v) \to a(t, u, v) \text{ is continuous on } [0, T] \times V \times V \qquad (3.104)$$

$$\exists \alpha_* > 0, \lambda \in \mathbb{R}: \quad a(t, v, v) \geq \alpha_* \|v\|_V^2 - \lambda \|v\|_H^2 \qquad \forall v \in V, \forall t \in [0, T] \qquad (3.105)$$

Then for every $L \in L^2(0, T; V')$ and $u_0 \in H$ there exists a unique $u$ satisfying

$$u \in L^2(0, T; V) \cap H^1(0, T; V') \qquad u(0) = u_0$$
$$\langle u'(t), v \rangle + a(t, u(t), v) = \langle L(t), v \rangle \qquad \forall v \in V, \text{almost everywhere in } ]0, T[ \qquad (3.106)$$

and we have the estimate (with $c$ independent of $u_0$ and $L$)

$$\|u\|_{L^2(V) \cap H^1(V')} \leq c(\|u_0\|_H + \|L\|_{L^2(V')}) \qquad (3.107)$$

In the case of hyperbolic problems the corresponding abstract result is as follows.

<u>THEOREM 3.20</u>  Let $V \hookrightarrow H \hookrightarrow V'$ be a Hilbert triplet (see Sec. 1.4G in Part 1) and $a(t, \cdot, \cdot)$ a family of continuous bilinear forms on $V \times V$ such that:

$$\text{The maps } (t, u, v) \to a(t, u, v) \text{ and } (t, u, v) \to a'(t, u, v) \text{ are continuous on } [0, T] \times V \times V \qquad (3.108)$$

where $a'(t_0, u_0, v_0)$ is the derivative at $t = t_0$ of the map $t \rightarrow a(t, u_0, v_0)$; moreover assume (3.105) and

$$a(t, u, v) = a(t, v, u) \qquad \forall u, v \in V, \forall t \in [0, T] \qquad (3.109)$$

Then for every $L_1 \in L^2(0, T; H)$, $L_2 \in H^1(0, T; V')$, $u_0 \in V$, and $u_1 \in H$ there exists a unique $u$ satisfying

$$u \in C^0([0, T]; V) \cap C^1([0, T]; H) \cap H^2(0, T; V') \qquad u(0) = u_0; \; u'(0) = u_1$$

$$\langle u''(t), v \rangle + a(t, u(t), v) = \langle L_1(t) + L_2(t), v \rangle \qquad \forall v \in V, \text{almost everywhere in } ]0, T[ \qquad (3.110)$$

and we have the estimate

$$\|u\|_{C^0(V) \cap C^1(H) \cap H^2(V')} \le c(\|u_0\|_V + \|u_1\|_H + \|L_1\|_{L^2(H)} + \|L_2\|_{H^1(V')}) \qquad (3.111)$$

where $c$ does not depend on $u_0$, $u_1$, $L_1$, and $L_2$.

**REMARK 3.25**  The assumption (3.109) can be weakened as follows: $a(t, u, v) = a_0(t, u, v) + a_1(t, u, v)$, where $a_0(\cdot, \cdot, \cdot)$ satisfies (3.105), (3.108), and (3.109); $a_1(\cdot, \cdot, \cdot)$ satisfies (3.108); and

$$|a_1(t, u, v)| \le M(\|u\|_V \|v\|_H + \|u\|_H \|v\|_V) \qquad \forall u, v \in V, \forall t \in [0, T] \qquad (3.112)$$

Let us consider now the applicability of Theorems 3.19 and 3.20 to the parabolic problems (3.102) and (3.103) or to the corresponding hyperbolic cases. For (3.102), it is sufficient to set $V = H_0^1(\Omega)$ and $H = L^2(\Omega)$; (3.104) is a regularity assumption on coefficients, surely implied by (3.23); (3.105) follows from (3.24) (see also Rem. 3.13); finally $L \in L^2(0, T; V')$ means $f \in L^2(0, T; H^{-1}(\Omega))$. For (3.103) instead, one chooses $V = H^1(\Omega)$ and $f \in L^2(0, T; H^{-1/2}(\Omega))$. Then Theorem 3.19 gives $u \in L^2(0, T; H^1(\Omega)) \cap H^1(0, T; (H^1(\Omega))')$ and one can show that actually $u_t \in L^2(0, T; H^{-1/2}(\Omega))$. It is clear that the choice

$$\langle L, v \rangle = \int_Q fv \qquad \text{with} \qquad f \in L^2(0, T; H^{-1/2}(\Omega))$$

is not the most general, but the use of a more general $L$ might cause problems in the interpretation of the boundary condition as in Rem. 3.23.

Similar considerations hold for the applicability of Theorem 3.20 to hyperbolic problems; for instance, the choices $V = H_0^1(\Omega)$ and $V = H^1(\Omega)$ give rise once again to Dirichlet or Neumann boundary conditions, respectively [in both cases $H = L^2(\Omega)$]. Let us say a few words on right-hand sides. For the Dirichlet problem we are allowed to choose $f = f_1 + f_2$ with $f_1 \in L^2(Q)$ and $f_2 \in H^1(0, T; H^{-1}(\Omega))$ [that is, $\partial f_2/\partial t \in L^2(0, T; H^{-1}(\Omega))$]; for the Neumann problem, instead, $f = f_1 + f_2$ with $f_1 \in L^2(Q)$ and $f_2 \in H^1(0, T; H^{-1/2}(\Omega))$, and again we do not use the full generality for $L_2$. Finally, note that in Rem. 3.25 the split $a = a_0 + a_1$ corresponds to a splitting of the operator $A = A_0 + A_1$, where $A_0$ is the principal part of $A$, which is assumed to be symmetric [see (3.67)], and (3.112) expresses the fact that $A_1$ is actually a first-order operator.

**REMARK 3.26**  The regularity assumptions (3.104) and (3.108) are stronger than necessary and could be replaced by boundedness and suitable measurability assumptions. In the applications we are thus allowed to choose $a_{ij}$, $b_i$, $c_i$, $d \in L^\infty(Q)$ for the parabolic case and $a_{ij}$, $b_i$, $c_i$, $d \in W^{1,\infty}(0, T; L^\infty(\Omega))$ for the hyperbolic case; moreover even weaker regularity can be allowed on $b_i$, $c_i$, $d$.

**REMARK 3.27**  In the study of the variational formulation for evolution problems we used test functions $v \in V$ independent of $t$. However, nothing changes if one requires, instead,

$$\int_0^T \{\langle u'(t), v(t)\rangle + a(t, u(t), v(t))\}\, dt = \int_0^T \langle L(t), v(t)\rangle\, dt \qquad \forall v \in L^2(0, T; V) \qquad (3.113)$$

and

$$\int_0^T \{\langle u''(t), v(t)\rangle + a(t, u(t), v(t))\}\, dt = \int_0^T \langle L_1(t) + L_2(t), v(t)\rangle\, dt \qquad \forall v \in L^2(0, T; V) \qquad (3.114)$$

respectively. However (3.113) and (3.114) suggest the introduction of weaker variational formulations that can be obtained integrating by parts the integrals $\int \langle u', v\rangle$ and $\int \langle u'', v\rangle$; in the second case one can also choose to perform one or two integrations by parts. In any case one has to assume for $v$ a greater regularity than $L^2(0, T; V)$ and suitable conditions of vanishing at $t = T$; at the same time the initial conditions on $u$ will appear in the right-hand side and less regularity for $u$ is required a priori. It has to be pointed out that some confusion is present in the literature about the meaning of the words *weak formulations*; for instance, some authors call *weak* what we called *variational*.

**REMARK 3.28**  Consider Eqs. (3.6) and (3.38) with homogeneous boundary conditions and multiply them by $u$; integrating over the domain, formally one has, by Green's formulae,

$$a(u, u) = \int_\Omega fu \qquad (3.115)$$

$$\int_\Omega |u(t)|^2 + 2\int_0^t a(\tau, u(\tau), u(\tau))\, d\tau = \int_\Omega u_0^2 + 2\int_0^t \int_\Omega fu \qquad (3.116)$$

Taking instead (3.68) in the simplest case where $a$ is symmetric and independent of $t$ and multiplying by $u'$, one gets

$$\int_\Omega |u'(t)|^2 + a(u(t), u(t)) = \int_\Omega u_1^2 + a(u_0, u_0) + 2\int_0^t \int_\Omega fu' \qquad (3.117)$$

These formulae generally express an *energy balance* and can be used for deriving a priori bounds on $u$ in suitable norms, which are strongly suggested by the corresponding left-hand sides. For instance, if $a(u, v) = \int \nabla u \cdot \nabla v$ and we are dealing with Dirichlet conditions, the left-hand sides dictate the energy norms

$$\|u\|^2_{L^\infty(L^2)} + \|u\|^2_{L^2(H^1)} \qquad \text{and} \qquad \|u'\|^2_{L^\infty(L^2)} + \|u\|^2_{L^\infty(H^1)}$$

In the more general case of an $H_0^1$-elliptic form $a(u, v)$, we have $a(u, u) \approx \|u\|^2_{1,\Omega}$ and the previous energy norms can still be used. In a general case one should first derive formally an energy balance which will suggest the "natural norm" and thus the regularity of the space $V$ to be used in the abstract formulation (see examples below).

## 3.5c  Examples

**EXAMPLE 3.33**  Take $V = \{v \in H^1(\Omega): v|_{\Gamma_0} = 0\}$, where $\Gamma_0$ is a "good" subset of $\Gamma$, and set $\Gamma_1 = \Gamma \backslash \bar{\Gamma}_0$. Let $a(u, v)$ be given by (3.12) and assume that (3.99) is satisfied [this will be the case, for instance, if $a(u, v) = \int \nabla u \cdot \nabla v$]. Suppose that $f \in H^{-1/2}(\Omega)$ and $g_1 \in (H_{00}^{1/2}(\Gamma_1))'$ and consider the problem

$$u \in V \qquad \text{and} \qquad a(u, v) = \int_\Omega fv + \int_{\Gamma_1} g_1 v \qquad \forall v \in V \qquad (3.118)$$

The unique solution given by Theorem 3.18 satisfies the *mixed boundary-value problem*: $Au = f$ in $\Omega$, $u = 0$ on $\Gamma_0$, and $\partial u/\partial \nu_A = g_1$ on $\Gamma_1$. With the same choice of $V$ in Theorems 3.19 and 3.20 one can deal with mixed boundary-value problems for evolution equations.

**EXAMPLE 3.34** In discussing the applicability of Theorem 3.18 we said that $L^\infty$-coefficients were allowed. However, in the case of discontinuous coefficients particular care must be taken when dealing with the associated operator $A$. In the sense of distributions, $A$ can always be written in the form (3.2), but it is forbidden in general to use the Leibnitz rule for derivatives of products. Hence one should always consider the equation $Au = f$ written in the form $-\text{div } w + z = f$, where $w_j = \sum_i a_{ij} D_i u + c_j u$ and $z = \sum_i b_i D_i u + du$. Note that this form is also, in general, the most meaningful physically. In particular, if we split $\Omega$ into two regions $\Omega^{(1)}$ and $\Omega^{(2)}$ by means of a smooth surface $S$, one has separately $u^{(i)} \in H^1(\Omega^{(i)})$ and $-\text{div } w^{(i)} + z^{(i)} = f^{(i)}$ in $\Omega^{(i)}$ ($i = 1, 2$, with obvious notations). Assuming now, for instance, $f \in L^2(\Omega)$ [$f \in H^s$ is allowed now with $s > -\tfrac{1}{2}$, but not with $s = -\tfrac{1}{2}$] because of (2.147) and (2.138) in Part 1 we also have globally $\text{div } w \in L^2(\Omega)$ and, of course, $u \in H^1(\Omega)$. This implies on $S$ the supplementary conditions $u^{(1)} = u^{(2)}$ and $w^{(1)} \cdot \nu^{(1)} + w^{(2)} \cdot \nu^{(2)} = 0$ (where $\nu^{(1)} + \nu^{(2)} \equiv 0$ on $S$). The last condition follows from (2.197) in Part 1 applied to $\Omega$ and $\Omega^{(i)}$ with $v \in \mathscr{D}(\Omega)$. The interesting case is when the coefficients are smooth separately on $\Omega^{(i)}$ and jump on $S$. Then we have a *transmission problem*: $Au^{(i)} = f^{(i)}$ in $\Omega^{(i)}$, with $u^{(1)} = u^{(2)}$ and $w^{(1)} \cdot \nu^{(1)} + w^{(2)} \cdot \nu^{(2)} = 0$ on $S$. To illustrate the "particular care" that must be taken, consider the following simple example: $\Omega = ]-1, 2[$, $\Omega^{(1)} = ]-1, 0[$, $\Omega^{(2)} = ]0, 2[$ (thus $S = \{0\}$), $k(x) = 1$ in $\Omega^{(1)}$ and $= 2$ in $\Omega^{(2)}$, $f(x) = -8k(x)$, $V = H_0^1(\Omega)$, and

$$a(u, v) = \int_{-1}^{2} ku'v'$$

Then $w = ku'$, $z = 0$, and $u$ is given by $u(x) = 4x^2 - 10 - 6x/k(x)$ (check both $-\text{div } w = f$ in $\Omega$ and the transmission conditions). On the other hand, one has $-u'' = -8$ in $\Omega^{(i)}$ ($i = 1, 2$), but not $-u'' = -8$ in $\Omega$; indeed $u$ can be written as $u(x) = 4x^2 - 6x - 10 + 3x^+$, so that $-u'' = -8 - 3\delta_0$.

**EXAMPLE 3.35** Recalling Rem. 3.23, consider the following example:

$$V = H^1(0, 1) \qquad a(u, v) = \int (u'v' + uv)$$

and

$$L(v) = \int (x^\alpha v(x) + \alpha x^{\alpha-1} v'(x)) \qquad \text{where} \qquad \alpha \notin \mathbb{N}$$

With the notations of Rem. 3.23, we thus have $f_0(x) = x^\alpha$, $F(x) = \alpha x^{\alpha-1}$. We need $\alpha > \tfrac{1}{2}$; otherwise the variational formulation is meaningless from Example 2.28 in Part 1. We are solving a Neumann problem for $-u'' + u = f$, with $f(x) = x^\alpha - \alpha(\alpha - 1)x^{\alpha-2}$, and the boundary conditions are $w(x) - F(x) = 0$ at $x = 0, 1$, where $w = u'$. The general solution of the equation is given by $u(x) = x^\alpha + c_1 Chx + c_2 Shx$; thus $w(x) - F(x) = c_1 Shx + c_2 Chx$, which is smooth for any $\alpha$. Now, for $\tfrac{1}{2} < \alpha < 1$, $f \in H^s$ with $-1 < s < -\tfrac{1}{2}$, both $w$ and $F$ are unbounded at $x = 0$, and the boundary condition $w(x) - F(x) = 0$ at $x = 0$ *cannot* be written $w(0) = F(0)$. When instead $\alpha > 1$, $f \in H^{-1/2}$ (at least), and the boundary conditions can now be written $w(x) = F(x)$ at $x = 0, 1$. Note that the solution was $u(x) = x^\alpha$ ($\forall \alpha > \tfrac{1}{2}$). Note also that $L(v)$ could be written as $L(v) = \int fv_0 + v(1) - v(0)$, where $v_0(x) = v(x) - v(0) - x(v(1) - v(0))$, and the term $v(1) - v(0)$ is in place of $\int_\Gamma gv$.

**EXAMPLE 3.36** Consider the *Neumann problem* $-\Delta u = f$ in $\Omega$, $\partial u/\partial \nu = g_1$ on $\Gamma$. The variational formulation should be

$$\int_\Omega \nabla u \cdot \nabla v = L(v) \equiv \int_\Omega fv + \int_\Gamma g_1 v \qquad \forall v \in H^1(\Omega)$$

Unfortunately the form $a(u, v) = \int_\Omega \nabla u \cdot \nabla v$ is (obviously!) not $H^1(\Omega)$-elliptic. Indeed the solution is never unique. We thus look for a $u$ satisfying $\int_\Omega u = 0$ and take accordingly $V = \{v \in H^1(\Omega): \int_\Omega v = 0\}$. Now one can prove that $a(\cdot, \cdot)$ is $V$-elliptic, and Theorem 3.18 applies. Let us see whether $u$ solves the original problem. If $\phi \in \mathcal{D}(\Omega)$, then $D_i\phi \in V$; hence $a(u, D_i\phi) = L(D_i\phi) \; \forall \phi \in \mathcal{D}(\Omega)$; that is, $-\Delta u = f + c$ for some constant $c$. Moreover, for $v \in V$, we have

$$L(v) = a(u, v) = \int_\Omega (-\Delta u)v + \int_\Gamma v\frac{\partial u}{\partial \nu}$$

$$= \int_\Omega (f + c)v + \int_\Gamma v\frac{\partial u}{\partial \nu} = \int_\Omega fv + \int_\Gamma v\frac{\partial u}{\partial \nu}$$

Thus $\partial u/\partial \nu = g_1$ on $\Gamma$. Let us compute $c$. Integrating the equation $-\Delta u = f + c$ over $\Omega$, we have

$$c \text{ meas } \Omega = -\int_\Omega f + \int_\Omega (-\Delta u) = -\int_\Omega f - \int_\Gamma \frac{\partial u}{\partial \nu} = -\int_\Omega f - \int_\Gamma g_1$$

But the original problem is solved iff $c = 0$, that is, iff $\int_\Omega f + \int_\Gamma g_1 = 0$, in agreement with Example 3.10.

**EXAMPLE 3.37** Theorem 3.18 can be applied even to a *nonuniformly elliptic equation*. Let us see a simple example. Consider the equation $-(xu')' = f$ in $]0, 1[$. Assuming for the sake of simplicity that $u(1) = 0$, the formal energy balance is

$$\int_0^1 x(u')^2 = \int_0^1 fu$$

which suggests the space

$$V = \left\{v \in \mathcal{D}'(0, 1): \int_0^1 x(v')^2 < \infty, v(1) = 0\right\}$$

the form

$$a(u, v) = \int_0^1 xu'v'$$

and the variational formulation

$$u \in V \qquad \text{and} \qquad a(u, v) = \int_0^1 fv \qquad \forall v \in V \qquad \text{where } f \in V'$$

One can prove that $V$ is a Hilbert space with respect to the norm $(a(u, u))^{1/2}$, that $\mathcal{D}(0, 1)$ is dense in $V$ [thus $V' \hookrightarrow \mathcal{D}'(0, 1)$ by Sec. 2.5H in Part 1], and that $V' = \{(\sqrt{x}\psi)': \psi \in L^2(0, 1)\}$. Therefore, taking $f = (\sqrt{x}\psi)'$ with $\psi \in L^2(0, 1)$, Theorem 3.18 applies and our problem has a unique solution $u$, which in particular satisfies

$$\int_0^1 x(u')^2 < \infty \qquad u(1) = 0 \qquad \text{and} \qquad -(xu')' = (\sqrt{x}\psi)'$$

Let us see whether the variational formulation contains further conditions on $u$. By a simple computation one can see that all solutions of the differential equation are given by

$$u(x) = c_1 + c_2 \ln x + \phi(x)$$

where

$$\phi(x) = \int_x^1 t^{-1/2} \psi(t) \, dt$$

Now $u(1) = 0$ means $c_1 = 0$ and one can easily see that $\phi \in V$ and $\ln x \notin V$, so that $u \in V$ means $c_2 = 0$; therefore, no further condition can be given on $u$ and we conclude that $u = \phi$. In particular, no boundary condition is satisfied at $x = 0$; indeed, the choice $\psi(x) = (x^{1/2} \ln (x/2))^{-1}$ gives $u(x) = -\ln |\ln (x/2)|$, which shows that the solution of our problem does not have in general any trace at $x = 0$. This follows from the degeneracy of the ellipticity of the operator at $x = 0$.

**EXAMPLE 3.38**  We want to deal now with a simple example of a *fourth-order elliptic equation* in the two-dimensional case: $\Delta^2 u = f$, where $\Delta^2 = \Delta\Delta = D_1^4 + 2 D_1^2 D_2^2 + D_2^4$. The energy balance suggests that the norm of $V$ must involve second derivatives; hence we look for spaces $V$ with $H_0^2 \hookrightarrow V \hookrightarrow H^2$. Choose first $V = H_0^2(\Omega)$. There are many possibilities for the bilinear form $a(\cdot, \cdot)$; for instance, $a(u, v) = \int (1-\sigma) \Sigma D_i D_j u D_i D_j v + \sigma \Delta u \Delta v)$ works and is $V$-elliptic for any $\sigma \in \mathbb{R}$. The condition $u \in V$ implies the two boundary conditions $u = \partial u / \partial \nu = 0$ on $\Gamma$. Choose now $V = H^2(\Omega) \cap H_0^1(\Omega)$. The above choice for $a(\cdot, \cdot)$ still gives $V$-ellipticity at least for $0 \leqslant \sigma \leqslant 1$. Now the condition $u \in V$ only involves $u = 0$ on $\Gamma$ and one expects a further boundary condition to emerge naturally from the variational formulation by means of Green's formula. Indeed one gets $M_\nu(u) \equiv (1-\sigma) \Sigma \nu_i \nu_j D_i D_j u + \sigma \Delta u = 0$ on $\Gamma$. Notice that this last condition depends on $\sigma$ and hence on the choice of $a(\cdot, \cdot)$ (see also Example 2.44 in Part 1). Many other choices are obviously possible for $V$ and $a(\cdot, \cdot)$, still being careful with the $V$-ellipticity condition. A third good choice is, for instance, $V = \{v \in H^2(\Omega): v = \partial v / \partial \nu = 0 \text{ on } \Gamma_0\}$ (with $\Gamma_0 \subset \Gamma$) and $a(\cdot, \cdot)$ as above. The corresponding natural conditions on $\Gamma \backslash \bar\Gamma_0$ are $M_\nu(u) = 0$ and $K_\nu(u) \equiv \partial \Delta u / \partial \nu + (1-\sigma) \Sigma \nu_i \tau_j \tau_k D_i D_j D_k u = 0$, where $\tau = (-\nu_2, \nu_1)$, which again depends on $\sigma$.

The same arguments apply to the corresponding evolution equations $u_t + \Delta^2 u = f$ and $u_{tt} + \Delta^2 u = f$.

**EXAMPLE 3.39**  Consider the *elliptic system* in the two unknowns $u^1(x_1, x_2)$, $u^2(x_1, x_2)$:

$$D_1^2 u^1 + \frac{1-\sigma}{2} D_2^2 u^1 - \frac{1-\sigma}{2} D_1 D_2 u^2 = f_1$$

$$\text{in } \Omega$$

$$\frac{1-\sigma}{2} D_1^2 u^2 + D_2^2 u^2 - \frac{1-\sigma}{2} D_1 D_2 u^1 = f_2$$

Taking $V = H_0^1(\Omega) \times H_0^1(\Omega)$ (which means homogeneous Dirichlet boundary conditions $u^1 = u^2 = 0$ on $\Gamma$) and $a(u, v) = \int \{(D_1 u^1 - \sigma D_2 u^2) D_1 v^1 - (\sigma D_1 u^1 - D_2 u^2) D_2 v^2 + 2^{-1}(1-\sigma)(D_2 u^1 - D_1 u^2) \times (D_2 v^1 - D_1 v^2)\}$, we have $V$-ellipticity from (the nontrivial!) Korn's inequality. The same result holds for $V = \{v \in H^1(\Omega) \times H^1(\Omega): v = 0 \text{ on } \Gamma_0\}$ (with $\Gamma_0 \subset \Gamma$); in this case a Neumann condition on $\Gamma \backslash \bar\Gamma_0$ appears, namely, $(D_1 u^1 - \sigma D_2 u^2) \nu_1 + 2^{-1}(1-\sigma)(D_2 u^1 - D_1 u^2) \nu_2 = -(\sigma D_1 u^1 - D_2 u^2) \nu_2 - 2^{-1}(1-\sigma) \times (D_2 u^1 - D_1 u^2) \nu_1 = 0$.

**EXAMPLE 3.40**  In all the previous examples $V$ was a functional space of infinite dimension. Assume here that $V = \mathbb{R}^n$. Then $a(\cdot, \cdot)$ has the form $a(u, v) = v^t A u$ with $A = n \times n$-matrix; Theorem 3.18 applies when $A$ is positive-definite and gives the solution of the system $Au = b$ for a given $b \in \mathbb{R}^n$. Let us consider now the corresponding evolution problems (with $V = H = \mathbb{R}^n$) $u'(t) + A(t)u(t) = b(t)$ and $u''(t) + A(t)u(t) = b(t)$. According to Rem. 3.26 we only need that the coefficient $A_{ij}(t)$ belong to

$L^\infty(0, T)$ and $W^{1,\infty}(0, T)$, respectively. As a by-product we have $u'A(t)u \geq -M\|u\|^2$, that is, (3.105) is always satisfied; moreover we can take $a_0 = 0$ in Rem. 3.25 and thus forget (3.109). We have in this way existence and uniqueness results for Cauchy problems for systems of *ordinary differential equations*.

### 3.5D Variational Inequalities

It is well known that the solution $u$ of the problem $-\Delta u = f$ in $\Omega$, $u = 0$ on $\Gamma$, with a given $f$, say, $f \in L^2(\Omega)$, minimizes the quadratic functional

$$J(v) = \tfrac{1}{2} \int_\Omega |\nabla u|^2 - \int_\Omega fv \tag{3.119}$$

on the space $H_0^1(\Omega)$. More generally, consider on a Hilbert space $V$ the *quadratic functional*

$$J(v) = \tfrac{1}{2}a(v, v) - L(v) \tag{3.120}$$

where $a(\cdot, \cdot)$ is a continuous bilinear form on $V \times V$ and $L \in V'$.

**THEOREM 3.21**   If $a(\cdot, \cdot)$ is $V$-elliptic [see (3.99)], then $J$ has a unique minimum $u$ on $V$. Moreover, $u$ satisfies

$$u \in V \quad \text{and} \quad a_s(u, v) = L(v) \quad \forall v \in V \tag{3.121}$$

where $a_s(u, v) = (a(u, v) + a(v, u))/2$.

In many applications one meets minimum problems with constraints; this means that the minimum has to be sought in a subset $K$ of $V$.

**THEOREM 3.22**   Let $V$ be a Hilbert space, $a(\cdot, \cdot)$ a continuous bilinear form on $V \times V$, and $K$ a nonempty closed convex subset of $V$. Set $K - K = \{v_1 - v_2: v_i \in K\}$ (in agreement with Def. 1.13 in Part 1) and assume the following $(K - K)$-ellipticity condition:

$$\exists \alpha_* > 0: a(v, v) \geq \alpha_* \|v\|_V^2 \quad \forall v \in K - K \tag{3.122}$$

Then for every $L \in V'$ there exists a unique $u \in K$ which minimizes (3.120) on $K$. Moreover, $u$ satisfies

$$u \in K \quad \text{and} \quad a_s(u, u - v) \leq L(u - v) \quad \forall v \in K \tag{3.123}$$

with $a_s$ as in Theorem 3.21.

In the literature, (3.123) is called a *variational inequality*. As in Theorem 3.18, we could consider the case of a nonsymmetric form $a(\cdot, \cdot)$.

**THEOREM 3.23**   *Lions–Stampacchia*. Under the assumptions of Theorem 3.22, for any $L \in V'$ there exists a unique $u$ satisfying the variational inequality

$$u \in K \quad \text{and} \quad a(u, u - v) \leq L(u - v) \quad \forall v \in K \tag{3.124}$$

Moreover, if $u_1$ and $u_2$ are the solutions corresponding to $L_1$ and $L_2$, respectively, we have the estimate

$$\|u_1 - u_2\|_V \leq \frac{1}{\alpha_*}\|L_1 - L_2\|_{V'} \tag{3.125}$$

**REMARK 3.29** It is worth noting that if $a \neq a_s$, both Theorems 3.22 and 3.23 provide a unique solution which, in general, is not the same.

**REMARK 3.30** In Theorem 3.23 one could assume the boundedness of $K$ and $\alpha_* \geq 0$ in (3.122). In this case we still have existence, but not uniqueness. On the contrary, if (3.122) does not hold and $K$ is unbounded, even existence will fail: take $K = V = \mathbb{R}^2$ and $a(u, v) = u_1 v_1$, $L(v) = v_2$.

**REMARK 3.31** In Theorem 3.23 the variational inequality (3.124) can be replaced by

$$u \in K \quad \text{and} \quad a(v, u - v) \leq L(u - v) \quad \forall v \in K \tag{3.126}$$

Indeed, more generally, whenever $a(v, v) \geq 0 \; \forall v \in K - K$, (3.124) holds iff (3.126) holds (Minty's trick).

**REMARK 3.32** If $0 \in K$ and $2K \subset K$ (see Def. 1.13 in Part 1), i.e., if $K$ is a *cone*, then (3.124) is equivalent to

$$u \in K \quad a(u, u) = L(u) \quad \text{and} \quad a(u, v) \geq L(v) \quad \forall v \in K \tag{3.127}$$

**REMARK 3.33** If $K$ has the form $K = v_0 + V_0$ (see Def. 1.13 in Part 1), with $v_0 \in V$ and $V_0$ a closed subspace of $V$, then $K - K = V_0$ and (3.124) is equivalent to

$$u \in K \quad \text{and} \quad a(u, v) = L(v) \quad \forall v \in V_0 \tag{3.128}$$

Even in this case one can find extensions of Theorem 3.23 to evolution problems. Some of those results are listed in the following theorems.

**THEOREM 3.24** Let $V \hookrightarrow H \hookrightarrow V'$ be a Hilbert triplet (see Sec. 1.4G in Part 1) and $a(\cdot, \cdot)$ a $V$-elliptic symmetric continuous bilinear form on $V \times V$. Let $K$ be a nonempty closed convex subset of $V$ and $\tilde{K}$ its closure in $H$. Then for every $u_0 \in \tilde{K}$ and $f \in L^2(0, T; H)$ there exists a unique $u$ satisfying

$$u \in L^2(0, T; V) \cap C^0([0, T]; H) \qquad t^{1/2}u' \in L^2(0, T; H) \qquad u(0) = u_0$$

$$u(t) \in K \quad \text{and} \quad \langle u'(t), u(t) - v \rangle + a(u(t), u(t) - v) \leq \langle f(t), u(t) - v \rangle \tag{3.129}$$

$$\forall v \in K \text{ almost everywhere in } ]0, T[$$

If, in addition, $f' \in L^1(0, T; H)$, then for every $t \in ]0, T[$, $u(t) \in K$, and the right derivative, $u'_+(t)$ exists and $tu' \in L^\infty(0, T; H)$.

**THEOREM 3.25** With the same assumptions and notations as in Theorem 3.24, for every $u_0 \in V$ and $L \in H^1(0, T; V')$, there exists a unique $u$ satisfying

$$u \in C^0([0, T]; V) \cap H^1(0, T; H) \qquad t^{1/2}u' \in L^2(0, T; V) \qquad u(0) = u_0$$

$$u'(t) \in K \quad \text{and} \quad \langle u'(t), u'(t) - v \rangle + a(u(t), u'(t) - v) \leq \langle L(t), u'(t) - v \rangle \tag{3.130}$$

$$\forall v \in K \text{ almost everywhere in } ]0, T[$$

If, in addition, $L \in H^2(0, T; V')$, then $tu' \in L^\infty(0, T; V')$.

**THEOREM 3.26**  With the same assumptions and notations as in Theorem 3.24, for every triplet $u_0 \in V$, $u_1 \in K$, $f \in H^1(0, T; H)$ such that

$$\exists w \in H: \langle w, u_1 - v \rangle \geq a(u_0, u_1 - v) \qquad \forall v \in K \tag{3.131}$$

there exists a unique $u$ satisfying

$$u \in W^{1,\infty}(0, T; V) \cap W^{2,\infty}(0, T; H) \qquad u(0) = u_0 \qquad u'(0) = u_1$$

$$u'(t) \in K \qquad \forall t \in [0, T] \tag{3.132}$$

$$\langle u''(t), u'(t) - v \rangle + a(u(t), u'(t) - v) \leq \langle f(t), u'(t) - v \rangle \qquad \forall v \in K \text{ almost everywhere in } ]0, T[$$

**REMARK 3.34**  A sufficient condition for (3.131) is $|a(u_0, v)| \leq M\|v\|_H \; \forall v \in V$, which in applications generally means a regularity assumption on $u_0$ (e.g., if $V = H_0^1$, $H = L^2$, and $a(u, v) = \int \nabla u \cdot \nabla v$, it means indeed $u_0 \in H^2$).

Moreover the $V$-ellipticity condition in Theorem 3.26 can be replaced by the weaker assumption (3.105).

## 3.5E Examples

**EXAMPLE 3.41**  The convexity assumption on $K$ is essential. On the one hand, trivial examples of nonuniqueness for a nonconvex $K$ can be given (e.g., $V = \mathbb{R}$, $K = \{-1, 1\}$, $J = x^2$). On the other hand, the existence of a minimizing $u$ can be proved for a nonconvex $K$ only in the finite-dimensional case. Consider, for instance, the following example: $V = L^2(0, 1)$, $K = \{v \in V: \|v\| = 1\}$, $L = 0$, and $a(u, v) = 2 \int (1+x)uv$, which clearly satisfies all assumptions of Theorem 3.23. Now $J(v) > \|v\|^2 = 1 \; \forall v \in K$ and $J(v_n) \to 1$, where $v_n(x) = n^{1/2}$ if $0 < x < 1/n$ or $= 0$ otherwise. Thus no minimizing $u \in K$ exists.

**EXAMPLE 3.42**  Consider the particular case where $a(\cdot, \cdot)$ is the scalar product of $V$. Let $w \in V$ be given. We want to minimize on $K$ the functional $\|v - w\|$. Since $w$ is fixed, this is clearly equivalent to minimizing $J(v) = (\|v - w\|_V^2 - \|w\|_V^2)/2 = 2^{-1}a(v, v) - (w, v)_V$, which has the form (3.120). Hence Theorem 3.22 ensures existence and uniqueness of a solution $u \in K$ that we call the *projection of $w$ on $K$*. Moreover, (3.125) becomes now $\|u_1 - u_2\|_V \leq \|w_1 - w_2\|_V$ (with obvious notations). Note that this agrees with Theorem 1.34 in Part 1 when $K$ is a closed subspace of $V$.

**EXAMPLE 3.43**  Take in Example 3.42 $V = L^2(\Omega)$ and $K = \{v \in V: v \geq 0\}$. The projection of $w$ on $K$ is $u = w^+$. More generally, if $\psi \in V$ and $K = \{v \in V: v \geq \psi$ (respectively, $v \leq \psi)\}$, the projection of $w$ on $K$ is $u = \max \{w, \psi\}$ (respectively, $u = \min \{w, \psi\}$). It is natural to ask whether for smoother $w$ and $\psi$ the corresponding $u$ is smooth. This is not the case in general; if $\Omega = ]-1, 1[$, $\psi = 0$, and $w(x) = x$, then $u(x) = x^+$, which does not belong to $W^{1+1/p,p}(-1, 1)$ ($1 \leq p < \infty$; see Example 2.28 in Part 1), nor to $C^1(-1, 1)$. However, one can see that $w, \psi \in W^{s,p}(\Omega)$ implies $u \in W^{s,p}(\Omega)$, $0 \leq s \leq 1$, $1 \leq p \leq \infty$. It is a "common belief" (unproved to our knowledge) that $w, \psi \in W^{s,p}(\Omega)$ implies $u \in W^{s,p}(\Omega)$, for $1 < s < 1 + 1/p$ and $1 \leq p < \infty$.

**EXAMPLE 3.44**  Consider the *nonhomogeneous Dirichlet problem* $Au = f$ in $\Omega$, $u = g_0$ on $\Gamma$, where $A$ is the elliptic operator associated with a bilinear form $a(\cdot, \cdot)$ as in (3.12), with $a_{ij}, b_i, c_i, d \in L^\infty(\Omega)$, which we assume to be $H_0^1(\Omega)$-elliptic. Suppose $f \in H^{-1}(\Omega)$ and $g_0 \in H^{1/2}(\Gamma)$ and let $v_0 \in H^1(\Omega)$ be such that $v_0|_\Gamma = g_0$. The variational formulation of the problem is obtained from Rem. 3.33 with $V = H^1(\Omega)$, $V_0 = H_0^1(\Omega)$, and $L(v) = \int fv$. In a similar way, one can deal with the mixed problem (see also Example 3.33) with a nonhomogeneous condition on $\Gamma_0$.

The following examples illustrate some particular choices of $K$ which are interesting in the applications. In all the following cases we assume that $a(\cdot,\cdot)$ is given by (3.12) with $L^\infty$-coefficients, $V = H^1(\Omega)$, and $a(\cdot,\cdot)$ is $(K-K)$-elliptic.

**EXAMPLE 3.45**  Assume that $\psi \in H^1(\Omega)$, $g_0 \in H^{1/2}(\Gamma)$, $f \in H^{-1}(\Omega)$, set $L(v) = \int fv$ and $K = \{v \in V : v \geqslant \psi$ and $v|_\Gamma = g_0\}$, and assume $\psi|_\Gamma \leqslant g_0$; hence $K \neq \varnothing$. Indeed, take $w \in H^1(\Omega)$ with $w|_\Gamma = g_0$ and note that $\max\{w, \psi\} \in K$ by Example 3.43. One can show that the unique solution $u$ of (3.124) satisfies $u \in H^1(\Omega)$, $u|_\Gamma = g_0$, and

$$u \geqslant \psi \qquad Au \geqslant f \qquad \text{and} \qquad Au = f \text{ in } \Omega^+ \equiv \{x \in \Omega : u(x) > \psi(x)\} \qquad (3.133)$$

The last property of (3.133) is formal; however, its meaning is clear whenever $u, \psi \in C^0(\Omega)$ since $\Omega^+$ becomes an open set. More generally, see Rem. 3.35. If $\Gamma$, the coefficient of $a(\cdot,\cdot)$, and the data are smoother, $u$ is also smoother up to the limit regularity $W^{s,p}(\Omega)$, $s < 2 + 1/p$, $1 \leqslant p < \infty$. In particular, the $W^{s,p}$-regularity, with $p < \infty$, is an easy consequence of Theorem 3.2 and of the Lewy–Stampacchia inequality

$$f \leqslant Au \leqslant \max\{f; A\psi\} \qquad (3.134)$$

To illustrate the upper bound for the regularity of $u$, consider the case where $\Omega = {]-1, 1[}$, $a(u, v) = \int u'v'$, $\psi = 0$, $f = 2$, $g_0(-1) = 0$, and $g_0(1) = 1$. Then $u(x) = (x^+)^2$, whose regularity is given by Example 2.28.

**REMARK 3.35**  The *complementarity conditions* (3.133) are particular cases of the following more general situations. Assume that $K$ has the following property: there exists a set $\Phi$ of smooth functions such that $v \in K$ implies $v + \phi \in K \ \forall \phi \in \Phi$; then the solution $u$ verifies

$$a(u, \phi) \geqslant L(\phi) \qquad \forall \phi \in \Phi \qquad (3.135)$$

Assume now that the solution $u$ satisfies for some $x_0 \in \bar\Omega$ and $\delta > 0$ the following property: $\forall \phi \in \mathscr{D}(B_\delta(x_0)) \ \exists \varepsilon > 0$ such that $u \pm \varepsilon\phi \in K$; then

$$a(u, \phi) = L(\phi) \qquad \forall \phi \in \mathscr{D}(B_\delta(x_0)) \qquad (3.136)$$

In the particular case of Ex. 3.45 one can take $\Phi = \{\phi \in \mathscr{D}(\Omega) : \phi \geqslant 0\}$, and (3.135) gives $Au \geqslant f$ (see Def. 3.2). If, in addition, $u, \psi \in C^0(\Omega)$ and $u(x_0) > \psi(x_0)$, one can take $B_\delta(x_0) \subset \Omega^+$, and (3.136) gives $Au = f$ in $B_\delta(x_0)$.

**EXAMPLE 3.46**  Another example of interest is obtained by choosing

$$K = \{v \in V : v|_\Gamma \geqslant g_0\} \qquad \text{and} \qquad L(v) = \int_\Omega fv + \int_\Gamma g_1 v$$

with $g_0 \in H^{1/2}(\Gamma)$, $f \in H^{-1/2}(\Omega)$, and $g_1 \in H^{-1/2}(\Gamma)$. The arguments of Rem. 3.35 give: $Au = f$ in $\Omega$ [take $\Phi = \mathscr{D}(\Omega)$ in (3.135)], $\partial u/\partial \nu_A \geqslant g_1$ [take now $\Phi = \{\phi \in C^\infty(\Omega) : \phi \geqslant 0$ on $\Gamma\}$ and use Green's formula], $u \geqslant g_0$ on $\Gamma$ (since $u \in K$), and $\partial u/\partial \nu_A = g_1$ on $\Gamma^+ \equiv \{x \in \Gamma : u(x) > g_0(x)\}$ formally [if $u \in C^0(\bar\Omega)$ and $g_0 \in C^0(\Gamma)$, argue as before]. Hence $u$ is the solution of the so-called *Signorini problem*. Even in this case we have an upper bound for the regularity of $u$. For instance, $u(x) = -\rho^{3/2}\sin(3\theta/2)$ satisfies near the origin in $\mathbb{R}_+^2$: $-\Delta u = 0$, $u(x_1, 0) = 0$ and $-D_2 u(x_1, 0) > 0$ for $x_1 > 0$, and $u(x_1, 0) > 0$ and $-D_2 u(x_1, 0) = 0$ for $x_1 < 0$; its regularity is $u \in W^{s,p}$ iff $s < \frac{3}{2} + 1/p$, $u \in C^{1,\alpha}$ iff $\alpha \leqslant \frac{1}{2}$. However, in the general case, it has been proved that for smooth data $u \in W^{1+2/p,p}$ ($1 \leqslant p < \infty$) and $u \in C^{1,\alpha}$ for some $\alpha > 0$.

**EXAMPLE 3.47**   Take $K = \{v \in H^1(\Omega): v \geq \psi\}$ and $L(v) = \int_\Omega fv + \int_\Gamma g_1 v$ with $\psi \in H^1(\Omega)$, $f \in H^{-1/2}(\Omega)$, and $g_1 \in H^{-1/2}(\Gamma)$. With the arguments of the previous examples one can show that $u$ satisfies $u \geq \psi$ in $\Omega$, $Au \geq f$ in $\Omega$, $Au = f$ in $\Omega^+ = \{u > \psi\}$, $u \geq \psi$ on $\Gamma$, $\partial u/\partial \nu_A \geq g_1$ on $\Gamma$, $\partial u/\partial \nu_A = g_1$ in $\Gamma^+ = \Gamma \cap \{u > \psi\}$.

**EXAMPLE 3.48**   Take $\Omega = ]0, 1[$, $a(u, v) = \int u'v'$, $K = \{v \in H_0^1(0, 1): v \geq \psi\}$ with $\psi(x) = (x - x^2)^{1/2}$, and $L = 0$. Then (3.124) has no solution! Indeed $K$ is *empty*. In fact, $v \in H_0^1(0, 1)$ implies

$$\int_0^{1/2} x^{-2} v^2 < \infty$$

by Theorem 2.16; on the other hand, $v \geq \psi$ implies

$$\int_0^{1/2} x^{-2} v^2 \geq \int_0^{1/2} x^{-2} \psi^2 = \infty$$

**EXAMPLE 3.49**   Another application of (3.136) is given as follows: take $K = \{v \in H_0^1(\Omega): |\nabla v| \leq 1\}$ and $L(v) = \int fv$. If $u \in C^1(\Omega)$ and $|\nabla u| < 1$ at $x_0 \in \Omega$, then $Au = f$ near $x_0$.

**EXAMPLE 3.50**   One can also consider the version of the above examples in the case of evolution problems. Consider, for instance, (3.129) with $V = H_0^1(\Omega)$, $H = L^2(\Omega)$, $K = \{v \in V: v \geq \psi\}$, $L(v) = \int_Q fv$, with, for example, $\psi \in H_0^1(\Omega)$, $f \in L^2(Q)$. Now $\tilde{K} = \{v \in H: v \geq \psi\}$. Then, if $u_0 \in \tilde{K}$, we have a unique solution $u$ which satisfies

$$u(x, t) \geq \psi(x) \qquad u_t(x, t) + Au(x, t) \geq f(x, t) \qquad u(x, 0) = u_0(x)$$
$$u_t(x, t) + Au(x, t) = f(x, t) \qquad \text{where } u(x, t) > \psi(x) \tag{3.137}$$

using arguments similar to those in Rem. 3.35.


## 3.6 REFERENCES

1. Agmon, S., *Lectures on Elliptic Boundary Value Problems*, Van Nostrand, Princeton, N.J., 1965.

2. Baiocchi, C., and A. Capelo, *Variational and Quasivariational Inequalities, Applications to Free Boundary Problems*, Wiley, Chichester, 1983.

3. Barbu, V., *Nonlinear Semigroups and Differential Equations in Banach Spaces*, Academiei Bucureşti/Noordhoff, Leyden, 1976.

4. Brezis, H., *Analyse Fonctionnelle: Théorie et Applications*, Masson, Paris, 1983.

5. Duvaut, G., and J. L. Lions, *Inequalities in Mechanics and Physics*, Springer, Berlin, 1976. (French ed., Dunod, Paris, 1972.)

6. Ekeland, I., and R. Temam, *Analyse Convexe et Problèmes Variationnels*, Dunod/Gauthier-Villars, Paris, 1974.

7. Friedman, A., *Partial Differential Equations of Parabolic Type*, Prentice-Hall, Englewood Cliffs, N.J., 1964.

8. Friedman, A., *Variational Principles and Free Boundary Problems*, Wiley, New York, 1982.

9. Giaquinta, M., *Multiple Integrals in the Calculus of Variations and Nonlinear Elliptic Systems*, Princeton University Press, Princeton, 1983.

10. Gilbarg, D., and N. S. Trudinger, *Elliptic Partial Differential Equations of Second Order*, Springer, Berlin, 1977.

11. Kinderlehrer, D., and G. Stampacchia, *An Introduction to Variational Inequalities and Their Applications*, Academic Press, New York, 1980.

12. Ladyženskaja, O. A., V. A. Solonnikov, and N. N. Ural'ceva, "Equations de types Paraboliques Linéaires et Quasi-Linéaires," *Translations*, **23**, American Mathematical Society, Providence, R.I., 1968.

13. Ladyženskaja, O. A., and N. N. Ural'ceva, *Equations aux Dérivées Partielles de Type Elliptique*, Dunod, Paris, 1968. (Russian ed., Nauka, Moscow, 1964.)

14. Lions, J. L., *Equations Différentielles Operationnelles et Problèmes aux Limites*, Springer, Berlin, 1961.

15. Lions, J. L., and E. Magenes, *Non-Homogeneous Boundary Value Problems and Applications*, vols. I and II, Springer, Berlin, 1972. (French ed., Dunod, Paris, 1968.)

16. Miranda, C., *Partial Differential Equations of Elliptic Type*, 2d ed., Springer, Berlin, 1970.

17. Mizohata, S., *The Theory of Partial Differential Equations*, Cambridge University Press, Cambridge, 1973.

18. Morrey, C. N., "Multiple integrals in the Calculus of Variations," *Grundlehren*, **130**, Springer, Berlin, 1966.

19. Nečas, J., *Les Méthodes Directes en Théorie des Equations Elliptiques*, Masson, Paris, Academia, Prague, 1967.

20. Pazy, A., *Semigroups of Linear Operators and Applications to Partial Differential Equations*, Springer, Berlin, 1983.

21. Protter, M. H., and H. F. Weinberger, *Maximum Principles in Differential Equations*, Prentice-Hall, Englewood Cliffs, N.J., 1967.

22. Schechter, M., *Modern Methods in Partial Differential Equations: An Introduction*, McGraw-Hill, New York, 1977.

# CHAPTER 4
# FINITE ELEMENT APPROXIMATION THEORY

This chapter is an introduction to finite elements and their assembly into finite element subspaces, and to the important idea of affine-equivalent finite elements. An outline of the concise and elegant interpolation theory which can be developed for affine-equivalent finite elements and for finite elements of class $\mathscr{C}^1$ which are "almost affine-equivalent" is then given. This theory has proved to be a pervading tool in the numerical analysis of various aspects of the finite-element method: isoparametric and curved finite elements, singular and rational finite elements, composite finite elements, numerical integration, nonconforming methods, and so forth.

## 4.1 THE FINITE-ELEMENT METHOD IN ITS SIMPLEST FORM

Consider the following abstract problem: Find $u \in V$ such that

$$\forall v \in V \qquad a(u, v) = f(v) \tag{4.1}$$

where the space $V$, the bilinear form $a(\cdot, \cdot)$, and the linear form $f$ satisfy the hypotheses of the Lax–Milgram lemma. The space $V$ is a Hilbert space, the bilinear form is continuous $[|a(u, v)| \leq M \|u\| \|v\|$ for all $u, v \in V]$ and $V$-elliptic [there exists $\alpha > 0$ such that $a(v, v) \geq \alpha \|v\|^2$ for all $v \in V]$, and the linear form is continuous.

A conforming approximate method for solving problem (4.1) consists of finding an *approximate* solution $u_h$ in a finite-dimensional subspace $V_h$ of the space $V$, $u_h$ being the solution of the following problem:

$$\forall v_h \in V_h \qquad a(u_h, v_h) = f(v_h) \tag{4.2}$$

That this problem has one and only one solution follows from the Lax-Milgram lemma.

Denoting by $\| \ \|$ the norm in $V$, we now turn to the problem of estimating the error $\|u - u_h\|$.

**THEOREM 4.1**   There exists a constant $C$ independent of the subspace $V_h$ such that

$$\|u - u_h\| \le C \inf_{v_h \in V_h} \|u - v_h\| \tag{4.3}$$

*Proof*   Let $w_h$ be an arbitrary element in $V_h$. It follows from (4.1) and (4.2) that $a(u - u_h, w_h) = 0$. Thus we have, for any $v_h \in V_h$,

$$\alpha \|u - u_h\|^2 \le a(u - u_h, u - u_h) = a(u - u_h, u - v_h) \le M \|u - u_h\| \|u - v_h\|$$

and the conclusion follows with $C = M/\alpha$.

The above result shows that the problem of estimating the error is thus reduced to a problem in approximation theory, namely, to evaluate the distance between the solution $u$ and the subspace $V_h$.

**REMARK 4.1**   In the case where the bilinear form is symmetric, the above method is known as the *Rayleigh–Ritz–Galerkin method.* Then the approximate solution $u_h$ also satisfies

$$J(u_h) = \min_{v_h \in V_h} J(v_h) \qquad \text{with} \qquad J(v) = \tfrac{1}{2} a(v, v) - f(v) \tag{4.4}$$

In addition, there is, in this case, a remarkable interpretation of the approximate solution: Since we have $a(u - u_h, w_h) = 0$ for all $w_h \in V_h$, it follows that $u_h$ is the projection over $V_h$ of the exact solution $u$, with respect to the inner product $a(\cdot, \cdot)$. Thus

$$a(u - u_h, u - u_h) = \inf_{v_h \in V_h} a(u - v_h, u - v_h)$$

Using the $V$-ellipticity and the continuity of the bilinear form, we deduce

$$\|u - u_h\| \le \sqrt{\frac{M}{\alpha}} \inf_{v_h \in V_h} \|u - v_h\| \tag{4.5}$$

which is an inequality *better* than (4.3) since we always have $M \ge \alpha$.

**REMARK 4.2**   Without any further assumption, we can see that the approximate solutions are bounded independently of the subspace $V_h$ (the *stability* condition):

$$\alpha \|u_h\|^2 \le a(u_h, u_h) = f(u_h) \le \|f\|_* \|u_h\|$$

In the case of a symmetrical bilinear form (cf. Rem. 4.1), this is even simpler to prove since we have in this case

$$a(u_h, u_h) \le a(u, u)$$

by a well-known property of the projection operator.

The *finite-element method*, in its simplest form at least, is a conforming approximate method in which the subspaces $V_h$ are of a particular form. To be more specific, assume that we are approximating a second-order elliptic equation, so that we are facing the problem of constructing a finite-dimensional subspace of the space $H^1(\Omega)$ or $H_0^1(\Omega)$.

Let us assume that the set $\bar{\Omega}$ is a polygon in $R^2$. Then we establish a *triangulation* $\mathscr{T}_h$ over the set $\bar{\Omega}$; i.e., the set $\bar{\Omega}$ is expressed as a finite union $\bigcup_{T \in \mathscr{T}_h}$ of triangles T in such a way that whenever $T_1$ and $T_2$ are two distinct triangles of $\mathscr{T}_h$, their intersection is either empty, or a vertex common to $T_1$ and $T_2$, or an edge common to $T_1$ and $T_2$. In the latter case, the two triangles are said to be *adjacent*. Figure 4.1 shows an example of a *forbidden* situation

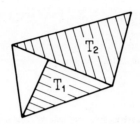

**FIG. 4.1**  Forbidden triangulation.

since the intersection of $T_1$ and $T_2$ is not an edge of $T_2$. With such a triangulation is associated a space $V_h$ of functions defined over $\bar{\Omega}$ whose restrictions to each triangle T belong to a finite-dimensional space $P_T$ of functions defined over the set T. Up to this point, the space $V_h$ is thus dependent upon a given triangulation $\mathscr{T}_h$ and the spaces $P_T$, $T \in \mathscr{T}$. Of course, even if the spaces $P_T$ consist of very smooth functions, there is no reason why the inclusion $V_h \subset H^1(\Omega)$ should hold. Hence an additional condition is needed, as the following simple result shows.

**THEOREM 4.2**  Assume that the inclusions $P_T \subset H^1(\overset{\circ}{T})$ for all $T \in \mathscr{T}_h$ and $V_h \subset \mathscr{C}^0(\bar{\Omega})$ hold. Then the inclusion $V_h \subset H^1(\Omega)$ holds. If, in addition, the functions in $V_h$ vanish along the boundary of the set $\Omega$, then the inclusion $V_h \subset H_0^1(\Omega)$ holds.

**Proof**  Let $v \in V_h$ be given. By definition of the space $H^1(\Omega)$, we must find, for $i = 1$ and 2, a function $v_i \in L^2(\Omega)$ such that

$$\forall \varphi \in \mathscr{D}(\Omega) \qquad \int_\Omega v_i \varphi \, dx = - \int_\Omega v \frac{\partial \varphi}{\partial x_i} \, dx$$

A natural candidate is the function whose restriction to each triangle T is the function $\partial(v|_T)/\partial x_i$. Since a triangle T has a Lipschitz-continuous boundary $\partial T$, we may apply Green's formula (cf. Sec. 2.9H in Part 1). For each $T \in \mathscr{T}_h$, we have

$$\int_T \frac{\partial(v|_T)}{\partial x_i} \varphi \, dx = - \int_T v|_T \frac{\partial \varphi}{\partial x_i} \, dx + \int_{\partial T} \varphi v_{i,T} \, d\gamma$$

where $v_{i,T}$ is the $i^{\text{th}}$ component of the outer normal vector along T. By summing over all triangles, we obtain

$$\int_\Omega v_i \varphi \, dx = \int_\Omega v \frac{\partial \varphi}{\partial x_i} \, dx + \sum_{T \in \mathscr{T}_h} \int_{\partial T} v|_T \varphi \nu_{i,T} \, d\gamma$$

and the proof follows if we notice that the sum

$$\sum_{T \in \mathscr{T}_h} \int_{\partial T} v|_T \varphi \nu_{i,T} \, d\gamma$$

vanishes: Either a portion of $\partial T$ is a portion of the boundary $\Gamma$ of $\Omega$, in which case $\varphi = 0$ along this portion, or the contribution of adjacent triangles is zero.

The boundary of a polygon being Lipschitz-continuous, the second part of the theorem follows from the characterization of the space $H_0^1(\Omega)$ (cf. Sec. 2.9ı in Part 1).

**REMARK 4.3**   We have given the proof in such a way that it readily extends to sets $\bar{\Omega}$ in $R^n$ which are finite unions of subsets with Lipschitz-continuous boundaries. We could likewise prove the following theorem.

**THEOREM 4.3**   Assume that the inclusions $P_T \subset H^2(\mathring{T})$ for all $T \in \mathscr{T}_h$ and $V_h \subset \mathscr{C}^1(\bar{\Omega})$ hold. Then the inclusion $V_h \subset H^2(\Omega)$ holds. If, in addition, the functions in $V_h$ and their normal derivative vanish along the boundary of the set $\Omega$, then the inclusion $V_h \subset H_0^2(\Omega)$ holds.

Finally, let us say a few words about how the discrete problem (4.2) is solved in practice. Let $(w_j)_{j=1}^M$ be a basis in $V_h$; then the solution $u_h = \sum_{j=1}^M u_j w_j$ of problem (4.2) is obtained by solving the linear system

$$\sum_{j=1}^M a(w_j, w_i) u_j = f(w_i) \qquad 1 \le i \le M \tag{4.6}$$

whose matrix is always invertible. When the bilinear form is symmetric, the matrix $(a(w_j, w_i))$ is also symmetric and positive-definite (in contrast to matrices arising from finite-difference methods over other than rectangular regions). This is an advantage for the numerical solution of system (4.6). In the choice of the basis $(w_j)_{j=1}^M$, it is of paramount importance, again from a numerical standpoint, that the resulting matrix possess as many zeros as possible. In practice, the coefficients of the matrix are integrals; in the case of the elliptic operator $-\Delta u + bu$, we have, for instance (cf. Chap. 5 in Part 1),

$$a(w_j, w_i) = \sum_{T \in \mathscr{T}_h} \int_T \left( \frac{\partial w_j}{\partial x_1} \frac{\partial w_i}{\partial x_1} + \frac{\partial w_j}{\partial x_2} \frac{\partial w_i}{\partial x_2} + b w_j w_i \right) dx$$

Thus $a(w_j, w_i) = 0$ whenever the intersection of the supports of $w_j$ and $w_i$ is of measure zero. As a consequence, we shall try to have basis functions $w_j$ whose supports are as small as possible.

## 4.2. EXAMPLES OF FINITE ELEMENTS

Before we give some examples, let us summarize the various requirements that a subspace $V_h$, as constructed in Sect. 4.1, should satisfy in order to be a good candidate for the finite-element method.

1. For all $T \in \mathcal{T}_h$, the space $P_T$ must consist of *polynomials,* for two reasons: First, this fact will be essential in proving the convergence of the method (cf. Chap. 5 in Part 1), and secondly, it has the obvious advantage of yielding simple computations for the coefficients of the linear system (4.6).

2. In view of Theorems 4.2 and 4.3, inclusions such as $V_h \subset \mathcal{C}^0(\bar{\Omega})$ or $V_h \subset \mathcal{C}^1(\bar{\Omega})$, depending essentially upon whether we are solving a second-order problem or a fourth-order problem, should hold. These *global* inclusions will be a consequence of appropriate choices for the basis of the *local* spaces $P_T$ (the coefficients in the expansion of a function of $P_T$ over such a basis will constitute what we shall call the set $\Sigma_T$), as the examples will show.

3. Eventually, we must check that there exists at least one basis in the space $V_h$ whose functions have small supports (see discussion at the end of Sec. 4.1).

We begin by examples of finite elements which yield the inclusion $V_h \subset \mathcal{C}^0(\bar{\Omega})$. We denote by $P_k$ the set of all polynomials of degree $\leq k$ in the $n$ variables $x_1, x_2, \ldots, x_n$. Note that

$$\dim (P_k) = \binom{n+k}{k}$$

We recall that in $R^n$, an *n-simplex* is the convex hull T of $n+1$ points $a_j = (a_{ij})_{i=1}^n \in R^n$, which are then called the *vertices* of the $n$-simplex, provided the matrix

$$A = \begin{bmatrix} a_{11} & a_{12} & \cdots & a_{1\,n+1} \\ a_{21} & a_{22} & \cdots & a_{2\,n+1} \\ \vdots & \vdots & & \vdots \\ a_{n1} & a_{n2} & \cdots & a_{n\,n+1} \\ 1 & 1 & \cdots & 1 \end{bmatrix} \tag{4.7}$$

is regular (equivalently, the $n+1$ points $a_j$ are not contained in a hyperplane). Thus,

$$T = \left\{ x = \sum_{j=1}^{n+1} \lambda_j a_j; \, 0 \leq \lambda_j \leq 1, 1 \leq j \leq n+1, \sum_{j=1}^{n+1} \lambda_j = 1 \right\} \tag{4.8}$$

Notice that a 2-simplex is a triangle and that a 3-simplex is a tetrahedron. The barycentric coordinates $\lambda_j = \lambda_j(x)$, $1 \leq j \leq n+1$, of any point $x \in R^n$ with respect to the $n+1$ points $a_j$ are the (unique) solutions of the linear system

$$\sum_{j=1}^{n+1} a_{ij}\lambda_j = x_i \qquad 1 \leq i \leq n$$

$$\sum_{j=1}^{n+1} \lambda_j = 1 \tag{4.9}$$

whose matrix is precisely the matrix $A$ of (4.7). By inverting the linear system (4.9), one sees that *the barycentric coordinates are affine functions of* $x_1, x_2, \ldots, x_n$:

$$\lambda_i = \sum_{j=1}^{n} b_{ij}x_j + b_{i\,n+1} \qquad 1 \leq i \leq n+1 \tag{4.10}$$

where the matrix $B = (b_{ij})$ is the inverse of the matrix $A$.

Since $\lambda_i(a_j) = \delta_{ij}$, $1 \le i, j \le n+1$, we have the identity

$$p = \sum_{i=1}^{n+1} p(a_i)\lambda_i \qquad \text{for all } p \in P_1 \tag{4.11}$$

Therefore *a polynomial of degree* $\le 1$ *is uniquely determined by its values* at the $n+1$ points $a_j$. This observation leads to the definition of the simplest *finite element* which we shall call *n-simplex of type 1*. The space $P_T$ is $P_1$, and the set $\Sigma_T$ of *degrees of freedom*, i.e., those parameters which uniquely define a function in the space $P_T$, consists of the values at the vertices, which we write symbolically as $\Sigma_T = \{p(a_i), 1 \le i \le n+1\}$; see Fig. 4.2 for $n = 2$.

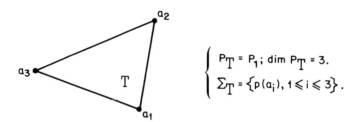

$$\begin{cases} P_T = P_1; \ \dim P_T = 3. \\ \Sigma_T = \{p(a_i), 1 \le i \le 3\}. \end{cases}$$

**FIG. 4.2**  Triangle of type 1.

Let us call $a_{ij} = (a_i + a_j)/2$ the midpoints of the edges of the $n$-simplex T. Since $\lambda_k(a_{ij}) = \frac{1}{2}(\delta_{ki} + \delta_{kj})$, it is easy to establish the identity

$$p = \sum_{i=1}^{n+1} \lambda_i(2\lambda_i - 1)p(a_i) + \sum_{i<j} 4\lambda_i\lambda_j p(a_{ij}) \qquad \text{for all } p \in P_2 \tag{4.12}$$

which yields the definition of a finite element, called the *n-simplex of type 2*: the space $P_T$ is $P_2$, and the set $\Sigma_T$ consists of the values at the vertices and at the midpoints of the edges (see Fig. 4.3) for $n = 2$.

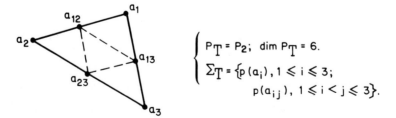

$$\begin{cases} P_T = P_2; \ \dim P_T = 6. \\ \Sigma_T = \{p(a_i), 1 \le i \le 3; \\ \qquad\quad p(a_{ij}), 1 \le i < j \le 3\}. \end{cases}$$

**FIG. 4.3**  Triangle of type 2.

Let $a_{iij} = (2a_i + a_j)/3$ for $i \neq j$, and $a_{ijk} = (a_i + a_j + a_k)/3$ for $i \neq j$, $j \neq k$, $k \neq i$. From the identity

$$p = \sum_{i=1}^{n+1} \frac{\lambda_i(3\lambda_i - 1)(3\lambda_i - 2)}{2} p(a_i) + \sum_{i \neq j} \frac{9\lambda_i\lambda_j(3\lambda_i - 1)}{2} p(a_{iij})$$

$$+ \sum_{i<j<k} 27\lambda_i\lambda_j\lambda_k p(a_{ijk}) \qquad \text{for all } p \in P_3 \qquad (4.13)$$

we likewise deduce the definition of the *n-simplex of type 3* (see Fig. 4.4) for $n = 2$.

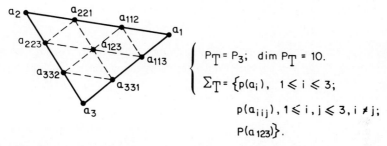

$$\begin{cases} P_T = P_3; \quad \dim P_T = 10. \\ \Sigma_T = \{p(a_i), \ 1 \leqslant i \leqslant 3; \\ \qquad p(a_{iij}), 1 \leqslant i, j \leqslant 3, i \neq j; \\ \qquad P(a_{123})\}. \end{cases}$$

**FIG. 4.4**   Triangle of type 3.

With a given triangulation, we now associate in a natural way a space $V_h$ with each type of finite element. With triangles of type 1, a function of $V_h$ (1) is in the space $P_T = P_1$ for each $T \in \mathcal{T}_h$, and (2) is completely determined by its values at all the vertices of the triangulation, by definition. Likewise, with triangles of type 2, a function of $V_h$ (1) is in the space $P_T = P_2$ for each $T \in \mathcal{T}_h$, and (2) is completely determined by its values at all the vertices and all midpoints of the edges of the triangulation, and similarly for triangles of type 3. In other words, a function in $V_h$ is specified by a set $\Sigma_h$ of *degrees of freedom*, its values at all the vertices for triangles of type 1, etc, in such a way that

$$\Sigma_h = \bigcup_{T \in \mathcal{T}_h} \Sigma_T$$

We now show that, in each instance, the functions in $V_h$ are continuous over the set $\bar{\Omega}$. Since a function $v_h \in V_h$ is already continuous in the interior of each finite element, it suffices to consider the two functions $v_h|_{T_1}$ and $v_h|_{T_2}$ along the common side $\Gamma$ of two adjacent triangles $T_1$ and $T_2$, e.g., triangles of type 2, as shown in Fig. 4.5. Let $t$ denote the abscissa along an

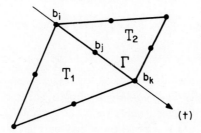

**FIG. 4.5**   Adjacent triangles of type 2.

axis containing the segment $\Gamma = [b_i, b_k]$. The two functions $v_h|_{T_1}$ and $v_h|_{T_2}$ along $\Gamma$ are quadratic polynomials of $t$ whose values coincide at the three points $b_i$, $b_j$, $b_k$; therefore, they are identical. A similar argument holds for the other types of triangles.

So far, requirements (1) and (2) are satisfied, and it remains to verify requirement (3), which states that there is indeed a canonical choice for basis functions with small supports. In each case, the set $\Sigma_h$ is of the form

$$\Sigma_h = \{v(b_j); \ 1 \leqslant j \leqslant M\} \tag{4.14}$$

Then if we define a basis $(w_j)_{j=1}^M$ by the conditions

$$w_j(b_i) = \delta_{ij} \qquad 1 \leqslant i, j \leqslant M \tag{4.15}$$

it is easily seen that this will result in functions with small supports. In Fig. 4.6 we have represented the three types of supports which are encountered when triangles of type 3 are employed.

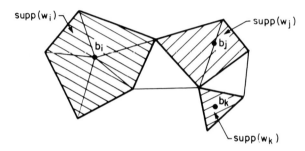

**FIG. 4.6**   Supports of the basis functions of triangles of type 3.

With the same notations as for the triangle of type 3, one can show that

$$\phi(p) \equiv 12p(a_{123}) + 2 \sum_{i=1}^{3} p(a_i) - 3 \sum_{\substack{i,j=1 \\ i \neq j}}^{3} p(a_{iij}) = 0 \qquad \text{for all } p \in P_2 \tag{4.16}$$

If we define the space (which contains $P_2$, by definition) as

$$P_3' = \{p \in P_3; \ \phi(p) = 0\} \tag{4.17}$$

one can prove that a polynomial $p \in P_3'$ is uniquely defined by the following set of degrees of freedom:

$$\Sigma_K = \{p(a_i), \ 1 \leqslant i \leqslant 3; \ p(a_{iij}), \ 1 \leqslant i, j \leqslant 3, \ i \neq j\} \tag{4.18}$$

From this result, one deduces the definition of a finite element, called the *triangle of type 3'*, whose associated space $V_h$ is again a subspace of the space $C^0(\bar{\Omega})$.

If it happens that the set $\bar{\Omega}$ is a rectangle, it may be conveniently triangulated by finite elements which are themselves *rectangles* with sides parallel to the sides of $\bar{\Omega}$. In the following, we let $Q_k$ denote the space of all polynomials of degree $\leqslant k$ with respect to each of the $n$ variables $x_1, x_2, \ldots, x_n$; i.e., a polynomial $p \in Q_k$ is of the form

$$p(x_1, x_2, \ldots, x_n) = \sum_{\alpha_i \leqslant k} a_{\alpha_1 \alpha_2 \cdots \alpha_n} x_1^{\alpha_1} x_2^{\alpha_2} \cdots x_n^{\alpha_n} \qquad 1 \leqslant i \leqslant n \qquad (4.19)$$

Observe that $\dim Q_k = (k+1)^n$ and that we have the inclusions

$$P_k \subset Q_k \subset P_{nk} \qquad (4.20)$$

Denoting by $K$ the unit hypercube $[0, 1]^n$ of $R^n$, we define its subset

$$\Xi_k = \left\{ x = \left( \frac{i_1}{k}, \frac{i_2}{k}, \ldots, \frac{i_n}{k} \right) \in R^n; \, i_j \in \{0, 1, \ldots, k\}, 1 \leqslant j \leqslant n \right\} \qquad (4.21)$$

for any given integer $k \geqslant 1$. In view of the identity

$$p = \sum_{\substack{0 \leqslant i_j \leqslant k \\ 1 \leqslant j \leqslant n}} \prod_{j=1}^{n} \left( \prod_{\substack{i'_j=0 \\ i'_j \neq i_j}}^{k} \frac{kx_j - i'_j}{i_j - i'_j} \right) p\left( \frac{i_1}{k}, \frac{i_2}{k}, \ldots, \frac{i_n}{k} \right) \qquad \text{for all } p \in Q_k \qquad (4.22)$$

we deduce the definition of finite elements which we call *hypercubes of type k*. Figures 4.7 to 4.9 show the special cases $k = 1, 2, 3$ and $n = 2$, as well as the notations which we use for the points of the corresponding sets $\Xi_k$.

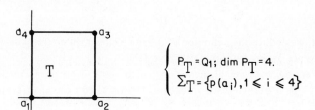

FIG. 4.7   Square of type 1.

$$\begin{cases} P_T = Q_1; \dim P_T = 4. \\ \Sigma_T = \{p(a_i), 1 \leqslant i \leqslant 4\} \end{cases}$$

With an argument identical to the one previously used for triangles of types 1, 2, and 3, we could show that the resulting subspaces $V_h$ are contained in $\mathscr{C}^0(\bar{\Omega})$. Of course, we could analogously extend the previous definitions, given for squares, to the case of rectangles with sides parallel to the coordinate axes. This would result in the definition of *rectangles of types 1, 2, and 3.*

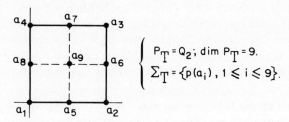

$$\begin{cases} P_T = Q_2; \dim P_T = 9. \\ \Sigma_T = \{p(a_i), 1 \leqslant i \leqslant 9\}. \end{cases}$$

FIG. 4.8   Square of type 2.

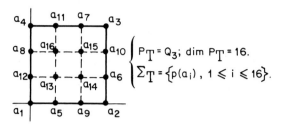

**FIG. 4.9**  Square of type 3.

Let $a_i$, $1 \leq i \leq 9$, be the nine points occurring in the definition of the square of type 2 as shown in Fig. 4.8. Then, the following identity holds:

$$\chi(p) = 4p(a_9) + \sum_{i=1}^{4} p(a_i) - 2 \sum_{i=5}^{8} p(a_i) = 0 \qquad \text{for all } p \in P_2 \qquad (4.23)$$

Defining the space (which contains $P_2$, by definition)

$$Q'_2 = \{p \in Q_2; \chi(p) = 0\} \qquad (4.24)$$

we can show that a polynomial $p \in Q'_2$ is uniquely determined by the following set of degrees of freedom:

$$\Sigma_K = \{p(a_i), 1 \leq i \leq 8\} \qquad (4.25)$$

From this result, we deduce the definition of a finite element called the *square of type 2'*. The corresponding space $V_h$ is again included in $\mathscr{C}^0(\bar{\Omega})$.

Let us now introduce finite elements on which some degrees of freedom are partial derivatives. Let T be a triangle with vertices $a_i$, $1 \leq i \leq 3$, and center of gravity $a_{123}$. Using the identity

$$\forall p \in P_3, \qquad p = \sum_{i=1}^{3} (-2\lambda_i^3 + 3\lambda_i^2 - 7\lambda_1\lambda_2\lambda_3)p(a_i) + 27\lambda_1\lambda_2\lambda_3 p(a_{123})$$

$$+ \sum_{i=1}^{3} \sum_{\substack{j=1 \\ j \neq i}}^{3} \lambda_i\lambda_j(2\lambda_i + \lambda_j - 1)Dp(a_i) \cdot (a_j - a_i) \qquad (4.26)$$

we deduce the definition of a finite element which we call the *Hermite triangle of type 3* (cf. Fig. 4.10) where the partial derivatives $Dp(a_i) \cdot (a_j - a_i)$ are now degrees of freedom. Notice that the knowledge of the two partial derivatives $Dp(a_i) \cdot (a_j - a_i)$ for $j \neq i$, $i \leq j \leq 3$, implies the knowledge of the first derivative $Dp(a_i)$ at each vertex $a_i$, which we indicate by one small circle centered at the point $a_i$. Since the first derivative $Dp(a_i)$ is equally well determined by the partial derivatives $(\partial p/\partial x_1)(a_i)$, $(\partial p/\partial x_2)(a_i)$, another equivalent set of degrees of freedom is

$$\Sigma'_T = \left\{p(a_i), \frac{\partial p}{\partial x_1}(a_i), \frac{\partial p}{\partial x_2}(a_i), 1 \leq i \leq 3; p(a_{123})\right\} \qquad (4.27)$$

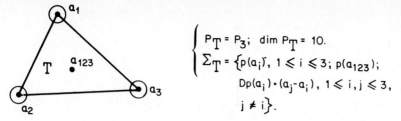

$$\begin{cases} P_T = P_3; \ \dim P_T = 10. \\ \Sigma_T = \{p(a_i), 1 \leqslant i \leqslant 3; \ p(a_{123}); \\ \quad Dp(a_i) \cdot (a_j - a_i), 1 \leqslant i, j \leqslant 3, \\ \quad j \neq i\}. \end{cases}$$

**FIG. 4.10**   Hermite triangle of type 3.

We now have to construct a space $V_h$. With a given triangulation, we associate a space $V_h$ as follows. By definition, a function $v_h$ belongs to the space $V_h$ if (1) it is in the space $P_T = P_3$ for each $T \in \mathcal{T}_h$ and (2) it is defined by its values at all the vertices $b_j$, $1 \leqslant j \leqslant J$, and centers of gravity $b_j$, $J + 1 \leqslant j \leqslant L$ of all triangles $T \in \mathcal{T}_h$, together with the values of its first partial derivatives at the vertices $b_j$, $1 \leqslant j \leqslant J$. In this case, the set of degrees of freedom is therefore

$$\Sigma_h = \left\{ p(b_j), \frac{\partial p}{\partial x_1}(b_j), \frac{\partial p}{\partial x_2}(b_j), 1 \leqslant j \leqslant J; p(b_j), J + 1 \leqslant j \leqslant L \right\} \tag{4.28}$$

Notice that we have again

$$\Sigma_h = \bigcup_{T \in \mathcal{T}_h} \Sigma_T$$

provided the degrees of freedom for each triangle are chosen in such a way that they do not change from one triangle to another. For instance, the set $\Sigma'_T$ of (4.27) has this property, while the set $\Sigma_T$ of Fig. 4.10 does not.

Then if we define a basis $(w_j, w_j^1, w_j^2)$ by the conditions

$$w_j(b_k) = \delta_{jk} \qquad 1 \leqslant j, k \leqslant L$$

$$\frac{\partial w_j}{\partial x_1}(b_k) = \frac{\partial w_j}{\partial x_2}(b_k) = 0 \qquad 1 \leqslant j \leqslant L, 1 \leqslant k \leqslant J$$

$$w_j^1(b_k) = 0 \qquad 1 \leqslant j \leqslant J, 1 \leqslant k \leqslant L$$

$$\frac{\partial w_j^1}{\partial x_1}(b_k) = \delta_{jk} \qquad \frac{\partial w_j^1}{\partial x_2}(b_k) = 0 \qquad 1 \leqslant j, k \leqslant J \tag{4.29}$$

$$w_j^2(b_k) = 0 \qquad 1 \leqslant j \leqslant J, 1 \leqslant k \leqslant L$$

$$\frac{\partial w_j^2}{\partial x_1}(b_k) = 0 \qquad \frac{\partial w_j^2}{\partial x_2}(b_k) = \delta_{jk} \qquad 1 \leqslant j, k \leqslant J$$

it is easily seen that these basis functions have "small" supports, exactly as in the sense previously understood.

Arguing as for the space $V_h$ made up of triangles of type 3, we can derive the inclusion $V_h \subset \mathscr{C}^0(\bar{\Omega})$ since, along the common side of two adjacent triangles, there is a unique polynomial of degree 3 in one variable which takes on prescribed values and prescribed first derivatives at the endpoints of the side.

We can show that the following identity holds:

$$\psi(p) \equiv 6p(a_{123}) - 2 \sum_{i=1}^{3} p(a_i) + \sum_{i=1}^{3} Dp(a_i) \cdot (a_i - a_{123}) \qquad \text{for all } p \in P_2 \qquad (4.30)$$

Defining the space (which, by definition, contains $P_2$)

$$P_3'' = \{p \in P_3; \ \psi(p) = 0\} \qquad (4.31)$$

we can show that a polynomial $p \in P_3''$ is uniquely determined by the following set of degrees of freedom:

$$\Sigma_T = \left\{ p(a_i), \frac{\partial p}{\partial x_1}(a_i), \frac{\partial p}{\partial x_2}(a_i), 1 \leq i \leq 3 \right\} \qquad (4.32)$$

The resulting finite element is called the *Hermite triangle of type 3'*, or, preferably, the *Zienkiewicz triangle*. The corresponding space $V_h$ is again included in $\mathscr{C}^0(\bar{\Omega})$.

We now examine examples of finite elements which yield the inclusion $V_h \subset \mathscr{C}^1(\bar{\Omega})$. Our first example will be based on the following result.

**THEOREM 4.4**  Let T be a triangle with vertices $a_i, 1 \leq i \leq 3$. Let $p \in P_5$ be a polynomial which satisfies the following relations:

$$p(a_i) = \frac{\partial p}{\partial x_1}(a_i) = \frac{\partial p}{\partial x_2}(a_i) = \frac{\partial^2 p}{\partial x_1^2}(a_i) = \frac{\partial^2 p}{\partial x_1 \partial x_2}(a_i) = \frac{\partial^2 p}{\partial x_2^2}(a_i) = 0, \qquad 1 \leq i \leq 3 \qquad (4.33)$$

$$\frac{\partial p}{\partial \nu}(a_{ij}) = 0, \qquad 1 \leq i < j \leq 3$$

where $(\partial p/\partial \nu)(a_{ij})$ denotes the exterior normal derivative at the midpoints $a_{ij}$ of the sides of T. Then $p = 0$.

*Proof*  Let $t$ denote an abscissa along the side $\Delta = [a_1, a_2]$. We have $p|_\Delta = 0$ since $q = p|_\Delta$ is a polynomial of degree 5 in $t$ satisfying

$$q(a_1) = \frac{dq}{dt}(a_1) = \frac{d^2q}{dt^2}(a_1) = q(a_2) = \frac{dq}{dt}(a_2) = \frac{d^2q}{dt^2}(a_2) = 0$$

Likewise, $\partial p/\partial \nu = 0$ along $\Delta$ since $r = \partial p/\partial \nu$ along $\Delta$ is a polynomial of degree 4 such that

$$r(a_1) = \frac{dr}{dt}(a_1) = r(a_2) = \frac{dr}{dt}(a_2) = r(a_{12}) = 0$$

Since we have $\partial p/\partial t = 0$ along $\Delta$ ($p = 0$ along $\Delta$), it follows that $p$ and its first derivative $Dp$ vanish identically along $\Delta$.

Therefore we conclude that the polynomial $\lambda_3^2$ is a factor of $p$. Arguing similarly with the other sides, we find that

$$p = q\lambda_1^2\lambda_2^2\lambda_3^2$$

Since the $\lambda_i$'s are polynomials of degree 1 which do not reduce to constants, it follows that $q = 0$ and thus $p = 0$.

Since dim $P_5 = 21$ is also the number of conditions which appeared in (4.33), we can define a new element called the *21-degrees-of-freedom triangle* or, preferably, the *Argyris triangle*.

Figure 4.11 is self-explanatory with regard to the graphical symbols used for representing the various degrees of freedom. We observe that at each vertex $a_i$, the first and second

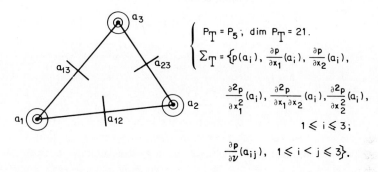

$$
\begin{cases}
P_T = P_5; \quad \dim P_T = 21. \\[2mm]
\Sigma_T = \left\{ p(a_i), \dfrac{\partial p}{\partial x_1}(a_i), \dfrac{\partial p}{\partial x_2}(a_i), \right. \\[3mm]
\qquad \dfrac{\partial^2 p}{\partial x_1^2}(a_i), \dfrac{\partial^2 p}{\partial x_1 \partial x_2}(a_i), \dfrac{\partial^2 p}{\partial x_2^2}(a_i), \\[3mm]
\qquad\qquad\qquad\qquad\qquad 1 \leqslant i \leqslant 3; \\[2mm]
\qquad \left. \dfrac{\partial p}{\partial \nu}(a_{ij}), \quad 1 \leqslant i < j \leqslant 3 \right\}.
\end{cases}
$$

**FIG. 4.11**    Argyris triangle.

derivatives $Dp(a_i)$ and $D^2 p(a_i)$ are known. With this observation in mind, we see that other equivalent definitions for the set of degrees of freedom are

$$
\Sigma_T' = \left\{ p(a_i), 1 \leqslant i \leqslant 3; \right.
$$

$$
Dp(a_i) \cdot (a_j - a_i), 1 \leqslant i, j \leqslant 3, j \neq i;
$$

$$
D^2 p(a_i) \cdot (a_j - a_i, a_k - a_i), 1 \leqslant i, j, k \leqslant 3, j \neq i, k \neq i;
$$

$$
\left. \frac{\partial p}{\partial \nu}(a_{ij}), 1 \leqslant i < j \leqslant 3 \right\} \tag{4.34}
$$

or the set used by J. H. Argyris:

$$
\Sigma_T'' = \{ p(a_i), Dp(a_i) \cdot (a_{i-1} - a_i), Dp(a_i) \cdot (a_{i+1} - a_i), 1 \leqslant i \leqslant 3,
$$

$$
D^2 p(a_i) \cdot (a_{j+1} - a_j)^2, 1 \leqslant i, j \leqslant 3;
$$

$$
Dp(a_{ij}) \cdot \nu_i; 1 \leqslant i < j \leqslant 3 \} \tag{4.35}
$$

where in the last expression of (4.35) the indices are numbered modulo 3, and the vector $\nu_i$ is the height issued from $a_i$.

Let us now show that the associated space $V_h$ is a subspace of $\mathscr{C}^1(\bar{\Omega})$. Let $T_1$ and $T_2$ be two adjacent triangles with a common side $\Gamma = [b_i, b_k]$ (cf. Fig. 4.12) and let $V_h$ be a function in the space $V_h$. Considered as functions of $t$, the functions $v_h|_{T_1}$ and $v_h|_{T_2}$ are along $\Gamma$ polynomials of degree 5 in the variable $t$. Call these polynomials $q_1$ and $q_2$. Since by definition

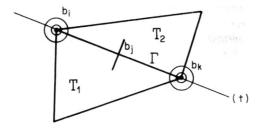

**FIG. 4.12**   Adjacent Argyris triangles.

of the set $\Sigma_h$, we have

$$q(b_i) = \frac{dq}{dt}(b_i) = \frac{d^2q}{dt^2}(b_i) = q(b_k) = \frac{dq}{dt}(b_k) = \frac{d^2q}{dt^2}(b_k) = 0$$

with $q = q_1 - q_2$, it follows that $q = 0$ and hence the inclusion $V_h \subset \mathscr{C}^0(\bar{\Omega})$ holds. Likewise, call $r_1$ and $r_2$ the restrictions to $\Gamma$ of the functions $(\partial v_h/\partial \nu)|_{T_1}$ and $(-\partial v_h/\partial \nu)/_{T_2}$. Then both $r_1$ and $r_2$ are polynomials of degree 4 in $t$ and, again by definition of the set $\Sigma_h$, we have

$$r(b_i) = \frac{dr}{dt}(b_i) = r(b_j) = r(b_k) = \frac{dr}{dt}(b_k) = 0$$

with $r = r_1 - r_2$, so that $r = 0$. We have thus proved the continuity of the normal derivative, which, combined with the continuity of the "tangential" derivative ($q = 0$ along $\Gamma$ implies $dq/dt = 0$ along $\Gamma$), shows that the first derivatives are also continuous on $\bar{\Omega}$.

Let $a_i$ and $a_j$ be two points and let $r$ be a function such that its restriction $r|_{[a_i, a_j]}$ is a polynomial of degree 4 in $t$, $t$ being an abscissa along an axis containing the points $a_i$ and $a_j$. $r|_{[a_i, a_j]}$ is a polynomial of degree 3 in $t$ if and only if

$$-8r(a_{ij}) + 4(r(a_i) + r(a_j)) + (Dr(a_i) \cdot (a_j - a_i) + Dr(a_j) \cdot (a_i - a_j)) = 0 \qquad (4.36)$$

where

$$a_{ij} = \frac{a_i + a_j}{2}$$

The let $P_5'$ denote the subspace of $P_5$ formed by those polynomials of $P_5$ whose normal derivatives along each side of a triangle with vertices $a_i$, $1 \leqslant i \leqslant 3$, are polynomials of degree 3 in $t$, $t$ being an abscissa along an axis containing the side. Notice that, by definition, the inclusions $P_4 \subset P_5' \subset P_5$ hold. Using the above result, we can show that a polynomial $p \in P_5'$ is uniquely determined by the following set of degrees of freedom:

$$\Sigma_T = \left\{ p(a_i), \frac{\partial p}{\partial x_1}(a_i), \frac{\partial p}{\partial x_2}(a_i), \frac{\partial^2 p}{\partial x_1^2}(a_i), \frac{\partial^2 p}{\partial x_1 \partial x_2}(a_i), \frac{\partial^2 p}{\partial x_2^2}(a_i), 1 \leqslant i \leqslant 3 \right\} \qquad (4.37)$$

The resulting finite element is called the *18-degrees-of-freedom triangle*. The associated space $V_h$ is again included in $\mathscr{C}^1(\bar{\Omega})$.

In the case of rectangular domains, the following finite element is also of interest. Let T denote a rectangle with its sides parallel to the coordinate axes. Then we can show that a function $p \in Q_3$ is uniquely determined by the set

$$\Sigma_T = \left\{ p(a_i), \frac{\partial p}{\partial x_1}(a_i), \frac{\partial p}{\partial x_2}(a_i), \frac{\partial^2 p}{\partial x_1 \, \partial x_2}(a_i); \ 1 \le i \le 4 \right\} \qquad (4.38)$$

(again, Fig. 4.13 is self-explanatory for the graphical notations), and that the corresponding space $V_h$ is contained in $\mathscr{C}^1(\bar{\Omega})$. This finite element is called the *Bogner–Fox–Schmit rectangle*.

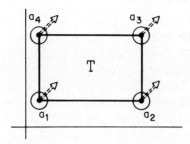

**FIG. 4.13**   Bogner–Fox–Schmit rectangle.

## 4.3 GENERAL PROPERTIES OF FINITE ELEMENTS†

With the previous examples in mind, we can now give the general definition of a finite element. A *finite element in $R^n$* is a triple $(T, P, \Sigma)$ where the data $T$, $P$, and $\Sigma$ have the following significations and relationships:

1. $T$ is a compact subset of $R^n$ with a nonempty interior and a Lipschitz-continuous boundary.
2. $P$ is a finite-dimensional space of real-valued functions defined over the set $T$, of dimension $N$.
3. $\Sigma$ is a set of $N$ linear forms $\varphi_i$, $1 \le i \le N$, defined over the space $P$, in such a way that the set $\Sigma$ is *P-unisolvent* in the sense that given any real scalars $\alpha_i$, $1 \le i \le N$, there exists a unique function $p \in P$ which satisfies

$$\varphi_i(p) = \alpha_i \qquad 1 \le i \le N \qquad (4.39)$$

Equivalently, there exist $N$ functions $p_i \in P$, $1 \le i \le N$, which satisfy

$$\varphi_j(p_i) = \delta_{ij} \qquad 1 \le j \le N \qquad (4.40)$$

which are called the *basis functions* of the finite element, since we have the identity

$$p = \sum_{i=1}^{N} \varphi_i(p) p_i \qquad \text{for all } p \in P \qquad (4.41)$$

---

† From here to the end of the chapter, T and $T$ may be considered as interchangeable.

In light of the definition of a finite element, let us now go back over the examples seen in the previous section.

We have seen that the set $T$ could be an $n$-simplex in $R^n$, i.e., a triangle in $R^2$ or a tetrahedron in $R^3$; a hypercube in $R^n$, i.e., a square in $R^2$ or a cube in $R^3$; or a rectangle in $R^2$. These are all special cases of *straight finite elements*, i.e., finite elements for which the set is a polyhedron in $R^n$. There exist also *curved finite elements*, i.e., those whose boundary is composed of curved surfaces (cf. Section 4.2 in Part 2).

In the examples, the sets $\Sigma$ of degrees of freedom consist of linear forms of some of the following forms:

$$\varphi_i^0 : p \to p(a_i^0)$$

$$\varphi_{ik}^1 : p \to Dp(a_i^1) \cdot \xi_{ik}^1 \tag{4.42}$$

$$\varphi_{ikl}^2 : p \to D_p^2(a_i^2) \cdot (\xi_{ik}^2, \xi_{il}^2)$$

where the points $a_i^r$, $r = 0, 1, 2$, belong to the finite element, and the nonzero vectors $\xi_{i,k}^1$, $\xi_{i,k}^2$, $\xi_{il}^2$ are either constructed from the geometry of the finite element [for example, $Dp(a_i) \cdot (a_j - a_i)$, $(\partial p/\partial \nu)(a_{ij}), \ldots]$ or fixed vectors of $R^n$ [for example, $(\partial p/\partial x_1)(a_i)$, $(\partial^2 p/\partial x_1 \partial x_2)(a_i), \ldots]$. The points $a_i^r$, $r = 0, 1, 2$, are called the *nodes of the finite element*.

Whereas only partial derivatives of order $r = 0, 1$, or 2 occurred in the examples, we could conceivably consider degrees of freedom which would be partial derivatives of arbitrarily high order, but these are seldom used in practice.

When all the degrees of freedom are of the form $\varphi_i : p \to p(a_i)$, we say that the associated finite element is a *Lagrange finite element*, while if at least one partial derivative occurs, then the associated finite element is a *Hermite finite element*.

Given a finite element $(T, P, \Sigma)$, we associate with any sufficiently smooth function $v : T \to R$ the *$(T, P, \Sigma)$-interpolate function*, denoted $\Pi v$ or $\Pi_T v$, of the function $v$, defined by the conditions

$$\Pi v \in P \quad \text{and} \quad \varphi_i(\Pi v) = \varphi_i(v) \quad 1 \le i \le N \tag{4.43}$$

Therefore, the $(T, P, \Sigma)$-interpolate can be expressed as

$$\Pi v = \sum_{i=1}^{N} \varphi_i(v) p_i \tag{4.44}$$

We have thus defined a $(T, P, \Sigma)$-interpolation operator $\Pi$, also denoted $\Pi_T$.

Whereas for a Lagrange finite element the set of degrees of freedom is unambiguously defined (indeed, it can be conveniently identified with the set of nodes), there are *always* several possible definitions for the degrees of freedom of a Hermite finite element which yield somehow the *same* finite element [cf., for instance, the sets $\Sigma_T$, $\Sigma_T'$, and $\Sigma_T''$ for the Argyris triangle shown in Fig. 4.11 and in (4.34) and (4.35)]. Let us now give a precise statement for this: *we do not distinguish between two finite elements $(T, P, \Sigma)$ and $(S, Q, \Xi)$ if we have*

$$T = S \quad \Pi_T = \Pi_S \quad \text{and} \quad P = Q \tag{4.45}$$

If this is the case, we say that the *sets $\Sigma$ and $\Xi$ are equivalent.*

For instance, the sets $\Sigma_T$ and $\Sigma'_T$ of Fig. 4.10 and of Eq. (4.27) are equivalent for the Hermite triangle of type 3 and the sets $\Sigma_T$, $\Sigma'_T$, and $\Sigma''_T$ are equivalent for the Argyris triangle.

Concerning the various spaces $P$ encountered in the examples, notice that they all contain a polynomial space $P_k$ for some integer $k \geq 1$, a property that will be shown in the next section to be as crucial as far as convergence properties are concerned.

We now come to an essential idea which we will apply to an example. Consider a *family* of triangles of type 2 (cf. Fig. 4.3). Our aim is then to describe such a family as simply as possible. Let $\hat{T}$ be a triangle with vertices $\hat{a}_i$ and midpoints of the sides $\hat{a}_{ij} = (\hat{a}_i + \hat{a}_j)/2$, $1 \leq i < j \leq 3$, and let $\hat{\Sigma} = \{p(\hat{a}_i), 1 \leq i \leq 3; p(\hat{a}_{ij}), 1 \leq i < j \leq 3\}$ so that the triple $(\hat{T}, \hat{P}, \hat{\Sigma})$ with $\hat{P} = p_2$ is also a triangle of type 2.

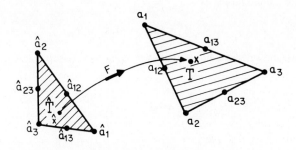

**FIG. 4.14**   Affine-equivalent triangles of type 2.

Given any finite element in the family (cf. Fig. 4.14), *there exists a unique invertible affine mapping*

$$F_T: \hat{x} \in R^2 \to F_T(\hat{x}) = B_T\hat{x} + b_T \in R^2 \tag{4.46}$$

i.e., with $B_T$ an invertible matrix and $b_T$ a vector of $R^2$, such that

$$F_T(\hat{a}_i) = a_i \qquad 1 \leq i \leq 3 \tag{4.47}$$

*Then it automatically follows that*

$$F_T(\hat{a}_{ij}) = a_{ij} \qquad 1 \leq i < j \leq 3 \tag{4.48}$$

This is so because the property for a point to be the midpoint of a segment is preserved by an affine mapping. Likewise, the points which we called $a_{iij}$ or $a_{ijk}$ keep their geometrical definition through an affine mapping.

Once we have established a bijection $\hat{x} \in \hat{T} \to x = F_T(\hat{x}) \in T$ between the points of the sets $\hat{T}$ and $T$, it is natural to associate the space

$$P_T = \{p: T \to R; p = \hat{p} \circ F_T^{-1}, \hat{p} \in \hat{P}\} \tag{4.49}$$

with the space $\hat{P}$. Then it follows that

$$P_T = P_2 \tag{4.50}$$

In other words, rather than prescribe such a family by the date $(T, P_T, \Sigma_T)$, it suffices to give one *reference finite element* $(\hat{T}, \hat{P}, \hat{\Sigma})$ and the affine mappings $F_T$ occurring in the family. Then we have the following relations:

$$T = F_T(\hat{T})$$

$$\Sigma_T = \{p(F_T(\hat{a}_i)), 1 \le i \le 3; p(F_T(\hat{a}_{ij})), 1 \le i < j \le 3\} \tag{4.51}$$

$$P_T = \{p: T \to R; p = \hat{p} \circ F_T^{-1}, \hat{p} \in \hat{P}\}$$

From this example, let us now derive the following *general definition.* Two finite elements $(\hat{T}, \hat{P}, \hat{\Sigma})$ and $(T, P, \Sigma)$ with degrees of freedom of the form (4.42) are *affine-equivalent* if there exists an invertible affine mapping

$$F: \hat{x} \in R^n \to F(\hat{x}) = B\hat{x} + b \in R^n \tag{4.52}$$

such that the following relations hold:

$$T = F(\hat{T}) \tag{4.53}$$

$$a_i^r = F(\hat{a}_i^r) \qquad r = 0, 1, 2, \ldots \tag{4.54}$$

$$\xi_{ik}^1 = B\hat{\xi}_{ik}^1 \qquad \xi_{ik}^2 = B\hat{\xi}_{ik}^2 \qquad \xi_{il}^2 = B\hat{\xi}_{il}^2$$

whenever the nodes $a_i^r$ and $\hat{a}_i^r$, and vectors $\xi_{ik}^1, \xi_{ik}^2, \xi_{il}^2$ and $\hat{\xi}_{ik}^1, \hat{\xi}_{ik}^2, \hat{\xi}_{il}^2$ occur in the definition of the set $\Sigma$ or $\hat{\Sigma}$, respectively,

$$P = \{p: T \to R; p = \hat{p} \circ F^{-1}, \hat{p} \in \hat{P}\} \tag{4.55}$$

We shall constantly use the bijections

$$\hat{x} \in \hat{T} \to x \in T \qquad \text{where} \qquad x = F(\hat{x})$$

$$\hat{p} \in \hat{P} \to p \in P \qquad \text{where} \qquad p = \hat{p} \circ F^{-1} \tag{4.56}$$

$$p(x) = \hat{p}(\hat{x}) \qquad \text{for all } x = F(\hat{x})$$

between the points and functions associated with two affine-equivalent finite elements $(\hat{T}, \hat{P}, \hat{\Sigma})$ and $(T, P, \Sigma)$. We now prove a crucial relationship between the $(\hat{T}, \hat{P}, \hat{\Sigma})$-interpolation operator $\hat{\Pi}$ and the $(T, P, \Sigma)$-interpolation operator $\Pi$, and also between the basis functions of affine-equivalent finite elements.

**THEOREM 4.5**   Let $(\hat{T}, \hat{P}, \hat{\Sigma})$ and $(T, P, \Sigma)$ be two affine-equivalent finite elements. Then, if $\hat{p}_i, 1 \le i \le N$, are the basis functions of the finite element $(\hat{T}, \hat{P}, \hat{\Sigma})$, the functions $p_i, 1 \le i \le N$, are the basis functions of the finite element $(T, P, \Sigma)$. The interpolation operators $\Pi$ and $\hat{\Pi}$ are such that

$$\widehat{\Pi v} = \hat{\Pi}\hat{v} \tag{4.57}$$

for any sufficiently smooth functions $v: T \to R$ and $\hat{v}: \hat{T} \to R$ associated in the correspondence

$$v \to \hat{v} \qquad \text{where} \qquad v = \hat{v} \circ F^{-1}$$

that is $\qquad\qquad\qquad\qquad v(x) = \hat{v}(\hat{x}) \qquad \text{for all } x = F(\hat{x})$ \hfill (4.58)

***Proof***  We know that

$$\Pi v = \sum_i v(a_i^0) p_i^0 + \sum_{i,k} \{Dv(a_i^1) \cdot \xi_{ik}^1\} p_{ik}^1 + \sum_{i,k,l} \{D^2 v(a_i^2) \cdot (\xi_{ik}^2, \xi_{il}^2)\} p_{ikl}^2$$

Using the derivation of composition of functions, we obtain

$$Dv(a_i^1) \cdot \xi_{ik}^1 = Dv(F(\hat{a}_i^1)) \cdot B\hat{\xi}_{ik}^1 = Dv(F(\hat{a}_i^1)) \cdot DF(\hat{a}_i^1) \cdot \hat{\xi}_{ik}^1$$

$$= D(v \cdot F)(\hat{a}_i^1) \cdot \hat{\xi}_{ik}^1 = D\hat{v}(\hat{a}_i^1) \cdot \hat{\xi}_{ik}^1$$

and    $$D^2 v(a_i^2) \cdot (\xi_{ik}^2, \xi_{il}^2) = D^2 v(F(\hat{a}_i^2)) \cdot (B\hat{\xi}_{ik}^2, B\hat{\xi}_{il}^2)$$

$$= D^2 v(F(\hat{a}_i^2)) \cdot (DF(\hat{a}_i^2)\hat{\xi}_{ik}^2, DF(\hat{a}_i^2)\hat{\xi}_{il}^2)$$

$$= D^2 (v \cdot F)(\hat{a}_i^2)(\hat{\xi}_{ik}^2, \hat{\xi}_{il}^2) = D^2 \hat{v}(\hat{a}_i^2) \cdot (\hat{\xi}_{ik}^2, \hat{\xi}_{il}^2)$$

Thus we also have

$$\Pi v = \sum_i \hat{v}(\hat{a}_i^0) p_i + \sum_{i,k} \{D\hat{v}(\hat{a}_i^1) \cdot \hat{\xi}_{ik}^1\} p_{ik}^1 + \sum_{i,k,l} \{D^2 \hat{v}(\hat{a}_i^2) \cdot (\hat{\xi}_{ik}^2, \hat{\xi}_{il}^2)\} p_{ikl}^2$$

from which we deduce, using the second correspondence (4.56), the identity

$$\widehat{\Pi v} = \sum_i \hat{v}(\hat{a}_i^0) \hat{p}_i^0 + \sum_{i,k} \{D\hat{v}(\hat{a}_i^1) \cdot \hat{\xi}_{ik}^1\} \hat{p}_{ik}^1 + \sum_{i,k,l} \{D^2 \hat{v}(\hat{a}_i^2) \cdot (\hat{\xi}_{ik}^2, \hat{\xi}_{il}^2)\} \hat{p}_{ikl}^2$$

This identity has two consequences: (1) if we apply it with $v \in P$, we find that the functions $\hat{p}_i^0$, $\hat{p}_{ik}^1$, $\hat{p}_{ikl}^2$ are the basis functions in the space $\hat{p}$; (2) using (1), we see that $\Pi v$ is, by definition, also equal to $\hat{\Pi} \hat{v}$.

A family of finite elements is called an *affine family* if all its finite elements are affine-equivalent to a single finite element, which is then called the *reference finite element* of the family.

***A Word of Caution***  A family of finite elements where some degrees of freedom are normal derivatives at midpoints of the sides is *not* in general an affine family. This is the case of the Argyris triangle, for example, and this is why when we study in Sec. 4.5 the approximation properties of this element, we use an "intermediate" finite element (the Hermite triangle of type 5) which *can* be imbedded in an affine family.

We conclude this section by examining the construction of the subspaces $V_h$. For the sake of brevity, our discussion will be essentially concerned with the two-dimensional case, but all the subsequent considerations apply equally well to arbitrary dimensions.

We consider a *triangulation* $\mathcal{T}_h$ of a polygonal domain $\bar{\Omega}$ in $R^2$, made up of finite elements $(T, P_T, \Sigma_T)$, $T \in \mathcal{T}_h$, which are all of the same type. Thus, for instance, we consider a triangulation made up of triangles of type 1, a triangulation made up of rectangles of type $2'$, etc.

As explained in Sec. 4.2, a space $V_h$ is then associated with such a triangulation. Of course, if $T_1$ and $T_2$ are two adjacent finite elements, some *compatibility conditions* must be satisfied by the two sets $\Sigma_{T_1}$ and $\Sigma_{T_2}$, if we are to define unambiguously a set $\Sigma_h$ of *degrees of freedom of the space* $V_h$, which are now linear functionals over the space $V_h$. Rather than give a general and cumbersome discussion, we merely consider the special cases discussed in some detail in the previous section. The second example shows that, if necessary, we must choose between equivalent sets $\Sigma_T$, $\Sigma'_T$, etc., so that the equality

$$\Sigma_h = \bigcup_{T \in \mathcal{T}_h} \Sigma_T \tag{4.59}$$

makes sense. When the degrees of freedom of the finite elements are of the form (4.42), the resulting degrees of freedom of the space $V_h$ are of the following form:

$$\varphi^0_{j,h}: v \to v(b^0_j)$$
$$\varphi^1_{jk,h}: v \to Dv(b^1_j) \cdot \eta^1_{jk} \tag{4.60}$$
$$\varphi^2_{jkl,h}: v \to D^2v(b^2_j) \cdot (\eta^2_{jk}, \eta^2_{jl})$$

where the points $b^r_j$, $r = 0, 1, 2$, are called the *nodes of space* $V_h$ (to be distinguished from the vertices of the triangulation).

If we write the set $\Sigma_h$ as

$$\Sigma_h = \{\varphi_{i,h}\}^M_{i=1} \tag{4.61}$$

then the *basis functions* $w_j$, $1 \leqslant j \leqslant M$, *of the space* $V_h$ are naturally defined by the relations

$$\varphi_{i,h}(w_j) = \delta_{ij} \qquad 1 \leqslant i \leqslant M \tag{4.62}$$

We leave it to the reader to verify on each example that the basis functions $w_j$ can be easily derived simply by "patching together" the basis functions of each finite element.

With any sufficiently smooth function $v: \bar{\Omega} \to R$, we associate the $V_h$-*interpolate function*, denoted $\Pi_h v$, of the function $v$, uniquely defined by the relations

$$\Pi_h v \in V_h \qquad \text{and} \qquad \varphi_{j,h}(\Pi_h v) = \varphi_{j,h}(v) \qquad 1 \leqslant j \leqslant M \tag{4.63}$$

if the set $\Sigma_h$ is written as in (4.61). Therefore, the $V_h$-interpolate is given by

$$\Pi_h v = \sum_{j=1}^{M} \varphi_{j,h}(v) w_j \tag{4.64}$$

The corresponding mapping $\Pi_h$ is called the $V_h$-*interpolation operator*.

In view of the relation $\Sigma_h = \bigcup_{T \in \mathcal{T}_h} \Sigma_T$, we note the following important relations:

$$\forall T \in \mathcal{T}_h \qquad \Pi_h v|_T = \Pi_T v \tag{4.65}$$

In all the examples which we have considered, the spaces $P_T$ always consist of very smooth functions (polynomials). As a consequence of Theorems 4.2 and 4.3, it therefore remains to satisfy either inclusion $V_h \subset \mathscr{C}^0(\bar{\Omega})$ or $V_h \subset \mathscr{C}^1(\bar{\Omega})$. Rather than go into a general theory, we simply give the following definition: a *finite element* (of a specific type) *is of class* $\mathscr{C}^0$, *or of class* $\mathscr{C}^1$, if whenever it is the generic finite element of a triangulation, the associate space $V_h$ satisfies the inclusion $V_h \subset \mathscr{C}^0(\bar{\Omega})$, or $V_h \subset \mathscr{C}^1(\bar{\Omega})$, respectively. Thus for instance, *all* the Lagrange finite elements seen in Sec. 4.2 are of class $\mathscr{C}^0$, while the Argyris triangle and the Bogner-Fox-Schmit rectangle are of class $\mathscr{C}^1$.

Actually, such "global" inclusions are indeed consequences of "local" properties, i.e., properties of the finite element itself. Let us briefly comment about this point. The Lagrange finite elements $(T, P_T, \Sigma_T)$ which we have considered all share the following crucial property: Let $\varphi_i \in \Sigma_T$ be of the form $\varphi_i : p \to p(a_i)$. Then the associated basis function $p_i$ is identically zero on any side of the finite element which does not contain the node $a_i$. This fact has the following three important consequences which the reader should check in detail.

1. Let $\Delta$ denote a face of $T$. Then the restriction to $\Delta$ of a function in $P_T$ solely depends upon the degrees of freedom whose associated nodes are on $\Delta$. Therefore, as long as the space $P|_\Delta$ is the same for all faces, the corresponding finite element is of class $\mathscr{C}^0$.

2. Any basis function of $V_h$ constructed from the basis functions of the finite elements is automatically continuous over $\bar{\Omega}$.

3. If we are to construct a subspace of $H_0^1(\Omega)$, then it suffices that we equate to zero the degrees of freedom whose associated nodes are *boundary nodes*, i.e., those which lie on $\Gamma$. In other words, if we let $V_h$ denote the finite-element subspace "without boundary condition" [i.e., $V_h$ is an "approximation" of the space $H^1(\Omega)$], then the space

$$V_{0h} = \{v \in V_h; \forall a \in \Sigma_{0h} = \Sigma_h \cap \Gamma, v(a) = 0\} \tag{4.66}$$

is an approximation of the space $H_0^1(\Omega)$ (cf. Theorem 4.2), where in (4.66) we have identified $\Sigma_h$ with the set of all nodes of $\mathscr{T}_h$. As an important consequence, the $V_h$-interpolate of a sufficiently smooth function $v$ vanishing on the boundary $\Gamma$ is also the $V_{0h}$-interpolate of $v$.

We leave it to the reader to extend the previous considerations to the case of Hermite finite elements of class $\mathscr{C}^1$. In this case, the normal derivative along each side of the finite element also has to be taken into account.

## 4.4 INTERPOLATION THEORY FOR AFFINE FAMILIES OF FINITE ELEMENTS

Assume that we are approximating by means of the finite-element method a boundary-value problem whose solution $u$ is sufficiently smooth, so that the $V_h$-interpolate $\Pi_h u$ is well defined. Then, in view of the fundamental error bound (cf. Theorem 4.1), we have

$$\|u - u_h\| \le C \inf_{v_h \in V_h} \|u - v_h\| \le C \|u - \Pi_h u\| \tag{4.67}$$

where $u_h$ denotes the solution of the discrete problem and $C$ is a constant independent of the subspace $V_h$. Taking into account that we are essentially working with Sobolev norms $\|\cdot\|_{m,\Omega}$ with $m = 1$ or 2, and that $\Pi_h u|_T = \Pi_T u$ for all $T \in \mathscr{T}_h$ [cf. (4.65)], we can write

$$\|u - \Pi_h u\|_{m,\Omega} = \left(\sum_{T \in \mathscr{T}_h} \|u - \Pi_T u\|_{m,\mathring{T}}^2\right)^{1/2} \tag{4.68}$$

where $\mathring{T}$ denotes the interior of the set $T$. Therefore, the problem of finding an upper bound for $\|u-u_h\|$ is reduced to the local problem of evaluating quantities such as $\|u-\Pi_T u\|_m$, $\overset{\circ}{T}$. Solving this local problem is the object of this section.

In view of future needs, we will state and prove our results in the *Sobolev spaces* $W^{m,p}(\Omega)$ for any integer $m \geqslant 0$ and any number $p$ satisfying $1 \leqslant p \leqslant \infty$ which are defined as in Chapter 2 of Part 1.

We recall that Sobolev spaces are Banach spaces with the *norm*

$$\|v\|_{m,p,\Omega} = \left( \sum_{|\alpha| \leqslant m} \int_\Omega |\partial^\alpha v|^p \, dx \right)^{1/p} \tag{4.69}$$

We also use the *seminorms*

$$|v|_{m,p,\Omega} = \left( \sum_{|\alpha| = m} \int_\Omega |\partial^\alpha v|^p \, dx \right)^{1/p} \tag{4.70}$$

with the standard modification in the case of $p = \infty$. Also recall that

$$W^{m,2}(\Omega) = H^m(\Omega) \qquad \|\cdot\|_{m,2,\Omega} = \|\cdot\|_{m,\Omega} \qquad |\cdot|_{m,2,\Omega} = |\cdot|_{m,\Omega} \tag{4.71}$$

All the open sets $\Omega$ considered in this section will be assumed to have Lipschitz-continuous boundaries. Since this definition implies that $\Omega$ is bounded, it makes sense to consider the *quotient space* $W^{k+1,p}(\Omega)/P_k$, which becomes a Banach space when it is equipped with the usual *quotient norm*

$$\dot{v} \in W^{k+1,p}(\Omega)/P_k \to \|\dot{v}\|_{k+1,p,\Omega} = \inf_{p \in P_k} \|v+p\|_{k+1,p,\Omega} \tag{4.72}$$

where $v$ is any member of the equivalence class $\dot{v}$. Then the mapping

$$\dot{v} \in W^{k+1,p}(\Omega)/P_k \to |\dot{v}|_{k+1,p,\Omega} = |v|_{k+1,p,\Omega} \qquad \text{for any } v \in \dot{v} \tag{4.73}$$

is a priori a seminorm on the quotient space. It is a fundamental result that it is in fact a norm over this quotient space, which is in addition equivalent to the quotient norm, as we now prove.

**THEOREM 4.6** There exists a constant $C(\Omega)$ such that

$$\|\dot{v}\|_{k+1,p,\Omega} \leqslant C(\Omega)|\dot{v}|_{k+1,p,\Omega} \qquad \text{for all } \dot{v} \in W^{k+1,p}(\Omega)/P_k \tag{4.74}$$

**Proof** Let $N = \dim(P_k)$ and let $f_i$, $1 \leqslant i \leqslant N$, be a basis of the dual space of $P_k$. Using the Hahn-Banach extension theorem, there exist continuous linear forms over the space $W^{k+1,p}(\Omega)$, again denoted $f_i$, $1 \leqslant i \leqslant N$, such that for any $p \in P_k$, we have $f_i(p) = 0$, $1 \leqslant i \leqslant N$, if and only if $p = 0$. We will show that there exists a constant $C(\Omega)$ such that

$$\forall v \in W^{k+1,p}(\Omega) \qquad \|v\|_{k+1,p,\Omega} \leqslant C(\Omega)\left( |v|_{k+1,p,\Omega} + \sum_{i=1}^N |f_i(v)| \right) \tag{4.75}$$

Inequality (4.74) will then be a consequence of inequality (4.75). Given any function $v \in W^{k+1,p}(\Omega)$, let $q \in P_k$ be such that $f_i(v+q) = 0$, $1 \leqslant i \leqslant N$. Then,

$$\|\dot{v}\|_{k+1,p,\Omega} = \inf_{p \in P_k} \|v+p\|_{k+1,p,\Omega} \leqslant \|v+q\|_{k+1,p,\Omega} \leqslant C(\Omega)|v|_{k+1,p,\Omega}$$

which proves (4.74). Let us therefore prove (4.75). If it is false, there exists a sequence $(v_l)_{l=1}^{\infty}$ with $v_l \in W^{k+1,p}(\Omega)$, such that

$$\forall l \geq 1 \qquad \|v_l\|_{k+1,p,\Omega} = 1 \qquad \text{and} \qquad \lim_{l \to \infty} \left( |v_l|_{k+1,p,\Omega} + \sum_{i=1}^{N} |f_i(v_l)| \right) = 0 \qquad (4.76)$$

Since the sequence $(v_l)$ is bounded in $W^{k+1,p}(\Omega)$, there exists a subsequence, again denoted $(v_l)$, and a function $v \in W^{k,p}(\Omega)$ such that

$$\lim_{l \to \infty} \|v_l - v\|_{k,p,\Omega} = 0 \qquad (4.77)$$

(Apply the *Kondrasov–Rellich theorem* for $1 \leq p < \infty$ and *Ascoli's theorem* for $p = \infty$.) By (4.76),

$$\lim_{l \to \infty} |v_l|_{k+1,p,\Omega} = 0 \qquad (4.78)$$

and since the space $W^{k+1,p}(\Omega)$ is complete, we conclude from (4.77) and (4.78) that the sequence $(v_l)$ converges in the space $W^{k+1,p}(\Omega)$ to a function $v$ which satisfies

$$\|\partial^\alpha v\|_{0,p,\Omega} = \lim_{l \to \infty} \|\partial^\alpha v_l\|_{0,p,\Omega} = 0 \qquad \text{for all } \alpha \text{ with } |\alpha| = k+1$$

and thus $\partial^\alpha v = 0$ for any multi-index $\alpha$ with $|\alpha| = k+1$: the function $v$ is a polynomial of $P_k$. Using (4.76), we have

$$f_i(v) = \lim_{l \to \infty} f_i(v_l) = 0$$

so that we conclude that $v = 0$ from the properties of the linear forms $f_i$. But this contradicts the equality $\|v_l\|_{k+1,p,\Omega} = 1$ for all $l$.

We first derive an "abstract error bound," valid in general for *polynomial-invariant linear operators*, which plays a fundamental role. In the following, we shall indicate the inclusion $X \subset Y$ together with a continuous injection by the notation $X \hookrightarrow Y$.

**THEOREM 4.7**  Let $W^{k+1,p}(\Omega)$ and $W^{m,q}(\Omega)$ be Sobolev spaces satisfying the inclusion

$$W^{k+1,p}(\Omega) \hookrightarrow W^{m,q}(\Omega) \qquad (4.79)$$

and let $\Pi \in \mathscr{L}(W^{k+1,p}(\Omega); W^{m,q}(\Omega))$ be an operator which satisfies

$$\Pi p = p \qquad \text{for all } p \in P_k \qquad (4.80)$$

Then there exists a constant $C(\Omega)$ such that

$$|v - \Pi v|_{m,q,\Omega} \leq C(\Omega) \|I - \Pi\|_{\mathscr{L}(W^{k+1,p}(\Omega); W^{m,q}(\Omega))} |v|_{k+1,p,\Omega} \qquad \text{for all } v \in W^{k+1,p}(\Omega) \qquad (4.81)$$

*Proof*  In view of (4.80), we have the identity

$$v - \Pi v = (I - \Pi)(v + p) \qquad \text{for all } v \in W^{k+1,p}(\Omega), \ p \in P_k$$

from which we deduce, using inclusion (4.79), that

$$|v - \Pi v|_{m,q,\Omega} \leqslant \|v - \Pi v\|_{m,q,\Omega}$$

$$\leqslant \|I - \Pi\|_{\mathscr{L}(W^{k+1,p}(\Omega);\, W^{m,q}(\Omega))} \inf_{p \in P_k} \|v + p\|_{k+1,p,\Omega}$$

The conclusion follows from Theorem 4.6 and from the definition of the quotient norm (4.72).

For *polynomial-invariant linear forms*, we have another important corollary:

**THEOREM 4.8**  Bramble–Hilbert lemma. Let $f$ be a continuous linear form on the space $W^{k+1,p}(\Omega)$ which satisfies

$$f(p) = 0 \qquad \text{for all } p \in P_k \tag{4.82}$$

Then there exists a constant $C(\Omega)$ such that

$$|f(v)| \leqslant C(\Omega) \|f\|_{\mathscr{L}(W^{k+1,p}(\Omega);\, R)} |v|_{k+1,p,\Omega} \tag{4.83}$$

***Proof***  It is an immediate consequence of Theorem 4.6 and of the identity

$$f(v) = f(v + p) \qquad \text{for all } v \in W^{k+1,p}(\Omega), \; p \in P_k$$

We say that two open subsets $\Omega$ and $\hat{\Omega}$ of $R^n$ are *affine-equivalent* if there exists an invertible affine mapping .

$$F: \hat{x} \in \hat{\Omega} \to F(\hat{x}) = B\hat{x} + b \in \Omega \tag{4.84}$$

such that

$$\Omega = F(\hat{\Omega}) \tag{4.85}$$

As in the case of affine-equivalent finite elements [cf. (4.52) and (4.56)], we use the bijections

$$\hat{x} \in \hat{\Omega} \to x \in \Omega \qquad \text{where} \qquad x = F(\hat{x}),$$

$$\hat{v} \to v \qquad \text{where} \qquad v(x) = \hat{v}(\hat{x}) \qquad \text{for all } x = F(\hat{x}) \tag{4.86}$$

between points of the two sets and functions defined over the two sets, respectively.

The following simple result will be constantly used; it shows us how the Sobolev seminorms are related for functions $v$ and $\hat{v}$.

**THEOREM 4.9**  Let $\Omega$ and $\hat{\Omega}$ be two equivalent open subsets of $R^n$. Then there exist constants $C = C(m, n)$ such that

$$|v|_{m,p,\hat{\Omega}} \leqslant C \|B\|^m |\det (B)|^{-1/p} |v|_{m,p,\Omega} \qquad \text{for all } v \in W^{m,p}(\Omega) \tag{4.87}$$

$$|v|_{m,p,\Omega} \leqslant C \|B^{-1}\|^m |\det (B)|^{1/p} |\hat{v}|_{m,p,\hat{\Omega}} \qquad \text{for all } \hat{v} \in W^{m,p}(\hat{\Omega}), \tag{4.88}$$

where $\|\cdot\|$ is the euclidean norm, and $B$ is the matrix occurring in the mapping $F$ of (4.84).

***Proof***  The technical but otherwise straightforward proof is omitted. See Theorem 3.1.2 in Ref. [11].

In order to apply Theorem 4.9, we must evaluate the norms $\|B\|$, $\|B^{-1}\|$ in terms of simple geometric quantities; that is the object of the next theorem, where we will use the following notation:

$$h = \text{diam}\ (\Omega) \qquad \hat{h} = \text{diam}\ (\hat{\Omega}) \tag{4.89}$$

$$\rho = \sup\ \{\text{diam}\ (S);\ S\text{ is a ball contained in }\Omega\}$$
$$\hat{\rho} = \sup\ \{\text{diam}\ (S);\ S\text{ is a ball contained in }\hat{\Omega}\} \tag{4.90}$$

**THEOREM 4.10**   The following inequalities hold:

$$\|B\| \leq \frac{h}{\hat{\rho}} \qquad \text{and} \qquad \|B^{-1}\| \leq \frac{\hat{h}}{\rho} \tag{4.91}$$

**Proof**   We may write

$$\|B\| = \frac{1}{\hat{\rho}}\ \sup_{\|\xi\|=\hat{\rho}}\ \|B\xi\|$$

Given a vector $\xi$ satisfying $\|\xi\| = \hat{\rho}$, there exist two points $\hat{y}, \hat{z} \in \hat{\Omega}$ such that $\hat{y} - \hat{z} = \xi$, by definition of $\hat{\rho}$; see Fig. 4.15. Since $B\xi = F(\hat{y}) - F(\hat{z})$ with $F(\hat{y}) \in \bar{\Omega}$, $F(\hat{z}) \in \bar{\Omega}$, we deduce that $\|B\xi\| \leq h$, and thus the first inequality (4.91) is proved. The other inequality is proved in a similar fashion.

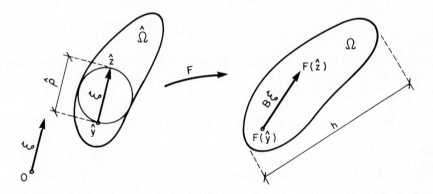

**FIG. 4.15**   Affine-equivalent open subsets of $\mathbb{R}^2$.

We now come to the main result of this section.

**THEOREM 4.11**   Let $(\hat{T}, \hat{P}, \hat{\Sigma})$ be a finite element, and let $s$ denote the greatest order of partial derivatives occurring in the definition of $\hat{\Sigma}$.† If the following inclusions hold, for some integers $m$

---

† Recall that, in practice, $s = 0$ for Lagrange finite elements and $s = 1$ or $2$ for Hermite finite elements (cf. Secs. 4.2 and 4.3).

and $k$,

$$W^{k+1,p}(\overset{\circ}{\hat{K}}) \hookrightarrow C^s(\hat{K}) \tag{4.92}$$

$$W^{k+1,p}(\overset{\circ}{\hat{K}}) \hookrightarrow W^{m,q}(\overset{\circ}{\hat{K}}) \tag{4.93}$$

$$P_k \subset \hat{P} \subset W^{m,q}(\hat{K}) \tag{4.94}$$

then there exists a constant $C(\hat{T}, \hat{P}, \hat{\Sigma})$ such that for all affine-equivalent finite elements $(T, P, \Sigma)$ and all functions $v \in W^{k+1,p}(\overset{\circ}{T})$,

$$|v - \Pi_T v|_{m,q,\overset{\circ}{T}} \le C(\hat{T}, \hat{P}, \hat{\Sigma})(\text{meas }(T))^{1/q-1/p} \frac{h_T^{k+1}}{\rho_T^m} |v|_{k+1,p,\overset{\circ}{T}} \tag{4.95}$$

where $\Pi_T v$ denotes the $(T, P, \Sigma)$-interpolate of the function $v$, and

$$h_T = \text{diam }(T) \tag{4.96}$$

$$\rho_T = \sup \{\text{diam }(S); S \text{ is a ball contained in } T\} \tag{4.97}$$

***Proof*** The inclusion $P_k \subset \hat{P}$ and the $\hat{P}$-unisolvence of the set imply that

$$\forall p \in P_k \qquad \hat{\Pi} p = p \tag{4.98}$$

where the $(\hat{T}, \hat{P}, \hat{\Sigma})$-interpolation operator takes the form

$$\hat{\Pi}\hat{v} = \sum_i \hat{v}(\hat{a}_i^0)\hat{p}_i^0 + \sum_{i,k} \{D\hat{v}(\hat{a}_i^1) \cdot \hat{\xi}_{ik}^1\}\hat{p}_{ik}^1 + \sum_{i,k,l} \{D^2\hat{v}(\hat{a}_i^2) \cdot (\hat{\xi}_{ik}^2, \hat{\xi}_{il}^2)\}\hat{p}_{ikl}^2$$

In view of the inclusions $W^{k+1,p}(\overset{\circ}{T}) \hookrightarrow C^s(T)$ and $\hat{P} \subset W^{m,q}(\overset{\circ}{T})$, we conclude from the above expansion that the operator $\hat{\Pi}$ belongs to the space $\mathscr{L}(W^{k+1,p}(\overset{\circ}{T}); W^{m,q}(\overset{\circ}{T}))$. Using Theorem 4.7 which we may apply in view of (4.94) and the inclusion (4.93), we obtain

$$|\hat{v} - \hat{\Pi}\hat{v}|_{m,q,\overset{\circ}{T}} \le C(\hat{T}, \hat{P}, \hat{\Sigma})|\hat{v}|_{k+1,p,\overset{\circ}{T}} \qquad \text{for all } \hat{v} \in W^{k+1,p}(\overset{\circ}{T}) \tag{4.99}$$

It follows from (4.57) that

$$\hat{v} - \hat{\Pi}\hat{v} = \widehat{v - \Pi_T v}$$

Since the open sets $\overset{\circ}{T}$ and $\overset{\circ}{\hat{T}}$ are equivalent, an application of Theorem 4.9 yields

$$|v - \Pi_T v|_{m,q,\overset{\circ}{T}} \le C\|B^{-1}\|^m|\det (B)|^{1/q}|\hat{v} - \hat{\Pi}\hat{v}|_{m,q,\overset{\circ}{T}} \tag{4.100}$$

$$|\hat{v}|_{k+1,p,\overset{\circ}{T}} \le C\|B\|^{k+1}|\det (B)|^{-1/p}|v|_{k+1,p,\overset{\circ}{T}}. \tag{4.101}$$

Combining inequalities (4.99) to (4.101) and using the relation

$$|\det (B)| = \frac{\text{meas }(T)}{\text{meas }(\hat{T})} \tag{4.102}$$

we eventually obtain inequality (4.95).

**REMARK 4.4**   Denoting by $\sigma_n$ the volume of the unit sphere in $R^n$, we sometimes use the inequalities

$$\sigma_n \rho_T^n \leq \text{meas (T)} \leq \sigma_n h_T^n \tag{4.103}$$

$$\hat{\sigma}_n \rho_T^n \leq |\det (B)| \leq \hat{\sigma}_n h_T^n \tag{4.104}$$

with $\hat{\sigma}_n = \sigma_n \text{ meas } (\hat{T})$.

We shall say that a family of finite elements $(T, P, \Sigma)$ is *regular* if the following three conditions are satisfied:

1. It is an affine family, in the sense of Sec. 4.3.                                        (4.105)
2. There exists a constant $\sigma$ such that

$$\frac{h_T}{T} \leq \sigma \qquad \text{for all the finite elements in the family} \tag{4.106}$$

3. The diameters $h_T$ approach zero.                                                      (4.107)

As an immediate consequence of Theorem 4.11 and Rem. 4.4, we then have the following theorem:

**THEOREM 4.12**   Let there be given a regular affine family of finite elements for which the assumptions (4.92) to (4.94) hold for the reference finite element of the family. Then there exists a constant $C$ such that for all finite elements in the family, and for all functions $v \in W^{k+1,p}(\hat{T})$,

$$|v - \Pi_T v|_{m,q,\hat{T}} \leq C(h_T)^{n(1/q - 1/p)} h_T^{k+1-m} |v|_{k+1,p,T} \tag{4.108}$$

To conclude this section, we define a property of a *family of triangulations*, which is often needed in error estimates (cf. Chapter 5 of Part 1). We say that a family of triangulations satisfies an *inverse assumption*, in view of the "inverse" inequalities (4.111) to be established in the next theorem, if there exists a constant $\nu$ such that

$$\frac{h}{h_T} \leq \nu \qquad \text{for all } T \in \mathcal{T}_h \text{ and all } \mathcal{T}_h \tag{4.109}$$

For such families, we are able to estimate the equivalence constants between Sobolev seminorms [recall that $\sigma$ is the constant which appears in the regularity assumption; cf. (4.106)].

**THEOREM 4.13**   Consider a family of finite-element spaces $V_h$ whose finite elements form a regular affine family, associated with a family of triangulations which satisfies an inverse assumption, and let there be given two pairs $(l, r)$ and $(m, q)$ with $l, m \geq 0$ and $(r, q) \in [1, \infty]$ such that

$$l \leq m \qquad \text{and} \qquad \hat{P} \subset W^{l,r}(\hat{K}) \cap W^{m,q}(\hat{K}) \tag{4.110}$$

Then there exists a constant $C = C(\sigma, \nu, l, r, m, q)$ such that

$$\left( \sum_{T \in \mathcal{T}_h} |v_h|_{m,q,\hat{T}}^q \right)^{1/q} \leq \frac{C}{h_T^{m-l+\max\{0,n(1/r-1/q)\}}} \left( \sum_{T \in \mathcal{T}_h} |v_h|_{l,r,\hat{T}}^r \right)^{1/r} \qquad \text{for all } v_h \in V_h \tag{4.111}$$

if $p, q < \infty$, with

$$\max_{T \in \mathcal{T}_h} |v_h|_{m,\infty,\dagger} \quad \text{in lieu of} \quad \left( \sum_{T \in \mathcal{T}_h} |v_h|^q_{m,q,\dagger} \right)^{1/q} \quad \text{if } q = \infty \tag{4.112}$$

$$\max_{T \in \mathcal{T}_h} |v_h|_{l,\infty,\dagger} \quad \text{in lieu of} \quad \left( \sum_{T \in \mathcal{T}_h} |v_h|^r_{l,r,\dagger} \right)^{1/r} \quad \text{if } r = \infty \tag{4.113}$$

**Proof** See Theorem 3.2.6 in Ref. [11].


## 4.5 INTERPOLATION THEORY FOR FINITE ELEMENTS OF CLASS $\mathscr{C}^1$

We now examine some finite elements of class $\mathscr{C}^1$. To begin, let us consider the Bogner-Fox-Schmit rectangle, introduced in Sec. 4.2 (cf. Fig. 4.13). For this element, we may apply the "affine" theory developed in Sec. 4.4. From the inclusion $P_3 \subset Q_3 = \hat{P}$, we conclude that, for a regular family of triangulations using this element (for simplicity, restricting ourselves to the case $p = 2$),

$$\|u - u_h\|_{2,\Omega} \le Ch^2 |u|_{4,\Omega} \quad \text{if } u \subset H^4(\Omega) \tag{4.114}$$

Let us now turn to the Argyris triangle, which was also introduced in Sec. 4.2 (cf. Fig. 4.11).

As we already observed, such a finite element *cannot* be imbedded in an affine family because of the degrees of freedom $(\partial p/\partial v)(a_{ij})$, $1 \le i \le j \le 3$. This is why we introduce the *Hermite triangle of type 5*, whose characteristics are indicated in Fig. 4.16.

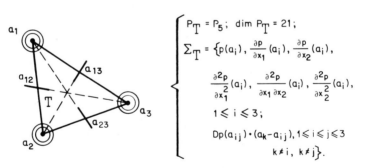

**FIG. 4.16** Hermite triangle of type 5.

Although this element is *not* a finite element of class $\mathscr{C}^1$ (it is of class $\mathscr{C}^0$ only), it will serve as a convenient *intermediary* for obtaining the interpolation error, because it *can* be imbedded in an affine family, as a straightforward analysis shows. Therefore, if we denote by $\Lambda_T$ the interpolation operator corresponding to the Hermite triangle of type 5, it follows from Theorem 4.11 that for all functions $v \in H^6(\hat{T})$ (restricting ourselves, for simplicity, to the case $p = 2$)

$$|v - \Lambda_T v|_{m,\dagger} \le C \frac{h_T^6}{\rho_T^m} |v|_{6,\dagger} \quad 0 \le m \le 6 \tag{4.115}$$

for some constant $C$ independent of $T$. Denoting by $\Pi_T$ the interpolation operator corresponding to the Argyris triangle, we must next estimate the difference

$$\delta = \Pi_T v - \Lambda_T v \tag{4.116}$$

The function $\delta$ is a polynomial of degree $\leqslant 5$ which satisfies

$$\frac{\partial \delta}{\partial \nu_k}(a_{ij}) = \frac{\partial}{\partial \nu_k}(v - \Lambda_T v)(a_{ij}) \qquad 1 \leqslant k \leqslant 3 \tag{4.117}$$

since

$$\frac{\partial \Pi_T v}{\partial \nu_k}(a_{ij}) = \frac{\partial v}{\partial \nu_k}(a_{ij})$$

We have, on the other hand,

$$D\delta(a_{ij}) \cdot (a_k - a_{ij}) = \frac{\partial \delta}{\partial \nu_k}(a_{ij})\langle a_k - a_{ij}, \nu_k \rangle + \frac{\partial \delta}{\partial \tau_k}(a_{ij})\langle a_k - a_{ij}, \tau_k \rangle \tag{4.118}$$

where (cf. Fig. 4.17), $\nu_k$ and $\tau_k$ are the unit outer normal and tangential vectors, respectively,

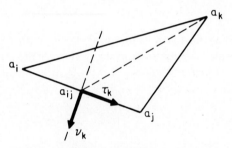

**FIG. 4.17** Unit outer normal and tangential vectors along a side of a triangle.

along the side opposite to the vertex $a_k$, and $\langle \cdot, \cdot \rangle$ is the usual inner product in $R^2$. Since

$$0 = \delta(a_i) = \frac{\partial \delta}{\partial x_1}(a_i) = \frac{\partial \delta}{\partial x_2}(a_i) = \frac{\partial^2 \delta}{\partial x_1^2}(a_i)$$

$$= \frac{\partial^2 \delta}{\partial x_1 \partial x_2}(a_i) = \frac{\partial^2 \delta}{\partial x_2^2}(a_i), \qquad 1 \leqslant i \leqslant 2 \tag{4.119}$$

the polynomial $\delta$ vanishes along each side of the triangle, and thus

$$\frac{\partial \delta}{\partial \tau_k}(a_{ij}) = 0 \qquad 1 \leqslant i < j \leqslant 3, \ k \neq i, \ k \neq j \tag{4.120}$$

Combining (4.117), (4.118), and (4.120), we obtain

$$D\delta(a_{ij})(a_k - a_{ij}) = \frac{\partial}{\partial \nu_k}(v - \Lambda_T v)(a_{ij})\langle a_k - a_{ij}, \nu_k \rangle \tag{4.121}$$

In view of relations (4.119) and (4.121), we may write

$$\delta = \Pi_T v - \Lambda_T v = \sum_{\substack{i<j \\ k \ne i, k \ne j}} \{D\delta(a_{ij}) \cdot (a_k - a_{ij})\} p_{ij}$$

$$= \sum_{\substack{i<j \\ k \ne i, l \ne j}} \frac{\partial}{\partial \nu_k} (v - \Lambda_T v)(a_{ij})\langle a_k - a_{ij}, \nu_k \rangle p_{ij} \tag{4.122}$$

where the functions $p_{ij}$ are the basis functions of the Hermite triangle of type 5 associated with the degrees of freedom $Dp(a_{ij}) \cdot (a_k - a_{ij})$. We have

$$|\langle a_k - a_{ij}, \nu_k \rangle| \le h_T \tag{4.123}$$

on the one hand, and

$$\left| \frac{\partial}{\partial \nu_k} (v - \Lambda_T v)(a_{ij}) \right| \le |v - \Lambda_T v|_{1,\infty,\hat{T}} \le C(\text{meas } T)^{-1/2} \frac{h_T^6}{\rho_T} |v|_{6,\hat{T}}$$

$$\le C \frac{h_T^6}{\rho_T^2} |v|_{6,\hat{T}} \tag{4.124}$$

on the other hand, by Theorem 4.11, with $m = 1$, $q = \infty$, $k = 5$, $p = 2$ (all necessary inclusions are satisfied). Let $\hat{p}_{ij}$ be the basis functions of the reference finite element which correspond to the functions $p_{ij}$. By Theorems 4.9 and 4.10, we infer that, for all integers $m$,

$$|p_{ij}|_{m,\hat{T}} \le C \frac{h_T}{\rho_T^m} |\hat{p}_{ij}|_{m,\hat{T}} \tag{4.125}$$

Combining (4.122) to (4.125), we eventually obtain

$$|\Pi_T v - \Lambda_T v|_{m,\hat{T}} \le C \frac{h_T^8}{\rho_T^{m+2}} |v|_{6,\hat{T}} \tag{4.126}$$

so that, using (4.115) and (4.126), we have proved the following.

**THEOREM 4.14**   There exists a constant $C$ such that, for all Argyris triangles and for all functions $v \in H^6(\hat{T})$,

$$|v - \Pi_T v|_{m,\hat{T}} \le C \frac{h_T^6}{\rho_T^m} \left( 1 + \left( \frac{h_T}{\rho_T} \right)^2 \right) |v|_{6,\hat{T}} \qquad 0 \le m \le 6 \tag{4.127}$$

where $\Pi_T v$ is the associated $(T, P, \Sigma)$-interpolate of the function $v$.


## 4.6 REFERENCES

1. Apprato, D., R. Arcangéli, and J. L. Gout, "Sur les Éléments Finis Rationnels de Wachspress," *Numer. Math.*, **32**:247–270 (1979).

2. Arcangéli, R., and J. L. Gout, "Sur l'Évaluation de l'Erreur d'Interpolation de Lagrange dans un Ouvert de $R^n$," *Rev. Fr. Autom. Inf. Rech. Oper.*, **10**(3):5-27 (1976).

3. Attéia, M., "Fonctions 'Spline' et Méthode d'Éléments Finis," *Rev. Fr. Autom. Inf. Rech. Oper.*, **R-2**: 13-40 (1975).

4. Birkhoff, G., "Tricubic Interpolation in Triangles," *Proc. Nat. Acad. Sci.*, **68**:1162-1164 (1971).

5. Birkhoff, G., and L. Mansfield, "Compatible Triangular Finite Elements," *J. Math. Anal. Appl.*, **47**:531-553 (1974).

6. Bramble, J. H., and S. R. Hilbert, "Estimation of Linear Functional on Sobolev Spaces with Application to Fourier Transforms and Spline Interpolation," *SIAM J. Numer. Anal.*, 7:113-124 (1970).

7. Bramble, J. H., and S. R. Hilbert, "Bounds for a Class of Linear Functions with Applications to Hermite Interpolation," *Numer. Math.*, **16**:362-369 (1971).

8. Bramble, J. H., and M. Zlámal, "Triangular Elements in the Finite Element Methods," *Math. Comp.*, **24**:809-820 (1970).

9. Ciarlet, P. G., "Sur l'Élément de Clough et Tocher," *Rev. Fr. Autom. Inf. Rech. Oper.*, **R-2**:19-27 (1974).

10. Ciarlet, P. G., *Numerical Analysis of the Finite Element Method*, Université de Montréal, Montreal, 1976.

11. Ciarlet, P. G., *The Finite Element Method for Elliptic Problems*, North-Holland, Amsterdam, 1978.

12. Ciarlet, P. G., "Interpolation Error Estimates for the Reduced Hsieh-Clough-Tocher Triangle," *Math. Comp.*, **32**:335-344 (1978).

13. Ciarlet, P. G., and P. A. Raviart, "General Lagrange and Hermite Interpolation in $R^n$ with Applications to Finite Element Methods," *Arch. Ration. Mech. Anal.*, **46**:177-199 (1972).

14. Ciarlet, P. G., and P. A. Raviart, "Interpolation Theory over Curved Elements, with Applications to Finite Element Methods," *Comput. Meth. Appl. Mech. Eng.*, 1:217-249 (1972).

15. Ciarlet, P. G., and C. Wagschal, "Multipoint Taylor Formulas and Applications to the Finite Element Method," *Numer. Math.*, **17**:84-100 (1971).

16. Ciavaldini, J. F., and J. C. Nédélec, "Sur l'Élément de Fraeijs de Veubeke et Sander," *Rev. Fr. Autom. Inf. Rech. Oper.*, **R-2**:29-45 (1974).

17. Clément, P., "Approximation by Finite Element Functions Using Local Regularization," *Rev. Fr. Autom. Inf. Rech. Oper.*, **R-2**:77-84 (1975).

18. Coatmélec, C., "Approximation et Interpolation des Fonctions Différentiables de Plusieurs Variables," *Ann. Sci. Ecole Normale Sup.*, **83**:271-341 (1966).

19. Dupont, T., and R. Scott, "Constructive Polynomial Approximation in Sobolev Spaces," C. de Boor and G. H. Golub (eds.), *Recent Advances in Numerical Analysis*, Academic Press, New York, 1978, pp. 31-44.

20. Gout, J. L., "Estimation de l'Erreur d'Interpolation d'Hermite dans $\mathbb{R}^n$," *Numer. Math.*, **28**:407-429 (1977).

21. Gout, J. L., "Interpolation Error Estimates on Hermite Rational 'Wachspress Type' Third Degree Element," *Comp. Math. Appl.*, **5**:349-357 (1979).

22. Jamet, P., "Estimations d'Erreur Pour des Éléments Finis Droits presque Dégénérés," *Rev. Fr. Autom. Inf. Rech. Oper.*, **10**:43-61 (1976).

23. Jamet, P., "Estimation de l'Erreur d'Interpolation dans un Domaine Variable et Application aux Éléments Finis Quadrilatéraux Dégénérés," in *Méthodes Numériques en Mathématiques Appliquées*, Presses de l'Université de Montréal, Montreal, 1976, pp. 55-100.

24. Mansfield, L. E., "Higher Order Compatible Triangular Finite Elements," *Numer. Math.*, **22**:89-97 (1974).

25. Meinguet, J., "Realistic Estimates for Generic Constants in Multivariate Pointwise Approximation," in J. J. H. Miller (ed.), *Topics in Numerical Analysis II*, Academic Press, New York, 1975, pp. 89–107.

26. Meinguet, J., "Structure et Estimations de Coefficients d'Erreur," *RAIRO Anal. Numer.*, **11**:355–368 (1977).

27. Meinguet, J., "A Practical Method for Estimating Approximation Errors in Sobolev Spaces," D. C. Handscomb (ed.), *Multivariate Approximation*, Academic Press, London, 1978, pp. 169–187.

28. Meinguet, J., and J. Descloux, "An Operator-Theoretical Approach to Error Estimation," *Numer. Math.*, **27**:307–326 (1977).

29. Natterer, F., "Berechenbare Fehlerschranken für die Methode der finiten Elemente," in *ISNM*, **28**:109–121, Birkhäuser, Basel, 1975.

30. Nicolaides, R. A., "On a Class of Finite Elements Generated by Lagrange Interpolation," *SIAM J. Numer. Anal.*, **9**:435–445 (1972).

31. Percell, P., "On Cubic and Quartic Clough-Tocher Finite Elements," *SIAM J. Numer. Anal.*, **13**:100–103 (1976).

32. Rabier, P., "Interpolation Harmonique," *RAIRO Anal. Numer.*, **11**:159–180 (1977).

33. Scott, R., "Finite Element Techniques for Curved Boundaries," Ph.D. dissertation, Massachusetts Institute of Technology, Cambridge, Mass., 1973.

34. Strang, G., "Approximation in the Finite Element Method," *Numer. Math.*, **19**:81–98 (1972).

35. Ženíšek, A., "Interpolation Polynomials on the Triangle," *Numer. Math.*, **15**:283–296 (1970).

36. Ženíšek, A., "Polynomial Approximation on Tetrahedrons in the Finite Element Method," *J. Approximation Theory*, **7**:334–351 (1973).

37. Ženíšek, A., "A General Theorem on Triangular Finite $C^m$-Elements," *RAIRO*, **R-2**:119–127 (1974).

38. Zienkiewicz, O. C., *The Finite Element Method in Engineering Science*, McGraw-Hill, London, 1971.

39. Zlámal, M., "On the Finite Element Method," *Numer. Math.*, **12**:394–409, 1968.

40. Zlámal, M., "A Finite Element Procedure of the Second Order of Accuracy," *Numer. Math.*, **16**:394–402 (1970).

41. Zlámal, M., "The Finite Element Method in Domains with Curved Boundaries," *Int. J. Numer. Meth. Eng.*, **5**:367–373 (1973).

42. Zlámal, M., "Curved Elements in the Finite Element Method, I," *SIAM J. Numer. Anal.*, **10**:229–240 (1973).

43. Zlámal, M., "Curved Elements in the Finite Element Method, II," *SIAM J. Numer. Anal.*, **11**:347–362 (1974).

# CHAPTER 5
# FINITE-ELEMENT METHODS FOR ELLIPTIC BOUNDARY-VALUE AND EIGENVALUE PROBLEMS

The purpose of this chapter is to present an introduction to the mathematics of Galerkin finite-element methods as applied to boundary-value problems and eigenvalue problems for linear elliptic equations. The aim is to give an idea of what kinds of results are available with an explanation of what they mean. Only a few proofs will be presented in order to provide an understanding of how the simplest results may be derived mathematically. Because we are intentionally not emphasizing generality, only second-order problems will be discussed. In particular, we will consider only Laplace's operator in two dimensions, and proofs will be given only in the case where the domains are smooth. To further avoid clouding the understanding with technicalities, we will concentrate on specific simple examples of finite elements which, from a mathematical point of view, are vector spaces whose elements consist of piecewise polynomial functions in two variables.

Section 5.1 introduces notation and presents some basic well-known results concerning boundary-value problems. Also presented here are some fundamental results concerning approximation by piecewise polynomial functions. In Sec. 5.2 the Ritz approximation is introduced for Dirichlet's problem, and the most fundamental error estimate is proved. In Section 5.3 we discuss the Neumann problem and give examples of results which are contained in the literature. The so-called negative norm estimates are derived in this case. Such estimates will be seen to be central to the types of results presented in the later sections. Section 5.4 is concerned with local estimates. In particular, some local maximum norm and $L_2$-estimates are given. In Sec. 5.5 the question of postprocessing to obtain greater accuracy is discussed. Finally, in Sec. 5.6 the eigenvalue problem is considered. Error estimates are given for the convergence rates of eigenvalues and eigenfunctions.

## 5.1 NOTATION AND PRELIMINARIES

In this section we introduce various model problems, some well-known results concerning their regularity, and some fundamental results concerning piecewise polynomial functions.

Let $\Omega$ be a bounded convex plane domain with smooth boundary $\partial\Omega$, and consider the boundary-value problem

$$
\begin{aligned}
-\Delta u &= f \quad \text{in } \Omega \\
u &= 0 \quad \text{on } \partial\Omega
\end{aligned}
\tag{5.1}
$$

where $\Delta u$ is the laplacian $\partial^2 u/\partial x_1^2 + \partial^2 u/\partial x_2^2$. This is the classical Dirichlet problem for Poisson's equation with homogeneous (zero) boundary condition. In order to discuss properties of the solution of this problem and others, we introduce some standard notation. Throughout this chapter we denote by $\|\cdot\|_0$ the $L_2$-norm over $\Omega$ and by $\|\cdot\|_k$ that in the Sobolev space $H^k(\Omega) = W_2^k(\Omega)$. Thus for real-valued functions $v$,

$$
\|v\|_0 = \left( \int_\Omega v^2 \, dx \right)^{1/2}
$$

and for $k$ a positive integer,

$$
\|v\|_k = \left( \sum_{|\alpha| \leq k} \|D^\alpha v\|_0^2 \right)^{1/2}
\tag{5.2}
$$

where $\alpha$ is a multi-index [that is, $\alpha = (\alpha_1, \alpha_2)$, with $\alpha_1$ and $\alpha_2$ nonnegative integers], $|\alpha| = \alpha_1 + \alpha_2$, and $D^\alpha v \equiv \partial^{|\alpha|} v/\partial x_1^{\alpha_1} \partial x_2^{\alpha_2}$. For example,

$$
\|v\|_2 = \left( \|v\|_0^2 + \left\|\frac{\partial v}{\partial x_1}\right\|_0^2 + \left\|\frac{\partial v}{\partial x_2}\right\|_0^2 + \left\|\frac{\partial^2 v}{\partial x_1^2}\right\|_0^2 + \left\|\frac{\partial^2 v}{\partial x_1 \partial x_2}\right\|_0^2 + \left\|\frac{\partial^2 v}{\partial x_2 \partial x_1}\right\|_0^2 + \left\|\frac{\partial^2 v}{\partial x_2^2}\right\|_0^2 \right)^{1/2}
$$

From a mathematical point of view results for the finite-element method (to be described in the next section) are most easily derived using as our norms the $H^k(\Omega)$-norms given by (5.2). From a computational standpoint, pointwise estimates for the error are often more interesting, but they are much more difficult to prove than the average estimates provided by the $H^k(\Omega)$-norms. Such pointwise estimates will appear in Sec. 5.4.

A main result, which will be needed in proving our later estimates, gives a precise statement of what smoothness we may expect for the solution $u$ of (5.1) given a certain degree of smoothness of $f$. Unless specifically stated, it will be assumed throughout that $\partial\Omega$ is smooth.

**LEMMA 5.1**  Given any nonnegative integer $k$, there is a constant $C$ such that for any $f \in H^k(\Omega)$ with $u$ the corresponding solution of (5.1), we have

$$
\|u\|_{k+2} \leq C\|f\|_k
\tag{5.3}
$$

Hence $u \in H^{k+2}(\Omega)$.

This result may be found in Ref. [7]; it states a well-known regularity property associated with elliptic equations.

We also want to consider the following model Neumann problem:

$$-\Delta u + u = f \quad \text{in } \Omega$$

$$\frac{\partial u}{\partial n} = 0 \quad \text{on } \partial\Omega$$

(5.4)

where $\partial u/\partial n$ is the outward normal derivative on $\partial\Omega$. Corresponding to this problem there is also a smoothing property.

**LEMMA 5.2**   Given any nonnegative integer $k$, there is a constant $C$ such that for any $f \in H^k(\Omega)$ with $u$ the corresponding solution of (5.4), we have

$$\|u\|_{k+2} \leqslant C\|f\|_k$$

(5.5)

Hence $u \in H^{k+2}(\Omega)$.

Fundamental mathematical results, such as those given by these two lemmas, concerning the regularity of solutions of elliptic boundary-value problems are the principal tools needed for proving the less superficial properties of the errors in finite-element approximations.

We want to approximate the solutions of (5.1) and (5.4) by certain piecewise polynomial functions defined on $\Omega$. In order to avoid the confusion of generality, which adds little to the understanding of the underlying mathematical treatment of our approximations, we will concentrate on studying the most classical of finite-element functions, namely, the piecewise linear functions.

Before proceeding to the approximation of the solutions of (5.1) or (5.4), we examine the problem of approximation of smooth functions on $\Omega$. First we consider smooth functions which vanish on $\Omega$, of which the solution $u$ of (5.1) is one.

Let $\mathcal{I}_h$ denote a partition of $\Omega$ into disjoint triangles $\tau$ such that no vertex of any triangle lies on the interior of a side of another triangle and such that the union of the triangle determines a polygonal domain $\Omega_h \subset \Omega$ ($\Omega$ convex) whose boundary vertices lie on $\partial\Omega$ (cf. Fig. 5.1).

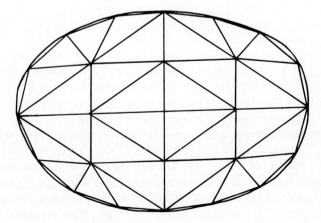

**FIG. 5.1**   Triangulation of domain with convex boundary.

Let $h$ denote the maximal length of a side of the triangulation $\mathcal{T}_h$. Thus $h$ is a parameter which decreases as the triangulation is made finer. We will assume that the angles of the triangulation are bounded below, independently of $h$, and often also that the triangulations are quasi-uniform in the sense that the triangles $\mathcal{T}_h$ are of essentially the same size, which may be expressed by demanding that the area of any $\tau$ in $\mathcal{T}_h$ is bounded below by $ch^2$ with $c > 0$ independent of $h$.

Now let $S_h$ denote the continuous functions on the closure $\bar\Omega$ of $\Omega$ which are linear in each triangle of $\mathcal{T}_h$ and which vanish outside $\Omega_h$. Let $\{P_j\}^{N_h}$ be the interior vertices of $\mathcal{T}_h$. A function in $S_h$ is uniquely determined by its values at the points $P_j$ and thus depends on $N_h$ parameters. Let $\phi_j$ be the "pyramid function" in $S_h$ which takes the value 1 at $P_j$ but vanishes at the other vertices. Then $\{\phi_j\}^{N_h}$ forms a basis for $S_h$, and every $\chi$ in $S_h$ admits the representation

$$\chi(x) = \sum_{j=1}^{N_h} \alpha_j \phi_j(x) \qquad \text{with} \qquad \alpha_j = \chi(P_j)$$

Given a smooth function $v$ on $\Omega$ which vanishes on $\partial\Omega$, we can interpolate $v$ into $S_h$ by defining the interpolant of $v$, $I_h v$ in $S_h$, as that function in $S_h$ satisfying

$$I_h v(P_j) = v(P_j) \qquad \text{for } j = 1, \dots, N_h$$

Hence
$$I_h v(x) = \sum_{j=1}^{N_h} v(P_j)\phi_j(x)$$

The following error estimates for the interpolant $I_h v$ are well known, namely (cf. Ref. [5]),

$$\|I_h v - v\|_0 \leqslant Ch^2 \|v\|_2 \tag{5.6a}$$

and
$$\|\nabla I_h v - \nabla v\|_0 \leqslant Ch \|v\|_2 \tag{5.6b}$$

where we assume that $v$ is sufficiently regular so that $\|v\|_2$ is finite. Here $\nabla v = \text{grad } v$ (where grad is the standard abbreviation for gradient) and

$$\|\nabla v\|_0 = \left( \left\|\frac{\partial v}{\partial x_1}\right\|_0^2 + \left\|\frac{\partial v}{\partial x_2}\right\|_0^2 \right)^{1/2}$$

The orders of these estimates, $O(h^2)$ and $O(h)$, respectively, are the optimal orders to which the functions and their gradients can be approximated in $S_h$ in the sense that the powers of $h$ in (5.6a) cannot be increased with (5.6b) remaining valid for a fixed $C$ and all $v \in H^2(\Omega)$ vanishing on $\partial\Omega$. We shall show in the next section that the piecewise linear Galerkin approximation to the solution of (5.1) satisfies similar inequalities.

In considering the approximation of the solution of (5.4) we must consider sets of functions $S_h$ which do not necessarily vanish on $\partial\Omega$. Details of such functions and their properties will be given in later chapters in which many different finite elements are discussed. What is needed to carry out the analysis of the error in the approximation of (5.4) are statements similar to (5.6a) and (5.6b) but for $v \in H^2(\Omega)$ not necessarily vanishing on $\partial\Omega$ and with $I_h v$ some interpolant into a finite-element space of functions which are restrictions to $\Omega$ of piecewise polynomials on a triangulation containing $\Omega$ (cf. Fig. 5.2).

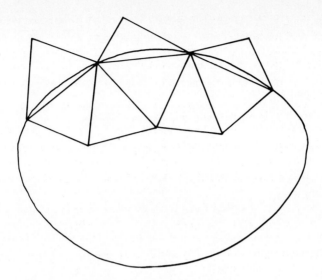

**FIG. 5.2**  Triangulation of domain containing $\Omega$.

## 5.2 THE RITZ APPROXIMATION FOR DIRICHLET'S PROBLEM

To define the Ritz approximation of (5.1) we multiply the equation by a smooth function $\phi$ which vanishes on $\partial\Omega$, integrate over $\Omega$, and apply Green's formula to the second term to obtain, for all such $\phi$, with $(v, w)$ denoting the inner product $\int_\Omega vw\,dx$ in $L_2(\Omega)$,

$$(\nabla u, \nabla \phi) = (f, \phi) \tag{5.7}$$

We may then pose the approximate problem to find $u_h$ in $S_h$ such that

$$(\nabla u_h, \nabla \chi) = (f, \chi) \qquad \text{for all } \chi \in S_h \tag{5.8}$$

In terms of the basis $\{\phi_j\}^{N_h}$ introduced above, we may restate the problem as follows: Find the coefficients $\alpha_1, \ldots, \alpha_{N_h}$ defining

$$u_h(x) = \sum_{j=1}^{N_h} \alpha_j \phi_j(x)$$

such that

$$\sum_{j=1}^{N_h} \alpha_j (\nabla \phi_j, \nabla \phi_k) = (f, \phi_k) \qquad k = 1, \ldots, N_h \tag{5.9}$$

Defining the symmetric matrix $B = (b_{jk})$ with $b_{jk} = (\nabla \phi_j, \nabla \phi_k)$ and the vector $\tilde{f} = (f_k)$ with $f_k = (f, \phi_k)$, denoting by $\alpha$ the vector with components $\alpha_k$, we may rewrite Eq. (5.9) in matrix notation

$$B\alpha = \tilde{f} \tag{5.10}$$

The matrix $B$ is the so-called stiffness matrix.

Now for functions in $H^1(\Omega)$ which vanish on $\partial\Omega$ it is well known that there is a constant $C_0$ such that for such functions

$$\|v\|_0 \le C_0 \|\nabla v\|_0$$

Thus from this and the definition of the norm in $H^1(\Omega)$ it is obvious that

$$\|\nabla v\|_0 \le \|v\|_1 \le (1 + C_0^2)^{1/2} \|\nabla v\|_0$$

This means that if $v = 0$ on $\partial\Omega$ and $\|\nabla v\|_0 = 0$, then $v = 0$ in $\Omega$. Now we make the observation that (5.8) has a unique solution $u_h$ in $S_h$. Uniqueness follows by considering any two solutions $u_h^1$ and $u_h^2$ and setting $v_h = u_h^1 - u_h^2$. Then $v_h$ satisfies

$$(\nabla v_h, \nabla \chi) = 0 \qquad \text{for all } \chi \in S_h$$

Hence setting $\chi = v_h$, we find that $\|\nabla v_h\|_0 = 0$, and by the above discussion, $v_h = 0$ or $u_h^1 = u_h^2$. But this just means that the matrix $B$ in (5.10) is nonsingular so that (5.10) is uniquely solvable, given any right-hand side $\tilde{f}$.

Now that we know that (5.10) is uniquely solvable, we want to compare its solution $u_h$ (obtained from an $N_h \times N_h$ matrix equation) with the solution $u$ of (5.1). The easiest comparison is given with respect to the norm $\|\cdot\|_1$. We first prove the following theorem.

**THEOREM 5.1**

$$\|\nabla(u_h - u)\|_0 \le Ch^{s-1} \|u\|_s \qquad \text{for } s = 1, 2 \tag{5.11}$$

**Proof**  Observe that

$$(\nabla(u_h - u), \nabla\chi) = 0 \qquad \text{for any } \chi \in S_h \tag{5.12}$$

Hence for $\chi \in S_h$ arbitrary

$$(\nabla(u_h - u), \nabla(u_h - u)) = (\nabla(u_h - u), \nabla(\chi - u))$$

Using Schwarz's inequality we have

$$\|\nabla(u_h - u)\|_0 \le \|\nabla(\chi - u)\|_0 \tag{5.13}$$

Now the choice $\chi \equiv 0$ in (5.13) yields (5.11) with $s = 1$ and $C = 1$. The choice $\chi = I_h u$ together with (5.6b) yields (5.11) with $s = 2$.

The two important facts which the above shows are as follows:

1. $u_h$ is the best approximation in $S_h$ (in the sense of the norm $\|\nabla \cdot\|_0$ on $S_h$) of the function $u$; in other words, $u_h$ is the orthogonal projection of $u$ onto $S_h$ (with norm $\|\nabla \cdot\|_0$).

2. $u_h$ may be computed directly from the "data" $f$.

Theorem 5.1 shows that the Ritz approximation $u_h$ imitates the optimality property of the interpolant (5.6b), which is, of course, natural in view of fact 1. We note here the well-known fact that $u$ minimizes the functional $\frac{1}{2}\|\nabla v\|_0^2 - (f, v)$ for all $v$ in $H^1(\Omega)$ which vanish on $\partial\Omega$.

This property is imitated by $u_h$ in that $u_h$ minimizes the same functional for functions in $S_h$. We next prove the important fact that the Ritz approximation has an optimality property with respect to the $L_2(\Omega)$-norm. Thus we will prove a property analogous to (5.6a) for $u_h$.

**THEOREM 5.2**

$$\|u_h - u\|_0 \leq Ch^s \|u\|_s \qquad \text{for } s = 1, 2 \tag{5.14}$$

**Proof** Let $w$ be the solution of a problem of type (5.1) with $f = u_h - u$. That is,

$$-\Delta w = u_h - u \quad \text{in } \Omega$$
$$w = 0 \qquad \text{on } \partial\Omega \tag{5.15}$$

(This function is introduced solely as an analytical tool and never has to be computed. Only its properties are needed.) Now

$$\|u_h - u\|_0^2 = (u_h - u, -\Delta w) = (\nabla(u_h - u), \nabla w) \tag{5.16}$$

by Green's formula. Using (5.12) with $\chi = I_h w$ and combining with (5.16) yields

$$\|u_h - u\|_0^2 = (\nabla(u_h - u), \nabla(w - I_h w))$$

Now apply Schwarz's inequality to obtain

$$\|u_h - u\|_0^2 \leq \|\nabla(u_h - u)\|_0 \|\nabla(I_h w - w)\|_0$$

Next use (5.6b) with $v = w$:

$$\|u_h - u\|_0^2 \leq \|\nabla(u_h - u)\|_0 Ch \|w\|_2$$

The next step is to apply the regularity estimate, Lemma 5.1, with $f = u_h - u$ and $k = 0$; that is,

$$\|w\|_2 \leq C \|u_h - u\|_0$$

Thus combining these last two estimates and dividing by $\|u_h - u\|_0$ yields

$$\|u_h - u\|_0 \leq Ch \|\nabla(u_h - u)\|_0 \tag{5.17}$$

Theorem 5.1 together with (5.17) yields Theorem 5.2.

The preceding argument in which the auxiliary function $w$ is introduced, and from it properties of the error deduced, is commonly called a *duality argument* in the mathematical literature on finite-element methods. It was first published by Aubin [1], Nitsche [8], and Oganesian [10], all independently and at approximately the same time. It is often referred to as *Nitsche's trick*. This technique has found widespread application in the mathematical analysis of the finite-element method, and its importance cannot be overemphasized.

## 5.3 THE RITZ APPROXIMATION FOR THE NEUMANN PROBLEM

We now turn our attention to the problem (5.4):

$$-\Delta u + u = f \quad \text{in } \Omega$$

$$\frac{\partial u}{\partial n} = 0 \quad \text{on } \partial \Omega$$

(5.4)

This problem is in a sense simpler to treat than (5.1) since the boundary condition is a so-called natural boundary condition and, as we shall see, the approximate solution will not be required to satisfy any boundary condition.

We start as before by multiplying by an arbitrary function $\phi$ (not required to satisfy any particular boundary condition) and then apply Green's formula to obtain

$$(\nabla u, \nabla \phi) + (u, \phi) = (f, \phi)$$

(5.18)

This of course uses the fact that the solution $u$ of (5.4) has a vanishing normal derivative on $\partial \Omega$. With (5.18) as a starting point we now consider finite-element spaces $S_h$ not required to satisfy boundary conditions. Examples of these may be found in later chapters, but here we will just be concerned with knowledge of certain properties of these functions in order to deduce statements relative to our approximate solution of (5.4).

The Ritz approximation is now given as the solution of the following problem: Find $u_h$ in $S_h$ such that

$$(\nabla u_h, \nabla \chi) + (u_h, \chi) = (f, \chi)$$

(5.19)

for all $\chi$ in $S_h$.

We see immediately from (5.18) and (5.19) that

$$(\nabla(u_h - u), \nabla \chi) + (u_h - u, \chi) = 0$$

(5.20)

for all $\chi$ in $S_h$. In mathematical terminology, (5.20) states that $u_h$ is the orthogonal projection of $u$ onto $S_h$ [with respect to the $H^1(\Omega)$-norm]. The orthogonal projection is the function in $S_h$ which is "closest" to $u$ in the sense that

$$\|u_h - u\|_1 = \inf_{\chi \in S_h} \|\chi - u\|_1$$

(5.21)

Expression (5.21) is an immediate consequence of (5.20) using Schwarz inequality. Now in case we have properties analogous to (5.6$a$ and $b$), we may again use the best approximation property and the duality argument to prove the following theorem.

**THEOREM 5.3**

$$\|u_h - u\|_0 + h\|u_h - u\|_1 \le Ch^s \|u\|_s \quad \text{for } s = 1, 2$$

Now let us assume that (5.6a and b) hold but somewhat more generally:

$$\|I_h v - v\|_0 \leqslant Ch^s \|v\|_s \qquad (5.21a)$$

$$\|\nabla(I_h v - v)\|_0 \leqslant Ch^{s-1} \|v\|_s \qquad (5.21b)$$

with $2 \leqslant s \leqslant r$ for some $r$. Here $I_h v$ may be some function in $S_h$; the interpolant was chosen before so as to be specific, but any such function will do.

An example of functions satisfying (5.21a and b) is provided by the continuous, piecewise bicubic polynomials on a square mesh of width $h$, restricted to the region $\Omega$. In this case $r = 4$.

Under the assumptions (5.21a and b) we obtain the following.

**THEOREM 5.4**

$$\|u_h - u\|_0 + h\|u_h - u\|_1 \leqslant Ch^s \|u\|_s \qquad \text{for } s = 1, 2, \ldots, r$$

The proof of this is the same as that for the previous result.

Now an examination of the duality argument shows that we have not used the full strength of (5.21a and b) or that of the regularity estimate (5.5) of Lemma 5.2. Let us examine more closely this argument. In proving the estimate for $\|u_h - u\|_0$, we want to introduce an auxiliary function which will not appear in the final result. Instead of $(u_h - u, u_h - u) \equiv \|u_h - u\|_0^2$, let us consider the expression $(u_h - u, v)$ and introduce the function $w$ satisfying

$$-\Delta w + w = v \qquad \text{in } \Omega$$

$$\frac{\partial w}{\partial n} = 0 \qquad \text{on } \partial \Omega$$

We proceed as before. Thus

$$(u_h - u, v) = (\nabla(u_h - u), \nabla w) + (u_h - u, w)$$

$$= (\nabla(u_h - u)\nabla(w - \chi)) + (u_h - u, w - \chi)$$

for any $\chi$ in $S_h$, where we have used Green's formula and (5.20). We now apply Schwarz' inequality to obtain

$$|(u_h - u, v)| \leqslant \|u_h - u\|_1 \|\chi - w\|_1$$

By setting $\chi = I_h w$ and using (5.21a and b), we find that

$$|(u_h - u, v)| \leqslant Ch^{s-1} \|w\|_s \|u_h - u\|_1$$

for $2 \leqslant s \leqslant r$. Finally we use Lemma 5.2 with $k = s - 2$ and $f = v$ to obtain

$$|(u_h - u, v)| \leqslant Ch^{s-1} \|v\|_{s-2} \|u_h - u\|_1$$

Dividing by $\|v\|_{s-2}$, we find that

$$\frac{|(u_h - u, v)|}{\|v\|_{s-2}} \leqslant Ch^{s-1} \|u_h - u\|_1 \qquad (5.22)$$

for $2 \leqslant s \leqslant r$ and any smooth function $v$ defined on $\Omega$. We now make the following observations. If we choose $s = 2$, then the choice $v = u_h - u$ yields the estimate for the $L_2(\Omega)$-norm contained in Theorem 5.3. However, for $s > 2$, noting that the right-hand side of (5.22) does not depend on $v$, we have

$$\sup_{v \in H^{s-2}(\Omega)} \frac{|(u_h - u, v)|}{\|v\|_{s-2}} \leqslant Ch^{s-1} \|u_h - u\|_1 \tag{5.23}$$

The expression on the left when $s = 2$ is equal to $\|u_h - u\|_0$ and when $s > 2$ can be shown also to be a norm. Let us define then, for $k = 0, 1, 2, \ldots$, the norms

$$\|\phi\|_{-k} = \sup_{v \in H^k(\Omega)} \frac{|(\phi, v)|}{\|v\|_k} \tag{5.24}$$

Our result (5.23) may now be rephrased as

$$\|u_h - u\|_{-(s-2)} \leqslant Ch^{s-1} \|u_h - u\|_1 \tag{5.25}$$

The norms defined by (5.24) are said to be defined by duality and are the so-called negative norms. Clearly, if $k_1 < k_2$, then

$$\|\phi\|_{-k_2} \leqslant \|\phi\|_{-k_1}$$

Hence, in particular, if $k_1 = 0$, we see that, for $k = 0, 1, 2, \ldots$,

$$\|\phi\|_{-k} \leqslant \|\phi\|_0$$

Thus the estimate (5.25) shows that, in general, the "rate of convergence" of $u_h$ to $u$ is higher when measured in the weaker negative norms. Thus we may state the following theorem.

**THEOREM 5.5**

$$\|u_h - u\|_{-(s-2)} \leqslant Ch^{s+l-2} \|u\|_l \tag{5.26}$$

where $2 \leqslant s \leqslant r$ and $1 \leqslant l \leqslant r$.

**Proof**  This is just a consequence of (5.25) and Theorem 5.4 with $s = l$.

In particular, the highest rate is obtained from Theorem 5.5 when $s = l = r$, and we have

$$\|u_h - u\|_{-(r-2)} \leqslant Ch^{2r-2} \|u\|_r$$

Note that in the case of piecewise linear finite elements $r = 2$, and we simply recapture the estimate of Theorem 5.3. Another interesting particular case of (5.26) is, for example, $s = r$, $l = 2$:

$$\|u_h - u\|_{-(r-2)} \leqslant Ch^r \|u\|_2 \tag{5.27}$$

Thus even in the case in which $f$ (the right-hand side) is such that the solution will be only in $H^2(\Omega)$, we may still conclude that the $H^{-(r-2)}(\Omega)$-norm of the error tends to zero quite rapidly with $h = 0$. We shall see that this is particularly important in studying the local behavior of the error in the next section. In fact, we shall see in the next three sections that the negative norm estimates, though they might appear superficially to be only a mathematical curiosity, have important applications to the study of local $L_2$ as well as local pointwise estimates, higher-order accuracy by postprocessing, and estimates for eigenvalues.

Finally it should be noted that the proof of the negative norm estimates was crucially dependent upon Lemma 5.2, which in turn depends upon the smoothness of $\partial\Omega$. Hence it may be that for domains with reentrant corners, for example, the rates of convergence do not increase for weaker norms (cf. Ref. [13]).


## 5.4 LOCAL ESTIMATES

In this section we present some results of Nitsche and Schatz [9] and Schatz and Wahlbin [11] on local estimates for the error in Ritz–Galerkin methods for elliptic problems.

Let us consider an arbitrary subdomain $\Omega_0$ of $\Omega$ whose closure is contained in $\Omega$. Now on $\Omega$ we suppose, as in Secs. 5.2 and 5.3, that we have the finite-element spaces $S_h$. Let $\Omega$ be between $\Omega_0$ and $\Omega$ in the sense that the closure of $\Omega_0$ is in $\Omega_1$ and the closure of $\Omega_1$ is in $\Omega$. Let $\mathring{S}_h(\Omega_1)$ be that subspace of $S_h$ consisting of those functions which vanish outside of $\Omega_1$. For example, in the example of the piecewise linear function in Sect. 5.1, the space $\mathring{S}_h(\Omega_1)$ consists of functions of the form

$$\chi(x) = \sum_{j=1}^{N_h} \alpha_j \phi_j(x)$$

with $\alpha_j = 0$ if $\phi_j(x) \neq 0$ for some $x$ outside of $\Omega_1$.

We may now consider the "interior equations." These are the analogues of the differential equation but in "variational form." Let $B(\phi, \psi)$ denote the bilinear form corresponding to the equation in either (5.1) or (5.4), i.e.,

$$B(\phi, \psi) = (\nabla\phi, \nabla\psi)$$

or

$$B(\phi, \psi) = (\nabla\phi, \nabla\psi) + (\phi, \psi)$$

Now let $u$ satisfy $-\Delta u = f$ in $\Omega$ or $-\Delta u + u = f$ in $\Omega$ without regard to boundary condition on $\partial\Omega$. Let $\psi$ vanish outside $\Omega_1$ and belong to $H^1(\Omega)$. Then

$$B(u, \psi) = (f, \psi) \tag{5.28}$$

for any such $\psi$. Now for $u_h$ defined by (5.8) or (5.19) we have, for $\chi$ in $\mathring{S}_h(\Omega_1)$,

$$B(u_h, \chi) = (f, \chi) \tag{5.29}$$

so that combining (5.28) and (5.29) yields

$$B(u_h - u, \chi) = 0 \tag{5.30}$$

for all $\chi$ in $\mathring{S}_h(\Omega_1)$. Equation (5.29) or (5.30) is the finite-element interior equation. For some cases finite-element equations may be identified with finite-difference equations. In such cases, particular choices of $\chi$ in (5.29) yield the local finite-difference equations. Hence it makes sense to think of (5.29) as a local equation. Problems (5.1) and (5.4) are just examples of problems with such local equations. Clearly many other problems satisfy such conditions.

We now give the local $L_2(\Omega_0)$-estimates of Nitsche and Schatz [9]. They require that certain technical conditions be satisfied by the spaces $S_h$. For a precise statement of these conditions refer to Ref. [9]. For our purposes here it suffices to say that the triangular elements constructed in Bramble and Zlámal [5] on a quasi-uniform triangulation such as that described in Sec. 5.1 satisfy all the Nitsche–Schatz conditions. We will assume then that these conditions are satisfied. In that case we have the following.

**THEOREM 5.6**  Let $u_h$ satisfy (5.29) and suppose that $u \in H^l(\Omega_1)$ with $2 \leq l \leq r$. Then for any fixed integer $p$, we have the estimate

$$\|u_h - u\|_{L_2(\Omega_0)} \leq C(h^l \|u\|_{H^l(\Omega_1)} + \|u_h - u\|_{-p}) \tag{5.31}$$

where $C$ depends on $p$, $\Omega_0$, and $\Omega_1$. Here the norms are those in the indicated Sobolev spaces.

The proof of a more general version of this theorem may be found in Ref. [9].

The meaning of (5.31) is quite clear. The local behavior of the error given by $\|u_h - u\|_{L_2(\Omega_0)}$ depends strongly on the local behavior of $u$ in the sense that $\|u\|_{H^l(\Omega_1)}$ is required to be finite, but very weakly on outside influences (in general). That is, the contribution to the error due to nonlocal effects is no greater than that due to the weakest norm for which we have a strong estimate. For example, for the Neumann problem (5.4) we have the result (5.27). Hence, if we take $l = r$, then the local $L_2$-convergence is governed by the norms $\|u\|_{H^r(\Omega_1)}$ and $\|u\|_{H^2(\Omega)}$. Thus, for example, if $r = 4$, we obtain the estimate

$$\|u_h - u\|_{L_2(\Omega_0)} \leq ch^4 (\|u\|_{H^4(\Omega_1)} + \|u\|_{H^2(\Omega)}) \tag{5.32}$$

This estimate is in general much stronger than (5.26).

The next result which we want to mention concerns the convergence of difference quotients of $u_h$ to derivatives of $u$. To state the result of Nitsche and Schatz [9], we require that the subspace $S_h(\Omega_0)$ have certain translational properties on $\Omega_1$. We will only give an example. Let $S_h$ consist of the restrictions to $\Omega$ of bilinear splines on a uniform mesh of width $h$. Then the difference quotient defined by

$$(Q_h^1 v)(x) = (2h)^{-1}[v(x_1 + h, x_2) - v(x_1 - h, x_2)]$$

is a second-order approximation to $D^1 v(x) = (\partial v / \partial x)(x)$. An example of a much more general result of Ref. [9] is the following theorem in which we assume the above special condition.

**THEOREM 5.7**  The error $u_h - u$ in (5.28) satisfies

$$\|Q_h^1 u_h - D^1 u\|_{L_2(\Omega_0)} \leq ch^2 (\|u\|_{H^3(\Omega_1)} + \|u\|_{H^2(\Omega)})$$

Thus certain difference quotients converge to derivatives locally provided that strong local and weak global conditions are satisfied. The rate of local convergence is the same as that for the error itself.

The theorem in Ref. [9] gives similar results for difference quotients approximating derivatives of arbitrary order.

We next state the maximum norm estimates given by Schatz and Wahlbin [11]. Again we are only looking at our particular examples to give an idea of what kinds of results are available and what might be expected. We write for any continuous function $v$ on a domain $D$

$$\|v\|_{L_\infty(D)} = \sup_{x \in D} |v(x)|$$

We now state the following.

**THEOREM 5.8**  Let $u_h$ satisfy (5.29) and let $p$ be any nonnegative integer. Then, for $h$ small enough and any $\chi$ in $S_h(\Omega_1)$,

$$\|u_h - u\|_{L_\infty(\Omega_0)} \leq c\{|\ln h|^{\bar{r}} \|u - \chi\|_{L_\infty(\Omega_1)} + \|u_h - u\|_{-p}\} \tag{5.33}$$

where $c$ depends on $p, \Omega_0$, and $\Omega_1$ and

$$\bar{r} = \begin{cases} 1 & \text{if } r = 2 \\ 0 & \text{if } r \geq 3 \end{cases}$$

Now most of the finite-element spaces used satisfy approximation properties analogous to (5.21$a$) with respect to the $L_\infty$-based Sobolev norms. To describe these we define the norms, for functions defined on a domain $D$, by

$$\|v\|_{W_\infty^k(D)} = \sum_{|\alpha| \leq k} \|D^\alpha v\|_{L_\infty(D)}$$

where, as in (5.2), $\alpha$ is a multi-index. Now the interpolant $I_h v$ of (5.6) also satisfies, for $\Omega_1 \subset \Omega$,

$$\|I_h v - v\|_{L_\infty(\Omega_1)} \leq ch^2 \|v\|_{W_\infty^2(\Omega_1)}$$

We can also assert that, in the more general situation described in Sec. 5.3, the interpolant given there satisfies

$$\|I_h v - v\|_{L_\infty(\Omega_1)} \leq ch^s \|v\|_{W_\infty^s(\Omega_1)} \tag{5.34}$$

with $1 \leq s \leq r$.

Now the theorem is best understood when combined with such estimates and when we consider a case where we may estimate the negative norm on the right. For example, take $u_h$ and $u$ as in Sec. 5.3. Let us take the case in which $r \geq 3$. Then $\bar{r} = 0$ and we may choose $\chi = I_h u$ and $p = -(r - 2)$ in (5.33). Now we may combine (5.33) with (5.34) and (5.27) to see that

$$\|u_h - u\|_{L_\infty(\Omega_0)} \leq ch^r \{\|u\|_{W_\infty^r(\Omega_1)} + \|u\|_2\}$$

Thus, as in the local $L_2$-estimate, we see here that the local maximum norm (or pointwise value of the error) depends locally on the pointwise best approximation properties of $S_h$, but globally only on a weak norm. Even more specifically, for example, if $r = 4$, then the error tends to zero as $h^4$ at an interior point of $r$, provided $u$ has bounded fourth-order partial derivatives in a domain $\Omega_1$ containing the point, and if $u$ has second partial derivatives which are square-integrable.

We wish to emphasize that the results exemplified here are not at all restricted to the special case of the laplacian or of the boundary conditions of Secs. 5.2 and 5.3.

## 5.5 HIGHER-ORDER LOCAL ACCURACY BY AVERAGING

In this section we give examples of results which, as in the preceding section, depend on the knowledge of negative norm estimates. The general idea, which is fully developed in Ref. [4], is that in the case that our finite-element space is uniform on a certain interior subregion of $\Omega$ it is possible to average our finite-element solution $u_h$ in a systematic way so as to obtain, in many cases, higher accuracy for the averaged values than is possessed by the approximation $u_h$ itself. As will be seen by the estimates, a crucial step is provided by the higher-order convergence of the solution $u_h$ to $u$, when measured in a negative norm.

Let $\Omega_0$ and $\Omega_1$ be subregions of $\Omega$ as described in Sec. 5.4. Let $\rho$ be the "least distance" between $\partial\Omega_0$ and $\partial\Omega_1$; that is,

$$\rho - \min_{y_0 \in \partial\Omega_0, y_1 \in \partial\Omega_1} |y_0 - y_1|$$

Suppose that $K_h$ is a function which is sufficiently smooth and whose support has diameter less than $\rho$. Then for any function $v$ defined on $\Omega_1$ the new function

$$(K_h * v)(x) = \int K_h(x - y)v(y)\, dy$$

with $x \in \Omega_0$ is a function obtained by "averaging" the values of $v$ on $\Omega_1$.

We will consider specific functions $K_h$ which have the following properties:

1. $K_h$ has small support.
2. $K_h$ is independent of the specific choice of $S_h$.
3. $K_h * u_h$ is easily computable from $u_h$.

As always, $u_h$ will be the solution of (5.29). As previously mentioned, the results will depend on having a space $S_h$ that is based on a mesh which is regular on $\Omega_1$.

Once again, in order to avoid excessive generality, we will consider piecewise polynomials defined on a square mesh of width $h$ in the plane (cf. Fig. 5.3) or on a regular triangulation of the plane obtained by this same square mesh and the set of positively sloping diagonals (cf. Fig. 5.4). The functions in $S_h$, when restricted to $\Omega_1$, will be continuous on $\Omega_1$ and polynomials on each square, in the first example, or polynomials on each triangle in the second. A convenient way of describing the one important feature of such spaces is as follows: For $x \in \Omega_1$ and $U$ in $S_h$ there are functions $\phi_1, \ldots, \phi_k$ which are piecewise polynomials with compact support such that

$$U(x) = \sum_{j=1}^{k} \sum_{\alpha \in \mathbb{Z}^2} a_\alpha^j \phi_j(h^{-1}x - \alpha)$$

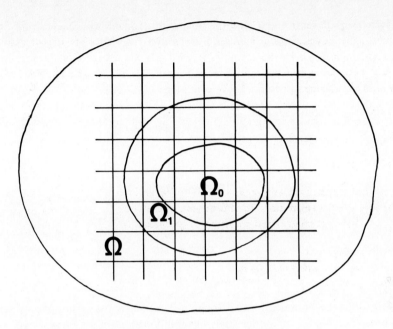

**FIG. 5.3** Discretization of subdomains with square mesh.

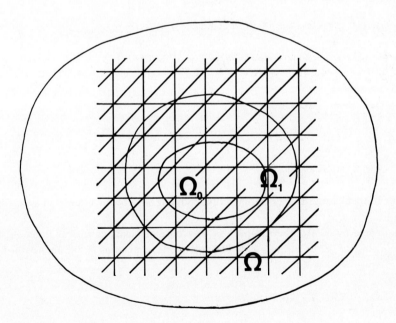

**FIG. 5.4** Triangulation of subdomains with positive-slope diagonals.

Here $a^j_\alpha$ are real coefficients and $\mathbb{Z}^2$ are the points in the plane with integer coordinates. (This property may be described as an interior translation invariance property; clearly such a property is demonstrated by the examples in Figs. 5.3 and 5.4.) We emphasize that the uniformity is a condition which is only required locally. Thus many finite-element spaces which are used in practice satisfy the above conditions.

To define the function $K_h$ we need to introduce the so-called smooth splines. In fact, we choose $K_h$ to be a particular smooth spline depending on the index $r$ associated with the space $S_h$.

For $t$ real, define

$$\chi(t) = \begin{cases} 1 & \text{for } |t| \leq \frac{1}{2} \\ 0 & \text{for } |t| > \frac{1}{2} \end{cases}$$

and for $x = (x_1, x_2)$

$$\psi(x) = \chi(x_1)\chi(x_2)$$

For $l$ a positive integer set

$$\psi^{(l)}(x) = (\psi * \cdots * \psi)(x), \ (l-1) \text{ times}$$

The function $\psi^{(l)}$ is the $N$-dimensional $B$-spline of Schoenberg [12]. The space of smooth splines of order $l$ on a mesh of width $h$ consists of all functions of the form

$$U(x) = \sum_{\alpha \in \mathbb{Z}^2} a_\alpha \psi^{(l)}(h^{-1}x - \alpha)$$

for some coefficients $a_\alpha$.

The following proposition is proved in Ref. [4].

**PROPOSITION 5.1**  Let $l$ and $t$ be two given positive integers. The smooth spline

$$K_h(x) = \sum_{\alpha \in \mathbb{Z}^2} k_\alpha \psi^{(l)}(h^{-1}x - \alpha) \tag{5.35}$$

may be chosen so that

1. $k_\alpha = 0$ when $|\alpha_j| > t-1$ for some $j$. With $h$ small enough, the support of $K_h$ is less than $\rho$, and we have

2. $\|v - K_h * v\|_{L_\infty(\Omega_0)} \leq Ch^{2t}\|v\|_{W^{2t}_\infty(\Omega_1)}$, and

3. $\|v - K_h * v\|_{L_2(\Omega_0)} \leq Ch^{2t}\|v\|_{H^{2t}(\Omega_1)}$.

This function $K_h$ is the aforementioned function in terms of which our local averages will be defined.

Let us denote by $\mathring{S}_h(\Omega_1)$ the subspace of $S_h$ whose elements consist of functions in $S_h$ with support in $\Omega_1$. Let us suppose now that the interior equations (5.30) are satisfied; that is,

$$B(u_h - u, \chi) = 0$$

for all $\chi \in \mathring{S}_h(\Omega_1)$.

We now state the main result which may be found in Ref. [4].

**THEOREM 5.9**  Let $p$ be an arbitrary but fixed integer. Let $l = r - 2$ and $t = r - 1$. Then there is a constant $C$ such that for $u \in H^{2r-2}(\Omega_1)$

$$\|u - K_h * u_h\|_{L_2(\Omega_0)} \leq C\{h^{2r-2}\|u\|_{H^{2r-2}(\Omega_1)} + \|u - u_h\|_{-p}\} \tag{5.36}$$

and, for $u \in H^{2r}(\Omega_1)$,

$$\|u - K_h * u_h\|_{L_\infty(\Omega_0)} \leq C\{h^{2r-2}\|u\|_{H^{2r}(\Omega_1)} + \|u - u_h\|_{-p}\} \tag{5.37}$$

To understand the significance of these results, we consider some specific examples. Let $S_h^{(r)}(\Omega)$ consist of smooth splines of order $r$ (restricted to $\Omega$). Let $u$ be the solution of (5.4) and $u_h$ satisfy (5.19). Then for $\phi \in S_h^{(r)}$ we see that $K_h * \phi \in S_h^{(2r-2)}$. It is known that for some $U_h \in S_h^{(2r-2)}$

$$u - U_h = O(h^{2r-2}) \quad \text{as } h \to 0$$

for smooth $u$. The theorem says that in fact the special smooth spline $K_h * u_h$ is such that

$$u - K_h * u_h = O(h^{2r-2}) \quad \text{as } h \to 0$$

in the interior of $\Omega$ provided that for some $p$

$$\|u - u_h\|_{H^{-p}(\Omega_1)} = O(h^{2r-2})$$

As we see from Theorem 5.5,

$$\|u_h - u\|_{-(r-2)} \leq Ch^{2r-2}\|u\|_r$$

Hence choosing $p = r - 2$, we obtain, from (5.36) in this case,

$$\|u - K_h * u_h\|_{L_2(\Omega_0)} \leq Ch^{2r-2}\{\|u\|_{H^{2r-2}(\Omega_1)} + \|u\|_r\} \tag{5.38}$$

and

$$\|u - K_h * u_h\|_{L_\infty(\Omega_0)} \leq Ch^{2r-2}\{\|u\|_{H^{2r}(\Omega_1)} + \|u\|_r\} \tag{5.39}$$

We see once again that to obtain the local estimates (5.38) or (5.39) we need $u \in H^{2r-2}(\Omega_1)$ [or $H^{2r}(\Omega_1)$] and the weaker result with respect to the behavior of $u$ on $\Omega$ that $u \in H^r(\Omega)$. Even more specifically, looking at (5.39) for $r = 4$ (cubic splines), we have

$$\|u - K_h * u_h\|_{L_\infty(\Omega_0)} \leq Ch^6\{\|u\|_{H^8(\Omega_1)} + \|u\|_4\}$$

Thus we obtain sixth-order convergence in the interior for the Galerkin solution to (5.4) when $S_h$ consists of cubic splines.

We emphasize that $S_h$ need not be chosen to be smooth splines locally (as a special case represented by Fig. 5.3) but may be chosen from a much larger class of approximating subspaces of $H^1(\Omega)$.

Although $K_h * u_h$ can be calculated at arbitrary points, we shall write down explicitly the expression for it at mesh points in the case $\overset{\circ}{S}_h(\Omega_1)$ consists of smooth splines.

Generally, if $u_h$ has the form

$$u_h(x) = \sum_{j=1}^{k} \sum_{\alpha \in \mathbb{Z}^2} a_\alpha^j \phi_j(h^{-1}x - \alpha)$$

in $\Omega_1$, then, for $h$ sufficiently small and $\gamma \in \mathbb{Z}^2$,

$$(K_h * u_h)(h\gamma) = h^2 \sum_{j=1}^{k} \sum_{\alpha \in \mathbb{Z}^2} a_{\gamma-\alpha}^j d_\alpha^j$$

where

$$d_\alpha^j = \sum_{\beta \in \mathbb{Z}^2} k_\beta (\psi^{(r-2)} * \phi_j)(\alpha - \beta)$$

The values of $d_\alpha^j$ may be computed a priori, and once the values of $a_\alpha^j$ are known, it is an easy matter to form $(K_h * u_h)(h\gamma)$.

In the case of smooth splines, $k = 1$ and $\phi_1 = \psi^{(r)}$. Then $d_\alpha \equiv d_\alpha^1$ and hence

$$(K_h * u_h)(h\gamma) = h^2 \sum_{\alpha \in \mathbb{Z}^2} a_{\gamma-\alpha} d_\alpha$$

with

$$d_\alpha = \sum_{\beta \in \mathbb{Z}^2} k_\beta \psi^{(2r-2)}(\alpha - \beta)$$

Note that $d_\alpha = 0$ whenever $|\alpha_j|$ is large for some $j$. Hence the above sum is finite.

The quantities $k_\alpha$ may be computed as follows. Let $k_j'$ be the coefficients in the case of one dimension and take $k_j' = k_{-j}'$. Then

$$k_\alpha = k_{\alpha_1}' k_{\alpha_2}'$$

so that

$$K_h(x) = \prod_{j=1}^{2} \left[ \sum_{n=-(t-1)}^{t-1} k_n' \psi_1^{(l)}(h^{-1}x_j - n) \right]$$

where $\psi_1^{(l)}$ corresponds to the one-dimensional $B$-spline. Tables 5.1 and 5.2 list values of $k_n'$ corresponding to various values of $l$ and $t$.

**TABLE 5.1** $k_j'$, $l = r - 2$, $t = r - 1$

| $j \backslash r$ | 3 | 4 | 5 | 6 |
|---|---|---|---|---|
| 0 | $\dfrac{13}{12}$ | $\dfrac{37}{30}$ | $\dfrac{346{,}517}{241{,}920}$ | $\dfrac{76{,}691}{45{,}360}$ |
| 1 | $\dfrac{-1}{24}$ | $\dfrac{-23}{180}$ | $\dfrac{-81{,}329}{322{,}560}$ | $\dfrac{-48{,}061}{113{,}400}$ |
| 2 | | $\dfrac{1}{90}$ | $\dfrac{6337}{161{,}280}$ | $\dfrac{20{,}701}{226{,}800}$ |
| 3 | | | $\dfrac{-3229}{967{,}680}$ | $\dfrac{-1573}{113{,}400}$ |
| 4 | | | | $\dfrac{479}{453{,}600}$ |

**TABLE 5.2**   $k'_j, \; l = t = r$

| $j\backslash r$ | 1 | 2 | 3 | 4 |
|---|---|---|---|---|
| 0 | 1 | $\dfrac{7}{6}$ | $\dfrac{437}{320}$ | $\dfrac{12{,}223}{7560}$ |
| 1 |  | $\dfrac{-1}{12}$ | $\dfrac{-97}{480}$ | $\dfrac{-919}{2520}$ |
| 2 |  |  | $\dfrac{37}{1920}$ | $\dfrac{311}{5040}$ |
| 3 |  |  |  | $\dfrac{-41}{7560}$ |

Similarly, let $d'_n$ correspond to the case $N = 1$. Then

$$d_\alpha = d'_{\alpha_1} d'_{\alpha_2} = \prod_{j=1}^{2} \left[ \sum_{n=-(t-1)}^{t-1} k'_n \psi_1^{(2r-2)}(\alpha_j - n) \right]$$

Table 5.3 lists some values of $d'_j$ for various indices $l$ and $t$.

**TABLE 5.3**   $d'_j$

| $j\backslash r$ | 3 | 4 | 5 | 6 |
|---|---|---|---|---|
| 0 | $\dfrac{51}{72}$ | $\dfrac{673}{1080}$ | $\dfrac{33{,}055{,}739}{58{,}060{,}800}$ | $\dfrac{967{,}356{,}037}{1{,}828{,}915{,}200}$ |
| 1 | $\dfrac{11}{72}$ | $\dfrac{4283}{21{,}600}$ | $\dfrac{3{,}589{,}969}{16{,}257{,}024}$ | $\dfrac{3{,}841{,}481{,}473}{16{,}460{,}236{,}800}$ |
| 2 | $\dfrac{-1}{144}$ | $\dfrac{-61}{5400}$ | $\dfrac{-12{,}162{,}977}{1{,}625{,}702{,}400}$ | $\dfrac{31{,}253{,}191}{82{,}301{,}184{,}000}$ |
| 3 |  | $\dfrac{29}{21{,}600}$ | $\dfrac{4{,}795{,}283}{2{,}438{,}553{,}600}$ | $\dfrac{48{,}179{,}483}{27{,}433{,}728{,}000}$ |
| 4 |  | $\dfrac{1}{10{,}800}$ | $\dfrac{26{,}273}{270{,}950{,}400}$ | $\dfrac{89{,}711}{514{,}382{,}400}$ |
| 5 |  |  | $\dfrac{-58{,}243}{812{,}851{,}200}$ | $\dfrac{-2{,}905{,}789}{16{,}460{,}236{,}800}$ |
| 6 |  |  | $\dfrac{-3229}{4{,}877{,}107{,}200}$ | $\dfrac{25{,}867}{1{,}097{,}349{,}120}$ |
| 7 |  |  |  | $\dfrac{117{,}083}{82{,}301{,}184{,}000}$ |
| 8 |  |  |  | $\dfrac{479}{164{,}602{,}368{,}000}$ |

## 5.6 EIGENVALUES AND EIGENVECTORS

In this section we consider the eigenvalue problems corresponding to (5.1) and (5.4). That is, we want to find a real number $\lambda$ and a nonzero function $u$ such that

$$-\nabla u = \lambda u \quad \text{in } \Omega$$
$$u = 0 \quad \text{on } \partial\Omega$$

$$(5.40)$$

This is the eigenvalue problem corresponding to (5.1). The problem corresponding to (5.4) is to find a real $\lambda$ and a nonzero function $u$ such that

$$-\Delta u + u = \lambda u \quad \text{in } \Omega$$
$$\frac{\partial u}{\partial n} = 0 \quad \text{on } \partial\Omega$$

$$(5.41)$$

The number $\lambda$ is called an *eigenvalue* and $u$ is a corresponding *eigenfunction*. Clearly, for $\lambda$ and $u$ satisfying (5.40) we have

$$\|\nabla u\|_0^2 = \lambda \|u\|_0^2$$

so that $\lambda > 0$. Similarly, for $\lambda$ and $u$ satisfying (5.40) we have

$$\|\nabla u\|_0^2 + \|u\|_0^2 = \lambda \|u\|_0^2$$

so that here also $\lambda > 0$. In the case of (5.40) every such $\lambda$ is positive and for (5.41), choosing $u \equiv 1$ shows that $\lambda = 1$ is an eigenvalue. It is known that in each case there is a sequence

$$\{\lambda_j\}_{j=1}^\infty \quad \text{with} \quad \lim_{j\to\infty} \lambda_j = \infty \quad \text{and} \quad 0 < \lambda_1 \le \lambda_2 \le \cdots$$

We will suppose that we are looking at either (5.40) or (5.41).

It is well known that corresponding to each real number $\lambda$ there is at most a finite number of eigenvalues $\lambda_j$ with $\lambda_j = \lambda$. This number is the multiplicity of $\lambda_j$.

Now it is convenient to formulate (5.40) and (5.41) in terms of the solution operators corresponding to (5.1) or (5.4). Define the operator $T : L_2(\Omega) \to L_2(\Omega)$ by $Tf = u$ in the case of (5.1) or (5.4). Then we may rephrase (5.40) as

$$T(\lambda u) = u$$

or

$$Tu = \frac{1}{\lambda} u$$

$$(5.42)$$

Setting $\mu = 1/\lambda$ we write

$$Tu = \mu u$$

$$(5.43)$$

Thus in either case we have that there is a sequence

$$\{\mu_j\}_{j=1}^\infty \quad \text{with } \mu_j > 0 \quad \text{for all } j, \ \mu_1 \ge \mu_2 \ge \cdots > 0 \quad \text{and} \quad \lim_{j\to\infty} \mu_j = 0$$

Now as in the case of the boundary-value problems, we wish to introduce the Galerkin eigenvalue problems and give results showing how the Galerkin eigenvalues and eigenfunctions approximate the ones in (5.40) or (5.41).

It is convenient to introduce the solution operator $T_h$ corresponding to (5.8) or (5.19). Thus we define $u_h \equiv T_h f$. The theorems of Secs. 5.2 and 5.3 are statements about $Tf - T_h f$ which we will also subsequently rephrase in terms of operator norm on $T - T_h$. First let us introduce the Galerkin eigenvalue problem. That is, we want to find $\mu(h)$ real such that there corresponds a function $w \in S_h$ with

$$T_h w = \mu(h) w \tag{5.44}$$

Now using the notation of Sec. 5.4 and applying (5.8) or (5.19), we have

$$\mu(h) B(w, \phi) = (w, \phi) \tag{5.45}$$

for all $\phi \in S_h$. Choosing a basis for $S_h$, as was done, for example, in Sec. 5.2, we seek

$$w = \sum_{j=1}^{N_h} \gamma_j \phi_j$$

Hence (5.45) becomes

$$\mu(h) \sum_{j=1}^{N_h} \gamma_j B(\phi_j, \phi_l) = \sum_{j=1}^{N_h} \gamma_j (\phi_j, \phi_l)$$

for $l = 1, \ldots, N_h$. This is a symmetric-matrix eigenvalue problem for the determination of $\mu(h)$ and $\gamma_1, \ldots, \gamma_{N_h}$ (which defines $w$). Ways of solving such matrix problems will be discussed in other chapters. Here we consider the relationship of (5.44) to (5.43) as $h \to 0$. We follow the development in Ref. [3], where more general elliptic operators, including non-self-adjoint operators, are considered. The two examples given in this section could have been treated by other methods (cf. Ref. [2]) which do not generalize directly.

The closure of the set of positive real numbers $\{\mu_j\}_{j=1}^{\infty}$ is commonly called the *spectrum of T*. One statement which can be made from rather general considerations (cf. Ref. [6]) is as follows. Suppose $\mu$ is an eigenvalue of $T$ and has multiplicity $M$. Then for $h$ sufficiently small there is a set of $M$ eigenvalues of $T_h$, $\mu_1(h), \ldots, \mu_M(h)$ with $\mu_1(h) \leq \cdots \leq \mu_M(h)$ and

$$\lim_{h \to 0} \mu_j(h) = \mu \qquad j = 1, \ldots, M$$

Note that the $\mu_j(h)$'s could be distinct though each converges to $\mu$. We want to study how $\mu_j(h) \to \mu$ in terms of the properties of $S_h$ which are reflected in the relationship of $T_h$ to $T$. Let us define the following operator norms. We write, for $s, s_1 \geq 0$,

$$\|T - T_h\|_{-s, s_1} = \sup_{g \in H^{s_1}(\Omega)} \frac{\|(T - T_h)g\|_{-s}}{\|g\|_{s_1}}$$

Thus we have in this notation another statement of Theorem 5.1.

**Theorem 5.10**  Let $T$ and $T_h$ be the solution operators corresponding to (5.1) and (5.8), respectively. Then

$$\|(T - T_h)\|_{0,s} \leq Ch^s \qquad \text{for } s = 1, 2$$

Similarly, we have a restatement of Theorem 5.5.

**Theorem 5.11**  Let $T$ and $T_h$ correspond to (5.4) and (5.19), respectively. Then

$$\|T - T_h\|_{-(s-2),l} \leq Ch^{s+l-2}$$

where $2 \leq s \leq r$ and $1 \leq l \leq r$.

With these statements we now give the estimates for the convergence of eigenfunctions. We need first some remarks. Corresponding to $\mu$ the linear span of the set of eigenfunctions corresponding to $\mu$ is $M$-dimensional. Similarly, the linear span of the set of eigenfunctions corresponding to $\mu_1(h), \ldots, \mu_M(h)$ is also $M$-dimensional. In (5.43), if $u$ is an eigenfunction corresponding to $\mu$, then so is any nonzero constant times $u$. Hence we assume that $u$ has been normalized so that $\|u\|_0 = 1$. We similarly normalize $w$ in (5.44).

The following is contained in Ref. [3].

**Theorem 5.12**  Let $w_j$ be an eigenfunction corresponding to $\mu_j(h)$ with $1 \leq j \leq M$. Then there is an eigenfunction $u_j$ corresponding to $\mu$ such that

$$\|u_j - w_j\|_{-q} \leq C\{\|T - T_h\|_{-q,s} + \|T - T_h\|_{-q,0}\|T - T_h\|_{0,s} + \|T - T_h\|_{0,s}^2\}$$

holds for $0 \leq q \leq r - 2$, $1 \leq s \leq r$, where $C$ is a constant independent of $h$ and $h$ is sufficiently small. Here $C$ depends on $\mu$.

Finally, we give the estimate for the eigenvalues, which is also contained in Ref. [3].

**Theorem 5.13**  For $k = 1, \ldots, M$,

$$|\mu - \mu_k(h)| \leq C\{\|T - T_h\|_{-(r-2),r} + \|T - T_h\|_{-(r-2),0}\|T - T_h\|_{0,r} + \|T - T_h\|_{0,r}^2\}$$

where $C$ is a constant independent of $h$, for $h$ sufficiently small.

We see that for $r > 2$ the negative norm estimates play an important role. From Theorem 5.11 we have

$$\|T - T_h\|_{-(r-2),r} \leq Ch^{2r-2}$$

$$\|T - T_h\|_{-(r-2),0} \leq Ch^{r-2}$$

and
$$\|T - T_h\|_{0,r} \leq Ch^r$$

so that these results with Theorem 5.13 give

$$|\mu - \mu_k(h)| \leq C\{h^{2r-2} + h^{2r}\} \leq C_1 h^{2r-2}$$

Similarly, taking $q = 0$ in Theorem 5.12, we obtain the $L_2$-estimates for the normalized eigenfunctions

$$\|u_j - w_j\|_0 \le Ch^r$$

It is interesting to note that for $r > 2$ the convergence rate for the eigenvalues is greater than that for the eigenfunctions. For example, in the case of piecewise quadratic polynomials ($r = 3$) we see that

$$|\mu - \mu_k(h)| = O(h^4)$$

and in the case of piecewise cubic polynomials

$$|\mu - \mu_k(h)| = O(h^6)$$

## 5.7 REFERENCES

1. Aubin, J. P., "Behavior of the Error of the Approximate Solutions of Boundary Value Problems for Linear Elliptic Operators by Galerkin's and Finite Difference Methods," *Ann. Scuola Norm. Supp. Pisa*, **21**:599–637 (1967).

2. Babuška, I., and A. K. Aziz, "Survey Lectures on the Mathematical Foundations of the Finite Element Method," in A. K. Aziz (ed.), *The Mathematical Foundations of the Finite Element Method with Applications to Partial Differential Equations*, Academic Press, New York, 1972, pp. 3–359.

3. Bramble, J. H., and J. E. Osborn, "Rate of Convergence Estimates for Nonselfadjoint Eigenvalue Approximations," *Math. Comp.*, **27**:525–549 (1973).

4. Bramble, J. H., and A. H. Schatz, "Higher Order Local Accuracy by Averaging in the Finite Element Method," *Math. Comp.*, **31**:94–111 (1977).

5. Bramble, J. H., and M. Zlámal, "Triangular Elements in the Finite Element Method," *Math. Comp.*, **24**:809–920 (1970).

6. Kato, T., "Perturbation Theory for Linear Operators," *Die Grundlehren der mathematischen Wissenschaften*, Band 132, Springer-Verlag, New York, 1966.

7. Lions, J. L., and E. Magenes, *Problèmes aux Limites non Homogènes et Applications*, vol. I, *Travaux et Recherches Mathematiques*, No. 17, Dunod, Paris, 1968.

8. Nitsche, J. A., "Ein Kriterium für die Quasi-optimalität des Ritzche Verfahrens," *Numer. Math.*, **11**:346–348 (1981).

9. Nitsche, J., and A. H. Schatz, "Interior Estimates for Ritz–Galerkin Methods," *Math. Comp.*, **28**:937–958 (1974).

10. Oganesjan, L. A., and P. A. Rukhovets, "Investigation of the Convergence Rate of Variational-Difference Schemes for Elliptic Second Order Equations in a Two-Dimensional Domain with a Smooth Boundary," *Z. Vycisl. Mat. Mat. Fyz.*, **9**:1102–1120 (1969).

11. Schatz, A. H., and L. B. Wahlbin, "Interior Maximum Norm Estimates for Finite Element Methods," *Math. Comp.*, **31**:414–442 (1977).

12. Schoenberg, I. J., "Contributions to the Problem of Approximation of Equidistant Data by Analytic Functions," pt. A, *Q. Appl. Math.*, **4**:45–99, 112–141 (1946).

13. Wahlbin, L. B., "On the Sharpness of Certain Local Estimates for $\mathring{H}^1$ Projections into Finite Element Spaces: Influence of a Reentrant Corner," *Math. Comp.*, **42**:1–8 (1984).

# CHAPTER 6
# FINITE-ELEMENT METHODS FOR TIME-DEPENDENT PROBLEMS

Our purpose in the present chapter is to give a survey of the mathematics of Galerkin finite-element methods as applied to initial boundary-value problems for linear evolution equations. In doing so we will emphasize basic principles rather than generality, and we will refer to the literature for more complete results and more stringent analysis.

The bulk of the chapter deals with parabolic problems. In the introductory Sec. 6.1 we consider the simplest finite-element method for the heat equation, using a standard weak formulation of the differential equation and employing piecewise linear approximating functions. For this model problem we prove the simplest error estimates in mean-square norms, first for the semidiscrete problem resulting from discretization in the space variables only, and then also for some basic completely discrete time-stepping procedures. This section is the longest of the chapter and is intended to give some familiarity with basic tools and concepts.

The next four sections all deal with different aspects of the semidiscrete problem. Section 6.2 discusses the extension to more general situations concerning the approximating functions, and Sec. 6.3 is devoted to estimates which require little regularity of the exact solution to be approximated. Uniform or maximum-norm estimates are outlined in Sec. 6.4, and Sec. 6.5 is a brief account of the related concepts of negative-norm estimates and superconvergence. Section 6.6 is then devoted to discretization in time of the semidiscrete equations.

In the following two sections certain variants of the Galerkin method treated so far are discussed, namely, in Sec. 6.7 the method of lumping the mass matrix and in Sec. 6.8 the so-called $H^1$ and $H^{-1}$ methods which are based on other than the standard weak formulations of the differential equation.

In the final two sections we consider hyperbolic problems. Thus, in Sec. 6.9 we describe methods and error estimates relating to the wave equation, and in Sec. 6.10 we present some results for a model first-order hyperbolic problem.

## 6.1 THE STANDARD GALERKIN METHOD

In this introductory section we consider, in some detail, the model problem of approximating the solution of the heat equation in two space dimensions by means of Galerkin's method, using piecewise linear trial functions.

Let $\Omega$ be a bounded convex plane domain with smooth boundary $\partial\Omega$, and consider the initial boundary-value problem

$$
\begin{aligned}
u_t - \Delta u = f \qquad & \text{in } \Omega \times [0, \infty) \\
u = 0 \qquad & \text{on } \partial\Omega \times [0, \infty) \\
u(x, 0) = v(x) \qquad & \text{on } \Omega
\end{aligned}
\tag{6.1}
$$

where $u_t$ denotes $\partial u/\partial t$ and $\Delta$ the laplacian $\partial^2/\partial x_1^2 + \partial^2/\partial x_2^2$. In the first step we want to approximate $u(x, t)$ by means of a function $u_h(x, t)$ which, for each fixed $t$, is a piecewise linear function of $x$ over a triangulation $\mathcal{T}_h$ of $\Omega$, thus depending on a finite number of parameters. We then proceed to discretize (6.1) also in the time variable.

Before we proceed with the differential equation, we consider the problem of approximation of smooth functions on $\Omega$, vanishing on $\partial\Omega$, by such piecewise linear functions.

Thus let $\mathcal{T}_h$ denote a partition of $\Omega$ into disjoint triangles $\tau$ such that no vertex of any triangle lies on the interior of a side of another triangle and such that the union of the triangles determines a polygonal domain $\Omega_h \subset \Omega$ whose boundary vertices lie on $\partial\Omega$.

Let $h$ denote the maximal length of a side of the triangulation $\mathcal{T}_h$. Thus $h$ is a parameter which decreases as the triangulation is made finer. We assume that the angles of the triangulations are bounded below, independently of $h$, and often also that the triangulations are quasi-uniform in the sense that the triangles of $\mathcal{T}_h$ are of essentially the same size, which may be expressed by demanding that the area of $\tau$ in $\mathcal{T}_h$ is bounded below by $ch^2$ with $c > 0$ independent of $h$.

Now let $S_h$ denote the continuous functions on the closure $\bar{\Omega}$ of $\Omega$ which are linear in each triangle of $\mathcal{T}_h$ and which vanish outside $\Omega_h$. Let $\{P_j\}_1^{N_h}$ be the interior vertices of $\mathcal{T}_h$. A function in $S_h$ is then uniquely determined by its values at the points $P_j$ and thus depends on $N_h$ parameters. Let $\varphi_j$ be the "pyramid function" in $S_h$ which takes the value 1 at $P_j$ but vanishes at the other vertices. Then $\{\varphi_j\}_1^{N_h}$ forms a basis for $S_h$, and every $\chi$ in $S_h$ admits the representation

$$
\chi(x) = \sum_{j=1}^{N_h} \alpha_j \varphi_j(x) \qquad \text{with} \qquad \alpha_j = \chi(P_j)
$$

Given a smooth function $v$ on $\Omega$ which vanishes on $\partial\Omega$, we can now approximate it by its interpolant $I_h v$ in $S_h$, which we define by requiring that it agrees with $v$ at the interior vertices; that is, $I_h v(P_j) = v(P_j)$ for $j = 1, \ldots, N_h$. We now need some results concerning the error in this interpolation.

Throughout this chapter we denote by $\|\cdot\|$ the $L_2$, or mean-square, norm over $\Omega$ and by $\|\cdot\|_r$ that in the Sobolev space $H^r(\Omega) = W_2^r(\Omega)$. Thus, for real-valued functions $v$,

$$\|v\| = \left( \int_\Omega v^2 \, dx \right)^{1/2}$$

and for $r$ a positive integer,

$$\|v\|_r = \left( \sum_{|\alpha| \leq r} \|D^\alpha v\|^2 \right)^{1/2}$$

where $D^\alpha$ is an arbitrary derivative with respect to $x$ of order $|\alpha|$, so that the sum contains all such derivatives of order at most $r$. We recall that for functions in $H_0^1(\Omega)$, i.e., the functions $v$ with $\nabla v = \mathrm{grad}\, v$ in $L_2(\Omega)$ and which vanish on $\partial\Omega$, $\|\nabla v\|$ and $\|v\|_1$ are equivalent norms.

The following error estimates for the interpolant just defined are well known, namely,

$$\|I_h v - v\| \leq Ch^2 \|v\|_2$$

and
$$\|\nabla I_h v - \nabla v\| \leq Ch \|v\|_2 \qquad (6.2)$$

where, as will always be the case in the following discussion, the statements of the inequalities assume that $v$ is sufficiently regular for the norms on the right to be finite.

The orders of these estimates, $O(h^2)$ and $O(h)$, respectively, are the optimal orders to which the functions and their gradients can be approximated in $S_h$, and we attempt below to obtain approximations of these orders for the solution of the heat equation.

For the purpose of defining thus an approximate solution to the initial boundary-value problem (6.1), we multiply the heat equation by a smooth function $\varphi$ which vanishes on $\partial\Omega$, integrate over $\Omega$, and apply Green's formula to the second term, to obtain, for all such $\varphi$, with $(v, w)$ denoting the inner product $\int_\Omega vw \, dx$ in $L_2(\Omega)$,

$$(u_t, \varphi) + (\nabla u, \nabla \varphi) = (f, \varphi) \qquad \text{for } t \geq 0$$

We may then pose the approximate problem to find $u_h(t)$, belonging to $S_h$ for each $t$, such that

$$(u_{h,t}, \chi) + (\nabla u_h, \nabla \chi) = (f, \chi) \qquad \text{for all } \chi \text{ in } S_h, t \geq 0 \qquad (6.3)$$

together with the initial condition

$$u_h(0) = v_h$$

where $v_h$ is some approximation of $v$ in $S_h$. Since we have only discretized in the space variables, this is referred to as a *semidiscrete* problem. Later, we will discretize also in the time variables to produce completely discrete schemes.

In terms of the basis $\{\varphi_j\}_1^{N_h}$ introduced previously our semidiscrete problem may be stated: Find the coefficients $\alpha_j(t)$ in

$$u_h(x, t) = \sum_{j=1}^{N_h} \alpha_j(t) \varphi_j(x)$$

such that
$$\sum_{j=1}^{N_h} \alpha_j'(t)(\varphi_j, \varphi_k) + \sum_{j=1}^{N_h} \alpha_j(t)(\nabla\varphi_j, \nabla\varphi_k) = (f, \varphi_k) \qquad k = 1, \ldots, N_h$$

and, with $\gamma_j$ the nodal values of the given initial approximation $v_h$,

$$\alpha_j(0) = \gamma_j \qquad j = 1, \ldots, N_h$$

In matrix notation this may be expressed as

$$A\alpha'(t) + B\alpha(t) = \tilde{f} \qquad \text{for } t \geq 0, \text{ with } \alpha(0) = \gamma$$

where $A = (a_{jk})$ is the mass matrix with elements $a_{jk} = (\varphi_j, \varphi_k)$, $B = (b_{jk})$ the stiffness matrix with $b_{jk} = (\nabla\varphi_j, \nabla\varphi_k)$, $\tilde{f} = (f_k)$ the vector with entries $f_k = (f, \varphi_k)$, $\alpha(t)$ the vector of unknowns $\alpha_j(t)$, and $\gamma = (\gamma_k)$. The dimension of each of these items equals $N_h$, the number of interior vertices of the triangulation.

Since the mass matrix $A$ is a Gram matrix, and thus in particular positive-definite and invertible, the above system of ordinary differential equations may be written

$$\alpha'(t) + A^{-1}B\alpha(t) = A^{-1}\tilde{f} \qquad \text{for } t \geq 0, \text{ with } \alpha(0) = \gamma$$

and hence obviously has a unique solution for positive $t$.

We will prove the following estimate for the error between the solutions of the semidiscrete and continuous problems.

**THEOREM 6.1** Let $u_h$ and $u$ be the solutions of (6.3) and (6.1), respectively. Then

$$\|u_h(t) - u(t)\| \leq \|v_h - v\| + Ch^2 \left\{ \|v\|_2 + \int_0^t \|u_t\|_2 \, ds \right\} \qquad \text{for } t \geq 0$$

Here we require, of course, that the solution of the continuous problem has the regularity implicitly assumed by the presence of the norms on the right. Note also that for $v_h = I_h v$, (6.2) shows that the first term on the right is dominated by the second. The same holds true if $v_h = P_h v$, where $P_h$ denotes the $L_2$-projection of $v$ onto $S_h$, since this choice is the best approximation of $v$ in $S_h$ with respect to the $L_2$-norm. Another such optimal order choice of $v_h$ is the projection to be defined next.

For the purpose of the proof of Theorem 6.1 we introduce the so-called elliptic, or Ritz, projection $R_h$ onto $S_h$ as the orthogonal projection with respect to the inner product $(\nabla v, \nabla w)$, so that

$$(\nabla R_h u, \nabla \chi) = (\nabla u, \nabla \chi) \qquad \text{for } \chi \text{ in } S_h \qquad (6.4)$$

In fact, $R_h u$ is the finite-element approximation of the solution of the corresponding elliptic problem whose exact solution is $u$. From the well-established error analysis for the elliptic problem we quote the following lemma.

**LEMMA 6.1** With $R_h$ defined by (6.4) we have

$$\|R_h v - v\| + h\|\nabla(R_h v - v)\| \leq Ch^s \|v\|_s \qquad \text{for } s = 1, 2$$

We now turn to the proof of Theorem 6.1. In the main step we compare the solution of the semidiscrete problem to the elliptic projection of the exact solution. We write

$$u_h - u = (u_h - R_h u) + (R_h u - u) = \theta + \rho \tag{6.5}$$

The second term is easily estimated because it is bounded by Lemma 6.1. Thus

$$\|\rho(t)\| \leq Ch^2 \|u(t)\|_2 = Ch^2 \left\| v + \int_0^t u_t \, ds \right\|_2 \leq Ch^2 \left( \|v\|_2 + \int_0^t \|u_t\|_2 \, ds \right)$$

In order to estimate $\theta$, we note that

$$(\theta_t, \chi) + (\nabla \theta, \nabla \chi) = (u_{h,t}, \chi) + (\nabla u_h, \nabla \chi) - (R_h u_t, \chi) - (\nabla R_h u, \nabla \chi)$$

$$= (f, \chi) - (R_h u_t, \chi) - (\nabla u, \nabla \chi) = (u_t - R_h u_t, \chi) \tag{6.6}$$

or $\qquad\qquad (\theta_t, \chi) + (\nabla \theta, \nabla \chi) = -(\rho_t, \chi) \qquad$ for $\chi$ in $S_h$ $\qquad\qquad$ (6.7)

In this derivation we have used the definition of $R_h$ and the easily established fact that this operator commutes with time differentiation. Since $\theta$ belongs to $S_h$, we may choose $\chi = \theta$ in (6.7) and conclude

$$(\theta_t, \theta) + \|\nabla \theta\|^2 = -(\rho_t, \theta)$$

or since the first term equals $\frac{1}{2}(d/dt)\|\theta\|^2$ and the second is nonnegative,

$$\frac{1}{2} \frac{d}{dt} \|\theta\|^2 \leq \|\rho_t\| \|\theta\|$$

This yields

$$\frac{d}{dt} \|\theta\| \leq \|\rho_t\|$$

or, after integration,

$$\|\theta(t)\| \leq \|\theta(0)\| + \int_0^t \|\rho_t\| \, ds$$

Here

$$\|\theta(0)\| = \|v_h - R_h v\| \leq \|v_h - v\| + \|R_h v - v\| \leq \|v_h - v\| + Ch^2 \|v\|_2$$

and further

$$\|\rho_t\| = \|R_h u_t - u_t\| \leq Ch^2 \|u_t\|_2$$

Together these estimates show the theorem.

We shall briefly look at another approach to the proof of Theorem 6.1, which consists in working with the equation for $\theta$ in operator form. For this purpose we introduce a "discrete laplacian" $\Delta_h$, which we think of as an operator from $S_h$ into itself, by

$$(\Delta_h\psi, \chi) = -(\nabla\psi, \nabla\chi) \qquad \text{for } \psi, \chi \text{ in } S_h \tag{6.8}$$

this analogue of Green's formula clearly defines

$$\Delta_h\psi = \sum_{j=1}^{N_h} d_j\varphi_j$$

from
$$\sum_{j=1}^{N_h} d_j(\varphi_j, \varphi_k) = -(\nabla\psi, \nabla\varphi_k) \qquad k = 1, \ldots, N_h$$

since the matrix of this system is the positive-definite mass matrix encountered above. The operator $\Delta_h$ is easily seen to be self-adjoint and $-\Delta_h$ is positive-definite. With $P_h$ again the $L_2$-projection onto $S_h$, the equation for $\theta$ takes the form

$$(\theta_t, \chi) - (\Delta_h\theta, \chi) = -(P_h\rho_t, \chi) \qquad \text{for } \chi \text{ in } S_h$$

or
$$(\theta_t - \Delta_h\theta + P_h\rho_t, \chi) = 0 \qquad \text{for } \chi \text{ in } S_h$$

or, finally, noting that the first factor is in $S_h$, so that $\chi$ may be chosen equal to it,

$$\theta_t - \Delta_h\theta = -P_h\rho_t \tag{6.9}$$

Let us denote by $E_h(t)$ the solution operator of the homogeneous semidiscrete equation

$$u_{h,t} - \Delta_h u_h = 0 \qquad \text{for } t \geq 0$$

i.e., the operator which takes the initial data $u_h(0) = v_h$ into the solution $u_h(t)$ at time $t$, so that $u_h(t) = E_h(t)v_h$. (This operator can also be thought of as the semigroup generated by $-\Delta_h$.) Duhamel's principle then tells us that the solution of the inhomogeneous equation (6.9) is

$$\theta(t) = E_h(t)\theta(0) - \int_0^t E_h(t-s)P_h\rho_t(s) \, ds$$

We now note that $E_h(t)$ is stable in $L_2$, or

$$\|E_h(t)v_h\| \leq \|v_h\| \qquad \text{for } v_h \text{ in } S_h$$

In fact, choosing $\chi = u_h$ in the homogeneous form of (6.3), we have

$$\frac{1}{2}\frac{d}{dt}\|u_h\|^2 + \|\nabla u_h\|^2 = 0$$

Since the second term is nonnegative, we conclude that the first is nonpositive and hence $\|u_h\|^2$ is nonincreasing, which shows the stability. Since obviously $P_h$ has unit norm in $L_2$, we have therefore

$$\|\theta(t)\| \leq \|\theta(0)\| + \int_0^t \|\rho_t(s)\| \, ds$$

from which the theorem follows as above. The desired estimate for $\theta$ is thus a consequence of the stability estimate for $E_h(t)$ combined with the error estimate for the elliptic problem applied to $\rho_t = (R_h - I)u_t$.

In a similar way we may prove the following estimate for the error in the gradient:

**THEOREM 6.2**   Under the assumptions of Theorem 6.1 we have for $t \geq 0$,

$$\|\nabla u_h(t) - \nabla u(t)\| \leq C\|\nabla v_h - \nabla v\| + Ch\left\{\|v\|_2 + \|u(t)\|_2 + \left(\int_0^t \|u_t\|_1^2 \, ds\right)^{1/2}\right\}$$

**Proof**   As before, we write the error in the form (6.5). Here by Lemma 6.1,

$$\|\nabla \rho(t)\| = \|\nabla(R_h u(t) - u(t))\| \leq Ch\|u(t)\|_2$$

In order to estimate $\nabla\theta$ we use again (6.7), now with $\chi = \theta_t$. We obtain

$$\|\theta_t\|^2 + \frac{1}{2}\frac{d}{dt}\|\nabla\theta\|^2 = -(\rho_t, \theta_t) \leq \tfrac{1}{2}\|\rho_t\|^2 + \tfrac{1}{2}\|\theta_t\|^2$$

so that
$$\frac{d}{dt}\|\nabla\theta\|^2 \leq \|\rho_t\|^2$$

or
$$\|\nabla\theta(t)\|^2 \leq \|\nabla\theta(0)\|^2 + \int_0^t \|\rho_t\|^2 \, ds$$

$$\leq (\|\nabla(v_h - v)\| + \|\nabla(R_h v - v)\|)^2 + \int_0^t \|\rho_t\|^2 \, ds$$

Hence, in view of Lemma 6.1,

$$\|\nabla\theta(t)\|^2 \leq C\|\nabla(v_h - v)\|^2 + Ch^2\left(\|v\|_2^2 + \int_0^t \|u_t\|_1^2 \, ds\right) \tag{6.10}$$

which completes the proof.

Note that if $v_h = I_h v$ or $R_h v$, then

$$\|\nabla v_h - \nabla v\| \leq Ch\|v\|_2$$

so that the first term on the right in Theorem 6.2 is again dominated by the second.

We make the following observation concerning $\theta = u_h - R_h u$: Assume that we have chosen $v_h = R_h v$ so that $\theta(0) = 0$. Then in addition to (6.10) we have

$$\|\nabla\theta(t)\| \leq C\left(\int_0^t \|\rho_t\|^2 \, ds\right)^{1/2} \leq Ch^2\left(\int_0^t \|u_t\|_2^2 \, ds\right)^{1/2}$$

Hence the gradient of $\theta$ is $O(h^2)$, whereas the gradient of the total error is only $O(h)$, for small $h$. Thus $\nabla u_h$ is a better approximation to $\nabla R_h u$ than is possible to $\nabla u$. This is an example of a phenomenon which is sometimes referred to as *superconvergence*. We shall return later to other examples.

We now turn our attention to some simple schemes for discretization also with respect to the time variable. We begin by the backward Euler–Galerkin method. If we let $k$ be the time step and $U^n$ the approximation in $S_h$ of $u(t)$ at $t = t_n = nk$, this method is defined by replacing the time derivative in (6.3) by a backward-difference quotient, or if $\bar{\partial}_t U^n = k^{-1}(U^n - U^{n-1})$,

$$(\bar{\partial}_t U^n, \chi) + (\nabla U^n, \nabla\chi) = (f(t_n), \chi) \qquad \text{for } \chi \text{ in } S_h$$
$$U^0 = v_h$$

$$(6.11)$$

This defines $U^n$ implicitly by means of $U^{n-1}$ from the elliptic problem

$$(U^n, \chi) + k(\nabla U^n, \nabla\chi) = (U^{n-1} + kf(t_n), \chi) \qquad \text{for } \chi \text{ in } S_h$$

We shall prove the following error estimate.

**THEOREM 6.3**  With $U^n$ and $u$ the solutions of (6.11) and (6.1), respectively, we have

$$\|U^n - u(t_n)\| \le \|v_h - v\| + Ch^2\left(\|v\|_2 + \int_0^{t_n} \|u_t\|_2 \, ds\right) + Ck \int_0^{t_n} \|u_{tt}\| \, ds \qquad \text{for } n \ge 0$$

**Proof**  In analogy with (6.5) we write

$$U^n - u(t_n) = (U^n - R_h u(t_n)) + (R_h u(t_n) - u(t_n)) = \theta^n + \rho^n$$

As before,
$$\|\rho^n\| \le Ch^2\|u(t_n)\|_2 \le Ch^2\left(\|v\|_2 + \int_0^{t_n} \|u_t\|_2 \, ds\right)$$

This time, a calculation corresponding to (6.6) yields

$$(\bar{\partial}_t \theta^n, \chi) + (\nabla\theta^n, \nabla\chi) = -(\omega^n, \chi)$$

where
$$\omega^n = R_h \bar{\partial}_t u(t_n) - u_t(t_n)$$
$$= (R_h - I)\bar{\partial}_t u(t_n) + (\bar{\partial}_t u(t_n) - u_t(t_n))$$
$$= \omega_1^n + \omega_2^n$$

Choosing $\chi = \theta^n$, we have

$$(\bar{\partial}_t \theta^n, \theta^n) \le \|\omega^n\| \cdot \|\theta^n\|$$

or
$$\|\theta^n\|^2 - (\theta^{n-1}, \theta^n) \le k\|\omega^n\|\|\theta^n\|$$

so that
$$\|\theta^n\| \le \|\theta^{n-1}\| + k\|\omega^n\|$$

and, by repeated application,

$$\|\theta^n\| \le \|\theta^0\| + k\sum_{j=1}^n \|\omega^j\| \le \|\theta^0\| + k\sum_{j=1}^n \|\omega_1^j\| + k\sum_{j=1}^n \|\omega_2^j\|$$

Here, as before,
$$\|\theta^0\| = \|v_h - R_h v\| \le \|v_h - v\| + Ch^2\|v\|_2$$

Note now that

$$\omega_1^j = (R_h - I)k^{-1} \int_{t_{j-1}}^{t_j} u_t \, ds = k^{-1} \int_{t_{j-1}}^{t_1} (R_h - I)u_t \, ds$$

whence

$$k \sum_{j=1}^{n} \|\omega_1^j\| \leq \sum_{j=1}^{n} \int_{t_{j-1}}^{t_j} Ch^2 \|u_t\|_2 \, ds = Ch^2 \int_0^{t_n} \|u_t\|_2 \, ds$$

Further,

$$\omega_2^j = k^{-1}(u(t_j) - u(t_{j-1})) - u_t(t_j) = -k^{-1} \int_{t_{j-1}}^{t_j} (s - t_{j-1})u_{tt}(s) \, ds$$

so that

$$k \sum_{j=1}^{n} \|\omega_2^j\| \leq \sum_{j=1}^{n} \left\| \int_{t_{j-1}}^{t_j} (s - t_{j-1})u_{tt}(s) \, ds \right\| \leq k \int_0^{t_n} \|u_{tt}\| \, ds$$

Together our estimates complete the proof of the theorem.

Notice that because of the nonsymmetric choice of the discretization in time, the backward Euler-Galerkin method is only first order in time.

We now turn to the Crank-Nicolson-Galerkin method, in which the semidiscrete equation is discretized in a symmetric fashion around the point $t_{n+1/2} = (n + \frac{1}{2})k$, which will produce a method which is second-order accurate in time. More precisely, we define $U^n$ in $S_h$ recursively by

$$(\bar{\partial}_t U^n, \chi) + \left( \nabla \frac{(U^n + U^{n-1})}{2}, \nabla \chi \right) = (f(t_{n-1/2}), \chi) \qquad \text{for } \chi \text{ in } S_h, n = 1, 2, \ldots$$

$$U^0 = v_h$$

(6.12)

This time the error estimate reads as follows; its proof is similar to that of Theorem 6.3.

**THEOREM 6.4**  With $U^n$ and $u$ the solutions of (6.12) and (6.1), respectively, we have for $n \geq 0$,

$$\|U^n - u(t_n)\| \leq \|v_h - v\| + Ch^2 \left( \|v\|_2 + \int_0^{t_n} \|u_t\|_2 \, ds \right)$$

$$+ Ck^2 \int_0^{t_n} (\|u_{ttt}\| + \|\Delta u_{tt}\|) \, ds$$

The material in this section is now standard; for some early references, see Refs. [13], [19], [28], and [40].

## 6.2 SOME RESULTS FOR MORE GENERAL SEMIDISCRETE APPROXIMATIONS

In this section we discuss the extension to more general situations of the treatment in Sec. 6.1 of discretization of the parabolic problem (6.1) with respect to the space variables.

Let us first note that the only properties of the spaces $S_h$ of approximating functions that entered into the analysis of the semidiscrete problem were the error estimates of Lemma 6.1

for the elliptic problem, which in turn follow from the properties that $S_h \subset H_0^1(\Omega)$ and that

$$\|v - I_h v\| + h \|\nabla(v - I_h v)\| \leqslant Ch^2 \|v\|_2$$

where $I_h v$ denotes the interpolant of $v$.

Through the proofs of Theorems 6.1 and 6.2 it is easy to see that if the latter property is replaced by the assumption that for some $r \geqslant 2$,

$$\min_{\chi \in S_h} \{\|v - \chi\| + h\|\nabla(v - \chi)\|\} \leqslant Ch^s\|v\|_s \qquad \text{for } s = 1, 2, \ldots, r \tag{6.13}$$

so that sufficiently smooth functions may be approximated to order $h^r$ and their gradients to order $h^{r-1}$, then similar improvements follow for the solutions of the elliptic and parabolic problems. This conclusion applies equally well to the case when $\Omega$ is a domain in $d$-dimensional space $R^d$ with a smooth boundary $\partial\Omega$.

In particular, defining the elliptic projection $R_h$ onto $S_h$ as earlier by

$$(\nabla R_h v, \nabla \chi) = (\nabla v, \nabla \chi) \qquad \text{for } \chi \text{ in } S_h \tag{6.14}$$

we have the following lemma.

**LEMMA 6.2**   If (6.13) holds, then for $v$ vanishing on $\partial\Omega$,

$$\|R_h v - v\| + h\|\nabla(R_h v - v)\| \leqslant Ch^s\|v\|_s \qquad \text{for } s = 1, \ldots, r$$

Further, considering the parabolic problem

$$u_t - \Delta u = f \qquad \text{in } \Omega \times [0, \infty)$$

$$u = 0 \qquad \text{on } \partial\Omega \times [0, \infty) \tag{6.15}$$

$$u(\cdot, 0) = v \qquad \text{in } \Omega$$

and its semidiscrete analogue

$$(u_{h,t}, \chi) + (\nabla u_h, \nabla \chi) = (f, \chi) \qquad \text{for } \chi \text{ in } S_h$$

$$u_h(0) = v_h \tag{6.16}$$

we may state the following theorem.

**THEOREM 6.5**   If (6.13) holds, then for $u_h$ and $u$ the solutions of (6.16) and (6.15), respectively, we have for $t \geqslant 0$,

$$\|u_h(t) - u(t)\| \leqslant \|v_h - v\| + Ch^r \left( \|v\|_r + \int_0^t \|u_t\|_r \, ds \right)$$

and $\qquad \|\nabla u_h(t) - \nabla u(t)\| \leqslant C\|\nabla v_h - \nabla v\| + Ch^{r-1} \left\{ \|v\|_r + \|u(t)\|_r + \left( \int_0^t \|u_t\|_{r-1}^2 \, ds \right)^{1/2} \right\}$

Spaces $S_h$ with the property (6.13) could consist, for instance, of continuous functions which reduce to polynomials of degree $\leqslant r - 1$ on the triangles of a triangulation $\mathcal{T}_h$ of $\Omega$ of the type we have considered above. The case of piecewise linear approximating functions would then be included as the special case $r = 2$, and an increase in the degree of the polynomials would result in a corresponding increase in the order of approximation.

For $r > 2$ and $\partial\Omega$ curved, however, there are difficulties in constructing the spaces $S_h$ so that the condition $S_h \subset H_0^1(\Omega)$ is satisfied, as this requires that the approximating functions satisfy the boundary condition $u = 0$ on $\partial\Omega$ exactly. Even if this is possible to accomplish, in principle, by mapping a curved-boundary triangle onto a straight-edged reference triangle and using the appropriate polynomials there (isoparametric elements), a variety of other procedures for the elliptic problems have been devised which dispense with the condition $S_h \subset H_0^1(\Omega)$ in various ways. For example, one method which has been proposed by Nitsche [25] uses the following bilinear form to define the solution of the elliptic problem, namely, with $\langle v, w \rangle = \int_{\partial\Omega} vw \, dS$, $n$ the exterior normal to $\partial\Omega$, and $\gamma$ an appropriate positive number,

$$B_h(v, w) = (\nabla v, \nabla w) - \left\langle \frac{\partial v}{\partial n}, w \right\rangle - \left\langle v, \frac{\partial w}{\partial n} \right\rangle + \gamma h^{-1} \langle v, w \rangle$$

In another method, analyzed by Scott [30], the approximating functions are made to satisfy the boundary condition $u = 0$ only at certain interpolation points between the boundary vertices.

With these considerations in mind, we now describe an approach developed in Ref. [5] to space discretization of the parabolic problem, which allows considerable generality in the treatment of the elliptic term.

We assume thus that we have associated with the elliptic problem,

$$-\Delta u = f \quad \text{in } \Omega \qquad u = 0 \quad \text{on } \partial\Omega \tag{6.17}$$

an approximate solution $u_h = T_h f$ in $S_h$ such that the linear operator $T_h$ has the following two properties, shared by several finite-element-type approximations, namely:

1. $T_h$ is self-adjoint, positive-semidefinite on $L_2$, and positive-definite on $S_h$.
2. With $u = Tf$ the exact solution of (6.17),

$$\| T_h f - T f \| \leqslant C h^s \| f \|_{s-2} \qquad \text{for } s = 2, \ldots, r$$

If we write the parabolic equation in the form $-\Delta u = f - u_t$, it is natural to demand that the approximate solution in $S_h$ satisfy $u_h = T_h(f - u_{h,t})$, and we therefore formulate our semidiscrete problem as

$$T_h u_{h,t} + u_h = T_h f \qquad \text{for } t \geqslant 0$$
$$u_h(0) = v_h \tag{6.18}$$

It follows easily from the positive-definiteness of $T_h$ that a unique solution of (6.18) exists in $S_h$ for $t \geqslant 0$.

For the standard Galerkin method the approximate solution operator $T_h$ would be defined by

$$(\nabla T_h f, \nabla \chi) = (f, \chi) \qquad \text{for } \chi \text{ in } S_h$$

so that, if $u = Tf$, one finds that $T_h f = R_h u = R_h Tf$. Using the definition of $T_h$, we have

$$(f, T_h g) = (\nabla T_h f, \nabla T_h g) = (T_h f, g)$$

so that $T_h$ is self-adjoint, and also, as is seen by choosing $g = f$, positive-semidefinite. To show that $T_h$ is positive-definite on $S_h$, we let $f_h \in S_h$ be such that $T_h f_h = 0$ and conclude

$$\|f_h\|^2 = (f_h, f_h) = (\nabla T_h f_h, \nabla f_h) = 0$$

Thus, condition 1 is satisfied for this choice, and condition 2 is a consequence of Lemma 6.2 since

$$\|T_h f - Tf\| = \|u_h - u\| \leq Ch^s \|u\|_s \leq Ch^s \|f\|_{s-2}$$

where in the last step we have used a well-known regularity estimate for the elliptic equation.

In terms of the operator $T_h$, the semidiscrete standard Galerkin equation may now be written

$$(\nabla T_h u_{h,t}, \nabla \chi) + (\nabla u_h, \nabla \chi) = (\nabla T_h f, \nabla \chi) \qquad \text{for } \chi \text{ in } S_h$$

or, since $\chi$ is arbitrary in $S_h$, as (6.18). In the case of Nitsche's bilinear form, the problem (6.18) corresponds to taking the semidiscrete equation

$$(u_{h,t}, \chi) + B_h(u_h, \chi) = (f, \chi) \qquad \text{for } \chi \text{ in } S_h$$

and the situation is similar for other methods.

Our previous $L_2$-error estimate now extends to the present degree of generality:

**THEOREM 6.6** Assume that conditions 1 and 2 hold. Then, if $u_h$ is the solution of (6.18) and $u$ the exact solution of (6.15), we have

$$\|u_h(t) - u(t)\| \leq \|v_h - v\| + Ch^r \left( \|v\|_r + \int_0^t \|u_t\|_r \, ds \right) \qquad \text{for } t \geq 0$$

For special choices of $T_h$ the estimate for the gradient of Theorem 6.5 also generalizes. In general, if $S_h$ satisfies the "inverse" assumption

$$\|\nabla \chi\| \leq Ch^{-1} \|\chi\| \qquad \text{for } \chi \text{ in } S_h \tag{6.19}$$

which often holds for quasi-uniform triangulations, one may show the following.

**THEOREM 6.7** Under the assumptions of Theorem 6.6 and if (6.19) holds, we have

$$\|\nabla u_h(t) - \nabla u(t)\| \leq Ch^{-1} \|v_h - v\| + Ch^{r-1} \left( \|v\|_r + \int_0^t \|u_t\|_r \, ds \right) \qquad \text{for } t \geq 0$$

In particular, if $v_h$ is chosen as the best approximation of $v$ with respect to the $L_2$-norm, the $L_2$-projection $P_h v$ of $v$ onto $S_h$, we conclude from (6.13) that the first term in either of the above error bounds is dominated by the second, and hence may be omitted. This conclusion remains valid for all choices of $v_h$ such that $\|v_h - v\| \leq Ch^r \|v\|_r$.

For the homogeneous equation, i.e., the case $f = 0$ in (6.15), it can be shown that the last term in the error estimate of Theorem 6.6 may be omitted. More precisely, we have the following:

**THEOREM 6.8**  Under the assumptions of Theorem 6.6, and with $f = 0$, assume that $v$ is compatible with the differential equation on $\partial\Omega$ in the sense that $\Delta^j v - 0$ on $\partial\Omega$ for $j < r/2$. Then

$$\|u_h(t) - u(t)\| \leq \|v_h - v\| + Ch^r\|v\|_r \qquad \text{for } t \geq 0$$

The above remark, concerning the choice of $v_h$ applies again so that, in particular, if $v_h = P_h v$, for example, then

$$\|u_h(t) - u(t)\| \leq Ch^r\|v\|_r \qquad (6.20)$$

We close this section by remarking that the above theory extends to the more general parabolic equation

$$u_t - \sum_{j,k=1}^{d} \frac{\partial}{\partial x_j}\left(a_{jk}\frac{\partial u}{\partial x_k}\right) - \sum_{j=1}^{d} b_j \frac{\partial u}{\partial x_j} - cu = f$$

where $a_{jk}$, $b_j$, and $c$ are smooth functions of both $x$ and $t$, and $(a_{jk})$ is a uniformly positive-definite matrix (cf. Ref. [22] and its references).

## 6.3 NONSMOOTH DATA ESTIMATES

In the preceding section we presented error estimates for the semidiscrete problem which were of optimal order $h^r$, under the appropriate assumptions about the approximating spaces $S_h$. In order for these estimates to be valid, however, relatively stringent regularity assumptions had to be imposed on the exact solution. For the homogeneous heat equation, for instance, to infer the optimal-order estimate (6.20) it was necessary not only that $v \in H^r(\Omega)$ but also that certain compatibility conditions be satisfied on $\partial\Omega$.

In this section we shall see that optimal-order estimates for the homogeneous equation are valid also without such stringent regularity assumptions, provided the time at which the error is considered is bounded away from zero and the discrete initial data are appropriately chosen. We shall then apply this fact to the nonhomogeneous equation to find that optimal-order error estimates are valid provided the exact solution is regular near the time at which the error is appraised.

Let us thus consider the continuous problem, with $\Omega \subset R^d$,

$$u_t = \Delta u \qquad \text{in } \Omega \times [0, \infty)$$

with $\qquad u = 0 \qquad$ on $\partial\Omega \times [0, \infty) \qquad$ and $\qquad u(0) = v \qquad$ (6.21)

and its semidiscrete counterpart,

$$T_h u_{h,t} + u_h = 0 \qquad \text{for } t \geq 0 \qquad \text{with } u_h(0) = v_h = P_h v \qquad (6.22)$$

where $u_h \in S_h$ and $T_h$ satisfies conditions 1 and 2 of Sec. 6.2. Recall that if $S_h \in H_0^1(\Omega)$ and

(6.13) holds, then such an operator $T_h$ could be defined in a manner which makes (6.22) the standard weak formulation of the heat equation. Observe that we have now restricted the choice of the discrete initial data to the $L_2$-projection of the given $v$.

The following error estimate holds (see Ref. [5] and references).

**THEOREM 6.9**   Under the present assumptions,

$$\|u_h(t) - u(t)\| \le Ch^r t^{-r/2} \|v\| \qquad \text{for } t > 0$$

This optimal-order estimate thus only requires $v$ to be in $L_2(\Omega)$ but it deteriorates as $t$ becomes small.

The proof is related to a smoothing property of parabolic equations: For the exact solution of (6.21) one has for $v$ appropriate

$$\|u(t)\|_p \le Ct^{-(p-q)/2} \|v\|_q \qquad \text{for } 0 \le q \le p \tag{6.23}$$

and it is not difficult to formulate and show a corresponding result for the semidiscrete problem. In particular, with our previous notation,

$$\|\Delta_h E_h(t) v_h\| = \|E_h(t)\Delta_h v_h\| \le Ct^{-1/2} \|v_h\|_1 \qquad \text{for } v_h \text{ in } S_h \tag{6.24}$$

To give some indication of how such an estimate may yield an error estimate of the type stated, we shall show

$$\|u_h(t) - u(t)\| \le Ch^{1/2} t^{-1/4} \|v\| \qquad \text{for } t > 0 \tag{6.25}$$

in the case of the standard Galerkin method, and under the additional assumption that $P_h$ is bounded in $H_0^1(\Omega)$, which holds, for instance, if $S_h$ satisfies the inverse assumption (6.19). An error estimate with a higher power of $ht^{-1/2}$ may be obtained from (6.25) by an iteration argument by Helfrich [21], which will not be carried out here.

In the demonstration of (6.25) it suffices, by stability, to consider $h \le t^{1/2}$. We write the error

$$u_h - u = (u_h - P_h u) + (P_h u - u) = \eta + \omega$$

Here, using (6.23) with $p = 1$, $q = 0$,

$$\|\omega(t)\| = \|P_h u(t) - u(t)\| \le Ch\|u(t)\|_1 \le Cht^{-1/2}\|v\| \le Ch^{1/2} t^{-1/4}\|v\| \tag{6.26}$$

A simple calculation shows

$$(\eta_t, \chi) + (\nabla \eta, \nabla \chi) = -(\nabla \omega, \nabla \chi) = -(\nabla R_h \omega, \nabla \chi)$$

or

$$\eta_t - \Delta_h \eta = \Delta_h R_h \omega = \Delta_h P_h (I - R_h) u$$

Now since $\eta(0) = 0$, we have

$$\eta(t) = \int_0^t E_h(t - s) \Delta_h P_h (I - R_h) u(s) \, ds$$

and hence by (6.24), using the boundedness of $P_h$ in $H_0^1(\Omega)$, and again (6.23) with $p = 1$, $q = 0$,

$$\|\eta(t)\| \le C \int_0^t (t-s)^{-1/2} \|(I - R_h)u(s)\|_1 \, ds$$

Here, using Lemma 6.2 with $s = 1$ and 2 and then (6.23), we have

$$\|(I - R_h)u(s)\|_1 \le C(h\|u(s)\|_2)^{1/2} \|u(s)\|_1^{1/2} \le Ch^{1/2}s^{-3/4}\|v\|$$

whence

$$\|\eta(t)\| \le Ch^{1/2} \int_0^t (t-s)^{-1/2} s^{-3/4} \, ds \|v\| = Ch^{1/2}t^{-1/4}\|v\| \qquad (6.27)$$

Together, (6.26) and (6.27) show (6.25).

Estimates similar to the above are valid for time derivatives of the error:

**THEOREM 6.10**   Under the same assumptions as above, we have for $l \ge 0$,

$$\left\|\left(\frac{d}{dt}\right)^l (u_h(t) - u(t))\right\| \le Ch^r t^{-r/2-l}\|v\| \qquad \text{for } t > 0$$

We complete this section by the following result for the nonhomogeneous equation

$$u_t - \Delta u = f \qquad \text{in } \Omega \times [0, \infty)$$

with the usual boundary and initial conditions, and its discrete counterpart,

$$T_h u_{h,t} + u_h = T_h f \qquad \text{for } t \ge 0, \; u_h(0) = P_h v$$

where again $T_h$ is assumed to satisfy conditions 1 and 2 of Sec. 6.2 (cf. Ref. [34]).

**THEOREM 6.11**   Under the present assumptions, and with $\delta > 0$ and $l \ge 0$ we have for $t \ge \delta$,

$$\left\|\left(\frac{d}{dt}\right)^l (u_h(t) - u(t))\right\| \le Ch^r \left\{ \|v\| + \int_0^t \|f\| \, ds + \sum_{j=0}^{l+1} \int_{t-\delta}^t \left\|\left(\frac{d}{dt}\right)^j u\right\|_r ds \right\}$$

This result shows that optimal-order estimates are valid at time $t$ for the error and its successive derivatives with respect to time, provided the exact solution is sufficiently regular in a short interval preceding $t$. The proof uses the above results for the homogeneous equation.

The results of this section generalize to more general parabolic equations (cf. Ref. [22] and references).

## 6.4 MAXIMUM-NORM ESTIMATES

In this section we present some maximum-norm stability and corresponding uniform error estimates from Ref. [31].

We return to the model problem of the introduction and consider thus the initial boundary-value problem

$$u_t - \Delta u = f \quad \text{in } \Omega \times [0, \infty)$$

$$u = 0 \quad \text{on } \partial\Omega \times [0, \infty)$$

$$u(\cdot, 0) = v \quad \text{in } \Omega$$

where $\Omega$ is a smooth, bounded convex domain in the plane. Let $S_h \subset H_0^1(\Omega)$ be the piecewise linear functions on a quasi-uniform triangulation $\mathcal{T}_h$ of $\Omega$ with its boundary vertices on $\partial\Omega$, and which vanish outside the polygonal domain $\Omega_h$ defined by $\mathcal{T}_h$. We consider the corresponding semidiscrete problem to find $u_h(t) \in S_h$ such that

$$(u_{h,t}, \chi) + (\nabla u_h, \nabla \chi) = (f, \chi) \quad \text{for } t \geq 0, \text{ for all } \chi \text{ in } S_h$$

$$u_h(0) = v_h$$

Recall that the solution operator $E_h(t)$ of the corresponding homogeneous equation is stable in $L_2$,

$$\|E_h(t)v_h\| \leq \|v_h\|$$

and that this fact could be used in the $L_2$-error analysis. With regard to the maximum norm one may show the following.

**THEOREM 6.12**  Under the present assumptions, we have for $t \geq 0$,

$$\|E_h(t)v_h\|_{L_\infty} \leq C \ln \frac{1}{h} \|v_h\|_{L_\infty} \quad \text{where} \quad \|v\|_{L_\infty} = \sup_{x \in \Omega} |v(x)|$$

For the continuous problem the well-known maximum principle would imply an analogous result, but with the factor $C \ln(1/h)$ replaced by unity. In this form the result does not carry over to the finite-element situation, but as we shall see, the weaker maximum principle of Theorem 6.12 is almost equally effective in deriving error estimates. It is not known whether or not $C \ln(1/h)$ could be replaced by, say, a constant.

Let us briefly comment on the proof of the theorem. One notes first that the solution of the homogeneous equation may be written by means of a discrete fundamental solution as

$$u_h(t) = E_h(t)v_h(x) = (\Gamma_h^x(t), v_h)$$

where $\Gamma_h^x$ is also a solution of the homogeneous semidiscrete equation but with initial values $\delta_h^x$, the discrete $\delta$-function defined by

$$(\delta_h^x, \chi) = \chi(x) \quad \text{for all } \chi \text{ in } S_h$$

The theorem would therefore follow from

$$\|\Gamma_h^x\|_{L_1} \leq C \ln \frac{1}{h}$$

In order to get into a situation where energy arguments and $L_2$-based norms may be used, one introduces the weight function $\omega(y) = \omega_h^x(y) = (|x-y|^2 + h^2)^{1/2}$ and finds by Schwarz' inequality

$$\|\Gamma_h^x\|_{L_1} \leq \|\omega^{-1}\|_{L_2} \|\omega \Gamma_h^x\|_{L_2}$$

Here a simple calculation shows that the first factor is bounded by $C[\ln (1/h)]^{1/2}$, and the result is therefore a consequence of the fact that the second is also so bounded, as may be demonstrated by means of a considerable technical arsenal.

The stability result of Theorem 6.12 has an analogue in the case of one space dimension (cf. Ref. [36]), but to our knowledge generalizations to more than two dimensions have not been explicitly stated in the literature.

For the purpose of error analysis we recall a maximum-norm error estimate for the elliptic problem (cf. Ref. [26] and references), expressed in terms of the elliptic projection $R_h$:

**LEMMA 6.3**   We have

$$\|R_h v - v\|_{L_\infty} \leq Ch^2 \ln \frac{1}{h} \|v\|_{W_\infty^2} \qquad \text{where} \qquad \|v\|_{W_\infty^2} = \sum_{j,k=1}^{2} \left\| \frac{\partial^2 v}{\partial x_j \, \partial x_k} \right\|_{L_\infty}$$

We now state the maximum-norm error estimate analogous to Theorem 6.1.

**THEOREM 6.13**   We have for $t \geq 0$,

$$\|u_h(t) - u(t)\|_{L_\infty} = C \ln \frac{1}{h} \|v_h - v\|_{L_\infty} + Ch^2 \left( \ln \frac{1}{h} \right)^2 \left( \|v\|_{W_\infty^2} + \int_0^t \|u_t\|_{W_\infty^2} \, ds \right)$$

To see this, recall from the proof of Theorem 6.1 that with $\theta = u_h - R_h u$, $\rho = R_h u - u$, we have

$$\theta(t) = E_h(t)\theta(0) - \int_0^t E_h(t-s) P_h \rho_t(s) \, ds$$

Since the $L_2$-projection $P_h$ can be shown to be bounded in the maximum norm, we conclude

$$\|\theta(t)\|_{L_\infty} \leq C \ln \frac{1}{h} \|v_h - R_h v\|_{L_\infty} + C \ln \frac{1}{h} \int_0^t \|\rho_t\|_{L_\infty} \, ds$$

which is bounded as stated by Lemma 6.3. Together with the bound for $\rho(t)$ supplied by Lemma 6.3 this completes the proof.

Maximum-norm error estimates are known in greater generality, also in more dimensions (cf. Refs. [11], [12], [27]).

We quote also a nonsmooth data maximum-norm error estimate (cf. Ref. [31]):

**THEOREM 6.14**   With $v_h = P_h v$ we have for any $\varepsilon > 0$,

$$\|u_h(t) - u(t)\|_{L_\infty} \leq C_\varepsilon h^{2-3\varepsilon} t^{-2+\varepsilon} \|v\|_{L_1} \qquad \text{for } t > 0$$

This result thus states that even with initial data only in $L_1(\Omega)$, the error is essentially optimal order $O(h^2)$ in the maximum norm away from $t = 0$. We will not discuss its proof here.

## 6.5 NEGATIVE-NORM ESTIMATES AND SUPERCONVERGENCE

In this section we give a brief account of the related concepts of negative-norm estimates and superconvergence, extracted from Ref. [34].

Consider again the initial boundary-value problem, with $\Omega \subset R^d$,

$$
\begin{aligned}
u_t - \Delta u = f \quad &\text{in } \Omega \times [0, \infty) \\
u = 0 \quad &\text{on } \partial\Omega \times [0, \infty) \\
u(\cdot, 0) = v \quad &\text{in } \Omega
\end{aligned}
\tag{6.28}
$$

and its semidiscrete analogue

$$
\begin{aligned}
(u_{h,t}, \chi) + (\nabla u_h, \nabla \chi) = (f, \chi) \quad &\text{for } t \ge 0, \ \chi \text{ in } S_h \\
u_h(0) = v_h
\end{aligned}
\tag{6.29}
$$

where $S_h \subset H_0^1(\Omega)$ and satisfies, for some $r \ge 2$,

$$
\inf_{\chi \in S_h} \{\|v - \chi\| + h\|\nabla(v - \chi)\|\} \le Ch^s\|v\|_s \qquad \text{for } 1 \le s \le r
\tag{6.30}
$$

[We have chosen to work with the case $S_h \subset H_0^1(\Omega)$ for simplicity only; what follows carries over to the general situation employing approximate solution operators $T_h$ as described in Sec. 6.2.]

We first recall the following error estimate for the elliptic problem associated with (6.28) with respect to the negative norm defined by

$$
\|v\|_{-s} = \sup \left\{ \frac{(v, \varphi)}{\|\varphi\|_s}; \ \varphi \in H^s(\Omega) \right\}
$$

which may be derived by a simple duality argument.

**LEMMA 6.4** With $R_h$ the standard elliptic projection onto $S_h$ we have

$$
\|R_h v - v\|_{-s} \le Ch^{s+r}\|v\|_r, \qquad \text{for } 0 \le s \le r - 2
$$

Note in particular the case $s = r - 2$,

$$
\|R_h v - v\|_{-(r-2)} \le Ch^{2r-2}\|v\|_r
$$

showing convergence in the negative norm specified of order $h^{2r-2}$, which is faster than $O(h^r)$ if $r > 2$.

Our purpose now is to show similar estimates for the parabolic problem and briefly discuss some applications which will exhibit higher-order approximations than might be expected from (6.30). This sort of phenomenon is referred to as *superconvergence*.

It will be convenient to modify the definition of the negative norm by taking the supremum over functions satisfying certain boundary conditions, or

$$\|v\|_{-s} = \sup\left\{\frac{(v, \varphi)}{\|\varphi\|_s}; \ \varphi \in H^s(\Omega), \ \Delta^j\varphi = 0 \text{ on } \partial\Omega \text{ for } j < \frac{s}{2}\right\}$$

With this new definition Lemma 6.4 remains valid and we have the following.

**THEOREM 6.15**    Assume that $v_h$ is chosen such that

$$\|v_h - v\|_{-s} \leq Ch^{s+r}\|v\|_r, \qquad \text{for } 0 \leq s \leq r-2$$

Then for $u_h$ and $u$ the solutions of (6.29) and (6.28), respectively, we have for $t \geq 0$,

$$\|u_h(t) - u(t)\|_{-(r-2)} \leq Ch^{2r-2}\left(\|v\|_r + \int_0^t \|u_t\|_r \, ds\right)$$

The assumption for $v_h$ is satisfied, for instance, by the elliptic projection $R_h v$ and the $L_2$-projection $P_h v$ of $v$ onto $S_h$.

In our applications below we will need an estimate also for time derivatives, which we state here only for $v_h = P_h v$.

**THEOREM 6.16**    Let $l \geq 0$, and $v_h = P_h v$. Then, with $u_h$ and $u$ as above, we have for $t \geq \delta > 0$,

$$\left\|\left(\frac{d}{dt}\right)^l (u_h(t) - u(t))\right\|_{-(r-2)} \leq Ch^{2r-2}\left\{\sum_{j=0}^l \left\|\left(\frac{d}{dt}\right)^j u(t)\right\|_r + \int_{t-\delta}^t \left\|\left(\frac{d}{dt}\right)^{l+1} u\right\|_r ds + \int_0^t \|u_t\|_r \, ds\right\}$$

As a first, very simple, application, assume one is interested in computing the integral $F(u) = \int_\Omega ug\, dx$, where $g$ is a function in $H^{r-2}(\Omega)$ satisfying the boundary conditions $\Delta^j g = 0$ on $\partial\Omega$ for $j < \frac{1}{2}r - 1$. Then it follows immediately that $F(u_h)$ is a superconvergent-order approximation of $F(u)$:

$$|F(u_h) - F(u)| = |(u_h - u, g)| \leq C\|u_h - u\|_{-(r-2)}\|g\|_{r-2} \leq C(u)h^{2r-2}$$

In our next application we shall assume that the triangulation $\mathcal{T}_h$ is uniform in some interior subdomain $\Omega_1$ of $\Omega$ (in a sense which we refrain from making precise here). We shall see that by postprocessing the semidiscrete solution in a simple fashion it is possible to determine a superconvergent-order approximation of $u$. For this purpose we shall denote by $\psi$ the $B$-spline of order $r-2$ in $R^d$, that is, the convolution $\psi_0 * \psi_0 * \cdots * \psi_0$ with $r-2$ factors, where $\psi_0$ is the function with value 1 for $-\frac{1}{2} \leq x_j \leq \frac{1}{2}, j = 1, \ldots, d$, and which vanishes elsewhere. The following theorem results from a combination of a construction of a local averaging operator in Ref. [4] and some interior estimates for difference quotients of the error in (6.29).

**THEOREM 6.17**   There exists a function $K_h$ of the form

$$K_h(x) = h^{-d} \sum_{\gamma} k_\gamma \psi(h^{-1}x - \gamma)$$

with $k_\gamma = 0$ for $|\gamma_j| \geq r - 1$, such that if $\mathcal{T}_h$ is uniform in a neighborhood $\Omega_1$ of the interior domain $\Omega_0$, then, for $u_h$ and $u$ as above, we have at time $t$, with $d_0 > d/2$,

$$\|K_h * u_h - u\|_{L_\infty(\Omega_0)} \leq Ch^{2r-2} \sum_{2l < 2r-2+d_0} \left\|\left(\frac{d}{dt}\right)^l u\right\|_{H^{2r-2+d_0-2l}(\Omega_1)}$$

$$+ C \sum_{2l \leq r+d_0} \left\{ h^{r-2}\left\|\left(\frac{d}{dt}\right)^l (u_h - u)\right\| + \left\|\left(\frac{d}{dt}\right)^l (u_h - u)\right\|_{-(r-2)} \right\}$$

The coefficients $k_\gamma$ of $K_h$ can easily be determined by manipulations with Fourier transforms.

As a consequence we find in view of our previous Theorem 6.16 that for positive time and suitable initial data,

$$\|K_h * u_h(t) - u(t)\|_{L_\infty(\Omega_0)} \leq C(u)h^{2r-2}$$

with stringent regularity assumptions only near $t$.

The above procedure may be modified in such a way that an arbitrary derivative of $u$ with respect to the space variables may be approximated to superconvergent order $h^{2r-2}$ by means of a convolution of a difference quotient of $u_h$ by a simple function (cf. Refs. [33] and [34]).

We shall present one more application of these ideas. This concerns the case of one space dimension so that the elliptic problem reduces to the two-point boundary-value problem

$$Au \equiv -\frac{d}{dx}\left(a\frac{du}{dx}\right) + cu = f \quad \text{in } I = [0, 1] \quad \text{with } a > 0, c \geq 0$$

$$u(0) = u(1) = 0$$

(6.31)

where we have introduced the smooth coefficients $a$ and $c$ to make what follows nontrivial. We now work with the finite-dimensional space $S_h$ consisting of continuous functions in $I$ vanishing at $x = 0$ and $x = 1$ and which reduce to polynomials of degree at most $r - 1$ in each interval of the partition $0 = x_0 < x_1 < \cdots < x_M = 1$, with $\kappa h \leq x_j - x_{j-1} \leq h$. Such a family satisfies the analogue of the approximation assumption (6.30) above. This time the bilinear form associated with the problem is

$$A(v, w) = \int_0^1 (av'w' + cvw)\, dx$$

and the discrete solution of (6.31) is defined by

$$A(u_h, \chi) = (f, \chi) \quad \text{for } \chi \text{ in } S_h$$

Let now $g = g_{\bar{x}}$ be the Green's function of (6.31) with singularity at a node $\bar{x}$ of the partition. Then, by the definition of the Green's function, we find that $w(\bar{x}) = A(w, g)$ for any $w \in H_0^1(I)$. In particular, we have for the error, using its orthogonality to $S_h$ with respect to $A(\cdot,\cdot)$,

$$(u_h - u)(\bar{x}) = A(u_h - u, g) = A(u_h - u, g - \chi) \qquad \text{for } \chi \text{ in } S_h$$

Note now that although $g_{\bar{x}}$ is not smooth at $\bar{x}$ it may still be approximated well by a function in $S_h$ since it is smooth outside $\bar{x}$ and the discontinuity of the derivative at $\bar{x}$ can be accommodated in $S_h$. Therefore, with a suitable choice of $\chi$ in $S_h$, using the known $H^1$-error estimate for $u_h$, we find

$$\left| (u_h - u)(\bar{x}) \right| \leqslant C \| u_h - u \|_1 \| g - \chi \|_1 \leqslant (Ch^{r-1} \| u \|_r) C(g) h^{r-1} = Ch^{2r-2} \| u \|_r$$

that is, superconvergence occurs at the nodes of the partition.

Consider now the corresponding parabolic problem

$$u_t + Au = f \qquad \text{in } I \times [0, \infty)$$

$$u = 0 \qquad \text{at } x = 0, 1$$

$$u(\cdot, 0) = v \qquad \text{in } I$$

and its semidiscrete analogue

$$(u_{h,t}, \chi) + A(u_h, \chi) = (f, \chi) \qquad \text{for } \chi \text{ in } S_h$$

$$u_h(0) = v_h$$

Using ideas employed above for the two-point boundary-value problem one may show the following (see Ref. [34]).

**THEOREM 6.18**   Let $\bar{x}$ be one of the nodes of the partition. Then, with $u_h$ and $u$ as above, we have for any $n \geqslant 0$,

$$\left| u_h(\bar{x}, t) - u(\bar{x}, t) \right| \leqslant C \left\{ h^{r-1} \sum_{j=0}^{n} \left\| \left( \frac{d}{dt} \right)^j (u_h - u)(t) \right\|_1 + h^r \left\| \left( \frac{d}{dt} \right)^{n+1} (u_h - u)(t) \right\| \right.$$

$$\left. + \left\| \left( \frac{d}{dt} \right)^{n+1} (u_h - u)(t) \right\|_{-2n} \right\}$$

Once more, we may appeal to known error estimates of order $h^{r-1}$ in $\| \cdot \|_1$, $h^r$ in $\| \cdot \|$, and $h^{2r-2}$ in $\| \cdot \|_{-(r-2)}$ to conclude that under the appropriate regularity assumptions and with suitable choice of $v_h$, we have for $t > 0$,

$$\left| u_h(\bar{x}, t) - u(\bar{x}, t) \right| \leqslant C(t, u) h^{2r-2}$$

For another approach to the present problem, using so-called quasi projections of the exact solution, see Ref. [16].

## 6.6 COMPLETELY DISCRETE SCHEMES

In this section we discuss, more generally than in Sec. 6.1, time-stepping procedures for the heat equation which are obtained by discretization in time of a semidiscrete problem. We shall present error bounds of the form $O(h^r + k^\nu)$ where $O(h^r)$ is the order of the error in the semidiscrete solution and where, with $k$ the time step, $O(k^\nu)$ is the contribution from the discretization in time. We first discuss the homogeneous equation and then state some results for the nonhomogeneous case.

We consider thus the initial boundary-value problem, with $\Omega \subset R^d$,

$$u_t = \Delta u \qquad \text{in } \Omega \times [0, \infty)$$

$$u = 0 \qquad \text{on } \partial\Omega \times [0, \infty) \tag{6.32}$$

$$u(\cdot, 0) = v \qquad \text{in } \Omega$$

Following the presentation in Ref. [3], we assume that we are given a family of subspaces $S_h$ and a corresponding family of approximate solution operators $T_h$ of the associated elliptic problem such that conditions 1 and 2 of Sec. 6.2 are satisfied. The semidiscrete approximation to (6.32) is then

$$T_h u_{h,t} + u_h = 0 \qquad \text{for } t \geqslant 0 \qquad \text{with } u_h(0) = v_h$$

If we set $\Delta_h = -T_h^{-1}$ on $S_h$, which is possible since $T_h$ is positive-definite, this problem may be written

$$u_{h,t} = \Delta_h u_h \qquad \text{for } t \geqslant 0 \qquad \text{with } u_h(0) = v_h$$

which formally has the exact solution

$$u_h(t) = E_h(t)v_h = \exp(t\Delta_h)v_h$$

Note that the present definition of $\Delta_h$ coincides with the definition in (6.8) in the particular case treated in Sec. 6.1.

For the purpose of defining a completely discrete method, let $k$ be the time step and let $r(z)$ be a rational function approximating $e^z$ with accuracy $\nu$, that is,

$$r(z) = e^z + O(z^{\nu+1}) \qquad \text{as } z \to 0 \tag{6.33}$$

and satisfying certain boundedness conditions on the negative real axis, to be specified below. Assuming, in particular, that $r(z)$ has no pole at any eigenvalue of $k\Delta_h$, we may then define the approximate solution $U^n$ in $S_h$ at time $t_n = nk$ recursively by

$$U^{n+1} = r(k\Delta_h)U^n \qquad n = 0, 1, \ldots$$

$$U^0 = v_h \tag{6.34}$$

For example, consider the case that $S_h \subset H_0^1(\Omega)$ so that $\Delta_h$ may be defined by (6.8). Then the equation

$$(\bar{\partial}_t U^{n+1}, \chi) + (\nabla(\theta U^{n+1} + (1-\theta)U^n), \nabla\chi) = 0 \qquad \text{for } \chi \text{ in } S_h$$

may be written $\qquad\qquad (I - k\theta\Delta_h)U^{n+1} = (I + k(1-\theta)\Delta_h)U^n$

which corresponds to taking

$$r(z) = \frac{1 + (1-\theta)z}{1 - \theta z} \tag{6.35}$$

The cases $\theta = 0$ and $\theta = 1$ are the forward and backward Euler schemes, and for $\theta = \frac{1}{2}$ we recognize the Crank–Nicolson method.

More generally, if

$$r(z) = c \prod_{j=1}^{M} (\alpha_j - z)^{-1} \prod_{j=1}^{N} (\beta_j - z)$$

then Eq. (6.34) may be written in the form

$$\prod_{j=1}^{M} (\alpha_j - k\Delta_h) U^{n+1} = c \prod_{j=1}^{N} (\beta_j - k\Delta_h) U^n$$

which shows that $U^{n+1}$ may be obtained from $U^n$ through the solution of a finite number of elliptic finite-element problems.

For the analysis, it is convenient to interpret (6.34) by means of a spectral representation. Thus, let $\{\Lambda_j\}_1^{N_h}$ be the eigenvalues of the positive-definite operator $-\Delta_h$ on $S_h$ and $\{\phi_j\}_1^{N_h}$ the corresponding eigenfunctions. Then for any $v_h \in S_h$,

$$U^n(x) = r(k\Delta_h)^n v_h = \sum_{j=1}^{N_h} r(-k\Lambda_j)^n (v_h, \phi_j) \phi_j(x) \tag{6.36}$$

We note at once that the scheme (6.34) will be stable in $L_2(\Omega)$ if $|r(-k\Lambda_j)| \leq 1$ for all $j$, for then, by Parseval's relation,

$$\|U^n\|^2 \leq \sum_{j=1}^{N_h} (v_h, \phi_j)^2 = \|v_h\|^2$$

We shall now classify the rational functions involved according to the following successively more restrictive conditions for their behavior on the negative real axis:

**I.** $|r(\lambda)| < 1$     for $-\alpha < \lambda < 0$ for some $\alpha > 0$

**II.** $|r(\lambda)| < 1$     for $\lambda < 0$,

**III.** $|r(\lambda)| < 1$     for $\lambda < 0$, $|r(\infty)| < 1$

**IV.** $|r(\lambda)| < 1$     for $\lambda < 0$, $r(\infty) = 0$

Letting $\Lambda_{max}$ be the maximal eigenvalue of $-\Delta_h$, we say that a scheme is of type

**I'.** if $r(z)$ is of type I and $k\Lambda_{max} < \alpha_0$ for some $\alpha_0$ in $(0, \alpha)$,

**II'.** if $r(z)$ is of type II and $k\Lambda_{max} < \alpha_1$ for some $\alpha_1 > 0$.

A scheme of type II, III, or IV will simply be one for which $r(z)$ satisfies condition II, III, or IV, respectively, with no restriction on $k\Lambda_{max}$.

Examples of rational functions of types I, II, and IV are provided by the above-diagonal, diagonal, and below-diagonal entries, respectively, of the Padé table for $e^z$. The rational function in (6.35) is of type I if $\theta < \frac{1}{2}$, II if $\theta = \frac{1}{2}$, III if $\frac{1}{2} < \theta < 1$, and IV if $\theta = 1$; it is accurate of order $\nu = 2$ for $\theta = \frac{1}{2}$ and $\nu = 1$ for $\theta \neq \frac{1}{2}$. Another example of a scheme of type III with $r(\infty) \neq 0$ is furnished by the third-order accurate Calahan scheme, which uses

$$r(z) = 1 + \frac{z}{1 - bz} + \frac{\sqrt{3}}{6}\left(\frac{z}{1 - bz}\right)^2 \quad \text{with} \quad b = \frac{1}{2}\left(1 + \frac{\sqrt{3}}{3}\right)$$

In order that $k\Lambda_{\max} \leqslant \tau_0$ it is sufficient that $\Lambda_{\max} \leqslant \kappa_0 h^{-2}$ and that the mesh-ratio condition $k/h^2 \leqslant \tau_0/\kappa_0$ hold, where, for the standard Galerkin method, the former condition would follow from the inverse assumption (6.19).

We may now state two error estimates, the first of which is valid when the solution of (6.32) is smooth uniformly for $t \geqslant 0$ and where the second is a nonsmooth data estimate.

**THEOREM 6.19**  Let the discretization be of type I' or II. Then, with $U^n$ and $u$ as above, we have for $v$ appropriately regular and compatible with (6.32),

$$\|U^n - u(t_n)\| \leqslant \|v_h - v\| + C\{h^r\|v\|_r + k^\nu\|v\|_{2\nu}\} \quad \text{for } t \geqslant 0$$

**THEOREM 6.20**  Let the discretization be of type I', II', or III. Then, with $U^n$ and $u$ as above, we have for $v_h = P_h v$,

$$\|U^n - u(t_n)\| \leqslant C\{h^r t^{-r/2} + k^\nu t^{-\nu}\}\|v\| \quad \text{for } t > 0$$

The proofs depend on spectral representation as in (6.36). Observe that the nonsmooth data result places more restrictions on $r(z)$ for large negative $z$ than does the smooth data estimate.

We now turn to completely discrete schemes for the inhomogeneous equation

$$u_t = \Delta u + f \quad \text{in } \Omega \times [0, \infty) \tag{6.37}$$

and to isolate the effect of the inhomogeneity we assume that $u$ vanishes for $t = 0$. The semidiscrete problem is now

$$u_{h,t} = \Delta_h u_h + P_h f \quad \text{for } t \geqslant 0 \quad \text{with } u_h(0) = 0 \tag{6.38}$$

Generalizing from the case of the homogeneous equation, we consider a scheme of the form (cf. Refs. [6] and [8])

$$U^{n+1} = r(k\Delta_h)U^n + k\sum_{j=1}^{m} r_j(k\Delta_h)P_h f(t_n + k\tau_j) \tag{6.39}$$

where $r_j(z)$ are rational functions without poles on the negative real axis and $\{\tau_j\}_1^m$ distinct real numbers in $[0, 1]$.

It turns out that this scheme is an approximation to the semidiscrete problem of order $\nu$ if and only if (6.33) holds together with the equations

$$\sum_{j=1}^{m} \tau_j^l r_j(z) = \frac{l!}{z^{l+1}}\left(r(z) - \sum_{j=0}^{l} \frac{z^j}{j!}\right) + O(z^{\nu-l}) \quad \text{as } z \to 0 \text{ for } 0 \leqslant l \leqslant \nu - 1$$

The schemes have particularly advantageous properties if the $O(z^{\nu-l})$-remainder terms vanish, and we call such a scheme *strictly accurate of order $\nu$*.

For example, the Crank–Nicolson scheme

$$(I - \tfrac{1}{2}k\Delta_h)U^{n+1} = (I + \tfrac{1}{2}k\Delta_h)U^n + kf(t_n + \tfrac{1}{2}k)$$

corresponds to

$$r(z) = \frac{1 + \tfrac{1}{2}z}{1 - \tfrac{1}{2}z} \qquad m = 1, \ \tau_1 = \tfrac{1}{2}, \ r_1(z) = \frac{1}{1 - \tfrac{1}{2}z}$$

It is strictly accurate of order 2.

We say that the scheme (6.39) is of type I', II, etc., if the associated scheme for the homogeneous equation is of this respective type. We now present some error estimates for (6.39), where in the first two we include only the error between the completely discrete and semidiscrete problems. We use the notation $f^{(l)} = (d/dt)^l f$.

**THEOREM 6.21**   Assume that the scheme (6.39) is of type I' or II and accurate of order $\nu$. Then, provided $f$ is appropriately regular and satisfies the boundary conditions $\Delta^s f^{(l)} = 0$ on $\partial\Omega$ for $s < \max(\tfrac{1}{2}r, \nu) - l$, $l < \nu$, we have for $t_n \leq t^* < \infty$, with $U^n$ and $u_h$ the solutions of (6.39) and (6.38),

$$\|U^n - u_h(t_n)\| \leq Ch^r \sum_{l=0}^{\nu-1} \sup_{t \leq t_n} \|f^{(l)}(t)\|_{\max(r-2l,0)} + Ck^\nu \left\{ \sum_{l=0}^{\nu-1} \sup_{t \leq t_n} \|f^{(l)}(t)\|_{2\nu-2l} + \int_0^{t_n} \|f^{(\nu)}\| \, ds \right\}$$

**THEOREM 6.22**   Assume that the scheme (6.39) is of type I' or II and strictly accurate of order $\nu$. Then, if $f$ is appropriately regular and satisfies the above boundary conditions on $\partial\Omega$ for $t = 0$, we have for $t_n \leq t^*$, with $U^n$ and $u_h$ as above,

$$\|U^n - u_h(t_n)\| \leq Ch^r \sum_{l=0}^{\nu} \|f^{(l)}(0)\|_{\max(r-2l,0)} + Ck^\nu \left\{ \sum_{l=0}^{\nu} \|f^{(l)}(0)\|_{2r-2l} + \int_0^{t_n} \|f^{(\nu+1)}\| \, ds \right\}$$

The advantage of the stricter accuracy condition is that the artificial boundary conditions of Theorem 6.21 may be dropped for $t > 0$.

We end by stating a complete error estimate for $t$ bounded away from zero. Similarly to the situation for the semidiscrete problem we find that smoothness with respect to the $x$-variables is only required in a short interval preceding the time at which the error is sought.

**THEOREM 6.23**   Let the scheme (6.39) be of type I', II', or IV, and strictly accurate of order $\nu$. Then, with $U^n$ and $u$ the solutions of (6.39) and (6.37), we have for $0 < \delta \leq t_n \leq t^*$,

$$\|U^n - u(t_n)\| \leq Ch^r \left\{ \int_{t_n-\delta}^{t_n} (\|u\|_r + \|u_t\|_r) \, ds + \int_0^{t_n} \|f\| \, ds \right\}$$

$$+ Ck^\nu \left\{ \sum_{l=0}^{\nu-1} \|f^{(l)}(0)\| + \int_{t_n-\delta}^{t_n} \|f^{(\nu-1)}\| \, ds + \int_0^{t_n} \|f^{(\nu)}\| \, ds \right\}$$

The methods treated above are all of single-step type in that they express the approximation at a given time level in terms of the approximation at the previous time level only. For some studies of multistep methods, involving more than two time levels, compare Refs. [9], [24], and [42].

## 6.7 THE LUMPED-MASS METHOD

In this section we consider a modification of the standard Galerkin method discussed in Sec. 6.1, the method of lumping the mass matrix. We consider thus again the case of the initial boundary-value problem (6.1), with $\Omega$ a smooth, convex plane domain, and let $S_h$ consist of continuous piecewise linear functions on the triangulation $\mathcal{T}_h$, vanishing on $\partial\Omega$.

Recall that the standard Galerkin method,

$$(u_{h,t}, \chi) + (\nabla u_h, \nabla \chi) = (f, \chi) \qquad \text{for } \chi \text{ in } S_h, \, t \geq 0 \tag{6.40}$$

can be written in matrix form

$$A\alpha'(t) + B\alpha(t) = \tilde{f}(t) \qquad \text{for } t \geq 0 \tag{6.41}$$

where the mass and stiffness matrices have elements $a_{jk} = (\varphi_j, \varphi_k)$ and $b_{jk} = (\nabla\varphi_j, \nabla\varphi_k)$, respectively. One way of defining the *lumped-mass method* is to replace the mass matrix $A$ in (6.41) by the diagonal matrix $\bar{A}$ obtained by taking for its diagonal elements

$$\bar{a}_{jj} = \sum_{k=1}^{N_h} a_{jk}$$

or by lumping all masses in one row into the diagonal entry. This makes the inversion of the matrix $\bar{A}$ a triviality.

This procedure may also be interpreted as resulting from evaluating the first term in (6.40) by numerical quadrature: Let $\tau$ be a triangle of the triangulation $\mathcal{T}_h$, let $P_{\tau,j}$, $j = 1, 2, 3$, be its vertices, and consider the quadrature formula

$$Q_{\tau,h}(f) = \text{area } \tau \cdot \frac{1}{3} \sum_{j=1}^{3} f(P_{\tau,j}) \approx \int_{\tau} f\, dx$$

We may then define an approximation of the $L_2$-inner product by

$$(\psi, \chi)_h = \sum_{\tau \in \mathcal{T}_h} Q_{\tau,h}(\psi\chi)$$

and find by simple calculation that the lumped-mass method may be written as

$$(u_{h,t}, \chi)_h + (\nabla u_h, \nabla \chi) = (f, \chi) \qquad \text{for } \chi \in S_h \tag{6.42}$$

The procedure just discussed is a special case of a family of quadrature schemes analyzed in Ref. [29], where it is also shown to be the only viable such method of diagonal type.

We are now ready to state the error estimates for the lumped-mass method (6.42).

THEOREM 6.24   If $u_h$ and $u$ are the solutions of (6.42) and (6.1), respectively, then for $t \geq 0$,

$$\|u_h(t) - u(t)\| \leq C\|v_h - v\| + Ch^2 \left\{ \|v\|_2 + \|u(t)\|_2 + \left( \int_0^t \|u_t\|_2^2 \, ds \right)^{1/2} \right\}$$

and

$$\|\nabla u_h(t) - \nabla u(t)\| \leq C\|\nabla v_h - \nabla v\| + Ch \left\{ \|v\|_2 + \|u(t)\|_2 + \left( \int_0^t \|u_t\|_2^2 \, ds \right)^{1/2} \right\}$$

We shall not include the proof. We note that the regularity requirements in these results are slightly more stringent than in the corresponding results for the standard Galerkin method. We also remark that a superconvergence result is again valid for $\nabla(u_h - R_h u)$, and one may prove as a consequence a maximum-norm error bound of the form (cf. Ref. [7])

$$\|u_h(t) - u(t)\|_{L_\infty} \leq C(t, u) h^2 \ln \frac{1}{h} \qquad \text{for } t \geq 0$$

The method of lumped masses may, of course, also be employed in connection with discretization with respect to time. One could, for instance, consider the backward Euler method, with $\bar{\partial}_t$ as usual denoting the backward-difference quotient,

$$(\bar{\partial}_t U^n, \chi)_h + (\nabla U^n, \nabla \chi) = (f(t_n), \chi) \qquad \text{for } \chi \text{ in } S_h, \, n = 1, 2, \ldots$$
$$U^0 = v_h \tag{6.43}$$

or in matrix form, with $\alpha^n$ the vector of the nodal values of $U^n$ and $F^n$ the vector with components $(f(t_n), \varphi_k)$, $k = 1, \ldots, N_h$,

$$\alpha^n = (\bar{A} + kB)^{-1} \bar{A} \alpha^{n-1} + (\bar{A} + kB)^{-1} F^n \qquad \text{for } n = 1, 2, \ldots$$

with $\alpha^0$ given from $v_h$. One may then prove the following.

**THEOREM 6.25**   If $U^n$ and $u$ are the solutions of (6.43) and (6.1), respectively, then for $t_n = nk \geq 0$,

$$\|U^n - u(t_n)\| \leq C \|v_h - v\| + Ch^2 \left\{ \|v\|_2 + \|u(t)\|_2 + \left( \int_0^{t_n} \|u_t\|_2^2 \, ds \right)^{1/2} \right\} + Ck \left( \int_0^{t_n} \|u_{tt}\|^2 \, ds \right)^{1/2}$$

An interesting property of the lumped-mass method is that, in contrast to the situation for the standard Galerkin method, an exact maximum principle holds under the specific assumption that the triangulation contains no obtuse triangles. Letting $\bar{E}_h(t)$ denote the solution operator associated with the semidiscrete method (6.42), one may prove the following (cf. Ref. [20]).

**THEOREM 6.26**   Assume that all angles of the triangulation $\mathcal{T}_h$ are bounded above by $\pi/2$. Then for all $v_h \in S_h$,

$$\min\left(0, \min_\Omega v_h(x)\right) \leq \bar{E}_h(t) v_h(x) \leq \max\left(0, \max_\Omega v_h(x)\right) \tag{6.44}$$

In particular, $\qquad\qquad\qquad\qquad \|\bar{E}_h(t) v_h\|_{L_\infty} \leq \|v_h\|_{L_\infty}$

To give an indication of the proof of (6.44), we note that the solution of the system of ordinary differential equations corresponding to (6.41) may be written

$$\alpha(t) = \exp\left(-\bar{A}^{-1} B t\right) \gamma = G(t) \gamma \qquad \text{where } \gamma = \alpha(0)$$

It is then easy to see that (6.44) follows if we can show that all elements of $G(t)$ are nonnegative and all its row sums are bounded by 1. For the purpose of showing the first statement, one observes that the off-diagonal elements of the stiffness matrix $B$ are nonpositive. In fact, since $\nabla \varphi_j$ are constant on each $\tau \in \mathcal{T}_h$,

$$b_{jk} = (\nabla \varphi_j, \nabla \varphi_k) = \sum_{\tau \in \mathcal{T}_h} \nabla \varphi_j|_\tau \cdot \nabla \varphi_k|_\tau \text{ area } \tau$$

Now since $\nabla \varphi_j|_\tau$ is the direction of the normal to the side of $\tau$ opposite to $P_j$, we have, since there are no obtuse triangles in $\mathcal{T}_h$, $\nabla \varphi_j|_\tau \cdot \nabla \varphi_k|_\tau \leq 0$, and hence $b_{jk} \leq 0$.

It is not difficult to show, as a result of this fact, that the positive-definite matrix $\bar{A} + kB$ has an inverse with nonnegative elements, and hence also the elements of $(I + k\bar{A}^{-1}B)^{-1} = (\bar{A} + kB)^{-1}\bar{A}$ and its powers are nonnegative. Since $G(t) = \lim_{n \to \infty} (I + tn^{-1}\bar{A}^{-1}B)^{-n}$, this shows the same property for $G(t)$.

The proof that the row sums of $G(t)$ are bounded by 1 is similar and depends on showing first that the row sums of $B$ are nonnegative. We shall not go into the details.

It follows implicitly from the above discussion that the maximum principle extends to the backward Euler method.

For an analysis of lumping in connection with eigenvalue problems, see Ref. [38].

## 6.8 THE $H^1$- AND $H^{-1}$-METHODS

In this section we consider briefly some alternatives to the Galerkin methods considered above which consist in using inner products other than the one in $L_2(\Omega)$ to formulate the semidiscrete problems. For simplicity we describe the situation of the simple heat equation in one space dimension, and use only semidiscrete methods.

We consider thus the initial boundary-value problem

$$
\begin{aligned}
u_t - u_{xx} &= f && \text{in } I \times [0, \infty) \text{ where } I = [0, 1] \\
u(0, t) &= u(1, t) = 0 && \text{for } t \geq 0 \\
u(\cdot, 0) &= v && \text{in } I
\end{aligned}
$$
(6.45)

For $r$ and $k$ integers with $r \geq 4$ and $1 \leq k \leq r - 2$ and with $0 = x_0 < x_1 < \cdots < x_M = 1$ a partition of $I$, let now (with $\Pi_s$ the polynomials of degree at most $s$)

$$S_h = \{\chi \in C^k(I), \chi|_{(x_{j-1}, x_j)} \in \Pi_{r-1} ; \chi(0) = \chi(1) = 0\}$$

Then, in particular, $S_h \subset H^2(I) \cap H_0^1(I)$, and we have for $v$ vanishing at $x = 0$ and 1,

$$\inf_{\chi \in S_h} \{\|v - \chi\| + h\|v - \chi\|_1 + h^2\|v - \chi\|_2\} \leq Ch^s\|v\|_s \qquad \text{for } 2 \leq s \leq r$$

The semidiscrete $H^1$-method for (6.45) is then defined by, with primes denoting differentiation with respect to $x$,

$$
\begin{aligned}
(u'_{h,t}, \chi') + (u''_h, \chi'') &= -(f, \chi'') && \text{for } \chi \text{ in } S_h, t \geq 0 \\
u_h(0) &= v_h
\end{aligned}
$$
(6.46)

This weak formulation is obtained from multiplying the heat equation by $\chi''$, integrating over $I$, and integrating by parts in the first term.

We may also think of this method as resulting from the weak formulation with respect to the semi-inner product $(v, w)_1 = (v', w')$ in $H^1(I)$, namely,

$$(u_t, \chi)_1 - (u'', \chi)_1 = (f, \chi)_1$$

Since $u'' + f = u_t$ vanishes at $x = 0$ and 1, an integration by parts brings this into the form (6.46).

With $\{\varphi_j\}_1^{N_h}$ a basis for $S_h$ this semidiscrete problem may be written in matrix form

$$A\alpha'(t) + B\alpha(t) = \tilde{f}(t) \qquad \text{for } t \geq 0, \ \alpha(0) = \gamma$$

where the elements of $A$ and $B$ are $(\varphi_j', \varphi_k')$ and $(\varphi_j'', \varphi_k'')$, respectively. Both $A$ and $B$ are thus symmetric and positive-definite.

This time one may use an elliptic projection $R_h$ from $H^2(I) \cap H_0^1(I)$ into $S_h$ defined by

$$((R_h v)'', \chi'') = (v'', \chi'') \qquad \text{for } \chi \text{ in } S_h$$

and one finds easily

$$\|R_h v - v\| + h\|(R_h v - v)'\| + h^2\|(R_h v - v)''\| \leq C h^s \|v\|_s, \qquad 2 \leq s \leq r \tag{6.47}$$

We have now the following error estimates which are proved by a standard energy argument (cf. Refs. [14], [15], and [35]).

**THEOREM 6.27**   Let $u_h$ and $u$ be the solutions of (6.46) and (6.45), respectively, and let $u_h(0) = R_h v$. Then for $t \geq 0$,

$$\|u_h(t) - u(t)\| \leq C h^r \left\{ \|u(t)\|_r + \left( \int_0^t \|u_t\|_r^2 \, ds \right)^{1/2} \right\}$$

and

$$h\|(u_h(t) - u(t))'\| + h^2\|(u_h(t) - u(t))''\| \leq C h^r \left\{ \|u(t)\|_r + \left( \int_0^t \|u_t\|_{r-1}^2 \, ds \right)^{1/2} \right\}$$

For $r > 4$ the regularity assumptions in the $L_2$-estimate may be reduced to those in $H^1$ and $H^2$. For $k = 1$ and 2 in the definition of $S_h$, superconvergence of order $O(h^{2r-4})$ occurs at the nodes of the partition (for $k = 1$ also for the derivatives) provided that the discrete initial values are appropriately chosen (cf. Ref. [14]).

We now turn to the $H^{-1}$-method for (6.45). This time we will use two different finite-dimensional spaces as our trial and test spaces. Let $r$ be a fixed positive integer and let $k$ be an integer with $-1 \leq k \leq r - 2$. With the partition introduced above let now

$$S_h = \{\chi \in C^k(I); \ \chi|_{(x_{j-1}, x_j)} \in \Pi_{r-1}\}$$

[where $C^{-1}(I)$ is interpreted as $L_2(I)$, say, so that discontinuities may occur at the nodes] and

$$V_h = \{\psi \in C^{k+2}(I); \ \psi|_{(x_{j-1}, x_j)} \in \Pi_{r+1}; \ \psi(0) = \psi(1) = 0\}$$

Note that $V_h$ is two orders smoother than $S_h$, that $S_h$ has no prescribed boundary values, and that $S_h$ and $V_h$ have the same dimension.

The semidiscrete $H^{-1}$-Galerkin (or Galerkin–Petrov) method is then to determine $u_h(t)$ in $S_h$ such that

$$(u_{h,t}, \psi) - (u_h, \psi'') = (f, \psi) \qquad \text{for } \psi \text{ in } V_h, \, t \geqslant 0 \tag{6.48}$$

with $u_h(0)$ a given approximation of $v$ in $S_h$, which for simplicity will be taken here to be the $L_2$-projection $P_h v$ onto $S_h$.

To appreciate why this method is called the $H^{-1}$-method, we reformulate (6.48) somewhat. For this purpose we introduce the solution operator $G$ of the two-point boundary-value problem

$$-u'' = f \qquad \text{in } I$$

$$u(0) = u(1) = 0$$

(so that its solution may be written $u = Gf$) and note that $V_h = GS_h$. Since it is easy to see that $G$ is symmetric and positive-definite on $L_2(I)$, we may define the inner product $\langle v, w \rangle = (v, Gw)$ and observe that for the corresponding norm $|v| = \langle v, v \rangle^{1/2}$,

$$|v|^2 = (v, Gv) = -((Gv)'', Gv) = \|(Gv)'\|^2$$

We find easily, with $c > 0$,

$$c|v| \leqslant \sup_{w \in H_0^1(I)} \frac{(v, w)}{\|w\|_1} = \sup_{w \in H_0^1(I)} \frac{((Gv)', w')}{\|w\|_1} \leqslant C|v|$$

whence $|\cdot|$ may be interpreted as a norm in the dual space $H^{-1}(I)$ of $H_0^1(I)$. The semidiscrete method may now be written in the form of the ordinary Galerkin method

$$\langle u_{h,t}, \chi \rangle + (u_h, \chi) = \langle f, \chi \rangle \qquad \text{for } \chi \text{ in } S_h$$

where thus $\langle \cdot, \cdot \rangle$ is an $H^{-1}$-inner product and where the $L_2$-inner product plays the role of the bilinear form $(v', w')$ in the standard Galerkin method. The elliptic projection appropriate to this problem turns out to be the $L_2$-projection onto $S_h$, and by our standard methods we may prove, for instance, the following (cf. Refs. [23] and [41]).

**THEOREM 6.28**  In the situation under consideration, with $v_h = P_h v$, we have

$$\|u_h(t) - u(t)\| \leqslant Ch^r \left\{ \|u(t)\|_r + \left( \int_0^t \|u_t\|_{r-1}^2 \, ds \right)^{1/2} \right\} \qquad \text{for } t \geqslant 0$$

We will not carry out the details. The result generalizes to more general operators, and nonsmooth data estimates are also available, as are certain superconvergence results for $k = -1$ in the definitions of $S_h$ and $V_h$.

## 6.9 DISCRETIZATION OF THE WAVE EQUATION

In this section we discuss briefly some results concerning semidiscrete and completely discrete schemes for the wave equation,

$$u_{tt} - \Delta u = f \quad \text{in } \Omega \times [0, \infty), \Omega \subset R^d$$

with initial and boundary conditions

$$u = 0 \quad \text{on } \partial\Omega \times [0, \infty)$$

$$u(\cdot, 0) = v \quad \text{in } \Omega$$

$$u_t(\cdot, 0) = w \quad \text{in } \Omega$$

We assume that we are given a family of subspaces $S_h$ of $H_0^1(\Omega)$ with the property

$$\inf_{\chi \in S_h} \{\|v - \chi\| + h\|\nabla(v - \chi)\|\} \leqslant Ch^s\|v\|_s \quad \text{for } 1 \leqslant s \leqslant r$$

The semidiscrete analogue of our problem is then to find $u_h(t) \in S_h$ such that

$$(u_{h,tt}, \chi) + (\nabla u_h, \nabla \chi) = (f, \chi) \quad \text{for } \chi \text{ in } S_h$$

$$u_h(0) = v_h \tag{6.49}$$

$$u_{h,t}(0) = w_h$$

This may be thought of as an initial-value problem for a system of ordinary differential equations of second order for the coefficients with respect to a basis $\{\varphi_j\}_1^{N_h}$ of $S_h$. If

$$u_h(t) = \sum_{j=1}^{N_h} \alpha_j(t)\varphi_j(x)$$

(6.49) is equivalent to     $A\alpha''(t) + B\alpha(t) = \tilde{f}(t) \quad \text{for } t \geqslant 0$

where the elements of $A$ and $B$ are $(\varphi_j, \varphi_k)$ and $(\nabla \varphi_j, \nabla \varphi_k)$, respectively, and $\tilde{f}_j = (f, \varphi_j)$. The initial conditions are

$$\alpha(0) = \beta \qquad \alpha'(0) = \gamma$$

where $\qquad\qquad v_h = \sum_{j=1}^{N_h} \beta_j\varphi_j \qquad w_h = \sum_{j=1}^{N_h} \gamma_j\varphi_j$

The following error estimates are valid, where $R_h$ denotes the standard elliptic projection (see Ref. [17]).

**THEOREM 6.29** With $u_h$ and $u$ as above, we have for $t$ bounded,

$$\|u_h(t) - u(t)\| \leqslant C\|\nabla(v_h - R_h v)\| + C\|w_h - R_h w\| + Ch^r\left\{\|u(t)\|_r + \left(\int_0^t \|u_{tt}\|_r^2\, ds\right)^{1/2}\right\}$$

$$\|u_{h,t}(t) - u_t(t)\| \leqslant C\|\nabla(v_h - R_h v)\| + C\|w_h - R_h w\| + Ch^r\left\{\|u_t(t)\|_r + \left(\int_0^t \|u_{tt}\|_r^2\, ds\right)^{1/2}\right\}$$

and
$$\|\nabla(u_h - u)(t)\| \leqslant C\|\nabla(v_h - R_h v)\| + C\|w_h - R_h w\|$$
$$+ Ch^{r-1}\left\{\|u(t)\|_r + \left(\int_0^t \|u_{tt}\|_{r-1}^2 \, ds\right)^{1/2}\right\}$$

**Proof** Writing as usual $u_h - u = (u_h - R_h u) + (R_h u - u) = \theta + \rho$, we have

$$(\theta_{tt}, \chi) + (\nabla\theta, \nabla\chi) = (\rho_{tt}, \chi) \qquad \text{for } \chi \text{ in } S_h$$

Choosing $\chi = \theta_t$ yields

$$\frac{1}{2}\frac{d}{dt}(\|\theta_t\|^2 + \|\nabla\theta\|^2) = (\rho_{tt}, \theta_t) \leqslant \tfrac{1}{2}\|\rho_{tt}\|^2 + \tfrac{1}{2}\|\theta_t\|^2$$

and hence by Gronwall's lemma,

$$\|\theta_t(t)\|^2 + \|\nabla\theta(t)\|^2 \leqslant C(\|\theta_t(0)\|^2 + \|\nabla\theta(0)\|^2) + C\int_0^t \|\rho_{tt}\|^2 \, ds$$

Hence, using the standard elliptic estimate for $\rho_{tt}$,

$$\|\theta_t(t)\| + \|\nabla\theta(t)\| \leqslant C(\|w - R_h w\| + \|\nabla(v_h - R_h v)\|) + Ch^r\left(\int_0^t \|u_{tt}\|_r^2 \, ds\right)^{1/2} \tag{6.50}$$

Together with the obvious estimate for $\rho$ and $\rho_t$, this implies the first two estimates of the theorem. The proof of the third is similar.

Note in Theorem 6.29 that the choices $v_h = R_h v$ and $w_h = R_h w$ give optimal-order error estimates for all three quantities considered, but that other optimal choices of $v_h$ could cause a loss of one power of $h$ because of the gradient in the first term on the right. With a slightly more refined argument, however, the following $L_2$-error bound may be shown, where $P_h$ denotes the $L_2$-projection onto $S_h$ (cf. Refs. [1] and [2]).

**THEOREM 6.30** With $u_h$ and $u$ as above, we have for $t \geqslant 0$,

$$\|u_h(t) - u(t)\| \leqslant C(\|v_h - R_h v\| + \|w_h - P_h w\|) + Ch^r\left\{\|u(t)\|_r + \int_0^t \|u_t\|_r \, ds\right\}$$

Optimal-order error estimates thus result for arbitrary optimal-order choices of $v_h$ and $w_h$. Note also that the regularity requirements for the solution are weaker in the latter theorem.

We now make some observations concerning the discretization also in time, and let $U^n$ denote the approximation in $S_h$ at $t = t_n = nk$, where $k$ is the time step. One possible method for the wave equation is

$$(k^{-2}(U^{n+1} - 2U^n + U^{n-1}), \chi) + (\nabla(\tfrac{1}{4}U^{n+1} + \tfrac{1}{2}U^n + \tfrac{1}{4}U^{n-1}), \nabla\chi) = (\tfrac{1}{4}f(t_{n+1})$$
$$+ \tfrac{1}{2}f(t_n) + \tfrac{1}{4}f(t_{n-1}), \chi) \qquad \text{for } \chi \text{ in } S_h \tag{6.51}$$

with $U^0$ and $U^1$ given approximations of $u(0) = v$ and $u(k)$, respectively. The choice of the linear combination in the second term and the right-hand side is motivated by a combination of stability and accuracy considerations. Using the most direct analogue of the arguments in the proof of Theorem 6.29 above, one may show the following analogue of (6.50), where we use the notation $\theta^n = U^n - R_h u(t_n)$ and $\bar{\partial}_t U^n = k^{-1}(U^n - U^{n-1})$:

$$\|\bar{\partial}_t \theta^n\| + \left\|\frac{\nabla(\theta^n + \theta^{n-1})}{2}\right\| \leq C(\|\bar{\partial}_t \theta^1\| + \|\nabla\theta^0\| + \|\nabla\theta^1\|)$$

$$+ Ch^r\left(\int_0^{t_n} \|u_{tt}\|_r^2\,ds\right)^{1/2} + Ck^2\left(\int_0^{t_n} \|u_{tttt}\|^2\,ds\right)^{1/2}$$

It is clear that together with error estimates for $R_h u$ this will yield error bounds for approximations of $u_t$, $u$, and $\nabla u$ at $t = t_n - k/2$. We will not write down these estimates in precise form but only state the following (cf. Ref. [17]).

**THEOREM 6.31**   With $U^n$ and $u$ as above, assume that the initial values $U^0$ and $U^1$ are chosen in such a way that

$$\|\bar{\partial}_t \theta^1\| + \|\nabla\theta^0\| + \|\nabla\theta^1\| \leq Ch^r$$

Then, under the appropriate regularity conditions for $u$, we have for $t_n$ bounded,

$$\left\|\tfrac{1}{2}(U^n + U^{n-1}) - u\left(t_n - \tfrac{1}{2}k\right)\right\| \leq C(u)(h^r + k^2)$$

$$\left\|\bar{\partial}_t U^n - u_t\left(t_n - \tfrac{1}{2}k\right)\right\| \leq C(u)(h^r + k^2)$$

and

$$\left\|\nabla\left(\frac{U^n + U^{n-1}}{2}\right) - \nabla u\left(t_n - \tfrac{1}{2}k\right)\right\| \leq C(u)(h^r + k^2)$$

The conditions for the initial values may be satisfied by taking $U^0 = R_h u$ and $U^1 = R_h(v + kw + \tfrac{1}{2}k^2 u_{tt}(0)) = R_h(v + kw + \tfrac{1}{2}k^2(\Delta v + f))$.

We briefly consider another approach to the time discretization and consider now the semidiscrete problem for the homogeneous equation, which, from the definition (6.8) of the discrete laplacian $\Delta_h$, may be written

$$u_{h,tt} - \Delta_h u_h = 0 \quad \text{for } t \geq 0 \quad \text{with } u_h(0) = v_h,\ u_{h,t}(0) = w_h$$

Setting

$$\tilde{u}_h = \begin{pmatrix} u_h \\ u_{h,t} \end{pmatrix} \quad J_h = \begin{pmatrix} 0 & I \\ \Delta_h & 0 \end{pmatrix}$$

the semidiscrete problem may be written

$$\tilde{u}_{h,t} - J_h \tilde{u}_h = 0 \quad \text{for } t \geq 0 \quad \text{with } \tilde{u}_h(0) = (v_h, w_h)^T$$

and this has the exact solution

$$\tilde{u}_h(t) = \exp(tJ_h)\tilde{u}_h(0)$$

It is now natural to discretize the problem in time by using a rational function $r(z)$ approximating $e^z$ with accuracy $\nu$ to define an approximation $\tilde{U}^n$ of $\tilde{u}_h(t_n)$ recursively by

$$\tilde{U}^{n+1} = r(kJ_n)\tilde{U}^n \qquad \text{for } n \geq 0 \qquad \text{with } \tilde{U}^0 = (v_h, w_h)^T$$

Since, as is easily seen, $J_h$ has its spectrum on the imaginary axis, it is only the behavior of $r(z)$ there that is relevant to the performance of the method. In analogy with the situation in the parabolic case one may consider different stability conditions here, such as

**Ĩ.** $|r(i\lambda)| \leq 1$ \qquad for $-\alpha < \lambda < \alpha$

**ĨĨ.** $|r(i\lambda)| \leq 1$ \qquad for all real $\lambda$

The second type will result in unconditionally stable methods, whereas mesh-ratio and inverse-type hypotheses will be needed in the first case.

We only state a convergence result for the second type (cf. Ref. [2]).

**THEOREM 6.32**  Assume that the rational function $r(z)$ is accurate of order $\nu$ and of type $\tilde{II}$ and let $\tilde{U}^n$ and $u$ be as above. Then for the first component $U^n$ of $\tilde{U}^n$, we have for $t_n$ bounded,

$$\|U^n - u(t_n)\| \leq C(\|v_h - v\| + \|w_h - w\|) + Ch^r(\|v\|_{r+1} + \|w\|_r) + Ck^\nu(\|v\|_{\nu+1} + \|w\|_\nu)$$

Examples of rational functions to which this result may be applied are entries in the diagonal and first two subdiagonals of the Padé table for $e^z$; these functions satisfy the stronger condition $|r(z)| \leq 1$ for $\text{Re } z \leq 0$. Other such functions with advantageous features and which have poles on both sides of the imaginary axis have also been developed. Let us close by remarking that the second-order diagonal Padé approximation $r(z) = (1 - \frac{1}{2}z)^{-1}(1 + \frac{1}{2}z)$ reproduces Eq. (6.51) after elimination of the second component of $\tilde{U}^n$.

## 6.10 SOME RESULTS FOR FIRST-ORDER HYPERBOLIC EQUATIONS

In this section we consider as an example of first-order hyperbolic equations the model problem

$$u_t - u_x = f \qquad \text{for } t \geq 0, \ x \in (-\infty, \infty)$$
$$u(\cdot, 0) = v \qquad \text{on } (-\infty, \infty)$$

(6.52)

where we assume that $f$ and $v$ are periodic in $x$ with period 1 and where the solution sought is 1-periodic as well. In this context the $L_2$-inner products and the norms used will have to be based on an interval of length 1, for example,

$$(v, w) = \int_0^1 vw \, dx \qquad \|v\|^2 = \int_0^1 v^2 \, dx$$

For the purpose of defining an approximate solution, we let $r$ be an integer with $r \geq 2$ and $k$ a nonnegative integer with $k \leq r - 2$, and introduce the finite-dimensional space

$$S_h = \left\{ \chi \in C^k(R); \ \chi|_{(x_{j-1}, x_j)} \in \Pi_{r-1}, \ \chi \text{ 1-periodic} \right\}$$

where $0 = x_0 < x_1 < \cdots < x_M = 1$ is a partition of the basic interval $I = [0, 1]$. It is then possible to show the existence of an interpolation operator $Q_h$ into $S_h$ such that for 1-periodic $v$, with $h = \max\{x_{j-1} - x_j ; j = 0, \ldots, M-1\}$,

$$\|Q_h v - v\| + h\|(Q_h v - v)'\| \leq Ch^s \|v\|_s \qquad 1 \leq s \leq r \tag{6.53}$$

and such that $Q_h$ commutes with time differentiation, so that $Q_h(u_t) = (Q_h u)_t$.

The standard Galerkin method for the present problem is then to find $u_h(t) \in S_h$ such that

$$(u_{h,t}, \chi) - (u_{h,x}, \chi) = (f, \chi) \qquad \text{for } t \geq 0 \text{ and } \chi \text{ in } S_h$$
$$u_h(0) = v_h \tag{6.54}$$

In terms of a basis $\{\varphi_j\}_1^{N_h}$ of $S_h$ this may again be written in the form

$$A\alpha'(t) + B\alpha(t) = \tilde{f}(t) \qquad \text{for } t \geq 0, \text{ with } \alpha(0) = \gamma$$

where as usual $A$ is the symmetric positive-definite matrix with elements $(\varphi_j, \varphi_k)$, so that in particular the problem has a well-defined unique solution for $t \geq 0$, but where the matrix $B$ with elements $-(\varphi_j', \varphi_k) = (\varphi_j, \varphi_k')$ is now skew-symmetric.

We begin our discussion by proving the following simple error estimate (cf. Ref. [32]).

**THEOREM 6.33**   Let $u_h$ and $u$ be the solutions of (6.54) and (6.52), respectively. Then for $t \geq 0$,

$$\|u_h(t) - u(t)\| \leq \|v_h - v\| + Ch^{r-1}\left\{\|v\|_{r-1} + \int_0^t (\|u_t\|_{r-1} + \|u\|_r)\, ds\right\}$$

*Proof*   This time we write $u_h - u = (u_h - Q_h u) + (Q_h u - u) = \theta + \rho$, where $Q_h$ is the interpolation operator of (6.53). Obviously then

$$\|\rho(t)\| \leq Ch^{r-1}\|u(t)\|_{r-1} \leq Ch^{r-1}\left(\|v\|_{r-1} + \int_0^t \|u_t\|_{r-1}\, ds\right)$$

In order to estimate $\theta$ we note that

$$(\theta_t, \chi) - (\theta_x, \chi) = -(\rho_t - \rho_x, \chi) \qquad \text{for } \chi \text{ in } S_h$$

so that with $\chi = \theta$,

$$\frac{1}{2}\frac{d}{dt}\|\theta\|^2 - (\theta_x, \theta) \leq \|\rho_t - \rho_x\|\|\theta\|$$

Observing that by periodicity,

$$(\theta_x, \theta) = \int_0^1 \frac{1}{2}\frac{d}{dx}\theta^2\, dx = \tfrac{1}{2}(\theta(1)^2 - \theta(0)^2) = 0$$

we conclude

$$\frac{1}{2}\frac{d}{dt}\|\theta\|^2 = \|\theta\|\frac{d}{dt}\|\theta\| \leq (\|\rho_t\| + \|\rho_x\|)\|\theta\|$$

or, after cancellation of $\|\theta\|$ and integration,

$$\|\theta(t)\| \leq \|\theta(0)\| + \int_0^t (\|\rho_t\| + \|\rho_x\|) \, ds$$

$$\leq \|v_h - v\| + \|Q_h v - v\| + \int_0^t (\|Q_h u_t - u_t\| + \|(Q_h u - u)_x\|) \, ds$$

$$\leq \|v_h - v\| + Ch^{r-1} \left\{ \|v\|_{r-1} + \int_0^t (\|u_t\|_{r-1} + \|u\|_r) \, ds \right\} \tag{6.55}$$

thus completing the proof.

We observe that the estimate of Theorem 6.33 is of nonoptimal order $h^{r-1}$, as a result of the fact that the first derivative of the error in $Q_h u$ occurs on the right-hand side of (6.55).

For special cases more accurate results are known, for example, the following result for the homogeneous equation $u_t - u_x = 0$ (cf. Refs. [19] and [37]).

**THEOREM 6.34**  Let the partition used in the definition of $S_h$ be uniform, so that $x_j - x_{j-1} = h = 1/M$ for all $j$, and let $k = r - 2$, so that $S_h$ consists of smooth splines. Then, with $u_h$ and $u$ the solutions of (6.54) and (6.52), respectively, with $f = 0$, we have for $t$ bounded,

$$\|u_h(t) - u(t)\| \leq \|v_h - v\| + Ch^r \|v\|_{r+1}$$

It may also be shown, however, that the improvement to optimal order is not always possible (cf. Ref. [18]).

**THEOREM 6.35**  Let $S_h$ be defined by a uniform partition and with $r = 4$, $k = 1$ (Hermite cubics). Then, if $v$ is a nonconstant analytic 1-periodic function and $v_h \in S_h$ is arbitrary, we have for $u_h$ and $u$ the solutions of (6.54) and (6.52), respectively, with $f = 0$, and any $t^* > 0$,

$$\sup_{t \in (0, t^*)} \|u_h(t) - u(t)\| \geq ch^3 \qquad \text{with } c > 0$$

We remark that in the situation of Theorem 6.34 superconvergence takes place at the nodes in the sense described in the following (cf. Ref. [37] and references).

**THEOREM 6.36**  Under the assumptions of Theorem 6.34 let $I_h v$ denote the function in $S_h$ which agrees with $v$ at the nodes of the partition. Then, if $v_h = I_h v$, we have for $t$ bounded,

$$\|u_h(t) - I_h u(t)\| \leq Ch^{2r} \|v\|_{2r+1}$$

or

$$\left( h \sum_{j=1}^{M} (u_h(jh, t) - u(jh, t))^2 \right)^{1/2} \leq Ch^{2r} \|v\|_{2r+1}$$

The proofs of Theorems 6.34 and 6.36 are based on the observation that in this case the ordinary Galerkin method may be interpreted as a finite-difference method for the coefficients with respect to a basis for $S_h$. Known results from finite-difference theory may then be applied to yield the present ones.

Since, in view of Theorem 6.35 it is impossible to obtain optimal-order estimates even for uniform partitions for general $k$ and $r$, modifications of the standard Galerkin method have been proposed which do not exhibit this deficiency (cf. Refs. [10] and [39]). Thus, for example, considering again the nonhomogeneous equation, we may define a semidiscrete solution $u_h(t)$ in $S_h$ by

$$(u_{h,t} - u_{h,x}, \chi - h\chi') = (f, \chi - h\chi') \qquad \text{for } \chi \text{ in } S_h$$

$$u_h(0) = v_h$$

(6.56)

Writing this as a system of ordinary differential equations,

$$A\alpha'(t) + B\alpha(t) = \tilde{f} \qquad \text{for } t \geq 0 \qquad \text{with } \alpha(0) = \gamma$$

the matrix $A$ this time has elements $(\varphi_j, \varphi_k) - h(\varphi_j, \varphi_k')$. Thus $A = A_0 - hA_1$ where $A_0$ is symmetric and positive-definite and $A_1$ is skew-symmetric. In particular, $A$ is invertible.

The following error estimate holds in the present case (Ref. [39]).

**THEOREM 6.37** Let $S_h$ be defined on a uniform partition and let $0 \leq k \leq r - 2$. Then for $u_h$ and $u$ the solutions of (6.56) and (6.52), respectively, we have for $t$ bounded,

$$\|u_h(t) - u(t)\| \leq C\|v_h - v\| + Ch^r \left\{ \|v\|_r + \left( \int_0^t \|u_t\|_r^2 \, ds \right)^{1/2} \right\}$$

We will not give the details of the proof.

## 6.11 REFERENCES

1. Baker, G. A., "Error Estimates for Finite Element Methods for Second Order Hyperbolic Equations," *SIAM J. Numer. Anal.*, **13**:564–576 (1976).

2. Baker, G. A., and J. H. Bramble, "Semidiscrete and Single Step Fully Discrete Approximations for Second Order Hyperbolic Equations," *RAIRO Anal. Numér.*, **13**:75–100 (1979).

3. Baker, G. A., J. H. Bramble, and V. Thomée, "Single Step Galerkin Approximations for Parabolic Problems," *Math. Comp.*, **31**:818–847 (1977).

4. Bramble, J. H., and A. H. Schatz, "Higher Order Local Accuracy by Averaging in the Finite Element Method," *Math. Comp.*, **31**:94–111 (1977).

5. Bramble, J. H., A. H. Schatz, V. Thomée, and L. B. Wahlbin, "Some Convergence Estimates for Galerkin Type Approximations for Parabolic Equations," *SIAM J. Numer. Anal.*, **14**:218–241 (1977).

6. Brenner, P., M. Crouzeix, and V. Thomée, "Single Step Methods for Inhomogeneous Linear Differential Equations in Banach Space," *RAIRO Anal. Numér.*, **16**:5–26 (1982).

7. Chen, C. M., and V. Thomée, "The Lumped Mass Finite Element Method for a Parabolic Problem," *J. Austr. Math. Soc.*, ser. B, **26**:329–354 (1985).

8. Crouzeix, M., "Sur l'Approximation des Équations Différentielles Opérationnelles Linéaires par des Méthodes de Runge-Kutta," Thesis, University of Paris VI, Paris, 1975.

9. Crouzeix, M., and P. A. Raviart, "Approximation d'Équations d'Évolution linéaires par des Méthodes a pas Multiples, *C. R. Acad. Sci. Paris*, **283**:367–370 (1976).

10. Dendy, J. E., "Two Methods of Galerkin Type Achieving Optimum $L^2$ Rates of Convergence for First Order Hyperbolics," *SIAM J. Numer. Anal.*, **11**:637–653 (1974).

11. Dobrowolski, M., "$L^\infty$-Convergence of Finite Element Approximation to Quasilinear Initial Boundary Value Problems," *RAIRO Anal. Numér.*, **12**:247–266 (1978).

12. Dobrowolski, M., "$L^\infty$-Convergence of Linear Finite Element Approximations to Nonlinear Parabolic Problems," *SIAM J. Numer. Anal.*, **17**:663–674 (1980).

13. Douglas, J., Jr., and T. Dupont, "Galerkin Methods for Parabolic Equations," *SIAM J. Numer. Anal.*, **7**:575–626 (1970).

14. Douglas, J., Jr., T. Dupont, and M. F. Wheeler, "Some Superconvergence Results for an $H^1$ Galerkin Procedure for the Heat Equation," *Lecture Notes in Computer Science*, Springer-Verlag, New York, 1974, vol. 10, pp. 288–311.

15. Douglas, J., Jr., T. Dupont, and M. F. Wheeler, "$H^1$-Galerkin Methods for the Laplace and Heat Equations," *Mathematical Aspects of Finite Elements in Partial Differential Equations*, Academic Press, New York, 1974, pp. 383–416.

16. Douglas, J., Jr., T. Dupont, and M. F. Wheeler, "A Quasi-Projection Analysis of Galerkin Methods for Parabolic and Hyperbolic Equations," *Math. Comp.*, **32**:345–362 (1978).

17. Dupont, T., "$L^2$-Estimates for Finite Element Methods for Second Order Hyperbolic Equations," *SIAM J. Numer. Anal.*, **10**:880–889 (1973).

18. Dupont, T., "Galerkin Methods for First-Order Hyperbolics: An Example," *SIAM. J. Numer. Anal.*, **10**:890–899 (1973).

19. Fix, G., and N. Nassif, "On Finite Element Approximations in Time Dependent Problems," *Numer. Math.*, **19**:127–135 (1972).

20. Fujii, H., "Some Remarks on Finite Element Analysis of Time-Dependent Field Problems," *Theory and Practice in Finite Element Structural Analysis*, University of Tokyo Press, Tokyo, 1973, pp. 91–106.

21. Helfrich, H. P., "Fehlerabschätzungen für das Galerkinverfahren zur Lösung von Evolutionsgleichungen," *Manuscripta Math.*, **13**:219–235 (1974).

22. Huang, M., and V. Thomée, "Some Convergence Estimates for Semidiscrete Type Schemes for Time-Dependent Nonselfadjoint Parabolic Equations," *Math. Comp.*, **37**:327–346 (1981).

23. Huang, M., and V. Thomée, "An Error Estimate for the $H^{-1}$ Galerkin Method for a Parabolic Problem with Non-Smooth Initial Data," *Calcolo*, **19**:115–124 (1982).

24. Le Roux, M.-N., "Semidiscretization in Time for Parabolic Problems," *Math. Comp.*, **33**:919–931 (1979).

25. Nitsche, J. H., "Über ein Variationsprinzip zur Lösung von Dirichlet-Problemen by Verwendung von Teilräumen die keinen Randbedingungen unterworfen sind," *Abh. Sem. Univ. Hamburg*, **36**:9–15 (1971).

26. Nitsche, J. H., "$L_\infty$-Convergence of Finite Element Approximations," *Mathematical Aspects of Finite Element Methods, Lecture Notes in Mathematics*, Springer-Verlag, New York, 1977, vol. 606, pp. 261–274.

27. Nitsche, J. H., "$L_\infty$-Convergence of Finite Element Galerkin Approximations on Parabolic Problems," *RAIRO Anal. Numér.*, **13**:31–54 (1979).

28. Price, H. S., and R. S. Varga, "Error Bounds for Semi-Discrete Galerkin Approximations of Parabolic Problems with Application to Petroleum Reservoir Mechanics," *Numerical Solution of Field Problems in Continuum Physics*, American Mathematical Society, Providence, R.I., 1970, pp. 74–94.

29. Raviart, P. A., "The Use of Numerical Integration in Finite Element Methods for Solving Parabolic Equations," in J. J. H. Miller (ed.), *Topics in Numerical Analysis*, Academic Press, New York, 1973, pp. 233–264.

30. Scott, R., "Interpolated Boundary Conditions in the Finite Element Method," *SIAM J. Numer. Anal.*, **12**:404–427 (1975).

31. Schatz, A. H., V. Thomée, and L. B. Wahlbin, "Maximum Norm Stability and Error Estimates in Parabolic Finite Element Equations," *Comm. Pure Appl. Math.*, **33**:265–304 (1980).

32. Swartz, B., and B. Wendroff, "Generalized Finite-Difference Schemes," *Math. Comp.*, **23**:37–49 (1969).

33. Thomée, V., "High Order Local Approximations to Derivatives in the Finite Element Method," *Math. Comp.*, **31**:652–660 (1977).

34. Thomée, V., "Negative Norm Estimates and Superconvergence in Galerkin Methods for Parabolic Problems," *Math. Comp.*, **34**:93–113 (1980).

35. Thomée, V., and L. B. Wahlbin, "On Galerkin Methods in Semilinear Parabolic Problems," *SIAM J. Numer. Anal.*, **12**:378–389 (1975).

36. Thomée, V., and L. B. Wahlbin, "Maximum-Norm Stability and Error Estimates in Galerkin Methods for Parabolic Equations in One Space Variable," *Numer. Math.*, **41**:345–371 (1983).

37. Thomée, V., and B. Wendroff, "Convergence Estimates for Galerkin Methods for Variable Coefficient Initial-Value Problems," *SIAM J. Numer. Anal.*, **11**:1059–1068 (1974).

38. Tong, P., T. H. H. Pian, and L. L. Bucciarelli, "Mode Shapes and Frequencies by Finite Element Method Using Consistent and Lumped Masses," *J. Comp. Struct.*, **1**:623–638 (1970).

39. Wahlbin, L. B., "A Dissipative Galerkin Method Applied to Some Quasilinear Hyperbolic Equations," *RAIRO Anal. Numér.*, **8**:109–117 (1974).

40. Wheeler, M. F., "A Priori $L_2$ Error Estimates for Galerkin Approximations to Parabolic Partial Differential Equations," *SIAM J. Numer. Anal.*, **10**:723–759 (1973).

41. Wheeler, M. F., "An $H^{-1}$ Galerkin Method for Parabolic Problems in a Single Space Variable," *SIAM J. Numer. Anal.*, **12**:803–817 (1975).

42. Zlámal, M., "Finite Element Multistep Discretizations of Parabolic Boundary Value Problems," *Math. Comp.*, **29**:350–359 (1975).

# CHAPTER 7
# FINITE-ELEMENT METHODS FOR VARIATIONAL INEQUALITIES

## 7.1 ABSTRACT ELLIPTIC VARIATIONAL INEQUALITIES: EXISTENCE, UNIQUENESS, APPROXIMATION

In this section we consider some simple classes of *elliptic variational inequalities* (EVI) and their approximation by *Galerkin-type methods*. More specific examples are considered in the next section. Iterative methods for solving approximate variational inequalities are treated in the third section. Then, in the fourth section, the approximation of the obstacle problem by mixed finite-element methods is presented.

### 7.1A Functional Context

We introduce the following mathematical objects:

A real Hilbert space $V$ equipped with the inner product $(\cdot, \cdot)$ and the corresponding norm $\|\cdot\|$

A bilinear continuous form $a: V \times V \to \mathbb{R}$, $V$-elliptic [that is, $\exists \alpha > 0$ such that $a(v, v) \geq \alpha \|v\|^2 \; \forall v \in V$]; we do not assume that $a(\cdot, \cdot)$ is symmetric

A form $L: V \to \mathbb{R}$, linear and continuous

A closed, convex, nonempty subset $K$ of $V$

A functional $j: V \to \bar{\mathbb{R}}$ ($\equiv \mathbb{R} \cup \{+\infty\} \cup \{-\infty\}$), convex, lower semicontinuous, proper (that is, $j(v) > -\infty \; \forall v \in V, j \not\equiv +\infty$)

## 7.1B Two Classes of Elliptic Variational Inequalities

Let us now consider the two problems

$$(\text{EVI})_1 \quad \begin{cases} \text{Find } u \in K \text{ such that} \\ a(u, v - u) \geq L(v - u) \qquad \forall v \in K \end{cases}$$

and
$$(\text{EVI})_2 \quad \begin{cases} \text{Find } u \in V \text{ such that} \\ a(u, v - u) + j(v) - j(u) \geq L(v - u) \qquad \forall v \in V \end{cases}$$

In what follows $(\text{EVI})_1$ and $(\text{EVI})_2$ will be denoted respectively as EVI of the *first* and *second* kinds.

**REMARK 7.1**  We can find in the literature more complicated EVI (see, for example, Ref. [2]) and also the generalization called *quasi-variational inequalities* (QVI) introduced by Bensoussan and Lions (see, for example, Refs. [3, 4] and the bibliographies therein).

**REMARK 7.2**  If $K = V$ in $(\text{EVI})_1$ and $j \equiv 0$ in $(\text{EVI})_2$, then both problems reduce to the standard *linear variational equation*

$$\begin{cases} \text{Find } u \in V \text{ such that} \\ a(u, v) = L(v) \qquad \forall v \in V \end{cases} \tag{7.1}$$

**REMARK 7.3**  The distinction between $(\text{EVI})_1$ and $(\text{EVI})_2$ is rather artificial (theoretically, at least) since $(\text{EVI})_1$ is equivalent to

$$\begin{cases} \text{Find } u \in V \text{ such that} \\ a(u, v - u) + I_K(v) - I_K(u) \geq L(v - u) \qquad \forall v \in V \end{cases} \tag{7.2}$$

where $I_K$ is defined by

$$I_K(v) = \begin{cases} 0 \text{ if } v \in K \\ +\infty \text{ if } v \notin K \end{cases}$$

The functional $I_K$ is called the *indicator functional* of $K$, and since $K$ is a *closed, convex, nonempty* subset of $V$, $I_K$ is *lower semicontinuous, convex,* and *proper*. Therefore $(\text{EVI})_1$ is a special case of $(\text{EVI})_2$; however, formulation $(\text{EVI})_1$ is usually more practical.

**REMARK 7.4**  If $a(\cdot, \cdot)$ is symmetric, $(\text{EVI})_1$ and $(\text{EVI})_2$ are respectively equivalent to the *minimization problems*

$$(\pi_1) \quad \begin{cases} \text{Find } u \in K \text{ such that} \\ J(u) \leq J(v) \qquad \forall v \in K \end{cases}$$

where
$$J(v) = \tfrac{1}{2}a(v, v) - L(v) \tag{7.3}$$

and $\qquad\qquad (\pi_2)\qquad$ $\begin{cases} \textit{Find } u \in K \text{ such that} \\ J(u)+j(u) \leq J(v)+j(v) \end{cases}$

where $J(\,\cdot\,)$ is again defined by (7.3).

## 7.1c Existence and Uniqueness Results for $(\mathrm{EVI})_1$ and $(\mathrm{EVI})_2$

From Lions and Stampacchia [5] we have the following theorem.

**THEOREM 7.1**  If the above hypotheses on $V$, $a$, $L$, and $K$ hold, then $(\mathrm{EVI})_1$ has a unique solution.

**Proof**  **1.** *Uniqueness.* Let $u_1$ and $u_2$ be two solutions. Then

$$a(u_1, v-u_1) \geq L(v-u_1) \qquad \forall v \in K, u_1 \in K \qquad (7.4)$$

$$a(u_2, v-u_2) \geq L(v-u_2) \qquad \forall v \in K, u_2 \in K \qquad (7.5)$$

Taking $v = u_2$ in (7.4) and $v = u_1$ in (7.5), we obtain by addition and using the $V$-ellipticity of $a(\,\cdot\,,\cdot\,)$

$$\alpha \|u_2 - u_1\|^2 \leq a(u_2 - u_1, u_2 - u_1) \leq 0$$

which implies the uniqueness.

**2.** *Existence.* It is known from the *Riesz representation theorem* that there exists $A \in \mathscr{L}(V, V)$ and $l \in V$ such that

$$a(u, v) = (Au, v) \qquad \forall u, v \in V \qquad (7.6)$$

$$L(v) = (l, v) \qquad \forall v \in V \qquad (7.7)$$

Then, if $u$ is the solution of $(\mathrm{EVI})_1$, we have

$$(Au, v-u) \geq (l, v-u) \qquad \forall v \in K, u \in K \qquad (7.8)$$

which is equivalent to $(\mathrm{EVI})_1$. Problem (7.8) is equivalent to

$$(u - \rho(Au - l) - u, v - u) \leq 0 \qquad \forall v \in K, u \in K, \rho > 0 \qquad (7.9)$$

and (7.9) is equivalent to $\qquad u = P_K(u - \rho(Au - l)) \qquad \rho > 0 \qquad (7.10)$

where in (7.10) $P_K$ is the *projection operator* from $V$ to $K$ in the $\|\cdot\|$-norm. It follows from (7.10) that every solution of $(\mathrm{EVI})_1$ is also a solution of the *fixed-point problem* (7.10) for any $\rho > 0$, and, conversely, if there exists a particular $\rho > 0$ such that (7.10) has a solution, this solution is also a solution of $(\mathrm{EVI})_1$.

A sufficient condition for (7.10) to have a solution is that the mapping from $V$ to $V$

$$v \rightarrow P_K(v - \rho(Av - l))$$

is *strictly* and *uniformly contracting* for $\rho$ well-chosen. Let us denote by $w$ the vector $P_K(v - \rho(Av - l))$ and consider

$$w_i = P_K(v_i - \rho(Av_i - l)) \qquad i = 1, 2$$

Since the projection mapping $P_K$ is a contraction, we have

$$\|w_2 - w_1\| \leqslant \|v_2 - v_1 - \rho A(v_2 - v_1)\| \tag{7.11}$$

From (7.6) and (7.11) we obtain

$$\|w_2 - w_1\|^2 \leqslant \|v_2 - v_1\|^2 - 2\rho a(v_2 - v_1, v_2 - v_1) + \rho^2 \|A(v_2 - v_1)\|^2$$

$$\leqslant \|v_2 - v_1\|^2 - 2\rho\alpha\|v_2 - v_1\|^2 + \rho^2\|A\|^2\|v_2 - v_1\|^2$$

so that         $$\|w_2 - w_1\|^2 \leqslant (1 - 2\rho\alpha + \rho^2\|A\|^2)\|v_2 - v_1\|^2 \tag{7.12}$$

From (7.12) the above mapping will be strictly and uniformly contracting if

$$0 < \rho < \frac{2\alpha}{\|A\|^2} \tag{7.13}$$

If $\rho$ fulfills (7.13), the fixed-point problem (7.10) has a solution which is also the solution of $(EVI)_1$, and we know that this solution is unique.

**REMARK 7.5**   The proof of Theorem 7.1 suggests the following algorithm for solving $(EVI)_1$:

Given                               $$u^0 \in V \tag{7.14}$$

then for $n \geqslant 0$            $$u^{n+1} = P_K(u^n - \rho(Au^n - l)) \tag{7.15}$$

From the proof of Theorem 7.1 it follows that for $0 < \rho < 2\alpha/\|A\|^2$ the sequence $\{u^n\}_n$ defined by (7.14) and (7.15) *converges strongly* in $V$ to the solution $u$ of $(EVI)_1$.

Interest in (7.14) and (7.15) is quite limited in most applications (at least in the above form), since we usually do not know $l$ or $A$, and to project on $K$ is, in most cases, a very complicated operation. We should observe that if $a(\cdot, \cdot)$ is symmetric, then $A$ is also symmetric and (7.14), (7.15) is a *gradient with projection* algorithm (see, for example, Ref. [6] for a study of these methods).

For the case of $(EVI)_2$ we have the following theorem from Ref. [5].

**THEOREM 7.2**   If the above hypotheses on $V$, $a$, $L$, and $j$ hold, then $(EVI)_2$ has a unique solution.

We refer for the proof to Refs. [1, 5]; in fact in this proof, which is a variant of the proof of Theorem 7.1, one still uses a fixed-point technique.

## 7.1D Internal Approximation of $(EVI)_1$

The assumptions on $V$, $a$, $K$, $L$ are those of Sec. 7.1A.

*Approximation of V and K*   The parameter $h$ is taken to converge to zero and the space $V$ is approximated by the family $\{V_h\}_h$, where the $V_h$ are *closed* subspaces of $V$; the $V_h$ are usually *finite-dimensional*. The convex set $K$ is then approximated by $\{K_h\}_h$, where the $K_h$

are *closed convex* subsets of $V_h$; we do not assume that $K_h \subset K$. We do assume, however, that $\{K_h\}_h$ has the following two properties:

**1.** If $\{v_h\}_h$ is such that $v_h \in K_h$ $\forall h$, then all the weak cluster points of $\{v_h\}_h$ belong to $K$.

**2.** There exists $\chi$, $\bar{\chi} = K$ and $r_h: \chi \to K_h$ such that $\lim_{h \to 0} r_h v = v$ strongly in $V$, $\forall v \in \chi$.

<u>**REMARK 7.6**</u>   If $K_h \subset K$ $\forall h$, then property 1 is automatically satisfied.

**Approximation of** $(\text{EVI})_1$   We approximate $(\text{EVI})_1$ by

$$(\text{EVI})_{1h} \quad \begin{cases} \text{Find } u_h \in K_h \text{ such that} \\ a(u_h, v_h - u_h) \geq L(v_h - u_h) \qquad \forall v_h \in K_h \end{cases}$$

<u>**REMARK 7.7**</u>   In most cases it will be necessary to approximate also $a(\cdot, \cdot)$ and $L(\cdot)$, respectively, by $a_h(\cdot, \cdot)$ and $L_h(\cdot)$ [in practical cases, they are usually derived from $a(\cdot, \cdot)$ and $L(\cdot)$ by a *numerical integration* procedure]. Since there is nothing special about this point for variational inequalities as opposed to linear equalities, we shall not discuss it further and simply instead refer to Ref. [7].

The following proposition is easily proved.

<u>**PROPOSITION 7.1**</u>   Problem $(\text{EVI})_{1h}$ has a unique solution.

**Convergence Results**   Let us prove now the following convergence theorem.

<u>**THEOREM 7.3**</u>   If the above hypotheses on $\{V_h\}_h$ and $\{K_h\}_h$ hold, then

$$\lim_{h \to 0} \|u_h - u\| = 0 \tag{7.16}$$

where $u$ and $u_h$, respectively, are solutions of $(\text{EVI})_1$ and $(\text{EVI})_{1h}$.

**Proof**   **1.** *Estimates for $u_h$.* We have from $(\text{EVI})_{1h}$ that

$$a(u_h, u_h) \leq a(u_h, v_h) - L(v_h - u_h) \qquad \forall v_h \in K_h$$

which implies $\forall v_h \in K_h$ that

$$\alpha \|u_h\|^2 \leq \|A\| \|u_h\| \|v_h\| + \|L\|_* \|v_h\| + \|L\|_* \|u_h\| \tag{7.17}$$

From property 2 above and from (7.17), we obtain

$$\alpha \|u_h\|^2 \leq \|A\| \|u_h\| \|r_h v\| + \|L\|_* \|r_h v\| + \|L\|_* \|u_h\| \qquad \forall v \in \chi$$

Now take $v_0 \in \chi$. Then with $C_i$ denoting various constants depending on $v_0$, but not on $h$, we have from property 2 above that

$$\|r_h v\| \leq C_0 \qquad \forall h$$

which implies that

$$\alpha \|u_h\|^2 \leq C_1 \|u_h\| + C_2 \qquad \forall h \tag{7.18}$$

In turn (7.18) implies the *boundedness* of $\{u_h\}_h$ in $V$.

**2.** *Weak convergence of* $\{u_h\}_h$. We can extract from $\{u_h\}_h$ a subsequence, still denoted by $\{u_h\}_h$, such that

$$u_h \to u^* \text{ weakly in } V \tag{7.19}$$

From property 1 above, we have $\qquad\qquad u^* \in K \tag{7.20}$

From (7.19) and property (2) and taking the limit in

$$a(u_h, u_h) \leqslant a(u_h, r_h v) - L(r_h v - u_h) \qquad \forall v \in \chi$$

we obtain $\qquad\qquad \liminf_{h \to 0} a(u_h, u_h) \leqslant a(u^*, v) - L(v - u^*) \qquad \forall v \in \chi \tag{7.21}$

Then we observe that

$$\alpha \|u_h - u^*\|^2 \leqslant a(u_h - u^*, u_h - u^*) = a(u_h, u_h) + a(u^*, u^*) - a(u_h, u^*) - a(u^*, u_h)$$

implies in the limit $\qquad\qquad \liminf_{h \to 0} a(u_h, u_h) \geqslant a(u^*, u^*) \tag{7.22}$

which is a (well-known) weak lower semicontinuity property. From (7.21) and (7.22) it follows that

$$a(u^*, u^*) \leqslant a(u^*, v) - L(v - u^*) \qquad \forall v \in \chi \tag{7.23}$$

Since $\bar{\chi} = K$, inequality (7.23) also holds $\forall v \in K$, so that with (7.20) we have

$$a(u^*, v - u^*) \geqslant L(v - u^*) \qquad \forall v \in K \qquad u^* \in K$$

Thus $u^*$ is a solution of $(\text{EVI})_1$. But from the *uniqueness* of such a solution we have $u^* = u$. The uniqueness property implies also that the *whole* sequence $\{u_h\}_h$ converges weakly to $u$.

**3.** *Strong convergence of* $\{u_h\}_h$. We have that

$$\alpha \|u_h - u\|^2 \leqslant a(u_h - u, u_h - u) = a(u_h, u_h) + a(u, u) - a(u_h, u) - a(u, u_h)$$

$$\leqslant a(u_h, r_h v) - L(r_h v - u_h) + a(u, u) - a(u_h, u) - a(u, u_h) \qquad \forall v \in \chi$$

From the above relation, from property 2, and from the weak convergence of $\{u_h\}_h$, we have in the limit that

$$\alpha \limsup \|u_h - u\|^2 \leqslant a(u, v) - L(v - u) - a(u, u)$$

$$= a(u, v - u) - L(v - u) \qquad \forall v \in \chi$$

But since $\bar{\chi} = K$ we also have that

$$\alpha \limsup \|u_h - u\|^2 \leqslant a(u, v - u) - L(v - u) \qquad \forall v \in K \tag{7.24}$$

Taking $v = u$ in (7.24) it follows that

$$\alpha \limsup \|u_h - u\|^2 \leqslant 0$$

which implies that $\lim_{h \to 0} \|u_h - u\| = 0$, that is, the *strong convergence*.

**REMARK 7.8** Error estimates for some EVIs of the first type have been obtained by several authors (see Sec. 7.2 for more details). But, as in many *nonlinear* problems, the methods used to obtain these estimates are specific to the particular problem under consideration. This remark still holds for the approximation of EVIs of the second kind, which is the subject of the next subsection.

## 7.1E Internal Approximation of $(EVI)_2$

The assumptions on $V$, $a(\cdot,\cdot)$, $L(\cdot)$, and $j(\cdot)$ are those given in Sec. 7.1A, and furthermore, we assume, for simplicity, that

$$j(\cdot) \text{ is continuous over } V \tag{7.25}$$

In Sec. 7.5 an important family of $(EVI)_2$'s for which $j(\cdot)$ is noncontinuous will also be considered.

**Approximation of $V$**   The space $V$ is approximated by the family $\{V_h\}_h$, $V_h$ being a closed subspace of $V$ (dim $V_h < +\infty$ in applications). We assume that $\{V_h\}_h$ has the following property:

**1.** There exist $\mathscr{V} \subset V$, $\bar{\mathscr{V}} = V$, and $r_h : \mathscr{V} \to V_h$ such that

$$\lim_{h \to 0} r_h v = v \text{ strongly in } V \qquad \forall v \in \mathscr{V}$$

**Approximation of $j(\cdot)$**   The functional $j(\cdot)$ is approximated by $\{j_h\}_h$, where

$$\begin{aligned} &j_h : V_h \to \bar{\mathbb{R}} \\ &j_h \text{ is convex, lower semicontinuous, uniformly proper in } h \end{aligned} \tag{7.26}$$

The last property implies the existence of $\lambda : V \to \mathbb{R}$, linear and continuous, and of $\mu \in \mathbb{R}$ such that

$$j_h(v_h) \geq \lambda(v_h) + \mu \qquad \forall v_h \in V_h, \forall h \tag{7.27}$$

We shall assume also that $\{j_h\}_h$ obeys the following properties:

**2.** If $v_h \to v$ weakly in $V$, then $\liminf j_h(v_h) \geq j(v)$.

**3.** $\displaystyle\lim_{h \to 0} j_h(r_h v) = j(v) \qquad \forall v \in \mathscr{V}.$

<u>**REMARK 7.9**</u>   In all the applications that we know, if $j(\cdot)$ is continuous, then it is always possible to construct continuous $j_h(\cdot)$ obeying properties 2 and 3.

<u>**REMARK 7.10**</u>   If $j_h = j \,\forall h$, then (7.26) and properties 2 and 3 are automatically satisfied.

**Approximation of $(EVI)_2$**   We approximate $(EVI)_2$ by

$$(EVI)_{2h} \qquad \begin{cases} \text{Find } u_h \in V_h \text{ such that} \\ a(u_h, v_h - u_h) + j_h(v_h) - j_h(u_h) \geq L(v_h - u_h) \qquad \forall v_h \in V_h \end{cases}$$

The following proposition is then easily proved.

**PROPOSITION 7.2**   If the above hypotheses on $\{V_h\}_h$ and $\{j_h\}_h$ hold, then $(\text{EVI})_{2h}$ has a unique solution.

**REMARK 7.11**   Remark 7.7 of Sec. 7.1D still holds for $(\text{EVI})_{2h}$.

**Convergence Results**   Using a variant of the proof of Theorem 7.3, we obtain the following theorem (see Ref. [1] for more details).

**THEOREM 7.4**   If the above hypotheses on $\{V_h\}_h$ and $\{j_h\}_h$ hold, then

$$\lim_{h \to 0} \|u_h - u\| = 0 \qquad \lim_{h \to 0} j_h(u_h) = j(u)$$

where $u$ and $u_h$, respectively, are the solutions of $(\text{EVI})_2$ and $(\text{EVI})_{2h}$.


## 7.2 SPECIFIC EXAMPLES AND ERROR ESTIMATES FOR CONFORMING FINITE-ELEMENT METHODS

### 7.2A Stationary Obstacle Problems

Stationary obstacle problems are fairly simple but provide good mathematical models for several important applications. Furthermore, obstacle problems are those which have received most attention in the deriving of finite-element-approximation error analysis.

**Formulation of a Particular Obstacle Problem**   Let $\Omega$ be a bounded domain of $\mathbb{R}^N$ with a smooth boundary $\Gamma = \partial\Omega$. We consider with $x = \{x_i\}_{i=1}^N$ and $\nabla = \{\partial/\partial x_i\}_{i=1}^N$ the particular obstacle problem

$$\begin{cases} \text{Find } u \in K \text{ such that} \\[2mm] \displaystyle\int_\Omega \nabla u \cdot \nabla(v-u)\,dx \geqslant \int_\Omega f(v-u)\,dx \qquad \forall v \in K \end{cases} \tag{7.28}$$

where, in (7.28), $f \in L^2(\Omega)$ and $K$ is defined by

$$K = \{v \in H^1(\Omega),\ v \geqslant \psi \text{ almost everywhere on } \Omega,\ v|_\Gamma = g\} \tag{7.29}$$

where $\psi$ and $g$ are given functions defined respectively on $\Omega$ and $\Gamma$.

**Physical Interpretation**   Assume that $\Omega \subset \mathbb{R}^2$; then a classical interpretation of (7.28) and (7.29) is that $u$ represents the *small vertical displacements* of an *elastic membrane* $\Omega$ under the effects of a field of vertical forces whose *intensity* is given by $f$ ($f$ represents a *surface density* of vertical forces). This membrane is fixed on its boundary $\Gamma$ ($u = g$) and lies over an *obstacle* whose height is given by $\psi$, ($u \geqslant \psi$); see Fig. 7.1 for a geometrical description of the phenomenon.

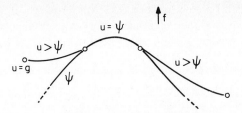

**FIG. 7.1**   Membrane lying over an obstacle.

*Other Phenomena Related to Obstacle Problems*   Similar EVIs also occur, sometimes with other types of boundary conditions and/or nonsymmetric bilinear forms, in mathematical models for the following problems:

*Lubrication phenomena.* See, for example, Cryer [8, 9], Marzulli [10], and Glowinski, Lions, and Trémolières [11] for finite-difference treatments and more references, and Capriz [12] for a discussion of the mathematical modeling.

*Filtration of liquids in porous media.* See, in particular, Baiocchi [13–15]; Comincioli [16]; Baiocchi, Brezzi, and Comincioli [17]; Cryer and Fetter [18]; Baiocchi and Capelo [4]; Oden and Kikuchi [19]; and the numerous references therein.

*Two-dimensional potential flows of inviscid fluids.* See Brezis and Stampacchia [20, 21]; Brezis [22], Ciavaldini, Pogu, and Tournemine [23]; Roux [24]; and the references therein.

*Wake problems.* See Bourgat and Duvaut [25].

This list is far from complete, and there also are applications in such fields as biomathematics, economics, and semiconductors.

*Interpretation of (7.28) and (7.29) as a Free-Boundary Problem*   Let us define from the solution $u$ of (7.28) and (7.29)

$$\Omega^+ = \{x \mid x \in \Omega, u(x) > \psi(x)\} \qquad \Omega^0 = \{x \mid x \in \Omega, u(x) = \psi(x)\}$$

$$\gamma = \partial\Omega^+ \cap \partial\Omega^0 \qquad \text{and} \qquad u_+ = u|_{\Omega^+} \qquad u_0 = u|_{\Omega^0}$$

Classically (7.28) and (7.29) have been formulated as the problem of finding $\gamma$ (the *free boundary*) and $u$ such that

$$-\Delta u = f \qquad \text{on } \Omega^+ \tag{7.30}$$

$$u = \psi \qquad \text{on } \Omega^0 \tag{7.31}$$

$$u = g \qquad \text{on } \Gamma \tag{7.32}$$

$$u_+|_\gamma = u_0|_\gamma \tag{7.33}$$

The physical interpretation of (7.30) to (7.33) is the following: (7.30) means that on $\Omega^+$ the membrane is *strictly above the obstacle* and has a *purely elastic* behavior; (7.31) means that on $\Omega^0$ the membrane is *in contact* with the obstacle; (7.32) is a *transmission relation* on the free boundary.

In fact, (7.30) to (7.33) are not sufficient to characterize $u$, and it is therefore necessary to add other *transmission properties*; for instance, if $\psi$ is smooth enough [let us say $\psi \in H^2(\Omega)$], we should require the *continuity* of $\nabla u$ on $\gamma$ [we may ask $\nabla u \in H^1(\Omega) \times H^1(\Omega)$].

**REMARK 7.12**  This kind of free-boundary interpretation holds for the other examples considered in what follows.

***Existence, Uniqueness, and Regularity of the Solution***  With regard to the existence and uniqueness of a solution of (7.28) and (7.29), we can easily prove the following theorem.

**THEOREM 7.5**  Assume that $\Gamma$ is smooth and that $\psi \in H^1(\Omega)$, $g \in H^{1/2}(\Gamma)$ with $\psi|_\Gamma \leqslant g$ almost everywhere on $\Gamma$; then (7.28), (7.29) has a unique solution.

**REMARK 7.13**  The above theorem holds for $f \in (H^1(\Omega))'$ and for fairly discontinuous $\psi$.

As far as the *regularity* of $u$ is concerned, let us recall the following classical result due to Brezis and Stampacchia [26]: If $\Gamma$ is sufficiently smooth and if, for $p \in\, ]1, +\infty[$, $f \in L^p(\Omega) \cap (H^1(\Omega))'$, $\psi \in W^{2,p}(\Omega)$, and $g = \tilde{g}|_\Gamma$ with $\tilde{g} \in W^{2,p}(\Omega)$, then $u \in W^{2,p}(\Omega)$.

The above results have actually been refined by Brezis [27, 28], and very sophisticated properties of the solution and of the free boundary have been obtained by Lewy and Stampacchia, Brezis, Kinderlehrer, Nirenberg, Schaeffer, etc.; a detailed account of these properties is given in the monograph of Kinderlehrer and Stampacchia [29].

***Finite-Element Approximations of (7.28) and (7.29)***

*I. Piecewise Linear Approximations*  We now consider conforming finite-element approximations of order 1 of the obstacle problem (7.28) and (7.29). Piecewise quadratic approximations and nonconforming approximations of mixed type are considered in later sections.

We assume for simplicity that $\Omega$ is a bounded polygonal domain of $\mathbb{R}^2$ and also that $\psi \in H^1(\Omega) \cap C^0(\bar{\Omega})$, $g \in H^{1/2}(\Gamma) \cap C^0(\Gamma)$. We introduce a standard *triangulation* $\mathcal{T}_h$ of $\bar{\Omega}$ such that $\bigcup_{T \in \mathcal{T}_h} T = \bar{\Omega}$, with, as usual, $h = $ length of the largest side of $\mathcal{T}_h$. Let us define now

$$\Sigma_h = \{P \in \bar{\Omega}, P \text{ vertex of } T \in \mathcal{T}_h\}$$

$$\mathring{\Sigma}_h = \{P \in \Sigma_h, P \notin \Gamma\} = \Sigma_h \cap \Omega$$

We then approximate $H^1(\Omega)$ and $K$, respectively, by

$$V_h = \{v_h \in C^0(\bar{\Omega}), v_{h|T} \in P_1 \; \forall T \in \mathcal{T}_h\} \tag{7.34}$$

$$K_h = \{v_h \in V_h, v_h(P) \geqslant \psi(P) \; \forall P \in \mathring{\Sigma}_h, v_h(P) = g(P) \; \forall P \in \Sigma_h \cap \Gamma\} \tag{7.35}$$

where in (7.34) and the sequel (for $k \geqslant 0$) $P_k = $ *space of polynomials in two variables of degree* $\leqslant k$.

Finally, we approximate (7.28) and (7.29) by (7.35) and

$$\begin{cases} \text{Find } u_h \in K_h \text{ such that} \\[2mm] \displaystyle\int_\Omega \nabla u_h \cdot \nabla(v_h - u_h) \, dx \geqslant \int_\Omega f(v_h - u_h) \, dx \qquad \forall v_h \in K_h \end{cases} \tag{7.36}$$

**PROPOSITION 7.3** The approximate obstacle problem (7.35), (7.36) has a unique solution.

For treatment of the *convergence* of the approximate solutions as $h \to 0$, we refer to Glowinski (Chap. 2 of Ref. [1]) for the case where $u$ is not very smooth. We shall below briefly consider the derivation of *error estimates*, in the $H^1(\Omega)$-norm, if $u$, $\psi$, $g \in H^2(\Omega)$. We follow very closely the analysis of Brezzi, Hager, and Raviart (Sec. 4 of Ref. [30]), in which

$$a(u, v) = \int_\Omega \nabla u \cdot \nabla v \, dx + \int_\Omega uv \, dx.$$

To obtain these error estimates we need the following.

**LEMMA 7.1** Assume that $u \in H^2(\Omega)$; then

$$-\Delta u - f \geq 0 \text{ almost everywhere on } \Omega \tag{7.37}$$

$$(-\Delta u - f)(u - \psi) = 0 \text{ almost everywhere on } \Omega \tag{7.38}$$

*Proof* See Brezis [31].

**LEMMA 7.2** Let $u$ and $u_h$, respectively, be solutions of (7.28), (7.29) and (7.35), (7.36). Then

$$a(u_h - u, u_h - u) \leq a(u_h - u, v_h - u) + a(u, v_h - u_h) - \int_\Omega f(v_h - u_h) \, dx \qquad \forall v_h \in K_h \tag{7.39}$$

*Proof* Following Brezzi, Hager, and Raviart [30], we have, $\forall v_h \in K_h$,

$$a(u_h - u, u_h - u) = a(u_h - u, v_h - u) + a(u_h - u, u_h - v_h)$$

$$= a(u_h - u, v_h - u) + a(u, v_h - u_h) - \int_\Omega f(v_h - u_h) \, dx$$

$$+ \int_\Omega f(v_h - u_h) \, dx - a(u_h, v_h - u_h)$$

Since $v_h$ obeys (7.36), we have

$$\int_\Omega f(v_h - u_h) \, dx - a(u_h, v_h - u_h) \leq 0 \qquad \forall v_h \in K_h$$

which, combined with the above equation, implies (7.39).

We prove now the following theorem.

**THEOREM 7.6** If $f \in L^2(\Omega)$, $\psi \in H^2(\Omega)$, $g = \tilde{g}|_\Gamma$, $\tilde{g} \in H^2(\Omega)$, and if the angles of $\mathcal{T}_h$ are bounded below by $\theta_0 > 0$ independent of $h$, then

$$\|u_h - u\|_{H^1(\Omega)} = O(h) \tag{7.40}$$

where $u$ and $u_h$, respectively, are solutions of (7.28), (7.29) and (7.35), (7.36).

**Proof** We follow again Brezzi, Hager, and Raviart ([30], Theorem 4.1); see also Falk [32]. We have from Green's formula that

$$a(u, v) = \int_\Omega \nabla u \cdot \nabla v \, dx = -\int_\Omega \Delta u \, v \, dx + \int_\Gamma \frac{\partial u}{\partial n} v \, d\Gamma \qquad \forall v \in H^1(\Omega) \tag{7.41}$$

Since $v_h - u_h \in H_0^1(\Omega) \ \forall v_h \in K_h$, it follows from (7.41) that

$$a(u, v_h - u_h) - \int_\Omega f(v_h - u_h) \, dx = \int_\Omega (-\Delta u - f)(v_h - u_h) \, dx \qquad \forall v_h \in K_h \tag{7.42}$$

Let $\pi_h$ be the operator of $V_h$-interpolation on $\Sigma_h$. Then since $\Omega \subset \mathbb{R}^2$, we have that $H^2(\Omega) \subset C^0(\bar\Omega)$ and $u \in H^2(\Omega)$, $u \geq \psi$ on $\Omega$ imply

$$\pi_h u \in K_h \tag{7.43}$$

Taking $v_h = \pi_h u$ in (7.39) and (7.42), we obtain

$$a(u_h - u, u_h - u) \leq a(u_h - u, \pi_h u - u) + \int_\Omega (-\Delta u - f)(\pi_h u - u_h) \, dx \tag{7.44}$$

Observe that

$$\pi_h u - u_h = (\pi_h u - u) + (\psi - \pi_h \psi) + (u - \psi) + (\pi_h \psi - u_h) \tag{7.45}$$

Let $w = -\Delta u - f$; then $w \in L^2(\Omega)$, and from (7.45),

$$\int_\Omega w(\pi_h u - u_h) \, dx = \int_\Omega w(\pi_h u - u) \, dx + \int_\Omega w(\psi - \pi_h \psi) \, dx$$

$$+ \int_\Omega w(u - \psi) \, dx + \int_\Omega w(\pi_h \psi - u_h) \, dx \tag{7.46}$$

Since Lemma 7.1 holds, we have that $w \geq 0$ and $w(u - \psi) = 0$ almost everywhere; moreover, since $u_h \in K_h$, we have $\pi_h \psi - u_h \leq 0$ on $\bar\Omega$. It follows that

$$\int_\Omega w(\pi_h u - u_h) \, dx \leq \|w\|_{L^2(\Omega)} (\|\pi_h u - u\|_{L^2(\Omega)} + \|\pi_h \psi - \psi\|_{L^2(\Omega)}) \tag{7.47}$$

Since $u, \psi \in H^2(\Omega)$, we have (since the *angle condition* holds) that

$$\|\pi_h u - u\|_{H^1(\Omega)} \leq Ch \|u\|_{H^2(\Omega)}$$
$$\|\pi_h u - u\|_{L^2(\Omega)} \leq Ch^2 \|u\|_{H^2(\Omega)} \tag{7.48}$$

$$\|\pi_h \psi - \psi\|_{H^1(\Omega)} \leq Ch \|\psi\|_{H^2(\Omega)}$$
$$\|\pi_h \psi - \psi\|_{L_2(\Omega)} \leq Ch^2 \|\psi\|_{H^2(\Omega)} \tag{7.49}$$

where the $C$'s are independent of $h$, $u$, $\psi$. It follows then from (7.44) and (7.47) to (7.49) that

$$|u_h - u|_{1,\Omega} = O(h) \tag{7.50}$$

where $|v|_{1,\Omega} = (\int_\Omega |\nabla v|^2 \, dx)^{1/2}$ (and where below $\|v\|_{1,\Omega} = \|v\|_{H^1(\Omega)}$). To estimate $\|u_h - u\|_{1,\Omega}$, we observe that, since $\Omega$ is bounded,

$$\|v\|_{1,\Omega} \leq C|v|_{1,\Omega} \qquad \forall v \in H_0^1(\Omega), \ C \text{ independent of } v \tag{7.51}$$

It follows then from (7.51) and from $u_h - \pi_h u \in H_0^1(\Omega)$ that

$$\|u_h - u\|_{1,\Omega} \leq \|u_h - \pi_h u\|_{1,\Omega} + \|\pi_h u - u\|_{1,\Omega}$$
$$\leq C|u_h - \pi_h u|_{1,\Omega} + \|\pi_h u - u\|_{1,\Omega}$$
$$\leq C|u_h - u|_{1,\Omega} + C|u - \pi_h u|_{1,\Omega} + \|\pi_h u - u\|_{1,\Omega} \tag{7.52}$$

Finally, (7.40) follows clearly from (7.48), (7.50), and (7.52).

To our knowledge, the first $O(h)$ estimates for $\|u_h - u\|_{1,\Omega}$ were obtained, for *piecewise linear approximations*, by Falk [32] and then by Mosco and Strang [33]. These works were followed by Falk [34, 35] (see also Glowinski, Lions, and Trémolières [11], Chap. 1 and Appendix; and Ciarlet [7]). In our opinion one finds in Ref. [35] the most complete analysis for piecewise linear approximations, since it also considers *nonconvex* and/or *nonpolygonal* $\Omega$. The problem of obtaining, via a generalization of the Aubin-Nitsche trick, $L^2$-estimates (of optimal order) is not yet completely solved; however, for some partial results in that direction see Natterer [36] and Mosco [37] and the references therein. To conclude with piecewise linear approximations, let us mention that under suitable hypothesis Baiocchi [38] and Nitsche [39] have obtained for the obstacle problem $\|u_h - u\|_{L^\infty(\Omega)} = O(h^{2-\varepsilon})$, $\varepsilon > 0$ arbitrarily small and $\|u_h - u\|_{L^\infty(\Omega)} = O(h^2|\log h|)$, respectively.

### Finite-Element Approximations of (7.28) and (7.29)

**II. Piecewise Quadratic Approximations**   With $\Sigma_h$, $\overset{\circ}{\Sigma}_h$ as above, we define

$$\Sigma_h' = \{P \in \bar{\Omega}, \ P \text{ midpoint of a side of } T \in \mathcal{T}_h\}$$

$$\overset{\circ}{\Sigma}_h' = \{P \in \Sigma_h', \ P \notin \Gamma\} \qquad \Sigma_h'' = \Sigma_h \cup \Sigma_h' \qquad \overset{\circ}{\Sigma}_h'' = \overset{\circ}{\Sigma}_h'' \cup k\overset{\circ}{\Sigma}_h'$$

We approximate $H^1(\Omega)$ and $K$ by

$$V_h = \{v_h \in C^0(\bar{\Omega}), \ v_h|_T \in P_2 \ \forall T \in \mathcal{T}_h\} \tag{7.53}$$

$$K_h^1 = \{v_h \in V_h, \ v_h(P) \geq \psi(P) \ \forall P \in \overset{\circ}{\Sigma}_h'', \ v_h(P) = g(P) \ \forall P \in \Sigma_h'' \cap \Gamma\} \tag{7.54a}$$

$$K_h^2 = \{v_h \in V_h, \ v_h(P) \geq \psi(P) \ \forall P \in \overset{\circ}{\Sigma}_h', \ v_h(P) = g(P) \ \forall P \in \Sigma_h'' \cap \Gamma\} \tag{7.54b}$$

We observe that in $K_h^2$ the condition $v_h(P) \geq \psi(P)$ is required only on the side midpoints. We approximate the obstacle problem (7.27) to (7.29) by:

$$\begin{cases} \text{Find } u_h^i \in K_h^i \text{ such that} \\ \\ \displaystyle\int_\Omega \nabla u_h^i \cdot \nabla(v_h - u_n^i) \, dx \geq \int_\Omega f(v_h - u_h^i) \, dx \qquad \forall v_h \in K_h^i \end{cases} \tag{7.55}_i$$

where $i = 1, 2$.

**PROPOSITION 7.4**   The approximate problem $(7.55)_i$ has a unique solution.

For the convergence of the approximate solution we refer to Glowinski [1], where $\lim_{h\to 0}\|u_h^i - u\|_{1,\Omega} = 0$ is proved, for $i = 1, 2$, by assuming the usual angle condition. The error-estimate analysis is much more complicated than with $k = 1$, and we refer to Brezzi, Hager, and Raviart [30], where under suitable assumptions on $f$, $u$, $\psi$, $g$, and the free boundary, one proves that, $\forall i = 1, 2$, $\|u_h^i - u\|_{H^1(\Omega)} = O(h^{3/2-\varepsilon})$, $\varepsilon > 0$ arbitrarily small, if the angle condition holds.

**Concluding Remarks**  Nonlinear obstacle problems have been considered by Janovsky and Whiteman [40]. For the numerical solution of the approximate obstacle problems we refer to Sec. 7.3, where several methods of solution are described.

## 7.2B The Elastoplastic Torsion Problem

The problem we now consider is more complicated than the obstacle problem of Sec. 7.2A. It is related to the *elastoplastic torsion of a cylindrical bar of infinite length*. It is a fairly simple plasticity problem, but it is of great interest from both theoretical and numerical points of view.

**Formulation of the Continuous Problem**  Let $\Omega$ be a bounded domain of $\mathbb{R}^2$ with a smooth boundary $\Gamma = \partial\Omega$. We consider the following problem:

$$\begin{cases} \text{Find } u \in K \text{ such that} \\ \displaystyle\int_\Omega \nabla u \cdot \nabla(v - u)\, dx \geq \int_\Omega f(v - u)\, dx \qquad \forall v \in K \end{cases} \tag{7.56}$$

where $f \in L^2(\Omega)$ and

$$K = \{v \in H_0^1(\Omega), |\nabla v| \leq 1 \text{ almost everywhere}\} \tag{7.57}$$

We recall that

$$H_0^1(\Omega) = \overline{\mathscr{D}(\Omega)}^{H^1(\Omega)} = \{v | v \in H^1(\Omega),\ v = 0 \text{ on } \partial\Omega\}$$

**REMARK 7.14**  Since the bilinear form $a(\cdot, \cdot)$ occurring in (7.56) is symmetric, that is, $a(u, v) = \int_\Omega \nabla u \cdot \nabla v\, dx$, (7.56) is indeed equivalent to the following minimization problem:

$$\begin{cases} \text{Find } u \in K \text{ such that} \\ J(u) \leq J(v) \qquad \forall v \in K \end{cases} \tag{7.58}$$

where

$$J(v) = \tfrac{1}{2}\int_\Omega |\nabla v|^2\, dx - \int_\Omega fv\, dx$$

**Physical Interpretation**  Let us consider an infinitely long cylindrical bar of cross section $\Omega$, where $\Omega$ is *simply connected*. Assume that this bar is made of an isotropic, elastic, perfectly plastic material whose *plasticity yield* is given by the *von Mises criterion* (see Ref. [41, Chap. 5], for a general discussion of plasticity phenomena). Starting from a zero-stress initial state, an increasing torsion moment is applied to the bar. The torsion is characterized by $C$, its *torsion angle per unit length.* It follows then from the *Haar-Karman principle* that the stress field can be obtained through the solution of the following variational problem:

$$\min_{v \in K} \left\{ \tfrac{1}{2} \int_{\Omega} |\nabla v|^2 \, dx - C \int_{\Omega} v \, dx \right\} \tag{7.59}$$

which is a particular case of (7.56) and (7.58), with $f = C$.

The *stress vector* $\boldsymbol{\sigma}$ in $\Omega$ is obtained from $u$ by the relation $\boldsymbol{\sigma} = \nabla u$. Hence $u$ appears as a *stress potential.*

**REMARK 7.15**   If $\Omega$ is not simply connected, the formulation of the elastoplastic problem has to be modified, and we refer to Glowinski and Lanchon [42] for the new formulation.

**Existence and Uniqueness Results: Regularity and Further Properties**   The conditions of Sec. 7.1 being fulfilled, we can apply Theorem 7.1; then we have the following.

**PROPOSITION 7.5**   Problems (7.56) and (7.58) have a unique solution.

For the proof we refer to Glowinski, Lions, and Trémolières [11, Chap. 3]. For regularity properties it follows from Brezis and Stampacchia [26] that if $\partial\Omega$ is smooth (or $\Omega$ convex) and if $f \in L^p(\Omega)$ with $p \geq 2$, then the solution $u$ of (7.56) and (7.58) satisfies $u \in W^{2,p}(\Omega) \cap K$. If, in particular, $f = \text{constant}$ [as in (7.59)], then $u \in W^{2,p}(\Omega)$ for $p$ arbitrarily large. If, for example, $\Omega$ is a disk and $f = \text{constant}$, then for $f$ large enough $u \in W^{2,\infty}(\Omega) \cap H^s(\Omega) \ \forall s < 5/2$, but $u \notin C^2(\bar{\Omega})$, $u \notin H^3(\Omega)$.

**REMARK 7.16**   If $f = \text{constant}$, Brezis and Sibony [43] have proved that the solution $u$ of (7.56) and (7.58) is also the unique solution of the *two-obstacles* problem

$$\min_{v \in K^*} \left\{ \tfrac{1}{2} \int_{\Omega} |\nabla v|^2 \, dx - C \int_{\Omega} v \, dx \right\} \tag{7.60}$$

where
$$K^* = \{v \in H_0^1(\Omega), |v(x)| \leq \delta(x, \Gamma) \text{ almost everywhere}\}$$

with $\delta(x, \Gamma) = \text{distance of } x \text{ from } \Gamma = \partial\Omega$.

**REMARK 7.17**   For the *free-boundary* aspect of the elastoplastic problem we refer, for example, to Glowinski, Lions, and Trémolières [11]. Actually, Shaw [44] has solved (7.59) numerically as a free-boundary problem using finite-difference approximations.

**Finite-Element Approximations of (7.56) and (7.58)**   We assume $\Omega$ polygonal, define $\mathcal{T}_h$ as in "Piecewise Linear Approximations" in Sec. 7.2A, and introduce

$$V_{oh} = \{v_h \in C^0(\bar{\Omega}), \ v_h|_{\Gamma} = 0, \ v_h|_T \in P_1 \ \forall T \in \mathcal{T}_h\}$$

$$K_h = \{v_h \in V_h, |\nabla v_h| \leq 1 \text{ almost everywhere}\} = K \cap V_{oh}$$

Then we approximate (7.56) by:

$$
\begin{cases}
\text{Find } u_h \in K_h \text{ such that} \\[2mm]
\displaystyle\int_\Omega \nabla u_h \cdot \nabla(v_h - u_h)\, dx \geq \int_\Omega f(v_h - u_h)\, dx \quad \forall v_h \in K_h
\end{cases}
\tag{7.61}
$$

It is clear that (7.61) has a unique solution.

**REMARK 7.18**   Since $v_h$ is a *piecewise constant*, the condition $v_h \in K_h$ amounts to Card $(\mathcal{T}_h)$–quadratic constraints ($|\nabla v_h|^2 \leq 1$ on $T$, $\forall T \in \mathcal{T}_h$). If instead of a piecewise linear approximation, one uses a piecewise quadratic, requiring that $|\nabla v_h| \leq 1$ almost everywhere, then $v_h \in K_h$ would amount to 3 Card $(\mathcal{T}_h)$–quadratic constraints (see Glowinski, Lions, and Trémolières [11, Chap. 3], for more details).

**REMARK 7.19**   The numerical analysis of (7.56) via (7.60) is given for the case $f = $ constant by Glowinski, Lions, and Trémolières [11, Chap. 3].

***Convergence Analysis***   Since $\overline{\mathcal{D}(\Omega) \cap K}^{H_0^1(\Omega)} = K$ [where $\mathcal{D}(\Omega) = \{v \in C^\infty(\Omega),\ v$ has a compact support in $\Omega\}$], we can prove, using the general approximation results of Sec. 7.1, that

$$
\lim_{h \to 0} \|u_h - u\|_{1,\Omega} = 0
\tag{7.62}
$$

if the angle condition holds. For the proof of (7.62) and of the above density result, see, e.g., Glowinski, Lions, and Trémolières [11, Chap. 3] and Glowinski [1, Chap. 2].

Moreover if $f \in L^p(\Omega)$ and $u \in W^{2,p}(\Omega)$ with $p > 2$, it is proved in Falk [31] (see also Glowinski [1, Chap. 2]) that

$$
\|u_h - u\|_{1,\Omega} = O(h^{1/2 - 1/p})
\tag{7.63}
$$

In Falk [31] the case in which $\Omega$ is nonpolygonal is also considered.

**REMARK 7.20**   If $\Omega \subset \mathbb{R}$, then $f \in L^2(\Omega)$ implies that $\|u_h - u\|_{1,\Omega} = O(h)$ instead of (7.63). This result is related to the fact that in the monodimensional case the *piecewise linear interpolate* of $v \in K$ is still in $K$, which is no longer true in $\mathbb{R}^2$.

The iterative solution of the approximate problems is discussed in Sec. 7.3B.

The solution of (7.56) by *spectral methods*, and the convergence of the approximate solutions, are discussed in the Chap. 3 of Ref. [11] with numerical experiments showing the possibilities of such methods.

## 7.2c  Flow of a Bingham Medium in a Pipe

In the two preceding sections we have considered examples of EVIs of the first kind. In this section we discuss an EVI of the second kind related to the flow of a Bingham's viscous-plastic medium in a pipe. This section follows Glowinski [1] and Glowinski, Lions, and Trémolières [11, Chap. 5] (see also Duvaut and Lions [41, Chap. 6]) for a more precise mechanical interpretation.

***Formulation of the Continuous Problem***   Let $\Omega$ be a *bounded* domain of $\mathbb{R}^2$ with a smooth boundary $\Gamma = \partial\Omega$. Let $j(\cdot)$ be defined by

$$j(v) = \int_\Omega |\nabla v|\, dx \qquad (7.64)$$

$j(\cdot)$ is *Lipschitz-continuous* but *not differentiable*.

Let us consider now the following EVI of the second kind [with $f \in L^2(\Omega)$]:

$$\begin{cases} \text{Find } u \in H_0^1(\Omega) \text{ such that} \\[2mm] \mu \int_\Omega \nabla u \cdot \nabla (v - u)\, dx + gj(v) - gj(u) \geq \int_\Omega f(v - u)\, dx \qquad \forall v \in H_0^1(\Omega) \end{cases} \qquad (7.65)$$

which is equivalent to

$$\min_{v \in H_0^1(\Omega)} \left\{ \frac{\mu}{2} \int_\Omega |\nabla v|^2\, dx + gj(v) - \int_\Omega fv\, dx \right\} \qquad (7.66)$$

If we assume that $\mu > 0$ and $g \geq 0$, Prop. 7.6 follows from Theorem 7.2 of Sec. 7.1C.

<u>PROPOSITION 7.6</u>   The two equivalent problems (7.65) and (7.66) have a unique solution.

***Practical Interpretation***   If $f = \text{constant} = C (C > 0$, for example), it follows from Lions and Duvaut [41, Chap. 6] that (7.65) and (7.66) model the *laminar stationary flow* of a *Bingham's viscous-plastic fluid* in a cylindrical pipe of cross section $\Omega$, with $u(x)$ the velocity at $x$. The above constant $C$ is the linear decay of pressure and $\mu$, $g$ are, respectively, the viscosity and the plasticity yield of the medium. The above medium behaves like a viscous fluid (of viscosity $\mu$) in

$$\Omega^+ = \{x \,|\, x \in \Omega, |\nabla u(x)| > 0\}$$

and like a rigid medium in

$$\Omega^0 = \{x \,|\, x \in \Omega, \nabla u(x) = 0\}$$

We refer to Mossolov and Miasnikov [45–47] for a detailed analysis of the properties of $\Omega^+$ and $\Omega^0$.

***Regularity Properties: Existence of Multipliers***   With regard to the regularity of the solution $u$ of (7.65) and (7.66), Brezis [48] has proved that $u \in H^2(\Omega) \cap H_0^1(\Omega)$ and also, if $\Omega$ is convex, that

$$\|u\|_{H^2(\Omega)} \leq \frac{\gamma(\Omega)}{\mu} \|f\|_{L^2(\Omega)} \qquad (7.67)$$

If $\Omega$ is a disk and $f = \text{constant}$, then we have $u \in W^{2,\infty}(\Omega) \cap H^s(\Omega) \; \forall s < 5/2$, but if $g$ is small enough, $u \notin C^2(\bar{\Omega})$, $u \notin H^3(\Omega)$. Let us also mention that if $g$ is large enough, then $u = 0$.

With regard to characterization involving multipliers, let us define

$$\Lambda = \{\mathbf{q} \,|\, \mathbf{q} \in L^2(\Omega) \times L^2(\Omega), |\mathbf{q}(x)| \leqslant 1 \text{ almost everywhere}\}$$

where $|\mathbf{q}| = \sqrt{q_1^2 + q_2^2}$. It follows, for example, from Ref. [11, Chap. 5], that the solution $u$ of (7.65) and (7.66) is characterized by the existence of $p$ such that

$$\mu \int_\Omega \boldsymbol{\nabla} u \cdot \boldsymbol{\nabla} v \, dx + g \int_\Omega \mathbf{p} \cdot \boldsymbol{\nabla} v \, dx = \int_\Omega fv \, dx \qquad \forall v \in H_0^1(\Omega), u \in H_0^1(\Omega) \qquad (7.68)$$

$$\boldsymbol{p} \cdot \boldsymbol{\nabla} u = |\boldsymbol{\nabla} u| \text{ almost everywhere} \qquad p \in \Lambda \qquad (7.69)$$

**Finite-Element Approximations**   Since the regularity of the solution of (7.65) and (7.66) is usually low, we concentrate here only on piecewise linear approximations, and assume that $\Omega$ is a polygonal domain. We define $\mathcal{T}_h$ as in Sec. 7.2A and $V_{oh}$ as in Sec. 7.2B and then approximate (7.65) and (7.66) by

Find $u_h \in V_h$ such that $\forall v_h \in V_{oh}$

$$\mu \int_\Omega \boldsymbol{\nabla} u_h \cdot \boldsymbol{\nabla}(v_h - u_h) \, dx + g \int_\Omega |\boldsymbol{\nabla} v_h| \, dx - g \int_\Omega |\boldsymbol{\nabla} u_h| \, dx \geqslant \int_\Omega f(v_h - u_h) \, dx \qquad (7.70)$$

The approximate problem (7.70) clearly has a unique solution. For the convergence of $u_h$ to $u$ as $h \to 0$ we have the following.

**THEOREM 7.7**   Assume that the angles of $\mathcal{T}_h$ are uniformly bounded from below by $\theta_0 > 0$, as $h \to 0$; then

$$\lim_{h \to 0} \|u_h - u\|_{1,\Omega} = 0 \qquad (7.71)$$

If furthermore $u \in H^2(\Omega)$, then

$$\|u_h - u\|_{1,\Omega} = O(h^{1/2}) \qquad (7.72)$$

**Proof**   We follow Glowinski [1]. Taking $v_h = 0$ in (7.70), we obtain

$$|u_h|_{1,\Omega} \leqslant \frac{1}{\mu} \|f\|_{L^2(\Omega)} \|u_h\|_{L^2(\Omega)} \qquad \forall h \qquad (7.73)$$

Since $\Omega$ is bounded, $|v|_{1,\Omega} = (\int_\Omega |\boldsymbol{\nabla} v|^2 \, dx)^{1/2}$ defines on $H_0^1(\Omega)$ a norm equivalent to $\|v\|_{1,\Omega}$. We have moreover that

$$\|v\|_{L^2(\Omega)} \leqslant \frac{1}{\lambda_0^{1/2}} |v|_{1,\Omega} \qquad \forall v \in H_0^1(\Omega)$$

where $\qquad\qquad\qquad \lambda_0 = $ smallest eigenvalue of $-\Delta$ over $H_0^1(\Omega)$                    (7.74)

It follows then from (7.73) and (7.74) that

$$|u_h|_{1,\Omega} \leqslant \frac{1}{\mu \lambda_0^{1/2}} \|f\|_{L^2(\Omega)} \qquad (7.75)$$

From other considerations we have that

$$\mu \int_{\Omega} \nabla u_h \cdot \nabla (v_h - u_h) \, dx + gj(v_h) - gj(u_h) \geq \int_{\Omega} f(v_h - u_h) \, dx \qquad \forall v_h \in V_h$$

$$\mu \int_{\Omega} \nabla u \cdot \nabla (u_h - u) \, dx + gj(u_h) - gj(u) \geq \int_{\Omega} f(u_h - u) \, dx$$

and hence by addition we obtain

$$\mu |u_h - u|^2_{1,\Omega} \leq gj(v_h) - gj(u) + \mu \int_{\Omega} \nabla u_h \cdot \nabla (v_h - u) \, dx - \int_{\Omega} f(v_h - u) \, dx \qquad \forall v_h \in V_h \qquad (7.76)$$

From (7.75), (7.76), and

$$j(v) = \int_{\Omega} |\nabla v| \, dx \leq \sqrt{\text{meas} \, (\Omega)} \, |v|_{1,\Omega} \qquad \forall v \in H_0^1(\Omega) \qquad (7.77)$$

we obtain

$$|u_h - u|^2_{1,\Omega} \leq \frac{1}{\mu} \left( g \sqrt{\text{meas} \, (\Omega)} + \frac{2}{\sqrt{\lambda_0}} \|f\|_{L^2(\Omega)} \right) |v_h - u|_{1,\Omega} \qquad \forall v_h \in V_h \qquad (7.78)$$

Let $\phi \in \mathscr{D}(\Omega)$; we denote by $\pi_h \phi$ the $V_{oh}$-interpolate of $\phi$ on $\mathscr{T}_h$; that is,

$$\pi_h \phi \in V_{oh}, \qquad \pi_h \phi(P) = \phi(P) \qquad \forall P \text{ vertex of } \mathscr{T}_h$$

Since the angle condition holds, we have

$$|\pi_h \phi - \phi|_{1,\Omega} \leq C \|\phi\|_{H^2(\Omega)} h \qquad \forall \phi \in \mathscr{D}(\Omega) \qquad (7.79)$$

with $C$ independent of $h$ and $\phi$. From (7.78), (7.79), and the triangular inequality we obtain, taking $v_h = \pi_h \phi$ in (7.78),

$$|u_h - u|^2_{1,\Omega} \leq \frac{1}{\mu} \left( g \sqrt{\text{meas} \, (\Omega)} + \frac{2}{\sqrt{\lambda_0}} \|f\|_{L^2(\Omega)} \right) (|\phi - u|_{1,\Omega} + C \|\phi\|_{H^2(\Omega)} h) \qquad \forall \phi \in \mathscr{D}(\Omega) \qquad (7.80)$$

Since $\mathscr{D}(\Omega)$ is *dense in* $H_0^1(\Omega)$, (7.80) clearly implies (7.71). To prove (7.72) we use (7.78) directly; indeed if $u \in H^2(\Omega) \cap H_0^1(\Omega)$, then $u \in C^0(\bar{\Omega})$ and $\pi_h u$ can be defined. We have furthermore that

$$|\pi_h u - u|_{1,\Omega} \leq Ch \|u\|_{H^2(\Omega)} \qquad (7.81)$$

Then, if we take $v_h = \pi_h u$ in (7.78), it is clear that (7.81) implies (7.72), and this completes the proof of Theorem 7.7.

**REMARK 7.21** If we assume some extra regularity conditions (satisfied if $\Omega$ is a disk and if $f =$ constant), it is shown in Refs. [1, Chap. 2] and [49] that $\|u_h - u\|_{1,\Omega} = O(|\log h|^{1/2} h)$.

*Iterative methods* for solving (7.65) and (7.70) are described in Sec. 7.3C.

## 7.2D Error Estimates of Optimal Order
### for the Elastoplastic Torsion and
### Bingham's Flow Problems via a New Formulation

Here we briefly describe some of the results of Falk and Mercier [50], who via a new variational formulation of the problems just discussed have obtained error estimates of optimal order.

***The Elastoplastic Torsion Problem*** We consider again the elastoplastic problem (7.56) and assume that $\Omega$ is simply connected (which corresponds precisely to the physical problem). Then we have the following.

<u>**PROPOSITION 7.7**</u>  Assume that $\Omega$ is simply connected; then the variational problem (7.56) is equivalent to:

$$\begin{cases} \text{Find } \mathbf{p} \in \Lambda \cap H \text{ such that} \\ \displaystyle\int_\Omega \mathbf{p} \cdot (\mathbf{q}-\mathbf{p})\, dx \geq \int_\Omega \boldsymbol{\phi} \cdot (\mathbf{q}-\mathbf{p})\, dx \qquad \forall \mathbf{q} \in \Lambda \cap H \end{cases} \tag{7.82}$$

where $\boldsymbol{\phi} = \{\phi_1, \phi_2\}$ is any solution of $f = \partial\phi_1/\partial x_2 - \partial\phi_2/\partial x_1$ and where

$$\Lambda = \{\mathbf{q} \in L^2(\Omega) \times L^2(\Omega), |\mathbf{q}| \leq 1 \text{ almost everywhere on } \Omega\} \tag{7.83}$$

$$H = \left\{ \mathbf{q} \in L^2(\Omega) \times L^2(\Omega), \int_\Omega \mathbf{q} \cdot \nabla w\, dx = 0 \ \forall w \in H^1(\Omega) \right\} \tag{7.84}$$

The solutions $u$ of (7.56) and $\mathbf{p}$ of (7.82) are related by

$$\mathbf{p} = \left\{ \frac{\partial u}{\partial x_2}, -\frac{\partial u}{\partial x_1} \right\} \tag{7.85}$$

<u>**REMARK 7.22**</u>  It is clear that $\mathbf{q} \in H$ is equivalent to

$$\mathbf{q} \in L^2(\Omega) \times L^2(\Omega) \qquad \nabla \cdot \mathbf{q} = 0 \text{ almost everywhere on } \Omega \qquad \mathbf{q} \cdot \mathbf{n} = 0 \text{ a.e. on } \partial\Omega$$

where $\mathbf{n}$ is the outward unit normal vector at $\Omega$.

<u>**REMARK 7.23**</u>  If $f = \text{constant} = C$, one can take $\phi_1 = Cx_2$, $\phi_2 = 0$.

If $f$ is not constant and $\partial\Omega$ smooth or $\Omega$ convex, it is always possible to construct from $f \in L^2(\Omega)$, $\phi_1$, $\phi_2 \in H^1(\Omega)$ such that $f = \partial\phi_1/\partial x_2 - \partial\phi_2/\partial x_1$. For instance, we solve

$$\Delta u_0 = f \text{ on } \Omega \qquad u_0 \in H^1_0(\Omega)$$

which produces $u_0 \in H^2(\Omega) \cap H^1_0$. It suffices then to take $\phi_1 = \partial u_0/\partial x_2$, $\phi_2 = -\partial u_0/\partial x_1$.

As far as the approximate problem is concerned, we assume, for simplicity, that $\Omega$ is a polygonal bounded convex domain of $\mathbb{R}^2$; let $\mathcal{T}_h$ be a triangulation of $\Omega$ as in the above sections. We approximate $H^1(\Omega)$, $L^2(\Omega) \times L^2(\Omega)$, and $H$, respectively, by

$$V_h = \{v_h \in C^0(\bar{\Omega}),\, v_h|_T \in P_1 \; \forall T \in \mathcal{T}_h\}$$

$$L_h = \{\mathbf{q}_h \in L^2(\Omega) \times L^2(\Omega),\, \mathbf{q}_h|_T \in \mathbb{R}^2 \; \forall T \in \mathcal{T}_h\}$$

$$H_h = \left\{\mathbf{q}_h \in L_h,\, \int_\Omega \mathbf{q}_h \cdot \nabla w_h \, dx = 0 \; \forall w_h \in V_h\right\}$$

and then approximate (7.82) by

$$\begin{cases} \text{Find } p_h \in \Lambda \cap H_h \text{ such that} \\[2mm] \displaystyle\int_\Omega \mathbf{p}_h \cdot (\mathbf{q}_h - \mathbf{p}_h)\, dx \geq \int_\Omega \boldsymbol{\phi}(\mathbf{q}_h - \mathbf{p}_h)\, dx \qquad \forall \mathbf{q}_h \in \Lambda \cap H_h \end{cases} \tag{7.86}$$

The approximate problem (7.86) has a unique solution, and it is proved in Falk and Mercier [50] that if some convenient properties of $u$ and $\mathbf{p}$ hold, together with the usual angle condition, then

$$\|\mathbf{p}_h - \mathbf{p}\|_{L^2(\Omega) \times L^2(\Omega)} = O(h) \tag{7.87}$$

If, for example, $f = $ constant, which corresponds to the physical problem, then (7.87) holds. We refer to Falk and Mercier [50] for more details.

***Concluding Remark***   By a change of formulation an error estimate of optimal order has been obtained. It seems, however, that (7.86) is more complicated to solve numerically than (7.61) (see, however, Ref. [11], Appendix 3, where a conjugate gradient method with preconditioning for solving (7.82) is fully described).

***The Bingham's Flow Problem***   We consider now the Bingham's flow problem of Sec. 7.2C. We then have the following.

PROPOSITION 7.8   The variational problem (7.65) is equivalent to:

$$\begin{cases} \text{Find } \mathbf{p} \in H \text{ such that} \\[2mm] \displaystyle\mu \int_\Omega \mathbf{p} \cdot (\mathbf{q} - \mathbf{p})\, dx + g j(\mathbf{q}) - g j(\mathbf{p}) \geq \int_\Omega \boldsymbol{\phi} \cdot (\mathbf{q} - \mathbf{p})\, dx \qquad \forall \mathbf{q} \in H \end{cases} \tag{7.88}$$

where $\phi$ and $H$ are as in the statement of Prop. 7.7 and where $j(\mathbf{q}) = \int_\Omega |\mathbf{q}|\, dx$. The solutions $u$ of (7.65) and $\mathbf{p}$ of (7.88) are related by $\mathbf{p} = \{\partial u/\partial x_2, -\partial u/\partial x_1\}$.

***The Approximate Problem***   With $V_h$, $L_h$, $H_h$ as above, we approximate (7.88) by:

$$\begin{cases} \text{Find } \mathbf{p}_h \in H_h \text{ such that} \\[2mm] \displaystyle\mu \int_\Omega \mathbf{p}_h \cdot (\mathbf{q}_h - \mathbf{p}_h)\, dx + g j(\mathbf{q}_h) - g j(\mathbf{p}_h) \geq \int_\Omega \boldsymbol{\phi} \cdot (\mathbf{q}_h - \mathbf{p}_h)\, dx \qquad \forall \mathbf{q}_h \in H_h \end{cases} \tag{7.89}$$

The approximate problem (7.89) has a unique solution and, under suitable assumptions on

$u$ and $\mathbf{p}$, it follows from Falk and Mercier [50] that

$$\|\mathbf{p}_h - \mathbf{p}\|_{L^2(\Omega) \times L^2(\Omega)} = O(h)$$

(we again assume that the angle condition holds).

The concluding remark for the elastoplastic torsion problem still holds for (7.89).

## 7.2E Further Problems

We have not considered here the numerical analysis via finite elements of problems of the form

$$\begin{cases} \text{Find } u \in K \text{ such that} \\ \displaystyle\int_\Omega \nabla u \cdot \nabla (v - u)\, dx \geq \int_\Omega f(v - u)\, dx \qquad \forall v \in K \end{cases} \tag{7.90}$$

with
$$K = \{v \in H^1(\Omega),\ v|_{\Gamma_0} = g,\ v \geq \psi \text{ a.e. on } \Gamma_1\}$$

where $\Gamma_0$ and $\Gamma_1$ are such that $\Gamma_0 \cap \Gamma_1 = \varnothing$, $\Gamma_0 \cup \Gamma_1 = \partial\Omega$, or of the form

$$\begin{cases} \text{Find } u \in H^1(\Omega) \text{ such that} \\ \displaystyle\int_\Omega \nabla u \cdot \nabla (v - u)\, dx + j(v) - j(u) \geq \int_\Omega f(v - u)\, dx \qquad \forall v \in H^1(\Omega) \end{cases} \tag{7.91}$$

with
$$j(v) = g \int_{\partial\Omega} |v|\, d\Gamma$$

For finite-element approximations of these problems by conforming methods refer to Refs. [1, Chap. 2; 11, Chap. 4; 30; 51; and 52].

## 7.3 ITERATIVE METHODS FOR SOLVING THE APPROXIMATE VARIATIONAL INEQUALITIES OF SEC. 7.2

In this section we give some brief indications on the actual solution by iterative methods of the approximate problems of Sec. 7.2. For more details and other applications, refer to Refs. [1, 11, 52, 53], the references therein, and the references below. In fact the methods to follow are closely related to nonlinear programming.

### 7.3A Iterative Solution of the Obstacle Problem

**Orientation**  The obstacle problem and its variants [possibly involving nonsymmetric $a(\cdot, \cdot)$] may be solved by several methods. We shall concentrate on successive overrelaxation (SOR) with truncation and duality methods, and give some indication of the use of penalty methods.

The solution of discrete variational inequalities through the use of the so-called *complementarity methods* has also been studied in recent years; in that direction refer to such works as

Cottle [54, 55]; Cottle, Golub, and Sacher [56]; and Mosco and Scarpini [57]. However, in our opinion these methods are less effective (at least for most discrete EVIs) than the methods which follow and will therefore not be considered here.

***Methods of SOR with Truncation***   These methods have been by far the most popular for solving discrete obstacle problems and are, in our opinion, the simplest to program and the most economical in terms of computer storage.

The various discrete obstacle problems discussed in Sec. 7.2B are in fact particular cases of

$$\min_{y \in C} \{\tfrac{1}{2}(\mathbf{A}\mathbf{y}, \mathbf{y}) - (\mathbf{f}, \mathbf{y})\} \tag{7.92}$$

where $\mathbf{y} = \{y_1, \ldots, y_N\} \in \mathbb{R}^N$, $\mathbf{A}$ is an $N \times N$ positive-definite matrix,

$$(\mathbf{x}, \mathbf{y}) = \sum_{i=1}^{N} x_i y_i \qquad \mathbf{f} \in \mathbb{R}^N$$

and
$$C = \{\mathbf{y} \in \mathbb{R}^N, a_i \leqslant y_i \leqslant b_i \ \forall i = 1, \ldots, N\} \tag{7.93}$$

with $a_i \leqslant b_i \ \forall i = 1, \ldots, N$. Some of the $a_i$'s and $b_i$'s can possibly be equal to $-\infty$ and $+\infty$, respectively.

If $\mathbf{A} = (a_{ij})_{1 \leqslant i, j \leqslant N}$, then a typical *SOR truncation* algorithm is

$$\mathbf{x}^0 \in \mathbb{R}^N \qquad \text{arbitrarily given} \tag{7.94}$$

assuming $\mathbf{x}^n$ known, one computes $\mathbf{x}^{n+1}$ from $\mathbf{x}^n$ component by component as follows:

For $i = 1, \ldots, N$ compute

$$x_i^{n+1/2} = \frac{1}{a_{ii}} \left\{ f_i - \sum_{j<i} a_{ij} x_j^{n+1} - \sum_{j>i} a_{ij} x_j^n \right\} \tag{7.95}_i$$

$$x_i^{n+1} = P_i(x_i^n + \omega(x_i^{n+1/2} - x_i^n)) \tag{7.96}_i$$

with
$$P_i(y_i) = \sup (a_i, \inf (b_i, y_i))$$

For the convergence we have the following.

**THEOREM 7.8**   If $0 < \omega < 2$, then $\forall \mathbf{x}^0 \in \mathbb{R}^N$,

$$\lim_{n \to +\infty} \mathbf{x}^n = \mathbf{x}$$

where $\mathbf{x}$ is the unique solution of (7.92).

For the proof of Theorem 7.8 refer to Cryer [9], Cea and Glowinski [58], Comincioli [59], and Glowinski, Lions, and Trémolières [11, Chap. 2]. In some of these references generalizations to block algorithms in Hilbert spaces are also considered.

It appears that the optimal value $\omega_{\text{opt}}$ of $\omega$ (i.e., this giving the fastest convergence for a given norm) is a function of $C$ and $\mathbf{f}$. Therefore for the discrete obstacle problems discussed above it will be a function of $f$, $g$, and $\psi$. In practice, several strategies can be used; one can either use the optimal $\omega$ of the corresponding linear problem $(Ax = b)$ or apply the Young's method (see Varga [60]; Young [61]). In fact the last method has given very good results even for matrices $A$ which are not $M$-matrices.

**REMARK 7.24**   In practice, when using SOR with truncation to solve discrete obstacle problems, the first components of $\mathbf{x}^n$ to converge are those for which the discrete solution coincides with $\psi$. It appears in fact that most of the computational time is used to compute the approximate solution of $-\Delta u = f$ on $\Omega^+ = \{x \in \Omega, u(x) > \psi(x)\}$, with $u|_{\partial\Omega^+} = \psi|_{\partial\Omega^+}$ as boundary condition. Indeed we have observed that the optimal value of $\omega$ corresponds to the optimal choice for the approximate solution of the corresponding linear Dirichlet problem on $\Omega^+$.

In conclusion, the main advantages of SOR methods with truncation are that they are easy to program and they require little computer storage. They have, however, some drawbacks in that they are mainly limited to second-order potential problems. Indeed they usually show a fairly slow convergence when applied to the solution of obstacle problems related to $\Delta^2$ or to elasticity operators; the block variants of algorithm (7.94) to (7.96) are not easy to program since the truncation has to be replaced by a more complicated projection step.

**Solution of the Obstacle Problem by Duality Methods**   Several dual problems may be associated with the obstacle problem (7.28) and (7.29) (see Sec. 7.4 below for one of them). Among these dual formulations the following is well suited for computations. Let us define

$$\Lambda = \{\mu \in L^2(\Omega), \mu \geq 0 \text{ a.e.}\}$$

$$V_g = \{v \in H^1(\Omega), v = g \text{ on } \partial\Omega\}$$

and a lagrangian functional $\mathscr{L}: H^1(\Omega) \times L^2(\Omega) \to \mathbb{R}$ by

$$\mathscr{L}(v, \mu) = \tfrac{1}{2} \int_\Omega |\nabla v|^2 \, dx - \int_\Omega fv \, dx - \int_\Omega \mu(v - \psi) \, dx$$

Assume that the solution $u$ of (7.28) and (7.29) belongs to $H^2(\Omega)$; then $\lambda = -\Delta u - f$ is the unique solution of the dual problem

$$\max_{\mu \in \Lambda} \min_{v \in V_g} \mathscr{L}(v, \mu) \tag{7.97}$$

Moreover we can easily prove that $\{u, \lambda\}$ is the unique saddlepoint of $\mathscr{L}$ over $V_g \times \Lambda$.

From these properties we can use *Uzawa's algorithm*, discussed in Glowinski, Lions, and Trémolières [11, Chap. 2], which takes the following form:

$$\lambda^0 \in L^2(\Omega) \qquad \text{arbitrarily given } (\lambda^0 = 0, \text{ for example}) \tag{7.98}$$

then for $n \geq 0$, assuming $\lambda^n$ known, we obtain $u^n$ and $\lambda^{n+1}$ from

$$-\Delta u^{n+1} = f + \lambda^n \text{ in } \Omega \qquad u^{n+1} = g \text{ on } \partial\Omega \tag{7.99}$$

$$\lambda^{n+1} = P_+(\lambda^n + \rho(\psi - u^n)), \qquad \rho > 0 \tag{7.100}$$

where $P_+(\mu) = \sup (0, \mu)$.

Using Glowinski, Lions, and Trémolières [11, Chap. 2], we can prove the following.

**THEOREM 7.9**   Assume that $u \in H^2(\Omega)$; then $\forall \lambda^0 \in L^2(\Omega)$ we have

$$\lim_{n \to +\infty} \|u^n - u\|_{H^1(\Omega)} = 0$$

if $0 < \rho < 2\beta_0$ where $\beta_0$ is the smallest eigenvalue in

$$-\Delta w = \beta w \text{ in } \Omega \qquad w = 0 \text{ on } \partial\Omega$$

**Comments**   If one uses $\lambda^0 = 0$, it has been observed that the smaller $\Omega^0 = \{x \in \Omega, u(x) = \psi(x)\}$ is, the faster the convergence is. The above method (in its discrete form) is very well suited to users having at their disposal *finite-difference* or *finite-element elliptic solvers*. Another advantage of this duality approach is that it gives directly $\lambda$, for which the mechanical interpretation is interesting since it is *the reaction force of the obstacle on the membrane*. Variants of the above algorithm have been successfully used with $\Delta$ replaced by $\Delta^2$, or the *elasticity operator* (see, e.g., Ref. [11]).

**Solution of the Obstacle Problem by Penalty Methods**   We now focus our attention on the continuous obstacle problem whose formalism is simpler. With $V_g$ again as in the preceding section, we consider

$$\min_{v \in V_g} \left\{ \tfrac{1}{2} \int_\Omega |\nabla v|^2 \, dx - \int_\Omega fv \, dx + j_\varepsilon(x) \right\} \tag{7.101}$$

with

$$j_\varepsilon(v) = \frac{1}{2\varepsilon} \int_\Omega |(\psi - v)^+|^2 \, dx \tag{7.102}$$

where $q^+ = \sup(0, q)$.

The minimization problem (7.101) is in fact equivalent to the *nonlinear Dirichlet problem*

$$-\Delta u_\varepsilon - \frac{1}{\varepsilon} (\psi - u_\varepsilon)^+ = f \text{ in } \Omega \qquad u_\varepsilon = g \text{ on } \partial\Omega \tag{7.103}$$

For the convergence of $u$ to the solution $u$ of (7.28) and (7.29) it can be proved that

$$\lim_{\varepsilon \to 0} \|u_\varepsilon - u\|_{H^1(\Omega)} = 0$$

The nonlinear problem (7.101), (7.103) (in fact its discrete variants) can be solved by various methods, such as, for example, nonlinear SOR, conjugate gradients with scaling (see Concus, Golub, and O'Leary [62]; Douglas and Dupont [63]), using as scaling operator a discrete form of $-\Delta$, or an operator obtained by *incomplete Cholesky decomposition* (see Meijerink Van de Vorst [64] for details).

**Comments**   The main inconvenience of the penalty method is that it requires a small $\varepsilon$ in order to have $u_\varepsilon - u$ small. In this situation (7.101) and (7.103) are *ill-conditioned* problems. However, this technique has been successfully used in optimal-control or optimal-design problems in which the state equation is replaced by a variational inequality.

***Other Methods***   The above obstacle problem can also be solved by *conjugate-gradient-with-truncation* methods (see, e.g., Trémolières [52]) or by using a *discrete time-dependent* approach requiring at each time step the solution of a problem of similar type but better conditioned.

We can also use *augmented lagrangian* methods (refer to Chan and Glowinski [65]).

### 7.3B Iterative Solution of the Elastoplastic Torsion Problem

In this section we describe one algorithm and refer the reader to Glowinski, Lions, and Trémolières [11, Chap. 3]; Cea, Glowinski, and Nedelec [66]; Fortin and Glowinski [67, Chap. 3]; and Fortin, Glowinski, and Marrocco [68] for more details and/or other methods.

The problem under consideration is (7.56); we associate with this a *lagrangian functional* $\mathcal{L}: H_0^1(\Omega) \times L^\infty(\Omega) \to \mathbb{R}$ defined by

$$\mathcal{L}(v, \mu) = \tfrac{1}{2} \int_\Omega |\nabla v|^2 \, dx - \int_\Omega fv \, dx + \int_\Omega \mu(|\nabla v|^2 - 1) \, dx \qquad (7.104)$$

If $\Lambda = \{\mu \in L^\infty(\Omega),\ \mu \geq 0 \text{ a.e.}\}$, then we can easily prove that if $\{u, \lambda\}$ is a saddlepoint of $\mathcal{L}$ over $H_0^1(\Omega) \times \Lambda$, then $u$ is the solution of (7.56). If $f =$ constant the existence of such a saddlepoint has been proved by Brezis [69]; for more general $f$ the situation is not clear at the moment. However, the existence of such a saddlepoint has been proved for the finite-difference or finite-element approximations of the elastoplastic problem (see Glowinski, Lions, and Trémolières [11, Chap. 3] and Cea, Glowinski, and Nedelec [66] for further information). From the above properties it is then natural to use the following algorithm to compute the saddlepoints of $\mathcal{L}$ and hence $u$:

$$\lambda^0 \in \Lambda \qquad \text{arbitrarily given} \qquad (7.105)$$

then for $n \geq 0$ compute $u^n$ and $\lambda^{n+1}$ from

$$-\nabla \cdot (1 + \lambda^n)\nabla u^n = f \text{ in } \Omega \qquad u^n|_{\partial\Omega} = 0 \qquad (7.106)$$

$$\lambda^{n+1} = P_+(\lambda^n + \rho(|\nabla u^n|^2 - 1)) \qquad \rho > 0 \qquad (7.107)$$

with $P_+$ as above.

For the convergence of (7.105) to (7.107), see Refs. [11, 66].

We observe that the solution of (7.106) requires at each iteration the solution of a Dirichlet problem whose right-hand side depends upon $n$ (via $\lambda^n$). However, (7.105) to (7.107) appear as an efficient algorithm for solving (7.56).

### 7.3c Iterative Solution of the Bingham Flow Problem in a Pipe

In this section, we consider the iterative solution of (7.65), (7.66). The simplest method for solving this problem is based on the characterization (7.68), (7.69). The algorithm is the following:

$$\mathbf{p}^0 \in L^2(\Omega) \times L^2(\Omega) \text{ is arbitrarily given } (\mathbf{p}^0 = \mathbf{0}, \text{ for example})$$

Then for $n \geq 0$ one defines $u^n$ and $\mathbf{p}^{n+1}$ from $\mathbf{p}^n$ and from

$$-\mu \Delta u^n = f + g\nabla \cdot \mathbf{p}^n \text{ in } \Omega \qquad u^n|_{\partial\Omega} = 0 \tag{7.108}$$

$$\mathbf{p}^{n+1} = P_\Lambda(\mathbf{p}^n + \rho\nabla u^n) \qquad \rho > 0 \tag{7.109}$$

where $\qquad \Lambda = \{\mathbf{q} \in L^2(\Omega) \times L^2(\Omega), |\mathbf{q}(x)| \leq 1 \text{ almost everywhere}\}$

and $\qquad\qquad P_\Lambda(\mathbf{q}) = \dfrac{\mathbf{q}}{\sup(1, |\mathbf{q}|)} \qquad \forall \mathbf{q} \in L^2(\Omega) \times L^2(\Omega) \tag{7.110}$

Theorem 7.10 follows then from Cea and Glowinski [70] and Glowinski, Lions, and Trémolières [11, Chaps. 2, 5].

**THEOREM 7.10**  Assume that we have $0 < \rho < 2/g$; then $\forall \mathbf{p}^0 \in L^2(\Omega) \times L^2(\Omega)$ we have

$$\lim_{n \to +\infty} \|u^n - u\|_{H^1(\Omega)} = 0$$

$$\lim_{n \to +\infty} \mathbf{p}^n = \mathbf{p} \text{ in } L^\infty(\Omega) \times L^\infty(\Omega) \text{ weak-*}$$

where $u$ is the solution of (7.65), (7.66) and where $\mathbf{p}$ is such that $\{u, \mathbf{p}\}$ obeys (7.68), (7.69).

**REMARK 7.25**  The above function $\mathbf{p}$ is actually a solution of the dual problem

$$\max_{\mathbf{q} \in \Lambda} \min_{v \in H_0^1(\Omega)} \left\{ \frac{\mu}{2} \int_\Omega |\nabla v|^2 \, dx - \int_\Omega fv \, dx + g \int_\Omega \mathbf{q} \cdot \nabla v \, dx \right\}$$

**REMARK 7.26**  More efficient algorithms based on *augmented lagrangian* techniques are described in Gabay and Mercier [71], Fortin [72], Fortin and Glowinski [67], and Fortin, Glowinski, and Marrocco [68]. These algorithms are more complicated to handle than (7.108) to (7.110), which definitely offer the simpler efficient method for solving (7.65), (7.66) and their discrete variants.

## 7.4 APPROXIMATION OF THE OBSTACLE PROBLEM BY MIXED FINITE-ELEMENT METHODS

### 7.4A Orientation

Following Brezzi, Hager, and Raviart [73], we consider in this section *mixed finite-element approximations* of the *obstacle problem* (7.28), (7.29) (for related studies see also Hlavacek [74]). For more complicated variational inequalities, solved also by mixed finite-element methods, refer to Johnson [75, 76]; Brezzi, Johnson, and Mercier [77]; and Begis and Glowinski [78].

### 7.4B A Dual Formulation of the Obstacle Problem

It is clear that (7.28), (7.29) also has the following formulation:

$$\min_{\{v,\mathbf{q}\} \in \mathcal{K}} \left\{ \frac{1}{2} \int_\Omega |\mathbf{q}|^2 \, dx - \int_\Omega fv \, dx \right\} \tag{7.111}$$

where

$$\mathcal{K} = \{\{v, \mathbf{q}\} \in H^1(\Omega) \times (L^2(\Omega))^N, \mathbf{q} = \nabla v, \ v = g \text{ on } \partial\Omega, \ v \geq \psi \text{ a.e. on } \Omega\} \tag{7.112}$$

We associate with (7.111), (7.112) the lagrangian

$$\mathcal{L}(v, \mathbf{q}, \boldsymbol{\mu}) = \tfrac{1}{2} \int_\Omega |\mathbf{q}|^2 \, dx - \int_\Omega fv \, dx + \int_\Omega \boldsymbol{\mu} \cdot (\nabla v - \mathbf{q}) \, dx$$

and then consider the dual problem of (7.28), (7.29), related to $\mathcal{L}$; that is,

$$\max_{\boldsymbol{\mu} \in (L^2(\Omega))^N} \ \min_{\{v, \mathbf{q}\} \in \tilde{\mathcal{K}}} \ \mathcal{L}(v, q, \mu) \tag{7.113}$$

where $\qquad \tilde{\mathcal{K}} = \{\{v, \mathbf{q}\} \in H^1(\Omega) \times (L^2(\Omega))^N, \ v = g \text{ on } \partial\Omega, \ v \geq \psi \text{ a.e. on } \Omega\}$

Fortunately the explicit form of (7.113) is known and is

$$\min_{q \in C} \left\{ \tfrac{1}{2} \int_\Omega |\mathbf{q}|^2 \, dx + \int_\Omega \psi \nabla \cdot \mathbf{q} \, dx - \int_\Omega g\mathbf{q} \cdot \mathbf{n} \, d\Gamma \right\} \tag{7.114}$$

with $\qquad C = \{\mathbf{q} \in H(\mathrm{div}, \Omega), \ \nabla \cdot \mathbf{q} + f \leq 0 \text{ a.e. on } \Omega\} \tag{7.115}$

where $\qquad H(\mathrm{div}, \Omega) = \{\mathbf{q} \in (L^2(\Omega))^N, \ \nabla \cdot \mathbf{q} \in L^2(\Omega)\}$

Conversely (7.114) has a unique solution $\mathbf{p}$ such that $\mathbf{p} = \nabla u$, where $u$ is the solution of the obstacle problem (7.28), (7.29). Define

$$\Lambda = \{\mu \in L^2(\Omega), \ \mu \geq 0 \text{ a.e. on } \Omega\}$$

then $\qquad \mathbf{q} \in C \Leftrightarrow \mathbf{q} \in H(\mathrm{div}, \Omega) \quad \displaystyle\int_\Omega (\nabla \cdot \mathbf{q} + f)\mu \, dx \leq 0 \qquad \forall \mu \in \Lambda \tag{7.116}$

## 7.4c A Mixed Approximation of the Dual Problem (7.114), (7.115)

We again assume that $\Omega$ is a polygonal domain of $\mathbb{R}^2$ and $\mathcal{T}_h$ a standard triangulation of $\Omega$. Let us consider the following approximations of $H(\mathrm{div}, \Omega)$, $L^2(\Omega)$, $\Lambda$, and $C$, respectively:

$$H_h = \{\mathbf{q}_h \in H(\mathrm{div}, \Omega), \ \mathbf{q}_h|_T \in P_{k+1} \times P_{k+1} \qquad \forall T \in \mathcal{T}_h$$

and $\qquad \mathbf{q}_h \cdot \mathbf{n}|_S \in P_k \qquad \forall S \text{ side of a } T \in \mathcal{T}_h\}$

($\mathbf{n}$ is a unit vector normal to $S$).

$$L_h = \{\mu_h \in L^2(\Omega), \ \mu_h|_T \in P_k \qquad \forall T \in \mathcal{T}_h\}$$

$$\Lambda_h = \Lambda \cap L_h = \{\mu_h \in L_h, \ \mu_h \geq 0 \text{ a.e. on } \Omega\}$$

$$C_h = \left\{ \mathbf{q}_h \in H_h, \ \int_\Omega (\nabla \cdot \mathbf{q}_h + f)\mu_h \, dx \leq 0 \qquad \forall \mu_h \in \Lambda_h \right\}$$

An approximate form of (7.114), (7.115) is

$$
\begin{cases}
\text{Find } \mathbf{p}_h \in C_h \text{ such that} \\
\displaystyle\int_\Omega \mathbf{p}_h \cdot (\mathbf{q}_h - \mathbf{p}_h)\, dx + \int_\Omega \psi \boldsymbol{\nabla} \cdot (\mathbf{q}_h - \mathbf{p}_h)\, dx \geq \int_\Gamma g(\mathbf{q}_h - \mathbf{p}_h) \cdot \mathbf{n}\, d\Gamma \qquad \forall \mathbf{q}_h \in C_h
\end{cases}
\tag{7.117}
$$

Problem (7.117) clearly has a unique solution. An equivalent mixed formulation of (7.117) is

$$
\begin{cases}
\text{Find } \{\mathbf{p}_h, \lambda_h\} \in H_h \times \Lambda_h \text{ such that} \\
\displaystyle\int_\Omega \mathbf{p}_h \cdot \mathbf{q}_h\, dx + \int_\Omega (\lambda_h + \psi)\boldsymbol{\nabla} \cdot \mathbf{q}_h\, dx = \int_\Omega g\mathbf{q}_h \cdot \mathbf{n}\, d\Gamma \qquad \forall \mathbf{q}_h \in H_h \\
\displaystyle\int_\Omega (\boldsymbol{\nabla} \cdot \mathbf{p}_h + f)(\mu_h - \lambda_h)\, dx \leq 0 \qquad \forall \mu_h \in \Lambda_h
\end{cases}
\tag{7.118}
$$

It follows from Brezzi, Hager, and Raviart [73] that (7.118) has a unique solution and $p_h$ is the solution of (7.117).

For the convergence of $\mathbf{p}_h$ and $\lambda_h$ as $h \to 0$, Brezzi, Hager, and Raviart [73] have proved that if $(\mathcal{T}_h)$ is a *regular family* of triangulations, if $f \in L^2(\Omega)$, $u \in H^2(\Omega)$ [then $g \in H^{3/2}(\Gamma)$], and if $k = 0$, then

$$
\|\mathbf{p}_h - \boldsymbol{\nabla} u\|_{L^2(\Omega)} = \|\lambda_h - (u - \psi)\|_{L^2(\Omega)} = O(h)
$$

The above authors have also proved that if $k = 1$ and if $f \in L^\infty(\Omega)$, $u, \psi \in W^{2,\infty}(\Omega)$, $u \in W^{s,\alpha}(\Omega)$ $\forall \alpha \in \,]1, +\infty[$, and $s < 2 + 1/\alpha$, then

$$
\|p_h - \boldsymbol{\nabla} u\|_{L^2(\Omega)} = \|\lambda_h - (u - \psi)\|_{L^2(\Omega)} = O(h^{3/2 - \varepsilon})
$$

with $\varepsilon > 0$ arbitrarily small.

**REMARK 7.27**   The numerical solution of (7.117), (7.118) is more complicated than that of the approximate problems of Sec. 7.2, which correspond to standard conforming (displacement) finite-element approximations.

## 7.5 CONCLUSION AND FURTHER COMMENTS

The variational-inequality methodology appears to be an efficient tool for solving problems which may originally be formulated in a more classical way. Let us consider two examples of such a situation.

**EXAMPLE 7.1**   *A family of mildly nonlinear elliptic problems.* Let $\Omega$ be a bounded domain of $\mathbb{R}^N$ with smooth boundary, $A: H_0^1(\Omega) \to H^{-1}(\Omega)\,[=(H_0^1(\Omega))']$ a *strongly elliptic isomorphism*, $f \in H^{-1}(\Omega)$, $\phi : \mathbb{R} \to \mathbb{R}$, $\phi \in C^0$, $\phi$ nondecreasing [we can always suppose that $\phi(0) = 0$]. We consider then the following nonlinear elliptic problem (of monotone type)

$$
Au + \phi(u) = f
\tag{7.119}
$$

Let us define $a : H_0^1(\Omega) \times H_0^1(\Omega) \to \mathbb{R}$, bilinear continuous, and $H_0^1(\Omega)$-elliptic from

$$a(v, w) = \langle Av, w \rangle$$

where $\langle \cdot, \cdot \rangle$ denotes the duality pairing between $H^{-1}(\Omega)$ and $H_0^1(\Omega)$. Let us also define $j : H_0^1(\Omega) \to \bar{\mathbb{R}}$ by

$$j(v) = \int_\Omega \Phi(v) \, dx \quad \text{where} \quad \Phi(t) = \int_0^t \phi(\tau) \, d\tau$$

It is clear that $j(\cdot)$ is convex, proper, and lower semicontinuous. Actually from the point of view of solving (7.119) it is convenient to consider the following $(\text{EVI})_2$:

$$\begin{cases} \text{Find } u \in H_0^1(\Omega) \text{ such that} \\ a(u, v - u) + j(v) - j(u) \geq \langle f, v - u \rangle \quad \forall v \in H_0^1(\Omega) \end{cases} \tag{7.120}$$

In Chan and Glowinski [65] (see also Glowinski [1]) it is proved that (7.120) has a unique solution which is also the unique solution of (7.119) in $H_0^1(\Omega)$. We consider also in the two cited references the approximation of (7.119), (7.120) by piecewise linear finite elements. This is precisely a situation in which the convergence results cannot be applied (directly at least), since $j(\cdot)$ is in general *not continuous* on $H_0^1(\Omega)$.

However, the strong convergence of the approximate solution can be proved (see Refs. [1, 65] for more details).

**EXAMPLE 7.2**  *Transonic, potential flows.* This problem is far more important and difficult than the problem of Example 7.1. In fact it is not an elliptic problem unless the flow remains purely subsonic. The problem is to find a velocity potential $\phi$ defined on $\Omega$ (the domain of the flow) such that

$$\begin{cases} \boldsymbol{\nabla} \cdot (\rho(\phi)\boldsymbol{\nabla}\phi) = 0 \quad \text{in } \Omega \\ + \text{convenient boundary conditions} \end{cases} \tag{7.121}$$

with

$$\rho(\phi) = \rho_0 \left( 1 - \frac{|\boldsymbol{\nabla}\phi|^2}{(\gamma+1)/(\gamma-1)} C_*^2 \right)^{1/\gamma-1}$$

where $\rho_0 = \text{constant}$, $\gamma = 1.4$ in air, $C_* = \text{critical velocity}$. The flow velocity is given by $\mathbf{v} = \boldsymbol{\nabla}\phi$.

If $\Omega$ is not simply connected, $\phi$ has to obey a circulation condition given by the *Kutta-Joukowsky* condition (see Landau and Lifchitz [79] for more details, and also the references below). Actually the above relations are not sufficient to obtain only *physical solutions*, i.e., solutions *without expansion shocks*. In order to avoid these nonphysical solutions an *entropy condition* has to be prescribed. We have found it convenient to require that

$$(\Delta\phi)^+ \in L^p(\Omega) \quad \forall p > 1 \tag{7.122}$$

The most common values of $p$ are $p = 2$ and $p = +\infty$. In order to solve (7.121), taking (7.122) into account, we have introduced the variational problem

$$\min_{w \in X} \left\{ \int_\Omega |\boldsymbol{\nabla}\phi(w)|^2 \, dx + \mu \int_\Omega |(\Delta w - C)^+|^2 \, dx \right\} \tag{7.123}$$

where $X$ is a set (usually convex) of admissible velocity potentials, $\mu$ is a positive parameter, $C$ is a given constant (or function), and $\phi(w)$ is the solution of the elliptic problem

$$
\begin{cases}
\Delta\phi(w) = \nabla \cdot (\rho(w)\nabla w) & \text{in } \Omega \\
+ \text{boundary conditions} + (\text{possibly}) \text{ Kutta–Joukowsky conditions}
\end{cases}
\tag{7.124}
$$

In fact (7.123), (7.124) is a least-squares formulation of (7.121) taking (7.122) into account. Problem (7.123), which is indeed a nonlinear fourth-order variational problem, has been solved by a mixed finite-element method coupled to a conjugate-gradient algorithm with scaling. For further details refer to Glowinski and Pironneau [80, 81], Bristeau [82, 83], Bristeau, Glowinski, Périaux, Perrier, Pironneau, and Poirier [84], where references to other methods for solving (7.121) are also given; see also the sections of this handbook devoted to transonic flow calculations.

To conclude this survey on elliptic variational inequalities, we mention several books or reports relevant to the subject: Duvaut and Lions [41] and Hlavacek, Haslinger, Necas, and Lovisek [85] for mathematical aspects and applications to mechanics and physics; Cea [6], Glowinski, Lions, and Trémolières [11], Glowinski [1, 49], Trémolières [52] for numerical analysis (approximation and iterative solution); Bensoussan and Lions [3] for quasi-variational inequalities; Baiocchi and Capelo [4] for applications to the solution of the free-boundary problems related to flows in porous media (see also Baiocchi, Comincioli, Magenes, and Pozzi [86]; Cryer and Fetter [18]; and Oden and Kikuchi [19]).

## 7.6 REFERENCES

1. Glowinski, R., *Numerical Methods for Nonlinear Variational Problems*, Springer-Verlag, New York, 1984.

2. Lions, J. L., *Quelques Méthodes de Résolution des Problèmes aux Limites Non Linéaires*, Dunod, Paris, 1969.

3. Bensoussan, A., and J. L. Lions, *Contrôle Impulsionnel et Inéquations Quasi-Variationnelles*, Dunod, Paris, 1982.

4. Baiocchi, C., and A. Capelo, *Disequazioni Variazionali e Quasi-Variazionali: Applicazioni a Problemi di Frontiera Libera*, Quaderni 4 e 7 dell' Unione Mathematica Italiana, Pitagora Editrice, Bologna, 1978.

5. Lions, J. L., and G. Stampacchia, "Variational Inequalities," *Comm. Pure Appl. Math.*, **20**:493–519 (1967).

6. Cea, J., *Optimisation: Théorie et Algorithmes*, Dunod, Paris, 1970.

7. Ciarlet, P. G., *The Finite Element Method for Elliptic Problems*, North-Holland, Amsterdam, 1978.

8. Cryer, C. W., "The Method of Christoferson for Solving Free Boundary Problems for Infinite Journal Bearings by Means of Finite Differences," *Math. Comp.*, **75**:435–443 (1971).

9. Cryer, C. W., "The Solution of a Quadratic Programming Problem Using Systematic Over-relaxation," *SIAM J. Control*, **9**:385–392 (1971).

10. Marzulli, P., "Rizoluzione alle Differenze Finite di Equazioni alle Derivate Parziali di Tipo Ellittico con Condizioni su un Conterno Libero," *Calcolo*, **1**:1–22 (1968).

11. Glowinski, R., J. L. Lions, and R. Trémolières, *Numerical Analysis of Variational Inequalities*, North-Holland, Amsterdam, 1981.

12. Capriz, G., "Variational Techniques for the Analysis of a Lubrication Problem," in I. Galligani and E. Magenes (eds.), *Mathematical Aspects of Finite Element Methods, Lecture Notes in Mathematics,* Springer-Verlag, Berlin, 1977, vol. 606, pp. 47-55.

13. Baiocchi, C., "Sur un Problème à Frontière Libre Traduisant le Filtrage de Liquides à Travers des Milieux Poreux," *C. R. Acad. Sci. Paris,* **273A**:1215-1217 (1971).

14. Baiocchi, C., "Sur un Problema di Frontiera Libera Connesso a Questioni di Idraulica," *Ann. Mat. Pura Appl.,* **4**:107-127 (1972).

15. Baiocchi, C., "Free Boundary Problems in the Theory of Fluid Flow through Porous Media," *Proceedings of the International Congress of Mathematics (Vancouver 1974),* 1975, vol. 2, pp. 237-243.

16. Comincioli, V., "On Some Oblique Derivative Problems Arising in the Fluid Flow in Porous Media: A Theoretical and Numerical Approach," *Appl. Math. Optimization,* **1**:313-336 (1975).

17. Baiocchi, C., F. Brezzi, and V. Comincioli, "Free Boundary Problems in Fluid Flow through Porous Media," *Proc. 2d Int. Symp. Finite Element Methods in Flow Problems,* Santa Margherita, 1976, pp. 407-420.

18. Cryer, C. W., and H. Fetter, "The Numerical Solution of Axisymmetric Free Boundary Porous Flow Well Problems Using Variational Inequalities," MRC-Technical Summary Report 1761, University of Wisconsin, Madison, 1977.

19. Oden, J. T., and N. Kikuchi, "Theory of Variational Inequalities with Application to Problems of Flow through Porous Media, *Int. J. Eng. Soc.,* **18**:1173-1284 (1980).

20. Brezis, H., and G. Stampacchia, Une Nouvelle Méthode pour l'Étude d'Écoulements Stationnaires, *C.R. Acad. Sci. Paris,* **276A**:129-132 (1973).

21. Brezis, H., and G. Stampacchia, "The Hodograph Method in Fluid Dynamics in the Light of Variational Inequalities," *Arch. Ration. Mech. Anal.,* **61**:1-18 (1976).

22. Brezis, H., "A New Method in the Study of Subsonic Flows," in J. Goldstein (ed.), *Partial Differential Equations and Related Topics, Lecture Notes in Mathematics,* Springer-Verlag, Berlin, 1975, vol. 446.

23. Ciavaldini, J. F., M. Pogu, and G. Tournemine, "Une Méthode Variationnelle Non Linéaire pour l'Étude dans le Plan Physique d'Écoulements Compressibles Subcritiques en Atmosphère Infinie," *C. R. Acad. Sci. Paris,* **281A**:1105-1108 (1975).

24. Roux, J., "Résolution Numérique d'un Problème d'Écoulement Subsonique de Fluides Compressibles," *Rev. Fr. Autom. Inf. Rech. Oper. Anal. Numer.,* **11**:197-208 (1977).

25. Bourgat, J. F., and G. Duvaut, "Numerical Analysis of Flow with or without Wake Past a Symmetric Two-Dimensional Profile with or without Incidence," *Int. J. Numer. Meth. Eng.,* **11**:975-993 (1977).

26. Brezis, H., and G. Stampacchia, Sur la Régularité de la Solution d'Inéquations Elliptiques, *Bull. Soc. Math. Fr.,* **96**:153-180 (1968).

27. Brezis, H., "Nouveaux Théorèmes de Régularité pour les Problèmes Unilatéraux," *Proceedings of the Joint Meeting of Theoretical Physicists and Mathematicians,* Strasbourg, 1971, vol. 12.

28. Brezis, H., "Seuil de Régularité pour Certains Problèmes Unilatéraux," *C. R. Acad. Sci. Paris,* **273A**:35-37 (1971).

29. Kinderlehrer, D., and G. Stampacchia, *An Introduction to Variational Inequalities and their Applications,* Academic Press, New York, 1980.

30. Brezzi, F., W. W. Hager, and P. A. Raviart, "Error Estimates for the Finite Element Solution of Variational Inequalities: I—Primal Theory," *Numer. Math.,* **28**:431-443 (1977).

31. Brezis, H., "Problèmes Unilatéraux," *J. Math. Pures Appl.* Ser. 72, **9**:1-168 (1971).

32. Falk, R. S., *Approximate Solutions of Some Variational Inequalities with Order of Convergence Estimates,* Ph.D. thesis, Cornell University, Ithaca, N.Y., 1971.

33. Mosco, U., and G. Strang, "One Sided Approximation and Variational Inequalities," *Bull. Am. Math. Soc.,* **80**:308-312 (1974).

34. Falk, R. S., "Error Estimates for the Approximation of a Class of Variational Inequalities," *Math. Comp.*, **28**:963–971 (1974).

35. Falk, R. S., "Approximation of an Elliptic Boundary Value Problem with Unilateral Constraints," *Rev. Fr. Autom. Inf. Rech. Oper.*, **R2**:5–12 (1975).

36. Natterer, F., "Optimale $L_2$-Konvergenz finiten Elemente bei Variationsungleichungen," *Bonn Math. Schr.*, **89**:1–12 (1976).

37. Mosco, U., "Error Estimates for Some Variational Inequalities," in I. Galligani and E. Magenes (eds.), *Mathematical Aspects of Finite Element Methods, Lecture Notes in Mathematics*, Springer-Verlag, Berlin, 1977, vol. 606, pp. 224–236.

38. Baiocchi, C., "Estimations d'Erreur dans $L^\infty$ pour les Inéquations à Obstacle," in I. Galligani and E. Magenes (eds.), *Mathematical Aspects of Finite Element Methods, Lecture Notes in Mathematics*, Springer-Verlag, Berlin, 1977, vol. 606, pp. 27–34.

39. Nitsche J., "$L^\infty$-Convergence of Finite Element Approximation," in I. Galligani and E. Magenes (eds.), *Mathematical Aspects of Finite Element Methods, Lecture Notes in Mathematics*, Springer-Verlag, Berlin, 1977, vol. 606, pp. 261–274.

40. Janovsky, V., and J. R. Whiteman, "Error analysis of Finite Element Methods for Mildly Nonlinear Variational Inequalities," *Numer. Functional Anal. Optimization*, **1**:223–232 (1979).

41. Duvaut, G., and J. L. Lions, *Les Inéquations en Mécanique et en Physique*, Dunod, Paris, 1972.

42. Glowinski, R., and H. Lanchon, "Torsion Elasto-Plastique d'une Barre Cylindrique de Section Multiconnexe," *J. Mecanique*, **12**:151–171 (1973).

43. Brezis, H., and M. Sibony, "Equivalence de Deux Inéquations Variationnelles et Applications," *Arch. Ration. Mech. Anal.*, **41**:254–265 (1971).

44. Shaw, F. S., "The Torsion of Solid and Hollow Prisms in the Elastic and Plastic Range by Relaxation Methods," Rep. ACA-11, Australian Council of Aeronautics, 1944. (See *Engineering Index*, 1945, p. 1064.)

45. Mossolov, P. P., and V. P. Miasnikov, "Variational Methods in the Theory of Viscous–Plastic Medium," *J. Mech. Appl. Math. (P.M.M.)*, **29**:468–492 (1965).

46. Mossolov, P. P., and V. P. Miasnikov, "On Stagnant Flow Regions of a Viscous-Plastic Medium in Pipes," *J. Mech. Appl. Math. (P.M.M.)*, **30**:707–717 (1966).

47. Mossolov, P. P., and V. P. Miasnikov, "On Qualitative Singularities of the Flow of a Viscous-Plastic Medium in Pipes," *J. Mech. Appl. Math. (P.M.M.)*, **31**:581–585 (1967).

48. Brezis, H., "Monotonicity Methods in Hilbert Spaces and Some Applications to Nonlinear Partial Differential Equations," in E. Zarantonello (ed.), *Contributions to Nonlinear Functional Analysis*, Academic Press, New York, 1971, pp. 101–156.

49. Glowinski, R., "Sur l'Approximation d'une Inéquation Variationnelle Elliptique de Type Bingham," *Rev. Fr. Autom. Inf. Rech. Oper.*, **10**:13–30 (1976).

50. Falk, R. S., and B. Mercier, "Error Estimates for Elasto-Plastic Problems," *Rev. Fr. Autom. Inf. Rech. Oper.*, **11**:135–144 (1977).

51. Scarpini, F., and M. A. Vivaldi, "Error Estimates for the Approximation of Some Unilateral Problems," *Rev. Fr. Autom. Inf. Rech. Oper. Anal. Numer.*, **11**:197–208 (1977).

52. Trémolières, R., *Inéquations Variationnelles: Existence, Approximation, Résolution*, Thesis, Université Pierre et Marie Curie, Paris, 1972.

53. Mercier, B., *Sur la Théorie et l'Analyse Numérique de Problèmes de Plasticité*, Thesis, Université Pierre et Marie Curie, Paris, 1977.

54. Cottle, R. W., "Computational Experience with Large Scale Linear Complementarity Problems," in S. Karamardian (ed.), *Fixed Points: Algorithms and Applications*, Academic Press, New York, 1977, pp. 281–313.

55. Cottle, R. W., "Numerical Methods for Complementarity Problems in Engineering and Applied Sciences," in R. Glowinski and J. L. Lions, (eds.), *Computing Methods in Applied Sciences and Engineering*, 1977, **1**, *Lecture Notes in Mathematics*, Springer-Verlag, Berlin, 1979, vol. 704, pp. 37–52.

56. Cottle, R. W., Golub, G. H., and R. J. Sacher, "On the Solution of Large, Structured, Linear Complementarity Problems: The Block Partitioned Case," *Appl. Math. Optim.*, **4**:347–364 (1978).

57. Mosco, U., and F. Scarpini, "Complementarity Systems and Approximation of Variational Inequalities," *Rev. Fr. Autom. Inf. Rech. Oper.*, **R-1**:83–104 (1975).

58. Cea, J., and R. Glowinski, "Sur des Méthodes d'Optimisation par Relaxation," *Rev. Fr. Autom. Inf. Rech. Oper.*, **R-3**:5–32 (1973).

59. Comincioli, V., "Metodi di Rilassamento per la Minimizzazione in uno Spazio Prodotto," *L.A.N.-C.N.R.*, **20**, Pavia, 1971.

60. Varga, R. S., *Matrix Iterative Analysis*, Prentice-Hall, Englewood Cliffs, N.J., 1962.

61. Young, D. M., *Iterative Solution of Large Linear Systems*, Academic Press, New York, 1971.

62. Concus, P., G. H. Golub, and D. P. O'Leary, "Numerical Solution of Nonlinear Partial Differential Equations by a Generalized Conjugate Gradient Method," *Computing*, **19**:321–340 (1977).

63. Douglas, J., and T. Dupont, "Preconditioned Conjugate Gradient Iteration Applied to Galerkin Methods for a Mildly Nonlinear Dirichlet Problem," in J. R. Bunch and D. J. Rose (eds.), *Sparse Matrix Computations*, Academic Press, New York, 1976, pp. 333–348.

64. Meijerink, J. A., and H. A. Van der Vorst, "An Iterative Solution Method for Linear Systems of Which the Coefficient Matrix Is a Symmetric M-Matrix," *Math. Comp.*, **31**:148–162 (1977).

65. Chan, T. F., and R. Glowinski, "Numerical Methods for Solving Some Mildly Nonlinear Elliptic Partial Differential Equations," Stanford Report STAN-CS-78-674, 1978.

66. Cea, J., R. Glowinski, and J. C. Nedelec, "Application des Méthodes d'Optimisation, de Différences et d'Éléments Finis à l'Analyse Numérique de la Torsion Elasto-Plastique d'une Barre Cylindrique," in *Approximations et Méthodes Itératives de Résolution d'Inéquations Variationnelles et de Problèmes Non Linéaires, Cahier de l'IRIA*, 1974, vol. 12, pp. 7–138.

67. Fortin, M., and R. Glowinski, "Sur des Méthodes de Décomposition-Coordination par Lagrangiens Augmentés," in M. Fortin and R. Glowinski (eds.), *Méthodes de Lagrangien Augmenté*, Dunod, Paris, 1981, pp. 91–136.

68. Fortin, M., R. Glowinski, and A. Marrocco, "Application à la Résolution de Problèmes aux Limites d'Ordre Deux Fortement Non Linéaires," in M. Fortin and R. Glowinski (eds.), *Méthodes de Lagrangien Augmenté*, Dunod, Paris, 1981, pp. 159–201.

69. Brezis, H., "Multiplicateur de Lagrange en Torsion Elasto-Plastique," *Arch. Ration. Mech. Anal.*, **49**:32–40 (1972).

70. Cea, J., and R. Glowinski, "Méthodes Numériques pour l'Écoulement Laminaire d'un Fluide Rigide Visco-Plastique Incompressible," *Int. J. Comp. Math.*, B, **3**:225–255 (1972).

71. Gabay, D., and B. Mercier, "A Dual Algorithm for the Solution of Nonlinear Variational Problems via Finite Element Approximations," *Comp. Math. Appl.*, **2**:17–40 (1976).

72. Fortin, M., "Minimization of Some Nondifferentiable Functionals by the Augmented Lagrangian Method of Hestenes and Powell," *Appl. Math. Optim.*, **2**:236–250 (1976).

73. Brezzi, F., W. W. Hager, and P. A. Raviart, "Error Estimates for the Finite Element Solution of Variational Inequalities: II—Mixed Methods," *Numer. Math.*, **31**:1–16 (1978).

74. Hlavacek, I., "Dual Finite Element Analysis for Unilateral Boundary Value Problems," *Appl. Matematiky*, **22**:14–51 (1977).

75. Johnson, C., "A Mixed Finite Element Method for Plasticity Problems with Hardening," *SIAM J. Numer. Anal.*, **14**:575–583 (1977).

76. Johnson, C., "An Elasto-Plastic Contact Problem," *Rev. Fr. Autom. Inf. Rech. Oper. Numer. Anal.*, **27**:59–74 (1978).

77. Brezzi, F., C. Johnson, and B. Mercier, "Analysis of a Mixed Finite Element Method for Elasto-Plastic Plates," *Math. Comp.*, **31**:809–817 (1977).

78. Begis, D., and R. Glowinski, "Application à la Simulation Numérique d'Écoulements Bidimension-nels de Fluides Visco-Plastiques Incompressibles," in M. Fortin and R. Glowinski (eds.), *Méthodes de Lagrangien Augmenté*, Dunod, Paris, 1981, pp. 219–240.

79. Landau, L., and E. Lifchitz, *Mécanique des Fluides*, Mir, Moscow, 1953.

80. Glowinski, R., and O. Pironneau, "On the Computation of Transonic Flows," in H. Fujita (ed.), *Functional Analysis and Numerical Analysis*, Japanese Society for the Promotion of Science, Tokyo, 1978, pp. 143–173.

81. Glowinski, R., and O. Pironneau, "Least Squares Solution of Nonlinear Problems in Fluid Dynamics," G. M. de la Penha and L. A. Medeiros (eds.), *Contemporary Developments in Continuum Mechanics and P.D.E.*, North-Holland, Amsterdam, 1978, pp. 171–224.

82. Bristeau, O., "Application of Optimal Control Theory to Transonic Flow Computations by Finite Element Methods," in R. Glowinski and J. L. Lions (eds.), *Computing Methods in Applied Sciences and Engineering*, pt. II, *Lecture Notes in Physics*, Springer-Verlag, Berlin, 1979, vol. 91, pp. 103–124.

83. Bristeau, O., "Application of a Finite Element Method to Transonic Flow Problems Using an Optimal Control Approach," in W. Kollmann (ed.), *Computational Fluid Dynamics*, Hemisphere Publications, Washington, D.C., 1980, pp. 281–328.

84. Bristeau, M. O., R. Glowinski, J. Périaux, P. Perrier, O. Pironneau, and G. Poirier, "Transonic Flow Simulations by Finite Elements and Least Square Methods," in R. H. Gallagher, D. M. Norrie, J. T. Odlen, and O. C. Zienkiewicz (eds.), *Finite Elements in Fluids*, Wiley, Chichester, 1982, vol. 4, pp. 453–482.

85. Hlavacek, I., J. Haslinger, J. Necas, and J. Lovisek, *Riesenie Variacnych Nerovnosti v Mechanike*, S.N.T.L., Prague, 1982.

86. Baiocchi, C., V. Comincioli, E. Magenes, and G. A. Pozzi, *Fluid Flow through Porous Media: A New Theoretical and Numerical Approach*, Pub. 69, *L.A.N.-C.N.R.*, Pavia, 1974.

# FEM FUNDAMENTALS

# CHAPTER 1
# VARIATIONAL PRINCIPLES

## 1.1 VARIATIONAL PRINCIPLES IN ELASTICITY†

### 1.1A Introduction

Given the body of evidence which has accrued in the course of the last thirty years for the utility of variational formulations in connection with the approximate solution of problems in small- and large-deformation theories of elasticity, the present account is an attempt to review the basic developments in this field in historical perspective.

It is possible to undertake such a presentation within the framework of large (finite) deformation, or *geometrically nonlinear* theory, at the outset, with the results for small (infinitesimal) deformations, or *geometrically linear* theory, being deduced by specialization. However, in order to achieve a clearer understanding, it seems preferable to adopt a contrary procedure. Thus, we begin with a self-contained account of the results which apply when *geometric* linearity is assumed for *physically* linear as well as nonlinear problems. Discussion of the geometrically nonlinear problem then follows.

We begin with a statement of the differential equations and boundary conditions of geometrically linear theory of elasticity with mutually compatible surface displacement and/or traction conditions. We then show how some portions of these relations are equations of *constraint* and how complementary portions are *consequences* (Euler equations) of the classical "one-field" variational equations for displacements *or* for stresses. We proceed from this, in a synthetic way, to a statement of a two-field variational equation for displacements *and*

† The writing of Sec. 1.1 has been supported in part by National Science Foundation Grant No. CEE-8213256.

stresses in which there are no equations of constraint and all the differential equations and boundary conditions are consequences of the variational equation. Subsequent to this we describe the ingeniously simple invention of a three-field variational equation for displacements, stresses, *and* strains, which obtains when we change the status of the expression for strains, in terms of displacement derivatives, from defining relations to component parts of the system of differential equations of the theory.

The discussion of variational equations (theorems or principles) for geometrically *non*-linear elasticity theory is preceded by a *natural* approach to the differential equations via a consideration of "edge" vectors for deformed and undeformed "infinitesimal boxes." This leads to defining relations for components of finite strain, in the sense of Green, as well as to defining (pseudo) stress components as components of force per unit of *un*deformed area having the direction of the edge vectors of the deformed box, as done by Kirchhoff and Trefftz. From the above "natural" description of finite strain and stress, we deduce the equations which apply when the cartesian projections of the Kirchhoff–Trefftz stress components are introduced. These we designate as components of Piola stress. We also deduce the equations which apply when the displacement-component derivatives are introduced in place of the strain components of Green. These are conjugate measures in the same sense that the Kirchhoff–Trefftz stresses and Green strains are conjugate measures.

Given the above static and kinematic relations of geometrically nonlinear theory, it is a straightforward matter to reformulate the variational theorem for *displacements* of geometrically linear theory to make it valid for geometrically nonlinear theory. On the other hand, attempts at a corresponding reformulation of the variational principle for *stresses* so that it applies in the geometrically nonlinear range have not, in essence, been successful. The reasons for this will become apparent when we inspect the form of the Euler differential equations which one hopes to associate with such a theorem. In contrast to this, the serendipitous attempt to reformulate, again synthetically, the *two*-field variational theorem of geometrically linear theory so that it becomes a variational theorem for stresses and displacements of geometrically nonlinear theory in terms of Green strains and Kirchhoff–Trefftz stresses does lead to the "expected" result. Similarly, there is no difficulty in reformulating the three-field problem of linear theory so as to become an appropriate variational theorem of nonlinear theory for Kirchhoff–Trefftz stresses, Green strains, and displacements. Additionally, for this *three*-field problem, the step from using Kirchhoff–Trefftz stresses and Green strains to using Piola stresses and displacement-component derivatives also presents no difficulty.

The impossibility of obtaining a variational theorem for stresses and displacements in terms of Piola stresses and (translational) displacements has in recent times been overcome by variational formulations in terms of what we here designate as *distinguished generalized* Piola stresses, in conjunction with rotational, in addition to translational, displacement components. We conclude our discussion by a brief description of these developments.

### 1.1B Differential Equations and Boundary Conditions of Geometrically Linear Theory

Given a cartesian coordinate system $x_i$ we are concerned with a system of differential equations for *components of stress* $\sigma_{ij}$ and *components of displacement* $u_i$ of the form

$$\sigma_{ij,i} + \frac{\partial P}{\partial u_j} = 0 \qquad \sigma_{ij} = \frac{\partial \Sigma}{\partial u_{ij}} \tag{1.1a, b}$$

where $\sigma_{ij} = \sigma_{ji}$ and $u_{ij} = u_{ji} \equiv \frac{1}{2}(u_{i,j} + u_{j,i})$, with $P$ and $\Sigma$ being given functions of $u_i$ and $u_{ij}$, respectively.

Equations $(1.1a, b)$ are to be solved in the interior of a given domain $V$, subject to prescribed conditions on the domain surface $A$, of the mixed form

$$u_i = \frac{\partial U}{\partial t_i} \text{ on } A_u \qquad t_i = \frac{\partial T}{\partial u_i} \text{ on } A_t \qquad A_u \cup A_t = A \tag{1.2a, b}$$

where $t_i = \sigma_{ji}\nu_j$, with $\nu_j = \cos(x_j, \nu)$ and with $U$ and $T$ being given functions of $t_i$ and $u_i$, respectively.

With regard to the notation used above note that we have written $u_{ij}$ in place of the usual $\varepsilon_{ij}$ for *components of strain* and that it is customary to designate the quantities $t_i$ as *traction components*.

With regard to the functions $P, \Sigma, U, T$ we assume that all the indicated derivatives exist, and in addition that the *strain-energy density* $\Sigma$ has a unique inverse *complementary strain-energy density* $\Gamma$ such that

$$u_{ij} = \frac{\partial \Gamma}{\partial \sigma_{ij}} \tag{1.1c}$$

The problem as stated is *physically* as well as geometrically linear in the event that

$$P = P_1 + P_2 \qquad \Sigma = \Sigma_1 + \Sigma_2 \qquad U = U_1 + U_2 \qquad T = T_1 + T_2 \qquad \Gamma = \Gamma_1 + \Gamma_2 \tag{1.3}$$

with the subscripts designating polynomials of degree 1 and 2, respectively.

Of particular interest for what follows are cases for which

$$P = P_1 = \bar{p}_i u_i \qquad U = U_1 = \bar{u}_i t_i \qquad T = T_1 = \bar{t}_i u_i \tag{1.4}$$

with $\bar{p}_i, \bar{u}_i, \bar{t}_i$ being *prescribed body-force, surface-displacement*, and *traction* components, respectively.

With regard to the *mixed* system of boundary conditions, Eqs. $(1.2a, b)$, we note the possibility of stipulating, in extension of the obvious specialization of Eqs. $(1.2a, b)$ which is given upon choosing $U$ and $T$ as in $(1.4)$,

$$u_i = \bar{u}_i \text{ on } A_{u_i} \qquad t_i = \bar{t}_i \text{ on } A_{t_i} \qquad A_{u_i} \cup A_{t_i} = A \tag{1.5a, b}$$

with this latter version being relevant in much of what follows.†

## 1.1c The Classical Variational Theorems of Linear Theory

Given Eqs. $(1.1a$ to $c)$ and $(1.5a, b)$ with $P = P_1$, $\Sigma = \Sigma_2$, and $\Gamma = \Gamma_2$, the classical considerations of Green, Castigliano, and Menabrea, as summarized succinctly by Tefftz [25a], imply the validity of the following two *one-field* variational theorems.

---

† A corresponding restatement of Eqs. $(1.2a, b)$ would involve a subdivision of $A$ into *eight* nonoverlapping portions $A_i$ and will not be pursued here.

*The Variational Theorem for Displacements*   The variational equation

$$\delta I_u = \delta \left\{ \int [\Sigma_2(u_{ij}) - \bar{p}_i u_i] \, dV - \int \bar{t}_i u_i \, dA \right\} = 0 \tag{1.6}$$

where Eqs. (1.1$b$) and (1.5$a$) are conditions of constraint and the extent of the surface integration is consistent with Eq. (1.5$b$), has Eqs. (1.1$a$) and (1.5$b$) as Euler differential equations and boundary conditions.†

*The Variational Theorem for Stresses*   The equation

$$\delta I_\sigma = \delta \left\{ \int \Gamma_2(\sigma_{ij}) \, dV - \int \bar{u}_i t_i \, dA \right\} = 0 \tag{1.7}$$

where Eqs. (1.1$a$) and (1.5$b$) are equations of constraint and the surface integration is consistent with Eq. (1.5$a$), has Eqs. (1.1$c$) and (1.5$a$) as Euler differential equations and boundary conditions.

*Verification of the Variational Theorems for Displacements or for Stresses*   The verification of both statements involves use of the divergence-theorem (integration by parts) relation

$$\int \sigma_{ij} u_{ij} \, dV = \int t_i u_i \, dA - \int \sigma_{ji,j} u_i \, dV \tag{1.8}$$

in conjunction with $\delta u_{i,j} = (\delta u_i)_{,j}$ and $\delta(\sigma_{ij,j}) = (\delta \sigma_{ij})_{,j}$ and, for the $I_\sigma$-problem, the possibility of an appropriate interim a priori introduction of the Euler equations $u_{ij} = \partial \Gamma_2 / \partial \sigma_{ij}$.

For some applications it is useful to know that the stipulations $\delta I_u = 0$ and $\delta I_\sigma = 0$, in conjunction with their constraint conditions, are in fact equivalent to stipulations $I_u = \min$ and $I_\sigma = \min$, with the verification of these properties depending on the positive definiteness of $\Sigma_2$ and $\Gamma_2$. For examples of such applications, see Refs. [18] and [23].

## 1.1D The Variational Theorem for Stresses and Displacements of Geometrically Linear Theory

Given that in the use of the variational theorem for displacements or of the theorem for stresses, for obtaining *approximate* solutions of boundary-value problems (in the sense of Rayleigh and Ritz) certain *parts* of the complete system of differential equations and boundary conditions must be satisfied *exactly* while the remaining parts are only *approximately* satisfied, "it is natural to ask whether it might not be possible to use the calculus of variations for the purpose of obtaining approximate solutions in such a manner that there is no preferential treatment for either one of the two kinds of equations which occur in the theory. In what follows this question is answered in the affirmative" [14], as follows.

---

† Here and in what follows we speak of *Euler boundary conditions* in place of the generally used expression natural boundary conditions.

Among all differentiable states of stress and displacement the actually occurring state, which satisfies the differential equations (1.1a, c) and the boundary conditions (1.5a, b), is determined by the variational equation

$$\delta I_{u\sigma} = \delta \left\{ \int \left[ u_{ij}\sigma_{ij} - \Gamma(\sigma_{ij}) - P(u_i) \right] dV - \int \bar{t}_i u_i \, dA - \int (u_i - \bar{u}_i) t_i \, dA \right\} = 0 \qquad (1.9)$$

with the extent of the surface integration in this now being consistent with the form of Eqs. (1.5a) *and* (1.5b).†

The validity of the theorem as stated may be verified by the usual procedures of the calculus of variations. Some extensions and corollaries are as follows.

**The Theorem for Mixed and Physically Nonlinear Boundary Conditions**   In the event that the boundary conditions which are to result in Euler boundary conditions are as in (1.2a, b) the function $I_{u\sigma}$ is, in accordance with Ref. [17],

$$I_{u\sigma} = \int \left[ u_{ij}\sigma_{ij} - \Gamma(\sigma_{ij}) - P(u_i) \right] dV - \int T \, dA - \int (u_i t_i - U) \, dA \qquad (1.10)$$

The corresponding result for mixed *linear* boundary conditions, consistent with Eq. (1.3), has been stated previously in Ref. [16].

**The Stress and Displacement Theorem with Constraint Equilibrium Conditions**   Use of Eqs. (1.1a) and (1.2b) as conditions of constraint, in conjunction with $I_{u\sigma}$ as in Eq. (1.10), and application of the integration-by-parts formula (1.8) results in a modified functional

$$I_{u\sigma}^* = \int \left( u_i \frac{\partial P}{\partial u_i} - P - \Gamma \right) dV + \int \left( u_i \frac{\partial T}{\partial u_i} - T \right) dA + \int U \, dA \qquad (1.11)$$

When $P = P_1$, $T = T_1$, $U = U_1$, and $\Gamma = \Gamma_2$, then $I_{u\sigma}^* = -I_\sigma$ and the variational equation $\delta I_{u\sigma}^* = 0$ reduces to the classical variational theorem (1.7).

A generalization of (1.7), which antedates the general result in accordance with Eq. (1.11), results when the restriction $P = P_1$ is replaced by a restriction $P = P_1 + P_2$, with which $P - u_i \, \partial P / \partial u_i = -P_2$. The ensuing variational equation, now with $T = T_1$ and $U = U_1$, is

$$\left\{ \int (P_2 - \Gamma) \, dV + \int U_1 \, dA \right\} = 0 \qquad (1.12)$$

with this becoming the result in Ref. [13] upon stipulating that $P_2 = \frac{1}{2}\rho\omega^2 u_i u_i$.††

---

† The original formulation of this theorem [14], which was arrived at *synthetically*, that is, by mathematical experimentation with various possible modifications of $I_u$ and $I_\sigma$, had the boundary conditions (1.5a) as constraint conditions, with this entailing absence of the second set of surface integrals in Eq. (1.9). The above version, including the second set of surface integrals, was stated subsequently by Fraeijs de Veubeke [2] and also by Langhaar [9].

†† Note that the derivation of the result in [13] depended on the use of *interrelated* variations of stress and displacement prior to the use of *independent* variations of stress and displacement in [14].

*A Variational Theorem for Boundary Values*  In the event that Eqs. (1.1$a$) and (1.1$c$) are taken as conditions of constraint, the functional $I_{u\sigma}$ may be transformed, upon using (1.8) in connection with *one-half* the term $u_{ij}\sigma_{ij}$, into an expression

$$I_{u\sigma}^{**} = \int \left( \tfrac{1}{2}u_i \frac{\partial P}{\partial u_i} - P + \tfrac{1}{2}\sigma_{ij}\frac{\partial \Gamma}{\partial \sigma_{ij}} - \Gamma \right) dV + \int_{A_t} (\tfrac{1}{2}u_i t_i - T)\, dA - \int_{A_u} (\tfrac{1}{2}u_i t_i - U)\, dA \qquad (1.13)$$

The functional $I_{u\sigma}^{**}$ becomes one involving boundary integrals only upon stipulating that $\Gamma = \Gamma_2$ and $P = P_2$, that is, upon stipulating that equilibrium differential equations as well as stress-displacement differential equations are linear and *homogeneous* in the variables $\sigma_{ij}$ and $u_i$ [17]. While it does not seem, at first, that the ensuing variational equation

$$\delta \left\{ \int (\tfrac{1}{2}u_i t_i - T)\, dA - \int (\tfrac{1}{2}u_i t_i - U)\, dA \right\} = 0 \qquad (1.14)$$

has the boundary conditions (1.1$a$, $b$) as Euler equations, it can be shown [17] that this is in fact the case, upon verifying that when $\Gamma = \Gamma_2$ and $P = P_2$ then $\int u_i\, \delta t_i\, dA = \int t_i\, \delta u_i\, dA$ and therewith, as a consequence of Eq. (1.14),

$$\int_{A_t} \left( t_i - \frac{\partial T}{\partial u_i} \right) \delta u_i\, dA \quad \int_{A_u} \left( u_i - \frac{\partial U}{\partial t_i} \right) \delta t_i\, dA = 0 \qquad (1.15)$$

Applications of this result, in the sense of Rayleigh and Ritz, as in [10], evidently depend upon using particular solutions $\sigma_{ij}^{(k)}$, $u_i^{(k)}$ of the linear homogeneous version of (1.1$a$, $b$) in the form $u_i = c_k u_i^{(k)}$, $t_i = c_k t_i^{(k)}$ so as to obtain from Eq. (1.15) a "best" set of values $c_k$.

### 1.1E The Variational Theorem for Stresses, Displacements, and Strains

Given that technically significant elasticity boundary-value problems involve prescriptions for surface stress and/or displacement, it does not, at first sight, seem fruitful to deviate from the expressions for components of strain in terms of components of displacement being no more than defining relations for the former. That this conclusion is not, in actuality, warranted was first observed by H. C. Hu [8] and K. Washizu [27], who discovered that, upon rewriting Eq. (1.1$b$) in the form

$$\sigma_{ij} = \frac{\partial \Sigma}{\partial \varepsilon_{ij}} \qquad \varepsilon_{ij} = \frac{u_{i,j} + u_{j,i}}{2} \qquad (1.1b', c)$$

it is possible to formulate a *three-field* variational theorem, with independent stress, displacement, *and* strain variations, without having to make use of the inverted relation (1.1$c$).

Just as the variational theorem for stresses and displacements is formulated most simply by direct synthesis, so it is with the theorem involving independent strain variations. With prior knowledge of the form of the surface integrals in Eq. (1.9) it is readily seen that the variational equation

$$\delta I_{u\sigma\varepsilon} = \delta \left\{ \int [(u_{ij} - \varepsilon_{ij})\sigma_{ij} + \Sigma(\varepsilon_{ij}) - P(u_i)]\, dV - \int \bar{t}_i u_i\, dA - \int (u_i - \bar{u}_i)t_i\, dA \right\} = 0 \qquad (1.16)$$

with arbitrary $\delta u_i$, $\delta\sigma_{ij}$, and $\delta\varepsilon_{ij}$ does in fact have the differential equations (1.1$a$ to $c$) and the boundary conditions (1.5$a$, $b$) as Euler equations.†

It is to be expected that (1.16) would *imply* the validity of the corresponding statements concerning $I_u$, $I_\sigma$, and $I_{u\sigma}$. The verification of this for $I_u$ is immediate, inasmuch as all that needs to be done in this case is to use (1.1$c$) and (1.5$a$) as constraint conditions, with this reducing Eq. (1.16), in appropriate generalization of Eq. (1.6), to

$$\delta I_u = \delta \left\{ \int [\Sigma(u_{ij}) - P(u_i)] \, dV - \int \bar{t}_i u_i \, dA \right\} = 0 \tag{1.17}$$

with the subsequent use of the constraint (1.1$b$) then leading to Eqs. (1.1$a$) and (1.5$b$) as Euler equations.

The analogous *formal* reduction of Eq. (1.16) to the form (1.9) and to a generalization of (1.7) depends, as must be expected, on an inversion of (1.1$b'$) and on the introduction of $\Gamma$ in the Legendre form $\Gamma(\sigma) = \varepsilon(\sigma)\sigma - \Sigma[\varepsilon(\sigma)]$, in conjunction with the constraint condition (1.1$c$), into (1.16). The step from (1.9) to the generalization

$$\delta I_\sigma = \delta \left\{ \int \Gamma(\sigma_{ij}) \, dV - \int \bar{u}_i t_i \, dA \right\} = 0 \tag{1.18}$$

of (1.7) through use of Eq. (1.8) and with $P = P_1$ is, of course, immediate.

It seems worth stating that, evidently, the *derivation* of Eq. (1.9) from (1.16), involving as it does the Legendre transformation concept, is a more difficult matter than the earlier *ad hoc* formulation in Ref. [14].

We finally note that among the conclusions in Hu's work [8] is one that an introduction of *all differential* equations as constraint conditions into $I_{u\sigma\varepsilon}$ reduces the equation $\delta I_{u\sigma\varepsilon} = 0$ to the special case of Eq. (1.15), which is given when $T = \bar{t}_i u_i$ and $U = \bar{u}_i t_i$.††

---

† A modification of (1.16), so as to have (1.2$a$, $b$) in place of (1.5$a$, $b$) as Euler equations, is a simple matter and will not be stated here.

†† In this connection we recall an early insight of Trefftz for the two-dimensional problem $\nabla^2 u = 0$, with $u = \bar{u}(s)$ along the boundary [24]. Trefftz observes that it should be practical to obtain approximations $v$, with $\nabla^2 v = 0$, for the function $u$ through use of the variational equation

$$\delta \int \int [(v-u)^2_{,x} + (v-u)^2_{,y}] \, dx \, dy = \int \int [(v-u)_{,x}\delta v_{,x} + (v-u)_{,y}\delta v_{,y}] \, dx \, dy = 0 \tag{i}$$

and that, upon an integration by parts so as to eliminate derivatives of $(v-u)$ (rather than of $\delta v$) one is left with the relation

$$\oint (v-\bar{u})\delta v_{,n} \, ds = 0 \tag{ii}$$

It seems worth noting that the same result follows upon departing, in the spirit of Hu, from a variational equation

$$\delta \left\{ \int \int \{[u_{,i} - \varepsilon_i]\sigma_i + \tfrac{1}{2}\varepsilon_i\varepsilon_i\} \, dA - \oint (u-\bar{u})\sigma_n \, ds \right\} = 0 \tag{iii}$$

where, in the developed form of this equation, $u \approx v$, with $\sigma_i = \varepsilon_i = v_{,i}$ and $\sigma_{i,i} = 0$.

### *Supplementary Results*

From among possible extensions and consequences of the variational equations described so far, we mention in particular an equation for displacements and pressure by Herrmann [7] and its generalization in [19], a two-field equation for strains and displacements by Oden and Reddy [12], and equations for displacements and *some* stresses in [20] and [21]. The analysis in [7] was motivated by computational difficulties in the application of the equation for displacements only to problems for incompressible or nearly incompressible materials. The analysis in [20] was motivated by analytical advantages in connection with computational problems in the analysis of *laminated* shear-deformable plates and shells.

## 1.1F Basic Relations of Geometrically Nonlinear Theory

We take as the essence of geometrically nonlinear theory a recognition of the fact that the displacement-component derivative combinations $u_{i,j}$ are appropriate measures of deformations only in the event that these deformations are sufficiently small, with an appreciation of the meaning of the adjective *sufficiently* depending on knowledge of the elements of an analysis of states of deformation without a priori assumption of smallness.

Given again the cartesian coordinate system $x_i$ we now use the vectorial representations $\mathbf{x} = x_i \mathbf{e}_i$ and $\mathbf{u} = u_i(x)\mathbf{e}_i$, as well as the abbreviation $\mathbf{z} = z_i(x)\mathbf{e}_i = \mathbf{x} + \mathbf{u}$, and we observe that an element of volume with edge vectors $\mathbf{e}_1 \, dx_1$, $\mathbf{e}_2 \, dx_2$, $\mathbf{e}_3 \, dx_3$ in its natural state is deformed into an element with edge vectors $\mathbf{z}_{,1} \, dx_1$, $\mathbf{z}_{,2} \, dx_2$, $\mathbf{z}_{,3} \, dx_3$. With these edge vectors we have the quantities $|\mathbf{z}_{,i}| - 1$ as expressions for relative changes of length, and the changes $\gamma_{ij} = \gamma_{ji}$ of originally right angles are determined by the relations $\mathbf{z}_{,i} \cdot \mathbf{z}_{,j} = |\mathbf{z}_{,i}||\mathbf{z}_{,j}| \cos\left(\frac{1}{2}\pi - \gamma_{ij}\right)$.

On the basis of the form of these expressions, we introduce as defining relations, having appropriate transformation properties in connection with coordinate-system rotations, for *components of finite strain*

$$\varepsilon_{ij} = \varepsilon_{ji} = \tfrac{1}{2}(\mathbf{z}_{,i} \cdot \mathbf{z}_{,j} - \delta_{ij}) \tag{1.19}$$

with the assumed representation of the vector $\mathbf{z}$ then giving in terms of the components $z_i$ and $u_i$, respectively,

$$\varepsilon_{ij} = \tfrac{1}{2}(z_{k,i}z_{k,j} - \delta_{ij}) = \tfrac{1}{2}(u_{i,j} + u_{j,i} + u_{k,i}u_{k,j}) \tag{1.20}$$

It is customary to designate these quantities $\varepsilon_{ij}$, which reduce to the corresponding quantities of geometrically linear theory upon neglect of nonlinear-displacement derivative terms, in order to distinguish them from other analytically possible measures of deformations, as Green's components of strain or, more simply, as *Green strains*.

With these defining relations for Green strains one is led to defining relations for *conjugate* components of stress $\sigma_{ij} = \sigma_{ji}$, which we here designate as *Kirchhoff–Trefftz stresses*, in essence on the basis of stipulating that

$$\sigma_{ij} = \frac{\partial \Sigma(\varepsilon_{11}, \varepsilon_{12}, \varepsilon_{21}, \dots)}{\partial \varepsilon_{ij}} \tag{1.21a}$$

in order that $\sigma_{ij}\delta\varepsilon_{ij} = \delta\Sigma$, so as to have the possibility of deducing equations of equilibrium for stress as a consequence of a variational principle for displacements [25b].

It turns out to be consistent with the above procedure for deducing equilibrium equations to introduce, in accordance with [26], a system of (pseudo) stress *vectors* $\boldsymbol{\sigma}_i$ acting on the faces of the deformed element of volume, with components in the direction of the edge vectors of the deformed box, in the form

$$\boldsymbol{\sigma}_i = \sigma_{ij}\mathbf{z}_{,j} \tag{1.22}$$

with these being force vectors per unit of *un*deformed area.

With the further introduction of a *body-force vector* per unit of *un*deformed volume $\bar{\mathbf{p}}$, it is then possible to deduce the simple relation

$$\boldsymbol{\sigma}_{i,i} + \bar{\mathbf{p}} = 0 \tag{1.23}$$

as equation of force equilibrium for the deformed elements of volume, with the associated equation of moment equilibrium being of the form

$$\mathbf{z}_{,i} \times \boldsymbol{\sigma}_i = 0 \tag{1.24}$$

An introduction of the formulas $\boldsymbol{\sigma}_i = \sigma_{ij}z_{k,j}\mathbf{e}_k$ and $\bar{\mathbf{p}} = \bar{p}_k\mathbf{e}_k$ into (1.23) and (1.24) now gives as a system of component equations of equilibrium

$$(z_{k,j}\sigma_{ij})_{,i} + \bar{p}_k = 0 \quad \text{and} \quad \sigma_{ij} - \sigma_{ji} = 0 \tag{1.25a, b}$$

with the conditions of moment equilibrium being consistent, as they must be, with the implications of Eq. (1.21a).

With regard to the form of (1.21a) we assume, in generalization of a corresponding assumption for the problem of geometrically linear theory, one-to-one invertibility, so as to have

$$\varepsilon_{ij} = \frac{\partial\Gamma(\sigma_{11}, \sigma_{12}, \sigma_{21}, \ldots)}{\partial\sigma_{ij}} \tag{1.21b}$$

with the *formal* justification of this involving, of course, an application of the inverse-function theorem, and of the Legendre transformation concept.

It is possible, with regard to the formulation of variational theorems of geometrically nonlinear theory as generalizations of the corresponding theorems of linear theory, to limit the treatment of the differential equations of geometrically nonlinear theory to Eqs. (1.20) to (1.25). A celebrated alternative proposal in the literature on variational theorems makes it, however, necessary to introduce at least one alternative description of stress and strain, in terms of components of stress, which will be designated as *Piola stresses*, and in terms of their conjugate components of strain, which turn out to be the ordinary displacement-component derivatives.

Given the vectorial introduction (1.22) of the Kirchhoff–Trefftz components of stress, we have as analogous introduction of *Piola components of stress* the representation

$$\boldsymbol{\sigma}_i = s_{ik}\mathbf{e}_k \tag{1.26}$$

and therewith, as relations between Kirchhoff–Trefftz stresses and Piola stresses,

$$s_{ik} = \sigma_{ij} z_{k,j} \tag{1.27}$$

where, in general, $s_{ik} \neq s_{ki}$ and where we have $t_i = s_{ji} \nu_j$ as expressions for cartesian traction components, in generalization of the defining relations of linear theory which follow Eqs. (1.2a, b).

Use of the representation (1.26) implies the apparent simplification of a step from the nonlinear system of force-equilibrium equations (1.25a) to the linear system

$$s_{ik,i} + \bar{p}_k = 0 \tag{1.28a}$$

This simplification is, however, associated with a complication, by way of changing the linear system of moment-equilibrium equations (1.25b) into the nonlinear system

$$(\delta_{ij} + u_{j,i}) s_{ik} - (\delta_{ik} + u_{k,i}) s_{ij} = 0 \tag{1.28b}$$

The form of (1.28a) implies the quantities $u_{k,i}$ as the deformation measures which are conjugate to the stress measures $s_{ik}$. It follows from this that relations between stresses and strains which take the place of Eq. (1.21a) must be of the form

$$s_{ik} = \frac{\partial S(u_{1,1}, u_{1,2}, u_{2,1}, \ldots)}{\partial u_{k,i}} \tag{1.29a}$$

where, it must be emphasized, the function $S$ of the nine variables $u_{k,i}$ must be such as to be compatible with satisfaction of the three partial differential equations (1.28b).

With regard to the solution of this system of three equations, we limit ourselves here to two observations. The first is that it can be verified that Eq. (1.28b) will in fact be satisfied whenever

$$S(u_{1,1}, u_{1,2}, u_{2,1}, \ldots) = \Sigma(\varepsilon_{11}, \varepsilon_{12}, \varepsilon_{21}, \ldots) \tag{1.30}$$

with $\varepsilon_{ij}$ as in (1.20). The second observation is that *in the event of an existence of the inversion*

$$u_{k,i} = \frac{\partial G(s_{11}, s_{12}, s_{21}, \ldots)}{\partial s_{ik}} \tag{1.29b}$$

Eqs. (1.28b) impose as restrictions on the possible form of the function $G$ the three partial differential equations

$$\left( \delta_{ij} + \frac{\partial G}{\partial s_{ij}} \right) s_{ik} = \left( \delta_{ik} + \frac{\partial G}{\partial s_{ik}} \right) s_{ij} \tag{1.31}$$

as appears to have been pointed out first by Fraeijs de Veubeke [3]. One must in this context, however, also make reference to considerations by Hamel [5], which, because of unconventional terminology and lack of concern with specific applications, appear to be almost unknown.

## 1.1G Variational Theorems of Geometrically Nonlinear Theory

Since introduction $(1.21a)$ and $(1.20)$ into the force-equilibrium equations $(1.25a)$ results in a system of three simultaneous differential equations for the three components $u_i$, there should be a straightforward generalization to nonlinear theory of the variational theorem for *displacements* of geometrically linear theory, in terms of a functional $I_u$ analogous to the functionals in Eqs. (1.6) and (1.17). That this in fact is so follows readily from a consideration of the variational equation

$$\delta\left\{\int \left[\Sigma(\varepsilon_{11}, \varepsilon_{12}, \ldots) - \bar{p}_k u_k\right] dV - \int \bar{t}_k u_k \, dA\right\} = 0 \tag{1.32}$$

with $\varepsilon_{ij}$ as in (1.20), $\sigma_{ij}$ as in $(1.21a)$, and $\delta u_i = 0$ on $A_u$ and arbitrary in the interior as well as on $A_t$. The evaluation of (1.32) leads, as it should, to $(1.25a)$ as Euler differential equations, and to the conditions $t_k = \bar{t}_k$ on $A_t$ as Euler boundary conditions [25b].

While in geometrically linear theory an analogous variational theorem for *stresses* could be *expected*, on the basis of the absence of an explicit influence of the state of deformation on the conditions of equilibrium, the fact that this absence is no longer given for geometrically nonlinear theory would lead one *not* to expect the existence of a variational theorem involving variations of stress components without simultaneous involvement of variations of displacement components. Notwithstanding this, attempts to establish just such a theorem, in terms of Piola stress components, have occurred repeatedly.

## 1.1H The Variational Theorem for Displacements and Stresses

The result which is described next owes its origin to the idea that while one could reasonably expect obstacles in the path of a variational theorem for stresses alone, in going from a geometrically linear to a geometrically nonlinear formulation, no such obstacles need exist for a theorem for stresses and displacements. This, in conjunction with the earlier synthetic formulation for geometrically linear theory [14], led to the *conjecture* of a possible form of such a theorem for geometrically nonlinear theory, with the proof of the theorem having to be no more than a *verification*, which is introduced in Ref. [15] with these words:

> In the following we formulate a variational theorem of the theory of finite elastic deformations which is characterized by the fact that the Euler equations of the variational equation consist of the differential equations of equilibrium *and* the stress displacement relations, and for which stress *and* displacement boundary conditions are natural boundary conditions.
>
> A corresponding result for infinitesimal deformations has been indicated earlier [14]. It is found that the generalization to finite deformations is quite direct if one works with the notion of stress introduced by Trefftz [26] . . . .†

---

† "This was first reported in a colloquium at Brown University on March 14, 1952. The same result was found independently by B. Frayes de Veubeke." (Footnote reproduced from Ref. [15].)

The Introduction in [15] is followed by a summary of the contents of equations (1.20) to (1.25). The essence of the contents of [15] may be indicated by the following further quotation:

**The variational theorem.** The following theorem will be proved. *The state of stress and displacement which satisfies the differential equations of equilibrium and the stress displacement relations in the interior of the body and the conditions of prescribed stress on the part $A_t$ and of prescribed displacement on the part $A_u$ of the surface of the body is determined by the variational equation*

$$\delta \left[ \int (\sigma_{ij}\varepsilon_{ij} - \Gamma - \bar{p}_i u_i)\, dV - \int \bar{t}_i u_i\, dA - \int (u_i - \bar{u}_i) t_i\, dA \right] = 0 \qquad (1.33)$$

In order to see the validity of (1.33), it is noted that according to the rules of the calculus of variations ... equation (1.33) is equivalent to

$$\int [(\varepsilon_{ij} - \partial\Gamma/\partial\sigma_{ij})\delta\sigma_{ij} + \sigma_{ij}\delta\varepsilon_{ij} - \bar{p}_i\delta u_i]\, dV$$

$$- \int \bar{t}_i\delta u_i\, dA - \int [(u_i - \bar{u}_i)\delta t_i + t_i\delta u_i]\, dA = 0 \qquad (1.34)$$

where

$$\delta\varepsilon_{ij} = \frac{1}{2}[\delta(u_{j,i} + u_{i,j}) + u_{k,i}\delta u_{k,j} + u_{k,j}\delta u_{k,i}] \qquad (1.35)$$

The verification of the theorem continues with two intermediate transformations which lead to the relation

$$\int \{(\varepsilon_{ij} - \partial\Gamma/\partial\sigma_{ij})\delta\sigma_{ij} - \{[(\delta_{jk} + u_{k,j})\sigma_{ij}]_{,i} + \bar{p}_k\}\delta u_k\}\, dV$$

$$+ \int (t_k - \bar{t}_k)\delta u_k\, dA - \int (u_k - \bar{u}_k)\delta t_k\, dA = 0 \qquad (1.36)$$

Since in the interior we have $\delta\sigma_{ij}$ and $\delta u_k$ arbitrary, with $\delta u_k$ also arbitrary on $A_u$ and $\delta t_k$ arbitrary on $A_t$, it follows that the variational equation (1.36) is equivalent to the [indicated] differential equations and boundary conditions. This proves the theorem.

**Hellinger's Considerations**   The fact that the two-field variational Eq. (1.33) is often thought to be equivalent to the consequences of earlier considerations by Hellinger [6] which are relatively unavailable at this time suggests that a translation of Ref. [6] (aside from an unessential consideration of body-force terms, and with suitably modified notation) would be of interest. This translation is as follows:

**Direct Determination of the Components of Stress**   For some purposes, a transformation of the principle of minimum potential energy [$\delta\Phi = 0$, where $\Phi = \int \phi(z_{1,1}, z_{1,2}, \ldots)\, dV$] which is analogous to the so-called canonical transformation of dynamics of discrete media is important. [This transformation] consists in the introduction of the nine associated stress components $s_{ij} = \partial\phi/\partial z_{j,i}$ in place of the nine derivatives $z_{i,j}$, subject to an assumption of the non-vanishing of the associated Jacobian. If one then introduces a function

$$H = \phi(z_{1,1}, z_{1,2}, \ldots) - z_{i,j}s_{ji} = H(s_{11}, s_{12}, \ldots) \tag{1.37}$$

one shows readily, with the help of the known methods of the calculus of variations, that the relation $\delta\Phi = 0$ is equivalent to the relation

$$\delta \int [H(s_{11}, s_{12}, \ldots) - z_{i,j}s_{ji}]\, dV = 0 \tag{1.38}$$

with $s_{ij}$ and $z_i$ as unknown functions. From this follows the new canonical form of the equilibrium differential equations

$$s_{ij,i} = 0 \quad \text{and} \quad z_{i,j} = \frac{\partial H}{\partial s_{ji}} \tag{1.39a, b}$$

with Eqs. (1.39$b$) playing an essential role in the theory of elasticity, inasmuch as they are explicit expressions for strains in terms of components of stress.

The characteristic property of this new *variational principle, involving stress components rather than strain measures*, makes it possible to replace (1.38) by the following *variational principle with side conditions* which is analogous to the *Menabrea–Castigliano principle* in the theory of framed structures. *Let*

$$\delta \int H(s_{11}, s_{12}, \ldots)\, dV = 0 \tag{1.40}$$

*subject to the conditions* (1.39$a$). A designation of the associated Lagrange multipliers by $z_j$ then does in fact lead from (1.40) to (1.39$b$). Elimination of the Lagrange multipliers in (1.39$b$) gives as six *compatibility conditions* of the theory of elasticity for the nine functions $s_{ij}$

$$\left(\frac{\partial H}{\partial s_{11}}\right)_{,2} = \left(\frac{\partial H}{\partial s_{21}}\right)_{,1}, \quad \text{etc.} \tag{1.41}$$

with these conditions expressing that a state of stress which satisfies (1.39$a$) can in fact be an equilibrium state in a medium with energy density $\phi$ or $H$, respectively.

While the absence of any consideration of boundary integrals in the above is generally known, other difficulties appear not to have been noted previously. These include the entirely casual reference to the matter of the invertibility of the relations $s_{ij} = \partial\phi/\partial z_{j,i}$ (which is, of course, a much more significant restriction than the corresponding condition for $\sigma_{ij} = \partial\Sigma/\partial\varepsilon_{ij}$), the absence of a concern with conditions on $\phi$ or $H$ so as to ensure moment equilibrium, and, most importantly, the unqualified conclusion concerning the statement of a general variational theorem for *stresses* alone, as an obvious consequence of (1.38), with this clearly being the purpose of this section, given the wording of the heading of the section. Altogether, these difficulties make it questionable whether it is in fact historically meaningful to consider Hellinger's considerations as a stepping-stone to the variational theorem for displacements and stresses in Ref. [15].

**The Three-Field Theorem for Geometrically Nonlinear Theory**  Given the ingeniously simple Hu–Washizu formulation of the theorem for geometrically linear theory [8, 27] it is not unexpected that a corresponding formulation is possible for geometrically nonlinear theory. The form of Eqs. (1.16) and (1.33) evidently suggests that the appropriate three-field variational equation will be

$$\delta\left\{\int \{[\tfrac{1}{2}(u_{i,j}+u_{j,i}+u_{k,i}u_{k,j})-\varepsilon_{ij}]\sigma_{ij}+\Sigma(\varepsilon_{ij})-\bar{p}_i u_i\}\,dV\right.$$

$$\left.-\int \bar{t}_i u_i\,dA-\int (u_i-\bar{u}_i)t_i\,dA\right\}=0 \qquad (1.42)$$

with independent $\delta u_i$, $\delta\sigma_{ij}$, and $\delta\varepsilon_{ij}$ in the interior, and independent $\delta u_i$ and $\delta t_i$ on appropriate portions of the surface of the body. The verification that (1.42) is indeed associated with the totality of differential equations and boundary conditions of the problem as Euler equations is carried out in the usual manner and need not be shown here.

The result in this form seems to have been first stated by Fung in 1965 [4], and there considered as an alternative version of the content of Eq. (1.33). The difference between (1.42) and (1.33), as well as the relation of (1.42) to the earlier Hu–Washizu result of linear theory, is discussed by Washizu [28].

A *formal* derivation of (1.33), as a consequence of (1.42), by the Legendre transformation procedure, is, as it must be, possible, but is of conceptual rather than technical interest.

An alternative statement of the three-field theorem, in terms of Piola stresses $s_{ij}$ and conjugate-strain measures $\alpha_{ij}=u_{i,j}$, can be verified to be of the form [29]

$$\delta\left\{\int [(u_{i,j}-\alpha_{ij})s_{ji}+S(\alpha_{ij})-\bar{p}_i u_i]\,dV-\int \bar{t}_i u_i\,dA-\int (u_i-\bar{u}_i)t_i\,dA\right\}=0 \qquad (1.43a)$$

where $S(\alpha_{ij})=\Sigma[\tfrac{1}{2}(\alpha_{ij}+\alpha_{ji}+\alpha_{ki}\alpha_{kj})]$.

Remarkably, as was also shown by Washizu [29], this result may be transformed into a two-field principle not involving $u_i$ by taking the force-equilibrium equations (1.28a), as well as the stress boundary conditions which are associated with (1.43a), as equations of constraint. With these constraint conditions we obtain, upon application of the integration-by-parts formula (1.8), an associated variational equation

$$\delta\left\{\int [S(\alpha_{ij})-\alpha_{ij}s_{ji}]\,dV+\int \bar{u}_i t_i\,dA\right\}=0 \qquad (1.43b)$$

With regard to the significance of this result we can do no better than to quote from Washizu [29]:

If it were possible to eliminate $\alpha_{ij}$ from Eq. (1.43b) by the use of the relations

$$s_{ji}=\left(\frac{\partial\Sigma}{\partial\varepsilon_{mn}}\right)\left(\frac{\partial\varepsilon_{mn}}{\partial\alpha_{ij}}\right) \qquad (1.44)$$

we might obtain a functional entirely in terms of $s_{ij}$ and similar in form to that of the variational theorem for stresses in geometrically linear theory. However, this elimination is difficult in general. Consequently, it would seem advantageous, for practical applications to Finite Element Methods, not to struggle with the elimination to obtain a variational theorem for stresses only, but to be satisfied with (1.43b), taking $s_{ij}$ and $\alpha_{ij}$ as independent quantities subject to variation under the indicated constraint stipulations.

## 1.1ı Variational Theorem for Distinguished Generalized Piola Stresses and Translational and Rotational Displacements

Given that the variational considerations of Hellinger [6] had been in terms of the Piola stresses $s_{ij}$ in conjunction with the displacement gradient component $u_{j,i} = z_{j,i} - \delta_{ij}$, without provision for the requirements of moment equilibrium and of the realizability of the formally associated constitutive equations, it is of interest to describe the following approach in terms of a system of *generalized* Piola stresses $\tau_{ij}$ in conjunction with a system of *generalized* displacement-gradient components $\gamma_{ij}$.

Introduction of the components $\tau_{ij}$ is effected by writing

$$\boldsymbol{\sigma}_i = \tau_{ij}\mathbf{t}_j \tag{1.45a}$$

where

$$\mathbf{t}_j = \alpha_{jk}\mathbf{e}_k \quad \text{and} \quad \mathbf{e}_j = \alpha_{kj}\mathbf{t}_k \tag{1.45b, c}$$

with

$$\alpha_{ik}\alpha_{jk} = \alpha_{ki}\alpha_{kj} = \delta_{ij} \tag{1.45d}$$

and where then, in accordance with (1.23) and (1.24)

$$(\tau_{ij}\alpha_{jk})_{,k} = \bar{p}_k \quad \text{and} \quad z_{i,m}\alpha_{nm}e_{njk}\tau_{ij} = 0 \tag{1.45e, f}$$

Introduction of the components $\gamma_{ij}$ follows from an observation of the relations $\boldsymbol{\sigma}_i \cdot \delta\mathbf{z}_{,i} = \tau_{ij}\delta\gamma_{ij}$, with $\mathbf{z}_{,i} = (\delta_{in} + \gamma_{in})\mathbf{t}_n$ and with this resulting in the expression

$$\gamma_{ij} = (\delta_{ik} + u_{k,i})\alpha_{jk} - \delta_{ij} \tag{1.45g}$$

A complementation of the force-equilibrium equation (1.45e) and the strain-displacement equation (1.45g) by a system of constitutive equations

$$\gamma_{ij} = \frac{\partial H}{\partial \tau_{ij}} \tag{1.45h}$$

with the $\alpha_{ij}$ as a system of *given* functions, may be thought of as being associated with a *generalized* Hellinger variational equation

$$\delta \int (H - \gamma_{ij}\tau_{ij} - \bar{p}_k u_k) \, dV = 0 \tag{1.45i}$$

with independent $\delta\tau_{ij}$ and $\delta u_k$ and with (1.45e) and (1.45h) as Euler equations. The original Hellinger result follows from this upon setting $\alpha_{ij} = \delta_{ij}$.

Given that (1.45i), with prescribed $\alpha_{ij} = \alpha_{ij}(x)$, is in general associated with stress and displacement states which imply nonsatisfaction of the moment equation (1.45f), it is remarkable that this difficulty can be made to disappear by a change of status of the $\alpha_{ij}$ from given functions to dependent variables with arbitrary variations $\delta\alpha_{ij}$. The relations $\alpha_{ik}\delta\alpha_{jk} = \alpha_{jk}\delta\alpha_{ik}$ which are implied by (1.45d) then imply the further relations $\alpha_{np}\delta\alpha_{jp} = e_{jnk}\delta\omega_k$ with arbitrary $\delta\omega_k$. Observation of this, in conjunction with equation (1.45$g$), leads to the conclusion that the variational equation (1.45$i$) has, with arbitrary $\delta\tau_{ij}$, $\delta u_k$, *and* $\delta\omega_k$, not only (1.45$h$) and (1.45$e$) but also (1.45$f$) as Euler equations.

With (1.45$i$) now being free of one of the deficiencies of the considerations in [6], there remains the deficiency concerning the physical reasonableness of the constitutive equation (1.45$h$). An as yet nonrigorous way of dealing with this deficiency is as follows. We stipulate, on intuitive grounds, that the deficiency will disappear upon assuming that the function $H$ of the nine arguments $\tau_{ij}$ should depend on the six arguments $(\tau_{ij} + \tau_{ji})/2$ only. With this restriction on the form of $H$, we then have strain-symmetry conditions $\gamma_{ij} = \gamma_{ji}$ as supplementary Euler equations of (1.45$i$), with the meaning of the conditions $\gamma_{ij} = \gamma_{ji}$ being, in essence, that the directions of the $\tau_{ij}$ will be parallel to the edges of those rectangular elements of volume which are most nearly congruent with the deformed (in general, oblique) elements of volume. This, in turn, makes the generalized Piola components of stress into *distinguished* generalized Piola components.

The notion of a finite-elasticity variational equation, with rotational in addition to translational displacement variations, is considered to be due to Fraeijs de Veubeke [2]. Extensions and modifications of the analysis in [2] can be found in the work of Murakawa and Atluri [11], Bufler [1], and in [22], as well as in the literature cited in these articles.

## 1.2 REFERENCES FOR SEC. 1.1

1. Bufler, H., "The Biot Stresses in Nonlinear Elasticity and the Associated Generalized Variational Principles," *Ing. Arch.*, **55**:450–462 (1985).

2. Fraeys (Fraeijs) de Veubeke, B., "*Diffusion des Inconnues Hyperstatiques dans les Voilures á Longerons Couplés*," *Bulletin Service Technique Aeronautique*, no. 24, 1951, chap. I, pp. 1–18.

3. Fraeijs de Veubeke, B., "A New Variational Principle for Finite Elastic Deformations," *Intern. J. Eng. Science*, **10**:745–763 (1962).

4. Fung, Y. C., *Foundations of Solid Mechanics*, Prentice-Hall, Englewood Cliffs, N. J., 1965, pp. 299–300, 455–456.

5. Hamel, G., *Theoretische Mechanik*, Springer, Berlin, 1949, pp. 368–375.

6. Hellinger, E., "Die allgemeinen Ansätze der Mechanik der Kontinua," *Enzyklopädae der Mathematischen Wissenschaften*, 1914, vol. IV, 4, art. 30, pp. 654–655.

7. Herrmann, L. R., "Elasticity Equations for Incompressible or Nearly Incompressible Materials by a Variational Theorem," *AIAA J.*, **3**:1896–1900 (1965).

8. Hu, H. C., "On Some Variational Principles in the Theory of Elasticity and the Theory of Plasticity," *Sci. Sin.*, **4**:33–54 (1955).

9. Langhaar, H. L., *Energy Methods in Applied Mechanics*, Wiley, New York, 1962, pp. 130–133.

10. Lardner, T. J., and E. Reissner, "Application of a Variational Theorem for Boundary Value Problems in Shell Theory," *J. Strain Anal.*, **1**:83–85 (1965).

11. Murakawa, H., and S. N. Atluri, "Finite Elasticity Solutions Using Hybrid Finite Elements based on a Complementary Energy Principle," *J. Appl. Mech.*, **45**:539–547 (1978).

12. Oden, J. T., and J. N. Reddy, "Variational Methods in Theoretical Mechanics," 2d ed., Springer, New York, 1983, p. 116.

13. Reissner, E., "Note on the Method of Complementary Energy," *J. Math. & Phys.*, **27**:159–160 (1948).

14. Reissner, E., "On a Variational Theorem in Elasticity," *J. Math. & Phys.*, **29**:90–95 (1950).

15. Reissner, E., "On a Variational Theorem for Finite Elastic Deformations," *J. Math. & Phys.*, **32**:129-135 (1953).

16. Reissner, E., "On Variational Principles in Elasticity," *Proc. Symp. Appl. Math.*, **8**:1-6 (1958).

17. Reissner, E., "On Some Variational Theorems in Elasticity," in *Problems of Continuum Mechanics* (Muskelisvili Anniversary Volume), SIAM, Philadelphia, 1961, pp. 370-381.

18. Reissner, E., "On Bounds for the Torsional Stiffness of Shafts of Varying Circular Cross Section," *J. Elasticity*, **8**:221-225 (1978).

19. Reissner, E., "On a Variational Principle for Elastic Displacements and Pressure," *J. Appl. Mech.*, **51**:444-445 (1984).

20. Reissner, E., "On a Certain Mixed Variational Equation and a Proposed Application," *Int. J. Numer. Meth. Eng.*, **20**:1366-1368 (1984).

21. Reissner, E., "On a Mixed Variational Theorem and on Shear Deformable Plate Theory," *Int. J. Numer. Meth. Eng.*, **23**:193-198 (1986).

22. Reissner, E., "Some Aspects of the Variational Principles Problem in Elasticity," *Computational Mechanics*, **1**:3-9 (1986).

23. Reissner, E., and M. B. Sledd, "Bounds on Influence Coefficients for Circular Cylindrical Shells," *J. Math. & Phys.*, **36**:1-19 (1957).

24. Trefftz, E., "Ein Gegenstück zum Ritzschen Verfahren," *Proc. 2d Intern. Cong. Appl. Mech.*, 1927, pp. 17-28.

25. Trefftz, E., "Mathematische Elastizitätstheorie," *Handbuch der Physik*, Springer, Berlin, 1927, vol. 6, ch. 2, (*a*) pp. 71-72, (*b*) p. 140.

26. Trefftz, E., "Über die Ableitung der Stabilitätskriterien des elastischen Gleichgewichts," *Proc. 3d Int. Cong. Appl. Mech*, 1931, pp. 44-50.

27. Washizu, K., "On the Variational Principles of Elasticity and Plasticity," Aeroelastic and Structures Res. Lab., Tech. Rep. No. 25-18, Massachusetts Institute of Technology, Cambridge, Mass., March 1955.

28. Washizu, K., *Variational Methods in Elasticity and Plasticity*, Pergamon Press, New York, 1968, pp. 68-69.

29. Washizu, K., *Variational Methods in Elasticity and Plasticity* 2d ed., Pergamon Press, New York, 1975, pp. 383-384.

# 1.3 VARIATIONAL PRINCIPLES IN FLUID MECHANICS AND HEAT TRANSFER

## 1.3A Introduction

The variational principle provides an alternative statement of the differential equations that lends itself to the finite-element method. The finite-element method can be applied either with a variational method, based on a variational principle, or with the Galerkin method, which is applicable to all problems. The variational method is always equivalent to a Galerkin method, although the reverse is not true. In this section, following an explanation of terminology to clarify what is meant by a variational principle, the practical implications of the existence of a variational principle are identified. Variational principles are then listed for a variety of situations in fluid mechanics. Perfect, inviscid fluids are treated in both the steady and unsteady state. The Navier-Stokes equations are treated in a variety of special cases, including waves and free surfaces. The Navier–Stokes equations apply to a newtonian fluid, in which the shear stress is proportional to the shear rate. More general nonnewtonian fluids are also amenable to variational principles, and some of these are listed. Variational principles are provided for the heat-transfer equations that are solved in conjunction with both fluid- and solid-mechanical problems.

A variational principle exists when a functional is defined. This functional is made stationary with respect to changes in the function, and in doing so the Euler–Lagrange equation is derived. Natural and essential boundary conditions are also identified in the variational principle. The second variation indicates whether the principle might be of a minimum or maximum type when the Euler–Lagrange equation is satisfied.

Reciprocal or dual variational principles are sometimes possible (see Table 1.1 for terminology), and these may provide upper and lower bounds on the functional. These bounds can sometimes be used to provide error bounds on the solution. Several examples are given below, but general treatments on how to generate dual variational principles are available in Refs. [1, 2].

Some authors have used the term *variational principle* in a more general way. The terminology used here corresponds with classical treatments [3, 4]. In a restricted variational principle, the functional depends on two variables: the dependent variable and a stand-in for the dependent variable, and variations are allowed for the dependent variable but not

**TABLE 1.1**   List of Variational Principles

| Situation | Type† |
|---|---|
| Perfect fluid, steady state, incompressible | · Reciprocal |
| Perfect fluid, steady state, compressible | Reciprocal |
| Perfect fluid, unsteady state | Stationary |
| Navier–Stokes equations | |
|    Slow flow | Reciprocal |
|    Laminar flow in duct | Reciprocal |
|    Complete equations | Adjoint and dual |
|    $u, v, \omega$, 2D | Stationary |
|    $\psi, \omega$, 2D | Stationary and dual |
| Perfect fluid, free surface | Stationary |
| Nonnewtonian fluid, slow flow | Stationary |
| Droplets and bubbles | (See references) |
| Porous media | Adjoint and convolution |
| Heat transfer: | |
|    Steady-state conduction | Reciprocal |
|    Steady-state convection | Adjoint |
|    Unsteady-state conduction | Adjoint and convolution (see references) |

† *Reciprocal* means a minimum and maximum principle. *Stationary* means a stationary principle. *Dual* means a saddlepoint for an expanded set of equations. *Adjoint* means a stationary principle for an expanded set of equations. *Convolution* means a stationary principle for an integral version of the equations.

for its stand-in. After the variation the stand-in is equated to the original dependent variable. Such "principles" are easy to derive but have none of the useful properties of true variational principles. Application of the principle is equivalent to Galerkin's method. Restricted variational principles are not given here.

Another use of the term variational principle applies to cases where no functional is defined. In this case a variational equation is given, as in the case of the Hamilton principle when nonconservative external forces are involved.

The existence of variational principles for a given differential equation and set of boundary conditions is an important question that has been answered recently [5–8]. We should note that it is possible to define a functional which has as its Euler–Lagrange equations the original equations and an expanded equation or adjoint equation. These principles are discussed elsewhere [7, 8], and examples are given below.

If a finite-element method is based on a variational principle, several advantages accrue. The matrix is symmetric when a variational principle exists; this means that special methods for solving the resulting algebraic equations can be used, saving up to 50% of the computational time. The splitting of boundary conditions between natural and essential boundary conditions is clearly represented by the variational principle. The user must of course make the trial functions satisfy the essential boundary conditions, whereas the natural boundary conditions will be satisfied by the variational principle as the number of parameters becomes large. Sometimes error bounds can be found in terms of the value of the variational integral under different levels of approximation.

Restricted variational principles, such as the local potential method, and quasi-variational principles, resulting in a Galerkin method, do not possess the above advantages derived from variational principles. These methods are critiqued elsewhere [9, 10]. A list of the variational principles in fluid mechanics and heat transfer is given in Table 1.1.

Throughout we use both vector notation $\mathbf{u}$ and indicial notation $u_i$ to denote the velocity of a material particle. The divergence of a vector is denoted in three possible ways.

$$( \nabla \cdot \mathbf{u}) \qquad \frac{\partial u_i}{\partial x_i} \qquad u_{i,i} \tag{1.46}$$

The summation convention is used throughout in that repeated indices in an equation are to be summed from 1 to 3 for a three-dimensional problem. In some of the more complicated equations the notation $u_{i,j}$ is used to mean $\partial u_i / \partial x_j$, where $x_j$ are cartesian spatial coordinates. A material derivative is given by

$$\frac{dc}{dt} = \frac{\partial c}{\partial t} + u_i \frac{\partial c}{\partial x_i} = \frac{\partial c}{\partial t} + \mathbf{u} \cdot \nabla c \tag{1.47}$$

The equations are defined for three dimensions in a volume $V$ bounded by a space $S$. Variational principles are given without specifying the space of trial functions, except for boundary conditions and constraint equations. Generally, piecewise continuous derivatives are needed as they appear in the variational functional. It is noted that in general an eulerian approach is used in fluid mechanics: the solution is defined at a fixed spatial location.

### 1.3ʙ Steady, Incompressible, Perfect Fluid

The equations for the steady, irrotational flow of an incompressible, perfect fluid are

$$\mathbf{u} = \nabla \phi \qquad \text{in } V \tag{1.48}$$

$$\nabla \cdot \mathbf{u} = 0 \qquad \text{in } V \tag{1.49}$$

$$\rho \mathbf{n} \cdot \mathbf{u} = f \qquad \text{on } S \tag{1.50}$$

One variational principle is as follows [28].

Minimize the functional $I(u)$ among all velocity functions $\mathbf{u}$ satisfying Eqs. (1.49), (1.50), where

$$I(\mathbf{u}) = \tfrac{1}{2}\rho \int_V \mathbf{u} \cdot \mathbf{u} \, dV \tag{1.51}$$

The function which does so satisfies Eq. (1.48), which is the Euler equation. In practice, Eq. (1.49) is satisfied by means of a Lagrange multiplier. The reciprocal variational principle is as follows.

Maximize $J(\phi)$, where

$$J(\phi) \equiv -\tfrac{1}{2}\rho \int_V \nabla \phi \cdot \nabla \phi \, dV + \int_S \phi f \, dS \tag{1.52}$$

The Euler equation is

$$\nabla^2 \phi = 0 \tag{1.53}$$

which is equivalent to Eq. (1.49). The natural boundary condition is

$$\rho \mathbf{n} \cdot \nabla \phi = f \tag{1.54}$$

which is equivalent to Eq. (1.50).

For any function $\mathbf{u}$ satisfying the conditions of the variational principle (1.51) and $\phi$ satisfying the conditions of the variational principle (1.52), we have [4, 7]

$$J(\phi) \leq J(\bar{\phi}) = I(\bar{u}) \leq I(u) \tag{1.55}$$

where the kinetic energy is the exact value for the flow defined by Eqs. (1.48) to (1.50). $\bar{\phi}$ and $\bar{u}$ are the exact solutions.

### 1.3c Steady, Compressible, Perfect Fluid

The equations for the steady, irrotational flow of a compressible, perfect fluid are

$$p^2 = \rho^2 \frac{du}{d\rho} \qquad \text{in } V \tag{1.56}$$

$$\tfrac{1}{2}\mathbf{u} \cdot \mathbf{u} + \frac{d}{d\rho}(\rho u) = 0 \qquad \text{in } V \tag{1.57}$$

$$\mathbf{u} = \nabla \phi \qquad \text{in } V \tag{1.58}$$

$$\nabla \cdot (\rho \mathbf{u}) = 0 \qquad \text{in } V \tag{1.59}$$

$$\rho \mathbf{n} \cdot \mathbf{u} = f \qquad \text{on } S \tag{1.60}$$

The Bateman–Kelvin principle [4] is as follows.

Minimize the functional $I(\mathbf{u})$, where

$$I(\mathbf{u}) \equiv \int_V (p + \rho \mathbf{u} \cdot \mathbf{u}) \, dV \tag{1.61}$$

among all velocity fields satisfying Eqs. (1.56), (1.57) and (1.59), (1.60). The velocity field that does so is irrotational; the Euler-Lagrange equation is (1.58). The reciprocal principle is due to Bateman [4, 12].

Maximize $J(\phi)$, where

$$J(\phi) \equiv \int_V p \, dV + \int_S \phi f \, dS \tag{1.62}$$

among all functions $\phi$ satisfying Eqs. (1.56) to (1.58).

The Euler equation is Eq. (1.59) and the natural boundary condition is Eq. (1.60). For any function $\mathbf{u}$ satisfying the conditions of the variational principle (1.61) and function $\phi$ satisfying the conditions of the variational principle (1.62), we have [4, 7]

$$J(\phi) \leqslant \int (\bar{p} + \rho \bar{\mathbf{u}} \cdot \bar{\mathbf{u}}) \, dV \leqslant I(\mathbf{u}) \tag{1.63}$$

Thus any approximate solution $\mathbf{u}$ and $\phi$ provide lower and upper bounds on the exact value of the integral Eq. (1.63).

## 1.3D Unsteady, Compressible, Perfect Fluid

To handle the unsteady flow of a perfect fluid we introduce the entropy $S$, a vector $\mathbf{a}(\mathbf{x}, t)$ representing the position at time $t = 0$ of a fluid element which has position $\mathbf{x}$ at time $t$, and the jacobian

$$J = \frac{\partial(x, y, z)}{\partial(a_1, a_2, a_3)} \tag{1.64}$$

The conservation of mass is then expressed as

$$\rho(\mathbf{x}(\mathbf{a}, t))J = \rho_0 \equiv \rho(\mathbf{a}, 0) \tag{1.65}$$

and the conservation of entropy for a perfect fluid is

$$\frac{\partial S(\mathbf{a}, t)}{\partial t} = 0 \tag{1.66}$$

The internal energy is $U$. The conservation of momentum is

$$\left(\frac{\partial^2 x_i}{\partial t^2}\right)_a = -\frac{\partial p}{\partial x_i} - \frac{\partial \Phi}{\partial x_i} \tag{1.67}$$

and this is rewritten as

$$\left(\frac{\partial^2 x_i}{\partial t^2}\right)_a = -\frac{1}{\rho_0} \sum_j J_{ij}\frac{\partial p}{\partial a_j} - \frac{\partial \Phi}{\partial x_i} \tag{1.68}$$

where

$$J\frac{\partial a_j}{\partial x_i} = J_{ij} \tag{1.69}$$

The first variational principle is for the lagrangian formulation [13, 14].
    Make stationary $I(\rho, S, \mathbf{u})$, where

$$I(\rho, S, \mathbf{u}) = \int_{t_1}^{t_2}\int_{V_a} [\tfrac{1}{2}\rho\mathbf{u} \cdot \mathbf{u} - (U + \Phi)]J\,d\mathbf{a}\,dt] \tag{1.70}$$

among functions $\rho(\mathbf{a}, t)$, $S(\mathbf{a}, t)$, and $\mathbf{x}(\mathbf{a}, t)$ which satisfy Eqs. (1.64) to (1.66). $S(\mathbf{a}, t)$ and $\mathbf{x}(\mathbf{a}, t)$ take prescribed values at $t = t_1$ and $t_2$, and $\mathbf{n}_a \cdot \mathbf{x}$ takes prescribed values on the boundary of $V_a$ for all $t$. $V_a$ is a region in a space with normal $\mathbf{n}_a$.
    The Euler equations are

$$\tfrac{1}{2}\mathbf{u} \cdot \mathbf{u} - (U + \Phi) - \frac{P}{\rho} - \alpha = 0 \tag{1.71}$$

$$\frac{\partial \beta}{\partial t} = \rho_0 \left(\frac{\partial U}{\partial S}\right)_\rho \equiv \rho_0 T \tag{1.72}$$

$$-\rho J\left(\frac{\partial^2 x_i}{\partial t^2}\right)_a - \rho J\frac{\partial \Phi}{\partial x_i} - \frac{\partial}{\partial a_j}\left\{[\tfrac{1}{2}\rho\mathbf{u} \cdot \mathbf{u} - \rho(U + \Phi) - \rho\alpha]\frac{\partial J}{\partial x_{ij}}\right\} = 0 \tag{1.73}$$

These can be rearranged to give Eq. (1.67) (see Ref. [7]).
    The second variational principle is for the eulerian formulation [4, 13]. The equations of conservation of mass are

$$\frac{\partial \rho}{\partial t} + \nabla \cdot (\rho\mathbf{u}) = 0 \tag{1.74}$$

$$\frac{d\mathbf{a}}{dt} = 0 \tag{1.75}$$

The conservation of entropy is

$$\frac{dS}{dt} = 0 \tag{1.76}$$

and the conservation of momentum is

$$\frac{d\mathbf{u}}{dt} = -\frac{1}{\rho}\nabla p - \nabla \Phi \tag{1.77}$$

Make stationary $I(\rho, S, \mathbf{u})$, where

$$I(\rho, S, \mathbf{u}) = \int_{t_1}^{t_2} \int_V [\tfrac{1}{2}\rho\mathbf{u}\cdot\mathbf{u} - \rho(U+\Phi)]\,dV\,dt \tag{1.78}$$

among functions $\rho$, $S$, and $\mathbf{u}$ which satisfy Eqs. (1.74) to (1.76) and take prescribed values in $V$ at time $t_1$ and $t_2$, while $\rho$, $S$, and $\mathbf{n}\cdot\mathbf{u}$ take prescribed values on the boundary of $V$.

The Euler equations are derived by introducing Lagrange multipliers $\alpha$, $\gamma$, and $\beta$ for Eqs. (1.74) to (1.76):

$$\mathbf{u} + \nabla\alpha - \beta\nabla S - \boldsymbol{\gamma}\cdot\nabla a = 0 \tag{1.79}$$

$$\tfrac{1}{2}\mathbf{u}\cdot\mathbf{u} - (U+\Phi) - \frac{p}{\rho} + \frac{d\alpha}{dt} - \beta\frac{dS}{dt} - \boldsymbol{\gamma}\cdot\frac{d\mathbf{a}}{dt} = 0 \tag{1.80}$$

$$-\rho T + \rho\frac{d\beta}{dt} = 0 \tag{1.81}$$

$$\frac{d\boldsymbol{\gamma}}{dt} = 0 \tag{1.82}$$

where

$$T = \left(\frac{\partial U}{\partial S}\right)_\rho \quad \text{and} \quad \frac{p}{\rho^2} = \left(\frac{\partial U}{\partial \rho}\right)_s \tag{1.83}$$

These equations can be combined to give the conservation-of-momentum equation (1.77) (see [7]).

## 1.3E Navier–Stokes Slow Flow

The equations for a perfect fluid include the inertial terms but must, by definition, include no viscosity. We next turn to equations which include viscosity but not the inertial terms. We limit ourselves to incompressible, steady flows. The continuity equation is the same as (1.49), that is $u_{i,i} = 0$. The Cauchy momentum equation is

$$\frac{\partial \tau'_{ji}}{\partial x_j} - \frac{\partial p}{\partial x_i} + \rho F_i = 0 \tag{1.84}$$

Here $\tau'_{ji}$ is the deviatoric stress, whereas $\tau_{ji}$ is the total stress. A newtonian, incompressible fluid is one whose stress is related to velocity gradients by

$$\tau'_{ji} = \mu\left(\frac{\partial u_j}{\partial x_i} + \frac{\partial u_i}{\partial x_j}\right) \tag{1.85}$$

giving
$$\frac{\partial}{\partial x_j}\left[\mu\left(\frac{\partial u_j}{\partial x_i}+\frac{\partial u_i}{\partial x_j}\right)\right]-\frac{\partial p}{\partial x_i}+\rho F_i = 0 \tag{1.86}$$

Equation (1.84) is the Stokes, slow-flow approximation to the full Navier–Stokes equation including inertial terms.

The first variational principle is [15] as follows.

Minimize $I(\mathbf{u}, p)$, where

$$I(\mathbf{u}, p) = \int_V \left\{\frac{\mu}{4}\left(\frac{\partial u_i}{\partial x_j}+\frac{\partial u_j}{\partial x_i}\right)\left(\frac{\partial u_i}{\partial x_j}+\frac{\partial u_j}{\partial x_i}\right) - pu_{i,i} - \rho F_i u_i\right\} dV - \int_S g_i u_i \, dS \tag{1.87}$$

among functions $\mathbf{u}(\mathbf{x})$ that obey the prescribed conditions both normal and tangential to $S_2$.

In this statement we have included the incompressibility constraint (1.49) by introducing a Lagrange multiplier $p$ into Eq. (1.87). This gives Eq. (1.86) as one Euler equation (for variations $\delta u_i$) and Eq. (1.49) as the other Euler equation (for variations $\delta p$).

In the penalty method, we replace $(pu_{i,i})$ in (1.87) by $(1/2\varepsilon)(u_{i,i})^2$, where $\varepsilon$ is taken between $10^{-6}$ and $10^{-12}$ (see Chap. 9 in Part 2 on the penalty method). In this case the Euler equation is the same as (1.86) when the quantity $(-1/\varepsilon)(u_{i,i})$ is interpreted as hydrostatic pressure $p$. The variation of Eq. (1.87) can be easily shown to be

$$\delta I = \int_V \left[\delta u_i\left\{-\mu\frac{\partial}{\partial x_j}\left(\frac{\partial u_i}{\partial x_j}+\frac{\partial u_j}{\partial x_i}\right) - \rho F_i + \frac{\partial p}{\partial x_i}\right\} - \delta p \frac{\partial u_i}{\partial x_i}\right] dV$$

$$+ \int_S \delta u_t \left[\mu t_i n_j\left(\frac{\partial u_i}{\partial x_j}+\frac{\partial u_j}{\partial x_i}\right) - t_i g_i\right] ds$$

$$+ \int_S \delta u_n \left[\mu n_i n_j\left(\frac{\partial u_i}{\partial x_j}+\frac{\partial u_j}{\partial x_i}\right) - p - n_i g_i\right] ds = 0 \tag{1.88}$$

The Euler equation, the coefficient of $\delta u_i$ in the volume integral, is clearly the desired Eq. (1.86). In the surface integrals, the virtual velocities $\delta u_t$ and $\delta u_n$ in directions tangential and normal to the boundary, respectively, are used. (Here $t_i$ and $n_i$ are, respectively, the direction cosines of a unit tangent and normal to the boundary.) From the vanishing of these surface integrals, one obtains the essential boundary conditions that $\delta u_t = 0$, or the term in brackets following $\delta u_t$ being zero as the natural boundary condition. A similar set of essential or natural conditions normal to the boundary can be obtained from the last term in (1.88).

When the user applies the variational principle (1.87), two boundary conditions must be chosen on each surface. If a normal velocity is not specified as an essential boundary condition, then the variational method leads to satisfaction of the natural boundary condition even if $g_i = 0$. If a tangential velocity is not specified as an essential boundary condition, then the variational method leads to satisfaction of the natural boundary condition. This principle allows a free surface whose location must be determined by the solution.

An alternative variational principle is available and is given for two-dimensional problems.

Minimize $I(u, v)$, where

$$I(u, v) = \int_V \frac{\mu}{2}\left[\left(\frac{\partial u}{\partial x}\right)^2 + \left(\frac{\partial u}{\partial y}\right)^2 + \left(\frac{\partial v}{\partial x}\right)^2 + \left(\frac{\partial v}{\partial y}\right)^2\right] dy\, dx - \int p\frac{\partial u_i}{\partial x_i}\, dy\, dx$$

$$- \int \rho F_i u_i\, dx\, dy - \int_s g_i u_i\, dS \tag{1.89}$$

among all functions $u(x, y)$ and $v(x, y)$ that take prescribed values on all boundaries. The Euler equations are

$$-\mu\left(\frac{\partial^2 u}{\partial x^2} + \frac{\partial^2 u}{\partial y^2}\right) - \rho F_1 + \frac{\partial p}{\partial x} = 0 \tag{1.90}$$

$$-\mu\left(\frac{\partial^2 v}{\partial x^2} + \frac{\partial^2 v}{\partial y^2}\right) - \rho F_2 + \frac{\partial p}{\partial y} = 0 \tag{1.91}$$

which are equivalent to (1.86) in two dimensions when (1.49) is used in (1.86). The natural boundary conditions are not force balances and do not represent physical conditions [16]. This principle (1.89) can only be used with essential boundary conditions.

The variational principle that is reciprocal to Eq. (1.87) is as follows [17, 39, 40].
Maximize $J(\tau'_{ij})$, where

$$J(\tau'_{ij}) = -\int_V \frac{1}{4\mu}\tau'_{ij}\tau'_{ij}\, dV + \int_s (n_j\tau'_{ji} - pn_i)f_i\, dS \tag{1.92}$$

among functions $\tau_{ij}$ and $p$ that satisfy Eq. (1.84) and

$$n_j\tau'_{ji} - pn_i = g_i \qquad \text{on } S_3 \tag{1.93}$$

The Euler–Lagrange equations are Eqs. (1.49) and (1.85) and the velocity boundary conditions.
For any functions satisfying the conditions of the variational principles, we have

$$J(\tau'_{ij}) \leqslant J(\bar{\tau}'_{ij}) = I(\bar{u}) \leqslant I(u) \tag{1.94}$$

where $\tau'_{ij}$ and $\bar{u}$ are the exact solution of the problem.

## 1.3F Navier–Stokes Equations

The full Navier-Stokes equations for an incompressible newtonian fluid in steady flow are

$$\rho u_j u_{i,j} = -p_{,i} + \mu u_{i,jj} \tag{1.95}$$

$$u_{i,i} = 0 \tag{1.96}$$

These equations are called the *u-p* formulation since they are written in terms of primary variables, velocity and pressure. Millikan [19] first answered the question of whether there exists a lagrangian giving Eqs. (1.95) and (1.96) as the Euler–Lagrange equations. His answer was no, when the lagrangian was a polynomial of the velocities and their derivatives. Finlayson

[20] used Fréchet differentials to prove the same thing for any form of the lagrangian. He concluded that the *u-p* formulation, Eqs. (1.95) and (1.96), had a variational principle only if either $\mathbf{u} \times (\nabla \times \mathbf{u}) = 0$ or $\mathbf{u} \cdot \nabla \mathbf{u} = 0$.

Variational principles for the Navier–Stokes equations and an adjoint system of equations have been derived by Bateman [21], Finlayson [20], and Usher and Craik [22]. We present the latter derivation because it has been used in analyzing wave interactions in shear flows [22].

The variational integral is

$$I(\mathbf{u}, \mathbf{u}^*, p, p^*) \equiv \int_0^t \left( \int_V L \, dV + \int_{S_1} M_1 \, dS + \int_{S_2} M_2 \, dS \right) dt \tag{1.97}$$

with

$$L = \tfrac{1}{2}(u_{i,j}^* + u_{j,i}^*)(p\delta_{ij} - \mu(u_{i,j} + u_{j,i}) + \rho u_i u_j) + \rho(u_i u_{i,t}^*) + p^* u_{i,i} \tag{1.98}$$

$$M_1 = -\rho n_i u_j^* u_i u_j - u_i^* g_i \tag{1.99}$$

$$M_2 = -n_i u_i^* + \mu n_i u_j^* (u_{i,j} + u_{j,i})$$

$$\qquad - \rho n_i u_j^* [u_i^p u_j + u_j^p (u_i - u_i^p)] - \mu |\mathbf{u} - \mathbf{u}^p|_{,k} \varepsilon_{ijk} n_i u_j \tag{1.100}$$

The Euler–Lagrange equations are (1.95) and (1.96) with $u_{i,t}$ on the left-hand side and with natural boundary conditions appearing in (1.88), when the variation is with respect to $u^*$ and $p^*$. When the variation is with respect to $u$ and $p$, the Euler–Lagrange equations are

$$\rho \frac{\partial u_i^*}{\partial t} + \rho u_j (u_{i,j}^* + u_{j,i}^*) = +\frac{\partial p}{\partial x_i} - \mu \frac{\partial}{\partial x_j} \frac{\partial u_i^*}{\partial x_j} \tag{1.101}$$

$$\frac{\partial u_i^*}{\partial x_i} = 0 \tag{1.102}$$

and the natural boundary condition is

$$n_i(p^* - \rho u_j^* u_j) - n_j \left[ \mu \left( \frac{\partial u_i^*}{\partial x_j} + \frac{\partial u_j^*}{\partial x_i} \right) + \rho u_i^* u_j \right] = 0 \tag{1.103}$$

The variations are taken such that $\delta u_i^*$ vanishes at $t = 0$ and $t$, and $\delta u_i = 0$ on $S_2$.

Another approach to the same problem is by using dual variational principles. Barrett et al. [23] give the functional as

$$I(\mathbf{u}, \mathbf{u}^*) = \int \left( \frac{\mu}{2} \frac{\partial u_i}{\partial x_j} \frac{\partial u_i}{\partial x_j} - \frac{\mu}{2} \frac{\partial u_i^*}{\partial x_j} \frac{\partial u_i^*}{\partial x_j} + \rho u_i^* u_j \frac{\partial u_i^*}{\partial x_j} - \rho u_i^* u_j^* \frac{\partial u_i}{\partial x_j} \right) dV \tag{1.104}$$

where $\mathbf{u}$ and $\mathbf{u}^*$ are incompressible. The Euler–Lagrange equations are

$$\rho u_j^* \frac{\partial u_j^*}{\partial x_i} + \rho \frac{\partial}{\partial x_j}(u_i^* u_j^*) = -\frac{\partial p}{\partial x_i} + \mu \frac{\partial}{\partial x_j} \frac{\partial u_i}{\partial x_j} \tag{1.105}$$

$$\rho u_j^* \frac{\partial u_j}{\partial x_i} + \rho \frac{\partial}{\partial x_j}(u_i^* u_j) + \rho u_j^* \frac{\partial u_i}{\partial x_j} - \rho u_j \frac{\partial u_i^*}{\partial x_j} = -\frac{\partial p^*}{\partial x_i} + \mu \frac{\partial}{\partial x_j} \frac{\partial u_i}{\partial x_j} \tag{1.106}$$

These equations differ from Eqs. (1.95) and (1.102) in the convection terms, and the adjoint or dual variable $\mathbf{u}^*$ affects the original equation. The solution to Eqs. (1.105), (1.016) is the solution to the Navier-Stokes equations, when

$$u_i = u_i^*  \tag{1.107}$$

It is not proved by Barrett et al. [23] that Eqs. (1.105), (1.106) have only the solution satisfying Eq. (1.107).

These variational principles involving adjoint equations or dual equations lead to general variational methods. If the same trial functions are used for both $\mathbf{u}^*$ and $\mathbf{u}$, then the variational methods are equivalent to the Galerkin method.

For further discussions of mixed variational formulations for Navier-Stokes equations, see [40, 41].

## 1.3G  Navier–Stokes Vorticity Formulation, 2D

Ecer [24] considers the two-dimensional Navier-Stokes equations in terms of $u$, $v$ and the vorticity $\omega$:

$$u\omega_x + v\omega_y = \nu(\omega_{xx} + \omega_{yy})  \tag{1.108}$$

$$u_x + v_y = 0 \qquad \omega = v_x - u_y  \tag{1.109}$$

The functional is the kinetic energy, and this is minimized with Eqs. (1.108) and (1.109) as constraints. By using Lagrange multipliers we get

$$I(u, v, \omega, \phi, \beta, \eta) = \iint \left[ \tfrac{1}{2}(u^2 + v^2) + \phi(u_x + v_y) \right.$$
$$\left. + \beta(-v_x + u_y + \omega) + \eta(u\omega_x + v\omega_y - \nu\nabla^2\omega) \right] dx\,dy  \tag{1.110}$$

The Euler-Lagrange equations are Eqs. (1.108) and (1.109), and

$$u = \phi_x + \beta_y - \eta\omega_x  \tag{1.111}$$

$$v = \phi_y - \beta_x - \eta\omega_y  \tag{1.112}$$

$$\beta = \eta_x u + \eta_y v + \nu\nabla^2\eta  \tag{1.113}$$

The natural boundary conditions are

$$\int_c u_n \delta\phi \, dC = 0  \tag{1.114}$$

$$\int_c u_t \delta\beta \, dC = 0  \tag{1.115}$$

$$\int_c \eta^2 \left[ u_n\left(\frac{\partial\omega}{\eta}\right) - \nu\frac{\partial}{\partial n}\left(\frac{\delta\omega}{\eta}\right) \right] dC = 0  \tag{1.116}$$

Here $u_n$ and $u_t$ are normal and tangential components of velocity on the surface. If a boundary is a solid boundary with $u_n$ and fully developed flow, where $u_t = 0$ and $u_n$ can be found, then this variational principle can be used since Eqs. (1.114) and (1.115) provide proper natural boundary conditions. Inhomogeneous terms can be added to Eq. (1.110) to get proper boundary conditions.

Adding

$$-\int_c g\phi \, dC \tag{1.117}$$

makes the natural boundary condition

$$\int_c (u_n - g)\delta\phi \, dC = 0 \tag{1.118}$$

The last condition (1.116) is not a standard condition, so we require $\eta = 0$ on the boundary.

### 1.3H Navier–Stokes Stream-Function Vorticity, 2D

Ecer [24] also proves a functional for the stream-function–vorticity formulation.

$$I(\psi, \omega, \beta, \eta) = \int\int [\tfrac{1}{2}(\psi_x^2 + \psi_y^2) + \beta(\nabla^2\psi - \omega) + \eta(-\psi_y\omega_x + \psi_x\omega_y - \nu\nabla^2\omega)] \, dx \, dy \tag{1.119}$$

giving the Euler–Lagrange equations

$$-\nabla^2\psi + \nabla^2\beta + (\eta\omega_x)_y - (\eta\omega_y)_x = 0 \tag{1.120}$$

$$\nabla^2\psi = \omega \tag{1.121}$$

$$-\psi_y\omega_x + \psi_x\omega_y - \nu\nabla^2\omega = 0 \tag{1.122}$$

$$-\beta + \eta_x\psi_y - \eta_x\psi_x - \nu\nabla^2\eta = 0 \tag{1.123}$$

Equations (1.121) and (1.122) are the required equations. Ecer also gives a formulation for the fourth-order equation involving the stream function.

An alternative principle for the stream-function–vorticity formulation is provided by Barrett [25] using a dual variational principle. The functional is

$$
\begin{aligned}
I(\psi_1, \psi_2, \omega_1, \omega_2) = \int\int \Bigg\{ & \left(\frac{\partial\psi_1}{\partial x}\frac{\partial\omega_1}{\partial x} + \frac{\partial\psi_1}{\partial y}\frac{\partial\omega_1}{\partial y}\right) + \frac{\omega_1^2}{2} - \left(\frac{\partial\psi_2}{\partial x}\frac{\partial\omega_2}{\partial x} + \frac{\partial\psi_2}{\partial y}\frac{\partial\omega_2}{\partial y}\right) - \frac{\omega_2^2}{2} \\
& - \frac{\rho}{2\mu}\left[\left(\frac{\partial\psi_1}{\partial y}\frac{\partial\omega_1}{\partial x} - \frac{\partial\psi_1}{\partial x}\frac{\partial\omega_1}{\partial y}\right)\psi_2 - \left(\frac{\partial\psi_2}{\partial y}\frac{\partial\omega_2}{\partial x} - \frac{\partial\psi_2}{\partial x}\frac{\partial\omega_2}{\partial y}\right)\psi_1\right] \Bigg\} \, dx \, dy \\
& + \int_{S_2} \psi f_1 \, dS - \int_{S_4} \omega f_2 \, dS
\end{aligned}
\tag{1.124}
$$

The Euler–Lagrange equations are

$$\nabla^2 \omega_1 - \frac{\rho}{\mu}\left[\frac{\partial \psi_2}{\partial y}\left(\frac{\partial \omega_1}{\partial x} + \frac{\partial \omega_2}{\partial x}\right) - \left(\frac{\partial \psi_2}{\partial x}\right)\left(\frac{\partial \omega_1}{\partial y} + \frac{\partial \omega_2}{\partial y}\right)\right] = 0 \qquad (1.125)$$

$$\nabla^2 \psi_1 + \omega_1 - \frac{\rho}{\mu}\left(\frac{\partial \psi_2}{\partial x}\frac{\partial \psi_1}{\partial y} - \frac{\partial \psi_2}{\partial y}\frac{\partial \psi_1}{\partial x}\right) = 0 \qquad (1.126)$$

The natural boundary conditions are

$$\delta\psi_1: \qquad \frac{\partial \omega_1}{\partial n} + \frac{\rho}{2\mu}\frac{\partial \omega_1}{\partial s}\psi_1 = f_1 \qquad \text{on } S_2 \qquad (1.127)$$

$$\delta\omega_1: \qquad \frac{\partial \psi_1}{\partial n} - \frac{\rho}{2\mu}\frac{\partial \psi_1}{\partial s}\psi_2 = f_2 \qquad \text{on } S_4 \qquad (1.128)$$

First consider the case when the Reynolds number is small (set $\rho = 0$). We then get the appropriate equations, (1.121) and (1.122). The boundary conditions are that either $\psi_1$ is given or Eq. (1.127) holds on all portions of the boundary; in addition, either $\omega_1$ is given or Eq. (1.128) holds on all portions of the boundary. On a solid boundary the stream function is usually known and the no-flow condition involves $\partial\psi_1/\partial n = 0$. On an inflow or outflow boundary with fully developed flow we also can find $\psi_1$ and use $\partial\psi_1/\partial n = 0$. Thus these boundary conditions are appropriate for all cases except a free boundary. When the Reynolds number is not small, Eq. (1.128) may present problems. It is also necessary to show that $\psi_1 = \psi_2$ and $\omega_1 = \omega_2$, provided they satisfy some of the boundary conditions, and Barrett [25] does this.

We thus see that there are a variety of variational principles applicable to the Navier–Stokes equations (1.97), (1.104), (1.110), (1.119), and (1.124). When the flow is turbulent, variational principles have not been found; treatments using energy methods are available [7, 26].

## 1.31 Perfect Fluid, Free Surface

We next consider the motion of a perfect fluid with a free surface. The velocity is given by Eq. (1.48), and the equation of conservation of mass is Eq. (1.53).

We consider a two-dimensional problem with one free surface at $y = h(x, t)$. The Bernoulli equation on the surface is

$$\tfrac{1}{2}\nabla\phi \cdot \nabla\phi + \frac{\partial \phi}{\partial t} + gy = 0 \qquad \text{on } y = h \qquad (1.129)$$

while the condition of no flow normal to the surface is

$$\mathbf{n} \cdot \nabla\phi - \frac{\partial h}{\partial t} = 0 \qquad \text{on } y = h \qquad (1.130)$$

The variational principle is by Luke [27].

Make the functional

$$I(\phi, h) \equiv \int_{t_1}^{t_2} \int_{x_1}^{x_2} \int_0^{h(x,t)} \left( \tfrac{1}{2} \nabla \phi \cdot \nabla \phi + \frac{\partial \phi}{\partial t} + gy \right) dy \, dx \, dt \tag{1.131}$$

stationary among functions $\phi$ and $h$ subject to the restrictions that the values of $\phi$ and $h$ are set at $x = x_1$ or $x_2$, $t = t_1$ or $t_2$.

The Euler–Lagrange equations are then Eq. (1.53) with natural boundary conditions (1.129) and (1.130). Thus the equations for the classical wave problem can be derived from a variational principle. The functional (1.131) is the pressure, as in Eq. (1.62).

### 1.3J Nonnewtonian Fluids

We next consider purely viscous nonnewtonian fluids in steady, incompressible flow. The Cauchy equation of motion is

$$\frac{\partial \tau'_{ji}}{\partial x_j} - \frac{\partial p}{\partial x_i} + \rho F_i = 0 \tag{1.132}$$

and the deviatoric stress tensor is given by

$$\tau'_{ji} = \frac{\partial \Gamma(d_{pq})}{\partial d_{ji}} \tag{1.133}$$

where $\Gamma$ is a given, symmetric function of the rate-of-deformation tensor, $d_{pq}$:

$$d_{pq} = \frac{\partial u_p}{\partial x_q} + \frac{\partial u_q}{\partial x_p} \tag{1.134}$$

Likewise we can replace Eq. (1.133), through a contact transformation, with

$$d_{ij} = \frac{\partial \hat{\Gamma}(\tau'_{pq})}{\partial \tau_{ij}} \tag{1.135}$$

Equations (1.133) and (1.135), after definition of $\Gamma$ and $\hat{\Gamma}$, determine the type of nonnewtonian fluid. In addition, we need the incompressibility constraint, Eq. (1.49), and boundary conditions discussed in connection with (1.88).

The functional

$$I(\mathbf{u}) = \int_V (\Gamma - \rho F_i u_i) - \int_S g_i u_i \, dS \tag{1.136}$$

is made stationary (or minimized for special $\Gamma$) among functions $u$ satisfying Eqs. (1.49) and (1.133) and the prescribed conditions on velocity at the boundary.

The Euler–Lagrange equation is Eq. (1.132), and the natural boundary conditions are the tractions at the boundary.

A reciprocal principle also exists. The functional

$$J(\tau', p) = -\int_V \Gamma \, dV + \int (\tau'_{ji} n_j - p n_i) f_i \, dS \tag{1.137}$$

is made stationary (maximized for certain $\hat{\Gamma}$) among functions $\tau'_{ji}$ satisfying Eq. (1.132) and the prescribed traction conditions at the boundary.

For functions which are admissible to their respective variational principles we have, in certain cases,

$$J(\tau') \leqslant J(\bar{\tau}') \qquad I(\bar{\mathbf{u}}) \leqslant I(\mathbf{u}) \tag{1.138}$$

When the constitutive equation (1.133) is

$$\tau'_{ji} = 2\eta(\mathrm{II}) d_{ji} \tag{1.139}$$

where II is the second invariant of $d_{ji}$,

$$\mathrm{II} = d_{ji} d_{ij} \tag{1.140}$$

the function $\Gamma$ is

$$\Gamma = \int^{\mathrm{II}} \eta(\mathrm{II}') \, d\,\mathrm{II}' \tag{1.141}$$

Then $I(u)$ is a minimum provided [24]

$$\eta + 2\frac{d\eta}{d\,\mathrm{II}} \mathrm{II} > 0 \tag{1.142}$$

This is always true for a common viscosity relation, the Bird–Carreau representation [45]

$$\eta = \frac{\eta_0}{[1 + (\lambda \mathrm{II})^2]^{(1-n)/2}} \tag{1.143}$$

provided $n \leqslant 1$, the usual case. These variational principles were first presented by Johnson [7, 29, 30].


## 1.3κ Droplets and Bubbles

The equations of fluid motion often must be solved when there are particles or droplets on bubbles which can move with the fluid. Variational principles have been developed for these cases with newtonian fluids [31, 32] and nonnewtonian fluids [7]. In this case the boundary conditions between fluid regions must be carefully treated, and the Euler–Lagrange equations must include equations governing the movement of the particles and droplets.

## 1.3L Porous Media

The equations for the flow of water in porous media are

$$S\frac{\partial h}{\partial t} = \frac{\partial}{\partial x_i}\left(K_{ij}\frac{\partial h}{\partial x_j}\right) + q \tag{1.144}$$

where $K_{ij} = K_{ji}$ is the transmissibility, $q$ is an injection rate, $S$ is the specific storage (confined flow) or porosity (unconfined flow), and $h$ is a hydrostatic head. The variational principle is given for Eq. (1.144), and its adjoint is given in the manner developed by Morse and Feshbach [33].

Make the functional $I(h, h^*)$ stationary among all functions $h$ and $h^*$ which satisfy $h = h_0$ at $t = 0$, $h^* = h_0$ at $t = t_f$, $h = h_1$ and $h^* = h_2$ on $S_1$.

$$
\begin{aligned}
I(h, h^*) = &\int_0^{t_f}\int_V\left[K_{ij}\frac{\partial h}{\partial x_i}\frac{\partial h}{\partial x_j} + \frac{1}{2}\left(h^*\frac{\partial h}{\partial t} - h\frac{\partial h^*}{\partial t}\right)\right]dV\,dt \\
&- \int_0^{t_f}\int_V q(h + h^*)\,dV + \frac{1}{2}\int_V S[h_0(h^* - h)]\Big|_0^{t_f}\,dS \\
&+ \int_0^{t_f}\int_{S_2}(h + h^*)f\,dS
\end{aligned}
\tag{1.145}
$$

The Euler equations are (1.144) and its adjoint

$$-S\frac{\partial h^*}{\partial t} = \frac{\partial}{\partial x_j}\left(K_{ji}\frac{\partial h}{\partial x_i}\right) + q \tag{1.146}$$

The natural boundary conditions are

$$-n_i K_{ij}\frac{\partial h^*}{\partial x_j} = f \qquad \text{on } S_2 \tag{1.147}$$

$$-n_i K_{ij}\frac{\partial h}{\partial x_j} = f \qquad \text{on } S_2 \tag{1.148}$$

This principle is similar to that derived by Neuman and Witherspoon [34]. A related principle using the dual variables is by Herrera and Bielak [35].

## 1.3M Steady-State Heat Transfer

Flow problems are often coupled with heat transfer. Consider first heat conduction with no motion. The governing equations are

$$\nabla \cdot (k\nabla T) = f(\mathbf{x}) \qquad \text{in } V \tag{1.149}$$

$$T = T_1(\mathbf{x}) \qquad \text{on } S_1 \tag{1.150}$$

$$-k\mathbf{n} \cdot \nabla T = q_2(\mathbf{x}) \qquad \text{on } S_2 \tag{1.151}$$

$$-k\mathbf{n} \cdot \nabla T = h(T - T_3(\mathbf{x})) \qquad \text{on } S_3 \tag{1.152}$$

Make stationary the function $I(T)$ among functions $T(\mathbf{x})$ satisfying Eq. (1.152).

$$I(T) = \int_V \left[\tfrac{1}{2}k\nabla T \cdot \nabla T + Tf(x)\right] dV + \int_{S_2} q_2 T \, dS + \tfrac{1}{2}\int_{S_3} h(T - T_3)^2 \, dS \qquad (1.153)$$

The Euler–Lagrange equation is (1.149), and the natural boundary conditions are (1.151), (1.152). Other variations are possible: having $k(T)$, $h(T)$, a radiation boundary condition, and a nonlinear rate of heat generation, $f(T)$ [7]. A reciprocal variational principle can also be defined in terms of the heat flux [7, 18].

### 1.3N  Convective Heat Transfer

When there is convection, the equation is

$$\rho C_p \mathbf{u} \cdot \nabla T = \nabla \cdot (k\nabla T) \qquad (1.154)$$

where $\mathbf{u}$ satisfies Eq. (1.49). Fréchet derivatives can be used to show that Eq. (1.154) has a variational principle in terms of only $T$ only if $\mathbf{u}$ is a potential function; see Eq. (2.6) in Ref. [7]. This is an unlikely event, so we give a variational principle using the adjoint equations.

Make stationary $I(T, T^*)$ among functions $T$ and $T^*$ which take prescribed values on $S_1$.

$$I(T, T^*) = \int_V \left(k\frac{\partial T}{\partial x_i}\frac{\partial T^*}{\partial x_i} + \rho C_p T^* \mathbf{u} \cdot \nabla T\right) dV + \int_{S_2} q_2(T + T^*) \, dS \qquad (1.155)$$

The Euler equations are (1.154) and

$$-\rho C_p \mathbf{u} \cdot \nabla T^* = \nabla \cdot (k\nabla T^*) \qquad (1.156)$$

The natural boundary conditions are (1.151) and

$$-k\mathbf{n} \cdot \nabla T^* - \rho C_p \mathbf{n} \cdot \mathbf{u} T^* = q_2 \qquad (1.157)$$

If this principle is applied and the same trial functions are used for $T$ and $T^*$, then the $T$ equations can be solved separately and are the same as those derived with the Galerkin method.

### 1.3O  Unsteady Heat Conduction

For unsteady-state conduction the equation is similar to Eq. (1.144), and the corresponding variational principle follows from (1.145). Other treatments of the unsteady equations use convolution integrals [36–38]. In application these are all equivalent to the Galerkin method.

## 1.4 REFERENCES FOR SEC. 1.3

1. Arthurs, A. M., *Complementary Variational Principles*, Clarendon Press, Oxford, 1970.
2. Noble, B., and M. J. Sewell, "On Dual Extremum Principles in Applied Mathematics," *J. Inst. Math. Appl.*, **9**:123–193 (1972).
3. Courant, R., and D. Hilbert, *Methods of Mathematical Physics*, Interscience, New York, 1953, vol. I.

4. Serrin, J., in S. Flugge (ed.), *Handbuch der Physik*, Springer-Verlag, Berlin, 1959, vol. 8, pt. 1.

5. Tonti, E., "Variational Formulation of Nonlinear Differential Equations, I, II," *Bull. Acad. R. Belg. (Cl. Sci.)*, **55**(5):137–165, 262–278 (1969).

6. Vainberg, M. M., *Variational Methods for the Study of Nonlinear Operators*, Holden-Day, San Francisco, 1964.

7. Finlayson, B. A., *The Method of Weighted Residuals and Variational Principles*, Academic Press, New York, 1972.

8. Atherton, R. W., and G. M. Homsy, "On the Existence and Formulation of Variational Principles for Nonlinear Differential Equations," *Stud. Appl. Math.*, **54**:31–60 (1975).

9. Finlayson, B. A., and L. E. Scriven, "On the Search for Variational Principles," *Int. J. Heat Mass Transfer*, **10**:799–821 (1967).

10. MacDonald, D. A., "On the Method of the Local Potential as Applied to the Solution of the Equations of Diffusion," *Int. J. Heat Mass Transfer*, **17**:393–400 (1974).

11. Thomson, W., "On the Vis-Viva of a Liquid in Motion," *Cambridge Dub. Math. J.*, **4**:90–94 (1849).

12. Lush, P. E., and T. M. Cherry, "The Variational Method in Hydrodynamics," *Q. J. Mech. Appl. Math.*, **9**:6–21 (1956).

13. Herivel, J. W., "The Derivation of the Equations of Motion of an Ideal Fluid by Hamilton's Principle," *Proc. Cambridge Phil. Soc.*, **51**:344–349 (1955).

14. Eckart, C., "Variation Principles of Hydrodynamics," *Phys. Fluids*, **3**:421–427 (1960).

15. Lamb, H., *Hydrodynamics*, 6th ed., Dover, New York, 1945.

16. Chang, P. W., T. W. Patten, and B. A. Finlayson, "Collocation and Galerkin Finite Element Methods for Viscoelastic Fluid Flow, I," *Comp. Fluids*, **7**:267–283 (1979).

17. Hill, R., and G. Power, "Extremum Principles for Slow Flow and the Approximate Calculation of Drag," *Q. J. Mech. Appl. Math.*, **9**:313–319 (1956).

18. Sani, R. L., "Dual Variational Statements Viewed from Function Space," *A.I.Ch.E. J.*, **9**:277–278 (1963).

19. Millikan, C. B., "On the Steady Motion of Viscous Incompressible Fluids; with Particular Reference to a Variation Principle," *Phil. Mag.*, **7**(7):641–662 (1929).

20. Finlayson, B. A., "Existence of Variational Principles for the Navier–Stokes Equation," *Phys. Fluids*, **15**:963–967 (1972).

21. Dryden, H. L., F. P. Murnaghan, and H. Bateman, *Hydrodynamics*, 7th ed., Dover, New York, 1956.

22. Usher, J. R., and A. D. D. Craik, "Nonlinear Wave Interactions in Shear Flows: 1. A Variational Formulation," *J. Fluid Mech.*, **66**:209–221 (1974).

23. Barrett, K. E., G. Demunshi, and D. N. Shields, "A Minimax Principle for Navier–Stokes Equations," in P. W. Hemker and J. J. N. Miller (eds.), *Numerical Analysis of Singular Perturbation Problems*, Academic Press, New York, 1979.

24. Ecer, A., "Variational Formulation of Viscous Flows," *Int. J. Numer. Meth. Eng.*, **15**:1355–1361 (1980).

25. Barrett, K. A., "A Variational Principle for the Stream Function–Vorticity Formulation of the Navier–Stokes Equations Incorporating No-Slip Conditions," *J. Comp. Phys.*, **26**:153–161 (1978).

26. Busse, F. H., "Bounds for Turbulent Shear Flow," *J. Fluid Mech.*, **41**:219–240 (1970).

27. Luke, J. C., "A Variational Principle for a Fluid with a Free Surface," *J. Fluid Mech.*, **27**:395–397 (1967).

28. Bird, R. B., R. C. Armstrong, and O. Hassager, *Dynamics of Polymeric Liquids*, Wiley, New York, 1977, vol. 1.

29. Johnson, M. W., Jr., "Some Variational Theorems for Non-Newtonian Flow," *Phys. Fluids*, **3**:871–878 (1960).

30. Johnson, M. W., Jr., "On Variational Principles for Non-Newtonian Fluids," *Trans. Soc. Rheol.*, **5**:9–21 (1961).

31. Keller, J. B., L. A. Rubenfeld, and J. E. Molyneux, "Extremum Principles for Slow Viscous Flows with Applications to Suspensions," *J. Fluid Mech.*, **30**:97–125 (1967).

32. Skalak, R., "Extensions of Extremum Principles for Slow Viscous Flows," *J. Fluid Mech.*, **42**:527–548 (1970).

33. Morse, P. M., and H. Feshbach, *Methods of Theoretical Physics*, McGraw-Hill, New York, 1953, vol. I.

34. Neuman, S. P., and P. A. Witherspoon, "Variational Principles for Confined and Unconfined Flow of Ground Water," *Water Resources Res.*, **6**:1376–1382 (1970).

35. Herrera, I., and J. Bielak, "Dual Variational Principles for Diffusion Equations," *Q. Appl. Math.*, **34**:85–102 (1976).

36. Gurtin, M. E., "Variational Principles for Linear Initial-Value Problems," *Q. Appl. Math.*, **22**:252–256 (1964).

37. Filippov, V. M., and A. N. Skorokhodov, "A Quadratic Functional for the Heat-Conduction Equation," *Diff. Eqn.*, **13**:770–776 (1977).

38. Reddy, J. N., "Note on Mixed Variational Principles for Initial-Value Problems," *Q. J. Mech. Appl. Math.*, **28**:123–132 (1975).

39. Bratianu, C., and S. N. Atluri, "A Hybrid Finite Element Method for Stokes Flow: I. Formulation and Numerical Studies," and L.-A. Ying and S. N. Atluri, "II. Stability and Convergence Studies," *Comput. Meth. Appl. Mech. Eng.*, **36**:23–37, 39–60 (1983).

40. Yang, C.-T., and S. N. Atluri, "An Assumed Deviatoric-Stress-Pressure-Velocity Mixed Finite Element Method for Unsteady, Convective, Incompressible Viscous Flow: I. Theoretical Development," *Int. J. Numer. Meth. Fluids*, **3**:377–398 (1983).

41. Yang, C. T., and S. N. Atluri, "An Assumed Deviatoric-Stress–Pressure–Velocity Mixed Finite Element Method for Unsteady, Convective, Incompressible Viscous Flow: Part II, Computational Studies," *Int. J. Numer. Meth. Fluids*, **4**:43–69 (1984).

# CHAPTER 2
# CONSTITUTIVE EQUATIONS IN MECHANICS

## 2.1 NONLINEAR MECHANICS OF MATERIALS

### 2.1A Introduction and Notations

The continuum model is the basis for calculations of practically all theories of deformation of solids and liquids and much of the theory of gases and is used throughout this volume. This chapter contains a number of results based on the continuum model which are needed for numerical calculations. They are presented largely without proof but with references to sources where more detailed developments can be found. General treatments of continuum mechanics with a notation similar to that used in this section can be found in Malvern [9]. This chapter and all recent treatments draw heavily on the books by Truesdell and Noll [5] and Truesdell and Toupin [2]. For convenience, we are listing below the notation and definitions encountered in this chapter.

$$\mathbf{e}_k = \text{orthonormal basis}$$

$$\mathbf{v} = v_k \mathbf{e}_k \quad \text{(vector)}$$

$$\mathbf{T} = T_{km} \mathbf{e}_k \mathbf{e}_m \quad \text{(second-order tensor)}$$

$$\mathbf{T} \cdot \mathbf{S} = T_{km} S_{mn} \mathbf{e}_k \mathbf{e}_n$$

$$\mathbf{T} : \mathbf{S} = T_{km} S_{km} = \overline{\mathbf{T} \cdot \mathbf{S}^T} \quad \text{(inner product of a pair of tensors)}†$$

---

† A superposed bar, such as $\bar{\mathbf{T}}$, indicates the trace of a tensor.

$$\nabla = \mathbf{e}_k \frac{\partial}{\partial x_k} \qquad (\nabla \text{ operator})$$

$$\nabla \cdot \mathbf{T} = \frac{\partial T_{mk}}{\partial x_m} \mathbf{e}_k \qquad (\text{divergence of } T)$$

$$\boldsymbol{\phi} = \phi_{kmrs} \mathbf{e}_k \mathbf{e}_m \mathbf{e}_r \mathbf{e}_s \qquad (\text{fourth-order tensor})$$

## 2.1B Kinematics

Let us choose a fixed point in space as the origin 0 and denote by $\mathbf{r}(\tau)$ the position vector from 0 to the point occupied by the particle $\mathscr{P}$ in the configuration $\imath(\tau)$. Similarly, let $\mathbf{x}$ denote the position vector from the common origin 0 to the position of the same particle $\mathscr{P}$ in a (fixed) configuration $\mathscr{R}$ of the body, at some particular time, called the *reference configuration.*

The material particle can be mathematically identified by the position vector $\mathbf{x}$, and the correspondence between points and particles in the continuum model is then expressed by the relation

$$\mathbf{r}(\tau) = f(\mathbf{x}, \tau) \tag{2.1}$$

between the position of the particle at the reference time and other times $\tau$, $-\infty \leqslant \tau \leqslant \infty$. Equation (2.1) describes mathematically the motion of the material particle. The aim of numerical analysis is to calculate the position of all particles at all times, i.e., to determine the function $f$.

The velocity vector is the rate of change of position vector for a fixed particle,

$$\mathbf{v}(\tau) = \frac{d\mathbf{r}(\tau)}{d\tau} \tag{2.2}$$

The acceleration vector is the rate of change of velocity vector for a fixed particle,

$$\mathbf{a}(\tau) = \frac{d\mathbf{v}(\tau)}{d\tau} = \frac{d^2\mathbf{r}(\tau)}{d\tau^2} \tag{2.3}$$

Only smooth deformations are considered here. The function $f$ in (2.1) is assumed to be continuous and invertible with a continuous derivative at each time. Thus for fixed $\tau$, $d\mathbf{r}(\tau) = \mathbf{F}(\tau) \cdot d\mathbf{x}$, where

$$\mathbf{F}(\tau)^T = \nabla \mathbf{r}(\tau) \tag{2.4}$$

The derivative $\mathbf{F}(\tau)$ of $f(\cdot, \tau)$ is commonly called the *deformation gradient.* Invertibility of $f$ implies that

$$|\mathbf{F}(\tau)| > 0 \tag{2.5}$$

Note that $\mathbf{r}(\tau)$, $\mathbf{v}(\tau)$, $\mathbf{a}(\tau)$, and $\mathbf{F}(\tau)$ all depend on $\mathbf{x}$ although that dependence is not explicitly indicated.

It is often convenient to use a reference configuration which changes with time and may not even be an actual configuration of the body. One may, for example, wish to use a rigidly moving body which coincides with the actual configuration at time $\tau = 0$ and moves so as to remain near the deformed body [29]. Such reference configurations are useful in analyzing motions with small strain, and are commonly used in the analysis of stability and control of aerospace vehicles.

For the present discussion, the only variable reference configuration which will be explicitly considered is the actual configuration at a particular time $t$. In that case, the position vector of the particle $\mathcal{P}$ is $\mathbf{r} \equiv \mathbf{r}(t)$ and the region occupied by the body is $\imath \equiv \imath(t)$. In the usual application $t$ is regarded as the "present time," and $\tau$ is any past or future time. In numerical calculations, the fundamental problem is the calculation of the motion for subsequent time $\tau$, $\tau > t$, when the motion has been determined for $\tau \leq t$ and the configuration $\imath$ has been established.

The deformation gradient tensor $\mathbf{F}$ can be decomposed into parts which separately characterize the strain and the rotation. One way to do this is by use of the following (right) polar decomposition:

$$\mathbf{F}(\tau) = \mathbf{R}(\tau) \cdot \mathbf{U}(\tau) \tag{2.6}$$

$$\mathbf{R}(\tau)^{-1} = \mathbf{R}(\tau)^{T} \tag{2.7}$$

$$|\mathbf{R}(\tau)| = +1 \tag{2.8}$$

$$\mathbf{U}(\tau)^{T} = \mathbf{U}(\tau) \tag{2.9}$$

$$|\mathbf{U}(\tau)| > 0 \tag{2.10}$$

The tensors $\mathbf{R}$ and $\mathbf{U}$ are uniquely determined by $\mathbf{F}$. The symmetric positive-definite tensor $\mathbf{U}(\tau)$ is called the (right) *stretch tensor*.†

When it is necessary to identify the reference configuration that is used for some formulation, such as the definition (2.4) of $\mathbf{F}(\tau)$, a subscript identifying the time when the material body occupied the reference configuration will be used. Thus, $\mathbf{F}_0(\tau)$ is the deformation gradient with respect to the configuration $\mathcal{R} = \imath(0)$, and $\mathbf{F}_t(\tau)$ is the deformation gradient with respect to the configuration $\mathcal{R} = \imath(t)$ as a reference configuration.

The tensor $\mathbf{F}_t(\tau)$ is called the relative deformation gradient (relative to the configuration at time $t$). The decomposition (2.6) for $\mathbf{F}_t$ is $\mathbf{F}_t(\tau) = \mathbf{R}_t(\tau) \cdot \mathbf{U}_t(\tau)$. Since the deformed and reference configurations coincide‡ at $\tau = t$, $\mathbf{F}_t(t) = \mathbf{R}_t(t) = \mathbf{U}_t(t) = \mathbf{I}$.

The relation between deformation gradients for the same deformed configuration but different reference configurations is found from the compositions of mappings as the product of deformation gradients of each, e.g.,

$$\mathbf{F}_0(\tau) = \mathbf{F}_t(\tau) \cdot \mathbf{F}_0(t) \tag{2.11}$$

The rate of deformation can be similarly analyzed. The *velocity gradient* with respect to the configuration at time $t$ as a reference is the tensor $\mathbf{L}$ such that $d\mathbf{v}(\tau) = \mathbf{L}(\tau) \cdot d\mathbf{r}$ for each

---

† The proper orthogonal tensor $\mathbf{R}(\tau)$ is called the *rotation tensor*.

‡ The tensor $\mathbf{I}$ is the unit tensor. It has the components $\delta_{rm}$ on an orthonormal basis, where $\delta$ is the Kronecker delta.

time $\tau$. Thus

$$\mathbf{L}(\tau)^T = \nabla_t \mathbf{v}(\tau) \tag{2.12}$$

From (2.2) and (2.4), it follows that

$$\mathbf{L}(\tau) = \dot{\mathbf{F}}(\tau) \cdot \mathbf{F}(t)^{-1} \tag{2.13}$$

For $\tau = t$, $\mathbf{L}(t)$ coincides with the spatial velocity gradient. Using (2.6),

$$\mathbf{L} = \dot{\mathbf{R}} \cdot \mathbf{R}^T + \mathbf{R} \cdot \dot{\mathbf{U}} \cdot \mathbf{U}^{-1} \cdot \mathbf{R}^T \tag{2.14}$$

where the argument $t$ has been omitted to simplify the formula. This simplified notation will be frequently used for quantities evaluated at time $t$.

The symmetric part of $\mathbf{L}$ is called the *rate-of-strain* tensor,

$$\mathbf{D} = \tfrac{1}{2}(\mathbf{L} + \mathbf{L}^T) \tag{2.15}$$

The skew-symmetric part of $\mathbf{L}$ is the *spin tensor*,

$$\mathbf{W} = \tfrac{1}{2}(\mathbf{L} - \mathbf{L}^T) \tag{2.16}$$

For the special case when the configuration at time $t$ is used as reference configuration for calculation of the deformation gradient, Eqs. (2.13) to (2.16) yield

$$\mathbf{L} = \dot{\mathbf{F}}_t(t) \tag{2.17}$$

$$\mathbf{D} = \dot{\mathbf{U}}_t(t) \tag{2.18}$$

$$\mathbf{W} = \dot{\mathbf{R}}_t(t) \tag{2.19}$$

Now, let us consider the global body. For a surface in $\mathcal{R}$, an area element with adjacent edges $d\mathbf{x}_1$, and $d\mathbf{x}_2$ has the area $dA$ and normal $\mathbf{N}$: $\mathbf{N}\, dA = d\mathbf{x}_1 \times d\mathbf{x}_2$. The deformed area element has edges $d\mathbf{r}_1$ and $d\mathbf{r}_2$, area $da$, and normal $\mathbf{n}$: $\mathbf{n}\, da = d\mathbf{r}_1 \times d\mathbf{r}_2$. It follows from (2.4) that

$$\mathbf{n}\, da = |\mathbf{F}| \mathbf{F}^{-T} \cdot \mathbf{N}\, dA \tag{2.20}$$

The volume element with adjacent edges $d\mathbf{x}_1, d\mathbf{x}_2, d\mathbf{x}_3$, and volume $dV = d\mathbf{x}_1 \cdot (d\mathbf{x}_2 \times d\mathbf{x}_3)$, is deformed into the volume element with edges $d\mathbf{r}_1, d\mathbf{r}_2, d\mathbf{r}_3$ and volume $dv$. It follows from (2.4) that

$$dv = |\mathbf{F}|\, dV \tag{2.21}$$

If $\rho_{\mathcal{R}}$ is the density of the material in $\mathcal{R}$ and $\rho$ the density in $\imath$, the conservation of mass then yields

$$\rho(\tau)|\mathbf{F}(\tau)| = \rho_{\mathcal{R}} \tag{2.22}$$

Turning now to the fundamental problem of calculation of the deformation for time $\tau > t$, let $\mathbf{u}(\tau)$ denote the incremental displacement

$$\mathbf{u}(\tau) = \mathbf{r}(\tau) - \mathbf{r} \tag{2.23}$$

The displacement from the reference configuration is not explicitly used in this chapter.

Each quantity also depends on the material particle, identified either by the position $\mathbf{x}$ in the reference configuration $\mathscr{R}$ or by the position $\mathbf{r}$ in the configuration at time $\imath(t)$.

When an arbitrary fixed reference configuration is used,

$$d\mathbf{u}(\tau) = \mathbf{H}(\tau) \cdot d\mathbf{x} \tag{2.24}$$

The tensor $\mathbf{H}(\tau)$ is called the *gradient of incremental displacement*. It follows from (2.23) and (2.4) that

$$\mathbf{H}(\tau) = \mathbf{F}(\tau) - \mathbf{F} \tag{2.25}$$

When the configuration at time $t$ is used as a reference, it follows from (2.23) and (2.4) that the gradient of incremental displacement for that reference configuration is given by

$$\mathbf{H}_t(\tau) = \mathbf{F}_t(\tau) - \mathbf{I} \tag{2.26}$$

The velocity vector (2.2) and acceleration vector (2.3) are directly determined by the incremental displacement:

$$\mathbf{v}(\tau) = \frac{d\mathbf{u}(\tau)}{d\tau} \tag{2.27}$$

$$\mathbf{a}(\tau) = \frac{d^2\mathbf{u}(\tau)}{d\tau^2} \tag{2.28}$$

## 2.1c Stress, Balance of Momentum, Mechanical Power

The balance of momentum for each volume element of the material requires that there exists a tensor $\mathbf{T}$ called the (Cauchy) *true-stress tensor* such that†

$$\mathbf{t}(\tau) = \mathbf{n}(\tau) \cdot \mathbf{T}(\tau) \tag{2.29}$$

where $\mathbf{n}$ is the unit exterior normal vector to the surface.

The balance of angular momentum of a volume element requires that the true-stress tensor is symmetric:

$$\mathbf{T}(\tau)^T = \mathbf{T}(\tau) \tag{2.30}$$

It is also useful to introduce the vector $\mathbf{p}$ such that $\mathbf{p}\,dA = \mathbf{t}\,da$; that is, $\mathbf{p}$ is the stress vector per unit area of the reference configuration, the so-called *nominal stress*. Using (2.20),

---

† The vector $\mathbf{t}(\tau)$ is the contact force per unit deformed area.

it follows that

$$\mathbf{p}(\tau) = \mathbf{N} \cdot \mathbf{P}(\tau) \tag{2.31}$$

where, by definition, $\qquad \mathbf{P}(\tau) = |\mathbf{F}(\tau)| \mathbf{F}(\tau)^{-1} \cdot \mathbf{T}(\tau) \tag{2.32}$

The nonsymmetric tensor $\mathbf{P}$ is called the *nominal-stress tensor*. The transpose of $\mathbf{P}$ is called the first Piola–Kirchhoff tensor in Truesdell and Toupin [2].

The tensor $\mathbf{P}$ depends on the choice of reference configuration. Thus $\mathbf{P}_0(\tau)$ is the stress tensor relative to the configuration at $\tau = 0$; $\mathbf{P}_t(\tau)$ is the stress tensor relative to the configuration at $\tau = t$ as a reference. Note that $\mathbf{P}_t(t) = \mathbf{T}(t)$.

The body force is assumed to be fully prescribed and has the value $\mathbf{b}(\tau)$ per unit mass of the particle.

The global balance of linear momentum is then expressible in the following form:

$$\int_{\mathcal{S}} \mathbf{p}(\tau)\, dA + \int_{V} \rho_{\mathcal{R}} \mathbf{b}(\tau)\, dV = \int_{V} \rho_{\mathcal{R}} \mathbf{a}(\tau)\, dV \tag{2.33}$$

Integration is over each part $\mathcal{V}$ of the reference configuration $\mathcal{R}$ with surface $\mathcal{S}$.

Integration by parts then yields

$$\nabla \cdot \mathbf{P}(\tau) + \rho_{\mathcal{R}} \mathbf{b}(\tau) = \rho_{\mathcal{R}} \mathbf{a}(\tau) \tag{2.34}$$

At points where $\mathbf{P}(\tau)$ is discontinuous, and at exterior surfaces, a local pointwise balance with the exterior loads must hold.

Equation (2.34) holds for an arbitrary reference configuration. The two most commonly used special cases are the configuration at $t = 0$, for which (2.34) becomes

$$\nabla_0 \cdot \mathbf{P}_0(\tau) + \rho_0 \mathbf{b}(\tau) = \rho_0 \mathbf{a}(\tau) \tag{2.35}$$

and the case when the reference configuration is the configuration at time $t$, for which (2.34) becomes

$$\nabla_t \cdot \mathbf{P}_t(\tau) + \rho \mathbf{b}(\tau) = \rho \mathbf{a}(\tau) \tag{2.36}$$

For the particular time $\tau = t$, eq. (2.36) is the so-called eulerian form of the balance of momentum;

$$\nabla_t \cdot \mathbf{T}(t) + \rho \mathbf{b} = \rho \mathbf{a} \tag{2.37}$$

When $\mathbf{a}(\tau) = 0$, Eq. (2.34) is referred to as the *equation of mechanical equilibrium*.

For the static or quasi-static problem (when inertia is neglected), the equations governing the rate of change of stress can be established directly by differentiation of (2.34) with respect to time $\tau$:

$$\nabla \cdot \dot{\mathbf{P}}(\tau) + \rho_{\mathcal{R}} \dot{\mathbf{b}}(\tau) = 0 \tag{2.38}$$

It follows from the definition of $\mathbf{P}$ and the kinematical definitions of Sec. 2.2 that the rate of mechanical working of surface tractions on a volume element is given by

$$d\mathscr{P}(\tau) = \mathbf{P}(\tau)^T : \dot{\mathbf{F}}(\tau) \, dV \tag{2.39}$$

Thus, $\mathbf{P}(\tau)^T : \dot{\mathbf{F}}(\tau)$ is the mechanical power per unit volume of the reference configuration.

## 2.1D Strain Measures, Stress Measures, Strain Energy

The stretch tensor $\mathbf{U}$ completely determines the stretch and shear of fibers of the material body with respect to the reference configuration. Any other tensor $\mathbf{E}$ in one-to-one correspondence with $\mathbf{U}$ would also determine the strain,

$$\mathbf{E} = f(\mathbf{U}) \qquad \mathbf{E} = \mathbf{E}^T \tag{2.40}$$

where $f$ is invertible.

Commonly used examples of strain tensors include the following:

$$\mathbf{E} = \mathbf{U} - \mathbf{I} \tag{2.41a}$$

$$\mathbf{E} = \mathbf{I} - \mathbf{U}^{-1} \tag{2.41b}$$

$$\mathbf{E} = \tfrac{1}{2}(\mathbf{U}^2 - \mathbf{I}) \tag{2.41c}$$

$$\mathbf{E} = \tfrac{1}{2}(\mathbf{I} - \mathbf{U}^{-2}) \tag{2.41d}$$

Each of these possible strain tensors has been used by various authors. For example, the first was called the *extension tensor* by Dill [19]. The third is commonly called *Green's strain tensor* [2]. The fourth is called *Almansi's strain tensor* by Hill [22]. There is no reason, however, to prefer one strain tensor over another.

A similar arbitrariness of choice of measure of stress also exists. To illustrate the situation, consider the general constitutive relation of an elastic material, which can be written in the form

$$\tilde{\mathbf{T}} = \mathscr{F}(\mathbf{U}) \tag{2.42}$$

where $\tilde{\mathbf{T}}$ is defined by $\qquad\qquad \tilde{\mathbf{T}} = \mathbf{R}^T \cdot \mathbf{T} \cdot \mathbf{R} \tag{2.43}$

The tensor $\tilde{\mathbf{T}}$ is called the *rotated-stress tensor*. Equation (2.42) shows that the strain determines the stress tensor, through the constitutive relation, only to within the rotation of the particle.

Clearly any symmetric tensor $\mathbf{S}$ which is in one-to-one correspondence with $\tilde{\mathbf{T}}$ for each $\mathbf{U}$ would be an equally usable *measure of stress*:

$$\mathbf{S} = g(\tilde{\mathbf{T}}, \mathbf{U}) \qquad \mathbf{S} = \mathbf{S}^T \tag{2.44}$$

where $g$ is invertible for each $\mathbf{U}$. Since $\tilde{\mathbf{T}}$ is invariant under superposed rigid-body motion, the stress measure $\mathbf{S}$ is also invariant.

The specific choice of stress measure is usually made in conjunction with the choice of strain measure in such a way that the expression for mechanical power (2.39) has the form

$d\mathscr{P}(\tau) = \mathbf{S}(\tau) : \dot{\mathbf{E}}(\tau)\, dV$. That is,

$$\mathbf{S}(\tau) : \dot{\mathbf{E}}(\tau) = \mathbf{P}(\tau)^T : \dot{\mathbf{F}}(\tau) \tag{2.45}$$

In this case $\mathbf{S}$ and $\mathbf{E}$ are said to be *conjugate* measures.

When $\mathbf{S}$ and $\mathbf{E}$ are conjugate, the relation between $\mathbf{S}$ and $\mathbf{T}$ has a simple form. This can be seen by noting that $\mathbf{U}$ is a function of $\mathbf{F}$ and therefore $\mathbf{E}$ is a function of $\mathbf{F}$ by definition (2.40). Thus

$$\dot{\mathbf{E}} = \boldsymbol{\varepsilon} : \dot{\mathbf{F}} \tag{2.46}$$

where the fourth-order tensor $\boldsymbol{\varepsilon}$ has the following components on an orthonormal basis:

$$\varepsilon_{ijkm} = \frac{\partial E_{ij}}{\partial F_{km}} \qquad \varepsilon_{ijkm} = \varepsilon_{jikm} \tag{2.47}$$

Since the relation (2.45) is required to hold identically in $\dot{\mathbf{F}}$, it follows that

$$\mathbf{S} : \varepsilon = \mathbf{P}^T = \frac{\rho_{\mathscr{R}}}{\rho} \mathbf{T} \cdot \mathbf{F}^{-T} \tag{2.48}$$

Using (2.32), 
$$\mathbf{T} = \frac{\rho}{\rho_{\mathscr{R}}} (\mathbf{S} : \varepsilon) \cdot \mathbf{F}^T \tag{2.49}$$

The stress measures conjugate to the special strain measures (2.41*a* to *d*) are readily calculated. They are, respectively,

$$\mathbf{S} = \frac{\rho_{\mathscr{R}}}{2\rho} (\mathbf{F}^{-1} \cdot \mathbf{T} \cdot \mathbf{R} + \mathbf{R}^T \cdot \mathbf{T} \cdot \mathbf{F}^{-T}) \tag{2.50a}$$

$$\mathbf{S} = \frac{\rho_{\mathscr{R}}}{2\rho} (\mathbf{R}^T \cdot \mathbf{T} \cdot \mathbf{F} + \mathbf{F}^T \cdot \mathbf{T} \cdot \mathbf{R}) \tag{2.50b}$$

$$\mathbf{S} = \frac{\rho_{\mathscr{R}}}{\rho} \mathbf{F}^{-1} \cdot \mathbf{T} \cdot \mathbf{F}^{-T} \tag{2.50c}$$

$$\mathbf{S} = \frac{\rho_{\mathscr{R}}}{\rho} \mathbf{F}^T \cdot \mathbf{T} \cdot \mathbf{F} \tag{2.50d}$$

The first has been called the *Jaumann tensor* [11]; the fourth has been called the convected-stress tensor [5], apart from the factor $\rho_{\mathscr{R}}/\rho$; and the third is commonly called the second (symmetric) Piola–Kirchhoff tensor [2]. Note that the definitions (2.50) coincide with the stress measures implicit in the forms of the elasticity relations.

The various stress measures have physical interpretations in terms of the surface tractions with respect to appropriate reference configurations and computational advantages in simplicity of component relations on imbedded or corotational coordinate systems [28].

For any pair of conjugate-stress and strain measures $\mathbf{S}$ and $\mathbf{E}$, the constitutive relation for an elastic material can be written in terms of $\mathbf{S}$ and $\mathbf{E}$:

$$\mathbf{S} = \mathscr{F}(\mathbf{E}) \tag{2.51}$$

when the reference configuration is the stress-free undeformed state, and, of course, $\mathscr{F}$ denotes a different function from that in (2.42). Owing to the invariance of $\mathbf{S}$ and $\mathbf{E}$ under superposed rigid-body motion, the required invariance of the constitutive relation is automatically achieved.

If it is further assumed, as is normally done, that the specific mechanical power is the time derivative of a function $\mathscr{U}$ of the strain tensor (called the *strain energy*), then the choice of $\mathbf{S}$ and $\mathbf{E}$ as conjugate measures ensures that $\mathscr{F}$ is the derivative of $\mathscr{U}$. Using an orthonormal basis,

$$\mathscr{F}(\mathbf{E})_{ij} = \frac{\partial \mathscr{U}(\mathbf{E})}{\partial E_{ij}} \tag{2.52}$$

Consequently,† 

$$\dot{\mathbf{S}} = \boldsymbol{\phi}[\dot{\mathbf{E}}] \tag{2.53}$$

where the fourth-order tensor $\boldsymbol{\phi}$ is given by

$$\phi_{ijrs} = \frac{\partial^2 \mathscr{U}(\mathbf{E})}{\partial E_{ij} \partial E_{rs}} \tag{2.54}$$

and therefore has the following symmetries:

$$\phi_{ijrs} = \phi_{jirs} = \phi_{ijsr} = \phi_{rsij} \tag{2.55}$$

Of course, $\boldsymbol{\phi}$ depends on $\mathbf{E}$ in general, but not on $\dot{\mathbf{E}}$.

When a constitutive relation for $\mathbf{S}$ has been established, such as (2.53), the dependence of $\mathbf{P}$ on the deformation can be found by differentiating (2.48). First, from (2.47),

$$\dot{\varepsilon}_{ijkm} = \Delta_{ijkmpq} \dot{F}_{pq} \tag{2.56}$$

where the sixth-order tensor $\boldsymbol{\Delta}$ has the components

$$\Delta_{ijkmpq} = \frac{\partial^2 E_{ij}}{\partial F_{km} \partial F_{pq}} \tag{2.57}$$

Because the sequence of derivatives may be reversed,

$$\Delta_{ijkmpq} = \Delta_{ijpqkm} \tag{2.58}$$

$\boldsymbol{\Delta}$ is also symmetric in the first pair of indices. Now, differentiating (2.48),

$$\dot{P}_{mk} = \dot{S}_{ij} \varepsilon_{ijkm} + S_{ij} \Delta_{ijkmpq} \dot{F}_{pq} \tag{2.59}$$

In the direct notation, 

$$\dot{\mathbf{P}}^T = \dot{\mathbf{S}} : \boldsymbol{\varepsilon} + \mathbf{S} : \boldsymbol{\Delta} : \dot{\mathbf{F}} \tag{2.60}$$

A general form for the constitutive relation for $\dot{\mathbf{S}}$ and the formula for $\dot{\mathbf{P}}$ will be considered in Sec. 2.6.

---

† For fourth-order tensors the rotation $\boldsymbol{\phi}(\dot{\mathbf{E}}) \equiv \boldsymbol{\phi} : \dot{\mathbf{E}} = \phi_{kmrs} \dot{E}_{rs} \mathbf{e}_k \mathbf{e}_m$ is used here and below.

For the particular case when $\mathbf{S}$ is the second Piola–Kirchhoff tensor (2.50c) and $\mathbf{E}$ is Green's strain tensor (2.41c), one finds by direct calculation that

$$\varepsilon_{ijkm} = \tfrac{1}{2}(\delta_{im}F_{kj} + F_{ki}\delta_{jm}) \tag{2.61}$$

and

$$\Delta_{ijkmpq} = \tfrac{1}{2}(\delta_{im}\delta_{kp}\delta_{jq} + \delta_{kp}\delta_{iq}\delta_{jm}) \tag{2.62}$$

For the Jaumann tensor (2.50a) it is generally necessary to proceed indirectly. For later use, it is noted here that when $\mathbf{S}$ is the Jaumann tensor defined by (2.50a),

$$\mathbf{S}:\dot{\mathbf{U}} = (\mathbf{P}\cdot\mathbf{R}):\dot{\mathbf{U}}$$

## 2.1E  Objective Stress Flux

For rate-type relations such as those that occur in plasticity or viscoelasticity, constitutive relations are often developed directly between "stress rate" and "strain rate." The corresponding form of the constitutive relation for stress as a function of the history of deformation may not be known. In such cases, the objective stress flux plays a direct role. A systematic way to generate objective stress fluxes will be considered in this section.

For any tensor $\mathbf{S}_t(\tau)$ such that

$$\mathbf{S}_t(t) = \mathbf{T}(t) \tag{2.63}$$

the time derivative at $\tau = t$, $\dot{\mathbf{S}}_t(t)$, will be called a *stress flux*. If, in a pair of motions differing only by a rigid translation and rotation at each time $t$, the following relation holds for $\dot{\mathbf{S}}_t(t)$,

$$\dot{\mathbf{S}}_t^*(t) = \mathbf{Q}\cdot\dot{\mathbf{S}}_t(t)\cdot\mathbf{Q}^T \tag{2.64}$$

then the stress flux will be called *objective*.†

The commonly encountered objective stress fluxes are generated by using a stress measure relative to the configuration of time $t$ as a reference configuration. The simplest examples are generated by the following five examples of relative stress measures.

$$\mathbf{S}_t(\tau) = \mathbf{R}_t(\tau)^T\cdot\mathbf{T}(\tau)\cdot\mathbf{R}_t(\tau) \tag{2.65a}$$

$$\mathbf{S}_t(\tau) = \mathbf{F}_t(\tau)^{-1}\cdot\mathbf{T}(\tau)\cdot\mathbf{F}_t(\tau)^{-T} \tag{2.65b}$$

$$\mathbf{S}_t(\tau) = \mathbf{F}_t(\tau)^T\cdot\mathbf{T}(\tau)\cdot\mathbf{F}_t(\tau) \tag{2.65c}$$

$$\mathbf{S}_t(\tau) = \mathbf{F}_t(\tau)^T\cdot\mathbf{T}(\tau)\cdot\mathbf{F}_t(\tau)^{-T} \tag{2.65d}$$

$$\mathbf{S}_t(\tau) = \mathbf{F}_t(\tau)^{-1}\cdot\mathbf{T}(\tau)\cdot\mathbf{F}_t(\tau) \tag{2.65e}$$

In each case, differentiating with respect to $\tau$ and then evaluating for $\tau = t$, using (2.17) to (2.19), yields the following five basic objective stress fluxes:

$$\dot{\mathbf{S}}_t(t) = \dot{\mathbf{T}} + \mathbf{W}^T\cdot\mathbf{T} + \mathbf{T}\cdot\mathbf{W} \tag{2.66a}$$

$$\dot{\mathbf{S}}_t(t) = \dot{\mathbf{T}} - \mathbf{L}\cdot\mathbf{T} - \mathbf{T}\cdot\mathbf{L}^T \tag{2.66b}$$

---

† The tensors S and S* are the stress fluxes in the two motions and Q is the relative rotation tensor.

$$\dot{\mathbf{S}}_t(t) = \mathbf{T} + \mathbf{L}^T \cdot \mathbf{T} + \mathbf{T} \cdot \mathbf{L} \tag{2.66c}$$

$$\dot{\mathbf{S}}_t(t) = \dot{\mathbf{T}} + \mathbf{L}^T \cdot \mathbf{T} - \mathbf{T} \cdot \mathbf{L}^T \tag{2.66d}$$

$$\dot{\mathbf{S}}_t(t) = \dot{\mathbf{T}} - \mathbf{L} \cdot \mathbf{T} + \mathbf{T} \cdot \mathbf{L} \tag{2.66e}$$

The first is commonly called the *corotational stress flux* [5] or the *Jaumann flux* [22]. Such a combination of terms also occurs naturally when one uses a coordinate system which rotates with the particle (corotational frame). The last four objective fluxes occur naturally when one uses an imbedded (convected) coordinate system. Differentiation of the covariant components of the stress tensor on the convected bases leads to (2.66c), contravariant components lead to (2.66b), and mixed components lead to the other two forms (see Ref. [2] for a general treatment of convected derivatives).

The stress measures (2.50a to d) expressed relative to the configuration at time $t$ as a reference could also be used to generate objective stress fluxes. Apart from the factor $\rho_{\mathcal{R}}/\rho$ the cases (2.50c and d) have already been treated. The other two lead to combinations of (2.66a) and (2.66b) or (2.66c). Inclusion of the weighting factor $\rho_{\mathcal{R}}/\rho$ generates a term $(t_l \mathbf{L})\mathbf{I} = (t_l \mathbf{D})\mathbf{I}$. The new term is an objective tensor, and its presence, or lack of it, in the definition of stress flux does not affect the objectivity of the flux.

## 2.1F  General Constitutive Relation, Rate Potentials

The constitutive relation (2.47) only characterizes elastic materials. For inelastic materials, the constitutive function $\mathscr{F}$ generally depends on the entire history of strain, and the rate form (2.49) contains an additional term which is independent of $\dot{\mathbf{E}}$ but depends on the entire past history of strain:

$$\dot{\mathbf{S}} = \boldsymbol{\phi}[\dot{\mathbf{E}}] + \boldsymbol{\alpha} \tag{2.67}$$

where $\boldsymbol{\alpha}$ is a second-order tensor, and $\boldsymbol{\phi}$ a fourth-order tensor, which may depend on the history of the strain measure $\mathbf{E}$. Note that the assumption of dependence on the history of $\mathbf{E}$ includes the special case when that dependence is expressible in terms of the present value of $\mathbf{S}$.

When (2.67) holds, we say the material has *instantaneous modulus* $\boldsymbol{\phi}$. In the usual physical theories, the modulus tensor has the symmetry expressed by (2.55):

$$\phi_{ijrs} = \phi_{jirs} = \phi_{ijsr} = \phi_{rsij} \tag{2.68}$$

on an orthonormal basis.

If we assume that $\mathbf{S}$ and $\mathbf{E}$ are conjugate measures, it follows from (2.60) that

$$\dot{\mathbf{P}}^T = \boldsymbol{\Phi}[\dot{\mathbf{F}}] + \boldsymbol{\beta} \tag{2.69}$$

where the fourth-order tensor $\boldsymbol{\Phi}$ is defined by

$$\boldsymbol{\Phi} = \boldsymbol{\varepsilon}^T : \boldsymbol{\phi} : \boldsymbol{\varepsilon} + \mathbf{S} : \boldsymbol{\Delta}$$

$$\Phi_{kmpq} = \varepsilon_{ijkm} \phi_{ijrs} \varepsilon_{rspq} + S_{ij} \Delta_{ijkmpq} \tag{2.70}$$

and the second-order tensor $\boldsymbol{\beta}$ is defined by

$$\boldsymbol{\beta} = \boldsymbol{\varepsilon}^T : \boldsymbol{\alpha}$$
$$\beta_{km} = \varepsilon_{ijkm}\alpha_{ij} \tag{2.71}$$

Note that $\boldsymbol{\beta} : \dot{\mathbf{F}} = \boldsymbol{\alpha} : \dot{\mathbf{E}}$.

It then follows from (2.68) that $\boldsymbol{\Phi}$ is a function of $\mathbf{F}$ with the symmetry property

$$\Phi_{kmpq} = \Phi_{pqkm} \tag{2.72}$$

For example, if $\mathbf{E}$ is Green's strain tensor (2.41c) the conjugate-stress measure is the second Piola–Kirchhoff tensor (2.50c). In that case Eq. (2.48) becomes

$$\mathbf{P}^T = \mathbf{F} \cdot \mathbf{S} \tag{2.73}$$

and Eq. (2.70) becomes     $$\Phi_{kmpq} = F_{ki}F_{pj}\phi_{imjq} + S_{mq}\delta_{kp} \tag{2.74}$$

For the Jaumann tensor (2.50a) it is again necessary to proceed indirectly.

For a particular history of strain there is a multitude of histories of deformation gradient $\mathbf{F}$. That is, $\mathbf{F}$ determines the strain but not vice versa. The history of $\mathbf{F}$ determines the history of $\mathbf{R}$ and $\mathbf{U}$, and therefore the strain measure $\mathbf{E}$, and also $\mathbf{S}$, $\mathbf{P}$, and $\mathbf{T}$, through the constitutive relation. Conversely, the history of stress measure $\mathbf{S}$, except for certain degenerate materials, determines $\mathbf{E}$, and therefore $\mathbf{U}$, through the inverse of the constitutive relation, but not $\mathbf{R}$ and therefore not $\mathbf{F}$. Likewise, the history of $\mathbf{T}$ does not determine $\mathbf{F}$ in general, nor does $\mathbf{P}$ determine $\mathbf{F}$. This situation is evident for elastic materials from (2.42), where the function $\mathscr{F}$ is generally assumed to be invertible, but still neither $\mathbf{P}$ nor $\mathbf{T}$ is sufficient to determine $\mathbf{F}$. This matter is discussed more fully by Dill [19] and Ogden [20].

**Elasticity**   The constitutive relations already cited for the theory of elasticity are, of course, included as a special case of (2.67) in which $\boldsymbol{\alpha}$ is zero and $\phi$ depends only on the present value of $\mathbf{E}$. The constitutive function $\mathscr{F}$ is generally invertible, although there are special cases, such as incompressible materials, where the function may not be single-valued. It is also generally assumed that $\mathscr{F}$ is derivable from a potential and consequently $\phi$ has the symmetries (2.68).

**Viscoelasticity**   Coleman's theory [4] of the thermodynamics of viscoelastic materials provides another example of a simple material with instantaneous modulus. In that theory, the potential $\mathcal{U}$ is a function of the history of strain which is differentiable when viewed as a function on the Banach space of strain histories with "fading-memory" norm, and $\mathscr{F}$ is the partial derivative with respect to the present value of the strain. More explicitly, if $\mathbf{S}$ is the second Piola–Kirchhoff tensor (2.50c) and $\mathbf{E}$ is the conjugate-strain measure (2.41c), there exists a reference configuration for which $\mathcal{U} = \mathcal{U}(\mathbf{E}_r^t, \mathbf{E}(t))$. The function $\mathbf{E}_r^t$ is the past history of strain defined by $\mathbf{E}_r^t(s) = \mathbf{E}(t-s)$, $s > 0$. The instantaneous modulus $\phi$ is again determined by (2.50), where the derivatives are partial derivatives holding the past history fixed. The tensor $\boldsymbol{\alpha}$ is determined by the partial derivative of $\mathcal{U}$ with respect to the past history and depends on the history of strain and the past history of rate of strain. The instantaneous modulus $\phi$ consequently has the symmetry (2.68). For a fuller treatment see Dill [15].

*Plasticity*  In Hill's rate theory of plasticity [1], the rate of strain relative to the configuration at time $t$ is assumed to be linearly related to the corotational (Jaumann) flux of stress given by $(2.66a)$. That is, the stress measure $\mathbf{S}_t(\tau)$ is the rotated-stress tensor relative to the configuration at time $t$, and the strain measure is the Green's strain tensor $\mathbf{E}_t(\tau)$ relative to the configuration at time $t$. Then

$$\dot{\mathbf{S}}_t(t) = \boldsymbol{\phi}_t[\dot{\mathbf{E}}_t(t)] \tag{2.75}$$

In Hill's theory, the tensor $\boldsymbol{\phi}_t$ is symmetric and depends on the history in a simplified way, reducing to a dependence on $\mathbf{S}_t(t) = \mathbf{T}$ alone. The general restrictions on symmetry of $\boldsymbol{\phi}_t$ are not well established, but it appears likely that (2.68) does hold in accepted theories which relate conjugate measures. Of course, $\boldsymbol{\alpha} = 0$ in this case, as for any rate-independent theory. For a fuller explanation, see McMeeking and Rice [16] and Atluri [39].

*Rate Potentials*  The general constitutive relation of a material with instantaneous elastic response is (2.67). When $\boldsymbol{\phi}$ has the symmetry property (2.68), it is possible to introduce a function $\mathcal{W}(\dot{\mathbf{E}})$ such that $\dot{\mathbf{S}}$ is the derivative of $\mathcal{U}$ with respect to $\dot{\mathbf{E}}$:

$$\mathcal{W}(\dot{\mathbf{E}}) = \tfrac{1}{2}\dot{\mathbf{E}} : \boldsymbol{\phi} : \dot{\mathbf{E}} + \boldsymbol{\alpha} : \dot{\mathbf{E}} \tag{2.76}$$

Then, since $\boldsymbol{\alpha}$ also a symmetric tensor and both $\boldsymbol{\phi}$ and $\boldsymbol{\alpha}$ are independent of $\dot{\mathbf{E}}$,

$$\dot{\mathbf{S}}_{ij} = \frac{\partial \mathcal{W}(\dot{\mathbf{E}})}{\partial \dot{E}_{ij}} \tag{2.77}$$

In coordinate-free notation

$$\dot{\mathbf{S}} = \partial_{\dot{\mathbf{E}}}\mathcal{W} \tag{2.78}$$

The function $\mathcal{W}$ is called a *rate potential* for the stress measure $\mathbf{S}$. Of course, $\mathcal{W}$ also depends implicitly on the history of strain, and the differentiation in (2.77) is for constant-strain history. Rate potentials are useful in formulating the variational theorems for incremental displacements.

A potential function $\mathcal{U}(\dot{\mathbf{F}})$ for $\mathbf{P}^T$ can also be introduced when $\boldsymbol{\Phi}$ has the symmetry (2.72):

$$\mathcal{U}(\dot{\mathbf{F}}) = \tfrac{1}{2}\dot{\mathbf{F}} : \boldsymbol{\Phi} : \dot{\mathbf{F}} + \boldsymbol{\beta} : \dot{\mathbf{F}} \tag{2.79}$$

Then, it follows from (2.69) that

$$\dot{P}_{mk} = \frac{\partial \mathcal{U}(\dot{\mathbf{F}})}{\partial \dot{F}_{km}} \tag{2.80}$$

In coordinate-free notation,

$$\dot{\mathbf{P}}^T = \partial_{\dot{\mathbf{F}}}\mathcal{U} \tag{2.81}$$

Of course, $\mathcal{U}$ implicitly depends on $\mathbf{F}$ through $\boldsymbol{\Phi}$.

It follows from the relation (2.70) between $\boldsymbol{\phi}$ and $\boldsymbol{\Phi}$ that $\mathcal{U}(\dot{\mathbf{F}})$ and $\mathcal{W}(\dot{\mathbf{E}})$ are related by the following transformation:†

$$\mathcal{U}(\dot{\mathbf{F}}) = \mathcal{W}(\dot{\mathbf{E}}) + \tfrac{1}{2}\mathbf{S} : \Delta[\dot{\mathbf{F}}, \dot{\mathbf{F}}]$$
$$\mathcal{U}(\dot{\mathbf{F}}) = \mathcal{W}(\dot{\mathbf{E}}) + \tfrac{1}{2}S_{ij}\Delta_{ijkmpq}\dot{F}_{km}\dot{F}_{pq} \tag{2.82}$$

---

† For sixth-order tensors the notation $\Delta[\mathbf{A}, \mathbf{B}] = \Delta_{ijkmpq}A_{km}B_{pq}\mathbf{e}_i\mathbf{e}_j$ is used here and below.

Alternatively, one may use      $$\mathbf{S}:\mathbf{\Delta}[\dot{\mathbf{F}},\dot{\mathbf{F}}]=\dot{\mathbf{P}}^T:\dot{\mathbf{F}}-\dot{\mathbf{S}}:\dot{\mathbf{E}}$$      (2.83)

when $\mathbf{\Delta}$ is difficult to establish.

For example, when $\mathbf{S}=\mathbf{P}\cdot\mathbf{F}^{-T}$ is the second Piola–Kirchhoff tensor and $\mathbf{E}=\frac{1}{2}(\mathbf{F}^T\cdot\mathbf{F}-\mathbf{I})$ is Green's strain tensor, $\mathbf{\Delta}$ is given by (2.57), and (2.82) becomes

$$\mathcal{U}(\dot{\mathbf{F}})=\mathcal{W}(\dot{\mathbf{E}})+\frac{1}{2}\overline{\mathbf{S}\cdot\dot{\mathbf{F}}^T\cdot\dot{\mathbf{F}}}$$      (2.84)

For the Jaumann tensor (2.50a), $\mathbf{S}=\frac{1}{2}(\mathbf{PR}+\mathbf{R}^T\mathbf{P}^T)$, and the extension tensor $\mathbf{E}=\mathbf{U}-\mathbf{I}$, one finds from (2.83) that

$$\mathcal{U}(\dot{\mathbf{F}})=\mathcal{W}(\dot{\mathbf{E}})-\overline{\mathbf{P}\dot{\mathbf{R}}\mathbf{U}}-\frac{1}{2}\overline{\mathbf{P}\dot{\mathbf{R}}\mathbf{R}^T\dot{\mathbf{R}}\mathbf{U}}$$      (2.85)

where the requirement that $\mathbf{P}$ correspond to a symmetric true-stress tensor has been used.

In accord with the remarks in Sec. 2.4 about invertibility of the constitutive relations, the tensor $\boldsymbol{\phi}$ is normally such that the relation (2.67) can be inverted to express $\dot{\mathbf{E}}$ as a function of $\dot{\mathbf{S}}$ and the past history of deformation:

$$\dot{\mathbf{E}}=\bar{\boldsymbol{\phi}}[\dot{\mathbf{S}}]+\bar{\boldsymbol{\alpha}}$$      (2.86)

where the fourth-order tensor $\bar{\boldsymbol{\phi}}$ has the symmetry property (2.68) and $\bar{\boldsymbol{\alpha}}$ is symmetric.

When the inverse relation exists, one may introduce a potential function for $\dot{\mathbf{E}}$:

$$\mathcal{E}(\dot{\mathbf{S}})=\dot{\mathbf{S}}:\dot{\mathbf{E}}-\mathcal{W}$$      (2.87)

Then                    $$\dot{\mathbf{E}}=\partial_{\dot{\mathbf{S}}}\mathcal{E}(\dot{\mathbf{S}})$$      (2.88)

It is not possible in general to express $\dot{\mathbf{F}}$ as a function of $\dot{\mathbf{P}}$ (see Sec. 2.3). It may be possible when $\mathbf{F}(t)\neq\mathbf{I}$, that is, when the particle is not in the reference state. When the inverse does exist,

$$\dot{\mathbf{F}}=\bar{\boldsymbol{\Phi}}:\dot{\mathbf{P}}^T+\bar{\boldsymbol{\beta}}$$      (2.89)

The new fourth-order tensor $\boldsymbol{\Phi}$ has the symmetry property (2.72). Both $\bar{\boldsymbol{\Phi}}$ and $\bar{\boldsymbol{\beta}}$ depend in general on the history of $\mathbf{F}$. A rate potential can then be defined for $\dot{\mathbf{F}}$:

$$\mathcal{G}(\dot{\mathbf{P}})=\dot{\mathbf{P}}^T:\dot{\mathbf{F}}-\mathcal{U}$$      (2.90)

and                    $$\dot{\mathbf{F}}^T=\partial_{\dot{\mathbf{P}}}\hat{\mathcal{G}}$$

A detailed discussion of rate potentials when the reference configuration is the initial configuration or the current configuration is given by Atluri and Murakawa [28].

### 2.1G Incremental and Rate Formulations of the Field Equations

In nonlinear field theories of inelastic materials, numerical solutions are commonly obtained by proceeding step by step in time to construct a solution. For a typical step, the various quantities have been calculated for all times up to some instant $t$ and the motion for $\tau > t$ is to be determined.

Any reference configuration, actual or hypothetical, may be used for calculation of the incremental displacement. The most common choices are the configuration at a single fixed time $\tau = 0$ (total lagrangian), the configuration at time $t$ (updated lagrangian), or a rigidly translating and rotating configuration (for airplane stability and control problems). A level of generality will be maintained here which allows a choice of reference configuration.

The fundamental problem of the numerical analysis is the determination of the motion for a small increment of time $\Delta t$, subsequent to time $t$, following previous calculations which have established the value of all variables up to and including time $t$. For mechanical problems the fundamental variable is the incremental displacement $\hat{\mathbf{u}} = \mathbf{r}(t + \Delta t) - \mathbf{r}(t)$. The gradient of $\hat{\mathbf{u}}$ is $\hat{\mathbf{F}} = \hat{\mathbf{F}}(t + \Delta t)$ or $\hat{\mathbf{F}}_t$, depending on the reference configuration.

In general, a superposed caret ( $\hat{\ }$ ) will be used to indicate the increment of a field variable, for example, $\hat{\mathbf{P}} = \mathbf{P}(t + \Delta t) - \mathbf{P}(t)$. We will assume here that the first-order approximation is made for all field variables except possibly the velocity and the acceleration, that is, $\mathbf{P}(t + \Delta t) = \mathbf{P}(t) + \dot{\mathbf{P}}(t) \Delta t$. Thus, a quantity with a superposed caret may be regarded as the time derivative multiplied by $\Delta t$, for example, $\hat{\mathbf{P}} \doteq \dot{\mathbf{P}}(t) \Delta t$, and is small with $\Delta t$.

The incremental displacement $\hat{\mathbf{u}} \doteq \mathbf{v} \Delta t$ is also regarded as small. Likewise, $\hat{\mathbf{F}} \doteq \dot{\mathbf{F}}(t) \Delta t$ is small.

It is assumed that the material has instantaneous elastic response so that the constitutive relation is of the form treated in Sec. 2.6. Using (2.69) with $\hat{\boldsymbol{\beta}} = \boldsymbol{\beta} \, \Delta t$, the fundamental material relation for the incremental field is $\hat{\mathbf{P}} = \boldsymbol{\Phi}[\hat{\mathbf{F}}] + \hat{\boldsymbol{\beta}}$. Recall that $\boldsymbol{\Phi}$ is a fourth-order tensor and $\boldsymbol{\beta}$ a second-order tensor, and both may depend on the history of deformation up through time $t$ but not on the rate of deformation at $t$. Furthermore, the material functions are subject to the restrictions implied by objectivity of material behavior, any symmetry of material properties, and the requirement that the stress tensor $\mathbf{T}$ determined from $\mathbf{P}$ by (2.32) is symmetric. These restrictions are automatically satisfied if $\boldsymbol{\Phi}$ is derived from a properly formulated constitutive relation by (2.54).

The increment in boundary tractions referred to the reference configuration is

$$\hat{\mathbf{p}} = \mathbf{p}(t + \Delta t) - \mathbf{p}(t) = \mathbf{N} \cdot \hat{\mathbf{P}} \tag{2.91}$$

where Eq. (2.31) has been used.

In summary, the fundamental kinematical, momentum, and constitutive relations for the incremental deformation are the following:

$$\hat{\mathbf{F}} = \nabla \hat{\mathbf{u}}^T \tag{2.92}$$

$$\nabla \cdot \hat{\mathbf{P}} + \nabla \cdot \mathbf{P}(t) + \rho_{\mathcal{R}} \mathbf{b}(\tau) = \rho_{\mathcal{R}} \mathbf{a}(\tau) \tag{2.93}$$

$$\hat{\mathbf{P}} = \boldsymbol{\Phi}[\hat{\mathbf{F}}] + \hat{\boldsymbol{\beta}} \tag{2.94}$$

It is assumed that the material relation (2.94) is such that symmetry of the stress tensor is ensured and $\boldsymbol{\Phi}$ has the symmetry (2.72).

Since $\mathbf{P}(t)$ also satisfies the equation of balance of momentum (2.34), the relation (2.93) can alternatively be written as

$$\nabla \cdot \hat{\mathbf{P}} + \rho_{\mathcal{R}} \hat{\mathbf{b}} = \rho_{\mathcal{R}} \hat{\mathbf{a}} \tag{2.95}$$

In this case one has to use a numerical-integration procedure for increment of acceleration

$\hat{\mathbf{a}}$ rather than for $\mathbf{a}(t+\Delta t)$. Consequently, the form (2.95) is most often used for statical–quasi-statical problems where the inertial forces are neglected; that is, $\hat{\mathbf{a}}$ is set to zero.

The fields are subject to specification of load or displacement at each point of the boundary $\mathcal{S}$ of $\mathcal{R}$. These boundary conditions are assumed here for simplicity to be of the following form:

$$\hat{\mathbf{p}} = \hat{\mathbf{p}}^0 \qquad \text{on } \mathcal{S}_1 \tag{2.96}$$

$$\hat{\mathbf{u}} = \hat{\mathbf{u}}^0 \qquad \text{on } \mathcal{S}_2 \tag{2.97}$$

where the union of the parts $\mathcal{S}_1$ and $\mathcal{S}_2$ is the whole external boundary $\mathcal{S}$ of $\mathcal{R}$.

For statical problems of rate-independent materials (e.g., elastoplastic materials), the explicit use of time as an ordering parameter is artificial, but it is a useful device. One may, for example, increment the magnitude of the load by means of a parameter $t$. However, it is also possible to deal directly with increments instead of derivatives by discarding nonlinear terms in $\mathbf{u}$, $\hat{\mathbf{F}}$, $\hat{\mathbf{P}}$, etc. Such a procedure also has the advantage of generality of formulation which allows a more complicated formula for estimating the incremental value than the simple first forward difference.

Alternative forms of (2.95) are often encountered. Recall that the $\nabla$ operator is formed by using the coordinates of the reference configuration which may be arbitrarily selected. The two common choices are initial or current configuration, corresponding to the forms (2.35) to (2.37) of the momentum balance, and may be applied directly to (2.95). Secondly, the nominal-stress tensor may be expressed in terms of any stress measure by (2.45), $\mathbf{P}^T = \mathbf{S} : \boldsymbol{\varepsilon}$. The fourth-order tensor $\boldsymbol{\varepsilon}$ depends on the strain measure $\mathbf{E}$ and therefore on $\mathbf{F}$. Using again the approximation $\hat{\mathbf{S}} = \dot{\mathbf{S}}\,\Delta t$, $\hat{\boldsymbol{\varepsilon}} = \dot{\boldsymbol{\varepsilon}}\,\Delta t$,

$$\hat{\mathbf{P}}^T = \hat{\mathbf{S}} : \boldsymbol{\varepsilon} + \mathbf{S} : \hat{\boldsymbol{\varepsilon}} \tag{2.98}$$

In the particular case when $\mathbf{S}$ is the second Piola–Kirchhoff tensor (2.50c), $\mathbf{P}^T = \mathbf{F} \cdot \mathbf{S}$, Eq. (2.98) becomes

$$\hat{\mathbf{P}}^T = \mathbf{F} \cdot \hat{\mathbf{S}} + \hat{\mathbf{F}} \cdot \mathbf{S} \tag{2.99}$$

When the reference configuration is that at time $t$, Eq. (2.99) becomes

$$\hat{\mathbf{P}}_t^T = \hat{\mathbf{S}}_t + \hat{\mathbf{F}}_t \cdot \mathbf{T} \tag{2.100}$$

The incremental-momentum balance for this choice of $\mathbf{S}$, using, respectively, the initial and current configurations for reference, becomes

$$\nabla_0 \cdot (\hat{\mathbf{S}}_0 \cdot \mathbf{F}_0^T + \mathbf{S}_0 \cdot \hat{\mathbf{F}}^T) + \rho_0 \hat{\mathbf{b}} = \rho_0 \hat{\mathbf{a}} \tag{2.101}$$

or

$$\nabla_t \cdot (\hat{\mathbf{S}}_t + \mathbf{T} \cdot \dot{\mathbf{F}}_t^T) + \rho \hat{\mathbf{b}} = \rho \hat{\mathbf{a}} \tag{2.102}$$

There are infinitely many possibilities.

## 2.1H Variational Formulae for the Rate Equations

It is well known that the field equations of linear elasticity can be regarded as following from the requirement that the derivative of a functional of the field variables be zero. A general treatment has been given by Washizu [7]. The complete set of equations results from the condition that the first derivative (variation) of the Hu–Washizu functional is zero. The equilibrium equations result from the derivative of the potential energy. The kinematical relations follow from the complementary energy. The virtual-work formula occurs in that context as the first derivative of the potential-energy function. Similar variational formulations are possible for nonlinear elasticity, but the finite rotation plays a special role [19].

In this subsection, the equations governing the rate of deformation from the (known) state at $\tau = t$ are considered for the equilibrium or quasi-static problems. The reference configuration is arbitrary but fixed for this study. The specific choice of the configuration at $\tau = 0$ (the total lagrangian method) or at $\tau = t$ (the updated lagrangian method) as a reference configuration are but two of the many useful choices. The rate equations are linear, and therefore variational theorems similar to those of the classical linear theory can be developed.

The displacement rate $\dot{\mathbf{u}}$ (the velocity), the gradient of displacement rate $\dot{\mathbf{F}}$, and the rate-of-nominal-stress tensor $\dot{\mathbf{P}}$ are governed by the field equations (2.4), (2.38), and (2.69), which are repeated here using the rate potential (2.81):

$$\dot{\mathbf{F}} = \nabla \dot{\mathbf{u}}^T \tag{2.103}$$

$$\nabla \cdot \dot{\mathbf{P}} + \rho_{\mathscr{R}} \dot{\mathbf{b}} = 0 \tag{2.104}$$

$$\dot{\mathbf{P}} = \partial_{\dot{\mathbf{F}}} \mathscr{U}(\dot{\mathbf{F}}) \tag{2.105}$$

These equations hold in $\mathscr{R}$. When the first-order approximations $\hat{\mathbf{P}} = \dot{\mathbf{P}} \Delta t$ and $\hat{\mathbf{F}} = \dot{\mathbf{F}} \Delta t$ are used, these equations also coincide with incremental Eqs. (2.92) to (2.94).

The symmetry of the true-stress tensor requires by (2.32) that $\mathbf{F}(\tau) \cdot \mathbf{P}(\tau)$ is symmetric. For the nominal-stress rate, $\mathbf{F} \cdot \dot{\mathbf{P}} + \mathbf{P} \cdot \dot{\mathbf{F}}$ must be symmetric. The material relation (2.105) is required to be such that these equations are satisfied. This means that $\mathscr{U}$ cannot be an arbitrary function of $\dot{\mathbf{F}}$. The form of $\mathscr{U}$ is further restricted by the requirement of invariance under superposed rigid motion.

The field equations are supplemented by the boundary conditions (2.96) and (2.97) expressing load and support conditions. For the incremental variables,

$$\mathbf{N} \cdot \dot{\mathbf{P}} = \dot{\mathbf{p}}^0 \qquad \text{on } \mathscr{S}_1 \tag{2.106}$$

$$\dot{\mathbf{u}} = \dot{\mathbf{u}}^0 \qquad \text{on } \mathscr{S}_2 \tag{2.107}$$

Note the load rate is expressed in terms of the traction-rate vector $\dot{\mathbf{p}}$ per unit area of the reference configuration. The choice of reference configuration in a practical calculation is generally that one for which $\dot{\mathbf{p}}$ is readily prescribed.

For the general case of conjugate-stress and strain measures, $\dot{\mathbf{E}} = \boldsymbol{\varepsilon} : \dot{\mathbf{F}}$ and $\dot{\mathbf{P}}^T = \dot{\mathbf{S}} : \boldsymbol{\varepsilon} + \mathbf{S} : \boldsymbol{\Delta} : \dot{\mathbf{F}}$. Consequently the basic relations corresponding to (2.103) to (2.105) are the following:

$$\dot{\mathbf{E}} = \boldsymbol{\varepsilon} : \nabla \dot{\mathbf{u}}^T \tag{2.103$a$}$$

$$\nabla \cdot (\dot{\mathbf{S}} : \boldsymbol{\varepsilon} + \mathbf{S} : \boldsymbol{\Delta} : \nabla \dot{\mathbf{u}}^T)^T + \rho_{\mathscr{R}} \dot{\mathbf{b}} = 0 \tag{2.104$a$}$$

$$\dot{\mathbf{S}} = \partial_{\dot{\mathbf{E}}} \mathscr{W}(\dot{\mathbf{E}}) \tag{2.105$a$}$$

Balance of angular momentum requires that $\dot{\mathbf{S}}$ be symmetric. The boundary conditions on traction (2.106) become

$$\mathbf{N}\cdot(\dot{\mathbf{S}}:\boldsymbol{\varepsilon}+\mathbf{S}:\boldsymbol{\Delta}:\nabla\dot{\mathbf{u}}^T)^T=\dot{\mathbf{p}}^0 \qquad \text{on } \mathscr{S}_1 \qquad (2.106a)$$

The rate equations are linear, and consequently relations analogous to the classical relations of linear theory can be developed. Corresponding to the Hu–Washizu principle, let

$$\Pi_W(\dot{\mathbf{u}},\dot{\mathbf{F}},\dot{\mathbf{P}})=\int_{\mathscr{R}} \{\mathscr{U}(\dot{\mathbf{F}})-\rho_{\mathscr{R}}\mathbf{b}\cdot\dot{\mathbf{u}}+\dot{\mathbf{P}}^T:(\nabla\dot{\mathbf{u}}^T-\dot{\mathbf{F}})\}\,dV$$

$$-\int_{\mathscr{S}_1} \dot{\mathbf{p}}^0\cdot\dot{\mathbf{u}}\,dA-\int_{\mathscr{S}_2}\mathbf{N}\cdot\dot{\mathbf{P}}\cdot(\dot{\mathbf{u}}-\dot{\mathbf{u}}^0)\,dA \qquad (2.108)$$

The field equations (2.103) to (2.105) and boundary conditions (2.106) and (2.107) result from the requirement that the derivative of the function $\Pi_W$ be zero. The balance of angular momentum is ensured by the structure of $\mathscr{U}$.

When $\dot{\mathbf{P}}$ is determined by the material relation (2.105), $\dot{\mathbf{F}}$ is determined by the kinematical relation (2.103), and the incremental displacement satisfies the boundary conditions (2.107), one obtains, as a special case, the potential-energy functional

$$\Pi_p(\dot{\mathbf{u}})=\int_{\mathscr{R}}\{\mathscr{U}(\dot{\mathbf{F}})-\rho_{\mathscr{R}}\mathbf{b}\cdot\dot{\mathbf{u}}\}\,dV-\int_{\mathscr{S}_1}\dot{\mathbf{p}}^0\cdot\dot{\mathbf{u}}\,dA \qquad (2.109)$$

The requirement that the first derivative of $\Pi_p(\dot{\mathbf{u}})$ be zero is expressed by virtual work and is equivalent to the remaining field equation (2.104) and boundary condition (2.106) on load. A principle of this type was given in Ref. [1].

For any choice of conjugate-stress and strain measure, using (2.82), the Hu–Washizu function (2.108) becomes the following:

$$\Pi_W(\dot{\mathbf{u}},\dot{\mathbf{E}},\dot{\mathbf{S}})=\int_{\mathscr{R}}\{\mathscr{W}(\dot{\mathbf{E}})+\tfrac{1}{2}\mathbf{S}:\boldsymbol{\Delta}[\dot{\mathbf{F}},\dot{\mathbf{F}}]-\rho_{\mathscr{R}}\mathbf{b}\cdot\dot{\mathbf{u}}-\dot{\mathbf{S}}:(\dot{\mathbf{E}}-\boldsymbol{\varepsilon}:\dot{\mathbf{F}})\}\,dV$$

$$-\int_{\mathscr{S}_1}\dot{\mathbf{p}}^0\cdot\dot{\mathbf{u}}\,dA-\int_{\mathscr{S}_2}\mathbf{N}\cdot(\dot{\mathbf{S}}:\boldsymbol{\varepsilon}+\mathbf{S}:\boldsymbol{\Delta}:\dot{\mathbf{F}})^T\cdot(\dot{\mathbf{u}}-\dot{\mathbf{u}}^0)\,dA \qquad (2.110)$$

Here $\dot{\mathbf{F}}=\nabla\dot{\mathbf{u}}^T$ is regarded as a function of $\dot{\mathbf{u}}$. This relation can be written in other forms by using, for instance, Eq. (2.83). For the particular choice of $\mathbf{S}$ as the second Piola–Kirchhoff tensor, $\mathbf{S}:\boldsymbol{\Delta}[\dot{\mathbf{F}},\dot{\mathbf{F}}]=\mathbf{S}:(\dot{\mathbf{F}}^T\cdot\dot{\mathbf{F}})$ and $\dot{\mathbf{E}}=\tfrac{1}{2}(\dot{\mathbf{F}}^T\cdot\mathbf{F}+\mathbf{F}^T\cdot\dot{\mathbf{F}})$. For the choice $\mathbf{E}=\mathbf{U}-\mathbf{I}$ and $\mathbf{S}=\tfrac{1}{2}(\mathbf{PR}+\mathbf{R}^T\mathbf{P}^T)$, the Jaumann tensor, (2.85), may be used.

The function $\Pi_W$ is defined for vectors $\dot{\mathbf{u}}$ and symmetric tensors $\dot{\mathbf{E}}$ and $\dot{\mathbf{S}}$. The requirement that the derivative of $\Pi_W$ be zero for $\dot{\mathbf{u}}$, $\dot{\mathbf{E}}$, and $\dot{\mathbf{S}}$ is equivalent to the full set of incremental equations (2.103) to (2.105) and boundary conditions (2.104) and (2.105), with $\dot{\mathbf{P}}$ replaced by $\dot{\mathbf{S}}:\boldsymbol{\varepsilon}+\mathbf{S}:\boldsymbol{\Delta}:\nabla\dot{\mathbf{u}}^T$. The balance of angular momentum is assured by the symmetry of $\mathbf{S}$.

As already pointed out, the general material relation for $\mathbf{P}$ has a multivalued inverse for every material. The material relation (2.69) for the rate of change $\dot{\mathbf{P}}$ of the nominal-stress tensor in terms of the rate of change $\dot{\mathbf{F}}$ of displacement gradients generally has a unique inverse, however, except for certain specific configurations (e.g., for an elastic material when the current local configuration coincides with a stress-free reference configuration). When the inverse exists, the functional corresponding to the complementary energy of linear theory may be introduced by using the potential $\mathscr{G}$ of (2.90). Special attention must be paid in that case to the angular-momentum balance since it is not ensured by the material relation (2.80) for arbitrary $\mathbf{P}$ [24].

In the following development, the finite rotation is explicitly considered and only the inverse of the general constitutive relation (2.67) is used, so that difficulties occurring in the direct analogue of the complementary energy of the small-deformation theory are avoided. The result is the rate form of the generalized complementary-energy theorem of nonlinear elasticity [11].

If the inverse of the constitutive relation (2.67) is used, the complementary potential $\mathscr{E}(\dot{\mathbf{S}})$ may be introduced in place of $\mathscr{W}(\dot{\mathbf{E}})$ by (2.87), the usual contact or Legendre transformation, to obtain a Hellinger–Reissner-type principle:

$$\Pi_R(\dot{\mathbf{u}}, \dot{\mathbf{S}}) = \int_{\mathscr{R}} \{-\mathscr{E}(\dot{\mathbf{S}}) + \dot{\mathbf{S}}:\dot{\mathbf{E}} + \tfrac{1}{2}\mathbf{S}:\Delta[\dot{\mathbf{F}}, \dot{\mathbf{F}}] - \rho_{\mathscr{R}}\dot{\mathbf{b}}\cdot\dot{\mathbf{u}}\} \, dV$$

$$- \int_{\mathscr{S}_1} \dot{\mathbf{p}}^0\cdot\dot{\mathbf{u}} \, dA - \int_{\mathscr{S}_2} \mathbf{N}\cdot\dot{\mathbf{P}}\cdot(\dot{\mathbf{u}}-\dot{\mathbf{u}}^0) \, dA \qquad (2.111)$$

where $\dot{\mathbf{F}} \equiv \nabla\dot{\mathbf{u}}^T$ and $\dot{\mathbf{E}} = \boldsymbol{\varepsilon}:\nabla\dot{\mathbf{u}}^T$ and $\dot{\mathbf{P}}$ is similarly determined by $\dot{\mathbf{S}}$ and $\dot{\mathbf{u}}$. A number of alternative forms are possible by using, for instance, Eq. (2.83).

The function $\Pi_R$ is defined for vectors $\dot{\mathbf{u}}$ and symmetric tensors $\dot{\mathbf{S}}$. The condition that the derivative of $\Pi_R$ be zero for $\dot{\mathbf{u}}$ and $\dot{\mathbf{S}}$ is equivalent to the equations and boundary conditions (2.104) to (2.107), where $\dot{\mathbf{E}}$ and $\dot{\mathbf{F}}$ are determined by the kinematical relations, $\dot{\mathbf{P}}^T$ is expressed by $\dot{\mathbf{S}}:\boldsymbol{\varepsilon}+\mathbf{S}:\Delta:\dot{\mathbf{F}}$, and the material relation (2.105) is replaced by (2.88). The balance of angular momentum is ensured by the symmetry of $\mathbf{S}$.

When $\dot{\mathbf{P}}$ is required to satisfy the equilibrium equations (2.104) and to satisfy the traction boundary conditions (2.105), one may integrate the term $\dot{\mathbf{P}}:\nabla\dot{\mathbf{u}}$ in (2.107) by parts, and introduce the complementary potential $\mathscr{E}$, to obtain a (generalized) complementary-energy principle:

$$\Pi_c(\dot{\mathbf{F}}, \dot{\mathbf{S}}) = \int_{\mathscr{R}} \{-\mathscr{E}(\dot{\mathbf{S}}) - \tfrac{1}{2}\mathbf{S}:\Delta[\dot{\mathbf{F}}, \dot{\mathbf{F}}]\} \, dV + \int_{\mathscr{S}_2} \mathbf{N}\cdot(\dot{\mathbf{S}}:\boldsymbol{\varepsilon}+\mathbf{S}:\Delta:\dot{\mathbf{F}})^T\cdot\dot{\mathbf{u}}^0 \, dA \qquad (2.112)$$

Again, various forms are possible.

The special case when $\mathbf{S} = \tfrac{1}{2}(\mathbf{P}\cdot\mathbf{R}+\mathbf{R}^T\cdot\mathbf{P}^T) \equiv \mathbf{J}$, the Jaumann tensor, and $\mathbf{E} = \mathbf{U}-\mathbf{I}$, the extension tensor, is of importance because $\dot{\mathbf{U}}$ does not occur in (2.112) and the dependence on $\dot{\mathbf{F}}$ reduces to a dependence on the rate of rotation $\dot{\mathbf{R}}$. Using (2.85), one finds that $\Pi_c$ becomes

$$\Pi_c(\dot{\mathbf{R}}, \dot{\mathbf{P}}) = \int_{\mathscr{R}} \{-\mathscr{E}(\dot{\mathbf{J}}) - \overline{\dot{\mathbf{P}}\mathbf{R}\mathbf{U}} - \tfrac{1}{2}\overline{\mathbf{P}\dot{\mathbf{R}}\mathbf{R}^T\dot{\mathbf{R}}\mathbf{U}}\} \, dV + \int_{\mathscr{S}_2} \mathbf{N}\cdot\dot{\mathbf{P}}\cdot\mathbf{u}^0 \, dA \qquad (2.113)$$

This result was presented by Atluri [27].

The function $\Pi_c(\dot{\mathbf{F}}, \dot{\mathbf{S}})$ is defined for general tensors $\dot{\mathbf{F}}$ and symmetric tensors $\dot{\mathbf{S}}$ such that the momentum balance (2.104a) and the traction boundary condition (2.106a) are satisfied for $\dot{\mathbf{P}}^T = \dot{\mathbf{S}}:\boldsymbol{\varepsilon}+\mathbf{S}:\Delta:\dot{\mathbf{F}}$. The condition that the derivative of $\Pi_c$ be zero for such a pair of tensors $\dot{\mathbf{F}}$ and $\dot{\mathbf{S}}$ ensures the existence of a velocity field $\dot{\mathbf{u}}$ such that (2.103) and (2.107) hold, and the relation (2.105) is satisfied. The balance of angular momentum is ensured by the symmetry of $\mathbf{S}$.

The function $\Pi_c(\dot{\mathbf{R}}, \dot{\mathbf{P}})$ is defined for tensors $\dot{\mathbf{R}}$ such that $\dot{\mathbf{R}}\mathbf{R}^T = -\mathbf{R}\dot{\mathbf{R}}^T$ and tensors $\dot{\mathbf{P}}$ such that (2.104) and (2.106) are satisfied. The condition that the derivative of $\Pi_c$ be zero for such a pair $\dot{\mathbf{R}}$ and $\dot{\mathbf{P}}$ ensures the existence of a velocity field $\dot{\mathbf{u}}$ such that (2.103), (2.105), and (2.107) are satisfied, and $\dot{\mathbf{P}}$ such that the balance of angular momentum is satisfied.

As repeatedly emphasized above the reference configuration remains to be selected to suit the particular application. If the configuration at $\tau = 0$ is used, then $\mathbf{F} = \mathbf{F}_0$, $\mathbf{P} = \mathbf{P}_0$, etc. If the configuration at time $\tau = t$ is used, considerable simplification of the foregoing formulas result because the time derivative is also evaluated at $\tau = t$.

When $\mathcal{R} = \varkappa(t)$, $\mathbf{F}_t(t) = \mathbf{U}_t(t) = \mathbf{R}_t(t) = \mathbf{I}$, $\mathbf{P}_t(t) = \mathbf{T}$, $\dot{\mathbf{F}}_t(t) = \mathbf{L}$, and $\dot{\mathbf{R}}_t(t) = \mathbf{W}$. The functions (2.108) to (2.113) then have the following forms:

$$\Pi_W(\dot{\mathbf{u}}, \mathbf{L}, \dot{\mathbf{P}}_t) = \int_* \{\mathcal{U}_t(\mathbf{L}) - \rho\dot{\mathbf{b}} \cdot \dot{\mathbf{u}} + \dot{\mathbf{P}}_t^T : (\nabla_t \dot{\mathbf{u}}^T - \mathbf{L})\} \, dv$$

$$- \int_{\sigma_1} \dot{\mathbf{p}}_t^0 \cdot \dot{\mathbf{u}} \, da - \int_{\sigma_2} \mathbf{n} \cdot \dot{\mathbf{P}}_t \cdot (\dot{\mathbf{u}} - \dot{\mathbf{u}}^0) \, da \qquad (2.108a)$$

$$\Pi_p(\dot{\mathbf{u}}) = \int_* \{\mathcal{U}_t(\mathbf{L}) - \rho\dot{\mathbf{b}} \cdot \dot{\mathbf{u}}\} \, dv - \int_{\sigma_1} \dot{\mathbf{p}}_t^0 \cdot \dot{\mathbf{u}} \, da \qquad (2.109a)$$

$$\Pi_W(\dot{\mathbf{u}}, \dot{\mathbf{E}}_t, \dot{\mathbf{S}}_t) = \int_* \{\mathcal{W}_t(\dot{\mathbf{E}}_t) + \tfrac{1}{2}\mathbf{S}_t : \Delta[\mathbf{L}, \mathbf{L}] - \rho\dot{\mathbf{b}} \cdot \dot{\mathbf{u}} - \dot{\mathbf{S}}_t : (\dot{\mathbf{E}}_t - \boldsymbol{\varepsilon}_t : \mathbf{L})\} \, dv$$

$$- \int_{\sigma_1} \dot{\mathbf{p}}_t^0 \cdot \dot{\mathbf{u}} \, da - \int_{\sigma_2} \mathbf{n} \cdot \dot{\mathbf{P}}_t \cdot (\dot{\mathbf{u}} - \dot{\mathbf{u}}^0) \, da \qquad (2.110a)$$

$$\Pi_R(\dot{\mathbf{u}}, \dot{\mathbf{S}}_t) = \int_* \{-\mathcal{E}_t(\dot{\mathbf{S}}_t) + \dot{\mathbf{S}}_t : \dot{\mathbf{E}}_t + \tfrac{1}{2}\mathbf{S}_t : \Delta[\mathbf{L}, \mathbf{L}] - \rho\dot{\mathbf{b}} \cdot \dot{\mathbf{u}}\} \, dv$$

$$- \int_{\sigma_1} \dot{\mathbf{p}}_t^0 \cdot \dot{\mathbf{u}} \, da - \int_{\sigma_2} \dot{\mathbf{p}}_t \cdot (\dot{\mathbf{u}} - \dot{\mathbf{u}}^0) \, da \qquad (2.111a)$$

$$\Pi_c(\mathbf{L}, \dot{\mathbf{S}}_t) = \int_* \{-\mathcal{E}_t(\dot{\mathbf{S}}_t) - \tfrac{1}{2}\mathbf{S}_t : \Delta[\mathbf{L}, \mathbf{L}]\} \, dv + \int_{\sigma_2} \mathbf{n} \cdot \dot{\mathbf{P}}_t \cdot \mathbf{u}^0 \, da \qquad (2.112a)$$

$$\Pi_c(\mathbf{W}, \dot{\mathbf{P}}_t) = \int_* \{-\mathcal{E}_t(\dot{\mathbf{J}}_t) - \dot{\mathbf{P}}_t^T : \mathbf{W} - \tfrac{1}{2}\mathbf{T} : (\mathbf{W} \cdot \mathbf{W})\} \, dv + \int_{\sigma_2} \mathbf{n} \cdot \dot{\mathbf{P}}_t \cdot \dot{\mathbf{u}}^0 \, da \qquad (2.113a)$$

In (2.113a), $\mathbf{J}$ is the Jaumann tensor. In (2.111a), $\mathbf{L}$, $\dot{\mathbf{E}}_t$, and $\dot{\mathbf{p}}_t$ are to be regarded as expressed in terms of $\dot{\mathbf{u}}$ and $\dot{\mathbf{S}}_t$. Recall that when $\mathbf{S}$ is the second Piola-Kirchhoff tensor, $\mathbf{S}_t : \Delta(\mathbf{L}, \mathbf{L}) = \mathbf{T} : (\mathbf{L}^T \cdot \mathbf{L})$ in the above equations.

A rate form for potential energy was given by Hill [1]. The remaining principles have been presented in essence by Atluri [24, 27], who also has discussed the practical difficulties of using these functions.

## 2.1ı Selected Finite-Element Literature for Nonlinear Solids

The finite-element method was first applied to nonlinear continuum problems in Ref. [3]. That paper, and early work in general, was concerned with the development of simplified theories for engineering design. A general theory for elasticity and plasticity was given in Ref. [10]. The paper [14] provides a clear exposition for elastic, plastic, and hypoelastic materials. Among the other contributions to the theory and applications to nonlinear problems are the papers [12, 13, 16, 17, 21]. All the foregoing use the direct stiffness method based on the virtual-work formula or the potential-energy function. Application of the complementary principles has been discussed in Refs. [18, 23, 24, 26, 28, 55, 56].

## 2.2 PROPERTIES OF MATERIALS

### 2.2ᴀ Introduction and Notations

In this section, we consider certain elementary theories of material response such as elasticity, viscoelasticity, plasticity, viscoplasticity, and creep.

Herein, we employ cartesian coordinates exclusively. We use a fixed cartesian system with base vectors $e_i$ ($i = 1, 2, 3$). The coordinates of a material particle before and after deformation are $x_i$ and $y_i$, respectively. The deformation gradient, denoted as $F_{ij}$, is defined to be

$$F_{ij} = \frac{\partial y_i}{\partial x_j} \equiv y_{i,j} \qquad (2.114)$$

The displacement components will be denoted by $u_i$ ($= y_i - x_i$), such that

$$F_{ij} = \delta_{ij} + u_{i,j} \qquad (2.115)$$

where $\delta_{ij}$ is a Kronecker delta. The Green–Lagrange strain tensor, $\varepsilon_{ij}$, is given by

$$\varepsilon_{ij} = \tfrac{1}{2}[F_{ki}F_{kj} - \delta_{ij}] \equiv \tfrac{1}{2}[u_{i,j} + u_{j,i} + u_{k,i}u_{k,j}] \qquad (2.116)$$

When displacements and their gradients are infinitesimal, (2.116) may be approximated as

$$\varepsilon_{ij} = \tfrac{1}{2}[u_{i,j} + u_{j,i}] \equiv u_{(i,j)} \qquad (2.117)$$

A wide variety of other strain measures may be derived [27, 30].

Let $(da)$ be a differential area in the *deformed* body, and let $n_i$ be direction cosines of a unit outward normal to $(da)$. If the differential force acting on this area is $df_i$, the *true stress*, or *Cauchy stress*, $\tau_{ij}$, is defined from the relation

$$df_i = (da)n_j\tau_{ji} \qquad (2.118)$$

Thus, $\tau_{ij}$ is stress per unit area in the deformed body. The *nominal stress* (or the transpose of the so-called first Piola–Kirchhoff stress) $t_{ij}$, and the *second Piola–Kirchhoff stress*, $S_{ij}$, are defined through the relations

$$df_i = (dA)N_j t_{ji} \qquad (2.119)$$

$$= (dA)N_j S_{jk} y_{i,k} \qquad (2.120)$$

where $(dA)N_j$ is the image in the undeformed configuration of the oriented area $(da)n_j$ in the deformed configuration. Note that both $t_{ji}$ and $S_{ji}$ are stresses per unit area in the undeformed configuration, and $t_{ji}$ is unsymmetric, while $S_{ji}$ is, by definition, symmetric [27, 30]. It should also be noted that a wide variety of other stress measures may be derived [27, 30].

From the geometric theory of deformation [31], it follows that

$$(da)n_j = (J)(dA)N_k \left(\frac{\partial x_k}{\partial y_i}\right) \tag{2.121}$$

where

$$J = \frac{dv}{dV} = \frac{\rho_0}{\rho} \tag{2.122}$$

In the above $(dv)$ is a differential volume in the deformed body, and $(dV)$ is its image in the undeformed body. From (2.118) to (2.122) it follows that

$$t_{ij} = J \frac{\partial x_i}{\partial y_k} \tau_{kj} \qquad S_{ij} = J \frac{\partial x_i}{\partial y_m} \tau_{mn} \frac{\partial x_j}{\partial y_n} \tag{2.123}$$

Another useful stress tensor is the so-called Kirchhoff stress tensor, denoted $\sigma_{ij}$, and defined as

$$\sigma_{ij} = J\tau_{ij} \tag{2.124}$$

When displacements and their gradients are infinitesimal, $J \approx 1$, $\partial x_i/\partial y_k \approx \delta_{ik}$, etc.; and thus, the distinction between all the stress measures largely disappears. Hence, in an infinitesimal-deformation theory, one may speak of *the* stress tensor $\sigma_{ij}$.

## 2.2B Elementary Theories of Material Responses

The mathematical characterization of behavior of solids is one of the most baffling aspects of solid mechanics. Most of the time, the general behavior of a material defies our mathematical ability to characterize it. The below-discussed theories must be viewed simply as *idealizations* of regimes of material response under specific types of loading and/or environmental conditions.

*Elasticity* In this idealization, the underlying assumption is that stress is a single-valued function of strain and is independent of the *history* of straining. Also, for such materials, one may define a "potential" for stress in terms of strain, in the form of a *strain-energy density function*, denoted here as $W$. It is customary [30] to measure $W$ per unit of *undeformed* volume. In the general case of finite deformations different stress measures are related to the derivative of $W$ with respect to specific strain measures, labeled as *conjugate-strain measures*. Thus, it may be shown [30] that

$$t_{ij} = \frac{\partial W}{\partial F_{ji}} \qquad S_{ij} = \frac{\partial W}{\partial \varepsilon_{ij}} \tag{2.125}$$

Note that, for finite deformations, the Cauchy stress does not have a simple conjugate-strain measure. When $W$ does not depend on the location of the material particle (in the undeformed configuration), the material is said to be *homogeneous*. A material is said to be *isotropic* if $W$ depends on $\varepsilon_{ij}$ only through the basic *invariants* of $\varepsilon_{ij}$. These invariants may be defined as

$$I_1 = 3 + 2\varepsilon_{kk} \qquad I_2 = 3 + 4\varepsilon_{kk} + 2(\varepsilon_{kk}\varepsilon_{mm} - \varepsilon_{km}\varepsilon_{km})$$

and 
$$I_3 = \det|\delta_{mn} + 2\varepsilon_{mn}| \equiv 1 + 2\varepsilon_{kk} + 2(\varepsilon_{kk}\varepsilon_{mm} - \varepsilon_{km}\varepsilon_{km}) + \tfrac{4}{3}e_{ijk}e_{rst}\varepsilon_{ir}\varepsilon_{js}\varepsilon_{kt} \qquad (2.126)$$

where $e_{ijk}$ is equal to $+1$ if $(ijk)$ take on values (123) in a cyclic order, is equal to $-1$ if in anticyclic order, and is zero if two of the indices take on identical values. Sometimes, invariants $J_1$, $J_2$, and $J_3$ defined as

$$J_1 = I_1 - 3 \qquad J_2 = I_2 - 2I_1 + 3 \qquad J_3 = I_3 - I_2 + I_1 - 1 \qquad (2.127)$$

are also used. When the material is isotropic, the Kirchhoff stress tensor may be shown to be the derivative of $W$ with respect to a certain logarithmic strain measure [30]. Also, by decomposing the deformation gradient $F_{ij}$ into pure stretch and rigid rotation [27, 30], one may derive certain other useful stress measures such as the Biot–Luré stress and Jaumann stress, among others [30].

An isotropic, nonlinear elastic material may be characterized, in its behavior at finite deformations, by

$$W = \sum_{r,s,t=0}^{\infty} C_{rst}(I_1-3)^r(I_2-3)^s(I_3-1)^t \qquad C_{000} = 0 \qquad (2.128)$$

The ratio of volume change due to deformation, $dv/dV$, is given, for finite deformations, by $I_3$. Thus, for incompressible materials, $I_3 = 1$. For incompressible materials, stress is determined from strain only to within a scalar function called the *hydrostatic pressure*. For such materials, one may define a "modified" strain-energy function, say $\bar{W}$, in which the incompressibility condition, $I_3 = 1$, is introduced as a constraint through the Lagrange multiplier $p$. Thus,

$$\bar{W} = W(\varepsilon_{ij}) + p(I_3 - 1) \qquad (2.129)$$

that is 
$$t_{ij} = \frac{\partial W}{\partial F_{ji}} + p\frac{\partial I_3}{\partial F_{ji}} \qquad S_{ij} = \frac{\partial W}{\partial \varepsilon_{ij}} + p\frac{\partial I_3}{\partial \varepsilon_{ij}} \qquad (2.130)$$

For isotropic incompressible elastic materials,

$$W(\varepsilon_{ij}) = W(I_1, I_2) \qquad (2.131)$$

Thus, (2.130) and (2.131) yield, for instance,

$$S_{ij} = 2\frac{\partial W}{\partial I_1}\delta_{ij} + 4[\delta_{ij}(1+\varepsilon_{mm}) - \delta_{im}\delta_{jn}\varepsilon_{mn}]$$

$$+ p[\delta_{ij}(1+2\varepsilon_{mm}) - 2\delta_{im}\delta_{jn}\varepsilon_{mn} + 2e_{imn}e_{jrs}\varepsilon_{mr}\varepsilon_{ns}] \qquad (2.132)$$

A well-known representation of (2.131) is due to Mooney [32], where

$$W(I_1 I_2) = C_1(I_1 - 3) + C_2(I_2 - 3) \qquad (2.133)$$

So far, we have discussed isotropic materials. In general, for a homogeneous solid, one may write:

$$W = E_{ij}\varepsilon_{ij} + \tfrac{1}{2}E_{ijmn}\varepsilon_{ij}\varepsilon_{mn} + \tfrac{1}{3}E_{ijmnrs}\varepsilon_{ij}\varepsilon_{mn}\varepsilon_{rs} + \cdots \qquad (2.134)$$

We use, for convenience, $S_{ij}$ and $\varepsilon_{ij}$ as conjugate measures of stress and strain. Since $S_{ij}$ and $\varepsilon_{ij}$ are both symmetric, one must have

$$E_{ij} = E_{ji} \qquad E_{ijmn} = E_{jimn} = E_{ijnm} = E_{mnij}$$

$$E_{ijmnrs} = E_{jimnrs} = E_{ijnmrs} = E_{ijmnsr} = \cdots = E_{rsijmn} \cdots \qquad (2.135)$$

Thus, 
$$S_{ij} = E_{ij} + E_{ijmn}\varepsilon_{mn} + E_{ijmnrs}\varepsilon_{mn}\varepsilon_{rs} + \cdots \qquad (2.136)$$

Henceforth, we will consider the case when deformations are *infinitesimal*. Thus, $\varepsilon_{ij} \approx \tfrac{1}{2}(u_{i,j} + u_{j,i})$. Further, the differences in the definitions of various stress measures disappear, and one may speak of *the* stress $\sigma_{ij}$. Thus, (2.136) may be rewritten as

$$\sigma_{ij} = E_{ij} + E_{ijmn}\varepsilon_{mn} + E_{ijmnrs}\varepsilon_{mn}\varepsilon_{rs} \qquad (2.137)$$

A material is said to be linearly elastic if a linear approximation of (2.137) is valid for the magnitude of strains under consideration. For such a material,

$$\sigma_{ij} = E_{ij} + E_{ijmn}\varepsilon_{mn} \qquad (2.138)$$

The stress at zero strain, that is, $E_{ij}$, most commonly is due to temperature variation from a reference state. The simplest assumption in thermal problems is to set

$$E_{ij} = -\beta_{ij}\,\Delta T$$

where $\Delta T(= T - T_0)$ is the temperature increment from the reference value $T_0$.

For an anisotropic linear-elastic solid, in view of the symmetries in (2.136), one has 21 independent elastic constants $E_{ijkl}$, and six constants $\beta_{ij}$. In the case of isotropic linear-elastic materials, an examination of (2.126) to (2.128) reveals that the number of independent elastic constants $E_{ijkl}$ is reduced to two, and the number of independent $\beta$'s to one. Thus, for an isotropic elastic material,

$$\sigma_{ij} = \lambda\varepsilon_{kk}\delta_{ij} + 2\mu\varepsilon_{ij} - \beta\,\Delta T\delta_{ij} \qquad (2.139a)$$

where $\lambda$ and $\mu$ are Lamé parameters, which are related to Young's modulus $E$ and Poisson's ratio $\nu$, through

$$\lambda = \frac{E\nu}{(1+\nu)(1-2\nu)} \qquad \mu = \frac{E}{2(1+\nu)}$$

The bulk modulus $K$ is defined as

$$K = \frac{3\lambda + 2\mu}{3}$$

The inverse of (2.139a) is

$$\varepsilon_{ij} = -\frac{\nu}{E}\sigma_{mm}\delta_{ij} + \frac{1+\nu}{E}\sigma_{ij} + \alpha\Delta T\delta_{ij} \tag{2.139b}$$

where $\beta$ and $\alpha$ are related through

$$\beta = \frac{E\alpha}{1-2\nu} \tag{2.139c}$$

and $\alpha$ is the linear coefficient of thermal expansion.

The state of "plane strain" is characterized by the conditions of validity that $u_\alpha = u_\alpha(x_\beta)$; $\alpha, \beta = 1, 2$; and $u_3 = 0$. Thus, $\varepsilon_{3i} = 0$, $i = 1, 2, 3$. In plane strain,

$$\varepsilon_{11} = \frac{1-\nu^2}{E}\left(\sigma_{11} - \frac{\nu}{1-\nu}\sigma_{22}\right) + \alpha(1+\nu)\Delta T \tag{2.140a}$$

$$\varepsilon_{22} = \frac{1-\nu^2}{E}\left(\sigma_{22} - \frac{\nu}{1-\nu}\sigma_{11}\right) + \alpha(1+\nu)\Delta T \tag{2.140b}$$

$$\varepsilon_{12} = \frac{1+\nu}{E}\sigma_{12} \tag{2.140c}$$

and

$$\sigma_{33} = \nu(\sigma_{11} + \sigma_{22}) - \alpha E\Delta T \tag{2.140d}$$

The state of "plane stress" is characterized by the conditions of validity that $\sigma_{3k} = 0$, $k = 1, 2, 3$. Here, one has

$$\varepsilon_{11} = \frac{1}{E}(\sigma_{11} - \nu\sigma_{22}) + \alpha\Delta T \tag{2.141a}$$

$$\varepsilon_{22} = \frac{1}{E}(\sigma_{22} - \nu\sigma_{11}) + \alpha\Delta T \tag{2.141b}$$

$$\varepsilon_{12} = \frac{1+\nu}{E}\sigma_{12} \tag{2.141c}$$

and

$$\varepsilon_{33} = -\frac{\nu}{E}(\sigma_{11} + \sigma_{22}) + \alpha\Delta T \tag{2.141d}$$

Note that in (2.140c) and (2.141c), $\varepsilon_{12}$ is the tensor component of strain. Sometimes it is customary to use the engineering strain component $\gamma_{12} = 2\varepsilon_{12}$. Note also that in the case of a linear-elastic material, the strain-energy density $W$ is given by

$$W = \tfrac{1}{2}\sigma_{ij}\varepsilon_{ij} = \tfrac{1}{2}(\sigma_{11}\varepsilon_{11} + \sigma_{22}\varepsilon_{22} + \sigma_{33}\varepsilon_{33} + 2\varepsilon_{12}\sigma_{12} + 2\varepsilon_{13}\sigma_{13} + 2\varepsilon_{23}\sigma_{23})$$

$$= \tfrac{1}{2}(\sigma_{11}\varepsilon_{11} + \sigma_{22}\varepsilon_{22} + \sigma_{33}\varepsilon_{33} + \gamma_{12}\sigma_{12} + \gamma_{23}\sigma_{23} + \gamma_{13}\sigma_{13}) \tag{2.142}$$

From (2.139b) it is seen that, for linear-elastic isotropic materials,

$$\varepsilon_{kk} = \frac{1-2\nu}{E}\sigma_{mm} + 3\alpha\Delta T \equiv \frac{\sigma_{mn}}{3k} + 3\alpha\Delta T \tag{2.143}$$

when the bulk modulus $k \to \infty$ (or $\nu \to \frac{1}{2}$), it is seen that $\varepsilon_{kk} \to 3\alpha \Delta T$, and is independent of mean stress. Note also from (2.139c) that $\beta \to \infty$ as $\nu \to \frac{1}{2}$. For such materials, the mean stress is indeterminate from deformation alone. In this case, the relation (2.139a) is replaced by

$$\sigma_{ij} = -p\delta_{ij} + 2\mu\varepsilon'_{ij} \tag{2.144a}$$

with the constraint
$$\varepsilon_{kk} = 3\alpha \Delta T \tag{2.144b}$$

where $p$ is the *hydrostatic pressure* and $\varepsilon'_{ij}$ the deviator of the strain. Note that the strain-energy density of a linear-elastic incompressible material is

$$W = \mu\varepsilon'_{ij}\varepsilon'_{ij} - p(\varepsilon_{kk} - 3\alpha \Delta T) \tag{2.145}$$

wherein $p$ acts as a Lagrange multiplier to enforce (2.144b).

**Viscoelasticity**   A linear-elastic solid, by definition, is one which has the memory of only its unstrained state. Viscoelastic materials are those for which the current deformation is a function of the entire history of loading, and conversely, the current stress is a function of the entire history of straining. Linear-viscoelastic materials are those for which the above hereditary relations are expressed in terms of linear-superposition integrals, which, for infinitesimal strains, take the forms

$$\sigma_{ij}(t) = \varepsilon_{kl}(0^+)E_{ijkl}(t) + \int_0^t E_{ijkl}(t-\tau)\frac{\partial \varepsilon_{kl}}{\partial \tau}\, d\tau \tag{2.146a}$$

$$\equiv E_{ijkl}(0^+)\varepsilon_{kl}(t) + \int_0^t \varepsilon_{kl}(t-\tau)\frac{\partial E_{ijkl}}{\partial \tau}\, d\tau \tag{2.146b}$$

In the above it has been assumed that $\sigma_{kl} = \varepsilon_{kl} = 0$ for $t < 0$, and that $\varepsilon_{ij}(t)$ and $E_{ijkl}(t)$ are piecewise-continuous. $E_{ijkl}(t)$ is called the *relaxation tensor*. Conversely, one may write

$$\varepsilon_{ij}(t) = \sigma_{kl}(0^+)C_{ijkl}(t) + \int_0^t C_{ijkl}(t+\tau)\frac{\partial \sigma_{kl}}{\partial \tau}\, d\tau \tag{2.147}$$

where $C_{ijkl}(t)$ is called the creep-compliance tensor.

For isotropic linear-viscoelastic materials,

$$E_{ijkl}(t) = \mu(t)(\delta_{ik}\delta_{jm} + \delta_{im}\delta_{jk}) + \lambda(t)\delta_{ij}\delta_{km} \tag{2.148}$$

where $\mu(t)$ is the shear-relaxation modulus, and $B(t) \equiv [3\lambda(t) + 2\mu(t)]/3$ is the bulk-relaxation modulus. It is often assumed that $B(t)$ is independent of time; thus, the material is assumed to have purely elastic volumetric change. The definition of a Poisson's ratio is somewhat ambiguous in viscoelasticity. For instance, in a uniaxial-tension test, let stress be $\sigma_{11}$, longitudinal strain $\varepsilon_{11}$, and lateral strain $\varepsilon_{22}$. For creep at constant stress, the ratio of lateral contraction, denoted as $\nu_c(t)$, is $\nu_c(t) \equiv -\varepsilon_{22}(t)/\varepsilon_{11}(t)$. For relaxation at constant strain, $\nu_R(t) \equiv -\varepsilon_{22}(t)/\varepsilon_{11}$. One may write

$$B(t) = \frac{2\mu(t)[1 + \nu_R(t)]}{1 - 2\nu_R(t)}$$

It is often convenient to assume that $\nu_R = $ constant, which renders $B(t)$ similar to $\mu(t)$. In this case, the material is said to have a constant Poisson's ratio.

The Laplace transforms of Eqs. (2.146) and (2.147) may be written as

$$\bar{\sigma}_{ij}(p) = p\bar{E}_{ijkl}(p)\bar{\varepsilon}_{kl}(p) \tag{2.149a}$$

and

$$\bar{\varepsilon}_{ij}(p) = p\bar{C}_{ijkl}(p)\bar{\sigma}_{kl}(p) \tag{2.149b}$$

where the overbar indicates the Laplace transform, and $p$ is the Laplace variable. From (2.149a and b), it follows that

$$p^2 \bar{E}_{ijkl}\bar{C}_{klmn} = \delta_{im}\delta_{nj} \tag{2.150}$$

It is also customary to represent the relaxation moduli $\mu(t)$ and $B(t)$ in series form as

$$\mu(t) = \mu_0 + \sum_{m=1}^{M} \mu_m \exp(-\alpha_m t)$$

$$B(t) = B_0 + \sum_{m=1}^{M} B_m \exp(-\beta_m t)$$

**Plasticity**   Most structural metals behave elastically for only very small values of strain, after which the materials yield. During yielding, the apparent instantaneous "tangent" moduli of the material are reduced from those in the prior elastic state. Removal of load causes the material to unload elastically with the initial elastic moduli. Such materials are usually labeled as *elastic-plastic*. Observed phenomena in the behavior of such materials include the so-called Bauschinger effect (a specimen initially loaded in tension often yields at a much reduced stress when reloaded in compression), cyclic hardening (when a specimen is subjected to cyclic straining of amplitude $-\varepsilon$ to $+\varepsilon$, the stress for the same value of tensile strain $\varepsilon$, prior to unloading, increases monotonically with the number of cycles and eventually saturates), etc. Various levels of sophistication of elastic–plastic constitutive theories are necessary to incorporate some or all of these observed phenomena. Here we give a rather cursory review of this still burgeoning literature.

In most theories of metal plasticity, it is assumed that plastic deformations are entirely distortional in nature, and that volumetric strain is purely elastic in nature.

The elastic limit of the material is assumed to be specified by a *yield function* which is a function of stress (or of strain, but most commonly of stress). Since plastic deformation is assumed to be insensitive to hydrostatic pressure, the yield function is assumed, in general, to depend on the stress deviator, $\sigma'_{ij}$ ($\sigma'_{ij} = \sigma_{ij} - \frac{1}{3}\sigma_{mm}\delta_{ij}$). The commonly used yield functions are

von Mises:       $f(\sigma_{ij}) = J_2 - k^2 = 0$       $J_2 = \frac{1}{2}\sigma'_{ij}\sigma'_{ij}$ \hfill (2.151)

Tresca:     $f(\sigma_{ij}) = [(\sigma_1 - \sigma_2)^2 - 4k^2][(\sigma_2 - \sigma_3)^2 - 4k^2][(\sigma_1 - \sigma_3)^2 - 4k^2] = 0$ \hfill (2.152)

In (2.151) and (2.152) $k$ may be a function of plastic strain. Both (2.151) and (2.152) imply the equality of the tensile and compressive yield stresses at all times—the so-called isotropic hardening. Thus, the yield surface expands while its center remains fixed in the stress space.

The relation of $k$ to test data is as follows: (1) In (2.151), $k = (\bar{\sigma}/\sqrt{3})$, where $\bar{\sigma}$ is the yield stress in uniaxial tension, which may be a function of plastic strain for strain-hardening materials, or $k = \bar{\tau}$, where $\bar{\tau}$ is the yield stress in pure shear. (2) In (2.152), $k = \bar{\sigma}/2$ or $\bar{\tau}$. Experimental data appear to favor the use of the von Mises condition [33, 34].

To account for the Bauschinger effect, one may use the representation of the yield surface:

$$f(\sigma_{ij} - \alpha_{ij}) = 0 = \tfrac{1}{2}(\sigma'_{ij} - \alpha'_{ij})(\sigma'_{ij} - \alpha'_{ij}) - \tfrac{1}{3}\bar{\sigma}^2 = 0 \tag{2.153}$$

where $\alpha'_{ij}$ represents the center of the yield surface in the deviatoric stress space. The evolution equations suggested for $\alpha_{ij}$ by Prager [35] and Ziegler [36], respectively, are

$$d\alpha'_{ij} = cd\varepsilon^p_{ij} \tag{2.154}$$

and

$$d\alpha_{ij} = d\mu(\sigma_{ij} - \alpha_{ij}) \tag{2.155}$$

In the above, the prime is used to denote the deviatoric part of the corresponding second-order tensor, and an additive decomposition of differential strain into elastic and plastic parts; that is, $d\varepsilon_{ij} = d\varepsilon^e_{ij} + d\varepsilon^p_{ij}$ has been used.

Elastic processes (with no increase in plastic strain) and plastic processes (with increase in plastic strain) are defined [34] as follows:

Elastic process:     $f < 0$     or     $f = 0$     and     $\dfrac{\partial f}{\partial \sigma_{ij}} d\sigma_{ij} \leqslant 0$ \hfill (2.156)

Plastic process:     $f = 0$     and     $\dfrac{\partial f}{\partial \sigma_{ij}} d\sigma_{ij} > 0$ \hfill (2.157)

The flow rule for strain-hardening materials, arising out of consideration of stress-working in a cyclic process and stability of the process—often referred to as Drucker's [37] postulates— is given by

$$d\varepsilon^p_{ij} = d\lambda \frac{\partial f}{\partial \sigma_{ij}} \tag{2.158}$$

The scalar $(d\lambda)$ is determined from the fact that $df = 0$ during a plastic process—the so-called consistency condition. Using the isotropic-hardening $J_2$-flow theory for which $f$ is given in (2.151), this consistency condition then leads to

$$d\varepsilon_{ij} = \tfrac{9}{4}\sigma'_{ij} \frac{\sigma'_{mn} d\sigma_{mn}}{H'\bar{\sigma}^2} \tag{2.159}$$

where $H'$ is the slope of the stress versus plastic-strain curve in uniaxial tension (or more correctly, the slope of the true-stress versus logarithmic-strain curve in pure tension). On the other hand, for linear-kinematic-hardening rules of Prager, given in (2.153) and (2.154), the consistency condition leads to

$$d\varepsilon^p_{ij} = \frac{3}{2c\bar{\sigma}^2}[(\sigma'_{mn} - \alpha'_{mn})d\sigma_{mn}](\sigma'_{ij} - \alpha'_{ij}) \tag{2.160}$$

For pressure-insensitive plasticity, the stress–strain laws may be written as

$$d\sigma_{mn} = (3\lambda + 2\mu)d\varepsilon_{mm} \tag{2.161a}$$

$$d\sigma'_{ij} = 2\mu(d\varepsilon'_{ij} - d\varepsilon^P_{ij}) \tag{2.161b}$$

Choosing a parameter $\alpha$ such that $\alpha = 1$ when $d\varepsilon^P_{ij} \neq 0$ and $\alpha = 0$ when $d\varepsilon^P_{ij} = 0$, we have

$$d\sigma'_{ij} = 2\mu\left(d\varepsilon'_{ij} - \tfrac{9}{4}\sigma'_{ij}\frac{\sigma'_{mn}d\sigma_{mn}\alpha}{H'\bar\sigma^2}\right) \tag{2.162}$$

for isotropic hardening, and

$$d\sigma'_{ij} = 2\mu\left[d\varepsilon'_{ij} - \frac{3}{2c\sigma^2}(\sigma'_{mn} - \alpha'_{mn})d\sigma_{mn}(\sigma'_{ij} - \alpha'_{ij})\alpha\right] \tag{2.163}$$

for Prager's linear-kinematic hardening. Taking the tensor product of both sides of Eq. (2.162) with $\sigma'_{ij}$ (and noting that $\sigma'_{mn}d\sigma_{mn} \equiv \sigma'_{mn}d\sigma'_{mn}$ by definition), we have

$$d\sigma'_{ij}\sigma'_{ij} = 2\mu\left(d\varepsilon'_{ij}\sigma'_{ij} - \frac{3\alpha}{2H'}\sigma'_{mn}d\sigma'_{mn}\right) \tag{2.164a}$$

or

$$d\sigma'_{ij}\sigma'_{ij} = \left(\frac{2\mu H'}{H'+3\mu}\right)d\varepsilon'_{ij}\sigma'_{ij} \tag{2.164b}$$

Use of (2.164b) and (2.162) results in

$$d\sigma'_{ij} = 2\mu\left[2\varepsilon'_{ij} - 2\mu\frac{9\alpha}{4(H'+3\mu)\bar\sigma^2}\sigma'_{ij}\sigma'_{mn}d\varepsilon'_{mn}\right] \tag{2.165}$$

Combining (2.161a) and (2.165), one may write the *isotropic-hardening* elastic-plastic constitutive law in differential form as

$$d\sigma_{ij} = \left[2\mu\delta_{im}\delta_{jn} + \lambda\delta_{ij}\delta_{mn} - 2\mu\frac{9\alpha\mu}{(2H'+6\mu)\bar\sigma^2}\sigma'_{ij}\sigma'_{mn}\right]d\varepsilon_{mn} \tag{2.166}$$

wherein $\sigma'_{mn}d\varepsilon'_{mn} \equiv \sigma'_{mn}d\varepsilon_{mn}$ has been noted. Similarly, by taking the tensor product of (2.163) with $\sigma'_{ij} - \alpha'_{ij}$ and repeating steps analogous to those in (2.164) to (2.166), one may write the kinematic-hardening elastoplastic constitutive law as

$$d\sigma_{ij} = \left[2\mu\delta_{im}\delta_{jn} + \lambda\delta_{ij}\delta_{mn} - 2\mu\frac{3\mu}{(c+2\mu)\bar\sigma^2}(\sigma'_{ij} - \alpha'_{ij})(\sigma'_{mn} - \alpha'_{mn})\right]d\varepsilon_{mn} \tag{2.167}$$

Note that all the above developments are restricted to the infinitesimal-strain and small-deformation case. Discussion of finite-deformation plasticity is beyond the scope of this work. Here, the objectivity of stress-strain relations plays an important role. Refer to Refs. [27, 38, 39, 54].

We now briefly examine the elastic-plastic stress-strain relations, in the isotropic-hardening case, for plane strain and plane stress, while leaving it to the reader to derive similar relations for kinematic hardening. In the plane-strain case, $d\varepsilon_{3n} = 0$, $n = 1, 2, 3$. Using this in (2.166), we have

$$d\sigma_{\alpha\beta} = \left[ 2\mu\delta_{\alpha\theta}\delta_{\beta\nu} + \lambda\delta_{\alpha\beta}\delta_{\theta\nu} - 2\mu \frac{9\alpha\mu}{(2H' + 6\mu)\bar{\sigma}^2} \sigma_{\alpha\beta}\sigma_{\theta\nu} \right] d\varepsilon_{\theta\nu} \tag{2.168}$$

and

$$d\sigma_{33} = \lambda d\varepsilon_{\theta\theta} - 2\mu \frac{9\alpha\mu}{(2H' + 6\mu)\bar{\sigma}^2} \sigma'_{33}\sigma_{\theta\nu}d\varepsilon_{\theta\nu} \tag{2.169}$$

for

$$\alpha, \beta, \theta, \nu = 1, 2 \tag{2.170}$$

Note that in the plane-strain case, $\sigma_{33}$ as integrated from (2.169) enters the yield condition.

In the plane-stress case, the stress-strain relation is somewhat tedious.

Noting that in the plane-stress case, $d\varepsilon_{\alpha\beta} = d\varepsilon^e_{\alpha\beta} + d\varepsilon^p_{\alpha\beta}$, one may, using the elastic strain-stress relations as given in (2.141), write that

$$d\varepsilon_{\alpha\beta} = d\varepsilon^e_{\alpha\beta} + d\varepsilon^p_{\alpha\beta} = \frac{1}{2\mu}\left( d\sigma_{\alpha\beta} - \frac{\nu}{1+\nu} d\sigma_{\theta\theta}\delta_{\alpha\beta} \right) + d\varepsilon^p_{\alpha\beta} \tag{2.171}$$

$$= \frac{1}{2\mu}\left( d\sigma_{\alpha\beta} - \frac{\nu}{1+\nu} d\sigma_{\theta\theta}\delta_{\alpha\beta} \right) + \sigma'_{\alpha\beta}(\sigma'_{\theta\nu}d\sigma_{\theta\nu}) \frac{9}{4H'\bar{\sigma}^2} \tag{2.172}$$

wherein (2.159) has been used. Equation (2.172) may be inverted to obtain $d\sigma_{\alpha\beta}$ in terms of $d\varepsilon_{\theta\nu}$. This $3 \times 3$ matrix inversion may be carried out, leading to the following result [40]:

$$\left(\frac{Q}{E}\right) d\sigma_{11} = [(\sigma'_{22})^2 + 2P]d\varepsilon_{11} + (-\sigma'_{11}\sigma'_{22} + 2\nu P)d\varepsilon_{22} - \frac{\sigma'_{11} + \nu\sigma'_{22}}{1+\nu}\sigma_{12}2d\varepsilon_{12}$$

$$\left(\frac{Q}{E}\right) d\sigma_{22} = (-\sigma'_{11}\sigma'_{22} + 2\nu P)\, d\varepsilon_{11} + [(\sigma'_{11})^2 + 2P]d\varepsilon_{22} - \frac{\sigma'_{22} + \nu\sigma'_{11}}{1+\nu}\sigma_{12}2\varepsilon_{12}$$

$$\left(\frac{Q}{E}\right) d\sigma_{12} = -\left(\frac{\sigma'_{11} + \nu\sigma'_{22}}{1+\nu}\sigma_{12}\right) d\varepsilon_{11} - \frac{\sigma'_{22} + \nu\sigma'_{11}}{1+\nu}\sigma_{12}d\varepsilon_{22} + \left[\frac{R}{2(1+\nu)} + \frac{2H'}{9E}(1-\nu)\bar{\sigma}^2\right]d\varepsilon_{12}$$

where

$$P = \frac{2H'}{9H}\bar{\sigma}^2 + \frac{\sigma_{12}^2}{1+\nu} \qquad Q = R + 2(1 - \nu^2)P$$

and

$$R = \sigma_{11}'^2 + 2\nu\sigma'_{11}\sigma'_{22} + \sigma_{22}'^2 \tag{2.173}$$

As noted earlier, the classical plasticity theory has several limitations. Intense research is under way to improve constitutive modeling in cyclic plasticity. Some notable avenues of current research are: multisurface plasticity models, endochronic theories, and related internal-variable theories (see Refs. [41–47], for instance).

**Viscoplasticity and Creep**   A viscoplastic solid is similar to a viscous fluid, except that the former can resist shear stress even in a rest configuration; but when the stresses reach critical values as specified by a yield function, the material flows. Consider, for instance, the loading case of simple shear with the only applied stress being $\sigma_{12}$. Restricting ourselves to infinitesimal deformations and strains, let the shear-strain rate be $\dot{\varepsilon}_{12}(= d\varepsilon_{12}/dt)$.

Until the magnitude of $\sigma_{12}$ reaches a value $k$, called the *yield stress*, $\dot{\varepsilon}_{12} = 0$. When $|\sigma_{12}| > k$, $\dot{\varepsilon}_{12}$, by definition for a simple viscoplastic material, is proportional to $|\sigma_{12}| - k$ and has the same sign as $\sigma_{12}$. Thus, if we define $F^1$ for this one-dimensional problem as

$$F^1 = \frac{|\sigma_{12}|}{k} - 1 \tag{2.174}$$

the property may be characterized by the equation

$$2\eta\dot{\varepsilon}_{12} = k\langle F^1 \rangle \sigma_{12} \tag{2.175}$$

where $\langle F^1 \rangle$ is a specific function defined as

$$
\begin{aligned}
\langle F^1 \rangle &= 0 && \text{if } F^1 < 0 \\
\langle F^1 \rangle &= F^1 && \text{if } F^1 \geq 0
\end{aligned} \tag{2.176}
$$

and where $\eta$ is the coefficient of viscosity.

The above relation for simple shear is due to Bingham [48]. Recognizing that $J = \sigma_{12}^2$ for simple shear, Hohenemser and Prager [49] gave a generalization of the above for the three-dimensional case as

$$2\eta\dot{\varepsilon}_{ij}^{vp} = 2k\langle F \rangle \frac{\partial F}{\partial \sigma_{ij}} \tag{2.177a}$$

and

$$F = \frac{J_2^{1/2}}{k} - 1 \equiv \frac{(\sigma_{ij}'\sigma_{ij}'/2)^{1/2}}{k} - 1 \tag{2.177b}$$

and the specific function $\langle F \rangle$ is defined similarly to $\langle F^1 \rangle$.

For an elasto-viscoplastic solid undergoing infinitesimal straining, one may use the additive decomposition

$$\dot{\varepsilon}_{ij} = \dot{\varepsilon}_{ij}^e + \dot{\varepsilon}_{ij}^{vp} \tag{2.178}$$

and the stress-strain–rate relation

$$\dot{\sigma}_{ij} = E_{ijkl}(\dot{\varepsilon}_{kl} - \dot{\varepsilon}_{kl}^{vp}) \tag{2.179}$$

where $E_{ijkl}$ are the instantaneous *elastic* moduli. Note that the viscoplastic strains in (2.177a) are purely deviatoric, since $\partial F / \partial \sigma_{ij} = \sigma_{ij}'/2$ is deviatoric. Thus, for an isotropic solid, Eq. (2.179) may be written as

$$\dot{\sigma}_{mm} = (3\lambda + 2\mu)\dot{\varepsilon}_{mm} \tag{2.180a}$$

and

$$\dot{\sigma}_{ij}' = 2\mu(\dot{\varepsilon}_{ij}' - \dot{\varepsilon}_{ij}^{vp}) \tag{2.180b}$$

On the other hand, for metals operating at elevated temperatures, the strain in uniaxial tension is known to be a function of time, for constant stress of magnitude even below the conventional elastic limit. Most often, on the basis of extensive experimental data [50], the creep strain under costant stress, in uniaxial tests, is expressed as

$$\varepsilon_c = A\sigma^n t^m \tag{2.181}$$

where $\sigma$ is the uniaxial stress and $t$ the time. The creep rate may be written as

$$\dot{\varepsilon}^c = f(\sigma, t) = mA\sigma^n t^{m-1} \tag{2.182a}$$

or, equivalently,

$$\dot{\varepsilon}^c = g(\sigma, \varepsilon_c) = mA^{1/m}\sigma^{n/m}\varepsilon_c^{1-1/m} \tag{2.182b}$$

Expression (2.182a) is often referred to as time-hardening and (2.182b) as *strain-hardening*. Inasmuch as Eqs. (2.181) and (2.182a, b) are valid for constant stress, Eqs. (2.182a and b), when integrated for variable-stress hsitories, do not necessarily give the same results. Usually strain-hardening leads to better agreement with experimental findings for variable stresses.

In the study of creep at long times, the so-called steady-state creep, or the creep-strain rate in uniaxial loading, is usually expressed as

$$\dot{\varepsilon}^c = f(\sigma, T) \tag{2.183}$$

where $T$ is the temperature. Assuming that the effect of $\sigma$ and $T$ are separable, the relation

$$\dot{\varepsilon}^c = f_1(\sigma) \times f_2(T) \tag{2.184a}$$

$$= A\sigma^n \times f_2(T) = B\sigma^n \tag{2.184b}$$

where $B$ is thus a function of temperature, is usually employed.

The steady-state creep strains are associated largely with plastic deformations and are usually observed to involve no volume change. Thus, in the multiaxial case, $\dot{\varepsilon}^c_{ij}$ is a deviatoric tensor. The relation (2.184) may be generalized to the multiaxial case as

$$\dot{\varepsilon}^c_{eq} = B\sigma^n_{eq} \tag{2.185}$$

where the subscript *eq* denotes an "equivalent" quantity, defined analogously to the case of plasticity, as

$$\sigma_{eq} = (\tfrac{3}{2}\sigma'_{ij}\sigma'_{ij})^{1/2} \quad \text{and} \quad \dot{\varepsilon}^c_{eq} = (\tfrac{2}{3}\dot{\varepsilon}_{ij}\dot{\varepsilon}_{ij})^{1/2} \tag{2.186}$$

such that $\sigma_{eq}\dot{\varepsilon}^c_{eq} = \sigma'_{ij}\dot{\varepsilon}^c_{ij}$. Thus, Eq. (2.185) implies that

$$\dot{\varepsilon}^c_{ij} = \tfrac{3}{2}B(\sigma_{eq})^{n-1}\sigma'_{ij} \tag{2.187}$$

For the elastic-creeping solid, one may again write

$$\dot{\varepsilon}_{ij} = \dot{\varepsilon}^e_{ij} + \dot{\varepsilon}^e_{ij} \tag{2.188}$$

and once again, stress-strain–rate relation may be written as

$$\dot{\varepsilon}_{ij} = E_{ijkl}(\dot{\varepsilon}_{ij} - \dot{\varepsilon}^c_{ij}) \tag{2.189}$$

In the above, the applied-stress level has been assumed to be such that the material remains within the elastic limit. If the applied loads are of such a magnitude as to cause the material to exceed its yield limit, one must account for plastic or viscoplastic strains.

An interesting unified viscoplastic-plastic-creep constitutive law has been proposed by Perzyna [51]. Under multiaxial conditions, the relation for inelastic-strain rate suggested in [51] is

$$\dot{\varepsilon}_{ij}^a = A \langle \psi(f) \rangle \frac{\partial q}{\partial \sigma_{ij}} \tag{2.190}$$

where $A$ is the fluidity parameter, superscript $a$ denotes an elastic-strain rate, and $f$ is a loading function, expressed analogously to the plasticity case, as

$$f(\sigma_{ij}, k) = \phi(\sigma_{ij}) - k = 0 \tag{2.191}$$

$q$ is a viscoplastic potential defined as

$$q = q(\sigma_{ij}) \tag{2.192}$$

and $\langle \psi(f) \rangle$ is a specific function such that

$$\begin{aligned} \langle \psi(f) \rangle &= 0 & \text{if } f < 0 \\ \langle \psi(f) \rangle &= \psi(f) & \text{if } f \geq 0 \end{aligned} \tag{2.193}$$

If $q \equiv f$ one has the so-called associative and if $q \neq f$ one has a "nonassociative" law. Perzyna [51] suggests a fairly general form for $\psi$ as

$$\psi(f) = f^n \tag{2.194a}$$

and
$$f = (\tfrac{3}{2} \sigma_{ij}' \sigma_{ij}')^{1/2} - \bar{\sigma} = \sigma_{eq} - \bar{\sigma} \tag{2.194b}$$

By letting $\bar{\sigma} = 0$ and $q = f$, one may easily verify that $\dot{\varepsilon}_{ij}^a$ of (2.190) tends to the creep-strain rate $\dot{\varepsilon}_{ij}^c$ of (2.187).

Letting $\bar{\sigma}$ be a specified value and $q = f$, we obtain, using (2.194) in (2.190),

$$\dot{\varepsilon}_{ij}^a = \tfrac{3}{2} A (\sigma_{eq} - \bar{\sigma})^n \frac{\sigma_{ij}'}{\sigma_{eq}} \qquad \text{for } f > 0 \qquad \text{that is } \sigma_{eq} > \bar{\sigma} \tag{2.195}$$

The equivalent inelastic strain may be written as

$$\dot{\varepsilon}_{eq}^a = (\tfrac{2}{3} \dot{\varepsilon}_{ij}^a \dot{\varepsilon}_{ij}^a)^{1/2} = A (\sigma_{eq} - \bar{\sigma})^n \tag{2.196a}$$

or
$$\sigma_{eq} - \bar{\sigma} = \left( \frac{1}{A} \dot{\varepsilon}_{eq}^a \right)^{1/n} \tag{2.196b}$$

Thus, if a stationary solution of the present inelastic model, i.e., when $\dot{\varepsilon}_{eq}^a \to 0$, is obtained, it is seen that $\sigma_{eq} \to \bar{\sigma}$. Thus, a classical inviscid-plasticity solution is obtained. This fact has been utilized in obtaining classical rate-independent plasticity solutions from the general model of Eq. (2.190) by Zienkiewicz and Cormeau [52]. An alternative way of obtaining the inviscid-plastic solution from Perzyna's model is to let $A \to \infty$. This concept has been implemented numerically by Argyris and Kleiber [53].

Also, as seen from (2.196$b$), $\sigma_{eq}$, or equivalently the size of the yield surface, is governed by (1) isotropic work-hardening effects as characterized by the dependence of $\bar{\sigma}$ on viscoplastic work and (2) the strain-rate effect as characterized by the term $(\dot{\varepsilon}_{eq}^{q})^{1/n}$. Thus, the rate-sensitive plastic problems may also be treated by Perzyna's model [51].

Thus, by appropriate modifications, the general relation (2.177) may be used to model creep, rate-sensitive plasticity, and rate-insensitive plasticity. By a linear combination of strain rates resulting from these individual types of behavior, combined creep, plasticity, and viscoplasticity may be modeled. However, such a model is more or less formalistic and does not lead to any physical insights into the problem of *interactive effects* between creep, plasticity, and viscoplasticity. Modeling of such interactions is the subject of a large number of current research studies [44–47].

## 2.3 REFERENCES

1. Hill, R., "Some Basic Principles in the Mechanics of Solids without a Natural Time," *J. Mech. Phys. Solids*, **7**:209–225 (1959).

2. Truesdell, C., and R. A. Toupin, "The Classical Field Theories," in S. Flugge (ed.), *Encyclopedia of Physics*, Springer-Verlag, Berlin, 1960, vol. VII, art. 3.

3. Turner, M. J., E. H. Dill, H. C. Martin, and R. L. Melosh, "Large Deflection of Structures Subjected to Heating and External Loads," *J. Aerospace Sci.*, **27**:97–102, 127 (1960).

4. Coleman, B. D., "Thermodynamics of Materials with Memory," *Arch. Ration. Mech. Anal.*, **17**:1–46 (1964).

5. Truesdell, C., and W. Noll, "The Nonlinear Field Theories of Mechanics," in S. Flugge (ed.), *Encyclopedia of Physics*, Springer-Verlag, Berlin, 1965, vol. VII, art. 3.

6. Eringen, A. C., *Mechanics of Continua*, 2d ed., Wiley, New York, 1967.

7. Washizu, K., *Variational Methods in Elasticity and Plasticity*, Pergamon Press, New York, 1967, 2d ed., 1975.

8. Hill, R., "On Constitutive Inequalities for Simple Materials: I," *J. Mech. Phys. Solids*, **16**:229–242 (1968).

9. Malvern, L. E., *Introduction to the Mechanics of a Continuous Medium*, Prentice-Hall, Englewood Cliffs, N. J., 1969.

10. Hibbitt, H. D., P. V. Marcal, and J. R. Rice, "A Finite Element Formulation for Problems of Large Strain and Large Displacement," *Intern. J. Solids Struct.*, **6**:1069–1086 (1970).

11. Fraeijis de Veubeke, B., "A New Variational Principle for Finite Elastic Displacements," *Intern. J. Eng. Sci.*, **10**:745–763 (1972).

12. Needleman, A., "A Numerical Study of Necking in Circular Cylindrical Bars," *J. Mech. Phys. Solids*, **20**:111–127 (1972).

13. Hutchinson, J. W., "Finite Strain Analysis of Elastic-Plastic Solids and Structures," in R. F. Hartung (ed.), *Numerical Solution of Nonlinear Structural Problems*, American Society of Mechanical Engineers, New York, 1973, pp. 17–31.

14. Bathe, K. J., E. Ramm, and E. L. Wilson, "Finite Element Formulation for Large Deformation Dynamic Analysis," *Int. J. Numer. Meth. Eng.*, **9**:353–386 (1975).

15. Dill, E. H., "Simple Materials with Fading Memory," in A. C. Eringen (ed.), *Continuum Physics*, Academic Press, New York, 1975, vol. II, pt. II, chap. 4.

16. McMeeking, R. M., and J. R. Rice, "Finite Element Formulation for Problems," *Int. J. Solids Struct.*, **11**:601–606 (1975).

17. Nemat-Nasser, S., and M. Taya, "Model Studies of Ductile Fracture: I. Formulation," *J. Franklin Inst.*, **302**:463–472 (1976).

18. Atluri, S. N., and H. Murakawa, "On Hybrid Finite Element Models in Nonlinear Solid Mechanics," P. G. Bergan et al. (eds.), *Finite Elements in Nonlinear Mechanics*, Tapir, Trondheim, Norway, 1977, vol. I, pp. 3–41.

19. Dill, E. H., "The Complementary Energy Principle in Nonlinear Elasticity," *Lett. Appl. Eng. Sci.*, **5**:95–106 (1977).

20. Ogden, R. W., "Inequalities Associated with the Inversion of Elastic Stress-Deformation Relations and Their Implications," *Proc. Cambridge Phil. Soc.*, **81**:313–324 (1977).

21. Yamada, H., T. Hirakawa, and A. S. Wifi, "Analysis of Large Deformation and Bifurcation in Plasticity Problems by the Finite Element Method," in P. G. Bergan et al. (eds.), *Finite Element in Nonlinear Mechanics*, Tapir, Trondheim, Norway, 1977, vol. I, pp. 393–413.

22. Hill, R., "Aspects of Invariance in Solid Mechanics," *Advances in Applied Mechanics*, Academic Press, New York, 1978, vol. 18, pp. 1–75.

23. Murakawa, H., and S. N. Atluri: "Finite Elasticity Solutions Using Hybrid Finite Elements Based on a Complementary Energy Principle," *J. Appl. Mech., Trans. ASME*, **45**:539–548 (1978).

24. Atluri, S. N., "On Rate Principles for Finite Strain Analysis of Elastic and Inelastic Nonlinear Solids," in *Recent Research on Mechanical Behavior of Solids* (Miyamoto Anniversary Volume), University of Tokyo Press, Tokyo, 1979, pp. 79–107.

25. Dill, E. H., "The Finite Element Method for Nonlinear Field Theories of Mechanics," in R. Vichnevetsky et al. (eds.), *Advances in Computer Methods for Partial Differential Equations, Proc. 3d IMACS Symp.*, Rutgers University, New Brunswick, N. J., 1979, vol. III, pp. 48–52.

26. Murakawa, H., and S. N. Atluri, "Finite Element Solutions of Finite Strain Elastic-Plastic Problems, Based on a New Complementary Energy Rate Principle," in R. Vichnevetsky (ed.), *Advances in Computer Methods for PDE, Proc. 3d IMACS Symp.*, Rutgers University, New Brunswick, N. J., 1979.

27. Atluri, S. N., "On Some New General and Complementary Energy Principles for Rate Problems of Finite Strain, Classical Elastoplasticity," *J. Struct. Mech.*, **8**:61–92 (1980).

28. Atluri, S. N., and H. Murakawa, "New General and Complementary Energy Theorems, Finite Strain, Rate Sensitive Inelasticity and Finite Elements: Some Computational Studies," in W. Wunderlich et al. (eds.), *Nonlinear Finite Element Analysis in Structural Mechanics*, Springer-Verlag, Berlin, 1981, pp. 28–48.

29. Dill, E. H., "The Finite Element Method Using a Convected Rigid Reference Configuration," in R. Vichnevetsky et al. (eds.), *Advances in Computer Methods for Partial Differential Equations, Proc. 4th IMACS Symp.*, Rutgers University, New Brunswick, N. J., 1981, vol. IV, pp. 345–350.

30. Atluri, S. N., "Alternate Stress and Conjugate Strain Measures, and Mixed Variational Formulations Involving Rigid Rotations, for Computational Analyses of Finitely Deformed Solids, with Application to Plates and Shells: I. Theory," *Computers and Structures*, **18**:93–116 (1984).

31. Eringen, A. C., *Nonlinear Theory of Continuous Media*, McGraw-Hill, New York, 1962.

32. Mooney, M., "A Theory of Large Elastic Deformation," *J. Appl. Phys.*, **11**:582–592 (1940).

33. Taylor, G. I., and H. Quinney, "The Plastic Deformation of Metals," *Phil. Trans. R. Soc. (London)*, Ser. A, **230**:323–362 (1931).

34. Hill, R., *The Mathematical Theory of Plasticity*, Oxford University Press, Oxford, 1950.

35. Prager, W., "A New Method of Analyzing Stresses and Strains in Work-Hardening Plastic Solids," *J. Appl. Mech.*, **23**:493–496 (1956).

36. Ziegler, H., "A Modification of Prager's Hardening Rule," *Q. Appl. Math.*, **17**:55–65 (1959).

37. Drucker, D. C., "A More Fundamental Approach to Plastic Stress Strain Relations," *Proc. 1st U.S. Nat. Congr. Appl. Mech.*, 1951, pp. 487–491.

38. Nemat-Nasser, S., "Continuum Bases for Consistent Numerical Formulations of Finite Strains in Elastic and Inelastic Structures," in T. Belytschko et al. (eds.), *Finite Element Analysis of Transient Nonlinear Structural Behavior*, American Society of Mechanical Engineers, New York, 1975, AMD vol. 14, pp. 85–98.

39. Atluri, S. N., "On Constitutive Relations at Finite Strain: Hypoelasticity and Elasto-Plasticity with Isotropic or Kinematic Hardening," *Comput. Meth. Appl. Mech. Eng.*, **43**:137–171 (1984).

40. Yamada, Y., N. Yoshimura, and T. Sakurai, "Plastic Stress-Strain Matrix and Its Application to the Solution of Elastic-Plastic Problems by the Finite Element Method," *Int. J. Mech. Sci.*, **10** (1968).

41. Valanis, K. C., "Fundamental Consequences of a New Intrinsic Tune Measure: Plasticity as a Limit of the Endochronic Theory," *Arch. Mech.* **32**(2):171–191 (1980).

42. Mroz, Z., "An Attempt to Describe the Behavior of Metals Under Cyclic Loads Using a More General Workhardening Model," *Acta Mech.*, **7**:199–212 (1969).

43. Atluri, S. N., "Notes and Comments on Computational Elasto-Plasticity: Some New Models and Their Numerical Implementation," in *Finite Elements in Computational Mechanics*, T. Kant (ed.), Pergamon Press, New York, vol. 1:271–291 (1985).

44. Watanabe, O., and S. N. Atluri, "A New Endochronic Approach to Computational Elastoplasticity: Example of a Cyclically Loaded Cracked Plate," *J. Appl. Mech.*, **52**:857–864 (1985).

45. Watanabe, O., and S. N. Atluri, "Internal Time, General Internal Variable, and Multi-Yield Surface Theories of Plasticity and Creep: A Unification of Concepts," *Intern. J. of Plasticity*, **2**:37–57 (1986).

46. Watanabe, O., and S. N. Atluri, "Constitutive Modeling of Cyclic Plasticity and Creep, Using an Internal Time Concept," *Intern. J. of Plasticity*, **2**:126–154 (1986).

47. Atluri, S. N., "An Endochronic Approach and Other Topics in Small and Finite Deformation Computational Elasto-plasticity," in *Proc. Europe-U.S. Symposium, Finite Element Methods for Nonlinear Problems*, Trondheim, Norway, Aug. 1985, Springer (in print).

48. Bingham, E. C., *Fluidity and Plasticity*, McGraw-Hill, New York, 1922.

49. Hohenemser, K., and W. Prager, "Uber die Ansatze der Mechanik isotroper Kontinua," *Z. Angew. Math. Mech.*, **12**:216–226 (1932).

50. Finnie, I., and W. R. Heller, *Creep of Engineering Materials*, McGraw-Hill, New York, 1959.

51. Perzyna, P., "The Constitutive Equations for Rate Sensitive Plastic Materials," *Q. J. Appl. Math. Mech.*, **20**(4):321–332 (1963).

52. Zienkiewicz, O. C., and I. C. Cormeau, "Visco-plasticity, Plasticity, and Creep in Elastic Solids—A Unified Numerical Solution Approach," *Int. J. Numer. Meth. Eng.*, **8**:821–845 (1974).

53. Argyris, J. H., and M. Kleiber, "Incremental Formulation in Nonlinear Mechanics and Large Strain Elasto-plasticity—Natural Approach: I," *Comput. Meth. Appl. Mech. Eng.*, **11**:215–247 (1977).

54. Reed, K. W., and S. N. Atluri, "Constitutive Modeling and Computational Implementation in Finite Strain Plasticity," *Intern. J. of Plasticity*, **1**:63–87 (1985).

55. Reed, K. W., and S. N. Atluri, "Analysis of Large Quasistatic Deformations of Inelastic Bodies by a New Hybrid-Stress Finite Element Algorithm," *Comp. Meth. Appl. Mech. and Eng.*, **39**:245–295 (1983), and "II. Applications," **40**:171–198 (1983).

56. Reed, K. W., and S. N. Atluri, "Hybrid-Stress Finite Elements for Large Deformations of Inelastic Solids," *Computers & Structures* (Prof. K. Washizu Memorial Issue), **19**:175–182 (1984).

# CHAPTER 3
# BASIC CONCEPTS OF THE FINITE-ELEMENT METHOD

## 3.1 INTRODUCTION

The basic concept of the finite-element method is not new. It has been used throughout centuries for evaluating certain quantities (particularly area and volume) by adding or counting well-defined geometric figures (elements). Today's understanding of the finite-element method, however, is finding an approximate solution to a boundary- and initial-value problem by assuming that the domain is divided into well-defined subdomains (elements) and that the unknown function of the *state variable* is defined approximately within each element. With these individually defined functions matching each other at the element nodes or at certain points at the interfaces, the unknown function is approximated over the entire domain.

There are, of course, many other approximate methods for the solution of boundary-value problems, such as finite-difference methods, weighted-residual methods, Rayleigh–Ritz methods, Galerkin methods, and more. The primary difference between the finite-element method and most other methods is that in the finite-element method the approximation is confined to relatively small subdomains. It is, in a way, the localized version of the Rayleigh–Ritz method. Instead of finding an admissible function satisfying the boundary conditions for the entire domain, which, particularly for irregular domains, is often difficult, in the finite-element methods the admissible functions are defined over element domains with simple geometry and pay no attention to complications at the boundaries. This is one of the reasons that the finite-element method has gained superiority over the other approximate methods.

Since the entire domain is divided into numerous elements and the function is approximated in terms of its values at certain points (nodes), it is inevitable that the evaluation of such a function will require solution of simultaneous equations. Because of this, the finite-element methods were not widely used until the middle of this century, at which time the computer became a powerful computational tool.

Figure 3.1 illustrates various components of the problem to be solved by using the finite-element method. The difficulty most often stems from the definition of the problem and the irregularities of the domain (geometrically as well as physically). If the conditions at the boundaries of the domain are well defined and simple (e.g., rectangular or circular plate under uniform loading in solid mechanics), one *need not* refer to a finite-element method to find the solution. Real-life problems, however, seldom fall into this category.

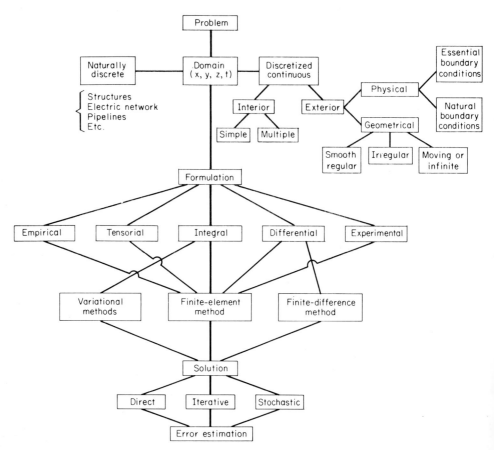

**FIG. 3.1**   Components of finite-element analysis.

## 3.2 BASIC STEPS IN THE FINITE-ELEMENT METHOD

Regardless of the physical nature of the problem, a standard finite-element method primarily involves the following steps. Each step requires a great deal of different planning and operations depending upon the physical nature and the mathematical modeling of the problem.

***Step 1. Definition of the Problem and Its Domain*** In finite-element methods, there are primarily three sources of approximation. The first one is the definition of the domain (physically and geometrically); the other two are the discretization and the solution algorithms. The approximations used in defining the physical characteristics of different regions of the domain are very much problem-oriented. The geometric definition of the domain, however, requires establishing *global coordinate* axes in reference to which the coordinates of certain points (nodes), which define the equations of the line and surfaces of elements, are to be described. This coordinate system need not be rectangular and cartesian (as is often done); some curvilinear systems may actually be better suited to the specific problem.

The domain can be *bounded* or *unbounded* (some portion extends to infinity). For the bounded region of the domain, the idealization is done by using finite elements and for the unbounded portion by using *infinite elements* or *boundary elements.* Quite often, the entire domain is also made up of subdomains, as in the case of interaction problems (see Chap. 5 in Part 2). The interface conditions between subdomains must also be defined prior to discretization.

***Step 2. Discretization of the Domain*** Since the problem is usually defined over a continuous domain, the governing equations, with the exception of the essential boundary conditions, are valid for the entirety of, as well as for any portion of, that domain. This allows idealization of the domain in the form of interconnected finite-sized domains (elements) of different size and shape (see Fig. 3.2). By doing this, certain approximations are introduced (e.g., cutting the corners, making curved lines straight and curved elements flat). Putting enough numbers of nodes between the elements (higher-order elements, etc.) also comes into the picture at this stage of the method. Here, one should be concerned with how well the *idealized* discrete domain represents the *actual* continuous domain. To a certain extent, it is

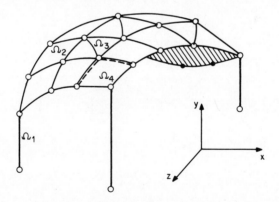

$\Omega_1$ = prismatic line element

$\Omega_2$ = quadrilateral curved element

$\Omega_3$ = curvilinear triangular element

$\Omega_4$ = quadrilateral linear element

**FIG. 3.2** Discretization of domain with various finite elements.

true that the smaller elements (finer mesh) produce better results. But it is also true that the finer mesh results in a larger number of equations to be solved and decreases the accuracy, thereby contrasting with the purpose of using the method. The question then arises: What is the most efficient element type, size, and pattern? A partial answer to this question is given in the literature under the key word *modeling*. *Adaptive processes* or *mesh refinements* and *automatic mesh generation* are also techniques relevant to the discretization of the domain. Chapter 2 in Part 4 is devoted to this issue.

In finite-element idealization of the domain, we shall, in general, make reference to the following elements: (a) *finite element* $\Omega_e$ and *master element* $\hat{\Omega}_e$. Finite elements are those which, when put together, result in the discrete version of the actual continuous domain. Finite elements are generally straight-sided (or -surfaced), particularly at the interior of the domain. They can be curved (as the higher-order elements) mainly at the boundaries or contain curved surfaces (as in shells). The curved elements, therefore, may contain geometric approximations in addition to physical approximations. Their geometric approximations are controlled by the number of nodes utilized at the exterior of the elements to define their shape. The physical approximations are controlled by the total number of nodes (exterior as well as interior) utilized in defining the *trial functions* (shape functions) for the state variable.

Master elements are those which are used in place of finite elements in order to facilitate computations in the element domain. The definition of shape functions and particularly of the integration shown in Eq. (3.15) becomes simpler in master elements. Figure 3.3 illustrates an actual finite element $\Omega_e$ and the corresponding master element $\hat{\Omega}_e$ with associated coordinate axes. In general, the master elements are straight lines, right triangles or prisms, squares, and cubes. They are defined in reference to normalized coordinate axes $(\xi, \eta, \zeta)$. The actual elements can be of any shape and size.

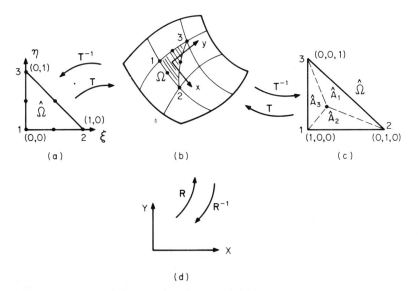

**FIG. 3.3**  Demonstration of coordinate axes for a triangular finite element. (*a*) Master element with natural coordinate axes. (*b*) Triangular element and local coordinate axes. (*c*) Master element with area coordinates. (*d*) Global axes.

***Step 3. Identification of State Variable(s)***   Until this step, no reference has been made to the physical nature of the problem. Whether it is a heat-transfer problem, fluid- or solid-mechanics problem, etc., comes into the picture at this stage. The mathematical description of steady-state physical phenomena, for instance, leads to an elliptic boundary-value problem in which the formula contains the *state variable* and the *flux*. These variables are related to each other by a *constitutive equation* representing a mathematical expression of a particular physical law. Table 3.1 presents various physical problems with associated state variables and constitutive equations [1].

Once the state variable and the flux have been identified, the formulation can take place containing either or both. The choice is usually dictated by the problem. Table 3.2, for instance, demonstrates this choice for problems in solid mechanics [2]. Various finite-element methods, in general, are the result of such choices. Comprehensive discussions of alternative formulations of finite element methods in mechanics may be found in [29–31].

***Step 4. Formulation of the Problem***   Very often a physical problem is formulated either via a set of *differential equations*

$$\mathbf{L}u = \mathbf{f} \tag{3.1}$$

with the boundary conditions or by an *integral equation* (a functional)

$$\pi = \int_\Omega G(x, y, z, u) \, d\Omega + \int_\Gamma g(x, y, z, u) \, d\Gamma \tag{3.2}$$

subject to stationary requirement (maximum, minimum, or saddle). While Eq. (3.1) is referred to as the *operational form* of the physical problem, Eq. (3.2) is referred to as the *variational form* of the same problem. Solution of either equation (inversion of $\mathbf{L}$ or minimization of $\pi$) yields the same results.

For a heat-conduction problem in 2D space, for instance, Eqs. (3.1) and (3.2) take the following forms:

$$\nabla^2 u - c = 0$$

$$\pi = \int_A \{\tfrac{1}{2}(u)^2 + cu\} \, dA$$

In general, if a functional [Eq. (3.2)] exists, the associated *Euler–Lagrange* differential equation (3.1) can be found. The reverse, however, is not necessarily true. For instance, the integrand involving several variables $u_i$ and the derivatives $u_i^{(n)}$

$$\pi = \int F(x, u_i, u_i^{(1)}, u_i^{(2)}, \ldots, u_i^{(n)}) \, dx \tag{3.3}$$

is the functional corresponding to the following differential equation [3]:

$$\sum_{j=0}^{n} (-1)^{n-j} \frac{d^{n-j}}{dx^{n-j}} \left( \frac{F}{u_i^{(n-j)}} \right) = 0 \tag{3.4}$$

Obtaining Eq. (3.4) from Eq. (3.3) is often referred to as the *Euler–Lagrange minimization*

**TABLE 3.1** Classification of Various Physical Problems

| Physical problem | Conservation principle | State variable | Flux | Material constants | Source | Constitutive equation |
|---|---|---|---|---|---|---|
| Deformation of an elastic body | Equilibrium of forces | Displacement or forces | Stress or strain | Young's modulus of elasticity, Poisson's constant | Body forces or surface | Hooke's law |
| Electric network | Equilibrium of currents | Voltage or ampere | Electric flux | Electric conductivity | External electric charge | Kirchhoff's law |
| Torsion | Conservation of potential energy | Stress function or warping function | Rate of twist | Shear | $-2 \times$ angle of twist | Hooke's law |
| Heat transfer | Conservation of energy | Temperature | Heat flux | Thermal conductivity | Internal or external heat | Fourier's law |
| Fluid flow | Conservation of momentum | Velocity | Shear stress | Viscosity | Body forces | Stokes's law |
| Flow through porous media | Conservation of mass | Hydraulic head | Flow rate | Permeability | Fluid sources | Darcy's law |
| Electrostatics | Conservation of electric flux | Electric potential | Electric flux | Permittivity | Charge | Coulomb's law |
| Magnetostatic | Conservation of magnetic potential | Magnetic potential | Magnetic flux | Magnetic permeability | Current | Maxwell's law |

**TABLE 3.2**   Various Finite-Element Methods in Solid Mechanics

| Model | Variational principle | Assumed inside each element | Along interelement boundary | Unknown in final equations |
|---|---|---|---|---|
| Compatible | Minimum potential energy | Continuous displacements | Displacement compatibility | Nodal displacements |
| Equilibrium | Minimum complementary energy | Continuous and equilibrating stresses | Equilibrium boundary tractions | Stress parameters Generalized nodal displacements |
| Hybrid 1 | Modified complementary energy | Continuous and equilibrating stresses | Assumed compatible displacements | Nodal displacements |
| Hybrid 2 | Modified potential energy | Continuous displacements | Assumed equilibrating boundary tractions | Displacement parameters and boundary forces |
| Hybrid 3 | Modified potential energy | Continuous displacements | Assumed boundary tractions for each element and assumed boundary displacements | Nodal displacements |
| Mixed | Reissner's principle | Continuous stresses and displacements | Different combinations of boundary displacements and tractions | Different combinations of boundary displacements and tractions |

*Source*: T. H. H. Pian and P. Tong, "Basis of Finite Element Methods for Solid Continua," *Intern. J. Numer. Meth. Eng.*, **1**(1):26, 1969.

*procedure.* While the differential equation may be approximated over a set of discrete points by using finite differences, the associated functional can be minimized over a set of discrete domains by using the finite-element method. A parallel treatment of the two classes of formulation can be found in a fine text by Strang and Fix on finite-element analysis [4], as well as in Ref. [5].

To demonstrate the variational and differential form of a problem, let us consider the following functional.

$$\pi = \int_0^l (\dot{u}^2 - u^2)\, dx$$

Minimization of this functional yields

$$\delta\pi = \int_0^l (2u\,\delta\dot{u} - 2u\,\delta u)\, dx = 0$$

Integrating by parts $\qquad \delta\pi = 2\dot{u}\,\delta u\big|_0^l - \displaystyle\int_0^l (2\ddot{u} + 2u)\,\delta u\,dx = 0$

results in the corresponding Euler–Lagrange equation

$$\ddot{u} + u = 0$$

and the associated boundary condition

$\qquad \dot{u}\big|_0^l = 0 \qquad$ *natural* boundary condition

$\qquad \delta u\big|_0^l = 0 \qquad$ *essential* boundary condition (also referred to as *kinematic* or *geometric* boundary condition)

This simple problem demonstrates that a boundary-value problem is, in general, subject to the following boundary conditions.

***Essential Boundary Condition*** The value of the state variable $u$ at the boundary is specified. This is often referred to as the *Dirichlet* problem

$$(u)_\Gamma = g_1$$

***Natural Boundary Condition*** Either the flux at the boundary is specified, as in the case of the *Neumann* problem

$$\left(\frac{\partial u}{\partial n}\right)_\Gamma = g_2$$

or the combination of the flux and the state variable is specified, as in the case of *mixed* boundary-value problems (*Cauchy* type)

$$g_3(u)_\Gamma + g_4\left(\frac{\partial u}{\partial \eta}\right)_\Gamma = g_5$$

where $g_i$ are prescribed functions of position on $\Gamma$. For problems in which the functional contains derivatives higher than the first order (e.g., the corresponding Euler–Lagrange differential equations are of the order of 4), the essential boundary conditions involve first derivatives as well as the state variable, and the natural boundary conditions involve the second derivatives.

To exemplify these boundary conditions, let us consider a steady-state heat flow in a homogeneous solid where the temperature $u(x, y, z)$ satisfies the Laplace equation $\nabla^2 u = 0$. Depending upon whether (1) the temperature, (2) the heat flux, or (3) both are prescribed throughout the boundary surface, we have the Dirichlet, Neumann, or mixed boundary-value problem, respectively. Another simple example is the cantilever arm in which the conditions at the fixed end are Dirichlet type ($u = \dot{u} = 0$) and at the free end are Neumann type ($\ddot{u} = c_1$, $\dddot{u} = c_2$). Because of this, in solid mechanics the Dirichlet and Neumann conditions are sometimes known as *displacement* and *force* (or stress) boundary conditions, respectively. It should be noted that the essential boundary conditions enter the problem during the definition of the physical space (step 1) and that they differ from problem to problem even within same class of problem. The natural boundary conditions, on the other hand, are the part of the functional which defines the problem. See step 10 for a detailed treatment of essential boundary conditions.

To begin, let us assume that the functional in Eq. (3.2) has been defined over a region $\Omega$. The true solution $u$ to this problem will make this functional stationary and will satisfy natural and essential boundary conditions. To find such a solution, we may choose an admissible approximate solution $\tilde{u}(x, y, z)$ and see whether it makes the functional stationary. If the functional represents energy, the stationary requirement represents the "least-energy principle." This principle states that among *all* approximate solutions, the one that minimizes the total energy is the *true* solution. The minimization of a functional in respect to a trial approximate function is not difficult. The difficulty stems from the fact that the trial function must be admissible by satisfying all conditions at the boundaries of the entire domain. Often, the domains of real-life engineering problems are irregular (complicated) in geometry, and therefore, to find an approximate trial function is difficult. If, on the other hand, the domain $\Omega$ is divided into simple geometric subdomains (elements) $\Omega_e$, the functional can be expressed as

$$\pi = \Sigma \pi_e \tag{3.5}$$

and the trial functions $\tilde{u}_e(x, y, z)$ for each element can be constructed without much difficulty. Thus

$$\tilde{u}_e(x, y, z) = N(x, y, z)\mathbf{u}_e \tag{3.6}$$

in which $N(x, y, z)$ is the approximate trial function (often referred to as the *shape function*) and $\mathbf{u}_e$ is the vector containing the unknown value of the function at certain points (nodes) of the element. Substituting $\tilde{u}_e(x, y, z)$ in $\pi_e$, which is in identical form to Eq. (3.2), and minimizing with respect to $\mathbf{u}_e$

$$\frac{\partial \pi_e}{\partial \mathbf{u}_e} = 0 \tag{3.7}$$

yields
$$\mathbf{k}_e \mathbf{u}_e + \mathbf{f}_e = 0 \tag{3.8}$$

which is known as the *element-matrix equation*. The assembly of this equation in accordance with the summation indicated in Eq. (3.5) results in

$$\mathbf{KU} + \mathbf{F} = 0 \tag{3.9}$$

which is the complete-matrix equation for the entire domain.

The finite-element method is used because it is easier to construct an admissible approximate function $\tilde{u}_e(x, y, z)$ for each type of geometrically well-defined element than for the entire domain. If, on the other hand, the entire domain has simple geometry (such as rectangular or circular) and the boundary conditions are well defined, other approximate methods or even analytical methods might produce faster and more accurate results. The researcher should investigate all alternatives at this stage of the problem. Although the finite-element method is often the easiest to use, it is not necessarily the best method for every physical problem.

**TABLE 3.3** Natural Coordinate System for Various Elements

| Natural coordinates $(L_1, L_2, L_3, L_4)$ | Mapping $\mathbf{T}$ and $\mathbf{T}^{-1}$ | Differentiation | Integration |
|---|---|---|---|
| **(a) Line element** $L_1 + L_2 = 1$ | $$\begin{bmatrix} 1 \\ x \end{bmatrix} = \begin{bmatrix} 1 & 1 \\ x_1 & x_2 \end{bmatrix}\begin{bmatrix} L_1 \\ L_2 \end{bmatrix}$$ $$\begin{bmatrix} L_1 \\ L_2 \end{bmatrix} = \frac{1}{l}\begin{bmatrix} x_2 & -1 \\ -x_1 & 1 \end{bmatrix}\begin{bmatrix} 1 \\ x \end{bmatrix}$$ | $$\frac{d}{dx} = \sum_{i=1}^{2} \frac{\partial L_i}{\partial x}\frac{\partial}{\partial L_i}$$ For shape functions see Table 4.1 in Part 2 | $$\int_p L_1^p L_2^q \, dl = \frac{p!\,q!}{p+q+1}\, l$$ |
| **(b) Triangular element** $L_1 + L_2 + L_3 = 1$   $L_i = \dfrac{A_i}{A}$ $A_{ij}$ = Area of $(ij0)$ triangle where 0 is the origin of the $x$ and $y$ axes | $$\begin{bmatrix} 1 \\ x \\ y \end{bmatrix} = \begin{bmatrix} 1 & 1 & 1 \\ x_1 & x_2 & x_3 \\ y_1 & y_2 & y_3 \end{bmatrix}\begin{bmatrix} L_1 \\ L_2 \\ L_3 \end{bmatrix}$$ $$\begin{bmatrix} L_1 \\ L_2 \\ L_3 \end{bmatrix} = \frac{1}{2A}\begin{bmatrix} 2A_{23} & b_1 & a_1 \\ 2A_{31} & b_2 & a_2 \\ 2A_{12} & b_3 & a_3 \end{bmatrix}\begin{bmatrix} 1 \\ x \\ y \end{bmatrix}$$ $a_1 = x_3 - x_2 \qquad b_1 = y_2 - y_3$ $a_2 = x_1 - x_3 \qquad b_2 = y_3 - y_1$ $a_3 = x_2 - x_1 \qquad b_3 = y_1 - y_2$ $$2A = \begin{vmatrix} 1 & x_1 & y_1 \\ 1 & x_2 & y_2 \\ 1 & x_3 & y_3 \end{vmatrix}$$ | $$\frac{\partial}{\partial x} = \sum_{i=1}^{3} \frac{\partial L_i}{\partial x}\frac{\partial}{\partial L_i}$$ $$= \sum_{i=1}^{3} \frac{b_i}{2A}\frac{\partial}{\partial L_i}$$ $$\frac{\partial}{\partial y} = \sum_{i=1}^{3} \frac{\partial L_i}{\partial y}\frac{\partial}{\partial L_i}$$ $$= \sum_{i=1}^{3} \frac{a_i}{2A}\frac{\partial}{\partial L_i}$$ For shape functions see Table 4.2 in Part 2 | $$\int_A L_1^p L_2^q L_3^r \, dA = \frac{p!\,q!\,r!}{p+q+r+2}\, 2A$$ Examples For $p = q = r = 1$, $$\int_A L_1 L_2 L_3 \, dA = \frac{1!}{5!}2A = \frac{A}{60}$$ For $p = 3$, $q = r = 0$, $$\int_A L_1^3 L_2^0 L_3^0 \, dA = \frac{3!}{5!}2A = \frac{A}{10}$$ |

## (c) Tetrahedral element

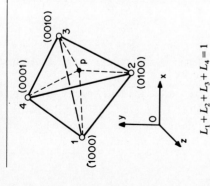

$$L_1 + L_2 + L_3 + L_4 = 1$$

$$L_i = \frac{V_i}{V}$$

$$6V = \begin{vmatrix} 1 & 1 & 1 & 1 \\ x_1 & x_2 & x_3 & x_4 \\ y_1 & y_2 & y_3 & y_4 \\ z_1 & z_2 & z_3 & z_4 \end{vmatrix}$$

---

$$\begin{bmatrix} 1 \\ x \\ y \\ z \end{bmatrix} = \begin{bmatrix} 1 & 1 & 1 & 1 \\ x_1 & x_2 & x_3 & x_4 \\ y_1 & y_2 & y_3 & y_4 \\ z_1 & z_2 & z_3 & z_4 \end{bmatrix} \begin{bmatrix} L_1 \\ L_2 \\ L_3 \\ L_4 \end{bmatrix}$$

$$\begin{bmatrix} L_1 \\ L_2 \\ L_3 \\ L_4 \end{bmatrix} = \frac{1}{6V} \begin{bmatrix} V_{234} & a_1 & b_1 & c_1 \\ V_{341} & a_2 & b_2 & c_2 \\ V_{412} & a_3 & b_3 & c_3 \\ V_{123} & a_4 & b_4 & c_4 \end{bmatrix} \begin{bmatrix} 1 \\ x \\ y \\ z \end{bmatrix}$$

$V_{ijk}$ = volume of tetrahedron with vertices $ijk0$

$a_i, b_i, c_i$ = projected areas of face $i$ onto $x$-, $y$-, and $z$-coordinate planes, respectively. For example,

$$a_2 = \begin{vmatrix} 1 & 1 & 1 \\ y_1 & y_3 & y_4 \\ z_1 & z_3 & z_4 \end{vmatrix}$$

$$c_3 = \begin{vmatrix} 1 & 1 & 1 \\ x_1 & x_2 & x_3 \\ z_1 & z_2 & z_3 \end{vmatrix}$$

---

$$\frac{\partial}{\partial x} = \sum_{i=1}^{4} \frac{\partial L_i}{\partial x}\frac{\partial}{\partial L_i} = \sum_{i=1}^{4} \frac{a_i}{6V}\frac{\partial}{\partial L_i}$$

$$\frac{\partial}{\partial y} = \sum_{i=1}^{4} \frac{\partial L_i}{\partial y}\frac{\partial}{\partial L_i} = \sum_{i=1}^{4} \frac{b_i}{6V}\frac{\partial}{\partial L_i}$$

$$\frac{\partial}{\partial z} = \sum_{i=1}^{4} \frac{\partial L_i}{\partial z}\frac{\partial}{\partial L_i} = \sum_{i=1}^{4} \frac{c_i}{6V}\frac{\partial}{\partial L_i}$$

---

$$\int_V L_1^p L_2^q L_3^r L_4^s \, dv = \frac{p!\,q!\,r!\,s!}{p+q+r+s+3}\, 6V$$

Examples

For $p = q = r = s = 1$,

$$\int_V L_1 L_2 L_3 L_4 \, dv = \frac{6V}{7!} = \frac{V}{840}$$

For $p = q = 0, r = s = 1$,

$$\int_V L_1^0 L_2^0 L_3 L_4 \, dv = \frac{1}{5!}6V = \frac{V}{20}$$

For shape function see Table 4.3 in Part 2

***Step 5. Establishing Coordinate Systems***    There are primarily two reasons for choosing special coordinate axes for the elements in addition to the global axes for the entire system. The first is the ease of constructing the trial functions for the elements and the second is the ease of integration within the elements. However, since the elements will be assembled in the global frame, this step introduces additional computations in the form of *coordinate transformations*. Although the entire finite-element analysis can be carried out directly in the global system, the benefit does not warrant the price paid for it. Since the coordinate transformation between any two coordinate systems is well defined, using the most suitable coordinate axes for each type of element is strongly recommended.

Depending upon the element shape, one usually chooses cartesian or curvilinear axes located within the element in reference to which the element matrix equation will be obtained. Other coordinate systems, known as *natural coordinates* such as *area* or *volume coordinates*, are often employed in finite-element analysis because the numerical integration [Eq. (3.15)] is much simpler in respect to these coordinates.

Figure 3.3 illustrates local-, global-, and master-element coordinate axes. Note that the dimensions of these coordinate systems are not usually the same. For instance, a one- or two-dimensional element may lie in a two- or three-dimensional space. Typical examples of this are trusses and flat-shell elements.

The transformation of entities from an element to a corresponding master element or vice versa involves mapping. One is the image of the other. Transformation from the element coordinate system to global coordinates, however, involves only rotations. If both coordinate systems, local $(x, y, z)$ and global $(X, Y, Z)$, are chosen so as to be orthogonal, the rotation matrix $\mathbf{R}$ is also orthogonal; that is, $\mathbf{R}^T = \mathbf{R}^{-1}$. This greatly facilitates the transformation between the two coordinate systems.

Once the coordinate axes are established, the element equations are ordinarily computed first in a master element $\hat{\Omega}_e$. They are then transformed into $\Omega_e$ and finally into the global system for assembly.

The following illustrates the sequence of mapping between the master element and the finite element. While matrix $\mathbf{T}$ maps the master-element equation into $\Omega_e$, matrix $\mathbf{R}$ transforms it into the global system.

$$\hat{\mathbf{p}}_e = \hat{\mathbf{k}}_e \hat{\mathbf{u}}_e \qquad \text{in } \hat{\Omega}_e$$

$$\mathbf{T} \downarrow \qquad\qquad\qquad\qquad \uparrow \mathbf{T}^{-1}$$

$$\mathbf{p}_e = \mathbf{k}_e \mathbf{u}_e \qquad \text{in } \Omega_e$$

$$\mathbf{R} \downarrow \qquad\qquad\qquad\qquad \uparrow \mathbf{R}^{-1} \text{ or } \mathbf{R}^T$$

$$\mathbf{p}_e = \mathbf{K}_e \mathbf{U}_e \qquad \text{in } \Omega$$

In some cases, however, the mapping of master-element computations can be done directly into the global coordinate systems.

Table 3.3 presents the natural coordinate systems, various master elements, and mapping. For detailed information on master-element shape functions, see Chap. 4 in Part 2.

After the solution of simultaneous equations, the *inverse* transformation takes place in order to compute the physical entities (such as stresses and strains in the case of solid-mechanics problems) in the element domain.

***Step 6. Constructing Approximate Functions for the Elements***   Once the state vari-
able(s) and the local coordinate system have been chosen, the function can be approximated
in numerous ways. The *approximation theory* in mathematics is one of the major disciplines.
We mention here only the approximation in terms of algebraic functions. The reader is
reminded that there are two entities that need to be approximated. The first is *physical* (the
state variable) and the second is *geometrical* (the shape of the element). If the element is
actually made of straight lines or planes, the coordinates of primary nodes (those at the
extremes of the elements) will define the element shape accurately. In this case, the geometric
approximation does not enter into the picture. Because of this, discretization of the entire
domain is most often made by straight-line (linear) elements. For some problems, however,
linear elements (i.e., flat elements in shells) may introduce unacceptable errors, and discretization must be done by using isoparametric elements (see Fig. 3.4).

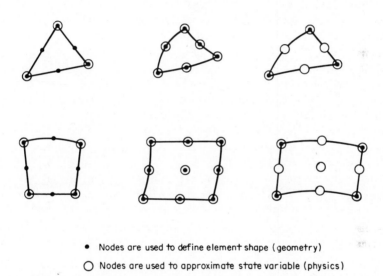

● Nodes are used to define element shape (geometry)

○ Nodes are used to approximate state variable (physics)

**FIG. 3.4**   Examples of subparametric, isoparametric, and superparametric
elements.

   A similar argument is, of course, valid for the approximation of the state variable. It can
be approximated in the form of a linear function or a higher-order function (i.e., quadratic,
cubic, etc.). The analyst then must decide whether to approximate *physics* (state variable)
and *geometry* (element shape) equally or to give preference to one or the other in various
regions of the domain. This leads to three different categories of elements with $m$ and $n$
representing the degree of approximation for element shape and for the state variable,
respectively. Figure 3.4 illustrates examples for (*a*) subparametric ($m < n$), (*b*) isoparametric
($m = n$), and (*c*) superparametric ($m > n$) elements. Approximation of any function can be
made in the form of a family of *transcendental* or *algebraic* equations. Figures 3.5 to 3.7
illustrate the families of trial functions in the form of algebraic polynomials. These triangular

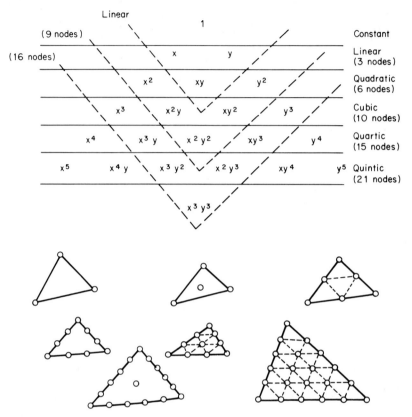

**FIG. 3.5** Pascal's triangle to generate various trial functions and corresponding elements.

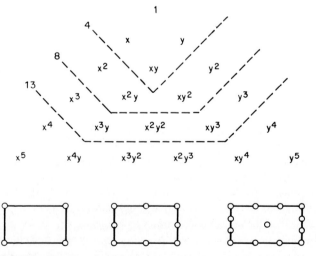

**FIG. 3.6** Pascal's triangle to generate various trial functions and corresponding rectangular elements.

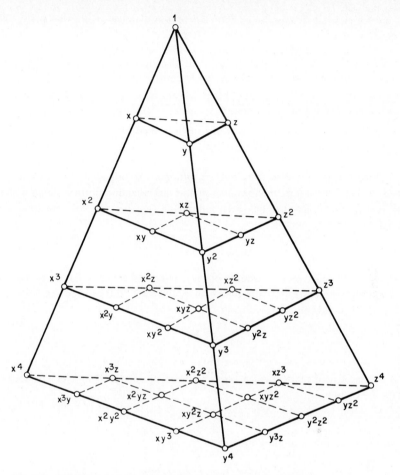

**FIG. 3.7**  Families of trial functions for various tetrahedral elements.

arrays (sometimes referred to as the *Pascal triangles*) can be constructed as a *dyadic* product of polynomials of the desired degree.

$$
\begin{bmatrix} 1 \\ x \\ x^2 \\ x^3 \\ \vdots \end{bmatrix}
\begin{bmatrix} 1 & y & y^2 & y^3 & \cdots \end{bmatrix} =
\begin{bmatrix}
1 & y & y^2 & y^3 & \cdots \\
x & xy & xy^2 & xy^3 & \cdots \\
x^2 & x^2y & x^2y^2 & x^2y^3 & \cdots \\
x^3 & x^3y & x^3y^2 & x^3y^3 & \cdots \\
\vdots & & & &
\end{bmatrix}
$$

At this point one is tempted to say that the finite-element solution may converge to the exact solution either by increasing the degrees of polynomials (these often correspond to the number of nodes in the element) or by decreasing the element size. Each has advantages and disadvantages. Since, however, the finite-element method is a procedure for constructing the solution for the entire domain from local approximations, the convergence can be attained if the functional itself converges as the size of the element diminishes. It is therefore recommended that:

1. The local functions be so constructed that their discontinuities (in terms of their derivatives as well) should not make the functional itself undefined over the entire domain. In other words, not only the local functions but the derivatives of one order less than that occurring in the functional must be continuous.

2. The integrand of the functional must be single-valued and represent a constant as the element size approaches zero.

***Step 7. Obtain Element Matrices and Equations***  At this stage, we assume that the modeling of the problem (i.e., the formulation and discretization of the domain with desired element shapes and functions) has been completed. Let the approximate function for a steady-state problem be written as

$$\tilde{u}_e(x, y, z) = \phi(x, y, z)\mathbf{c} \tag{3.10}$$

where $\phi(x, y, z)$ is a row vector made up of the polynomial terms of the desired degree and vector $\mathbf{c}$ contains the corresponding unknown coefficients. Substituting the coordinates of element nodes into this equation yields

$$\mathbf{c} = \mathbf{b}\mathbf{u}_e \tag{3.11}$$

in which $\mathbf{u}_e$ is the vector representing the unknown values of $u(x, y, z)$ at the element nodes and $\mathbf{b}$ is the associated matrix which contains the coordinates of the element nodes. From Eq. (3.10) we obtain

$$\tilde{u}_e(x, y, z) = \phi(x, y, z)\mathbf{b}\mathbf{u}_e \tag{3.12}$$

Note that this equation is often written as

$$\tilde{u}_e(x, y, z) = \mathbf{N}(x, y, z)\mathbf{u}_e \tag{3.13}$$

where $\mathbf{N}(x, y, z)$ is referred to as the *shape function*. It is called the shape function because it contains not only the approximation made for the state variable but also the coordinates of the element nodes which define the shape of the element. The shape function can be written as

$$\mathbf{N}(x, y, z) = [N_1 \quad N_2 \quad \cdots \quad N_n]$$

where $n$ represents the number of nodes of the element and $N_i$ is the shape function corresponding to node $i$. Substitution of Eq. (3.13) into Eq. (3.2) written for $\mathbf{\Omega}_e$, where the first term is often a quadratic form of $u$ and its derivatives, yields

$$\pi_e = \int_{\Omega_e} \mathbf{u}_e^T \mathbf{B}^T \mathbf{D} \mathbf{B} \mathbf{u}_e \, d\Omega_e + \int_{\Gamma} \mathbf{u}_e^T \mathbf{N}^T \mathbf{p} \, d\Gamma \tag{3.14}$$

Matrix $\mathbf{B}$ contains the shape function and its derivatives as well as the constitutive relationships of the problem. Matrix $\mathbf{D}$ represents the physical parameters of the domain, and $\mathbf{p}$ represents disturbances (traction forces) at the boundaries. In general, the minimization of this equation with respect to $\mathbf{u}_e$ yields

$$\int_{\Omega_e} \mathbf{B}^T \mathbf{DB} \, d\Omega \mathbf{u}_e + \int_{\Gamma} \mathbf{N}^T \mathbf{p} \, d\Gamma = 0 \qquad (3.15)$$

Carrying out the integrations (often numerically) results in the following matrix equation:

$$\mathbf{k}_e \mathbf{u}_e + \mathbf{p}_e = 0 \qquad (3.16)$$

In the case of solid-mechanics problems, one may refer to Castigliano's two theorems to obtain the above equation [6]. These theorems are referred to by Castigliano [7] as parts II and I, respectively,

$$\frac{\partial w_e}{\partial u_{iq}} = p^{iq} \qquad \text{and} \qquad \frac{\partial w}{\partial p^{iq}} = u_{iq}$$

in which $w_e$ represents the strain energy stored in an element, $i$ represents the node of the element, and $q$ represents the direction of the coordinate axes. Since the strain energy stored in an element is equal to the external work done by the forces at the same element, then

$$w_e = \tfrac{1}{2} p^{iq} u_{iq} \qquad \text{(repeated indices represent summation)}$$

According to Castigliano's first theorem, then

$$p^{jr} = \frac{1}{2} \frac{\partial (p^{iq} u_{iq})}{\partial u_{jr}} = \frac{1}{2} \frac{\partial p^{iq}}{\partial u_{jr}} u_{iq} + \frac{1}{2} p^{iq} \frac{\partial u_{iq}}{\partial u_{jr}}$$

Since $\qquad\qquad \dfrac{\partial u_{iq}}{\partial u_{jr}} = 1 \qquad$ for $i, q = j, r$; zero otherwise

the above equation reduces to

$$p^{iq} = \frac{\partial p^{iq}}{\partial u_{jr}} u_{jr} \qquad (3.17)$$

in which $\qquad\qquad \dfrac{\partial p^{iq}}{\partial u_{jr}} = k^{iqjr}$

represents the *stiffness tensor* of the element. Equation (3.17), which is the tensorial form of Eq. (3.16), indicates that the stiffness tensor can be obtained analytically, as is often done, but can also be obtained *experimentally* for elements with very irregular geometry and with many physical properties. The latter is of increasing interest in recent years. One can see that the above procedure can be repeated by using Castigliano's second theorem, in which case Eq. (3.17) takes the form

$$u_{jr} = \frac{\partial u_{jr}}{\partial p^{iq}} p^{iq} \qquad (3.18)$$

where $\qquad\qquad \dfrac{\partial u_{jr}}{\partial p^{iq}} = d^{jriq}$

represents the *flexibility* tensor of the element. Both tensors (stiffness and flexibility) can also be written in terms of strain energy as

$$k^{iqjr} = \frac{\partial^2 w}{\partial u_{iq}\,\partial u_{jr}}$$

$$d^{jriq} = \frac{\partial^2 w}{\partial p^{jr}\,\partial p^{iq}}$$

Further examination of Eqs. (3.17) and (3.18) reveals many other properties of entities which might otherwise be overlooked.

Regardless of the methods employed, one and sometimes both these equations must be evaluated for all elements and assembled according to the topological configurations of the elements.

Table 3.4 demonstrates the derivation of the element-matrix equation for a functional in one-dimensional space. The steps are presented side by side in local and global coordinates.

**TABLE 3.4** Computation of Element Matrices in Global and Local Coordinate Axes for a Problem in 1D Space

Functional

$$\pi = \int_0^1 (\dot{y}^2 - y^2 - 2xy)\,dx$$

| In global coordinates | In local coordinates |
|---|---|
| **Discretization** | |
| $\pi_e = \int_{x_i}^{x_{i+1}} (\dot{y}^2 - y^2 - 2xy)\,dx$ <br> $\pi = \Sigma \pi_e$ | $\pi_e = \int_0^h \{\dot{y}^2 - y^2 - 2(x_i + x)y\}\,dx$ <br> $\pi = \Sigma \pi_e$ |
| **Approximate function (linear)** | |
| $\tilde{y}_e = [1 \quad x]\mathbf{c}$ <br> $\begin{bmatrix} y_i \\ y_{i+1} \end{bmatrix} = \begin{bmatrix} 1 & x_i \\ 1 & x_{i+1} \end{bmatrix}\begin{bmatrix} c_1 \\ c_2 \end{bmatrix}$ <br> $\mathbf{c} = \frac{1}{x_{i+1}-x_i}\begin{bmatrix} x_{i+1} & -x_i \\ -1 & 1 \end{bmatrix}\mathbf{y}_e$ <br> $\mathbf{c} = \mathbf{b}\mathbf{y}_e$ | $\tilde{y}_e = [1 \quad x]\mathbf{c}$ <br> $\begin{bmatrix} y_i \\ y_{i+1} \end{bmatrix} = \begin{bmatrix} 1 & 0 \\ 1 & h \end{bmatrix}\begin{bmatrix} c_1 \\ c_2 \end{bmatrix}$ <br> $\mathbf{c} = \frac{1}{h}\begin{bmatrix} 1 & 0 \\ -1 & 1 \end{bmatrix}\mathbf{y}_e$ <br> $\mathbf{c} = \mathbf{b}\mathbf{y}_e$ |
| **Shape function** | |
| $\tilde{y}_e = [1 \quad x]\mathbf{b}\mathbf{y}_e$ <br> $\tilde{y}_e = [N_1 \quad N_2]\mathbf{y}_e$ <br> $\tilde{y}_e = \mathbf{N}_e\mathbf{y}_e$ | $\tilde{y}_e = [1 \quad x]\mathbf{b}\mathbf{y}_e$ <br> $\tilde{y}_e = [N_1 \quad N_2]\mathbf{y}_e$ <br> $\tilde{y}_e = \mathbf{N}_e\mathbf{y}_e$ |

**TABLE 3.4**—*cont.*

---

### Derivatives

$$\tilde{y}_e = \frac{d\mathbf{N}_e}{dx}\mathbf{y}_e$$

$$\tilde{y}_e = \frac{d\mathbf{N}_e}{dx}\mathbf{y}_e$$

---

### Functional over element domain

$$\pi_e = \int_{x_i}^{x_{i+1}}\left(\mathbf{y}_e^T\frac{d\mathbf{N}_e^T}{dx}\frac{d\mathbf{N}_e}{dx}\mathbf{y}_e\right.$$

$$\left. -\mathbf{y}_e^T\mathbf{N}_e^T\mathbf{N}_e\mathbf{y}_e - 2xy_e^T\mathbf{N}_e^T\right)dx$$

$$\pi_e = \int_{0}^{h}\left\{\mathbf{y}_e^T\frac{d\mathbf{N}_e^T}{dx}\frac{d\mathbf{N}_e}{dx}\mathbf{y}_e\right.$$

$$\left. -\mathbf{y}_e^T\mathbf{N}_e^T\mathbf{N}_e\mathbf{y}_e - 2(x_i+x)\mathbf{y}_e^T\mathbf{N}_e^T\right\}dx$$

---

### Integration and minimization

$$\frac{\partial \pi_e}{\partial \mathbf{y}_e} = 0$$

$$\frac{\partial \pi_e}{\partial \mathbf{y}_e} = 0$$

---

### Element equation

Lengthy expressions

$$\begin{bmatrix} \dfrac{1}{h} & -\dfrac{h}{3} \\[2mm] -\dfrac{1}{h} & -\dfrac{h}{6} \end{bmatrix}\begin{bmatrix} -\dfrac{1}{h} & \dfrac{h}{6} \\[2mm] \dfrac{1}{h} & -\dfrac{h}{3} \end{bmatrix}\begin{bmatrix} y_i \\[2mm] y_{i+1} \end{bmatrix} = \frac{h}{2}\begin{bmatrix} \dfrac{h}{3}+x_i \\[2mm] \dfrac{2h}{3}+x_i \end{bmatrix}$$

$$\mathbf{K}_e\mathbf{Y}_e = \mathbf{P}_e$$

$$\mathbf{k}_e\mathbf{y}_e = \mathbf{p}_e$$

---

### Corresponding Euler–Lagrange differential equation

$$F = \dot{y}^2 - y^2 - 2xy$$

$$\frac{\partial F}{\partial y} - \frac{\partial}{\partial x}\left(\frac{\partial F}{\partial \dot{y}}\right) = 0$$

$$\ddot{y} + \dot{y} + x = 0$$

---

Although not evident in Table 3.4, the integrations given by Eq. (3.15) become very cumbersome for higher-order elements if they are done directly in the global axes. As mentioned earlier, in order to overcome this difficulty a master element $\hat{\Omega}_e$ and a special coordinate system are often employed. However, since the geometry of element $\Omega_e$ is defined in reference to the global frame, the coordinate transformations and inverse transformations must be done for all elements.

***Step 8. Coordinate Transformations***    Coordinate transformations of physical entities such as vectors and matrices follow well-defined rules. They are often done in the form of a *jacobian matrix*. For instance, let us assume that there are two different coordinate systems, for example, $x$, $y$, $z$ located in the element domain and $\xi$, $\eta$, $\zeta$ located in the master element.

Let the relationship between these coordinate systems be continuous and differentiable.

$$x = x(\xi, \eta, \zeta)$$

**T:**     $$y = y(\xi, \eta, \zeta) \tag{3.19}$$

$$z = z(\xi, \eta, \zeta)$$

This relationship maps a point or a sequence of points from $\hat{\Omega}$ into $\Omega_e$. An infinitesimal line segment (or area and volume) in one coordinate system can thus be transformed into another by following the usual rules of differentiation.

$$
\begin{bmatrix} dx \\ dy \\ dz \end{bmatrix} =
\begin{bmatrix}
\dfrac{\partial x}{\partial \xi} & \dfrac{\partial x}{\partial \eta} & \dfrac{\partial x}{\partial \zeta} \\[2mm]
 & \dfrac{\partial y}{\partial \eta} & \dfrac{\partial y}{\partial \zeta} \\[2mm]
\text{Symm.} & & \dfrac{\partial z}{\partial \zeta}
\end{bmatrix}
\begin{bmatrix} d\xi \\ d\eta \\ d\zeta \end{bmatrix}
\tag{3.20}
$$

The matrix on the right-hand side of this equation is known as a *jacobian* and is often written as

$$\mathbf{J} = J\frac{x, y, z}{\xi, \eta, \zeta}$$

Equation (3.20) transforms the line segments in $\hat{\Omega}_e$ into line segments in $\Omega_e$. The inverse transformation which defines mapping of element $\Omega_e$ back into the master element $\hat{\Omega}_e$ follows a similar rule. This we refer to as the *inverse transformation*

$$
\begin{bmatrix} d\xi \\ d\eta \\ d\zeta \end{bmatrix} = \mathbf{J}^{-1}
\begin{bmatrix} dx \\ dy \\ dz \end{bmatrix}
\tag{3.21}
$$

where $\mathbf{J}^{-1}$ is the inverse matrix of the jacobian in Eq. (3.20). This implies that the condition of $|J| > 0$ must be satisfied for every point in both domains.

In step 7 we pointed out that to obtain an element-matrix equation requires integration of shape functions over the element domain. This, in turn, necessitates the change of integration limits from element to element and becomes very cumbersome if element geometry contains curved lines and surfaces. Therefore, element calculations are usually done in $\hat{\Omega}_e$ and then transformed into $\Omega_e$.

In step 1 we stated that in finite-element methods there are primarily two approximations to be made: one for the state variable and one for the shape of the element. Both approximations make use of the coordinates of certain element nodes in $\Omega$. Whether both approximations are of the same degree or not (as in the case of iso-, sub-, and superparametric elements), an approximation for any function $\phi(\xi, \eta, \zeta)$ can be constructed in terms of the shape function $\hat{N}(\xi, \eta, \zeta)$ and the nodal values of $\phi$:

$$\hat{\phi}(\xi, \eta, \zeta) = \phi_j N_j(\xi, \eta, \zeta) \qquad j = 1, 2, \ldots, n \tag{3.22}$$

where $\phi_j = \phi(\xi_j, \eta_j, \zeta_j)$ and $n$ is the number of nodes defined in the master element. Since the computations are usually done on $\hat{\Omega}_e$, the shape functions will be defined over the master element. Consequently, mapping of $\hat{\Omega}_e$ into $\Omega_e$ will be done as

$$x_i = x_{ij}\hat{N}_j(\xi, \eta, \zeta) \qquad i = 1, 2, 3$$
$$j = 1, 2, \ldots, n \tag{3.23}$$

where $x_{ij}$ are the coordinates $(x, y, z)$ of node $j$ in $\Omega_e$. This equation is an explicit version of Eq. (3.19) which maps $\hat{\Omega}_e$ into $\Omega_e$. Similarly, the transformation of shape functions and their derivatives can be written as

$$N(x, y, z) = \hat{N}_j(\xi(x, y, z), \eta(x, y, z), \zeta(x, y, z))$$

$$\frac{\partial N_j}{\partial x_i} = \frac{\partial \hat{N}_j}{\partial \xi}\frac{\partial \xi}{\partial x_i} + \frac{\partial \hat{N}_j}{\partial \eta}\frac{\partial \eta}{\partial x_i} + \frac{\partial \hat{N}_j}{\partial \zeta}\frac{\partial \zeta}{\partial x_i} \qquad i = 1, 2, 3 \tag{3.24}$$

The integration of a scalar-valued function $\phi(x, y, z)$ in $\Omega_e$ can be written as

$$\int_{\Omega_e} \phi(x, y, z)\, \partial\Omega_e = \int_{\hat{\Omega}_e} \hat{\phi}(\xi, \eta, \zeta)|J(\xi, \eta, \zeta)|\, \partial\hat{\Omega}_e \tag{3.25}$$

in which

$$\hat{\phi}(\xi, \eta, \zeta) = \phi(x_j\hat{N}_j(\xi, \eta, \zeta), y_j\hat{N}_j(\xi, \eta, \zeta), z_j\hat{N}_j(\xi, \eta, \zeta)) \qquad j = 1, 2, \ldots, n$$

and $|J(\xi, \eta, \zeta)|$ is the determinant of the jacobian matrix.

An excellent treatment of coordinate transformations (mapping) in this respect can be found in Ref. [1].

As a result of the transformation rules, the integrations over $\Omega_e$ [similar to the integration in Eq. (3.15)] can be replaced by Eq. (3.25) over $\hat{\Omega}_e$. These transformation rules, furthermore, can be extended to all coordinate systems, including *area* and *volume* coordinates, which are widely utilized in finite-element analysis.

**Step 9. Assembly of Element Equations** The assembly of element-matrix equations $(p_e = k_e u_e)$ is done according to the topological configuration of the elements after this equation is transformed into the global system. The assembly is done through the nodes at the interfaces which are common to the adjacent elements. At these nodes the continuities are established in respect to the state variable and possibly in respect to its derivatives. Sometimes this assembly is done through certain nodes only, referred to as the *primary nodes* (e.g., corner nodes), instead of to all the nodes at the interfaces. This reduces the overall size of the assembled matrix. The nodes that are not used in the assembly, the so-called *secondary nodes*, are used together with the primary nodes to increase the degree of approximation at the element level. Assume that the complete element matrix is partitioned as follows:

$$\begin{bmatrix} P_I \\ P_{II} \end{bmatrix} = \begin{bmatrix} K_{I,I} & K_{I,II} \\ K_{II,I} & K_{II,II} \end{bmatrix}\begin{bmatrix} U_I \\ U_{II} \end{bmatrix} \tag{3.26}$$

in which subscripts I and II identify the portions of the equations corresponding to primary and secondary nodes, respectively. This equation can be brought to the following form:

$$\mathbf{P}_\mathrm{I} - \mathbf{K}_\mathrm{I,II}\mathbf{K}_\mathrm{II,II}^{-1}\mathbf{P}_\mathrm{II} = [\mathbf{K}_\mathrm{I,I} \quad -\mathbf{K}_\mathrm{I,II}\mathbf{K}_\mathrm{II,II}^{-1}\mathbf{K}_\mathrm{II,I}]\mathbf{U}_\mathrm{I} \tag{3.27}$$

which, in short, can be written as $\qquad \mathbf{P}_e = \mathbf{K}_e\mathbf{U}_e \qquad\qquad\qquad$ (3.28)

This is the final equation to be assembled. It contains the unknown value of the function at the primary nodes only. To illustrate the assembly, let us assume that domain $\Omega$ in 2D space consists of three elements (rectangular, triangular, and line elements), as shown in Fig. 3.8.

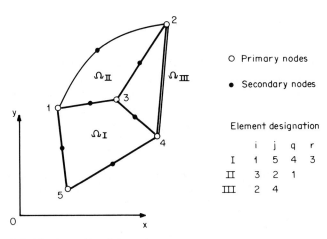

**FIG. 3.8**   Assembly of three elements.

The element submatrices are identified as the *dyadic* product of element designations using primary nodes ($i, j, q, r$ are the numbers assigned to nodes)

$$\begin{bmatrix} i \\ j \\ q \\ r \end{bmatrix}[i \quad j \quad q \quad r] = \begin{bmatrix} ii & ij & iq & ir \\ & jj & jq & jr \\ & & qq & qr \\ \text{Symm.} & & & rr \end{bmatrix}$$

With this designation, the assembled version of the complete matrix of the configuration shown in Fig. 3.8 will be

$$\mathbf{K} = \begin{bmatrix} \mathbf{K}_{ii}^\mathrm{I} + \mathbf{K}_{qq}^\mathrm{II} & \mathbf{K}_{qj}^\mathrm{I} & \mathbf{K}_{ir}^\mathrm{I} + \mathbf{K}_{qi}^\mathrm{II} & \mathbf{K}_{iq}^\mathrm{I} & \mathbf{K}_{ij}^\mathrm{I} \\ & \mathbf{K}_{jj}^\mathrm{II} + \mathbf{K}_{ii}^\mathrm{III} & \mathbf{K}_{ji}^\mathrm{II} & \mathbf{K}_{ij}^\mathrm{III} & 0 \\ & & \mathbf{K}_{rr}^\mathrm{I} + \mathbf{K}_{ii}^\mathrm{II} & \mathbf{K}_{rq}^\mathrm{I} & \mathbf{K}_{rj}^\mathrm{I} \\ & & & \mathbf{K}_{qq}^\mathrm{I} + \mathbf{K}_{jj}^\mathrm{III} & \mathbf{K}_{qj}^\mathrm{I} \\ \text{Symm.} & & & & \mathbf{K}_{jj}^\mathrm{I} \end{bmatrix} \tag{3.29}$$

The submatrices in $\mathbf{K}$ are the element submatrices corresponding to particular primary nodes of $\mathbf{K}_e$ in Eq. (3.28), which are already a condensed version of the overall element matrix in accordance with Eq. (3.27). The assembly for $\mathbf{P}_e$, the left-hand side of Eq. (3.28), follows a similar procedure [i.e., integration of the second term in Eq. (3.15), transformation into the global coordinate system, and equilibrium at the nodes].

The *complete equation* for the discrete domain shown in Fig. 3.8, for example, becomes

$$
\begin{bmatrix} \mathbf{P}_1 \\ \vdots \\ \mathbf{P}_5 \end{bmatrix} = \begin{bmatrix} \mathbf{K}_{11} & \cdots & \mathbf{K}_{15} \\ & \ddots & \vdots \\ \text{Symm.} & & \mathbf{K}_{55} \end{bmatrix} \begin{bmatrix} \mathbf{U}_1 \\ \vdots \\ \mathbf{U}_5 \end{bmatrix}
\tag{3.30}
$$

***Step 10. Introduction of Boundary Conditions***   At this stage, the essential boundary conditions are introduced. As a result of this, the complete set of equations, such as Eq. (3.30), will be reduced or condensed to its final form. In better algorithms, the essential boundary conditions are introduced in step 9 (i.e., during the assembly), which results in a reduction of machine time and memory, but it requires skillful programming.

The essential boundary conditions are the prescribed values of the function (or its first derivatives, as in the case of fourth-order differential equations) at the boundaries. They are often prescribed as zero or constant (equivalent to fixity or to specified displacements at the nodes, respectively) or as a function of the left-hand-side vector (elastic support in solid-mechanics problems). Let the complete set of equations be partitioned to reflect these conditions at the boundaries:

$$
\begin{bmatrix} \mathbf{P}_{\mathrm{I}} \\ \mathbf{P}_{\mathrm{II}} \\ \mathbf{P}_{\mathrm{III}} \end{bmatrix} = \begin{bmatrix} \mathbf{K}_{\mathrm{I,I}} & \mathbf{K}_{\mathrm{I,II}} & \mathbf{K}_{\mathrm{I,III}} \\ \mathbf{K}_{\mathrm{II,I}} & \mathbf{K}_{\mathrm{II,II}} & \mathbf{K}_{\mathrm{II,III}} \\ \mathbf{K}_{\mathrm{III,I}} & \mathbf{K}_{\mathrm{III,II}} & \mathbf{K}_{\mathrm{III,III}} \end{bmatrix} \begin{bmatrix} \mathbf{U}_{\mathrm{I}} \\ \mathbf{U}_{\mathrm{II}} = \pmb{\mathscr{k}}\mathbf{P}_{\mathrm{II}} \\ \mathbf{U}_{\mathrm{III}} = \mathbf{0} \end{bmatrix}
\tag{3.31}
$$

where $\pmb{\mathscr{k}}$ can be linear or nonlinear, which in solid-mechanics problems represents a matrix of spring constants. Solution of these three simultaneous equations (in terms of submatrices) yields

$$
\mathbf{P}_{\mathrm{I}} = \{\mathbf{K}_{\mathrm{I,I}} + \mathbf{K}_{\mathrm{I,II}}\pmb{\mathscr{k}}[\mathbf{I} - \mathbf{K}_{\mathrm{II,II}}\pmb{\mathscr{k}}]^{-1}\mathbf{k}_{\mathrm{II,I}}\}\mathbf{U}_{\mathrm{I}}
\tag{3.32}
$$

In short,
$$
\mathbf{P}_{\mathrm{I}} = \bar{\mathbf{K}}_{\mathrm{I,I}}\mathbf{U}_K
\tag{3.33}
$$

where $\bar{\mathbf{K}}_{\mathrm{I,I}}$ is the final matrix and this equation is the final equation to be solved. Notice that the introduction of zero boundary conditions (i.e., $\mathbf{U}_{\mathrm{III}} = \mathbf{0}$) is equivalent to erasing the corresponding rows and columns from the complete set, which certainly reduces the number of equations to be solved. If zero boundary conditions are prescribed in reference to a coordinate system other than the global (as in the case of inclined supports in solid mechanics), a rotational transformation is needed between the two coordinate systems. For instance, let the complete set be partitioned as

$$
\begin{bmatrix} \mathbf{P}_{\mathrm{I}} \\ \mathbf{P}_{\mathrm{II}} \end{bmatrix} = \begin{bmatrix} \mathbf{K}_{\mathrm{I,I}} & \mathbf{K}_{\mathrm{I,II}} \\ \mathbf{K}_{\mathrm{II,I}} & \mathbf{K}_{\mathrm{II,II}} \end{bmatrix} \begin{bmatrix} \mathbf{U}_{\mathrm{I}} \\ \mathbf{U}_{\mathrm{II}} \end{bmatrix}
$$

where $\mathbf{U}_{\mathrm{II}}$ contains zero boundary conditions in directions *other* than global (say, a primed coordinate system). Let **R** represent the rotational matrix which rotates a vector from global to primed coordinate axes. If both coordinate systems are cartesian, the elements of **R** represent the directional cosines of the primed coordinate axes with respect to the global axes. The above equation can then be written

$$\begin{bmatrix} \mathbf{P}_I \\ \mathbf{P}'_{II} \end{bmatrix} = \begin{bmatrix} \mathbf{K}_{I,I} & \mathbf{K}_{I,II}\mathbf{R} \\ \mathbf{R}^T\mathbf{K}_{II,I} & \mathbf{R}^T\mathbf{K}_{II,II}\mathbf{R} \end{bmatrix} \begin{bmatrix} \mathbf{U}_I \\ \mathbf{U}'_{II} \end{bmatrix}$$

because $\mathbf{P}_{II} = \mathbf{R}^T\mathbf{P}_{II}$ and $\mathbf{U}_{II} = \mathbf{R}^T\mathbf{U}_{II}$.

The introduction of zero boundary conditions (certain components of **U'**) now follows the same procedure (i.e., discarding corresponding rows and columns). Explicit treatment of essential boundary conditions can be found in Ref. [8].

***Step 11. Solution of the Final Set of Simultaneous Equations***   Until this step, we have made no reference to whether the problem is linear or nonlinear, or to whether it is an eigenvalue problem or not. Regardless of the nature of the problem, the finite-element methods eventually yield the solution of a set of simultaneous equations. The solution procedure for simultaneous equations can, in general, be categorized into three parts: (1) *direct*, (2) *iterative*, and (3) *stochastic*. The direct and iterative methods are presented in detail in Chap. 1 of Part 4. Stochastic-solution procedures, on the other hand, have thus far received very little attention because the finite-element methods are generally applied to *deterministic* rather than to *probabilistic* problems.

The direct-solution techniques (originally proposed by Gauss a century ago) consist of a set of systematic steps and are used a good deal in finite-element solutions. The accuracy of results is largely determined by the condition of equations (*well* or *ill*), the number of equations, and the computer (double precision, single precision, etc.). The symmetry and banded properties of equations can be well taken care of with these methods. The *Gauss elimination* and *Cholesky's factorization* (**LU** *decomposition*) are the most commonly used direct procedures. These methods are well suited to a small or moderate number of equations.

When systems are of a very large order, iterative procedures such as *Gauss–Seidel* or *Jacobi iterations* are more suited. Iterative methods are, in general, *self-correcting*, and the accuracy of the solution depends upon the number of iterations. Convergence is not always assured, but when convergence does occur, the sequence of equations plays an important role. The solution time is considerably less than that required by a direct procedure. On the other hand, the iterative methods are not suited for sets with multiple right-hand sides (e.g., multiple loading conditions in solid-mechanics problems).

When the set of equations to be solved is nonlinear, the *Newton–Raphson iteration* and its *modified* version appear to be the most commonly used methods. In recent years, the *quasi-Newton* method [9] has also received considerable attention in nonlinear finite-element analysis. A detailed presentation of the solution of simultaneous equations (linear and nonlinear) by using various procedures and with corresponding algorithms is presented in Secs. 1.1 and 1.2 of Part 4.

***Step 12. Interpretation of the Results***   The previous step resulted in the approximate values of the state variable at discrete points (nodes) of the domain. Normally these values are interpreted and used for calculation of other physical entities, such as flux, either throughout the domain or in certain regions of it. Activities taken at this step are often referred to as *postprocessing*. In solid-mechanics problems, for instance, this step involves plotting the contour for the deformed shape of the domain, calculating stress and strain, plotting the contour for the principal stresses, etc. Comparison of the calculated values against their allowable values (design criteria) enters into the picture at this stage as well.

This is the decision-making step and is probably the most important step in the entire process. Two important questions must be answered at this point: *How good are the results?* and *What should be done with them?* The first requires the estimation of *error bounds*, and the second involves the physical nature of the problem. The answers to these questions either terminate the analysis or require that certain steps be repeated. In some cases, the reanalysis begins with step 1 (i.e., redefinition of the problem with new physical parameters, new discretization using different size and shapes for the elements, etc.). For the majority of problems in practice, however, reliable results are obtained only by comparing various analyses (based on various discretizations) of the same problem. There are processes which are built into the software in order to increase the accuracy by *a posteriori* error estimates. These are known as *adaptive processes* [10, 11] and *automatic-mesh-generation* techniques and are presented in Sec. 3.4 of Part 4. Treatment of error estimates, efficient finite-element techniques, interpretation of results, etc., appear in Chap. 8 of Part 3. Efficient reanalysis procedures are presented in Chap. 2 of Part 4. More detailed information on the fundamentals of finite-element methods can be found in Refs. [12–28].

## 3.3 IMPLEMENTATION OF THE FINITE-ELEMENT METHOD

We have so far presented the basic steps for a standard finite-element method. Computer implementation of these steps consists of three basic units, namely, the *preprocessor*, *processor*, and *postprocessor*. The main functions of these processors are, respectively, (1) to input and/or

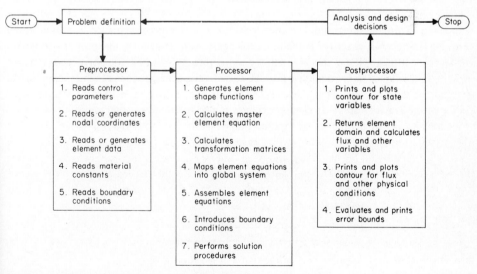

**FIG. 3.9**  Flowchart for finite-element implementation.

generate problem parameters, (2) to set up and solve equations, and (3) to print and/or plot the solution. The success of any finite-element code basically depends on the efficiency of each processor. Figure 3.9 summarizes the major operations which take place in these three processors. More information on the implementation of finite-element methods can be found in Chaps. 1 to 5 of Part 4.

## 3.4 NUMERICAL INTEGRATION

Numerical integration plays an important role in finite-element methods. For instance, evaluation of element matrices requires integration of certain functions over the element domains (see step 7 in Sec. 3.2). In order to facilitate these integrations [Eq. (3.15)], simple geometric elements (triangular, rectangular, etc.) and special coordinate systems (cartesian, natural, etc.) are normally chosen. Integration becomes particularly important when dealing with curved elements. In this case, all numerical integrations are done over a *master element* with simple geometry and coordinates, and then mapping is done to transform all entities to the real domain of the element (see step 8 in Sec. 3.2).

Integration can be done either analytically or numerically. The former method often becomes complicated and lengthy. There are numerous techniques to integrate a function numerically (trapezoidal or Simpson's rule, Newton–Cotes and Gauss–Legendre quadratures, etc.). There are also integration tables (e.g., see Table 3.8) for simple functions. Here we demonstrate how to integrate a function by using gaussian quadrature.

In the gaussian quadrature, the function $f(x, y, z)$ is usually transformed into non-dimensional form $\phi(\xi_1, \xi_2, \xi_3)$ and is evaluated at various points (integration points) within the domain. The approximate value of the integration is then obtained by summing the terms multiplied by weighting factors $w_j$ (see Tables 3.5 to 3.7 following). Thus

$$I = \iiint f(x, y, z)\, dx\, dy\, dz \approx V \sum_{j=1}^{n} w_j \phi(\xi_1, \xi_2, \xi_3)_j$$

For single or double integrations over a line or area, $V$ should be replaced by length $L$ and area $A$. The result is exact for polynomials of degree $(2n-1)$ with $n$ integration points. For instance, two integration points are required in a direction for which the polynomial is cubic.

The following example demonstrates the use of various techniques for the integration of two functions over a triangular domain. The results happen to be exact for the reason stated in the previous paragraph. The same procedure can be extended to other element shapes and functions using any number of integration points.

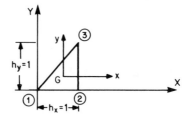

**FIG. 3.10**

**EXAMPLE 3.1** Integrate the following functions over the triangular element shown in Fig. 3.10 using various techniques.

$$I_1 = \int x^2 \, dA \qquad I_2 = \int xy \, dA$$

**A.** Using Table 3.3 and $\xi_1, \xi_2, \xi_3$ in place of $L_1, L_2, L_3$

$$x = x_1\xi_1 + x_2\xi_2 + x_3\xi_3 \qquad y = y_1\xi_1 + y_2\xi_2 + y_3\xi_3$$

$$I_1 = \int x^2 \, dA = \int (x_1\xi_1 + x_2\xi_2 + x_3\xi_3)^2 \, dA$$

$$= \int (x_1^2\xi_1^2 + x_2^2\xi_2^2 + x_3^2\xi_3^2 + x_1x_2\xi_1\xi_2 + \cdots) \, dA$$

$$= \int (\xi_2^2 + \xi_3^2 + 2\xi_2\xi_3) \, dA \qquad \text{since} \qquad x_1 = 0; \; x_2 = x_3 = 1$$

$$= \left\{ \frac{0!2!0!}{(0+2+0+2)!} + \frac{0!0!2!}{(0+0+2+2)!} + 2\frac{0!1!1!}{(1+1+1+2)!} \right\} 2A$$

$$= \tfrac{1}{4} \qquad \text{since} \qquad 0! = 1 \quad \text{and} \quad A = \tfrac{1}{2}$$

similarly,

$$I_2 = \int xy \, dA$$

$$= \int (x_1\xi_1 + x_2\xi_2 + x_3\xi_3)(y_1\xi_1 + y_2\xi_2 + y_3\xi_3) \, dA$$

$$= \int (\xi_2\xi_3 + \xi_3^2) \, dA \qquad \text{since} \qquad x_1 = y_1 = y_2 = 0; \; x_2 = x_3 = y_3 = 1$$

$$= \left\{ \frac{0!1!1!}{(0+1+1+2)!} + \frac{0!0!2!}{(0+0+2+2)!} \right\} 2A$$

$$= \tfrac{1}{8}$$

**B.** Using Table 3.6 and $\xi_1, \xi_2, \xi_3$ in place of $L_1, L_2, L_3$. Since the function is quadratic, three integration points will result in the exact answer (see cols. 2 and 3 of Table 3.6).

$$I_1 = \int x^2 \, dA = A \sum_{j=1}^{3} w_j \phi(\xi_1, \xi_2, \xi_3)_j$$

$$= A \sum_{j=1}^{3} w_j (x_1\xi_1 + x_2\xi_2 + x_3\xi_3)_j^2$$

$$= A\{ \tfrac{1}{3}(x_2\tfrac{1}{2} + x_3\tfrac{1}{2})^2 + \tfrac{1}{3}(x_1\tfrac{1}{2} + x_3\tfrac{1}{2})^2 + \tfrac{1}{3}(x_1\tfrac{1}{2} + x_2\tfrac{1}{2})^2 \}$$

$$= \frac{A}{12}\{ (x_2 + x_3)^2 + (x_1 + x_3)^2 + (x_1 + x_2)^2 \}$$

$$= \frac{A}{2} = \tfrac{1}{4} \qquad \text{since} \qquad x_1 = 0; \; x_2 = x_3 = 1$$

$$I_2 = \int xy \, dA = A \sum_{j=1}^{3} w_j (x_1\xi_1 + x_2\xi_2 + x_3\xi_3)_j (y_1\xi_1 + y_2\xi_2 + y_3\xi_3)_j$$

$$= \frac{A}{12}\{(x_2+x_3)(y_2+y_3)+(x_1+x_3)(y_1+y_3)+(x_1+x_2)(y_1+y_2)\}$$

$$= \frac{A}{12}\{(1+1)(0+1)+(0+1)(0+1)+(0+1)(0+0)\}$$

$$= \frac{A}{12}(3) = \tfrac{1}{8}$$

**C.** Using Table 3.8 with Eq. (3.25)

$$X = x+\tfrac{2}{3} \qquad Y = y+\tfrac{1}{3} \qquad J = I \qquad |J| = 1$$

$$I_1 = \int_A x^2 \, dx \, dy = \int_A (x+\tfrac{2}{3})^2 |J| \, dx \, dy$$

$$= \frac{A}{12}(\tfrac{4}{9}+\tfrac{1}{9}+\tfrac{1}{9}) + 0 + A\tfrac{4}{9}$$

$$= \tfrac{1}{4}$$

$$I_2 = \int xy \, dx \, dy = \int_A (x+\tfrac{2}{3})(y+\tfrac{1}{3})|J| \, dx \, dy$$

$$= \frac{A}{12}\{\tfrac{2}{3}(\tfrac{1}{3})+\tfrac{1}{3}(-\tfrac{1}{3})\} + 0 + 0 + A\tfrac{2}{9} = \tfrac{1}{8}$$

**D.** Using analytical integration

$$I_1 = \int_0^1 \int_0^x x^2 \, dy \, dx = \int_0^1 |x^2 y|_0^x \, dx = \int_0^1 x^3 \, dx = \frac{x^4}{4}\Big|_0^1 = \tfrac{1}{4}$$

$$I_2 = \int_0^1 \int_0^x xy \, dy \, dx = \int_0^1 \left| x\frac{y^2}{2}\right|_0^x dx = \int_0^1 \frac{x^3}{2} \, dx = \frac{x^4}{8} = \tfrac{1}{8}$$

or

$$I_1 = \int_0^1 \int_y^1 x^2 \, dx \, dy = \int_0^1 \left|\frac{x^3}{3}\right|_y^1 dy = \int_0^1 \left(\frac{1}{3}-\frac{y^3}{3}\right) dy = \tfrac{1}{4}$$

$$I_2 = \int_0^1 \int_y^1 xy \, dx \, dy = \int_0^1 \left|\frac{x^2}{2}y\right|_y^1 dy = \int_0^1 \left(\frac{y}{2}-\frac{y^3}{2}\right) dy = \tfrac{1}{8}$$

Note the order and limit of integration in the analytical procedure.

**TABLE 3.5**  Gaussian Integration Constants for Line Elements

| Figure | $n$† | $\pm\xi_i$ | $w_j$ |
|---|---|---|---|
| | 1 | 0.0 | 2.00000 00000 00000 |
| | 2 | 0.57735 02691 89626 | 1.00000 00000 00000 |
| | 3 | 0.77459 66692 41483 | 0.55555 55555 55556 |
| | | 0.00000 00000 00000 | 0.88888 88888 88889 |
| | 4 | 0.86113 63115 94053 | 0.34785 48451 37454 |
| | | 0.33998 10435 84856 | 0.65214 51548 62546 |
| | 5 | 0.90617 98459 38664 | 0.23692 68850 56189 |
| | | 0.53846 93101 05683 | 0.47862 86704 99366 |
| | | 0.00000 00000 00000 | 0.56888 88888 88889 |
| | 6 | 0.93246 95142 03152 | 0.17132 44923 79170 |
| | | 0.66120 93864 66265 | 0.36076 15730 48139 |
| | | 0.23861 91860 83197 | 0.46791 39345 72691 |
| | 7 | 0.94910 79123 42759 | 0.12948 49661 68870 |
| | | 0.74153 11855 99394 | 0.27970 53914 89277 |
| | | 0.40584 51513 77397 | 0.38183 00505 05119 |
| | | 0.00000 00000 00000 | 0.41795 91836 73469 |
| | 8 | 0.96028 98564 97536 | 0.10122 85362 90376 |
| | | 0.79666 64774 13627 | 0.22238 10344 53374 |
| | | 0.52553 24099 16329 | 0.31370 66458 77887 |
| | | 0.18343 46424 95650 | 0.36268 37833 78362 |
| | 9 | 0.96816 02395 07626 | 0.08127 43883 61574 |
| | | 0.83603 11073 26636 | 0.18064 81606 94857 |
| | | 0.61337 14327 00590 | 0.26061 06964 02935 |
| | | 0.32425 34234 03809 | 0.31234 70770 40003 |
| | | 0.00000 00000 00000 | 0.33023 93550 01260 |
| | 10 | 0.97390 65285 17172 | 0.06667 13443 08688 |
| | | 0.86506 33666 88985 | 0.14945 13491 50581 |
| | | 0.67940 95682 99024 | 0.21908 63625 15982 |
| | | 0.43339 53941 29247 | 0.26926 67193 09996 |
| | | 0.14887 43389 81631 | 0.29552 42247 14753 |

Figure column details:

$f(x)$, $f(x)$ curve from $x_a$ to $x_b$.

For $n = 4$: $\phi(\xi)$ over $-1$ to $+1$, $\xi$.

$0.33998\cdots$

$0.86113\cdots$

$$I = \int_a^b f(x)\,dx$$

$$= \int_{-1}^{+1} \phi(\xi)|J|\,d\xi$$

$$= \frac{L}{2}\sum_{j=1}^{n} w_j\phi(\xi_i)_j$$

† Answers are exact for polynomials of degree $(2n-1)$ or less; i.e., two integration points are required for a cubic polynomial.

# TABLE 3.6  Gaussian Integration Constants for Triangular Elements

$$I = \iint f(x, y)\,dx\,dy$$

$$= \int_{-1}^{1}\int_{-1}^{1} \phi(\xi, \eta)|J|\,d\xi\,d\eta$$

$$= A \sum_{j=1}^{n} w_j\phi(\xi_1, \xi_2, \xi_3)_j$$

$\alpha_1 = 0.81684757$

$\alpha_2 = 0.10810302$

$\alpha_3 = 0.79742699$

$\alpha_4 = 0.05971587$

$\beta_1 = 0.09157621$

$\beta_2 = 0.44594849$

$\beta_3 = 0.10128651$

$\beta_4 = 0.47014206$

| Figure† | $n$ | Order error | Points | $L_1$ | $L_2$ | $L_3$ | $w_j$ |
|---|---|---|---|---|---|---|---|
| | 1 | Linear $O(h^2)$ | $a$ | $\frac{1}{3}$ | $\frac{1}{3}$ | $\frac{1}{3}$ | 1 |
| | 3 | Quadratic $O(h^3)$ | $b_1$ | 0 | 0.5 | 0.5 | $\frac{1}{3}$ |
| | | | $b_2$ | 0.5 | 0 | 0.5 | $\frac{1}{3}$ |
| | | | $b_3$ | 0.5 | 0.5 | 0 | $\frac{1}{3}$ |
| | 3 | Quadratic $O(h^3)$ | $c_1$ | $\frac{2}{3}$ | $\frac{1}{6}$ | $\frac{1}{6}$ | $\frac{1}{3}$ |
| | | | $c_2$ | $\frac{1}{6}$ | $\frac{2}{3}$ | $\frac{1}{6}$ | $\frac{1}{3}$ |
| | | | $c_3$ | $\frac{1}{6}$ | $\frac{1}{6}$ | $\frac{2}{3}$ | $\frac{1}{3}$ |
| | 4 | Cubic $O(h^4)$ | $a$ | $\frac{1}{3}$ | $\frac{1}{3}$ | $\frac{1}{3}$ | $-0.5625$ |
| | | | $c_1$ | 0.6 | 0.2 | 0.2 | |
| | | | $c_2$ | 0.2 | 0.6 | 0.2 | 0.5208333 |
| | | | $c_3$ | 0.2 | 0.2 | 0.6 | |
| | 6 | Quartic $O(h^5)$ | $c_1$ | $\alpha_1$ | $\beta_1$ | $\beta_1$ | |
| | | | $c_2$ | $\beta_1$ | $\alpha_1$ | $\beta_1$ | 0.10995174 |
| | | | $c_3$ | $\beta_1$ | $\beta_1$ | $\alpha_1$ | |
| | | | $d_1$ | $\alpha_2$ | $\beta_2$ | $\beta_2$ | |
| | | | $d_2$ | $\beta_2$ | $\alpha_2$ | $\beta_2$ | 0.22338159 |
| | | | $d_3$ | $\beta_2$ | $\beta_2$ | $\alpha_2$ | |
| | 7 | Quintic $O(h^6)$ | $a$ | $\frac{1}{3}$ | $\frac{1}{3}$ | $\frac{1}{3}$ | 0.225 |
| | | | $c_1$ | $\alpha_3$ | $\beta_3$ | $\beta_3$ | |
| | | | $c_2$ | $\beta_3$ | $\alpha_3$ | $\beta_3$ | 0.12593918 |
| | | | $c_3$ | $\beta_3$ | $\beta_3$ | $\alpha_3$ | |
| | | | $d_1$ | $\alpha_4$ | $\beta_4$ | $\beta_4$ | |
| | | | $d_2$ | $\beta_4$ | $\alpha_4$ | $\beta_4$ | 0.13239415 |
| | | | $d_3$ | $\beta_4$ | $\beta_4$ | $\alpha_4$ | |
| | 7 | Quintic $O(h^6)$ | $a$ | $\frac{1}{3}$ | $\frac{1}{3}$ | $\frac{1}{3}$ | 0.45 |
| | | | $b_1$ | 0 | 0.5 | 0.5 | |
| | | | $b_2$ | 0.5 | 0 | 0.5 | 0.1333 |
| | | | $b_3$ | 0.5 | 0.5 | 0 | |
| | | | $e_1$ | 1 | 0 | 0 | |
| | | | $e_2$ | 0 | 1 | 0 | 0.05 |
| | | | $e_3$ | 0 | 0 | 1 | |

† Three nondimensional coordinates $\xi_1 = L_1$, $\xi_2 = L_2$, $\xi_3 = L_3$ are used.

2.104

**TABLE 3.7** Gaussian Integration Constants for Tetrahedral Elements

| Figure† | $n$ | Order error | Points | $L_1$ | $L_2$ | $L_3$ | $L_4$ | $w_j$ |
|---|---|---|---|---|---|---|---|---|
| | 1 | Linear $O(h^2)$ | $a$ | 0.25 | 0.25 | 0.25 | 0.25 | 1 |
| | 4 | Quadratic $O(h^3)$ | $b_1$ | $\alpha$ | $\beta$ | $\beta$ | $\beta$ | 0.25 |
| | | | $b_2$ | $\beta$ | $\alpha$ | $\beta$ | $\beta$ | 0.25 |
| | | | $b_3$ | $\beta$ | $\beta$ | $\alpha$ | $\beta$ | 0.25 |
| | | | $b_4$ | $\beta$ | $\beta$ | $\beta$ | $\alpha$ | 0.25 |
| | 5 | Cubic $O(h^4)$ | $a$ | $\frac{1}{4}$ | $\frac{1}{4}$ | $\frac{1}{4}$ | $\frac{1}{4}$ | −0.8 |
| | | | $c_1$ | $\frac{1}{3}$ | $\frac{1}{6}$ | $\frac{1}{6}$ | $\frac{1}{6}$ | 0.45 |
| | | | $c_2$ | $\frac{1}{6}$ | $\frac{1}{3}$ | $\frac{1}{6}$ | $\frac{1}{6}$ | 0.45 |
| | | | $c_3$ | $\frac{1}{6}$ | $\frac{1}{6}$ | $\frac{1}{3}$ | $\frac{1}{6}$ | 0.45 |
| | | | $c_4$ | $\frac{1}{6}$ | $\frac{1}{6}$ | $\frac{1}{6}$ | $\frac{1}{3}$ | 0.45 |

$$I = \iiint f(x, y, z)\, dx\, dy\, dz$$

$$= \int_{-1}^{1} \int_{-1}^{1} \int_{-1}^{1} \phi(\xi, \eta, \zeta)|J|\, d\xi\, d\eta\, d\zeta$$

$$= V \sum_{j=1}^{n} w_j \phi(\xi_1, \xi_2, \xi_3, \xi_4)_j$$

$\alpha = 0.58541020$

$\beta = 0.13819660$

† Four nondimensional coordinates $\xi_1 = L_1$, $\xi_2 = L_2$, $\xi_3 = L_3$, $\xi_4 = L_4$ are used.

**TABLE 3.8**  Integration Formulae Based on Centroidal Axes

| Triangular element | Tetrahedral element |
|---|---|

$$\Sigma x_i = \Sigma y_i = 0 \qquad i = 1, 2, 3$$

$$\int dA = \frac{1}{2}\begin{vmatrix} 1 & x_1 & y_1 \\ 1 & x_2 & y_2 \\ 1 & x_3 & y_3 \end{vmatrix} = A$$

$$\int x\, dA = 0$$

$$\int y\, dA = 0$$

$$\int x^2\, dA = \frac{A}{12}\Sigma x_i^2$$

$$\int y^2\, dA = \frac{A}{12}\Sigma y_i^2$$

$$\int xy\, dA = \frac{A}{12}\Sigma x_i y_i$$

$$\Sigma x_i = \Sigma y_i = \Sigma z_i = 0 \qquad i = 1, 2, 3, 4$$

$$\int dv = \frac{1}{6}\begin{vmatrix} 1 & x_1 & y_1 & z_1 \\ 1 & x_2 & y_2 & z_2 \\ 1 & x_3 & y_3 & z_3 \\ 1 & x_4 & y_4 & z_4 \end{vmatrix} = V$$

$$\int x\, dv = 0$$

$$\int y\, dv = 0$$

$$\int z\, dv = 0$$

$$\int x^2\, dv = \frac{v}{20}\Sigma x_i^2$$

$$\int y^2\, dv = \frac{v}{20}\Sigma y_i^2$$

$$\int z^2\, dv = \frac{v}{20}\Sigma z_i^2$$

$$\int xy\, dv = \frac{v}{20}\Sigma x_i y_i$$

$$\int xz\, dv = \frac{v}{20}\Sigma x_i z_i$$

$$\int yz\, dv = \frac{v}{20}\Sigma y_i z_i$$

## 3.5 REFERENCES

1. Becker, E. B., G. F. Carey, and J. T. Oden, *Finite Elements: An Introduction*, Prentice-Hall, Englewood Cliffs, N. J., 1981, vol. 1.
2. Pian, T. H. H., and P. Tong, "Basis of Finite Element Methods for Solid Continua," *Int. J. Numer. Meth. Eng.*, **1**(1):26 (1969).
3. Martin, H. C., and G. F. Carey, *Introduction to Finite Element Analysis*, Prentice-Hall, Englewood Cliffs, N. J., 1973.
4. Strang, G., and G. J. Fix, *An Analysis of the Finite Element Method*, Prentice-Hall, Englewood Cliffs, N. J., 1973.
5. Kardestuncer, H., *Discrete Mechanics—A Unified Approach*, Springer-Verlag, Vienna, 1975.
6. Kardestuncer, H., *Finite Element Methods via Tensors*, Springer-Verlag, Vienna, 1972.
7. Castigliano, A., "Nuova Teoria Intorno all'Equilibrio dei Sistemi Elastici," *Trans. Acad. Sci. (Torino)*, 1876.
8. Kardestuncer, H., *Elementary Matrix Analysis of Structures*, McGraw-Hill, New York, 1974.
9. Matthies, H., and G. Strang, "The Solution of Nonlinear Finite Element Equations," *Int. J. Numer. Meth. Eng.*, **1**:1613–1626 (1979).
10. Babuska, I., and W. C. Rheinboldt, "Adaptive Approaches and Reliability Estimations in Finite Element Analysis," *Comput. Meth. Appl. Mech. Eng.*, **17–18**:519–540 (1979).
11. Kelly, D. W., J. Gago, O. C. Zienkiewicz, and I. Babuska, "A Posteriori Error Analysis and Adaptive Processes in the Finite Element Method," *Int. J. Numer. Meth. Eng.* (in press).
12. Bathe, K.-J., *Finite Element Procedures in Engineering Analysis*, Prentice-Hall, Englewood Cliffs, N. J., 1982.
13. Brebbia, C. A., and J. C. Connor, *Fundamentals of Finite Element Techniques for Structural Engineers*, Butterworth, London, 1975.
14. Ciarlet, P. G., *The Finite Element Method for Elliptic Problems*, North-Holland, New York, 1978.
15. Cheung, Y. K., and M. F. Yeo, *A Practical Introduction to Finite Element Analysis*, Pitman, London, 1979.
16. Cook, R. D., *Concepts and Applications of Finite Element Analysis*, 2d ed., Wiley, New York, 1981.
17. Desai, C. S., *Elementary Finite Element Method*, Prentice-Hall, Englewood Cliffs, N. J., 1979.
18. Gallagher, R. H., *Finite Element Analysis Fundamentals*, Prentice-Hall, N. J., 1976.
19. Irons, B. M., and S. Ahmed, *Techniques of Finite Elements*, Ellis Horwood, Chichester, 1979.
20. Martin, H. C., and G. Carey, *Introduction to Finite Element Analysis*, McGraw-Hill, New York, 1973.
21. Norrie, D. H., and G. deVries, *Finite Element Method: Fundamentals and Applications*, Academic Press, New York, 1973.
22. Norrie, D. H., and G. deVries, *An Introduction to Finite Element Analysis*, Academic Press, New York, 1978.
23. Oden, J. T., and J. N. Reddy, *An Introduction to the Mathematical Theory of Finite Elements*, Wiley, New York, 1976.
24. Segerlind, L. J., *Applied Finite Element Analysis*, Wiley, New York, 1976.
25. Strang, G., and G. J. Fix, *An Analysis of the Finite Element Method*, Prentice-Hall, Englewood Cliffs, N. J., 1973.
26. Tong, P., and J. N. Rosettos, *Finite Element Method: Basic Technique and Implementation*, MIT Press, Cambridge, Mass., 1977.
27. Zienkiewicz, O. C., *The Finite Element Method*, 3d ed., McGraw-Hill, New York, 1977.

28. Zienkiewicz, O. C., and K. Morgan, *Finite Elements and Approximations*, McGraw-Hill, New York, 1983.

29. Atluri, S. N., R. H. Gallagher, and O. C. Zienkiewicz, *Hybrid and Mixed Finite Element Methods*, Wiley, Chichester, 1983.

30. Atluri, S. N., and N. Perrone, *Computer Methods for Nonlinear Solid and Structural Mechanics*, ASME AMD, vol. 54, American Society of Mechanical Engineers, New York, 1983.

31. Spilker, R. L., and K. W. Reed, *Hybrid and Mixed Finite Element Methods*, ASME AMD, vol. 73, American Society of Mechanical Engineers, New York, 1985.

# CHAPTER 4

# FINITE ELEMENTS BASED ON DISPLACEMENT FIELDS

## 4.1 THEORY AND GENERAL REMARKS

### 4.1A Interpolation and Shape Functions

The most widely used elements in structural mechanics are based on assumed displacement fields. Thus, the $xyz$-displacement components $\{u \ v \ w\}$ of an arbitrary point within an element are interpolated from nodal displacements $\boldsymbol{\delta}$ according to the expression

$$\begin{bmatrix} u \\ v \\ w \end{bmatrix} = \mathbf{N}\boldsymbol{\delta} \tag{4.1}$$

Matrix $\mathbf{N}$ is called the shape-function matrix. It contains the interpolation polynomial. For example, if linear interpolation is used for points on the axis of the bar in Fig. 4.1, we write

$$\begin{bmatrix} u \\ v \\ w \end{bmatrix} = \begin{bmatrix} N_1 & 0 & 0 & N_1 & 0 & 0 \\ 0 & N_1 & 0 & 0 & N_2 & 0 \\ 0 & 0 & N_1 & 0 & 0 & N_2 \end{bmatrix} \begin{bmatrix} u_1 \\ v_1 \\ w_1 \\ u_2 \\ v_2 \\ w_2 \end{bmatrix} \tag{4.2}$$

where
$$N_1 = \frac{L-s}{L} \quad \text{and} \quad N_2 = \frac{s}{L} \tag{4.3}$$

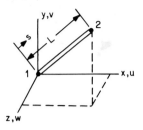

**FIG. 4.1**   A straight bar of length $L$, arbitrarily oriented in space.

Note that Eq. (4.2) reduces to $\{u \; v \; w\} = \{u_1 \; v_1 \; w_1\}$ if $s = 0$ and to $\{u \; v \; w\} = \{u_2 \; v_2 \; w_2\}$ if $s = L$. This behavior (that end values be met) is required of any interpolation scheme. In general, a term $N_i$ in $\mathbf{N}$ describes displacements within the element associated with a unit value of an element degree of freedom.

The foregoing linear interpolation provides interelement continuity of displacements ($C_0$-continuity). To provide continuity of first derivatives as well ($C_1$-continuity), rotations must be added to the list of nodal degrees of freedom and the polynomial must be of higher degree. The beam element of Fig. 4.2 is a case in point. Its lateral displacement $v$ must

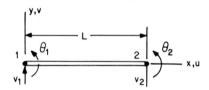

**FIG. 4.2**   A straight beam element with the four degrees of freedom needed to define its lateral displacement $v$.

contain cubic terms if slopes as well as displacements are to match between elements. Here it is not obvious what the $N_i$ must be in terms of $x$, so we start with generalized coordinates $\mathbf{a}^T = [a_1 \; a_2 \; a_3 \; a_4]$ instead of the nodal displacements $\boldsymbol{\delta} = \{v_1 \; \theta_1 \; v_2 \; \theta_2\}$. Let

$$v = \mathbf{N}_a \mathbf{a} \qquad \text{where} \qquad \mathbf{N}_a = [1 \quad x \quad x^2 \quad x^3] \qquad (4.4)$$

End values to be met are

$$v = v_1 \qquad \text{and} \qquad \frac{dv}{dx} = \theta_1 \qquad \text{at } x = 0$$

$$\qquad (4.5)$$

$$v = v_2 \qquad \text{and} \qquad \frac{dv}{dx} = \theta_2 \qquad \text{at } x = L$$

Here, in accord with small-deflection theory, we have assumed that slope $dv/dx$ may be taken as an angle of rotation. Substitution of Eq. (4.5) into Eq. (4.4) yields $\boldsymbol{\delta} = \mathbf{Aa}$, where

$$\boldsymbol{\delta} = \begin{bmatrix} v_1 \\ \theta_1 \\ v_2 \\ \theta_2 \end{bmatrix} \qquad \mathbf{A} = \begin{bmatrix} 1 & 0 & 0 & 0 \\ 0 & 1 & 0 & 0 \\ 1 & L & L^2 & L^3 \\ 0 & 1 & 2L & 3L^2 \end{bmatrix} \tag{4.6}$$

Therefore
$$\mathbf{a} = \mathbf{A}^{-1}\boldsymbol{\delta} \tag{4.7}$$

and Eq. (4.4) becomes $v = \mathbf{N}_a \mathbf{A}^{-1}\boldsymbol{\delta}$. We recognize the shape-function matrix as $\mathbf{N} = \mathbf{N}_a\mathbf{A}^{-1}$. This procedure is generally applicable when $\mathbf{N}$ must be extracted from an assumed field written in terms of generalized coordinates $\mathbf{a}$.

For adequate accuracy, an interpolation polynomial of low degree should span data points that are not far apart. Or, a polynomial of higher degree might span a larger number of degrees of freedom at more separated points. In a finite-element context this means that we must use a sufficiently fine mesh of simple elements or a coarser mesh of more competent elements. *Excessive* refinement is expensive. It may also be useless because of uncertainties about loads, construction errors, material properties, and so on.

## 4.1B General Formulae for Element Matrices

One can derive general expressions for the element stiffness matrix $\mathbf{k}$ and the vector of nodal loads $\mathbf{p}$ that arise from nonnodal forces within elements. These expressions are applicable to all elements based on assumed displacement fields. The derivation involves little more than identifying certain groups of terms in potential-energy expressions.

The potential-energy expression for one element and linear elasticity is

$$\Pi_{pe} = \int_V (\tfrac{1}{2}\boldsymbol{\varepsilon}^T \mathbf{E}\boldsymbol{\varepsilon} - \boldsymbol{\varepsilon}^T \mathbf{E}\boldsymbol{\varepsilon}_0 + \boldsymbol{\varepsilon}^T \boldsymbol{\sigma}_0)\, dV - \int_V \begin{bmatrix} u \\ v \\ w \end{bmatrix}^T \mathbf{X}\, dV - \int_S \begin{bmatrix} u \\ v \\ w \end{bmatrix}^T \mathbf{T}\, dS \tag{4.8}$$

Here the strains are
$$\boldsymbol{\varepsilon}^T = [\varepsilon_x \quad \varepsilon_y \quad \varepsilon_z \quad \gamma_{xy} \quad \gamma_{yz} \quad \gamma_{zx}]$$

Similarly arrayed vectors $\boldsymbol{\varepsilon}_0$ and $\boldsymbol{\sigma}_0$ contain initial strains and initial stresses, respectively, produced perhaps by swelling, temperature change, or other factors.

As a one-dimensional example, if an axially loaded prismatic bar of length $L$ is $e$ units too long and is heated $Y$ degrees, we can write $\varepsilon_0 = e/L$ and $\sigma_0 = -E\alpha_t Y$, where $\alpha_t$ is the coefficient of thermal expansion. Matrix $\mathbf{E}$ contains elastic constants ($E$, $\mu$, and $G$ in commonplace notation) to fit the stress-strain relation $\boldsymbol{\sigma} = \mathbf{E}(\boldsymbol{\varepsilon} - \boldsymbol{\varepsilon}_0) + \boldsymbol{\sigma}_0$. For the aforementioned prismatic bar, if length change is prohibited so that the mechanical strain $\varepsilon$ is zero, the stress-strain relation gives $\sigma = -Ee/L - E\alpha_t Y$ as expected. Body forces per unit volume are $\mathbf{X} = \{X \ Y \ Z\}$ in the coordinate directions. Similarly, surface-traction components are $\mathbf{T} = \{T_x \ T_y \ T_z\}$, and $dS$ is an element of the surface. In many practical problems, $\boldsymbol{\varepsilon}_0 = \boldsymbol{\sigma}_0 = \mathbf{X} = \mathbf{T} = 0$. Then the structure is loaded by prescribed values of displacements, or by external loads (forces and/or moments) applied at one or more structure nodes. These loads do not appear in Eq. (4.8).

We now define $\{u \ v \ w\}$ in terms of nodal displacements $\boldsymbol{\delta}$ by Eq. (4.1). Strains $\boldsymbol{\varepsilon}$ are

$$\boldsymbol{\varepsilon} = \mathbf{L} \begin{bmatrix} u \\ v \\ w \end{bmatrix} \tag{4.9}$$

where $\mathbf{L}$ is the standard operator matrix that yields strains from displacements; for example, $\varepsilon_x = (\partial/\partial x)u$. Hence from Eqs. (4.1) and (4.9)

$$\boldsymbol{\varepsilon} = \mathbf{B}\boldsymbol{\delta} \qquad \text{where} \qquad \mathbf{B} = \mathbf{LN} \tag{4.10}$$

We see that $\mathbf{B}$ is completely defined when shape functions $\mathbf{N}$ are chosen. Substitution of Eqs. (4.1) and (4.10) into (4.8) yields

$$\Pi_{pe} = \tfrac{1}{2}\boldsymbol{\delta}^T \mathbf{k}\boldsymbol{\delta} - \boldsymbol{\delta}^T \mathbf{p} \tag{4.11}$$

where the following definitions have been made. The element stiffness matrix $\mathbf{k}$ is

$$\mathbf{k} = \int_V \mathbf{B}^T \mathbf{E}\mathbf{B} \, dV \tag{4.12}$$

Loads applied by an element to its nodes are

$$\mathbf{p} = \int_V \mathbf{B}^T \mathbf{E}\boldsymbol{\varepsilon}_0 \, dV - \int_V \mathbf{B}^T \boldsymbol{\sigma}_0 \, dV + \int_V \mathbf{N}^T \mathbf{X} \, dV + \int_S \mathbf{N}^T \mathbf{T} \, dS \tag{4.13}$$

The last integral is zero unless the element boundary is subject to a traction. Equation (4.13) gives the "consistent" vector of nodal loads. Alternatively, but with noticeable loss of accuracy in a coarse mesh, it may be possible to replace $\mathbf{p}$ by statically equivalent concentrated forces applied to structure nodes.

An alternative expression for $\mathbf{k}$ is sometimes useful. As in Eq. (4.4) the displacement field can be written $\{u \ v \ w\} = \mathbf{N}_a \mathbf{a}$, where $\mathbf{N}_a$ is a shape-function matrix that operates on generalized coordinates $\mathbf{a}$ rather than on nodal degrees of freedom $\boldsymbol{\delta}$. In view of Eqs. (4.7) and (4.10)

$$\mathbf{B} = \mathbf{B}_a \mathbf{A}^{-1} \qquad \text{where} \qquad \mathbf{B}_a = \mathbf{LN}_a \tag{4.14}$$

Equation (4.12) can therefore be written

$$\mathbf{k} = \mathbf{A}^{-T} \int_V \mathbf{B}_a^T \mathbf{E}\mathbf{B}_a \, dV \, \mathbf{A}^{-1} \tag{4.15}$$

Equation (4.15) postpones until last the transformation from $\mathbf{a}$ to $\boldsymbol{\delta}$. This approach is convenient for certain elements, such as shells of revolution.

Equation (4.12) is easily adapted to particular element geometries. For example, let the bar of Fig. 4.1 lie along the $x$-axis and be permitted only $x$-direction displacements. It is therefore a two-force member, and $\varepsilon_x$ is the only strain that must be accounted for.

Accordingly,

$$N = \begin{bmatrix} \dfrac{L-x}{L} & \dfrac{x}{L} \end{bmatrix} \qquad B = \frac{\partial}{\partial x} N = \begin{bmatrix} -\dfrac{1}{L} & \dfrac{1}{L} \end{bmatrix} \tag{4.16}$$

$$k = \int_L B^T E B A \, dx = \frac{AE}{L} \begin{bmatrix} 1 & -1 \\ -1 & 1 \end{bmatrix} \tag{4.17}$$

where $A =$ cross-sectional area and $E =$ elastic modulus. We recognize Eq. (4.17) as the stiffness matrix of a truss element. It is symmetric, as expected from the form of Eq. (4.12).

Strain energy in an element is $U = \frac{1}{2}\delta^T k \delta$. From this more general point of view, **B** and **E** represent displacement derivatives and material coefficients appropriate to the problem at hand.

## 4.1c Nodal Loads Produced by Traction and Body Force

Equation (4.13) shows how loads associated with surface tractions **T** and body forces **X** should be allotted to element nodes. These loads are called *consistent* because they are based on the same shape function used to generate stiffness coefficients. Sometimes this allotment follows "common sense." For example, to account for the weight $W$ of a linear element, Eq. (4.13) requires that force $W/4$ be placed at each of the four nodes of a rectangular plane element and that force $W/8$ be placed at each of the eight nodes of a rectangular solid element. These loads might be anticipated. If the element is not rectangular, the fraction of $W$ that should appear at each node is not obvious. Figure 4.3 illustrates the consistent nodal loads for various elements.

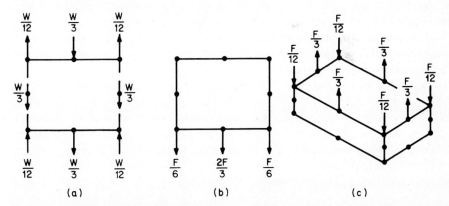

**FIG. 4.3** Consistently derived nodal loads on rectangular quadratic elements with midside nodes. (*a*) Weight $W$ of a plane uniform element. (*b*) Force $F$ uniformly distributed along the lower edge. (*c*) Force $F$ uniformly distributed over the upper face of a solid element.

If elements have side nodes as well as corner nodes, the side and corner nodes should not have the same fraction of the total load, even if the load is uniform and the element is rectangular. Cases in point are shown in Fig. 4.3. Note that nodal loads may not all act in the same direction.

Formulations for nodal forces due to surface tractions on curved edges and warped surfaces are presented in Ref. [6].

Instead of using consistent nodal forces derived by application of Eq. (4.13), one can apply statically equivalent nodal loads arrived at by an *ad hoc* method. *Ad hoc* lumping might make side nodes and corner nodes carry equal loads in Fig. 4.3, or might omit nodal moments at the ends of a beam element under uniform load. Answers will be less accurate if the mesh is coarse, but with mesh refinement there will be convergence toward correct results.

### 4.1D  Stress Computation

Stress computation usually begins (and may end) with finding stresses at one or more points in each element. With $\varepsilon = \mathbf{B}\boldsymbol{\delta}$, the stresses

$$\boldsymbol{\sigma} = \mathbf{E}(\varepsilon - \varepsilon_0) + \boldsymbol{\sigma}_0 \tag{4.18}$$

can be computed when nodal displacements $\boldsymbol{\delta}$ are known. Matrix $\mathbf{B}$ is, in general, a function of the coordinates and must be evaluated at the point where stresses are desired. A *stress matrix* can be defined as $\mathbf{S} = \mathbf{EB}$. Either of the vectors $\varepsilon_0$ and $\boldsymbol{\sigma}_0$ can be used to account for thermally induced stresses.

Stresses computed by Eq. (4.18) are more accurate at some points than others. Often the element center is best, midsides are good, and corners are worst. At points common to two or more elements, stresses should be averaged. A need for mesh refinement is suggested if numbers that are averaged are appreciably different from the average itself. Averaging between dissimilar materials or across sudden thickness changes must be avoided. Another form of averaging is to fit a polynomial to stresses at the nodes of several elements in the region of interest [1, 2]. A contour plot of stresses allows the analyst to visually estimate stresses at a given point.

An iterative method can greatly improve computed stresses [3]. It begins by computing node-point average stresses, which we call $\bar{\boldsymbol{\sigma}}$. Stresses within an element are interpolated from the node-point averages:

$$\boldsymbol{\sigma} = \mathbf{N}\bar{\boldsymbol{\sigma}} \tag{4.19}$$

where $\mathbf{N}$ is a shape-function matrix. The element $\boldsymbol{\sigma}$-fields join to produce a continuous stress field over the structure. Element nodal forces associated with $\boldsymbol{\sigma}$ are given by the volume integral over $\mathbf{B}^T \boldsymbol{\sigma}$ (analogous to the integral that contains $\boldsymbol{\sigma}_0$ in Eq. (4.13)). These nodal forces are summed over all $m$ elements of the structure and subtracted from $\mathbf{P}$, the vector of all nodal forces applied to the structure. We write

$$\mathbf{K}\, d\boldsymbol{\Delta} = \mathbf{P} - \sum_{i=1}^{m} \left( \int_V \mathbf{B}^T \boldsymbol{\sigma}\, dV \right)_i \tag{4.20}$$

If $\boldsymbol{\sigma}$ is exact, the right-hand side of Eq. (4.20) is zero. Otherwise, the right-hand side is a force unbalance that drives the solution toward a displacement state that reduces the unbalance. We compute increments $d\boldsymbol{\Delta}$ and add them to the existing $\boldsymbol{\Delta}$ to obtain a new displacement state. Stresses are computed from the new displacements and the process repeats until convergence. The same $\mathbf{K}$ is used throughout.

## 4.1E Approximate Nature of the Solution

An exact solution of an elasticity problem satisfies compatibility equilibrium and boundary conditions. A finite-element solution is usually able only to approximate these conditions, as follows.

Compatibility is satisfied within elements because the polynomial displacement field is continuous. Unintentional incompatibilities may appear if element shapes are badly chosen. Compatibility is enforced at nodes because nodes are the connection points between elements. At interfaces, however, elements may or may not be compatible, depending upon their assumed displacement fields.

Equilibrium prevails at nodes in the sense that the structural equations $\mathbf{K\Delta} = \mathbf{P}$ are equilibrium equations. If correctly solved for $\mathbf{\Delta}$, internally generated forces $\mathbf{K\Delta}$ will balance applied loads $\mathbf{P}$. This observation says nothing about whether the computational model is good or bad. Equilibrium is rarely satisfied at element boundaries. Most often, a step change in stress is seen as we move from one element to another. Consider the case of plane stress. If displacements are only $C_0$-continuous, strains will be discontinuous because they are first derivatives of displacement. Interelement continuity of strain and stress is achieved by $C_1$-elements, but at the cost of adding displacement derivatives to the list of nodal degrees of freedom.

Displacement boundary conditions are easily introduced at nodes where they are prescribed. Stress boundary conditions, as from pressure against a surface, traction, etc., are converted to equivalent nodal loads by the last integral of Eq. (4.13). In this form stress boundary conditions are easy to impose. However, computed values of stress $\sigma_n$ normal to the boundary and shear stress $\tau$ tangent to the boundary will seldom agree exactly with prescribed surface tractions. If the solution is satisfactory, one expects good agreement. At a free surface, computed values of $\sigma_n$ and $\tau$ will not be exactly zero.

## 4.2 ISOPARAMETRIC FAMILIES OF ELEMENTS

### 4.2A Definitions and Justifications

Isoparametric elements appeared in the literature in 1966 [4]. Distinguishing features of isoparametric elements include their ability to have curved sides and their use of an intrinsic coordinate system for formulating the element stiffness matrix. Intrinsic coordinates and element formulation are considered in this section. The term *isoparametric*, meaning "same parameters," follows from use of the same interpolation scheme to define both the geometry and the displacement field of an element. Consider, for example, the $x$-direction displacement $u$ in an element ($y$- and $z$-direction displacements would be written similarly). Let $u_i$ represent nodal displacements and $x_i$ represent nodal $x$-coordinates. The interpolation formulae are

$$u = \sum_{i=1}^{m} N_i u_i \qquad x = \sum_{i=1}^{n} N_i' x_i \tag{4.21}$$

where $N_i$ and $N_i'$ are shape functions written in terms of the intrinsic coordinates. These two equations give the value of $u$ and the value of $x$ at a point within the element, in terms of nodal values of $u_i$ and $x_i$, when the (intrinsic) coordinates of the internal point are given.

Similar equations describe coordinates $y$ and $z$ and displacement components $v$ and $w$. Terms are defined as follows.

1. The element is *isoparametric* if $m = n$, $N_i = N_i'$, and the same nodal points are used to define both element geometry and element displacement (Fig. 4.4$a$).

2. The element is *subparametric* if $m > n$, the order of $N_i$ larger than $N_i'$ (Fig. 4.4$b$).

3. The element is *superparametric* if $m < n$, the order of $N_i$ smaller than $N_i'$ (Fig. 4.4$c$).

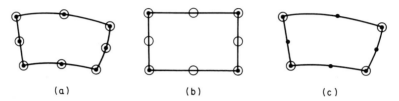

(a)          (b)          (c)

**FIG. 4.4**   The symbol · indicates a point whose coordinates are prescribed so as to define the geometry of an element. The symbol ∘ indicates a point with displacement degrees of freedom. The respective elements are ($a$) isoparametric, ($b$) subparametric, and ($c$) superparametric.

The isoparametric elements can correctly display rigid-body and constant-strain modes. Consider the displacement field

$$u = a_1 + a_2 x + a_3 y + a_4 z$$

$$v = a_5 + a_6 x + a_7 y + a_8 z \tag{4.22}$$

$$w = a_9 + a_{10} x + a_{11} y + a_{12} z$$

By suitable choice of the constants $a_i$ this field yields any desired state of rigid-body motion or constant strain. We wish to show that this field prevails within the element when nodal degrees of freedom are assigned values consistent with the field [5]. For instance, $u$ at node $i$ is

$$u_i = a_1 + a_2 x_i + a_3 y_i + a_4 z_i \tag{4.23}$$

where $x_i$, $y_i$, and $z_i$ are nodal coordinates. By definition, $u = \Sigma N_i u_i$, so

$$u = a_1 \Sigma N_i + a_2 \Sigma N_i x_i + a_3 \Sigma N_i y_i + a_4 \Sigma N_i z_i \tag{4.24}$$

But, also by definition, for the *iso*parametric element,

$$x = \Sigma N_i x_i \qquad y = \Sigma N_i y_i \qquad z = \Sigma N_i z_i \tag{4.25}$$

Therefore, if $\Sigma N_i = 1$ (as will be true for any correct interpolation scheme), Eq. (4.24) reduces to the first of Eqs. (4.22). Thus we conclude that isoparametric elements are valid in that they display the behavior required for convergence toward exact results as a mesh is refined.

The foregoing argument applies also to the subparametric element of Fig. 4.4$b$ if the side nodes are at midsides: then one can show that Eqs. (4.25) yield the same $x$, $y$, and $z$ expressions that are given by the four shape functions of a corner-node element. However, the argument usually fails for superparametric elements. A linear displacement field in a quadratically shaped element (Fig. 4.4c) does not produce a state of constant strain [6]. Certain superparametric elements, such as shell elements of varying thickness, can work because strains in the thickness direction are not used in formulating stiffness coefficients.

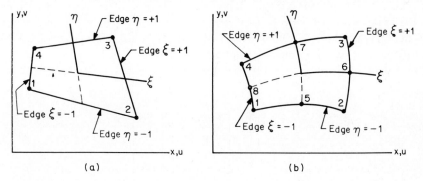

FIG. 4.5   (a) Linear plane isoparametric element. (b) Quadratic plane isoparametric element.

## 4.2B Quadrilateral Isoparametric Elements in Plane-Stress Problems

Consider the "linear" element of Fig. 4.5a, so-called because its sides are straight lines and the displacements are assumed to vary linearly:

$$x = \Sigma N_i x_i \qquad y = \Sigma N_i y_i \tag{4.26}$$

$$u = \Sigma N_i u_i \qquad v = \Sigma N_i v_i \tag{4.27}$$

where $i$ runs from 1 to 4, spanning the node numbers. The element has eight degrees of freedom (two degrees of freedom at each node). The shape functions are

$$N_1 = \tfrac{1}{4}(1-\xi)(1-\eta) \qquad N_2 = \tfrac{1}{4}(1+\xi)(1-\eta)$$
$$N_3 = \tfrac{1}{4}(1+\xi)(1+\eta) \qquad N_4 = \tfrac{1}{4}(1-\xi)(1+\eta) \tag{4.28}$$

which $\xi$ and $\eta$ are intrinsic coordinates. Regardless of the shape or physical size of the element, element edges are at $\xi = \pm 1$ and $\eta = \pm 1$. With the $N_i$ given in Eq. (4.28), node 1 is always at $\xi = \eta = -1$, node 2 at $\xi = +1$ and $\eta = -1$, and so on. Displacements $u$ and $v$ are, respectively, $x$-parallel and $y$-parallel, not $\xi$-parallel and $\eta$-parallel.

To establish the strain-displacement matrix **B** we must deal with $x$ and $y$ derivatives of $u$ and $v$. Since $u$ and $v$ are given in terms of $\xi$ and $\eta$, a coordinate transformation of derivatives is required. Consider displacement $u$. By the chain rule,

$$\begin{bmatrix} \dfrac{\partial u}{\partial \xi} \\[2mm] \dfrac{\partial u}{\partial \eta} \end{bmatrix} = \mathbf{J} \begin{bmatrix} \dfrac{\partial u}{\partial x} \\[2mm] \dfrac{\partial u}{\partial y} \end{bmatrix} \qquad \text{where} \qquad \mathbf{J} = \begin{bmatrix} \dfrac{\partial x}{\partial \xi} & \dfrac{\partial y}{\partial \xi} \\[2mm] \dfrac{\partial x}{\partial \eta} & \dfrac{\partial y}{\partial \eta} \end{bmatrix} \tag{4.29}$$

A similar expression applies to derivatives of $v$. From Eqs. (4.26),

$$\frac{\partial x}{\partial \xi} = \Sigma \frac{\partial N_i}{\partial \xi} x_i, \quad \frac{\partial y}{\partial \xi} = \Sigma \frac{\partial N_i}{\partial \xi} y_i, \quad \ldots \tag{4.30}$$

Matrix $\mathbf{J}$ is $2 \times 2$ for all plane elements. It is called the *jacobian matrix* and is defined by the geometry of the element.

Matrix $\mathbf{B}$ in the relation $\boldsymbol{\varepsilon} = \mathbf{B\delta}$ is given by the product of the rectangular matrices in the following three equations, in the order written.

$$\boldsymbol{\varepsilon} = \begin{bmatrix} \varepsilon_x \\ \varepsilon_y \\ \gamma_{xy} \end{bmatrix} = \begin{bmatrix} 1 & 0 & 0 & 0 \\ 0 & 0 & 0 & 1 \\ 0 & 1 & 1 & 0 \end{bmatrix} \begin{bmatrix} \dfrac{\partial u}{\partial x} \\ \dfrac{\partial u}{\partial y} \\ \dfrac{\partial v}{\partial x} \\ \dfrac{\partial v}{\partial y} \end{bmatrix} \tag{4.31}$$

$$\begin{bmatrix} \dfrac{\partial u}{\partial x} \\ \dfrac{\partial u}{\partial y} \\ \dfrac{\partial v}{\partial x} \\ \dfrac{\partial v}{\partial y} \end{bmatrix} = \begin{bmatrix} \mathbf{J}^{-1} & \\ & \mathbf{J}^{-1} \end{bmatrix} \begin{bmatrix} \dfrac{\partial u}{\partial \xi} \\ \dfrac{\partial u}{\partial \eta} \\ \dfrac{\partial v}{\partial \xi} \\ \dfrac{\partial v}{\partial \eta} \end{bmatrix} \tag{4.32}$$

$$\begin{bmatrix} \dfrac{\partial u}{\partial \xi} \\ \dfrac{\partial u}{\partial \eta} \\ \dfrac{\partial v}{\partial \xi} \\ \dfrac{\partial v}{\partial \eta} \end{bmatrix} = \begin{bmatrix} \dfrac{\partial N_1}{\partial \xi} & 0 & \cdots \\ \dfrac{\partial N_1}{\partial \eta} & 0 & \cdots \\ 0 & \dfrac{\partial N_1}{\partial \xi} & \cdots \\ 0 & \dfrac{\partial N_1}{\partial \eta} & \cdots \end{bmatrix} \begin{bmatrix} u_1 \\ v_1 \\ u_2 \\ v_2 \\ \vdots \end{bmatrix} \tag{4.33}$$

The element stiffness matrix is, with $t = $ thickness,

$$\mathbf{k} = \iint \mathbf{B}^T \mathbf{E} \mathbf{B} t \, dx \, dy = \int_{-1}^{1} \int_{-1}^{1} \mathbf{B}^T \mathbf{E} \mathbf{B} t J \, d\xi \, d\eta \tag{4.34}$$

where $\mathbf{E}$ is a $3 \times 3$ array of elastic constants. Physically, $J$ is the scale factor that yields area

$dx\,dy$ from $d\xi\,d\eta$. Matrix **B** is a function of $\xi$ and $\eta$ in both the numerators and the denominators of its terms. This circumstance makes numerical integration appropriate.

Higher-order plane quadrilateral isoparametric elements can be generated. A "quadratic" element, whose sides can displace as quadratic curves, is shown in Fig. 4.5b. Its **K** is $16 \times 16$ and the shape function is given by Table 4.2, serial number 2.

## 4.2c  Additional Isoparametric Elements

The isoparametric formulation extends easily from two dimensions to three. Consider, for example, the linear hexahedral element (Fig. 4.6a). Its six faces are, in general, warped

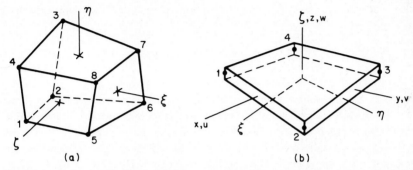

**FIG. 4.6**  (a) The linear eight-node brick. It has 24 degrees of freedom. (b) A four-node isoparametric element for plate-bending analysis. Plane $z = \zeta = 0$ is the plate midsurface.

quadrilaterals that have intrinsic coordinates $\xi = \pm 1$, $\eta = \pm 1$, and $\zeta = \pm 1$. To Eqs. (4.26) and (4.27) we add

$$z = \Sigma N_i z_i \qquad w = \Sigma N_i w_i \tag{4.35}$$

where $w$ is the $z$-direction displacement component. Shape functions of an eight-node element (often referred to as a *brick element*) are

$$N_i = \tfrac{1}{8}(1 \pm \xi)(1 \pm \eta)(1 \pm \zeta) \tag{4.36}$$

The eight possible permutations of sign yield eight shape functions, as required. The jacobian matrix becomes $3 \times 3$.

$$\mathbf{J} = \begin{bmatrix} \dfrac{\partial x}{\partial \xi} & \dfrac{\partial y}{\partial \xi} & \dfrac{\partial z}{\partial \xi} \\[2mm] \dfrac{\partial x}{\partial \eta} & \dfrac{\partial y}{\partial \eta} & \dfrac{\partial z}{\partial \eta} \\[2mm] \dfrac{\partial x}{\partial \zeta} & \dfrac{\partial y}{\partial \zeta} & \dfrac{\partial z}{\partial \zeta} \end{bmatrix} \tag{4.37}$$

Equation (4.31) must expand to allow for six strains and nine displacement derivatives, so the rectangular array of 1s and 0s becomes $6 \times 9$. The next two equations are also expanded.

The element stiffness matrix is

$$\mathbf{k} = \int_{-1}^{1} \int_{-1}^{1} \int_{-1}^{1} \mathbf{B}^T \mathbf{EB} J \, d\xi \, d\eta \, d\zeta \tag{4.38}$$

where $\mathbf{E}$ is a $6 \times 6$ array of elastic constants and $J$ is the determinant of the $3 \times 3$ jacobian matrix. Of the preceding equations in this section, only the shape functions [Eq. (4.36)] are specific to a particular solid element.

Isoparametric elements are also used for plates and shells. A plate element such as the one in Fig. 4.6b exhibits the lateral displacement $w$ and rotations $\theta_x$ and $\theta_y$ of a line that is normal to the midsurface in the undeformed plate. If $\theta_x$ and $\theta_y$ are taken as vectors in the positive $x$- and $y$-directions according to the right-hand rule, then the element displacement field is

$$u = z \Sigma N_i \theta_{yi} \qquad v = -z \Sigma N_i \theta_{xi} \qquad w = \Sigma N_i w_i \tag{4.39}$$

where shape functions $N_i$ depend only on $\xi$ and $\eta$. The formulation proceeds almost as if the element were three-dimensional, so that transverse-shear deformation is included. However, strain $\varepsilon_z$ is undefined and is omitted from the strain vector $\boldsymbol{\varepsilon}$. Matrix $\mathbf{B}$ therefore contains five rows rather than six. With axes $\xi$ and $\eta$ in the $z = 0$ plane, matrix $\mathbf{J}$ contains $J_{13} = J_{23} = J_{31} = J_{32} = 0$ and $J_{33} = t/2$, where $t$ is the plate thickness. Material property matrix $\mathbf{E}$ is written for a state of plane stress in the $z = 0$ plane. Thus, for isotropy, $E_{11} = E_{22} = E/(1 - \mu^2)$, $E_{12} = E_{21} = \mu E/(1 - \mu^2)$, and $E_{33} = E_{44} = E_{65} = G$, where $E$ = elastic modulus, $G$ = shear modulus, and $\mu$ = Poisson's ratio. The integration in the $\zeta$-direction is done explicitly. The in-plane ($\xi$ and $\eta$) integrations are done numerically.

Isoparametric elements for shells are similar to those for plates. However, stretching as well as bending must be accounted for. There are typically five degrees of freedom per node (three displacements, plus two rotations about lines tangent to the midsurface). Expressions become lengthier because of the need to deal with the geometric and the physical complexity of a general shell.

## 4.3 ISOPARAMETRIC FINITE ELEMENTS

Tables 4.1 to 4.3 present a catalog of one-, two-, and three-dimensional isoparametric finite elements.

## 4.4 CURVED-BEAM AND ARCH ELEMENTS

A large part of the effort put into the development of arch elements, as evidenced by the available published work, has been concerned with the *circular arch* and has been based on *first-approximation arch theory*. This type of arch is considered first here; other arch elements are described thereafter. Also, for the most part, only displacement-based formulations are discussed.

**TABLE 4.1** One-Dimensional (Line) Isoparametric Elements ($\xi_0 = \xi_i\xi$ for Node $i$)

| Serial no. | Element name | Configuration | DOF | Shape functions | Advantages | Disadvantages | Ref. |
|---|---|---|---|---|---|---|---|
| 1 | Two-node linear element†† | | † | $N_i = \frac{1}{2}(1+\xi_0); \ i = 1,2$ | Simple geometric shape | Only constant strain possible | [7] |
| 2 | Three-node parabolic element | | † | $N_i = \frac{1}{2}\xi_0(1+\xi_0); \ i=1,3$ $N_i = (1-\xi^2); \ i=2$ | Curve possible | ..... | [7] |
| 3 | Four-node cubic element | | † | $N_i = \frac{1}{16}(1+\xi_0)(9\xi^2-1)$ $i=1,4$ $N_i = \frac{9}{16}(1+9\xi_0)(1-\xi^2)$ $i=2,3$ | Curve possible | ..... | [7] |
| 4 | Five-node quartic element | | † | $N_i = \frac{1}{6}(1+\xi_0)\{4\xi_0(1-\xi^2)+3\xi_0\}$ $i=1,5$ $N_i = 4\xi_0(1-\xi^2)(1+4\xi_0)$ $i=2,4$ $N_3 = (1-4\xi^2)(1-\xi^2)$ | Curve possible | ..... | [8] |

† These elements can be used in 1D($u$), 2D($u$, $v$), and 3D($u$, $v$, $w$) cartesian coordinate spaces.
†† Referred to as a *truss element* in structural engineering.

**TABLE 4.2** Two-Dimensional (Plane) Isoparametric Elements† ($\xi_0 = \xi_i\xi$; $\eta_0 = \eta_i\eta$ for Node $i$)

| Serial no. | Element name | Configuration | DOF | Shape functions | Advantages | Disadvantages | Ref. |
|---|---|---|---|---|---|---|---|
| 1 | Four-node plane quadrilateral‡ | | $u, v$ | $N_i = \frac{1}{4}(1+\xi_0)(1+\eta_0)$ <br> $i = 1, 2, 3, 4$ | Simple geometric shape | Poor approximating power <br> Decline of accuracy with shape distortion | [7] |
| 2 | Eight-node plane quadrilateral‡ | | $u, v$ | $N_i = \frac{1}{4}(1+\xi_0)(1+\eta_0)(\xi_0+\eta_0-1)$ <br> $i = 1, 3, 5, 7$ <br> $N_i = \frac{1}{2}(1-\xi^2)(1+\eta_0)$ <br> $i = 2, 6$ <br> $N_i = \frac{1}{2}(1-\eta^2)(1+\xi_0)$ <br> $i = 4, 8$ | Curved sides possible <br> Easily adaptable to crack tip by moving midside nodes <br> Ideal for nonlinear formulations | Decline of accuracy with excessive shape distortion | [7] |
| 3 | Twelve-node plane quadrilateral | | $u, v$ | $N_i = \frac{1}{32}(1+\xi_0)(1+\eta_0)(-10+9(\xi^2+\eta^2))$ <br> $i = 1, 4, 7, 10$ <br> $N_i = \frac{9}{32}(1+\xi_0)(1+\eta^2)(1+9\eta_0)$ <br> $i = 5, 6, 11, 12$ <br> $N_i = \frac{9}{32}(1+\eta_0)(1-\xi^2)(1+9\xi_0)$ <br> $i = 2, 3, 8, 9$ | Curved sides possible <br> Easily adaptable to fracture-mechanics applications <br> Ideal for nonlinear formulations | Decline of accuracy with excessive shape distortion | [7] |

| | | | | | | |
|---|---|---|---|---|---|---|
| 4 | Six-node plane quadrilateral | | $u, v$ | $N_i = \dfrac{\xi_0}{4}(1+\xi_0)(1+\eta_0)$ $i = 1, 3, 4, 6$ $N_i = \dfrac{1}{2}(1-\xi^2)(1+\eta_0)$ $i = 2, 5$ | Curved sides possible Ideal for nonlinear formulations Useful for transitioning from parabolic to linear elements or vice versa | Decline of accuracy with excessive shape distortion | [8] |
| 5 | Eight-node plane quadrilateral | | $u, v$ | $N_i = \dfrac{1}{32}(1+\xi_0)(-1+9\xi^2)(1+\eta_0)$ $i = 1, 4, 5, 8$ $N_i = \dfrac{9}{32}(1-\xi^2)(1+9\xi_0)(1+\eta_0)$ $i = 2, 3, 6, 7$ | Curved sides possible Ideal for nonlinear formulations Useful for transitioning from cubic to linear elements or vice versa | Decline of accuracy with excessive shape distortion | [8] |
| 6 | Seven-node plane quadrilateral | | $u, v$ | $N_1 = -\dfrac{1}{4}(1-\xi)(1-\eta)(1+\xi+\eta)$ $N_2 = \dfrac{1}{2}(1-\eta)(1-\xi^2)$ $N_3 = \dfrac{\xi}{4}(1+\xi)(1-\eta)$ $N_4 = \dfrac{\xi}{4}(1+\xi)(1+\eta)$ $N_5 = \dfrac{1}{2}(1+\eta)(1-\xi^2)$ $N_6 = -\dfrac{1}{4}(1-\xi)(1+\eta)(1+\xi-\eta)$ $N_7 = \dfrac{1}{2}(1-\eta^2)$ | Curved sides possible Ideal for nonlinear formulations Useful for transitioning from parabolic to linear elements or vice versa | Decline of accuracy with excessive shape distortion | [8] |

† For plane stress, plane strain, axisymmetric solid, etc.
‡ Behavior improves by adding an internal node.

2.123

**TABLE 4.2** Two-Dimensional (Plane) Isoparametric Elements† ($\xi_0 = \xi_i\xi$; $\eta_0 = \eta_i\eta$ for Node i) (*Continued*)

| Serial no. | Element name | Configuration | DOF | Shape functions | Advantages | Disadvantages | Ref. |
|---|---|---|---|---|---|---|---|
| 7 | Nine-node plane quadrilateral | | $u, v$ | $N_i = \frac{1}{32}(1+\xi_0)\{-9(1-\xi^2)+\eta_0(1-9\xi^2)+8\eta^2\}$<br>$i = 1, 8$<br>$N_i = \frac{1}{32}(1+\xi_0)(-1+9\xi^2)(1+\eta_0)$<br>$i = 4, 5$<br>$N_i = \frac{9}{32}(1-\xi^2)(1+9\xi_0)(1+\eta_0)$<br>$i = 2, 3, 6, 7$<br>$N_9 = \frac{1}{2}(1-\xi)(1-\eta^2)$ | Curved sides possible<br>Ideal for nonlinear formulations<br>Useful for transitioning from cubic to parabolic and linear elements | Decline of accuracy with excessive shape distortion | [8] |
| 8 | Ten-node plane quadrilateral | | $u, v$ | $N_i = \frac{1}{32}(1+\xi_0)(1+\eta_0)\{-10+9(\xi^2+\eta^2)\}$<br>$i = 1, 8$<br>$N_i = \frac{1}{32}(1+\xi_0)(-1+9\xi^2)(1+\eta_0)$<br>$i = 4, 5$<br>$N_i = \frac{9}{32}(1-\xi^2)(1+9\xi_0)(1+\eta_0)$<br>$i = 2, 3, 6, 7$<br>$N_i = \frac{9}{32}(1+\xi_0)(1-\eta^2)(1+9\eta_0)$<br>$i = 9, 10$ | Curved sides possible<br>Ideal for nonlinear formulations<br>Useful for transitioning from cubic to linear elements or vice versa | Decline of accuracy with excessive shape distortion | [8] |
| 9 | Six-node plane quadrilateral | | $u, v$ | $N_1 = \frac{1}{4}(1-\xi)(1-\eta)$<br>$N_2 = \frac{-\eta}{4}(1+\xi)(1-\eta)$<br>$N_3 = \frac{1}{4}(1+\xi)(1-\eta^2)$<br>$N_4 = \frac{1}{4}(1+\xi)(1+\eta)(\xi+\eta-1)$<br>$N_5 = \frac{1}{2}(1+\eta)(1-\xi^2)$<br>$N_6 = -\frac{\xi}{4}(1-\xi)(1+\eta)$ | Curved sides possible<br>Ideal for nonlinear formulations<br>Useful for transitioning from parabolic to linear elements or vice versa | Decline of accuracy with excessive shape distortion | [8] |

| | Element | | u, v | Shape functions | | | |
|---|---|---|---|---|---|---|---|
| 10 | Three-node plane triangle | | $u, v$ | $N_1 = L_1$<br>$N_2 = L_2$<br>$N_3 = L_3$ | Simple geometric shape<br>Good modeling aid for complex shapes with sharp corners | Only constant strain possible | [7] |
| 11 | Six-node plane triangle | | $u, v$ | $N_1 = L_1(2L_1 - 1)$<br>$N_2 = 4L_1L_2$<br>$N_3 = L_2(2L_2 - 1)$<br>$N_4 = 4L_2L_3$<br>$N_5 = L_3(2L_3 - 1)$<br>$N_6 = 4L_3L_1$ | Curved sides possible<br>Ideal for nonlinear formulations<br>Good modeling aid for complex shapes with sharp corners | Decline of accuracy with excessive shape distortion | [7] |
| 12 | Ten-node plane triangle | | $u, v$ | $N_1 = \frac{1}{2}(3L_1 - 1)(3L_1 - 2)L_1$<br>$N_2 = \frac{9}{2}L_1L_2(3L_1 - 1)$<br>$N_3 = \frac{9}{2}L_1L_2(3L_2 - 1)$<br>$N_4 = \frac{3}{4}(3L_2 - 1)(3L_2 - 2)L_2$<br>$N_5 = \frac{9}{2}L_2L_3(3L_2 - 1)$<br>$N_6 = \frac{9}{2}L_2L_3(3L_3 - 1)$<br>$N_7 = \frac{1}{2}(3L_3 - 1)(3L_3 - 2)L_3$<br>$N_8 = \frac{9}{2}L_3L_1(3L_3 - 1)$<br>$N_9 = \frac{9}{2}L_3L_1(3L_1 - 1)$<br>$N_{10} = 27L_1L_2L_3$ | Curved sides possible<br>Ideal for nonlinear formulations<br>Good modeling aid for complex shapes with sharp corners | Decline of accuracy with excessive shape distortion | [7] |

2.125

**TABLE 4.3** Three-Dimensional (Solid) Isoparametric Elements ($\xi_0 = \xi_i\xi$, $\eta_0 = \eta_i\eta$, $\zeta_0 = \zeta_i\zeta$ for Node $i$)

| Serial no. | Element name | Configuration | DOF | Shape functions | Advantages | Disadvantages | Ref. |
|---|---|---|---|---|---|---|---|
| 1 | Eight-node 3D solid† | | $u, v, w$ | $N_i = \frac{1}{8}(1+\xi_0)(1+\eta_0)(1+\zeta_0)$<br>$i = 1, 2, \ldots 8$ | Simple geometric shape | Poor approximating power. Decline of accuracy with shape distortion | [7] |
| 2 | Twenty-node 3D solid† | | $u, v, w$ | $N_i = \frac{1}{8}(1+\xi_0)(1+\eta_0)(1+\zeta_0)(\xi_0 + \eta_0 + \zeta_0 - 2)$<br>$i = 1, 3, 5, 7, 13, 15, 17, 19$<br>$N_i = \frac{1}{4}(1-\xi^2)(1+\eta_0)(1+\zeta_0)$<br>$i = 2, 6, 14, 18$<br>$N_i = \frac{1}{4}(1-\eta^2)(1+\xi_0)(1+\zeta_0)$<br>$i = 4, 8, 16, 20$<br>$N_i = \frac{1}{4}(1-\zeta^2)(1+\xi_0)(1+\eta_0)$<br>$i = 9, 10, 11, 12$ | Curved sides and faces possible. Easily adaptable to fracture-mechanics applications. Ideal for nonlinear formulations | Decline of accuracy with excessive shape distortion | [7] |
| 3 | Thirty-two-node 3D solid | | $u, v, w$ | $N_i = \frac{1}{64}(1+\xi_0)(1+\eta_0)(1+\zeta_0)$<br>$\times \{9(\xi^2 + \eta^2 + \zeta^2) - 19\}$<br>$i = 1, 4, 7, 10, 21, 24, 27, 30$<br>$N_i = \frac{9}{64}(1-\xi^2)(1+9\xi_0)(1+\eta_0)(1+\zeta_0)$<br>$i = 2, 3, 8, 9, 22, 28, 29$<br>$N_i = \frac{9}{64}(1-\eta^2)(1+9\eta_0)(1+\xi_0)(1+\zeta_0)$<br>$i = 5, 6, 11, 12, 25, 26, 31, 32$<br>$N_i = \frac{9}{64}(1-\zeta^2)(1+9\zeta_0)(1+\xi_0)(1+\eta_0)$<br>$i = 13, 14, 15, 16, 17, 18, 19, 20$ | Curved sides possible. Easily adaptable to fracture-mechanics applications. Ideal for nonlinear formulations | Decline of accuracy with excessive shape distortion | [7] |

| | | $u, v, w$ | Curved sides and faces possible | Decline of accuracy with excessive shape distortion | [8] |
|---|---|---|---|---|---|
| 4 | Sixteen-node 3D solid | $N_i = \frac{1}{8}(1+\xi_0)(1+\eta_0)(\xi_0 + \eta_0 - 1)(1+\zeta_0)$ $i = 1, 3, 5, 7, 9, 11, 13, 15$ $N_i = \frac{1}{4}(1-\xi^2)(1+\eta_0)(1+\zeta_0)$ $i = 2, 6, 10, 14$ $N_i = \frac{1}{4}(1-\eta^2)(1+\xi_0)(1+\zeta_0)$ $i = 4, 8, 12, 16$ | Ideal for nonlinear formulations Useful for transitioning from parabolic to linear elements or vice versa | | |
| 5 | Twenty-four-node 3D solid | $N_i = \frac{1}{64}(1+\xi_0)(1+\eta_0)$ $\times(-10+9(\xi^2+\eta^2))(1+\zeta_0)$ $i = 1, 4, 7, 10, 13, 16, 19, 22$ $N_i = \frac{9}{64}(1+\xi_0)(1-\eta^2)(1+9\eta_0)(1+\zeta_0)$ $i = 5, 6, 11, 12, 17, 18, 23, 24$ $N_i = \frac{9}{64}(1+\eta_0)(1-\xi^2)(1+9\xi_0)(1+\zeta_0)$ $i = 2, 3, 8, 9, 14, 15, 20, 21$ | Curved sides and faces possible Ideal for nonlinear formulations Useful for transitioning from cubic to linear elements or vice versa | Decline of accuracy with excessive shape distortion | [8] |
| 6 | Eighteen-node 3D solid | $N_i = \frac{1}{8}(1+\xi_0)(1+\eta_0)(1+\zeta_0)(\xi_0 + \eta_0 + \zeta_0 - 2)$ $i = 1, 3, 5, 7$ $N_i = \frac{1}{4}(1-\eta^2)(1+\xi_0)(1+\zeta_0)$ $i = 2, 6$ $N_i = \frac{1}{4}(1-\zeta^2)(1+\xi_0)(1+\eta_0)$ $i = 4, 8$ $N_i = \frac{1}{8}(1+\xi_0)(1+\eta_0)(1+\zeta_0)(\xi - (1+\eta_0))$ $i = 10, 12, 15, 17$ $N_i = \frac{1}{4}(1+\eta_0)(1-\zeta^2)(1+\zeta_0)$ $i = 9, 13, 14, 18$ $N_i = \frac{1}{4}(1-\eta^2)(1+\xi_0)(1+\zeta_0)$ $i = 11, 16$ | Curved sides possible Ideal for nonlinear formulations Useful for transitioning from parabolic to linear elements or vice versa | Decline of accuracy with excessive shape distortion | [8] |

† Behavior improves by adding an internal node.

2.127

**TABLE 4.3** Three-Dimensional (Solid) Isoparametric Elements ($\xi_0 = \xi_i\xi$, $\eta_0 = \eta_i\eta$, $\zeta_0 = \zeta_i\zeta$ for Node $i$) (*Continued*)

| Serial no. | Element name | Configuration | DOF | Shape functions | Advantages | Disadvantages | Ref. |
|---|---|---|---|---|---|---|---|
| 7 | Twenty-eight-node 3D solid | | $u, v, w$ | $N_i = \frac{1}{64}(1+\xi_0)(1+\eta_0)(1+\zeta_0)$ $\times \{9(\xi^2+\eta^2+\zeta^2)-19\}$ <br> $i = 1, 4, 7, 10$ <br><br> $N_i = \frac{1}{64}(1-\eta^2)(1+\xi_0)(1+9\eta_0)(1+\zeta_0)$ <br> $i = 2, 3, 8, 9$ <br><br> $N_i = \frac{9}{64}(1-\zeta^2)(1+\xi_0)(1+\eta_0)(1+9\zeta_0)$ <br> $i = 5, 6, 11, 12$ <br><br> $N_i = \frac{9}{64}(1-\xi^2)(1+9\xi_0)(1+\eta_0)(1+\zeta_0)$ <br> $i = 13, 14, 19, 20, 21, 22, 27, 28$ <br><br> $N_i = \frac{1}{64}(1+\xi_0)(1+\eta_0)(1+\zeta_0)\{9(\xi^2+\eta^2)-10\}$ <br> $i = 15, 18, 23, 26$ <br><br> $N_i = \frac{9}{64}(1+\xi_0)(1+\zeta_0)(1+9\eta_0)(1-\eta^2)$ <br> $i = 16, 17, 24, 25$ | Curved sides possible <br> Ideal for nonlinear formulations <br> Useful for transitioning from cubic to linear elements or vice versa | Decline of accuracy with excessive shape distortion | [8] |
| 8 | Four-node linear tetrahedron | | $u, v, w$ | $N_1 = L_1$ <br> $N_2 = L_2$ <br> $N_3 = L_3$ <br> $N_4 = L_4$ | Simple geometric shape <br> Good modeling aid for complex solids with sharp corners | Only constant strain possible | [7] |

| | | | $u, v, w$ | | | |
|---|---|---|---|---|---|---|
| 9 | Ten-node parabolic tetrahedron | | $N_1 = L_1(2L_1-1); N_2 = 4L_1L_2$ <br> $N_3 = L_2(2L_2-1); N_4 = 4L_2L_3$ <br> $N_5 = L_3(2L_3-1); N_6 = 4L_3L_1$ <br> $N_7 = 4L_1L_4; N_8 = 4L_2L_4$ <br> $N_9 = 4L_3L_4; N_{10} = L_4(2L_4-1)$ | Curved sides and faces possible Ideal for nonlinear formulations Good modeling aid for complex solids with sharp corners | Decline of accuracy with excessive shape distortion | [7] |
| 10 | Twenty-node cubic tetrahedron | | $N_1 = \frac{1}{2}(3L_1-1)(3L_1-2)L_1;$ <br> $N_2 = \frac{9}{2}L_1L_2(3L_1-1);$ <br> $N_3 = \frac{9}{2}L_1L_2(3L_2-1);$ <br> $N_4 = \frac{1}{2}(3L_2-1)(3L_2-2)L_2;$ <br> $N_5 = \frac{9}{2}L_2L_3(3L_2-1);$ <br> $N_6 = \frac{9}{2}L_2L_3(3L_3-1);$ <br> $N_7 = \frac{1}{2}(3L_3-1)(3L_3-2)L_3;$ <br> $N_8 = \frac{9}{2}L_3L_4(3L_3-1);$ <br> $N_9 = \frac{9}{2}L_3L_4(3L_4-1); N_{10} = 27L_1L_2L_3$ <br> $N_{11} = \frac{9}{2}L_1L_4(3L_1-1); N_{12} = \frac{9}{2}L_2L_4(3L_2-1);$ <br> $N_{13} = \frac{9}{2}L_3L_4(3L_3-1); N_{14} = \frac{9}{2}L_1L_4(3L_4-1);$ <br> $N_{15} = \frac{9}{2}L_2L_4(3L_4-1); N_{16} = \frac{9}{2}L_2L_4(3L_4-1);$ <br> $N_{17} = \frac{1}{2}(3L_4-1)(3L_4-2)L_4; N_{18} = 27L_1L_3L_4$ <br> $N_{19} = 27L_1L_2L_4; N_{20} = 27L_2L_3L_4$ | Curved sides and faces possible Ideal for nonlinear formulations Good modeling aid for complex solides with sharp corners | Decline of accuracy with excessive shape distortion | [7] |

**TABLE 4.3** Three-Dimensional (Solid) Isoparametric Elements ($\xi_0 = \xi_i\xi$, $\eta_0 = \eta_i\eta$, $\zeta_0 = \zeta_i\zeta$ for Node $i$) (*Continued*)

| Serial no. | Element name | Configuration | DOF | Shape functions | Advantages | Disadvantages | Ref. |
|---|---|---|---|---|---|---|---|
| 11 | Six-node linear wedge | | $u, v, w$ | $N_i = \frac{1}{2}L_1(1+\zeta_0)$; $i = 1, 4$ <br> $N_i = \frac{1}{2}L_2(1+\zeta_0)$; $i = 2, 5$ <br> $N_i = \frac{1}{2}L_3(1+\zeta_0)$; $i = 3, 6$ | Good modeling aid for complex solids with sharp corners | Poor approximating power | [7] |
| 12 | Fifteen-node parabolic wedge | | $u, v, w$ | $N_i = \frac{1}{2}L_1(2L_1-1)(1+\zeta_0) - \frac{1}{2}L_1(1-\zeta^2)$ <br> $i = 1, 10$ <br> $N_i = \frac{1}{2}L_2(2L_2-1)(1+\zeta_0) - \frac{1}{2}L_2(1-\zeta^2)$ <br> $i = 3, 12$ <br> $N_i = \frac{1}{2}L_3(2L_3-1)(1+\zeta_0) - \frac{1}{2}L_3(1-\zeta^2)$ <br> $i = 5, 14$ <br> $N_7 = 2L_1L_2(1+\zeta_0)$; $i = 2, 11$ <br> $N_7 = 2L_2L_3(1+\zeta_0)$; $i = 4, 13$ <br> $N_7 = 2L_3L_1(1+\zeta_0)$; $i = 6, 15$ <br> $N_7 = L_1(1-\zeta^2)$ <br> $N_8 = L_2(1-\zeta^2)$ <br> $N_9 = L_3(1-\zeta^2)$ | Curved sides and faces possible <br> Ideal for nonlinear formulations <br> Good modeling aid for complex solids with sharp corners | Decline of accuracy with excessive shape distortion | [7] |

| 13 | Nine-node wedge | | $u, v, w$ | $N_i = \frac{L_1}{2}\zeta_0(1+\zeta_0); i = 1,7$ <br> $N_i = \frac{L_2}{2}\zeta_0(1+\zeta_0); i = 2,8$ <br> $N_i = \frac{L_3}{2}\zeta_0(1+\zeta_0); i = 3,9$ <br> $N_4 = L_1(1-\zeta^2)$ <br> $N_5 = L_2(1-\zeta^2)$ <br> $N_6 = L_3(1-\zeta^2)$ | Curved sides possible <br> Good modeling aid for complex solids with sharp corners <br> Useful for transitioning | Poor approximating power | [8] |
| 14 | Twelve-node wedge | | $u, v, w$ | $N_i = \frac{1}{2}L_1(2L_1-1)(1+\zeta_0); i = 1,7$ <br> $N_i = \frac{1}{2}L_2(2L_2-1)(1+\zeta_0); i = 3,9$ <br> $N_i = \frac{1}{2}L_3(2L_3-1)(1+\zeta_0); i = 5,11$ <br> $N_i = 2L_1L_2(1+\zeta_0); i = 2,8$ <br> $N_i = 2L_2L_3(1+\zeta_0); i = 4,10$ <br> $N_i = 2L_3L_1(1+\zeta_0); i = 6,12$ | Curved sides and faces possible <br> Good modeling aid for complex solids with sharp corners <br> Useful for transitioning | Decline of accuracy with excessive shape distortion | [8] |

2.131

### 4.4A Classical Circular-Arch Elements

A prismatic arch of circular centerline is shown in Fig. 4.7, wherein the pertinent parameters are illustrated.

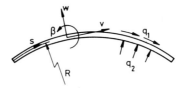

**FIG. 4.7**   Circular-arch geometry.

The assumptions of a "classical," or "first-approximation," arch theory include statements that the arch is slender, the deflections are small, material behavior is elastic, the transverse normal stress is negligible, and normals to the middle surface of the arch remain normal to it and undergo no change in length during the deformation process. The normalcy condition (the Kirchhoff–Love condition) means that transverse-shear effects are ignored, and this, together with the assumption regarding transverse normal stress, means that the strain energy of the arch is expressible as the sum of membrane and bending energies only [9, 10].

The extensional strain of the middle surface is

$$\varepsilon = \frac{dv}{ds} + \frac{w}{R} \tag{4.40}$$

the cross-sectional rotation is

$$\beta = \frac{dw}{ds} - \frac{v}{R} \tag{4.41}$$

and the curvature change due to loading is

$$\kappa = \frac{d\beta}{ds} = \frac{d^2 w}{ds^2} - \frac{1}{R}\frac{dv}{ds} \tag{4.42}$$

The strain energy $U$ is

$$U = \frac{E}{2} \int_s (A_c \varepsilon^2 + I\kappa^2)\, ds \tag{4.43}$$

where $A_c$ and $I$ are the cross-sectional area and second moment of area, respectively, while the potential energy of an applied distributed loading $q_1$ and $q_2$ per unit length, as shown in Fig. 4.7, is

$$\Omega = - \int_s (q_1 v + q_2 w)\, ds \tag{4.44}$$

The tangential force $N$ and the bending moment $M$ at a section are defined as

$$N = EA\varepsilon \qquad \text{and} \qquad M = EI\kappa \tag{4.45}$$

The differential equations of equilibrium in the tangential and radial directions are of interest and hence are presented here:

$$\frac{d^2v}{ds^2} + \frac{1}{R}\frac{dw}{ds} + e\left(\frac{1}{R^2}\frac{d^2v}{ds^2} - \frac{1}{R}\frac{d^3w}{ds^3}\right) = -\frac{q_1}{AE} \tag{4.46}$$

$$\frac{1}{R}\frac{dv}{ds} + \frac{w}{R^2} + e\left(\frac{d^4w}{ds^4} - \frac{1}{R}\frac{d^3v}{ds^3}\right) = -\frac{q_2}{AE} \tag{4.47}$$

where $e = I/A$.

For an arch finite element to be adjudged satisfactory it must perform efficiently in all situations; i.e., it must be able to represent accurately (but not necessarily exactly) both strain-free and strain-inducting states as appropriate.

When $q_1 = q_2 = 0$, the exact solutions to Eqs. (4.46) and (4.47) can be written [11, 12] in the form:

$$v = a_1\left(\frac{s}{R}\cos\frac{s}{R} - f\sin\frac{s}{R}\right) - a_2\left(\frac{s}{R}\sin\frac{s}{R} + f\cos\frac{s}{R}\right)$$

$$+ a_3\cos\frac{s}{R} - a_4\sin\frac{s}{R} - a_5\frac{s}{R} + a_6 \tag{4.48a}$$

$$w = a_1\frac{s}{R}\sin\frac{s}{R} + a_2\frac{s}{R}\cos\frac{s}{R} + a_3\sin\frac{s}{R} + a_4\cos\frac{s}{R} + a_5 \tag{4.48b}$$

where $f = (1 - I/AR^2)/(1 + I/AR^2)$.

On the basis of this displacement field, the exact stiffness matrix can be established [11]. Of course, the above solution is restricted to prismatic, end-loaded circular arches only.

The strain energy of the arch element given in Eq. (4.43) contains the first derivative of $v$ and the second derivative of $w$. Hence, a kinematically admissible arch element will require $C_0$-continuity for $v$ and $C_1$-continuity for $w$.

Here, we present five arch elements with uncoupled interpolating functions for $v$ and $w$. (All the degrees of freedom are assumed to be located at the two end nodes, but other arrangements of freedom are possible for the higher-order modes, for example by using internal nodes and hence restricting the freedoms at the nodes to those that are essential for inter-element compatibility requirements.)

1. The basic cubic-$w$–linear-$v$ (CL) model with

$$v = a_1 + a_2 s \tag{4.49a}$$

$$w = a_3 + a_4 s + a_5 s^2 + a_6 s^3 \tag{4.49b}$$

and degrees of freedom $v$, $w$, and $dw/ds$.

2. A cubic–cubic (CC) model with

$$v = a_1 + a_2 s + a_3 s^2 + a_4 s^3 \tag{4.50a}$$

$$w = a_5 + a_6 s + a_7 s^2 + a_8 s^3 \tag{4.50b}$$

and degrees of freedom $v$, $dv/ds$, $w$, and $dw/ds$.

3. A quintic–cubic (QC) model with

$$v = a_1 + a_2 s + a_3 s^2 + a_4 s^3 \tag{4.51a}$$

$$w = a_5 + a_6 s + a_7 s^2 + a_8 s^3 + a_9 s^4 + a_{10} s^5 \tag{4.51b}$$

and degrees of freedom $v$, $dv/ds$, $w$, $dw/ds$, and $d^2w/ds^2$.

4. A cubic–quintic (CQ) model with

$$v = a_1 + a_2 s + a_3 s^2 + a_4 s^3 + a_5 s^4 + a_6 s^5 \tag{4.52a}$$

$$w = a_7 + a_8 s + a_9 s^2 + a_{10} s^3 \tag{4.52b}$$

and degrees of freedom $v$, $dv/ds$, $d^2v/ds^2$, $w$, and $dw/ds$.

5. A quintic–quintic (QQ) model with

$$v = a_1 + a_2 s + a_3 s^2 + a_4 s^3 + a_5 s^4 + a_6 s^5 \tag{4.53a}$$

$$w = a_7 + a_8 s + a_9 s^2 + a_{10} s^3 + a_{11} s^4 + a_{12} s^5 \tag{4.53b}$$

and degrees of freedom $v$, $dv/ds$, $d^2v/ds^2$, $w$, $dw/ds$, and $d^2w/ds^2$.

The CL and CC models have been used in Refs. [12, 15–17], while the CC, QC, and QQ models have been studied in Refs. [13, 14]. In addition, two models which are based on coupled displacement fields and which have been fully tested in numerical applications can be identified as follows.

6. The rigid-body (RB) model with

$$v = A_1 \cos \frac{s}{R} - A_2 \sin \frac{s}{R} - A_3 R \left( 1 - \cos \phi \cos \frac{s}{R} \right) + A_4 s \tag{4.54a}$$

$$w = A_1 \sin \frac{s}{R} + A_2 \cos \frac{s}{R} + A_3 R \cos \phi \sin \frac{s}{R} + A_5 s^2 + A_6 s^3 \tag{4.54b}$$

where $2\phi$ is the angle subtended by the arch element.
The degrees of freedom at the end nodes are the basic ones, namely, $v$, $w$, and $\beta$ [15, 18].

7. The assumed strain-curvature (SC) model with

$$\varepsilon = \frac{dv}{ds} + \frac{w}{R} = B_1 \quad \text{and} \quad \kappa = \frac{d^2w}{ds^2} - \frac{1}{R}\frac{dv}{ds} = B_2 + B_3 s \tag{4.55a, b}$$

The corresponding displacement field is

$$v = a_1 + a_2 \sin \frac{s}{R} + a_3 \cos \frac{s}{R} + a_5 s + \tfrac{1}{2} a_6 s^2 \tag{4.56a}$$

$$w = -a_2 \cos \frac{s}{R} + a_3 \sin \frac{s}{R} + a_4 - a_6 R s \tag{4.56b}$$

The performance of several of these elements has been tested both by theoretical error estimates [17, 19, 20] and in detailed numerical studies [12–17].

The pertinent features of the "exact" model [based on the displacement field given by Eq. (4.48)] and of the QQ, CC, and SC models are summarized under arch elements 1 to 4, respectively, of Table 4.5.

## 4.4b Other Arch Elements

For a more general arch geometry, use of the type of formulation described above for a circular arch becomes more difficult and other approaches can be envisaged. For the arbitrary arch (see Fig. 4.8), the curvilinear coordinate is $\alpha$ and $A$ is a parameter such that $A\,d\alpha$ is

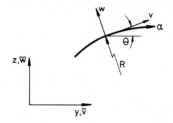

**FIG. 4.8**   Arbitrary arch geometry.

the line element along $\alpha$ (that is, $A\,d\alpha \equiv ds$). The radius of curvature $R$ in this case is variable. The expressions for the extensional strain $\varepsilon$, rotation $\beta$, and curvature change $\kappa$ are

$$\varepsilon = \frac{1}{A}\frac{dv}{d\alpha} + \frac{w}{R} \qquad \beta = \frac{1}{A}\frac{dw}{d\alpha} - \frac{v}{R} \qquad \kappa = \frac{1}{A}\frac{d\beta}{d\alpha} \qquad (4.57)$$

Here $1/R = -\theta' \cos\theta$, where $\theta = \tan^{-1}(z')$, and the prime denotes differentiation with respect to $y$. Table 4.4 summarizes the equations for $\varepsilon$, $\beta$, and $\kappa$, and for the rigid-body motion, for two types of formulation. For each type of formulation the exact arch strain-displacement equations for arbitrary geometry are given, followed by equations corresponding to two levels of approximation. For each of the six sets of strain-displacement equations, there are also recorded the rigid-body displacements $v_r$ and $w_r$, or $\bar{v}_r$ and $\bar{w}_r$, which correspond to zero extensional strain and curvature change in each case.

Curved finite elements have been developed on the basis of the four types of formulation symbolized by the sets of Eqs. (4.60) to (4.63) [21]. These formulations are approximate since each involves at least the assumption of shallow geometry.

In Table 4.5, in addition to the exact QQ, CC, and SC models for circular geometry summarized under arch elements 1 to 4, can be found three other models summarized respectively under arch elements 5 to 7. Elements 5 and 6 are based on the use of approximate first-order theory in the context of arbitrary shallow and arbitrary deep geometry, respectively. Element 7, on the other hand, is based on the use of a theory in which the Kirchhoff–Love condition is relaxed, allowing the analysis of arches of arbitrary geometry in which the effects of transverse shear deformation are included.

**TABLE 4.4** Equations for Various Types of Arch†

| Geometry | Formulation in terms of surface displacements and cartesian coordinates | Formulation in terms of cartesian displacements and coordinates |
|---|---|---|
| Arbitrary | $\varepsilon = v' \cos\theta + \dfrac{w}{R}$ <br><br> $\beta = w' \cos\theta - \dfrac{v}{R}$    (4.58a) <br><br> $\kappa = \cos\theta \dfrac{d}{dy}\left(w' \cos\theta - \dfrac{v}{R}\right)$ <br><br> where $\theta = \tan^{-1}(z')$ and $\dfrac{1}{R} = -\theta' \cos\theta$ <br><br> $v_r = \cos\theta\delta_y + \sin\theta\delta_z + \cos\theta(z - yz')\omega_x$    (4.58b) <br><br> $w_r = -\sin\theta\delta_y + \cos\theta\delta_z - \cos\theta(y + zz')\omega_x$ | $\varepsilon = \cos^2\theta(\bar{v}' + \bar{w}'z')$ <br><br> $\beta = \cos^2\theta(\bar{w}' - \bar{v}'z')$    (4.59a) <br><br> $\kappa = \cos^3\theta\{\bar{w}'' - \bar{v}''z' - \bar{v}'z'' - 2z'z'' \cos^2\theta(\bar{w}' - \bar{v}'z')\}$ <br><br> $\bar{v}_r = \delta_y + z\omega_x$    (4.59b) <br><br> $\bar{w}_r = \delta_y - y\omega_x$ |

## Shallow
### $(\cos\theta \approx 1,\ (z')^2 \ll 1,\ \text{etc.})$

$$\varepsilon = v' + \frac{w}{R}$$

$$\beta = w' - \frac{v}{R} \tag{4.60a}$$

$$\kappa = w'' - \frac{v'}{R}$$

where $R$ is assumed constant.

$$v_r = a_1 + a_2 \sin\frac{y}{R} - a_3 \cos\frac{y}{R}$$

$$w_r' = a_2 \cos\frac{y}{R} + a_3 \sin\frac{y}{R} \tag{4.60b}$$

$$\varepsilon = \bar{v}' + \bar{w}'z'$$

$$\beta = \bar{w}' - \bar{v}'z'$$

$$\kappa = \bar{w}'' - \bar{v}''z' - \bar{v}'z'' - 2z'z''\bar{w}' \tag{4.61a}$$

$$\bar{v}_r = \delta_y + z\omega_x$$

$$\bar{w}_r = \delta_z - y\omega_x \tag{4.61b}$$

## Shallow;
### neglect of $v$ or $\bar{v}$ derivatives in expressions for $\beta$ and $\kappa$

$$\varepsilon = v' + \frac{w}{R}$$

$$\beta = w' \tag{4.62a}$$

$$\kappa = w''$$

where $R$ is assumed constant.

$$u_r = a_1 + \frac{xa_2 - x^2 a_3/2}{R}$$

$$w_r = a_2 - xa_3 \tag{4.62b}$$

$$\varepsilon = \bar{v}' + \bar{w}'z'$$

$$\beta = \bar{w}'$$

$$\kappa = \bar{w}'' \tag{4.63a}$$

$$\bar{v}_r = \delta_y + z\omega_x$$

$$\bar{w}_r = \delta_z - y\omega_x \tag{4.63b}$$

† An overbar denotes differentiation with respect to $y$. $\delta_y$, $\delta_z$, and $\omega_x$ are, respectively, a rigid-body translation in the $y$-direction, a rigid-body translation in the $z$-direction, and a rigid-body rotation about the $x$-axis.

**2.137**

**TABLE 4.5**   Catalog of Arch Elements

---

Arch element 1, exact model

---

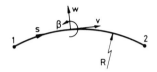

**FIG. A**

*Nodes and DOF*   Two end nodes with DOF $v$, $w$, and $\beta$.

*Displacement field*   Coupled field in terms of the curvilinear coordinate $s$, as Eq. (4.48).

*Geometry*   Uniform $R$.

*Advantages*   Gives exact solution, within classical arch theory, for any case involving nodal loads only.

*Disadvantages*   Philosophy cannot be extended to more general geometry.

*Reference*   [11].

---

Arch element 2, QQ model (see Fig. A)

---

*Nodes and DOF*   Two end nodes with DOF $v$, $dv/ds$, $d^2v/ds^2$, $w$, $dw/ds$, and $d^2w/ds^2$. Other arrangements can be used, however, to redistribute the 12 DOF [e.g., by the creation of two internal nodes at the $\frac{1}{3}$-points having DOF $v$, $dv/ds$, and $w$, with the end nodes left with the basic DOF $v$, $w$, $dw/ds$ (or $\beta$) only]. Alternatively, the nonbasic DOF can be eliminated by static condensation to leave a 6-DOF element.

*Displacement field*   Independent quintic interpolation in $s$, as Eq. (4.53).

*Geometry*   Uniform $R$ but capable of extension to general geometry.

*Advantages*   Very high accuracy for full range of depth and thinness of arch.

*Disadvantages*   In its basic form connection of all six freedoms at a node linking adjacent elements provides undesirable excessive continuity; this can be avoided, however, if element degrees of freedom are redistributed or the nonbasic freedoms are eliminated as described above.

*References*   [13, 14].

---

Arch element 3, CC model (see Fig. A)

---

*Nodes and DOF*   Two end nodes with DOF $v$, $dv/ds$, $w$, and $dw/ds$ (or $\beta$). The $dv/ds$ freedoms can be eliminated by static condensation to leave a 6-DOF element.

*Displacement field*   Independent cubic interpolation in $s$, as Eq. (4.50).

*Geometry*   Uniform $R$ but capable of extension to general geometry.

*Advantages*   Relatively simple element giving reasonable accuracy in situations of shallow and/or thick geometry.

*Disadvantages*   Efficiency of the element is problem-dependent and is poor when arch geometry is deep and thin; severe fluctuations of tangential-force distribution in latter circumstances.

*References*   [12–14, 16, 17].

**TABLE 4.5**   Catalog of Arch Elements (*Continued*)

---

Arch element 4, SC model (see Fig. A)

---

*Nodes and DOF*   Two end nodes with DOF $v$, $w$, $\beta$.

*Displacement field*   Coupled field in $s$, as Eq. (4.56).

*Geometry*   Uniform $R$.

*Advantages*   Good accuracy for full range of depth and thinness of arch. Precise representation of rigid-body motions and of states of uniform extensional strain and linear variation of curvature change. Uses basic nodal freedoms only.

*Disadvantages*   Difficult to extend the philosophy of the element to general geometry.

*Reference*   [12]

---

Arch element 5

---

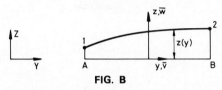

**FIG. B**

*Nodes and DOF*   Two end nodes with DOF $\bar{v}$, $\bar{w}$, and $\bar{w}'$.

*Displacement field*   Coupled field for cartesian components $\bar{v}$ and $\bar{w}$, as

$$\bar{v} = a_1 + a_2 y - a_3 z - 2a_4\left(yz - \int_0^y z\,dy\right) - 3a_5\left(y^2 z - \int_0^y 2yz\,dy\right)$$

$$\bar{w} = a_6 + a_3 y + a_4 y^2 + a_5 y^3$$

*Geometry*   The arch height $z = z(y)$ above its baseline $AB$ is interpolated in the same way as is $w$. The element is shallow ($z'^2 \ll 1$) and strain-displacement Eqs. (4.63$a$) apply. Local axes $y$, $z$ are aligned in the same directions as global axes $Y$, $Z$.

*Advantages*   Good accuracy for general shallow-arch geometry. The displacement field includes precise representation of rigid-body motions and of states of uniform extensional strain and linear variation of curvature change. Uses basic nodal freedoms only.

*Disadvantages*   The arch theory used is approximate, though errors involved are very small for shallow geometry.

*References*   [21, 22].

---

Arch element 6

---

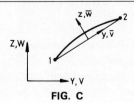

**FIG. C**

This element is simply the (shallow) arch element 5 used now in the analysis of deep arches. Details

**TABLE 4.5**   Catalog of Arch Elements (*Continued*)

with regard to the local axes *y*, *z* are as for arch element 5, with the specialization that the ends *A* and *B* of the local base line now coincide with nodes 1 and 2, which lie on the centerline of an arch. Transformation of the local translational freedoms $\bar{v}$ and $\bar{w}$ is required to corresponding global freedoms. These latter may be *V* and *W* or may, for a smooth arch, be surface components of displacement. This approach extends the range of shallow arch element 5 to provide an element which demonstrates good accuracy for deep, thin arch geometry [21]. It is noted that the further specialization that $z = 0$ for all *y* produces the simple, straight bar or beam element which has been used in arch analysis [17, 23].

---

Arch element 7

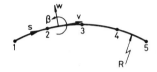

**FIG. D**

*Nodes and DOF*   Five nodes with DOF *v*, *w*, and $\beta$.

*Displacement field*   Independent interpolation of each of *v*, *w*, and $\beta$ by lagrangian polynomial functions (of *s*) of fourth degree.

*Geometry*   *R* interpolated in the same way as *v*, *w*, and $\beta$.

*Advantages*   Generally good accuracy for full range of depth and thinness of arch. Transverse-shear effects are included.

*Disadvantages*   Some fluctuations of tangential-force distributions for noncircular, deep arches.

*Reference*   [24].

---

The use of straight finite elements is another approach that can be employed to develop displacement-based elements to solve arch problems when using other than classical, or first-approximation, theory. Within the straight element there is no coupling at all between extensional and bending behavior, and this makes the representation of basic states, such as rigid-body motion and constant-strain states, a trivial matter: the coupling effect only comes into play on connecting adjacent elements together. It has been demonstrated, by Moan [17] and Kikuchi [23], that the straight-element approach does in fact provide convergence to the exact solution of Timoshenko arch theory as the element mesh is refined.

## 4.5 CIRCULAR CYLINDRICAL SHELL ELEMENTS

Almost all the cylindrical shell elements which have appeared in the literature have their counterparts in the simpler world of circular-arch analysis. These elements are usually based on a classical, first-approximation shell theory.

Koiter [26] has shown that it is permissible to add terms of the type $\varepsilon / R$ ($\varepsilon$ being any middle-surface strain component and *R* any initial radius of curvature of the middle surface) to expressions for curvature changes and that curvature-change expressions which differ only by terms of this type are equivalent in first-approximation theory. The question as to whether the strain-displacement equations of various first-approximation shell theories are consistent with a general rigid-body motion has been examined in Refs. [27, 28].

The cylindrical shell geometry, coordinates, and displacements (at the middle surface) are shown in Fig. 4.9. The shell is assumed to have uniform thickness $h$ and uniform radius

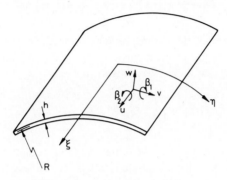

**FIG. 4.9** Cylindrical shell geometry.

of curvature (of its middle surface) $R$, and to be made of isotropic material. In first approximation shell theory, six strain-type quantities are defined in terms of the displacements for a cylindrical shell as in Ref. [1].

$$\varepsilon_1 = \frac{\partial u}{\partial \xi} \qquad \varepsilon_2 = \frac{\partial v}{\partial \eta} + \frac{w}{R} \qquad \gamma_{12} = \frac{\partial u}{\partial \eta} + \frac{\partial v}{\partial \xi}$$

$$\kappa_1 = \frac{\partial^2 w}{\partial \xi^2} \qquad \kappa_2 = \frac{\partial^2 w}{\partial \eta^2} - \frac{1}{R}\frac{\partial v}{\partial \eta} \qquad \text{and} \qquad \kappa_{12} = \frac{\partial^2 w}{\partial \xi \partial \eta} - \frac{1}{R}\frac{\partial v}{\partial \xi} \tag{4.64}$$

Here $\varepsilon_1$ and $\varepsilon_2$ are the extensional strains along $\xi$ and $\eta$, respectively; $\gamma_{12}$ is the shear strain; and $\kappa_1$, $\kappa_2$, and $\kappa_{12}$ are the components of the changes of curvature and twist referred to the $\xi$-, $\eta$-coordinates. The rotations $\beta_1$ and $\beta_2$ of the tangents to the middle surface along the $\xi$- and $\eta$-axes, respectively, are defined as

$$\beta_1 = \frac{\partial w}{\partial \xi} \qquad \text{and} \qquad \beta_2 = \frac{\partial w}{\partial \eta} - \frac{v}{R} \tag{4.65}$$

The stress resultants ($N_1$, $N_2$, and $N_{12}$) corresponding to ($\varepsilon_1$, $\varepsilon_2$, and $\gamma_{12}$) and couples ($M_1$, $M_2$, and $M_{12}$) corresponding to ($\kappa_1$, $\kappa_2$, and $\kappa_{12}$) are defined as

$$N_1 = C(\varepsilon_1 + \nu \varepsilon_2) \qquad N_2 = C(\varepsilon_2 + \nu \varepsilon_1) \qquad N_{12} = \tfrac{1}{2}(1-\nu)C\gamma_{12}$$

$$M_1 = D(\kappa_1 + \nu \kappa_2) \qquad M_2 = D(\kappa_2 + \nu \kappa_1) \qquad \text{and} \qquad M_{12} = D(1-\nu)\kappa_{12} \tag{4.66}$$

where $C = Eh/(1-\nu^2)$, $D = Eh^3/12(1-\nu^2)$.

In first-approximation theory the strain energy is expressed simply as the sum of membrane and bending energies in the form

$$U = \tfrac{1}{2} \int \int_{A_s} \left\{ C\left[ (\varepsilon_1 + \varepsilon_2)^2 - 2(1-\nu)\left( \varepsilon_1 \varepsilon_2 - \frac{\gamma_{12}^2}{4} \right) \right] \right.$$

$$\left. + D[(\kappa_1 + \kappa_2)^2 - 2(1-\nu)(\kappa_1 \kappa_2 - \kappa_{12}^2)] \right\} dA_s \qquad (4.67)$$

where $A_s$ denotes the area of the middle surface of the shell. The potential energy of an applied distributed loading having components $q_1$, $q_2$, and $q_3$ per unit surface area acting in the positive directions of $u$, $v$, and $w$, respectively, is

$$\Omega = -\int \int_{A_s} (q_1 u + q_2 v + q_3 w) \, dA_s \qquad (4.68)$$

When the integrals in Eqs. (4.67) and (4.68) are taken over a finite element, the expressions for $U$ and $\Omega$ provide the basis for the development of the stiffness matrix and the consistent load vector, respectively.

In the development of cylindrical shell elements, close consideration has often been given to the representation of the general rigid body motion. It is noted that in such a motion, the components of displacement have the form (with subscript $r$ implying rigid body motion),

$$u_r = Ra_2 \cos \frac{\eta}{R} + Ra_4 \sin \frac{\eta}{R} + a_5$$

$$v_r = (a_1 + a_2 \xi) \sin \frac{\eta}{R} - (a_3 + a_4 \xi) \cos \frac{\eta}{R} + a_6$$

$$w_r = -(a_1 + a_2 \xi) \cos \frac{\eta}{R} - (a_3 + a_4 \xi) \sin \frac{\eta}{R}$$

A displacement field for a simple conforming rectangular element with a total of 24 degrees of freedom is

$$u = a_1 + a_2 \xi + a_3 \eta + a_4 \xi \eta$$

$$v = a_5 + a_6 \xi + a_7 \eta + a_8 \xi \eta$$

$$w = a_9 + a_{10}\xi + a_{11}\eta + a_{12}\xi^2 + a_{13}\xi\eta + a_{14}\eta^2 + a_{15}\xi^3 + a_{16}\xi^2\eta + a_{17}\xi\eta^2 + a_{18}\eta^3$$

$$\qquad + a_{19}\xi^3\eta + a_{20}\xi^2\eta^2 + a_{21}\xi\eta^3 + a_{22}\xi^3\eta^2 + a_{23}\xi^2\eta^3 + a_{24}\xi^3\eta^3 \qquad (4.69)$$

The degrees of freedom at the corner nodes of this element are $u$, $v$, $w$, $\partial w/\partial \xi$, $\partial w/\partial \eta$, and $\partial^2 w/\partial \xi \partial \eta$. However, this element is extremely inefficient, and is the cylindrical shell element equivalent of circular-arch model CL. An improvement is obtained if $u$ and $v$ are interpolated in the same way as $w$, resulting in a 48-DOF element [29] which is designated cylindrical shell element 1 and is detailed in Table 4.6.

**TABLE 4.6**   Catalog of Cylindrical Shell Elements

---

Circular cylindrical shell element 1

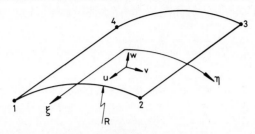

**FIG. A**

*Nodes and DOF*   Four corner nodes with DOF $u$, $\partial u/\partial \xi$, $\partial u/\partial \eta$, $\partial^2 u/\partial \xi \partial \eta$, $v$, $\partial v/\partial \xi$, $\partial v/\partial \eta$, $\partial^2 v/\partial \xi \partial \eta$, $w$, $\partial w/\partial \xi$, $\partial w/\partial \eta$, and $\partial^2 w/\partial \xi \partial \eta$: 48 DOF in total.

*Displacement field*   Independent bicubic polynomial interpolation for each of $u$, $v$, and $w$. Thus, for the $u$-component,

$$u = a_1 + a_2 \xi + a_3 \eta + a_4 \xi^2 + a_5 \xi \eta + a_6 \eta^2$$
$$+ a_7 \xi^3 + a_8 \xi^2 \eta + a_9 \xi \eta^2 + a_{10} \eta^3 + a_{11} \xi^3 \eta + a_{12} \xi^2 \eta^2$$
$$+ a_{13} \xi \eta^3 + a_{14} \xi^3 \eta^2 + a_{15} \xi^2 \eta^3 + a_{16} \xi^3 \eta^3$$

Expressions for $v$ and $w$ are similar.

*Advantages*   Fully conforming. Reasonably good accuracy for shells which are shallow or moderately deep and/or moderately thick.

*Disadvantages*   Efficiency of the element is problem-dependent and is generally poor for deep, thin geometry when severe fluctuations of calculated membrane-force distributions can be expected. Elements are connected together at nodes with excessive continuity.

*Reference*   [29].

---

Circular cylindrical shell element 2 (see Fig. A)

---

*Nodes and DOF*   Four corner nodes with DOF $u$, $v$, $w$, $\beta_1$ and $\beta_2$: 20 DOF in all.

*Displacement field*   The coupled field,

$$u = Ra_2 \cos \frac{\eta}{R} + Ra_4 \sin \frac{\eta}{r} + a_5 + a_7 \xi + (a_{11} + R^2 a_{19} - Ra_{20}) \frac{\eta}{R}$$

$$- \tfrac{1}{2} Ra_{17} \eta^2 + \frac{a_8}{R} \xi \eta - \tfrac{1}{6} a_{19} \eta^3$$

$$v = (a_1 + a_2 \xi) \sin \frac{\eta}{R} - (a_3 + a_4 \xi) \cos \frac{\eta}{R} + a_6$$

$$+ (-R^2 a_{19} + Ra_{20}) \xi + Ra_{16} \eta + Ra_{17} \xi \eta + \frac{a_{18}}{2} \eta^2 + \frac{a_{19}}{2} \xi \eta^2$$

$$w = -(a_1 + a_2 x) \cos \frac{\eta}{R} - (a_3 + a_4 x) \sin \frac{\eta}{R} + (Ra_9 - R^2 a_{16})$$

$$+ (Ra_{10} - R^2 a_{17}) \xi - Ra_{18} \eta - \frac{a_{12}}{2} \xi^2 - Ra_{19} \xi \eta - \frac{a_{13}}{6} \xi^3 - \frac{a_{14}}{2R} \xi^2 \eta - \frac{a_{15}}{6R} \xi^3 \eta$$

**TABLE 4.6**  Catalog of Cylindrical Shell Elements (*Continued*)

|  |  |
|---|---|
| *Advantages* | Rigid-body motions are represented exactly, as are basic states of strain and curvature. The only nodal freedoms used are the essential ones. Accuracy of the element appears to be usually good (despite the nonconformity) for thin and thick, deep and shallow geometry. |
| *Disadvantage* | The element is nonconforming. |
| *Reference* | [31]. |

Circular cylindrical shell element 3

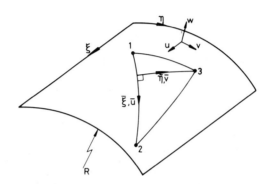

**FIG. B**  An arbitrarily oriented, straight-sided triangle in the developed surface of a cylinder.

|  |  |
|---|---|
| *Nodes and DOF* | Three corner nodes with global DOF $u$, $\partial u/\partial \xi$, $\partial u/\partial \eta$, $v$, $\partial v/\partial \xi$, $\partial v/\partial \eta$, $w$, $\partial w/\partial \xi$, $\partial w/\partial \eta$, $\partial^2 w/\partial \xi^2$, $\partial^2 w/\partial \xi \partial \eta$, and $\partial^2 w/\partial \eta^2$: 36 DOF in all. |
| *Displacement field* | The (local) $\bar{u}$-, $\bar{v}$-, and $\bar{w}$-components are independently interpolated in polynomial form. Basically $\bar{u}$ and $\bar{v}$ are represented by two-dimensional cubic expressions in $\bar{\xi}$ and $\bar{\eta}$, $\bar{w}$ by a two-dimensional quintic expression. Thus, initially, |

$$\bar{u} = a_1 + a_2\bar{\xi} + a_3\bar{\eta} + a_4\bar{\xi}^2 + a_5\bar{\xi}\bar{\eta} + a_6\bar{\eta}^2 + a_7\bar{\xi}^3 + a_8\bar{\xi}^2\bar{\eta} + a_9\bar{\xi}\bar{\eta}^2 + a_{10}\bar{\eta}^3$$

$$\bar{v} = a_{11} + a_{12}\bar{\xi} + a_{13}\bar{\eta} + a_{14}\bar{\xi}^2 + a_{15}\bar{\xi}\bar{\eta} + a_{16}\bar{\eta}^2 + a_{17}\bar{\xi}^3 + a_{18}\bar{\xi}^2\bar{\eta} + a_{19}\bar{\xi}\bar{\eta}^2 + a_{20}\bar{\eta}^3$$

$$\bar{w} = a_{21} + a_{22}\bar{\xi} + a_{23}\bar{\eta} + a_{24}\bar{\xi}^2 + a_{25}\bar{\xi}\bar{\eta} + a_{26}\bar{\eta}^2 + a_{27}\bar{\xi}^3$$
$$+ a_{28}\bar{\xi}^2\bar{\eta} + a_{29}\bar{\xi}\bar{\eta}^2 + a_{30}\bar{\eta}^3 + a_{31}\bar{\xi}^4 + a_{32}\bar{\xi}^3\bar{\eta} + a_{33}\bar{\xi}^2\bar{\eta}^2$$
$$+ a_{34}\bar{\xi}\bar{\eta}^3 + a_{35}\bar{\eta}^4 + a_{36}\bar{\xi}^5 + a_{37}\bar{\xi}^4\bar{\eta} + a_{38}\bar{\xi}^3\bar{\eta}^2 + a_{39}\bar{\xi}^2\bar{\eta}^3 + a_{40}\bar{\xi}\bar{\eta}^4 + a_{41}\bar{\eta}^5$$

|  |  |
|---|---|
|  | This field contains a total of 41 terms, whereas the element has only 36 DOF. The number of terms is brought into balance with the number of DOF by applying three subsidiary conditions on $\bar{w}$ and by condensing out one freedom associated with each of $\bar{u}$ and $\bar{v}$. |
| *Advantages* | The element is fully conforming, and its triangular shape is advantageous both for modeling geometric features (such as holes in the shell) and for mesh refinement. Accuracy of the element is good for shells of moderate depth and thickness. |
| *Disadvantages* | Accuracy is problem-dependent and generally reduces for deep, thin geometries where membrane forces can exhibit considerable fluctuations. Elements are connected together at nodes with excessive continuity. |
| *Reference* | [32]. |

**TABLE 4.6**   Catalog of Cylindrical Shell Elements (*Continued*)

---

Circular cylindrical shell element 4 (see Fig. B)

---

*Nodes and DOF*   Three corner nodes with global DOF $u$, $\partial u/\partial \xi$, $\partial u/\partial \eta$, $\partial^2 u/\partial \xi^2$, $\partial^2 u/\partial \xi \partial \eta$, $\partial^2 u/\partial \eta^2$, $v$, $\partial v/\partial \xi$, $\partial v/\partial \eta$, $\partial^2 v/\partial \xi^2$, $\partial^2 v/\partial \xi \partial \eta$, $\partial^2 v/\partial \eta^2$, $w$, $\partial w/\partial \xi$, $\partial w/\partial \eta$, $\partial^2 w/\partial \xi^2$, $\partial^2 w/\partial \xi \partial \eta$, and $\partial^2 w/\partial \eta^2$: 54 DOF in all.

*Displacement field*   The (local) $\bar{u}$-, $\bar{v}$-, and $\bar{w}$-components are each independently interpolated in the same way, being represented by two-dimensional quintic expressions in $\bar{\xi}$ and $\bar{\eta}$. Thus, initially,

$$\bar{u} = a_1 + a_2\bar{\xi} + a_3\bar{\eta} + a_4\bar{\xi}^2 + a_5\bar{\xi}\bar{\eta} + a_6\bar{\eta}^2 + a_7\bar{\xi}^3 + a_8\bar{\xi}^2\bar{\eta}$$
$$+ a_9\bar{\xi}\bar{\eta}^2 + a_{10}\bar{\eta}^3 + a_{11}\bar{\xi}^4 + a_{12}\bar{\xi}^3\bar{\eta} + a_{13}\bar{\xi}^2\bar{\eta}^2 + a_{14}\bar{\xi}\bar{\eta}^3$$
$$+ a_{15}\bar{\eta}^4 + a_{16}\bar{\xi}^5 + a_{17}\bar{\xi}^4\bar{\eta} + a_{18}\bar{\xi}^3\bar{\eta}^2 + a_{19}\bar{\xi}^2\bar{\eta}^3 + a_{20}\bar{\xi}\bar{\eta}^4 + a_{21}\bar{\eta}^4$$

with similar expressions for $\bar{v}$ and $\bar{w}$. The complete field contains a total of 63 terms, whereas the element has only 54 DOF. The number of terms is brought into balance with the number of DOF by applying three subsidiary conditions on each of $u$, $v$, and $w$.

*Advantages*   The element is fully conforming, and its triangular shape is advantageous both for modeling geometric features and for mesh refinement. Accuracy of the element is very good for the full range of shell geometry, being largely unaffected by depth or thinness considerations.

*Disadvantage*   Elements are connected together at nodes with excessive continuity.

*Reference*   [33].

---

A different approach was adopted by Cantin and Clough [18], who gave priority to the exact representation of the rigid-body motions. This element is the shell equivalent of the circular-arch model RB (see Sec. 4.4) and would be expected to be inefficient for deep, thin-shell geometry. In a later paper Cantin [30] developed a method to include the rigid-body motions as an *a posteriori* correction in a stiffness analysis which is based on a displacement field that is otherwise acceptable. The element is completely strain-free under any rigid-body motion, but the complete displacements are not fully compatible at element boundaries.

For the simple geometry of the circular cylindrical shell, it is possible to develop a rectangular element based on an assumed strain (rather than displacement) field [31],

$$\varepsilon_1 = a_7 + a_8 \frac{\eta}{R}$$

$$\varepsilon_2 = a_9 + a_{10}\xi - \frac{a_{12}}{2R}\xi^2 - \frac{a_{13}}{6R}\xi^3 - \frac{a_{14}}{2R^2}\xi^2\eta - \frac{a_{15}}{6R^2}\xi^3\eta$$

$$\gamma_{12} = a_{11} + \frac{a_8\xi}{R} \tag{4.70}$$

$$\kappa_1 = a_{12} + a_{13}\xi + \frac{a_{14}\eta}{R} + \frac{a_{15}\xi\eta}{R}$$

$$\kappa_2 = a_{16} + a_{17}\xi + \frac{a_{18}\eta}{R} + \frac{a_{19}\xi\eta}{R}$$

$$\kappa_{12} = a_{20} + \frac{a_{14}\xi}{R} + \frac{a_{15}\xi^2}{2R} + a_{17}\eta + \frac{a_{19}}{2R}\eta^2 \qquad (4.70)$$

The complete displacement field is obtained by addition of the rigid body motion displacements to the displacements corresponding to equations (4.70). Unfortunately the field is a nonconforming one. This element is designated circular cylindrical shell element 2 in Table 4.6. It reduces to circular-arch model SC (arch element 4) when appropriate substitutions are made (see Table 4.5).

As far as triangular shell elements are concerned, two of these are presented in Table 4.6 as shell elements 3 and 4. They are shell-equivalents of circular-arch models QC and QQ in Table 4.5.

## 4.6 SHELLS OF REVOLUTION

Table 4.7 presents a catalog of elements for shells of revolution.

**TABLE 4.7**   Catalog of Elements for Shells of Revolution

| Truncated conical element |
|---|

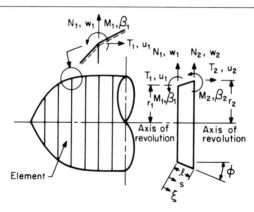

**FIG. A**

*Degrees of freedom*   Three degrees of freedom per nodal circle.

*Shape functions*

$$u = (1-\xi)u_1 + \xi u_2 - (\xi - 2\xi^2 + \xi^3)[\beta_1 l$$
$$+ (u_2 - u_1)\sin\phi - (w_2 - w_1)\cos\phi]\sin\phi$$
$$+ \xi^2(1-\xi)[\beta_2 l + (u_2 - u_1)\sin\phi - (w_2 - w_1)\cos\phi]\sin\phi$$

$$w = (1-\xi)w_1 + \xi w_2 + (\xi - 2\xi^2 + \xi^3)[\beta_1 l$$
$$+ (u_2 - u_1)\sin\phi - (w_2 - w_1)\cos\phi]\cos\phi$$
$$- \xi^2(1-\xi)[\beta_2 l + (u_2 - u_1)\sin\phi - (w_2 - w_1)\cos\phi]\cos\phi$$

$$\beta = \frac{dw}{ds}\cos\phi - \frac{du}{ds}\sin\phi$$

**TABLE 4.7**  Catalog of Elements for Shells of Revolution (*Continued*)

where $u$, $w$, $\beta$ = meridional and circumferential displacements and meridional rotation, respectively.

*Advantages*   Allows a cubic interpolation for $u$ and $w$.

*Disadvantages*   Does not represent curved meridian properly. Axisymmetrical loading only.

*Reference*   [34].

---

Conical frusta element

---

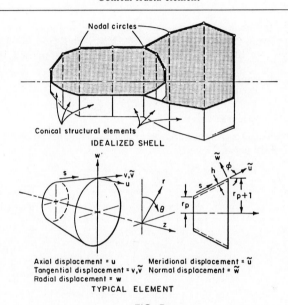

Axial displacement = u    Meridional displacement = $\tilde{u}$
Tangential displacement = v,$\tilde{v}$  Normal displacement = $\tilde{w}$
Radial displacement = w

TYPICAL ELEMENT

**FIG. B**

*Degrees of freedom*   Four degrees of freedom per nodal circle, namely, $u$, $v$, $w$, the meridional, circumferential, and normal displacements and $\beta$, the meridional rotation.

$$u_p(\theta) = q_{4p-3}^0 + \sum_{j=1}^{m} q_{4p-3}^j \cos j\theta + \sum_{j=1}^{m} \bar{q}_{4p-3}^j \sin j\theta$$

$$v_p(\theta) = q_{4p-2}^0 + \sum_{j=1}^{m} q_{4p-2}^j \sin j\theta + \sum_{j=1}^{m} \bar{q}_{4p-2}^j \cos j\theta$$

$$w_p(\theta) = q_{4p-1}^0 + \sum_{j=1}^{m} q_{4p-1}^j \cos j\theta + \sum_{j=1}^{m} \bar{q}_{4p-1}^j \sin j\theta$$

$$\beta_p(\theta) = q_{4p}^0 + \sum_{j=1}^{m} q_{4p}^j \cos j\theta + \sum_{j=1}^{m} \bar{q}_{4p}^j \sin j\theta$$

where $p$ = node number and $q$ = generalized displacement at node $p$.

*Advantages*   Incorporated in SABOR III, which allows the determination of the displacements and estimates the stress resultants and stress couples.

*Disadvantages*   Inaccurate representation of the shell geometry; inaccurate treatment of the singularity at the apex.

*References*   [35, 39].

**TABLE 4.7**   Catalog of Elements for Shells of Revolution (*Continued*)

---

Truncated conical shell element

---

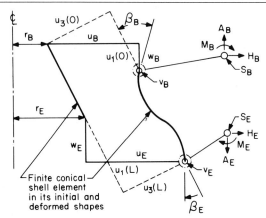

**FIG. C**   The circumferential displacement $v$ and force $s$ missing in the above diagram have their positive sense out of the plane of the paper.

*Degrees of freedom*   Four degrees of freedom per nodal circle.

*Shape functions*

$$
\begin{bmatrix} u_1 \\ u_2 \\ u_3 \end{bmatrix} = \sum_{n=0}^{\infty} \begin{bmatrix} \cos n\theta & & \\ & \sin n\theta & \\ & & \cos n\theta \end{bmatrix} \begin{bmatrix} u_{1:n} \\ u_{2:n} \\ u_{3:n} \end{bmatrix}
$$
$$
+ \sum_{m=0}^{\infty} \begin{bmatrix} \sin m\theta & & \\ & \cos m\theta & \\ & & \sin m\theta \end{bmatrix} \begin{bmatrix} u_{1:m} \\ u_{2:m} \\ u_{3:m} \end{bmatrix} \cdots
$$

where $u_1$, $u_2$, $u_3 =$ meridional, circumferential, and normal displacements, respectively.

*Advantages*   The element can model laminated orthotropic shell of revolution under arbitrary loads.

*Disadvantages*

*References*   [37].

---

Curved shell element

---

*Degrees of freedom*   Six degrees of freedom per nodal circle.

*Shape functions*   $\{\bar{u}^{(1)}, \bar{w}^{(1)}, \bar{\beta}^{(1)}, \bar{u}^{(2)}, \bar{w}^{(2)}, \bar{\beta}^{(2)}\} = [B][L]\{\bar{a}_2, \bar{a}_5, \dots, \bar{a}_9\}$

where $u$, $w =$ meridional and normal displacements, respectively, and $\beta =$ the meridional rotation, or

$\{\bar{u}^{(1)}, \bar{w}^{(1)}, \bar{\beta}^{(1)}, \bar{u}^{(2)}, \bar{w}^{(2)}, \bar{\beta}^{(2)}\} = [\lambda]\{u^{(1)}, w^{(1)}, \beta^{(1)}, u^{(2)}, w^{(2)}, \beta^{(2)}\}$

where $[\beta] =$ constant transformation matrix, $[L] =$ algebraic transformation matrix, and $[\lambda] =$ trigonometric transformation matrix.

*Advantages*   Accurate results for a spherical shell presented. Number of elements needed is less than for conical element.

**TABLE 4.7**  Catalog of Elements for Shells of Revolution (*Continued*)

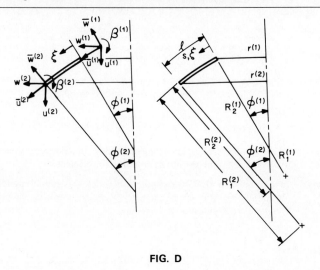

**FIG. D**

*Disadvantages*   Results for an elliptical shell required a large number of elements to minimize errors.

*Reference*   [36].

Curved element

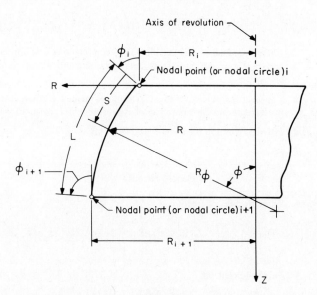

**FIG. E**

*Degrees of freedom*   Four degrees of freedom per nodal circle.

**TABLE 4.7** Catalog of Elements for Shells of Revolution (*Continued*)

---

*Shape functions*

$$u_i = \sum_{j=0}^{\infty} u_i^{(j)}(s) \cos j\theta$$

$$v_i = \sum_{j=0}^{\infty} v_i^{(j)}(s) \sin j\theta$$

$$w_i = \sum_{j=0}^{\infty} w_i^{(j)}(s) \cos j\theta$$

$$\beta_{\phi i} = \sum_{j=0}^{\infty} \beta_{\phi i}^{(j)}(s) \cos j\theta$$

where $u_i$, $v_i$, $w_i$ = meridional, circumferential, and normal displacements, respectively and $\beta_{\phi i}$ = the meridional rotation for element $i$.

*Advantages*   Incorporated in SHORE computer programs. Has curved meridian, high-order interpolations, and exact geometry. Can treat nonaxisymmetrical loading. Dynamic capabilities in later versions.

*Disadvantages*   Linear-elastic capability only.

*References*   [38, 44].

---

Frustum of the meridional curve (see Fig. E)

---

*Degrees of freedom*   Five degrees of freedom.

*Shape functions*   Polynomial functions

$$\{Y^{(j)}(s)\} = \{u^{(j)} \quad v^{(j)} \quad w^{(j)} \quad m_\phi^{(j)} \quad m_\theta^{(j)} \quad m_{\theta\varphi}^{(j)}\}$$
$$= \{y_1(s) \quad y_2(s) \quad y_3(s) \quad y_4(s) \quad y_5(s) \quad y_6(s)\}$$

in which

$$y_l(s) = (1-s)y_l(0) + sy_l(1) + s(1-s)\sum_{m=1}^{I} y_{lm}s^{m-1} \qquad (l=1,6)$$

where $u$, $v$, and $w$ = the meridional, circumferential, and normal displacements, and $m_\phi$, $m_\theta$, and $m_{\theta\varphi}$ = the meridional, circumferential, and twisting stress couples.

*Advantages*   Improved accuracy over the displacement-method solution for the same number of elements and the same order of expansion. Direct calculation of stress couples.

*Disadvantages*   Provides solution for a static problem only.

*Reference*   [41].

---

Curved element

---

*Degrees of freedom*   Three degrees of freedom.

*Shape functions*

$$\begin{Bmatrix} u \\ v \\ w \end{Bmatrix} = \Sigma N_i \begin{Bmatrix} u_i \\ v_i \\ w_i \end{Bmatrix} + \Sigma N_i \zeta \frac{t_i}{2}[\hat{\mathbf{v}}_{1i} - \hat{\mathbf{v}}_{2i}]\begin{Bmatrix} \alpha_i \\ \beta_i \end{Bmatrix}$$

Parabolic element:

Corner nodes   $N_i = \frac{1}{4}(1+\xi_0)(1+\eta_0)(\xi_0+\eta_0-1)$

Midside nodes   $(\xi_i = \pm 1, \eta_i = 0)$

$$N_i = \frac{1}{2}(1+\xi_0)(1-\eta^2)$$

with $\xi_0 = \xi\xi_i$ and $\eta_0 = \eta\eta_i$.

**TABLE 4.7** Catalog of Elements for Shells of Revolution (*Continued*)

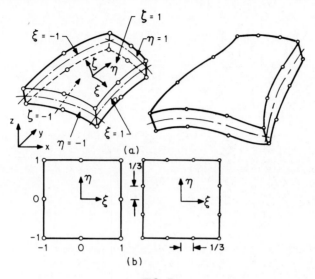

**FIG. F**

The other functions are deduced by interchanging $\xi$ and $\eta$.

Cubic element:

    Corner nodes    $N_i = \frac{1}{32}(1+\xi_0)(1+\eta_0)\{-10+9(\xi^2+\eta^2)\}$

    Midside nodes  $(\xi = \pm 1,\ n_i = \pm\frac{1}{3})$

$$N_i = \frac{9}{32}(1+\xi_0)(1-\eta^2)(1+9\eta_0),\ldots$$

where $u$, $v$, and $w$ are displacements in the directions of the global $x$-, $y$-, and $z$-axes, respectively.

*Advantages*  Presents solution for thick and thin shells.

*Reference*  [40].

---

Curved element

*Degrees of freedom*  Eight degrees of freedom (two internal).

*Shape function*

$$\begin{Bmatrix} u_i \\ u_j \\ u_k \end{Bmatrix} = \begin{bmatrix} \mathbf{T}_i & 0 & 0 \\ 0 & \mathbf{T}_j & 0 \\ 0 & 0 & \mathbf{I} \end{bmatrix} \begin{Bmatrix} r_i \\ r_j \\ r_k \end{Bmatrix}$$

    $8\times 1$          $8\times 1$    $3\times 1$

                                   $3\times 1$

                                   $2\times 1$

$$u_1 = \alpha_1 + \alpha_2\xi + a_3\xi^2 + \alpha_4\xi^3$$

$$u_2 = \alpha_5 + \alpha_6\xi + \alpha_7\xi^2 + \alpha_8\xi^3$$

$$\{\mathbf{r}\}^T = \langle u_r^i u_z^i \chi^i \mid u_r^j u_z^j \chi^j \mid u_1^m u_1^n \rangle$$

$$\{\mathbf{r}\}^T = \langle U^i W^i \chi^i \mid U^j W^j \chi^j \mid u_1^m u_1^n \rangle$$

where the $\alpha$'s are the generalized coordinates and $u_1$ and $u_2$ are the meridional and normal displacements, respectively.

**TABLE 4.7**   Catalog of Elements for Shells of Revolution (*Continued*)

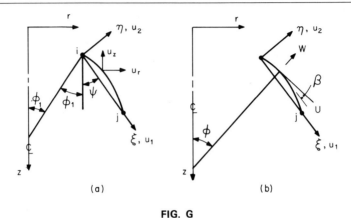

(a)                  (b)

**FIG. G**

*Advantages*   Can be used for the analysis of elastic-plastic shells of revolution.

*Reference*   [42].

Frustum of curved element

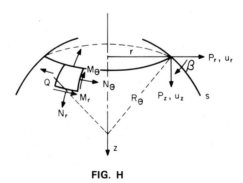

**FIG. H**

*Degrees of freedom*   Four degrees of freedom per node.

*Shape functions*   Piecewise linear.

*Advantages*   The possibility of using piecewise linear functions of the meridional arc length to represent the basic unknowns.

*Reference*   [43].

Superparametric curved element

*Degrees of freedom*   Four degrees of freedom per node, where $u$, $v$, and $w$ are the displacements at any point in the shell along the $\theta$-, $y$-, and $R$-directions, respectively, and $\gamma$ is the rotation of the normal to the shell in the $YR$-plane.

**TABLE 4.7** Catalog of Elements for Shells of Revolution (*Continued*)

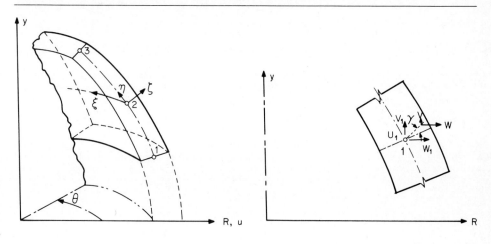

**FIG. I**

*Shape functions*

$$N_1 = \tfrac{1}{2}(-\eta + \eta^2)$$
$$N_2 = 1 - \eta^2$$
$$N_3 = \tfrac{1}{2}(\eta + \eta^2)$$
$$u = \Sigma N_i u_i$$
$$\left\{\frac{V}{W}\right\} = \Sigma N_i \left\{\frac{V_i}{W_i}\right\} + \Sigma N_i \frac{t_i}{2}\zeta V_{2i}$$

*Advantages*   Provides solution for laminated anisotropic shell of revolution.

*Disadvantages*   Treats axisymmetric loading only.

*Reference*   [45].

---

Curved element (see Fig. J, next page)

---

*Degrees of freedom*   Four degrees of freedom per nodal circle, where $u_r$, $u_z$ are radial and axial displacements; and $M_r$, $M_\theta$ are meridional and circumferential stress couples.

*Shape functions*   Fifth-order polynomials.

*Advantages*   The use of Newton–Raphson iteration. Provides very good accuracy in solving problems with geometric nonlinearity.

*Reference*   [46].

---

Conical element and quadratic curved element (see Fig K, next page)

---

*Degrees of freedom*   Three degrees of freedom per nodal-point element.

*Shape functions*   For two-nodal-point elements,

$$h_{21} = \tfrac{1}{2}(1 + \xi) \qquad \text{and} \qquad h_{22} = \tfrac{1}{2}(1 - \xi)$$

**TABLE 4.7**   Catalog of Elements for Shells of Revolution (*Continued*)

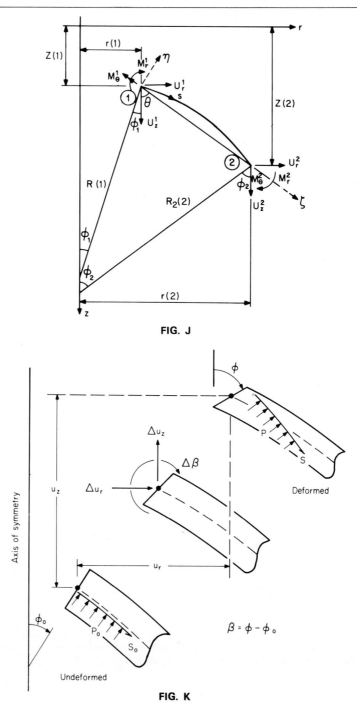

**FIG. J**

**FIG. K**

$$\beta = \phi - \phi_o$$

**TABLE 4.7**   Catalog of Elements for Shells of Revolution (*Continued*)

For three-nodal-point elements,

$$h_{31} = \tfrac{1}{2}\xi(1+\xi) \qquad h_{32} = -\tfrac{1}{2}\xi(1-\xi) \qquad \text{and} \qquad h_{33} = 1 - \xi^2$$

$$H(\xi) = \begin{bmatrix} h_{m1} & \cdots & h_{mm} & 0 & 0 \\ 0 & \cdots & 0 & h_{mm} & 0 \\ 0 & \cdots & 0 & 0 & h_{mm} \end{bmatrix}$$

where $m$ = number of nodal points in an element, and $\xi$ = normalized meridional coordinate for shell element.

*Advantages*   Provides solution for linear problems and for problems with large membrane strains, large rotations, and nonlinear material.

*Reference*   [47].

---

Transitional shell element

---

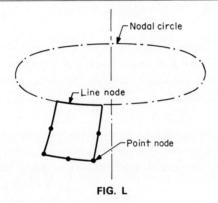

**FIG. L**

*Degrees of freedom*   Five degrees of freedom per node.

*Shape functions*   Parabolic element:

Corner nodes    $N_i = \tfrac{1}{4}(1+\xi_0)(1+\eta_0)(\xi_0 + \eta_0 - 1)$

Midside nodes    $(\xi_i = \pm 1,\ \eta_i = 0)$

$$N_i = \tfrac{1}{2}(1+\xi_0)(1-\eta^2)$$

with $\xi_0 = \xi\xi_i$ and $\eta_0 = \eta\eta_i$.

The other functions are deduced by interchanging $\xi$ and $\eta$.

Cubic element:

Corner nodes    $N_i = \tfrac{1}{32}(1+\xi_0)(1+\eta_0)\{-10+9(\xi^2+\eta^2)\}$

Midside nodes    $(\xi = \pm 1,\ \eta_i = \pm\tfrac{1}{3})$

$$N_i = \tfrac{9}{32}(1+\xi_0)(1-\eta^2)(1+9\eta_0), \ldots$$

$$N_6 = 0 \cdot 25(1-\xi)(1+\eta)(-\xi+\eta-1)$$

$$N_7 = 0 \cdot 25(1+\xi)(1+\eta)(\xi+\eta-1)$$

$$N_8 = 0 \cdot 5(1-\xi^2)(1+\eta)$$

$$\Lambda(\xi,\eta) = \sum_{i=6}^{8} N_i\lambda_i = N_6\lambda_6 + N_7\lambda_7 + N_8\lambda_8$$

**TABLE 4.7** Catalog of Elements for Shells of Revolution (*Continued*)

| | |
|---|---|
| *Advantages* | The development of a line node, where any shape function can be specified along the line. Provides a transition between a general shell element and a ring element so that *locally* nonaxisymmetrical shells can be analyzed. |
| *Reference* | [48]. |

## 4.7 PLATE-BENDING ELEMENTS

A very large number of plate elements has been proposed in the literature [49–51]. An ideal plate element has the following properties [52, 53]:

- The formulation should be based on continuum mechanics and plate theory with mechanistically clear assumptions and no numerically adjusted factors. The element nodal-point degrees of freedom are the engineering transverse displacement $w$ and sectional rotations $\theta_x$ and $\theta_y$.

- The element should be "numerically sound" and convergent for any plate structure. The element stiffness matrix must contain the three rigid-body modes and no spurious zero-energy mode. The element should not "lock" in thin-plate analyses.

- The predictive capability of the element should be relatively insensitive to element geometric distortions.

- Since a plate structure is a special case of a shell structure, and plates in large deformations exhibit shell characteristics, plate elements are best developed as special cases of general shell elements. This way the same element formulation can be employed for general plate and shell analyses.

These element characteristics are important when an element is to be employed in general engineering practice, and the value of an element should be measured on whether (or how closely) these properties are met.

The catalog of plate elements presented in Table 4.8 only summarizes some of the many plate elements available. Some additional elements that are presented as shell elements, but which can also be employed as plate elements, are catalogued in Sec. 4.8.

**TABLE 4.8** Catalog of Plate-Bending Elements

| | |
|---|---|
| | Discrete Kirchhoff theory three-node triangular (DKT) element |

| | |
|---|---|
| *Degrees of freedom* | The three engineering degrees of freedom $w$, $\theta_x$, $\theta_y$ are used at each of the three corner nodes. |
| *Remarks* | The element formulation starts with the kinematic description of the Mindlin-Reissner plate theory with shear-deformation effects neglected. The section rotations and transverse displacement are interpolated independently, and the Kirchhoff hypothesis of zero-transverse-shear strains is used at judiciously selected points on the element to tie the transverse displacement to the section |

**TABLE 4.8**   Catalog of Plate-Bending Elements (*Continued*)

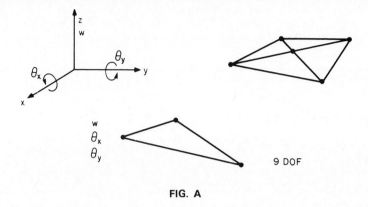

**FIG. A**

rotations. The variation of transverse displacements along the element sides is cubic. In mesh construction the diamond pattern of four elements assembled to a general quadrilateral is employed. The internal degrees of freedom can be statically condensed out. The element is also employed in the analysis of shells and nonlinear problems.

*Advantages*   The element satisfies the patch tests, does not lock, and has no spurious zero-energy mode. It is a simple and effective element, and has been used in many applications.

*Disadvantages*   With use of triangular elements, the element-mesh layout can significantly affect the solution results. The use of the diamond pattern is frequently effective. The element can only be employed for thin-plate and shell problems. For shell analyses an artificial out-of-plane bending stiffness is frequently defined.

*References*   [50, 54].

Hybrid-stress method (HSM) three-node triangular element (see Fig. A)

*Degrees of freedom*   The three engineering degrees of freedom $w$, $\theta_x$, $\theta_y$ are used at each of the three corner nodes.

*Remarks*   The element formulation is based on the Kirchhoff plate theory and hybrid-stress formulation. A linear variation of bending moments in the element and a cubic transverse-displacement variation along the element sides are assumed. In mesh construction, the diamond pattern of four elements assembled to a quadrilateral is employed.

*Advantages*   The element satisfies the patch tests, does not lock, and has no spurious zero-energy mode. It is a simple and effective element.

*Disadvantages*   With use of triangular elements, the element-mesh layout can significantly affect the solution results. The use of the diamond pattern is frequently effective. The element can only be employed for thin-plate and shell problems. For shell analyses an artificial out-of-plane bending stiffness is frequently introduced.

*References*   [50, 55, 56]; see also [77, 78, 79].

**TABLE 4.8** Catalog of Plate-Bending Elements (*Continued*)

DKQ four-node quadrilateral element

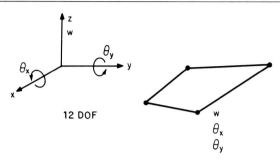

12 DOF

**FIG. B**

*Degrees of freedom* The three engineering degrees of freedom $w$, $\theta_x$, $\theta_y$ are used at each of the four corner nodes.

*Remarks* The element formulation is similar to the formulation of the DKT triangular element. The kinematic description of the Mindlin–Reissner plate theory is used, the shear-deformation effects are neglected, and the transverse displacement and section rotations are interpolated independently but tied to each other by ensuring that the transverse-shear strains are zero along the sides of the element.

*Advantages* The element satisfies the patch tests, does not lock, and has no spurious zero-energy mode. The element shows good convergence characteristics.

*Disadvantages* The element can only be employed for analysis of thin-plate and shell problems. For shell analyses an artificial out-of-plane bending stiffness is defined.

*Reference* [51].

Eight-node, isoparametric, reduced-integrated element

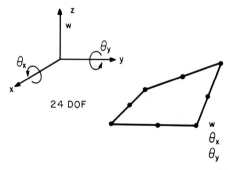

24 DOF

**FIG. C**

*Degrees of freedom* The three engineering degrees of freedom $w$, $\theta_x$, $\theta_y$ are used at each of the eight nodes.

*Remarks* The element formulation is based on the Mindlin–Reissner plate theory including shear deformations. The isoparametric interpolation of geometry and transverse-displacement and section rotations with eight nodes is used. The bending and

**TABLE 4.8**    Catalog of Plate-Bending Elements (*Continued*)

shear-strain contributions are integrated using $2 \times 2$ gaussian integration, which represents underintegration of the stiffness matrix.

The same concept is also used for the nine-node element. Both the eight- and nine-node element performances are somewhat improved by using selective integration ($3 \times 3$ gaussian integration for the bending energy and $2 \times 2$ gaussian integration for the shear-strain energy). Another closely related element is the heterosis element.

The element formulation is used in the analysis of shells and has also been extended to nonlinear analysis. However, in these cases the 16-node element based on the same formulation with full or selective integration is frequently most effective.

*Advantages*    The element is simple to formulate and works well in many thin- and thick-plate and shell problems.

*Disadvantages*    The (eight-node reduced-integrated) element has one spurious zero-energy mode and does not pass important patch tests. The element is sensitive to geometric distortions. Because of these deficiencies, the element can generate poor solutions and must be employed with care.

*References*    [57–61].

---

Selective reduced-integrated four-node element (see Fig. B)

---

*Degrees of freedom*    The three engineering degrees of freedom $w$, $\theta_x$, $\theta_y$ are used at each of the four corner nodes.

*Remarks*    The element formulation is based on the Mindlin–Reissner plate theory including shear deformations. The isoparametric interpolation of geometry and transverse-displacement and section rotations is used. The bending energy is integrated using $2 \times 2$ gaussian integration, the shear-strain energy is integrated with one-point integration. Some modifications to these integrations are proposed for very thin and thick-plate applications.

*Advantages*    Relatively few computations are required for the evaluation of the element stiffness matrix. The element has been used effectively in various applications.

*Disadvantages*    The element stiffness matrix contains two spurious zero-energy modes which can lead to unacceptable results.

*Reference*    [62].

---

QUAD4—Four-node element (see Fig. B)

---

*Degrees of freedom*    The three engineering degrees of freedom $w$, $\theta_x$, $\theta_y$ are used at each of the four corner nodes.

*Remarks*    The element is developed primarily along isoparametric principles but with some special provisions. The transverse-shear flexibility is included, but corrections are used to improve the bending energy for curvatures resulting from isoparametric displacements and rotations. The element coupled with a formulation for membrane action is also used extensively for shell analyses, and the formulation has been extended to nonlinear analysis.

*Advantages*    The element passes the patch tests, has no spurious zero-energy mode, and performs well in many applications.

**TABLE 4.8**  Catalog of Plate-Bending Elements (*Continued*)

| | |
|---|---|
| *Disadvantages* | The formulation is not particularly transparent. |
| *Reference* | [63]. |

LORA plate element (see Fig. B)

| | |
|---|---|
| *Degrees of freedom* | The three engineering degrees of freedom $w$, $\theta_x$, $\theta_y$ are used at each of the four corner nodes. |
| *Remarks* | The element is based on equilibrium stress functions, with compatible virtual boundary displacement functions used to express equilibrium between the nodal forces and the stress functions. The element has nine independent stress functions, four bilinear bending-moment functions for each direction (including transverse shear in the linear bending terms), and a constant twisting moment. The local element axes connect midpoints of opposite sides; these axes are used to interpolate the stresses. The element formulation has also been extended for use in shell analysis. |
| *Advantages* | The element satisfies the patch tests and converges well for a variety of applications. |
| *Disadvantages* | Nonlinear formulations have not yet been developed. |
| *Reference* | [64]. |

MITC4—Four-node element based on mixed interpolation of tensorial components (see Fig. B)

| | |
|---|---|
| *Degrees of freedom* | The three engineering degrees of freedom $w$, $\theta_x$, $\theta_y$ are used at each of the four corner nodes. |
| *Remarks* | The element is formulated using the Mindlin–Reissner plate theory including shear deformations. The geometry, transverse displacement, and section rotations are interpolated bilinearly. The transverse-shear strains (tensor components) are separately interpolated, and their intensities are tied to the nodal transverse displacements and section rotations. The element is obtained as a special case of a general shell element for linear and nonlinear analysis. |
| *Advantages* | The element does not lock, passes the patch tests, and has no spurious zero-energy mode. The element can be used for thin- and thick-plate analysis. In shell analyses the element is defined using five or six engineering degrees of freedom per node, and no artificial spring stiffness (corresponding to the out-of-plane rotation) is introduced. The element performs very well. |
| *Disadvantages* | The predictive capability of transverse-shear strains is low. |
| *References* | [65, 66]. |

MITC8—Eight-node element based on mixed interpolation of tensorial components (see Fig. C)

| | |
|---|---|
| *Degrees of freedom* | The three engineering degrees of freedom $w$, $\theta_x$, $\theta_y$ are used at each of the eight nodes. |
| *Remarks* | The element is formulated using the Mindlin–Reissner plate theory including shear deformations. The geometry, transverse displacement, and section rotations are interpolated using the isoparametric interpolation functions. The membrane strains and transverse-shear strains (tensor components) are interpolated sepa- |

**TABLE 4.8**   Catalog of Plate-Bending Elements (*Continued*)

|  |  |
|---|---|
|  | rately, and their intensities are tied to the nodal-point displacements and rotations. The element is obtained as a special case of a shell element for linear and nonlinear analysis. |
| *Advantages* | The element does not lock, passes the patch tests (with straight element sides), and has no spurious zero-energy mode. The element can be employed for thin- and thick-plate and shell problems. In shell analyses the element is defined using five or six engineering degrees of freedom per node, and no artificial spring stiffness (corresponding to the out-of-plane rotation) is introduced. The element performs very well. |
| *Disadvantages* | The element formulation does not contain the biquadratic displacement term (no internal ninth node is used). |
| *Reference* | [53]. |

## 4.8 GENERAL SHELL ELEMENTS

Many general shell elements have been developed in the literature. The catalog of general shell elements presented in Table 4.9 is limited to those elements which are based on the displacement method or stiffness approach, including some discrete Kirchhoff formulations. The catalog is not intended to be comprehensive. The nine elements are typical examples of the many approaches that are used to formulate shell elements.

**TABLE 4.9**   Catalog of General Shell Elements

CURSHL—High-precision triangular shell element

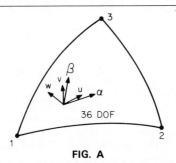

**FIG. A**

|  |  |
|---|---|
| *Degrees of freedom* | Twelve degrees of freedom at each corner node (three translations, six first-order derivatives, and three second-order derivatives of the normal component of displacement). |
| *Remarks* | A restricted quintic polynomial (containing a complete quartic) is chosen for the normal displacement field. A complete cubic field is chosen for each of the in-plane displacements. By imposing cubic normal rotations along each edge, the derivation satisfies interelement continuity. The centroidal values of the in-plane displacements are eliminated by static condensation. The resulting stiffness matrix has 36 degrees of freedom. No explicit consideration has been made in the derivation for rigid-body modes of displacement. |

**TABLE 4.9**   Catalog of General Shell Elements (*Continued*)

*Advantages*   CURSHL gives extremely accurate results and has a high convergence rate. The stresses are determined uniquely. CURSHL, a computer code by the authors, has options for different shell theories, including that of Koiter and Sanders.

*Disadvantages*   Numerical integration is used with a 13-point gaussian quadrature rule. This makes the element expensive, particularly for nonlinear analysis. The nodal continuity of the second derivatives of the normal displacement may lead to practical difficulties in the analysis of nonsmooth shells.

*References*   [67, 68].

SHEBA-6—Six-node triangular shell element

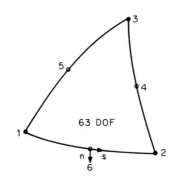

$$\bullet\ [u\ \ u,_\alpha\ \ u,_\beta\ \ u,_{\alpha\alpha}\ \ u,_{\alpha\beta}\ \ u,_{\beta\beta}$$
$$v\ \ v,_\alpha\ \ v,_\beta\ \ v,_{\alpha\alpha}\ \ v,_{\alpha\beta}\ \ v,_{\beta\beta}$$
$$w\ \ w,_\alpha\ \ w,_\beta\ \ w,_{\alpha\alpha}\ \ w,_{\alpha\beta}\ \ w,_{\beta\beta}]$$

$$\circ\ [u,_n\ \ v,_n\ \ w,_n]$$

**FIG. B**

*Degrees of freedom*   The corner nodes have three translational displacements, all six first derivatives, and all nine second derivatives. Interelement continuity is assured by the use of midside nodes having all three normal derivatives as degrees of freedom.

*Remarks*   This is a $C^1$-continuous triangular element with curvilinear boundaries and varying curvature. The formulation employs complete 21-term quintic polynomials for all three displacement components. The condition of zero strain under rigid-body motion is satisfied exactly by using the same interpolation functions for the surface location as for the displacements. The natural strain concept plays a central role in the shell theory employed. The extension of this theory for large displacements is readily available. Incorporated in ASKA general-purpose program.

*Advantages*   SHEBA-6 produces extremely accurate solutions.

*Disadvantages*   Calculation of individual element matrices is expensive. Owing to the presence of midside nodes, the bandwidth, when expressed as a percentage of total degrees of freedom, may be very high in comparison with simpler elements.

*Reference*   [69].

**TABLE 4.9**  Catalog of General Shell Elements (*Continued*)

Triangular thin-shell finite element based on a generalized potential-energy principle

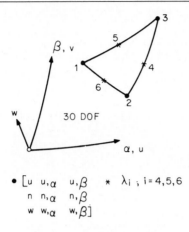

**FIG. C**

*Degrees of freedom*  Nine degrees of freedom at each corner node consisting of three displacements and six first-order derivatives. One Lagrange multiplier at each of the three midside nodes.

*Remarks*  The element uses a conventional potential-energy approach, with the three displacement components interpolated by cubic polynomials. Since these functions do not provide slope compatibility between elements, such continuity requirements are written as constraints and imposed by a Lagrange multiplier technique. Koiter's deep-shell, strain-displacement equations are used. Geometrically nonlinear behavior (small strain, finite displacement) is modeled.

*Advantages*  Satisfies $C^1$-continuity requirement without resorting to subregions.

*Disadvantages*  The use of Lagrange multipliers increases the problem size and requires careful numbering of degrees of freedom or a pivoting strategy in the solution scheme. The criterion of zero-strain energy under rigid-body motion is only approximated.

*Reference*  [70].

GDS3—Quadrangular conforming finite element based on the concept of subregions

*Degrees of freedom*  Five degrees of freedom at each corner node, consisting of the displacements and the rotations of the normal. One tangential rotation at the midpoint of each side. Two tangential displacements along the element interfaces at two nodes. A total of 40 degrees of freedom per element.

*Remarks*  This element is an extension of the well-known conforming quadrilateral plate element of Fraeijs de Veubeke. Each element is subdivided into four regions, in each of which a complete cubic polynomial is used for the normal displacement component. GDS3 provides cubic representation for all three components of displacements. A family of elements which contain linear or quadratic interpolation for in-plane displacements, along with cubic interpolation for the normal displacement component, is given in the reference.

**TABLE 4.9**  Catalog of General Shell Elements (*Continued*)

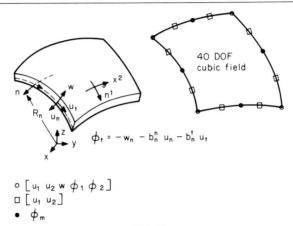

$$\phi_t = -w_n - b_n^n u_n - b_n^t u_t$$

○ $[u_1 \ u_2 \ w \ \phi_1 \ \phi_2]$
□ $[u_1 \ u_2]$
● $\phi_m$

**FIG. D**

*Advantages*  The element is strictly conforming even in the case where discontinuities of the curvature occur.

*Disadvantages*  The element stiffness computation is expensive.

*Reference*  [71].

Triangular thin-shell element based on discrete Kirchhoff theory

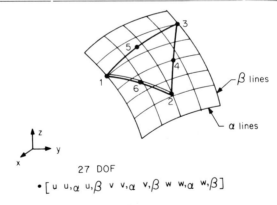

27 DOF
● $[u \ u_{,\alpha} \ u_{,\beta} \ v \ v_{,\alpha} \ v_{,\beta} \ w \ w_{,\alpha} \ w_{,\beta}]$

**FIG. E**

*Degrees of freedom*  Nine degrees of freedom at each corner node (the three components of displacement and their first-order derivatives).

*Remarks*  A linear shear-deformation theory forms the basis of the formulation. Independent assumptions are made for displacement and rotation vectors. Complete cubic polynomials are used for the displacements, and quadratic polynomials are used for the rotation vectors. Isoparametric representation of the shell geometry may be used. Convergence to the thin-shell solution is achieved by enforcement of the Kirchhoff hypothesis at a discrete number of points in the element. (Note: The discrete Kirchhoff theory approach to deep-shell elements

**TABLE 4.9**   Catalog of General Shell Elements (*Continued*)

is common, and there are many more elements of this category. The formulation described here is a typical example of this class of elements.)

*Advantages*   The element provides satisfactory solutions for a number of standard problems including patch tests.

*Disadvantages*   The element is expensive for nonlinear applications.

*Reference*   [72].

Semi-Loof thin-shell element

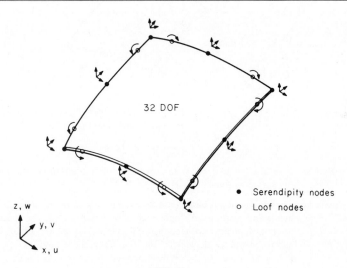

32 DOF

● Serendipity nodes
○ Loof nodes

z, w

y, v

x, u

**FIG. F**

*Degrees of freedom*   The global displacement components at the corners and midside nodes, and the normal rotations at the two Gauss points along each side, are used.

*Remarks*   Displacements are interpolated using lagrangian shape functions. Rotations are interpolated by a Loof family of shape functions from values at the central node and the two Gauss points along each edge of the element. A bubble function is added to aid in passing the patch test. These 43 degrees of freedom are reduced to 32 by employing 11 constraints; 8 of these constraints impose vanishing of transverse-shear strains, in the plane of the edge, at the Loof nodes. At each Loof node, only the rotation around the edge is retained as a degree of freedom. Three more constraints in an integral form over the area of the elements are enforced.

*Advantages*   The element is well behaved and demonstrates good convergence. FORTRAN coding of the shape functions and constraints is readily available with extensive documentation.

*Disadvantages*   The semi-Loof element is built around a complicated "black-box" interpolator routine in which the constraints are eliminated numerically. This makes the element expensive. The performance of the element deteriorates somewhat when it is distorted. The element contains a spurious kinematic mode, but this is rarely

**TABLE 4.9**   Catalog of General Shell Elements (*Continued*)

activated in practical cases. The element appears to be too flexible under the action of point loads.

*Reference*   [73].

---

Quadrilateral with one-point integration and singularity control via artificial stiffness

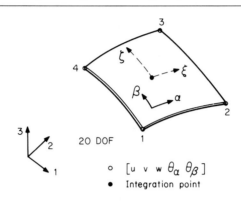

20 DOF

○  $[u \ v \ w \ \theta_\alpha \ \theta_\beta]$
●  Integration point

**FIG. G**

*Degrees of freedom*   Five degrees of freedom at each node (three translations and two rotations of the surface normal).

*Remarks*   The formulation is based on independent bilinear interpolation for the displacements and rotations. A single integration point is used. The spurious kinematic modes, which are a consequence of underintegration, are eliminated by a stabilization procedure in which additional generalized strains are defined by the kinematic modes only. Artificial stiffness parameters are used with these nonphysical strain components. Reference [2] describes a nine-node lagrangian shell element based on similar concepts.

*Advantages*   The element is inexpensive, especially for nonlinear applications, as it employs a single numerical integration point. The element is efficient in spite of its simplicity.

*Disadvantages*   The criterion for the selection of the artificial stiffness parameters and their influence in large-scale nonlinear analysis are not fully established. The element behaves poorly if it is distorted far from being rectangular.

*References*   [74, 75].

---

Eight- or nine-node general shell element with reduced integration

---

*Degrees of freedom*   Five degrees of freedom at each node (three displacement components and two rotations of the surface normal).

*Remarks*   The element is shear-flexible, as independent assumptions are made for displacements and rotations. Serendipity or Lagrange interpolation functions are employed for the geometry, displacements, and rotations. Conditions of zero strain for any general rigid-body motion are satisfied. Reduced integration of the stiffness coefficients eliminates shear-locking in the case of thin shells. The shear rigidity is considered as a penalty on the shear constraints, with its value

**TABLE 4.9**    Catalog of General Shell Elements (*Continued*)

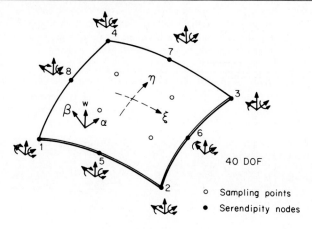

40 DOF

○    Sampling points
●    Serendipity nodes

**FIG. H**

chosen to provide physically correct behavior while avoiding numerical difficulties, for all applications ranging from thick to thin shells.

*Advantages*    The element is simple and works well if it is not distorted.

*Disadvantages*    The element is sensitive to distortion. It contains two spurious kinematic modes, but these modes are rarely activated in practical cases.

*References*    [6, 7].

HS2—Heterosis nonlinear shell element

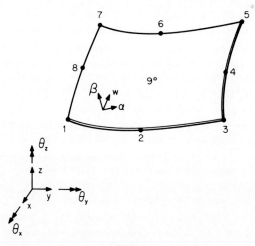

**FIG. I**

*Degrees of freedom*    Five degrees of freedom at each corner and midside nodes. Two rotation components at the internal node.

**TABLE 4.9**   Catalog of General Shell Elements (*Continued*)

| | |
|---|---|
| *Remarks* | The heterosis concept eliminates the spurious zero-energy mode in the nine-node, selectively integrated Lagrange element. Implementation of the heterosis element begins on the lines of a Lagrange element. A projection matrix is constructed from the serendipity shape functions (associated with the boundary nodes), which in turn will eliminate all translational degrees of freedom from the internal node. |
| *Advantages* | The element has correct rank and is rapidly convergent in many cases. The authors have documented an approximate finite-strain formulation for this element. |
| *Disadvantages* | The formulation involves considerable numerical cost. The element is sensitive to distortion. |
| *Reference* | [76]. |

## 4.9 REFERENCES

1. Oden, J. T., and H. Brauchli, "On the Calculation of Consistent Stress Distributions in Finite Element Approximations," *Int. J. Numer. Meth. Eng.*, **3**(3):317–325 (1971).

2. Stein, E., and R. Ahmad, "An Equilibrium Method for Stress Calculation Using Finite Element Displacement Models," *Comput. Meth. Appl. Mech. Eng.*, **10**(2):175–198 (1977).

3. Loubignac, G., G. Cantin, and G. Touzot, "Continuous Stress Fields in Finite Element Analysis," *AIAA J.*, **15**(11):1645–1647 (1977).

4. Irons, B. M., "Engineering Applications of Numerical Integration in Stiffness Methods," *AIAA J.* **4**(11):2035–2037 (1966).

5. Ergatoudis, I., B. M. Irons, and O. C. Zienkiewicz, "Curved Isoparametric, 'Quadrilateral' Elements for Finite Element Analysis," *Int. J. Solids Struct.*, **4**(1):31–42 (1968).

6. Cook, R. D., *Concepts and Applications of Finite Element Analysis*, 2d ed., Wiley, New York, 1981.

7. Zienkiewicz, O. C., *The Finite Element Method*, 3d ed., McGraw-Hill, New York, 1977.

8. Surana, K. S., *FINESSE (Finite Element System for Nonlinear Analysis) Theoretical Manual*, McDonnell Douglas Automation Company, St. Louis, 1983.

9. Timoshenko, S., and S. Woinowsky-Krieger, *Theory of Plates and Shells*, 2d ed., McGraw-Hill, Kogakusha, 1959, art. 121.

10. Flugge, W., *Stresses in Shells*, 2d ed., Springer-Verlag, Berlin, 1973.

11. Yamada, Y., and Y. Ezawa, "On Curved Finite Elements for the Analysis of Circular Arches," *Int. J. Numer. Meth. Eng.*, **11**:1635–1651 (1977).

12. Ashwell, D. G., A. B. Sabir, and T. M. Roberts, "Further Studies in the Application of Curved Finite Elements to Circular Arches," *Int. J. Mech. Sci.*, **13**:507–517 (1971).

13. Dawe, D. J., "Numerical Studies Using Circular Arch Finite Elements," *Comput. Struct.*, **4**:729–740 (1974).

14. Dawe, D. J., "Some High-Order Elements for Arches and Shells," in D. G. Ashwell and R. Gallagher (eds.), *Finite Elements for Thin Shells and Curved Members*, Wiley, London, 1976, Chap. 8.

15. Ashwell, D. G., and A. B. Sabir, "Limitations of Certain Curved Finite Elements when Applied to Arches," *Int. J. Mech. Sci.*, **13**:133–139 (1971).

16. Ashwell, D. G., and A. B. Sabir, "A Corrected Assessment of the Cylindrical Shell Finite Element of Bogner, Fox, and Schmit When Applied to Arches," *Int. J. Mech. Sci.*, **15**:325–327 (1973).

17. Moan, T., "A Note on the Convergence of Finite Element Approximations for Problems Formulated in Curvilinear Coordinate Systems," *Comp. Meth. Appl. Mech. Eng.*, **3**:209–235 (1974).

18. Cantin, G., and R. W. Clough, "A Curved Cylindrical Shell Finite Element," *AIAA J.*, **6**:1057–1062 (1968).

19. Fried, I., "Basic Computational Problems in the Finite Element Analysis of Shells," *Int. J. Solids Struct.*, **7**:1705–1715, 1971.

20. Fried, I., "Shape Functions and the Accuracy of Arch Finite Elements," *AIAA J.*, **11**:287–291 (1973).

21. Dawe, D. J., "Curved Finite Elements for the Analysis of Shallow and Deep Arches," *Comput. Struct.*, **4**:559–580 (1974).

22. Dawe, D. J., "A Finite Deflection Analysis of Shallow Arches by the Discrete Element Method," *Int. J. Numer. Meth. Eng.*, **3**:529–552, 1971.

23. Kikuchi, F., "On the Validity of the Finite Element Analysis of Circular Arches Represented by an Assemblage of Beam Elements," *Comput. Meth. Appl. Mech. Eng.*, **5**:253–276 (1975).

24. Noor, A. K., W. H. Greene, and S. J. Hartley, "Nonlinear Finite Element Analysis of Curved Beams," *Comput. Meth. Appl. Meth. Eng.*, **12**:289–307 (1977).

25. Noor, A. K., and J. M. Peters, "Mixed Models and Reduced/Selective Integration Displacement Models for Nonlinear Analysis of Curved Beams," *Int. J. Numer. Meth. Eng.*, **17**:615–631 (1981).

26. Koiter, W. T., "A Consistent First Approximation in the General Theory of Thin Elastic Shells," in W. T. Koiter (ed.), *Theory of Elastic Shells*, North-Holland, Amsterdam, 1960.

27. Cantin, G., "Strain Displacement Relationships for Cylindrical Shells," *AIAA J.*, **6**:1787–1788 (1968).

28. Dawe, D. J., "Rigid-Body Motions and Strain-Displacement Equations of Curved Shell Finite Elements," *Int. J. Mech. Sci.*, **14**:569–578 (1972).

29. Bogner, F. K., R. L. Fox, and L. A. Schmit, "A Cylindrical Shell Discrete Element," *AIAA J.*, **5**:745–750 (1967).

30. Cantin, G., "Rigid Body Motions in Curved Finite Elements," *AIAA J.*, **8**:1252–1255 (1970).

31. Ashwell, D. G., and A. B. Sabir, "A New Cylindrical Shell Finite Element Based on Simple Independent Strain Functions," *Int. J. Mech. Sci.*, **14**:171–183 (1972).

32. Lindberg, G. M., and M. D. Olson, "A High-Precision Triangular Cylindrical Shell Finite Element," *AIAA J.*, **9**:530–532 (1971).

33. Dawe, D. J., "High-Order Triangular Finite Element for Shell Analysis," *Int. J. Solids Struct.*, **11**:1097–1110 (1975).

34. Grafton, P. E., and D. R. Strome, "Analysis of Axisymmetrical Shells by the Direct Stiffness Method," *AIAA J.*, **1**:2342–2347 (1963).

35. Percy, J. H., T. H. H. Pian, S. Klein, and D. R. Navaratna, "Application of Matrix Displacement Method to Linear Elastic Analysis of Shells and Revolution," *AIAA J.*, **3**:2138–2145 (1965).

36. Jones, R. E., and D. R. Strome, "Direct Stiffness Method Analysis of Shells of Revolution Utilizing Curved Elements," *AIAA J.*, **4**:1519–1525 (1966).

37. Dong, S. B., "Analysis of Laminated Shells of Revolution," *J. Eng. Mech. Div. ASCE*, **EM6**:135–155 (1966).

38. Brombolich, L. J., and P. L. Gould, "Finite Element Analysis of Shells of Revolution by Minimization of the Potential Energy Functional," *Proceedings of the Conference for Applications of the Finite Element Method in Civil Engineering*, Vanderbilt University, Nashville, Tenn., 1969, pp. 279–307.

39. Witmer, E. A., and J. J. Kotanchik, *Proceedings of the 2d Conference on Matrix Methods in Structural Mechanics*, AFFDL-TR-68-150, 1969, pp. 1341–1453, Wright-Patterson Air Force Base, Ohio.

40. Sohrabuddin, A., B. M. Irons, and O. C. Zienkiewicz, "Analysis of Thick and Thin Shell Structures by Curved Finite Elements," *Int. J. Numer. Meth. Eng.*, **2**:419–451 (1970).

41. Gould, P. L., and S. K. Sen, "Refined Mixed Method Finite Elements for Shells of Revolution," *Proceedings of the 3d Conference on Matrix Methods in Structural Mechanics*, Wright-Patterson Air Force Base, Ohio, October 1971.

42. Popov, E. P., and P. Sharifi, "A Refined Curved Element for Thin Shells of Revolution," *Int. J. Numer. Meth. Eng.*, **3**:495–508 (1971).

43. Elias, Z. M., "Mixed Finite Element Method for Axisymmetric Shells," *Int. J. Numer. Meth. Eng.*, **4**:261–277 (1972).

44. Brombolich, L. J., and P. L. Gould, "Free Vibration of Shells of Revolution Using FEM," *J. Eng. Mech. Div. ASCE*, **100**(EM2):283–303 (1974).

45. Panda, S. C., and R. Natarajan, "Finite Element Analysis of Laminated Shells of Revolution," *Comput. Struct.*, **6**:61–64 (1976).

46. Tottenham, H., and S. Y. Barony, "Mixed Finite Element Formulation for Geometrically Non-Linear Analysis of Shells of Revolution," *Int. J. Numer. Meth. Eng.*, **12**:195–201 (1978).

47. Cook, W. A., "A Finite Element Model for Nonlinear Shells of Revolutions," *Int. J. Numer. Meth. Eng.*, **18**:135–149 (1982).

48. Han, K. J., and P. L. Gould, "Line Node and Transitional Shell Element for Rotational Shells," *Int. J. Numer. Meth. Eng.*, **18**:879–895 (1982).

49. Hrabok, M. M., and T. J. Hrudey, "A Review and Catalogue of Plate Bending Finite Elements," *J. Comput. Struct.*, **19**(3):479–495 (1984).

50. Batoz, J. L., K. J. Bathe, and L. W. Ho, "A Study of Three-Node Triangular Plate Bending Elements," *Int. J. Numer. Meth. Eng.*, **15**:1771–1812 (1980).

51. Batoz, J. L., and M. Ben Tahar, "Evaluation of a New Quadrilateral Thin Plate Bending Element," *Int. J. Numer. Meth. Eng.*, **18**:1655–1677 (1982).

52. Bathe, K. J., *Finite Element Procedures in Engineering Analysis*, Prentice-Hall, Englewood Cliffs, N. J., 1982, pp. 283–287.

53. Bathe, K. J., and E. N. Dvorkin, "A Formulation of General Shell Elements—The Use of Mixed Interpolation of Tensorial Components," *Int. J. Numer. Meth. Eng.*, **22**:697–722 (1986).

54. Bathe, K. J., and L. W. Ho, "A Simple and Effective Element for Analysis of General Shell Structures," *J. Comput. Struct.*, **13**:673–681 (1981).

55. Pian, T. H. H., and P. Tong, "Basis of Finite Element Methods for Solid Continua," *Int. J. Numer. Meth. Eng.*, **1**:3–28 (1969).

56. Allwood, R. J., and G. M. M. Cornes, "A Polygonal Finite Element for Plate Bending Problems Using the Assumed Stress Approach," *Int. J. Numer. Meth. Eng.*, **1**:135–149 (1969).

57. Ahmad, S., B. M. Irons, and O. C. Zienkiewicz, "Analysis of Thick and Thin Shell Structures by Curved Finite Elements," *Int. J. Numer. Meth. Eng.*, **2**:419–451 (1970).

58. Zienkiewicz, O. C., R. L. Taylor, and J. M. Too, "Reduced Integration Technique in General Analysis of Plates and Shells," *Int. J. Numer. Meth. Eng.*, **3**:275–290 (1971).

59. Pugh, E. D. L., E. Hinton, and O. C. Zienkiewicz, "A Study of Quadrilateral Plate Bending Elements with 'Reduced' Integration," *Int. J. Numer. Meth. Eng.*, **12**:1059–1079 (1978).

60. Hughes, T. J. R., and M. Cohen, "The 'Heterosis' Finite Element For Plate Bending," *J. Comput. Struct.*, **9**:445–450 (1978).

61. Bathe, K. J., and S. Bolourchi, "A Geometric and Material Nonlinear Plate and Shell Element," *J. Comput. Struct.*, **11**:23–48 (1980).

62. Hughes, T. J. R., R. L. Taylor, and W. Kanoknukulchai, "A Simple and Efficient Finite Element for Plate Bending," *Int. J. Numer. Meth. Eng.*, **11**:1529–1543 (1977).

63. MacNeal, R. H., "A Simple Quadrilateral Shell Element," *J. Comput. Struct.*, **8**:175–183 (1978).

64. Haggenmacher, G. W., "A Case for Stress Field Elements," in J. Robinson (ed.), *Proceedings Fourth World Congress on Finite Elements* (Interlaken, Switzerland, Sept. 1984), Robinson & Assoc., Dorset, England, pp. 17–21.

65. Bathe, K. J., and E. N. Dvorkin, "A Four Node Plate Bending Element Based on Mindlin–Reissner Plate Theory and a Mixed Interpolation," *Int. J. Numer. Meth. Eng.*, **21**:367–383 (1985).

66. Dvorkin, E. N., and K. J. Bathe, "A Continuum Mechanics Based Four Node Shell Element for General Nonlinear Analysis," *J. Eng. Computations*, **1**:77–88 (1984).

67. Cowper, G. R., "CURSHL: A High Precision Finite Element for Shells of Arbitrary Shape," Aeronautical Report LR-560, National Research Council of Canada, Ottawa, December 1971.

68. Cowper, G. R., G. M. Lindberg, and M. D. Olson, "Comparison of Two High-Precision Triangular Elements for Arbitrary Deep Shells," *Proceedings of the 3d Conference on Matrix Methods in Structural Mechanics*, Wright–Patterson Air Force Base, Ohio, October 1971.

69. Argyris, J. H., and D. Scharpf, "The SHEBA Family of Shell Elements for the Matrix Displacement Method," Aeronaut. J., **72**:873–883 (1968).

70. Thomas, G. R., and R. H. Gallagher, "A Triangular Element Based on Generalized Potential Energy Concepts," in D. G. Ashwell and R. H. Gallagher (eds.), *Finite Elements for Thin Shells and Curved Members*, Wiley, London, 1976, Chap. 9.

71. Sander, G., and S. Idelsohn, "A Family of Conforming Finite Elements for Deep Shell Analysis," *Int. J. Numer. Meth. Eng.*, **18**:363–380 (1982).

72. Batoz, J. L., "Analyse Non-Lineaire des Coques Minces Élastiques de Formes Arbitraires par Éléments Triangulaires Courbes," D.Sc. thesis, Universite Laval, Quebec, 1977.

73. Irons, B. M., "The SemiLoof Shell Element," in D. G. Ashwell and R. H. Gallagher (eds.), *Finite Elements for Thin Shells and Curved Members*, Wiley, London, 1976.

74. Belytschko, T., and Chen-Shyh Tsay, "A Stabilization Procedure for the Quadrilateral Plate Element with One Point Quadrature," *Int. J. Numer. Meth. Eng.*, **19**:405–419 (1983).

75. Belytschko, T., W.-K. Liu, and J. S.-J. Ong, "Nine Node Lagrange Shell Elements with Spurious Mode Control," *25th Structures, Structural Dynamics and Materials Conference*, AIAA/ASME/AHS, Palm Springs, Calif., May 1984.

76. Hughes, T. J. R., and W. K. Liu, "Nonlinear Finite Element Analysis of Shells," *Comput. Meth. Appl. Mech. Eng.*, **26**:331–362 (1981).

77. Karamanlidis, D., and S. N. Atluri, "Mixed Finite Element Models for Plate Bending Analysis— Theory," *Computers and Structures*, **19**:431–445 (1984).

78. Karamanlidis, D., H. L. The, and S. N. Atluri, "Mixed Finite Element Models for Plate Bending Analysis: A New Element and Its Applications," *Computers and Structures*, **19**:565–581 (1984).

79. Hrabok, M. M., and T. M. Hrudey, "A Review and Catalogue of Plate Bending Finite Elements," *Computers and Structures*, **19**:479–495 (1984).

# CHAPTER 5
# MIXED AND HYBRID FINITE-ELEMENT METHODS

## 5.1 INTRODUCTION

The two basic variational principles in structural mechanics are the principle of minimum potential energy and the principle of minimum complementary energy. These are "one-field" variational principles. The corresponding finite-element models are the compatible displacement model and the equilibrium model, which are called the *primal finite-element models*. More general variational principles can be derived by including the conditions of constraint and corresponding Lagrange multipliers. These variational principles contain more than one field variable in an element. The corresponding finite-element methods are called *mixed models*. For finite-element formulations, the constraint conditions and corresponding field variables along the interelement boundary may also be included. The resulting finite-element methods are called the *hybrid models*.

Mixed and hybrid finite-element models were initially developed to circumvent the difficulty in constructing a compatible displacement field for plate-bending problems which are governed by fourth-order differential equations. It was later found that these models also have advantages for problems governed by second-order equations.

In the next section a most general variational principle in structural mechanics, the Hu–Washizu principle, and its extended hybrid versions are discussed. By satisfying a priori some of the Euler's equations of the field variables, a variety of variational principles can be derived. Mixed, hybrid, and mixed-hybrid elements are, in fact, derived using these extended variational principles. A flowchart for the various variational principles and the corresponding finite-element models is given in Fig. 5.1. This chapter follows many of the basic developments discussed in Ref. [1].

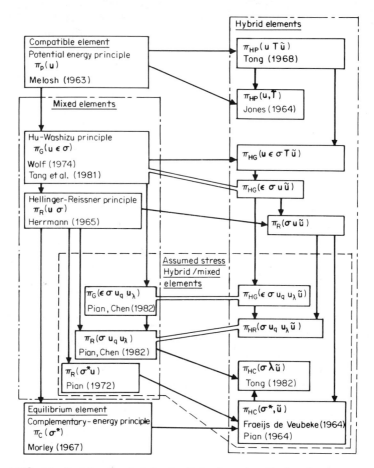

**FIG. 5.1** Variational principles for finite-element methods. $\sigma^* =$ stresses which satisfy equilibrium equations.

In this chapter, a fixed cartesian system is employed. A boldface letter denotes a vector or a matrix, and an italic boldface letter represents a tensor. A boldface Greek letter represents a vector or a tensor. The notations used are defined as follows:

$(\bar{\ })$         Overbar denotes a prescribed quantity

$(\tilde{\ })$         Tilde denotes a quantity defined only at element boundary

$\mathbf{a} = \boldsymbol{B}.\mathbf{C}.$        Implies $a_i = B_{ik}C_k$ (repeated subscript denotes sum)

$\boldsymbol{B}:\boldsymbol{C}$        Denotes $B_{ij}C_{ij}$

$\boldsymbol{\nabla}$        Gradient operator, $\boldsymbol{\nabla} = \mathbf{e}_i\,(\partial/\partial x_i)$, where $\mathbf{e}_i$ are the unit base vectors and $x_i$ are the spacial coordinates

$\boldsymbol{\tau}$        Stress tensor

$\boldsymbol{\varepsilon}$        Strain tensor

$\mathbf{F}$        Body-force vector

| | |
|---|---|
| $M$ | Moment tensor |
| **n** | Unit outward normal vector |
| **u** | Displacement vector |
| **T** | Boundary traction vector |
| $\Omega_m$ | Domain of an element |
| $\partial\Omega_m, S_m$ | Element boundary |
| $A(\boldsymbol{\varepsilon})$ | Strain-energy density |
| $B(\boldsymbol{\varepsilon})$ | Complementary-energy density |

## 5.2 GENERAL VARIATIONAL PRINCIPLE IN LINEAR SOLID MECHANICS

In the regular finite-element method in solid mechanics, a compatible displacement field is used as the dependent variable. The finite-element equations are derived from the principle of minimum potential energy, which has as its Euler equations the equilibrium conditions and the traction boundary conditions. The finite-element analysis is simply an approximation of these Euler equations. Similarly, a finite-element formulation can also be based on the principle of minimum complementary energy by employing an equilibrating stress field which satisfies the traction boundary conditions. The finite-element equations are, in fact, approximations of the compatibility equations and displacement boundary conditions. If, in the principle of minimum potential energy, the displacement compatibility and displacement boundary conditions are treated as conditions of constraint through the Lagrange multipliers, one obtains the Hu–Washizu variational principle [2, 3], which states the stationary condition of a functional with stresses, strains, and displacements as field variables. On the other hand, if, in the complementary-energy principle, the conditions of stress equilibrium are introduced as *a posteriori* constraints through Lagrange multipliers, one is led to the Reissner principle [4, 5], which states the stationary condition of a functional with stresses and displacements as field variables. The Reissner functional may also be obtained directly from the Hu–Washizu functional by eliminating the strain variables using the stress–strain relation. Thus, the Hu–Washizu principle may be considered as the more general variational principle in solid mechanics.

Consider a solid continuum which is discretized into $N$ finite elements $\Omega_m$, $m = 1, 2, \ldots, N$ ($\Omega = \sum_1^N \Omega_m$), whose boundaries are $\partial\Omega_m$. In general, $\partial\Omega_m = S_m + S_{tm} + S_{um}$, where $S_m$ is the interelement boundary, and $S_{tm}$ and $S_{um}$ are, respectively, the segments of $\partial\Omega_m$ with prescribed tractions $\bar{\mathbf{T}}$ and displacements $\bar{\mathbf{u}}$. For elements not adjoining the boundary of the solid, $S_{tm}$ and $S_{um}$ are zero. The Hu–Washizu principle is stated as the stationary condition of the variational functional

$$\pi_G(\mathbf{u}, \boldsymbol{\varepsilon}, \boldsymbol{\tau}) = \sum_m^N \left[ \pi_{Gm} - \int_{S_{tm}} \bar{\mathbf{T}} \cdot \mathbf{u} \, ds - \int_{S_{um}} \mathbf{n} \cdot \boldsymbol{\tau} \cdot (\mathbf{u} - \bar{\mathbf{u}}) \, dS \right] \qquad (5.1)$$

where

$$\pi_{Gm} = \int_{\Omega_m} \{ A(\boldsymbol{\varepsilon}) + \boldsymbol{\tau} : [\tfrac{1}{2}(\boldsymbol{\nabla}\mathbf{u}) + \tfrac{1}{2}(\boldsymbol{\nabla}\mathbf{u})^T - \boldsymbol{\varepsilon}] - \bar{\mathbf{F}} \cdot \mathbf{u} \} \, d\Omega \qquad (5.2)$$

The admissible condition at the interelement boundary $S_m$ is displacement continuity,

$$\mathbf{u}^+ = \mathbf{u}^- \tag{5.3}$$

at $S_m$, where the superscripts $+$ and $-$ denote the two sides of the interelement boundary. The corresponding Euler equations are

$$\nabla \cdot \boldsymbol{\tau} + \bar{\mathbf{F}} = 0 \qquad \text{in } \Omega_m \tag{5.4}$$

$$\boldsymbol{\tau} = \frac{\partial A}{\partial \boldsymbol{\varepsilon}} \qquad \text{in } \Omega_m \tag{5.5}$$

$$\boldsymbol{\varepsilon} = \tfrac{1}{2}[\nabla \mathbf{u} + (\nabla \mathbf{u})^T] \qquad \text{in } \Omega_m \tag{5.6}$$

$$\mathbf{n} \cdot \boldsymbol{\tau} = \bar{\mathbf{T}} \qquad \text{on } S_{tm} \tag{5.7}$$

$$\mathbf{u} = \bar{\mathbf{u}} \qquad \text{on } S_{um} \tag{5.8}$$

An alternative form of the variational functional obtained by using the divergence theorem is

$$\pi'_G(\mathbf{u}, \boldsymbol{\varepsilon}, \boldsymbol{\tau}) = \sum_m \left[ \pi'_{Gm} - \int_{S_{tm}} (\bar{\mathbf{T}} - \mathbf{n} \cdot \boldsymbol{\tau}) \cdot \mathbf{u} \, dS + \int_{S_{um}} \mathbf{n} \cdot \boldsymbol{\tau} \cdot \bar{\mathbf{u}} \, dS \right] \tag{5.9}$$

where

$$\pi'_{Gm} = \int_{\Omega_m} [A(\boldsymbol{\varepsilon}) - (\nabla \cdot \boldsymbol{\tau} + \bar{\mathbf{F}}) \cdot \mathbf{u} - \boldsymbol{\tau} : \boldsymbol{\varepsilon}] \, d\Omega \tag{5.10}$$

with the following admissible condition along $S_m$,

$$(\mathbf{n} \cdot \boldsymbol{\tau})^+ + (\mathbf{n} \cdot \boldsymbol{\tau})^- = 0 \tag{5.11}$$

i.e., the reciprocity of the tractions at the two sides of the interelement boundary. Note that the surface normals $\mathbf{n}^+ = -\mathbf{n}^-$ at $S_m$.

The admissibility requirement on the displacement fields for Eq. (5.1) may not provide flexibility in the finite-element application to a variety of problems in solid mechanics. For example, in problems involving thin plates and shells, the displacements are usually subject to the approximation of the Kirchhoff assumption such that the normal to the midsurface remains normal to the surface after deformation. If $x_\alpha$ ($\alpha = 1, 2$) are the in-plane coordinates and $x_3$ is normal to the plate or shell midsurface, the Kirchhoff assumption results in a kinematic constraint on $u_\alpha$ such that

$$u_\alpha = u_{\alpha 0} - x_3 u_3|_\alpha$$

where $u_{\alpha 0}$ is the value of $u_\alpha$ at the midplane of the thin structure and $(\ )|_\alpha$ denotes covariant differentiation with respect to $x_\alpha$. In order for all $u_i$ ($i = 1, 2, 3$) to be continuous at $S_m$, it is necessary that not only $u_3$ but also $u_3|_\alpha$ be continuous. The requirement that both $u_3$ and $u_3|_\alpha$ be continuous was a major difficulty in the early finite-element development and still is a source that leads to the complicated formulation of a displacement model for plates and shells. To ease such a difficulty, we can relax the interelement compatibility requirement with a Lagrange multiplier. It can be shown that the Lagrange multiplier field $\tilde{\mathbf{T}}$ for enforcing interelement displacement compatibility at $S_m$ has the meaning of interelement tractions, and should obey a priori the condition that $\tilde{\mathbf{T}}^+ + \tilde{\mathbf{T}}^- = 0$. Including these Lagrange multipliers in the variational functional, we obtain the *hybrid* finite-element functional from Eq. (5.1)

$$\pi_{HG}(\mathbf{u}, \boldsymbol{\varepsilon}, \boldsymbol{\tau}, \tilde{\mathbf{T}}) = \sum_{m=1}^{N} \left( \pi_{Gm} - \int_{S_m} \tilde{\mathbf{T}} \cdot \mathbf{u} \, dS \right) - \int_{S_{tm}} \tilde{\mathbf{T}} \cdot \mathbf{u} \, dS - \int_{S_{um}} \mathbf{u} \cdot \boldsymbol{\tau} \cdot (\mathbf{u} - \bar{\mathbf{u}}) \, dS \quad (5.12)$$

where $\pi_{Gm}$ is as defined in Eq. (5.2). This is called a *hybrid functional* because the fields $\mathbf{u}$, $\boldsymbol{\varepsilon}$, $\boldsymbol{\tau}$ are used in $\Omega_m$ while $\tilde{\mathbf{T}}$ is used only at $S_m$.

It is noted that if the reciprocating condition $(\mathbf{n} \cdot \boldsymbol{\tau})^+ = -(\mathbf{n} \cdot \boldsymbol{\tau})^- = \tilde{\mathbf{T}}^+$ is satisfied, Eq. (5.12) is simply reduced to Eq. (5.9).

In practice, it is not convenient to use a reciprocating traction $\tilde{\mathbf{T}}$ at $S_m$, because most of the available finite-element programs have adopted the displacementlike field as the basic unknown variable. This reciprocity condition can be relaxed by further modifying the functional in Eq. (5.12) through another Lagrange multiplier field $\tilde{\mathbf{u}}$ on $S_m$. The resulting functional becomes

$$\pi_{HG_1}(\mathbf{u}, \boldsymbol{\varepsilon}, \boldsymbol{\tau}, \tilde{\mathbf{T}}, \tilde{\mathbf{u}}) = \sum_{m} \left[ \pi_{Gm} - \int_{\partial\Omega_m} \tilde{\mathbf{T}} \cdot (\mathbf{u} - \tilde{\mathbf{u}}) \, dS - \int_{S_{tm}} \bar{\mathbf{T}} \cdot \tilde{\mathbf{u}} \, dS \right] \quad (5.13)$$

where $\tilde{\mathbf{u}} = \bar{\mathbf{u}}$ at $S_{um}$. This is the most general variational functional for the finite-element formulation.

It can be shown that the stationary condition of the functional in Eq. (5.13) leads to Eqs. (5.3) to (5.7) in $\Omega_m$, at $S_{tm}$ and at $S_{um}$, respectively, and

$$(\mathbf{n} \cdot \boldsymbol{\tau})^{\pm} = \tilde{\mathbf{T}}^{\pm} \quad (5.14)$$

$$\tilde{\mathbf{T}}^+ + \tilde{\mathbf{T}}^- = 0 \quad (5.15)$$

$$\mathbf{u}^{\pm} = \tilde{\mathbf{u}} \quad (5.16)$$

at $S_m$. As a result, the required interelement reciprocity and compatibility constraints, $(\mathbf{n} \cdot \boldsymbol{\tau})^+ + (\mathbf{n} \cdot \boldsymbol{\tau})^- = 0$ and $\mathbf{u}^+ = \mathbf{u}^-$ at $S_m$, are satisfied.

It should be noted that $\mathbf{T}^+ = (\mathbf{n} \cdot \boldsymbol{\tau})^+$ and $\mathbf{T}^- = (\mathbf{n} \cdot \boldsymbol{\tau})^-$ on $S_m$ can be easily satisfied in advance; and in practice the following hybrid functional with only four field variables $\mathbf{u}$, $\boldsymbol{\varepsilon}$, $\boldsymbol{\tau}$, and $\tilde{\mathbf{u}}$ is more commonly used:

$$\pi_{HG_2}(\mathbf{u}, \boldsymbol{\varepsilon}, \boldsymbol{\tau}, \tilde{\mathbf{u}}) = \sum_{m} \left[ \pi_{Gm} - \int_{\partial\Omega_m} \mathbf{n} \cdot \boldsymbol{\tau}(\mathbf{u} - \tilde{\mathbf{u}}) \, dS - \int_{S_{tm}} \bar{\mathbf{T}} \cdot \tilde{\mathbf{u}} \, dS \right] \quad (5.17)$$

The functional above can also be derived directly from Eq. (5.9) by enforcing the interelement reciprocity requirement, Eq. (5.11), through the Lagrange multiplier field $\tilde{\mathbf{u}}$.

By satisfying some of Eqs. (5.3) to (5.7) and (5.14) to (5.16) a priori and having the rest to be the *a posteriori* constraints resulting from the stationary condition of the reduced functionals, we can derive a variety of hybrid, mixed, and hybrid-mixed finite-element models. The most general modified variational functionals, and the variety of finite-element methods derivable therefrom, were first discussed in [49], and their extensions to nonlinear problems were later considered in [50].

In Eqs. (5.13) and (5.17), besides the interelement displacement $\tilde{\mathbf{u}}$, all field variables from different elements are independent. In other words, the field variables of one element are not necessarily the same as those of the other elements. One can ensure that this is so by having, in advance, different sets of Euler equations satisfied in different elements. This feature, which makes the hybrid method most versatile, allows one to select the best local solutions within the elements for construction of an approximate solution for the continuum.

The equations given above are for a three-dimensional solid continuum. Similar equations can be written for other structural-mechanics problems. For example, the strain energy of thin plates contains the second derivatives of lateral displacement $w$. This is because the strains are in terms of the displacement's second derivative. The equations of equilibrium are in terms of the stress couples and are also of the second order. There exist many alternative versions of mixed variational functionals with different combinations of the compatibility and reciprocity conditions along the interelement boundaries. For thin-shell problems, because the in-plane and out-of-plane stresses and strains may take different types of variational functionals, there exist even more variational principles for the finite-element formulations [6].

## 5.3 HYBRID STRESS METHOD

In Eq. (5.17) when the stress–strain relations, Eq. (5.5), are satisfied a priori, the strain can be eliminated through the contact transformation, $A(\boldsymbol{\varepsilon}) - \boldsymbol{\tau}:\boldsymbol{\varepsilon} = B(\boldsymbol{\tau})$. Equation (5.17) is then reduced to a functional for the Hellinger–Reissner principle which will be discussed in more detail in Sect. 5.5. If in addition the equations of equilibrium, Eq. (5.3), and the displacement boundary conditions, Eq. (5.7), are also imposed, the variational functional through the use of the divergent theorem becomes

$$\pi_{HS}(\boldsymbol{\tau}, \tilde{\mathbf{u}}) = \sum_m \pi_{HSm}(\boldsymbol{\tau}, \tilde{\mathbf{u}}) \tag{5.18}$$

where 
$$\pi_{HSm}(\boldsymbol{\tau}, \tilde{\mathbf{u}}) = \int_{\Omega_m} -B(\boldsymbol{\tau})\, d\Omega + \int_{\partial\Omega_m} \mathbf{n} \cdot \boldsymbol{\tau} \cdot \tilde{\mathbf{u}}\, dS - \int_{S_{tm}} \bar{\mathbf{T}} \cdot \tilde{\mathbf{u}}\, dS \tag{5.19}$$

where $\tilde{\mathbf{u}}$ are displacements only along the boundary of the elements. The Euler equations are the compatibility of strains in terms of stresses in $\Omega_m$, the reciprocity of $\mathbf{n} \cdot \boldsymbol{\tau}$ at $S_m$,'and the prescribed traction condition $\mathbf{n} \cdot \boldsymbol{\tau} = \bar{\mathbf{T}}$ at $S_{tm}$. It is seen that the variable $\tilde{\mathbf{u}}$, indeed, serves as the Lagrange multiplier to enforce the interelement traction reciprocity and traction boundary conditions for the principle of stationary complementary energy. Equation (5.19) is the hybrid functional used for the assumed-stress hybrid element [7–9].

In the derivation of the finite-element equations using Eq. (5.19), an equilibrating field $\boldsymbol{\tau}$ in $\Omega_m$ and an interelement boundary displacement $\tilde{\mathbf{u}}$ at $S_m$ are independently assumed in terms of a finite number of unknown parameters. Specifically, we approximate

$$\boldsymbol{\tau} = \boldsymbol{\tau}_h + \boldsymbol{\tau}_p \tag{5.20}$$

$$\tilde{\mathbf{u}} = \mathbf{Lq} \tag{5.21}$$

Here and in later developments in finite-element formulations, stresses and strains are expressed in vector form. In Eqs. (5.20)

$$\tau_h = \mathbf{P}\boldsymbol{\beta} \tag{5.22}$$

$$\tau_p = \mathbf{P}_p \boldsymbol{\beta}_p \tag{5.23}$$

where $\mathbf{L}$, $\mathbf{P}$, $\mathbf{P}_P$ are matrices of known function, $\boldsymbol{\beta}_p$ is a known column vector, and $\boldsymbol{\beta}$ and $\mathbf{q}$ are vectors of the unknown parameters for $\tau$ and $\tilde{\mathbf{u}}$, respectively. The matrices $\mathbf{P}$, $\mathbf{P}_P$, and $\boldsymbol{\beta}_p$ are selected such that $\tau_h$ and $\tau_p$ are, respectively, the homogeneous and particular solutions of the equilibrium equations. A substitution of Eqs. (5.22) and (5.23) in Eq. (5.19) yields

$$\pi_{HSm} = -\tfrac{1}{2}\boldsymbol{\beta}^T \mathbf{H}\boldsymbol{\beta} - \boldsymbol{\beta}^T \mathbf{Q}_1 + \boldsymbol{\beta}^T \mathbf{G}\mathbf{q} - \mathbf{Q}_0^T \mathbf{q} + \text{constant} \tag{5.24}$$

where

$$\tfrac{1}{2}\boldsymbol{\beta}^T \mathbf{H}\boldsymbol{\beta} = \int_{\Omega_m} B(\tau_h)\, d\Omega \tag{5.25}$$

$$\boldsymbol{\beta}^T \mathbf{Q}_1 = \int_{\Omega_m} B(\tau_h, \tau_p)\, d\Omega \tag{5.26}$$

$$\boldsymbol{\beta}^T \mathbf{G}\mathbf{q} = \int_{\partial\Omega_m} \mathbf{n} \cdot \tau_h \cdot \tilde{\mathbf{u}}\, dS \tag{5.27}$$

$$\mathbf{Q}_0^T \mathbf{q} = \int_{\partial\Omega_m} \mathbf{n} \cdot \tau_p \cdot \tilde{\mathbf{u}}\, dS + \int_{S_{tm}} \bar{\mathbf{T}} \cdot \tilde{\mathbf{u}}\, dS \tag{5.28}$$

where $B(\tau)$ is a quadratic function of $\tau$, and $\mathbf{H}$ is a positive-definite symmetric matrix except for incompressible materials. Since $\tau$ is an independent field within each individual element, the stationary condition of $\pi_{HSm}$ with respect to the unknown parameters implies

$$\mathbf{H}\boldsymbol{\beta} + \mathbf{Q}_1 = \mathbf{G}\mathbf{q} \tag{5.29}$$

If the above equation is used to eliminate $\boldsymbol{\beta}$ in Eq. (5.24), one obtains

$$\pi_{HSm} = \tfrac{1}{2}\mathbf{q}^T \mathbf{k}\mathbf{q} - \mathbf{Q}^T \mathbf{q} + \text{constant} \tag{5.30}$$

where

$$\mathbf{k} = \mathbf{G}^T \mathbf{H}^{-1} \mathbf{G} \tag{5.31}$$

$$\mathbf{Q} = \mathbf{Q}_0 + \mathbf{G}^T \mathbf{H}^{-1} \mathbf{Q}_1 \tag{5.32}$$

The matrix $\mathbf{k}$ is referred to as the *hybrid-stress-element stiffness matrix*, and $\mathbf{Q}$ is the consistent load factor. It is seen that the hybrid stress method leads to an equivalent stiffness approach in finite-element analysis.

The matrix $\mathbf{k}$ is symmetric and positive-semidefinite. If $\mathbf{k}$ is of order $n$ and $r$ is the allowable number of rigid-body degrees of freedom, and if the rank of $\mathbf{k}$ is less than $n - r$, the element is said to possess kinematic (deformation) mode(s) [8, 51]. The existence of such mode(s) can lead to spurious solutions for a continuum. More details are discussed in Sec. 5.6.

By choosing the same functions in Eq. (5.21) for $\tilde{\mathbf{u}}$ at the common boundary of two adjoining elements, one assures the interelement compatibility. This is a very significant feature of the hybrid stress method. It is particularly important for problems involving high-order field equations such as those of plate bending and shells because of the requirement of continuity in both the normal displacement and out-of-plane rotations.

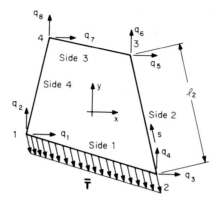

**FIG. 5.2** Quadrilateral two-dimensional element.

As an illustrative example in constructing the hybrid element, we consider a two-dimensional element of isotropic elastic material, as shown in Fig. 5.2. The functional, Eq. (5.19)

$$\pi_{HSm}(\boldsymbol{\tau}, \tilde{\mathbf{u}}) = -\frac{1}{2} \int_{\Omega_m} \begin{bmatrix} \tau_{xx} \\ \tau_{yy} \\ \tau_{xy} \end{bmatrix}^T [D] \begin{bmatrix} \tau_{xx} \\ \tau_{yy} \\ \tau_{xy} \end{bmatrix} d\Omega + \int_{\partial\Omega_m} \mathbf{n} \cdot \boldsymbol{\tau} \cdot \tilde{\mathbf{u}} \, dS - \int_{S_{tm}} \bar{\mathbf{T}} \cdot \tilde{\mathbf{u}} \, dS \quad (5.33)$$

where

$$\mathbf{D} = \frac{1}{E} \begin{bmatrix} \xi & -\nu\eta & 0 \\ -\nu\eta & \xi & 0 \\ 0 & 0 & 2(1+\nu) \end{bmatrix} \quad (5.34)$$

in which $E$ and $\nu$ are Young's modulus and Poisson's ratio with

$$\begin{aligned} \xi = 1 \qquad \eta = 1 \qquad &\text{for a plane-stress problem} \\ \xi = 1 - \nu^2 \qquad \eta = 1 + \nu \qquad &\text{for a plane-strain problem} \end{aligned} \quad (5.35)$$

$\Omega_m$ is the area of the quadrilateral, and $\partial\Omega_m$ consists of the four sides with nodes 1 to 4. If $\partial\Omega_m$ does not adjoin the stress prescribed boundary, $S_{tm}$ is zero.

In the present case, $S_{tm}$ is side 1 and the prescribed traction $\bar{\mathbf{T}}$ is constant at $S_{tm}$. We also assume that the body force is constant within $\Omega_m$ and is represented by its two components $\bar{F}_x$ and $\bar{F}_y$. A simple set of equilibrating stresses and compatible boundary displacements can be written in matrix form as

$$\boldsymbol{\tau} = \begin{bmatrix} \tau_{xx} \\ \tau_{yy} \\ \tau_{xy} \end{bmatrix} = \mathbf{P}\boldsymbol{\beta} + \boldsymbol{\tau}_p$$

$$= \begin{bmatrix} 1 & 0 & 0 & y & 0 \\ 0 & 1 & 0 & 0 & x \\ 0 & 0 & 1 & 0 & 0 \end{bmatrix} \begin{bmatrix} \beta_1 \\ \beta_2 \\ \vdots \\ \beta_5 \end{bmatrix} + \begin{bmatrix} x\bar{F}_x \\ y\bar{F}_y \\ 0 \end{bmatrix} \quad (5.36)$$

and
$$\tilde{\mathbf{u}} = \begin{bmatrix} u_x \\ u_y \end{bmatrix} = \mathbf{Lq}$$

$$= \begin{bmatrix} 1 - \dfrac{s}{l_i} & 0 & \dfrac{s}{l_i} & 0 \\ 0 & 1 - \dfrac{s}{l_i} & 0 & \dfrac{s}{l_i} \end{bmatrix} \begin{bmatrix} q_{2i-1} \\ q_{2i} \\ q_{2i+1} \\ q_{2i+2} \end{bmatrix} \tag{5.37}$$

for side $i$, with $i = 1, \ldots, 4$. The first and second terms of Eq. (5.37) are, respectively, the homogeneous and particular solutions of the assumed equilibrating stresses; $l_i$ is the length of side $i$; and $s$ is the distance measured from node $i$ to $i+1$. The assumed boundary-displacement variation is linear. Therefore, the interelement compatibility is assured if the nodal displacements of adjacent elements are matched. It can be shown that if the $x$- or $y$-axis is parallel to one of the element sides, no kinematic mode exists for this set of stresses and displacements.

A substitution of Eqs. (5.36) and (5.37) into Eq. (5.33) yields

$$\mathbf{H} = \int_{\Omega_m} \mathbf{P}^T \mathbf{D} \mathbf{P} \, d\Omega \tag{5.38}$$

$$\mathbf{Q}_1 = \int_{\Omega_m} P^T E \begin{bmatrix} x\bar{F}_x \\ y\bar{F}_y \\ 0 \end{bmatrix} d\Omega \tag{5.39}$$

The matrices $\mathbf{G}$ and $\mathbf{Q}_0$ are obtained by summing the integration as defined in Eqs. (5.27) and (5.28) along the four sides. The contribution to components $G_{I,J}$ from side $i$ is given by

| $J\backslash I$ | $2i-1$ | $2i$ | $2i+1$ | $2i+2$ |
|---|---|---|---|---|
| 1 | $\dfrac{l_i C_i}{2}$ | 0 | $\dfrac{l_i C_i}{2}$ | 0 |
| 2 | 0 | $\dfrac{l_i S_i}{2}$ | 0 | $\dfrac{l_i S_i}{2}$ |
| 3 | $\dfrac{l_i S_i}{2}$ | $\dfrac{l_i C_i}{2}$ | $\dfrac{l_i S_i}{2}$ | $\dfrac{l_i C_i}{2}$ |
| 4 | $l_i C_i \left( \dfrac{y_i}{3} + \dfrac{y_{i+1}}{6} \right)$ | 0 | $l_i C_i \left( \dfrac{y_i}{6} + \dfrac{y_i + 1}{3} \right)$ | 0 |
| 5 | 0 | $l_i S_i \left( \dfrac{x_i}{3} + \dfrac{x_{i+1}}{6} \right)$ | 0 | $l_i S_i \left( \dfrac{x_i}{6} + \dfrac{x_{i+1}}{3} \right)$ |

(5.40)

The contribution to the components $Q_J$ of $\mathbf{Q}_0$ from the same side is given by

| $J$ | $2i-1$ | $2i$ | $2i+1$ | $2i+2$ |
|---|---|---|---|---|
| | $C_i l_i \bar{F}_x \left( \dfrac{x_i}{3} + \dfrac{x_{i+1}}{6} \right)$ | $S_i l_i \bar{F}y \left( \dfrac{y_i}{3} + \dfrac{y_{i+1}}{6} \right)$ | $C_i l_i \bar{F}_x \left( \dfrac{x_i}{6} + \dfrac{x_{i+1}}{3} \right)$ | $S_i l_i \bar{F}_y \left( \dfrac{y_i}{6} + \dfrac{y_i + 1}{3} \right)$ |
| | $+ \varepsilon \bar{T}_x l_{i/2}$ | $+ \varepsilon \bar{T}_y l_{i/2}$ | $+ \varepsilon \bar{T}_x l_{i/2}$ | $+ \varepsilon \bar{T}_y l_{i/2}$ |

(5.41)

In the equations above, $\varepsilon = 1$ for side $i$, $\varepsilon = 0$ for all the other sides, $(x_i, y_i)$ are the coordinates of node $i$, and $(C_i, S_i)$ are the direction cosines of the normal on side $i$. The parameters and the nodal coordinates are related by the equations

$$l_i = [(x_{i+1} - x_i)^2 + (y_{i+1} - y_i)^2]^{1/2} \tag{5.42}$$

$$C_i = \frac{y_{i+1} - y_i}{l_i}$$
$$S_i = \frac{x_i - x_{i+1}}{l_i} \tag{5.43}$$

The matrices $\mathbf{H}$ and $\mathbf{Q}_i$ can be evaluated easily by numerical integration. In particular, if the element is a rectangle with its coordinates coinciding with the element principal axes, we have

$$\mathbf{H} = 4x_1 y_1 \begin{bmatrix} D_{11} & & & & & \\ D_{12} & D_{22} & & & \text{Symm.} & \\ 0 & 0 & D_{33} & & & \\ 0 & 0 & 0 & \frac{2D_{11}y_1^2}{3} & & \\ 0 & 0 & 0 & 0 & \frac{2D_{22}x_1^2}{3} \end{bmatrix} \tag{5.44}$$

and

$$\mathbf{Q}_0 = \tfrac{8}{3} D_{12} x_1 y_1 \begin{bmatrix} 0 \\ 0 \\ 0 \\ y_1^2 \bar{F}_y \\ x_1^2 \bar{F}_x \end{bmatrix} \tag{5.45}$$

The matrix $\mathbf{H}$ can be inverted explicitly.

In the case that the assumed stresses satisfy both the equilibrium and compatibility conditions, the volume integral in Eq. (5.19) can be reduced to a surface integral along the boundary of the element. The variational functional [10] can be expressed as

$$\pi^*_{HS} = \sum_m \left[ \int_{\partial\Omega_m} (-\tfrac{1}{2}\mathbf{n}\cdot\boldsymbol{\tau}\cdot\mathbf{u} + \mathbf{n}\cdot\boldsymbol{\tau}\cdot\tilde{\mathbf{u}})\,d\Omega - \int_{S_{tm}} \bar{\mathbf{T}}\cdot\tilde{\mathbf{u}}\,d\Omega \right] \tag{5.46}$$

where $\mathbf{u}$ and $\boldsymbol{\tau}$ are related through the stress–strain relations. In the finite-element formulation, let

$$\mathbf{u} = \mathbf{U}\boldsymbol{\beta} + \mathbf{U}_p\boldsymbol{\beta}_p \tag{5.47}$$

$$\mathbf{n}\cdot\boldsymbol{\tau} = \mathbf{R}\boldsymbol{\beta} + \mathbf{R}_p\boldsymbol{\beta}_p \tag{5.48}$$

then the resulting functional is of the same form as Eq. (5.24) except that the $\mathbf{H}$ matrix is defined as

$$\mathbf{H} = \tfrac{1}{2}\int_{\partial\Omega_m} (\mathbf{R}^T\mathbf{U} + \mathbf{U}^T\mathbf{R})\,d\Omega \tag{5.49}$$

A typical application of this variational functional $\pi_{HS}^*$ is the plane-elasticity problem with stress singularity such as the linear fracture-mechanics problem [10]. The standard technique of complex stress functions in plane-elasticity problems permits the construction at the neighborhood of the singularity an approximate series solution which satisfies the equilibrium and compatibility equations as well as the stress-free boundary conditions at the surface of the crack. A special element, which contains an embedded crack, can thus be derived to be employed in conjunction with conventional finite elements for the determination of elastic-stress intensity factors. Since the functional $\pi_{HS}^*$ contains only boundary integrals, the difficulty of area integration including a singularity can be avoided. In a similar manner, this method can be applied to problems for which the nature of the solution at infinity is known. A typical problem is the determination of surface waves near an offshore structure [11, 17].

The convergence behavior of the hybrid stress method was studied in Refs. [8, 12, 52, 53]. It was shown that the strain energy of a hybrid element is bounded from above by that of the displacement method with the same element boundary displacements. When problems with stress singularity of $1/r^\alpha$, $\alpha > 0$, are solved by the regular-displacement finite-element methods, the convergence of the strain energy is dominated by the singularity and is of order $h^{2\alpha}$, where $h$ is the size of the element. However, when the proper singular behavior is included in the assumed stresses and displacements in the hybrid method, the normal higher-order convergence rate is restored [13].

One significant advantage of the assumed-stress hybrid method is the absence of locking phenomena in its solution in certain limiting cases. The locking phenomena often appear for nearly incompressible materials and for thin plates derived by using the Reissner theory when the conventional assumed-displacement method is used. In these cases, several constraints are introduced to the element displacements.

In applying the assumed-stress hybrid elements to incompressible solids the flexibility matrix **H** will become singular, on account of the linear dependence of the columns which correspond to normal stress terms. It is shown [14, 15], in turn, that the incompressibility condition will lead to only one constraint, which, in fact, specifies that the volume of the element be maintained constant. It has been demonstrated that by including this constraint the assumed-stress hybrid element can yield very accurate solutions for materials which are very nearly incompressible, for example, for an isotropic material with Poisson's ratio equal to 0.4999. For applications of hybrid methods to incompressible fluids, see [54, 55].

For plate elements with the transverse-shear strain accounted for, it has been shown [16] that the flexibility matrix **H** does not become singular when the thickness of the plate approaches zero. Hence **H** can be inverted.

The direct inversion of **H** in Eqs. (3.31) and (5.32) can be time-consuming and can introduce numerical inaccuracy, especially for large **H**. A better way is to evaluate **k** and $\mathbf{H}^{-1}\mathbf{Q}_1$ using the triple factoring technique [17]. First, one factors **H** in the form $\mathbf{LDL}^T$, where **L** is a lower triangular matrix with all diagonals being 1 and **D** is a diagonal matrix. We then define **X** and **x** by solving the equations

$$\mathbf{LX} = \mathbf{C}$$

$$\mathbf{Lx} = \mathbf{Q}_1$$

(5.50)

It can be shown that the stiffness matrix and the load vector are simply

$$\mathbf{k} = \mathbf{X}^T \mathbf{D}^{-1} \mathbf{X} \tag{5.51}$$

$$\mathbf{Q} = \mathbf{Q}_0 + \mathbf{X}^T \mathbf{D}^{-1} \mathbf{x} \tag{5.52}$$

## 5.4 HYBRID DISPLACEMENT METHOD

If, in Eq. (5.17), the strain-displacement relations are satisfied a priori, we obtain the hybrid displacement function [18]

$$\pi_{HD}(\mathbf{u}, \tilde{\mathbf{T}}, \tilde{\mathbf{u}}) = \sum_m \pi_{HDm}(\mathbf{u}, \tilde{\mathbf{T}}, \tilde{\mathbf{u}}) \tag{5.53}$$

where

$$\pi_{HDm} = \int_{\Omega_m} [A(\boldsymbol{\varepsilon}) - \bar{\mathbf{F}}_0 \cdot \mathbf{u}] \, d\Omega - \int_{\partial\Omega_m} \tilde{\mathbf{T}} \cdot (\mathbf{u} - \tilde{\mathbf{u}}) \, dS - \int_{S_{tm}} \bar{\mathbf{T}} \cdot \mathbf{u} \, dS \tag{5.54}$$

and $\tilde{\mathbf{u}} = \bar{\mathbf{u}}$, the prescribed displacements at $S_{um}$. The Euler equations of the above functional are the equilibrium conditions, Eq. (5.3), in $\Omega_m$, the boundary traction conditions, Eq. (5.6), at $S_{tm}$, and the traction reciprocity and displacement compatibility, Eqs. (5.14) to (5.16), at $S_m$. In these Euler equations, the stress $\boldsymbol{\tau}$ is in terms of $\mathbf{u}$ through Eqs. (5.4) and (5.5)

$$\mathbf{u} = \mathbf{U}\boldsymbol{\gamma} \qquad \text{in } \Omega_m \tag{5.55}$$

$$\tilde{\mathbf{T}} = \mathbf{R}\boldsymbol{\alpha} \qquad \text{in } \Omega_m \tag{5.56}$$

$$\tilde{\mathbf{u}} = \mathbf{L}\mathbf{q} \qquad \text{in } \partial\Omega_m \tag{5.57}$$

where $\mathbf{U}$, $\mathbf{R}$, and $\mathbf{L}$ are matrices of known functions, and $\boldsymbol{\gamma}$, $\boldsymbol{\alpha}$, and $\mathbf{q}$ are column vectors of unknown parameters. Substituting Eqs. (5.3) to (5.5) into Eq. (5.2), we have

$$\pi_{HDm} = \tfrac{1}{2}\boldsymbol{\gamma}^T \mathbf{H}\boldsymbol{\gamma} - \boldsymbol{\gamma}^T \mathbf{Q}_1 - \boldsymbol{\alpha}^T \mathbf{G}_1\boldsymbol{\gamma} + \boldsymbol{\alpha}^T \mathbf{G}\mathbf{q} - \mathbf{q}^T \mathbf{Q}_0 \tag{5.58}$$

where

$$\boldsymbol{\gamma}^T \mathbf{H}\boldsymbol{\gamma} = 2 \int_{\partial\Omega_m} A(\boldsymbol{\varepsilon}) \, d\Omega \tag{5.59}$$

$$\boldsymbol{\gamma}^T \mathbf{Q}_1 = \int_{\Omega_m} \bar{\mathbf{F}} \cdot \mathbf{u} \, d\Omega \tag{5.60}$$

$$\boldsymbol{\alpha}^T \mathbf{G} \cdot \boldsymbol{\gamma} = \int_{\partial\Omega_m} \tilde{\mathbf{T}} \cdot \mathbf{u} \, dS \tag{5.61}$$

$$\boldsymbol{\alpha}^T \mathbf{G}\mathbf{q} = \int_{\partial\Omega_m} \tilde{\mathbf{T}} \cdot \tilde{\mathbf{u}} \, dS \tag{5.62}$$

$$\mathbf{q}^T \mathbf{Q}_0 = \int_{S_{t_m}} \bar{\mathbf{T}} \cdot \tilde{\mathbf{u}} \, dS \tag{5.63}$$

Since both $\mathbf{u}$ and $\mathbf{T}$ are independent fields, the stationary of $\pi_{HD}$ with respect to $\mathbf{u}$ and $\mathbf{T}$ implies

$$\mathbf{H\gamma} - \mathbf{G}_1^T \boldsymbol{\alpha} = \mathbf{Q}_1 \tag{5.64}$$

$$-\mathbf{G}_1 \boldsymbol{\gamma} = \mathbf{Gq} \tag{5.65}$$

From the above equations both $\boldsymbol{\gamma}$ and $\boldsymbol{\alpha}$ can be solved in terms of $\mathbf{q}$. A substitution into Eq. (5.57) reduces $\pi_{HDm}$ to the same form as $\pi_{HSm}$ in Eq. (5.30). Therefore, the hybrid displacement method, like the hybrid stress method, also leads to a stiffness-matrix approach.

The values of $\mathbf{k}$ and $\mathbf{Q}$, and the procedure for their evaluation, depend on the approximations of $\mathbf{u}$, $\mathbf{T}$, and $\tilde{\mathbf{u}}$. For example, if $\mathbf{u}$ and $\mathbf{T}$ are chosen so that $\mathbf{G}_1$ is a nonsingular square matrix, $\boldsymbol{\gamma}$ can be solved in terms of $\mathbf{q}$ from Eq. (5.65). Then, in turn, $\boldsymbol{\alpha}$ can be solved in terms of $\mathbf{q}$ from Eq. (5.64).

Another hybrid displacement model can be constructed by enforcing additional constraints. If the traction conditions at $S_{tm}$ and the traction-reciprocity conditions at $S_m$ are satisfied, all the terms in Eqs. (5.52) and (5.53) associated with $\mathbf{u}$ can be eliminated. The reduced variational functional, first derived by Jones [19], contains only two fields $\mathbf{u}$ and $\boldsymbol{\alpha}$, where $\boldsymbol{\alpha} = \mathbf{T}^+ = -\mathbf{T}^-$. Since most of the finite-element computer programs employ displacement degrees of freedom, it is not convenient to adapt this version of the hybrid displacement model in the existing programs. In plate bending, the corresponding field variables are the displacement $w$ in $\Omega_m$, the boundary displacement $w$ and its derivatives $w_{,n}$ and $w_{,s}$, and the boundary moments and shear $(M_n, M_{ns}, Q_n)$ at $\partial\Omega_m$, where the subscripts $n$ and $s$ denote, respectively, the normal and tangential directions at $\partial\Omega_m$. A practical hybrid displacement model [20, 21] is to select the field variables such that $w = \tilde{w}$ and $M_n^+ + M_n^- = 0$ at $\partial\Omega_m$. In this case, the boundary displacement and its derivatives can be eliminated. The remaining variables are $w$, which is continuous only at $\partial\Omega_m$, and $M_n$, which satisfies the reciprocity condition at $\partial\Omega_m$.

As with the hybrid stress method, it is desirable to have the proper approximations for $\mathbf{u}$, $\hat{\mathbf{T}}$, and $\tilde{\mathbf{u}}$ to avoid the possibility of kinematic modes. Also, if a field, say $\hat{\boldsymbol{\tau}}$, is readily available which satisfied $\mathbf{n} \cdot \hat{\boldsymbol{\tau}} = \tilde{\mathbf{T}}$ at $\partial\Omega_m$, the integration over $\partial\Omega_m$ in Eq. (5.60) can be converted to integration over $\Omega_m$. If, in addition, a field $\hat{\mathbf{u}}$ is also available with $\hat{\mathbf{u}} = \tilde{\mathbf{u}}$ at $\partial\Omega_m$, Eq. (5.61) can be evaluated by integration over $\Omega_m$. The numerical integration over $\Omega_m$ can be more convenient than that over $\partial\Omega_m$ for three-dimensional problems, provided there is no singularity in $\hat{\boldsymbol{\tau}}$ and $\tilde{\mathbf{u}}$.

The hybrid displacement method, unlike the hybrid stress method, which requires an equilibrating field, can be easily applied to shell problem [22]. This method has also been applied extensively to 2D- and 3D-crack problems [23, 24].

## 5.5 MIXED METHOD

Mixed finite elements can be formulated using the Hu–Washizu principle given by Eqs. (5.1) and (5.9) or Eq. (5.17). More commonly one employs the Hellinger–Reissner principle, which can be derived from the Hu–Washizu principle. In Eqs. (5.1) and (5.9), by imposing the stress–strain relation, Eq. (5.5), we can eliminate the strain $\boldsymbol{\varepsilon}$ through the contact transformation, $A(\boldsymbol{\tau}) - \boldsymbol{\varepsilon} : \boldsymbol{\tau} = B(\boldsymbol{\tau})$. Then these equations reduce to the following two corresponding functionals, respectively, for the Reissner principle:

$$\pi_R(\mathbf{u}, \boldsymbol{\tau}) = \sum_m \left\{ \pi_{Rm} - \int_{S_{tm}} \bar{\mathbf{T}} \cdot \mathbf{u} \, dS - \int_{S_{um}} \mathbf{n} \cdot \boldsymbol{\tau} \cdot (\mathbf{u} - \bar{\mathbf{u}}) \, dS \right\} \tag{5.66}$$

where

$$\pi_{RM} = \int_{\Omega_m} [-B(\boldsymbol{\tau}) + \boldsymbol{\tau} : [\tfrac{1}{2}(\nabla\mathbf{u}) + \tfrac{1}{2}(\nabla\mathbf{u})^T - \bar{\mathbf{F}} \cdot \mathbf{u}] \, d\Omega \tag{5.67}$$

and

$$\pi'_R(\mathbf{u}, \boldsymbol{\tau}) = \sum_m \left\{ \pi'_{Rm} - \int_{S_{tm}} (\bar{\mathbf{T}} - \mathbf{n} \cdot \boldsymbol{\tau}) \cdot \mathbf{u} \, dS + \int_{S_{um}} \mathbf{n} \cdot \boldsymbol{\tau} \cdot \bar{\mathbf{u}} \, dS \right\} \tag{5.68}$$

where

$$\pi'_{Rm} = \int_{\Omega_m} \{-B(\boldsymbol{\tau}) - (\nabla \cdot \boldsymbol{\tau} + \bar{\mathbf{F}}) \cdot \mathbf{u}\} \, d\Omega \tag{5.69}$$

Most of the existing mixed finite elements based on the Reissner principle [25] can be classified into two basic types:

1. Resulting mixed equations are of mixed form with both nodal displacements and stresses as unknowns.

2. Stress parameters are eliminated in the element level, and the resulting matrix equations contain only nodal displacements as unknowns.

Descriptions of these two types of mixed elements are followed by a mixed formulation for reduction of constraint conditions for certain limiting problems in structural mechanics.

## 5.5A Mixed Elements in Mixed Form

A mixed element in mixed form is used largely for thin plates and shells for which $C^1$-continuity for the normal displacement $w$ is required when the variational functional equivalent to $\pi_R$ of Eq. (5.67) is used. In order to relax such a constraint condition, Herrmann [26] used the alternative form equivalent to $\pi'_R$ of Eqs. (5.68) and (5.69) for bending of thin plates.

The variational functional is

$$\begin{aligned}
\pi'_R = \sum_m \Bigg\{ &\int_{A_m} [-B(\mathbf{M}) - (\nabla \cdot \mathbf{M}) \cdot \nabla w - \bar{F}w] \, dA \\
&+ \int_{S_{tm}} [\mathbf{n} \cdot (\mathbf{M} - \bar{\mathbf{M}}) \cdot \nabla w + \mathbf{n} \cdot (\nabla \cdot \bar{\mathbf{M}})w] \, dS \\
&+ \int_{S_{um}} [\mathbf{n} \cdot \mathbf{M} \cdot \nabla \bar{w} + \mathbf{n} \cdot (\nabla \cdot \mathbf{M})(w - \bar{w})] \, dS \Bigg\}
\end{aligned} \tag{5.70}$$

The a priori constraints at $S_m$ are the interelement displacement compatibility

$$w^+ = w^- \tag{5.71}$$

and the interelement moment reciprocity

$$(\mathbf{n} \cdot \mathbf{M})^+ (\mathbf{n} \cdot \mathbf{M})^- = 0 \tag{5.72}$$

The resulting variational functional still has only $M$ and $w$ as field variables, and only $C^0$-continuity is required for $w$.

In the finite-element formulation the stress couples $M\ (= M^{\alpha\beta})$ and the displacement $w$ are expressed, respectively, in terms of the $\mathbf{p}$ and $\mathbf{q}$ as

$$M = \mathbf{Zp} \tag{5.73}$$

$$w = \mathbf{Nq} \tag{5.74}$$

in which the displacement and normal moment at the boundaries are made to satisfy the prescribed values. Equation (5.74) may be expressed in the form of

$$\pi_R = \sum_m (-\tfrac{1}{2}\mathbf{p}^T\mathbf{H}_n\mathbf{p} + \mathbf{p}^T\mathbf{G}_n\mathbf{q} + \mathbf{q}^T\mathbf{Q}_n) \tag{5.75}$$

which, after summing over all elements, may be written as

$$\pi_R = -\tfrac{1}{2}\mathbf{p}^T\mathbf{Hp} + \mathbf{p}^T\mathbf{Gq} + \mathbf{q}^T\mathbf{Q} \tag{5.76}$$

The resulting matrix equation is

$$\begin{bmatrix} \mathbf{H} & \mathbf{G} \\ \mathbf{G}^T & \mathbf{0} \end{bmatrix} \begin{pmatrix} \mathbf{p} \\ \mathbf{q} \end{pmatrix} = \begin{pmatrix} \mathbf{0} \\ \mathbf{Q} \end{pmatrix} \tag{5.77}$$

In the triangular element developed by Herrmann [26], the distribution of $w$ is linear, and the distributions for $M_x$, $M_y$, and $M_{xy}$ are constant and are expressed in terms of the normal moments $M_n$ that are uniformly distributed along each edge. The number of unknowns per element is six. The $\mathbf{G}_n$-matrix in Eq. (5.75) is actually obtained from the boundary-integral term. Since the strains are the derivatives of the displacement, it is obvious that in a mixed element the corresponding assumed stresses should be approximated by an expansion of lower order than that of the assumed displacements.

Finite-element methods by mixed elements have an obvious advantage in balanced accuracy for stresses and displacements. However, because of the use of both nodal displacements and stresses as unknowns, the mixed model would contain a larger number of unknowns for the same finite-element mesh. Also, the resulting matrix equation contains a non-positive-definite matrix, and hence cannot be handled by the conventional finite-element codes which are designed only for positive-definite stiffness matrices.

Noor et al. [27] have applied this mixed formulation to laminated composite plates and shells with transverse-shear effects and evaluated the efficiency of the mixed elements by considering both the computing effort required to generate the element stiffness matrices and the time required for solving the global-matrix equation. They have found that a symbolic algebraic manipulation language can be employed for the evaluation of numerous integrals in the element-matrix formulation. Also, the number of numerical coefficients to be calculated can be reduced considerably by the use of the group-theoretic technique [28]. Mirza and Olson [29] have studied the convergence behavior of this mixed finite-element method and have shown numerically that, for problems with $1/r^{1/2}$-stress singularity, the convergence of the strain energy is $O(h^2)$, where $h$ is the size of the element. When such a problem is solved by finite-element methods using element stiffness matrices, the convergence of the energy is $O(h)$.

## 5.5B Mixed Elements with Discontinuous Stresses

Since in applying the Reissner principle of Eq. (5.66) it is not necessary to maintain the continuity of stresses or even the traction reciprocity along the interelement boundary, it is permissible to express the stresses in terms of stress parameters which are independent from one element to the others. The stress parameters can then be expressed in terms of the nodal displacements, and the resulting matrix equations will have only the nodal displacements as unknowns in the same manner as the assumed-displacement finite-element method. In Eqs. (5.66) and (5.67) consider $\mathbf{u} = \bar{\mathbf{u}}$ at $S_{um}$ and in $\Omega_m$. Let

$$\mathbf{u} = \mathbf{N}\mathbf{q} \tag{5.78}$$

and

$$\boldsymbol{\tau} = \mathbf{P}\boldsymbol{\beta} \tag{5.79}$$

Then $\pi_R$ can be written in the form

$$\pi_R = \sum_m (-\tfrac{1}{2}\boldsymbol{\beta}^T\mathbf{H}\boldsymbol{\beta} + \boldsymbol{\beta}^T\mathbf{G}\mathbf{q} - \mathbf{Q}_0^T\mathbf{q}) \tag{5.80}$$

where

$$\tfrac{1}{2}\boldsymbol{\beta}^T\mathbf{H}\boldsymbol{\beta} = \int_{\Omega_m} B(\boldsymbol{\tau})\, d\Omega \tag{5.81}$$

$$\boldsymbol{\beta}^T\mathbf{G}\mathbf{q} = \int_{\Omega_m} \boldsymbol{\tau} : [\tfrac{1}{2}(\boldsymbol{\nabla}\mathbf{u}) + \tfrac{1}{2}(\boldsymbol{\nabla}\mathbf{u})^T]\, d\Omega \tag{5.82}$$

$$\mathbf{Q}_0^T\mathbf{q} = \int_{\Omega_m} \bar{\mathbf{F}} \cdot \mathbf{u}\, d\Omega + \int_{S_{tm}} \bar{\mathbf{T}} \cdot \mathbf{u}\, dS \tag{5.83}$$

Equation (5.80) is of the same form as Eq. (5.24); hence, by following the procedures in Sec. 5.3, one can obtain

$$\pi_R = \sum_n (\tfrac{1}{2}\mathbf{q}^T\mathbf{k}\mathbf{q} - \mathbf{Q}_0^T\mathbf{q}) \tag{5.84}$$

where the element stiffness matrix is

$$\mathbf{k} = \mathbf{G}^T\mathbf{H}^{-1}\mathbf{G} \tag{5.85}$$

It is, however, clear that if the space $\boldsymbol{\nabla}\mathbf{u}$ is a subspace of $\boldsymbol{\tau}$, which is not subject to any constraints, the resulting stresses from the variational formulation will be those associated with the strains derived from the assumed displacements; and the resulting elements will be identical to those derived by the conventional finite-element method using the same assumed displacements.

In formulating mixed elements with discontinuous stresses it is, thus, desirable that some constraints be applied to the assumed stresses. One obvious idea is to satisfy a priori the homogeneous stress-equilibrium condition. In this case the $\mathbf{G}$ in Eq. (5.82) is identical to the $\mathbf{G}$ obtained in Eq. (5.27), and the element stiffness matrix $\mathbf{k}$ is identical to that obtained by the hybrid stress method.

It is noted that, by satisfying the equilibrium equations in advance, the assumed-stress components will be coupled and the resulting $\mathbf{H}$-matrix can be fully populated. An alternative approach [30] in the hybrid stress method is to assume that the stress components are decoupled initially. The equilibrium equation is enforced only through a lagrangian multiplier. The resulting $\mathbf{H}$, although it can still be fully populated, is in such a special form that it allows great simplification in the evaluation of $\mathbf{H}^{-1}$. Pian and Chen [32] achieved that same approach in a mixed formulation by dividing the assumed displacements into two components $\mathbf{u}_q$ and $\mathbf{u}_\lambda$

$$\mathbf{u}_q = \mathbf{Nq} \tag{5.86}$$

$$\mathbf{u}_\lambda = \mathbf{M\lambda} \tag{5.87}$$

where $\mathbf{q}$ are nodal displacements, $\mathbf{N}$ are compatible shape functions, and $\boldsymbol{\lambda}$ are internal parameters that can be eliminated in the element level. By applying the divergence theorem to the term with $\mathbf{u}_\lambda$, one obtains

$$\pi_R = \sum_m \left( \int \{ -B(\boldsymbol{\tau}) + \boldsymbol{\tau} : [\tfrac{1}{2}(\nabla \mathbf{u}_q) + \tfrac{1}{2}(\nabla \mathbf{u}_q)^T - \bar{\mathbf{F}} \cdot \mathbf{u}_q] \right.$$
$$\left. - (\nabla \boldsymbol{\tau} + \bar{\mathbf{F}}) \cdot \mathbf{u}_\lambda \} \, d\Omega - \int_{S_{tm}} [\bar{\mathbf{T}} \cdot \mathbf{u}_q + (\bar{\mathbf{T}} - \mathbf{n} \cdot \boldsymbol{\tau}) \cdot \mathbf{u}_\lambda] \, dS \right) \tag{5.88}$$

In arriving at the above equation it is assumed that $\mathbf{u}_\lambda$ does not vanish along $\partial \Omega_m$; hence the variational functional $\pi_R$ should be modified by adding a Lagrange multiplier term $-\int_{S_m} \mathbf{n} \cdot \boldsymbol{\tau} (\mathbf{u} - \tilde{\mathbf{u}}) \, dS$ with $\mathbf{u} - \tilde{\mathbf{u}} = \mathbf{u}_\lambda$ along the interelement boundary $S_m$.

It is seen that the terms associated with $\mathbf{u}_\lambda$ are the stress-equilibrium conditions with the Lagrange multiplier. In the finite-element formulation the stress-equilibrium conditions are not considered initially; they are enforced *a posteriori* through the $\mathbf{u}_\lambda$ terms. With appropriate choice for $\mathbf{u}$ such equilibrium conditions can be satisfied exactly and the resulting finite-element method is again identical to the hybrid stress method. This development, however, points out that the equilibrium conditions need not be completely satisfied. Indeed it has been found that more accurate solutions can be obtained when the equilibrium equations for the higher-order polynomial terms are not satisfied for some 3D solid elements [31]. The relaxation in equilibrium conditions means an improvement in computing efficiency when the present decoupled stresses are used. Also, being decoupled, the stress components may be expanded in terms of natural coordinates and the formulation becomes simplified. This formulation using decoupled stresses also leads to improved efficiency in computer implementation.

The Hu–Washizu principle can also be used for finite-element formulations by judicious selection of assumed functions for the field variables. In applying the variational functional $\pi_G$ in Eqs. (5.1) and (5.2) for finite-element implementation [32, 33], the key step is to use the same polynomial expansions for corresponding stress and strain components, i.e.,

$$\boldsymbol{\varepsilon} = \mathbf{P\alpha} \tag{5.89}$$

and $$\boldsymbol{\tau} = \mathbf{P\beta} \tag{5.90}$$

The element displacements can again be expressed in terms of nodal displacements $\mathbf{q}$. If we assume $\mathbf{u} = \bar{\mathbf{u}}$ on $S_{um}$, the variational function can then be expressed as

$$\pi_G = \sum_m (\tfrac{1}{2}\boldsymbol{\alpha}^T \mathbf{Z}\boldsymbol{\alpha} - \boldsymbol{\beta}^T \mathbf{H}\boldsymbol{\alpha} + \boldsymbol{\beta}^T \mathbf{Gq} - \mathbf{q}^T \mathbf{Q}_n) \tag{5.91}$$

where
$$\tfrac{1}{2}\boldsymbol{\alpha}^T \mathbf{Z}\boldsymbol{\alpha} = \int_{\Omega_m} A(\boldsymbol{\varepsilon})\, d\Omega \tag{5.92}$$

$$\boldsymbol{\beta}^T \mathbf{H}\boldsymbol{\alpha} = \int_{\Omega_m} \boldsymbol{\tau} : \boldsymbol{\varepsilon}\, d\Omega \tag{5.93}$$

$$\boldsymbol{\beta}^T \mathbf{G}\mathbf{q} = \int_{\Omega_m} \boldsymbol{\tau} : [\tfrac{1}{2}(\nabla \mathbf{u}) + \tfrac{1}{2}(\nabla \mathbf{u})^T]\, d\Omega \tag{5.94}$$

and
$$\mathbf{q}^T \mathbf{Q}_n = \int_{\Omega_m} \bar{\mathbf{F}} \cdot \mathbf{u}\, d\Omega + \int_{S_{tm}} \bar{\mathbf{T}} \cdot \mathbf{u}\, dS \tag{5.95}$$

Here both $\boldsymbol{\alpha}$ and $\boldsymbol{\beta}$ are independent from one element to the other and hence can be expressed in terms of the nodal displacements $\mathbf{q}$ by using the variational principle. The resulting variational functional can thus be reduced to

$$\pi_G = \sum_m (\tfrac{1}{2}\mathbf{q}^T \mathbf{k}\mathbf{q} - \mathbf{q}^T \mathbf{Q}_n) \tag{5.96}$$

where the element stiffness matrix is

$$\mathbf{k} = \mathbf{G}^T \mathbf{H}^{-1} \mathbf{Z}\mathbf{H}^{-1} \mathbf{G} \tag{5.97}$$

Here the assumed-stress components and hence also the strain components are necessarily uncoupled and unconstrained. If the space $\nabla \mathbf{u}$ is a subspace and the expansion $\boldsymbol{\varepsilon} = \mathbf{P}\boldsymbol{\alpha}$ is complete, it is expected again that the resulting element stiffness matrix will be identical to that obtained by a simple assumed-displacement method. In this case, the element displacements $\mathbf{u}$ can be resolved into $\mathbf{u}_q$ and $\mathbf{u}_\lambda$ so that the stress-equilibrium conditions can be introduced.

For linear-elastic problems the expression for $\mathbf{H}$ is simply

$$\mathbf{H} = \int_{\Omega_m} \mathbf{P}^T \mathbf{P}\, d\Omega = \begin{bmatrix} \mathbf{H}_1 & & & \\ & \mathbf{H}_2 & & \\ & & \ddots & \\ & & & \mathbf{H}_n \end{bmatrix} \tag{5.98}$$

and
$$\mathbf{H}^{-1} = \begin{bmatrix} \mathbf{H}_1^{-1} & & & \\ & \mathbf{H}_2^{-1} & & \\ & & \ddots & \\ & & & \mathbf{H}_n^{-1} \end{bmatrix} \tag{5.99}$$

The inversion of the $\mathbf{H}$-matrix can always be reduced to that of the submatrices, which are of a much smaller order than that of $\mathbf{H}$. Many finite elements derived by $\pi_R$ can be made identical to the assumed-stress hybrid element. These elements are grouped together as hybrid-mixed finite elements as shown in Fig. 5.1.

## 5.5c  Mixed Formulation for Reduction of Constraint Conditions

In many structural-mechanics problems conditions of constraint exist for the strain components in certain limiting cases. In those cases the formulation of finite-element methods based on the principle of stationary potential energy would not be applicable. In practice, even in the nearly limiting case, the conventional assumed-displacement finite element may lead to very rigid element stiffness matrices and hence may yield very inaccurate solutions.

For example, for incompressible materials the condition of constraint is zero dilatation. Thus, in analyzing a problem of nearly incompressible material by the conventional assumed-displacement method, the condition of zero dilatation pointwise may introduce a number of constraint conditions to the assumed displacements; hence the resulting element stiffness matrix may become extremely rigid.

Another example is the derivation of element stiffness matrices for plates and shells that takes transverse-shear effects into account. The requirement of interelement continuity of normal derivative $w_{,n}$ is replaced by that of boundary rotations which are now independent of $w$. The scheme would break down when the plates or shells were very thin so that the condition of diminishing shear strain would introduce a severe constraint to the element displacements. A third example is very thin shells for which the inextensional condition for membrane strains is a condition of constraint.

An effective remedy to these problems is the use of a modified version of the Reissner principle [25, 34]. In many structural-mechanics problems the total strain energy can be separated into two parts respectively due to two strain vectors $\varepsilon_1$ and $\varepsilon_2$, where the latter is the one to be constrained in the limiting case. In a modified variational principle only the strain energy of the latter is to be reduced to the form of the Reissner functional. The variational functional is thus

$$\pi_R = \int_\Omega [A_1(\varepsilon_1) - B_2(\tau_2) + \tau_2 : \varepsilon_2]\, d\Omega + W \tag{5.100}$$

where $\tau_2$ represents the stresses corresponding to $\varepsilon_2$. $A_1$ is the strain-energy density due to $\varepsilon_1$, $B_2$ is the complementary energy due to $\varepsilon_2$, and $W$ is the potential energy due to applied load. The strains $\varepsilon_1$ and $\varepsilon_2$ are expressed in terms of displacements, and, in the finite-element formulation, they are represented by nodal displacements $\mathbf{q}$. For example, in the variational functional proposed by Key [34] for incompressible and nearly incompressible materials $\varepsilon_1$ represents deviatoric strains and $\varepsilon$ is the mean strain.

In the finite-element formulation if $\varepsilon_2$ are independent for different elements, the resulting equation will have only nodal displacements as unknowns. It can be shown that the number of equations of constraint to the displacement functions is equal to the number of stress parameters representing $\tau_2$. Thus, to remove the locking phenomena one can simply use a smaller number of stress parameters for $\tau_2$. In solving problems of nearly incompressible materials by Key's method a lower approximation is used for the spherical strain energy. For the analysis of plates and shells, it turns out that by proper choice of the stress parameters the mixed formulation yields an element stiffness matrix which is identical to that of the assumed-displacement method using reduced and selective numerical integration [35]. This version of the mixed formulation thus offers a rational justification of the reduced-integration scheme in the finite-element methods.

## 5.6 KINEMATIC DEFORMATION MODES

In formulating a finite element by the assumed-stress hybrid model described in Sec. 5.3 or by the equivalent mixed model described in Sec. 5.5, it is important to make proper choice of the assumed stresses for a given assigned displacements $\tilde{\mathbf{u}}$ along the boundary or $\mathbf{u}$ in the element. Let $n$ be the number of element displacement parameters and $r$ be the number of possible rigid-body degrees of freedom of the solid continuum. Then a necessary condition for the resulting element stiffness matrix to be rank-sufficient is that $m$, the number of independent stress parameters, be greater than or equal to $n-r$. A rank deficiency of the stiffness matrix is an indication of the existence of kinematic deformation modes [8, 51–53].

The source of the kinematic deformation modes can be examined from the element deformation energy $U_d$ due to the assumed stresses and displacements [36]. That is, in Eq. (5.2),

$$2U_d = \int_{\Omega_m} \boldsymbol{\tau} : \boldsymbol{\varepsilon} \, d\Omega = \int_{\Omega_m} \boldsymbol{\tau} : [\tfrac{1}{2}(\nabla\mathbf{u}) + \tfrac{1}{2}(\nabla\mathbf{u})^T] \, d\Omega \tag{5.101}$$

and in Eq. (5.9)

$$2U_d = \int_{\partial\Omega_m} \mathbf{n} \cdot \boldsymbol{\tau} \cdot \mathbf{u} \, dS \tag{5.102}$$

In both cases

$$2U_d = \boldsymbol{\beta}^T \mathbf{G} \mathbf{q} \tag{5.103}$$

Now by means of Eq. (5.101) the element displacement $\mathbf{u}$ can also be expressed in terms of $n$ independent displacement modes in the form of

$$\mathbf{u} = \bar{\mathbf{N}} \begin{bmatrix} \boldsymbol{\alpha} \\ \mathbf{R} \end{bmatrix} \tag{5.104}$$

where $\mathbf{R}$ represents the $r$ rigid-body displacements. The two vectors $\mathbf{q}$ and $(\boldsymbol{\alpha}, \mathbf{R})$ can be related by linear transformation:

$$\mathbf{q} = \mathbf{T} \begin{bmatrix} \boldsymbol{\alpha} \\ \mathbf{R} \end{bmatrix} \tag{5.105}$$

The deformation energy is then

$$2U_d = \boldsymbol{\beta}^T \mathbf{G} \mathbf{T} \begin{bmatrix} \boldsymbol{\alpha} \\ \mathbf{R} \end{bmatrix} = \boldsymbol{\beta}^T [\mathbf{G}_\alpha \, \mathbf{G}_R] \begin{bmatrix} \boldsymbol{\alpha} \\ \mathbf{R} \end{bmatrix} = \boldsymbol{\beta}^T \mathbf{G}_\alpha \boldsymbol{\alpha} \tag{5.106}$$

since there is no deformation energy in the rigid-body modes.

When, for the given assumed-stress modes, the deformation energy $U_d$ becomes zero for any combination of the basic modes, $\alpha$'s, that combined mode is a kinematic mode. This will also include the case of zero energy for any individual deformation mode $\alpha_i$. Thus, the kinematic deformation modes are also called *zero-energy deformation modes*. For example, consider an eight-node brick-shaped hexahedral element with its vertices located at $(\pm l, \pm m, \pm n)$. The element displacements **u** are trilinear and contain the modes $u, v, w = xyz$. The resulting strains will have the terms $xy, yz$, and $xz$. It is seen that if the assumed stresses $\tau$ are only up to the linear terms the deformation energy $U$ will be zero for these deformation modes. For rectangular elements in two-dimensional solids, for regular brick elements, and for rectangular plate elements in bending, the assumed-stress terms must be judicially chosen to avoid kinematic modes [36, 37, 51, 56–58]. Kinematic modes can also exist in plate elements [38, 39].

Elements which are rank-deficient may often work satisfactorily if the boundary of the entire continuum is adequately constrained or if they are used together with other elements which are not rank-deficient. One can also find examples that superelements made of two or more elements do not have any kinematic deformation modes even if all individual elements are unstable by themselves [40]. However, for an element to be foolproof it is advisable that all kinematic deformation modes be suppressed in the construction of the element.

## 5.7 EXAMPLES IN ASSUMED-STRESS HYBRID ELEMENTS

In this section some examples on the formation of assumed-stress hybrid elements are given.

### 5.7A Four-Node Quadrilateral Plane Elements

The four-node plane-elasticity element presented in Sec. 5.3 was used in the original development of the assumed-stress hybrid element [7]. For rectangular geometry the logical arrangement is to have the reference axes coincide with those of the element, and the five stress terms given in Eq. (5.36) are the optimal choices.

In finite-element analyses the global axes may, in general, be at an angle with the element axes. Because the assumed stresses are not complete polynomials, the resulting element properties will be different when the global axes are used as the reference axes. In fact, it has been shown that when one of the reference axes is lined up with a diagonal of a rectangular element, a zero-energy deformation mode appears [41], furthermore, when the element geometry is distorted, it is not easy to choose the reference axes that will yield the best result. It turns out that a rational procedure for formulating invariant hybrid stress elements is the mixed formulation given in Sec. 5.5B. The stress-equilibrium conditions are not satisfied a priori but are enforced in an average sense within the element through lagrangian parameters representing the internal displacements $\mathbf{u}_\lambda$.

For plane problems the stress components $\tau = \{\tau_{xx}, \tau_{yy}, \tau_{xy}\}$ are expressed in complete linear terms in the rational coordinates $\xi$ and $\eta$; that is,

$$\tau = \begin{bmatrix} \tau_{xx} \\ \tau_{yy} \\ \tau_{xy} \end{bmatrix} = \begin{bmatrix} 1 & \xi & \eta & 0 & 0 & 0 & 0 & 0 & 0 \\ 0 & 0 & 0 & 1 & \xi & \eta & 0 & 0 & 0 \\ 0 & 0 & 0 & 0 & 0 & 0 & 1 & \xi & \eta \end{bmatrix} \begin{bmatrix} \beta_1 \\ \vdots \\ \beta_9 \end{bmatrix} \tag{5.107}$$

The assumed displacements are divided into two parts; the compatible displacements $\mathbf{u}_q$ are interpolated in terms of nodal displacements $u_{x_i}$ and $u_{y_i}$ by

$$\mathbf{u}_q = \begin{bmatrix} u_{x_q} \\ u_{y_q} \end{bmatrix} = \sum_{i=1}^{4} \tfrac{1}{4}(1+\xi_i\xi)(1+\eta_i\eta)\begin{bmatrix} u_{x_i} \\ u_{y_i} \end{bmatrix} \tag{5.108}$$

In the limiting case of rectangular geometry the resulting element should be identical to the five-$\beta$ element of Ref. [7], which can represent the bending nodes exactly and hence has no shear-lock difficulty; thus the present element must also have in the end only five independent stress parameters. The internal displacement $\mathbf{u}_\lambda$ hence must be expressed in terms of four $\beta$-parameters.

Indeed they are terms that contain $\xi^2$ and $\eta^2$ so that both displacements $u_x$ and $u_y$ are complete in quadratic terms. These displacements can be made identical to those used by Wilson et al. [42] in their incompatible displacement element.

In the actual formulation, it turns out that the four $\lambda$-terms yield only two independent equations of constraints for $\beta$'s. However, by imposing small perturbations of the shape $1-\eta^2$ to two opposite edges of the element, the four $\lambda$-terms now yield four equations of constraints. The resulting assumed stresses with five new parameters are as follows [43]:

$$\begin{bmatrix} \tau_{xx} \\ \tau_{yy} \\ \tau_{xy} \end{bmatrix} = \begin{bmatrix} 1 & 0 & 0 & a_1^2\eta & a_2^2\xi \\ 0 & 1 & 0 & b_1^2\eta & b_2^2\xi \\ 0 & 0 & 1 & a_1b_1\eta & a_2b_2\xi \end{bmatrix} \begin{bmatrix} \beta_1 \\ \vdots \\ \beta_5 \end{bmatrix} \tag{5.109}$$

where $a_1$, $a_2$, $b_1$, and $b_2$ are in terms of the coordinates $(x_i, y_i)$ of the four corner nodes.

$$\begin{aligned}
a_1 &= \tfrac{1}{4}(-x_1 + x_2 + x_3 - x_4) \\
a_2 &= \tfrac{1}{4}(-x_1 - x_2 + x_3 + x_4) \\
b_1 &= \tfrac{1}{4}(-y_1 + y_2 + y_3 - y_4) \\
b_2 &= \tfrac{1}{4}(-y_1 - y_2 + y_3 + y_4)
\end{aligned} \tag{5.110}$$

In the case of a rectangular element with $\xi$ and $\eta$ parallel to $x$ and $y$, $b_1$ and $a_2$ vanish and the five $\beta$-terms of Eq. (5.36) are obtained.

This is a proof that for rectangular geometry Wilson's element and the hybrid stress element are equivalent, as was pointed out by Froier et al. [44]. For hybrid stress elements, particularly of higher orders, there exist many possible choices for the assumed stresses. The present mixed formulation, thus, leads to a procedure for establishing the appropriate stress terms both for elements of regular shapes and for geometrically distorted elements.

Because the present formulation is based on natural coordinates, the resultant element stiffness matrix is always invariant with respect to the choice of global axes. It can also be shown that it always has sufficient rank. The element, of course, also passes the constant-strain patch test.

It turns out that the same result can be obtained when the stresses are based upon covariant basis vectors of the natural coordinates and are expressed as

$$\begin{bmatrix} \tau^{11} \\ \tau^{22} \\ \tau^{12} \end{bmatrix} = \begin{bmatrix} 1 & 0 & 0 & \eta & 0 \\ 0 & 1 & 0 & 0 & \xi \\ 0 & 0 & 1 & 0 & 0 \end{bmatrix} \begin{bmatrix} \beta_1 \\ \vdots \\ \beta_5 \end{bmatrix} \tag{5.111}$$

In converting the tensor stress $\tau^{ij}$ to the physical component $\sigma^{ij}$ by

$$\sigma^{ij} = J^i_k J^j_l \tau^{kl}$$

the value of the jacobian at $(\xi, \eta) = (0, 0)$ is used. By such a step the constant-stress state can be maintained; hence the resulting element will pass the patch test. For further discussions of a four-node isoparametric quadrilateral hybrid-stress element, see [52, 57].

A tapered and swept panel under shear load along one edge as shown in Fig. 5.3 is used to illustrate the advantage of the invariant hybrid stress element. The elements included in

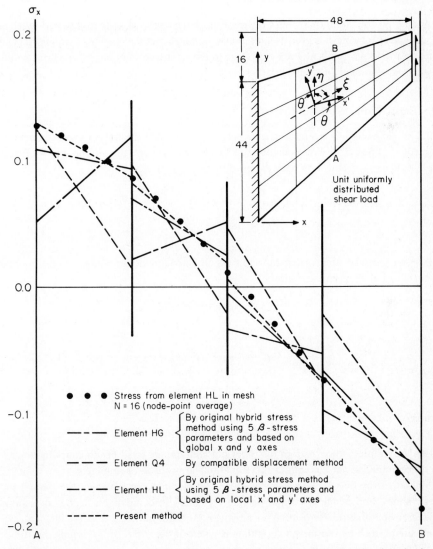

**FIG. 5.3**  Normal stress $\sigma_x$ along line $AB$ (mesh $N = 4$) for tapered panel under shear load at the tip.

the comparison are as follows:

1. Element $Q4$, which is the bilinear assumed-displacement element.

2. Element $HG$, which is based on the original hybrid stress method with five $\beta$-parameters and with the global axes $x$ and $y$ as reference axes.

3. Element $HL$, which is based on the original hybrid stress method with five $\beta$-parameters and with the reference $x'$- and $y'$-axes located at equal angles with the natural $\xi$- and $\eta$-axes [45].

4. The present invariant hybrid stress element.

A solution for the normal stress distribution at the midspan station obtained by element $HL$ using a $16 \times 16$ mesh is used as a reference. It is seen that the result by the present element using only a $4 \times 4$ mesh is already very close to the reference solution, while all the solutions by the other elements have much larger errors.

### 5.7B Eight-Node Solid Element

For solid elements it is again most convenient to formulate the hybrid stress element using the method of Sec. 5.5B. For an eight-node hexahedral element, the interpolations of element displacements $u$, $v$, and $w$ in natural coordinates $(\xi, \eta, \zeta)$ are

$$\begin{bmatrix} u \\ v \\ w \end{bmatrix} = \sum_{i=1}^{8} \tfrac{1}{8}(1 + \xi_i\xi)(1 + \eta_i\eta)(1 + \zeta_i\zeta) \begin{bmatrix} u_i \\ v_i \\ w_i \end{bmatrix} \qquad (5.112)$$

A set of assumed stresses that can suppress all kinematic deformation modes for a regular brick-shaped element are as follows:

$$\sigma_x = \beta_1 + \beta_7 y + \beta_8 z + \beta_{16} yz$$

$$\sigma_y = \beta_2 + \beta_9 x + \beta_{10} z + \beta_{17} xz$$

$$\sigma_z = \beta_3 + \beta_{11} x + \beta_{12} y + \beta_{18} xy$$

$$\tau_{xy} = \beta_4 + \beta_{13} z$$

$$\tau_{yz} = \beta_5 + \beta_{14} x$$

$$\tau_{xz} = \beta_6 + \beta_{15} y$$

$$(5.113)$$

This is the simplest stress pattern that does not contain any equilibrium coupling among the stress components; yet the equilibrium equations are satisfied completely.

Similar to the five-$\beta$ plane element, this solid element can represent the plane-bending stress modes, and hence is a more desirable element in comparison to the corresponding trilinear isoparametric element. Also an invariant eight-node hexahedral element can be formulated either by the mixed formulation given in Sec. 5.5B or by expressing the stress distribution in covariant basis vectors of the natural coordinates $\xi$, $\eta$, and $\zeta$ with 18-$\beta$ stress parameters of the same form as Eqs. (5.113). It has been demonstrated that this element is again least sensitive to geometric distortions [43]. A comprehensive study of various choices of stress fields for an 8-noded isoparametric solid element is reported in [51, 52, 56, 57].

### 5.7c  Bending of Thin-Plate Elements

The formulation of plate-bending elements by the assumed-stress hybrid method is illustrated here. Since this problem involves $C^1$-continuity for the lateral displacement $w$, the best approach is to use the modified complementary-energy principle to avoid the construction of element displacement. Exactly the same approach can be used for formulation of plate elements of any arbitrary number of sides [46].

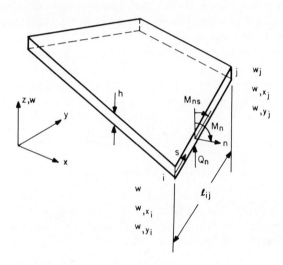

**FIG. 5.4**  Boundary tractions and nodal displacements of polygonal thin-plate element.

For given lateral displacements along the boundary of a thin-plate element (Fig. 5.4) the total complementary energy $\pi_c$ is

$$\pi_c = \int_A \tfrac{1}{2}[M_x \ M_y \ M_{xy}] \frac{12}{Eh^2} \begin{bmatrix} 1 & -\nu & 0 \\ -\nu & 1 & 0 \\ 0 & 0 & 2(1+\nu) \end{bmatrix} \begin{bmatrix} M_x \\ M_y \\ M_{xy} \end{bmatrix} dA$$

$$- \int_{\partial A} [-M_n \tilde{\omega}_{,n}, -M_{ns} \tilde{w}_{,s}, Q_n \tilde{w}] \, ds \tag{5.114}$$

where $M_x$, $M_y$, and $M_{xy}$ are the stress couples, $E$ is the module, $h$ is the plate thickness, $A$ is the area of the element, and $n$ and $s$ are the normal and tangential directions, respectively, of the boundary of the elements. Along the boundary $A$ the tractions are represented by the bending moment $M_n$, the twisting moment $M_{ns}$, and the transverse shear $Q_n$.

In the finite-element formulation for the plate-bending problem, the assumed-stress couples are made to satisfy the homogeneous equilibrium equations

$$M_{x,xx} + 2M_{xy,xy} + M_{y,yy} = 0 \tag{5.115}$$

Thus in the expression $\boldsymbol{\sigma} = \mathbf{P\beta}$, where $\boldsymbol{\sigma} = \{M_x \ M_y \ M_{xy}\}$, the P-matrix may take the following form:

$$\mathbf{P} = \begin{bmatrix} 1 & 0 & 0 & x & y & 0 & 0 & 0 & 0 & x^2 & xy & y^2 & 0 & 0 & 0 & 0 & 0 & \cdots \\ 0 & 1 & 0 & 0 & 0 & x & y & 0 & 0 & 0 & 0 & 0 & x^2 & xy & y^2 & 0 & 0 & \cdots \\ 0 & 0 & 1 & 0 & 0 & 0 & 0 & x & y & -xy & 0 & 0 & 0 & 0 & -xy & x^2 & y^2 & \cdots \end{bmatrix} \tag{5.116}$$

When complete linear stress terms are included, nine $\beta$'s are needed, and when complete quadratic stress terms are included, seventeen $\beta$'s are needed. Similarly, ten more $\beta$'s should be added for complete cubic stresses.

In common practice the nodal displacement used for plate-bending elements are the lateral displacement and its two derivatives $w_{,x}$ and $w_{,y}$ at the corner nodes. Along any side of the element the derivatives of $w$ with respect to the normal and tangential directions can then be expressed in terms of $w_{,x}$ and $w_{,y}$ by

$$\begin{bmatrix} w_{,n} \\ w_{,s} \end{bmatrix} = \begin{bmatrix} \cos nx & \sin nx \\ -\sin nx & \cos nx \end{bmatrix} \begin{bmatrix} w_{,x} \\ w_{,y} \end{bmatrix} \tag{5.117}$$

The lateral displacement along the side $ij$ is represented by cubic hermitian interpolation functions

$$w(\zeta) = H_{01}^1(\zeta)w_i + H_{02}^1(\zeta)w_j + H_{11}^1(\zeta)w_{,s_i} + H_{12}^1(\zeta)w_{,s_j}$$

where $\zeta$ is the nondimensional coordinate along the edge $\zeta = s/l_{ij}$, with $l_{ij}$ the length of the side $ij$ and

$$\begin{aligned} H_{01}^1 &= 1 - 3\zeta^2 + 2\zeta^3 \\ H_{02}^1 &= 3\zeta^2 - 2\zeta^3 \\ H_{11}^1 &= l_{ij}(\zeta - 2\zeta^2 + \zeta^3) \\ H_{12}^1 &= l_{ij}(-\zeta^2 + \zeta^3) \end{aligned} \tag{5.118}$$

The normal derivative $w_{,n}$ is represented by linear interpolation functions

$$w_{,n} = (1 - \zeta)w_{,n_i} + \zeta w_{,n_j} \tag{5.119}$$

The simplest plate element is a three-node triangular element with nine degrees of freedom. According to the rule given in Sec. 5.6, the necessary minimum number of stress parameters for the suppression of the kinematic deformation mode should be six. An element formulated by using nine complete linear-stress terms has been demonstrated to be a very efficient element [47]. For a 12-DOF quadrilateral element, the use of nine complete linear-stress terms will also satisfy the rule given in Sec. 5.6. Indeed, if the geometry of a quadrilateral plate element is not of rectangular shape, a 12-DOF element so derived will have no kinematic deformation mode. However, for regular rectangular elements two kinematic deformation modes appear and two higher-order stress terms are needed to suppress them [38].

## 5.8 CONCLUDING REMARKS

This chapter covers primarily the foundation of hybrid-mixed finite-element formulation. References are provided for readers who are interested in the details of specific models. Recent monographs on the subject of hybrid and mixed methods may also be consulted [59, 60].

The hybrid-mixed concept provides the finite-element method a versatile framework for construction of approximate solutions for continua. The hybrid-mixed method allows the use of different fields over separate subregions to form an optimal entire solution. These local solutions can be in terms of different fields and can involve singularities, special functions, or other features such as infinite domain, boundary layers, or known solutions of special configurations (e.g., circular or elliptical holes). Such flexibilities can greatly enhance the efficiency and accuracy of the finite-element method. It should also be emphasized that this flexibility ought to be used only for this purpose, i.e., to enhance efficiency and accuracy.

## 5.9 REFERENCES

1. Atluri, S. N., P. Tong, and H. Murakawa, "Recent Studies in Hybrid and Mixed Finite Element Methods in Mechanics," in S. N. Atluri, R. H. Gallagher, and O. C. Zienkiewicz (eds.), *Hybrid and Mixed Finite Element Methods*, Wiley, New York, 1983, pp. 51–71.

2. Hu, H. C., "On Some Variational Principles in the Theory of Elasticity and the Theory of Plasticity," *Sci. Sinica (Peking)*, **4**:33–54 (1955).

3. Washizu, K., "On the Variational Principles of Elasticity and Plasticity," Rep. 25-18, Contract N5 Ori-07833, Aeroelastic and Structures Research Laboratory, Massachusetts Institute of Technology, Cambridge, Mass., March 1955.

4. Hellinger, E., "Die allgemeine Ausatz der Mechanik der Kontinua," in F. Klei and C. Muller (eds.), *Encyklopedie der Mathematischen Wissenschaften*, Tubner, Leipzig, 1914, vol. 4, pt. 4, pp. 602–694.

5. Reissner, E., "On a Variational Theorem in Elasticity," *J. Math. Phys.*, **29**:90–95 (1950).

6. Atluri, S., and T. H. H. Pian, "Numerical Formulation of Finite Element Methods in Linear-Elastic Analysis of General Shells," *J. Struct. Mech.*, **1**:1–41 (1972).

7. Pian, T. H. H., "Derivation of Element Stiffness Matrices by Assumed Stress Distributions," *AIAA J.*, **2**:1333–1336 (1964).

8. Tong, P., and T. H. H. Pian, "A Variational Principle and Convergence of a Finite Element Method Based on Assumed Stress Distribution," *Int. J. Solids Struct.*, **5**:463–472 (1969).

9. Pian, T. H. H., and P. Tong, "Basis of Finite Element Methods for Solid Continua," *Int. J. Numer. Meth. Eng.*, **1**:3–28 (1969).

10. Tong, P., T. H. H. Pian, and S. Lasry, "A Hybrid-Element Approach to Crack Problems in Plane Elasticity," *Int. J. Numer. Meth. Eng.*, **7**:297–308 (1973).

11. Mei, C. C., and H. S. Chen, "A Hybrid Element Method for Study of Linearized Free-Surface Flow," *Int. J. Numer. Meth. Eng.*, **10**:1153–1175 (1976).

12. Brezzi, F., "On the Existence, Uniqueness, and Approximation of Saddle Point Problems Arising from Lagrangian Multipliers," *RAIRO Anal. Numer.*, **8**:129–151 (1974).

13. Tong, P., and T. H. H. Pian, "On the Convergence of the Finite Element Method for Problems with Singularity," *Int. J. Solids Struct.*, **9**:313–321 (1973).

14. Tong, P., "An Assumed Stress Hybrid Finite Element Method for Incompressible or Nearly Incompressible Material," *Int. J. Solids Struct.*, **5**:455–461 (1969).

15. Pian, T. H. H., and S. W. Lee, "Notes on Finite Elements for Nearly Incompressible Materials," *AIAA J.*, **14**:824–826 (1976).

16. Spilker, R. L., and N. I. Munir, "The Hybrid-Stress Model for Thin Plates," *Int. J. Numer. Meth. Eng.*, **15**:1239–1260 (1980).

17. Tong, P., and J. N. Rossettos, *Finite Element Method—Basic Technique and Implementation*, MIT Press, Cambridge, Mass., 1977.

18. Tong, P., "New Displacement Hybrid Finite Element Model for Solid Continua," *Int. J. Numer. Meth. Eng.*, **2**:78–83 (1970).

19. Jones, R. E., "A Generalization of the Direct Stiffness Model for Solid Continua," *AIAA J.*, **2**:78–83 (1964).

20. Harvey, J., and S. Kelsey, "Triangular Plate Bending Element with Enforced Compatibility," *AIAA J.*, **9**:1023–1026 (1971).

21. Thomas, G. R., and R. H. Gallagher, "A Triangular Thin Shell Finite Element: Linear Analysis," NASA CR-2482, National Aeronautics and Space Administration, 1975.

22. Atluri, S. N., and T. H. H. Pian, "Finite Element Analysis of Shells of Revolution by Two Doubly Curved Quadrilateral Elements," *J. Struct. Mech.*, **1**:393–416 (1973).

23. Atluri, S. N., A. S. Kobayashi, and M. Nakagaki, "An Assumed Displacement Hybrid Finite Element Model for Linear Fracture Mechanics," *Int. J. Fracture*, **11**:257–271 (1975).

24. Atluri, S. N., and K. Kathiresan, "On a 3-D Singularity Element for Computation of Combined Mode Stress Intensities," NASA CP-2001, *Adv. Eng. Sci.*, **1** (13th Ann. Meeting Soc. Eng. Sci.): 267–274 (1976).

25. Pian, T. H. H., and P. Tong, "Reissner's Principle in Finite Element Formulations," in S. Nemat-Nasser (ed.), *Mechanics Today*, Pergamon Press, New York, 1980, vol. 5, pp. 377–395.

26. Herrmann, L. R., "Finite Element Bending Analysis for Plates," *J. Eng. Mech. Div. ASCE*, **98**(EM5):13–26 (1967).

27. Noor, A. K., and M. D. Mathers, "Shear-Flexible Finite Element Models of Laminated Composite Plates and Shells," NASA TN D-8044, National Aeronautics and Space Administration, 1975.

28. Noor, A. K., and C. M. Andersen, "Mixed Isoparametric Finite Element Models of Laminated Composite Shells," *Comput. Meth. Appl. Mech. Eng.*, **11**:255–280 (1977).

29. Mirza, F. A., and M. D. Olson, "Energy Convergence and Evaluation of Stress Intensity Factor $K_I$ for Stress Singular Problems by Mixed Finite Element Method," *Int. J. Fracture*, **14**:555–573 (1978).

30. Tong, P., "A Family of Hybrid Plate Elements," *Int. J. Numer. Meth. Eng.*, **18**:1455–1468 (1982).

31. Pian, T. H. H., D. P. Chen, and D. Kang, "A New Formulation of Hybrid/Mixed Finite Element," *Comput. Struct.*, **16**:81–87 (1983).

32. Pian, T. H. H., and D. P. Chen, "Alternative Ways for Formulation of Hybrid Stress Elements," *Int. J. Numer. Meth. Eng.*, **18**:1679–1684 (1982).

33. Tang, L. M., W. J. Chen, and Y. X. Liu, "Quasi-Conforming Element and Generalized Variational Illegalities," *Proc. Symp. Finite Element Meth.*, Hefei, Anhui, China, Science Press, Peking, 1981, pp. 353–369.

34. Key, S. W., "A Variational Principle for Incompressible and Nearly Incompressible Anisotropic Elasticity," *Int. J. Solids Struct.*, **5**:824–826 (1969).

35. Malkus, D. S., and T. J. Hughes, "Mixed Finite Element Methods—Reduced and Selective Integration Techniques: A Unification of Concept," *Comput. Meth. Appl. Mech. Eng.*, **15**:63–81 (1978).

36. Pian, T. H. H., and D. P. Chen, "Zero Energy Deformation Modes in Assumed Stress Finite Elements," *Int. J. Numer. Meth. Eng.*, **19**:1741-1752 (1983).

37. Yang, C. T., R. Rubinstein, and S. N. Atluri, "On Some Fundamental Studies into the Stability of Hybrid/Mixed Finite Element Methods for Navier-Stokes Equations in Solid/Fluid Mechanics," in H. Kardestuncer (ed.), *Proceedings of the 6th Invitational Symposium on the Unification of Finite Elements—Finite Differences and Calculus of Variations*, University of Connecticut, Storrs, Conn., 1982, pp. 25-75.

38. Pian, T. H. H., and S. T. Mau, "Some Recent Studies in Assumed Stress Hybrid Models," in J. T. Oden, R. W. Clough, and Y. Yamamoto (eds.), *Advances in Computational Methods in Structural Mechanics and Design*, UAH Press, Huntsville, Ala., 1972, pp. 87-106.

39. Allman, D. J., "A Simple Cubic Displacement Element for Plate Bending," *Int. J. Numer. Meth. Eng.*, **10**:263-281 (1976).

40. Sander, G., "Application of Dual Analysis Principle," in B. Fraeijs de Veubeke (ed.), *High Speed Computing of Elastic Structures*, University of Liège, Liège, Belgium, 1971, pp. 167-207.

41. Spilker, R. L., S. M. Maskeri, and E. Kania, "Plane Isoparametric Hybrid-Stress Elements: Invariance and Optimal Sampling," *Int. J. Numer. Meth. Eng.*, **17**:1469-1496 (1981).

42. Wilson, E. L., R. L. Taylor, W. P. Doherty, and J. Ghaboussi, "Incompatible Displacement Models," in S. J. Fenves et al. (eds.), *Numerical and Computer Methods in Structural Mechanics*, Academic Press, New York, 1973, pp. 43-57.

43. Pian, T. H. H., K. Sumihara, and D. Kang, "New Variational Formulations of Hybrid Stress Elements," presented at NASA-Lewis/Industry/University Workshop on Nonlinear Structural Analysis, NASA Lewis Research Center, Cleveland, Ohio, April 19, 20, 1983.

44. Froier, M., L. Nilsson, and A. Samuelsson, "The Rectangular Plane Stress Element by Turner, Pian and Wilson," *Int. J. Numer. Meth. Eng.*, **8**:433-437 (1974).

45. Cook, R. D., "Improved Two-Dimensional Finite Elements," *ASCE J. Struct. Div.*, **ST9**:1851-1863 (September 1974).

46. Allwood, R. J., and G. M. M. Cornes, "A Polygonal Finite Element for Plate Bending Problems Using the Assumed Stress Approach," *Int. J. Numer. Meth. Eng.*, **1**:135-149 (1969).

47. Batog, J. L., K.-J. Bathe, and L.-W. Ho, "A Study of Three Node Triangular Plate Bending Elements," *Int. J. Numer. Meth. Eng.*, **15** (1900).

48. Pian, T. H. H., and S. T. Mau, "Some Recent Studies in Assumed Stress Hybrid Models," in J. T. Oden, R. W. Clough, and Y. Yamamotu (eds.) *Advances in Computational Mechanics and Design*, UAH Press, University of Alabama, Huntsville, Ala., 1972, pp. 87-106.

49. Atluri, S. N., "On Hybrid Finite Element Models in Solid Mechanics," in R. Vischnevefsky (ed.), *Advances in Computer Methods for Partial Differential Equations*, AICA, Rutgers University, NJ, 1975, pp. 346-355.

50. Atluri, S. N., and H. Murakawa, "On Hybrid Finite Element Models in Nonlinear Solid Mechanics," in P. G. Bergan et al. (eds.), *Finite Elements in Nonlinear Mechanics*, Tapir, Trondheim, Norway, 1977, vol. 1, pp. 3-41.

51. Rubinstein, R., E. F. Punch, and S. N. Atluri, "An Analysis of, and Remedies for, Kinematic Modes in Hybrid-Stress Finite Elements: Selection of Stable, Invariant Stress Fields," *Computer Methods in Applied Mechanics and Engineering*, **38**:63-92 (1983).

52. Xue, W-M., L. A. Karlovitz, and S. N. Atluri, "On the Existence and Stability Conditions for Mixed-Hybrid Finite Element Solutions Based on Reissner's Variational Principle," *Int. J. Solids and Structures*, **21**:97-116 (1985).

53. Xue, W-M., and S. N. Atluri, "Existence and Stability, and Discrete BB and Rank Conditions, for General Mixed-Hybrid Finite Elements in Elasticity," in R. L. Spilker et al. (eds.), *Hybrid and Mixed Finite Element Methods*, AMD vol. 73, ASME, New York, 1985, pp. 91-112.

54. Bratianu, C., and S. N. Atluri, "A Hybrid Finite Element Method for Stokes Flow: I. Formulation and Numerical Studies," and L-A. Ying and S. N. Atluri, "A Hybrid Finite Element Method for Stokes Flow: II. Stability and Convergence Studies," *Comp. Meth. Appl. Mech. Eng.*, **36**:23–37 and 39–60 (1983).

55. Yang, C. T., and S. N. Atluri, "An Assumed Deviatoric-Stress–Pressure–Velocity Mixed Method for Unsteady, Convective, Incompressible Viscous Flow: 1. Theoretical Development," *Int. J. Numer. Meth. Fluids*, **3**:377–398 (1983).

56. Punch, E. F., and S. N. Atluri, "Applications of Isoparametric Three-Dimensional Hybrid-Stress Finite Elements with Least-Order Stress Fields," *Computers and Structures*, **19**:409–430 (1984).

57. Punch, E. F., and S. N. Atluri, "Development and Testing of Stable, Invariant, Isoparametric Curvilinear 2- and 3-D Hybrid Stress Elements," *Comp. Meth. Appl. Mech. and Eng.*, **47**:331–356 (1984).

58. Atluri, S. N., "Computational Solid Mechanics (Finite Elements and Boundary Elements): Present Status and Future Directions," *The Chinese Journal of Mechanics*, **3**:1–19 (1985).

59. Spilker, R. L., and K. W. Reed (eds.), *Hybrid and Mixed Finite Element Methods*, ASME-AMD, vol. 73, ASME, New York, 1985.

60. Atluri, S. N., R. H. Gallagher, and O. C. Zienkiewicz (eds.), *Hybrid and Mixed Finite Element Methods*, Wiley, New York, 1983.

# CHAPTER 6
# OTHER FINITE-ELEMENT METHODS

## 6.1 FINITE-ELEMENT METHOD WITH SINGULARITIES

The presence of a singularity in a boundary-value problem causes a deterioration in the performance of a *standard* finite-element technique for its numerical solution. This is due to the fact that near a singularity, gradients of the solution are large and are also subject to abrupt changes, so that the solution cannot locally be accurately approximated by a piecewise polynomial function on a quasi-uniform mesh. As a result many special adaptations of finite-element methods, suited to particular singularities, have been proposed. These are generally based on some knowledge of the form of the singularity, which is exploited either *directly* in such adaptations as special *singular* elements for use near the point of singularity or the augmenting of the trial-function space, or *indirectly* in a technique such as local mesh refinement to control the number of levels of refinement employed.

The types of problem which are considered are second-order Poisson problems either with *Dirichlet* or *Neumann boundary conditions* and reentrant corners and edges or with *mixed boundary conditions*, fourth-order problems involving the biharmonic operator in regions with reentrant corners and including the case of flow of viscous fluids near sharp corners and edges, and problems of linear elasticity with reentrant corners and edges and in particular the case of linear-elastic fracture.

## 6.1A Singularities in Poisson Problems

For Poisson problems in 3D space, the solution satisfies

$$-\Delta[u(x, y, z)] = f_1(x, y, z) \qquad (x, y, z) \in \Omega$$

$$u(x, y, z) = g_1(x, y, z) \qquad (x, y, z) \in \partial\Omega_1 \qquad (6.1)$$

$$\frac{\partial u(x, y, z)}{\partial \nu} = g_2(x, y, z) \qquad (x, y, z) \in \partial\Omega_2$$

where $\Omega^3$ is a simply connected, open, bounded domain, and the boundary is $\partial\Omega$ consisting of disjoint parts $\partial\Omega_1, \partial\Omega_2$ such that $\partial\Omega \equiv \partial\Omega_1 \, \partial\Omega_2$. $\partial/\partial\nu$ is the derivative in the direction of the outward normal to the boundary.

For simplicity we consider first the 2D case where $g_1(x, y) = 0$ and $\partial\Omega_2 = \phi$ (Dirichlet condition) so that for the weak problem $u \in H_0^1(\Omega)$. In this situation it is well known [1, 2] that if $\partial\Omega$ contains a corner, with internal angle $\alpha$, then the behavior of $u$ near the corner is dominated by a term having the form

$$r^{\pi/\alpha} \left( \ln \frac{1}{r} \right)^{1/m} \sin \frac{\pi\theta}{\alpha} \qquad (6.2)$$

where $(r, \theta)$ are local polar coordinates centered on the corner with one of the arms of the corner as zero angle. When $\alpha > \pi$ so that the corner is *reentrant*, the function $u$ has unbounded derivatives as $r \to 0$ and hence has a singularity at the corner. In the case that $\alpha \neq \pi/2$, $\pi/3, \ldots$, the form simplifies to

$$r^{\pi/\alpha} \sin \frac{\pi\theta}{\alpha} \qquad (6.3)$$

For the case of homogeneous Neumann conditions on the arms of a corner, the form (6.3) contains a cosine rather than a sine term, and a singularity again occurs if the corner is reentrant. In a problem with mixed boundary conditions similar singularities can occur at points where parts of $\partial\Omega_1$ and $\partial\Omega_2$ intersect.

The common characteristics of the above for the three types of boundary condition is that in each case the solution $u$ of the problem has, near the corner or point of change of boundary condition, the form $r^\gamma F_\gamma(\Omega)$, where $F_\gamma(\theta)$ is a trigonometric function depending on $\gamma$. For the special case $\alpha = 2\pi$ (slit) the singularity has an $r^{1/2}$-form while for $\alpha = 3\pi/2$ (L-shape) it has an $r^{2/3}$-form.

We turn now to three-dimensional problems. In this case one has to consider not only reentrant corners, but also reentrant edges, and the associated singularities [3-7]. A typical case is illustrated in Fig. 6.1. Homogeneous Dirichlet boundary conditions are prescribed on all three planes. Spherical coordinates $(r, \theta, \phi)$ and cylindrical coordinates $(\rho, \phi, z)$ centered on 0 are as shown. A weak form of (6.1) is set up in a manner analogous to the two-dimensional case, and near the edge the dominant part of the weak solution has the form [7]

$$r^{1/\pi/\alpha} (\sin \theta)^{\pi/\alpha} \cos \theta \sin \frac{\pi\phi}{\alpha} \qquad \rho^{\pi/\alpha} \sin \frac{\pi\phi}{\alpha} z \qquad (6.4)$$

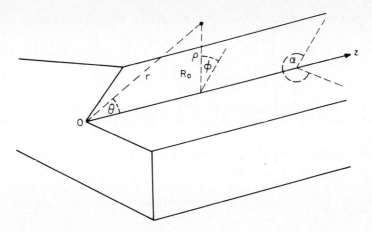

**FIG. 6.1**   Reentrant edges in 3D space.

It is clear from (6.4) that, for the case of a reentrant edge, $\alpha > \pi$, the solution $u$ will contain a singularity and that, in any plane orthogonal to the edge at a point interior to the edge, the singularity will have the same form as for the two-dimensional case. For this three-dimensional case the solution has near the edge the form $r^{\gamma+1}F_\gamma(\theta, \phi)$. The boundary conditions of these problems are such that $u$ does not have a singularity at the origin.

### 6.1B Singularities in Biharmonic Problems

The Dirichlet problem for the biharmonic operator in SD has the form

$$\Delta^2[u(x, y)] = f(x, y) \qquad (x, y) \in \Omega \tag{6.5}$$

$$u(x, y) = g_1(x, y) \qquad (x, y) \in \partial\Omega \tag{6.6}$$

$$\frac{\partial u(x, y)}{\partial \nu} = g_2(x, y) \qquad (x, y) \in \partial\Omega \tag{6.7}$$

In the plane-strain two-dimensional context of linear elasticity, if $f \equiv 0$ in $\Omega$, then $u(x, y)$ is the Airy stress function. We consider in particular the case where $\Omega$ contains a slit with the arms of the slit being $\theta = \pm\pi$. If the boundary conditions (6.6)–(6.7) are such that an opening-mode (mode I) fracture situation exists, so that there are stress-free boundary conditions on $u = \partial u/\partial \nu = 0$ on the arms of the slit, then it has been shown by Williams [9] that the biharmonic function satisfying these boundary conditions is

$$\dot{u}(r, \theta) = \sum_{n=1}^{\infty} (-1)^{n-1} a_{2n-1} r^{n+1/2} \left\{ -\cos\left(n - \tfrac{3}{2}\right)\theta + \frac{2n-3}{2n+1} \cos\left(n + \tfrac{1}{2}\right)\theta \right\}$$

$$+ (-1)^n a_{2n} r^{n+1}\{-\cos(n-1)\theta + \cos(n+1)\theta\} \tag{6.8}$$

where the unknown coefficients $a_n$ are determined by the remaining boundary conditions of the problem. The same form for the Airy stress function has been obtained by Steinberg [10] using two harmonic functions $P$ and $Q$ and seeking biharmonic functions of the form $u = r^2 P + Q$.

It is clear from (6.8) that there is a singularity at the crack tip $(r = 0)$ because, at that point, the second derivatives of $u$ are unbounded. In particular

$$\sigma_{yy} \equiv \frac{\partial^2 u}{\partial x^2} = -\frac{a_1}{r^{1/2}} \cos \frac{\theta}{2} \left( 1 + \sin \frac{\theta}{2} \sin \frac{3\theta}{2} \right) + \cdots \tag{6.9}$$

Biharmonic problems involving Eq. (6.5) with $f = 0$ also occur in the context of two-dimensional flow of a viscous fluid. In this case the dependent variable $u$ is the stream function and $\Omega$ is the Stokes equation. For the more complicated case described by the Navier–Stokes equations, terms involving the Reynolds number $R$ of the flow, as well as derivatives of the stream function and the vorticity $\omega$, occur in the right-hand side of (6.5). With Stokes flow $(R = 0)$ it has been shown by Moffat [11] for flow near a sharp corner formed by two straight lines and with a variety of boundary conditions that the stream function again has the form $r^\gamma F_\gamma(\theta)$, once more in terms of local polar coordinates. A typical example of this is the rectangular *driven-cavity* problem in which the driving wall meets the cavity at two corners where singularities occur. Problems of this type have been treated by Taylor [12] and Temam [13], while for small Reynolds numbers Gupta, Manohar, and Noble [14] have obtained the singular forms explicitly.

Regularity results for the weak forms of the Stokes problem in polygonal domains have also been obtained by Osborn [15] and Kellogg and Osborn [16].

## 6.1c  Singularities in Linear-Elastic Fracture

The Williams form (6.8) for the Airy stress function in a two-dimensional, plane-strain, mode I linear-elastic fracture problem, and the associated stress (6.9), have been given in the context of a biharmonic formulation. Problems of two-dimensional linear elasticity, and also of three-dimensional linear elasticity, can of course also be formulated in terms of displacements. In this case in $\Omega$ the displacement vector $\mathbf{u}$ satisfies the equations of equilibrium, and displacement of traction boundary conditions are specified on $\partial\Omega$. Weak forms of the two- and three-dimensional problems are defined respectively for $\mathbf{u} \equiv \{u, v\}^T \in (H^1(\Omega))^2$ and $\mathbf{u} \equiv \{u, v, w\}^T \in (H^1(\Omega))^3$; see, e.g., Ciarlet [17].

For mode I, two-dimensional linear-elastic fracture problems Irwin [18] has shown that the stress and displacement fields in the neighborhood of the crack tip have, respectively, the forms

$$\left\{ \begin{matrix} \sigma_{xx} \\ \tau_{xy} \\ \sigma_{yy} \end{matrix} \right\} = \frac{K_I}{(2\pi r)^{1/2}} \cos \frac{\theta}{2} \left\{ \begin{matrix} 1 - \sin \dfrac{\theta}{2} \sin \dfrac{3\theta}{2} \\[2mm] \sin \dfrac{\theta}{2} \cos \dfrac{3\theta}{2} \\[2mm] 1 + \sin \dfrac{\theta}{2} \sin \dfrac{3\theta}{2} \end{matrix} \right\} \tag{6.10}$$

and
$$\begin{Bmatrix} u \\ v \end{Bmatrix} = \frac{K_I}{2G}\left(\frac{r}{2\pi}\right)^{1/2}\begin{Bmatrix} \cos\dfrac{\theta}{2}\left(\kappa - 1 + 2\sin\dfrac{\theta}{2}\right) \\[2ex] \sin\dfrac{\theta}{2}\left(\kappa + 1 - 2\cos\dfrac{\theta}{2}\right) \end{Bmatrix} \tag{6.11}$$

where $\kappa = 3 - 4\nu$, with $\nu$ being Poisson's ratio, $G$ is the shear modulus, and $K_I$ is the opening-mode stress-intensity factor. Comparison of (6.9) and (6.10) indicates that near the crack tip the forms for $\sigma_{yy}$ are the same, so that $K_I = -\sqrt{2\pi}a_1$. It follows from the constitutive relationship for linear elasticity that the strains $\varepsilon$ near the crack tip will have the $r^{-1/2}$ for (6.10).

Irwin also produced expressions of the same nature as (6.10) and (6.11) but involving $K_{II}$ for mode II fracture, and also expressions involving $K_{III}$ for the stresses and displacement of mode III fracture; details can also be found in Rice [19].

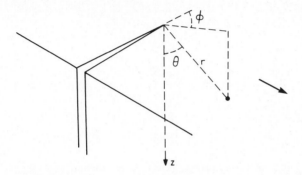

**FIG. 6.2**   3D solids with planar crack along the $z$-axis.

For three-dimensional linear-elastic fracture we consider first a situation as in Fig. 6.2, which is again mode I and in which the solid contains a planar crack with crack front along the $z$-axis. For points interior to the crack front it is assumed that a situation of plane strain exists so that in any plane in the solid orthogonal to the front the near-tip stress field is that of (6.10). However, the situation at 0, where the crack front intersects the stress-free top surface (intersection point), is more complicated. Starting with the general equations for the equilibrium of an elastic solid in terms of the displacements $\mathbf{u} \equiv \{u, v, w\}^T$ and using the method of Kelvin (see, e.g., Sneddon and Berry [20]) to derive the spherical polar components of $\mathbf{u}$ in terms of three Boussinesq functions, each of which is harmonic, Thompson and Whiteman [21] are able to show that near to the intersection point the stresses in the surface also have the $r^{-1/2}$-form, characteristic of other points on the crack front. The form of these stresses at the intersection point has been the subject of much recent discussion; see, e.g., Folias [22, 23], Benthem [24, 25], Kawai et al. [26], and Rao [27].

### 6.1D Error Estimates for Singularities

The *standard* piecewise polynomial or a quasi-uniform-mesh finite-element method can be used to derive approximations $u_h$ to the solutions $u$ of the weak formulations of problems of Poisson, biharmonic and linear elasticity by setting up approximating problems in finite-dimensional subspaces $(S^h)$ of the relevant Sobolev spaces $(H)$. The space $S^h$ usually consists of piecewise polynomial functions defined on a partition of $\Omega$. Numerical analysts seek to derive for the finite-element error bounds of the form

$$\| u - u_h \| \leqslant K(p) h^\mu |u|_k \tag{6.12}$$

See, e.g., Zlamal [28], Barnhill and Whiteman [29], and Whiteman [30], where $h$ is a generic constant denoting the mesh size; $p$ is the degree of the polynomial in each element; $K(p)$ is a constant depending on $p$ but independent of $h$ or $u$; $\|\cdot\|$ and $|\cdot|_k$ are appropriate norms (e.g., $L_2$, $H_1$, $L_\infty$) and seminorms, respectively; and $\mu$ depends on both $p$ and $k$. It is clearly attractive to have $\mu$ as large as possible, thus giving a high rate of convergence with decreasing mesh size provided that $|u|_k$ is bounded. Unfortunately, for problems involving singularities the regularity conditions satisfied by $u$ cause only low-order seminorms of $u$ to be bounded and thus preclude high orders of convergence of $u_h$ to $u$ as $h \to 0$. Typically, for weak forms of Poisson problems containing boundary singularities $u \in H^1(\Omega) - H^2(\Omega)$, for biharmonic problems $u \in H^2(\Omega) - H^3(\Omega)$, and for problems of linear elasticity $\mathbf{u} \in (H^1(\Omega))^m - (H^2(\Omega))^m$, $m = 2$ or 3. The rate of convergence is in these cases lower than that for problems without singularities, and there is a corresponding deterioration in the accuracy of the computed solutions. Thus special adaptations of the finite-element method are employed to rectify the situation. Such methods have been surveyed in Refs. [31, 32].

In the treatment of problems involving singularities with finite-element methods the intention always is to produce an approximation which mirrors the form of the singular behavior. As has been indicated earlier, this is not possible with a *standard* piecewise polynomial trial function on a quasi-uniform mesh, so that many special finite-element adaptations for singularities have been proposed. Three types of adaptation are now discussed: *augmentation of the trial-function space, singular elements, and local mesh refinement.*

## 6.1E Augmentation of the Trial-Function Space

The finite-element trial-function space usually consists of piecewise polynomial functions defined over the partition of $\Omega$, and for this the basis functions are also piecewise polynomial functions. When the trial-function space is augmented with basis functions having the form of the dominant part of a singularity, the augmenting basis functions are so defined that they have the appropriate singular form local to the singularity; they are zero except in the neighborhood of the point of singularity and they have suitable global continuity over $\Omega$. The advantage of these latter two properties is that, although the augmented function has the appropriate local singular form, the boundary conditions of the problem can be accommodated in the manner normal for finite-element methods.

Methods of this type were first proposed by Fix [33]. They have since been extended by Barnhill and Whiteman [34], Stephan and Whiteman [7], and Stephan [35]. Numerical experiments in the context of two-dimensional torsion problems have been undertaken by Fix, Gulati, and Wakoff [36]. More recently, using an idea first suggested by Babuska, Mejzlik, and Vitasel [37], a new technique has been used by Blum and Dobrowolski [38], Blum [39], and Dobrowolski [40] in which the trial- and test-function spaces are augmented respectively with functions having the form of the singularity and with functions having the form of the singularity associated with the adjoint of the differential operator of the defining differential equation.

Methods for implementing augmentation techniques have been discussed by Whiteman and Akin [41]. The usual approach is to associate each augmenting basis function with a nodeless *system* variable, which appears as an extra unknown in the final system of global stiffness equations. Clearly the structure of the global stiffness matrix is affected by the augmentation, and there is an increase in the bandwidth. The compensation for this is the fact that approximations to the coefficients of singular terms in the solution (e.g., the stress-intensity factor) are obtained automatically without the need for postprocessing calculations [41].

Augmentation techniques also have the advantage that it is possible to modify the error bound [see Eq. (6.12)] and so prove that an increase in the rate of convergence can be achieved. This arises from the fact [2] that in the seminorm on the right-hand side of, e.g., Eq. (6.12), combinations of appropriate singular functions can be subtracted from $u$, thus producing a function with greater regularity, which in turn allows larger values to be taken for $k$.

## 6.1F Singular Elements

In solving an elliptic boundary-value problem with a finite-element method it is convenient to employ a formulation which allows the use of a $C^0(\Omega)$-conforming trial function. This means that each element $\Omega^e$ can be mapped in a simple manner onto a *standard* element, that the approximation can be defined on this element, and that all the calculations for setting up the local stiffness matrix for $\Omega^e$ can be done on the standard element while maintaining compatibility over $\Omega$. This is the normal practice adopted in most finite-element packages. While similar mapping techniques do exist for $C^1(\Omega)$-trial functions (see, e.g., Kratochvil et al. [42]), they are much more complicated and make the *biharmonic* type of formulation much less attractive. We limit the discussion here to $C^0(\Omega)$-methods.

The most used mapping technique is that involving *isoparametric* elements in which the mapping function and the local approximating function have the same form. We illustrate this for the two-dimensional case with the single unknown function $u(x, y)$. Each element $\Omega^e$ of the $(x, y)$-plane is mapped onto a standard element in the local $(\xi, \eta)$-plane by means of a transformation of the form

$$\mathbf{x} \equiv \mathbf{x}(\xi, \eta) = \sum_{i=1}^{q} N_i(\xi, \eta)\mathbf{x}_i \tag{6.13}$$

where $\mathbf{x} = \{x, y\}^T$, the $N_i$ are the finite-element basis functions local to the element, and the $\mathbf{x}_i$ are point evaluations of $\{x, y\}^T$ at the $q$-nodes of the element. The dependent variable $u(x, y)$ in the element is transformed into $\hat{u}(\xi, \eta)$ in the standard element. This in turn is approximated by

$$\hat{u}_h(\xi, \eta)|_e = \sum_{i=1}^{q} N_i(\xi, \eta)(u_h)_i \tag{6.14}$$

where the $(u_h)_i$ are the (unknown) nodal-point values of $u_h$. The weak form or energy

formulation of the boundary-value problem in the physical space involves the global deriva-
tives $u_x$ and $u_y$. As a result of the mapping these are transformed into local derivatives $\hat{u}_\xi$, $\hat{u}_\eta$,
so that

$$\begin{bmatrix} u_x \\ u_y \end{bmatrix} = \mathbf{J}^{-1} \begin{bmatrix} \hat{u}_\xi \\ \hat{u}_\eta \end{bmatrix} \tag{6.15}$$

where $\mathbf{J}$ is the jacobian of the transformation. As in Ref. [41] we adopt for (6.15) the notation

$$\{\partial u_{\text{glob}}\} = \mathbf{J}^{-1}\{\partial \hat{u}_{\text{loc}}\} \tag{6.16}$$

The application of the approximation (6.14) to (6.16) leads for each element to

$$\{\partial(u_h)_{\text{glob}}\} = \mathbf{J}^{-1}\{\partial(\hat{u}_h)_{\text{loc}}\} \tag{6.17}$$

For problems involving singularities near a singular point the solutions have the general
form $r^\gamma F_\gamma(\theta)$, which has unbounded derivatives as $r \to 0$. It is the aim with *singular elements*
to introduce the appropriate singular form into $u_h|_e$ for elements involving the singularity.
From (6.17) it is clear that this can be done either via the jacobian $\mathbf{J}$ or via the approximating
function $\hat{u}_h$.

We consider first the jacobian. In a transformation of type (6.13) the inverse of the jacobian
will become singular if $|\mathbf{J}| = 0$. The transformation is normally so constructed that this effect
occurs at a point outside $\Omega^e$, thus avoiding any detrimental effect on the numerical calculations.
However, it is possible to harness the effect of jacobian singularity to produce an approximating function with the requisite form of the original (boundary) singularity. This has been
done in three ways: by distorting the shape of the element, by moving certain modes within
the element, and by modifying the form of the mapping functions of the transformation.

Irons [43] noted that the distorting of elements to degenerate forms can cause jacobian
singularities to develop. This idea was exploited by Tracey [44], who mapped a triangle into
a square and was thus able to produce $r^{1/2}$-type singularities, and by Pu, Hussain, and
Lorensen [45].

The second approach involves the displacing of certain nodes within an element to produce
a singularity in the approximating function at a desired point. Henshell and Shaw [46] were
among the first to notice that the point at which the jacobian becomes singular can be
controlled in this way to produce the required behavior. The technique is most easily described
in a one-dimensional context for the *quadratic* isoparametric case. Consider the transformation
between the element $[x_i, x_{i+2}]$ in the physical $x$-space, with nodes $x_i$, $x_{i+1}$, $x_{i+2}$, where
$x_{i+1} = x_i + qh$, $x_{i+2} = x_i + 2h$, $0 < q < 2$, and the standard element $[-1, 1]$, with nodes $-1, 0, 1$,
in the $\xi$-space. The transformation (6.13) now has the form

$$x(\xi) = x_i \frac{\xi(\xi-1)}{2} + x_{i+1}(1-\xi^2) + x_{i+2}\frac{\xi(\xi+1)}{2} \tag{6.18}$$

while the approximation (6.14) has the form

$$\hat{u}_h(\xi)|_e = (u_h)_{i+1} + \frac{\xi}{2}\{(u_h)_{i+2} - (u_h)_i\} + \frac{\xi^2}{2}\{(u_h)_{i+2} - 2(u_h)_{i+1} + (u_h)_i\} \tag{6.19}$$

For the case $q = \frac{1}{2}$, so that $x_{i+1}$ is a point one-quarter of the distance from $x_i$ to $x_{i+2}$, it follows from (6.18) that

$$\xi = \left\{\frac{2(x - x_i)}{h}\right\}^{1/2} - 1$$

so that from (6.19) in the $x$-space, $u_h(x)|_e \equiv \hat{u}_h(\xi)$ has the form

$$A + B(x - x_i)^{1/2} + C(x - x_i) \tag{6.20}$$

where $A$, $B$, $C$ are terms involving $(u_h)_i$, $(u_h)_{i+1}$, $(u_h)_{i+2}$. Thus a square-root singularity has been introduced into $u_h(x)$ at the point $x_i$ through the expedient of displacing the midpoint node to the "$\frac{1}{4}$-point" node. The two-dimensional case of a rectangular element, for which the singular form is required at a corner and in which the midside nodes on the two sides meeting at the corner (see Fig. 6.3) are moved to the $\frac{1}{4}$-point positions, is also considered in Ref. [46].

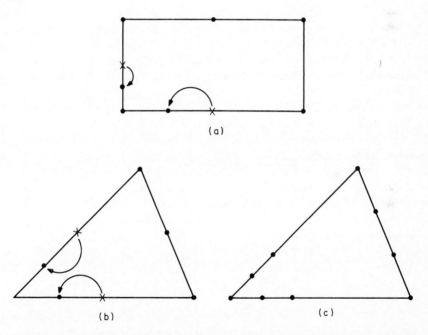

**FIG. 6.3**  (*a*) Quadratic $\frac{1}{4}$-point rectangular singular element. (*b*) Quadratic $\frac{1}{4}$-point triangular singular element. (*c*) Quadratic displaced-node triangular singular element.

Many papers on $\frac{1}{4}$-point techniques in straight-sided two-dimensional elements for treating $r^{1/2}$-type singularities followed the paper of Henshell and Shaw [46]. A six-node quadratic triangular element is shown in Fig. 6.4 [47, 48], which exhibits the required form in all radial directions from the corner within the element. Hibbitt [49] discussed the $r^{1/2}$-case further for two-dimensional straight-sided elements. Several schemes for displacing nodes for various-order trial functions and elements have been proposed for producing $r^\gamma$-type

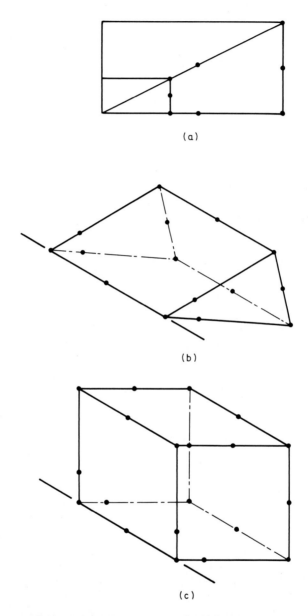

**FIG. 6.4** (*a*) Two-dimensional quadratic transition element. (*b*) Two-dimensional prismatic $\frac{1}{4}$-point element. (*c*) 20-node $\frac{1}{4}$-point brick element.

singularities (see, e.g., Henshell [50], Wait [51–53], and Atluri and Kumar [54]) which use higher-order polynomials. When elements of this type are used, the technique is to surround the singular point completely with a layer of singular elements, so that for each it is a corner node. The singular treatment is thus restricted to the first surrounding element layer, although the singular form of the solution frequently extends out beyond this from the singular point. This prompted Lynn and Ingraffea [55] to propose the use of transition elements, where the singular form is constrained to be at a point external to the element, which form a second layer of elements around the singularity (Fig. 6.4). Numerical experiments concerning the use of transition elements in two (and three) dimensions have been undertaken by Thompson [57].

The above discussion has been in a two-dimensional context. Line singularities in three-dimensional problems can be treated with three-dimensional elements of the $\frac{1}{4}$-point type as shown in Fig. 6.4. Barsoum [47] suggested the use of this type of element, the performance of which has been studied further both by Thompson [56] and by Harrison and Whiteman [59]. Transition elements can also be extended to three dimensions, as has been done in Ref. [57].

An extensive discussion on the effectiveness of various quadratic isoparametric $\frac{1}{4}$-point elements for representing singular forms, particularly strains in linear-elastic fracture, for two and three dimensions is given by Thompson and Whiteman [57]. It should also be noted that special two-dimensional elements for treating singularities arising at the tips of *curved* cracks have been given by Morris and Wait [58].

As with other singularity adaptations the purpose of using $\frac{1}{4}$-point elements is to improve both accuracy and the rate of convergence with decreasing mesh size of the finite-element solution. Referring again to the error bound [see Eq. (6.12)], it is found that the use of $\frac{1}{4}$-point elements does not increase the rate of convergence ($\mu$), so that the definite improvement in accuracy which can occur must be associated with a decrease in the size of the constant $K(p)$.

Another method for modifying the jacobian $\mathbf{J}$ has been proposed by Okabe [60]. With this type of technique, there is no reason why one should be limited to the use of *isoparametric* elements, for which the shape functions in the transformation (6.13) are the same as those of the approximation (6.14). Okabe changes the shape functions in the transformation and is thus able to treat a more general class of element shapes and also singularities of the form $r^\gamma$.

We turn now to the second class of singular elements. In (6.17) these introduce the singular form into $u_h$, not as previously via the jacobian but rather now via the local approximation $u_h$. One class of two-dimensional elements of this type is that due to Akin [61], which can treat singularities of the $r^\gamma$-form. Under the Akin scheme the standard shape functions, such as $N_i (\xi, \eta)$ of (6.14), are in the standard element modified by forming first $W(\xi, \eta) = 1 - N_1(\xi, \eta)$, where node 1 is located at the origin of the $(\xi, \eta)$-coordinate, and then setting

$$H_1(\xi, \eta) = 1 - \{W(\xi, \eta)\}^{1-\gamma}$$

$$H_i(\xi, \eta) = \frac{N_i(\xi, \eta)}{(W(\xi, \eta))^\gamma} \qquad i = 1, 2, 3, \ldots, q$$

The $r^\gamma$-singular form is thus produced at the origin, while along those element sides which do not pass through the point of singularity the resulting approximation is compatible with the corresponding standard element. This technique has been extended to three dimensions by Akin [61], and has been tested numerically for a three-dimensional problem containing a line singularity [59].

Singular approximating functions have also been introduced on the triangle by Tracey [44] and by Blackburn [62], who uses quotients in his shape functions or triangles and quadrilaterals. In its simplest form in the standard triangle, with vertices $(0, 0)$, $(1, 0)$, $(0, 1)$, the Blackburn form of $\hat{u}_h(\xi, \eta)$, which has linear variation along the side opposite the point of singularity, may be written as

$$\hat{u}_h(\xi, \eta) = u_h(0, 0) + \frac{(u_h(1, 0) - u_h(0, 0))\xi + (u_h(0, 1) - u_h(0, 0))\eta}{(\xi + \eta)^{1/2}}$$

In a manner similar to the corresponding Akin function this $\hat{a}_h$ has linear variation along the side $\xi + \eta = 1$, thus making it compatible with corresponding standard adjacent elements. The scheme has been extended to three dimensions by Blackburn and Hellen [63].

Singular approximating functions have also been produced by Benzley [64]. In this work the standard polynomial function is augmented with functions having the required singular form. The coefficients of these singular terms become global variables in the global stiffness equation. It is seen immediately that this is a variation of the augmentation methods described in Sec. 6.1E. This method has the disadvantage that, in order that compatibility may be produced, it is necessary to modify also the layer of elements surrounding the singular elements. A three-dimensional extension, but without compatibility modifications, is given in Ref. [65].

Extensive surveys of singular elements are given by Whiteman and Akin [41], Whiteman [66], and Atluri [67].

### 6.1G Local Mesh Refinement

The technique of local mesh refinement is perhaps the oldest approach for dealing with a singularity, the philosophy being that by using a concentration of elements near the singular point the detrimental effect can be isolated. Local mesh refinement was therefore used for a long time, often to very good effect, but without any effective control on the number of levels of refinement that should be employed. The literature is full of examples. Specific examples for two-dimensional fracture problems can be found in Refs. [68, 69]. Without some form of theoretical *a posteriori* approach it is clear that one is liable to either underrefine, in which case sufficient improvement in accuracy will not be obtained, or overrefine, which will produce an overexpensive computation because unnecessary effort will have been expended.

Recently much work on *self-adaptive* local mesh refinement has been undertaken, particularly by Babuska and Rheinboldt. The approach is to define an initial mesh from which an initial finite-element solution is obtained. A local error estimator is then used to estimate the size of error in a particular element, and this is tested against a predesignated error size to determine whether or not the element should be subdivided. Starting with the work of Babuska [70], many powerful results have been obtained which are reported in a long series of papers. A survey of *a posteriori* error estimators and adaptive approaches in the finite-element method has been given by Babuska and Rheinboldt [71], and further details of these techniques can be obtained from the extensive list of references contained therein.

Another approach to mesh refinement, which is of interest theoretically, is that of Thatcher [72, 73], who for two-dimensional Poisson problems has considered the case of an infinite number of levels of local mesh refinement. The technique has been extended to biharmonic problems by Ying Lung-An [74].

For problems in linear and nonlinear fracture mechanics, for either stationary or propagating cracks wherein the nature of stress/strain singularity near the crack tip is known *a priori*, the "hybrid singular elements" offer a very powerful means of computing the relevant fracture parameters. Also, in three-dimensional fracture problems, the so-called "alternating method" appears to be the least expensive and the most accurate. These and other topics of computational fracture mechanisms are discussed in [164–179].

## 6.2 COLLOCATION FINITE-ELEMENT METHOD

Collocation methods satisfy the differential equation at specified points, the *collocation points*. For finite-element collocation methods the basis functions are piecewise polynomials, as in the Galerkin–finite-element method, and the residual is defined as before. However, the residual is set to zero at selected points, the collocation points, to generate the governing equations.

The collocation equations are usually easier to set up and solve than in the Galerkin method. The convergence properties of the two methods are comparable, and the collocation method may lead to a more sparse matrix than that given by the Galerkin method. Unfortunately, the lowest-order polynomial is a $C^1$-cubic, and such expansion functions may not be appropriate for all problems and may be inefficient for engineering accuracy. Meshes are not as easily distorted to handle irregular geometries as for isoparametric elements in the Galerkin method. Mesh refinement is not as easy because triangular elements have not been utilized with collocation methods. Progress has been made on all these problems, as described below.

### 6.2A One-Dimensional Lagrange Polynomials

An early version of orthogonal collocation on finite elements was presented by Carey and Finlayson [75]. The domain $0 \leqslant x \leqslant 1$ is divided into elements of size $h_e$, using knots at $0 = x_1, x_2, \ldots, x_{NE}, x_{NE+1} = 1$.

$$u = \frac{x - x_e}{h_e} \qquad h_e = x_{e+1} - x_e$$

The solution $y(x)$ is then expanded as $y_e(u)$ within the $e^{\text{th}}$ element, and the basis functions are taken as Lagrange polynomials.

$$y_e(u) = \sum_{i=1}^{N+2} a_i l_{i-1}(u) \tag{6.21}$$

where

$$l_i(u) = \frac{\displaystyle\prod_{j=1, j \neq i}^{N+2} (u - u_j)}{\displaystyle\prod_{j=1, j \neq i}^{N+2} (u_i - u_j)}$$

(6.22)

We then can differentiate this equation and evaluate the terms at the collocation points $u_j$ to obtain

$$y_e(u_j) = \sum_{i=1}^{N+2} a_i l_{i-1}(u_j)$$

$$\frac{dy_e}{du}(u_j) = \sum_{i=1}^{N+2} a_i \frac{dl_{i-1}}{du}(u_j)$$

$$\frac{d^2 y_e}{du^2}(u_j) = \sum_{i=1}^{N+2} a_i \frac{d^2 l_{i-1}}{du^2}(u_j)$$

We evaluate these equations at $N+2$ collocation points (including the endpoints of the element), which correspond with the $N+2$ unknowns in Eq. (6.21). We write these equations in matrix form

$$\mathbf{y}_e = \mathbf{Q} \mathbf{a}$$

$$\frac{d\mathbf{y}_e}{d\mathbf{u}} = \mathbf{C} \mathbf{a}$$

$$\frac{d^2 \mathbf{y}_e}{d\mathbf{u}^2} = \mathbf{D} \mathbf{a}$$

Then it is possible to solve for the coefficients, given the values of $y_j$ at the collocation points.

$$\mathbf{a} = \mathbf{Q}^{-1} \mathbf{y}_e$$

Using this equation we can rewrite the derivatives in terms of the values of the solution at the collocation points.

$$\frac{d\mathbf{y}_e}{d\mathbf{u}} = \mathbf{C}\mathbf{Q}^{-1} \mathbf{y}_e \equiv \mathbf{A}\mathbf{y}_e$$

$$\frac{d^2 \mathbf{y}_e}{d\mathbf{u}^2} = \mathbf{D}\mathbf{Q}^{-1} \mathbf{y}_e = \mathbf{B}\mathbf{y}_e$$

The collocation points are chosen to be the gaussian quadrature points, although other choices are possible [76]. The theoretical basis of the collocation method is to collocate at the gaussian quadrature points internal to an element. With this choice the matrices $\mathbf{A}_{ji}$ and $\mathbf{B}_{ji}$ can be calculated. They are given in Table 6.1 for $N=1$ and $N=2$ and can be easily derived for higher $N$.

**TABLE 6.1**  Matrices for Orthogonal Collocation

| $N$ | $W$ | $A$ | $B$ |
|---|---|---|---|
| 1 | $\begin{pmatrix} \frac{1}{6} \\ \frac{2}{3} \\ \frac{1}{6} \end{pmatrix}$ | $\begin{pmatrix} -3 & 4 & -1 \\ -1 & 0 & 1 \\ 1 & -4 & 3 \end{pmatrix}$ | $\begin{pmatrix} 4 & -8 & 4 \\ 4 & -8 & 4 \\ 4 & -8 & 4 \end{pmatrix}$ |
| 2 | $\begin{pmatrix} 0 \\ \frac{1}{2} \\ \frac{1}{2} \\ 0 \end{pmatrix}$ | $\begin{pmatrix} -7 & 8.196 & -2.196 & +1 \\ -2.732 & 1.732 & 1.732 & -0.7321 \\ 0.7321 & -1.732 & -1.732 & 2.732 \\ -1 & 2.196 & -8.196 & 7 \end{pmatrix}$ | $\begin{pmatrix} 24 & -37.18 & 25.18 & -12 \\ 16.39 & -24 & 12 & -4.392 \\ -4.392 & 12 & -24 & 16.39 \\ -12 & 25.18 & -37.18 & 24 \end{pmatrix}$ |

The element matrix for the collocation method consists of the differential equation, evaluated at the internal collocation points, plus continuity constraints. The function will be continuous upon assembly of the equations; to make the first derivatives continuous we require that the first derivative at the end of one element be equal to the first derivative at the beginning of the next element. The element matrix is then

$$
J_{ji}^e = \begin{cases} \dfrac{1}{h_e} A_{li} & j = 1 \\[2mm] \dfrac{1}{h_e^2} B_{ji} - \dfrac{Pe}{h_e} A_{ji} & j = 2, \ldots, N+1 \\[2mm] \dfrac{1}{h_e} A_{N+2,i} & j = N+2 \end{cases} \tag{6.23}
$$

The middle $N$ equations are written for the differential operator $y''-Pey'$. The element matrices are assembled in the usual fashion to derive a set of algebraic equations to solve for the nodal values $y_j$ at the collocation points (internal to each element), the knots (the points common to two elements), and the two endpoints. An illustration of application is given in Sec. 7.1 in Part 3.

## 6.2B  One-Dimensional Hermite Polynomials

If Lagrange polynomials are used, it is necessary to enforce the continuity of derivatives by means of an auxiliary equation. If Hermite polynomials are used, the continuity of the first derivative can be ensured automatically. We take the Hermite polynomials on the element (with $0 \leq u \leq 1$).

$$
\begin{aligned}
H_1 &= (1-u)^2(1+2u) \\
H_2 &= u(1-u)^2 h_e \\
H_3 &= u^2(3-2u) \\
H_4 &= u^2(u-1)h_e
\end{aligned} \tag{6.24}
$$

The representation in the $e^{\text{th}}$ element is then

$$y_e(u) = \sum_{i=1}^{4} a_i H_i(u)$$

and the first and second derivatives are

$$\frac{dy_e}{dx} = \frac{1}{h_e} \sum_{i=1}^{4} a_i \frac{dH_i(u)}{du^2}$$

$$\frac{d^2 ye}{dx^2} = \frac{1}{h_e^2} \sum_{i=1}^{4} a_i \frac{d^2 H_i(u)}{du^2}$$

The Hermite polynomials have the convenient feature that either the function or its derivative takes the value 1 at one endpoint and both are zero at the other endpoint. Thus $y_e(0) = a_1$, $y_e(1) = a_3$, $dy_e/dx(u = 0) = a_2$, $dy_e/dx(u = 1) = a_4$.

The collocation points are again taken to be the gaussian quadrature points. The derivative of the solution within an element is then

$$\frac{dy_e}{du} = \sum_{i=1}^{4} a_i \frac{dH_i}{du}$$

$$\frac{d^2 y_e}{du^2} = \sum_{i=1}^{4} a_i \frac{d^2 H_i}{du^2}$$

We write these equations in the form

$$\mathbf{y}_e = \mathbf{Ha}$$

$$\frac{d\mathbf{y}_e}{d\mathbf{u}} = \mathbf{Aa}$$

$$\frac{d^2\mathbf{y}_e}{d\mathbf{u}^2} = \mathbf{Ba}$$

where the matrices are given in Table 6.2 for cubic polynomials. We now solve for the values of $a_j$, which are functions or $x$-derivatives at the knots. For the same operator the element

**TABLE 6.2**   Matrices for Hermite Polynomials

| | |
|---|---|
| $\mathbf{H(u_j)}$ | $\begin{pmatrix} 0.88490\,0180 & 0.13144\,5856h_k & 0.11509\,9820 & -0.03522\,0811h_k \\ 0.11509\,9820 & 0.03522\,0811h_k & 0.88490\,0180 & -0.13144\,5856h_k \end{pmatrix}$ |
| $\mathbf{A}$ | $\begin{pmatrix} -1 & 0.28867\,5136h_k & 1 & -0.28867\,5136h_k \\ -1 & -0.28867\,5136h_k & 1 & 0.28867\,5136h_k \end{pmatrix}$ |
| $\mathbf{B}$ | $\begin{pmatrix} -3.4641\,01620 & -2.73205\,0810h_k & 3.46410\,1620 & -0.73205\,0810h_k \\ 3.4641\,01620 & 0.73205\,0810h_k & -3.46410\,1620 & 2.73205\,0810h_k \end{pmatrix}$ |

matrix is

$$\mathbf{J}^e_{ji} = \frac{1}{h^2_e}\mathbf{B}_{ji} - \frac{Pe}{h_e}\mathbf{A}_{ji}$$

Note that the element matrix is now a $2 \times 4$ matrix, and there is no overlap with any other element (i.e., the final jacobian matrix is the sum of each of these element matrices but each element matrix belongs in a unique position). See Sec. 7.1 in Part 3 for an illustration of how to apply the method.

## 6.2c One-Dimensional $B$-Splines

Another alternative for the choice of basis functions are $B$-splines. Efficient ways to calculate with $B$-splines are available [77–79], but here we present a method, which is more illustrative, for using cubic $B$-splines with collocation [80].

With cubic $B$-splines the basis functions are cubic polynomials on one element but are constructed so that the function and its first and second derivatives are continuous across element boundaries. Collocation is provided at the knots, or the points between the elements.

$$y(x) = \sum_{i=0}^{N+2} a_i B_i(x) \tag{6.25}$$

The values of $B_i$ and its derivatives are needed at the knots; these are provided in Table 6.3.

TABLE 6.3  $B$-Spline Values

|  | $x_{i-2}$ | $x_{i-1}$ | $x_i$ | $x_{i-1}$ | $x_{i+2}$ |
|---|---|---|---|---|---|
| $B_i$ | 0 | $\frac{1}{4}$ | 1 | $\frac{1}{4}$ | 0 |
| $B'_i$ | 0 | $\frac{3}{4h}$ | 0 | $\frac{-3}{4h}$ | 0 |
| $B''_i$ | 0 | $\frac{3}{2h^2}$ | $\frac{-3}{h^2}$ | $\frac{3}{2h^2}$ | 0 |

To handle the boundary conditions it is necessary to use linear combinations of the basis functions, since otherwise the basis functions are defined outside the boundary. For example, for the illustrative problem we would have at each knot (including the endpoints)

$$\sum a_i (B''_i(x_j) - PeB'_i(x_j)) = 0 \qquad j = 0, 1, \ldots, N$$

while various boundary conditions would be satisfied as follows.

$y(0) = 0$:         $\frac{1}{4}(a_0 + a_2) + a_1 = 0$

$y'(0) = 0$:         $a_2 - a_0 = 0$

$y(1) = 1$:         $\frac{1}{4}(a_{N+2} + a_N) + a_{N+1} = 0$

This is not the format of the most efficient method of calculation, but it illustrates the idea clearly; it requires fewer multiplications to use recursive relations to evaluate the $B$-splines and their derivatives [77–79].

### 6.2D One-Dimensional Collocation-Galerkin Methods

In the collocation method using lagrangian polynomials a condition was established to ensure the continuity of first derivatives across element boundaries. This condition is inconvenient for some problems, and a $C^0$-collocation method would be useful. Fortunately a collocation-Galerkin method provides such a possibility. In this method [82–84] the same conditions are applied at the collocation points interior to the element. In place of the continuity condition, however, we use a Galerkin equation obtained by multiplying the residual by a test function that is a "hat" function centered at the knot. The Galerkin equations are integrated by parts, and the resulting integrals are easy to calculate since the derivative of the test function is constant in an element.

### 6.2E One-Dimensional Upwind Collocation

For problems with strong convection, it is necessary to modify the collocation method to avoid oscillations in the solution. One modification [85] is to change the trial function. Rather than use Hermite functions, one uses the set of functions

$$\phi^{0j} = \tfrac{1}{4}(\eta + \eta_j)^2(\eta - 2\eta_j) - \alpha_0 \eta_j (\eta^2 - 1)^2$$

$$\phi^{1j} = \frac{h}{8}(\eta + \eta_j)^2(\eta - \eta_j) - \alpha_1 \eta_j h(\eta^2 - 1)^2$$

$$j = 1, 2, 3, 4 \qquad \eta_j = \pm 1 \qquad \eta = \frac{2(x - x_e)}{h_e} - 1$$

Here the parameters $\alpha_0$ and $\alpha_1$ determine the amount of asymmetry in the basis functions. There are optimal values (see Ref. [85]), but they generally are between 0.05 and 0.3. The terms multiplied by $\alpha$ are used only in the convection term.

   Another modification of the collocation method is to change the collocation points for problems with strong convection. Herbst [86] does this, and for cubic trial functions the collocation points are shifted according to the relationships

$$L = Pe\frac{\Delta x}{2} \qquad \alpha = \coth L - \frac{1}{L}$$

$$\mu^2 + 2(\alpha - 1)\mu - \alpha\left(1 + \frac{1}{L}\right) + 1 = 0$$

$$\mu = u_2 + u_3$$

where $u_2$ and $u_3$ are the two interior collocation points for cubic trial functions.

## 6.2F Convergence

For any method the rate of convergence as the mesh size $h_e$ is reduced is an important question. Douglas and Dupont [88] first provided a proof of convergence for cubic polynomials, with collocation at the gaussian quadrature points, for quasi-linear parabolic differential equations. De Boor and Swartz [89] generalized the proof by including higher-order piecewise polynomials but for boundary-value problems only. Generally the results indicate that for an $m^{\text{th}}$-order differential equation using polynomials of degree $k+1$ which have continuous $(m-1)^{\text{th}}$ order derivatives globally, the error goes as

$$\|D^i(y-y_{\text{exact}})\|_\infty \leq C_1|h|^{\min (n,k)}$$

for the $i^{\text{th}}$ derivative of the solution, where the exact solution is in $C^n$. A superconvergence result is valid, however, and the error at the knots converges faster. Thus with cubic polynomials ($k=2$) and a second-order differential equation ($m=2$) and a highly continuous exact solution, the error goes as $h^2$ globally but $h^4$ at the knots. Houstis [90] provides a similar proof for hyperbolic equations, in which case the error goes as $h^4$ and $\Delta t^2$ when the time integration is performed with the Crank–Nicolson method.

For extension of Secs. 6.2A to 6.2C to two-dimensional problems see Refs. [91–99].

## 6.2G Comparison

The primary advantage of the collocation method over the Galerkin method is that it is easier to set up the problem. There are fewer integrals to evaluate and fewer terms in the jacobian, which is much more sparse (for example, 16 terms in a row compared with 36 for the Galerkin method when both use bicubic Hermite functions). This comparison holds when both methods use the same trial functions. The Galerkin method is more general in that it allows triangular elements and trial functions that are linear or quadratic rather than cubic, which is the first possible trial function with collocation. Operation counts indicate that the LU decomposition of the matrices arising from the collocation method can require fewer multiplications than for matrices arising from the Galerkin method [96, 98]. Actual performance tests for mildly nonlinear elliptic problems also indicate a preference for collocation [100]. Both collocation and Galerkin–finite-element methods are inferior to special high-order difference schemes for problems with singularities on regular meshes [101].

## 6.3 RATIONAL FINITE ELEMENTS

A common approach to function approximation in finite elements uses lagrangian interpolation of nodal values of the function; the discussion here is restricted to such elements. The rational elements described in this section achieve global continuity of the function ($C^0$-approximation) only and not of its derivatives.

### 6.3A Elements with Polynomial Bases

The symbol $(p; q)$ denotes either the line determined by points $p$ and $q$ or a linear form, unique except for normalization, that vanishes on the line. The linear form normalized to unity at $s$ is denoted by $(p; q)_s$. Polynomial bases exist for continuous approximation over triangles, parallelograms, and a few maverick elements of little practical importance. The element index $e$ is suppressed henceforth. Degree-1 approximation is achieved over the triangle in Fig. 6.5a with basis functions $N(1; x, y) = (2; 3)_1$, $N(2; x, y) = (3; 1)_2$, and $N(3; x, y) = (1; 2)_3$. The linear variation over the triangle is uniquely determined by the three vertex values. The basis functions for degree-1 approximation over the parallelogram in Fig. 6.5b are of the form $N(1; x, y) = (2; 3)_1(3; 4)_1$. Similarly, a degree-2 element can be generated.

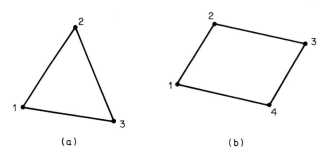

(a)                                   (b)

**FIG. 6.5**   Degree-1 elements. (*a*) Triangle. (*b*) Parallelogram.

### 6.3B  Isoparametric Elements

The earliest and still most prevalent generalization from triangles and parallelograms is the isoparametric element. The approximation and algebraic manipulation is performed in the isoparametric plane. This is described in detail in Sec. 4.2 in Part 2.

### 6.3c  Rational Elements

The inadequacy of polynomial bases is illustrated by consideration of a convex quadrilateral that is not a parallelogram (Fig. 6.6). The basis function associated with node 1 must vanish

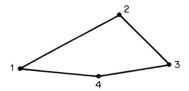

**FIG. 6.6**   A convex quadrilateral.

on the sides opposite vertex 1 in order that interelement continuity be maintained along these opposite sides independent of the function value at vertex 1. Thus $N(1; x, y) = (2; 3)_1(3; 4)_1 P(x, y)$, with $P$ a *polynomial in x and y* as the only acceptable polynomial form for the basis function associated with vertex 1. A polynomial of this form cannot vary linearly on sides (1; 2) and (1; 4) without vanishing identically on these sides unless $P$ is unity and the quadrilateral is a parallelogram. The next logical generalization is to rational basis functions. These will be denoted by $W(i; x, y)$ rather than $N(i; x, y)$. The simplest form for $W(1; x, y)$ for the convex quadrilateral is $W(1; x, y) = (2; 3)_1(3; 4)_1/(A; B)_1$.

One seeks a linear form $(A; B)$ such that $(2; 3)/(A; B)$ is constant on side $(1; 4)$ and $(3; 4)/(A; B)$ is constant on $(1; 2)$. Then $W$ will be linear on the sides adjacent to vertex 1 and the first obstacle will be overcome. Geometric considerations reveal that if lines $L$, $M$, and $N$ are concurrent (meet at a point), then there are constants $a$, $b$, and $c$ such that $aL + bM + cN = 0$, where $L$, $M$, $N$ now denote the linear forms that vanish on these lines. If $(2; 3)$, $(A; B)$, and $(1; 4)$ are concurrent and if $(3; 4)$, $(A; B)$, and $(1; 2)$ are concurrent, then $W$ has the required behavior. The unique line for which this is true is the exterior diagonal of the convex quadrilateral (Fig. 6.7). Convexity is required to ensure $(A; B) > 0$

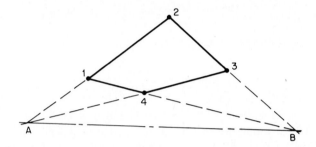

**FIG. 6.7**  The exterior diagonal.

over the element, this being necessary if the basis function is to be regular. Further study reveals that this same linear form suffices for the remaining basis functions:

$$W(2; x, y) = (3; 4)_2 \frac{(4; 1)_2}{(A; B)_2}$$

$$W(3; x, y) = (4; 1)_3 \frac{(1; 2)_3}{(A; B)_3}$$

and
$$W(4; x, y) = (1; 2)_4 \frac{(2; 3)_4}{(A; B)_4}$$

It remains to be shown that degree-1 approximation is achieved with these functions. The interpolation error for a linear function is

$$R(x, y) = L(x, y) - \sum_{i=1}^{4} L(x(i), y(i)) W(i; x, y)$$

Hence, $(A; B)R(x, y)$ is a quadratic in $x$ and $y$ for any linear $L$. This quadratic vanishes on the perimeter of order 4 and so must be the zero polynomial. Degree-1 approximation is thus established. That this is just the tip of the iceberg is suggested when one finds that elements such as the triangle with one curved side in Fig. 6.8 admit similar bases.

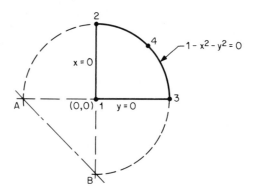

**FIG. 6.8**  A triangle with a curved side.

The simplest rational form for the basis function at vertex 1 is

$$W(l; x, y) = \frac{1 - x^2 - y^2}{(A; B)_1}$$

This is linear on side $(1; 2)$ when $(A; B)_1 = 1 + x + by$ and linear on side $(1; 3)$ when $(A; B)_1 = 1 + ax + y$. The only possibility is $(A; B)_1 = 1 + x + y$. If the sides are extended, it is found that, just as for the quadrilateral, the denominator is determined by the exterior intersection points of the element sides. It turns out that this denominator is common to all the basis functions for this three-sided element and that degree-1 approximation can be demonstrated. Note that a node is needed on the curved side for this purpose. The basis function associated with this side node is

$$W(4; x, y) = (1; 2)_4 \frac{(1; 3)_4}{(A; B)_4}$$

### 6.3D  Algebraic Geometry Foundations

The mathematical foundations for construction and analysis of rational basis functions for regular algebraic elements are in the field called *algebraic geometry*. Walker [103] provides an excellent introduction to this area of analysis for the more mathematically inclined reader. A concise summary of material essential for a thorough understanding of the construction of rational basis functions is given in Ref. [102].

### 6.3E  Construction of Rational Bases

The general recipe for constructing bases to achieve any degree of approximation over any regular algebraic element is given in Ref. [102]. For degree-1 approximation, each basis function is of the form

$$W(i; x, y) = k(i) \frac{P^i(x, y) R^i(x, y)}{Q(x, y)}$$

where $P^i$ is called the *opposite factor*, $R^i$ is called the *adjacent factor*, and $Q$ is the *adjoint factor*, which is common to all basis functions for the element. The constant $k(i)$ normalizes $W$ to unity at node $i$. Each factor will now be described. Factor $P^i$ is the polynomial of least degree that vanishes on all boundary segments of the element that do not contain node $i$. To remove arbitrary normalization one may set $P^i$ to unity at node $i$.

The adjoint factor is generated from the nonvertex multiple points of the boundary curve. If point $p$ has multiplicity $r$ on the boundary curve and $p$ is not a vertex, then point $p$ has multiplicity $r-1$ on the adjoint curve. Conversely, the only intersections of adjoint curve $Q$ with boundary curve $\partial$ are at multiple points of $\partial$. It has been shown [102] that for any regular algebraic element of order $m$ the multiple points of boundary curve $\partial$ determine a unique adjoint of maximal order $m-3$. Triangles and parallelograms have boundaries with no multiple points other than element vertices. For these elements, the unique adjoint is the polynomial of degree zero: $Q=1$. The exterior diagonal of a convex quadrilateral is the unique curve of maximal order 1 through the two "exterior" multiple points of the boundary of the quadrilateral. For a regular pentagon or hexagon, the unique adjoint is the circle through the exterior multiple points. For an irregular pentagon, the circle generalizes to a conic determined by the five exterior multiple points which no longer fall on a circle. For an irregular hexagon, the adjoint is in general a cubic curve through nine exterior multiple points, some of which may coalesce. Note that the number of intersections of six lines two at a time is $_6C_2=15$ and that six of these points are the vertices, leaving a total of nine (in the general case distinct) exterior intersection points for the hexagon. It has not yet been proved that the adjoint of any regular algebraic element contains no point in the element, a property necessary for regularity of the basis functions over the element. However, no violation of this condition has been uncovered. Analysis suggests that this is a reasonable conjecture.

The adjacent factor is unity for each side node on a conic side. It is also unity for each vertex at the intersection of two straight sides. Consider the vertex at the intersection of a conic side and a straight side. The adjacent factor is the linear form that vanishes on the line connecting the side node on the curved side through the vertex with the nonvertex intersection of that conic side and the straight side (Fig. 6.9a). The adjacent factor for a vertex at the intersection of two conic sides is the quadratic determined by the side nodes on the adjacent conic sides and the three exterior intersections of these sides. These five points determine a

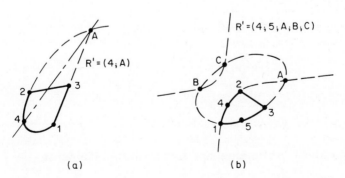

(a)                                    (b)

**FIG. 6.9**  Adjacent factors at "polycon" vertices. (a) A line-conic vertex. (b) A conic-conic vertex.

unique (except for normalization) quadratic. A "polycon" is an element with only linear and conic sides. Neither lines nor nondegenerate conics contain multiple points. Thus, the multiple points of a polycon boundary are just the points of intersection of its components. Construction of basis functions for elements with boundary components of an order higher than 2 is more complicated (see Ref. [102]) and will not be considered here. The construction described here will now be illustrated with the four-sided element of order $m = 5$ shown in Fig. 6.10.

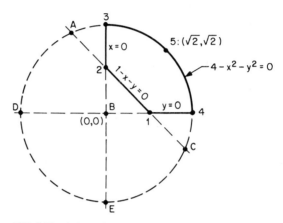

**FIG. 6.10**  A four-sided element of order 5.

The five exterior intersection points determine the unique adjoint of maximal order $m - 3 = 2$:

$$Q = x^2 + y^2 + 4xy + 2x + 2y$$

The five basis functions for this element are

$$W(1; x, y) = \frac{x(4 - x^2 - y^2)}{Q(x, y)}$$

$$W(2; x, y) = \frac{y(4 - x^2 - y^2)}{Q(x, y)}$$

$$W(3; x, y) = \frac{y(y + x - 1)\{y + 1 - (1 + 1/\sqrt{2})x\}}{Q(x, y)}$$

$$W(4; x, y) = \frac{x(y + x - 1)\{x + 1 - (1 + 1/\sqrt{2})y\}}{Q(x, y)}$$

$$W(5; x, y) = \frac{2(1 + \sqrt{2})xy(y + x - 1)}{Q(x, y)}$$

## 6.3F  Relative Merits of Rational and Isoparametric Elements

Rational bases are readily constructed for any regular algebraic element. Evaluation of integrals of products of basis functions and their derivatives of various orders over elements is a crucial part of finite-element application. Several approaches to integration have been fruitful (see, e.g., Andersen and McLeod [104]). However, the isoparametric formalism has an elegant simplicity that preempts use of rational bases in the physical coordinates whenever isoparametric elements are adequate. There are exceptional cases where rational bases are preferable. One must proceed with great care when one seeks higher than degree-1 approximation with isoparametric elements [105].

If the elements are sufficiently small, the approximation of true boundary curves by isoparametric arcs is reasonable. However, when the element structure is coarser, the rational elements introduce less error in boundary modeling. In the hierarchical elements (Sec. 6.4), accuracy is improved by increasing the degree of approximation within elements rather than by increasing the number of elements. The general class of regular algebraic elements is much larger than the class of isoparametric elements and thus provides greater modeling flexibility for hierarchical computation.

Another useful property of the rational bases is that they facilitate interpolation in physical coordinates. Isoparametric interpolation must often be done in the local (isoparametric) coordinates and then mapped into the physical plane. Evaluating a function known in the isoparametric plane at a specific point in the physical plane (other than an element node) is not a trivial task. Isoparametric elements are three- or four-sided. Regular algebraic elements may have any number of sides.

## 6.4 HIERARCHIC FINITE ELEMENTS

The approximating function in each finite element is constructed from simple functions, using polynomials, in such a way that certain continuity conditions are satisfied at interelement boundaries. Theoretically, the quality of approximation is completely determined by the finite-element mesh, the degree(s) of the polynomials, and the continuity at interelement boundaries. It is independent of how the polynomial shape functions are constructed.

Hierarchic finite elements have the property that shape functions corresponding to an element of order $p$ constitute a subset of the shape functions of all higher-order elements of the same kind. Thus the stiffness matrix of each hierarchic element is embedded in the stiffness matrices of all higher-order hierarchic elements of the same kind. This property, as well as near energy orthogonality of hierarchic shape functions, separates the global response of a finite-element model from its local behavior, ensures numerical stability, and can be exploited in obtaining efficient solutions for finite-element modeling.

The construction of shape functions for exactly and minimally conforming hierarchic $C^0$-finite elements is described here for one- and two-dimensional applications. Construction of $C^1$-elements in one and two dimensions is briefly discussed. For hierarchic elements in three dimensions, see Refs. [112–113].

### 6.4A $C^0$-Elements in One Dimension

Although the one-dimensional case is not of practical significance, it serves to introduce the idea of hierarchic shape functions in the simplest possible way. We define as our standard domain the line segment extending from $-1$ to $+1$: $-1 \leqslant \xi \leqslant 1$ which is mapped to the actual domain extending from $x_1$ to $s_2$ by the linear transformation

$$x = Q(\xi) = \tfrac{1}{2}(1-\xi)x_1 + \tfrac{1}{2}(1+\xi)x_2 \equiv L_1 x_1 + L_2 x_2 \tag{6.26}$$

with obvious definitions for $L_1$ and $L_2$. Note that $L_1 + L_2 = 1$; they are termed *natural coordinates*. An inverse transformation exists which will be denoted by

$$\xi = Q^{-1}(x) \tag{6.27}$$

The vertex modes are those shape functions which are associated with the endpoints of an element. There are two vertex modes in the case of one-dimensional elements: $L_1, L_2$. The internal modes are those shape functions which vanish at the endpoints of elements. The $p^{\text{th}}$-order $C^0$-element in one dimension has $p-1$ internal modes.

If we were concerned with the one-dimensional case only, then the most logical choice for the internal modes would be the first integrals of Legendre polynomials. Thus the $p^{\text{th}}$-order internal mode is

$$f_p(\xi) = \int_{-1}^{\xi} P_{p-1}(t)\, dt \qquad (p = 2, 3, \ldots) \tag{6.28}$$

in which $P_{p-1}(t)$ is the Legendre polynomial of degree $p-1$. We can also use the formula

$$f_p(\xi) = \frac{1}{2p-1}[P_p(\xi) - P_{p-2}(\xi)]$$

The orthogonality property of the Legendre polynomials ensures that the elemental stiffness matrix is diagonal. In fact, for $i, j \geq 3$ we have

$$k_{ij} = \int_{-1}^{1} f'_{i-1}(\xi) f'_{j-1}(\xi)\, d\xi = \begin{cases} 0 & i \neq j \\[2mm] \dfrac{2}{2i-3} & i = j \end{cases}$$

Another example of hierarchic internal modes in one dimension is

$$f_p(\xi) = \begin{cases} \dfrac{1}{p!}(\xi^p - 1) & p \text{ even} \\[3mm] \dfrac{\xi}{p!}(\xi^{p-1} - 1) & p \text{ odd} \end{cases} \tag{6.29}$$

The same internal modes in terms of natural coordinates are of the form

$$f_p(L_1, L_2) = \begin{cases} \dfrac{1}{p!}[(L_2 - L_1)^p - 1] & p \text{ even} \\[3mm] \dfrac{L_2 - L_1}{p!}[(L_2 - L_1)^{p-1} - 1] & p \text{ odd} \end{cases} \tag{6.30}$$

These hierarchic shape functions have the property that the shape functions corresponding to $p$ even are energy-orthogonal to those corresponding to $p$ odd. They have been normalized such that the $p^{\text{th}}$ derivative of the $p^{\text{th}}$-order shape function is unity.

It should be noted that in the one-dimensional case, because of the linearity of geometric mapping [Eq. (6.26)], the mapped shape functions will still be polynomials in $x$. Mapping can be used also for changing the character of the shape functions in such a way that the mapped shape functions are not polynomials or to induce singularities in the derivatives of the mapped function (see Sec. 6.1 for details).

## 6.4B $C^0$-Quadrilateral Elements

The most direct extension of the one-dimensional case is the quadrilateral element in two dimensions. The standard element is shown in Fig. 6.11.

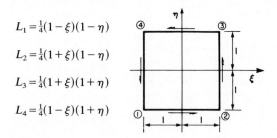

$$L_1 = \tfrac{1}{4}(1-\xi)(1-\eta)$$

$$L_2 = \tfrac{1}{4}(1+\xi)(1-\eta)$$

$$L_3 = \tfrac{1}{4}(1+\xi)(1+\eta)$$

$$L_4 = \tfrac{1}{4}(1-\xi)(1+\eta)$$

**FIG. 6.11**   $C^0$-quadrilateral element.

Note that $L_1 + L_2 + L_3 + L_4 = 1$ and $L_1 L_3 - L_2 L_4 = 0$. $L_1$, $L_2$, $L_3$, and $L_4$ are the vertex modes, i.e., the shape functions associated with nodes 1, 2, 3, and 4, respectively. These shape functions are equivalent to a polynomial of degree 1 in $\xi$, $\eta$ plus the monomial term $\xi\eta$. In other words, for any $a_1$, $a_2$, $a_3$, $a_4$ there is a set $b_1$, $b_2$, $b_3$, $b_4$ such that

$$a_1 + a_2\xi + a_3\eta + a_4\xi\eta = b_1 L_1 + b_2 L_2 + b_3 L_3 + b_4 L_4$$

The hierarchic $C^0$-quadrilaterals have $4(p-1)$ edge modes. The $p^{\text{th}}$-order edge modes associated with the four sides of the quadrilateral are

Side 1 $(\eta = -1)$:         $\phi_p^{(1)}(\xi, \eta) = \tfrac{1}{2}(1-\eta)f_p(\xi)$

Side 2 $(\xi = 1)$:          $\phi_p^{(2)}(\xi, \eta) = \tfrac{1}{2}(1+\xi)f_p(\eta)$

Side 3 $(\eta = 1)$:         $\phi_p^{(3)}(\xi, \eta) = \tfrac{1}{2}(1+\eta)f_p(-\xi)$

Side 4 $(\xi = -1)$:         $\phi_p^{(4)}(\xi, \eta) = \tfrac{1}{2}(1-\xi)f_p(-\eta)$

in which $f_p(\xi)$ is the function defined in Eq. (6.29).

These shape functions have been normalized such that the $p^{\text{th}}$ derivative of each edge mode along the side at which it does not vanish is unity. The positive sense of differentiation is shown by the arrows in Fig. 6.11.

The $C^0$-quadrilaterals have $\frac{1}{2}(p-2)(p-3)$ internal modes, $p \geq 4$. The general form for the $p^{\text{th}}$-order internal mode is

$$\psi_p(\xi, \eta) = (1 - \xi^2)(1 - \eta^2) P_{p-i-3}(\xi) P_{i-1}(\eta) \qquad i = 1, 2, \ldots, p-3$$

in which $P_j(\xi)$ is the Legendre polynomial of degree $j$.

It can be shown that the shape functions described herein are equivalent to complete polynomials of degree $p$ supplemented by the two monomial terms $\xi^p \eta$, $\xi \eta^p$; $p \geq 2$.

$C^0$-quadrilateral elements may be mapped either by standard iso- or subparametric transformations or by transformations based on linear blending.

## 6.4c  $C^0$-Triangular Elements

We select for our standard domain the equilateral triangle shown in Fig. 6.12. The natural coordinates and vertex modes for this element in terms of $\xi$ and $\eta$ are:

$$L_1 = \frac{1}{2}\left(1 - \xi - \frac{\eta}{\sqrt{3}}\right) \tag{6.31a}$$

$$L_2 = \frac{1}{2}\left(1 + \xi - \frac{\eta}{\sqrt{3}}\right) \tag{6.31b}$$

$$L_3 = \frac{\eta}{\sqrt{3}} \tag{6.31c}$$

Note that $L_1 + L_2 + L_3 = 1$. The vertex modes are equivalent to a polynomial of degree 1 in $\xi$, $\eta$ coordinates.

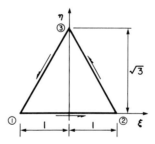

**FIG. 6.12**  $C^0$-triangular element.

The $C^0$-triangular elements have $3(p-1)$ edge modes. The edge modes are of the form of Eq. (6.30). In particular, for the side connecting nodes $i$, $j$ the $p^{\text{th}}$-order edge mode is

$$\phi_p(L_i, L_j) = L_i L_j q_{p-2}(L_j - L_i) \qquad p \geq 2 \tag{6.32a}$$

where $q_{p-2}$ is defined so that

$$f_p(\xi) = \frac{1}{4}(1 - \xi^2) q_{p-2}(\xi) \qquad p \geq 2 \tag{6.32b}$$

These shape functions have been normalized such that their $p^{\text{th}}$ derivative along the edge at which they do not vanish, in the direction shown by the arrows in Fig. 6.12, is unity.

The derivative along the side which connects nodes $i, j$ in the direction from $i$ to $j$ is

$$\frac{\partial}{\partial s_{ij}} = \frac{1}{2}\left(\frac{\partial}{\partial L_j} - \frac{\partial}{\partial L_i}\right)$$

There are $\frac{1}{2}(p-1)(p-2)$ internal modes, $p \geqslant 3$. The internal modes can be constructed in various ways. One possibility is the following:

$$\psi_p(L_1, L_2, L_3) = L_1 L_2 L_3 P_{p-i-2}(L_2 - L_1) P_{i-1}(2L_3 - 1) \qquad i = 1, 2, \ldots, p-2$$

in which $\psi_p$ denotes internal modes of degree $p$ and $P_j$ is the Legendre polynomial of degree $j$.

The shape functions of the triangular element are equivalent to a polynomial of degree $p$.

## 6.4D $C^0$-Tetrahedral Elements

The standard tetrahedral element is shown in Fig. 2.6.13. It is bounded by four equilateral triangles. The natural coordinates and vertex nodes for this element in terms of $\xi, \eta, \zeta$ are

$$L_1 = \frac{1}{2}\left(1 - \xi - \frac{\eta}{\sqrt{3}} - \frac{\zeta}{\sqrt{6}}\right)$$

$$L_2 = \frac{1}{2}\left(1 + \xi - \frac{\eta}{\sqrt{3}} - \frac{\zeta}{\sqrt{6}}\right)$$

$$L_3 = \frac{\eta}{\sqrt{3}} - \frac{\zeta}{2\sqrt{6}}$$

$$L_4 = \tfrac{1}{2}\sqrt{\tfrac{3}{2}}\,\zeta$$

The natural coordinates satisfy relationship $L_1 + L_2 + L_3 + L_4 = 1$. There are $4(p-1)$ edge modes which are of the form of Eq. (6.30). There are $2(p-1)(p-2)$ face modes, $p \geqslant 3$. These

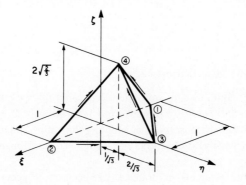

FIG. 6.13 $C^0$-tetrahedral element.

are analogous to the internal modes of the $C^0$-triangular elements. For example, the $p^{\text{th}}$-order face modes associated with the face that contains modes 1, 2, 3 are analogous to Eq. (6.32).

There are $\frac{1}{6}(p-1)(p-2)(p-3)$ internal modes, $p \geqslant 4$. A general form for the $p^{\text{th}}$-order internal modes can be given as

$$T_p(L_1, L_2, L_3, L_4) = L_1 L_2 L_3 L_4 P_i(L_2 - L_1) P_j(2L_2 + \tfrac{2}{3}L_4 - 1) P_k(2L_4 - 1)$$

in which $i, j, k = 0, 1, 2, \ldots, p-4$; $i + j + k = p - 4$.

The shape functions of the $C^0$-tetrahedral element of degree $p$ are equivalent to a complete polynomial of degree $p$ in $\xi$, $\eta$, $\zeta$.

### 6.4E $C^1$-Elements in One Dimension

The $C^1$-elements have four vertex modes and $p - 3$ internal modes, $p \geqslant 3$. The vertex modes are

$$\lambda_1 = L_1^2(1 + 2L_2) \qquad \text{(displacement at node 1)}$$

$$\lambda_2 = 2L_1^2 L_2 \qquad \text{(rotation at node 1)}$$

$$\lambda_3 = L_2^2(1 + 2L_1) \qquad \text{(displacement at node 2)}$$

$$\lambda_4 = -2L_1 L_2^2 \qquad \text{(rotation at node 2)}$$

in which $L_1$, $L_2$ are the natural coordinates given by (6.26). The first internal mode is $\frac{3}{2}L_1^2 L_2^2$, which has been normalized such that its fourth derivative is unity. The general form for the $p^{\text{th}}$-order internal mode is

$$\phi(L_1, L_2, p) = \frac{1}{p!}[(L_2 - L_1)^{p/2} - 1]^2 \qquad p \geqslant 4, \text{ even}$$

$$\phi(L_1, L_2, p) = \frac{L_2 - L_1}{p!}[(L_2 - L_1)^{(p-1)/2} - 1]^2 \qquad p \geqslant 5, \text{ odd}$$

Alternatively the internal modes can be constructed from the second integrals of Legendre polynomials. Thus the $p^{\text{th}}$-order internal mode is

$$\phi(\xi, p) = \int_{-1}^{\xi} \int_{-1}^{t} P_{p-2}(x)\, dx\, dt \qquad p \geqslant 4$$

### 6.4F $C^1$-Elements in Two Dimensions

Exact and minimal $C^1$-continuity in two dimensions cannot be enforced by means of local polynomial bases, as in the case of $C^0$-triangles and quadrilaterals. The continuity constraints must either be enforced in the process of assembling the stiffness matrix or the polynomial basis must be supplemented by rational functions. Detailed discussion of this point is available in Refs. [107–114].

The use of $C^1$-finite elements in practical applications is generally difficult because $C^1$-continuity is not preserved in curvilinear mapping.

## 6.4G Literature on Hierarchic Finite Elements

Hierarchic finite elements were first considered by Zienkiewicz et al. [106] in conjunction with joining finite elements of different polynomial order. The actual development of hierarchic finite elements is closely linked with the development of the $p$-version of the finite-element method. Hierarchic $C^0$-elements have been described in Refs. [107–112]. Hierarchic $C^1$-elements were presented in Refs. [106–108, 111, 114, 115, 117]. The computation of stiffness matrices and load vectors for hierarchic $C^0$-elements by precomputed arrays was described in Ref. [110]. Closed-form integration of the stiffness terms arising from the use of rational functions in hierarchic $C^1$-elements is presented in Ref. [116]. The round-off characteristics of the hierarchic $C^0$-triangles presented here were briefly discussed in Ref. [118].

## 6.5 THE PENALTY–FINITE-ELEMENT METHOD

The purpose of this section is limited to the introduction of the general concept of the penalty-function method and its applications to the finite-element modeling of some problems in viscous, incompressible flow and bending of elastic plates. Additional results, especially from the point of view of accuracy and stability of the penalty–finite-element approximations, can be found in Sec. 2.9 of this handbook.

Among several approaches available to solve problems with constraints, the Lagrange multiplier method dominates the applications. In the Lagrange multiplier method, one dependent variable per constraint is introduced in transforming a constrained-minimum problem to an unconstrained stationary problem. Thus, from the finite-element modeling point of view, the Lagrange multiplier formulation invariably leads to a large number of unknowns.

Another approach to solving a constrained-minimization problem is to construct a functional whose unconstrained minimum either is the true minimum $u_0$ itself, or is related to $u_0$ according to some known relation. The original problem can then be solved by formulating a sequence of *unconstrained* subproblems or possibly a single unconstrained subproblem. Such an approach was introduced, in a less formal form, in 1928 by Courant, Friedrichs, and Lewy [119] (see also Refs. [120, 121]). The method is now referred to as the *exterior-penalty method*. Thus method differs from the Lagrange multiplier method in that no additional dependent unknowns are introduced into the problem. Instead, a preassigned parameter, called the *penalty parameter*, is introduced with each constraint. The fact that no additional dependent unknowns are introduced and the original minimum character of the problem is retained in the unconstrained approximate problem, makes the penalty-function method very attractive from a finite-element computational point of view.

Although the idea was motivated by physical considerations, its value as a technique for transforming a given constrained-minimization problem into a (sequence of) unconstrained-minimization problem(s) was not recognized immediately. Rubin and Unger [122] took the original technique of Courant out of the realm of conjecture, generalized Courant's technique to problems with multiple variables and multiple equality constraints, and provided a convergence proof and a proof of the existence of Lagrange multipliers. The idea was extended to problems with inequality constraints by Zangwill [123], who showed that the Lagrange multiplier method can be obtained as the limit of the penalty method as the penalty parameter approaches the value of infinity. Since that time the technique is extensively used in mathematical programming and optimization (see Refs. [124, 125]). A complete mathematical treatment of the penalty method can be found in the books of Aubin [126] and Lions [127].

The first use of the penalty-function method in conjunction with the finite-element method was due to Babuska [128], who proved the existence and uniqueness of the finite-element solution to the penalty-function formulation of the Dirichlet problem for the Poisson's equation. The penalty method was brought into the finite-element analysis of viscous, incompressible fluid flows by Zienkiewicz [129]. In these problems the incompressibility condition (i.e., divergence of the velocity equal to zero) is viewed as a constraint on the velocity field that satisfies the momentum equations. However, difficulties were encountered in the numerical implementation of the method for fluid-flow problems. What was not realized then was the fact that there was a corresponding approximation of the pressure for each choice of the approximation of the velocity field. The use of reduced-order integration methods to evaluate the penalty terms (i.e., coefficients of the penalty parameter) proved to circumvent the difficulties [130, 131].

As the popularity of the penalty–finite-element method grew in the last decade, increased interest in the mathematical analysis and applications of the method took place (see Bercovier [132], Reddy [133–136], Oden and his colleagues [137–139], and Kikuchi [140]). Most of the continuum applications of the method are confined to problems of incompressible, conductive or convective flow (see Refs. [141–148], among many others). The shear-deformable theory of the elastic bending of plates can be interpreted as one derived from the classical plate theory by treating the zero-transverse-shear strains as constraints [149–152]; the penalty terms turn out to be the shear-energy terms, and therefore reduced integration of the shear-energy terms in the evaluation of stiffness coefficients is necessary.

### 6.5A The Penalty Method

Here we describe the penalty-function method for the general problem of finding $u$ that renders the functional

$$I(u) = \int_\Omega F(x, y, u, u_x, u_y)\, dx\, dy \tag{6.33}$$

a minimum and satisfies the constraint

$$G(u, u_x, u_y) = 0 \tag{6.34}$$

where $F$ and $G$ are, in general, nonlinear expressions involving $u$, $u_x = \partial u/\partial x$, and $u_y = \partial u/\partial y$.

In the Lagrange multiplier method (saddlepoint problem), we seek the stationary values $(u, \lambda)$ of the modified functional without constraints,

$$I_L(u, \lambda) = I(u) + \int_\Omega \lambda G(u, u_x, u_y)\, dx\, dy \tag{6.35}$$

where $\lambda$ denotes the *Lagrange multiplier*. The Euler equations of the new functional are given by (see [154])

$$\delta u: \qquad \frac{\partial F}{\partial u} - \frac{\partial}{\partial x}\left(\frac{\partial F}{\partial u_x}\right) - \frac{\partial}{\partial y}\left(\frac{\partial F}{\partial u_y}\right) + \lambda\left[\frac{\partial G}{\partial u} - \frac{\partial}{\partial x}\left(\frac{\partial G}{\partial u_x}\right) - \frac{\partial}{\partial y}\left(\frac{\partial G}{\partial u_y}\right)\right] = 0 \qquad (6.36)$$

$$\delta\lambda: \qquad\qquad\qquad\qquad G(u, u_x, u_y) = 0 \qquad\qquad\qquad\qquad (6.37)$$

Thus, the constraint condition is included (in its actual form) in the variational problem (6.35).

The penalty method reduces problems of conditional (or constrained) extrema to problems without constraints by the introduction of a penalty on the infringement of constraints. Instead of solving the original problem, one seeks the minimum of the quadratic penalty functional

$$I_p(u_\gamma) = I(u_\gamma) + J(u_\gamma) \qquad (6.38)$$

where $\gamma$ is a nonnegative parameter termed *penalty parameter* and

$$J(u_\gamma) = \frac{\gamma}{2}\int_\Omega [G(u, u_x, u_y)]^2 \, dx \, dy \qquad (6.39)$$

The functional $J(u_\gamma)$ is called the *penalty term*, which is assumed to be differentiable with respect to $u$, $u_x$, and $u_y$. The Euler equation of the functional $I_p$ is given by

$$\frac{\partial F}{\partial u} - \frac{\partial}{\partial x}\left(\frac{\partial F}{\partial u_x}\right) - \frac{\partial}{\partial y}\left(\frac{\partial F}{\partial u_y}\right) + \gamma G\left[\frac{\partial G}{\partial u} - \frac{\partial}{\partial x}\left(\frac{\partial G}{\partial u_x}\right) - \frac{\partial}{\partial y}\left(\frac{\partial G}{\partial u_y}\right)\right] = 0 \qquad (6.40)$$

A comparison of Eqs. (6.40) and (6.36) shows that an approximation to $\lambda$ is given by

$$\lambda_\gamma = \gamma G \qquad (6.41)$$

For increasing values of $\gamma$, say, $\gamma_1 < \gamma_2 < \gamma_3 < \cdots < \gamma_n < \infty$, the error between the true solution $(u_0, \lambda_0)$ and the penalty solution $(u_n, \lambda_n)$ can be shown to satisfy the following inequalities [153–155].

$$\|u_n - u_0\|_E \leq \frac{C_1}{2\gamma_n}\|\lambda_0\|_0$$

$$\qquad\qquad\qquad\qquad\qquad\qquad\qquad (6.42)$$

$$\|\lambda_n - \lambda_0\|_0 \leq \frac{C_1}{2\gamma_n}\|\lambda_0\|_0$$

where $\|u\|_E$ denotes the energy norm

$$\|u\|_E = \left\{\int_\Omega\left[u^2 + \left(\frac{\partial u}{\partial x}\right)^2 + \left(\frac{\partial u}{\partial y}\right)^2\right] dx \, dy\right\}^{1/2} \qquad (6.43)$$

and $\|u\|_0$ denotes the $L_2$-norm

$$\|u\|_0 = \left(\int_\Omega u^2 \, dx \, dy\right)^{1/2} \qquad (6.44)$$

Thus, the solution to the penalty problem converges to the true solution at the rate of $1/\gamma_n$.

For sufficiently large values of $\gamma_n$, one obtains an accurate approximation to the true solution. It should be pointed out the approximation error introduced by numerical modeling is in addition to the error introduced into the solution by the approximate satisfaction of the constraints.

We now consider application of the method to steady flow of a viscous incompressible fluid and the bending of elastic plates. With these examples we illustrate the application of the penalty method and finite-element modeling of the modified problems.

## 6.5B Application to Viscous Incompressible Flows

Consider the steady flow of a viscous incompressible fluid. The governing equations of the flow are given by

$$2\mu \frac{\partial^2 u}{\partial x^2} + \mu \frac{\partial}{\partial y}\left(\frac{\partial u}{\partial y} + \frac{\partial v}{\partial x}\right) - \frac{\partial P}{\partial x} = f_x$$

$$2\mu \frac{\partial^2 v}{\partial y^2} + \mu \frac{\partial}{\partial x}\left(\frac{\partial u}{\partial y} + \frac{\partial v}{\partial x}\right) - \frac{\partial P}{\partial y} = f_y \tag{6.45}$$

$$\frac{\partial u}{\partial x} + \frac{\partial v}{\partial y} = 0 \tag{6.46}$$

Here $(u, v)$ denotes the velocity components, $P$ the pressure, and $\mu$ the viscosity, and $f_x$ and $f_y$ denote the body-force components. The velocity field must also satisfy certain boundary conditions of the problem. For simplicity we assume that $u = v = 0$ on the boundary $\Gamma$ of $\Omega$.

It has been shown [155] that solving Eqs. (6.45) and (6.46) is equivalent to minimizing the functional

$$I_0(u, v) = \int_\Omega \left\{ \mu \left[ \left(\frac{\partial u}{\partial x}\right)^2 + \left(\frac{\partial v}{\partial y}\right)^2 + \frac{1}{2}\left(\frac{\partial u}{\partial y} + \frac{\partial v}{\partial x}\right)^2 \right] + f_x u + f_y v \right\} dx\, dy \tag{6.47}$$

such that 
$$u = v = 0 \qquad \text{on } \Gamma \tag{6.48}$$

$$\frac{\partial u}{\partial x} + \frac{\partial v}{\partial y} = 0 \qquad \text{in } \Omega \tag{6.49}$$

where $\Gamma$ denotes the boundary of the domain $\Omega$. We wish to include the incompressibility condition (6.49) as a constraint into the variational formulation by means of (1) the Lagrange multiplier method and (2) the penalty-function method. The essential boundary conditions in Eq. (6.48) can be readily imposed in the finite-element method, and therefore are not treated as constraints. Note that in the present case $G$ is given by

$$G(u_x, u_y) = \frac{\partial u}{\partial x} + \frac{\partial v}{\partial y} \tag{6.50}$$

1. **The Lagrange Multiplier Method**   Following the general idea described earlier, we seek the solution $(u, v, \lambda)$ that renders the following functional stationary:

$$I_L(u, v, P) = \int_\Omega \left\{ \mu \left[ \left( \frac{\partial u}{\partial x} \right)^2 + \left( \frac{\partial v}{\partial y} \right)^2 + \frac{1}{2} \left( \frac{\partial u}{\partial y} + \frac{\partial v}{\partial x} \right)^2 \right] + f_x u + f_y v \right\} dx\, dy$$

$$+ \int_\Omega \lambda \left( \frac{\partial u}{\partial x} + \frac{\partial v}{\partial y} \right) dx\, dy \tag{6.51}$$

Comparison of the Euler equations of the functional $I_L(\cdot)$ with the original equations (6.45) and (6.46) will show that the Lagrange multiplier $\lambda$ is indeed the negative of the pressure $P$:

$$\lambda = -P \tag{6.52}$$

Finite-element models based on the Lagrange multiplier formulation in Eq. (6.51) are called *mixed models* or *pressure-velocity models* (see Refs. [134, 155, 156]).

**2. The Penalty-Function Method**  The penalty formulation of the problem consists of finding the minimum of the modified functional

$$I_p(u_n, v_n) = I_0(u_n, v_n) + \frac{\gamma n}{2} \int_\Omega \left( \frac{\partial u_n}{\partial x} + \frac{\partial v_n}{\partial y} \right)^2 dx\, dy \tag{6.53}$$

subject to the conditions in (6.48) for any fixed (preassigned) parameter $\gamma_n$. In other words, the constraint (6.49) is satisfied in a least-squares sense. The degree to which the constraint is satisfied is directly proportional to the value of the penalty parameter $\gamma_n$. In fact one can show that the solution $(u_n, v_n)$ to the penalty problem converges to the solution $(u_0, v_0)$ of the original problem as $\gamma_n$ goes to infinity. The error between the two solutions is given by

$$[\|u_n - u_0\|_E^2 + \|v_n - v_0\|_E^2]^{1/2} \le \frac{c}{\gamma_n} \|P_0\|_0 \tag{6.54}$$

where $c$ is a constant and $P_0$ is the actual pressure.

The Euler equations of the functional $I_p$ are given by

$$2\mu \frac{\partial^2 u_n}{\partial x^2} + \mu \frac{\partial}{\partial y} \left( \frac{\partial u_n}{\partial y} + \frac{\partial v_n}{\partial x} \right) + \gamma_n \frac{\partial}{\partial x} \left( \frac{\partial u_n}{\partial x} + \frac{\partial v_n}{\partial y} \right) = f_x$$

$$\mu \frac{\partial}{\partial x} \left( \frac{\partial u_n}{\partial y} + \frac{\partial v_n}{\partial x} \right) + 2\mu \frac{\partial^2 v_n}{\partial y^2} + \gamma_n \frac{\partial}{\partial y} \left( \frac{\partial u_n}{\partial x} + \frac{\partial v_n}{\partial y} \right) = f_y \tag{6.55}$$

If we compare Eqs. (6.55) and (6.45), it follows that an approximation of the Lagrange multiplier is given by [in view of Eq. (6.52)]

$$P_n = -\gamma_n \left( \frac{\partial u_n}{\partial x} + \frac{\partial v_n}{\partial y} \right) \tag{6.56}$$

For finite-element applications of the formulation based on Eq. (6.53), see Refs. [141–148, 155, 156].

## 6.5c Application to Plate Bending

Here we consider the bending of thin isotropic elastic plates. From the classical theory of plates, the strain-energy functional is (see [157])

$$U_c(w) = \frac{D}{2} \int_\Omega [(w_{,xx})^2 + (w_{,yy})^2 + 2\nu w_{,xx} w_{,yy} + 2(1-\nu)(w_{,xy})^2] \, dx \, dy \qquad (6.57)$$

where $w$ is the transverse deflection, $D = Eh^3/12(1-\nu^2)$, $E$ is Young's modulus, $\nu$ is Poisson's ratio, and $h$ is the thickness of the plate. The slopes $\theta_x$ and $\theta_y$ are related to the derivatives of $w$ by

$$\frac{\partial w}{\partial x} - \theta_x = 0 \qquad \frac{\partial w}{\partial y} - \theta_y = 0 \qquad (6.58)$$

The strain energy in (6.57) can be written in terms of $\theta_x$ and $\theta_y$:

$$U_\theta(\theta_x, \theta_y) = \frac{D}{2} \int_\Omega \left[ \theta_{x,x}^2 + \theta_{y,y}^2 + 2\nu\theta_{x,x}\theta_{y,y} + \frac{1-\nu}{2}(\theta_{x,y} + \theta_{y,x})^2 \right] dx \, dy \qquad (6.59)$$

The first variation of the functional (6.57) yields the equilibrium equation in terms of the deflection $w$, and that in (6.59) yields equilibrium equations in terms of the slopes.

The strain energy associated with the thick-plate theory (see [156]) is given by

$$U_s = \frac{D}{2} \int_\Omega \left[ \phi_{x,x}^2 + \phi_{y,y}^2 + 2\nu\phi_{x,x}\phi_{y,y} + \frac{1-\nu}{2}(\phi_{x,y} + \phi_{y,x})^2 \right] dx \, dy$$

$$+ \frac{khG}{2} \int_\Omega [(w_{,x} - \phi_x)^2 + (w_{,y} - \phi_y)^2] \, dx \, dy \qquad (6.60)$$

where $\phi_x$ and $\phi_y$ are the slope functions and $k$ is the shear correction factor.

In the penalty method the problem of finding the critical points $(\theta_x, \theta_y)$ of the functional $U_\theta$ subject to the constraint conditions (6.58) is formulated as one of seeking the critical points $(\theta_x, \theta_y)$ of the modified functional

$$U_p(\theta_x, \theta_y, w) = U_\theta(\theta_x, \theta_y) + \frac{\gamma}{2} \int_\Omega [(w_{,x} - \theta_x)^2 + (w_{,y} - \theta_y)^2] \, dx \, dy \qquad (6.61)$$

Also note that the penalty functional $U_p$ is of the same form as the functional $U_s$ associated with shear-flexible theory with the following correspondence:

$$\phi_x \sim \theta_x \qquad \phi_y \sim \theta_y \qquad \gamma \sim khG \qquad (6.62)$$

Thus, the term involving $\gamma$ in (6.61) can be interpreted as the strain energy due to transverse shear, and a practical value for $\gamma$ in actual computation is $khG$. Reduced integration is used to evaluate the stiffness coefficients corresponding to the shear-energy terms.

Generalization of the above discussion to composite plates is straightforward. Inclusion of geometric or material nonlinearities does not alter the form of the penalty terms [149–152].

## 6.5D Computational Considerations: Selective Reduced Integration

In the usual numerical implementation of the penalty–finite-element models, one encounters spurious oscillations in the solution. The source of this problem lies in the numerical modeling of the penalty terms. A mathematical analysis of the discrete problem (i.e., finite-element approximation) reveals that the so-called Ladyzenskaya-Babuska-Brezzi (LBB) condition, a qualification for existence and consequently stability of the approximation scheme, is not satisfied unless the penalty terms in the finite-element matrices [156] are evaluated using reduced integration. Numerous studies, both theoretical and computational, have provided insight into the selection of elements and integration schemes to effectively implement the penalty–finite-element models [157–163]. These studies show that the reduced-order quadrature rule should be used for the penalty terms and the usual-order gaussian rule should be used for the nonpenalty terms. For example, when a bilinear quadrilateral element is used for incompressible flow (or plate bending), the one-point gaussian rule must be used to evaluate the penalty terms and the two-point (in each coordinate direction) rule must be used to evaluate the nonpenalty terms. This choice yields an accurate velocity (displacement) field. However, the pressure obtained in the postcomputation from (6.53) is oscillatory in most problems. Although these oscillations reduce with refined meshes, the oscillations are noticeable enough that they cannot be overlooked. To overcome this difficulty, several smoothing schemes are introduced [158–160]. These studies show that four-node rectangular elements with one-point quadrature and nine-node rectangular elements with three-point quadrature yield stable and convergent pressure fields [139]. Belytschko and his colleagues [163, 164] investigated the stability of the four-node quadrilateral elements for heat-conduction and plate-bending problems. It should be noted that most of the theoretical studies are conservative in nature (i.e., they give sufficient, but not necessary, conditions for convergence and stability). At this writing, most of the theoretical convergence and stability results available are limited to linear problems, especially in incompressible fluid-flow problems.

## 6.6 REFERENCES

1. Kondrat'ev, V. A., "Boundary Problems for Elliptic Equations in Domains with Conical or Angular Points," *Trans. Moscow Math. Soc.*, **16**:227–313 (1967).

2. Lehman, R. S., "Development at an Analytic Corner of Solutions of Elliptic Partial Differential Equations," *J. Math. Mech.*, **8**:727–760 (1959).

3. Grisvard, P., "Behaviour of the Solutions of an Elliptic Boundary Value Problem in a Polygonal or Polyhedral Domain," B. Hubbard (ed.), *Numerical Solution of Partial Differential Equations III*, SYNSPADE 1975, Academic Press, New York, 1976, pp. 207–274.

4. Grisvard, P., "Boundary Value Problems in Non-Smooth Domains," *Lecture Notes*, no. 19, Department of Mathematics, University of Maryland, College Park, 1980.

5. Maz'ja, V. G., and B. A. Plamenevskii, "On Boundary Value Problems for a Second Order Elliptic Equation in a Domain with Edges," *Vestnik Leningrad Univ. Math.*, **8**:99–106 (1980).

6. Stephan, E., "A Fix Method for the Laplacian in a Polyhedral Domain" (to appear).

7. Stephan, E., and J. R. Whiteman, "Singularities of the Laplacian at Corners and Edges of Three-Dimensional Domains and Their Treatment with Finite Element Methods," Technical Report BICOM 81/1, Institute of Computational Mathematics, Brunel University, England, 1981.

8. Walden, H., and R. B. Kellogg, "Numerical Determination of the Fundamental Eigenvalue for the Laplace Operator on a Spherical Domain," *J. Eng. Math.*, **11**:299–318 (1977).

9. Williams, M. L., "Stress Singularities Resulting from Various Boundary Conditions in Angular Corners of Plates in Extension," *J. Appl. Mech.*, **24**:526–528 (1952).

10. Steinberg, J., Private Communication, Brunel University, England, August 1979.

11. Moffat, H. K., "Viscous and Resistive Eddies near a Sharp Corner," *J. Fluid Mech.*, **18**:1–18 (1964).

12. Taylor, G. I., "Singularity Solutions of Hydrodynamics Problems," in N. S. Hoff and W. G. Vincenti (eds.), *Aeronautics and Astronautics*, Pergamon Press, Oxford, 1960, pp. 21–28.

13. Temam, R., *Navier Stokes Equations*, North-Holland, Amsterdam, 1977.

14. Gupta, M. M., R. P. Manohar, and B. Noble, "Nature of Viscous Flows near Sharp Corners," *Comput. Fluids*, **9**:379–388 (1981).

15. Osborn, J. E., "Regularity of Solutions of the Stokes Problem in a Polygonal Domain," in B. Hubbard (ed.), *Numerical Solution of Partial Differential Equations III*, SYNSPADE 1975, Academic Press, New York, 1976, pp. 393–411.

16. Kellogg, R. B., and J. E. Osborn, A Regularity Result for the Stokes Problem in a Convex Domain," **21**:397–431 (1976).

17. Ciarlet, P. G., *The Finite Element Method for Elliptic Problems*, North-Holland, Amsterdam, 1978.

18. Irwin, G. R., "Analysis of Stresses and Strains near the End of a Crack Traversing a Plate," *Trans. ASME J. Appl. Mech.*, **24**:361–364 (1957).

19. Rice, J. R., "Mathematical Analysis in the Mechanics of Fracture," in H. Liebowitz (ed.), *Fracture*, Academic Press, New York, 1969, vol. 2, pp. 191–311.

20. Sneddon, I. N., and D. S. Berry, "The Classical Theory of Elasticity," in S. Flügge (ed.), *Handbuch der Physik*, vol. VI: *Elastizität und Plastizität*, Springer-Verlag, Berlin, 1958, pp. 1–126.

21. Thompson, G. M., and J. R. Whiteman, "The Notch Problem in Three-Dimensional Linear Elasticity," Technical Report BICOM 82/1, Institute of Computational Mathematics, Brunel University, England, 1982.

22. Folias, E. S., "On the Three-Dimensional Theory of Cracked Plates," *J. Appl. Mech.*, **42**:663–673 (1975).

23. Folias, E. S., "Method of Solution of a Class of Three-Dimensional Problems under Mode I Loading," *Int. J. Fracture*, **16**:335–348 (1980).

24. Benthem, J. P., "State of Stress at the Vertex of a Quarter Infinite Crack in a Half-Space," *Int. J. Solids Struct.*, 479–492, 1977.

25. Benthem, J. P., "Three-Dimensional State of Stress at the Vertex of a Quarter-Infinite Crack in a Half-Space," Report WTHD No. 74, Dept. Mech. Eng., Delft University, Delft, 1975.

26. Kawai, T., Y. Fujitani, and K. Kumagai, "Analysis of Singularity at the Root of the Surface Crack Problem," in G. C. Sih and C. L. Chow (eds.), *Proc. Int. Conf. Fracture Mech. Technol.*, Noordhoff, Amsterdam, 1977, pp. 1157–1163.

27. Rao, M. N. B., "Three Dimensional Analysis of a Finite Thick Plate with a Through Crack," *Int. J. Fracture*, **17**:R43–R46 (1981).

28. Zlamal, M., "Some Recent Advances in the Mathematics," in J. R. Whiteman (ed.), *The Mathematics of Finite Elements and Applications*, Academic Press, London, 1973, pp. 59–81.

29. Barnhill, R. E., and J. R. Whiteman, "Error Analysis of Finite Element with Triangles for Elliptic Boundary Value Problems," J. R. Whiteman (ed.), *The Mathematics of Finite Elements and Applications*, Academic Press, London, 1973, pp. 83–112.

30. Whiteman, J. R., "Some Aspects of the Mathematics of Finite Element," in J. R. Whiteman (ed.), *The Mathematics of Finite Elements and Applications II*, MAFELAP 1975, Academic Press, London, 1976, pp. 25–43.

31. Whiteman, J. R., and J. E. Akin, "Finite Elements, Singularities and Fracture," in J. R. Whiteman (ed.), *The Mathematics of Finite Elements and Applications III*, MAFELAP 1978, Academic Press, London, 1979, pp. 35-54.

32. Whiteman, J. R., "Finite Elements for Singularities in Two- and Three-Dimensions," in J. R. Whiteman (ed.), *The Mathematics of Finite Elements and Applications IV*, MAFELAP 1981, Academic Press, London, 1982, pp. 37-55.

33. Fix, G., "Higher-Order Rayleigh-Ritz Approximations," *J. Math. Mech.*, **18**:645-657 (1969).

34. Barnhill, R. E., and J. R. Whiteman, "Error Analysis of Galerkin Methods for Dirichlet Problems Containing Boundary Singularities," *J. Inst. Math. Appl.*, **15**:121-125 (1975).

35. Stephan, E., "A Modified Fix Method for the Mixed Boundary Value Problem of the Laplacian in a Polyhedral Boundary," Preprint 538, Fachbereich Mathematik, Technische Hochschule Darmstadt, 1980.

36. Fix, G., S. Gulati, and G. I. Wakoff, "On the Use of Singular Functions with Finite Element Approximations," *J. Comp. Phys.*, **13**:209-228, 1973.

37. Babuska, I., L. Mejzlik, and E. Vitasel, "Effects of Artificial Cooling of Concrete in a Dam during Its Hardening," *Proc. VIIth Congr. des Grands Barrages*, Rome, 1961, pp. 1-13.

38. Blum, H., and M. Dobrowolski, "On Finite Element Methods for Elliptic Equations with Corners," Preprint 446, Sonderforschungsbereich 72, Approximation und Optimierung, Universität Bonn, Bonn, 1980.

39. Blum, H., "A Simple and Accurate Method for the Determination of Stress Intensity Factors and Solutions for Problems on Domains with Corners," in J. R. Whiteman (ed.), *The Mathematics of Finite Elements and Applications IV*, MAFELAP 1981, Academic Press, London, 1982, pp. 57-64.

40. Dobrowolski, M., "Numerical Approximation of Elliptic Interface and Corner Problems," Habilitationsschrift, Universität Bonn, Bonn, 1981.

41. Whiteman, J. R., and J. E. Akin, "Finite Elements, Singularities and Fracture," in J. R. Whiteman (ed.), *The Mathematics of Finite Elements and Applications IV*, MAFELAP 1981, Academic Press, London, 1982, pp. 35-54.

42. Kratochvil, J., A. Zenisek, and M. Zlamal, "A Simple Algorithm for the Stiffness Matrix of Triangular Plate Bending Elements," *Int. J. Numer. Meth. Eng.*, **3**:553-563 (1971).

43. Irons, B., "A Technique for Degenerating Brick-Type Isoparametric Elements Using Hierarchical Midside Nodes," *Int. J. Numer. Meth. Eng.*, **8**:203-209, 1974.

44. Tracey, D. M., "Finite Elements for the Determination of Crack Tip Elastic Stress Intensity Factors," *Eng. Fracture Mech.*, **3**:255-265 (1971).

45. Pu, S. L., M. A. Hussian, and W. E. Lorensen, "The Collapsed Cubic Isoparametric Element as a Singular Element for Crack Problems," *Int. J. Numer. Meth. Eng.*, **12**:1727-1742 (1978).

46. Henshell, R. D., and K. G. Shaw, "Crack Tip Elements Are Unnecessary," *Int. J. Numer. Meth. Eng.*, **9**:495-509 (1975).

47. Barsoum, R. S., "On the Use of Isoparametric Finite Elements in Linear Fracture Mechanics," *Int. J. Numer. Meth. Eng.*, **10**:25-37 (1976).

48. Barsoum, R. S., "Triangular Quarter Point Elements As Elastic Perfectly Plastic Crack Tip Elements," *Int. J. Numer. Meth. Eng.*, **12**:85-98 (1977).

49. Hibbitt, H. D., "Some Properties of Singular Isoparametric Elements," *Int. J. Numer. Meth. Eng.*, **11**:180-184 (1977).

50. Henshell, R. D., *PAFEC 75 Handbook: Theory and Results*, PAFEC Ltd., Nottingham, 1975.

51. Wait, R., "Singular Isoparametric Finite Elements," *J. Inst. Math. Appl.*, **20**:133-141 (1977).

52. Wait, R., "A Note on Quarter Point Triangular Elements," *Int. J. Numer. Meth. Eng.*, **12**:1333-1337 (1978).

53. Wait, R., "Finite Element Methods for Elliptic Problems with Singularities," *Comp. Meth. Appl. Mech. Eng.*, **13**:141–150 (1978).

54. Atluri, S. N., and K. V. Kumar, "$(i/r)^t$ Point Elements, Singular Transformations and Special Elements," Report 47, Center for the Adv. of Comp. Mech., Georgia Inst. of Tech., 1980.

55. Lynn, P. P., and A. R. Ingraffea, "Transition Elements To Be Used with Quarter-Point Crack Tip Elements," *Int. J. Numer. Meth. Eng.*, **12**:1031–1036 (1978).

56. Thompson, G. M., "The Finite Element Solution of Fracture Problems in Two- and Three-Dimensions," Ph.D. thesis, Department of Mathematics, Brunel University, England, 1982.

57. Thompson, G. M., and J. R. Whiteman, "An Analysis of Strain Representation in Both Singular and Non-Singular Finite Elements," Technical Report, Institute of Computational Mathematics, Brunel University, England (to appear).

58. Morris, J. L., and R. Wait, "Crack-Tip Elements with Curved Boundaries and Variable Nodes," *Appl. Math. Modelling*, **3**:259–262 (1979).

59. Harrison, D., and J. R. Whiteman, "A Test Example for Finite Element Techniques for Three-Dimensional Poisson Problems Containing Line Singularities" (to appear).

60. Okabe, M., "Fundamental Theory of the Semi-Radial Singularity Mapping with Applications to Fracture Mechanics," *Comp. Meth Appl. Mech. Eng.*, **26**:53–73 (1981).

61. Akin, J. E., "Generation Elements with Singularities," *Int. J. Numer. Meth. Eng.*, **10**:1249–1259 (1976).

62. Blackburn, W. S., "Calculation of Stress Intensity Factors at Crack Tips Using Special Finite Elements," in J. R. Whiteman (ed.), *The Mathematics of Finite Elements and Applications*, Academic Press, London, 1973, pp. 327–336.

63. Blackburn, W. S. and T. K. Hellen, "Calculation of Stress Intensity Factors in Three Dimensions by Finite Element Methods," *Int. J. Numer. Meth. Eng.*, **11**:211–229 (1977).

64. Benzley, S. E., "Representation of Singularities with Isoparametric Finite Element Methods," *Int. J. Numer. Meth. Eng.*, **8**:537–545 (1974).

65. Hilton, P. D., B. V. Kiefer, and G. C. Sih, "Specialised Finite Element Procedures for Three Dimensional Crack Problems," in A. R. Luxmore and D. J. R. Owen (eds.), *Numerical Methods in Fracture Mechanics*, Swansea Press, Swansea, Wales, 1978, pp. 411–421.

66. Whiteman, J. R., "Finite Element Methods for Singularities in Two- and Three-Dimensions," in J. R. Whiteman (ed.), *The Mathematics of Finite Elements and Applications IV*, MAFELAP 1981, Academic Press, London, 1982, pp. 37–55.

67. Atluri, S. N., "Higher Order, Special and Singular Finite Elements," in A. K. Noor and W. Pilkey (eds.), *State-of-the-Art Surveys on Finite Element Technology*, American Society of Mechanical Engineers, New York, 1983, chap. 4, pp. 87–126.

68. Gregory, J. A., D. Fischelov, B. Schiff, and J. R. Whiteman, "Local Mesh Refinement with Finite Elements for Elliptic Problems," *J. Comp. Phys.*, **28**:133–140 (1978).

69. Schiff, B., J. R. Whiteman, and D. Fishelov, "Determination of a Stress Intensity Factor Using Local Mesh Refinement," in J. R. Whiteman (ed.), *The Mathematics of Finite Elements and Applications III*, MAFELAP 1978, Academic Press, London, 1979, pp. 55–64.

70. Babuska, I., "The Self-Adaptive Approach in the Finite Element Method," in J. R. Whiteman (ed.), *The Mathematics of Finite Elements and Applications II*, MAFELAP 1975, Academic Press, London, 1976, pp. 125–142.

71. Babuska, I., and W. C. Rheinboldt, "A Survey of a Posteriori Error Estimators and Adaptive Approaches in the Finite Element Method," Technical Note BN-981, Institute for Physical Science and Technology, University of Maryland, College Park, 1982.

72. Thatcher, R. W., "Singularities in the Solution of Laplace's Equation in Two Dimensions," *J. Inst. Math. Appl.*, **16**:303–319 (1975).

73. Thatcher, R. W., "The Use of Infinite Grid Refinements at Singularities in the Solution of Laplace's Equation," *Numer. Math.*, **25**:163–178 (1976).

74. Ying Lung-An, "The Infinite Singular Element Method for Calculation of Stress Intensity Factors," *Sci. Sinica*, **21**:19–43 (1978).

75. Carey, G. F., and B. A. Finlayson, "Orthogonal Collocation on Finite Elements," *Chem. Eng. Sci.*, **30**:587–596 (1975).

76. Finlayson, B. A., *Nonlinear Analysis in Chemical Engineering*, McGraw-Hill, New York, 1980.

77. deBoor, C., "On Calculating with *B*-splines," *J. Approx. Theory*, **6**:50–62 (1972).

78. deBoor, C., "Package for Calculating with *B*-splines," *SIAM J. Numer. Anal.*, **14**:441–472 (1977).

79. Ascher, U., J. Christiansen, and R. D. Russell, "A Collocation Solver for Mixed Order Systems of Boundary Value Problems," *Math. Comput.*, **33**:659–679 (1979).

80. Sincovec, R. J., "On the Solution of the Equations Arising from Collocation with Cubic *B*-splines," *Math. Comput.*, **26**:893–895 (1972).

81. Ascher, U., J. Christiansen, and R. D. Russell, "Collocation Software for Boundary Value ODE's," *ACM TOMS*, **7**:209 (1981).

82. Dunn, R. J., Jr., and M. F. Wheeler, "Some Collocation-Galerkin Methods for Two-Point Boundary Value Problems," *SIAM J. Numer. Anal.*, **13**:720–733 (1976).

83. Diaz, J. C., "A Collocation-Galerkin Method for Two-Point Boundary Value Problems Using Continuous Piecewise Polynomial Spaces," *SIAM J. Numer. Anal.*, **14**:844–858 (1977).

84. Carey, G. F., D. Humphrey, and M. F. Wheeler, "Galerkin and Collocation-Galerkin Methods with Superconvergence and Optimal Fluxes," *Int. J. Numer. Meth. Eng.*, **17**:939–950 (1981).

85. Pinder, G. E., and A. Shapiro, "A New Collocation Method for the Solution of the Convection-Dominated Transport Equation," *Water Resources Res.*, **15**:1177–1182 (1979).

86. Herbst, B. M., "Collocation Methods and the Solution of Conduction-Convection Problems," *Int. J. Numer. Meth. Eng.*, **17**:1093–1102 (1981).

87. Ascher, U., J. Christiansen, and R. D. Russell, "Collocation Software for Boundary Value ODE's," *Trans. Math. Software*, **7**:209–220 (1981).

88. Douglas, J., Jr., and T. Dupont, "A Finite Element Collocation Method for Quasilinear Parabolic Equations," *Math. Comput.*, **27**:17–28 (1973).

89. deBoor, C., and B. Swartz, "Collocation at Gaussian Points," *SIAM J. Numer. Anal.*, **10**:582–606 (1973).

90. Houstis, E. N., "Application of Method of Collocation on Lines for Solving Nonlinear Hyperbolic Problems," *Math. Comput.*, **31**:443–456 (1977).

91. Prenter, P. M., and R. D. Russell, "Orthogonal Collocation for Elliptic Partial Differential Equations," *SIAM J. Numer. Anal.*, **13**:923–939 (1976).

92. Percell, P., and M. F. Wheeler, "A $C^1$ Finite Element Collocation Method for Elliptic Equations," *SIAM J. Numer. Anal.*, **17**:605–622 (1980).

93. Houstis, E. N., "Collocation Methods for Linear Elliptic Problems," *BIT*, **18**:301–310 (1978).

94. Houstis, E. N., "The Complexity of Numerical Methods for Elliptic Partial Differential Equations," *J. Comp. Appl. Math.*, **4**:191–197 (1978).

95. Hayes, L., G. Pinder, and M. Celia, "Alternating-Direction Collocation Method for Finite Element Approximations on Rectangles," *Comput. Math. Appl.*, **6**:45–60 (1980).

96. Chang, P. W., and B. A. Finlayson, "Orthogonal Collocation on Finite Elements for Elliptic Equations," *Math. Comp. Sim.*, **20**:83–92 (1978).

97. Diaz, J. C., "A Collocation-Galerkin Method for Poisson's Equation on Rectangular Regions," *Math. Comput.*, **33**:77–84 (1979).

98. Houstis, E. N., R. E. Lynch, J. R. Rice, and T. S. Papatheodorou, "Evaluation of Numerical Methods for Elliptic Partial Differential Equations," *J. Comp. Phys.*, **27**:323-350 (1978).

99. Frind, E. O., and G. F. Pinder, "A Collocation Finite Element Method for Potential Problems in Irregular Domains," *Int. J. Numer. Meth. Eng.*, **14**:681-702 (1979).

100. Houstis, E. N., W. F. Mitchell, and T. S. Papatheodorou, "Performance Evaluation of Algorithms for Mildly Nonlinear Elliptic Problems," *Int. J. Numer. Meth. Eng.*, **19**:665-709 (1983).

101. Houstis, E. N., and J. R. Rice, "High Order Methods for Elliptic Partial Differential Equations with Singularities," *Int. J. Numer. Meth. Eng.*, **18**:737-754 (1982).

102. Wachspress, E. L., *A Rational Finite Element Basis*, Academic Press, New York, 1975.

103. Walker, R., *Algebraic Curves*, Dover, New York, 1962.

104. Andersen, C. M., and R. J. Y. McLeod, "Integration Techniques for Isoparametric and Higher Order Bases on Finite Elements with a Curved Side," *Comput. Math. Appl.*, **5**:285-296 (1979).

105. Wachspress, E. L., "Higher Order Finite Elements," *Int. J. Numer. Meth. Eng.*, **17**:735-745 (1981).

106. Zienkiewicz, O. C., B. M. Irons, I. C. Scott, and J. S. Campbell, "Three Dimensional Stress Analysis," *Proc. IUTAM Symp. High Speed Computing of Elastic Structures*, Liège, Belgium, 1970.

107. Peano, A. G., "Hierarchies of Conforming Finite Elements," Doctoral dissertation, Washington University, St. Louis, 1975.

108. Peano, A. G., "Hierarchies of Conforming Finite Elements for Plane Elasticity and Plate Bending," *Comp. Math. Appl.*, **2**:211-224 (1976).

109. Katz, I. N., A. G. Peano, and M. P. Rossow, "Nodal Variables for Complete Conforming Finite Elements of Arbitrary Polynomial Order," *Comp. Math. Appl.*, **4**:85-112 (1978).

110. Rossow, M. P., and I. N. Katz, "Hierarchal Finite Elements and Precomputed Arrays," *Int. J. Numer. Meth. Eng.*, **12**:977-999 (1978).

111. Szabo, B. A., "Some Recent Developments in Finite Element Analysis," *Comp. Math. Appl.*, **5**:99-115 (1979).

112. Peano, A. G., A. Pasini, R. Riccioni, and L. Sardella, "Adaptive Approximations in Finite Element Structural Analysis," *Comput. Struct.*, **10**:333-342 (1979).

113. Peano, A. G., "Comments on the Paper: Simplex Elements of $C^0$ Continuity with Varying Polynomial Degree," *Int. J. Numer. Meth. Eng.*, **14**:1872-1873 (1979).

114. Peano, A. G., "Conforming Approximation for Kirchhoff Plates and Shells," *Int. J. Numer. Meth. Eng.*, **14**:1273-1291 (1979).

115. Peano, A., "Efficient High Order Finite Elements for Shells," *Meccanica, J. AIMETA*, **11**:42-47 (1967).

116. Katz, I. N., "Integration of Triangular Finite Elements Containing Corrective Rational Functions," *Int. J. Numer. Meth. Eng.*, **11**:107-114 (1977).

117. Wang, D. W., "The p-Version of the Finite Element Method for Problems Requiring $C^1$ Continuity," Doctoral dissertation, Washington University, St. Louis, August 1982.

118. Babuska, I., B. A. Szabo, and I. N. Katz, "The p-Version of the Finite Element Method," *SIAM J. Numer. Anal.*, **18**:512-545 (1981).

119. Courant, R., K. Friedrichs, and J. Lewy, "Uber die Partieller Differenzengleichungen der Mathematischen Physik," *Math. Annal.*, vol. **100**: p32 (1928) (English translation in *IBM Journal*, 1967).

120. Courant, R., "Variational Methods for the Solution of Problems of Equilibrium and Vibrations," *Bull. Am. Math. Soc.*, **49**:1-23 (1943).

121. Courant, R., "Calculus of Variations and Supplementary Notes and Exercises" (mimeographed notes), "Supplementary Notes" by M. Kruskal and H. Rubin, rev. and amended by J. Moser, New York University, New York, 1956-1957.

122. Rubin, H., and P. Unger, "Motion Under a Strong Constraining Force," *Commun. Pure Appl. Math.*, **10**:65–87 (1957).

123. Zangwill, W. I., "Nonlinear Programming via Penalty Functions," *Management Sci.*, **13**(5):344–358 (1967).

124. Fiacco, A. V., and G. P. McCormick, *Nonlinear Programming: Sequential Unconstrained Methods for Solving Constrained Minimization Techniques*, Wiley, New York, 1968.

125. Hestenes, M. R., *Optimization Theory: The Finite Dimensional Case*, Wiley-Interscience, New York, 1975.

126. Aubin, J. P., "Estimate of the Error in the Approximation of Optimization Problems with Constraints by Problems without Constraints," in A. V. Balakrishnan (ed.), *Control Theory and Calculus of Variations*, Academic Press, New York, 1969, pp. 153–173.

127. Lions, J. L., *Quelques Méthodes de Résolution des Problémes aux Limites Non Lineaires*, Dunod, Paris, 1969.

128. Babuska, I., "The Finite Element Method with Penalty," Tech. Note BN-710, Institute for Fluid Dynamics and Applied Mathematics, University of Maryland, College Park, August 1971.

129. Zienkiewicz, O. C., "Constrained Variational Principles and Penalty Function Methods in Finite Element Analysis," in G. A. Watson (ed.), *Lecture Notes in Mathematics: Conference on the Numerical Solution of Differential Equations*, Springer-Verlag, Berlin, 1974, pp. 207–214.

130. Zienkiewicz, O. C., R. L. Taylor, and J. M. Too, "Reduced Integration Technique in General Analysis of Plates and Shells," *Int. J. Numer. Meth. Eng.*, **3**:575–586 (1971).

131. Zienkiewicz, O. C., and E. Hinton, "Reduced Integration, Function Smoothing and Non-Conformity in Finite Element Analysis," *J. Franklin Inst.*, **302**:443–461 (1976).

132. Bercovier, M., "Perturbations of Mixed Variational Problems, Applications to Mixed Finite Element Methods," *RAIRO Anal. Numer.*, **12**:211–236 (1978).

133. Reddy, J. N., "On the Accuracy and Existence of Solutions to Primitive Variable Models of Viscous Incompressible Fluids," *Int. J. Eng. Sci.*, **16**:921–929 (1978).

134. Reddy, J. N., "On the Finite Element Model with Penalty for Incompressible Fluid Flow Problems," in J. R. Whiteman (ed.), *The Mathematics of Finite Elements and Applications III*, Academic Press, London, 1979, pp. 227–235.

135. Reddy, J. N., "On Penalty Function Methods in the Finite-Element Analysis of Flow Problems," *Int. J. Numer. Meth. Fluids*, **2**:151–171 (1982).

136. Reddy J. N., "The Penalty Function Method in Mechanics: A Review of Recent Advances," in J. N. Reddy (ed.), *Penalty-Finite Element Methods in Mechanics*, AMD-Vol. 51, American Society of Mechanical Engineers, 1982, pp. 1–20.

137. Oden, J. T., N. Kikuchi, and Y. J. Song, "An Analysis of Exterior Penalty Methods and Reduced Integration for Finite Element Approximations of Contact Problems in Incompressible Elasticity," TICOM Report 79-10, Texas Institute for Computational Mechanics, University of Texas, Austin, 1979.

138. Oden, J. T., and N. Kikuchi, "Finite Element Methods for Constrained Problems in Elasticity," TICOM Report 81-10, Texas Institute for Computational Mechanics, University of Texas, Austin, 1981.

139. Oden, J. T., and O. Jacqotte, "A Stable Second-Order Accurate, Finite Element Scheme for the Analysis of Two-Dimensional Incompressible Viscous Flows," *Proceedings of the Fourth International Symposium on Finite Elements in Flow Problems*, Tokyo, 1982.

140. Kikuchi, N., "Convergence of a Penalty Method for Variational Inequalities," TICOM Report 79-16, Texas Institute for Computational Mechanics, University of Texas, Austin, 1979.

141. Zienkiewicz, O. C., and P. N. Godbole, "Viscous, Incompressible Flow with Special Reference to Non-Newtonian (Plastic) Fluids," in R. H. Gallagher, J. T. Oden, C. Taylor, and O. C. Zienkiewicz, (eds.), *Finite Elements in Fluids*, Wiley-Interscience, London, 1975, vol. 1, pp. 25–55.

142. Hughes, T. J. R., R. L. Taylor, and J. F. Levy, "High Reynolds Number Steady, Incompressible Flow by a Finite Element Method," in R. H. Gallagher, J. T. Oden, C. Taylor, and O. C. Zienkiewicz (eds.), *Finite Elements in Fluids*, Wiley-Interscience, London, 1979, vol. 3, pp. 55–72.

143. Reddy, J. N., and K. H. Patil, "Alternate Finite Element Formulations of Incompressible Fluid Flow with Applications to Geological Folding," in L. C. Wellford, Jr. (ed.), *Applications of Computer Methods in Engineering*, University of Southern California, Los Angeles, 1977, vol. 1, pp. 179–190.

144. Marshall, R. S., J. C. Heinrich, and O. C. Zienkiewicz, "Natural Convection in a Square Enclosure by a Finite-Element Penalty Function Method Using Primitive Fluid Variables," *Numer. Heat Transfer*, **1**:315–330 (1978).

145. Hughes, T. J. R., W. K. Liu, and A. Brooks, "Finite Element Analysis of Incompressible Viscous Flows by the Penalty Function Formulation," *J. Comput. Phys.*, **30**:1–60 (1979).

146. Reddy, J. N., and A. Satake, "A Comparison of Various Finite-Element Models of Natural Convection in Enclosures," *J. Heat Transfer*, **102**:659–666 (1980).

147. Reddy, J. N., "Penalty Finite-Element Analysis of 3-D Navier-Stokes Equations," *Comput. Meth. Appl. Mech. Eng.*, **35**:87–106 (1982).

148. Reddy, J. N., "Penalty-Finite Element Methods in Conduction and Convection Heat Transfer," in R. W. Lewis, K. Morgan, and B. A. Shrefler (eds.), *Numerical Methods in Heat Transfer*, vol. II, Wiley, London, 1983, pp. 145–178.

149. Reddy, J. N., "Simple Finite Element with Relaxed Continuity for Nonlinear Analysis of Plates," in A. P. Kabaila and V. A. Pulmano (eds.), *Finite Element Methods in Engineering*, University of New South Wales, Sydney, 1979, pp: 265–281.

150. Hughes, T. J. R., R. L. Taylor, and W. Kanoknukulchai, "A Simple and Efficient Finite Element for Plate Bending," *Int. J. Numer. Meth. Eng.*, **11**:1529–1543 (1977).

151. Hughes, T. J. R., M. Cohen, and M. Haroun, "Reduced and Selective Integration Techniques in the Finite Element Analysis of Plates," *Nuclear Eng. Des.*, **46**:203–222 (1978).

152. Reddy, J. N., "A Penalty Plate-Bending Element for the Analysis of Laminated Anisotropic Composite Plates," *Int. J. Numer. Meth. Eng.*, **15**:1187–1206 (1980).

153. Polya, B. T., "The Convergence Rate of the Penalty Function Method," *Sh. Vychisl. Mat. Mat. fiz.*, **11**:3–11 (1971); *U.S.S.R. Comput. Math. Math. Phys.*, **11**:1–12 (1971).

154. Reddy, J. N., and M. L. Rasmussen, *Advanced Engineering Analysis*, Wiley-Interscience, New York, 1983.

155. Reddy, J. N., *Applied Functional Analysis and Variational Methods in Engineering*, McGraw-Hill, New York, 1986.

156. Reddy, J. N., *An Introduction to the Finite Element Method*, McGraw-Hill, New York, 1984.

157. Malkus, D. S., and T. J. R. Hughes, "Mixed Finite Element Methods—Reduced and Selective Integration Techniques: A Unification of Concepts," *Comput. Meth. Appl. Mech. Eng.*, **15**:63–81 (1978).

158. Engleman, M., R. L. Sani, P. M. Gresho, and M. Bercovier, "Consistent vs. Reduced Integration Penalty Methods for Incompressible Media Using Several Old and New Elements," *Int. J. Numer. Meth. Fluids*, **2**:25–42 (1983).

159. Kikuchi, N., and Y. J. Song, "Penalty/Finite Element Approximations of a Class of Unilateral Problems in Linear Elasticity," *Q. Appl. Math.*, **36**:1–22 (1981).

160. Kikuchi, N., "A Smoothing Technique for Reduced Integration Penalty Methods in Contact Problems," *Int. J. Numer. Meth. Eng.*, **18**:343–350 (1982).

161. Johnson, C., and Pitkaranta, "Analysis of Some Mixed Finite Element Methods Related to Reduced Integration," *Math. Comput.*, **38**:375–400 (1982).

162. Flanagan, D. P., and T. Belytschko, "A Uniform Strain Hexahedron and Quadrilateral with Orthogonal Hourglass Control," *Int. J. Numer. Meth. Eng.*, **17**:679–706 (1981).

163. Belytschko, T., W. K. Liu, and J. M. Kennedy, "Hourglass Control in Linear and Nonlinear Problems," in S. N. Atluri and N. Perrone (eds.), *Computer Methods for Nonlinear Solids and Structural Mechanics*, AMD-Vol. 54, American Society of Mechanical Engineers, New York, 1983.

164. Atluri, S. N., *Computational Methods in the Mechanics of Fracture*, North-Holland, Amsterdam, 1986.

165. Atluri, S. N., A. S. Kobayashi, and M. Nakagaki, "An Assumed Displacement Hybrid Finite Element Model for Linear Fracture Mechanics," *Int. J. Fracture*, 11:257-271 (1975).

166. Tong, P., T. H. H. Pian, and L. Lasry, "A Hybrid Element Approach to Crack Problems in Elasticity," *Int. J. Numer. Meth. Eng.*, 7:297-308 (1973).

167. Atluri, S. N., A. S. Kobayashi, and M. Nakagaki, "Fracture Mechanics Application of an Assumed Displacement Hybrid Finite Element Procedure," *AIAA Journal*, 13:734-739 (1975).

168. Atluri, S. N., A. S. Kobayashi, and M. Nakagaki, "A Finite-Element Program for Fracture Mechanics Analysis of Composite Materials," in *Fracture Mechanics of Composites*, ASTM STP 593, American Society for Testing and Materials, Philadelphia, 1975, pp. 86-98.

169. Atluri, S. N., and K. Kathiresan, "On a 3-D Singularity Element for Computation of Combined Mode Stress Intensities," NASA CP-2001, *Advances in Eng. Science*, 1 (13th Ann. Meeting Soc. Eng. Science), 267-274 (1976).

170. Nakagaki, M., and S. N. Atluri, "*J*-Integral Estimates for Strain Hardening Materials in Ductile Fracture Problems," *AIAA Journal*, 15:923-931 (1977).

171. Atluri, S. N., and K. Kathiresan, "3-D Analysis of Surface Flaws in Thick-Walled Reactor Pressure Vessels Using Displacement-Hybrid Finite Element Method," *Nuclear Engineering & Design*, 51:163-176 (1979).

172. Atluri, S. N., T. Nishioka, and M. Nakagaki, "Numerical Modeling of Dynamic and Nonlinear Crack Propagation in Finite Bodies, by Moving Singular Elements," in N. Perrone and S. N. Atluri (eds.), *Nonlinear and Dynamic Fracture Mechanics*, ASME-AMD, vol. 34, ASME, New York, 1979, pp. 37-66.

173. Nishioka, T., and S. N. Atluri, "Numerical Modeling of Dynamic Crack Propagation in Finite Bodies, by Moving Singular Elements," *J. Appl. Mech.*, 47:570-576 and 577-582 (1980).

174. Vijayakumar, K., and S. N. Atluri, "An Embedded Elliptical Crack, in an Infinite Solid, Subject to Arbitrary Crack-Face Conditions," *J. Appl. Mech.*, 48:88-96 (1981).

175. Nishioka, T., and S. N. Atluri, "Analytical Solution for Embedded Elliptical Cracks, and Finite Element Alternating Method for Elliptical Surface Cracks, Subjected to Arbitrary Loadings," *Eng. Fracture Mech.*, 17:247-268 (1982).

176. Nishioka, T., and S. N. Atluri, "An Inexpensive 3-D Finite Element-Alternating Method for the Analysis of Surface-Flawed Aircraft Structural Components," *AIAA Journal*, 21:749-758 (1983).

177. Atluri, S. N., and T. Nishioka, "Numerical Studies in Dynamic Fracture Mechanics," *Int. J. Fracture*, 27:245-261 (1985).

178. Nishioka, T., and S. N. Atluri, "Path-Independent Integral and Moving Isoparametric Elements for Dynamic Crack Propagation," *AIAA Journal*, 22:409-415 (1984).

179. O'Donoghue, P. E., T. Nishioka, and S. N. Atluri, "Mutliple Surface Flaws in Pressure Vessels," *Eng. Fracture Mech.*, 20:545-560 (1984).

# CHAPTER 7
# FINITE-ELEMENT METHOD FOR INSTABILITY ANALYSIS

## 7.1 INTRODUCTION

The analysis of most structures, by whatever means, is performed for the purpose of determining stresses, strains, or displacements which are then compared with allowable values that are based on material properties, various service requirements, or aesthetics. The analysis for the particular criterion of sudden collapse due to structural instability is performed much less often. When it is performed, however, it is of the utmost importance. Ample evidence of this is given by the dramatic failure in service of a number of monumental structures.

Although structural analysis prior to the emergence of the finite-element method had advanced to a point where there was a certain measure of sophistication in the treatment of complicated geometries, loadings, and phenomena, such was not the case with instability analysis. Available formulas, with some exceptions, were concerned with the buckling analysis of regular structures under simple load states.

The finite-element method has enabled the linear-elastic instability analysis of practical structures for complex load conditions. It has even brought to realization a capability for nonlinear-instability analysis. However, the largest share of literature has addressed this latter objective, and surprisingly little attention, or operational analysis capability, has been directed toward linear-elastic instability analysis. Nevertheless, linear-elastic instability analysis is a powerful, yet relatively inexpensive, approach to analysis which is realistic in many practical circumstances.

Section 7.2 describes representative conditions under which elastic instability occurs. Then, in Sec. 7.3, basic relationships which underlie most classes of instability problems are summarized. These are specialized in Sec. 7.4 to linear-elastic instability analysis; published applications for various classes of structures are reviewed.

Schemes for the prediction of another, more prevalent elastic-instability phenomenon, known as "snap-through," are given in Sec. 7.5. Next, in Sec. 7.6, methods for the determination of behavior in the postbuckling regime are examined. Calculation of elastic instability is far more expensive than calculation of stable response, and it is attractive to consider schemes for the reduction of the cost of analysis; approaches to this objective are taken up in the final section, Sec. 7.7.

## 7.2 TYPES OF LOAD-DISPLACEMENT RESPONSE

It is pertinent to review briefly some of the elementary situations that can arise in structural instability. Figure 7.1a and b illustrates the load-displacement behavior for these situations, tracing the response of a representative degree of freedom. Practical circumstances do not always evidence a behavior as simple as that portrayed here, but this does represent the response of a number of common situations in structural instability.

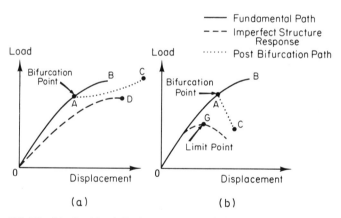

**FIG. 7.1**  Idealized load-displacement paths. (a) Bifurcation. (b) Limit-point situation.

The solid line in Fig. 7.1a and b applies to "perfect" structures. In these, the structure first displaces along the "fundamental path" (0A) with bifurcation to a secondary path at point A. The postbuckling path AC may rise (Fig. 7.1a) or descend (Fig. 7.1b), depending on the characteristics of the structure or the loading.

For certain structural forms, or when fabricational imperfections are taken into account for the types of perfect structures that are portrayed with the solid lines, the load-displacement behavior follows the paths indicated by the dashed lines, 0D. Structures with a rising postbuckling path (Fig. 7.1a) will have a strength exceeding the bifurcation load. The load-carrying capacity of a real (imperfect) structure with a descending postbuckling path (Fig. 7.1b) will be less than the bifurcation load of the corresponding perfect structure unless the load-displacement path rises again at larger displacements. This maximum load-carrying capacity, or *limit point*, occurs at point $G$. The associated form of elastic instability is called *snap-through*.

In view of the above, finite-element analysis procedures are needed for at least four different circumstances or load-displacement regimes: (1) general nonlinear analysis for tracing of the prebuckling load-displacement path, (2) calculation of a bifurcation point, (3) calculation of limit points, and (4) determination of the load-displacement response along a postbuckling path. The extensive literature on finite-element procedures for item 1 is detailed in Chap. 4 in Part 2 and is merely reviewed in the next section for the purpose of setting the stage for subsequent developments. This chapter emphasizes items 2 to 4.

## 7.3 BASIC EQUATIONS

For the problems to be discussed in this chapter it is necessary to consider only small strains and finite rotations. A lagrangian approach is adopted wherein the displacements of all points are referred to the undeformed state.

The basis of the theoretical developments to be presented resides in the principle of stationary potential energy. Alternative methods of formulation could be adopted, including virtual work and the method of weighted residuals, which would be more general. The potential-energy formulation, however, proves to be a convenient approach to the construction of the relevant equations.

The potential energy, denoted by $\Pi_p$, is given by

$$\Pi_p = U - V \tag{7.1}$$

where $U$ is the strain energy of deformation and $V$ is the potential of the applied loads. The formula for strain energy is

$$U = \tfrac{1}{2} \int_{\text{vol}} C_{ijkl} e_{kl} e_{ij} d(\text{vol}) \qquad (i, j, k, l = 1, 2, 3) \tag{7.2}$$

For a linear relationship between stress and strain

$$\sigma_{ij} = C_{ijkl} e_{kl} \tag{7.3}$$

where $C_{ijkl}$ is the material property tensor and $e_{kl}$ is the lagrangian strain tensor. As noted above, we utilize a lagrangian description of strains. The lagrangian strain tensor is expressed for cartesian coordinates, in terms of displacement derivatives, as

$$e_{ij} = \tfrac{1}{2}(u_{i,j} + u_{j,i}) + \tfrac{1}{2} u_{t,i} u_{t,j} \tag{7.4}$$

where $u_{i,j}$ denotes the displacement derivatives. For convenience we will group the terms on the right-hand side as linear-strain terms $[\varepsilon_{ij} = \tfrac{1}{2}(u_{i,j} + u_{j,i})]$ and nonlinear-strain terms $(\bar{\varepsilon}_{ij} = \tfrac{1}{2} u_{t,i} u_{t,j})$. Thus

$$e_{ij} = \varepsilon_{ij} + \bar{\varepsilon}_{ij} \tag{7.5}$$

Substitution of (7.5) into (7.4) results in

$$U = \tfrac{1}{2} \int_{\text{vol}} (C_{ijkl}\varepsilon_{kl}\varepsilon_{ij} + 2C_{ijkl}\varepsilon_{kl}\bar{\varepsilon}_{ij} + C_{ijkl}\bar{\varepsilon}_{kl}\bar{\varepsilon}_{ij}) \, d(\text{vol}) \qquad (7.6)$$

This is the basic form of the strain energy for nonlinear analysis under the above-listed limitations.

The finite-element concept involves the approximation of element displacements as a series of approximating (shape) functions times the values of the displacement at specified points (joints) of the element. This can be represented symbolically by

$$u_i = N_j^i u_j^i \qquad (j - 1, \ldots, m) \qquad (7.7)$$

where $N_j^i$ are the shape functions and $u_j^i$ are the element joint displacements. The element degrees of freedom are $m$ in number.

In subsequent developments, where we employ matrix rather than indicial notation, it will be convenient to designate the vector listing of joint displacements, taken over all relevant coordinate directions and all of the joints, as $\boldsymbol{\Delta}$. The relevant displacement components ($u_1$, $u_2$, and/or $u_3$) are denoted by $\mathbf{u}$ and the corresponding set of shape functions is $\mathbf{N}$. Thus, the matrix form of the relationships between the coordinate displacements is

$$\mathbf{u} = \mathbf{N}\boldsymbol{\Delta} \qquad (7.8)$$

If the displacements are differentiated to produce the strains, the strains are introduced into the strain energy, and the strain energy is integrated, the following algebraic form is obtained

$$U^e = \frac{\boldsymbol{\Delta}^T}{2} \mathbf{k}_0 \boldsymbol{\Delta} + \frac{\boldsymbol{\Delta}^T}{6} \mathbf{k}_1 \boldsymbol{\Delta} + \frac{\boldsymbol{\Delta}^T}{12} \mathbf{k}_2 \boldsymbol{\Delta} = \frac{\boldsymbol{\Delta}^T}{2} \hat{\mathbf{k}} \boldsymbol{\Delta} \qquad (7.9)$$

where

$$\hat{\mathbf{k}} = [\mathbf{k}_0 + \tfrac{1}{3}\mathbf{k}_1 + \tfrac{1}{6}\mathbf{k}_2] \qquad (7.10)$$

$\mathbf{k}_0$ is the stiffness matrix for linear, stable behavior; $\mathbf{k}_1$ is the *initial-stress*, or *geometric*, stiffness matrix (a linear function of $\boldsymbol{\Delta}$); and $\mathbf{k}_2$ is the *initial-displacement* stiffness matrix (a second-order function of $\boldsymbol{\Delta}$). Different ways of arranging terms in $\mathbf{k}_1$ and $\mathbf{k}_2$ are reviewed in Refs. [1, 2]. Alternatively, the strain energy can be written in indicial form:

$$U^e = \tfrac{1}{2} k_{0_{pq}} \Delta_p \Delta_q + \tfrac{1}{6} k_{1_{pqr}} \Delta_p \Delta_q \Delta_r + \tfrac{1}{12} k_{2_{pqrs}} \Delta_p \Delta_q \Delta_r \Delta_s \qquad (p, q, r, s = 1, \ldots, m) \qquad (7.11)$$

The strain energy for the complete structure is obtained by summing the element strain energies over all the elements

$$U = \Sigma U^e = \frac{\boldsymbol{\Delta}^T}{2} \hat{\mathbf{K}}\boldsymbol{\Delta} \qquad (7.12)$$

where

$$\hat{\mathbf{K}} = [\mathbf{K}_0 + \tfrac{1}{3}\mathbf{K}_1 + \tfrac{1}{6}\mathbf{K}_2] \qquad (7.13)$$

$\boldsymbol{\Delta}$ now includes the displacements at all $n$ degrees of freedom and $\hat{\mathbf{K}}$ is a global stiffness matrix obtained by appropriate summation of the element stiffness matrices. The detailed relationships for global behavior are of the same form as for element behavior and will not be written out here.

If external loads $P_p$ are concentrated, the joints and their direction remain unchanged throughout the displacement history, and the potential of these loads is

$$V = \mathbf{\Delta}^T \mathbf{P} \qquad (7.14)$$

or, in indicial notation, $\qquad V = \Delta_p P_p \qquad (p = 1, \ldots, n) \qquad (7.15)$

Distributed loads require consideration of their integrated effects and of the displacements of the surface over which they act but lead to the same algebraic form of $V$.

The potential energy is, by insertion of (7.9) and (7.14) into (7.1),

$$\Pi_p = \frac{\mathbf{\Delta}^T}{2} \hat{\mathbf{K}} \mathbf{\Delta} - \mathbf{\Delta}^T \mathbf{P} \qquad (7.16)$$

For equilibrium, the first derivative of $\Pi_p$ with respect to the displacements must be taken and set equal to zero. This gives the *equilibrium* or *secant* stiffness equations

$$\mathbf{K}\mathbf{\Delta} - \mathbf{P} = 0 \qquad (7.17)$$

where $\qquad \mathbf{K} = [\mathbf{K}_0 + \tfrac{1}{2}\mathbf{K}_1 + \tfrac{1}{3}\mathbf{K}_2] \qquad (7.18)$

The difference between $\hat{\mathbf{K}}$ (7.13) and $\mathbf{K}$ is in the multipliers of $\mathbf{K}_1$ and $\mathbf{K}_2$; this is the result of the differentiation process, which affects these matrices because they are functions of the displacement.

Most nonlinear-analysis processes involve solutions for a series of increments on the load-displacement path. If (7.17) is differentiated, the incremental equations are obtained

$$\mathbf{K}_T \,\delta\mathbf{\Delta} - \delta\mathbf{P} = 0 \qquad (7.19)$$

where $\mathbf{K}_T$, the global "tangent stiffness," is

$$\mathbf{K}_T = [\mathbf{K}_0 + \mathbf{K}_1 + \mathbf{K}_2] \qquad (7.20)$$

Here, the indicial form of $K_T$ is $(p, q, r, s = 1, \ldots, n)$

$$K_{T_{pq}} = K_{0_{pq}} + K_{1_{pqr}}\Delta_r + K_{2_{pqrs}}\Delta_r\Delta_s \qquad (7.21)$$

These relationships also serve as the basis for the analysis of certain instability phenomena. First, however, we discuss their modification for the special case of linear-stability analysis.


## 7.4 EIGENVALUE PROBLEMS

### 7.4A Linearized Prebuckling State

The classical approach to elastic-instability analysis involves the linearization of the prebuckling state; i.e., the fundamental path $0A$ in Fig. 7.1 is a straight line. It is assumed that the load state, represented here by the vector of joint forces **P**, increases in a manner such that the ratios of these forces to one another remains constant. This is termed *proportional loading*. Denoting a "reference," or normalized, vector of loads as $\hat{\mathbf{P}}$, and with $\lambda$ as the scalar load-intensity parameter, the joint forces at a specific level of intensity can be written as

$$\mathbf{P} = \lambda \hat{\mathbf{P}} \tag{7.22}$$

The intensity at which buckling occurs (point $A$, Fig. 7.1) is designated as $\lambda_{cr}$, where the subscript cr stands for "critical."

Linear-stability analysis requires the introduction of certain simplifications [3]. First, we add and subtract the higher-order nonlinear term $C_{ijkl}E_{kl}E_{ij}$ in the strain energy [Eq. (7.6)]

$$U = \tfrac{1}{2} \int_{\text{vol}} \{ C_{ijkl}\varepsilon_{kl}\varepsilon_{ij} + 2[ C_{ijkl}(\varepsilon_{kl} + \bar{\varepsilon}_{kl})]\bar{\varepsilon}_{kl} - C_{ijkl}\bar{\varepsilon}_{ij}\bar{\varepsilon}_{kl} \} \, d(\text{vol}) \tag{7.6a}$$

Also, the third (higher-order) term is discarded and substitutions are made for $e_{kl} = \varepsilon_{kl} + \bar{\varepsilon}_{kl}$ (7.5) and the constitutive relationship $\sigma_{ij} = C_{ijkl}e_{kl}$ (7.3). This gives

$$U = \tfrac{1}{2} \int_{\text{vol}} ( C_{ijkl}\varepsilon_{kl}\varepsilon_{ij} + 2\sigma_{ij}\bar{\varepsilon}_{ij}) \, d(\text{vol}) \tag{7.6b}$$

It is assumed, in utilization of this equation, that the internal stresses $\sigma_{ij}$ are known. They are obtained from a prior, independent analysis based on the linear-elastic stiffness $\mathbf{K}_0$ and the load vector **P**. In view of (7.18), $\sigma_{ij} = \lambda \hat{\sigma}_{ij}$, where $\hat{\sigma}_{ij}$ represents the stresses calculated with use of the reference vector $\hat{\mathbf{P}}$. Thus, the strain energy is now written as

$$U = \tfrac{1}{2} \int_{\text{vol}} ( C_{ijkl}\varepsilon_{kl}\varepsilon_{ij} + 2\lambda \hat{\sigma}_{ij}\bar{\varepsilon}_{ij}) \, d(\text{vol}) \tag{7.6c}$$

To obtain a finite-element algebraic representation the approximation for the displacement (7.8) is constructed and differentiated to give the strains $\varepsilon_{kl}$ and $\varepsilon_{ij}$, and the latter are substituted in (7.6c). After integration and summation of the strain energy of all elements of the finite-element representation

$$U = \frac{\mathbf{\Delta}^T}{2} \mathbf{K}_0\mathbf{\Delta} + \frac{\mathbf{\Delta}^T}{2} \lambda \bar{\mathbf{K}}_1\mathbf{\Delta} \tag{7.23}$$

where $\mathbf{K}_0$ is the linear stiffness matrix defined previously and

$$\bar{\mathbf{K}}_1 = \int_{\text{vol}} \hat{\sigma}_{ij}\bar{\varepsilon}_{ij} \, d(\text{vol}) \tag{7.24}$$

The condition for elastic instability is that the second variation of the potential energy is zero. This gives the condition

$$[\mathbf{K}_0 + \lambda \bar{\mathbf{K}}_1]\mathbf{a} = 0 \tag{7.25}$$

where **a** is the buckling-mode shape (eigenvector). Alternatively, the determinant of the matrix on the left must equal zero:

$$|[\mathbf{K}_0 + \lambda \bar{\mathbf{K}}_1]| = 0 \qquad (7.26)$$

At $\mathbf{P} = \lambda_{cr}\hat{\mathbf{P}}$ (Fig. 7.1, Point A) the intensity of load is such that alternative states of equilibrium are possible—the linear prebuckling state $(0A)$ and the postbuckling state $(AC)$. The external load $\mathbf{P}$ enters into the problem implicitly in the calculation of the internal load distribution, the intensity of which is denoted by the parameter $\lambda$. The external loads $\mathbf{P}$ play no explicit role in linear-bifurcation analysis because of the linearization of the prebuckling state and because the analysis represents a study of small displacements $\delta \mathbf{\Delta}$ about the bifurcation point.

Equations (7.25) and (7.26) are identical in form to the relationships that prevail in frequency and mode-shape calculation, where solution techniques are well established [4, 5]. All the techniques described in these references can be employed for calculation of the critical load. There are major differences in the desired results between dynamic and instability analysis, however. In frequency calculations, many roots and their associated displacement vectors are usually required. In bifurcation analysis the value of one root (the lowest) is sought, and on occasion the buckling-mode shape is only of incidental interest. For this reason a popular approach is to find the lowest root of the stability determinant, (7.26). One such approach, based on the "frontal" method of equation solution, is given in Ref. [6]. Another scheme, based on finding the lowest root of the determinant through extrapolation, is given in Ref. [7] and has been used in Ref. [8] and elsewhere.

## 7.4в Follower-Force Effects

Certain forces, especially distributed loads, might "follow" the displacements of the deformed structure; this is particularly important for problems of elastic instability, e.g., the buckling of pressure-loaded shells. In those cases the formulation of the load potential leads to an additional stiffness and complications in the sequence of analysis.

A detailed development of basic relationships for follower-force effects in finite-element instability analysis can be found in Refs. [9–13]. It suffices to say that the potential of the applied loads, given previously by Eq. (7.10), is now of the form

$$V = -\frac{\lambda}{2}\mathbf{\Delta}^T \mathbf{K}_p \mathbf{\Delta} + \lambda \mathbf{\Delta}^T \hat{\mathbf{P}} \qquad (7.27)$$

where due account has been taken of the proportional loading condition. $\mathbf{K}_p$ is a *pressure-stiffness matrix*; in general, its coefficients are functions of the displacements but it is often sufficient to treat them as constants. If $V$ is subtracted from the strain energy to give the potential energy (7.1) and the second variation is taken of the potential energy, the following eigenvalue problem is obtained

$$[\mathbf{K}_0 + \lambda[\bar{\mathbf{K}}_1 + \mathbf{K}_p]]\mathbf{a} = \mathbf{0} \qquad (7.28)$$

The techniques previously discussed for constant-direction loads can be employed for solution of the critical-load parameter $\lambda_{cr}$ and the associated eigenvector $\mathbf{a}$.

## 7.4c Nonlinear Prebuckling Behavior

Figure 7.1 indicates that the critical load is generally preceded by a nonlinear load-displacement path. In this section we describe methods that are intended for the solution of a bifurcation problem, as characterized by Eqs. (7.25) and (7.26), but which account for the nonlinear prebuckling behavior.

Analysis in the prebuckling regime is usually conducted in a series of steps, each of which is the solution of a linearized problem in a load increment $\delta\lambda$. Suppose these steps are carried to point $i$, just below the bifurcation point. The imminence of bifurcation can be sensed by monitoring the determinant of the tangent-stiffness matrix $\mathbf{K}_T$ or by use of the "current stiffness parameter," which will be described in Sec. 7.5A. At point $i$ the tangent stiffness is close to being singular and its determinant is close to zero, on account of nearness to the bifurcation point.

One approach to the calculation of the bifurcation point is by interpolation. Figure 7.2 illustrates this approach. For convenience we denote the determinant of the tangent stiffness, $|\mathbf{K}_T|$, as Det. The determinant of the tangent stiffness is calculated at points to either side of the bifurcation point, including points $i$ and $i+1$. Figure 7.2$b$ shows the variation of Det with the load parameter $\lambda$. Det $> 0$ for $0 < \lambda < \lambda_{\mathrm{cr}}$, as at point $i$. Det $< 0$ for $\lambda > \lambda_{\mathrm{cr}}$, as in the case of point $i+1$.

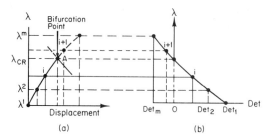

**FIG. 7.2**   Determination of a bifurcation point via interpolation.

If there are $m$ solution points, we can employ Lagrange interpolation to fit an $(m-1)\underline{\text{th}}$ polynomial through these points to give an expression for $\lambda$ in terms of Det. The bifurcation load is calculated by setting Det $= 0$ and solving for the associated value of the load intensity $\lambda_{\mathrm{cr}}$. The displacements and their derivatives at $\lambda_{\mathrm{cr}}$, needed for determination of the postbuckling path, may also be calculated by interpolation. These procedures are detailed in Ref. [14].

Alternative to the above is a procedure that creates an eigenvalue problem when a point just below the bifurcation point, such as point $i$ in Fig. 7.2, is reached [8, 15]. Designate the tangent stiffness and load parameter at point $i$ as $\mathbf{K}_T^i$ and $\lambda_i$. The load parameter is increased to $\lambda_{i+1}$, with stiffness $\mathbf{K}_T^{i+1}$. Denote $\delta\lambda = \lambda_{i+1} - \lambda_i$, $\delta\mathbf{K} = \mathbf{K}_T^{i+1} - \mathbf{K}_T^i$. If the tangent stiffness varies linearly in the interval $\delta\lambda$, with the critical value of the load parameter designated as $\lambda_{\mathrm{cr}}$, then

$$\mathbf{K}_T^{\mathrm{cr}} = \mathbf{K}_T^i - \frac{(\lambda_{\mathrm{cr}} - \lambda_i)}{\delta\lambda}\,\delta\mathbf{K} \tag{7.29}$$

and, multiplying through by $\delta\boldsymbol{\Delta}$ and noting that the tangent stiffness times the displacement at the limit point is zero,

$$\mathbf{K}_T^i \, \delta\boldsymbol{\Delta} - \frac{(\lambda_{cr} - \lambda_i)}{\delta\lambda} \, \delta\mathbf{K} \, \delta\boldsymbol{\Delta} = \mathbf{0} \tag{7.30}$$

or

$$\mathbf{K}_T^i - \omega \, \delta\mathbf{K} \, \delta\boldsymbol{\Delta} = \mathbf{0} \tag{7.31}$$

where

$$\omega = \frac{\lambda_{cr} - \lambda_1}{\delta\lambda} \tag{7.32}$$

This is an eigenvalue problem which can be solved by methods previously discussed.

## 7.4D Applications: Linear Eigenvalue Problems

To deal with applications one must introduce the specific assumptions of a class of structural behavior—beams, plates, or shells—into the general expressions previously presented. There is a very extensive literature on the instability analysis of structures composed of prismatic members (beams, frames, arches). The theory is presented in Refs. [16, 17]; finite-element applications are reviewed in Ref. [18]. We therefore discuss, in the following, applications of the finite-element method to flat and stiffened plates, flat-plate assemblies, and thin-shell instability analysis.

*Flat Plates*   The strain-energy expression for linearized elastic instability of flat plates is of the form

$$U = \frac{1}{2} \int_A \boldsymbol{\kappa}_f^T \mathbf{E}_f \boldsymbol{\kappa}_f \, dA + \frac{1}{2} \int_A N_x \left(\frac{\partial w}{\partial x}\right)^2 dA + \frac{1}{2} \int_A N_y \left(\frac{\partial w}{\partial y}\right)^2 dA$$

$$+ \int_A N_{xy} \left(\frac{\partial w}{\partial x}\right)\left(\frac{\partial w}{\partial y}\right) dA \tag{7.33}$$

where $w$ is the transverse displacement of the middle surface and $N_x$, $N_y$, and $N_{xy}$ are the known or otherwise calculated forces per unit length in the plate midsurface;

$$\boldsymbol{\kappa}_f = \left[\frac{\partial^2 w}{\partial x^2} \quad \frac{\partial^2 w}{\partial y^2} \quad 2\frac{\partial^2 w}{\partial x \, \partial y}\right]$$

$\mathbf{E}_f$ contains the plate flexural stiffness and material constants, and $A$ is the plate surface area.

The first integral in (7.33) is the usual expression for the flexural strain energy of thin plates and is the basis for the linear, stable stiffness matrix $\mathbf{K}_0$. The presence of second derivatives introduces the requirement that certain first derivatives, in particular the normal slope, be continuous across element interfaces. The next three integrals represent the instability effects and are the basis for the initial-stress stiffness matrix $\bar{\mathbf{K}}_1$. The extension of this formulation to geometrically nonlinear behavior leads to expressions which correspond to Von Karman's equations (see Ref. [19], pp. 415–420) and to the inclusion of the terms for the initial-displacement stiffness matrix.

The difficulty in the finite-element instability analysis of flat plates is in the choice of expressions which describe the transverse displacement ($w$) of the individual elements. The definition of functions which satisfy continuity of not only the transverse displacement itself, but also the slope continuity, has been the central problem.

This problem has not been difficult to solve for rectangles, however. The full product of the cubic function in the two perpendicular directions gives a 16-term "bicubic" function in $x$ and $y$. Considering a typical rectangle (Fig. 7.3), we see that at the four vertices there are three obvious displacements ($w, \partial w/\partial x, \partial w/\partial y$), for a total of 12 terms. To make up the total of 16 terms the usual approach taken is to introduce the twist derivative ($\partial^2 w/\partial x\, \partial y$) as a degree of freedom at each vertex. This gives accurate results for classical cases of buckling and nonlinear analysis [20–22], but the twist derivative is awkward to handle in many practical situations.

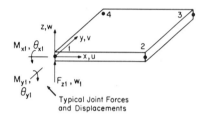

**FIG. 7.3**   Rectangular plate-bending element.

The triangle is the desired shape of element for geometric representation of practical structures, but the identification of displacement descriptions that are continuous across element interfaces, especially the normal slope ($\partial w/\partial n$), has not been easy. A quintic polynomial serves this purpose, but it contains 21 terms and the degrees of freedom of the corresponding element include all the second derivatives. This element is rarely used in practical computations. Fourth-order complete polynomials lack continuity of slope across element interfaces and also require many degrees of freedom (15).

Representation by means of third-order polynomials appears desirable because of the correspondence with beam flexure. It would also be desirable to represent the element in terms of a transverse displacement and two rotations at each vertex—9 degrees of freedom. A complete third-order polynomial has 10 terms, which seemingly presents no difficulties because the tenth term can be eliminated through algebraic operations, but it is unsatisfactory owing to a severe lack of slope continuity across element interfaces. Many special schemes have been proposed to define approximating functions of third order, and the most popular of these have been due to Bazeley, Cheung, Irons, and Zienkiewicz (for details, see Ref. [23]), a modification of such a function proposed in Ref. [24], and a formulation by Clough and Tocher [25]. Plate-buckling applications for these formulations are given in Ref. [26].

More recently, the entire issue of formulations for triangular-bending elements was given an extensive assessment by Batoz et al. [27]. They found that the elements of Refs. [23, 25] sustain a severe loss of accuracy, compared with equilateral triangles or 45° right triangles, when they are elongated. They also demonstrated that simple, reliable formulations for the triangle in bending can be established by use of discrete Kirchhoff concepts. A description of these concepts is beyond the scope of the present review, but it suffices to say that they result in an element stiffness matrix of conventional format, expressed in terms of the joint displacements of Fig. 7.4. Indeed, an explicit formulation of the discrete Kirchhoff formulation is available [28]. Results for plate-buckling problems have not yet appeared for this scheme.

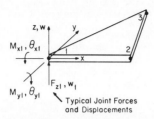

**FIG. 7.4** Triangular plate-bending element.

A rather different approach to beam-, plate-, and shell-bending behavior has appeared widely in the finite-element literature in recent years. This invokes Reissner–Mindlin plate theory [29, 30], wherein flexural behavior is expressed in terms of rotations of the normals to the midplane and terms are included which account for transverse-shear deformation. The latter are written in terms of the transverse displacement. A detailed account and background of this approach, encompassing buckling and large-displacement solutions, have been published by Pica et al. [31]. In general, such formulations do not converge to the correct solutions in the case of extreme thinness; the source of this difficulty is explained in Ref. [32]. The problem has been solved for a thin rectangular element in Ref. [33]. It appears that most Reissner–Mindlin formulations, for practical width/thickness ratios, are not adversely affected.

***Stiffened Flat Plates***   The most efficient form of construction of flat plates to resist buckling loads involves stiffeners. The finite-element method appears to be ideally suited to this class of problem because of its facility in the combination of different types of elements. Yet the combination of plate-bending elements and beam elements (for the stiffeners) is not always convenient. The beam element is based upon a cubic polynomial, but as explained in the previous section, not all the plate-bending elements are based on cubics. When the stiffener and plate-element displacements are consistent, care must be exercised in accounting for the eccentricity of the axis of the stiffeners and the middle surface of the plate [34].

Finite-element, stiffened-plate-buckling analyses are reported in Refs. [35, 36]. Hagedoorn [37] gives a thorough review of the topic, details of representation of stiffener eccentricity, and numerical comparisons of the finite-element approach, classical solutions for discretely stiffened plates, and solutions for "smeared" representation of the stiffeners.

***Flat-Plate Assemblies***   Flat-plate elements have been employed as the basic components of finite-element representations in the instability analysis of rolled and formed thin-walled structural members, such as I-beams and channels. Plate elements can also be employed to model stiffeners, an alternative to modeling them with beam elements. This requires that the finite-element representation of plate bending be combined with element representations of plane-stress conditions. Since the overall structural forms usually consist of rectangular segments, the finite elements can be rectangular and there is no difficulty in constructing a satisfactory analytical model with available element formulations. Akay, Johnson, and Will [38] describe analyses of thin-walled beams and frames modeled entirely with triangular flat-plate elements. Some background on finite-element representations of similar problems is found in their work.

An approach related to the finite-element method, known as the *finite-strip method*, has also been employed in this class of problem [39–41]. This involves the use of a series representation, or classical solution, in one direction and a finite-element discretization in the other direction. The former reduces the number of required elements and, therefore, the cost of solution.

***Shell Buckling*** Three popular approaches to finite-element analysis of curved thin-shell structures are (1) by means of three-dimensional (solid) elements with curved boundaries, (2) in "faceted" form with flat elements, and (3) via elements formulated on the basis of curved-shell theory.

An appeal of solid elements is that they stem directly from three-dimensional theory of elasticity. The curved boundaries are easily defined through use of "isoparametric" curvilinear coordinates, which employ the same form of description for both geometry and displacement. Conditions of the Love-Kirchhoff type are imposed, but this is insufficient to achieve economical solutions; it is necessary either to introduce certain supplementary displacement modes to describe bending action [42] or to deemphasize the representation of shear deformation by approximation (reduced numerical integration) of the shear-strain energy [43]. There has not been sufficient development of the nonlinear-analysis side of this approach to measure its effectiveness in thin-shell stability analysis.

The use of flat-plate elements is appealing in its simplicity. Among the objections to this approach, however, are the following: (1) it excludes coupling of stretching and bending within the element; (2) only triangular elements can be employed when general shells are to be handled; (3) it is difficult to treat junctions where all elements meeting at the point are coplanar; (4) the presence of "discontinuous" bending moments at element-juncture lines, which do not appear in the continuously curved actual structure, complicate the analysis; and (5) for stability analysis the geometric approximation influences the solution for imperfection-sensitive structures. We might add the problems of definition of displacement fields which meet interelement-continuity conditions, discussed already for flat elements, but these are even more serious for curved elements.

Flat finite elements represent the behavior of curved structures in the limit, and the errors due to objection 1 above can be made small by use of a refined element network. Nearly all finite-element programs suitable for stability analysis will contain triangles so that objection 2 is not so serious. In objection 3, coplanarity, a null stiffness corresponding to rotation about the axis normal to the plane, will be present, but steps can always be taken to identify and resolve the problem. Use of flat elements was one of the earliest approaches in finite-element thin-shell instability analysis [44], and it has been the basis of more recent investigations [45, 46].

The formulation and practical utilization of curved thin-shell finite elements raise a number of significant issues. Adequate means must be found for input of the structural and element geometry in curvilinear coordinates. It is difficult to establish a general procedure, although advances in interactive computer graphics give a comprehensive solution when the necessary equipment is available [47]. A satisfactory shell theory must be chosen; this has posed unresolved questions until relatively recently. Proper accounting for nonlinear terms is of particular importance [48]. Moreover, conditions basic to finite-element modeling that must be satisfied in the choice of approximating functions have proved difficult to meet. One challenging problem, for example, is to devise assumed displacement functions which give zero strain under rigid-body motion of the element. Also, in the presence of nonlinear strain-displacement relationships, the assumed displacements of linear flat-plate elements will generally not meet the conditions for convergence of finite-element solutions [49, 50]. Such functions are widely used as the basis for curved elements.

Formulations up through 1976 for curved thin-shell elements are reviewed in Ref. [51]. A number of developments have appeared since then. Many of the published thin-shell elements have been formulated to account for elastic instability and geometrically nonlinear behavior and applied to a wide variety of shell-buckling problems. Reference [7] reviews finite-element shell-buckling contributions (see also Refs. [52, 53]). A number of widely distributed finite-element programs also contain curved thin-shell elements which have been applied extensively to practical problems of shell instability.

A special type of thin-shell finite element is the axisymmetric element, which is useful for the analysis of shells of revolution. Application of this type of element to buckling problems is described in Ref. [54].

## 7.5 LIMIT-POINT BEHAVIOR

As Fig. 7.1b discloses, loss of stability, or snap-through, might occur at a "limit point," following a nonlinear load-displacement path. The limit-point phenomenon is far more prevalent than bifurcation and needs to be studied in its own right. Also, in considering postbuckling behavior, it is necessary to examine methods of tracing the load-displacement behavior across the limit point.

The tracing of load-displacement behavior across limit points is an aspect of the general problem of geometrically nonlinear analysis. It is characterized by the singularity of the tangent-stiffness matrix at the limit point. As we have already noted, close to that point the tangent-stiffness matrix is nearly singular. Consequently, simple incrementation of load results in an extremely large displacement and, by itself, is not a workable approach.

Many techniques have been proposed to deal with this problem. A review of developments up to 1972 was presented by Gallagher [55]. In 1980, Ramm [58] gave a critical review of techniques for identifying and crossing over limit points, including numerical comparisons; his review provides a framework for the following.

### 7.5A Suppression of Equilibrium Iterations

The *current-stiffness parameter* $(S_p)$ is a device introduced by Bergan et al. [56] as a means of controlling and rationally selecting step sizes in nonlinear finite-element analysis. This parameter is a key aspect of their approach to traveling over a limit point, which has also been characterized as the method of "suppression of equilibrium iterations."

The current-stiffness parameter is defined as follows:

$$S_p = \frac{\dot{\boldsymbol{\Delta}}_0^T \hat{\mathbf{P}}}{\dot{\boldsymbol{\Delta}}^T \hat{\mathbf{P}}} \tag{7.34}$$

where $\dot{\boldsymbol{\Delta}}_0^T$ is the rate of change of the displacements in the initial state with respect to load parameter $\boldsymbol{\lambda}$, and $\dot{\boldsymbol{\Delta}}^T$ is the rate at the current point on the load-displacement path. $\hat{\mathbf{P}}$, as before, is the reference load vector. Thus, $S_p$ is unity at the origin, it is less than unity if the system becomes "softer," and it is zero at the limit point. In an incremental-solution process with proportional loading it can be shown that

$$S_p = \left(\frac{\delta\lambda}{\delta\lambda_1}\right)^2 \frac{\delta\boldsymbol{\Delta}^1 \, \mathbf{K}_T^1 \, \delta\boldsymbol{\Delta}^1}{\delta\boldsymbol{\Delta}^j \, \mathbf{K}_T^i \, \delta\boldsymbol{\Delta}^j} \tag{7.35}$$

where the superscript 1 refers to the first increment and $j$ is the $j^{\text{th}}$, or current, increment.

The method of crossing the limit point proposed in Ref. [56] is as follows. At a point at which the prescribed value of the current-stiffness parameter (e.g., point $i$ in Fig. 7.5), is regarded as low enough to represent the imminence of a limit point, iterations within a load increment are discontinued because such iterations usually break down in the vicinity of the limit point. A single-step incremental analysis is performed, as between $i$ and $i+1$. If, at point $i+1$, the euclidian norm of displacement changes because the increment $\|\delta\boldsymbol{\Delta}\|$ exceeds a prescribed limit, they are linearly scaled back to an intermediate point.

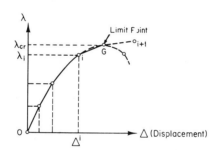

**FIG. 7.5**   Method of suppression of equilibrium iterations.

When negative diagonal elements in the tangent stiffness are detected, negative load increments are applied. Iteration within an increment is resumed when $S_p$ again reaches the prescribed value. The limit point $(G)$ is identified by interpolation of $S_p$ between this point and point $i$. This scheme generally requires the use of small load increments between the points at which $S_p$ is of the prescribed value.

## 7.5B Displacement Incrementation via Partitioning of the Tangent Stiffness

The most apparent approach to guiding the load-displacement response over a limit point is to increment a displacement component rather than the load parameter. To describe this we write the tangent-stiffness equations, for a point near the limit load, in the partitioned form (for simplicity we drop the subscript $T$ on the stiffness terms):

$$\begin{bmatrix} \mathbf{K}_{11} & \mathbf{K}_{12} \\ \mathbf{K}_{21} & \mathbf{K}_{22} \end{bmatrix} \begin{bmatrix} \delta\mathbf{\Delta}_1 \\ \delta\mathbf{\Delta}_2 \end{bmatrix} = \delta\lambda \begin{bmatrix} \hat{\mathbf{P}}_1 \\ \hat{\mathbf{P}}_2 \end{bmatrix} \tag{7.36}$$

where $\delta\mathbf{\Delta}_2$ is a *single* displacement component and $\delta\mathbf{\Delta}_1$ contains all the remaining degrees of freedom. The idea is to increment $\delta\mathbf{\Delta}_2$, and with this in mind the load vector and the final column of the stiffness equations are interchanged. This gives

$$\begin{bmatrix} \mathbf{K}_{11} & \hat{\mathbf{P}}_1 \\ \mathbf{K}_{21} & \hat{\mathbf{P}}_2 \end{bmatrix} \begin{bmatrix} \delta\mathbf{\Delta}_1 \\ \delta\lambda \end{bmatrix} = \delta\mathbf{\Delta}_2 \begin{bmatrix} \mathbf{K}_{12} \\ \mathbf{K}_{22} \end{bmatrix} \tag{7.37}$$

The equations on the left-hand side are unsymmetric. From a practical standpoint this problem can be avoided as follows. Solving the top partition,

$$\delta\mathbf{\Delta}_1 = \delta\mathbf{\Delta}_2 \cdot \mathbf{K}_{11}^{-1} \cdot \mathbf{K}_{12} - \delta\lambda \cdot \mathbf{K}_{11}^{-1} \cdot \mathbf{P}_1$$

and, from the bottom partition, after substitutions,

$$\delta\lambda = \frac{[\mathbf{K}_{22} - \mathbf{K}_{21}\,\mathbf{K}_{11}^{-1}\,\mathbf{K}_{12}]}{\mathbf{P}_2 - \mathbf{K}_{21}\,\mathbf{K}_{11}\,\mathbf{P}_1} \,\delta\mathbf{\Delta}_2 \tag{7.38}$$

The chosen displacement increment $\delta\mathbf{\Delta}_2$ can now be used to calculate the corresponding load increment $\delta\lambda$. With $\delta\lambda$ known the top partition can be written as

$$\mathbf{K}_{11}\delta\mathbf{\Delta}_1 = \delta\mathbf{\Delta}_2\mathbf{K}_{12} + \delta\lambda\,\mathbf{P}_1$$

One can solve this for $\delta\mathbf{\Delta}_1$; $\mathbf{K}_{11}$ is symmetric.

As we have already noted, when a load-displacement path is traced numerically and a solution point associated with a certain load level has been reached, the point will generally not correspond to the exact solution for that load level. Thus, for load level $\lambda_i$, with the displacement solution $\mathbf{\Delta}^i$, substitution of the latter into the left-hand side of the equilibrium equations [Eq. (7.17)] will yield an "out-of-balance" force vector $\mathbf{R}$. If we consider now an incremental analysis from load intensity $i$ to $i+1$, the incremental equations [previously given as (7.19)] are written as

$$\mathbf{K}_T\,\delta\mathbf{\Delta}^{i+1} = \delta\lambda_{i+1}\hat{\mathbf{P}} - \mathbf{R}^i \tag{7.39}$$

Equation (7.38), and other developments discussed here for limit-point calculation, can be readily modified to account for the out-of-balance force.

A severe disadvantage of the above approach is the algebraic effort required to partition the basic stiffness matrix and to perform the operations on the submatrices $\mathbf{K}_{11}$, $\mathbf{K}_{12}$, etc. The techniques to be discussed subsequently avoid this problem.

Before the latter are examined it is pertinent to observe that a limit point represents a rank deficiency of at least 1 in the tangent-stiffness matrix. Thus, the above scheme can be viewed as a method of isolation of one degree of freedom so as to remove this rank deficiency.

If there is a greater rank deficiency, a corresponding number of degrees of freedom can be isolated in $\boldsymbol{\Delta}_2$.

Steps can be taken to handle rank deficiency by use of other artifices. Sharifi and Popov [57] and Ramm [58] propose the introduction of an artificial spring for this purpose. Although this idea has worked for a number of specific problems, there is no unified approach to the selection of the spring constant and the method has not been viewed favorably in subsequent assessments. Another scheme is to perform a transient analysis [59]. The combination of the elastic restoring force and the inertial force involves a combination of matrices (stiffness and mass) that is, taken together, nonsingular. One can therefore march in time across the limit point, using standard methods of numerical integration in time, e.g., with use of Newmark's method.

## 7.5c  Displacement Incrementation without Partitioning of the Tangent Stiffness

Powell and Simons [60] have developed an approach to the iterative solution of nonlinear structures which carries the load-displacement behavior across limit points without disrupting the structure of the tangent-stiffness equations and which is effective in a wide variety of problems. It is a generalization of approaches taken by Haisler and Stricklin [61], Batoz and Dhatt [62], and Bergan et al. [56], to mention a few.

In this scheme two displacement components are calculated for an iteration within a load increment:

1. The displacement change due to the unbalanced loads associated with the solution from the prior increment:

$$\delta\boldsymbol{\Delta}_u = \mathbf{K}_T^{-1}\mathbf{R} \qquad (7.40)$$

2. The displacement change due to the reference load increment, $\delta\lambda\hat{\mathbf{P}}$:

$$\delta\boldsymbol{\Delta}_e = \delta\lambda\,\mathbf{K}_T^{-1}\hat{\mathbf{P}} \qquad (7.41)$$

The displacement increment $\delta\boldsymbol{\Delta}$ for the iteration is chosen to be a linear combination of the above two increments

$$\delta\boldsymbol{\Delta} = \alpha_u\delta\boldsymbol{\Delta}_u + \alpha_e\delta\boldsymbol{\Delta}_e \qquad (7.42)$$

where $\alpha_u$ and $\alpha_e$ are determined according to certain criteria.

Consider, for example, the imposition of the entire load unbalance in each iteration ($\alpha_u = 1$). For a specified displacement increment $\delta\bar{\Delta}_n$ in the $n^{\text{th}}$ degree of freedom, we have

$$\delta\bar{\Delta}_n = \delta\Delta_{u_n} + \alpha_e\delta\Delta_{e_n}$$

so that

$$\alpha_e = \frac{\delta\bar{\Delta}_n - \delta\Delta_{u_n}}{\delta\Delta_{e_n}} \qquad (7.43)$$

When this is substituted into (7.42), with $\alpha_u = 1$, the remaining displacement changes can be determined. These changes are used to calculate new $\mathbf{R}$, $\delta\boldsymbol{\Delta}_u$, and $\alpha_e$ in the subsequent iteration.

A number of criteria for the selection of $\alpha_u$ and $\alpha_e$ are described in Ref. [60].

### 7.5D Arc-Length Methods

Riks [63] and Wempner [64] have devised a scheme for the control of iterations in a nonlinear finite-element analysis which, in its simplest form, involves moving in constant arc lengths ($ds$) along the load-displacement path. In this approach the load step $\delta\lambda$ is constrained by the condition

$$\delta\boldsymbol{\Delta}^T\delta\boldsymbol{\Delta}+(\delta\lambda)^2=(ds)^2 \tag{7.44}$$

where $ds$ is the arc length. The implementation of this constraint, in the indicated format, introduces into the numerical analysis a number of undesirable complications. Crisfield [65, 66] and Wessels [67] have modified this approach in a manner such that these complications are circumvented. Studies based on numerical analysis of a variety of problems by Ramm [58] and Hinton and Lo [68] indicate that this approach is superior.

## 7.6  POSTBUCKLING ANALYSIS

### 7.6A Properties of the Critical Point

If buckling occurs at a limit point, the procedures described in the previous section are capable of utilization in the calculation of postbuckling response. The procedures for tracing postbuckling behavior beyond the critical point for bifurcation are more complicated on account of the discontinuity of the load-displacement path. Tracing of the postbuckling path beyond the critical point requires removal of the prebuckling behavior from the analytical equations.

Certain properties of the buckling state are pertinent to the following discussion. It has already been emphasized that the determinant of the tangent-stiffness matrix is zero, i.e., $|\mathbf{K}_T| = 0$. Also, for a single postbuckling path the tangent-stiffness matrix has a rank deficiency of 1. The latter property can be defined most conveniently in algebraic terms if the tangent-stiffness matrix is diagonalized. Thus, a modal matrix is formed, consisting of the eigenvectors of $\mathbf{K}_T$; denote this as $\mathbf{a}$, where an individual eigenvector is $\mathbf{a}^r$. The corresponding vector of generalized coordinates is $\mathbf{q}$. Applying the transformation to (7.19) results in

$$\bar{\mathbf{K}}_T\mathbf{q}=\dot{\lambda}\bar{\mathbf{P}} \tag{7.45}$$

where the diagonalized tangent-stiffness terms $\bar{K}_{T_{ij}} = \bar{K}_{T_{mn}}a_{mi}a_{nj}$ and the transformed load-vector component is $\bar{P}_i = \hat{P}_m a_{mi}$. Also, $\delta\lambda = \dot{\lambda}$ at the buckling point. Expanding (7.45) we obtain

$$\begin{bmatrix} \bar{K}_{T_{11}} & & \\ & \bar{K}_{T_{ii}} & \\ & & \bar{K}_{T_{nn}} \end{bmatrix}\begin{bmatrix} \dot{q}_1 \\ \dot{a}_i \\ \dot{q}_n \end{bmatrix}=\dot{\lambda}\begin{bmatrix} \bar{P}_1 \\ \bar{P}_i \\ \bar{P}_n \end{bmatrix} \tag{7.46}$$

The modal matrix is the basis of the transformation $\delta\Delta = \mathbf{aq}$. Now, since $\mathbf{K}_T$ has a rank deficiency of 1, one of the coefficients, $\bar{K}_{T_{11}}$, equals zero. If we choose this to be $\bar{K}_{T_{11}}$, it follows that $\dot{\lambda}\bar{P}_1 = 0$. If $\bar{P}_1 \neq 0$, then $\dot{\lambda} = 0$ and we have a limit-point situation. If $\bar{P}_1 = 0$, then $\dot{\lambda}$ is not necessarily zero and the condition of a bifurcation point prevails; this corresponds to the condition that the buckling mode is orthogonal to the loading ($a_{1i}P_i = 0$).

## 7.6B  Perturbation Method

The perturbation method has been the most widely used approach in classical studies of postbuckling behavior. There are many variants on the finite-element implementation of the perturbation method in postbuckling analysis. The one that is described here was employed by Thompson [69] and was developed further by Mau and Gallagher [70, 71]. Consider the load-displacement path for a single degree of freedom, portrayed in Fig. 7.6. Displacements

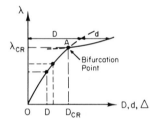

**FIG. 7.6**   Displacement coordinates for perturbation analysis.

on the prebuckling (fundamental) path are denoted by $D$, and the total displacement is given by $\Delta$. Thus,

$$\Delta = D + d \tag{7.47}$$

and the displacements along the postbuckling path, measured from the fundamental path, are denoted by $d$. The latter is expanded in polynomial series in terms of the path parameter $s$:

$$d_i = \dot{\Delta}_i s + \tfrac{1}{2}\ddot{\Delta}_i s^2 + \tfrac{1}{6}\dddot{\Delta}_i s^3 + \cdots \tag{7.48}$$

where an overdot signifies differentiation with respect to $s$. Similarly, the fundamental path is described by a series expansion.

$$D_i = D_i^c + (\lambda - \lambda_{cr})D_i^{c'} + \tfrac{1}{2}(\lambda - \lambda_{cr})^2 D_i^{c''} + \cdots \tag{7.49}$$

and, for the load parameter,

$$\lambda - \lambda_{cr} = \Gamma_1(\Delta_1) + \Gamma_2(\Delta_1)^2 + \Gamma_3(\Delta_1)^2 + \cdots \tag{7.50}$$

where the multipliers $\Gamma_1$, $\Gamma_2$, $\Gamma_3$, etc., are to be determined.

   If Eqs. (7.47) to (7.50), written for the full vectors of displacements, are substituted into Eq. (7.11), and the various terms are collected in like powers of $s$, one obtains, after use of the stationary-potential-energy principle,

$$K_{T_{jk}} \dot{\Delta}_i = 0 \tag{7.51}$$

and subsequent equations with the lead terms $K_{T_{ij}} \ddot{\Delta}_i$, etc. Equation (7.51) is first solved as an eigenvalue problem, with the terms in $\Delta_i$ referenced to $\Delta_1$. Then, with $\dot{\Delta}$ as a known, the subsequent equation is solved for $\Gamma_1$. Solution of the succeeding equations enables calculation of $\Gamma_2$, $\Gamma_3$, etc.

Connor and Morin [72] cover in detail most of the aspects of a general finite-element perturbation theory, as presented herein. Mau and Gallagher [70] also proposed an approach which covers all regimes of load-displacement response. Numerical solutions are given for a beam on an elastic foundation, a shallow arch, and a flat plate.

Mallett and Haftka [73] developed Koiter-type perturbation analysis in terms of finite-element (discrete) variables. As in the work of Lang and Hartz [74] the notion of a linear prebuckling state is preserved, but by modifying the energy functional of structures evidencing limit-point critical behavior a hypothetical "modified structure" with bifurcational buckling characteristics is created. Ecer [75] develops a thorough exposition of the perturbation approach in nonlinear structural mechanics and has applied his approach to the analysis of the postbuckling behavior of arches, the Euler column, and a rectangular plate that is analytically modeled with use of triangular finite elements. A study of the effect of neglecting various higher-order terms in the nonlinear stiffness equations is included. The numerical results demonstrate that acceptable solutions can be achieved with such simplifications.

Hangai and Kawamata [76] give one of the most thorough and lucid formulations of the static perturbation method for the full regime of load-displacement response. The numerical examples in Ref. [76] pertain to reticulated domes comprised of one-dimensional members. The critical behavior of this structural form under different systems of load and distribution of geometric imperfections is studied in detail.

Endo, Kawamata, and Hangai [77] adopt the perturbation approach in the problem of the critical behavior of shallow spherical shells under uniform pressure. The finite-element description of the structure consists of conical frusta whose assumed displacement fields are expanded in circumferential harmonics. This enables the distinction between asymmetric and axisymmetric algebraic representations of the structure. Since, in this case, asymmetric behavior corresponds to bifurcational buckling and axisymmetric behavior gives a limit-point phenomenon, the numerical solutions for both types of points are facilitated.

### 7.6c  Simplified Approach

Care et al. [78] have proposed a simple approach to postbuckling analysis. They recommend that a constraint condition be written and enforced upon the basic nonlinear (equilibrium) equations such that the component of displacement in the direction of the prebuckling (trivial) solution is zero. The proposed constraint is

$$\Delta^T G \Delta - \beta^2 = 0 \tag{7.52}$$

where $\beta$ is a preselected constant and the metric matrix $G$ is chosen to achieve the above-stated objective. The method of Lagrange multipliers is employed to enforce this constraint. Details of an approach to the construction of $G$ are given in Ref. [78].

## 7.7 REDUCED-BASIS TECHNIQUES

The idea of a reduced-basis technique is to supplant the vector of unknowns with a smaller (hopefully, much smaller) vector of surrogate unknowns, the "reduced basis." We will designate the latter as $\mathbf{Q}$. Thus, the following transformation must be created

$$\mathbf{\Delta} = \mathbf{\Gamma Q} \tag{7.53}$$

or

$$\mathbf{a} = \mathbf{\Gamma Q} \tag{7.54}$$

if the transformation is to be applied to the linearized buckling problem, Eq. (7.25). $\mathbf{\Gamma}$ will be referred to simply as the *transformation matrix* and its columns as the *basis vectors*.

Historically, most of the attention that has been drawn to reduced-basis techniques has been in the context of dynamic analysis [81–83]. As noted already, the algebraic format of the equations to be solved for instability and vibrational-frequency analysis is the same. The fact that only one buckling value (the lowest) is customarily required, while many frequencies are usually sought, has a major impact on the relative utility of reduced-basis approaches for the two problems. The operations associated with creation and utilization of the reduced basis have an associated cost that might not be recaptured in savings in the calculation of only one eigenvalue and eigenvector.

On the other hand, if the objective is general nonlinear analysis, including postbuckling, the use of a reduced basis might have the same payoff as dynamic analysis. Here, however, the detailed character of the component matrices is different, and an approach that is especially oriented toward the geometrically nonlinear problem is required.

Consider first the approach known as *Guyan reduction* [79]. We discuss it in terms of a linear stiffness analysis. The vector of unknowns must first be partitioned into the group which is to be removed ($\mathbf{\Delta}_r$) and the group which is to be kept ($\mathbf{\Delta}_k$); that is,

$$\mathbf{\Delta} = \begin{bmatrix} \mathbf{\Delta}_k \\ \mathbf{\Delta}_r \end{bmatrix}$$

Consider now the linear-stable stiffness equations with the loads set to zero:

$$\begin{bmatrix} \mathbf{K}_{kk} & \mathbf{K}_{kr} \\ \mathbf{K}_{rk} & \mathbf{K}_{rr} \end{bmatrix} \begin{bmatrix} \mathbf{\Delta}_k \\ \mathbf{\Delta}_r \end{bmatrix} = \begin{bmatrix} \mathbf{0} \\ \mathbf{0} \end{bmatrix} \tag{7.55}$$

By solving the lower partition for $\mathbf{\Delta}_r$ and substituting into the top equation, one can obtain the reduced stiffness equations

$$\mathbf{P}_k = [\mathbf{K}_{kk} - \mathbf{K}_{kr} \, \mathbf{K}_{rr}^{-1} \, \mathbf{K}_{rk}] \, \mathbf{\Delta}_k \tag{7.56}$$

It is easy to show that this is obtainable by use of the transformation

$$\begin{bmatrix} \mathbf{\Delta}_k \\ \mathbf{\Delta}_r \end{bmatrix} = \begin{bmatrix} \mathbf{I} \\ \mathbf{K}_{rr}^{-1} \, \mathbf{K}_{rk} \end{bmatrix} [\mathbf{\Delta}_k] \tag{7.57}$$

The matrix on the right is the desired transformation, $\mathbf{\Gamma}$. This same transformation can be used in elastic-instability analysis in Eq. (7.25).

It should be noted that a transformation matrix of this type can be established by using, as columns, equilibrium solutions to the stiffness equations. Thus, the series of solutions from a succession of nonlinear analyses could be employed.

The key issue is the selection of the degrees of freedom to be removed, $\Delta_r$. Instability problems pertain to structures in which bending is present, and these are described, for the most part, in terms of spatial $(u, v, w)$ and rotational $(\theta_x, \theta_y, \theta_z)$ degrees of freedom. It is usually possible to remove all but the spatial degrees of freedom. Selective removal of the latter is also possible. In all, some 90% of the basic degrees of freedom can often be removed without significant loss of accuracy; numerical evidence is given in Ref. [80].

Considerable study has been given to reduced-basis techniques for nonlinear, and therefore postbuckling, analysis. Besseling [84] and Nagy [85] have used linear-bifurcation modes to construct the basis vectors of $\Gamma$. Almroth et al. [86] use the linear solution and corrections to it as basis vectors.

More recently, Noor and Peters [87, 88] devised an alternative approach. They list four desirable qualities of basis vectors:

1. Linear independence and completeness.
2. Low cost of generation and simplicity of selection of their number.
3. High accuracy of solution for a large interval of the solution path.
4. Simplicity of tracing the postbuckling or post-limit-point behavior.

With these in mind they choose the vectors of the perturbation approach, i.e., the solution vector $\Delta$ and its derivatives $\dot{\Delta}, \ddot{\Delta}, \ldots$, with respect to the path parameters (see Sec. 7.6B). They give results of extensive numerical experimentation using this approach.

## 7.8 REFERENCES

1. Murray, D. W., and S. Rajasekaran, "Technique for Formulating Beam Equations," *Proc. ASCE J. Eng. Mech. Div.*, **101**(EM5):561–573 (October 1975).
2. Wood, R. D., and B. Schreffler, "Geometrically Nonlinear Analysis—A Correlation of Finite Element Notations," *Int. J. Numer. Meth. Eng.*, **12**(4):635–642 (1978).
3. Carey, G., "A Unified Approach to Three Finite Element Theories for Geometric Nonlinearity," *Comput. Meth. Appl. Mech. Eng.*, **4**:69–79 (1974).
4. Jensen, P. S., "Eigenvector Algorithms for Structural Analysis," in S. Zamrik and D. Dietrich (eds.), *Pressure Vessels and Piping: Design Technology, 1982. A Decade of Progress*, American Society of Mechanical Engineers, New York, 1980.
5. Bathe, K. J., and E. L. Wilson, "Solution Methods for Eigenvalue Problems in Structural Mechanics," *Int. J. Numer. Meth. Eng.*, **6**:213–236 (1973).
6. Cedolin, L., and R. H. Gallagher, "A Frontal-Based Solver for Frequency Analysis," *Int. J. Numer. Meth. Eng.*, **12**:1659–1666 (1978).
7. Gallagher, R. H., "The Finite Element Method in Shell Stability Analysis," *Comput. Struct.*, **3**:543–547 (1973).
8. Kiciman, O., and E. Popov, "Post-Buckling Analysis of Cylindrical Shells," *Proc. ASCE J. Eng. Mech. Div.*, **EM4**:751–762 (August 1978).

9. Loganathan, K., S. Chang, R. H. Gallagher, and J. F. Abel, "Finite Element Representation and Pressure Stiffness in Shell Stability Analysis," *Int. J. Numer. Meth. Eng.*, **14**:1413–1420 (1979).

10. Hibbitt, H. D., "Some Follower Forces and Load Stiffness," *Int. J. Numer. Meth. Eng.*, **14**:937–941 (1979).

11. Argyris, J. H., and S. Symeonidis, "Nonlinear Finite Element Analysis of Elastic Systems under Nonconservative Loading—Natural Formulation," *Comput. Meth. Appl. Mech. Eng.*, **26**:75–123 (1981).

12. Chan, A. S. L., and A. Firmin, "The Analysis of Cooling Towers by the Matrix Finite Element Method, Part II," *Aero. J.*, **74**:971–982 (1970).

13. Mang, H., and R. H. Gallagher, "On the Unsymmetric Eigenvalue Problem for the Buckling of Shells Under Pressure Loading," *J. Appl. Mech.*, **50**:95–100 (1983).

14. Gallagher, R. H., S. Lien, and S. T. Mau, "Finite Element Plate and Shell Pre-and-Post Buckling Analysis," *Proceedings of Third Conference on Matrix Methods in Structural Mechanics*, Dayton, Ohio, 1971.

15. Dupuis, G., D. Pfaffinger, and P. V. Marcal, "Effective Use of the Incremental Stiffness Matrices in Nonlinear Geometric Analysis," Report No. N00014-00715, Brown University, Providence, R.I., September 1970.

16. Gallagher, R. H., "Finite Element Analysis of Stability Problems," in T. Galambos (ed.), *Guide to Stability Design Criteria for Metal Structures*, 4th ed., Wiley, New York, Chap. 21 (to appear).

17. Gallagher, R. H., *Finite Element Analysis; Fundamentals*, Prentice-Hall, Englewood Cliffs, N.J., 1975.

18. Cook, R. D., *Concepts and Applications of Finite Element Analysis*, 2d ed., Wiley, N.Y., 1981.

19. Timoshenko, S., and S. Woinowsky-Kreiger, *Theory of Plates and Shells*, 2d ed., McGraw-Hill, N.Y., 1959.

20. Carson, W., and R. E. Newton, "Plate Buckling Analysis Using a Fully Compatible Finite Element," *AIAA J.*, **7**(3):527–529 (March 1969).

21. Yang, H. T. Y., "Finite Displacement Plate Flexure by Use of Matrix Incremental Approach," *Int. J. Numer. Meth. Eng.*, **4**:415–432 (1972).

22. Anderson, R. G., B. Irons, and O. C. Zienkiewicz, "Vibration and Stability of Plates Using Finite Elements," *Int. J. Solids Struct.*, **4**:1031–1055 (1968).

23. Zienkiewicz, O. C., *The Finite Element Method*, 3d ed., McGraw-Hill, New York, 1977, pp. 241–244.

24. Razzaque, A., "Program for Triangular Bending Element with Derivative Smoothing," *Int. J. Numer. Meth. Eng.*, **5**:588–589 (1973).

25. Clough, R. W., and J. S. Tocher, "Finite Element Stiffness Matrices for Analysis of Plates in Bending," *Proc. Conf. Matrix Meth. Struct. Mech.*, AFFDL-TR 66–80, Wright-Patterson Air Force Base, Ohio, 1965.

26. Vos, R., and W. Vann, "A Finite Element Tensor Approach to Plate Buckling and Postbuckling," *Int. J. Numer. Meth. Eng.*, **5**:351–366 (1973).

27. Batoz, J. L., K.-J. Bathe, and L. W. Ho, "A Study of Three-Node Triangular Plate Bending Elements," *Int. J. Numer. Meth. Eng.*, **15**:1771–1812 (1980).

28. Batoz, J. L., "An Explicit Formulation for an Efficient Triangular Plate-Bending Element," *Int. J. Numer. Eng.*, **18**:1077–1090 (1982).

29. Reissner, E., "Effect of Transverse Shear Deformation on the Bending of Elastic Plates," *J. Appl. Mech. Trans. ASME*, **67**:A-69–A-77 (1945).

30. Mindlin, R. D., "Influence of Rotatory Inertia and Shear on a Flexural Motion of Isotropic Elastic Plates," *J. Appl. Mech.*, **18**:31–38 (1951).

31. Pica, A., and R. D. Wood, "Postbuckling Behavior of Plates and Shells Using a Mindlin Shallow Shell Formulation," *Comput. Struct.*, **12**:759–768 (1980).

32. Prathap, G., and G. R. Bhashyam, "Reduced Integration and the Shear-Flexible Element," *Int. J. Numer. Meth. Eng.*, **18**(2):195–210 (1982).

33. Hughes, T. J. R., and M. Cohen, "The 'Heterosis' Finite Element for Plate Bending," *Comput. Struct.*, **10**:445–450 (1979).

34. Miller, R. E., "Reduction of Error in Eccentric Beam Modelling," *Int. J. Numer. Meth. Eng.*, **15**:575–582 (1980).

35. Crisfield, M., "Large Deflection Elasto-Plastic Buckling Analysis of Eccentrically-Stiffened Plates Using Finite Elements," Trans. Road R & S Lab Report 725, 1976.

36. Allman, D., "Calculation of the Elastic Buckling Loads of Thin Flat Reinforced Plates Using Triangular Finite Elements," *Int. J. Numer. Meth. Eng.*, **9**:415–432 (1975).

37. Hagedoorn, A. H., "An Elastic Finite Element Analysis of the Buckling of Eccentrically Stiffened Plates and Shells, Ph.D. dissertation, Dept. of Structural Eng., Cornell University, Ithaca, N.Y., 1973.

38. Akay, H., C. P. Johnson, and K. M. Will, "Local and Lateral Buckling of Beams and Frames," *Proc. ASCE J. Struct. Div.*, **103**(9):1821–1832 (September 1977).

39. Kleiber, M., and A. Zacharski, "Numerical Analysis of Local Instabilities in Elastic and Elasto-Plastic Prismatic Plate Assemblies," *Comput. Meth. Appl. Mech. Eng.*, **31**:2 (1982).

40. Hancock, G., "Local, Distortional and Lateral Buckling of I-Beams," *Proc. ASCE J. Struct. Div.*, **104**(11):1787–1798 (November 1978).

41. Plank, R., and W. Wittrick, "Buckling Under Combined Loading of Thin-Flat-Walled Structures by a Complex Finite Strip Method," *Int. J. Numer. Meth. Eng.*, **8**:323–334 (1974).

42. Wood, R. D., "The Application of Finite Element Methods to Geometrically Nonlinear Finite Element Analysis," Ph.D. thesis, University of Wales, Swansea, 1973.

43. Hughes, T. J. R., W. Kanok-Nukulchai, and R. L. Taylor, "A Large Deformation Formulation for Shell Analysis by the Finite Element Method," *Comput. Struct.*, **13**:19–30 (1981).

44. Gallagher, R. H., R. A. Gellatly, R. H. Mallett, and J. Padlog, "A Discrete-Element Procedure for Thin Shell Instability Analysis," *AIAA J.*, **5**(1):138–144 (January 1967).

45. Horrigmoe, G., and P. Bergan, "Nonlinear Analysis of Free Form Flat Shells by Flat Finite Elements," *Comput. Meth. Appl. Mech. Eng.*, **16**:11–35 (1978).

46. Argyris, J., P. C. Dunne, G. A. Malejannakis, and E. Schelke, "A Simple Triangular Facet Shell Element with Application to Linear and Non-Linear Equilibrium and Elastic Stability Problems," *Comput. Meth. Appl. Mech. Eng.*, **11**:97–131 (1977).

47. Haber, R., and J. F. Abel, "Discrete Transfinite Mappings for the Description and Meshing of Three-Dimensional Surfaces Using Interactive Computer Graphics," *Int. J. Numer. Meth. Eng.*, **18**:41–66 (1982).

48. Batoz, J. L., "Curved Finite Elements and Shell Theories with Particular Reference to the Buckling of a Circular Arch," *Int. J. Numer. Meth. Eng.*, **14**:774–779 (1979).

49. Dawe, D. J., "A Finite Deflection Analysis of Shallow Arches by the Discrete Element Method," *Int. J. Numer. Meth. Eng.*, **3**:529–552 (1971).

50. Allman, D. J., "Improved Finite Element Model for Large Displacement Bending and Postbuckling Analysis of Thin Plates," *Int. J. Solids Struct.*, **18**(9):737–762 (1982).

51. Gallagher, R. H., "Shell Elements," *Proceedings of First World Conference on Finite Elements*, Bournemouth, England, 1975.

52. Kanodia, V., R. H. Gallagher, and H. Mang, "Instability Analysis of Torispherical Pressure Vessel Heads with Triangular Thin-Shell Finite Elements," *Trans. ASME Ser. J. J. Press. Vess. Tech.*, **99**:64–74 (1977).

53. Matsui, T., and O. Matsuoka, "A New Finite Element Scheme for Instability Analysis of Thin Shells," *Int. J. Numer. Meth. Eng.*, **10**:145–170 (1976).

54. Venkateswara Rao, G., S. Radhamohan, and I. S. Raju, "Reinvestigation of Buckling of Shells of Revolution by a Refined Finite Element," *AIAA J.*, **12**(1):100–101 (January 1974).

55. Gallagher, R. H., "Geometrically Nonlinear Finite Element Analysis," *Proc. Spec. Conf. Finite Element Meth. Civ. Eng.*, McGill University, Montreal, June 1972.

56. Bergan, P. G., G. Horrigmoe, B. Krakeland, and T. Soreide, "Solution Techniques for Non-Linear Finite Element Problems," *Int. J. Numer. Meth. Eng.*, **12**:1677–1696 (1973).

57. Sharifi, P., and E. Popov, "Non-Linear Buckling Analysis of Sandwich Arches," *Proc. ASCE J. Eng. Mech. Div.*, **97**(EM5):1397–1412 (October 1971).

58. Ramm, E., "Strategies for Tracing the Non-Linear Response Near Limit Points," in W. Wunderlich, E. Stein, and K.-J. Bathe (eds.), *Non-Linear Finite Element Analysis in Structural Mechanics*, Springer-Verlag, New York, 1981, pp. 63–89.

59. McNamara, J. F., "Solution Schemes for Problems of Nonlinear Structural Dynamics," *Trans. ASME J. Press. Vess. Tech.*, **96**:96–102 (1974).

60. Powell, G. H., and J. Simons, "Improved Iteration Strategy for Nonlinear Structures," *Int. J. Numer. Meth. Eng.*, **17**:1455–1467 (1981).

61. Haisler, W. E., and J. A. Stricklin, "Displacement Incrementation in Nonlinear Structure Analysis by the Self-Correcting Method," *Int. J. Numer. Meth. Eng.*, **11**:3–10 (1977).

62. Batoz, J. L., and G. Dhatt, "Incremental Displacement Algorithms for Nonlinear Problems," *Int. J. Numer. Meth. Eng.*, **14**:1262–1267 (1979).

63. Riks, E., "An Incremental Approach to the Solution of Snapping and Buckling Problems," *Int. J. Solids Struct.*, **15**:529–551 (1979).

64. Wempner, G. A., "Discrete Approximations Related to Nonlinear Theories of Solids," *Int. J. Solids Struct.*, **17**:1581–1599 (1971).

65. Crisfield, M. A., "Finite Element Analysis for Combined Material and Geometric Nonlinearities," in W. Wunderlich, E. Stein, and K.-J. Bathe (eds.), *Nonlinear Finite Element Analysis in Structural Mechanics*, Springer-Verlag, New York, 1981.

66. Crisfield, M. A., "A Fast Incremental/Iterative Solution Procedure that Handles 'Snap Through,'" *Symposium on Computer Methods in Nonlinear Structural and Solid Mechanics*, Washington, D.C., 1980.

67. Wessels, M. "Das Statische und Dynamische Durchschlagsproblem," Dissertation, TU Hannover, 1977.

68. Hinton, E., and C. S. Lo, "Large Deflection Analysis of Imperfect Mindlin Plates Using the Modified Riks Method," in J. R. Whiteman (ed.), *The Mathematics of Finite Elements and Applications IV*, MAFELAP 1981, Academic Press, New York, 1982.

69. Thompson, J. M. T., and G. W. Hunt, *A General Theory of Elastic Stability*, Wiley, London, 1973.

70. Mau, S. T., and R. H. Gallagher, *A Finite Element Procedure for Nonlinear Pre-buckling and Initial Postbuckling Analysis*, NASA CR-1936, National Aeronautics and Space Administration, January 1972.

71. Gallagher, R. H., "Perturbation Procedures in Nonlinear Finite Element Structural Analysis," J. T. Oden (ed.), *Computational Mechanics, Lecture Notes in Mathematics*, 461, Springer-Verlag, New York, 1974.

72. Connor, J. J., and N. Morin, "Perturbation Techniques in the Analysis of Geometrically Non-linear Shells," in B. Fraeijs de Veubeke (ed.), *High Speed Computing of Elastic Structures*, University of Liège, Liège, 1971, vol. 2, pp. 683–706.

73. Mallett, R. H., and R. T. Haftka, "Progress in Nonlinear Finite Element Analysis Using Asymptotic Solution Techniques," in J. T. Oden et al. (eds.), *Advances in Computational Methods in Structural Mechanics and Design*, UAH Press, University of Alabama, Huntsville, 1972, pp. 357–374.

74. Lang, T. E., and B. J. Hartz, "Finite Element Matrix Formulation of Post-Buckling Stability and Imperfection Sensitivity," in B. Fraeijs de Veubeke (ed.), *High Speed Computing of Elastic Structures*, University of Liège, Liège, 1971, vol. 2, pp. 727-758.

75. Ecer, A., "Finite Element Analysis of the Postbuckling Behavior of Structures," *AIAA J.*, **11**:1532-1538 (November 1973).

76. Hangai, Y., and S. Kawamata, "Perturbation Method in the Analysis of Geometrically Nonlinear and Stability Problems," in J. T. Oden et al. (eds.), *Advances in Computational Methods in Structural Mechanics and Design*, UAH Press, University of Alabama, Huntsville, 1972, pp. 473-492.

77. Endo, A., S. Kawamata, and Y. Hangai, "Post-Bifurcation Analysis of Shallow Spherical Shells Under Uniform Pressure," *Seisan-Kenkyu Inst. Ind. Sci. Univ. Tokyo*, **26**(10), October 1974.

78. Care, R. F., R. E. Lawther, and A. Kabaila, "Finite Element Post-Buckling Analysis for Frames," *Int. J. Numer. Meth. Eng.*, **11**(5):833-850 (1977).

79. Guyan, R., "Reduction of Stiffness and Mass Matrices," *AIAA J.*, **3**(2):380 (February 1965).

80. Gallagher, R. H., and H. T. Y. Yang, "Elastic Instability Predictions for Doubly Curved Shells," *Proc. Second Conf. Matrix Meth. Struct. Mech.*, AFFDL TR-68-150, Wright-Patterson Air Force Base, Ohio, 1968.

81. Henshall, R., and J. Ong, "Automatic Masters for Eigenvalue Economization," *Earthquake Eng. Struct. Dyn.*, **3**:131-140 (1975).

82. Shah, V. N., and M. Raymond, "Analytical Selection of Masters for the Reduced Eigenvalue Problem," *Int. J. Numer. Meth. Eng.*, **18**:89-98 (1980).

83. Gerardin, M., "Error Bounds for Eigenvalue Analysis by Elimination of Variables," *J. Sound Vibr.*, **19**:111-132 (1971).

84. Besseling, J. F., "Post-Buckling and Nonlinear Analysis by the Finite Element Method as a Supplement to a Linear Analysis," *ZAMM*, **55**(4):T3-16 (1975).

85. Nagy, D., "Modal Representation of Geometrically Nonlinear Behavior by the Finite Element Method," *Comput. Struct.*, **10**:683-688 (August 1979).

86. Almroth, B., P. Stern, and F. Brogan, "Automatic Choice of Global Shape Function in Structural Analysis," *AIAA J.*, **16**:525-528 (May 1978).

87. Noor, A. K., and J. M. Peters, "Reduced Basis Techniques for Nonlinear Analysis of Structures," *AIAA J.*, **18**(4):455-462 (April 1980).

88. Noor, A. K., and J. M. Peters, "Recent Advances in Reduction Methods for Instability Analysis of Structures," *Comput. Struct.*, **16**:67-80 (1983).

# CHAPTER 8
# TRANSIENT RESPONSE ANALYSIS

## 8.1 INTRODUCTION

The finite-element method may be considered a process of approximation to continuum problems using a vector $\boldsymbol{\phi} = \{\phi_i\}$ of parameters to be determined and prescribed trial (or shape) functions $\{N_i\}$. The continuum problem is generally defined in a domain $\Omega$ of independent variables with sufficient boundary conditions given on the boundaries $\Gamma$. In the early days, the finite-element method was applied only to the space coordinates, and the result was then a semidiscretization in which the parameters remained time-variable. This gave a system of ordinary differential equations for the parameters $\phi_i$ which was solved either analytically or by the use of finite-difference techniques. Clearly, however, the use of the finite-element discretization in the time domain also was an obvious extension, and this has been introduced as a practical possibility by Oden [1], Argyris and Sharpf [2], Fried [3], Zienkiewicz [4, 5], and others.

Two distinct classes of finite element in the time domain exist. In the first, the finite-element process is applied to the system of ordinary differential equations resulting from the semidiscretization. In the second, direct finite-element shape functions are defined in the space-time domain.

Unless the problem space boundary is changing with time, the combined space-time domain is *prismatic* and the expansions used for the combined shape functions can be written in a product form as

$$N(\mathbf{x}, t) = \bar{N}(\mathbf{x})\hat{N}(t) \tag{8.1}$$

If this is the case, both processes of discretization can be made identical, and hence it is always desirable to proceed from the partially discretized forms. Indeed the large part of this section will be concerned with such a two-stage process, starting from ordinary matrix differential equations of the form

$$\mathbf{C}\dot{\boldsymbol{\phi}} + \mathbf{K}\boldsymbol{\phi} + \mathbf{f} = 0 \tag{8.2}$$

or

$$\mathbf{M}\ddot{\boldsymbol{\phi}} + \mathbf{C}\dot{\boldsymbol{\phi}} + \mathbf{K}\boldsymbol{\phi} + \mathbf{f} = 0 \tag{8.3}$$

The first of these equations arises from such problems as heat transfer, seepage, etc., by a semidiscretization of the relevant partial differential equations. The second is typical of dynamic behavior of solids. In all of the above equations, it is not essential to use the finite-element discretization in the space variables. Other legitimate approximations can be introduced, or indeed Eq. (8.2) or (8.3) may model a physically discrete situation.

On some occasions, such as those which may arise in the thermal behavior of ablating structures, the boundary-space surface may change with time and *nonprismatic* space-time elements may be desirable. Indeed this situation is encountered in a formulation of convective-diffusion heat-flow problems which utilizes the characteristic directions. We shall discuss this in a later section of this chapter in a general context. A particularly interesting application of this kind was recently introduced by Finn and Varoglu [6, 7].

In what follows we shall usually use a *weighted-residual*, or *Galerkin*, form of discretization. This allows us to obtain the more usual forms of finite-element approximation resulting from the stationariness of a specified functional as a special case. Other more interesting approximations will differ from such special cases when the weighting functions are not the same as the trial-function basis. Here we shall rediscover many standard finite-difference, alternatively derived, recurrence formulae. Indeed the process of applying finite elements in the time domain appears to encompass all alternative processes of time discretization and in addition brings up many new and interesting possibilities.

The notation and theoretical basis will mainly follow Zienkiewicz's text [8], but some more mathematical proofs may be found in other sources such as the excellent treatise by Strang and Fix [9].

## 8.2 SIMPLE ONE-STEP RECURRENCE RELATIONS FOR FIRST-ORDER EQUATIONS

### 8.2A Weighted-Residual Approach

Here we consider the first-order Eq. (8.2) and show how a simple recurrence scheme can be devised.

Proceeding in the usual manner of discretization, with time as the independent variable, we can write

$$\boldsymbol{\phi} \approx \hat{\boldsymbol{\phi}} = \Sigma N_l \boldsymbol{\phi}_l \tag{8.4}$$

where $\boldsymbol{\phi}_l$ stands for a nodal set of values of $\boldsymbol{\phi}$ at a time $t$.

The lowest order of polynomial for the trial function $N$ is that of the first order, as only first-order derivatives are involved in Eq. (8.2).

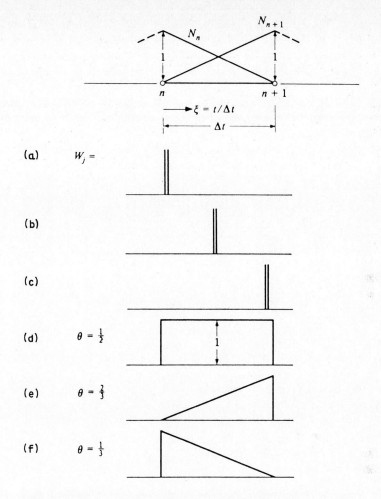

**FIG. 8.1**  Shape and weight functions for two-point recurrence formulae.

Consider now a typical time "element" of length $\Delta t$ with the set $\phi_l$ taking on nodal values $\phi_n$ and $\phi_{n+1}$ as shown in Fig. 8.1. The interpolation functions and their first time derivatives can be written in terms of local variables as

$$0 \leq \xi \leq 1 \qquad \xi = \frac{t}{\Delta t}$$

$$N_n = 1 - \xi \qquad \dot{N}_n = -\frac{1}{\Delta t} \qquad (8.5)$$

$$N_{n+1} = \xi \qquad \dot{N}_{n+1} = \frac{1}{\Delta t}$$

A typical weighted-residual equation can now be written by assuming that the full domain of investigation corresponds with that of one element in time:

$$\int_0^1 W\{C(\phi_n \dot{N}_n + \phi_{n+1}\dot{N}_{n+1}) + K(\phi_n N_n + \phi_{n+1}N_{n+1}) + \mathbf{f}\}\, d\xi = 0 \tag{8.6}$$

As the problem is an initial-value one, $\phi_n$ is assumed known and the equation will serve to determine $\phi_{n+1}$ approximately. Immediately on substituting from (8.5) one can write a recurrence relation as

$$\left(\mathbf{K}\int_0^1 W\xi\, d\xi + \mathbf{C}\int_0^1 W\frac{d\xi}{\Delta t}\right)\phi_{n+1}$$

$$+\left\{\mathbf{K}\int_0^1 W(1-\xi)\, d\xi - \mathbf{C}\int_0^1 W\frac{d\xi}{\Delta t}\right\}\phi_n + \int_0^1 W\mathbf{f}\, d\xi = 0 \tag{8.7}$$

in which various weighting functions $W$ can be inserted. In the above, matrices $\mathbf{K}$ and $\mathbf{C}$ have been assumed to be independent of $t$. Quite generally expression (8.7) can be rewritten for any weighting function as

$$\left(\frac{\mathbf{C}}{\Delta t} + \mathbf{K}\theta\right)\phi_{n+1} + \left\{-\frac{\mathbf{C}}{\Delta t} + \mathbf{K}(1-\theta)\right\}\phi_n + \bar{\mathbf{f}} = 0 \tag{8.8}$$

where

$$\theta = \frac{\displaystyle\int_0^1 W\xi\, d\xi}{\displaystyle\int_0^1 W\, d\xi} \tag{8.9a}$$

and

$$\bar{\mathbf{f}} = \frac{\displaystyle\int_0^1 W\mathbf{f}\, d\xi}{\displaystyle\int_0^1 W\, d\xi} \tag{8.9b}$$

From the above, $\phi_{n+1}$ can be found by solving the simultaneous equations as $\phi_n$ and $\bar{\mathbf{f}}$ are known.

It is logical and convenient to assume that the same interpolation is applied to the function $\bar{\mathbf{f}}$ as that used for the unknown vector $\phi$. If this interpolation is adopted, we find that

$$\bar{\mathbf{f}} = \theta\mathbf{f}_n + (1-\theta)\mathbf{f}_{n+1} \tag{8.10}$$

Such an interpolation is acceptable if the function varies smoothly in time, but on occasion may be misleading. In such cases, it is simpler to evaluate expression (8.9b) exactly. This allows *impulse* and other discontinuous inputs to be used.

At this stage, we observe that if $\theta = 0$ and $\mathbf{C}$ is a diagonal (lumped†) matrix, the solution for $\phi_{n+1}$ is trivial and each individual value can be computed directly from its precursor.

---

† If finite-element discretization is in fact used in the space domain, we find in general that such matrices as $\mathbf{C}$ are not diagonal, unlike those arising in finite-difference discretization. There are several possible methods for diagonalizing such matrices without loss of accuracy. A survey of the literature and descriptions of several such processes are given in Ref. [8, pp. 535–539].

Such schemes are known as *explicit*, while those in $\theta \neq 0$, requiring the solution of a non-diagonal system of equations, are known as *implicit*. We see later that the computational convenience of the explicit scheme is accompanied by a serious drawback which requires the use of $\Delta t$ not exceeding a certain magnitude.

The reader will recognize in Eq. (8.8) a well-known finite-difference formula with a modification of using a weighted loading term $\bar{\mathbf{f}}$. In Fig. 8.1, we show a series of weighting functions and the resulting values of $\theta$. The first three models, Fig. 8.1a to c, represent point-collocation weighting applied at $n$, $n + \frac{1}{2}$, and $n + 1$, respectively, and give the well-known forward-difference (Euler), middifference (Crank–Nicolson), and backward-difference formulae.

The schemes shown in Fig. 8.1d, e, and f represent Galerkin-type processes. The scheme (e), with $\theta = \frac{2}{3}$ (first suggested by Zienkiewicz), is equivalent to the normal use of the Galerkin procedure with the weighting corresponding to a trial function; it has shown considerable computational advantages.

In the foregoing, we have assumed the domain of the approximation to correspond to a time $\Delta t$ and established a recurrence relation between the two successive values of $\boldsymbol{\phi}_n$. The computation can obviously proceed in a step-by-step manner using a sequence of such domains. It is, however, possible to apply the procedure to the whole domain of time simultaneously, assuming this domain to be divided into a finite number of elements. Using, for instance, the linear expansions of Eq. (8.5) but integrating over the whole domain, we note that unless the weight functions are confined to a single element, several vectors $\boldsymbol{\phi}_i$ will be included simultaneously in a typical equation. For instance, if the Galerkin procedure is used and we assume that

$$W_j = N_j$$

then, if the whole domain is included, three successive values are involved in a typical equation, as shown in Fig. 8.2. For a constant time interval $\Delta t$ the following expression is

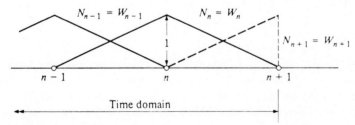

**FIG. 8.2** A Galerkin scheme with linear shape functions applied to the whole time domain.

obtained, which can be verified.

$$\left(\frac{\mathbf{C}}{2\Delta t} + \frac{\mathbf{K}}{6}\right)\boldsymbol{\phi}_{n+1} + \left(\frac{2\mathbf{K}}{3}\right)\boldsymbol{\phi}_n + \left(-\frac{\mathbf{C}}{2\Delta t} + \frac{\mathbf{K}}{6}\right)\boldsymbol{\phi}_{n-1} + \bar{\mathbf{f}} = 0$$

$$\bar{\mathbf{f}} = \frac{\mathbf{f}_{n+1}}{6} + \frac{2\mathbf{f}_n}{3} + \frac{\mathbf{f}_{n-1}}{6}$$

(8.11)

Provided that two initial values are known, such a formula can be used in a recurrent manner for evaluating $\phi_{n+1}$ from $\phi_n$ and $\phi_{n-1}$. We shall discuss such expressions further in Sec. 8.5.

## 8.2B Variational Approaches

As an alternative to the weighted-residual approach, it is often possible to use a variational functional whose stationariness corresponds to the correct differential equations discussed.

For instance, in the second-order dynamic equation, the Hamilton principle [11] could provide a starting basis. Gurtin [12, 13] establishes some other useful principles for both first- and second-order equations. Such variational functionals have been used by Wilson and Nickell [14], Fried [3], and Argyris [2, 15]. However, it is well known that such variational principles are equivalent to the use of Galerkin procedures and will yield no new alternative numerical schemes. Zienkiewicz and Parekh [4] have used, for the first time, the finite element in time based on weighted-residual forms.

One alternative which is not embedded explicitly in standard variational forms is the least-square procedure. In this we write a functional minimizing the square of the error. In the context of one element representing the whole domain and a linear interpolation function of Eq. (8.5), we thus minimize

$$\Pi = \int_0^1 |\mathbf{C}(\phi_n \dot{\mathbf{N}}_n + \phi_{n+1}\dot{\mathbf{N}}_{n+1}) + \mathbf{K}(\phi_n \mathbf{N}_n + \phi_{n+1}\mathbf{N}_{n+1}) + \mathbf{f}|^2 \, d\xi \tag{8.12}$$

with respect to the components of $\phi_{n+1}$. The reader can verify that the final recurrence scheme now obtained is

$$\left(\frac{\mathbf{C}^t\mathbf{C}}{\Delta t} + \frac{\mathbf{K}^t\mathbf{C} + \mathbf{C}^t\mathbf{K}}{2} + \mathbf{K}^t\mathbf{K}\frac{\Delta t}{3}\right)\phi_{n+1}$$

$$+ \left(-\frac{\mathbf{C}^t\mathbf{C}}{\Delta t} - \mathbf{K}^t\mathbf{C} - \frac{\mathbf{C}^t\mathbf{K}}{2} + \mathbf{K}^t\mathbf{K}\frac{\Delta t}{6}\right)\phi_n + \mathbf{K}^t\int_0^1 \mathbf{f}\xi\frac{d\xi}{\Delta t^2} + \mathbf{C}^t\int_0^1 \mathbf{f}\frac{d\xi}{\Delta t} = 0 \tag{8.13}$$

The above scheme obviously involves more computation but results in symmetric equations even if matrices $\mathbf{K}$ and $\mathbf{C}$ are not symmetric. Some experiments with such a scheme are given by Zienkiewicz and Lewis [16] and have been used successfully by others [17]. To compare the performance of various schemes outlined in this section we consider a simple single-variable equation with

$$K = C = 1 \qquad f = 0$$

for an initial value of $\phi_0 = 1$. In Fig. 8.3 we show results obtained using $\Delta t = 0.5$ and $\Delta t = 0.9$ for various schemes. The least-square process shows by far the greatest accuracy, but with associated larger computational cost. Here in the same example the central-difference schemes give "second-best" results, and this scheme has been used most frequently in practical applications. As we see later, however, it often leads to oscillatory solutions which are troublesome, and for that reason the backward-difference scheme ($\theta = 1$) is often preferred.

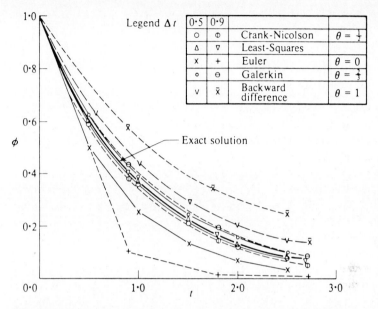

**FIG. 8.3** Comparison of various time-stepping schemes on an initial-value problem.

In Fig. 8.4 results for larger time steps, $t = 1.5$ and 2.5, are shown for the same problem. Here an interesting phenomenon occurs. The forward integration gives either oscillatory or divergent results while the other schemes still retain an acceptable accuracy. The behavior shown here is that of instability, which we shall discuss in the next section.

## 8.2c Oscillation and Instability for One-Step Recurrence Schemes

For stability considerations it will be convenient to consider the system of decoupled equations in terms of the modal participation variables $y_i$, i.e., to deal with a set of independent first-order scalar equations of the form

$$c_i \dot{y}_i + k_i y_i + f_i = 0 \qquad (8.14)$$

Clearly, since any response can be written as a sum of such modes, we are able to synthesize the total response for a multi-degree-of-freedom system with eigenvectors $\mathbf{u}_i$ as

$$\boldsymbol{\phi} = \Sigma y_i \mathbf{u}_i \qquad (8.15)$$

The recurrence relations written previously are obviously applicable here, and we shall consider the general recurrence relation of the form (8.8). For free response, i.e., with the forcing term set to zero, we can write this recurrence as

$$\left(\frac{c_i}{\Delta t} + k_i \theta\right) y_i^{n+1} + \left\{-\frac{c_i}{\Delta t} + k_i(1 - \theta)\right\} y_i^n = 0 \qquad (8.16)$$

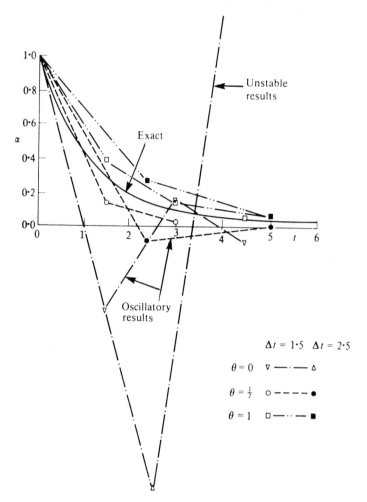

**FIG. 8.4**　Demonstration of instability in problems of Fig. 8.3.

Alternatively, writing

$$y_i^{n+1} = \lambda y_i^n \tag{8.17}$$

where $\lambda$ is the *amplification factor*, we have

$$\lambda\left(\frac{c_i}{\Delta t} + k_i\theta\right) + \left\{-\frac{c_i}{\Delta t} + k_i(1-\theta)\right\} = 0 \tag{8.18}$$

We see that an *unbounded* response will arise if $|\lambda| > 1$ and the problem will become unstable (for real solutions a damped behavior is generally noted). Further, if $\lambda < 0$, an oscillating behavior will arise which clearly does not represent the required solution well.

Equation (8.18), known as the *characteristic equation* of the recurrence scheme, gives

$$\lambda = \frac{1 - k_i(1-\theta)\,\Delta t/c_i}{1 + k_i\theta\,\Delta t/c_i} \tag{8.19}$$

If we require that $|\lambda| < 1$, the right-hand side of Eq. (8.19) must be greater than $-1$. Noting that $k_i/c_i = \omega_i$, the eigenvalue corresponding to a mode $i$, we can write this requirement as

$$1 - \omega_i \Delta t (1 - \theta) > -1 - \omega_i \Delta t \theta$$

or
$$\omega_i \Delta t (2\theta - 1) > -2 \qquad (8.20)$$

This condition is always satisfied for $\theta \geq \frac{1}{2}$, and schemes of this kind are unconditionally stable. When $0 < \theta < \frac{1}{2}$, stability is conditional, requiring

$$\omega_i \Delta t < \frac{2}{1 - 2\theta} \qquad (8.21)$$

This, in the example of Fig. 8.4, gives the limit of the time step as $\omega_i \Delta t \leq 2$ when the forward-difference scheme ($\theta = 0$) is used, and the violation of this condition has resulted in the divergent numbers shown.

The study of the characteristic value $\lambda$ gives us, however, more information. In Fig. 8.5, we show how $\lambda$ varies with $\omega_i \Delta t$ for some of the time-stepping schemes discussed. We note that, for many of these, $\lambda$ has negative values for a large time step, and in fact the backward-difference scheme with $\theta = 1$ is the only one not showing this property. This means that for any $\theta < 1$, oscillatory results can be given. Although mathematically it can be shown that the error for the middifference scheme with $\theta = \frac{1}{2}$ is of a higher order, this scheme can give less accurate results than the backward scheme for larger time steps as shown in Fig. 8.4.

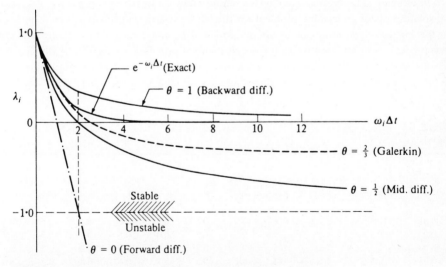

**FIG. 8.5**  Variation of $\lambda$ with $\omega_i \Delta t$ for various recurrence schemes.

The time response of a multi-degree-of-freedom system is a combination of all modal responses. Fortunately, the major part of the response corresponds generally to the modes with low eigenvalues $\omega_i$. When an unconditionally stable scheme is used for a multi-degree-of-freedom system, it usually involves time steps much in excess of those corresponding to good

accuracy for higher frequencies $\omega_i$; when the value of $\lambda$ for the unconditionally stable schemes
has a negative value, oscillations may not damp out as they should in practice. This is
particularly noticeable with the Crank–Nicolson scheme ($\theta = \frac{1}{2}$), and numerical devices have
to be used to eliminate such surplus oscillations [17, 18]. All such devices consist, in essence,
of averaging successive time steps of computation. We should note that the most severe input
starting such oscillations occurs at abrupt changes of the forcing term. Such abrupt changes
therefore should be avoided or particular care taken to deal with them (see Sec. 8.2D).

An alternative procedure which helps to iron out the oscillation is the use of $\theta > \frac{1}{2}$. In this
context a useful compromise has been found in the Galerkin scheme with $\theta = \frac{2}{3}$ and has been
shown to be very useful in practice with almost all oscillation and errors avoided. (Lambert
[19] suggests, by different reasoning, $\theta = 0.878 \approx \frac{7}{8}$ as optimal.) In Table 8.1, we show the
results of a one-dimensional finite-element problem where a bar at uniform initial temperature
is subjected suddenly to zero temperatures applied at its ends. Here, 10 linear elements are
used in the space dimension with $L = 1$. The oscillational errors occurring with $\theta = \frac{1}{2}$ are much
reduced for $\theta = \frac{2}{3}$. The time step used here is much longer than that corresponding to the
lowest eigenperiod, and the main cause of the oscillation is in the abrupt discontinuity of
temperature change.

Conditionally stable schemes, and in particular the explicit scheme, with $\theta = 0$, will
always result in instability as long as the time interval used in the calculation exceeds that
specified by the highest eigenvalue of the system. This is a serious limitation of the use of
explicit time schemes; nevertheless, the computational time-saving with no required matrix
inversion (or repeated solution) often compensates for the need to use many small time steps.

The estimate of the critical time step for conditionally stable schemes appears to necessitate
the solution of the eigenvalue problem for the whole system, but this is not so. The bound
on the highest eigenvalue can be simply obtained by the consideration of an individual
element. This is established by an important theorem proposed by Irons [20] which proves
that the highest system eigenvalue must always be less than the highest eigenvalue of the
individual elements. This theorem allows an easy estimate of critical time steps which will

**TABLE 8.1**   Percentage Errors for Finite Elements in Time ($\theta = \frac{2}{3}$) and by the Crank–Nicolson Scheme
($\theta = \frac{1}{2}$); $\Delta t = 0.01$

| $t$ | $x = 0.1$ | | $x = 0.2$ | | $x = 0.3$ | | $x = 0.4$ | | $x = 0.5$ | |
|---|---|---|---|---|---|---|---|---|---|---|
| | $\theta = \frac{2}{3}$ | $\theta = \frac{1}{2}$ | $\theta = \frac{2}{3}$ | $\theta = \frac{1}{2}$ | $\theta = \frac{2}{3}$ | $\theta = \frac{1}{2}$ | $\theta = \frac{2}{3}$ | $\theta = \frac{1}{2}$ | $\theta = \frac{2}{3}$ | $\theta = \frac{1}{2}$ |
| 0.01 | 10.8 | 28.2 | 1.6 | 3.2 | 0.5 | 0.7 | 0.6 | 0.1 | 0.5 | 0.2 |
| 0.02 | 0.5 | 3.5 | 2.1 | 9.5 | 0.1 | 0.0 | 0.5 | 0.7 | 0.7 | 0.4 |
| 0.03 | 1.3 | 9.9 | 0.5 | 0.7 | 0.8 | 3.1 | 0.5 | 0.2 | 0.5 | 0.6 |
| 0.05 | 0.5 | 4.5 | 0.4 | 0.2 | 0.5 | 2.3 | 0.4 | 0.8 | 0.5 | 1.0 |
| 0.10 | 0.1 | 1.4 | 0.1 | 2.0 | 0.1 | 1.5 | 0.1 | 1.9 | 0.1 | 1.6 |
| 0.15 | 0.3 | 2.2 | 0.3 | 2.1 | 0.3 | 2.2 | 0.3 | 2.1 | 0.3 | 2.2 |
| 0.20 | 0.6 | 2.6 | 0.6 | 2.6 | 0.6 | 2.6 | 0.6 | 2.6 | 0.6 | 2.6 |
| 0.30 | 1.4 | 3.5 | 1.4 | 3.5 | 1.4 | 3.5 | 1.4 | 3.5 | 1.4 | 3.5 |

NOTE:   Conductivity = specific heat = 1.
SOURCE:   Zlamal [10].

err on the safe side. It is important to note here that for first-order problems of the type of Eq. (8.2), the element eigenvalues increase as $h^{-2}$ (where $h$ = element size). This means a very rapid decrease of stable $\Delta t$ with mesh subdivision, and explicit schemes are therefore seldom used for such problems.

We have not discussed the stability conditions for either the three-point scheme given by Eq. (8.11) or the recurrence relation obtained from the least-square approximation given by Eq. (8.13). We leave these to the reader.

## 8.2D Accuracy and Initial Conditions

We have stated that in the first-order problems discussed here, the recurrence starts from some known initial conditions which are specified. However, as in the problem of a rapid change of boundary condition discussed previously, such initial conditions may cause an abrupt discontinuity to appear at the start, in which case an alternative formulation is physically preferable. Let us start the whole problem from a solution which represents the system at rest, i.e., in which $\phi$ = constant, and the change of the initial conditions or of any suddenly applied forcing terms can then be considered as a disturbance on this steady system. The initial conditions, therefore, correspond to those of the steady state and are given for all times prior to a certain instant.

If we consider as an example the simple initial-value problem on which we have based Figs. 8.3 and 8.4, then the problem can be restated as that requiring a solution of an equation

$$\dot{\phi} + \phi + f(t) = 0 \tag{8.22}$$

which is valid in the whole time domain, and where

$$f(t) = -1 \quad (t < 0) \quad \phi = 1$$

$$f(t) = 0 \quad (t \geqslant 0)$$

The resulting discontinuity in the new forcing term is shown in Fig. 8.6. Clearly such a discontinuity should be "smoothed," and this can be done in many ways, for instance, by placing an interval which straddles this discontinuity as shown. In the same figure we show the numerical results obtained in which such smoothing was applied for the very large time interval $\Delta t = 2.5$. Note that the smoothed solution does not show the violent oscillations previously noted and is thus more physically acceptable.

The process of starting from known steady solutions for $t < 0$ and smoothing out any discontinuities will simplify the computation for multistep schemes, as it implies the knowledge of all the vectors $\phi$ at times prior to the initial instant. We have now shown that this simplification does, in fact, lead to more realistic answers, and we shall invariably apply it in both first- and second-order equations. (The smoothing of the discontinuity is a natural consequence of the finite-element formulation in the time domain and does not appear naturally in finite-difference recurrence formulae.)

To show how important are the effects of starting conditions, we give (in Fig. 8.7) some results of applying the smoothing procedure in a realistic computation. The improvement of results with respect to application of a discontinuous initial condition is evident [73].

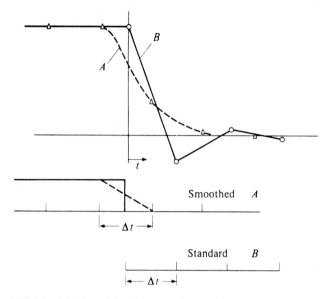

**FIG. 8.6** Initial conditions interpreted as step change on steady state. Effect of smoothing discontinuity: $\theta = \frac{1}{2}$, $\Delta t = 2.5$.

## 8.3 THREE-POINT RECURRENCE SCHEMES FOR SECOND-ORDER EQUATIONS

### 8.3A The Weighted-Residual Algorithm

The procedures of the previous section can be applied directly to the second-order Eq. (8.3), but the trial functions $N_i(t)$ must be at least of second order (parabolic) if $t$ as a second order is to be represented. Thus we need a minimum of three vectors to describe approximately the variation of this function. We can write

$$\mathbf{x} \approx \sum_{i=n-1}^{n+1} N_i(t)\mathbf{x}_i \tag{8.23}$$

replacing $\boldsymbol{\phi}$ by $\mathbf{x}_i$ in Eq. (8.3) to give the usual meaning in terms of displacements $\mathbf{x}_i$ at $t = (n-1)\Delta t$, $n\Delta t$, and $(n+1)\Delta t$.

The trial functions normalized to an interval $2\Delta t$, i.e., with $-1 \le \xi \le 1$, are the standard parabolic ones shown in Fig. 8.8 and can be written

$$N_{n+1} = \frac{\xi(1+\xi)}{2}$$

$$N_n = (1-\xi)(1+\xi) \tag{8.24}$$

$$N_{n-1} = \frac{-\xi(1-\xi)}{2}$$

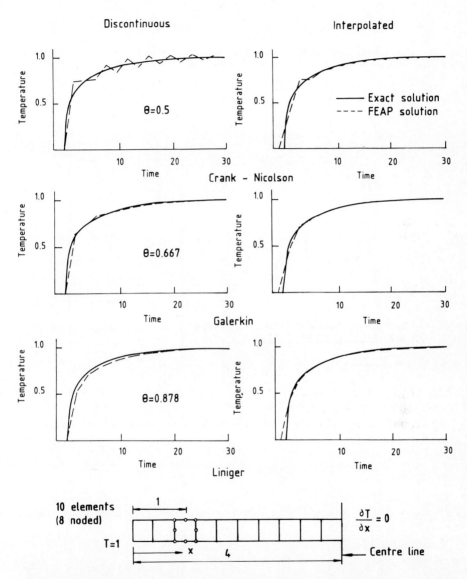

**FIG. 8.7** Transient heating of a bar; comparison of discontinuous and interpolation (smoothed) initial conditions for two-level schemes. FEAP = finite-element approximation.

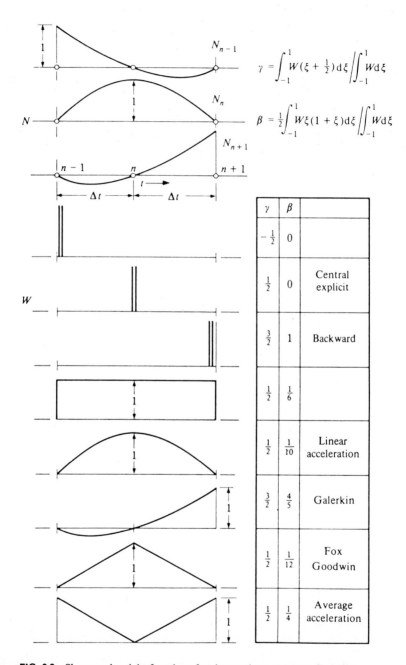

$$\gamma = \int_{-1}^{1} W(\xi + \tfrac{1}{2})\,d\xi \bigg/ \int_{-1}^{1} W\,d\xi$$

$$\beta = \tfrac{1}{2}\int_{-1}^{1} W\xi(1 + \xi)\,d\xi \bigg/ \int_{-1}^{1} W\,d\xi$$

| $\gamma$ | $\beta$ | |
|---|---|---|
| $-\tfrac{1}{2}$ | $0$ | |
| $\tfrac{1}{2}$ | $0$ | Central explicit |
| $\tfrac{3}{2}$ | $1$ | Backward |
| $\tfrac{1}{2}$ | $\tfrac{1}{6}$ | |
| $\tfrac{1}{2}$ | $\tfrac{1}{10}$ | Linear acceleration |
| $\tfrac{3}{2}$ | $\tfrac{4}{5}$ | Galerkin |
| $\tfrac{1}{2}$ | $\tfrac{1}{12}$ | Fox Goodwin |
| $\tfrac{1}{2}$ | $\tfrac{1}{4}$ | Average acceleration |

**FIG. 8.8** Shape and weight functions for three-point recurrence formulae.

where $\xi = t/\Delta t$. The time derivatives of these functions are

$$\dot{N}_{n+1} = \frac{\frac{1}{2}+\xi}{\Delta t} \qquad \ddot{N}_{n+1} = \frac{1}{\Delta t^2}$$

$$\dot{N}_n = \frac{-2\xi}{\Delta t} \qquad \ddot{N}_n = \frac{-2}{\Delta t^2} \qquad (8.25)$$

$$\dot{N}_{n-1} = \frac{-\frac{1}{2}+\xi}{\Delta t} \qquad \ddot{N}_{n-1} = \frac{1}{\Delta t^2}$$

We shall now use the period of the size of the element $2\Delta t$ as a *domain* of time and assume that $x_n$ and $x_{n-1}$ are prescribed, thus leaving $x_{n+1}$ to be determined. The assumption of two known values corresponds precisely to the requirement that two initial conditions be known in a second-order equation. Thus we write a single weighted-residual equation of the form

$$\int_{-1}^{1} W\{\mathbf{M}(\ddot{N}_{n-1}x_{n-1} + \ddot{N}_n x_n + \ddot{N}_{n+1}x_{n+1}) + \mathbf{C}(\dot{N}_{n-1}\mathbf{x}_{n-1} + \dot{N}_n \mathbf{x}_n + \dot{N}_{n+1}\mathbf{x}_{n+1})$$

$$+ \mathbf{K}(N_{n-1}x_{n-1} + N_n x_n + N_{n+1}x_{n+1}) + \mathbf{f}\} \, d\xi = 0 \qquad (8.26)$$

In an analysis similar to that used in deriving Eq. (8.8), we find that the above can be written

$$(\mathbf{M} + \gamma \Delta t \mathbf{C} + \beta \Delta t^2 \mathbf{K})x_{n+1} + \{-2\mathbf{M} + (1-2\gamma)\Delta t \mathbf{C} + (\tfrac{1}{2}-2\beta+\gamma)\Delta t^2 \mathbf{K}\}\mathbf{x}_n$$

$$+ \{\mathbf{M} - (1-\gamma)\Delta t \mathbf{C} + (\tfrac{1}{2}+\beta-\gamma)\Delta t^2 \mathbf{K}\}x_{n-1} + \bar{\mathbf{f}}\Delta t^2 = 0 \qquad (8.27)$$

in which

$$\gamma \equiv \frac{\int_{-1}^{1} W(\xi+\tfrac{1}{2}) \, d\xi}{\int_{-1}^{1} W \, d\xi}$$

$$\beta = \frac{\int_{-1}^{1} \tfrac{1}{2} W\xi(1+\xi) \, d\xi}{\int_{-1}^{1} W \, d\xi} \qquad (8.28)$$

$$\bar{\mathbf{f}} = \frac{\int_{-1}^{1} W\mathbf{f} \, d\xi}{\int_{-1}^{1} W \, d\xi}$$

If the same interpolation is used for $\mathbf{f}$ as implied for the displacement $\mathbf{x}$, then

$$\bar{\mathbf{f}} = \mathbf{f}_{n+1}\beta + \mathbf{f}_n(\tfrac{1}{2}-2\beta+\gamma) + \mathbf{f}_{n-1}(\tfrac{1}{2}+\beta-\gamma) \qquad (8.29)$$

From Eqs. (8.28) the weighting function $\mathbf{W}$ can be deduced as a quadratic function whose coefficients are functions of $\beta$ and $\gamma$.

The algorithm in Eq. (8.27) is closely linked to an algorithm derived by Newmark [21] by a completely different approach. The original Newmark method for the integration of Eq. (8.3) takes

$$\mathbf{x}_{n+1} = \mathbf{x}_n + \Delta t\, \mathbf{v}_n + \tfrac{1}{2}\Delta t^2[(1-2\beta)\mathbf{a}_n + 2\beta \mathbf{a}_{n+1}] \tag{8.30a}$$

and

$$\dot{\mathbf{x}}_{n+1} \equiv \mathbf{v}_{n+1} = \mathbf{v}_n + \Delta t[(1-\gamma)\mathbf{a}_n + \gamma \mathbf{a}_{n+1}] \qquad \mathbf{a}_{n+1} \equiv \ddot{\mathbf{x}}_{n+1} \tag{8.30b}$$

where $\mathbf{v}_n$, $\mathbf{a}_n$ are the approximate values of the velocity and acceleration, respectively, at $t = n\,\Delta t$.

Assuming we can substitute $\mathbf{x}_n$, $\mathbf{v}_n$, $\mathbf{a}_n$ into the differential Eq. (8.3) with $\phi$ replaced by $x$, we have

$$\mathbf{M}\mathbf{a}_j + \mathbf{C}\mathbf{v}_j + \mathbf{K}\mathbf{x}_j + \mathbf{f}_j = \mathbf{0} \tag{8.30c}$$

for $j = n-1$, $n$, $n+1$.

Then we can take the five equations (8.30a to c) and two more equations like (8.30a and b) relating quantities at $t = (n-1)\Delta t$ and $n\,\Delta t$, and from these seven independent equations we can eliminate the six quantities $\mathbf{a}_{n-1}$, $\mathbf{a}_n$, $\mathbf{a}_{n+1}$, $\mathbf{v}_{n-1}$, $\mathbf{v}_n$, $\mathbf{v}_{n+1}$ to give a recurrence relation in the displacements $\mathbf{x}_{n-1}$, $\mathbf{x}_n$, $\mathbf{x}_{n+1}$ which is exactly the same as Eq. (8.27). Thus the Newmark assumption of approximations (8.30a and b) for the displacement and velocity leads to the same recurrence in the displacements as does the assumption of a quadratic variation for the displacement and its insertion into the weighted-residual equation.

In Eq. (8.27), various forms of the weighting function $\mathbf{W}$ can be used, ranging from point collocation to Galerkin forms. In Fig. 8.8 we show the values of $\beta$ and $\gamma$ corresponding to a series of such weightings.

We note that if $\beta = 0$ and the matrices $\mathbf{M}$ and $\mathbf{C}$ are diagonal (lumped), then no inversion is necessary to determine $\mathbf{x}_{n+1}$ and the scheme is explicit. One such scheme, with $\gamma = \tfrac{1}{2}$, corresponds to the central-difference formula, which is extremely economical. However, just as in first-order equations, we find that stability here is conditional and the time interval $\Delta t$ has to be suitably limited. Such schemes have proved extremely efficient for many linear and nonlinear problems in practice and are discussed in Refs. [22–26].

In using Eq. (8.27), two starting values $\mathbf{x}_0$ and $\mathbf{x}_1$ are necessary to commence calculation. Frequently these are specified by the initial displacements and the initial velocity. This is inconvenient, and as recommended for the linear systems it is always easy to translate such a problem to that of an initially steady system to which a perturbation is applied. Alternatively, various starting schemes have to be used to predict two successive values of the displacement vector. Other methods are discussed subsequently.

## 8.3B Stability of Two-Step Recurrence Schemes

The stability of the schemes developed in the previous section can now be investigated using the procedures identical to those described for one-step recurrence schemes [27–31]. First we note that the response can be studied for a series of uncoupled equations of the general form

$$m_i \ddot{y}_i + c_i \dot{y}_i + k_i y_i + f_i = 0 \tag{8.31}$$

(assuming the matrices $\mathbf{M}$, $\mathbf{C}$, $\mathbf{K}$ have a common set of eigenvalues).

In general, to achieve such uncoupling, it is necessary to consider complex natural frequencies, but if the C-matrix can be assumed to be a linear combination of the mass and stiffness matrices, the mode decomposition can be accomplished using real eigenvalues of the free vibration

$$\omega_i^2 = \frac{k_i}{m_i} \tag{8.32}$$

This situation will be our main concern.

Once again we study the free response in which $f_1 = 0$ and assume a solution of the form

$$y_i^{n+1} = \lambda y_i^n \qquad n = 1, 2, \ldots \tag{8.33}$$

Substituting the above into the general-recurrence Eq. (8.27) [now written for the single-degree-of-freedom system of Eq. (8.31)], we have a characteristic equation

$$\lambda(m_i + \gamma \Delta t c_i + \beta \Delta t^2 k_i) + \lambda[-2m_i + (1 - 2\gamma)\Delta t c_i + (\tfrac{1}{2} - 2\beta + \gamma)\Delta t^2 k_i]$$

$$+ [m_i - (1 - \gamma)\Delta t c_i + (\tfrac{1}{2} + \beta - \gamma)\Delta t^2 k_i] = 0 \tag{8.34}$$

The roots of this equation can be found and will indicate the behavior of the numerical solution and, in particular, will show whether this grows in an unbounded manner, which, obviously, is physically unacceptable. The roots of the quadratic will generally be complex; this would be expected from the fact that the solution corresponds to one of a (damped) oscillation. However, we still require that the modulus of the complex root satisfies

$$|\lambda| \leqslant 1 \tag{8.35}$$

for the oscillation to remain unbounded.

The general case of a damped oscillation can be studied in detail by the reader, and here we consider answers only for the undamped case, i.e., putting the damping matrix $C_i = 0$. We know that for such cases the true solution must be of the form

$$y_j = \bar{y}_j e^{i\omega t} \qquad (i = \sqrt{-1}) \tag{8.36}$$

thus establishing the exact value of $\lambda$, which is

$$\lambda = \frac{y_j^{n+1}}{y_j^n} = \frac{e^{i\omega(t + \Delta t)}}{e^{i\omega t}} = e^{i\omega \Delta t} \tag{8.37}$$

This has unit modulus i.e.          $|\lambda| = 1$          (8.38)

thus indicating an undamped persisting oscillation.

Any numerical scheme which produces $|\lambda| < 1$ will give a stable but artificially damped solution. Considering now the solution of the characteristic equation, [Eq. (8.34)], in which

$$c_i = 0 \qquad \text{and} \qquad p_i = \frac{k_i}{m_i} \Delta t^2 = \omega_i^2 \Delta t^2$$

we have          $\lambda^2(1 + \beta p_i) + \lambda[-2 + (\tfrac{1}{2} - 2\beta + \gamma)p_i] + [1 + (\tfrac{1}{2} + \beta - \gamma)p_i] = 0$          (8.39)

Using the Routh–Hurwitz conditions [71] for $|\lambda| \leqslant 1$, we require that

$$2\beta \geqslant \gamma \geqslant \tfrac{1}{2} \tag{8.40}$$

for the stability to be unconditional for all values of $p_i$. (This also applies for $c_i > 0$.)

If the above conditions are not satisfied, stability can still be achieved, providing

$$p_i < p_{\text{crit}} = \frac{2}{\gamma - 2\beta} \tag{8.41}$$

Only two of the schemes shown in Fig. 8.8 are unconditionally stable ($\gamma = \tfrac{3}{2}$, $\beta = 1$, and $\gamma = 2\beta = \tfrac{1}{2}$); for all others stability is conditional. As remarked by Newmark, all schemes for which

$$\gamma = \tfrac{1}{2} \qquad \beta \geqslant \tfrac{1}{4} \tag{8.42}$$

are unconditionally stable and show no artificial damping; that is, $|\lambda| = 1$. For conditionally stable schemes such as the central-difference expression a simple calculation from inequality (8.41) shows that for $\gamma = \tfrac{1}{2}$, $\beta = 0$, we require for stability

$$p_i < 4 \tag{8.43}$$

or

$$\omega_i \Delta t < 2$$

Putting $\omega_i = 2\pi / T_i$, where $T_i$ is the period, we can write the stability condition as

$$\Delta t \leqslant \frac{1}{\pi} T_i \tag{8.44}$$

An alternative but popular scheme with

$$\gamma = \tfrac{1}{2} \qquad \beta = \tfrac{1}{6}$$

requires for stability that

$$\Delta t \leqslant \frac{\sqrt{3}}{\pi} T_i \tag{8.45}$$

as can easily be verified.

All schemes with $\gamma > \tfrac{1}{2}$ show an appreciable numerical damping leading to an inaccuracy of results. In Fig. 8.9, we show a plot of $|\lambda|$ against $\Delta t / T$ for various such schemes, showing how large this damping can be for larger values of $\Delta t$.

In practice some degree of numerical damping is desirable, as invariably $\Delta t$ used in unconditionally stable schemes will be much larger than that corresponding to the highest frequencies of the system, which cannot be reproduced exactly and only lead to numerical "noise." Ideally, therefore, we will seek schemes which have $|\lambda| \approx 1$ for $\Delta t / T < 1$ and show as much damping as possible when $\Delta t / T > 1$.

One way of obtaining such performance is to include, deliberately, a damping matrix of a form

$$\mathbf{C} = \varepsilon \mathbf{K} \Delta t \tag{8.46}$$

where $\varepsilon$ is a convenient parameter. Obviously as $\Delta t \to 0$ this damping will disappear, and when $\Delta t \to \infty$ it will have a large value.

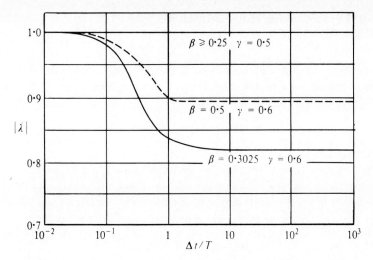

**FIG. 8.9**   Three-level (Newmark) expression. Spectral radius, $|\lambda|$ versus $\Delta t/T$.

Such artificial "adjustment" of numerical performance is of some interest and was used by Grant [32] to adjust the performance of an explicit Newmark scheme where $\gamma = \beta = 0$. A more sophisticated use is developed by Hilber et al. [33].

In addition to numerical damping, the value of $\lambda$ obtained from the characteristic Eq. (8.34), by comparison with the exact $\lambda$ of Eq. (8.37), gives information on the relative period error. Results are shown in Fig. 8.10 for the various schemes.

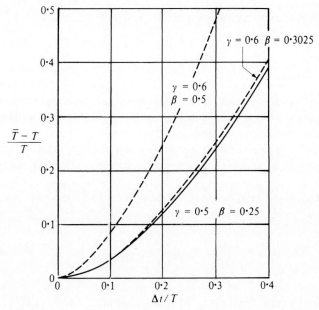

**FIG. 8.10**   Three-level (Newmark) expression. Relative period error versus $\Delta t/T$.

## 8.4 ONE-STEP RECURRENCE FORMULAE FOR SECOND-ORDER EQUATIONS

### 8.4A The Newmark Algorithm and Alternatives

Usually the Newmark algorithm is employed as a one-step formula to compute the vector $\mathbf{X}_{n+1}$ if the previous value $\mathbf{X}_n$ is known, where

$$\mathbf{X}_n = [\mathbf{x}_n, \Delta t \mathbf{v}_n, \Delta t^2 \mathbf{a}_n]$$

includes the displacement, velocity, and acceleration vectors.

With the one-step formula it is easy to vary the size of the time step $\Delta t$, which is a computational advantage. The algorithm can also be arranged to avoid repeated multiplications by the matrix $\mathbf{K}$, which is never diagonal, and thus save computer storage and operations. This can be done by taking the Newmark relations (8.30a and b) in the form

$$\mathbf{x}_{n+1} = \hat{\mathbf{x}}_{n+1} + \beta \Delta t^2 \mathbf{a}_{n+1} \tag{8.47}$$

$$\mathbf{v}_{n+1} = \hat{\mathbf{v}}_{n+1} + \gamma \Delta t \mathbf{a}_{n+1} \tag{8.48}$$

where

$$\hat{\mathbf{x}}_{n+1} = \mathbf{x}_n + \Delta t \mathbf{v}_n + (\tfrac{1}{2} - \beta) \Delta t^2 \mathbf{a}_n$$

and

$$\hat{\mathbf{v}}_{n+1} = \mathbf{v}_n + (1 - \gamma) \Delta t \mathbf{a}_n$$

the last two right-hand sides being available at the beginning of the time step.

Then taking the equation of motion in the form

$$\mathbf{M} \mathbf{a}_{n+1} + \mathbf{C} \mathbf{v}_{n+1} + \mathbf{K} \mathbf{x}_{n+1} + \mathbf{f}_{n+1} = \mathbf{0} \tag{8.49}$$

we can eliminate $\mathbf{a}_{n+1}$ and $\mathbf{v}_{n+1}$ using Eqs. (8.47) and (8.48) to obtain

$$\mathbf{x}_{n+1} = [\mathbf{M} + \gamma \Delta t \mathbf{C} + \beta \Delta t^2 \mathbf{K}]^{-1} [(\mathbf{M} + \gamma \Delta t \mathbf{C}) \hat{\mathbf{x}}_{n+1} - \beta \Delta t^2 \mathbf{C} \hat{\mathbf{v}}_{n+1} - \beta \Delta t^2 \mathbf{f}_{n+1}] \tag{8.50}$$

Then $\mathbf{a}_{n+1}$ and $\mathbf{v}_{n+1}$ follow from Eqs. (8.47) and (8.48) and no multiplication by $\mathbf{K}$ is necessary.

For starting this one-step algorithm we are usually given the starting values $\mathbf{x}_0$, $\mathbf{v}_0$ of the displacement and velocity vectors, and the acceleration $\mathbf{a}_0$ must be obtained by using the equation of motion at $t = 0$. We also note that Eq. (8.50) is using an unweighted form of the load vector, which may give misleading results.

An alternative arrangement of the Newmark equations is available if we only want to compute the vector $\mathbf{Y}_n = [\mathbf{x}_n, \Delta t \mathbf{v}_n]^T$ and not the accelerations [72]. We can first solve

$$\mathbf{M} \mathbf{u}_{n+1} = \left[ \gamma \mathbf{M} + \left( \beta - \frac{\gamma}{2} \right) \Delta t^2 \mathbf{K} \right] \mathbf{x}_n + \left[ (\gamma - \beta) \mathbf{M} + \left( \beta - \frac{\gamma}{2} \right) \Delta t \mathbf{C} \right] \Delta t \mathbf{v}_n + \left( \frac{\gamma}{2} - \beta \right) \Delta t^2 \mathbf{f} \tag{8.51}$$

for the vector

$$\mathbf{u}_{n+1} = \gamma \mathbf{x}_{n+1} - \beta \Delta t \mathbf{v}_{n+1} \tag{8.52}$$

Then we have

$$\gamma \mathbf{x}_{n+1} = [\mathbf{M} + \gamma \Delta t \mathbf{C} + \beta \Delta t^2 \mathbf{K}]^{-1} (\mathbf{M} + \gamma \Delta t \mathbf{C}) \mathbf{u}_{n+1} - \beta (1 - \gamma) \Delta t^2 \mathbf{K} \mathbf{x}_n$$

$$+ \beta [\mathbf{M} - \Delta t (1 - \gamma) \mathbf{C}] \Delta t \mathbf{v}_n + \beta \Delta t^2 [(1 - \gamma) \mathbf{f}_n + \gamma \mathbf{f}_{n+1}] \tag{8.53}$$

Equation (8.53) gives $\mathbf{x}_{n+1}$, and $\mathbf{v}_{n+1}$ is recovered from Eq. (8.52). Note that in this version of the algorithm we are using a weighted form of the load vector in the right-hand side of Eq. (8.53). With $\mathbf{C} = \mathbf{0}$ the conditions for unconditional stability are the same as before, i.e., inequalities (8.41).

It is also possible to obtain a one-step recurrence for $\mathbf{v}_n = [\mathbf{x}_n, \Delta t \mathbf{v}_n]^T$ via the finite-element approach. One way of doing this uses an idea [72] which is also useful in dealing with the higher-order formulae discussed in Sec. 8.5. Note that we need three independent parameters in terms of which to express the hypothesis that $\mathbf{x}$ is a quadratic in time.

1. If we choose $\mathbf{x}_{n+1}$, $\mathbf{x}_n$, $\mathbf{x}_{n-1}$ to be these three parameters as in Eq. (8.23), then the weighted-residual equation immediately gives the two-step recurrence in the displacements only, Eq. (8.27). This is convenient if we only need displacements.

2. If we need to evaluate velocities as well as displacements, we can express the quadratic variation in time in terms of $\mathbf{x}_{n+1}$, $\mathbf{x}_n$, $\mathbf{v}_n$. That is,

$$\mathbf{x} = \mathbf{x}_n + t\mathbf{v}_n + \frac{t^2}{\Delta t^2}(\mathbf{x}_{n+1} - \mathbf{x}_n - \Delta t \mathbf{v}_n) \tag{8.54}$$

This is not the conventional form using a "linear combination of basis functions" of finite-element trial functions as in Eq. (8.23), but it is equivalent.

Now substituting from Eq. (8.54) into the weighted-residual equation,

$$\int_0^{\Delta t} W_1 [\mathbf{M}\ddot{\mathbf{x}} + \mathbf{C}\dot{\mathbf{x}} + \mathbf{K}\mathbf{x} + \mathbf{f}] \, dt = 0 \tag{8.55}$$

we obtain immediately

$$\mathbf{x}_{n+1} = \mathbf{x}_n + \Delta t \mathbf{v}_n + [2\mathbf{M} + 2\gamma_z \Delta t \mathbf{C} + \beta_z \Delta t^2 \mathbf{K}]^{-1} \{-\Delta t^2 \mathbf{K} \mathbf{x}_n$$
$$- \Delta t^2 (\mathbf{C} + \gamma_z \Delta t \mathbf{K}) \mathbf{v}_n + \Delta t^2 \mathbf{F}\} \tag{8.56}$$

where $\gamma_z$, $\beta_z$ are new parameters defined as

$$\Delta t \gamma_z = \frac{\displaystyle\int_0^{\Delta t} W_1 t \, dt}{\displaystyle\int_0^{\Delta t} W_1 \, dt}$$

$$\Delta t^2 \beta_z = \frac{\displaystyle\int_0^{\Delta t} W_1 t^2 \, dt}{\displaystyle\int_0^{\Delta t} W_1 \, dt} \tag{8.57}$$

and $\mathbf{F}$ is a suitably interpolated form of the load vector $\mathbf{f}$.

Equation (8.56) is used to give $\mathbf{x}_{n+1}$ and then differentiating Eq. (8.54) and putting in $t = \Delta t$, we have

$$\Delta t \mathbf{v}_{n+1} = 2(\mathbf{x}_{n+1} - \mathbf{x}_n) - \Delta t \mathbf{v}_n \tag{8.58}$$

to give $\mathbf{v}_{n+1}$.

Equations (8.56) and (8.57) together thus constitute a one-step recurrence in $\mathbf{Y}_n = [\mathbf{x}_n, \Delta t v_n]^T$.

We can examine the stability of this scheme by putting $\mathbf{Y}_{n+1} = \lambda \mathbf{Y}_n$ and obtaining a stability polynomial which is a quadratic. By matching the coefficients of this with the quadratic polynomial Eq. (8.34), we find identity when

$$\gamma_z = \gamma \qquad \text{and} \qquad \beta_z = 2\beta \tag{8.59}$$

Noting that identical stability conditions must again apply, we find that by conditions of Eq. (8.40)

$$\beta_z \geqslant \gamma_z \geqslant \tfrac{1}{2} \tag{8.60}$$

for unconditional stability.

The new algorithm introduced here has considerable computational advantage over the standard Newmark process and deserves to be widely used.

Another algorithm using hermitian cubic interpolation functions (illustrated in Fig. 8.11) has been discussed by Argyris and Dunne [36]. For computational reasons, this algorithm has not become popular. See also references [34, 35].

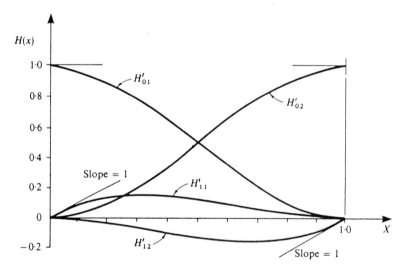

**FIG. 8.11**    Hermitian cubic interpolation functions in time.

## 8.5 HIGHER-ORDER RECURRENCE SCHEMES

The procedures for deriving recurrence schemes by the weighted-residual process can be extended by using higher-order interpolation in various ways. In this section we consider parabolic interpolation for the first-order equation and cubic interpolation for the second-order equation.

## 8.5A Two-Step Schemes for the First-Order Equation

We can use the same derivation as in Sec. 8.3. Putting $\mathbf{M} = 0$ in Eq. (8.27) to remove the second-order time derivative, we obtain the two-step recurrence

$$(\gamma\mathbf{C} + \beta\Delta t\mathbf{K})\mathbf{x}_{n+1} + [(1 - 2\gamma)\mathbf{C} + (\tfrac{1}{2} - 2\beta + \gamma)\Delta t\mathbf{K}]\mathbf{x}_n$$

$$+ [(\gamma - 1)\mathbf{C} + (\tfrac{1}{2} + \beta - \gamma)\Delta t\mathbf{K}]\mathbf{x}_{n-1} + \bar{\mathbf{f}} = 0 \tag{8.61}$$

where $\bar{\mathbf{f}}$ is given as before by interpolation of values of the forcing function [Eqs. (8.30)] and $\beta$, $\gamma$ have the same meaning as before [Eq. (8.28)].

$\gamma = \tfrac{1}{2}$, $\beta = \tfrac{1}{3}$ gives an algorithm due to Lees [37] often used for nonlinear problems [38]. $\gamma = \tfrac{1}{2}$, $\beta = \tfrac{1}{6}$ results from subdomain collocation [$W \equiv 1$ over $(n-1)\Delta t \leq t \leq (n+1)\Delta t$], shown in Fig. 8.8.

The conditions for unconditional stability are the same as before:

$$\gamma \geq \tfrac{1}{2} \qquad 2\beta \geq \gamma \tag{8.62}$$

Dahlquist [39] and Cryer [44] have also discussed this problem.

Conditions for conditional stability can be found if required. It is interesting to note that the central-difference scheme with $\gamma = \tfrac{1}{2}$ and $\beta = 0$ is unconditionally unstable and should never be used.

## 8.5B Cubic Schemes for Second-Order Equations

**1.** Zienkiewicz [40] obtained a very general higher-order formula by assuming the displacement $\mathbf{x}$ to be cubic in time (Fig. 8.12) and writing it in the form

$$\mathbf{x} = \sum_{i=n-2}^{n+1} \mathbf{x}_i N_i(t) \tag{8.63}$$

Substituted in the weighted-residual equation this immediately gives

$$\{\mathbf{M}(\gamma - 1) + (\tfrac{1}{2}\beta - \gamma + \tfrac{1}{3})\mathbf{C}\Delta t + (\tfrac{1}{6}\alpha - \tfrac{1}{2}\beta + \tfrac{1}{3}\gamma)\mathbf{K}\Delta t^2\}\mathbf{x}_{n+1}$$

$$+ \{\mathbf{M}(-3\gamma + 4) + (-\tfrac{3}{2}\beta + 4\gamma - \tfrac{3}{2})\mathbf{C}\Delta t + (-\tfrac{1}{2}\alpha + 2\beta - \tfrac{3}{2}\gamma)\mathbf{K}\Delta t^2\}\mathbf{x}_n$$

$$+ \{\mathbf{M}(3\gamma - 5) + (\tfrac{3}{2}\beta - 5\gamma + 3)\mathbf{C}\Delta t + (\tfrac{1}{2}\alpha - \tfrac{5}{2}\beta + 3\gamma)\mathbf{K}\Delta t^2\}\mathbf{x}_{n-1}$$

$$+ \{\mathbf{M}(-\gamma + 2) + (-\tfrac{1}{2}\beta + 2\gamma - \tfrac{11}{6})\mathbf{C}\Delta t + (-\tfrac{1}{6}\alpha + \beta - \tfrac{11}{6}\gamma + 1)\mathbf{K}\Delta t^2\}\mathbf{x}_{n-2}$$

$$+ \Delta t^2(\tfrac{1}{6}\alpha - \tfrac{1}{2}\beta + \tfrac{1}{3}\gamma)\mathbf{f}_{n+1} + (-\tfrac{1}{2}\alpha + 2\beta - \tfrac{3}{2}\gamma)\mathbf{f}_n\Delta t^2$$

$$+ (\tfrac{1}{2}\alpha - \tfrac{5}{2}\beta + 3\gamma)\mathbf{f}_{n-1}\Delta t^2 + (-\tfrac{1}{6}\alpha + \beta - \tfrac{11}{6}\gamma + 1)\mathbf{f}_{n-1}\Delta t^2 = 0 \tag{8.64}$$

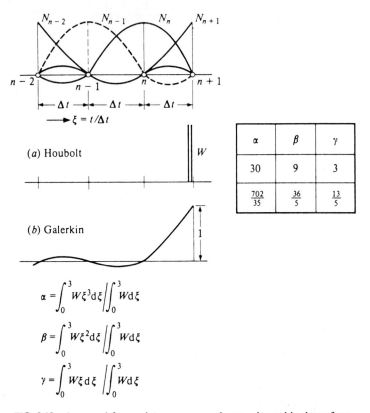

| $\alpha$ | $\beta$ | $\gamma$ |
|---|---|---|
| 30 | 9 | 3 |
| $\dfrac{702}{35}$ | $\dfrac{36}{5}$ | $\dfrac{13}{5}$ |

(a) Houbolt

(b) Galerkin

$$\alpha = \int_0^3 W\xi^3 d\xi \bigg/\!\!\bigg/ \int_0^3 W d\xi$$

$$\beta = \int_0^3 W\xi^2 d\xi \bigg/\!\!\bigg/ \int_0^3 W d\xi$$

$$\gamma = \int_0^3 W\xi d\xi \bigg/\!\!\bigg/ \int_0^3 W d\xi$$

**FIG. 8.12** A general four-point recurrence scheme using cubic shape functions: (a) Houbolt and (b) Galerkin as two special cases of weighting.

where

$$\Delta t\gamma = \frac{\displaystyle\int_{-2\Delta t}^{\Delta t} Wt\,dt}{\displaystyle\int_{-2\Delta t}^{\Delta t} W\,dt}$$

$$\Delta t^2\beta = \frac{\displaystyle\int_{-2\Delta t}^{\Delta t} Wt^2\,dt}{\displaystyle\int_{-2\Delta t}^{\Delta t} W\,dt}$$

$$\Delta t^3\alpha = \frac{\displaystyle\int_{-2\Delta t}^{\Delta t} Wt^3\,dt}{\displaystyle\int_{-2\Delta t}^{\Delta t} W\,dt}$$

(8.65)

The general stability properties of this three-step recurrence have been discussed in detail by Wood [41]. For unconditional stability we require

$$a > 0 \qquad b > 0 \qquad 3ab > c > 0 \qquad (8.66)$$

where $a$, $b$, $c$ are related to the $\alpha$, $\beta$, $\gamma$ in Eq. (8.65) by

$$\gamma = 1.5 + a \qquad \beta = 3 + 3a + b \qquad \alpha = 6.75 + 8.5a + 4.5b + c \qquad (8.67a)$$

Several well-known methods are particular cases of this. The Houbolt formula [42] is given by $\alpha = 27$, $\beta = 9$, $\gamma = 3$. This is unconditionally stable and has characteristics shown in Figs. 8.13 and 8.14. These can be compared with Figs. 8.9 and 8.10 for the Newmark method.

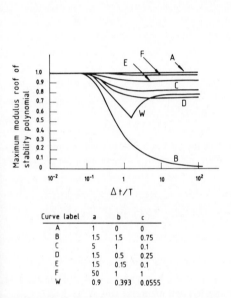

| Curve label | a | b | c |
|---|---|---|---|
| A | 1 | 0 | 0 |
| B | 1.5 | 1.5 | 0.75 |
| C | 5 | 1 | 0.1 |
| D | 1.5 | 0.5 | 0.25 |
| E | 1.5 | 0.15 | 0.1 |
| F | 50 | 1 | 1 |
| W | 0.9 | 0.393 | 0.0555 |

**FIG. 8.13** Maximum-modulus root of stability polynomial against $\Delta t / T$ (A) zero damping, minimum period elongation, (B) Houbolt, and (W) Wilson ($\theta = 1.4$).

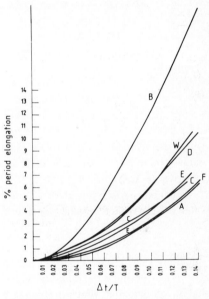

**FIG. 8.14** Percentage period elongation against $\Delta t / T$.

With

$$\alpha = 2 + 4\theta + 3\theta^2 + \theta^3 \qquad \beta = \tfrac{4}{3} + 2\theta + \theta^2 \qquad \gamma = 1 + \theta \qquad (8.67b)$$

the Wilson $\theta$-method is produced [27, 43]. This was introduced to obtain improved damping of the high-frequency modes. Values of $\theta$ such that $1.4 \leqslant \theta \leqslant 2.0$ have been used. For unconditional stability we must have $\theta > 1.366$ [41]. We note that $\theta = 1$ reduces the three-step scheme in the displacements given by Eq. (8.64) to the Newmark algorithm with $\gamma = \tfrac{1}{2}$, $\beta = \tfrac{1}{6}$. The algorithms proposed by Hilber [33] can also be identified with the three-step schemes with the introduction of artificial damping as in Eq. (8.46). The general algorithm given by

Eq. (8.64) has many other possibilities yet to be tested in practice. The corresponding form for first-order problems is available by putting $\mathbf{M} = \mathbf{0}$ in Eq. (8.64).

**2.** Instead of expressing the cubic variation in terms of four discrete values of the displacements as in Eq. (8.63), we can also express it in terms of four discrete values of displacement, velocity, and acceleration, as convenient. The weighted-residual equation then gives a relation between these four quantities. Thus we can express the cubic variation of displacement in terms of $\mathbf{x}_{n+1}$, $\mathbf{x}_n$, $\mathbf{x}_{n-1}$, $\mathbf{v}_n$ as follows:

$$\mathbf{x} = \mathbf{x}_n + t\mathbf{v}_n + \frac{t^2}{2\Delta t^2}(\mathbf{x}_{n+1} - 2\mathbf{x}_n + \mathbf{x}_{n-1}) + \frac{t^3}{2\Delta t^3}(\mathbf{x}_{n+1} - \mathbf{x}_{n-1} - 2\mathbf{v}_n\Delta t) \tag{8.67c}$$

Then substituting for $\mathbf{x}$, $\dot{\mathbf{x}}$, $\ddot{\mathbf{x}}$ in the weighted-residual form of Eq. (8.3), we obtain

$$\mathbf{M}[\mathbf{x}_{n+1} - 2\mathbf{x}_n + \mathbf{x}_{n-1} + 3\gamma_2(\mathbf{x}_{n+1} - \mathbf{x}_{n-1} - 2\Delta t\mathbf{v}_n)]$$

$$+ \Delta t\mathbf{C}\left[\Delta t\mathbf{v}_n + \gamma_2(\mathbf{x}_{n+1} - 2\mathbf{x}_n + \mathbf{x}_{n-1}) + \frac{3\beta_2}{2}(\mathbf{x}_{n+1} - \mathbf{x}_{n-1} - 2\Delta t\mathbf{v}_n)\right]$$

$$+ \Delta t^2\mathbf{K}\left[\mathbf{x}_n + \gamma_2\Delta t\mathbf{v}_n + \frac{\beta_2}{2}(\mathbf{x}_{n+1} - 2\mathbf{x}_n + \mathbf{x}_{n-1})\right.$$

$$\left. + \frac{\alpha_2}{2}(\mathbf{x}_{n+1} - \mathbf{x}_{n-1} - 2\Delta t\mathbf{v}_n)\right] + \Delta t^2\mathbf{F} = \mathbf{0} \tag{8.67d}$$

where the vector $\mathbf{F}$ is the result of a suitable interpolation on the forcing function $\mathbf{f}$. The parameters $\alpha_2$, $\beta_2$, $\gamma_2$ are given by formulae similar to those in Eqs. (8.65) with the integrals now over $(-\Delta t, \Delta t)$.

Equation (8.67d) thus gives $\mathbf{x}_{n+1}$ if the previous values $\mathbf{x}_n$, $\mathbf{x}_{n-1}$, and $\mathbf{v}_n$ are known. The value of $\mathbf{v}_{n+1}$ is then obtained by differentiating and substituting $t = \Delta t$ in Eq. (8.67c).

$$\Delta t\mathbf{v}_{n+1} = \tfrac{5}{2}\mathbf{x}_{n+1} - 2\mathbf{x}_n - \tfrac{1}{2}\mathbf{x}_{n-1} - 2\mathbf{v}_n\Delta t \tag{8.67e}$$

Equations (8.67d and e) together form a two-step recurrence for the vector $\mathbf{Y}_n = [\mathbf{x}_n, \Delta t\mathbf{v}_n]^T$.

We can examine the stability of this scheme by putting $\mathbf{Y}_{n+1} = \lambda\mathbf{Y}_n$ and obtaining the stability polynomial, which is a cubic. By matching the coefficients of this with those in the stability polynomial obtained by Wood [41] for the algorithm, Eq. (8.64), we find that taking

$$\gamma_2 = \gamma - \tfrac{4}{3}$$

$$\beta_2 = \beta - \tfrac{8}{3}\gamma + \tfrac{14}{9} \tag{8.67f}$$

$$\alpha_2 = \alpha - 4\beta + \tfrac{14}{3}\gamma - \tfrac{14}{9}$$

enables us to use the same stability conditions.

Working with the vector $\mathbf{Y}_n = [\mathbf{x}_n, \Delta t\mathbf{v}_n]^T$ can be useful when we are solving the second-order Eq. (8.3), and we do not need to evaluate accelerations.

**3.** We can obtain a one-step scheme in the vector $\mathbf{X}_n = [\mathbf{x}_n, \Delta t\mathbf{v}_n, \Delta t^2\mathbf{a}_n]^T$ by expressing the cubic variation in terms of the four discrete quantities $\mathbf{x}_n$, $\mathbf{v}_n$, $\mathbf{a}_n$, $\mathbf{a}_{n+1}$ as follows:

$$\mathbf{x} = \mathbf{x}_n + t\mathbf{v}_n + \tfrac{1}{2}t^2\mathbf{a}_n + \frac{t^3}{6\Delta t}(\mathbf{a}_{n+1} - \mathbf{a}_n) \tag{8.67g}$$

Substituting for $\mathbf{x}$, $\dot{\mathbf{x}}$, $\ddot{\mathbf{x}}$ in the weighted-residual equation, we obtain

$$\left[\gamma_3 \mathbf{M} + \frac{\beta_3}{2}\Delta t \mathbf{C} + \frac{\alpha_3}{6}\Delta t^2 \mathbf{K}\right]\mathbf{a}_{n+1} = -\mathbf{K}\mathbf{x}_n - (\mathbf{C} + \gamma_3 \Delta t \mathbf{K})\mathbf{v}_n$$

$$-\left[(1-\gamma_3)\mathbf{M} + \left(\gamma_3 - \frac{\beta_3}{2}\right)\Delta t \mathbf{C} + \frac{3\beta_3 - \alpha_3}{6}\Delta t^2 \mathbf{K}\right]\mathbf{a}_n + \Delta t^2 F \qquad (8.67h)$$

where $\alpha_3$, $\beta_3$, $\gamma_3$ are given by formulae similar to those in Eq. (8.65) with integrals now over $(0, \Delta t)$.

Equation (8.67h) gives $\mathbf{a}_{n+1}$ if $\mathbf{x}_n$, $\mathbf{v}_n$, $\mathbf{a}_n$ are known from the previous time step. Thus Eq. (8.67h), together with the equations

$$\mathbf{x}_{n+1} = \tfrac{1}{6}\Delta t^2 \mathbf{a}_{n+1} + \mathbf{x}_n + \Delta t \mathbf{v}_n + \tfrac{1}{3}\Delta t^2 \mathbf{a}_n \qquad (8.67i)$$

and $\qquad\qquad \Delta t \mathbf{v}_{n+1} = \tfrac{1}{2}\Delta t^2 \mathbf{a}_{n+1} + \Delta t \mathbf{v}_n + \tfrac{1}{2}\Delta t^2 \mathbf{a}_n \qquad (8.67j)$

[derived from Eq. (8.67g)] constitutes a convenient one-step recurrence in $\mathbf{X}_n$ such that only $\mathbf{a}_{n+1}$ requires a matrix inversion.

Again we can match coefficients in the stability polynomial arising from taking $\mathbf{X}_{n+1} = \lambda \mathbf{X}_n$ in order to use the results obtained by Wood [41]. We take

$$\gamma_3 = \gamma - 1$$
$$\beta_3 = \beta - 2\gamma + \tfrac{2}{3} \qquad\qquad (8.67k)$$
$$\alpha_3 = \alpha - 3\beta + 2\gamma$$

Then the conditions for unconditional stability [Eq. (8.66)] are again available via Eqs. (8.67a).


## 8.6 TIME-STEPPING SCHEMES FOR NONLINEAR PROBLEMS

The major application of time-stepping (or time-marching) procedures is to nonlinear problems, where one or more of the matrices $\mathbf{M}$, $\mathbf{C}$, $\mathbf{K}$, or $\mathbf{f}$ depend on the unknown vector $\boldsymbol{\phi}$. Here the alternatives of analytical solution present in linear situations do not exist. Clearly the weighted-residual expressions, such as those given by Eqs. (8.6) and (8.26) for first- and second-order systems, respectively, remain valid, but their simplified, integrated forms of Eqs. (8.8) and (8.27) are not. Indeed the full integration can only be carried out numerically, and, in general, iteration within each time step appears to be needed. Further, at each time step a different set of equations will require solution, thus making procedures costly.

With such nonlinear problems, point-collocation procedures (finite differences) have often been used in practice, thus avoiding the difficulties of integration in the time domain. This loses some of the accuracy of the computation, however, and alternatives exist. For instance, turning our attention to Eq. (8.6) and assuming $\mathbf{C}$ and $\mathbf{K}$ to be dependent on $\boldsymbol{\phi}$, we can apply the interpolation expressions $\dot{N}$ and $N$, respectively, to the product vectors

$$\tilde{\mathbf{C}} = \mathbf{C}\boldsymbol{\phi} \qquad \mathbf{p} = \mathbf{K}\boldsymbol{\phi} \tag{8.68}$$

Now, in place of Eq. (8.8), we have

$$\left(\frac{\tilde{\mathbf{C}}^{n+1}}{\Delta t} + \mathbf{p}^{n+1}\theta\right) + \left(-\frac{\tilde{\mathbf{C}}^{n}}{\Delta t} + \mathbf{p}^{n}(1-\theta)\right) + \tilde{\mathbf{f}} = \mathbf{0} \tag{8.69}$$

An iterative process, e.g. the Newton–Raphson method, can be used to solve the above set of equations for $\boldsymbol{\phi}_{n+1}$, noting that

$$\tilde{\mathbf{C}}^{n+1} = \tilde{\mathbf{C}}(\boldsymbol{\phi}^{n+1})$$
$$\mathbf{p}^{n+1} = \mathbf{p}(\boldsymbol{\phi}^{n+1}) \tag{8.70}$$

Tangent matrices must be computed, giving such derivatives as

$$\frac{\partial \tilde{\mathbf{C}}}{\partial \boldsymbol{\phi}^{n}} \qquad \frac{\partial \mathbf{p}}{\partial \boldsymbol{\phi}^{n}} \tag{8.71}$$

The vectors $\tilde{\mathbf{C}}^{n}$ and $\mathbf{p}^{n}$, however, are readily evaluated, and errors in incomplete iteration are, to some extent, corrected by a direct computation of these at the start of each interval.

In this manner, the procedure can be applied to second-order problems. Such processes once again appear to be more consistent than the pointwise imposition of the nonlinear equation in conventional finite-difference (or Newmark) schemes.

Iteration within a time interval can, however, be costly, and an alternative exists in making a cruder approximation to the variable matrices. Here, mean values of the appropriate matrices $\mathbf{M}$, $\mathbf{C}$, or $\mathbf{K}$ are established by extrapolation from previous steps, and the linear expressions previously derived are used in the interval. Such extrapolation leads to more stable solutions [45–47], as within each interval the usual linearized stability criteria hold and further instability which may sometimes arise solely due to iteration is avoided.

In a particular interval, a very simple extrapolation uses the values of the matrices corresponding to those at the last known value, i.e.,

$$\mathbf{M}^{n+1} = \mathbf{M}^{n} \qquad \mathbf{C}^{n+1} = \mathbf{C}^{n} \qquad \cdots \tag{8.72}$$

and for first-order problems any of the two- or three-point formulae previously developed can be used directly.

Culham and Varga [45] use such a scheme for the solution of a first-order equation with a variable $\mathbf{K}$ and combine it with a backward-difference ($\theta = 1$) numerical scheme. Their results show a better accuracy than that obtainable with other schemes where iteration has been used.

In explicit schemes with lumped matrices, the use of approximation [Eq. (8.72)] is natural. The term

$$\mathbf{K}^{n}\boldsymbol{\phi}^{n} = \mathbf{p}^{n} \tag{8.73}$$

is evaluated as a vector such as may be caused by a nonlinear material or geometrical behavior of a structure, and the matrix $\mathbf{K}$ is not explicitly formed. Such schemes appear extremely useful in many structural short-period investigations [23–25], and although the time interval is still subject to stability, the simplicity of computation makes the scheme very commendable.

Another use of the assumption of Eq. (8.72) is in the three-point schemes applied to first-order equations in which all the matrices are subject to nonlinearity. This has been demonstrated as an effective procedure by Comini et al. [38] for a heat-conduction problem in which conductivity of specific heat and heat generation both depend on temperature.

Indeed, at this point, we see a possible advantage of using the three-point formulation of the Newmark algorithm given by Eq. (8.27) rather than its conventional alternative [21]. In the former, $\mathbf{K}^n$ (etc.) correspond to midinterval values rather than to initial values and thus the error in linearization is less severe.

## 8.7 COMBINED IMPLICIT AND EXPLICIT PROCESSES

### 8.7A General Considerations

The computational advantages of explicit time-stepping schemes are counterbalanced by the very small size of time step necessary when some elements have high eigenvalues. In some problems, typified by Fig. 8.15, a part I of a region may be such that explicit processes with

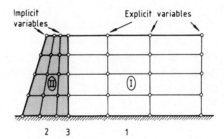

**FIG. 8.15**  A typical problem for which a mix of implicit and explicit processes is desirable.

a reasonable time-step size could be used, and a part II may be one in which the stiffness or size of element is such that for the same time step an implicit process is necessary. It is, in such cases, possible to use simultaneously both algorithms and take advantage of the partial diagonalization of the matrices in the explicit region I. The procedures were first introduced by Belytschko and Mullen [48–50] and were given an alternative form by Hughes and Liu [51, 52] and Park et al. [53–55]. Here we show that such a mixed formulation arises naturally with the process using a weighted, finite element in time. We illustrate the process on the first-order problem of Eq. (8.2) for which we have developed the two-point formula of Eq. (8.8). The extension to other algorithms and to second-order problems will follow identical lines and need not be discussed in detail.

Two possible approaches exist to the problem, i.e., *nodal* or *element* algorithm separations. In the first, the starting point is the semidiscretized set of ordinary differential equations. In the second, the separation is carried out at element levels. The first procedure results in algorithms similar to those of Belytschko and Park. The second is basically the process suggested by Hughes.

## 8.7B Nodal Algorithm Separation

We start with the semidiscretized form of Eq. (8.2), writing it as

$$\mathbf{C\dot{a} + Ka + f = 0} \tag{8.74}$$

in which $\mathbf{C}$ is assumed to be diagonal.

In the expansion following Eq. (8.4), we partition the vector $\mathbf{a}_i$ into components $\mathbf{a}_i^{\mathrm{I}}$ and $\mathbf{a}_i^{\mathrm{II}}$ associated with explicit and implicit regions, respectively. We now have

$$\mathbf{a} \approx \hat{\mathbf{a}} = \sum_{i=n}^{n+1} [\, N_i^{\mathrm{I}} \quad N_i^{\mathrm{II}}\,] \begin{bmatrix} \mathbf{a}_i^{\mathrm{I}} \\ \mathbf{a}_i^{\mathrm{II}} \end{bmatrix} \tag{8.75}$$

In the present case, we assume that $N_i^{\mathrm{I}} = N_i^{\mathrm{II}}$ and follow the forms given by Eq. (8.5), but obviously we could take different shape functions for each expansion. (If different shape functions are used, it is possible that a spatial discontinuity will be involved in the time-space domain, but this need not concern us at this stage where discrete equations are being solved.)

In weighted form analogous to that of Eq. (8.6), we now have

$$\int_0^{\Delta t} [\, W_i^{\mathrm{I}} \quad W_i^{\mathrm{II}}\,][\mathbf{C}(\mathbf{a}_n \dot{N}_n + \mathbf{a}_{n+1} N_{n+1}) + \mathbf{K}(\mathbf{a}_n N_n + \mathbf{a}_{n+1} N_{n+1}) + \mathbf{f}]\, dt = 0 \tag{8.76}$$

The weighting functions $W_i^{\mathrm{I}}$ and $W_i^{\mathrm{II}}$ can now be chosen to make the algorithm explicit for the vector of unknowns $\mathbf{a}_i^{\mathrm{I}}$ and implicit for $\mathbf{a}_i^{\mathrm{II}}$. Omitting algebraic detail, using the definitions of Eq. (8.9), and taking $\theta = 0$ for nodes in region I and $\theta = \bar{\theta}$ for nodes in region II, we can write Eq. (8.8) in a partitioned form as

$$\begin{bmatrix} \dfrac{1}{\Delta t}\mathbf{C}^{\mathrm{I,I}} & 0 \\[2ex] \mathbf{K}^{\mathrm{II,I}}\bar{\theta} & \dfrac{1}{\Delta t}\mathbf{C}^{\mathrm{II,II}} + \mathbf{K}^{\mathrm{II,II}}\bar{\theta} \end{bmatrix} \begin{bmatrix} \mathbf{a}^{\mathrm{I}} \\ \mathbf{a}^{\mathrm{II}} \end{bmatrix}_{n+1}$$

$$+ \begin{bmatrix} \dfrac{-1}{\Delta t}C^{\mathrm{I,I}} + K^{\mathrm{II}} & \mathbf{K}^{\mathrm{I,II}} \\[2ex] (1-\bar{\theta})\mathbf{K}^{\mathrm{II,I}} & \dfrac{-1}{t}\mathbf{C}^{\mathrm{II,II}} + (1-\bar{\theta})\mathbf{K}^{\mathrm{II,II}} \end{bmatrix} \begin{bmatrix} \mathbf{a}^{\mathrm{I}} \\ \mathbf{a}^{\mathrm{II}} \end{bmatrix}_n + \begin{bmatrix} \mathbf{f}^{\mathrm{I}} \\ \mathbf{f}^{\mathrm{II}} \end{bmatrix} = 0 \tag{8.77}$$

The above separation could have been implemented for any two or more values of $\bar{\theta}$, but it is useful only if one side leads to an explicit solution. We observe that the coefficients of the equations are no longer symmetric. However, the solution can readily be carried out sequentially using the symmetric properties of the submatrices. Indeed, this is the natural manner of utilizing the explicitness of the first variable.

In such a sequential solution, we proceed to determine from the known values of $\mathbf{a}_n$ first the vector $\mathbf{a}_{n+1}^{\mathrm{I}}$ and then, using the above values as boundary condition for the second part, determine $\mathbf{a}_{n+1}^{II}$. As determined by Park [55], this type of solution is best accomplished by simply combining two separate programs written for either implicit or explicit processes. We note, however, that if the first partition corresponds to a nonexplicit scheme, such as that given by $\theta \neq 0$, this is no longer possible and nonsymmetric solvers may have to be used or, alternatively, a "staggered" solution process adopted [55].

## 8.7c Element Algorithm Separation

We start from the fact that the semidiscretization was carried out, generally, by a spatial finite-element process and that the semidiscrete system of Eq. (8.74) is obtained by an element assembly of the standard form defined as

$$C_{ij} = \sum_{e=1}^{m} C_{ij}^{e} \cdots \tag{8.78}$$

where $e$ denotes the element contributions and the summation is carried out over all elements.

Now we consider two regions of elements I and II in the example of Fig. 8.15 and apply the same algorithm as before (i.e., $\theta = 0$ and $\theta = \bar{\theta}$) to the elements of each region.

Partitioning the vector $\mathbf{a}_i^{II}$ into two parts $(\mathbf{a}^2, \mathbf{a}^3)^T$, we write the equivalent to Eq. (8.8) as

$$
\begin{bmatrix}
\dfrac{1}{\Delta t}\mathbf{C}^{1,1} & \mathbf{0} & \mathbf{0} \\[2ex]
\mathbf{0} & \dfrac{1}{t}\mathbf{C}^{2,2}+\mathbf{A} & \mathbf{K}^{2,3}\bar{\theta} \\[2ex]
\mathbf{0} & \mathbf{K}^{3,2}\bar{\theta} & \dfrac{1}{\Delta t}\mathbf{C}^{3,3}+\mathbf{K}^{3,3}\bar{\theta}
\end{bmatrix}
\begin{bmatrix}
\mathbf{a}^1 \\[1ex] \mathbf{a}^2 \\[1ex] \mathbf{a}^3
\end{bmatrix}_{n+1}
$$

$$
+
\begin{bmatrix}
-\dfrac{1}{\Delta t}\mathbf{C}^{1,1}+\mathbf{K}^{1,1} & \mathbf{K}^{1,2} & \mathbf{0} \\[2ex]
\mathbf{K}^{1,2} & \dfrac{-1}{\Delta t}\mathbf{C}^{2,2}+\mathbf{B} & \mathbf{K}^{2,3}(1-\bar{\theta}) \\[2ex]
\mathbf{0} & \mathbf{K}^{3,2}(1-\bar{\theta}) & \dfrac{-1}{\Delta t}\mathbf{C}^{3,3}+\mathbf{K}^{3,3}(1-\bar{\theta})
\end{bmatrix}
\begin{bmatrix}
\mathbf{a}^1 \\[1ex] \mathbf{a}^2 \\[1ex] \mathbf{a}^3
\end{bmatrix}_{n+1}
+
\begin{bmatrix}
\mathbf{f}^1 \\[1ex] \mathbf{f}^2 \\[1ex] \mathbf{f}^3
\end{bmatrix}
= 0 \tag{8.79}
$$

In Eq. (8.79)

$$\mathbf{A} = \sum_{e}^{2} \mathbf{K}_e^{2,2}\bar{\theta}$$

$$\mathbf{B} = \sum_{e}^{1} \mathbf{K}_e^{2,2} + \sum_{e}^{2} \mathbf{K}_e^{2,2}(1-\bar{\theta})$$

and the summations marked 1 and 2 refer to the appropriate element regions.

The resulting equations are still explicit in the variables in vector $\mathbf{a}^1$ and in addition have a symmetry property which allows a simple symmetric program to be used throughout.

Which of the alternatives presented is superior depends on the usage and the problem presented. It is clear that either can be adapted to any of the algorithms discussed in this chapter and that indeed both forms spring directly from the concept of the "finite element in time."

Stability of the implicit–explicit processes has been studied extensively. Hughes and Liu [51] study the "element" procedures, while Park [55] gives a complete study of a variety of cases. It appears simply that in the mixed forms satisfaction of stability criteria within each separate domain automatically ensures stability of the whole scheme. This result is one which "heuristically" we would anticipate.

## 8.8 PROBLEMS WITH CHANGING BOUNDARIES

### 8.8A Convective-Diffusive Heat-Transport Equation

In the discretization of Eqs. (8.2) and (8.3) we have assumed that the matrices occurring there are positive-definite and therefore have real eigenvalues. If this is not the case, the conclusions concerning the stability of various algorithms are not valid and it is possible for instability to occur. A typical problem of this class arises in a semidiscretized form of the convective-diffusive (heat-) transport equation

$$c\frac{\partial T}{\partial t}+u\frac{\partial T}{\partial x}+v\frac{\partial T}{\partial y}-\frac{\partial}{\partial x}\left(k\frac{\partial T}{\partial x}\right)+\frac{\partial}{\partial y}\left(k\frac{\partial T}{\partial y}\right)+Q=0 \tag{8.80}$$

where $u(x, y, t)$ and $v(x, y, t)$ are known velocities. Note that the second and third terms result in a nonsymmetric semidiscretized form even if Galerkin–Petrov methods are used. Now, following exactly the same process that led to the semidiscretized form of Eq. (8.2), we have

$$\mathbf{C\dot{a}+Ka+f=0} \tag{8.81}$$

using $T \approx \hat{T} = \Sigma \bar{N}_i(x, y)a_i(t)$. The matrices $\mathbf{C}$, $\mathbf{K}$ and the vector $\mathbf{f}$ are given by

$$C_{ij} = \int_\Omega \bar{W}_j c \bar{N}_i \, dx \, dy$$

$$K_{ji} = \int_\Omega \left(k\frac{\partial \bar{W}_j}{\partial x}\frac{\partial \bar{N}_i}{\partial y}+k\frac{\partial \bar{W}_j}{\partial y}\frac{\partial \bar{N}_i}{\partial y}+\bar{W}_j u\frac{\partial \bar{N}_i}{\partial x}+\bar{W}_j v\frac{\partial \bar{N}_i}{\partial y}\right) dx \, dy \tag{8.82}$$

$$f_j = \int_\Omega \bar{W}_j Q \, dx \, dy$$

It can be shown that even with the spatial discretization in which $\bar{W}_j = \bar{N}_j$ we can obtain unstable (oscillatory) results. To overcome the difficulty in such problems, special forms of weighting functions can be used [56–61]. The use of such so-called *upwind-weighting techniques* has recently been extended to transient situations. With such spatial discretization although the matrices $\mathbf{K}$ of Eq. (8.81) are still nonsymmetric, stable computation with some of the algorithms previously discussed are still possible and the time discretization follows the path already described. A more complete discussion of this problem may be found in Refs. [62–65].

Here we pursue a different approach, which leads to a class of formulations with a standard diffusion (conduction) governing equation but with changing (spatial) boundaries.

Let us consider a coordinate change to be applied to Eq. (8.80). The new coordinates $x'$, $y'$, and $t'$ are related to $x$, $y$, and $t$ by the requirement

$$x' = x - \frac{ut}{c}$$

$$y' = y - \frac{vt}{c} \qquad (8.83)$$

$$t' = t$$

Noting that

$$\frac{\partial x'}{\partial x} = \frac{\partial y'}{\partial y} = \frac{\partial t'}{\partial t} = 1 \qquad \frac{\partial x'}{\partial t} = -\frac{u}{c} \qquad \frac{\partial y'}{\partial t} = -\frac{v}{c} \qquad \frac{\partial x'}{\partial y} = \frac{\partial y'}{\partial x} = \frac{\partial t'}{\partial x} = \frac{\partial t'}{\partial y} = 0$$

we can, by rules of partial differentiation, observe that

$$c\frac{\partial T}{\partial t} = -u\frac{\partial T}{\partial x'} - v\frac{\partial T}{\partial y'} + c\frac{\partial T}{\partial t'} \qquad \frac{\partial T}{\partial x} = \frac{\partial T}{\partial x'} \qquad \frac{\partial T}{\partial y} = \frac{\partial T}{\partial y'} \qquad (8.84)$$

Equation (8.80) transforms simply in the above set of coordinates to the standard heat-conduction form

$$\frac{\partial T}{\partial t'} - \frac{\partial}{\partial x'}\left(\frac{k}{c}\frac{\partial T}{\partial x'}\right) - \frac{\partial}{\partial y'}\left(\frac{k}{c}\frac{\partial T}{\partial y'}\right) + \frac{Q}{c} = 0 \qquad (8.85)$$

The discretized form of this equation with standard Galerkin weighting has been fully discussed in Sec. 8.7.

Further, since the coordinates $x'$, $y'$, and $t'$ can be determined exactly or by numerical integration of relationships (8.83), it appears that the convective-diffusion problem has been entirely reduced to the standard forms already known. However, a difficulty arises as the boundary conditions of the form

$$\left.\begin{array}{c} \phi = \bar{\phi} \\[2mm] k\frac{\partial \phi}{\partial n} = q \end{array}\right\} \qquad \text{on } \Gamma(x, y) \qquad (8.86)$$

are given generally on the true space domain whose shape does not change with time. Now, by virtue of relationships (8.83), the shape of the domain in the $x'$- and $y'$-coordinates changes. To illustrate the problem consider a simple physical one-dimensional case governed by equations

$$\frac{\partial T}{\partial t} + \frac{u}{c}\frac{\partial T}{\partial x} - \frac{k}{c}\frac{\partial^2 T}{\partial x^2} + \frac{Q}{c} = 0 \qquad (8.87)$$

with

$$\left.\begin{array}{ll} T = T_0 & x = 0 \\[1mm] T = T_L & x = L \end{array}\right\} \quad t \geq 0$$

In the above $c$, $u$, and $k$ are taken as constants for the sake of simplicity. Now the equation in transformed coordinates becomes simply

$$\frac{\partial T}{\partial t'} - \frac{k}{c}\frac{\partial^2 T}{\partial x'^2} + Q = 0 \tag{8.88}$$

Figure 8.16$a$ illustrates the time-space domain of the original problem and the lines of constant $x'$, which in fact represent "characteristics of the propagation." In Fig. 8.16$b$, the domain of the problem in the transformed coordinates is shown, indicating the change of boundaries with time.

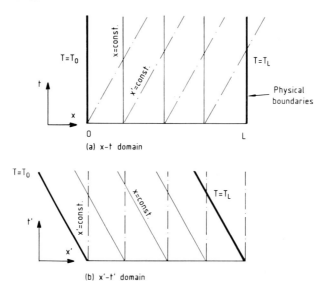

**FIG. 8.16** Convective-diffusive problem in one space dimension: ($a$) original and ($b$) transformed coordinates.

In Fig. 8.17$a$ and $b$ the same situation is illustrated for two-dimensional problems, showing the distortion of the space-time domain for a problem in which the velocities were not constant.

We note now that the simplification achieved by coordinate transformation is accompanied by an increase of difficulty due to the changes of spatial discretization.

Before proceeding further, we note the behavior of the solution for the limiting case when $k = 0$. Now, in the *transformed* coordinate we have simply

$$\frac{\partial T}{\partial t'} + \frac{Q}{c} = 0 \quad \rightarrow \quad T = -\int_0^t \frac{Q}{c}\, dt \tag{8.89}$$

and $T$ can be integrated exactly along the characteristic direction ($x' = $ constant) providing initial conditions are known. Indeed, we note that in the absence of heat generation the temperature remains constant along the characteristic, and in such a case the application of the boundary conditions where characteristics leave the physical region is physically incorrect. With the above remarks in mind, we note that two possible ways of proceeding are possible.

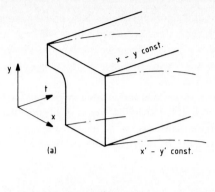

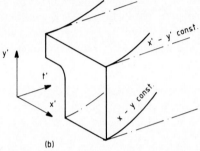

**FIG. 8.17** Convective-diffusive problem in two space dimensions: ($a$) original and ($b$) transformed domain.

In the first, limiting our attention to a time domain $[t, t + \Delta t]$, we choose $x = x'$ in the one-dimensional problem in Fig. 8.16 to apply at some point within the interval, e.g., at time $t + \frac{1}{2}\Delta t$ as illustrated in Fig. 8.18 for both sets of coordinates. The approximate region is also shown there. In the domain, we now solve Eq. (8.89) by standard means (semidiscretizing)

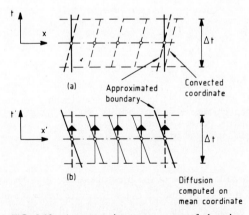

**FIG. 8.18** An approximate treatment of changing boundaries in convective-diffusive domain: ($a$) original and ($b$) transformed coordinate.

and by using, for instance, the algorithm of Eq. (8.8), and a new set of temperatures at time $t + \Delta t$ is available to start the next step. As the new values are given, however, at the coordinates $x'$ which can be evaluated, we change the space mesh at the next step and interpolate to new mesh positions. If the new interval is again defined in the coordinates $x' = x$, its e   polated position is again shown in Fig. 8.18.

The procedure turns out to be identical to that suggested by Connor and Brebbia [66] and Adey and Brebbia [67] and derived by them physically. Basically they note that the convection and conditions solutions can be used consecutively:

1. If we assume the velocities to be zero in the time interval $\Delta t$, a straightforward solution can be applied on the original mesh.

2. Turning off the conduction, we now are concerned with the pure-convection problem, and the new coordinates at which the results of step 1 are applicable are simply obtained by updating these to new positions given by $(u/c)\Delta t$. In practical computation to avoid changes of mesh at each time step, the temperatures are interpolated to the original mesh positions.

The second procedure is more precise. Here note is taken of the irregularity of the solution domain by using a full space–time element formulation. Such space–time elements can be drawn either in the original or transformed space domains of Fig. 8.19 and various forms of

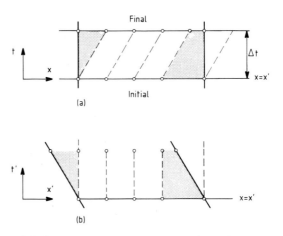

**FIG. 8.19** Irregular time-space elements (mainly) oriented along characteristics: (a) original and (b) transformed domains. (Reinterpolation to original mesh allows $x = x^1$ to be imposed at end of each step.)

solution techniques applied. Because of the presence of the first derivative of the equation, the equation will no longer be symmetric but will approximate symmetry if the directions are following the characteristics. This process applied in the original domain was first used by Finn and Varoglu [6, 7] and has achieved success in both one- and two-dimensional solutions. See also references [68–70].

## 8.8B  General Problems with Changing Boundaries

In the previous section we indicated the possibility of dealing with changing boundaries by various approximations. Some boundary-change problems occur in another context, e.g., in *ablating* bodies where the surface is subject to combustion. Again, various solution results are possible by following the details of the previous section.

## 8.9 REFERENCES

1. Oden, J. T., "The General Theory of Finite Elements: I. Applications," *Int. J. Numer. Meth. Eng.*, **1**:247-259 (1969).

2. Argyris, J. H., and D. W. Scharpf, "Finite Elements in Time and Space," *Aero. J. R. Aero. Soc.*, **73**:1041-1044 (1969).

3. Fried, I. "Finite Element Analysis of Time Dependent Phenomena," *AIAA J.*, **7**:1170-1172 (1969).

4. Zienkiewicz, O. C., and C. J. Parekh, "Transient Field Problems—Two and Three Dimensional; Analysis by Isoparametric Finite Elements," *Int. J. Numer. Meth. Eng.*, **2**:61-71 (1970).

5. Zienkiewicz, O. C., "The Finite Element Method in Engineering Science," McGraw-Hill, New York, 1971, pp. 335-339.

6. Finn, W. D. L., and E. Varoglu, "An Efficient Solution for Heat Transport Problems," in R. W. Lewis and K. Morgan (eds.), *Proceedings of the Conference on Numerical Methods in Thermal Problems*, University of Wales, Swansea, Wales, 1979.

7. Varoglu, E., and N. D. L. Finn, "A Finite Element Method for the Diffusion-Convection Equation With Constant Coefficients," *Adv. Water Resources*, **1**:337-341 (1973).

8. Zienkiewicz, O. C., "The Finite Element Method," 3d ed., McGraw-Hill, New York, 1977.

9. Strang, G., and G. I. Fix, *An Analysis of the Finite Element Method*, Prentice-Hall, Englewood Cliffs, N.J., 1973.

10. Zlamal, M., "Finite Element Methods in Heat Conduction Problems," in J. Whiteman (ed.), *Mathematics of Finite Elements and Applications II*, Academic Press, New York, 1977, pp. 85-104.

11. Washizu, K., *Variational Methods in Elasticity and Plasticity*, 2d ed., Pergamon Press, New York, 1975.

12. Gurtin, M., "Variational Principles for Linear Elastodynamics," *Arch. Nat. Mech. Anal.*, **16**:34-50 (1969).

13. Gurtin, M., "Variational Principles for Linear Elastodynamics and Plasticity," 2d ed., Pergamon Press, New York, 1975.

14. Wilson, E. L., and R. E. Nickell, "Application of Finite Element Method to Heat Conduction Analysis," *Nucl. Eng. Des.*, **4**:1-11 (1966).

15. Argyris, J. H., and D. W. Scharpf, "Finite Elements in Time and Space," *Nucl. Eng. Des.*, **10**:456-469 (1969).

16. Zienkiewicz, O. C., and R. H. Lewis, "An Analysis of Various Time Stepping Schemes for Initial Value Problems," *Int. J. Earthquake Eng. Struct. Dynam.*, **1**:407-408 (1973).

17. Wood, W. L., and R. W. Lewis, "A Comparison of Time Marching Schemes for the Transient Heat Conduction Equation," *Int. J. Numer. Meth. Eng.*, **9**:679-689 (1975).

18. Jones, D. G., and R. D. Henshell, "Oscillations in Transient Thermal Calculations" (to appear).

19. Lambert, T. D., *Computational Methods in Ordinary Differential Equations*, Wiley, New York, 1973.

20. Irons, B. M., *Applications of a Theorem on Eigenvalues to Finite Element Problems*, CR/132/70, Dept. Civ. Eng., University of Wales, Swansea, 1970.

21. Newmark, N. M., "A Method for Computation of Structural Dynamics," *Proc. Am. Soc. Civ. Eng.*, **85**(EM3):67–94 (1959).

22. Chan, S. P., H. L. Cox, and O. Benfield, "Transient Analysis of Forced Vibrations of Complex Structural Mechanical Systems," *J. R. Aero. Soc.*, **66**:457–460 (1962).

23. Belytschko, T., R. L. Chapetta, and H. D. Bartel, "Efficient Large Scale Non-Linear Transient Analysis by Finite Elements," *Int. J. Numer. Meth. Eng.*, **10**:579–596 (1976).

24. Shantaram, D., D. R. J. Owen, and O. C. Zienkiewicz, "Dynamic Transient Behaviour of Two and Three Dimensional Structures Including Plasticity, Large Deformation and Fluid Interaction," *Int. J. Earthquake Eng. Struct. Dynam.*, **4**:561–578 (1976).

25. Krieg, R. D., and S. W. Key, "Transient Shock Response by Numerical Time Integration," *Int. J. Numer. Meth. Eng.*, **7**:273–286 (1973).

26. Fu, C. C., "On the Stability of Explicit Methods for Numerical Integration of the Equations of Matrices in Finite Element Methods," *Int. J. Numer. Meth. Eng.* **4**:95–107 (1972).

27. Bathe, K. J., and E. L. Wilson, "Stability and Accuracy Analysis of Direct Integration Methods," *Int. J. Earthquake Eng. Struct. Dynam.*, **1**:283–291 (1973).

28. Nickell, R. E., "On the Stability of Approximation Operators in Problems of Structural Dynamics," *Int. J. Solids Struct.*, **7**:301–319 (1971).

29. Dunham, R. S. et al., "Integration Operators for Transient Structural Response," *J. Comp. Struct.*, **2** (1972).

30. Goudreau, G. L., and R. L. Taylor, "Evaluation of Numerical Integration Methods in Elasto Dynamics," *Comput. Meth. Appl. Mech. Eng.*, **2**:69–97 (1972).

31. Fox, L., and E. T. Goodwin, "Some New Methods for the Numerical Integration of Ordinary Differential Equations," *Proc. Camb. Phil. Soc.*, **49**:373–388 (1949).

32. Grant, J. E., "Response Computation Using Taylor Series," *Proc. ASCE*, **97**(EM2):295–303 (1971).

33a. Hilber, H. M., T. J. R. Hughes, and R. L. Taylor, "Improved Numerical Dissipation for Time Integration Algorithms in Structural Mechanics," *Int. J. Earthquake Struct. Dynam.*, **5**:283–292 (1977).

33b. Hilber, H. M., and T. J. R. Hughes, "Collocation, Dissipation and 'Overshoot' for Time Integration Schemes in Structural Dynamics," *Int. J. Earthquake Struct. Dynam.*, **6**:99–117 (1978).

34. Zienkiewicz, O. C., W. L. Wood, and R. L. Taylor, "An Alternative Single-Step Algorithm for Dynamic Problems," *Int. J. Earthquake Eng. Struct. Dynam.*, **8** (1980/81).

35. Collings, A. G., and C. J. Tee, "Generalized Euler Numerical Integration Schemes for New Solution of Problems in Structural Dynamics," *Proceedings of the Sixth Australasian Conference on the Mechanics of Structures and Materials*, Christchurch, New Zealand, 1977.

36a. Argyris, J. H., and P. R. Dunne, "Some Contributions to Non-Linear Solid Mechanics: II," *Int. Symp. on Comput. Meth. Appl. Sci. Eng. Lecture Notes in Computer Science*, 10, Springer-Verlag, New York, 1979.

36b. Argyris, J. H., and A. S. L. Chan, "Application of Finite Elements in Space and Time," *Ingenieur Archiv.*, **41**:235–257 (1972).

37. Lees, M., "A Linear Three Level Difference Scheme for Quasilinear Parabolic Equations," *Math. Comp.*, **20**:516–622 (1966).

38. Comini, G., S. Del Guidice, R. W. Lewis, and O. C. Zienkiewicz, "Finite Element Solution of Non-Linear Heat Conduction Problems with Special Reference to Phase Change," *Int. J. Numer. Meth. Eng.*, **8**:613–624 (1974).

39. Dahlquist, G., "A Special Stability Problem for Linear Multi-Step Methods," *BIT*, **3**:27–43 (1963).

40. Zienkiewicz, O. C., "A New Look at the Newmark, Houbolt and Other Time Stepping Schemes: A Weighted Residual Approach," *Int. J. Earthquake Eng. Struct. Dynam.*, **5**:413–418 (1977).

41a. Wood, W. L., "On the Zienkiewicz Four Time Level Scheme for the Numerical Integration of Vibration Problems," *Int. J. Numer. Meth. Eng.*, **11**:1519–1528 (1977).

41b. Wood, W. L., "On the Zienkiewicz Three and Four Time Level Schemes Applied to the Numerical Integration of Parabolic Equations," *Int. J. Numer. Meth. Eng.*, **12**:1717–1726 (1978).

42. Houbolt, J. C., "A Recurrence Matrix Solution for the Dynamic Response of Elastic Aircraft," *J. Aero. Sci.*, **17**:540–550 (1950).

43. Farhoomand, I., "Non-Linear Dynamic Stress Analysis of Two Dimensional Solids," Ph.D. dissertation, University of California, Berkeley, 1970.

44. Cryer, C. H., "A New Class of Highly Stable Methods: $A_0$-Stable Methods," *BIT*, **13**:153–159 (1973).

45. Culham, W. E., and R. S. Varga, "Numerical Methods for Time Dependent Non-Linear Boundary Value Problems," *J. Soc. Petrol. Eng.*, 374–387 (December 1971).

46. Boggs, P. T., "The Solution of Non-Linear Systems of Equations by $A$-Stable Integration Techniques," *SIAM J.*, **8**:767–785 (1975).

47. Stricklin, J. A. et al., "Non-Linear Dynamic Analysis of Shells of Revolution by Matrix Displacement Methods," *Proceedings of the Conference on Structural Dynamics*, American Society of Mechanical Engineers, Denver, 1971.

48. Belytschko, T., and R. Mullen, "Mesh Partitions of Explicit-Implicit Time Integration," in J. Bathe et al. (eds.), *Formulations and Computational Algorithms in Finite Element Analysis*, MIT Press, Cambridge, Mass., 1977.

49. Belytschko, T., and R. Mullen, "Stability of Explicit-Implicit Mesh Partitions in Time Integration," *Int. J. Numer. Meth. Eng.*, **12**:1575–1586 (1978).

50. Belytschko, T., H. J. Yen, and R. Mullen, "Mixed Methods for Time Integration," *Proc. Int. Conf. Finite Elements Non-Linear Mech.* (*FENOMECH 78*), University of Stuttgart, Stuttgart, September, 1978.

51. Hughes, T. J. R., and W. K. Liu, "Implicit-Explicit Finite Elements in Transient Analysis: Stability Theory," *J. Appl. Mech.*, **45**:371–374 (1978).

52. Hughes, T. J. R., and W. K. Liu, "Implicit-Explicit Finite Elements in Transient Analysis: Implementation and Numerical Examples," *J. Appl. Mech.*, **45**:375–378 (1978).

53. Park, K. C., C. A. Felippa, and H. A. Deruntz, "Stabilization of Staggered Solution Procedures for Fluid-Structure Interaction Analysis," in T. Belytschko and T. L. Geers (eds.), *Computational Methods for Fluid-Structure Interaction Problems*, ASME Appl. Mech. Symp. Ser., AMD, **26**:94–124 (1977).

54. Felippa, C. A., and K. C. Park, "Computational Aspects of Time Integration Procedures in Structural Dynamics," *J. Appl. Mech.*, **45**:595–602 (1978).

55. Park, K. C., "Partitioned Transient Analysis Procedures for Coupled Field Problems," *J. Appl. Mech.* (to appear).

56. Christie, I., D. F. Griffiths, A. R. Mitchell, and O. C. Zienkiewicz, "Finite Element Methods for Second Order Differential Equations with Significant First Derivative," *Int. J. Numer. Meth. Eng.*, **10**:1389–1396 (1976).

57. Heinrich, J. C., P. S. Huyakorn, O. C. Zienkiewicz, and A. R. Mitchell, "An 'Upwind' Finite Element Scheme for Two-Dimensional Convective-Transport Equation," *Int. J. Numer. Meth. Eng.*, **11**:1831–1844 (1977).

58. Heinrich, J. C., and O. C. Zienkiewicz, "Quadratic Finite Element Schemes for Two-Dimensional Convective Transport Problems," *Int. J. Numer. Meth. Eng.*, **11**:1831–1844 (1977).

59. Tabata, M., "A Finite Element Approximation Corresponding to the Upwind Finite Differencing," *Mem. Numer. Math.*, **4**:47–63 (1977).

60. Tabata, M., "Uniform Convergence of the Upwind Finite Element Approximation for Semilinear Parabolic Problems," *J. Math. Kyoto Univ.*, **18**:327–351 (1978).

61. Hughes, T. J. R., "A Simple Scheme for Developing 'Upwind' Finite Elements," *Int. J. Numer. Meth. Eng.*, **12**:1359–1365 (1978).

62. Donea, J., S. Giuliana, and H. Laval, "Explicit Finite Element Solutions to Transient Convective-Conductive Heat Transfer Problems," *Proceedings of the International Conference on Laminar and Turbulent Flow*, Swansea, Wales, July 1978.

63. Griffiths, D. F., "Towards Time Stepping Algorithms for Convective-Diffusion," *Proceedings of the Conference on the Numerical Analysis of Singular Perturbation Problems*, Catholic University, Nijmegen, Holland, May 1978, Academic Press, London, 1979.

64. Mitchell, A. R., and D. F. Griffiths, "Semi Discrete Galerkin Methods for Time Dependent Conduction Convection Problems," *Proceedings of the Third Conference on the Mathematics of Finite Elements and Applications*, Brunel, April 1978, Academic Press, New York, 1979, 19–34.

65. Morton, K. W., and A. K. Parrott, "Generalized Galerkin Methods for First Order Hyperbolic Equations," N.S. Rep. 4/78, University of Reading, Reading, 1978.

66. Connor, I. J., and C. A. Brebbia, *Finite Element Techniques for Fluid Flow*, Newness-Butterworth, London-Boston, 1976, pp. 33–42, 268–277.

67. Adey, R., and C. A. Brebbia, "Finite Element Solutions for Effluent Dispersion," in C. Brebbia and I. J. Connors (eds.), *Numerical Methods in Fluid Dynamics*, Pentech Press, London, 1974.

68. Leimkuhler, W. F. et al., "A Two Dimensional Finite Element Dispersion Model," *Modeling*, American Society of Civil Engineering, New York, 1975.

69. Morandi Cecchi, M., "Error Continuation for Finite Element Solutions of Heat Transfer Problems in the Square Time Domain," in C. J. Whiteman (ed.), *Mathematics of Finite Applications*, Academic Press, New York, 1976, Chap. 16, pp. 203–207.

70. Alducin, V., and J. T. Oden, "Qualitative Analysis of Galerkin Approximation of a Class of Non-Linear Convection-Diffusion Problems," T.I.C.OM Rep. 78.8, University of Texas, Austin, 1978.

71. Gantmacher, F. R., *The Theory of Matrices*, Chelsea Publishing Company, New York, 1959.

72. Wood, W. L., "A Further Look at Newmark, Houbolt, etc., Time Stepping Formulae," *Int. J. Numer. Meth. Eng.*, **20**:1009–1017 (1984).

73. Bettencourt, J. M., O. C. Zienkiewicz, and G. Cantin, "Consistent Use of Finite Elements in Time and the Performance of Various Recurrence Schemes for the Heat Diffusion Equation," *Int. J. Numer. Meth. Eng.*, **17**:931–938 (1981).

# CHAPTER 9

# CONVERGENCE OF FINITE-ELEMENT METHODS FOR LINEAR PROBLEMS IN MECHANICS

## 9.1 INTRODUCTION

Our aim here is to record some of the standard results on error estimates, convergence rates, and stability of finite-element methods for certain classes of linear-elliptic problems that arise in applications in solid and fluid mechanics. This chapter is divided into six sections: first, we summarize standard results and estimates on finite-element approximations of general elliptic problems of order $2m$; second, we cite some special $L^\infty$-results for linear-elasticity problems; third, we review certain features of mixed finite elements for linear problems with constraints; fourth, we list some special results on reduced-integration penalty methods for stokesian flow and incompressible linear elasticity; fifth, we present the stability conditions of reduced-integration penalty schemes; and finally, we include a detailed section on mixed and hybrid finite-element methods.

## 9.2 STANDARD RESULTS FOR LINEAR-ELLIPTIC BOUNDARY-VALUE PROBLEMS

Consider a $2m^{\underline{\text{th}}}$-order, linear, partial differential operator $A$ of the form

$$Au = \sum_{|\alpha|=|\beta|\leqslant m} (-1)^{|\alpha|} D^\alpha [a_{\alpha\beta}(\mathbf{x}) D^\beta u] \tag{9.1}$$

where $a_{\alpha\beta}$ are sufficiently differentiable functions of $\mathbf{x} = (x_1, x_2, \ldots, x_n)$, $\boldsymbol{\alpha}$ denotes an $n$-tuple of nonnegative integers,

$$\boldsymbol{\alpha} = (\alpha_1, \alpha_2, \dots, \alpha_n) \qquad \alpha_i \geqslant 0 \qquad \alpha_i = \text{integer}$$

$$|\boldsymbol{\alpha}| = \sum_{i=1}^{n} \alpha_i \qquad \mathbf{x}^{\boldsymbol{\alpha}} = x_1^{\alpha_1} x_2^{\alpha_2} \cdots x_n^{\alpha_n}$$

$$D^{\boldsymbol{\alpha}} = \frac{\partial^{|\alpha|}}{\partial x_1^{\alpha_1} \partial x_2^{\alpha_2} \cdots \partial x_n^{\alpha_n}} = \frac{\partial^{\alpha_1}}{\partial x_1^{\alpha_1}} \frac{\partial^{\alpha_2}}{\partial x_2^{\alpha_2}} \cdots \frac{\partial^{\alpha_n}}{\partial x_n^{\alpha_n}} \tag{9.2}$$

and $\Omega$ is an $n$-dimensional domain with a sufficiently smooth boundary $\partial\Omega$. An example of $A$ is given by the following second-order partial differential operator in two variables [that is, $m = 1$, $n = 2$, $\boldsymbol{\alpha} = (\alpha_1, \alpha_2)$, $\alpha_i = 0, 1$, $|\boldsymbol{\alpha}| = \alpha_1 + \alpha_2$]:

$$Au = a_{00}u - \frac{\partial}{\partial x_1}\left(a_{11}\frac{\partial u}{\partial x_1} + a_{12}\frac{\partial u}{\partial x_2}\right) - \frac{\partial}{\partial x_2}\left(a_{21}\frac{\partial u}{\partial x_1} + a_{22}\frac{\partial u}{\partial x_2}\right) \tag{9.3}$$

Now consider a boundary-value problem of the type (see Oden and Reddy [1], Reddy [2])

$$Au = f \qquad \text{in } \Omega$$

$$B_j u \equiv \frac{\partial^j u}{\partial n^j} = g_j \qquad \text{on } \Gamma \qquad j = 0, 1, \dots, m-1 \tag{9.4}$$

where $A$ is the $2m^{\text{th}}$-order (elliptic) partial differential operator defined in Eq. (9.1), $\{B_j\}_{j=0}^{m-1}$ is a (*normal*) system of boundary operators (covering $A$), and $f$ and $g_j$ are the data (i.e., given functions of position) of the problem. Equation (9.4) can be reduced to one with homogeneous (essential) boundary conditions by introducing a function $w$ such that $R_j w = g_j$, $0 \leqslant j \leqslant m-1$, on $\Gamma$. Then we have

$$A\hat{u} = \hat{f} \qquad \text{in } \Omega$$

$$B_j \hat{u} = 0 \qquad \text{on } \partial\Omega \tag{9.5}$$

where $\hat{u} = u - w$ and $\hat{f} = f - Aw$. The variational problem associated with (9.5) consists of finding the (generalized) solution $u$ from the linear vector space $V = H^r(\Omega) \cap H_0^m(\Omega)$ such that

$$a(v, u) = f(v) \text{ for every } v \in H_0^m(\Omega) \tag{9.6}$$

Here $r \geqslant 2m$, $H^m(\Omega)$ is the Hilbert space of order $m$ on $\Omega$, $H_0^m(\Omega)$ is the Hilbert space with compact support,

$$H_0^m(\Omega) = \left\{ u : u \in H^m(\Omega), \frac{\partial^j u}{\partial n^j} = 0, 0 \leqslant j \leqslant m-1, \text{ on } \partial\Omega \right\} \tag{9.7}$$

and $a(u, v)$ and $f(v)$ are the bilinear and linear forms, respectively,

$$a(v, u) = \int_{\Omega} \sum_{|\alpha||\beta| \leqslant m} a_{\alpha\beta} D^{\alpha} v\, D^{\beta} u\, dx$$

$$f(v) = \int_{\Omega} \hat{f} v\, d\mathbf{x} \tag{9.8}$$

For the operator in (9.3), the bilinear form is given by

$$a(v, u) = \int_{\Omega \subset \mathbb{R}^2} \left( a_{00} vu + a_{11} \frac{\partial v}{\partial x_1} \frac{\partial u}{\partial x_1} + a_{12} \frac{\partial v}{\partial x_1} \frac{\partial u}{\partial x_2} + a_{21} \frac{\partial v}{\partial x_2} \frac{\partial u}{\partial x_1} + a_{22} \frac{\partial v}{\partial x_2} \frac{\partial u}{\partial x_2} \right) dx \qquad (9.9)$$

For linear two-dimensional (anisotropic) elasticity equations,

$$-\frac{\partial}{\partial x_1} \left[ a_{11} \frac{\partial u_1}{\partial x_1} + a_{12} \frac{\partial u_2}{\partial x_2} + a_{13} \left( \frac{\partial u_1}{\partial x_2} + \frac{\partial u_2}{\partial x_1} \right) \right]$$

$$-\frac{\partial}{\partial x_2} \left[ a_{13} \frac{\partial u_1}{\partial x_1} + a_{23} \frac{\partial u_2}{\partial x_2} + a_{33} \left( \frac{\partial u_1}{\partial x_2} + \frac{\partial u_2}{\partial x_1} \right) \right] = f_1 \qquad \text{in } \Omega$$

$$-\frac{\partial}{\partial x_1} \left[ a_{13} \frac{\partial u_1}{\partial x_1} + a_{23} \frac{\partial u_2}{\partial x_2} + a_{33} \left( \frac{\partial u_1}{\partial x_2} + \frac{\partial u_2}{\partial x_1} \right) \right]$$

$$-\frac{\partial}{\nabla x_2} \left[ a_{12} \frac{\partial u_1}{\partial x_1} + a_{22} \frac{\partial u_2}{\partial x_2} + a_{23} \left( \frac{\partial u_1}{\partial x_2} + \frac{\partial u_2}{\partial x_1} \right) \right] = f_2 \qquad \text{in } \Omega \qquad (9.10a)$$

with the boundary conditions

$$u_1 = 0 \qquad u_2 = 0 \qquad \text{on } \partial\Omega \qquad (9.10b)$$

the bilinear and linear forms are given by (see Reddy and Rasmussen [2])

$$a(v_1, v_2; u_1, u_2) = \int_\Omega \left\{ \frac{\partial v_1}{\partial x_1} \left[ a_{11} \frac{\partial u_1}{\partial x_1} + a_{12} \frac{\partial u_2}{\partial x_2} + a_{13} \left( \frac{\partial u_1}{\partial x_2} + \frac{\partial u_2}{\partial x_1} \right) \right] \right.$$

$$+ \frac{\partial v_1}{\partial x_2} \left[ a_{13} \frac{\partial u_1}{\partial x_1} + a_{23} \frac{\partial u_2}{\partial x_2} + a_{33} \left( \frac{\partial u_1}{\partial x_2} + \frac{\partial u_2}{\partial x_1} \right) \right]$$

$$+ \frac{\partial v_2}{\partial x_1} \left[ a_{13} \frac{\partial u_1}{\partial x_1} + a_{23} \frac{\partial u_2}{\partial x_2} + a_{33} \left( \frac{\partial u_1}{\partial x_2} + \frac{\partial u_2}{\partial x_1} \right) \right]$$

$$\left. + \frac{\partial v_2}{\partial x_2} \left[ a_{12} \frac{\partial u_1}{\partial x_1} + a_{22} \frac{\partial u_2}{\partial x_2} + a_{23} \left( \frac{\partial u_1}{\partial x_2} + \frac{\partial u_2}{\partial x_1} \right) \right] \right\} dx_1 \, dx_2$$

$$f(v_1, v_2) = \int_\Omega (f_1 v_1 + f_2 v_2) \, dx_1 \, dx_2 \qquad (9.11)$$

The solution space $V$ for the elasticity problem is given by

$$V = [H_0^1(\Omega) \times H_0^1(\Omega)] \cap [H^r(\Omega) \times H^r(\Omega)] \qquad r \geq 2 \qquad (9.12)$$

By means of Korn's inequality (see [1–3]), it can be shown that the variational problem associated with (9.10) has a solution.

For the operator equation in (9.5), the Galerkin–finite-element approximation of (9.6) involves finding $u^h$ from the finite-element space $S_h(\Omega)$, a finite-dimensional subspace of $V$, such that

$$a(v_h, u_h) = f(v_h) \qquad \text{for all } v_h \text{ in } S_h(\Omega) \tag{9.13}$$

where $a(\cdot, \cdot)$ is the bilinear form obtained from (9.8) by replacing $v$ and $u$, respectively, by $v_h$ and $u_h$. Here $h$ denotes a geometric parameter (e.g., $h = \max\{h_e, 1 \le e \le E\}$). Equation (9.13) leads to the set of finite-element equations

$$\mathbf{K}^{(e)}\mathbf{u}^h = \mathbf{F}^{(e)} \tag{9.14}$$

where the element coefficient matrix $\mathbf{K}^{(e)}$ and column vector $\mathbf{F}^{(e)}$ are given by

$$K_{ij}^{(e)} = \int_{\Omega_e} \sum_{|\alpha|=|\beta|\le m} a_{\alpha\beta} D^\alpha \phi_i D^\beta \phi_j \, d\mathbf{x} = B_e(\phi_i, \phi_j)$$

$$F_i^{(e)} = \int_{\Omega_e} \phi_i f \, dx + \int_{\partial\Omega^e} \sum_{j=0}^{m-1} t_j \frac{\partial^j \phi_i}{\partial n^j} \, ds \tag{9.15}$$

where $\Omega^e$ is a typical finite element, $\partial\Omega^e$ is its boundary, and $t_j$ are interface tractions (see Oden and Reddy [1] or Lions and Magenes [4]). The second term in $F_i^{(e)}$ does not contribute to the global column vector because it is canceled by contributions from neighboring elements at the interelement boundaries and it is zero [because $u_h \in S_h(\Omega) \subset H_0^m(\Omega)$] on the boundary $\Gamma$; see Becker, Carey, and Oden [5] or Oden and Carey [6, 7].

Whenever the data $f$ are such that a solution $u_0 \in H^r(\Omega)$, $r \ge 2m$, exists and the boundary conditions $B_j u = 0$ are exactly satisfied, the error $e = u_0 - u_h$ between the exact solution and the finite-element solution is given by (see Ref. [1])

$$\|e\|_{H^\alpha(\Omega)} \le ch^p \|f\|_{H^{r-2m}(\Omega)} \tag{9.16}$$

$$p = \min(k+1-\alpha, 2(k+1-m), 2m+r-\alpha)$$

where $0 \le \alpha \le m$, $r \ge 0$, $k+1 > m$, and $k$ is the degree of the interpolation functions $\phi_i$ used to approximate $u$.

For example, consider the Dirichlet problem for the Poisson's equation

$$-\nabla^2 u = f \qquad \text{in } \Omega \subset R^2$$

$$u = 0 \qquad \text{on } \partial\Omega \tag{9.17}$$

Suppose that the linear triangular element (i.e., Lagrange simplex, $k = 1$) is used to solve the problem by the finite-element method. Then the error estimate (9.16) for the problem in (9.17) becomes

$$\|e\|_{H^1(\Omega)} \le ch \|f\|_{H^0(\Omega)} \tag{9.18a}$$

$$\|e\|_{H^0(\Omega)} \le ch^2 \|f\|_{H^0(\Omega)} \tag{9.18b}$$

In other words, the error in the $L_2$-norm is of the order $h^2$, whereas the error in the energy norm is of the order $h$.

As a second example consider the plane-elasticity problem in (9.10). The error $e = (u_1^0 - u_1^h, u_2^0 - u_2^h)$, where $u^0 = (u_1^0, u_2^0)$ is the exact solution and $u^h = (u_1^h, u_2^h)$ is the finite-element solution, is given by

$$\|u_1^0 - u_1^h\|_{H^\alpha(\Omega)}^2 + \|u_2^0 - u_2^h\|_{H^\alpha(\Omega)}^2 \leqslant ch^{2p}[\|f_1\|_{H^r(\Omega)}^2 + \|f_2\|_{H^{r-2m}(\Omega)}^2]$$

$$p = \min(k+1-\alpha, 2(k+1-m), 2m+r-\alpha) \tag{9.19}$$

If the linear triangular element (i.e., Lagrange simplex, $k = 1$) is used to approximate $u_1^h$ and $u_2^h$, the error is given by

$$\|u^0 - u^h\|_{\mathbf{H}^0(\Omega)} \leqslant ch^2\|f\|_{\mathbf{H}^0(\Omega)} \tag{9.20}$$

where

$$\|u\|_{\mathbf{H}^0(\Omega)} = [\|u_1\|_{H^0(\Omega)}^2 + \|u_2\|_{H^0(\Omega)}^2]^{1/2} \tag{9.21}$$

## 9.3 SOME $L^\infty$-ESTIMATES FOR FINITE-ELEMENT APPROXIMATIONS IN PLANE ELASTICITY

We now consider some more specialized results of Nitsche [9] applicable to standard, piecewise linear, finite-element approximations on triangles of the displacement equations of linear elastostatics for the case of plane strain. We consider the following boundary-value problem:

Find $\mathbf{u} = (u_1 u_2)$, $\mathbf{H} = [H_0^1(\Omega)]^2$ such that

$$\mathbf{a}(\mathbf{u}, \mathbf{v}) = f(\mathbf{v}) \qquad \forall \mathbf{v} \in \mathbf{H} \tag{9.22}$$

Here

$$a(\mathbf{u}, \mathbf{v}) = \int_\Omega \sigma_{ij}(\mathbf{u})\varepsilon_{ij}(\mathbf{v})\, dx$$

$$\sigma_{ij}(\mathbf{u}) = \text{the stress} = \lambda\varepsilon_{kk}(\mathbf{u})\delta_{ij} + 2\mu\varepsilon_{ij}(\mathbf{u})$$

$$\varepsilon_{ij}(\mathbf{v}) = \frac{u_{i,j} + u_{j,i}}{2} \tag{9.23}$$

$$f(\mathbf{v}) = \int_\Omega \mathbf{f} \cdot \mathbf{v}\, dx$$

$$\lambda, \mu = \text{Lamé constants}$$

$\Omega$ is a sufficiently smooth domain in $\mathbb{R}^2$, $dx = dx_1\, dx_2$, and standard indicial notation and the summation convention are used. It is well known that a unique solution $\mathbf{u}$ exists to (9.22), and if $f_i \in L^2(\Omega)$, then $\mathbf{u} \in \mathbf{H} \cap (H^2(\Omega))^2$ and

$$\|\mathbf{u}\|_2 \equiv \left\{ \int_\Omega (u_{i,jj}u_{i,kk} + u_{i,j}u_{i,j} + u_iu_i)\, dx \right\}^{1/2}$$

$$\leqslant c\|\mathbf{f}\|_{L^2(\Omega)}$$

A finite-element approximation of (9.22) is of the form

$$a(\mathbf{u}_h, \mathbf{v}_h) = f(\mathbf{v}_h) \qquad \forall \mathbf{v}_h \in H^h \tag{9.24}$$

where $H^h$ is the finite-element subspace of $\mathbf{H}$ generated by using a triangulated mesh over which the displacements are approximated using piecewise linear basis functions. For any triangle $T$ of the mesh, we assume that there are spheres $\underline{S}$, $\bar{S}$ with radii $\rho$, $\bar{\rho}$ such that $\underline{S} \subset T \subset \bar{S}$, $\gamma^{-1} h \leq \rho \leq \bar{\rho} \leq h$ with $\gamma$ a constant. Under these conditions, the space $H^h = (S_h)^2$ and $S_h$ has the following interpolation properties (see Ciarlet and Raviart [8] and Nitsche [9]):

**1.** $\forall v \in H^1(\Omega) \cap H^k(\Omega_h)$ there is a $\chi \in S_h(\Omega)$ such that

$$\|v - \chi\|_\alpha + h\|\nabla(v - \chi)\|_\alpha \leq c_1(\alpha) h^k \|\nabla^k v\|_\alpha^h$$

**2.** $\forall \chi \in S_h$ $\qquad \|\nabla \chi\|_\alpha \leq c_2(\alpha) h^{-1} \|\chi\|_\alpha$

$$|\nabla \chi|_\alpha \leq c_3(\alpha) h^{-1/2}(\|\chi\|_\alpha + \|\nabla \chi\|_\alpha)$$

where $k$ is an integer $> 0$,

$$H^k(\Omega_h) = \{v \in L^2(\Omega) | v|_{\Omega_e} \in H^k(\Omega_e)\}$$

$$\|v\|_\alpha = \left\{ \int_\Omega (|x - x_0|^2 + \rho^2)^{-\alpha} v^2 \, dx \right\}^{1/2} \qquad \alpha \in \mathbb{R}$$

$$\|\nabla^k v\|_\alpha = \left\{ \sum_{|\beta| = k} \|D^\beta v\|_\alpha^2 \right\}^{1/2}$$

Under these conditions, the error,

$$\mathbf{e}_h = \mathbf{u} - \mathbf{u}_h$$

in the approximation (9.24) satisfies the *a priori* estimates

$$\|\mathbf{e}_h\|_{H^1(\Omega)} \leq ch \|\mathbf{f}\|_{L^2(\Omega)}$$
$$\|\mathbf{e}_h\|_{L^2(\Omega)} \leq ch^{3/2} \|\mathbf{f}\|_{L^2(\Omega)} \tag{9.25}$$

It has been shown by Nitsche [9] that the $L^2$-result in (9.25) can be improved if, instead of (9.24), we approximate the equivalent problem with boundary terms,

$$a_1(\mathbf{w}, \mathbf{v}) = f(\mathbf{v}) \qquad \forall \mathbf{v} \in H$$
$$a_1(\mathbf{w}, \mathbf{v}) = a(\mathbf{w}, \mathbf{v}) + \oint_{\partial\Omega} n_i \{\sigma_{ik}(\mathbf{w}) v_k + c_{ik}(\mathbf{v}) w_k\} \, ds \tag{9.26}$$

Then, instead of (9.25), we have

$$\|\mathbf{e}_h\|_{L^2(\Omega)} \leq ch^2 \|\mathbf{f}\|_{L^2(\Omega)} \tag{9.27}$$

In addition, Nitsche [9] also derived the following $L^\infty$-estimates for the elasticity problem:

If the solution **u** has bounded second derivatives in $\Omega$, then

$$\inf_{v_h \in H^h} \{\|\mathbf{u} - \mathbf{v}_h\|_2 + \|\nabla(\mathbf{u} - \mathbf{v}_h)\|_1\} \le ch|\ln h|^{1/2} \|\nabla^2 \mathbf{u}\|'_{\mathbf{L}^\infty} \tag{9.28}$$

and if $\mathbf{u} \in (W^{2,\infty}(\Omega))^2$

$$\|\nabla \mathbf{e}_h\|_{L^\infty} \le ch|\ln h| \|\nabla^2 \mathbf{u}\|_{\mathbf{L}^\infty}$$

$$\|\mathbf{e}_h\|_{L^\infty} \le ch^2|\ln h| \|\nabla^2 \mathbf{u}\|_{\mathbf{L}^\infty} \tag{9.29}$$

## 9.4 PROBLEMS WITH CONSTRAINTS

Many important problems in solid and fluid mechanics involve elliptic boundary-value problems with constraints. We mention as examples the steady laminar flow of a viscous incompressible fluid, the deformation of an incompressible material, or the unilateral contact of an elastic body with a foundation. In this section, we review some theoretical aspects of the approximation of such problems by finite-element methods.

Let $V$ be a real Hilbert space with the natural norm $\|\cdot\|$ defined by the inner product $(\cdot, \cdot)_V$, and let $V'$ be the (topological) dual of $V$ with the norm $\|\cdot\|^*$. Let $a(\cdot, \cdot)$ be a continuous $V$-elliptic bilinear form on $V \times V$ such that

$$a(u, v) \le M\|u\|\|v\| \qquad \forall u, v \in V$$

$$a(u, u) \ge m\|u\|^2 \qquad \forall u \in V \tag{9.30}$$

for some positive constants $m$ and $M$. Let $f$ be a continuous linear functional on $V$ whose value is denoted by $f(v)$ or $\langle f, v \rangle_V$ by using the duality pairing on $V' \times V$.

Suppose that $B$ is a linear-continuous map from $V$ into another real Hilbert space $Q$; that is,

$$B(\alpha u + \beta v) = \alpha B(u) + \beta B(v) \qquad \forall \alpha, \beta \in \mathbb{R}, \ u, v \in V$$

$$|B(u)| \le C\|u\| \qquad \forall u \in V \tag{9.31}$$

where $|\cdot|$ is the norm defined for $Q$ by the inner product $(\cdot, \cdot)_Q$.

We consider two constrained problems in this section:

(P1)
$$u \in K_1: a(u, v - u) \ge f(v - u) \qquad \forall v \in K_1$$

$$K_1 = \{v \in V \mid Bu - g \le 0 \text{ in } Q\} \tag{9.32}$$

and

(P2)
$$u \in K_2: a(u, v - u) = f(v - u) \qquad \forall v \in K_2$$

$$K_2 = \{v \in V \mid Bu - g = 0 \text{ in } Q\} \tag{9.33}$$

The inequality symbol $\le$ in $K_1$ represents the partial-ordering system on $Q$ that is a generalization of the inequality on $\mathbb{R}$ into function spaces.

The first problem (P1) is related to contact problems in linear elasticity, and the second one (P2) is an abstract representation of the problem of Stokes flows or of incompressible linear-elastic materials. Since (P1) is more delicate than (P2), we shall make a detailed study for the first problem and provide only brief discussions on (P2).

## 9.4ᴀ Mixed Finite-Element Methods

The constrained problem (P1) can be alternately formulated by the so-called mixed method that introduces an additional unknown as a Lagrange multiplier for the constraint $Bv - g \leq 0$ in $Q$. Because of the inequality constraint in $K_1$, the Lagrange multiplier must be restricted into the negative cone $N$ in the dual space $Q'$ of $Q$:

$$N = \{q \in Q' \,|\, q \leq 0 \text{ in } Q'\} \tag{9.34}$$

Here the inequality symbol $\leq$ in $N$ is related to the one in $K_1$ through the relation that $q \leq 0$ in $Q'$ if and only if $\langle q, \phi \rangle_Q \geq 0$, $\forall \phi \leq 0$ in $Q$. If (P2) is considered, the Lagrange multiplier belongs to $Q'$, and need not introduce the negative cone $N$.

The mixed formulation to (P1) is given by

$$(u, p) \in V \times N:$$

$$a(u, v) - \langle p, Bv \rangle_Q = f(v) \qquad \forall v \in V \tag{9.35}$$

$$\langle q - p, Bu - g \rangle_Q \geq 0 \qquad \forall q \in N$$

It is clear that if there exists a solution $(u, p)$ to (9.35) the problem (P1) is also solved since $u$ satisfies (9.32). However, it is, in general, not obvious that the mixed formulation is well-posed for a given constraint operator $B$. Well-posedness of (9.35) depends upon whether or not the operator $B$ satisfies the LBB (Ladyszenskaya–Babuška–Brezzi) condition

$$\sup_{v \in V} \frac{\langle q, Bv \rangle_Q}{\|v\|} \geq \alpha |q|^* \qquad \forall q \in Q' \tag{9.36}$$

for a positive constant $\alpha$. This fact has been studied by Babuška [10] and Brezzi [11], and reference to it as the LBB condition acknowledges the work of Ladyszenskaya [12], who studied (9.36) for incompressible viscous flow. Roughly speaking, the condition (9.36) means that

$$\langle q, Bv \rangle_Q = 0 \qquad \forall v \in V \qquad \text{implies} \qquad q = 0 \text{ in } Q' \tag{9.37}$$

If this is not the case, the Lagrange multiplier $p$ is not uniquely determined, because

$$a(u, v) - \langle p, Bv \rangle = a(u, v) - \langle p + p^*, Bv \rangle = f(v)$$

for every $p^* \in \ker B^*$ defined by

$$\ker B^* = \{q^* \in Q' : \langle q^*, Bv \rangle = 0, \forall v \in V\} \tag{9.38}$$

If $\ker B^*$ is not trivial ($\neq \{0\}$), we need to consider the mixed method (9.35) on the quotient space $Q'/(\ker B^*)$ or on the orthogonal complement $(Q')^{\perp}$ to $\ker B^*$ in order to keep uniqueness of the Lagrange multiplier. We shall not, however, consider the case that $\ker B^*$ is not trivial in order to simplify the discussions.

Let $V_h$ and $Q'_h$ be approximations of the spaces $V$ and $Q'$ using finite-element methods such that $V_h \hookrightarrow V$ and $Q'_h \hookrightarrow Q'$, where $A \hookrightarrow B$ means that $A$ is included in $B$ and the identity map from $A$ into $B$ is continuous. Then a finite-element approximation of (9.35) is written by

$$(u_h, p_h) \in V_h \times N_h:$$

$$a(u_h, v_h) - \langle p_h, Bv_h \rangle_Q = f(v_h) \qquad \forall v_h \in V_h \tag{9.39}$$

$$\langle q_h - p_h, Bu_h - g \rangle_Q \geq 0 \qquad \forall q_h \in N_h$$

where
$$N_h = \{ q_h \in Q'_h : q_h \leq 0 \text{ in } Q'_h \} \tag{9.40}$$

Difficulties in the analysis of finite-element approximations of the mixed formulations are that well-posedness of (9.39) has to be checked independently of the original continuous problem (9.35) and that convergence of the methods is strongly dependent upon the LBB condition in the discrete finite-element approximation (9.39). Moreover, we must also take into account the fact that the ordering in the constrained set $N_h$ might be different from the one in $N$. Indeed, in order that (9.39) make sense, we need

$$\langle q_h, Bv_h \rangle_Q = 0 \qquad \forall v_h \in V_h \qquad \text{yields} \qquad q_h = 0 \tag{9.41}$$

that is, for a positive constant $\alpha_h$

$$\sup_{v_h \in V_h} \frac{\langle q_h, Bv_h \rangle_Q}{\|v_h\|} \geq \alpha_h |q_h|^* \qquad q_h \in Q'_h \tag{9.42}$$

Note that (9.42) cannot be concluded from (9.36) because $V_h \subset V$. Whenever (9.42) holds, the approximation of the mixed formulation (9.39) has a unique solution $(u_h, p_h) \in V_h \times N_h$. This follows from standard results in convex analysis; see Ekeland and Temam [13, Chap. 2] or Brezzi [11]. As discussed thoroughly by Fortin [14], if the constant $\alpha_h$ is independent of the mesh size, the convergence of the approximation (9.39) to (9.35) can be established together with an estimate of the rate of convergence. Then, the remaining questions are the existence of the constant $\alpha_h$ in (9.42) and what additional conditions need be imposed on $V_h$ and $Q'_h$ in order that $\alpha_h$ be independent of the mesh size $h$.

The first question is answered by noting that if the image of $V_h$ under the operator $B$ strictly contains the space $Q'_h$, the closed-range theorem (see Yosida [15]) implies the existence of $\alpha_h$ for a fixed $h$. In other words, if the contribution to the stiffness matrix from the term $\langle p_h, Bv_h \rangle$ has full rank, we have a positive constant $\alpha_h$. Roughly speaking, this may be equivalent to the requirement that the total degrees of freedom in $V_h$ must be balanced (generally greater than) the number of constraints $Bv_h = g$ in $Q'_h$. It is noted that the closed-range theorem merely guarantees the existence of $\alpha_h$ for given $V_h$ and $Q'_h$. Then, we cannot conclude that there exists a lower bound $\alpha_0 > 0$ of $\alpha_h$ for every $h$. Additional requirements on the choice of $V_h$ and $Q'_h$ for a lower bound $\alpha_0$ is stated by Fortin [14] as follows.

**PROPOSITION 9.1**    Suppose that there exists an operator $\Lambda_h$ from $V$ into $V_h$ such that

$$\langle q_h, B(v - \Lambda_h v)\rangle_Q = 0 \qquad \forall q_h \in Q'_h$$

$$\|\Lambda_h v\| \leqslant C\|v\| \tag{9.43}$$

Then, if the LBB condition (9.36) holds, there exists a lower bound $\alpha_0$ for every $h$ such that $\alpha_0 = \alpha/C$.

Under the assumption of the LBB condition, we shall derive several inequalities which lead to the error estimates on the finite-element approximation (9.39). Let $Q$ be imbedded in a real pivot Hilbert space $H$ with the natural norm $\|\|\cdot\|\|$, and let the identity map of $Q$ into $H$ be continuous. Suppose that $Q$ is dense in $H$. Then the duality pairing $\langle\cdot,\cdot\rangle_Q$ may be identified with the inner product $(\cdot,\cdot)_H$ on $H \times H$. If this new topological structure is introduced, the discrete LBB condition (9.42) can be represented by

$$\sup_{v_h \in V_h} \frac{\langle q_h, Bv_h\rangle_Q}{\|v_h\|} \geqslant \beta_h \|\|q_h\|\| \qquad \forall q_h \in Q'_h \tag{9.44}$$

Note that $\|\|\cdot\|\| = \|\|\cdot\|\|^* = \sqrt{(\cdot,\cdot)_H}$ since $H$ is assumed to be a pivot space.

**THEOREM 9.1**    Let $(u, p) \in V \times N$ and $(u_h, p_h) \in V_h \times N_h$ be solutions of (9.35) and (9.39), respectively. Suppose that (9.30), (9.31), and (9.44) hold. Then there exist positive constants $C_1$, $C_2$, and $C_3$ such that

$$\|u_h - u\| \leqslant C_1\left\{\|v_h - u\| + |q_h - p|^* + \frac{1}{\beta_h}\|\|B(u - v_h)\|\|\right\}$$

$$+ C_2\{\|\|p - q_h\|\|\|\|B(u - v_h)\|\| + (q - p_h + q_h - p, Bu - g)\}^{1/2} \tag{9.45}$$

and

$$\|\|p_h - p\|\| \leqslant \|\|q_h - p\|\| + \frac{C_3}{\beta_h}\{|q_h - p|^* + \|u - u_h\|\} \tag{9.46}$$

for every $q \in N$, $q_h \in N_h$, and $v_h \in V_h$.

**Proof.**    From (9.35) and (9.39)

$$a(u_h - u, v_h) = \langle p_h - p, Bv_h\rangle_Q \qquad \forall v_h \in V_h \tag{9.47}$$

Using this identity with $v_h$ replaced by $v_h - u_h$, we obtain

$$a(u_h - u, v_h - u) + a(u_h - u, u_h - v_h) = a(u_h - u, v_h - u) + \langle p_h - p, Bu_h - Bv_h\rangle_Q$$

We next observe that the following inequality holds:

$$\langle p_h - p, B(u_h - v_h)\rangle_Q = \langle p_h - p, B(u - v_h)\rangle_Q + \langle p_h - q_h, B(u_h - u)\rangle_Q + \langle q_h - p, B(u_h - u)\rangle_Q$$

$$\leqslant \langle p_h - p, B(u - v_h)\rangle_Q + \langle q - p_h + q_h - p, Bu - g\rangle_Q$$

$$+ \langle q_h - p, B(u_h - u)\rangle_Q \qquad \forall q \in N \qquad \forall q_h \in N_h$$

In this last step we have used the last inequalities in (9.35) and (9.39) to show that

$$\langle p_h - q_h, Bu_h - Bu \rangle_Q = \langle p_h - q_h, Bu_h - g \rangle_Q - \langle p_h - q_h, Bu - g \rangle_Q$$
$$\leq \langle q - p_h + q_h - p, Bu - g \rangle_Q - \langle q - p, Bu - g \rangle_Q$$
$$\leq \langle q - p_h - q_h - p, Bu - g \rangle_Q \qquad \forall q \in N \qquad \forall q_h \in N_h$$

Collecting these results, we have

$$a(u_h - u, u_h - u) \leq a(u_h - u, v_h - u) + \langle p_h - p, B(u - v_h) \rangle_Q$$
$$+ \langle q - p_h + q_h - p, Bu - g \rangle_Q + \langle q_h - p, B(u_h - u) \rangle_Q$$

for every $v_h \in V_h$, $q_h \in N_h$, and $q \in N$.

Thus, applying (9.30), we have

$$m \|u_h - u\|^2 \leq M \|u_h - u\| \|v_h - u\| + \||p_h - p\|| \||B(u - v_h)\||$$
$$+ \langle q - p_h + q_h - p, Bu - g \rangle_Q + C |q_h - p|^* \|u_h - u\| \qquad (9.48)$$

This is almost the desired result, (9.45), but we have not yet used the critical condition (9.44). Toward this end, we again apply (9.47) to obtain for each $q_h \in N_h$, $v_h \in V_h$,

$$\langle q_h - p_h, Bv_h \rangle_Q = \langle q_h - p, Bv_h \rangle_Q + a(u - u_h, v_h)$$

Thus, from (9.44) it follows that

$$\||q_h - p_h\|| \leq \frac{1}{\beta_h} (C |q_h - p|^* + M \|u - u_h\|)$$

Application of the triangle inequality yields (9.46).

The inequality (9.45) now follows from (9.48), (9.46), and Young's inequality, $ab \leq \varepsilon a^2 + (1/4\varepsilon) b^2$, $\varepsilon > 0$.

Finally, we show that we can obtain an estimate of $|p_h - p|^*$ instead of $\||p_h - p\||$ by using a duality argument.

**THEOREM 9.2**   Suppose that the conditions of Theorem 9.1 hold and that, for each $v \in V$, an element $v_h \in V_h$ exists such that

$$\||Bv - Bv_h\|| \leq C_1 h^\nu \|v\| \qquad \nu > 0$$
$$\|v_h\| \leq C_2 \|v\| \qquad\qquad\qquad (9.49)$$

Then there exists a positive constant $C_4$ such that

$$|p_h - p|^* \leq C_4 \{ h^\nu \||p_h - p\|| + \|u_h - u\| \} \qquad (9.50)$$

*Proof.*   By definition of the norm on the dual space of $Q$,

$$|p_h - p|^* = \sup_{\phi \in Q} \frac{|\langle p_h - p, \phi \rangle_Q|}{|\phi|} \qquad (\phi \neq 0)$$

According to Yosida [15, p. 206], the open-mapping theorem guarantees that if $Rg(B) = Q$, then a constant $c > 0$ exists such that, for each $\phi \in Q$, a $v_\phi \in V$ exists such that $Bv_\phi = \phi$ and $\|v_\phi\| \leq c|\phi|$. Thus, $|\phi|^{-1} \leq c\|v_\phi\|^{-1}$, $\phi \neq 0$. Hence, for any $v_h \in V_h$,

$$|p_h - p|^* \leq c \sup_{\phi \in Q} \frac{\langle p_h - p, Bv_\phi \rangle_Q}{\|v_\phi\|}$$

$$= c \sup_{\phi \in Q} \frac{\langle p_h - p, Bv_\phi - Bv_h \rangle_Q + a(u_h - u, v_h)}{\|v_\phi\|}$$

$$\leq c \sup_{\phi \in Q} \|v_\phi\|^{-1} \{ \|p_h - p\| \|Bv_\phi - Bv_h\| + M\|u_h - u\| \|v_h\| \}$$

Choosing $v_h$ to be the projectionn of $v_\phi$ satisfying (9.49) and simplifying yields (9.50).

For the second problem (P2), the corresponding finite-element approximation becomes

$$(u_h, p_h) \in V_h \times Q'_h:$$

$$a(u_h, v_h) - \langle p_h, Bv_h \rangle_Q = f(v_h) \qquad \forall v_h \in V_h \tag{9.51}$$

$$\langle q_h, Bu_h - g \rangle_Q = 0 \qquad \forall q_h \in Q'_h$$

Similar estimates to (9.45), (9.46), and (9.50) can be obtained for the approximation (9.51) with the equality constraint.

**THEOREM 9.3**   Suppose that the same conditions of Theorems 9.1 and 9.2 hold. Then for the solutions $(u_h, p_h) \in V_h \times Q'_h$ to (9.51) and $(u, p) \in V \times Q'$ to the problem

$$(u, p) \in V \times Q':$$

$$a(u, v) - \langle p, Bv \rangle_Q = f(v) \qquad \forall v \in V \tag{9.52}$$

$$\langle q, Bu - g \rangle_Q = 0 \qquad \forall q \in Q'$$

the following estimates hold:

$$\|u_h - u\| \leq C_1 \left\{ \|v_h - u\| + |q_h - p|^* + \frac{1}{\beta_h} \|B(u - v_h)\| \right\} \tag{9.53}$$

$$|p_h - p|^* \leq C_2 h^\nu \left\{ \|q_h - p\| + \frac{C_3}{\beta_h} (|q_h - p|^* + \|u_h - u\|) \right\} + \|u_h - u\| \tag{9.54}$$

for every $v_h \in V_h$ and $q_h \in Q'_h$.

## 9.4B Penalty–Finite-Element Methods

Another attractive and closely related method to the mixed method is the (exterior) penalty method that is widely used in finite-element analyses of constrained problems. To describe the penalty method, we consider the second problem (P2) and its lagrangian form (9.51).

Suppose that $Bu_h - g$ is perturbed by $\varepsilon p_h^\varepsilon$. Then (9.51) becomes

$$(u_h^\varepsilon, p_h^\varepsilon) \in V_h \times Q_h':$$

$$a(u_h^\varepsilon, v_h) - \langle p_h^\varepsilon, Bv_h \rangle_Q = f(v_h) \qquad \forall v_h \in V_h \qquad (9.55)$$

$$\langle q_h, \varepsilon p_h^\varepsilon + Bu_h^\varepsilon - g \rangle_Q = 0 \qquad \forall q_h \in Q_h'$$

where $\varepsilon$ is a sufficiently small positive number. Then if the second equation is solved as

$$p_h^\varepsilon = \frac{-(Bu_h^\varepsilon - g)}{\varepsilon} \qquad (9.56)$$

and if it is substituted into the first equation in (9.55), we formally obtain the penalty formulation

$$a(u_h^\varepsilon, v_h) + \frac{1}{\varepsilon} \langle Bu_h^\varepsilon - g, Bv_h \rangle_Q = f(v_h) \qquad \forall v_h \in V_h \qquad (9.57)$$

This shows that (9.57) is an approximation of the mixed formulation (9.51) in the parameter $\varepsilon > 0$. We expect that the solution $u_h^\varepsilon$ of (9.57) and the Lagrange multiplier $p_h^\varepsilon$ computed by (9.56) converge to the solution $(u_h, p_h)$ of (9.51) as $\varepsilon \to 0$. Advantage of the present formulation is that the function $u_h^\varepsilon$ is obtained without solving the two equations as in (9.51), and the Lagrange multiplier can be computed later using (9.56) if it is necessary.

It is noted that the expression (9.56) is merely formal. The Lagrange multiplier $p_h^\varepsilon$ is the result of solving the second equation of (9.55). If $Q_h'$ is constructed by nonconforming elements, the second equation in (9.55) is solved within each finite element. There are infinitely many choices of $Q_h'$ and methods for solving the second equation in (9.55). Once the Lagrange multiplier $p_h^\varepsilon$ has been computed, its substitution into the first equation yields the penalty method.

**THEOREM 9.4**    Let the conditions of Theorem 9.3 hold and let $(u_h^\varepsilon, p_h^\varepsilon)$ and $(u_h, p_h)$ be solutions of (9.55) and (9.51), respectively, $p_h^\varepsilon$ being given by (9.56). Then there exist positive constants $C_1$ and $C_2$, independent of $\varepsilon$, such that

$$\| u_h^\varepsilon - u_h \| \leqslant C_1 \frac{\varepsilon}{\beta_h} \|\!| p_h |\!\|$$

$$\qquad (9.58)$$

$$\|\!| p_h^\varepsilon - p_h |\!\| \leqslant C_2 \frac{\varepsilon}{\beta_h^2} \|\!| p_h |\!\|$$

**Proof.**    From (9.51) and (9.55), we have

$$a(u_h^\varepsilon - u_h, v_h) = \langle p_h^\varepsilon - p_h, Bv_h \rangle_Q \qquad \forall v_h \in V_h \qquad (9.59)$$

Assumption (9.44) yields

$$\|\!| p_h^\varepsilon - p_h |\!\| \leqslant \frac{M}{\beta_h} \| u_h^\varepsilon - u_h \| \qquad (9.60)$$

Putting $v_h = u_h^\varepsilon - u_h$ in (9.59), we get

$$a(u_h^\varepsilon - u_h, u_h^\varepsilon - u_h) = \langle p_h^\varepsilon - p_h, Bu_h^\varepsilon - Bu_h \rangle_Q$$

Next, noting that

$$\langle p_h^\varepsilon - p_h, Bu_h^\varepsilon - Bu_h \rangle_Q = \langle p_h^\varepsilon - p_h, Bu_h^\varepsilon - g \rangle_Q - \langle p_h^\varepsilon - p_h, Bu_h - g \rangle_Q \leqslant \langle p_h^\varepsilon - p_h, -\varepsilon p_h^\varepsilon \rangle_Q$$

we use (9.30) to obtain

$$a(u_h^\varepsilon - u_h, u_h^\varepsilon - u_h) \leqslant C\|\!|p_h^\varepsilon - p_h|\!\|\,\|\!|p_h|\!\|\varepsilon$$

Thus
$$\|u_h^\varepsilon - u_h\| \leqslant \frac{CM}{m}\,\frac{\varepsilon}{\beta_h}\|\!|p_h|\!\|$$

Inequality (9.58) now follows from (9.60).

The above theorem implies that the approximation (9.55), i.e., (9.57) of (9.51), is estimated in terms of the (penalty) parameter $\varepsilon$ and the constant $\beta_h$ in the LBB condition. If $\varepsilon \to 0$ much faster than $\beta_h$ as $h \to 0$, the penalty approximation (9.57) converges to the mixed formulation (9.51).

We shall not provide details of discussions on the first problem (P1) since similar results can be obtained using Theorem 9.4.

## 9.4c  Signorini's Problem in Linear Elasticity

One of the typical applications of the above general theory to constrained problems is Signorini's problem for a linearly elastic body. Application of the mixed method to this class of problems is studied by Paczelt [16] and Haslinger and Lovisek [17]. The theory in Ref. [17] is quite similar to that described above, although Theorems 9.1 to 9.3 are obtained from the study of penalty methods to contact problems by Kikuchi and Oden [18].

Let $E_{ijkl}$, $1 \leqslant i, j, k, l \leqslant N$, be the elasticity moduli such that

$$E_{ijkl} = E_{jikl} = E_{klij}$$

$$E_{ijkl}X_{kl}X_{ij} \geqslant mX_{ij}X_{ij} \qquad \forall X_{ij} = X_{ji} \tag{9.61}$$

$$\max_{x\in\Omega}\ \max_{i,j,k,l}\ |E_{ijkl}(\mathbf{x})| \leqslant M$$

and let
$$a(\mathbf{u}, \mathbf{v}) = \int_\Omega E_{ijkl}u_{k,l}v_{i,j}\, d\Omega$$

$$f(\mathbf{v}) = \int_\Omega f_i v_i\, d\Omega + \int_{\Gamma_{iF}} t_i v_i\, d\Gamma \tag{9.62}$$

The bilinear form $a(\cdot, \cdot)$ represents the virtual work of the elastic body characterized by (9.61) at the equilibrium $\mathbf{u}$ due to an arbitrary virtual displacement $\mathbf{v}$, and is continuous and $V$-elliptic on a subspace $V$ of the Sobolev space $\mathbf{H}^1(\Omega) = \{\mathbf{v} = v_i\mathbf{i}_i : v_i \in L^2(\Omega), \partial v_i/\partial x_\alpha \in L^2(\Omega), 1 \leqslant i, \alpha \leqslant N\}$ defined by

$$V = \{\mathbf{v} \in \mathbf{H}^1(\Omega)\,|\, V_i = 0 \text{ on } \Gamma_{iD}, 1 \leqslant i \leqslant N\} \tag{9.63}$$

if meas $(\Gamma_{iD}) > 0$ for each $i$.

Here the boundary $\Gamma$ of a lipschitzian domain $\Omega$ is covered by three parts $\Gamma_{iF}$, $\Gamma_{iD}$, and $\Gamma_C$ for each $i$, $1 \leq i \leq N$. That is, $\Gamma = \bar{\Gamma}_{iF} \cup \bar{\Gamma}_{iD} \cup \bar{\Gamma}_C$.

Signorini's problem is then defined by the variational inequality

$$\mathbf{u} \in K: a(\mathbf{u}, \mathbf{v} - \mathbf{u}) \geq f(\mathbf{v} - \mathbf{u}) \qquad \forall \mathbf{v} \in K$$

$$K = \{\mathbf{v} \in V \,|\, v_n - g \leq 0 \text{ on } \Gamma_C\}$$

(9.64)

where $v_n = v_i n_i$ is the normal component of the displacement $\mathbf{v}$ on $\Gamma$ and $\mathbf{n} = n_i \mathbf{i}_i$ is the unit vector outward normal to $\Gamma$. The inequality in the constrained (or admissible) set $K$ must be considered as the usual inequality applied almost everywhere on $\Gamma_C$. The function $g$ is the gap function of the elastic body and is assumed to be continuous on $\Gamma_C$.

Although the trace operators and related theorems must be introduced to define the boundary value of a function $\mathbf{v}$ in the mathematical theory, we shall not apply these to simplify the notation and explanations. Details of such delicate mathematics can be found in Kikuchi and Oden [18] or Necas [19, Chap. 2].

The mixed formulation to the variational inequality is given as

$$(\mathbf{u}, p) \in V \times N:$$

$$a(\mathbf{u}, \mathbf{v}) - \langle p, v_n \rangle_Q = f(\mathbf{v}) \qquad \forall \mathbf{v} \in V$$

$$\langle q - p, u_n - g \rangle_Q \geq 0 \qquad \forall q \in N$$

(9.65)

where $Q$ is the restriction of the space $H_n^{1/2}(\Sigma)$ into the part $\Gamma_C$ of the boundary $\Gamma$, and $H_n^{1/2}(\Sigma)$ is the range of the normal trace of $V$ that is orthogonal to the range of the tangential trace of $V$ under the assumption that $\Gamma_C \subset \Sigma = \Gamma - \Gamma_D$. If $q \in L^2(\Gamma_C)$, the duality pairing $\langle \cdot, \cdot \rangle_Q$ might be identified with the $L^2$-inner product on $\Gamma_C$. The admissible set $N$ is defined by

$$N = \{q \in Q': q \leq 0\}$$

(9.66)

In this case, the operator $B$ characterizing the constraint is the normal trace defined by $B\mathbf{v} = v_n$ and is linear, continuous, and surjective from $V$ into $H_n^{1/2}(\Sigma)$. Thus the LBB condition (9.36) holds for the continuous problem (9.65) (see the part of the closed-range theorem in Yosida [15]); that is, there exists a positive constant $\alpha > 0$ to the inequality

$$\sup_{v \in V} \frac{\langle q, v_n \rangle_Q}{\|\mathbf{v}\|} \geq \alpha |q|_Q^* \qquad \forall q \in Q'$$

(9.67)

where $\|\cdot\|$ is the norm of $V$ defined by

$$\|\mathbf{v}\| = \left( \int_\Omega v_{i,\alpha} v_{i,\alpha} \, d\Omega \right)^{1/2}$$

(9.68)

A formal finite-element approximation of the mixed formulation (9.65) is

$$(\mathbf{u}_h, p_h) \in V_h \times N_h:$$

$$a(\mathbf{u}_h, \mathbf{v}_h) - \langle p_h, v_{nh} \rangle_Q = f(\mathbf{v}_h) \qquad \forall \mathbf{v}_h \in V_h$$

$$\langle q_h - p_h, u_{nh} - g \rangle_Q \geq 0 \qquad \forall q_h \in N_h$$

(9.69)

for a proper pair $\{V_h, N_h\}$ defined by a finite-element method.

For simplicity, let us consider the plane problem in the subsequent discussions; i.e., let $\Omega \subset \mathbb{R}^2$.

Suppose that $V_h$ is constructed by four-node isoparametric quadrilateral elements (i.e., Q4-elements), and that $Q'_h$ is obtained by two-node line elements (i.e., L2-elements).

**LEMMA 9.1** Suppose that a piecewise linear polynomial $v_{nh}$ is the interpolation of $v_n$ by L2-elements such that $v_{nh} = v_n^\alpha N_\alpha(s)$, where $v_n^\alpha$ is the value of $\mathbf{v}_h \cdot \mathbf{n}$ and $N_\alpha$ is the shape function associated with the $\alpha$-node. Then, for every $q_h \in Q'_h$, that is, also constructed by L2-elements, we have

$$\langle q_h, v_{nh} \rangle_Q = \int_{\Gamma_C} q_h v_{nh} \, d\Gamma = |\!|\!| q_h |\!|\!| \, |\!|\!| v_{nh} |\!|\!| \tag{9.70}$$

if $q_h \equiv v_{nh}$, where $|\!|\!| \cdot |\!|\!|$ is the $L^2$-norm on $\Gamma_C$; that is,

$$|\!|\!| q_h |\!|\!| = \left( \int_{\Gamma_C} q_h^2 \, d\Gamma \right)^{1/2}$$

Here it has been assumed that the value of $v_n^\alpha$ is determined uniquely at each nodal point on $\Gamma_C$.

**LEMMA 9.2** Let $\Omega_e$ be a rectangular element of the size $h_s \times h_t$, and let $\Gamma_e$ be its boundary. Then, if $h_s / h_t = r > 0$, there exists a positive constant $C$ depending only upon $r$ such that

$$\int_{\Gamma_e} v_{hi} v_{hi} \, d\Gamma \geqslant ch \int_{\Omega_e} v_{hi,j} v_{hi,j} \, d\Omega \tag{9.71}$$

for every $\mathbf{v}_h \in V_h$.

The estimate (9.71) can be obtained directly by the evaluation of $v_{hi} = v_i^\alpha N_\alpha(s, t)$ and $v_{hi,j} = v_i^\alpha N_{\alpha,j}(s, t)$. Combining Lemmas 9.1 and 9.2, it is possible to verify the following result.

**LEMMA 9.3** Suppose that $\Omega$ is divided into regular Q4-elements $\{\Omega_e\}$ such that the ratio of the radii of two circles, one which contains $\Omega_e$ and the other of which is contained in $\Omega_e$, is bounded for every $e$, $1 \leqslant e \leqslant E$. Then there exists a positive constant $\beta_0 > 0$ independent of $h$ such that

$$\sup_{\mathbf{v}_h \in V_h} \frac{\langle q_h, v_{nh} \rangle_Q}{\|\mathbf{v}_h\|} \geqslant \beta_0 h^{1/2} |\!|\!| q_h |\!|\!| \qquad \forall q_h \in Q'_h \tag{9.72}$$

Applying the results in Theorems 9.1 and 9.2, and using the theory of interpolation of functions in, for example, Ciarlet [10] or Oden and Carey [6], we may conclude the following error estimates.

**THEOREM 9.5** Let (9.61) hold, and let the conditions in Lemma 9.3 be assumed. Suppose that

$$\mathbf{u} \in H^2(\Omega) \qquad p \in H^{1/2}(\Gamma_C) \qquad \text{and} \qquad g \in H^{3/2}(\Gamma_C) \tag{9.73}$$

Then for $V_h$ and $Q'_h$ constructed by $Q_4$-elements and L2-elements, respectively, we have

$$\|\mathbf{u} - u_n\| + |p - p_h|^* \leqslant Ch \tag{9.74}$$

for a proper constant $C$ independent of the mesh size $h$.

If the penalty method studied above is applied to the Signorini problem, the formulation (9.69) is changed by

$$\mathbf{u}_h \in V_h : a(\mathbf{u}_h, \mathbf{v}_h) + \frac{1}{\varepsilon} \int_{\Gamma_C} (u_{nh}^\varepsilon - g)^+ v_{nh} \, ds = f(\mathbf{v}_h) \qquad \forall \mathbf{v}_h \in V_h \tag{9.75}$$

where $(u_{nh}^\varepsilon - g)^+ = ((u_n^\varepsilon)^\alpha)^+ N_\alpha(s)$, and $\phi^+ = \max\{0, \phi\}$. Then the estimate (9.74) may be modified:

$$\|\mathbf{u} - \mathbf{u}_h^\varepsilon\| + |p - p_h^\varepsilon|^* \leq C(h + \varepsilon h^{-1/2}) \tag{9.76}$$

## 9.4D Stokes Flow Problems in Fluid Mechanics

Another application of combined mixed and penalty methods to solve constrained problems is the Stokes flow problem, which is a linearized version of Navier–Stokes flow problems. In this case, the flow is restricted into the divergence free space

$$K = \{\mathbf{v} \in V \mid \operatorname{div} \mathbf{v} = v_{i,i} = 0 \text{ in } \Omega\} \tag{9.77}$$

where $\mathbf{v}$ is the velocity field of the flow, and

$$V = \{\mathbf{v} \in \mathbf{H}^1(\Omega) \mid v_i = 0 \text{ on } \Gamma, 1 \leq i \leq N\} \tag{9.78}$$

If $\mu$ is the viscosity such that

$$\mu_0 \leq \mu(\mathbf{x}) \leq \mu \qquad \forall \mathbf{x} \in \Omega \tag{9.79}$$

the bilinear form $a(\cdot, \cdot)$ defined by

$$a(\mathbf{u}, \mathbf{v}) = \int_\Omega \mu u_{i,j} v_{i,j} \, dx \tag{9.80}$$

is continuous and $V$-elliptic on $V \times V$, and the linear form $f(\cdot)$ defined by

$$f(\mathbf{v}) = \int_\Omega f_i v_i \, dx \tag{9.81}$$

is bounded on $V$ for $\mathbf{f} \in \mathbf{L}^2(\Omega)$. The variational form to the Stokes flow problem is then given by

$$\mathbf{u} \in K; \ a(\mathbf{u}, \mathbf{v} - \mathbf{u}) = f(\mathbf{v} - \mathbf{u}) \qquad \forall \mathbf{v} \in K \tag{9.82}$$

and the corresponding mixed formulation becomes

$$(\mathbf{u}, p) \in V \times Q':$$

$$a(\mathbf{u}, \mathbf{v}) - \langle p, \operatorname{div} \mathbf{v} \rangle_Q = f(\mathbf{v}) \qquad \forall \mathbf{v} \in V \tag{9.83}$$

$$\langle q, \operatorname{div} \mathbf{u} \rangle_Q = 0 \qquad \forall q \in Q'$$

where $Q = L^2(\Omega)/\mathbb{R}$, and $\langle \cdot, \cdot \rangle_Q$ is identified with the $L^2$-inner product on $\Omega$. Since the divergence operator is linear-continuous and surjective from $V$ into $Q$, the mixed formulation (9.83) is well-posed.

A formal description of a finite-element approximation of (9.83) is

$$(\mathbf{u}_h, p_h) \in V_h \times Q'_h:$$

$$a(\mathbf{u}_h, \mathbf{v}_h) - \langle p_h, \operatorname{div} \mathbf{v}_h \rangle_Q = f(\mathbf{v}_h) \qquad \forall \mathbf{v}_h \in V_h \qquad (9.84)$$

$$\langle q_h, \operatorname{div} \mathbf{u}_h \rangle_Q = 0 \qquad \forall q_h \in Q'_h$$

The choice of $V_h$ and $Q'_h$ for the Stokes flow problem is much more delicate than the Signorini problem, since the operator $B$ for the constraint includes the first-order differential operators. Many studies on the choice of proper finite-element spaces have been studied so far. For example, Crouzeix and Raviart [21], Fortin [14], Girault and Raviart [22], Oden, Kikuchi, and Song [23], Oden and Jacquotte [24], Bercovier and Pironneau [25], Glowinski and Pironneau [26], Bercovier [27], and others applied various forms of both mixed and penalty methods to the Stokes flow problem. Details of analysis can be found in Girault and Raviart [22]. Studies on the conforming mixed methods that applied the different LBB condition from (9.36) to obtain error estimates are found in Bercovier and Pironneau [25] and Glowinski and Pironneau [26].

Here we summarize the results on a nonconforming scheme to the pressure field that has natural correspondence to the penalty method widely used in practice, following Oden, Kikuchi, and Song [23]. The proof of the discrete LBB condition is based upon the result in Prop. 9.1 derived by Fortin [14].

Let a domain in $\mathbb{R}^2$ be divided into the set of composite elements $\{\Omega_e\}$ such that each $\Omega_e$ consists of four equal-size four-node isoparametric quadrilateral elements. Let a finite-element space $V_h$ be constructed by such specially arranged Q4-elements, and let

$$Q'_h = \{q_h : q_h = \text{constant on } \Omega^i_e, 1 \le i \le 4,$$

$$q^1_h + q^3_h = q^2_h + q^4_h \text{ on } \Omega_e, 1 \le e \le E\} \qquad (9.85)$$

where

$$\bar{\Omega}_e = \bigcup_{i=1}^{4} \bar{\Omega}^i_e \qquad \text{and} \qquad q^i_h = q_h \qquad \text{on } \Omega^i_e$$

That is, the pressure field is assumed to be a piecewise constant function on each Q4-element, and it satisfies the special condition $q^1_h + q^3_h = q^2_h + q^4_h$ on each composite element $\Omega_e$. Then Oden, Kikuchi, and Song [23] prove the following result.

**LEMMA 9.4**  For the above choice of elements for $V_h$ and $Q'_h$, it is possible to find the operator $\Lambda_h$ of $V$ into $V_h$ such that Prop. 9.1 is satisfied; i.e., there exists a positive constant $\alpha_0$ such that

$$\sup_{\mathbf{v}_h \in V_h} \frac{\langle q_h, \operatorname{div} \mathbf{v}_h \rangle_Q}{\|\mathbf{v}_h\|} \ge \alpha_0 |q_h|^* \qquad \forall q_h \in Q'_h \qquad (9.86)$$

if the domain $\Omega$ is a rectangle.

Applying the theory of interpolation and the results in Theorems 9.1 and 9.2, we can obtain the following error estimates.

**THEOREM 9.6**  Let (9.79) hold, and let

$$\mathbf{u} \in H^2(\Omega) \quad \text{and} \quad p \in H^1(\Omega) \tag{9.87}$$

Then for the special composite element defined above and a rectangle $\Omega$, we have

$$\|\mathbf{u} - \mathbf{u}_h\| + |p - p_h|^* \leq Ch \tag{9.88}$$

for a positive constant $C > 0$ independent of the mesh size $h$, where $|\cdot|^*$ is the norm on the quotient space $Q = L^2(\Omega)/\mathbb{R}$.

The corresponding penalty method for the mixed formulation (9.84), using such composite elements, has to satisfy a special relation in the space $Q_h'$. It is clear that for the penalty formulation

$$\mathbf{u}_h^\varepsilon \in V_h : a(\mathbf{u}_h^\varepsilon, \mathbf{v}_h) + \frac{1}{\varepsilon} \int_\Omega \operatorname{div} \mathbf{u}_h^\varepsilon \operatorname{div} \mathbf{v}_h \, d\Omega = f(\mathbf{v}_h) \qquad \forall \mathbf{v}_h \in V_h \tag{9.89}$$

does not correspond to the mixed formulation (9.84), unless the condition

$$\operatorname{div} \mathbf{u}_h^\varepsilon|_1 + \operatorname{div} \mathbf{u}_h^\varepsilon|_3 = \operatorname{div} \mathbf{u}_h^\varepsilon|_2 + \operatorname{div} \mathbf{u}_h^\varepsilon|_4 \tag{9.90}$$

is satisfied, where $\operatorname{div} \mathbf{u}_h^\varepsilon|_i = \operatorname{div} \mathbf{u}_h^\varepsilon$ on $\Omega_e^i$.

Similar methods are used in Oden, Kikuchi, and Song [23] to prove the discrete LBB condition for the choice of nine-node $\Omega_2$-elements for $V_h$ and linear elements for $Q_h$.

## 9.4E Stability of Reduced-Integration Penalty Schemes

We return to the Stokes problem (9.83) and the discrete approximation (9.89). In most applications of exterior penalty methods for this problem, we have, instead of (9.89), the reduced-integration scheme

$$\mathbf{u}_h^\varepsilon \in V_h : a(\mathbf{u}_h, \mathbf{v}_h) - I(p_h^\varepsilon, \operatorname{div} \mathbf{v}_h) = f(\mathbf{v}_h)$$

$$I(q_h, \varepsilon p_h^\varepsilon + \operatorname{div} U_h^\varepsilon) = 0 \qquad \forall \mathbf{v}_h \in V_h, \ \forall q_h \in Q_h \tag{9.91}$$

where $I(\cdot, \cdot)$ is a numerical quadrature operator approximating $(\cdot, \cdot)_{L^2(\Omega)}$:

$$I(f, g) = \sum_{e=1}^E \sum_{j=1}^G W_j^e f(\xi_j^e) g(\xi_j^e) \tag{9.92}$$

where $W_j^e$ = quadrature weights, $\xi_j^e$ = quadrature points and $f, g \in C^0(\bar\Omega)$. In this case, the discrete LBB condition becomes the following.

There exists $\alpha_h > 0$ such that

$$\alpha_h \|q_h\|_{L^2(\Omega)/\ker \nabla_h} \leq \sup_{\mathbf{v}_h \in V_h} \frac{I(q_h, \operatorname{div} \mathbf{v}_h)}{\|\mathbf{v}_h\|} \qquad \forall q h \in Q_h \tag{9.93}$$

wherein $\nabla_h$ is the discrete approximation of the gradient (plus boundary conditions):

$$\langle \nabla_h q_h, \mathbf{v}_h \rangle = I(q_h, \operatorname{div} \mathbf{v}_h) \qquad q_h \in Q_h, \ \mathbf{v}_h \in V_h \tag{9.94}$$

The numerical stability of the method (9.91) and its convergence characteristics depend upon the parameter $\alpha_h$, as was noted earlier. For the case in which $\Omega$ is a rectangle, a uniform mesh is used, and Dirichlet boundary conditions are enforced. Estimates of $\alpha_h$ have been obtained by Oden, Kikuchi, and Song [23], Oden [28], and Oden and Jacquotte [24]. Following Oden [28], some of these results are given in Table 9.1.

**TABLE 9.1**

| Velocity approximation $V^h$ | Quadrature rule (pressure approximation $Q^h$) | $\beta_h$ | Rate of convergence |
|---|---|---|---|
| 1   $Q_1$ | $Q_2$ | $O(1)$ | Locks for small $\varepsilon$; $\varepsilon$ must be taken as dependent on $h$ |
| 2   $Q_1$ | $Q_0$ | $O(h)$ | Unstable pressure |
| 3   $1B$ | $Q_2$ | $O(1)$ | Locks for small $\varepsilon$; $\varepsilon$ must be taken as dependent on $h$ |
| 4   $I8$ | $Q_1$ | $O(h)$ | Unstable pressure |
| 5   $I8$ | $P_1$ | $O(h)$ | Unstable pressure |
| 6   $I8$ | $Q_0$ | $O(1)$ | Suboptimal $[O(h)]$ in velocity error in energy norm |
| 7   $Q_2$ | $Q_2$ | $O(1)$ | Locks for small $\varepsilon$; $\varepsilon$ must be taken as dependent on $h$ |

TABLE 9.1—*cont.*

| | Velocity approximation $V^h$ | Quadrature rule (pressure approximation $Q^h$) | $\beta_h$ | Rate of convergence |
|---|---|---|---|---|
| 8 | $Q_2$ | $Q_1$ | $O(h)$ | Unstable pressure |
| 9 | $Q_2$ | $P_1$ | $O(1)$ | Optimal: $\|\mathbf{u}-\mathbf{u}_h\|_V = O(h^2)$ $\|p-p_h\|_Q = O(h^2)$ |
| 10 | $Q_2$ | $Q_0$ | $O(1)$ | Suboptimal $[O(h)]$ in velocity error in energy norm |
| 11 | $Q_3$ | $Q_2$ | $O(h)$ | Unstable pressure† |
| 12 | $Q_3$ | $Q_0$ | $O(1)$ | Suboptimal $[O(h)]$ in velocity error in energy norm† |
| 13 | Composite $Q_2/18$ | Composite $4P_1$ | $O(1)$ | Optimal |
| 14 | Composite $4P_1$ | Composite $4P_1$ | $O(h)$ | Unstable pressures |
| | $P_2$ | $P_0$ | $O(1)$ | Suboptimal $[O(h)]$ in velocity error in energy norm |

† The behavior of these elements is only conjecture and has not been rigorously proved.

We use the notations

$p_k$ = space of complete piecewise polynomials of degree $k$ over an element

$Q_k$ = space of tensor products of complete polynomials of degree $K$

$I8$ = the eight-node isoparametric element

In Table 9.1, examples 1, 2, and 7 "lock" at small values of the penalty parameter $\varepsilon$. This means that for a given mesh size $h$, $\varepsilon$ cannot be taken arbitrarily small, as noted earlier. Of course, for an acceptable $\varepsilon$ for reasonable mesh sizes, $\varepsilon$ is so large that the constraint of incompressibility is not adequately satisfied. Hence, these elements should generally be avoided. Elements 2, 4, 5, 8, 11, and 14 are unstable since $\beta_h = O(h)$. Remarkably, these instabilities frequently are not observed on uniform meshes when the solution is very smooth. Mild irregularities in the solution or small perturbations in the mesh may, however, produce violent oscillations in computed pressures, the magnitudes of which increase without bound as $h$ tends to zero. In many cases, however, these oscillations disappear upon "filtering" the pressure solutions (i.e., upon averaging the pressures over one or more elements). In the case of elements 2 and 14, it has been proved mathematically (by N. Kikuchi and J. T. Oden) that certain filtering schemes will produce a stable and convergent method. However, it is not known if filtering can be used to stabilize and salvage the remaining unstable elements.

Elements 6 and 10 lead to stable and convergent schemes and are quite robust in the sense that they are insensitive to singularities in the solution. However, they are not too accurate and converge at a suboptimal rate.

Elements 5 and 9 are calculated using the perturbed lagrangian ideas discussed in Sec. 9.3: a piecewise linear approximation of the regularized pressure $p_\varepsilon$ is computed over each element. Then (9.91) leads to a discrete system for each element of the form

$$\mathbf{K}\mathbf{u}_\varepsilon - \mathbf{B}^T \mathbf{p}_\varepsilon = \mathbf{f} + \boldsymbol{\sigma}$$
$$\varepsilon \mathbf{M}\mathbf{p} + \mathbf{B}\mathbf{u}_\varepsilon = 0 \tag{9.95}$$

where $\mathbf{K}$ is the element stiffness matrix, $\mathbf{B}$ is the nonrectangular constraint matrix, $\mathbf{f}$ is the load vector, $\boldsymbol{\sigma}$ is the "connecting" vector (which sums to zero upon connecting elements together to form the mesh), and $\mathbf{M}$ is the Gram matrix corresponding to the linear shape functions for $p_\varepsilon$. Thus,

$$\mathbf{p}_\varepsilon = -\varepsilon^{-1} \mathbf{M}^{-1} \mathbf{B}^T \mathbf{u}_\varepsilon \tag{9.96}$$

i.e., the fact that $p_h^\varepsilon$ is discontinuous across interelement boundaries makes it possible to eliminate the pressure *at the element level* by (9.96). Then the penalty approximation over an element is characterized by

$$(\mathbf{K} + \varepsilon^{-1} \mathbf{B}^T \mathbf{M}\mathbf{B}) u_\varepsilon = \mathbf{f} + \boldsymbol{\sigma} \tag{9.97}$$

Thus, no reduced-integration rule is actually used in constructing elements 5 and 9.

Element 9 is clearly the superior of any listed: it is unconditionally stable, it provides both velocity and pressure approximations which converge at the optimal rate, and

$$\ker \nabla_h = \ker \nabla$$

Element 13 is somewhat of a novelty. While element 5 yields unstable pressure approxima-tions, Oden and Jacquotte [24] have shown that a composite of three $Q_2/P_1$-elements (number 9) and one $I8/P_1$-element (number 5) is stable.

The behavior of elements 11 and 12, marked with a dagger, is only conjectured here and has not been rigorously proved.

Extensions of these results to three-dimensional elements are straightforward.

## 9.5 HYBRID FINITE-ELEMENT METHODS

A large class of practically important problems in engineering can be written in the operator form

$$A^* LAu = f \tag{9.98}$$

Here $A^*$ is the adjoint of an $m^{\text{th}}$-order linear operator $A$, $L$ is a symmetric operator, and $f$ is a given function.

A majority of finite-element approximations of type (9.98) is based on either the minimum or maximum principle. Indeed, the use of conforming or nonconforming "displacement" ("primal") finite-element models dominated most of the applications in mechanics for many years.

In the primal method, the primary variables (e.g., displacements, temperature, potential) are first computed and then second quantities (e.g., stresses, flux, velocity), which are more important for design purposes, are calculated by numerically differentiating the approximate solutions, thereby introducing additional errors. On the other hand, the dual (or equilibrium) models which behave as mechanisms without a judicious choice of basis functions have found limited use in general-purpose computer codes.

Moreover, continuity requirements encountered in conforming primal models for higher-order problems lead to complicated elements resulting in a large system of equations to solve. Some of these problems can be overcome if mixed, hybrid, or generalized hybrid models are used.

Equations of the form (9.98), as suggested by the appearance of $A$ and $A^*$, can be decomposed into two lower-order equations by introducing a secondary variable, say, $\varepsilon = Au$ and treating it as another dependent variable, which naturally leads to the so-called mixed variational principle. Finite-element approximations based on this variational principle are called *mixed methods*, and they have gained some popularity (see, e.g., Refs. [17, 26, 27, and 29-34]).

The hybrid finite-element methods are based on the idea of providing independent approximations of lagrangian multipliers introduced by treating interelement-continuity requirements of certain variables as constraints. The concept was first introduced by Jones [35] and Pian [36] and was subsequently expanded and extensively applied by Pian and others [37-43]. Extensive references and computational accounts can be found in Refs. [44, 45]. Specific results of mathematical properties of mixed and hybrid methods can be found in Refs. [46-59]. See also Ref. [60] for interesting observations concerning variational formulations.

Quite general hybrid methods can be constructed for the abstract problem (9.98) by applying the concepts of the mixed and hybrid formulations. We outline here the basis of a mixed-hybrid variational formulation associated with (9.98) and discuss mathematical properties of some special cases that can be deduced from the general formulation.

### 9.5A General Approach

Let $\Omega$ be an open bounded domain with a piecewise smooth boundary $\partial\Omega$. We assume that the problem (9.98) is posed on $\Omega$ with proper boundary conditions so that a unique solution is guaranteed.

Hybrid variational problems, in general, are formulated on a partitioned domain with suitable constraints to guarantee that they are equivalent to the original problem in some sense. Because of this property, hybrid variational formulations provide a natural vehicle for the construction of corresponding finite-element approximations.

Let $P$ be a partition of $\Omega = \Omega_0$ into a collection of $E$ geometrically simple subdomains $\Omega_e$ (i.e., a regular finite-element mesh) with piecewise smooth boundaries $\partial\Omega_e$, $e = 1, 2, \ldots, E$, such that

1. $\bar{\Omega} = \bigcup_{e=1}^{E} \bar{\Omega}_e$ = closure of $\Omega$
2. $\Omega_e \cap \Omega_f = 0$      if $e \neq f \neq 0$
3. The boundary segments

$$\Gamma_{ef} = \partial\Omega_e \cap \partial\Omega_f, \qquad e > f, 0 < e, f \leq E$$

are smooth.

We assume that the collection of smooth boundary pieces

$$\Gamma = \Gamma(P) = \bigcup_{e>f}^{E} \Gamma_{ef}$$

is oriented so that $\Omega_e$ is on the left side of $\Gamma_{ef}$ whenever $1 \leq f < e \leq E$.

We use the notations

$$[[u, v]] = \sum_{e=1}^{E} [u, v]_e = \sum_{e=1}^{E} \int_{\partial\Omega_e} uv \, ds \qquad (9.99)$$

and
$$((u, v)) = \sum_{e=1}^{E} (u, v)_e = \sum_{e=1}^{E} \int_{\Omega_e} uv \, dx \qquad (9.100)$$

Consider now the functional defined by

$$J(\boldsymbol{\lambda}) = \tfrac{1}{2} B(\boldsymbol{\lambda}, \boldsymbol{\lambda}) - F(\boldsymbol{\lambda}) \qquad (9.101)$$

Here, $\boldsymbol{\lambda} = (u, v, \sigma, \tau, \mathbf{w})$, and

$$B(\boldsymbol{\lambda}, \bar{\boldsymbol{\lambda}}) = ((Lv - \sigma, \bar{v})) + ((Au - v, \bar{\sigma})) + ((\sigma, A\bar{u})) + [[\tau, \bar{\mathbf{w}} - \gamma\bar{u}]] + [[\mathbf{w} - \gamma u, \bar{\tau}]] \qquad (9.102)$$

$$F(\boldsymbol{\lambda}) = ((f, u)) + \langle g_2, \mathbf{w}\rangle_2 - \langle g_1, \tau\rangle_1 \qquad (9.103)$$

in which the overbar is used to denote an arbitrary function in the space of the corresponding variable; $\boldsymbol{\gamma} = \{\gamma_i\}_{i=0}^{m-1}$, where $m$ is the order of the operator $A$, and $\gamma_i = \partial^i/\partial n_e^i$, $\mathbf{n}_e$ being the outward normal to $\partial\Omega_e$; $\boldsymbol{\tau}$, $\mathbf{w}$, and $\mathbf{g}_\alpha$, $\alpha = 1, 2$, are sets of $m$-functions so that, for example, $[[\boldsymbol{\tau}, \boldsymbol{\gamma}u]] = \sum_{i=0}^{m-1} [[\tau^i, \gamma_i u]]$; and, for $\alpha = 1, 2$,

$$\langle \mathbf{g}_a, \mathbf{b}\rangle_\alpha = \sum_{i=0}^{m-1} \int_{\partial\Omega^\alpha} g_\alpha^i b^i \, ds$$

It is assumed that $\partial\Omega = \partial\Omega^1 \cup \partial\Omega^2$ and $\mathbf{g}_\alpha$ are prescribed functions on $\partial\Omega^\alpha$.

Obviously, the stationary-value problem of the functional $J(\cdot)$ is to seek an element $\boldsymbol{\lambda}$ in a proper space, say $\mathscr{X}$, such that

$$B(\boldsymbol{\lambda}, \bar{\boldsymbol{\lambda}}) = F(\bar{\boldsymbol{\lambda}}) \qquad \text{for every } \bar{\boldsymbol{\lambda}} \in \mathscr{X} \tag{9.104}$$

When the third term in (9.104) is integrated by parts by using Green's formula,

$$(Au, \sigma)_e = (A^*\sigma, u)_e + [\delta\sigma, \gamma u]_e \tag{9.105}$$

we obtain the following set of Euler's equations. For each $e = 1, 2, \ldots, E$,

$$\left.\begin{aligned} Au &= v \\ Lv &= \sigma \\ A^*\sigma &= f \end{aligned}\right\} \quad \text{in } \Omega_e \tag{9.106}$$

$$\left.\begin{aligned} \mathbf{w} &= \boldsymbol{\gamma}u \quad \text{and} \quad \delta\sigma = \boldsymbol{\tau} \quad \text{on } \partial\Omega_e \\ \boldsymbol{\gamma}u &= \mathbf{g}_1 \quad \text{on } \partial\Omega_e \cap \partial\Omega^1 \\ \boldsymbol{\tau} &= \mathbf{g}_2 \quad \text{on } \partial\Omega_e \cap \partial\Omega^2 \end{aligned}\right\} \tag{9.107}$$

and the weak-continuity condition of $\boldsymbol{\tau}$ over $\Gamma$

$$\sum_{e=1}^{E} \int_{\partial\Omega_e - \partial\Omega} \boldsymbol{\tau} \cdot \bar{\mathbf{w}} \, ds = 0 \qquad \text{for arbitrary } \bar{\mathbf{w}} \text{ defined on } \Gamma \tag{9.108}$$

We now have a set of weak canonical equations posed on each element with proper continuity and boundary conditions as constraints. Definite advantages of this type of formulation can be readily observed, namely, reduced smoothness requirements and a natural setting to handle interface conditions that may exist. Notice also that the weak solutions $u$ and $\sigma$ need to be smooth only in each subdomain $\Omega_e$ rather than in $\Omega$. This feature will play a greater role in the development of finite-element approximations for problems with singularities.

For future development we define some functional spaces over the partition described earlier. Let $H^l(\Omega)$ be the Hilbert space with the usual norm, and define

$$H^l(P) = \{u \in L_2(\Omega); u_e \in H^l(\Omega_e), 1 \le e \le E\} \tag{9.109}$$

and the norm in $H^l(P)$ by

$$\|u\|_{l,P} = \left( \sum_{e=1}^{E} \|u_e\|_{l,\Omega_e}^2 \right)^{1/2}$$

Let $\mathcal{W}(\Gamma) = $ completion of $C^\infty(\Gamma)$ in the norm

$$\|\psi\|_{\mathcal{W}} = \inf \{\|v\|_{1,\Omega}; \ v \in \tilde{H}_0^1(\Omega) \text{ such that } v|_\Gamma = \psi\} \tag{9.110}$$

and let

$$\mathcal{M}(\tilde{\Gamma}) = \prod_{e=1}^{E} H^{-1/2}(\partial\Omega_e) \tag{9.111}$$

where

$$\tilde{H}_0^1(\Omega) = \{u \in H^1(\Omega); \ \gamma_0 u = 0 \text{ on } \partial\Omega^1\}$$

and $H^{-1/2}(\partial\Omega_e)$ is the completion of $C^\infty(\partial\Omega_e)$ in the norm

$$\|\tau\|_{-1/2,\partial\Omega_e} = \sup_{\phi \in H^{1/2}(\partial\Omega_e)} \frac{\left| \oint \tau\phi \, ds \right|}{\|\phi\|_{1/2,\partial\Omega_e}} \tag{9.112}$$

Here

$$H^{1/2}(\partial\Omega_e) = \{\gamma_0 u; \ u \in H^1(\Omega_e)\} \tag{9.113}$$

The space $\mathcal{M}(\tilde{\Gamma})$ will be equipped with the norm

$$\|\tau\|_{\mathcal{M}} = \left( \sum_{e=1}^{E} \|\tau_e\|_{-1/2,\partial\Omega_e}^2 \right)^{1/2} \tag{9.114}$$

Technically speaking, $\tilde{\Gamma}$ should not contain corner nodal points so that the above definitions make sense.

Some examples of hybrid variational problems based on the general form (9.105) are briefly discussed below.

**EXAMPLE 9.1**   For a biharmonic equation, we have $A = A^* = \Delta$, where $\Delta$ is the laplacian operator $(m = 2)$, and $L = 1$. Then

$$\gamma = \{\gamma_0, \gamma_1\} \qquad \delta = \{-\gamma_1, \gamma_0\} \qquad \mathbf{w} = \{w^0, w^1\} \qquad \tau = \{\tau^0, \tau^1\} \tag{9.115}$$

If we set $Lv = \sigma$ in (9.102), (9.104) takes the form

$$B_4^6(\lambda, \bar{\lambda}) = F(\bar{\lambda}) \qquad \forall \bar{\lambda} \in \mathcal{X}^6 \tag{9.116}$$

where $\lambda = (u, \sigma, \tau^0, \tau^1, w^0, w^1)$ and the bilinear form $B_4^6(\cdot, \cdot)$ can be obtained from (9.102) with the aid of (9.115) and integration by parts.

$$B_4^6(\lambda, \bar{\lambda}) = \sum_{e=1}^{E} \left\{ b_e(u, \sigma; \bar{u}, \bar{\sigma}) + \int_{\partial\Omega_e} [(\sigma - \tau^1)\gamma_1 \bar{u} + (\bar{\sigma} - \bar{\tau}^1)\gamma_1 u + (w^0 - u)\bar{\tau}^0 \right.$$

$$\left. + (\bar{w}^0 - \bar{u})\tau^0 + \tau^1 \bar{w}^1 + w^1 \bar{\tau}^1] \, ds \right\} \tag{9.117}$$

where

$$b_e(u, \sigma; \bar{u}, \bar{\sigma}) = -\int_{\Omega_e} (\text{grad } u \cdot \text{grad } \bar{\sigma} + \sigma\bar{\sigma} + \text{grad } \sigma \cdot \text{grad } \bar{u}) \, dx$$

The space $\mathscr{X}^6$ can be identified as

$$\mathscr{X}^6 = H^1(P) \times H^1(P) \times \mathscr{M}(\tilde{\Gamma}) \times \mathscr{W}(\tilde{\Gamma}) \times \mathscr{W}(\Gamma) \times \mathscr{M}(\tilde{\Gamma}) \qquad (9.118)$$

Although the usefulness of such a complex formulation is questionable, one can provide a finite-element approximation of (9.116). One would assume independent approximations of $u$ and $\sigma$ in $\Omega e$, $\tau^0$ and $w^1$ on $\partial\Omega_e$, and $\tau^1$ and $w^0$ on the common boundary $\Gamma_{ef}$ so that they are continuous over $\Gamma$. Since $u$, $\sigma$, $\tau^0$, and $w^0$ are defined only locally (i.e., they are independent for each element), they can be eliminated prior to assembly of the global equation so that the final equation will have nodal values of $\tau^1$ and $w^0$ as unknowns.

**EXAMPLE 9.2**  A considerably simpler formulation can be obtained. If we replace $w^1$ by $\gamma_1 u$ and $\tau^0$ by $-\gamma_1\sigma$ in (9.117), we have

$$B_4^3(\boldsymbol{\lambda}, \bar{\boldsymbol{\lambda}}) = F(\bar{\boldsymbol{\lambda}}) \qquad \forall\bar{\boldsymbol{\lambda}} \in \mathscr{X}^3 \qquad (9.119)$$

where
$$B_4^3(\boldsymbol{\lambda}, \bar{\boldsymbol{\lambda}}) = \sum_{e=1}^{E} \left\{ b_e(u, \sigma; \bar{u}, \bar{\sigma}) + \oint_{\partial\Omega_e} [\sigma\gamma_1\bar{u} + \bar{\sigma}\gamma_1 u + (u - w)\gamma_1\bar{\sigma} + (\bar{u} - \bar{w})\gamma_1\sigma] \, ds \right\} \qquad (9.120)$$

in which
$$\boldsymbol{\lambda} = (u, \sigma, w) \qquad \text{with} \qquad w = w^0$$

$$\mathscr{X}^3 = H^1(P) \times H^1(P) \times \mathscr{W}(\Gamma) \qquad (9.121)$$

One can easily construct a finite-element subspace of $\mathscr{X}^3$ for a consistent approximation. For example,

$$\mathscr{X}_h^3 = \mathscr{P}_k(P) \times \mathscr{P}_r(P) \times \mathscr{P}_t(\Gamma) \subset \mathscr{X}^3 \qquad (9.122)$$

where
$$\mathscr{P}_k(P) = \{U \in L_2(\Omega); \ U_e \text{ is a } k^{\underline{\text{th}}}\text{-degree polynomial in each } \Omega_e\}$$

$$\mathscr{P}_t(\Gamma) = \{W \in \mathscr{W}(\Gamma): \ W_e \text{ is a } t^{\underline{\text{th}}}\text{-degree polynomial on each } \partial\Omega_e\}$$

The usual $C^0$-finite-element subspace can be effectively used to generate the subspace $\mathscr{P}_t(\Gamma)$.

The results are quite revealing in a sense that the usual nonconforming elements can be effectively employed to approximate fourth-order problems via the hybrid formulation provided here. Moreover, addition of singular functions in $\mathscr{P}_k$ and/or $\mathscr{P}_r$ when needed is easy to implement (see Ref. [57]).

**EXAMPLE 9.3**  The so-called "stress-assumed" (dual) hybrid model pioneered by Pian [36, 37] can also be obtained from the general approach. We begin by replacing $\sigma$ and $\tau^1$ by $\sigma_{ij}$, $\tau^0$ by $-\sigma_{ij,j}n_i$, $w^0$ by $w$, and $w^1$ by $\phi_i n_j$ in (9.117). Here, the index notations are adapted with $i, j = 1, 2$; a comma denotes a partial derivative; and $n_j$ are components of a unit outward normal to an element $\Omega_e$. Then, integrating area integrals by parts with the substitution $\sigma_{ij} = s_{ij} + P_{ij}$ where $s_{ij,ij} = 0$ and $P_{ij,ij} = f$ in each $\Omega_e$, we have

$$\tilde{B}_4^3(\boldsymbol{\lambda}, \bar{\boldsymbol{\lambda}}) = \tilde{F}(\bar{\boldsymbol{\lambda}}) \qquad \forall\bar{\boldsymbol{\lambda}} \in \tilde{\mathscr{X}}^3 \qquad (9.123)$$

where $\boldsymbol{\lambda} = (s_{ij}, w, \phi_i)$ and

$$\tilde{B}_4^3(\boldsymbol{\lambda}, \bar{\boldsymbol{\lambda}}) = \left[ \sum_{e=1}^{E} \int_{\Omega_e} s_{ij}\bar{s}_{ij} \, dx + \oint_{\partial\Omega_e} (w\bar{s}_{ij,j}n_i + s_{ij,j}n_i\bar{w} - \phi_i n_j\bar{s}_{ij} - s_{ij}n_j\bar{\phi}_i) \, ds \right] \qquad (9.124)$$

$$\tilde{F}(\bar{\boldsymbol{\lambda}}) = \sum_{e=1}^{E} \left[ -\int_{\Omega_e} P_{ij}\bar{s}_{ij} \, dx - \oint_{\partial\Omega_e} (P_{ij,j}n_i\bar{w} - P_{ij}n_j\bar{\phi}_i) \right] \qquad (9.125)$$

Here, it is assumed that $\partial\Omega^2 = \phi$ and $\mathbf{g}_1 = \mathbf{0}$ on $\partial\Omega^1 = \partial\Omega$ for convenience. The space of admissible functions can be identified as

$$\mathscr{X}^3 = \mathscr{S}^0(P) \times \mathscr{W}(\Gamma) \times \mathscr{W}(\Gamma) \qquad (9.126)$$

where
$$\mathscr{S}^0(P) = \{v_{ij} \in L_2(\Omega);\ v_{ij} = v_{ji},\ v_{ij,ij} = 0 \text{ in each } \Omega_e\}$$

It can be shown that the solution $\lambda$ of (9.123) has the relationship (in the weak sense)

$$w = u \qquad s_{ij} = u_{,ij} - P_{ij} \qquad \phi_i = u_{,i} \qquad (9.127)$$

if $u$ is the solution of     $\Delta^2 u = f$ in $\Omega$   and   $u = \dfrac{\partial u}{\partial n} = 0$ on $\partial\Omega$     (9.128)

This formulation appears to be slightly different from the original one given by Pian [36] in the sense that the function $\phi_i$ is treated as independent from $w$. One can identify $\phi_i$ in (9.123) by $w_{,i}$. Then the conditions $w$, $w_{,i} \in \mathscr{W}(\Gamma)$ can be met by selecting $w$ as the restriction of a function in $H_0^2(\Omega)$ to $\Gamma$, or, equivalently, $w \in H_0^2(\Omega)$ after applying Green's formula in (9.124). Mathematical analysis of the corresponding finite-element approximations including conditions for convergence are discussed in detail by Brezzi [52] and Brezzi and Marini [53].

Some mathematical results for second-order problems are discussed in the following section.

## 9.5b  A Sample Analysis

Consider a model problem

$$-\Delta\phi = f(x, y) \qquad \text{in } \Omega$$

$$\phi = 0 \quad \text{on } \partial\Omega^1 \qquad \text{and} \qquad \frac{\partial\phi}{\partial n} = g \quad \text{on } \partial\Omega^2 \qquad (9.129)$$

where $\Delta$ is the laplacian operator in $R^2$; $\partial\Omega^1$ and $\partial\Omega^2$ are portions of the piecewise smooth boundary $\partial\Omega$ of $\Omega$; and $f \in L_2(\Omega)$ and $g \in L_2(\partial\Omega^2)$ are given functions.

In this case, we have $A = \text{grad} = \nabla$, $A^* = -\nabla\cdot$, $L = I$, and $m = 1$. Considering the same partition $P$ described earlier and replacing $\sigma$ by $Ev = \mathbf{v}$ and $\tau^0$ by $\mathbf{v}_e \cdot \mathbf{n}_e$ in (9.102), we obtain, after integration by parts,

$$B(\lambda, \bar{\lambda}) = -((\nabla \cdot \mathbf{v}, \bar{\phi})) - ((\phi, \nabla \cdot \bar{\mathbf{v}})) - ((\mathbf{v}, \bar{\mathbf{v}})) \qquad (9.130a)$$

$$F(\bar{\lambda}) = ((f, \bar{\phi})) + \langle g, \bar{w} \rangle_2 \qquad (9.130b)$$

where $\lambda = (\phi, \mathbf{v}, w)$. The space $\mathscr{X}$ can be identified as

$$\mathscr{X} = L_2(P) \times \mathscr{S}(P) \times \mathscr{W}(\Gamma) \qquad (9.131)$$

together with the natural norm

$$\|\lambda\|_{\mathscr{X}} = (\|\phi\|_{0,P}^2 + \|\mathbf{v}\|_{\mathscr{S}}^2 + \|w\|_{\mathscr{W}}^2)^{1/2} \qquad (9.132)$$

so that $\boldsymbol{\lambda} \in \mathcal{X}$ would mean that $\phi \in L_2(P)$, $v \in S(P)$, and $w \in \mathcal{W}(\Gamma)$. Here, $L_2(P) = H^0(P)$ and $\mathcal{W}(\Gamma)$ are as in (9.109) and (9.110), and

$$\mathcal{S}(P) = \{ \mathbf{v} \in (L_2(\Omega))^2; \ \nabla \cdot \mathbf{v}_e \in L_2(\Omega_e) \text{ for each } \Omega_e \} \tag{9.133}$$

$$\|\mathbf{v}\|_{\mathcal{S}}^2 = \sum_{e=1}^{E} \{ \|\mathbf{v}\|_{0,\Omega_e}^2 + \|\nabla \cdot \mathbf{v}\|_{0,\Omega_e}^2 \}$$

Now the mixed-hybrid variational boundary-value problem corresponding to (9.129) is to find a triple $\boldsymbol{\lambda} = (\phi, v, w) \in \mathcal{X}$ such that

$$B(\boldsymbol{\lambda}, \bar{\boldsymbol{\lambda}}) = F(\bar{\boldsymbol{\lambda}}) \qquad \bar{\boldsymbol{\lambda}} \in \mathcal{X} \tag{9.134}$$

which is equivalent to the stationary-value problem for the functional

$$J(\boldsymbol{\lambda}) = \tfrac{1}{2} B(\boldsymbol{\lambda}, \boldsymbol{\lambda}) - F(\boldsymbol{\lambda}) \tag{9.135}$$

The functional of the type (9.135) was proposed by Wolf [43] in connection with elasticity problems. It is readily verified that the corresponding Euler's equations are, for each $e = 1, 2, \ldots, E$,

$$-\nabla \cdot \mathbf{v}_e = f_e \quad \text{and} \quad \mathbf{v}_e = \nabla \phi_e \quad \text{in } \Omega_e$$

$$w_e = \phi_e \quad \text{on } \partial\Omega_e \quad \text{and} \quad \mathbf{v}_e \cdot \mathbf{n} = g_e \quad \text{on } \partial\Omega_e^2 \tag{9.136}$$

$$\sum_{e=1}^{E} \int_{\partial\Omega_e^0} \mathbf{v}_e \cdot \mathbf{n} \bar{w}_e \, ds = 0 \qquad \bar{w} \in \mathcal{W}(\Gamma) \qquad \partial\Omega_e^0 = \partial\Omega_e - \partial\Omega \tag{9.137}$$

Notice that (9.137) implies a weak continuity of the vector $\mathbf{v}$ across the interelement boundaries and $w$ is the Lagrange multiplier defined continuously over $\Gamma$ and vanishing on $\partial\Omega$.

It can be shown that (see Refs. [56–59]) the mixed-hybrid formulation (9.134) has a unique solution. Furthermore, if the solution is smooth enough, (9.129) and (9.134) are equivalent.

The stage is now set to introduce finite-element approximations of the variational problem (9.134). We provide approximations of degree $k$, $r$, and $t$ for $\phi_e$, $\mathbf{v}_e$, and $w_e$, over each finite element $\bar{\Omega}_e$, respectively; i.e.,

$$\phi_e \approx \Phi_e = \sum_{i=1}^{K} b^i \psi_i(x_1, x_2) \qquad K = \dim \{\mathcal{P}_k(\Omega_e)\} \tag{9.138}$$

$$\mathbf{v}_e \approx \mathbf{V}_e = \sum_{i=1}^{R} (a_1^i \mathbf{e}_1 + a_2^i \mathbf{e}_2) \omega_i(x_1, x_2) \qquad R = \dim \{\mathcal{P}_r(\Omega_e)\}$$

$$w_e \approx W_e = \sum_{i=1}^{T} W^i N_i(s) \qquad T = M_e t = \dim \{\mathcal{P}_t(\partial\Omega_e)\} \tag{9.139}$$

where $\mathcal{P}_k(\Omega_e)$ is the space of polynomials of degree $k$, etc.; $\mathbf{e}_1$ and $\mathbf{e}_2$ are unit vectors; $M_e$ is the number of sides of $\Omega_e$; $W_e$ is continuously defined over $\Gamma_{ef}$ with nodal values $W^i$.

Introducing (9.138) and (9.139) in (9.134), we obtain, for each element,

$$\mathbf{A}_1^T \mathbf{a}_1 + \mathbf{A}_2^T \mathbf{a}_2 = -\mathbf{f}_e \tag{9.140}$$

$$\mathbf{A}_\alpha \mathbf{b} - \mathbf{B}\mathbf{a}_\alpha + \mathbf{C}_\alpha \mathbf{w} = 0 \qquad \alpha = 1, 2 \tag{9.141}$$

$$\sum_{e=1}^{E} (\mathbf{C}_1^T \mathbf{a}_1 + \mathbf{C}_2^T \mathbf{a}_2 - \mathbf{g}_e) = 0 \tag{9.142}$$

where $\mathbf{a}_\alpha$, $\mathbf{b}$, and $\mathbf{w}$ are vectors of unknown parameters and

$$\underset{(R \times K)}{\mathbf{A}_\alpha} = \int_{\Omega_e} \omega_{i,\alpha} \psi_j \, dA \qquad \underset{(R \times T)}{\mathbf{C}_\alpha} = \int_{\partial\Omega_e} \omega_i n_\alpha N_j \, ds$$

$$\underset{(R \times R)}{\mathbf{B}} = \int_{\Omega_e} \omega_i \omega_j \, dA \qquad \underset{(K)}{\mathbf{f}_e} = \int_{\Omega_e} f_e \psi_j \, dA \tag{9.143}$$

$$\mathbf{g}_e = \int_{\partial\Omega_e^2} g_e N_j \, ds \qquad \alpha = 1, 2 \qquad \partial\Omega_e^2 = \partial\Omega_e \cap \partial\Omega^2$$

Solving for $\mathbf{a}_\alpha$ (9.141) and using it in (9.140), we obtain

$$\mathbf{R}\mathbf{b} = \mathbf{D}\mathbf{w} + \mathbf{f}_e \tag{9.144}$$

where $\quad \underset{(K \times K)}{\mathbf{R}} = \mathbf{A}_1^T \mathbf{B}^{-1} \mathbf{A}_1 + \mathbf{A}_2^T \mathbf{B}^{-1} \mathbf{A}_2 \qquad \underset{(K \times T)}{\mathbf{D}} = \mathbf{A}_1^T \mathbf{B}^{-1} \mathbf{C}_1 + \mathbf{A}_2^T \mathbf{B}^{-1} \mathbf{C}_2$

Notice that if $r - 1 < k$, $\qquad$ Rank $(\mathbf{R}) \leqslant \min\{K, R'\} \leqslant R' < K$ $\tag{9.145}$

where $R' = \dim\{\mathscr{P}_{r-1}(\Omega_e)\}$, which implies that $\mathbf{R}$ is singular if $r - 1 < k$.

Assuming, for the moment, that $\mathbf{R}$ is invertible, we substitute $\mathbf{a}_\alpha$ into (9.142) after eliminating $\mathbf{b}$ to obtain

$$\sum_{e=1}^{E} (\mathscr{K}\mathbf{w} - \mathscr{F}_e) = 0 \tag{9.146}$$

in which $\qquad \underset{(T \times T)}{\mathscr{K}} = \mathbf{C}_1^T \mathbf{B}^{-1} \mathbf{C}_1 + \mathbf{C}_2^T \mathbf{B}^{-1} \mathbf{C}_2 - \mathbf{D}^T \mathbf{R}^{-1} \mathbf{D}$

$$\underset{(T)}{\mathscr{F}_e} = \mathbf{D}^T \mathbf{R}^{-1} \mathbf{f}_e - \mathbf{g}_e$$

Notice that the final form (9.146) is the usual "stiffness" type of equation having nodal values of $W$ as final unknowns.

We now introduce some subspaces to discuss mathematical properties associated with the method:

- $Q_k(P) = \{\Phi \in L_2(\Omega); \ \Phi_e \in \mathscr{P}_k(\Omega_e), \ k \geqslant 0, \ e = 1, 2, \ldots, E\}$

- $\mathbf{Q}_r(P) = \{\mathbf{V} \in \mathscr{S}(P); \ \mathbf{V}_e \in \mathscr{P}_r(\Omega_e), \ r \geqslant 1, \ e = 1, 2, \ldots, E\}$

- $Q_t(\Gamma) = \{W \in \mathscr{W}(\Gamma); \text{ there exists a } U \in \mathscr{P}_t(\Omega_e) \text{ such that}$

  $W_e = U \text{ on } \partial\Omega_e, \ t \geqslant 1, \ e = 1, 2, \ldots, E\}$

- $\mathscr{X}_h = Q_k(P) \times \mathbf{Q}_r(P) \times Q_t(\Gamma) \subset \mathscr{X}$ $\tag{9.147}$

Then the mixed-hybrid finite-element method can be stated as follows:

$$\text{Find } \Lambda = (\Phi, \mathbf{V}, W) \in \mathcal{X}_h \text{ such that}$$

$$B(\Lambda, \bar{\Lambda}) = F(\bar{\Lambda}) \qquad \forall \bar{\Lambda} \in \mathcal{X}_h \tag{9.148}$$

where $B(\cdot, \cdot)$ and $F(\cdot)$ are as in (9.120).

It can be shown that (see Refs. [56, 57]) if $r \geq t-1$ and $k \leq r-1$ there exists a unique solution to (9.148) and that the following a priori error estimates hold if the exact solution is smooth enough:

1. If $k = r-1$ and $r \geq t-1$, we expect convergence at the full rate; i.e.,

$$\|e\|_{\mathcal{X}} \approx h^{\alpha}(\cdot) \qquad \alpha = \min \{r, t\} \tag{9.149}$$

2. If $k < r-1$ and $r \geq t-1$, the convergence rate is reduced by 2; i.e.,

$$\|e\|_{\mathcal{X}} \approx h^{\alpha-2}(\cdot) \qquad \alpha = \min \{k+1, t\} \tag{9.150}$$

Notice from (9.150) that if $t = 1$, that is, a linear approximation of $\phi$ on interelement boundaries, we will have a divergent solution if $k < r-1$.

Several special cases can be deduced from the general theory presented by imposing various restrictions on the spaces $\mathcal{X}$ and $\mathcal{X}_h$. A brief discussion is given below.

***Dual-Hybrid Method***    Let $\mathbf{P} \in \mathcal{S}(P)$ be a fixed vector such that $-\nabla \cdot \mathbf{P}_e = f_e$ in $\Omega_e$, and let

$$\mathcal{S}^0(P) = \{\boldsymbol{\sigma} \in \mathcal{S}(P); \nabla \cdot \boldsymbol{\sigma}_e = 0 \text{ in } \Omega_e, e = 1, 2, \ldots, E\} \tag{9.151}$$

For a $\boldsymbol{\sigma} \in \mathcal{S}^0(P)$, if we set $\mathbf{v} = \boldsymbol{\sigma} + \mathbf{P}$ in (9.130), we obtain the dual-hybrid variational problem. Naturally, we set

$$\mathcal{X}^1 = \mathcal{S}^0(P) \times \mathcal{W}(\Gamma) \tag{9.152}$$

Then the dual-hybrid variational problem is to find a couple $\lambda = (\boldsymbol{\sigma}, w) \in \mathcal{X}^1$ such that

$$B^1(\lambda, \bar{\lambda}) = F^1(\bar{\lambda}) \qquad \forall \bar{\lambda} \in \mathcal{X}^1 \tag{9.153}$$

where

$$B^1(\lambda, \bar{\lambda}) = \sum_{e=1}^{E} \int_{\Omega_e} -\boldsymbol{\sigma} \cdot \bar{\boldsymbol{\sigma}} \, dA + \int_{\partial\Omega_e} (\boldsymbol{\sigma} \cdot \mathbf{n}\bar{w} + \bar{\boldsymbol{\sigma}} \cdot \mathbf{n}w) \, ds$$

$$F^1(\bar{\lambda}) = \sum_{e=1}^{E} \int_{\partial\Omega_e^2} (g - \mathbf{P} \cdot \mathbf{n}) \, ds$$

For a finite-element approximation, we set

$$\mathcal{X}_h^1 = \mathbf{Q}_r^0(P) \times Q_t(\Gamma) \tag{9.154}$$

where

$$\mathbf{Q}_r^0(P) = \{\mathbf{V} \in \mathbf{Q}_r(P); \nabla \cdot V_e = 0 \text{ in } \Omega_e\}$$

It can be shown that (see [56] or [57]), if $r \geq t-1$, there exists a unique finite-element solution to (9.153), and we have the following estimate:

$$\|\mathbf{e}\|_{\mathcal{X}^1} = h^\xi(\cdot) \qquad \xi = \min\{r, t\} \tag{9.155}$$

where $\mathbf{e}$ is the error.

**Dual-Mixed Method**  If we let $\phi = w$ in (9.130) and restrict the space $\mathscr{S}(P)$ to $\mathbf{H}^1(\Omega)$, we obtain the dual-mixed method. For this, we set

$$\mathcal{X}^2 = L_2(\Omega) \times \overset{\circ}{\mathbf{H}}{}^1(\Omega) \tag{9.156}$$

where $\qquad \overset{\circ}{\mathbf{H}}{}^1(\Omega) = \{\mathbf{v} \in \mathbf{H}^1(\Omega); \mathbf{v} \cdot \mathbf{n} = 0 \text{ on } \partial\Omega^2\}$

The dual-mixed variational problem consists of finding a couple $\bar{\boldsymbol{\lambda}} \in \mathcal{X}^2$ such that

$$B^2(\boldsymbol{\lambda}, \bar{\boldsymbol{\lambda}}) = F^2(\bar{\boldsymbol{\lambda}}) \qquad \forall \bar{\boldsymbol{\lambda}} \in \mathcal{X}^2 \tag{9.157}$$

where $\qquad B^2(\boldsymbol{\lambda}, \bar{\boldsymbol{\lambda}}) = \displaystyle\int_\Omega (-\boldsymbol{\nabla} \cdot \mathbf{v}\bar{\phi} - \phi\boldsymbol{\nabla} \cdot \bar{\mathbf{v}} - \mathbf{v} \cdot \bar{\mathbf{v}}) \, dA$

$$F^2(\bar{\boldsymbol{\lambda}}) = \int_\Omega f\bar{\phi} \, dA$$

For a finite-element approximation, we construct the subspace

$$\mathcal{X}_h^2 = Q_k(\Omega) \times \mathbf{Q}_r^1(\Omega) \subset \mathcal{X}^2 \tag{9.158}$$

where $\qquad Q_k(\Omega) = Q_k(P)$

and $\qquad Q_r^1(\Omega) = \{\mathbf{V} \in \overset{\circ}{\mathbf{H}}{}^1(\Omega); \mathbf{V}_e \in \mathscr{P}_r(\Omega_e), e = 1, 2, \ldots, N\}$

If $k \leqslant r - 1$, there exists a unique finite-element solution to (9.157) and the errors satisfy the following estimate [56]:

$$\|\mathbf{e}\|_{\mathcal{X}^2} = h^\beta(\cdot) \tag{9.159}$$

where $\qquad \beta = \begin{cases} \min\{k, r\} & \text{if } k = r - 1 \\ \min\{k, r\} - 2 & \text{if } k < r - 1 \end{cases}$

One drawback of this method is the increased number of unknowns in the final equations because $\mathbf{v}$ has to be connected into the global formulation and $\phi$ cannot be eliminated at the element level.

**(Primal-) Mixed Method**  By integrating (9.157) by parts, we obtain

$$B^3(\boldsymbol{\lambda}, \bar{\boldsymbol{\lambda}}) = F^3(\bar{\boldsymbol{\lambda}}) \qquad \forall \bar{\boldsymbol{\lambda}} \in \mathcal{X}^3 = \tilde{H}_0^1(\Omega) \times L_2(\Omega) \tag{9.160}$$

where $\qquad B^3(\boldsymbol{\lambda}, \bar{\boldsymbol{\lambda}}) = \displaystyle\int_\Omega [\boldsymbol{\nabla}\bar{\phi} \cdot \mathbf{v} + (\boldsymbol{\nabla}\phi - \mathbf{v}) \cdot \bar{\mathbf{v}}] \, dA$

$$F^3(\bar{\boldsymbol{\lambda}}) = \int_\Omega f\bar{\phi} \, dA + \int_{\partial\Omega^2} g\bar{\phi} \, ds$$

This is a well-known mixed method with the primary variable as the connector.

A finite-element subspace can be given as

$$\mathscr{X}_h^3 = Q_k^1(\Omega) \times \mathbf{Q}_r(\Omega) \tag{9.161}$$

where $\quad \mathbf{Q}_r(\Omega) = \mathbf{Q}_r(P) \quad$ and

$$Q_k^1 = \{\Phi \in \tilde{H}_0^1(\Omega), \Phi_e \in \mathscr{P}_k(\Omega_e), e = 1, 2, \ldots, E\}$$

There exists a unique finite-element solution to (9.160) if $k \leqslant r+1$ and the following estimates hold:

$$\|e\|_{\mathscr{X}^3} = h^k(\cdot) \tag{9.162}$$

$$\|\phi^* - \Phi^*\|_{0,\Omega} = h^{k+1}(\cdot) \tag{9.163}$$

## 9.5c Hybrid Models for Elastostatics

Suppose that a linear-elastic body is subjected to body force $f_i$, traction $g_i$ on $\partial\Omega^2$, and fixed-end condition on $\partial\Omega^1$. The general form (9.102) can be used to obtain the modified Reissner's principle proposed by Prager [61] by identifying operators and functional spaces properly. We let $v = Au$ be the strain-displacement relations and replace $v$ by $L^{-1}\sigma$, where $L$ is the elasticity tensor. Then (9.102) can be rewritten, using the index notation, as

$$B(\lambda, \bar{\lambda}) = \sum_{e=1}^{E} \left\{ \int_{\Omega_e} [\sigma_{ij}\bar{e}_{ij} + (e_{ij} - c_{ijkl}\sigma_{kl})\bar{\sigma}_{ij}] \, dv \right.$$

$$\left. + \int_{\partial\Omega_e} [\bar{\tau}_i(w_i - u_i) + \tau_i(\bar{w}_i - \bar{u}_i)] \, ds \right\} \tag{9.164a}$$

$$F(\bar{\lambda}) = \sum_{e=1}^{E} \left( \int_{\Omega_e} f_i\bar{u}_i \, dv + \int_{\partial\Omega_e^2} g_i w_i \, ds \right) \tag{9.164b}$$

where $\quad \lambda = (u_i, \sigma_{ij}, w_i, \tau_i) \qquad e_{ij} = \frac{1}{2}(u_{i,j} + u_{j,i})$
$\qquad w_i = \bar{w}_i = 0 \quad$ on $\partial\Omega^1$
$\qquad c_{ijkl}$ = elastic-compliance tensor
$\qquad f_i$ = body force

The space of admissible variation $\mathscr{X}$ for the functional can be identified as

$$\mathscr{X} = [L^1(P)]^3 \times [L_2(P)]^6 \times [\mathscr{W}(\Gamma)]^3 \times [\mathscr{M}(\Gamma)]^3 \tag{9.165}$$

where $\qquad L^1(P) = \{u \in L_2(\Omega); \nabla u \in L_2(\Omega_e), e = 1, 2, \ldots, E\}$

The variational problem can be shown to have a unique solution (see Ref. [58]). One can provide independent polynomial approximations of degree $k$, $r$, $t$, and $q$ for $u_i$, $\sigma_{ij}$, $w_i$, and $\tau_i$, respectively, over each element by constructing the finite-element subspace as

$$\mathscr{X}_h = [Q_k(P)]^3 \times [Q_r(P)]^6 \times [Q_t(\Gamma)]^3 \times [Q_q(\tilde{\Gamma})]^3 \tag{9.166}$$

where $\qquad Q_q(\tilde{\Gamma}) = \{\tau \in \mathscr{M}(\tilde{\Gamma}); \tau$ is a polynomial of degree $q$ on a side of $\partial\Omega_e\}$

A careful observation of the corresponding set of finite-element equations leads us to conclude that one way to solve it is to set

$$Q_q(\tilde{\Gamma}) = Q_k(P)|_{\tilde{\Gamma}} \tag{9.167}$$

which would mean that $k = q$.

The following results can be found in Ref. [58].

**LEMMA 9.5**   Let $k = q \geqslant t$. Then

$$\inf_{\|\Lambda\|_{\mathscr{X}}=1} \sup_{\|\bar{\Lambda}\|_{\mathscr{X}} \leqslant 1} |B(\Lambda, \bar{\Lambda})| \geqslant C_h \tag{9.168}$$

where
$$C_h = \min\{2\nu_e - 1, \tfrac{1}{2}\}C \qquad C > 0$$

$$\nu_e = \inf_{U_i \in P_k(V_e)} \frac{\|\pi_r U_{i,j}\|_0^2}{\|U_{i,j}\|_0^2} \tag{9.169}$$

$$\pi_r : [L_2(V_e)]^3 \to [P_r(V_e)]^3 \text{ is an } L_2\text{-projection}$$

**THEOREM 9.7**   Let $k = q \geqslant t$. Then the error satisfies the inequality

$$\|e\|_{\mathscr{X}} \leqslant C_h^* h^\mu(\cdot) \qquad \mu = \min\{t, r+1\} \tag{9.170}$$

where
$$C_h^* = C_2(1 + C_1/C_h) \text{ and } C_h \text{ is as in (9.169).}$$

It can be shown that

$$\nu_e = \begin{cases} =1 & \text{if } r \geqslant k-1 \\ <1 & \text{if } r < k-1 \end{cases}$$

Therefore, if $r \geqslant k-1$, $C_h = \tfrac{1}{2}C$ and $C_h^*$ in (9.170) is independent of $h$, which leads to a stable and convergent scheme.

The main result of this section is stated in the next theorem.

**THEOREM 9.8**   If $r+1 \geqslant q = k \geqslant t \geqslant 1$, the mixed-hybrid method is stable and converges at the rate of $h^t(\cdot)$.

We now discuss some special cases.

**Displacement-Assumed Hybrid (DH2)**   As proposed by Tong [38], to obtain the functional for DH2, we simply set, in (9.164),

$$\sigma_{ij} = E_{ijkl}e_{kl} \qquad \text{where} \qquad E_{ijkl} = c_{ijkl}^{-1}$$

Then
$$J^1(\lambda) = \tfrac{1}{2}B^1(\lambda, \lambda) - F(\lambda) \tag{9.171}$$

where
$$B^1(\lambda, \bar{\lambda}) = \sum_{e=1}^{E} \left\{ \int_{\Omega_e} (u_{i,j}E_{ijkl}\bar{u}_{k,l})\, dV + \int_{\partial\Omega_e} [\tau_i(\bar{w}_i - \bar{u}_i) + \bar{\tau}_i(w_i - u_i)]\, ds \right\} \tag{9.172}$$

and $F(\cdot)$ is the same as in (9.164b), and the vector $\lambda$ is a triple, that is, $\lambda = (u_i, w_i, \tau_i)$. We naturally replace the space $\mathscr{X}$ by

$$\mathscr{X}^1 = [L^1(P)]^3 \times [\mathscr{W}(\Gamma)]^3 \times [\mathscr{M}(\tilde{\Gamma})]^3 \qquad (9.173)$$

The corresponding finite-element subspace can be defined by

$$\mathscr{X}'_h = [Q_k(P)]^3 \times [Q_t(\Gamma)]^3 \times [Q_q(\tilde{\Gamma})]^3 \qquad (9.174)$$

We also require that $k = q$. We state the results without proof.

**THEOREM 9.9**  If $k = q \geq t$, the DH2 method has a unique stable solution and the error $e$ satisfies the inequality

$$\|e\|_{\mathscr{X}^1} \leq Ch^t(\cdot) \qquad (9.175)$$

where $C > 0$ is independent of $h$.

**Three-Field Mixed Hybrid (MH3)**  This model was first proposed by Wolf [43], and its mathematical properties are stated in the previous section in connection with a Poisson's equation in two dimensions. This model is also called *dual-mixed hybrid* simply because the functional contains derivatives of stresses rather than displacements.

If we let $\tau_i = \sigma_{ij} n_j$ in (9.164) and integrate the first and second terms by parts, we obtain

$$J^2(\lambda) = \tfrac{1}{2} B^2(\lambda, \lambda) - F(\lambda) \qquad (9.176)$$

where

$$B^2(\lambda, \bar{\lambda}) = \sum_{e=1} \left[ -\int_{\Omega_e} (u_i \bar{\sigma}_{ij,j} + \sigma_{ij,j} \bar{u}_i + c_{ijkl} \sigma_{ij} \bar{\sigma}_{kl}) \, dV \right.$$

$$\left. + \int_{\partial\Omega_e} (\sigma_{ij} n_j \bar{w}_i + \bar{\sigma}_{ij} n_j w_i) \, ds \right] \qquad (9.177)$$

and

$$\lambda = (u_i, \sigma_{ij}, w_i)$$

The natural choices of admissible spaces are

$$\mathscr{X}^2 = [L_2(P)]^3 \times [\mathscr{S}(P)]^6 \times [\mathscr{W}(\Gamma)]^3 \qquad (9.178)$$

$$\mathscr{X}^2_h = [Q_k(P)]^3 \times [Q_r(P)]^6 \times [Q_t(\Gamma)]^3 \subset \mathscr{X}^2 \qquad (9.179)$$

We summarize results in the following theorem.

**THEOREM 9.10**  If $k \leq r-1$ and $r \geq t-1$, the MH3 model has a unique solution and the following estimate holds:

$$\|e\|_{\mathscr{X}^2} \leq C_1(1 + C_2 \gamma_h) h^\alpha(\cdot) \qquad (9.180)$$

where $e$ is the error; $C_1, C_2 > 0$ are independent of $h$; $\alpha = \min\{k+1, t\}$; and

$$\gamma_h = \begin{cases} 1 & \text{if } k = r-1 \\ h^{-2} & \text{if } k < r-1 \end{cases} \qquad (9.181)$$

According to the estimate, the MH3 model is stable if $k = r - 1$ and $r > t - 1$, and converges at the full rate $h^\alpha$, where $\alpha = \min\{r, t\}$.

***Stress-Assumed Hybrid (SH)***   Let $P_{ij}$ be fixed functions such that $P_{ij,j} + f_i = 0$ in $\Omega_e$, and let

$$S^0(P) = \{\sigma_{ij}^0 \in S(P); \ \sigma_{ij,j}^0 = 0 \text{ in } \Omega_e, \ e = 1, 2, \ldots, E\} \tag{9.182}$$

Then, if we set $\sigma_{ij} = \sigma_{ij}^0 + P_{ij}$ in (9.177), we obtain the SH model. Naturally, we set

$$\mathscr{X}^3 = [S^0(P)]^6 \times [\mathscr{W}(\Gamma)]^3$$

Then the SH method is to find a couple $\lambda = (\sigma_{ij}, w_i) \in \mathscr{X}^3$ such that

$$B^3(\lambda, \bar{\lambda}) = F(\bar{\lambda})$$

for every $\bar{\lambda} \in \mathscr{X}^3$. A finite-element approximation will be to seek an approximate solution in the finite-dimensional submanifold

$$\mathscr{X}_h^3 = [Q_r^0(P)]^6 \times [Q_t(\Gamma)]^3$$

where          $Q_r^0(P) = \{\Sigma_{ij} \in Q_r(P): \Sigma_{ij,j} = 0 \text{ in } \Omega_e, \ e = 1, 2, \ldots, E)$

More special cases including mixed methods can be similarly derived.

## 9.6 REFERENCES

1. Oden, J. T., and J. N. Reddy, *An Introduction to the Mathematical Theory of Finite Elements*, Wiley-Interscience, New York, 1976.

2. Reddy, J. N., *Applied Functional Analysis and Variational Methods in Engineering*, McGraw-Hill, New York, 1986.

3. Oden, J. T., and J. N. Reddy, *Variational Methods in Theoretical Mechanics*, Springer-Verlag, Berlin, 1976.

4. Lions, J. L., and E. Magenes, *Non-Homogeneous Boundary Value Problems and Applications I*, trans. from rev. Fr. ed. by P. Kenneth, 1968, Springer-Verlag, New York, 1972.

5. Becker, E. B., G. F. Carey, and J. T. Oden, *Finite Elements: An Introduction*, Prentice-Hall, Englewood Cliffs, N.J., 1981.

6. Oden, J. T., and G. F. Carey, *Finite Elements: Mathematical Aspects*, Prentice-Hall, Englewood Cliffs, N.J., 1982.

7. Carey, G. F., and J. T. Oden, *Finite Elements: A Second Course*, Prentice-Hall, Englewood Cliffs, N.J., 1983.

8. Ciarlet, P. G., and P. A. Raviart, "General Lagrange and Hermite Interpolation in $\mathbb{R}^n$ with Applications to Finite Element Methods," *Arch. Rat. Mech. Anal.*, **46**:177–199 (1972).

9. Nitsche, J., "Finite Element Approximations for Solving the Elastic Problem," in R. Glowinski and J. L. Lions (eds.), *Computing Methods in Applied Sciences and Engineering, Lecture Notes in Economics and Mathematical Systems*, **134**:154–167 (1976).

10. Babuska, I., "The Finite Element Method with Lagrange Multipliers," *Numer. Math.*, **20**, 1973.

11. Brezzi, F., "On the Existence, Uniqueness and Approximation of Saddle Point Problems Arising from Lagrangian Multipliers," *RAIRO*, **8**:129-151 (1974).

12. Ladyszhenskaya, O., *Mathematical Theory of Viscous Incompressible Flow*, Gordon and Breach, New York, 1969.

13. Ekeland, I., and R. Temam, "Convex Analysis and Variational Problems," North-Holland, Elsevier, New York, 1976.

14. Fortin, M., "An Analysis of the Convergence of Mixed Finite Element Methods," *RAIRO*, **11**:341-354 (1977).

15. Yosida, K., *Functional Analysis*, Springer-Verlag, Berlin, 1965.

16. Paczelt, I., "Solution of Elastic Contact Problems by Finite Element Displacement Method," *Acta Tech. Acad. Sci. Hung.*, **82**:354-375 (1976).

17. Haslinger, J., and J. Lovisek, "Mixed Variational Formulation of Unilateral Problems," *Comm. Math. Univ. Carolina*, **21**:231-246 (1980).

18. Kikuchi, N., and J. T. Oden, "Contact Problems in Elasticity," *Siam J.* (to appear).

19. Necas, J., *Les Méthodes Directes en Théorie des Équations Élliptiques*, Masson & CIE, Paris, 1967.

20. Ciarlet, P. G., *The Finite Element Method For Elliptic Problems*, North-Holland, Amsterdam, 1978.

21. Crouzeix, M., and P. A. Raviart, "Conforming and Non-Conforming Finite Element Methods for Solving the Stationary Stokes Equations," *RAIRO*, **3**:33-76 (1974).

22. Girault, V., and P. A. Raviart, "Finite Element Approximation of the Navier-Stokes Equations," *Lecture Notes in Mathematics*, no. 749, Springer-Verlag, Berlin, 1979.

23. Oden, J. T., N. Kikuchi, and Y. J. Song, "Reduced Integration and Exterior Penalty Methods for Finite Element Approximations of Stokes Flow Problems," *Comput. Meth. Appl. Mech. Eng.*, **2**:297-329 (1982).

24. Oden, J. T., and O. Jacquotte, "A Stable Second Order Accurate, Finite Element Scheme for the Analysis of Two Dimensional Incompressible Viscous Flows," in R. H. Gallagher, J. T. Oden, and O. C. Zienkiewicz (eds.), *Finite Elements in Fluids*, Wiley, London, 1982, vol. IV.

25. Bercovier, M., and O. Pironneau, "Error Estimates for Finite Element Method Solution of the Stokes Problem in the Primitive Variables," *Numer. Math.*, **33**:211-224 (1979).

26. Glowinski, R., and O. Pironneau, "On a Mixed Finite Element Approximation of the Stokes Problem (I)," *Numer. Math.*, **33**:397-424 (1979).

27. Bercovier, M., "Perturbation of Mixed Variational Problems: Application to Mixed Finite Element Methods," *RAIRO*, **12**:211-236 (1978).

28. Oden, J. T., "Penalty Method and Reduced Integration for the Analysis of Fluids," *Symposium on Penalty Finite Element Methods in Mechanics*, ASME Winter Annual Meeting, Phoenix, November 1982.

29. Herrmann, L., "Finite Element Bending Analysis for Plates," *J. Mech. Div. ASCE*, **93**, EMS (1967).

30. Dunham, R. S. and K. S. Pister, "A Finite Element Application of the Bellinger-Reissner Variational Theorem," *Proceedings of the Conference of Matrix Methods in Structural Mechanics*, AFDL-TR68-150, Wright-Patterson Air Force Base, Ohio, 1968, pp. 471-487.

31. Visser, W., "A Refined Mixed-Type Plate Bending Element," *AIAA J.*, **7**(9):1801-1803 (September 1969).

32. Connor, J. J., and G. T. Will, "A Mixed Finite Element Shell Formulation," *Japan-U.S. Seminar on Matrix Methods of Structural Analysis and Design*, Tokyo, August 1969, *Recent Advances in Matrix Methods of Structural Analysis and Design*, University of Alabama Press, Huntsville, 1971.

33. Chatterjee, A., and A. V. Setlur, "A Mixed Finite Element Formulation for Plate Problems," *Int. J. Numer. Meth. Eng.*, **4**:67-84 (1972).

34. Elias, Z. H., "Mixed Finite Element Method for Axisymmetric Shells," *Int. J. Numer. Meth. Eng.*, **4**(2):261–278 (1972).

35. Jones, E., "A Generalization of the Direct-Stiffness Method of Structural Analysis," *AIAA J.*, **2**(5):821–826 (1964).

36. Pian, T. H. H., "Derivation of Element Stiffness Matrices by Assumed Stress Distributions," *AIAA J.*, **2**(7):1335–1336 (1964).

37. Pian, T. H. H., "Element Stiffness Matrices for Boundary Compatibility and for Prescribed Boundary Stresses," AFDL-TR-66-80, *Proceedings of the First Conference on Matrix Methods in Structural Mechanics*, Wright–Patterson Air Force Base, Ohio, 1965, 1966, pp. 457–477.

38. Tong, P., "New Displacement Hybrid Finite Element Models for Solid Continua," *Int. J. Numer. Meth. Eng.*, **2**:73–85 (1970).

39. Pian, T. H. H., P. Tong, and C. H. Luk, "Elastic Crack Analysis by a Finite Element Hybrid Method," *Proceedings of the Third Conference on Matrix Methods in Structural Mechanics*, Dayton, Ohio, October, 1971.

40. Cook, R. D., "Two Hybrid Elements for Analysis of Thick Thin and Sandwich Plates," *Int. J. Numer. Meth. Eng.*, **2**:277–288 (1972).

41. Atluri, S., "Finite-Element Analysis of Shells of Revolution by Two Doubly Curved Quadrilateral Elements," *J. Struct. Mech.*, **1**(3):393–416 (1973).

42. Tong, P., T. H. H. Pian and S. J. Larry, "A Hybrid-Element Approach to Crack Problems in Plane Elasticity," *Int. J. Numer. Meth. Eng.*, **7**:297–308 (1973).

43. Wolf, J. P., "Generalized Hybrid Stress Finite Element Models," *AIAA J.*, **11**(3):386–388 (1973).

44. Atluri, S. N., "On Hybrid Finite Element Models in Solid Mechanics," in R. L. Vishneuetsky (ed.), *Advances in Computer Methods for Partial Differential Equations*, AICA, Rutgers University, New Brunswick, N.J., 1975.

45. Pian, T. H. H., and P. Tong, "Reissner's Principle in Finite Element Formulations," *Mech. Today*, **5**, 1980.

46. Oden, J. T., "Some Contributions to the Mathematical Theory of Mixed Finite Element Approximations," in Y. Yamada and R. H. Gallagher (eds.), *Theory and Practice in Finite Element Structural Analysis*, University of Tokyo Press, Tokyo, 1973, pp. 3–23.

47. Reddy, J. N., and J. T. Oden, "Mathematical Theory of Mixed Finite Element Approximations," *Q. Appl. Math.*, **33**:255–280 (1975).

48. Ciarlet, P. G., and P. A. Raviart, "A Mixed Finite Element Method for the Biharmonic Equation," in C. deBoor (ed.), *Mathematical Aspects of Finite Elements in Partial Differential Equations*, Academic Press, New York, 1974, pp. 125–145.

49. Johnson, C., "On the Convergence of a Mixed Finite Element Method for Plate Bending Problems," *Numer. Math.*, **21**:43–62 (1973).

50. Raviart, P. A., "Hybrid Finite Element Methods for Solving 2nd Order Elliptic Equations," in J. J. H. Miller (ed.), *Topics in Numerical Analysis II, Proceedings of the Royal Irish Conference on Numerical Analysis*, 1974, Academic Press, New York, 1976.

51. Thomas, J. M., "Méthodes des Éléments Finis Hybrides Duaux pour les Problèmes Elliptiques du Second-Ordre," Rep. 75006, Univérsité Paris VI et Centre National de la Research Scientifique, Paris, 1975.

52. Brezzi, F., "Sur la Méthode des Éléments Finis Hybrides pour les Problèmes Biharmonique," *Numer. Math.*, **24**:103–131 (1975).

53. Brezzi, F., and L. D. Marini, "On the Numerical Solution of Plate Bending Problems by Hybrid Methods," *RAIRO Rep.* (1975).

54. Babuska, I., J. T. Oden, and J. K. Lee, "Mixed-Hybrid-Finite Element Approximations of Second-Order Elliptic Boundary-Value Problems," *Comput. Meth. Appl. Mech. Eng.*, **11** (1977).

55. Oden, J. T., and J. K. Lee, "Theory and Hybrid Finite-Element Approximations in Linear Elasticity," *Proc. IUTAM / IUM Symp. Appl. Meth. Functional Anal. Prob. Mech.*, Marseille, September 1975, *Lecture Notes in Mathematics*, no. 503, Springer-Verlag, Berlin, 1976.

56. Oden, J. T., and J. K. Lee, "Theory and Application of Dual Mixed-Hybrid Finite Element Methods to Two-Dimensional Potential Flow Problems," in O. C. Zienkiewicz et al. (eds.), *Finite Elements in Fluids*, Wiley, London, 1978, vol. 3.

57. Lee, J. K., "Convergence of Mixed-Hybrid Finite Element Methods," Ph.D. dissertation, University of Texas, Austin, 1976.

58. Lee, J. K., "Properties of Hybrid Finite Element Models," in L. C. Wellford (ed.), *Proceedings of the Symposium on Applications of Computer Methods in Engineering*, University of Southern California Press, Los Angeles, 1977.

59. Reddy, J. N., "Existence and Uniqueness of Solutions to a Stationary Finite Element Model of the Biharmonic Equation," *Comput. Math. Appl.*, **3**:135–147 (1977).

60. Fraeijs de Veubeke, B., "Variational Principles and the Patch Test," *Int. J. Numer. Meth. Eng.*, **8**, 1974.

61. Prager, W., "Variational Principles of Linear Elastostatics for Discontinuous Displacements, Strains and Stress," in B. Broberg, J. Hult, and F. Niordson (eds.), *Recent Progress in Applied Mechanics*, The Folke–Odqvist Volume, Almquist and Wiksell, Stockholm, 1967, pp. 463–474.

# P · A · R · T · 3

# FEM APPLICATIONS

# CHAPTER 1
# FINITE-ELEMENT APPLICATIONS IN SOLID MECHANICS

It is common knowledge that the finite-element method started, developed, and, to a certain extent, matured with researchers dealing primarily with solid-mechanics problems. Its earliest application in solids, though no reference was actually made to the term *finite elements*, was to structures (the naturally discrete systems made of one-dimensional elements). The application of the method to a solid continuum by using discretization was introduced by Hrenikoff, McHenry, Argyris, and Turner et al. [1–4]. The term *finite element* was first used by R. W. Clough [5] for the analysis of plane-stress problems in solid mechanics.

The concept of the finite-element method in the form of approximate solutions of differential equations and of estimation of area and volume of certain geometric figures dates to a much earlier time than those works cited above. Since the 1950s, the finite-element method has been applied to problems in solid mechanics much more so than to any other discipline in science and engineering. Finite-element analyses of problems in solid mechanics are innumerable, and even a very brief treatment of them would exceed the number of pages allocated to this chapter. Therefore, we categorize the solid-mechanics problems and demonstrate the application of the finite-element method to a few of these. In particular, we choose problems from structural analysis, 2- and 3D linear solids using the *h*- and *p*-version of finite-element methods, fracture mechanics, projectile-impact response, and high-temperature inelastic analysis. For other problems, we cite references where detailed treatments can be found (refer to Table 1.1).

## 1.1 CLASSIFICATION OF PROBLEMS IN SOLID MECHANICS

Figure 1.1 illustrates the general classification of solid-mechanics problems. If one draws a vertical line through the middle of this figure, the problems on the left can be classified as *elementary*. As one moves toward the right, the problems become *intermediate* and then *advanced*. For example, static-linear-skeletal problems are elementary, while dynamic-nonlinear-3D problems are more advanced. Table 1.1 lists key references for the problems classified in Fig. 1.1. The numbers in this table refer to works listed at the end of this chapter. It is understandable that some references, such as textbooks, cover more than one discipline, yet no reference covers all areas of solid mechanics. Since the amount of published material covering a variety of solid-mechanics problems is so large, we are unable to list all.

**TABLE 1.1**   References for Problems in Solid Mechanics†

| | | | Problem category | | | | |
|---|---|---|---|---|---|---|---|
| | | | | Nonlinear | | | |
| | | | | Geometric | | | Material |
| Type of finite element | | Linear | Large displacements | Instability | Fracture | Plastic | Viscoplastic |
| **1D elements, prismatic or nonprismatic** | a | 6, 7, 8 | 67, 147 | 74, 77 | 83, 141 | 120, 126 | 120 |
| | b | 6, 7, 8 | 74, 147 | 74, 77 | 141, 153 | 120, 126 | 120 |
| | c | 6, 7, 8 | 82, 147 | 101, 145 | 141, 153 | 120, 126 | 120 |
| | d | 6, 7, 8 | 82, 147 | 75, 77 | 141 | 120, 126 | 122 |
| | e | 60 | 67, 101 | | | 120 | |
| | f | 85, 134 | 85, 107 | | 141 | 107, 134 | |
| **2D elements — Thick** | a | 61, 145 | 71, 133 | 61, 101 | 25, 97 | 71, 120 | 71, 121 |
| | b | 61, 145 | 71, 133 | 61, 101 | 25, 96 | 71, 120 | 71, 121 |
| | c | 62, 65, 66 | 69, 71, 73 | 70, 143 | 93, 115 | 68, 70, 73 | 88, 122 |
| | d | 61, 64 | 72, 133 | 101, 143 | 84, 110 | 71, 72 | 88, 152 |
| | e | 61, 145 | 71, 72 | | 93, 115 | 71, 120 | 88, 122 |
| | f | 61, 145 | 72 | 78 | 93, 99 | 71, 89 | 86, 152 |
| | g | 61, 63 | 79, 133 | 78, 79 | 93, 99 | 71, 89 | 86, 152 |
| **2D elements — Thin** | a | 61, 143 | 71, 133 | 61, 143 | 92, 97 | 71 | 71, 152 |
| | b | 61, 143 | 71, 133 | 61, 143 | 92, 96 | 71, 112 | 71, 112 |
| | c | 61, 65, 66 | 69, 71 | 70, 76 | 93, 115 | 68, 70 | 71, 112 |
| | d | 61, 64 | 72, 133 | 77, 81 | 84, 115 | 72, 112 | 71, 112 |
| | e | 61, 125 | 71, 80 | | 93, 99 | 71, 112 | 88, 112 |
| | f | 61, 143 | 72, 133 | 78, 81 | 93, 99 | 71, 89 | 88, 112 |
| | g | 61, 63 | 72, 133 | 78, 81 | 93, 110 | 71, 89 | 86, 112 |
| **3D elements** | a | 61, 100 | 133 | 100 | 94, 142 | 136 | 61, 112 |
| | b | 61, 100 | 133 | 100 | 90, 95 | 136 | 61, 121 |
| | c | 61, 100 | 133 | 100 | 98, 142 | 87, 136 | 87, 121 |

(Left margin label, read vertically: **STATIC**)

**TABLE 1.1**  References for Problems in Solid Mechanics† (*Continued*)

| Type of finite element | | | Linear | Large displacements | Insta-bility | Fracture | Plastic | Visco-plastic |
|---|---|---|---|---|---|---|---|---|
| | | | | **Problem category** | | | | |
| | | | | **Nonlinear** | | | | |
| | | | | **Geometric** | | | **Material** | |
| **1D elements, prismatic** | | a | 100, 101 | 116, 155 | 124, 127 | 139, 141 | 127, 145 | 71, 148 |
| | | b | 100, 101 | 116, 155 | 124, 127 | 139, 141 | 127, 145 | 71, 148 |
| | | c | 102 | 116, 155 | 124, 127 | 139, 141 | 127, 145 | 122 |
| | | d | 102, 124 | 124 | 124, 127 | 139, 141 | 127, 145 | 122 |
| | | e | 106, 125 | 124 | | | 100 | 122 |
| | | f | 104 | 146 | 146 | 139, 153 | | 122 |
| **2D elements** | **Thick** | a | 61, 100 | 105, 113 | 71, 135 | 136, 137 | 105, 117 | 108, 128 |
| | | b | 61, 100 | 105, 113 | 71, 124 | 136, 137 | 105, 117 | 108, 128 |
| | | c | 103, 154 | 105, 118 | 71, 124 | 136, 144 | 105, 117 | 108, 132 |
| | | d | 61, 100 | 105, 113 | 124, 143 | 136, 144 | 105, 149 | 130, 131 |
| | | e | 102 | 105, 113 | | 136, 144 | 105, 149 | 130, 132 |
| | | f | 61, 119 | 105, 113 | 100, 124 | 136, 144 | 105, 149 | 121, 132 |
| | | g | 61, 119 | 105, 113 | 100, 124 | 136, 144 | 105, 149 | 121, 132 |
| | **Thin** | a | 60, 154 | 105, 113 | 71, 124 | 136, 137 | 105, 117 | 108, 151 |
| | | b | 100, 154 | 105, 113 | 71, 124 | 136, 137 | 105, 117 | 108, 151 |
| | | c | 103, 154 | 105, 118 | 71, 124 | 136, 138 | 105, 117 | 108, 150 |
| | | d | 100, 154 | 105, 113 | 124, 143 | 136, 140 | 105, 149 | 130, 151 |
| | | e | 102, 143 | 105, 113 | | 136, 138 | 105, 149 | 121, 151 |
| | | f | 61, 119 | 105, 113 | 100, 124 | 136, 156 | 105, 149 | 121, 151 |
| | | g | 61, 119 | 105, 113 | 100, 124 | 136, 156 | 105, 149 | 121, 151 |
| **3D elements** | | a | 100, 102 | 129, 133 | 100, 124 | 136, 140 | 124 | 124, 132 |
| | | b | 100, 102 | 129, 133 | 100, 124 | 136, 140 | 135 | 124, 132 |
| | | c | 100, 102 | 129, 133 | 100, 124 | 136, 144 | 135 | 124, 132 |

(Left margin vertical label spanning the 2D and 3D rows: **DYNAMIC**)

† Numbers refer to references at the end of the chapter. See Fig. 1.1 for a, b, c, etc.

One should keep in mind that a typical real-life problem in solid mechanics often encompasses most of the problem areas specified in Fig. 1.1. For instance, quite often problems are made up of a combination of 1-, 2-, and 3D elements, some of which behave linearly, others nonlinearly; some are subject to fracture and others to instability or viscoplasticity; etc. It is, therefore, not so simple to classify a real-life problem and identify a specific FEM technique applicable to its entirety. Practitioners often confront this issue which, in turn, necessitates (1) the definition of every region of the problem as accurately as possible, (2) the modeling of each region according to the definitions, (3) in-house development or choice of commercially available software suitable for each region. One should also keep in mind

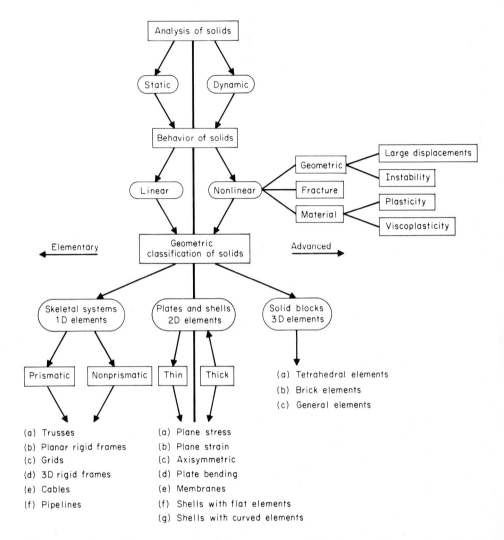

**FIG. 1.1**  Classification of solid-mechanics problems. The materials in these problems can be subjected to temperature variations and can be isotropic, anisotropic, orthotropic, or composite.

that for time- and path-dependent problems, the initial classification and modeling of the problem (at zero load and time level) change at each increment of load and time. There are many commercially available codes which, with certain limitations, take care of these changes.

Figure 1.2 illustrates a section of a typical civil-engineering structure. Regardless of the different moduli of elasticity (soil, concrete, steel, etc.), a problem of this kind can be classified as *simple* if it falls to the left in Fig. 1.1 (i.e., if it is static and linear, with 1-, 2-, and 3D elements). It would *not be so simple* if it fell to the right in Fig. 1.1 (i.e., if it were subject to

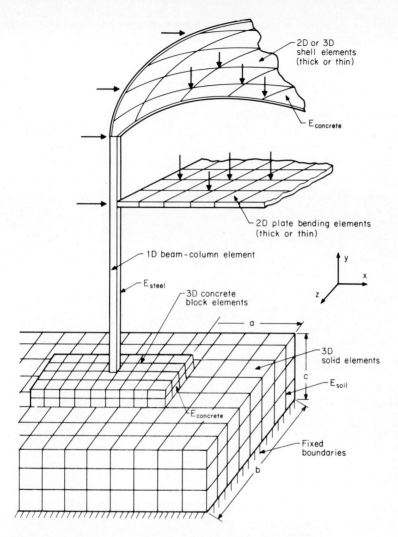

**FIG. 1.2**   A typical civil-engineering structure and its discretization.

dynamic loads and/or nonlinear behavior here and there). The problem becomes *more complicated* where fracture occurs and/or bonding between reinforcing bars and concrete yields. Even further complications arise when, in addition to fracture, buckling (instability) and/or viscoplasticity takes place in certain regions of the system. Behavior of soil, unusual boundary conditions, stress concentration, and so on, introduce additional difficulties. A realistic analysis of what seems to be a simple structure may involve so many difficulties that no commercially available code can completely handle the job without some in-house modification. In addition to the general classification of solid-mechanics problems as in Fig. 1.1, solids may also interact with other continuous media such as fluid, air, soil, and the like. Such interaction problems are treated in Chap. 5 of Part 3.

## 1.2 FINITE-ELEMENT ANALYSIS OF STRUCTURES (1D ELEMENTS)

Analysis of structures using the finite-element technique is commonly known as *matrix analysis of structures*. Since this type of system is naturally discrete (the assembly of one-dimensional finite elements), there is no need to discretize the system as in the case of continuous bodies such as plates, shells, and 3D solids.

The analysis usually starts with evaluation of the stiffness **k** or flexibility **d** matrices of each member (element). The explicit expression for **k** and **d** for prismatic members can be found in many textbooks [6–10]. For instance, the stiffness-matrix equation for a *prismatic beam* element in reference to principal coordinate axes of the cross section (neglecting shear deformations and higher-order terms) is given as

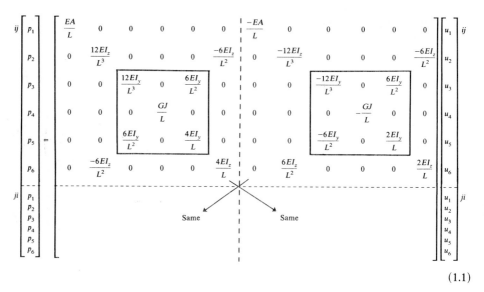

$$(1.1)$$

where $E$ = Young's modulus; $G$ = shear modulus; $J$ = torsion constant; $A$ = cross-sectional area; $I_y$, $I_z$ = moments of inertia with respect to $y$ and $z$ axes; $L$ = element length. In short,

$$\begin{bmatrix} \mathbf{p}_{ij} \\ \mathbf{p}_{ji} \end{bmatrix} = \begin{bmatrix} \mathbf{k}_{ii}^{j} & \mathbf{k}_{ij} \\ \mathbf{k}_{ji} & \mathbf{k}_{jj}^{i} \end{bmatrix} \begin{bmatrix} \mathbf{u}_{ij} \\ \mathbf{u}_{ji} \end{bmatrix}$$

where the first subscript represents the end under consideration. Two subscripts or the first subscript and a superscript designate a member. Matrices on the main diagonal are referred to as *direct-stiffness matrices* and those on the off-diagonal as *cross-stiffness matrices*.

For particular structures such as trusses, planar rigid frames, and grids, only a certain portion of the stiffness matrix shown in Eq. (1.1) is needed (i.e., the first row and column for trusses, the midportion shown boxed for grids, without the midportion for planar rigid frames, and the entirety for three-dimensional rigid frames). This matrix is obtained by integrating the following equation in which *linear* and *cubic* displacement functions in longitudinal (including torsion) and transverse directions, respectively, are employed (see

Chap. 4 in Part 2 for displacement functions). Thus

$$\mathbf{k}_e = \int_v \mathbf{B}^T \mathbf{D} \mathbf{B} \tag{1.2}$$

where matrix **B** in the transverse direction is

$$\mathbf{B} = -y \left[ \frac{6}{L^2} - \frac{12x}{L^3} \quad \frac{4}{L} - \frac{6x}{L^2} \quad -\frac{6}{L^2} + \frac{12x}{L^3} \quad \frac{2}{L} - \frac{6x}{L^2} \right]$$

and                     **D** = material matrix,† in this case, the modulus of elasticity

Note that the assumed displacement function for Eq. (1.1) is

$$u = c_1 + c_2 x$$

$$v = c_3 + c_4 x + c_5 x^2 + c_6 x^3$$

$$\omega = c_7 + c_8 x + c_9 x^2 + c_{10} x^3$$

$$\theta_x = c_{11} + c_{12} x$$

$$\theta_y = \frac{\partial \omega}{\partial x} = c_8 + 2 c_9 x + 3 c_{10} x^2$$

$$\theta_z = \frac{\partial v}{\partial x} = c_4 + 2 c_5 x + 3 c_6 x^2$$

The strain-displacement relationship is

$$\varepsilon_x = -y \frac{d^2 v}{dx^2}$$

The corresponding shape function becomes

$$\mathbf{N} = \left[ 1 - 3 \frac{x^2}{L^2} + 2 \frac{x^3}{L^3} \quad x - \frac{2x^2}{L} + \frac{x^3}{L^2} \quad 3 \frac{x^2}{L^2} - 2 \frac{x^3}{L^3} \quad -\frac{x^2}{L} + \frac{x^3}{L^2} \right]$$

Because of uncoupled effects, the integration of Eq. (1.2) can be carried out independently in both the xy- and xz-planes. In the axial direction, including torsion, the shape functions are assumed to be linear and uncoupled with transverse directions. Note that Eq. (1.2) can also be written in terms of shape function **N** as

$$\mathbf{k}_e = \int_v \frac{\partial^2 \mathbf{N}^T}{\partial x^2} \mathbf{D} \frac{\partial^2 \mathbf{N}}{\partial x^2} \, dv$$

The force-displacement relationship of each element in respect to local coordinate axes is

$$\mathbf{p}_{ij} = \mathbf{k}_{ii}^j \mathbf{u}_{ij} + \mathbf{k}_{ij} \mathbf{u}_{ji} \tag{1.3}$$

_____

† See Chap. 2 in Part 2 for material matrix **D** (constitutive relationship between stress and strain) for other problems.

Once this is known, the standard procedure is to transform these equations into the global coordinate axes so that

$$\mathbf{R}_{ij}^T \mathbf{p}_{ij} = \mathbf{R}_{ij}^T \mathbf{k}_{ii}^j \mathbf{R}_{ij} \mathbf{R}_{ij}^T \mathbf{u}_{ij} + \mathbf{R}_{ij}^T \mathbf{k}_{ij} \mathbf{R}_{ij} \mathbf{R}_{ij} \mathbf{u}_{ij} \tag{1.3a}$$

$$\mathbf{P}_{ij} = \mathbf{K}_{ii}^j \mathbf{U}_{ij} + \mathbf{K}_{ij} \mathbf{U}_{ji} \tag{1.3b}$$

and to assemble them to form the following matrix equation

$$\mathbf{P} = \mathbf{KU} \tag{1.4}$$

in which $\mathbf{K}$ is the assembled matrix (in accordance with the members' configuration), and $\mathbf{P}$ and $\mathbf{U}$ are the force and displacement vectors at the nodes.

$$\mathbf{P}_i = [P_{ix} \quad P_{iY} \quad P_{iZ} \quad M_{iX} \quad M_{iY} \quad M_{iZ}]$$

$$\mathbf{U}_i^T = [\Delta_{iX} \quad \Delta_{iY} \quad \Delta_{iZ} \quad \theta_{iX} \quad \theta_{iY} \quad \theta_{iZ}]$$

$$\mathbf{R}_{ii} = \begin{bmatrix} l_x & m_x & n_x \\ l_y & m_y & n_y \\ l_z & m_z & n_z \end{bmatrix}$$

Coordinate transformation for vectors and matrices can be found in Chap. 3 of Part 2 and in Ref. [6].

Introduction of the boundary conditions to Eq. (1.4) and solution of the remaining set of simultaneous equations yield the unknown nodal displacements.

Once the nodal displacements are known, internal member-end forces (axial, shear, bending, and torsion) can be calculated using Eq. (1.3). Determination of the corresponding stress and strain becomes a routine procedure.

The following examples demonstrate the analysis of two- and three-dimensional rigid frames using the stiffness-matrix method outlined above.

**EXAMPLE 1.1**   *Planar rigid frame.* This example demonstrates in detail the application of the *finite-element stiffness method* to the analysis of planar rigid frames. Note that the units are irrelevant because any system of units can be used. It is assumed that $EI/EA = 1000$ and is constant for all elements.

The structure and loads are as shown in the accompanying figure.

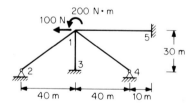

The complete equation [Eq. (1.4)] prior to boundary conditions is

$$\begin{bmatrix} P_1 \\ P_2 \\ P_3 \\ P_4 \\ P_5 \end{bmatrix} = \begin{bmatrix} K_{11} & K_{12} & K_{13} & K_{14} & K_{15} \\ & K_{22} & 0 & 0 & 0 \\ & & K_{33} & 0 & 0 \\ & \text{Symm.} & & K_{44} & 0 \\ & & & & K_{55} \end{bmatrix} \begin{bmatrix} U_1 \\ U_2 \\ U_3 \\ U_4 \\ U_5 \end{bmatrix}$$

The remaining equation after the introduction of the boundary conditions (deleting rows and columns corresponding to zero boundary displacements and rotations at joints 3 and 5) becomes

$$
\begin{bmatrix} P_1 \\ P_2 \\ P_4 \end{bmatrix} = \begin{bmatrix} K_{11} & K_{12} & K_{14} \\ K_{21} & K_{22} & 0 \\ K_{41} & 0 & K_{44} \end{bmatrix} \begin{bmatrix} U_1 \\ U_2 \\ U_4 \end{bmatrix}
$$

where
$$
\begin{aligned}
K_{11} &= K_{11}^2 + K_{11}^3 + K_{11}^4 + K_{11}^5 \\
K_{22} &= K_{22}^1 \\
K_{44} &= K_{44}^1
\end{aligned}
\qquad
R_{ij} = \begin{bmatrix} l & m & 0 \\ -m & l & 0 \\ 0 & 0 & 1 \end{bmatrix}
$$

Member direct stiffnesses in global coordinates are as follows.

Member 1, 2:

$$
\begin{aligned} l &= 0.8 \\ m &= 0.6 \end{aligned}
\quad
K_{11}^2 = EI \times 10^{-3} \begin{bmatrix} 0.0473 & -0.0365 & 1.44 \\ -0.0365 & 0.0684 & -1.92 \\ 1.44 & -1.92 & 80.0 \end{bmatrix}
\quad \text{since} \quad
R_{12} = \begin{bmatrix} 0.8 & 0.6 & 0 \\ -0.6 & 0.8 & 0 \\ 0 & 0 & 1 \end{bmatrix}
$$

Member 1, 3:

$$
\begin{aligned} l &= 0 \\ m &= 1 \end{aligned}
\quad
K_{11}^3 = EI \times 10^{-3} \begin{bmatrix} 0.444 & 0 & 6.66 \\ 0 & 0.033 & 0 \\ 6.66 & 0 & 133.3 \end{bmatrix}
\quad \text{since} \quad
R_{13} = \begin{bmatrix} 0 & 1 & 0 \\ -1 & 0 & 0 \\ 0 & 0 & 1 \end{bmatrix}
$$

Member 1, 4:

$$
\begin{aligned} l &= -0.8 \\ m &= 0.6 \end{aligned}
\quad
K_{11}^4 = EI \times 10^{-3} \begin{bmatrix} 0.0473 & 0.0365 & 1.440 \\ 0.0365 & 0.0684 & 1.920 \\ 1.440 & 1.920 & 80.0 \end{bmatrix}
\quad \text{since} \quad
R_{14} = \begin{bmatrix} -0.8 & 0.6 & 0 \\ -0.6 & -0.8 & 0 \\ 0 & 0 & 1 \end{bmatrix}
$$

Member 1, 5:

$$
\begin{aligned} l &= -1 \\ m &= 0 \end{aligned}
\quad
K_{11}^5 = EI \times 10^{-3} \begin{bmatrix} 0.020 & 0 & 0 \\ 0 & 0.096 & 2.40 \\ 0 & 2.40 & 80.0 \end{bmatrix}
\quad \text{since} \quad
R_{15} = \begin{bmatrix} -1 & 0 & 0 \\ 0 & -1 & 0 \\ 0 & 0 & 1 \end{bmatrix}
$$

The cross-stiffness matrices can be obtained from the above direct stiffnesses by modifications indicated in Eq. (1.1). The stiffness-matrix equation prior to the boundary conditions at supports 2 and 4 becomes

$$
\begin{bmatrix} P_{1X} \\ P_{1Y} \\ M_1 \\ P_{2X} \\ P_{2Y} \\ M_2 \\ P_{4X} \\ P_{4Y} \\ M_4 \end{bmatrix} = EI \times 10^{-3}
\begin{bmatrix}
0.559 & 0 & 9.546 & -0.0473 & 0.0365 & 1.440 & -0.0473 & -0.0365 & 1.440 \\
 & 0.266 & 2.40 & 0.0365 & -0.0686 & -1.920 & -0.0365 & -0.0684 & 1.920 \\
 & & 373.3 & -1.440 & 1.920 & 40.0 & -1.440 & -1.920 & 40.0 \\
 & & & 0.0473 & -0.0365 & -1.440 & 0 & 0 & 0 \\
 & & & & 0.0686 & 1.920 & 0 & 0 & 0 \\
 & & & & & 80.0 & 0 & 0 & 0 \\
 & & & & & & 0.0473 & 0.0364 & -1.440 \\
 & & & & & & & 0.0686 & -1.920 \\
\text{Symm.} & & & & & & & & 80.0
\end{bmatrix}
\begin{bmatrix} \Delta_{1X} \\ \Delta_{1Y} \\ \theta_1 \\ \Delta_{2X} \\ \Delta_{2Y} \\ \theta_2 \\ \Delta_{4X} \\ \Delta_{4Y} \\ \theta_4 \end{bmatrix}
$$

After introduction of the boundary conditions at 2 and 4, the final equation becomes

$$
\begin{bmatrix} -100 \\ 0 \\ 200 \\ 0 \\ 0 \end{bmatrix} = EI \times 10^{-3}
\begin{bmatrix}
0.559 & 0 & 9.546 & 1.440 & 1.440 \\
 & 0.266 & 2.400 & -1.920 & 1.920 \\
 & & 373.33 & 40.0 & 40.0 \\
 & & & 80.0 & 0 \\
\text{Symm.} & & & & 80.0
\end{bmatrix}
\begin{bmatrix} \Delta_{1X} \\ \Delta_{1Y} \\ \theta_1 \\ \theta_2 \\ \theta_4 \end{bmatrix}
$$

which gives the free-joint displacements as

$$\Delta_{1X} = \frac{-0.365}{EI} \times 10^6 \qquad \theta_1 = \frac{0.0105}{EI} \times 10^6$$

$$\Delta_{1Y} = \frac{-0.144}{EI} \times 10^6 \qquad \theta_2 = \frac{-0.00216}{EI} \times 10^6$$

$$\theta_4 = \frac{0.00478}{EI} \times 10^6$$

To calculate member-end forces,

$$\mathbf{p}_{ij} = \mathbf{k}_{ii}^j \mathbf{R}_{ij} \mathbf{U}_i + \mathbf{k}_{ij} \mathbf{R}_{ji} \mathbf{U}_j$$

$$\mathbf{p}_{12} = 10^3 \begin{bmatrix} 0.02 & 0 & 0 \\ 0 & 0.096 & -2.40 \\ 0 & -2.40 & 80.0 \end{bmatrix} \begin{bmatrix} 0.8 & 0.6 & 0 \\ -0.6 & 0.8 & 0 \\ 0 & 0 & 1 \end{bmatrix} \begin{bmatrix} -0.365 \\ -0.144 \\ 0.0105 \end{bmatrix}$$

$$+ 10^3 \begin{bmatrix} -0.02 & 0 & 0 \\ 0 & -0.096 & -2.40 \\ 0 & 2.40 & 40.0 \end{bmatrix} \begin{bmatrix} 0.8 & 0.6 & 0 \\ -0.6 & 0.8 & 0 \\ 0 & 0 & 1 \end{bmatrix} \begin{bmatrix} 0 \\ 0 \\ -0.00216 \end{bmatrix} = \begin{bmatrix} -7.58 \text{ N} \\ -10.15 \text{ N} \\ 507.6 \text{ N} \cdot \text{m} \end{bmatrix}$$

Similarly,

$$\mathbf{p}_{13} = \begin{bmatrix} -4.82 \text{ N} \\ 92.18 \text{ N} \\ -1032 \text{ N} \cdot \text{m} \end{bmatrix} \qquad \mathbf{p}_{14} = \begin{bmatrix} 4.10 \text{ N} \\ -4.59 \text{ N} \\ 230 \text{ N} \cdot \text{m} \end{bmatrix} \qquad \mathbf{p}_{15} = \begin{bmatrix} 7.3 \text{ N} \\ -11.36 \text{ N} \\ 494 \text{ N} \cdot \text{m} \end{bmatrix}$$

The above member-end forces are in reference to the local coordinate axes shown in the accompanying figure.

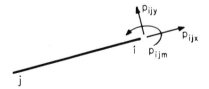

**Discussion**   This example illustrates the introduction of fixed and hinged boundary conditions in one problem. Notice that the last rows (columns) of $\mathbf{K}_{ij}$ corresponding to hinged supports remain in the equation. An experienced analyst should calculate only the last rows (columns) of the stiffness matrices for members 1, 2 and 1, 4. In order to illustrate how the fixed and hinged supports affect the complete equation, they are introduced separately in this example. Note that $l$, $m$, $n$ are the directional cosines of local coordinate axes in respect to global axes.

The cross-stiffness matrices are obtained from the direct stiffnesses by modifications instead of recalculation. Calculation of the stiffness matrices in local coordinates is also omitted in this example.

**EXAMPLE 1.2**   *Three-dimensional rigid frame.*   The analysis of 3D rigid frames makes use of the entire stiffness matrix shown in Eq. (1.1). Attention must be paid to the fact that the cross-sectional properties of members must be specified in reference to *principal coordinate axes*, which may not always coincide with the element (local) coordinate axes. In this case, the coordinate transformation between local and principal axes using the $\beta$-angle between the local $y$-axis and the principal $y$-axis must be done prior to transformation from local to global axes. Thus

$$\underbrace{\mathbf{R}^T_{ijp}\mathbf{p}_{ijp}}_{\mathbf{p}_{ij}} = \underbrace{\mathbf{R}^T_{ijp}\mathbf{k}^j_{iip}\mathbf{R}_{ijp}}_{\mathbf{k}^j_{ii}}\,\underbrace{\mathbf{R}^T_{ijp}\mathbf{u}_{ijp}}_{\delta_{ij}} + \underbrace{\mathbf{R}^T_{ijp}\mathbf{k}_{ijp}\mathbf{R}_{ijp}}_{\mathbf{k}_{ij}}\,\underbrace{\mathbf{R}^T_{ijp}\mathbf{u}_{jip}}_{\delta_{ji}}$$

where

$$\mathbf{R}_{ijp} = \begin{bmatrix} 1 & 0 & 0 & \\ 0 & \cos\beta & \sin\beta & \mathbf{0} \\ 0 & -\sin\beta & \cos\beta & \\ \hdashline & \mathbf{0} & & \text{Same} \end{bmatrix} \qquad \mathbf{R}_{ij} = \begin{bmatrix} l & m & n & \\ -\dfrac{m}{D} & \dfrac{l}{D} & 0 & 0 \\ -\dfrac{ln}{D} & -\dfrac{mn}{D} & D & \\ \hdashline & \mathbf{0} & & \text{Same} \end{bmatrix}$$

$$D = \sqrt{l^2 + m^2}$$

since the local $x$-axis and the principal $x_p$-axis usually coincide. Note that for this example the $\beta$-angle is assumed to be zero; therefore, the above rotation matrix becomes an identity matrix. Should the members rotate about their longitudinal axis, the $\beta$-angle will amount to that rotation.

Member properties (any system of units can be used):

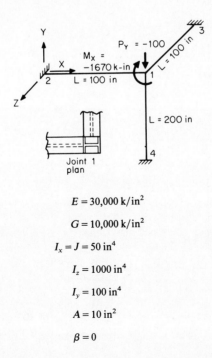

$$E = 30,000 \text{ k/in}^2$$

$$G = 10,000 \text{ k/in}^2$$

$$I_x = J = 50 \text{ in}^4$$

$$I_z = 1000 \text{ in}^4$$

$$I_y = 100 \text{ in}^4$$

$$A = 10 \text{ in}^2$$

$$\beta = 0$$

The final equation is
$$\mathbf{P}_1 = \mathbf{K}_{11}\boldsymbol{\Delta}_1$$

where
$$\mathbf{K}_{11} = \mathbf{K}_{11}^2 + \mathbf{K}_{11}^3 + \mathbf{K}_{11}^4 \quad \text{and} \quad \mathbf{K}_{ii}^j = \mathbf{R}_{ij}^T \mathbf{k}_{ii}^j \mathbf{R}_{ij}$$

Member 1, 2:

$$
\begin{aligned}
l &= 1 \\
m &= 0 \\
n &= 0
\end{aligned}
\quad
\mathbf{K}_{11}^2 =
\begin{bmatrix}
3000 & 0 & 0 & 0 & 0 & 0 \\
 & 360 & 0 & 0 & 0 & -18{,}000 \\
 & & 36 & 0 & 1{,}800 & 0 \\
 & & & 5000 & 0 & 0 \\
 & & & & 120{,}000 & 0 \\
\text{Symm.} & & & & & 1{,}200{,}000
\end{bmatrix}
\qquad
\mathbf{R}_{12} =
\begin{bmatrix}
I & 0 \\
0 & I
\end{bmatrix}
$$

Member 1, 3:

$$
\begin{aligned}
l &= 0 \\
m &= 0 \\
n &= 0
\end{aligned}
\quad
\mathbf{K}_{11}^3 =
\begin{bmatrix}
36 & 0 & 0 & 0 & -1{,}800 & 0 \\
 & 360 & 0 & 18{,}000 & 0 & 0 \\
 & & 3000 & 0 & 0 & 0 \\
 & & & 1{,}200{,}000 & 0 & 0 \\
 & & & & 120{,}000 & 0 \\
\text{Symm.} & & & & & 5000
\end{bmatrix}
\quad
\mathbf{R}_{13} =
\begin{bmatrix}
\begin{array}{ccc|c}
0 & 0 & 1 & \\
0 & 1 & 0 & 0 \\
-1 & 0 & 0 & \\
\hline
 & 0 & & \text{Same}
\end{array}
\end{bmatrix}
$$

Member 1, 4:

$$
\begin{aligned}
l &= 0 \\
m &= 1 \\
n &= 0
\end{aligned}
\quad
\mathbf{K}_{11}^4 =
\begin{bmatrix}
45 & 0 & 0 & 0 & 0 & 4{,}500 \\
 & 1500 & 0 & 0 & 0 & 0 \\
 & & 4.5 & -450 & 0 & 0 \\
 & & & 60{,}000 & 0 & 0 \\
 & & & & 2500 & 0 \\
\text{Symm.} & & & & & 600{,}000
\end{bmatrix}
\quad
\mathbf{R}_{14} =
\begin{bmatrix}
\begin{array}{ccc|c}
0 & 1 & 0 & \\
-1 & 0 & 0 & 0 \\
0 & 0 & 1 & \\
\hline
 & 0 & & \text{Same}
\end{array}
\end{bmatrix}
$$

The final equation, then, becomes

$$
\begin{bmatrix}
0 \\ -100 \\ 0 \\ -1670 \\ 0 \\ 0
\end{bmatrix}
=
\begin{bmatrix}
3081 & 0 & 0 & 0 & -1{,}800 & 4{,}500 \\
 & 2220 & 0 & 18{,}000 & 0 & -18{,}000 \\
 & & 3040 & -450 & 1{,}800 & 0 \\
 & & & 1{,}265{,}000 & 0 & 0 \\
 & & & & 242{,}500 & 0 \\
\text{Symm.} & & & & & 1{,}805{,}000
\end{bmatrix}
\begin{bmatrix}
\Delta_{1X} \\ \Delta_{1Y} \\ \Delta_{1Z} \\ \theta_{1X} \\ \theta_{1Y} \\ \theta_{1Z}
\end{bmatrix}
$$

from which

$$
\mathbf{K}^{-1} = 10^{-9}
\begin{bmatrix}
327{,}307 & -8226 & -1{,}427 & 116 & 2440 & -898 \\
 & 560{,}632 & -1{,}149 & -7978 & -52 & 5611 \\
 & & 330{,}371 & 134 & -2462 & -8 \\
 & & & 904 & -0.128 & -80 \\
 & & & & 4160 & -7 \\
\text{Symm.} & & & & & 612
\end{bmatrix}
$$

$$
\mathbf{U} =
\begin{bmatrix}
0.0006281 \text{ in} \\
-0.0427702 \text{ in} \\
-0.0001081 \text{ in} \\
-0.0007084 \text{ rad} \\
0.0000055 \text{ rad} \\
-0.0004278 \text{ rad}
\end{bmatrix}
$$

To compute member forces:     $\mathbf{p}_{ij} = \mathbf{k}_{ii}\mathbf{R}_{ij}\mathbf{U}_i + \mathbf{k}_{ij}\mathbf{R}_{ij}\mathbf{U}_j$

Member 1, 2: $\mathbf{U}_2 = 0$

$$
\mathbf{p}_{12} =
\begin{bmatrix}
3000 & 0 & 0 & 0 & 0 & 0 \\
 & 360 & 0 & 0 & 0 & -18{,}000 \\
 & & 36 & 0 & 1{,}800 & 0 \\
 & & & 5000 & 0 & 0 \\
 & & & & 120{,}000 & 0 \\
\text{Symm.} & & & & & 1{,}200{,}000
\end{bmatrix}
[\mathbf{I}][\mathbf{U}] =
\begin{bmatrix}
1.88^k \\
-7.69^k \\
0.0059^k \\
-3.542 \,\text{k}\cdot\text{in} \\
0.47 \,\text{k}\cdot\text{in} \\
256.58 \,\text{k}\cdot\text{in}
\end{bmatrix}.
$$

Member 1, 3:

$$\mathbf{p}_{13} = \mathbf{k}_{11}^3\mathbf{R}_{13}\mathbf{U}_1 \qquad \text{since} \qquad \mathbf{U}_3 = 0$$

$$
\mathbf{p}_{13} =
\begin{bmatrix}
3000 & 0 & 0 & 0 & 0 & 0 \\
 & 360 & 0 & 0 & 0 & -18{,}000 \\
 & & 36 & 0 & 1{,}800 & 0 \\
 & & & 5000 & 0 & 0 \\
 & & & & 120{,}000 & 0 \\
\text{Symm.} & & & & & 1{,}200{,}000
\end{bmatrix}
\left[
\begin{array}{ccc|c}
0 & 0 & 1 & \\
0 & 1 & 0 & \mathbf{0} \\
-1 & 0 & 0 & \\
\hline
 & \mathbf{0} & & \text{Same}
\end{array}
\right]
[\mathbf{U}] =
\begin{bmatrix}
-1.324^k \\
-28.15^k \\
0.013^k \\
-2.15 \,\text{k}\cdot\text{in} \\
-0.47 \,\text{k}\cdot\text{in} \\
1629.12 \,\text{k}\cdot\text{in}
\end{bmatrix}
$$

Member 1, 4:

$$\mathbf{p}_{14} = \mathbf{k}_{11}^4\mathbf{R}_{14}\mathbf{U}_1 \qquad \text{since} \qquad \mathbf{U}_4 = 0$$

$$
\mathbf{p}_{14} =
\begin{bmatrix}
1500 & 0 & 0 & 0 & 0 & 0 \\
 & 45 & 0 & 0 & 0 & -4{,}500 \\
 & & 4.5 & 0 & 450 & 0 \\
 & & & 2500 & 0 & 0 \\
 & & & & 60{,}000 & 0 \\
\text{Symm.} & & & & & 600{,}000
\end{bmatrix}
\left[
\begin{array}{ccc|c}
0 & 1 & 0 & \\
-1 & 0 & 0 & \mathbf{0} \\
0 & 0 & 1 & \\
\hline
 & \mathbf{0} & & \text{Same}
\end{array}
\right]
[\mathbf{U}] =
\begin{bmatrix}
-64.15^k \\
1.89^k \\
0.31^k \\
0.0137 \,\text{k}\cdot\text{in} \\
42.43 \,\text{k}\cdot\text{in} \\
-254.00 \,\text{k}\cdot\text{in}
\end{bmatrix}
$$

Verify the equilibrium of joint 1.

$$\sum_1 \mathbf{R}_{1j}^T\mathbf{p}_{1j} = \mathbf{P}_1 = \mathbf{R}_{12}^T\mathbf{p}_{12} + \mathbf{R}_{13}^T\mathbf{p}_{13} + \mathbf{R}_{14}^T\mathbf{p}_{14}$$

$$
\mathbf{P}_1 =
\left[
\begin{array}{ccc|ccc}
1 & 0 & 0 & 0 & 0 & 0 \\
0 & 1 & 0 & 0 & 0 & 0 \\
0 & 0 & 1 & 0 & 0 & 0 \\
\hline
0 & 0 & 0 & 1 & 0 & 0 \\
0 & 0 & 0 & 0 & 1 & 0 \\
0 & 0 & 0 & 0 & 0 & 1
\end{array}
\right]
\mathbf{p}_{12} +
\left[
\begin{array}{ccc|ccc}
0 & 0 & -1 & & & \\
0 & 1 & 0 & & \mathbf{0} & \\
1 & 0 & 0 & & & \\
\hline
 & & & 0 & 0 & -1 \\
 & \mathbf{0} & & 0 & 1 & 0 \\
 & & & 1 & 0 & 0
\end{array}
\right]
\mathbf{p}_{13}
$$

$$
+
\left[
\begin{array}{ccc|ccc}
0 & -1 & 0 & & & \\
1 & 0 & 0 & & \mathbf{0} & \\
0 & 0 & 1 & & & \\
\hline
 & & & 0 & -1 & 0 \\
 & \mathbf{0} & & 1 & 0 & 0 \\
 & & & 0 & 0 & 1
\end{array}
\right]
\mathbf{p}_{14} \approx
\begin{bmatrix}
0 \\
-100^k \\
0 \\
-1670 \,\text{k}\cdot\text{in} \\
0 \\
0
\end{bmatrix}
$$

*Discussion* This structure may be considered the smallest three-dimensional rigid frame since it contains only one free joint. Nevertheless, the analysis of a larger structure will follow the same procedure. Notice that the orientation of local axes for member 1, 3 does not follow the standard procedure presented. When a member is parallel to the $z$-axis, its local axes must be oriented in a special way as given in Ref. [6].

The orientation of the local axes for the other members, member 1, 4, for instance, was determined as in Ref. [6].

$$l_x = \frac{0-0}{200} = 0 \qquad m_x = \frac{0-(-200)}{200} = 1 \qquad n_x = \frac{0-0}{200} = 0 \qquad D = 1$$

Then the rotation matrix $\mathbf{R}_{14}$ becomes

$$\mathbf{R}_{14} = \left[\begin{array}{ccc|c} 0 & 1 & 0 & \\ -1 & 0 & 0 & \mathbf{0} \\ 0 & 0 & 1 & \\ \hline & \mathbf{0} & & \text{Same} \end{array}\right]$$

Notice that, since $\beta = 0$, the local axes and principal axes of the cross sections coincide; thus, $\mathbf{R}_{ijp} = \mathbf{I}$.

The procedure outlined here can be extended to structures with nonprismatic members. The only requirement is the evaluation of the member stiffness matrices similar to that given in Eq. (1.1) for prismatic members. This, in turn, requires a line integration [Eq. (1.2)] with variable cross-sectional properties of nonprismatic members. The rest of the procedure—i.e., assembly of member stiffness matrices, introduction of essential boundary conditions, and evaluation of nodal displacements, member-end forces, and stresses—is the same as before.

## 1.3 FINITE-ELEMENT ANALYSIS OF 2D SOLIDS

Figure 1.1 indicates the classification of 2D solids. The analysis of each group follows a similar procedure, except that the constitutive relationships and the approximating functions are different for each. Here, we briefly outline various 2D problems.

### 1.3A Plane-Stress and Plane-Strain Problems

Problems involving plane stress and strain occur when a 2D body is subject to in-plane forces and constraints. In this case, the lowest order of approximation for displacements for a triangular element (known as the constant-stress-and-strain triangle) is

$$\tilde{u} = c_1 + c_2 x + c_3 y + \cdots$$

$$\tilde{v} = c_4 + c_5 x + c_6 y + \cdots$$

The strain-displacement relationship is

$$\varepsilon_{xx} = \frac{\partial \tilde{u}}{\partial x} \qquad \varepsilon_{yy} = \frac{\partial \tilde{v}}{\partial y} \qquad \varepsilon_{xy} = \frac{\partial \tilde{u}}{\partial y} + \frac{\partial \tilde{v}}{\partial x}$$

The material matrix for an isotropic linearly elastic material is as follows.

*For plane-stress problems*:         *For plane-strain problems*:

$$\mathbf{D} = \frac{E}{1-\nu^2} \begin{bmatrix} 1 & \nu & 0 \\ \nu & 1 & 0 \\ 0 & 0 & \dfrac{1-\nu}{2} \end{bmatrix} \qquad \mathbf{D} = \frac{E}{(1+\nu)(1-2\nu)} \begin{bmatrix} 1-\nu & \nu & 0 \\ \nu & 1-\nu & 0 \\ 0 & 0 & \dfrac{1-2\nu}{2} \end{bmatrix}$$

Substituting element-node coordinates into the above approximate function for $\tilde{u}$ and $\tilde{v}$ yields (for node $i$ at the origin of the local coordinate axes and node $j$ on the $y$-axis)

$$\begin{bmatrix} u_i \\ u_j \\ u_m \\ v_i \\ v_j \\ v_m \end{bmatrix} = \begin{bmatrix} \begin{bmatrix} 1 & & \\ 1 & x_j & \\ 1 & x_m & y_m \end{bmatrix} & \mathbf{0} \\ \mathbf{0} & \begin{bmatrix} 1 & & \\ 1 & x_j & \\ 1 & x_m & y_m \end{bmatrix} \end{bmatrix} \begin{bmatrix} c_1 \\ c_2 \\ c_3 \\ c_4 \\ c_5 \\ c_6 \end{bmatrix}$$

In short, $\mathbf{u}_e = \mathbf{b}^{-1}\mathbf{c}$.

The inversion of the square matrix on the right-hand side of the above equation yields the coefficient vector $\mathbf{c}$, which in turn can be substituted into the expressions for strain

$$\boldsymbol{\varepsilon} = \mathbf{dc}$$

Once the total potential energy of the element is expressed in terms of strain energy and external work,

$$\pi = \int_A \frac{t}{2} \boldsymbol{\varepsilon}^T \mathbf{D} \boldsymbol{\varepsilon}\; dA - \mathbf{u}_e^T \mathbf{p}_e$$

the minimization of it as $\partial \pi / \partial \mathbf{u}_e = 0$ yields $\mathbf{P}_e = \mathbf{k}_e \mathbf{u}_e$. The element stiffness matrix $\mathbf{k}_e$ on the right-hand side of this equation requires integration given in Eq. (1.2), in which matrix $\mathbf{B}$ depends on the shape of the element and the order of approximations for displacements. It relates node displacements to strains as

$$\boldsymbol{\varepsilon} = \mathbf{dbu}_e = \mathbf{Bu}_e$$

For the *constant-strain-and-stress triangle*, these matrices become

$$\mathbf{d} = \begin{bmatrix} 0 & 1 & 0 & 0 & 0 & 0 \\ 0 & 0 & 0 & 0 & 0 & 1 \\ 0 & 0 & 1 & 0 & 1 & 0 \end{bmatrix}$$

$$\mathbf{b} = \frac{1}{x_j y_m} \begin{bmatrix} \begin{bmatrix} x_j y_m & 0 & 0 \\ -y_m & y_m & 0 \\ x_m - x_j & -x_m & x_j \end{bmatrix} & \mathbf{0} \\ \mathbf{0} & [\text{Same}] \end{bmatrix}$$

and the shape function is

$$\mathbf{N} = \begin{bmatrix} 1 & x & y & 0 & 0 & 0 \\ 0 & 0 & 0 & 1 & x & y \end{bmatrix} \mathbf{b} = \boldsymbol{\phi}(x, y)\mathbf{b}$$

The explicit stiffness matrix of a constant-stress triangular element (CST) is

$$\mathbf{k}_e = a_1 \begin{bmatrix} y_m^2 + a_2 a_3^2 & & & & & \text{Symm.} \\ -y_m^2 - a_2 a_3 x_m & y_m^2 + a_2 x_m^2 \\ (a_2 a_3 x_j) & -a_2 x_j x_m & a_2 x_j^2 \\ -(a_2 + \nu)y_m a_3 & y_m(a_2 x_m + \nu a_3) & -a_2 x_j y_m & a_2 y_m^2 + a_3 \\ y_m(a_2 a_3 + \nu x_m) & -x_m y_m(\nu + a_2) & a_z x_j y_m & -a_2 y_m^2 - x_m a_3 & a_2 y_m^2 + x_m^2 \\ -\nu x_j y_m & \nu x_j y_m & 0 & x_j a_3 & -x_j x_m & x_j \end{bmatrix}$$

where

$$a_1 = \frac{Et}{2 x_j y_m (1 - \nu^2)} \qquad a_2 = \frac{1 - \nu}{2} \qquad a_3 = x_m - x_j$$

The above stiffness matrix establishes the force-displacement relationship in reference to local coordinate axes

$$\mathbf{p}_e = \mathbf{k}_e \mathbf{u}_e$$

Note that the order of the terms in this matrix follows the same sequence set earlier, that is, $[u_i \ u_j \ u_m \ v_i \ v_j \ v_m]$. Rows and columns must be interchanged before the assembly of this matrix into $\mathbf{P} = \mathbf{KU}$.

High-order stiffness matrices for linear-stress triangles (LST) and for quadratic-stress triangles (QST) can be obtained simply by taking additional terms in the displacement function and consequently additional nodes at the interfaces. (Refer to Chap. 3 in Part 2 for families of displacement functions.)

The equivalent nodal-force vector is obtained by the following integration

$$\mathbf{p}_e = \int_v \mathbf{N}^T \mathbf{g} \, dv + \int_A \mathbf{N}^T \mathbf{p} \, dA$$

where $\mathbf{g}$ and $\mathbf{p}$ are the vectors representing body force and traction distribution over the body and boundary of the element.

Note that shape function $\mathbf{N}$ consists of two matrices. The first, $\boldsymbol{\phi}$, represents the *degree of approximation* (linear in this case), and the second, $\mathbf{b}$, represents the *shape of the element* (composed of nodal coordinates). The two together are referred to as the *shape function*. One should, therefore, keep in mind that the finite stiffness matrices in solid mechanics are formed by four entities: degree of approximation $\boldsymbol{\phi}(x, y, z)$, shape of the element $\mathbf{b}$, strain-displacement matrix $\mathbf{d}$, and material matrix $\mathbf{D}$. These matrices vary from problem to problem.

## 1.3ʙ Plate-Bending Problems

Planar two-dimensional systems subject to flexure are known as *plates*. General forces on these systems are usually separated into two components: in-plane forces and transverse (perpendicular) forces. Under the former forces, the plate is subject to in-plane stresses or strains; under the latter, it is subject to flexure (bending). In-plane forces have been treated in the previous section; we consider the latter here.

Plates can be thin or thick. When plates are thin, the transverse-shear deformations are negligible and the normals to the neutral surface remain normal after the deformation. The bending strains and stresses vary linearly through the thickness, and the strains of the midsurface and stresses normal to the midsurface of the plate are assumed to be zero.

There are usually three degrees of freedom at each node:

$$ w \qquad \theta_x = \frac{\partial w}{\partial y} \qquad \theta_y = -\frac{\partial w}{\partial x} $$

Occasionally in-plane warping $\partial^2 w/\partial x\,\partial y$ is taken into account as an additional degree of freedom at the node. The approximation for the transverse deflection $w(x, y)$ can be made to any degree depending upon the number of nodes of the element and the degree of freedom in each node.

$$ \tilde{w} = \begin{bmatrix} 1 & x & y & x^2 & xy & y^2 & x^3 & x^2y & xy^2 & y^3 & \cdots \end{bmatrix} \mathbf{c} $$

Differentiation of this function gives strains

$$ \varepsilon_{xx} = -z\frac{\partial^2 w}{\partial x^2} \qquad \varepsilon_{yy} = -z\frac{\partial^2 w}{\partial y^2} \qquad \varepsilon_{xy} = -2z\frac{\partial^2 w}{\partial x\,\partial y} $$

After substitution of the element coordinates into the assumed displacement function and utilization of the above strain components together with the material matrix in the energy functional, the stiffness matrix of a plate-bending element can be obtained by the familiar integration over the element domain

$$ \mathbf{k}_e = \int_A \mathbf{B}^T \mathbf{D}_b \mathbf{B}\, dA $$

In this equation, $\mathbf{D}_b$ is the plate flexural-rigidity matrix given below.

*For isotropic material:*             *For orthotropic material:*

$$ \mathbf{D}_b = \frac{Et^3}{12(1-\nu^2)}\begin{bmatrix} 1 & \nu & 0 \\ \nu & 1 & 0 \\ 0 & 0 & \dfrac{1-2}{2} \end{bmatrix} \qquad \mathbf{D}_b = \frac{t^3}{12(1-\nu_x\nu_y)}\begin{bmatrix} E_x & E_y\nu_x & 0 \\ E_y\nu_x & E_y & 0 \\ 0 & 0 & G(1-\nu_x\nu_y) \end{bmatrix} $$

And $\mathbf{B}$ is the derivation of the shape function $\mathbf{N}$ according to strain-displacement relationships such that

$$ \mathbf{B} = \begin{bmatrix} -\dfrac{\partial^2}{\partial x^2} & -\dfrac{\partial^2}{\partial y^2} & 2\dfrac{\partial^2}{\partial x\,\partial y} \end{bmatrix} \mathbf{N} $$

For a basic triangular element with three corner nodes, the usual matrices are

$$\tilde{\mathbf{u}}(x, y) = \begin{bmatrix} w \\ \theta_x \\ \theta_y \end{bmatrix}$$

$$= \begin{bmatrix} 1 & x & y & x^2 & xy & y^2 & x^3 & (x^2y + xy^2) & y^3 \\ 0 & 0 & 1 & 0 & x & 2y & 0 & (x^2 + 2xy) & 3y^2 \\ 0 & -1 & 0 & -2x & -y & 0 & -3x^2 & -(2xy + y^2) & 0 \end{bmatrix} \begin{bmatrix} c_1 \\ c_2 \\ \vdots \\ c_9 \end{bmatrix}$$

$$\mathbf{b}^{-1} = \begin{bmatrix} 1 & 0 & 0 & 0 & 0 & 0 & 0 & 0 & 0 \\ 0 & 0 & 1 & 0 & 0 & 0 & 0 & 0 & 0 \\ 0 & -1 & 0 & 0 & 0 & 0 & 0 & 0 & 0 \\ 1 & x_j & 0 & x_j^2 & 0 & 0 & x_j^3 & 0 & 0 \\ 0 & 0 & 1 & 0 & x_j & 0 & 0 & x_j^2 & 0 \\ 0 & -1 & 0 & -2x_j & 0 & 0 & -3x_j^2 & 0 & 0 \\ 1 & x_m & y_m & x_m^2 & x_m y_m & y_m^2 & x_m^3 & x_m^2 y_m + x_m y_m^2 & y_m^3 \\ 0 & 0 & 1 & 0 & x_m & 2y_m & 0 & x_m^2 + 2x_m y_m & 3y_m^2 \\ 0 & -1 & 0 & -2x_m & -y_m & 0 & -3x_m^2 & -(2x_m y_m + y_m^2) & 0 \end{bmatrix}$$

$$\mathbf{d} = -z \begin{bmatrix} 0 & 0 & 0 & 2 & 0 & 0 & 6x & 2y & 0 \\ 0 & 0 & 0 & 0 & 0 & 2 & 0 & 2x & 6y \\ 0 & 0 & 0 & 0 & -2 & 0 & 0 & -4(x+y) & 0 \end{bmatrix} \begin{bmatrix} c_1 \\ c_2 \\ \vdots \\ c_9 \end{bmatrix}$$

Using the above matrices, the stiffness matrix for a basic triangular element becomes

$$\mathbf{k}_e = \frac{\mathbf{b}^T E t^3}{12(1 - \nu^2)} \int_A$$

$$\begin{bmatrix} 0 & & & & 0 & & & \\ \hline & 4 & & & & & & \\ & 0 & 2(1-\nu) & & & & & \\ 0 & 4\nu & 0 & 4 & & & & \\ & 12x & 0 & 12\nu x & 36x^2 & & & \\ & 4(\nu x + y) & 4(1-\nu)(x+y) & 4(x + \nu y) & 12(\nu x + y)x & -8(1-\nu)xy & & \\ & & & & & +(12 - 8\nu)(x+y) & & \\ & 12\nu y & 0 & 12y & 36\nu xy & 12(x+\nu y)y & 36y^2 \end{bmatrix} \; dA \, \mathbf{b}$$

which is the explicit version of the standard expression of the stiffness matrices in solid mechanics:

$$\mathbf{k}_e = \int_v \mathbf{b}^T \mathbf{d}^T \mathbf{D} \mathbf{d} b \; dv$$

Note that **b**-matrices, which are made of the coordinates of the elements, are often left outside the integration.

In *thick plates*, the transverse-shear contribution to the stiffness matrix is significant; thus, shear-strain energy must be added to bending-strain energy. The total potential energy is written as

$$\pi_e = \frac{t}{2}\int_A \boldsymbol{\varepsilon}^T \mathbf{D}_b \boldsymbol{\varepsilon}\, dA + \frac{tc}{2}\int_A \boldsymbol{\gamma}^T \mathbf{D}_s \boldsymbol{\gamma}\, dA - \mathbf{u}_e^T \mathbf{p}_e$$

where
$$\mathbf{D}_s = \frac{E}{2(1+\nu)}\begin{bmatrix} 1 & 0 \\ 0 & 1 \end{bmatrix}$$

$t$ = thickness of the plate

$c$ = correction factor for nonuniformity of shear stresses through thickness, usually taken as $\frac{5}{6}$

After modification of the total potential energy to include the shearing effect, the analysis of thick plates follows the same procedure as for thin plates.

For a *basic quadrilateral element* with 12 degrees of freedom, one can take 12 terms in the approximate function for $\tilde{w}$. Thus

$$\tilde{w} = \begin{bmatrix} 1 & x & y & x^2 & xy & y^2 & x^3 & \cdots & xy^3 \end{bmatrix}\mathbf{c}$$

The corresponding matrices are similarly obtained. Note that in these approximations, the transverse displacements between the elements are compatible (continuous), but the slopes are not compatible (kinking occurs). The slopes in this case are quadratic and only two end values are prescribed. Discontinuous displacement functions are normally referred to as *nonconforming* shape functions. The slope's continuity can be established by higher-order approximations, a process which requires introducing additional nodes at the interfaces.

The equivalent nodal-force vector is obtained by the usual integration

$$\mathbf{p}_e = \int_v \mathbf{N}^T \mathbf{g}\, dv + \int_A \mathbf{N}^T \mathbf{p}\, dA$$

in which $\mathbf{g}$ is the body-force distribution and vector $\mathbf{p}$ consists of distributed transverse forces as well as moments and shears over the element and its boundaries. The element edge moments and shear forces are related to stresses as

$$\begin{bmatrix} M_x \\ M_y \\ M_{xy} \end{bmatrix} = \int_{-t/2}^{t/2} z \begin{bmatrix} \sigma_x \\ \sigma_y \\ \tau_{xy} \end{bmatrix} dz \qquad \begin{bmatrix} Q_x \\ Q_y \end{bmatrix} = \int_{-t/2}^{t/2} \begin{bmatrix} \tau_{zx} \\ \tau_{yz} \end{bmatrix} dz$$

The catalog of plate-bending elements can be found in Sec. 4.7 of Part 2.

## 1.3c Shells

Several theories are available for thick and thin shells. The finite-element analysis of shells in general makes use of elements which are (1) flat, (2) curved, and (3) solid. For thin shells, accurate results are often obtained by using *flat* elements which combine *membrane* and *flexural* effects. These two sets of components are uncoupled in the element domain, although coupling does occur in the global domain after the assembly takes place. If all elements at a particular node are coplanar, coupling may not take place. The element-matrix equation for flat-shell elements in local coordinate axes is

$$
\begin{bmatrix} \mathbf{p}_p \\ \mathbf{p}_b \\ \mathbf{m}_z \end{bmatrix} = \begin{bmatrix} \mathbf{k}_p & & \\ & \mathbf{k}_b & \\ & & \mathbf{0} \end{bmatrix} \begin{bmatrix} \mathbf{u}_p \\ \mathbf{u}_b \\ \mathbf{\theta}_z \end{bmatrix}
$$

in which $\mathbf{k}_p$ and $\mathbf{k}_b$ represent membrane and bending stiffness matrices, respectively. These are, in fact, the stiffness matrices of plane stress and bending elements given in Secs. 1.3A and 1.3B above.

In the case of coplanar elements, the singularity in-plane rotation can be avoided by inserting an arbitrary coefficient on the diagonal representing the in-plane rotational stiffness of the element. Reference [61] suggests using the following matrix on the diagonal of the above matrix for triangular elements:

$$
\begin{bmatrix} m_{iz} \\ m_{jz} \\ m_{kz} \end{bmatrix} = \alpha E V \begin{bmatrix} 1.0 & -0.5 & -0.5 \\ -0.5 & 1.0 & -0.5 \\ -0.5 & -0.5 & 1.0 \end{bmatrix} \begin{bmatrix} \theta_{iz} \\ \theta_{jz} \\ \theta_{kz} \end{bmatrix}
$$

$$
\mathbf{m}_z = \mathbf{k}_{\theta z} \mathbf{\theta}_z
$$

where $\alpha$ is some coefficient yet to be specified. A very small value of it ($10^{-6} \leqslant \alpha \leqslant 10^{-2}$) often produces good results. $V$ is the volume of the element.

It has also been suggested that $\mathbf{k}_{\theta z}$ be set equal to $10^{-4}$ times the smallest bending stiffness of the element [80].

Flat elements are often used for the analysis of folded shells. However, much care is needed when applying these elements to the analysis of general shells.

Most general isoparametric thin-shell elements are derived from 3D isoparametric solid elements by assuming that the displacements in the $x$- and $y$-directions vary linearly while $u_z$ remains constant throughout the thickness of the shell. Thus

$$
\tilde{u}_x = \tilde{u}_x^m + z\theta_y^m
$$

$$
\tilde{u}_y = \tilde{u}_y^m - z\theta_x^m
$$

$$
\tilde{u}_z = \tilde{u}_z^m
$$

where $m$ denotes the midsurface displacements. Their approximation is often made in accordance with standard polynomials presented in Sec. 3.2 of Part 2.

Axisymmetric shells have numerous applications in practice. Although general shell theories are applicable to axisymmetric shells, Zienkiewicz et al. [62] proposed an explicit stiffness matrix for linear, axisymmetric, thin-shell elements.

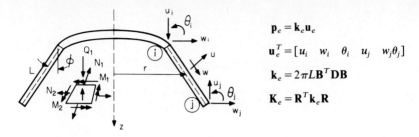

$$\mathbf{p}_e = \mathbf{k}_e \mathbf{u}_e$$

$$\mathbf{u}_e^T = [\, u_i \quad w_i \quad \theta_i \quad u_j \quad w_j \theta_j \,]$$

$$\mathbf{k}_e = 2\pi L \mathbf{B}^T \mathbf{D} \mathbf{B}$$

$$\mathbf{K}_e = \mathbf{R}^T \mathbf{k}_e \mathbf{R}$$

where

$$
\mathbf{B} =
\begin{bmatrix}
-\dfrac{1}{L} & 0 & 0 & \dfrac{1}{L} & 0 & 0 \\[2ex]
\dfrac{\sin\phi}{2r} & \dfrac{\cos\phi}{2r} & 0 & \dfrac{\sin\phi}{2r} & \dfrac{\cos\phi}{2r} & 0 \\[2ex]
0 & 0 & \dfrac{1}{L} & 0 & 0 & -\dfrac{1}{L} \\[2ex]
0 & 0 & -\dfrac{\sin\phi}{2r} & 0 & 0 & -\dfrac{\sin\phi}{2r} \\[2ex]
0 & -\dfrac{1}{L} & -\tfrac{1}{2} & 0 & \dfrac{1}{L} & -\tfrac{1}{2}
\end{bmatrix}
$$

$$
\mathbf{D} = \frac{E_1 t}{1 - \nu_1 \nu_2}
\begin{bmatrix}
1 & \nu_2 & 0 & 0 & 0 \\[2ex]
\nu_2 & \dfrac{E_2}{E_1} & 0 & 0 & 0 \\[2ex]
0 & 0 & \dfrac{t^2}{12} & \dfrac{\nu_2 t^2}{12} & 0 \\[2ex]
0 & 0 & \dfrac{\nu_2 t^2}{12} & \dfrac{E_2}{E_1}\dfrac{t^2}{12} & 0 \\[2ex]
0 & 0 & 0 & 0 & \dfrac{5}{6}\dfrac{G(1 - \nu_1 \nu_2)}{E_1}
\end{bmatrix}
$$

$$
\mathbf{R} = \begin{bmatrix} \hat{\mathbf{R}} & \mathbf{0} \\ \mathbf{0} & \hat{\mathbf{R}} \end{bmatrix}
\qquad
\hat{\mathbf{R}} = \begin{bmatrix} \cos\phi & \sin\phi & 0 \\ -\sin\phi & \cos\phi & 0 \\ 0 & 0 & 1 \end{bmatrix}
$$

And the stiffness-matrix coefficients are

$$K_{11} = K_{44} = -K_{14} = \frac{c(\cos^2\phi + a\sin^2\phi)}{L^2}$$

$$K_{24} = -K_{12} = \frac{c(a-1)\sin\phi\cos\phi}{L^2} + \frac{\nu_2 c\cos\phi}{2Lr}$$

$$K_{15} = -K_{45} = \frac{c(a-1)\sin\phi\cos\phi}{L^2} - \frac{\nu_2 c\cos\phi}{2Lr}$$

$$K_{34} = K_{46} = -K_{13} = -K_{16} = \frac{ca \sin \phi}{2L}$$

$$K_{23} = K_{26} = -K_{35} = -K_{56} = \frac{ca \cos \phi}{2L}$$

$$K_{22} = \frac{c(\sin^2 \phi + a \cos^2 \phi)}{L^2} + cb - \frac{v_2 c \sin \phi}{Lr}$$

$$K_{55} = \frac{c(\sin^2 \phi + a \cos^2 \phi)}{L^2} + cb + \frac{v_2 c \sin \phi}{Lr}$$

$$K_{25} = \frac{-c(\sin^2 \phi + a \cos^2 \phi)}{L^2 + cb}$$

$$K_{33} = \frac{ct^2}{12L^2} + \frac{cbt^2 \sin^2 \phi}{12} + \frac{ca}{4} - \frac{v_2 ct^2 \sin \phi}{12Lr}$$

$$K_{66} = \frac{ct^2}{12L^2} + \frac{cbt^2 \sin^2 \phi}{12} + \frac{ca}{4} + \frac{v_2 ct^2 \sin \phi}{12Lr}$$

$$K_{36} = \frac{-ct^2}{12L^2} + \frac{cbt^2 \sin^2 \phi}{12} + \frac{ca}{4}$$

where        $E_1, E_2$ = Young's moduli in meridional and circumferential directions

$\quad\quad\quad\quad v_1$ = Poisson's ratio in meridional direction

$\quad\quad\quad\quad v_2 = v_1 E_2 / E_1$

$\quad\quad\quad\quad G$ = transverse-shear modulus

$\quad\quad\quad\quad a = 5G(1 - v_1 v_2)/6E_1$

$\quad\quad\quad\quad b = E_2/4E_1 r^2$

$\quad\quad\quad\quad c = 2\pi r L E_1 t/(1 - v_1 v_2)$

The above stiffness matrix can also be used in plane problems such as deep beams, arches, and frames, in which case

$$E_2 = 0 \quad\quad r = \frac{\bar{b}}{2\pi}$$

where $\bar{b}$ is the width of the rectangular cross section.

The derivation of stiffness matrices for general thin-shell elements with single or double curvature requires a vigorous procedure. Those resulting from surface of revolutions are presented in Sec. 4.6 in Part 2. For thick shells, the practitioner often uses 3D solid elements. A catalog of general shell elements can be found in Sec. 4.8 of Part 2.

## 1.4 FINITE-ELEMENT ANALYSIS OF 3D SOLIDS

Discretization of 3D solids is often done using tetrahedral and hexahedral elements (refer to Fig. 1.8). The compatibilities among these elements are usually assumed to satisfy displacements but not derivatives (pin-connected nodes). A basic tetrahedron with linear approximations for $u$, $v$, $w$ and without any internal or interface nodes, therefore, has a total of 12 degrees of freedom. Primary matrices for tetrahedra can be obtained from plane-stress problems by introducing an additional dimension in the $z$-direction.

$$\tilde{u} = c_1 + c_2 x + c_3 y + c_4 z$$

$$\tilde{v} = c_5 + c_6 x + c_7 y + c_8 z$$

$$\tilde{w} = c_9 + c_{10} x + c_{11} y + c_{12} z$$

The strain-displacement relationship is

$$\varepsilon_{ij} = \frac{1}{2} \left( \frac{\partial \tilde{u}_i}{\partial x_j} + \frac{\partial \tilde{u}_j}{\partial x_i} \right) \qquad i, j = x, y, z$$

For isotropic materials, matrix $\mathbf{D}$ is

$$\mathbf{D} = \frac{E}{(1+\nu)e_2} \begin{bmatrix} e_1 & \nu & \nu & 0 & 0 & 0 \\ & e_1 & \nu & 0 & 0 & 0 \\ & & e_1 & 0 & 0 & 0 \\ & & & e_3 & 0 & 0 \\ & & & & e_3 & 0 \\ & & & & & e_3 \end{bmatrix}$$

where

$$e_1 = 1 - \nu \qquad e_2 = 1 - 2\nu, \qquad e_3 = \frac{e_2}{2}$$

With the orientation of local coordinate system and the sequence of displacement components as shown below,

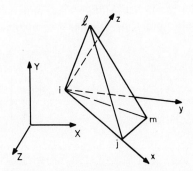

matrix $\mathbf{b}^{-1}$ (the shape matrix) becomes

$$
\begin{bmatrix} u_i \\ u_j \\ u_m \\ u_l \\ v_i \\ v_j \\ v_m \\ v_l \\ w_i \\ w_j \\ w_m \\ w_l \end{bmatrix} = \begin{bmatrix} \begin{bmatrix} 1 & 0 & 0 & 0 \\ 1 & x_j & 0 & 0 \\ 1 & x_m & y_m & 0 \\ 1 & x_l & y_l & z_l \end{bmatrix} & & 0 \\ & \begin{bmatrix} \text{Same} \end{bmatrix} & \\ & 0 & \begin{bmatrix} \text{Same} \end{bmatrix} \end{bmatrix} \begin{bmatrix} c_1 \\ c_2 \\ c_3 \\ c_4 \\ \vdots \\ \\ \\ \\ \\ \\ c_{12} \end{bmatrix}
$$

The shape function as usual is

$$ N(x, y, z) = \mathbf{\phi}(x, y, z)\mathbf{b} $$

where $\mathbf{\phi}$ is the approximate function for displacements; see Fig. 3.7 in Part 2.

From here on, the procedure is similar to that presented in Sec. 1.2 for plane-stress problems. Attention in this case, however, must be paid to the orientation of the local coordinate axes and to the coordinate transformations. Similarly, stress and strain calculations eventually require evaluation of the principal directions.

A basic *hexahedron* has 24 degrees of freedom. Cubic and brick elements are special types of hexahedrons and are frequently used in finite-element analysis of 3D solids. Table 4.3 in Part 2 lists commonly used elements.

## 1.4A Axisymmetric Solids

Problems involving axisymmetric solids are very common in practice and are similar to plane-stress problems. While out-of-plane stresses are zero in plane-stress problems, they are constant in axisymmetric-solids problems. The linear approximations for displacements are

$$
\begin{bmatrix} \tilde{u} \\ \tilde{v} \end{bmatrix} = \begin{bmatrix} 1 & r & y & 0 & 0 & 0 \\ 0 & 0 & 0 & 1 & r & y \end{bmatrix} \begin{bmatrix} c_1 \\ c_2 \\ \vdots \\ c_6 \end{bmatrix}
$$

where $r$ indicates the distance to the origin of the element coordinate axes from the axis of rotation. The strain vector is

$$
\boldsymbol{\varepsilon} =
\begin{bmatrix} \varepsilon_r \\ \varepsilon_y \\ \varepsilon_\theta \\ \gamma_{ry} \end{bmatrix}
=
\begin{bmatrix} \dfrac{\partial u}{\partial r} \\[6pt] \dfrac{\partial v}{\partial y} \\[6pt] \dfrac{u}{r} \\[6pt] \dfrac{\partial u}{\partial y} + \dfrac{\partial v}{\partial r} \end{bmatrix}
=
\begin{bmatrix}
0 & 1 & 0 & 0 & 0 & 0 \\
0 & 0 & 0 & 0 & 0 & 1 \\
\dfrac{1}{r} & 1 & \dfrac{-y}{r} & 0 & 0 & 0 \\
0 & 0 & 1 & 0 & 1 & 0
\end{bmatrix}
\begin{bmatrix} c_1 \\ c_2 \\ c_3 \\ c_4 \\ c_5 \\ c_6 \end{bmatrix}
$$

or, in short,

$$ \boldsymbol{\varepsilon} = \mathbf{d}\mathbf{c} $$

For isotropic and linearly elastic material, the matrix $\mathbf{D}$ is

$$
\mathbf{D} = \frac{E}{(1+\nu)(1-2\nu)}
\begin{bmatrix}
1-\nu & \nu & \nu & 0 \\
\nu & 1-\nu & \nu & 0 \\
\nu & \nu & 1-\nu & 0 \\
0 & 0 & 0 & \dfrac{1-2\nu}{2}
\end{bmatrix}
$$

The stiffness for an element which, in this case, is a ring with triangular cross section becomes

$$ \mathbf{k}_e = 2\pi \int_A \mathbf{B}^T \mathbf{D} \mathbf{B} r \, dA $$

where

$$
\mathbf{B} = \frac{1}{2A}
\begin{bmatrix}
0 & c_i & 0 & c_j & 0 & c_m \\
b_i & 0 & b_j & 0 & b_m & 0 \\
d_i & 0 & d_j & 0 & d_m & 0 \\
c_i & b_i & c_j & b_j & c_m & b_m
\end{bmatrix}
$$

and

$$ a_i = r_j z_m - r_m z_j $$
$$ b_i = z_j - z_m $$
$$ c_i = r_m - r_j $$
$$ d_i = a_i/r + b_i + c_i z/r \qquad \text{etc., in cyclic order} $$
$$ A = \text{cross-sectional area of the triangular ring element} $$

Table 4.7 in Part 2 lists various axisymmetric solid elements. These elements are often used for the analysis of thick shells of revolution. The following section demonstrates the application of the finite-element method to various problems involving 3D solids.

## 1.5 *h*- AND *p*-VERSION OF FEM MODELS IN SOLIDS

In this section some practical aspects of finite-element analysis of three-dimensional solids are reviewed with emphasis on static, linearly elastic systems.

### 1.5A Mesh Design†

In conventional finite-element computer models, the finite-element mesh must satisfy three requirements: (1) the essential geometrical details of the object to be modeled must be represented; (2) the element size $h$ must be sufficiently small to keep the error of approximation within acceptable bounds; (3) the aspect ratios of elements must be close to 1 in order to avoid degradation of their numerical performance. Taken together, these requirements can create formidable practical problems which, even when advanced mesh generators are available, impose serious limitations on the usefulness of three-dimensional models in engineering practice. For example, a conventional finite-element modeling of part of a gear case shown in Fig. 1.3 is done using an automatic mesh generator FASTDRAW. However, matching of element faces and nodal coordinates at the interfaces of the subdomains and verification of the topological data had to be performed manually. In two-dimensional analysis, it is practical to grade finite-element meshes so that fine meshes are used only where the stresses change very rapidly, such as at reentrant corners. In the three-dimensional case, mesh grading is a far more difficult task, and topological constraints usually force the analyst to use fine meshes over the entire domain if a fine mesh is required over one or more subdomains.

Relatively recent developments in finite-element technology have made it possible to control the error of approximation through the addition of polynomial shape functions (basis functions) of progressively increasing degree $p$. This approach to controlling the error of approximation is called the *p-version* of the finite-element method. A description of some hierarchical sequences of shape functions is presented in Sec. 6.4 of Part 2. The conventional approach to controlling the error of approximation by the size of the elements $h$ is called the *h-version* of the finite-element method.

One of the most important benefits provided by the $p$-version is a substantial simplification in model construction. For example, the gear-case model, pictured in Fig. 1.3, was reanalyzed by a $p$-version computer code, FIESTA, which resulted in a substantial reduction in the number of elements (Fig. 1.4). The required input data are the same for both models. With the $p$-version, however, the analyst is not required to match element faces and nodal coordinates at the interfaces. The importance of the $p$-version will continue to increase in engineering practice, particularly in the area of three-dimensional analysis.

### 1.5B Control of the Error of Approximation‡

Finite-element codes based on the displacement formulation produce an approximate solution which minimizes the error in strain energy or, more precisely, the error measured in the energy norm [11, 12]. The error of approximation measured in the energy norm is very closely

---

† See also Sec. 8.2 in Part 3.

‡ See also Sec. 8.1 in Part 3.

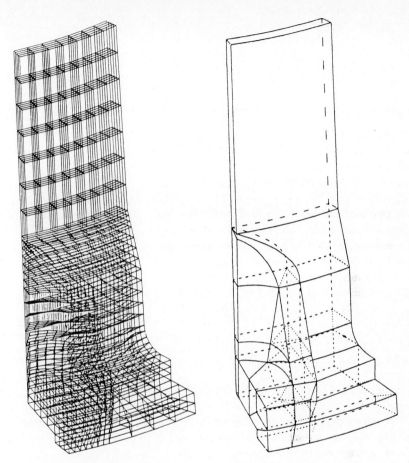

**FIG. 1.3**  Conventional finite-element model of part of a gear case.

**FIG. 1.4**  *p*-Version finite-element model of the gear case shown in Fig. 1.3.

related to the root-mean-square error in stresses. The energy norm and the root-mean-square measure of stresses are equivalent [13].

The degree of difficulty associated with achieving a given level of precision in the energy norm or in the root-mean-square measure of stresses, for example, 5% relative error, depends on the characteristics of the problem to be solved [14].

Most finite-element models of practical problems contain singularities; thus, their solution is not smooth. In structural mechanics the smoothness of the solution is determined by the presence of reentrant corners and edges, the way in which boundary conditions are specified, and the occurrence of sudden changes in material properties and loading. Of these, reentrant corners are the most commonly occurring sources of difficulty in practical analyses.

Characterization of reentrant corners in two-dimensional elasticity with respect to smoothness has been available since 1952 [15]. The essential features of the solutions of three-dimensional solids as reentrant edges are similar.

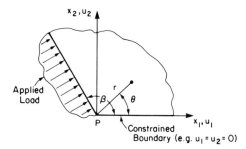

**FIG. 1.5** Typical section of a three-dimensional
body normal to an edge (*P*).

As an example, consider a section of a 3D body (Fig. 1.5) where the strain component in the direction of the edge is negligible, that is, $\varepsilon_3 = 0$.

The functional form of the exact solution in the immediate neighborhood of the edge $P$ in terms of polar coordinates $(r, \theta)$ centered on $P$ is

$$u = r^\mu F(\theta) + G(r, \theta) \tag{1.5}$$

in which $u = \{u_1, u_2\}^T$, $F$ and $G$ are smooth functions, and $\mu$ is a positive number (for homogeneous isotropic solids $\mu \geq \frac{1}{4}$) which depends on the angle $\beta$, the boundary conditions imposed on the planes intersecting at $P$, and Poisson's ratio $\nu$. The smoothness of $u$ is quantified by $\mu$. The greater $\mu$ is, the smoother the solution. By definition,

$$\mu = \min \operatorname{Re}(\lambda) \tag{1.6}$$

in which $\lambda$ is an eigenvalue determined from the condition that the exact solution must satisfy the governing differential equations and the boundary conditions in the vicinity of $P$ [15].

The root-mean-square (RMS) measure of stresses is defined as follows:

$$S(\sigma) = \sqrt{\frac{1}{V} \int_V [\sigma_x^2 + \sigma_y^2 + \sigma_z^2 + \tau_{xy}^2 + \tau_{yz}^2 + \tau_{zx}^2] \, dV} \tag{1.7}$$

where $V$ represents the volume of the entire three-dimensional model. The relative error in the RMS measure of stress is then

$$(e_r)_S = \frac{S(\sigma_{EX} - \sigma_{FE})}{S(\sigma_{EX})} \tag{1.8}$$

where $\sigma_{EX}$ is the stress field of the exact solution and $\sigma_{FE}$ is the stress field of the finite-element solution.

Theorems exist which establish relationships among $(e_r)_S$, the number of degrees of freedom $N$, the parameter $\mu$, and the degree of the polynomial basis functions. A schematic representation of two such relationships is given in Fig. 1.6.

The results of a typical case study are shown in Fig. 1.7. A short cantilever beam was analyzed under the assumptions of plane-strain conditions and Poisson's ratio $\nu = 0.3$. The initial mesh is shown in the inset of Fig. 1.7. Singularities occur at the intersections of the

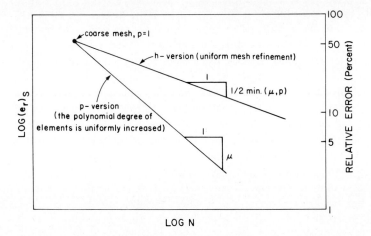

**FIG. 1.6**  Schematic respresentation of the asymptotic rates of convergence of the *h*-version (uniform mesh refinement) and the *p*-version (uniform *p*-distribution).

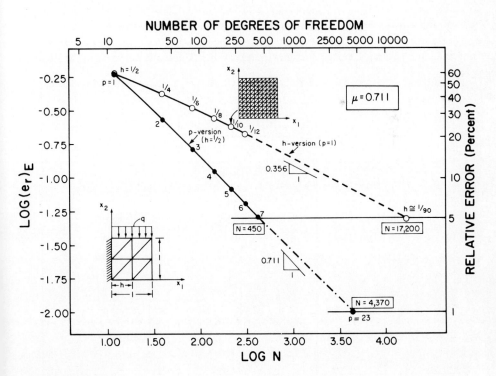

**FIG. 1.7**  Short cantilever problem, plane strain, $\mu = 3$. Relative error in energy norm versus number of degrees of freedom.

constrained face with the top and bottom surfaces of the cantilever. The value of the parameter $\mu$ is 0.711 [15]. In this case the relative error in the energy norm, $(e_r)_E$, rather than $(e_r)_S$, is plotted against $N$; however, $(e_r)_S$ is approximately the same as $(e_r)_E$.

It is of course good practice to use fine meshes only in the vicinity of singularities. With such meshes $(e_r)_E$ corresponding to a given $N$ is generally smaller than in the case of uniform meshes for both the $h$- and $p$-versions, but the asymptotic rates of convergence remain the same. There is one important exception, however: if the sequence of meshes is designed in such a way that the error contribution of each element to the total error of approximation is approximately the same, then the asymptotic rate of convergence depends only on the polynomial order of the elements rather than on the parameter $\mu$, and it can be made arbitrarily large simply by the selection of sufficiently large $p$ [16].

In addition to its higher rate of convergence and lesser sensitivity to mesh design, the $p$-version has two further advantages: it makes visualization of the convergence process feasible in practical analyses and it is more robust than the $h$-version [14]. For example, Poisson's ratio as large as 0.4999 will not noticeably downgrade the performance of $p$-version models. Also, large aspect ratios of finite elements are permissible in the case of the $p$-version.

## 1.5c Element Shapes

A rich variety of element shapes can be developed in three dimensions. The most commonly used elements are *hexahedra, pentahedra,* and *tetrahedra.* Other shapes, such as *pyramids, chisels,* and *anvils* (Fig. 1.8), are also available in some computer codes.

There is an important difference between hexahedra, tetrahedra, and pentahedra on the one hand and pyramids, chisels, and anvils on the other. The shape functions of the standard

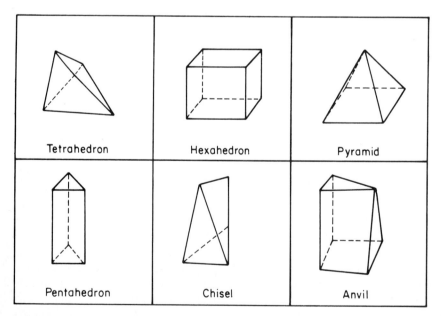

| Tetrahedron | Hexahedron | Pyramid |
| Pentahedron | Chisel | Anvil |

**FIG. 1.8**   Standard finite elements in three-dimensional analysis.

elements in the second group contain rational functions unless the polynomial degree of the elements is 1 [19, 20]. The shape functions for the standard pyramid and anvil elements are generated from the shape functions of the standard hexahedral element by assigning the same nodal coordinates to more than one node. The shape functions for the standard chisel element are generated from the shape functions of the standard pentahedron. These, in turn, introduce singularities into the quadratic and higher-order shape functions which tend to downgrade the numerical performance of these elements. More precisely, when the shape functions are not polynomials, then the performance of an element can be strongly problem-dependent. For this reason, pyramid, chisel, and anvil elements should be used with caution; the element sizes should be small so as to minimize the importance of quadratic and higher-order shape functions.

## 1.5D Stress Approximations

In many practical problems, reentrant edges and corners, abrupt changes in material properties, boundary conditions, and loading occur; consequently, the stress components computed by the theory of elasticity are infinite at one or more points. If one takes into account the fact that corners are rounded and constraints are smoothly changing, then the computed stresses will be finite. In three-dimensional finite-element models, the computed stress values are extremely sensitive to corner radii, which are very difficult to control within narrow bounds in practice.

One of two goals is usually set. The first is the determination of stress resultants (moments, shear forces) on certain sections deemed critical by the analyst. The second approach is to consider an asymptotic expansion of the stress field at the singularity. In this case, the functional form of the stress field is obtained from homogeneous solution terms of the Navier equations which satisfy the appropriate boundary conditions in the vicinity of singular points [15].

Both approaches avoid the conceptual and practical difficulties of having to deal with pointwise stress values in the neighborhood of singular points. There is an added benefit: it is much simpler to compute stress resultants and stress-intensity factors to a given level of precision than pointwise stresses.

The first and still most widely used approach to finite-element modeling of solids is based on linear displacement approximation. In this case, the state of stress within the element is constant. In the case of quadratic shape functions, the stress components vary linearly within the elements. Many computer codes will provide only the state of stress at the centroid of the standard element and report average stresses at nodes, i.e., the average of stresses computed for those elements which share the nodal point. This practice hides from the analyst the fact that the stress field computed by the finite-element method is discontinuous and provides a more pleasing, although less accurate, picture of the computed stress field. Unfortunately, true-stress concentrations are underestimated by averaging.

In the case of singular stress fields, the maximum stress increases with the polynomial degree and the computed stresses oscillate about their true value in those elements which have edges, vertices, faces, or interior points containing the stress singularity. The reason for this is that the oscillatory behavior of stresses at singular points yields the best approximation in the energy norm. This oscillatory behavior of stresses is the reason for the faster rate of convergence of the *p*-version in the energy norm and RMS stress norm, as illustrated in Fig. 1.6. It is important to remember that a finite-element model based on the displacement formulation will minimize the error in the energy norm only. The error of the finite-element solution measured in any other norm may not be small. Techniques exist, however, for the extraction of any functional value, for example, stress-intensity factors, stresses or displacements at any given point, stress resultants with precision comparable to that of the computed strain energy [21–23].

## 1.5E Examples

The following problems were solved by the Experimental Institute for Models and Structures (ISMES) in Bergamo, Italy, on a VAX 11/780 computer, by means of the *p*-version finite-element program FIESTA.

***Analysis of a Valve Body***    The purpose of this analysis is to understand the effect of certain changes in the dimensions of the valve body on the stress distribution. The finite-element mesh layout is shown in Fig. 1.9. The mesh is typical for *p*-version finite-element analysis; the number of elements is governed by the geometry of the model. The complexities of three-dimensional mesh design require the use of pentahedral elements at regions *A* and *B*. Note that large aspect ratios are permissible in the *p*-version finite-element method.

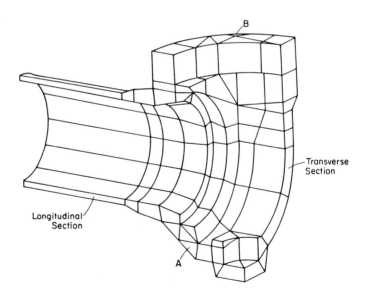

**FIG. 1.9**    *p*-version finite-element model of a valve-body.

The material is assumed to be linearly elastic and loading is 100 lb/in$^2$ internal pressure.
   Typical stress data are shown in Figs. 1.10 and 1.11. The contours represent octahedral shear stresses for polynomial degrees 3 and 4. Note that in those regions where there are no reentrant edges, or the reentrant edges are not highly stressed, the stress contours are smooth

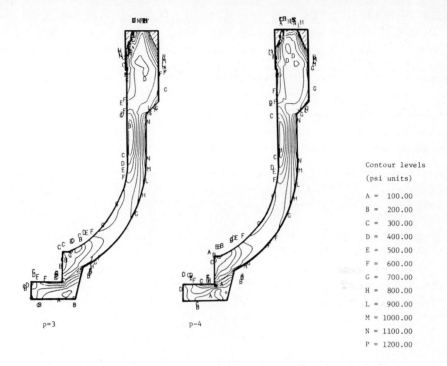

Contour levels
(psi units)

A =   100.00
B =   200.00
C =   300.00
D =   400.00
E =   500.00
F =   600.00
G =   700.00
H =   800.00
L =   900.00
M =  1000.00
N =  1100.00
P =  1200.00

**FIG. 1.10** Octahedral shear-stress contours on transverse section of a valve body.

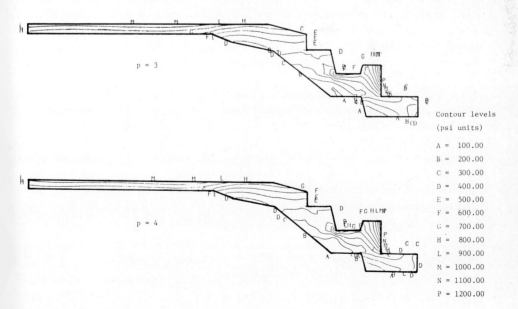

Contour levels
(psi units)

A =   100.00
B =   200.00
C =   300.00
D =   400.00
E =   500.00
F =   600.00
G =   700.00
H =   800.00
L =   900.00
M =  1000.00
N =  1100.00
P =  1200.00

**FIG. 1.11** Octahedral shear-stress contours on longitudinal section of a valve body.

and there is virtually no change in the stress distribution as the polynomial degree $p$ is increased from 3 to 4. In the immediate vicinity of highly stressed reentrant edges, on the other hand, a substantial increase in stress levels is evident as $p$ is increased from 3 to 4. Note that, given the geometric complexities of this model, accounting for roundedness of reentrant corners or edges would not be practicable.

***Analysis of an Elbow Pipe***   The purpose of the analysis is to validate design formulas for various diameter/thickness ratios in elbow pipes fabricated from segments of straight pipes. The pipe is modeled by three-dimensional finite elements as shown in Fig. 1.12. Although

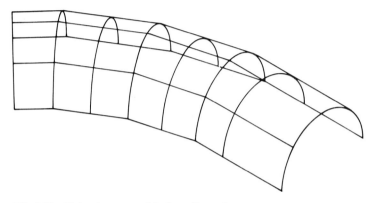

**FIG. 1.12**   Finite-element model of an elbow pipe.

the individual pipe segments are in fact thin shells, the usual assumptions of thin-shell theories are violated at the lines of intersection. The three-dimensional model is constructed to provide for proper evaluation of the stress states in the vicinity of the welded joints. In this sense, the problem is typical of many shell-intersection problems: at the intersections that are usually of greatest interest to analysts, the stress state is truly three-dimensional and the assumptions of shell theories are violated.

The three-dimensional model provides a basis for the assessment of errors caused by violations of the assumptions of various shell theories. In this case it is very advantageous to use elements with large aspect ratios, which are permissible when high-order elements are used.

The material is assumed to be linearly elastic and loading is 100 lb/in² internal pressure. Typical stress data are shown in Fig. 1.13. The contours of the octahedral shear stress computed for the external surface are illustrated. The polynomial degree of elements is 4. Note mild stress concentrations at the welded joints.

## 1.6 FINITE-ELEMENT ANALYSIS OF FRACTURE MECHANICS PROBLEMS

In this section, fracture-mechanics parameters will first be reviewed briefly and some interpretation of their physical significance will be given. Subsequently, the main portion of this

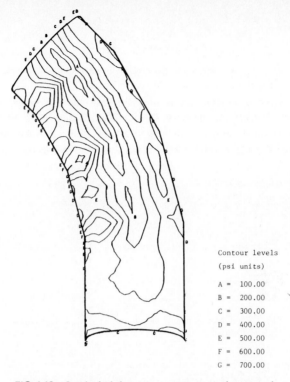

Contour levels
(psi units)

A =  100.00
B =  200.00
C =  300.00
D =  400.00
E =  500.00
F =  600.00
G =  700.00

**FIG. 1.13**  Octahedral shear-stress contours on the external surface of an elbow pipe.

section will discuss how the finite-element method can be applied to calculate these parameters. Finally, a number of examples will be used to demonstrate the techniques discussed.

## 1.6A Review of Fracture Mechanics

If the existence of a crack is postulated in a linear-elastic structure, the stress field in the vicinity of the crack tip has a specific form characterized by three parameters. These parameters are called the *stress-intensity factors* and are often identified as $K_I$, $K_{II}$, and $K_{III}$. The displacement and stress solutions are

$$u_i = K_I \sqrt{\frac{r}{2\pi}}\, f_i^I(\theta) + K_{II} \sqrt{\frac{r}{2\pi}}\, f_i^{II}(\theta) + K_{III} \sqrt{\frac{r}{2\pi}}\, f_i^{III}(\theta) \qquad (1.9a)$$

$$\sigma_{ij} = \frac{K_I}{\sqrt{2\pi r}} g_{ij}^I(\theta) + \frac{K_{II}}{\sqrt{2\pi r}} g_{ij}^{II}(\theta) + \frac{K_{III}}{\sqrt{2\pi r}} g_{ij}^{III} \qquad (1.9b)$$

Here, the coordinates $r$ and $\theta$ describe the position of a point relative to the crack tip, as shown in Fig. 1.14.

**FIG. 1.14**  Crack-tip coordinates.

The solutions $f_i$ and $g_{ij}$ correspond to three different modes of crack opening, as shown in Fig. 1.15. Mode I describes the opening of the crack due to applied tension loading perpendicular to the crack faces (*tensile mode*). Mode II describes the solution around the crack due to shear loading parallel to the crack faces but perpendicular to the crack tip (*plane-shear mode*), and mode III does the same but for shear loading parallel to crack faces and crack tip (*antiplane-shear mode*).

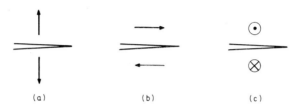

(a)                          (b)                          (c)

**FIG. 1.15**  Different crack loading types: (*a*) Mode I. (*b*) Mode II. (*c*) Mode III.

The stress-intensity factors not only describe the displacement and stress field in the vicinity of the crack tip, but also determine the *elastic-energy release rate G* associated with the crack. This *elastic-energy release rate* is the rate at which elastic energy is released from the structure as the crack grows parallel to itself if no work is done by applied loadings. This is the case if the stresses are induced by fixed kinematic constraints only. The relation between the $K$ factors and $G$ is

$$G = \frac{1-\nu^2}{E}(K_I^2 + K_{II}^2) + \frac{1}{E}K_{III}^2 \qquad (1.10)$$

In more general loading situations, $G$ is equal to the decrease in potential energy of the structure due to crack propagation.

$$G = -\frac{d\Pi}{dl} \qquad \Pi = \int_V w\,dV - \int_S P_i u_i\,dS \qquad (1.11)$$

where $l$ is the crack length and $w$ is the elastic-energy density.

For brittle materials, unstable crack propagation will occur if the energy-release rate is equal to the energy needed to create the free surface associated with the crack. This criterion is approximately valid for materials such as glass, but for the usual structural materials such as steel, the effects of plasticity need to be taken into account.

For many structural materials *critical-stress-intensity factors* $K_{I_C}$, $K_{II_C}$, and $K_{III_C}$ have been established which can be used as criteria for crack growth. Rules for crack growth under cyclic loading conditions have been developed which are based on average and alternating values of the stress-intensity factors. However, if the material is very ductile, this approach breaks down. In that case the plastic zone may grow to such a large size that the elastic solution disappears completely. Asymptotic solutions were obtained by Hutchinson [24] and Rice and Rosengren [25] for materials with power-law hardening. If the shear stress varies with the shear strain according to $\tau \sim \gamma^N$, the stress field has the characteristic form

$$\sigma_{ij} \sim r^{-N/(1+N)} G_{ij}(\theta_{ij} N) \tag{1.12}$$

Obviously, for $N = 1$, this reduces to the linear-elastic solution. An interesting case occurs when $N \to 0$ (a perfectly plastic material): the singularity in the stress vanishes. It can be established that this solution reduces to the solution for the Prandtl punch problem, which is shown in Fig. 1.16.

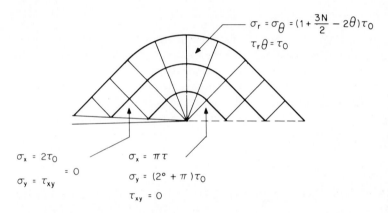

$$\sigma_r = \sigma_\theta = (1 + \frac{3N}{2} - 2\theta)\tau_0$$
$$\tau_r\theta = \tau_0$$

$$\sigma_x = 2\tau_0$$
$$\sigma_y = \tau_{xy} = 0$$

$$\sigma_x = \pi\tau$$
$$\sigma_y = (2° + \pi)\tau_0$$
$$\tau_{xy} = 0$$

**FIG. 1.16**   Prandtl plastic solution.

Note that in the Prandtl solution, the strain field has a $1/r$ singularity, which means that the velocity at the crack tip is nonunique. To deal with these strongly nonlinear problems, Rice proposed the use of the $J$-integral [26]. This integral is defined for nonlinear-elastic materials in terms of a contour $\Gamma$ which begins on the lower crack surface and ends on the upper one and has the form

$$J = \int_\Gamma \left[ w(\varepsilon)n_1 - \mathbf{n} \cdot \boldsymbol{\sigma} \cdot \frac{\partial \mathbf{u}}{\partial x_1} \right] d\Gamma \tag{1.13}$$

where $w$ is the elastic-energy density, $\mathbf{n}$ is the outward unit normal to the contour, and $n_1$ is the component of the normal in the $x_1$-direction; see Fig. 1.17.

For elastic materials, this integral is path-independent, and is in fact equal to the elastic-energy-release rate $G$.

For elastic-plastic materials, one can also obtain a $J$-integral by defining

$$W(\varepsilon) = \int_0^\varepsilon \sigma_{ij}\, d\varepsilon_{ij} \tag{1.14}$$

along the actual loading path. In this case, the $J$-integral is no longer strictly path-independent.

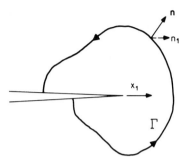

**FIG. 1.17**   *J*-integral.

However, numerical calculations [27] have shown that for most practical cases the deviations are no more than a few percent, even if the contour is completely within the plastic zone.

Because of the approximate path independence, it has been postulated that a criterion for the onset of crack growth can be stated in terms of attainment of a critical value $J_c$ [28, 29]. Experimental evidence indeed indicates that this is the case, provided that certain minimum specimen dimensions are exceeded. *Hence accurate evaluation of J is an important objective in analysis of nonlinear fracture-mechanics problems.*

The elastic-plastic approach as shown above has its limits. In particular, because of the singularity in the strain field, blunting of the crack tip occurs. Numerical studies indicate that the *J*-integral remains approximately path-independent if the contour is not too close to the tip [30]. If the size of the contour is less than 4 to 5 times the opening of the blunted crack tip, the *J*-integral seems to lose its significance.

Most studies in fracture mechanics deal with stationary cracks. However, it has been observed that in elastic-plastic situations the onset of cracking does not coincide with final fracture instability. As yet, no successful criteria have been established to characterize this instable growth. The absence of good criteria is caused by the difficulties in obtaining accurate numerical solutions as well as by the limited availability of plasticity models for complex nonproportional loading. Hence, in this section, we focus on finite-element analysis of stationary cracks.

### 1.6B  Finite-Element Analysis Procedures

The principal objective of the analysis of fracture-mechanics problems is the calculation of appropriate fracture-mechanics parameter(s) such as stress-intensity factor(s), energy-release rate, and/or *J*-integral. These parameters can be calculated in a variety of ways. Methods that have often been applied are described below.

***The Direct Method***   With the direct method, the fracture-mechanics parameters are determined directly from the stress, strain, and displacement fields in the vicinity of the crack tip. In order to obtain an accurate solution, a very fine mesh is needed near the crack tip, which makes the method rather expensive to use.

***The Superposition Method***   With the superposition method, the appropriate singular expression is superimposed on a conventional finite-element mesh. This expression does not satisfy all boundary conditions of the actual problem, and the disparities in loading are applied to the finite-element model. This method was originally developed for elastic problems [31] and has recently been extended successfully to certain types of nonlinear problems [32].

***The Singular-Element(s) Method***   The singular-element(s) method makes use of "special" elements near the crack tip together with conventional finite elements elsewhere. Originally, a considerable amount of research was carried out to develop such special elements [33]. However, in the mid seventies, it was demonstrated that a very close approximation to the linear-elastic, singular stress field could be obtained with ordinary quadratic isoparametric elements through the use of the so-called quarter-point node technique [34, 35]. In this technique a triangular or collapsed quadrilateral element is used around the crack tip where the nodes on the edges adjacent to the tip are put one-quarter of the edge length away from the tip (see Fig. 1.18a and b).

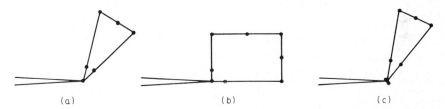

(a)                              (b)                              (c)

FIG. **1.18**   Quarter-point node elements: (a) triangle, (b) quadrilateral, (c) collapsed quadrilateral.

If, in addition, separate nodes are maintained in the collapsed element at the crack tip (Fig. 1.18c), a singularity in the strain field of the type $1/r$ is also present [33]. Hence, the collapsed quarter-point node element is very suitable for elastic-plastic analysis. Reasonably accurate values for the fracture-mechanics parameters can be obtained directly from the solution—the easiest and probably the most accurate values are derived from the crack-front displacements. The quarter-point node technique is readily applied in two- and three-dimensional problems with general-purpose finite-element programs. It has, therefore, gained considerable popularity.

***The J-Integral Method***   The J-integral, which is path-independent, can be evaluated directly from the finite-element solution. Its accurate evaluation requires a somewhat careful selection of the path because of the approximate nature of the finite-element solution. The method has been applied successfully for linear as well as nonlinear fracture-mechanics problems [36].

***The Energy-Release-Rate Method***   A fracture-mechanics parameter of relevance in both linear and nonlinear problems is the energy-release rate. The most obvious (though not the most efficient) way to calculate the energy-release rate consists of solving two finite-element problems with slightly different crack lengths, $l$ and $l + \Delta l$. In both analyses, the potential energy is calculated, and from the difference, the energy-release rate is obtained analogous to Eq. (1.11):

$$G = \frac{-\Delta\Pi}{t\Delta l} \tag{1.15}$$

with $t$ the thickness of the specimen.

Since the method requires at least two finite-element solutions, it takes considerable effort [37]. In addition, if the method is to be applied in nonlinear-elastic or pseudoelastic problems, care has to be taken that both problems are solved with exactly the same accuracy. In principle, the method can be applied in three-dimensional problems if the crack front is advanced over a certain distance $s$, in which case Eq. (1.15) transforms to the average value of the release rate (see Fig. 1.19)

$$G_{av} = \frac{-\Delta\Pi}{\displaystyle\int \Delta l(s)\, ds} \tag{1.16}$$

Multiple analyses would be necessary to obtain the energy-release-rate distribution along the crack front, but the cost of these would usually be prohibitively high.

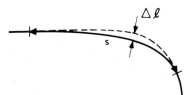

**FIG. 1.19**   Crack-front advance.

***Stiffness-Derivative Method***   With the stiffness-derivative method, the energy-release rate is evaluated directly in a single finite-element analysis by advancing the crack tip or crack front a small amount after each analysis. This changes the stiffness of some of the elements in the mesh. The change in potential energy can be calculated as follows [38].

$$\Delta\Pi = \tfrac{1}{2}\mathbf{u}^T \Delta\mathbf{K}\mathbf{u} + (\mathbf{u}^T\mathbf{K} - \mathbf{P}^T)\,\Delta\mathbf{u} \tag{1.17}$$

Several values of $\Delta\Pi$ can be obtained in one analysis by using different methods to advance the crack tip (see Fig. 1.20).

In Fig. 1.20a, only the crack tip is moved, causing changes in shape in the elements adjacent to the crack tip. In Fig. 1.20b, the complete inner ring of elements is moved, causing shape changes in the second ring of elements, whereas in Fig. 3.1.20c, the third ring of elements is changed in shape.

The method is very suitable for three-dimensional problems since the crack can be advanced in multiple ways all within one analysis. For nonlinear problems (elastic or pseudoelastic), the method can also be applied successfully [39]. The energy in an element can be written as

$$W = \sum_n A_n W_n = \sum_n A_n \int_0^{u_i} \boldsymbol{\sigma}_n \cdot \boldsymbol{\beta}_n^i \, du_i \tag{1.18}$$

where $A_n$ is the weight factor for integration point $n$ in the element. A change in shape of

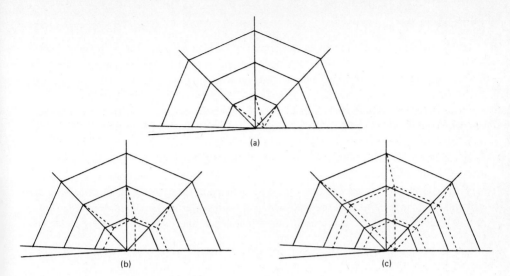

**FIG. 1.20** Three stiffness-derivative schemes.

the element in the final state yields the energy difference:

$$\Delta W = \sum_n [\Delta A_n W_n + A_n \boldsymbol{\sigma}_n \cdot \Delta \boldsymbol{\beta}_n^i u_i] \tag{1.19}$$

This expression strongly resembles Eq. (1.13) for the $J$-integral, and, in fact, in the limit of an infinitely narrow band of elements, it reduces to the $J$-integral. The stiffness-derivative technique is definitely the most efficient method for estimating fracture-mechanics parameters in both linear and nonlinear problems. When it is combined with a special element technique, such as the quarter-point node technique, it yields extremely accurate results without substantial mesh refinement. The method has been implemented in several general-purpose finite-element programs.

These methods are applicable only for the analysis of stationary cracks. To date, no efficient methods have been devised for the analysis of propagating cracks. Some methods employ finer meshes in the vicinity of the crack tip and propagate the crack tip by release of boundary conditions (Fig. 1.21).

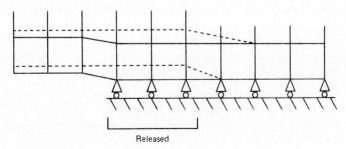

Released

**FIG. 1.21** Simulation of crack propagation.

## 1.6c Examples

A simple example of the use of quarter-point node elements and the stiffness-derivative technique is shown in Fig. 1.22 [40]. A double-edge notched (DEN) specimen is analyzed linearly. One-quarter of the specimen is modeled with only 20 ordinary eight-node quadrilateral elements. The quarter-point node technique is used near the crack tip, and the stiffness-derivative technique is used to obtain the energy-release rate with three different evaluations. From these values the $K_I$ factors are calculated with use of Eq. (1.10). The calculated and the exact values are shown in Fig. 1.22.

A more complicated problem is shown in Fig. 1.23. Here, a three-dimensional analysis is made of a single-edge notched band (SENB) specimen with nonlinear material properties [41]. In order to save computational cost, only the vicinity of the crack is modeled with 3D elements. For the remainder of the specimen, plane-stress elements are employed. The values of the $J$-integral along the crack front for various load values are shown in Fig. 1.24. The

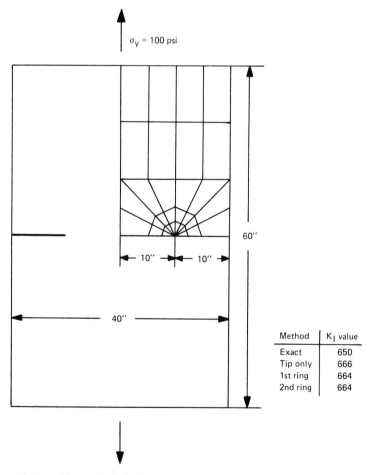

$\sigma_y = 100$ psi

60″

10″   10″

40″

| Method | $K_I$ value |
|---|---|
| Exact | 650 |
| Tip only | 666 |
| 1st ring | 664 |
| 2nd ring | 664 |

**FIG. 1.22**  Linear-elastic DEN specimen.

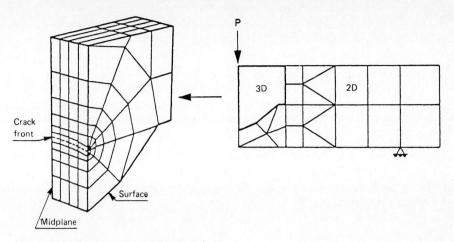

**FIG. 1.23**   Three-dimensional SENB specimen.

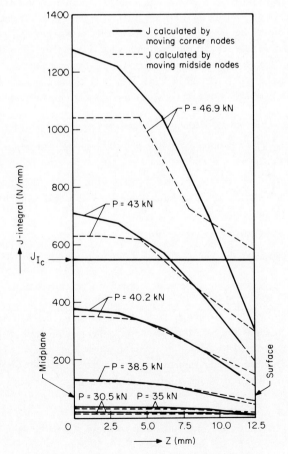

**FIG. 1.24**   *J*-integral distribution in SENB specimen.

stiffness-derivative method is used in combination with the collapsed-element quarter-point node technique to obtain the *J*-integral values, and the crack front is advanced by moving individual nodes on the crack front.

Note that there is a certain difference between moving the midside nodes or the corner nodes of the 20-node brick elements used in this analysis, particularly for the higher loads. The distortion of the elements causes additional error in the (pseudo)potential energy, which adds to the energy release due to crack propagation. Nevertheless, a good impression of the *J*-integral distribution is obtained.

## 1.7 FINITE-ELEMENT ANALYSIS OF PROJECTILE IMPACT RESPONSE

### 1.7A Definition of Problem

Projectiles are often required to survive target impact with minimal structural damage. Dynamic, nonlinear finite-element analyses are done to determine deformations and stresses in such projectiles. From this information, an assessment of survivability can be made.

The projectile and target each deform during impact. A complete finite-element treatment requires modeling of both components and their coupling at an interface. A simplified *two-part analysis technique* has been developed which involves finite-element modeling of the projectile only. This approach has several advantages over the more complete treatment:

1. The problem size can be greatly reduced because the target material need not be modeled.
2. Alternatively, for a given problem size, the projectile model can be more detailed, thus giving better resolution.
3. The loading history can be developed from a penetration analysis that incorporates a more accurate theory of material failure and flow than is possible with available finite-element-code material representations.

### 1.7B Loading Histories

Approximate loading histories have been developed for several common projectile-target combinations [42].

In the case of flat-fronted projectiles penetrating into concrete half spaces at normal incidence, loading histories are based on penetration-theory equations derived by Bernard and Creighton [43] preceded by an initial transient. These equations are for conical-nosed projectiles. It has been observed experimentally, however, that conical caps of target material form on the front of blunt projectiles shortly after initial impact and are carried along by the projectiles as they penetrate [44]. The presence of these caps means that all projectiles become effectively conical-nosed during penetration.

In the case of perforation of finite-thickness concrete slabs, the same loadings as for penetration into concrete half spaces can be applied and then truncated at the moment of breakthrough.

In the case of flat-fronted projectiles perforating thin steel plates at normal incidence, loading histories are derived primarily on the basis of the assumption that the forces on the projectile are associated with the acceleration of a punched-out disk of target material up to the speed of the projectile and that the strength of the steel can be neglected. Difficulties have been encountered in finite-element runs using these loadings because the nose of the projectile mushrooms, producing more extreme element distortion than the code can tolerate. Rezoning would be required to continue the solution.

Experimental firings of small projectiles have confirmed that these loading histories yield reasonable results for the deformed shapes of impacting projectiles [42, 45].

## 1.7c  Finite-Element Analysis

Using this two-part technique, an analysis was made of a kinetic-energy warhead penetrating a semi-infinite 10,000 lb/in$^2$ concrete target at 2400 ft/s and normal incidence [46]. A schematic drawing of the warhead is given in Fig. 1.25. The finite-element model of the warhead,

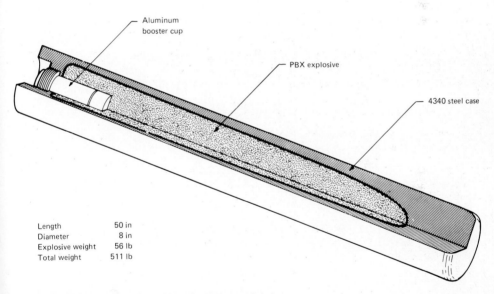

| | |
|---|---|
| Length | 50 in |
| Diameter | 8 in |
| Explosive weight | 56 lb |
| Total weight | 511 lb |

**FIG. 1.25**  Schematic drawing of kinetic-energy warhead.

which contains 1027 quadrilateral elements, is shown in Fig. 1.26. The finite-element analysis was performed using the HONDO code [47]. This program, which was created specifically for the large-deformation dynamic analysis of impulsively loaded solids of revolution, functions entirely in core. Explicit, central-difference time integration is used. The 4340 steel case, the PBX explosive, and the aluminum booster cup were modeled. Property values for these materials are given in Table 1.2.

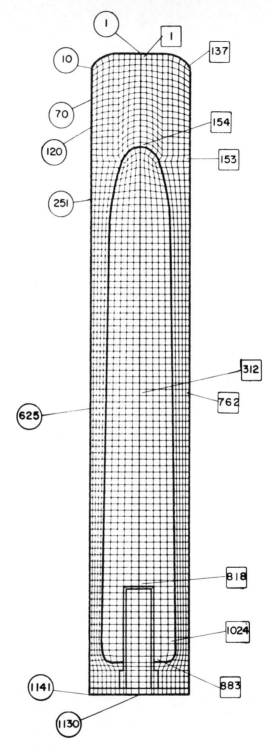

**FIG. 1.26** Finite-element model of warhead.

**TABLE 1.2**  Material Property Values

| Material | Elastic modulus, $\mathrm{lb/in^2} \times 10^6$ | Hardening modulus, $\mathrm{lb/in^2}$ | Poisson's ratio | Yield stress, $\mathrm{lb/in^2}$ | Density, $\mathrm{lb \cdot s^2/in^4}$ |
|---|---|---|---|---|---|
| 4340 steel | 30 | 77,000 | 0.3 | 148,000 | 0.000733 |
| PBX explosive | 1 | .... | 0.34 | .... | 0.000169 |
| Aluminum booster cup | 13 | .... | 0.34 | .... | 0.000246 |

The loading history (force-time curve) to be applied to the front of the warhead to represent the resistance of the target material to penetration is plotted in Fig. 1.27. The warhead was regarded as flat-fronted despite the slight rounding of the corner of the front end. The force was applied in the form of a normal pressure distributed over the front end of the warhead. The exact distribution of this pressure was not known, but was taken to be proportional to the cosine of the angle between the normal to the surface and the axis of the warhead. The resulting distribution is uniform over the flat portion of the front end and decreases on the curved portion near the outer edge. It is likely that near the outer edge of the front end there will be substantial shear stresses, in addition to normal forces.

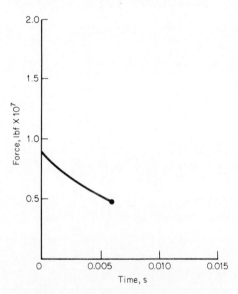

**FIG. 1.27**  Loading history for warhead impact-ing 10,000 $\mathrm{lb/in^2}$ concrete at 2400 ft/s.

A computer analysis using this loading history was made for a time of 1000 microseconds (the time for an elastic disturbance to travel the length of the warhead and back twice). Extensive plotting of output data was used to interpret the results. Plots of displacements and stresses versus time for selected nodes and elements, as well as stress-contour and deformed-structure plots at successive times, were made. Axial-stress contour plots for the steel case during the first 100 microseconds are given in Fig. 1.28. These plots show a compressive stress wave created by the sudden application of pressure over the front end propagating down the length of the warhead. At later times, two-dimensional effects and reflections from the irregular surfaces complicate the stress field so that it is no longer interpretable in one-dimensional terms. Deformed-structure plots for the first 1000 microseconds are shown in Fig. 1.29. A slight bulge in the case a short distance behind the front of the explosive cavity can be seen.

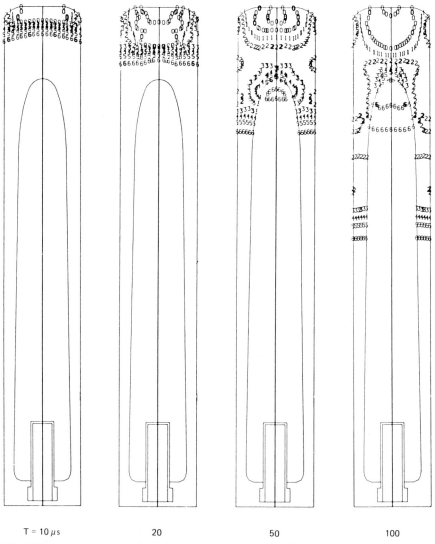

T = 10 μs                20                50                100

**FIG. 1.28**  Axial stress contours in case. Key (values in lb/in²): $0 = -145,000$; $1 = -120,000$; $2 = -95,000$; $3 = -70,000$; $4 = -45,000$; and $5 = -20,000$.

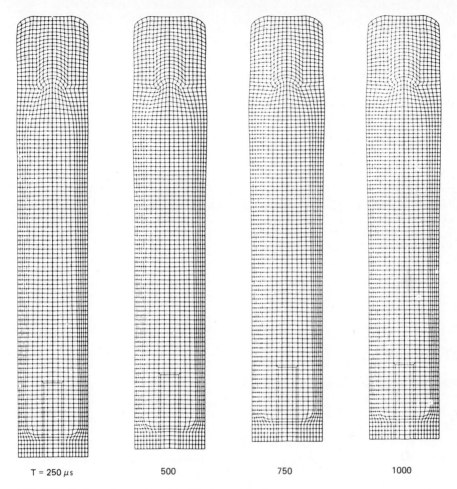

T = 250 $\mu$s            500              750              1000

**FIG. 1.29**  Deformed-structure plots. Displacements × 2.

The results of the analysis indicate that this warhead would survive impact with 10,000-lb/in$^2$ concrete at a 2400-ft/s impact velocity without case failure. About 6.5 ft of concrete would be penetrated. Examination of stress levels in the explosive indicates that deflagration of the explosive is a possibility.

## 1.8 FINITE-ELEMENT ANALYSIS OF HIGH-TEMPERATURE INELASTIC SOLIDS

### 1.8A Definition of Problem

A typical fission-reactor analysis will be demonstrated on a test model, shown in Fig. 1.30, consisting of a nozzle attachment in a pressure vessel. This model is composed of type 304

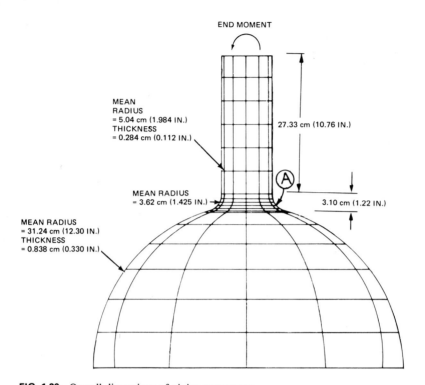

**FIG. 1.30**   Overall dimensions of piping component.

stainless steel and consists of a cylindrical nozzle–toroidal fillet–spherical shell configuration
that has been tested at Oak Ridge National Laboratory (ORNL) at 1100°F for a period of
21 weeks under combined internal pressure and end-moment loading. The loading histogram
is shown in Fig. 1.31.

## 1.8в Assumptions

The test model is discretized as shown in Fig. 1.30 with three-dimensional isoparametric
elements. The relation between creep-strain rate and time was modeled after experimental
findings which did not fit the usual "creep laws" based on powers of stress and time. The
data, presented in Ref. [48], was approximated by the expression

$$\varepsilon^c = \varepsilon_m t + \sum_{i=1}^{3} A_i [1 - \exp(-R_i t)]$$

where $\varepsilon^c$ and $t$ represent creep strain and time, respectively, and all other quantities represent
constants.

   The analysis methods are designed to accurately predict small-strain, isothermal, three-
dimensional, elastoplastic-creep responses of thick- and thin-shell structures under mechanical
and thermal loads [49, 50].

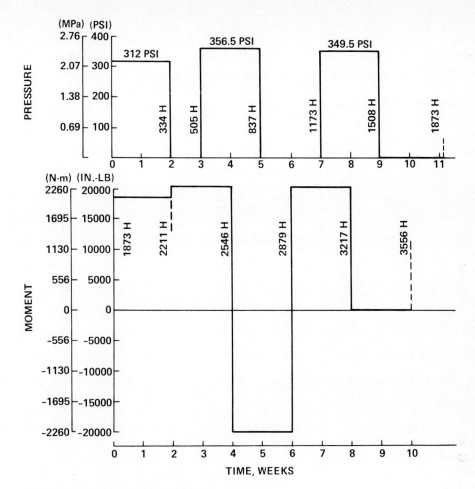

**FIG. 1.31**  Pressure and moment histogram. H = hours.

## 1.8c Constitutive Equations

Consistent with small-strain theory, we express the change in total strain as

$$de_{ij} = d\varepsilon_{ij}^e + d\varepsilon_{ij}^p + d\varepsilon_{ij}^c + d\varepsilon_{ij}^t \qquad (1.20)$$

where $de_{ij}$, $d\varepsilon_{ij}^e$, $d\varepsilon_{ij}^p$, $d\varepsilon_{ij}^c$, and $d\varepsilon_{ij}^t$ are the changes in total, elastic, plastic, creep, and thermal strain tensors, respectively. Here we choose the more classical approach of separating the inelastic strains into two parts, one time-dependent (creep) and the other time-independent (plasticity). This is in contrast to the unified theories, in which plasticity and creep are basically indistinguishable.

A detailed description of the complete elastoplastic-creep theory is presented in Ref. [51]. For the elastic-plastic theory this includes the von Mises yield criterion used to predict initial yield, the Prandtl-Reuss associative flow rule, the stress-strain relation, a hardening law based on the Prager-Ziegler kinematic hardening theory, and proportional and nonproportional cyclic loading conditions. The constitutive equations for the time-dependent creep are somewhat similar to those for plasticity and include a flow rule similar to the Prandtl-Reuss flow rule for plasticity; a "creep law" relating creep-strain rate to time; the strain-hardening and time-hardening rules; and an auxiliary procedure, described by Greenstreet et al. [52], used when stress reversals occur.

## 1.8D Solution Algorithm

From energy considerations the governing equation associated with the incremental initial-strain method is written as

$$\mathbf{K}\Delta\mathbf{U} = \Delta\mathbf{P} + \Delta\mathbf{Q}^c + \Delta\mathbf{Q}^p \tag{1.21}$$

where $\Delta\mathbf{U}$ is the incremental nodal-displacement vector from which total strains are obtained,

$$\Delta\mathbf{e} = \mathbf{B}\Delta\mathbf{U} \tag{1.22}$$

$\Delta\mathbf{P}$ is the incremental applied-load vector, including thermal loads; $\mathbf{K}$ is the elastic stiffness matrix defined as

$$\mathbf{K} = \int \mathbf{B}^T \mathbf{E} \mathbf{B} \, dV \tag{1.23}$$

and $\Delta\mathbf{Q}^p$ and $\Delta\mathbf{Q}^c$ are the pseudoload vectors associated with plastic and creep strains, respectively, and defined by

$$\Delta\mathbf{Q}^p = \int \mathbf{B}^T \mathbf{E} \Delta\boldsymbol{\varepsilon}^p \, dv$$

and

$$\Delta\mathbf{Q}^c = \int \mathbf{B}^T \mathbf{E} \Delta\boldsymbol{\varepsilon}^c \, dV \tag{1.24}$$

We assume that the differential equations, including the constitutive equations, can be integrated over a small but finite interval, $\Delta$, by using linear-functional forms during the interval.

The material constitutive model enters the governing matrix equation, Eq. (1.21), through the pseudoload vectors as described in Eq. (1.24). Note that the pseudoload vectors, and hence the right-hand side of Eq. (1.21), are unknown at the start of an incremental step. Note also that the formulation is isothermal in the sense that the elastic stiffness matrix does not change in time, as a function of temperature.

An iterative method for the solution of Eq. (1.21) is described in Ref. [53]. This procedure is an extension of the one outlined for creep by Mendelson et al. [54] and modified by Dahl [55].

Much attention has been given to the time-step incremental strategy since this governs efficiency and accuracy. The time step is always kept within certain bounds. If the time step is too large, accuracy suffers and instability may occur, and if the time step is too small, the expense of solving a problem may be very high. The criteria for the time-step solution follow those outlined by Zienkiewicz and Cormeau [56], and are described in Ref. [53].

## 1.8E Description of an Isoparametric Solid Element

The basic finite element used is an isoparametric solid element as described by Zienkiewicz et al. [57]. A variable number of nodes between eight and twenty is allowed for each element, as described by Levy [58]. In practice this variable-node feature is especially useful when a mesh changes character, e.g., in going from a coarser to a finer mesh. It is also applicable to problems in which the mechanical behavior is directional, e.g., when bending is significant in one direction and shear deformation is significant in another. The use of this "variable-node" isoparametric element allows the user to specify the number of nodes contained in an element without resorting to external methods such as node elimination or constraint equations, which may be costly.

## 1.8F Variable Inelastic Integration Points

The calculation of the incremental displacements, Eq. (1.21), requires the evaluation of integrals involving inelastic behavior. Consequently, the accuracy of the solution depends on the accuracy of the inelastic-strain representation. An accurate representation of the elastic-plastic creep behavior within an element is achieved by introducing a variable set of inelastic integration points, within an element, at which stress and strain histories are monitored. This procedure is described in the section on finite-element modeling (Chap. 3 of Part 4), as well as in Ref. [53].

The actual analysis was run in 15 segments using restart procedures. Typical results for the pressure phase are shown in Figs. 1.32 and 1.33. The experimental results shown were obtained from Clinard, Richardson, and Battiste [59]. The results show an overprediction of plastic strain during the pressure loading, which occurs predominantly during the first creep period where stress redistribution is pronounced. The discrepancies between experimental and analytic results can be accounted for qualitatively if we consider the interactive behavior between creep and plasticity which was not accounted for in the analysis; i.e., creep strains at high temperatures tend to reduce the development of subsequent plastic strains and accumulated creep strains tend to raise the yield stress of the material. The agreement between experimental results and analysis was excellent during the creep phase. Typical contour plots are shown in Figs. 1.34 and 1.35. Note that the geometry is distorted. Here we show contour plots of effective strain at the end of the pressure- and moment-loading phases. Creep strains are directly related to stresses, and therefore Figs. 1.34 and 1.35 represent the accumulated effect of the stress history. The stresses and creep strains developed in the spherical shell are almost completely due to the pressure loading, while those in the toroidal and cylindrical sections are redistributed due to the moment load. The peak stress occurs at gauge *A* (Fig. 1.30) in the toroidal region, except for the edge effect near the application of the moment.

In the near future, large-scale computer programs will be capable of analyzing nonisothermal, large-strain, inelastic three-dimensional behavior. Solution algorithms, finite elements, and modeling techniques are in a relatively advanced state and have been demonstrated by many researchers. The area of most uncertainty appears in the constitutive relations. It is

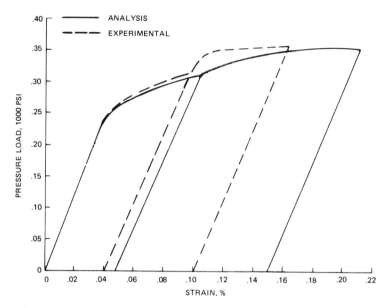

**FIG. 1.32**    Pressure load versus circumferential strain at gauge A, at 1100°F.

apparent that even for general cyclic-inelastic behavior alone (i.e., isothermal, small-displacement, inelastic behavior) the present state-of-the-art constitutive relations are inadequate. An accurate representation of the general inelastic material behavior must be established. Research in the areas of unified theories and interactive relations for a wide range of materials and environments may solve this problem.

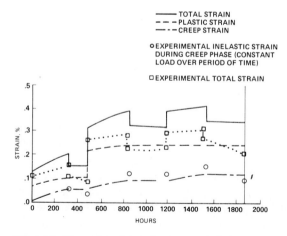

**FIG. 1.33**    Circumferential strain at gauge A during pressure loading, at 1100°F.

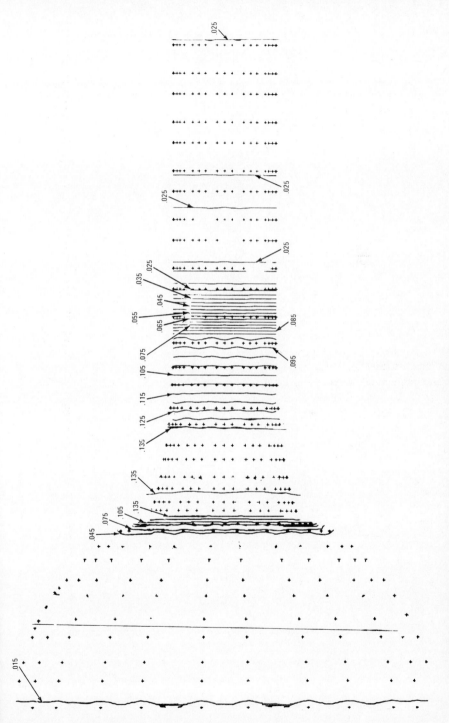

**FIG. 1.34**  Contour plot of effective creep-strain percent at end of pressure phase.

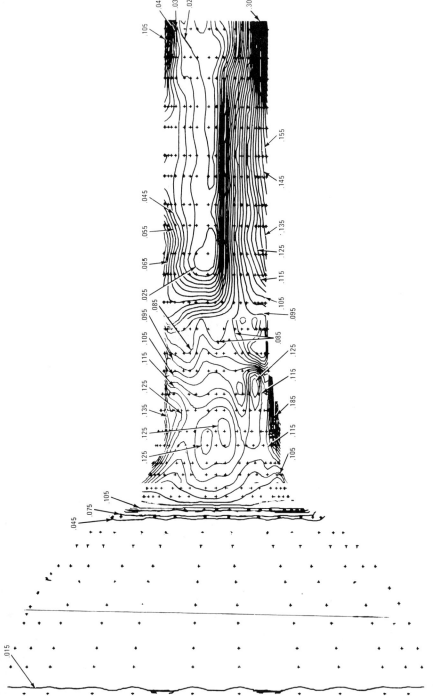

**FIG. 1.35**  Contour plot of effective strain percent at end of moment phase.

## 1.9 REFERENCES

1. Hrenikoff, A., "A Solution of Problems in Elasticity by the Frame Work Method," *J. Appl. Mech. A*, **8**:169–175 (1941).

2. McHenry, D., "A Lattice Analogy for the Solution of Plane Stress Problems," *J. Inst. Civ. Eng.*, **21**:59–82 (1943).

3. Argyris, J. H., "Energy Theorem and Structural Analysis," *Aircraft Eng.*, **26**:347–356 (1954).

4. Turner, J. J., R. W. Clough, H. C. Martin, and L. J. Topp, "Stiffness and Deflection Analysis of Coupled Structures," *J. Aero. Sci.*, **23**:805–823 (1956).

5. Clough, R. W., "The Finite Element in Plane Stress Analysis," *Proc. 2d ASCE Conf. Electronic Computation*, Pittsburgh, September 1960.

6. Kardestuncer, H., *Elementary Matrix Analysis of Structures*, McGraw-Hill, New York, 1974.

7. Livesley, R. K., *Matrix Methods of Structural Analysis*, Macmillan, New York, 1964.

8. Przemieniecki, J. S., *Theory of Matrix Structural Analysis*, McGraw-Hill, New York, 1968.

9. Meek, J. L., *Matrix Structural Analysis*, McGraw-Hill, New York, 1971.

10. Ghali, A., and A. M. Neville, *Matrix Structural Analysis*, Chapman & Hall, London, 1978.

11. Parks, D. M., "A Stiffness Derivative Finite Element Technique for Determination of Crack Tip Stress Intensity Factors," *Int. J. Fract.*, **10**:487–502 (1974).

12. Szabo, B. A., and A. K. Mehta, "*P*-Convergent Finite Element Approximations in Fracture Mechanics," *Int. J. Numer. Meth. Eng.*, **12**:551–560 (1978).

13. Szabo, B. A., and I. Babuska, "Stress Approximations by the *h* and *p* Versions of the Finite Element Method," Report WU/CCm-82/1, Center for Comp. Mech., Washington University, St. Louis, March 1982.

14. Babuska, I., and B. A. Szabo, "On the Rates of Convergence of the Finite Element Method," *Int. J. Numer. Meth. Eng.*, **18**:323–341 (1982).

15. Williams, M. L., "Stress Singularities Resulting from Various Boundary Conditions in Angular Corners of Plates in Extension," *J. Appl. Mech.*, **19**:526–528 (1952).

16. Babuska, I., R. B. Kellogg, and J. Pitkaranta, "Direct and Inverse Error Estimates for Finite Elements with Mesh Refinements," *J. Numer. Math.*, **33**:447–471 (1979).

17. Babuska, I., and W. C. Rheinboldt, "Reliable Error Estimation and Mesh Adaptations for the Finite Element Method," in J. T. Oden (ed.), *Computational Methods in Nonlinear Mechanics*, North-Holland, Amsterdam, 1980, pp. 67–108.

18. Babuska, I., and M. R. Dorr, "Error Estimates for the Combined *h* and *p* Versions of the Finite Element Method," *J. Numer. Math.*, **37**:257–277 (1981).

19. Irons, B. M., "A Technique for Degenerating Brick-Type Isoparametric Elements Using Hierarchical Midside Nodes," *Int. J. Numer. Meth. Eng.*, **8**:203–209 (1974).

20. Newton, R. E., "Degeneration of Brick-Type Isoparametric Elements," *Int. J. Numer. Meth. Eng.*, **7**:579–581 (1973).

21. Babuska, I., and A. Miller, "The Post-Processing Approach in the Finite Element Method: Part 1. Calculation of Displacements, Stresses and Other Higher Derivatives of the Displacements," *Int. J. Numer. Meth. Eng.*, **20**:1085–1109 (1984).

22. Babuska, I., and A. Miller, "The Post-Processing Approach in the Finite Element Method: Part 2. The Calculation of Stress Intensity Factors," *Int. J. Numer. Meth. Eng.*, **20**:1111–1129 (1984).

23. Babuska, I., and A. Miller, "The Post-Processing Approach in the Finite Element Method: Part 3. A Posteriori Error Estimates and Adaptive Mesh Selection," *Int. J. Numer. Meth. Eng.*, **20**:2311–2324 (1984).

24. Hutchinson, J. W., "Singular Behavior at the End of a Tensile Crack," *J. Mech. Phys. Solids*, **16**:13–31 (1960).

25. Rice, J. R., and G. F. Rosengren, "Plane Strain Deformation near a Crack Tip in a Power Low Hardening Material," *J. Mech. Phys. Solids*, **16**:1–12 (1968).

26. Rice, J. R., "A Path-Independent Integral and the Approximate Analysis of Strain Concentration by Notches and Cracks," *J. Appl. Mech.*, **35**:379–386 (1968).

27. Parks, D. M., "Some Problems in Elastic-Plastic Finite Element Analysis of Cracks," Ph.D. thesis, Brown University, Providence, R.I., 1975.

28. Begley, J. A., and J. D. Landes, "The *J*-Integral as a Fracture Criterion," *Fracture Toughness STP*, **514**:1–23 (1972).

29. Begley, J. A., and J. D. Landes, "Test Results from *J*-Integral Studies, and an Attempt to Establish a JIC Test Procedure," *Fracture Analysis STP*, **560** (1974).

30. McMeeking, R. M., "Finite Deformation Analysis of Crack Tip Opening in Elastic-Plastic Materials and Implications for Fracture," *J. Mech. Phys. Solids*, **25**:357–381 (1977).

31. Yamamoto, Y., and N. Tokuda, Determination of Stress Intensity Fracture in Cracked Plates by the Finite Element Method," *Int. J. Numer. Meth. Eng.*, **6**:427–439 (1973).

32. Yagawa, G., T. Aizawa, and Y. Ando, "Crack Analysis of Power Hardening Materials Using a Penalty Function and Superposition Method," *Proc. 12th Conf. Fracture Mechanics*, ASTM STP 700, 1980, pp. 439–452.

33. Rice, J. R., and D. M. Tracey, "Computational Fracture Mechanics," in S. J. Fenves et al. (eds.), *Numerical and Computer Methods in Structural Mechanics*, Academic Press, New York, 1973, pp. 585–623.

34. Henshell, R. D., and K. G. Shaw, "Crack Tip Finite Elements Are Unnecessary," *Int. J. Numer. Meth. Eng.*, **9**:495–507 (1975).

35. Barsoum, R. S., "On the Use of Isoparametric Finite Elements in Linear Fracture Mechanics," *Int. J. Numer. Meth. Eng.*, **10**:25–37 (1976).

36. Rice, J. R., R. M. McMeeking, D. M. Parks, and E. P. Sorensen, "Recent Finite Element Studies in Plasticity and Fracture Mechanics," *Comp. Meth. Appl. Mech. Eng.*, **17–18**:411–442 (1979).

37. Watwood, V. B., "Finite Element Method for Prediction of Crack Behavior," *Nucl. Eng. Des.*, **11**:323–332 (1970).

38. Parks, D. M., "A Stiffness Derivative Finite Element Technique for Determination of Crack Tip Stress Intensity Factors," *Int. J. Fract.*, **16**:487–502 (1974).

39. Parks, D. M., "Virtual Crack Extension Method for Nonlinear Material Behavior," *Comp. Meth. Appl. Mech. Eng.*, **12**:353–364 (1977).

40. *MARC User's Manuals*, Version J.2, MARC Analysis Research Corp., Palo Alto, Calif.

41. Bakker, A., "*J*-Integral Evaluations, a Sensitivity Study," *Proc. 6th SMIRT Conf.*, Paris, 1981.

42. Stronge, W. J., and J. C. Schulz, "Projectile Impact Damage Analysis," in A. K. Noor and Harvey G. McComb, Jr. (eds.), *Proceedings of Symposium on Computational Methods in Non-Linear Structural and Solid Mechanics*, Pergamon Press, New York, 1981; also published as special issue of *Comput. Struct.*, **13**:287–294 (1981).

43. Bernard, R. S., and D. C. Creighton, "Projectile Penetration in Earth Materials: Theory and Computer Analysis," Defense Nuclear Agency, Washington, D.C., 1977.

44. Backman, M. E., S. A. Finnegan, and K. G. Whitham, "The Formation of Stagnation Zones in Stable Penetrations of Brittle Material," *Proc. 6th Int. Symp. Ballistics*, Orlando, Fla., October 27–29, 1981.

45. Schulz, J. C., O. E. R. Heimdahl, and S. Finnegan, "Magnesium Projectile Impact Behavior," *Proceedings of the Army Symposium on Solid Mechanics, 1980—Designing for Extremes: Environment,*

*Loading and Structural Behavior*, Army Materials and Mechanics Research Center, Watertown, Mass., September 1982.

46. Schulz, J. C., "Finite Element Analysis of a Kinetic Energy Warhead Penetrating Concrete," *Proc. 4th Int. Symp. Ballistics*, Monterey, Calif., October 1978.

47. Key, S. W., Z. E. Beising, and R. D. Krieg, *HONDO II, a Finite Element Computer Program for the Large Deformation Dynamic of Axisymmetric Solids*, Sandia Laboratories, Albuquerque, N. Mex., 1978.

48. Clinard, J. A., "Creep Equation," *High Temperature Structural Design Program Semiannual Progress Report for Period Ending June 30, 1978*, ORNL-5433, Oak Ridge National Laboratory, Oak Ridge, Tenn., 1978, pp. 137–140.

49. Levy, A., "Development of the PLANS Computer Program for Elastic-Plastic Creep Analysis of Nuclear Reactor Structural Components," Grumman Research Dept. Rep. RE-567, ORNL-Sub-4485-2, Grumman Aerospace Corp., Bethpage, New York, 1979.

50. Levy, A., "Finite Element Three-Dimensional Elastic-Plastic-Creep Analysis," *Engineering Structures*, **3**:9–16 (1981).

51. Pifko, A. B., H. S. Levine, and H. Armen, Jr., "PLANS—A Finite Element Program for Nonlinear Analysis of Structures," vol. 1: *Theoretical Manual*, Grumman Research Dept. Rep. RE-501, Grumman Aerospace Corp., Bethpage, New York, 1974.

52. Greenstreet, W. L., J. M. Corum, C. E. Pugh, and K. C. Liu, "Currently Recommended Constitutive Equations for Inelastic Design Analysis for FFTF Components," ORNL-TM-36-02, Oak Ridge National Laboratory, Oak Ridge, Tenn., 1971.

53. Levy, A., and A. B. Pifko, "On Computational Strategies for Problems Involving Plasticity and Creep," *Int. J. Numer. Meth. Eng.*, **17**:747–771 (1981).

54. Mendelson, A., M. H. Herschberg, and S. S. Mason, "A General Approach to the Practical Solution of Creep Problems," *J. Basic Eng.*, **81**:585–593 (1959).

55. Dahl, N. C., "Discussion of A. Mendelson et al., 'A General Approach to the Practical Solution of Creep Problems'," (*J. Basic Eng.*, **81**:585–593), *J. Basic Eng.*, **81**:595 (1959).

56. Zienkiewicz, O. C., and J. C. Cormeau, "Viscoplasticity-Plasticity and Creep in Elastic Solids—A Unified Numerical Approach," *Int. J. Numer. Meth. Eng.*, **8**:821–845 (1974).

57. Zienkiewicz, O. C., J. E. Irons, S. Admad, and F. C. Scott, "Isoparametric and Associated Element Families for Two- and Three-Dimensional Analysis," in I. Holand and K. Bell (eds.), *Finite Element Methods in Stress Analysis*, Tapir Press, Trondheim, Norway, 1972, pp. 383–432.

58. Levy, A., "A Three Dimensional 'Variable Node' Isoparametric Solid Element," Grumman Research Dept. Rep. RM-587, Grumman Aerospace Corp., Bethpage, New York, 1974.

59. Clinard, J. A., M. Richardson, and R. L. Battiste, "Nozzle-to-Sphere Tests," *High Temperature Structural Design Program Semiannual Progress Report for Period Ending Dec. 31, 1979*, ORNL-5622, Oak Ridge National Laboratory, Oak Ridge, Tenn., 1979.

60. Peyrot, A. H., and A. M. Goulois, "Analysis of Flexible Transmission Lines," *J. Struct. Div.*, **104**(ST5):763–779 (1978).

61. Zienkiewicz, O. C., *The Finite Element Method*, 3d ed., McGraw-Hill, London, 1977.

62. Zienkiewicz, O. C., J. Bauer, K. Morgan, and E. Onate, "A Simple and Efficient Element for Axisymmetric Shells," *Int. J. Numer. Meth. Eng.*, **11**(10):1545–1558 (1977).

63. Ahmad, S., B. M. Irons, and O. C. Zienkiewicz, "Analysis of Thick and Thin Shell Structures by Curved Finite Elements," *Int. J. Numer. Meth. Eng.*, **2**(3):419–451 (1970).

64. Hughes, T. J. R., R. L. Taylor, and W. Kanoknukulchai, "A Simple and Efficient Element for Plate Bending," *Int. J. Numer. Meth. Eng.*, **11**:1529–1543 (1977).

65. Percy, J. H., T. H. H. Pian, S. Klein, and D. R. Navartna, "Application of Matrix Displacement Method to Linear Elastic Analysis of Shells of Revolution," *AIAA J.*, **3**:2138–2145 (1965).

66. Ahmad, S., B. M. Irons, and O. C. Zienkiewicz, "Curved Thick Shell and Membrane Elements with Particular Reference to Axisymmetric Problems," *WPAFB2 Conf.*, Wright Patterson Air Force Base, Ohio, 1966, pp. 539–572.

67. Baron, F., and M. S. Venkatesan, "Nonlinear Analysis of Cable and Truss Structures," *J. Struct. Div.*, **97**:679–710 (1971).

68. Marcal, P. V., "Large Deflection Analysis of Elastic-Plastic Shells of Revolution," *AIAA J.*, **8**:1627–1633 (1970).

69. Bushnell, D., "Large Deflection Elastic-Plastic Creep Analysis of Axisymmetric Shells," in R. F. Hartung (ed.), *Numerical Solution of Nonlinear Structural Problems*, Applied Mechanics Division 6, American Society of Mechanical Engineers, New York, 1973, pp. 103–138.

70. Bushnell, D., "BOSOR5—Program for Buckling of Elastic-Plastic Complex Shells of Revolution Including Large Deflections and Creep," *Comput. Struct.*, **6**:221–239 (1976).

71. Oden, J. T., *Finite Elements of Nonlinear Continua*, McGraw-Hill, New York, 1972.

72. Bathe, K. J., and S. Bolourchi, "A Geometric and Material Nonlinear Plate and Shell Element," *Comput. Struct.*, **11**:23–48 (1980).

73. Yaghmai, S., and E. P. Popov, "Incremental Analysis of Large Deflections of Shells of Revolution," *Int. J. Solids Struct.*, **7**:1375–1393 (1971).

74. Beskos, D. E., "Framework Stability by Finite Element Method," *J. Struct. Div.*, **103**:2273–2276 (1977).

75. Barsoum, R. S., and J. H. Gallagher, "Finite Element Analysis of Torsional and Torsional-Flexural Stability Problems," *Int. J. Numer. Meth. Eng.*, **2**:335–352 (1970).

76. Tong, P., and T. H. H. Pian, "Postbuckling Analysis of Shells of Revolution by the Finite Element Method," in Y. C. Fung and E. E. Sechler (eds.), *Thin-Shell Structures: Theory, Experiment and Design*, Prentice-Hall, Englewood Cliffs, N.J., 1974, pp. 435–452.

77. Przemieniecki, J. S., "Matrix Analysis of Local Instability in Plates, Stiffened Panels and Columns," *Int. J. Numer. Meth. Eng.*, **5**:209–216 (1972).

78. Bushnell, D., "Buckling of Shells—Pitfall for Designers," *21st SSDM Conf.*, May 1980, pp. 1–56.

79. Kanok-Nukulchai, W., R. L. Taylor, and T. J. R. Hughes, "A Large Deformation Formulation for Shell Analysis by the Finite Element Method," *Comput. Struct.*, **13**:19–27 (1981).

80. Bathe, K. J., and L. W. Ho, "A Simple and Effective Element for Analysis of General Shell Structures," *Comput. Struct.*, **13**:673–681 (1981).

81. Allman, D. J., "Improved Finite Element Models for the Large Displacement Bending and Post Buckling Analysis of Thin Plates," *Int. J. Solids Struct.*, **18**:737–762 (1982).

82. Milner, H. R., "Accurate Finite Element Analysis of Large Displacements in Skeletal Frames," *Comput. Struct.*, **14**:205–210 (1981).

83. Shis, C. F., H. G. deLorenzi, and M. D. German, "Crack Extension Modeling with Singular Quadratic Isoparametric Elements," *Int. J. Fract.*, **12**:647–651 (1976).

84. Barsoum, R. S., "A Degenerate Solid Element for Linear Fracture Analysis of Plate Bending and General Shells," *Int. J. Numer. Meth. Eng.*, **10**:551–564 (1976).

85. Bathe, K. J., and C. Almeida, "A Simple and Effective Pipe Elbow Element—Linear Analysis," *J. Appl. Mech.*, **47**:93–100 (1980).

86. Zienkiewicz, O. C., "Viscoplasticity, Plasticity, Creep and Viscoplastic Flow: Problems of Small, Large and Continuing Deformation," in *Computational Mechanics, Texas Inst. Comput. Mech. Lect. Notes Math.*, 461, Springer-Verlag, New York, 1975.

87. Taylor, R. L., K. Pister, and G. Goudreau, "Thermo-Mechanical Analysis of Visco-Elastic Solids," *Int. J. Numer. Meth. Eng.*, **2**:45–60 (1970).

88. Persyna, P., "Fundamental Problems in Viscoplasticity," *Adv. Appl. Mech.*, **9**:243–377 (1966).

89. Zienkiewicz, O. C., and I. C. Cormear, "Visco-Plasticity, Plasticity, and Creep in Elastic Solids—A Unified Numerical Solution Approach," *Int. J. Numer. Meth. Eng.*, **8**:821–845 (1974).

90. Bergan, P., and B. Aamodt, "Finite Element Analysis of Crack Propagation in Three-Dimensional Solids under Cyclic Loading," *Proc. 2d Int. Conf. Struct. Mech. Reactor Technol.*, Berlin, 1973, vol. III, pts. G–H.

91. Aamodt, B., "Efficient Formulations of the Finite Element Method in Linear and Nonlinear Fracture Mechanics," *Proceedings of World Congress on Finite Element Methods in Structural Mechanics*, Bournemouth, England, October 1975, vol. 2.

92. Gallagher, R. H., "Finite Element Analysis of Crack Tip Problems," *Proceedings of Symposium on Finite Element Method*, Hefei, China, Gordon and Breach Science Publishers, New York, 1982.

93. Rice, J., and D. Tracey, "Computational Fracture Mechanics," in S. J. Fenves et al. (eds.), *Numerical and Computer Methods in Structural Mechanics*, Academic Press, New York, 1973, pp. 555–624.

94. Cruse, T. A., and G. Meyers, "Three-Dimensional Fracture Mechanics Analysis," *J. Struct. Div.*, **103**:309–320 (1977).

95. Yamamoto, Y., and Y. Sumi, "Stress Intensity Factors for Three-Dimensional Cracks," *14th Int. Congr. Theor. Appl. Mech.*, Delft, 1976.

96. Levy, N., P. V. Marcal, W. Ostergren, and J. Rice, "Small Scale Yielding near a Crack in Plane Strain: A Finite Element Analysis," *Int. J. Fract. Mech.*, **7**:143–157 (1971).

97. Hellen, T. K., and W. S. Blackburn, "The Calculation of Stress Intensity Factors in Two- and Three-Dimensions Using Finite Elements in Computational Fracture Mechanics," in E. Rybicki and S. Benzley (eds.), *ASME Spec. Publ.*, American Society of Mechanical Engineers, New York, 1975.

98. Pian, T. H. H., and K. Moriya, "Three-Dimensional Fracture Analysis by Assumed Stress Finite Elements," *Proc. Int. Conf. Numer. Meth. Fract. Mech.*, Swansea, Wales, January 1978.

99. Atluri, S. et al., "Hybrid Finite Element Models for Linear and Nonlinear Fracture Mechanics," *Proc. 1st. Conf. Numer. Meth. Fract. Mech.*, Swansea, Wales, January 1978.

100. Bathe, K. J., *Finite Element Procedures in Engineering Analysis*, Prentice-Hall, Englewood Cliffs, N.J., 1982.

101. Cook, R. D., *Concepts and Applications of Finite Element Analysis*, 2d ed., Wiley, New York, 1981.

102. Belytschko, T., "A Survey of Numerical Methods and Computer Programs for Dynamic Structural Analysis," *Nucl. Eng. Des.*, **37**:23–34 (1976).

103. Surana, K. S., "Lumped Mass Matrices with Non-zero Inertia for General Shell and Axisymmetric Shell Elements," *Int. J. Numer. Meth. Eng.*, **12**:1635–1650 (1978).

104. Watwood, V. B., T. Y. Chow, Z. Zudans, and W. H. Miller, "Combined Analysis and Evaluation of Piping Systems Using the Computer," *Nucl. Eng. Des.*, **27**:334–342 (1974).

105. Belytschko, T., J. R. Osias, and P. V. Marcal (eds.), *Finite Element Analysis of Transient Nonlinear Structural Behavior*, Appl. Mech. Div. 1, American Society of Mechanical Engineers, New York, 1975, vol. 14.

106. Friberg, P. O., "Coupled Vibration of Beams—An Exact Dynamic Element Stiffness Matrix," *Int. J. Numer. Meth. Eng.*, **19**:479–493 (1983).

107. Othmer, O., "Nonlinear Flow Analysis in Pipe Networks," *Int. J. Numer. Meth. Eng.*, **19**:373–392 (1983).

108. Moore, C., G. W. Vickers, and S. N. Dwivedi, "Viscoplasticity Solution of Deformation Problems," *Int. J. Numer. Meth. Eng.*, **19**:257–269 (1983).

109. Shabaik, A. H., and E. G. Thomsen, "Computer Aided Viscoplasticity Solution of Some Deformation Problems," *Int. Symp. Found. Plasticity*, Noordhoff, Leyden, 1972.

110. Alwari, R. S. et al., "Three-Dimensional Finite Element Analysis of Cracked Thick Plates in Bending," *Int. J. Numer. Meth. Eng.*, **19**:293–303 (1983).

111. Fried, I., "Finite Element Computation of Large Rubber Membrane Deformation," *Int. J. Numer. Meth. Eng.*, **18**:653–660 (1982).

112. Dinis, L. M. S., and D. R. J. Owen, "Elasto-Viscoplastic and Elasto-Plastic Large Deformation Analysis of Thin Plates and Shells," *Int. J. Numer. Meth. Eng.*, **18**:591–609 (1982).

113. AIAA/ASME, *10th Structures, Structural Dynamics and Material Conference*, New Orleans, 1969.

114. Cook, W. A., "A Finite Element Model for Nonlinear Shells of Revolution," *Int. J. Numer. Meth. Eng.*, **18**:135–149 (1982).

115. *Proceedings of the 1st Conference on Numerical Methods in Fracture Mechanics*, Swansea, Wales, 1978.

116. Reddy, J. N., and I. R. Singh, "Large Deflection and Large Amplitude Free Vibrations of Straight and Curved Beams," *Int. J. Numer. Meth. Eng.*, **17**:829–852 (1981).

117. Levy, A., and A. B. Pifko, "On Computational Strategies for Problems Involving Plasticity and Creep," *Int. J. Numer. Meth. Eng.*, **17**:747–771 (1981).

118. Reddy, J. N., et al., "Large Deflection and Large Amplitude Vibrations of Axisymmetric Circular Plates," *Int. J. Numer. Meth. Eng.,* **17**:527–541 (1981).

119. Gupta, K. K., "Development of a Unified Numerical Procedure for Vibration Analysis of Structures," *Int. J. Numer. Meth. Eng.*, **17**:187–198 (1981).

120. Owen, D. R. J., and E. Hinton, *Finite Elements in Plasticity*, Pineridge Press, Swansea, Wales, 1980.

121. Nemat-Nasser, S. (ed.), *Variational Methods in the Mechanics of Solids*, Pergamon Press, New York, 1980.

122. Stricklin, J. A., and K. J. Saczalski (eds.), *Constitutive Equations in Viscoplasticity: Computational and Engineering Aspects*, Appl. Mech. Div., American Society of Mechanical Engineers, New York, 1976, vol. 20.

123. Bergan, P. G., et al., *FEM in Nonlinear Mechanics*, Tapir Press, Trondheim, Norway, 1978.

124. *Proc. 2d Int. Conf. Finite Elements Nonlinear Mechanics* (pts. I–III), in *Comput. Meth. Appl. Mech. Eng.*, **23** (September 1982).

125. Haber, R. B., and J. F. Abel, "Initial Equilibrium Method for Cable Reinforced Membranes," pts. I, II, *Comput. Meth. Appl. Mech. Eng.*, **30** (1982).

126. Argyris, J. H., et al., "Finite Element Analysis of Two- and Three-Dimensional Elasto-Plastic Frames—The Natural Approach," *Comput. Meth. Appl. Mech. Eng.*, **35** (1982).

127. Fried, I., "Nonlinear Finite Element Computation of the Equilibrium, Stability and Motion of the Extensional Beam and Ring," *Comput. Meth. Appl. Mech. Eng.*, **38** (1983).

128. Chung, T. J., and R. L. Edison, "Dynamic Analysis of Viscoelasto-Plastic Anisotropic Shells," *Comput. Struct.*, **3**:483–494 (1973).

129. Argyris, J. H., et al., "New Developments in the Inelastic Analysis for Quasistatic and Dynamic Problems," *Int. J. Numer. Meth. Eng.*, **13**:1813–1850 (1979).

130. Perzyna, P., "Fundamental Problems in Visco-Plasticity," *Adv. Appl. Mech.*, **9**:343–377 (1966).

131. Ghoreim, H., and Yu Chen, "A Viscoelastic-Viscoplastic Constitutive Equation and Its Finite Element Implementation," *Comput. Struct.*, **17**:499–509 (1983).

132. Cormeau, C., "Elastoplastic Thick Shell Analysis by Viscoplastic Solid Finite Element," *Int. J. Numer. Meth. Eng.*, **12**:203–227 (1978).

133. "Computational Methods in Nonlinear Structural and Solid Mechanics," *Comput. Struct.*, **13** (1981).

134. Bushnell, D., "Elastic-Plastic Bending and Buckling Analysis of Pipes and Elbows," *Comput. Struct.*, **13**:241–248 (1981).

135. Noor, A. K., and J. N. Hausner (eds.), "Advances and Trends in Structural and Solid Mechanics," *Comput. Struct.*, **16**:1–4 (1983).

136. Sih, G. C., *Methods of Analysis and Solutions of Crack Problems*, Noordhoff, Leyden, 1973.

137. Roman, I., and K. Ono, "Model for Fracture Toughness Alteration Due to Cyclic Loading," *Int. J. Fract.*, **19**:67–80 (1980).

138. Sih, G. C., and P. S. Theocaris, *Mixed Mode Crack Propagation*, Martinus Nijhoff, The Hague, 1980.

139. Perrone, N., et al., *Fracture Mechanics*, University of West Virginia Press, Morgantown, 1978.

140. Perrone, N., and S. Atluri (eds.), *Nonlinear and Dynamic Fracture Mechanics*, ASME-AMD 35, American Society of Mechanical Engineers, New York, 1979.

141. *Proceedings of the International Conferences on Numerical Methods in Fracture Mechanics*, Pineridge Press, Swansea, Wales, 1978, 1980, 1982.

142. Atluri, S., et al., "Hybrid-Finite Element Analysis of Some Nonlinear and 3-Dimensional Problems of Engineering Fracture Mechanics," *Comput. Struct.*, **12**:511–520 (1980).

143. Irons, B. M., and S. Ahmad, *Techniques of Finite Elements*, Ellis-Horwood, Chichester, 1980.

144. Atluri, S., and K. Kathiresan, "Three Dimensional Analysis of Surface Flows in Thick Walled Reactor Pressure Vessels Using Displacement-Hybrid Finite Element Methods," *Nucl. Eng. Des.*, **51**:163–176 (1979).

145. Bowman, P. (ed.), "Engineering Application of the Finite Element Method," *Comput. Struct.*, **12**(4) (1980).

146. Rega, G., and A. Luongo, "Natural Vibrations of Suspended Cables with Flexible Supports," *Comput. Struct.*, **12**:65–75 (1980).

147. Gallagher, R. H., *Finite Element Analysis Fundamentals*, Prentice-Hall, Englewood Cliffs, N.J., 1975.

148. Chon, C. T., and G. J. Weng, "Impact of a Finite Elastic-Viscoplastic Bar," *Int. J. Non-Linear Mech.*, **15**:195–209 (1980).

149. Cristescu, N., *Dynamic Plasticity*, North-Holland, Amsterdam, 1967.

150. Sarihan, V., and S. Mukherjee, "Axisymmetric Viscoplastic Deformation by the Boundary Element Method," *Int. J. Solids Struct.*, **18**:1129–1145 (1982).

151. Zienkiewicz, O. C., and I. C. Cormeau, "Viscoplasticity Solutions by Finite Element Process," *Proc. Colloque Meth. Calcul. Sci. Tech. IRIA*, Paris, 1978.

152. Telles, J. C. F., and C. A. Brebbia, "Elastic/Viscoplastic Problems Using Boundary Element," *Int. J. Mech. Sci.*, **24**:605–618 (1982).

153. Sih, G. C., *Mechanics of Fracture*, Martinus Nijhoff, The Hague, 1981.

154. Anderson, R. G., B. M. Irons, and O. C. Zienkiewicz, "Vibration and Stability of Plates Using Finite Elements," *Int. J. Solids Struct.*, **4** (1968).

155. Bathe, K. J., E. Ramm, and E. L. Wilson, "Finite Element Formulations for Large Deformation Dynamic Analysis," *Int. J. Numer. Meth. Eng.*, **9**:353–386 (1975).

156. Nishioko, T., and S. N. Atluri, "Analytical Solution for Embedded Elliptical Cracks and Finite Element Alternating Method for Elliptical Surface Cracks Subjected to Arbitrary Loadings," *Eng. Fract. Mech.*, **17**:247–268 (1983).

# CHAPTER 2
# FINITE-ELEMENT APPLICATIONS IN FLUID MECHANICS

Four basic conservation equations form the basis of most numerical modeling procedures in fluid dynamics. These are the Navier–Stokes equations, in which both mass and momentum are conserved, and the equations describing the conservation of energy and species.

For a three-dimensional cartesian orthogonal coordinate system these four equations can be written in the following forms [1, 2].

*Conservation of mass:*
$$\frac{\partial \hat{\rho}}{\partial t} + \frac{\partial}{\partial x_i}(\hat{\rho}\hat{u}_i) = 0 \tag{2.1}$$

*Conservation of momentum:*

$$\frac{\partial \hat{u}_i}{\partial t} + \hat{u}_j \frac{\partial \hat{u}_i}{\partial x_j} = -\frac{1}{\hat{\rho}}\frac{\partial \hat{p}}{\partial x_i} + \hat{F}_i + \frac{1}{\hat{\rho}}\frac{\partial}{\partial x_j}\left(\mu \frac{\partial \hat{u}_i}{\partial x_j}\right) + \frac{1}{3\hat{\rho}}\frac{\partial}{\partial x_i}\left(\mu \frac{\partial \hat{u}_i}{\partial x_i}\right) \qquad i,j = 1, 2, 3 \tag{2.2}$$

in which $\hat{u}_i$ and $\hat{p}$ are the instantaneous, pointwise values of the velocity and pressure, respectively; $\mu$ is the viscosity; $\hat{F}_i$ is a body force over and above that due to pressure which may be enthalpy- or species-dependent; and $t$ denotes time. Conservation of total enthalpy, $\hat{H}$, can be described by the following [2].

*Conservation of enthalpy:*
$$\frac{\partial \hat{H}}{\partial t} + \hat{u}_j \frac{\partial \hat{H}}{\partial x_j} = \frac{\hat{S}_H}{\hat{\rho}} + \frac{1}{\hat{\rho}}\frac{\partial}{\partial x_i}\left(K\frac{\partial \hat{T}}{\partial x_j}\right) \tag{2.3}$$

where
$$\hat{H} = C_p \hat{T} + \frac{\hat{u}_i^2}{2} + \hat{M}_{fu}\hat{H}_{fu}$$

in which $C_p$ is the specific heat of the fluid at constant pressure, $\hat{T}$ is the local instantaneous value of temperature, $\hat{S}_H$ is the result of extraneous work, $K$ is thermal conductivity, and $\hat{M}_{fu}\hat{H}_{fu}$ is the product of the mass fraction of fuel in a combustible system and its enthalpy of combusion per unit mass. This latter term can, obviously, be ignored in nonreacting flows. For an ideal fluid (2.3) becomes

$$\frac{\partial \hat{T}}{\partial t} + \hat{u}_j \frac{\partial \hat{T}}{\partial x_j} = \frac{\hat{S}_H}{\rho C_p} + \frac{1}{\rho C_p} \frac{\partial}{\partial x_j}\left( K \frac{\partial \hat{T}}{\partial x_j}\right) \tag{2.4}$$

The remaining conservation equation is for a species $s$:

*Conservation of species:* $\qquad \dfrac{\partial \hat{\rho}_s}{\partial t} + \dfrac{\partial}{\partial x_i}(\hat{\rho}_s \hat{u}_i) = \hat{M}_s + \dfrac{\partial}{\partial x_i}\left( \hat{\rho} D \dfrac{\partial \hat{M}_s}{\partial x_i}\right)$  (2.5)

where $\hat{\rho}_s$ is the mass density of the species $s$; $\hat{M}_s$ is the mass rate of creation of $s$ per unit volume per unit time; and, according to Fick's law of diffusion, $\hat{m}_s$ is defined by

$$\hat{\rho}_s(\hat{u}_s - \hat{u}_i) = -D\frac{\partial \hat{m}_a}{\partial x_i} \tag{2.6}$$

in which $u_s$ is the species rate of translation.

For laminar flow the variables $\hat{u}_i$, $\hat{H}$, $\hat{T}$, $\hat{\rho}$, and $\hat{\rho}_s$ need no further definition and Eqs. (2.1) to (2.6) can be used to predict the flow pattern, heat transfer, and species transfer relating to such problems.

In some instances the Navier–Stokes equations can be reduced by introducing simplifying assumptions. The two main assumptions are as follows.

**1.** Convective terms are insignificant and the momentum equations reduce to

$$\frac{\partial \hat{u}_i}{\partial t} = -\frac{1}{\hat{\rho}} \frac{\partial \hat{\rho}}{\partial x_i} + \hat{F}_i + \frac{1}{\hat{\rho}} \frac{\partial}{\partial x_j}\left( \mu \frac{\partial \hat{u}_i}{\partial x_j}\right) \tag{2.7}$$

**2.** Dissipation terms can be ignored, resulting in

$$\frac{\partial \hat{u}_i}{\partial t} + \hat{u}_j \frac{\partial \hat{u}_i}{\partial x_j} = -\frac{1}{\hat{\rho}} \frac{\partial \hat{p}}{\partial x_i} + \hat{F}_i \tag{2.8}$$

When turbulent flow is considered, variables are usually defined in terms of time-averaged mean quantities and instantaneous fluctuations from such quantities:

$$\hat{u}_i = u_i + u_i' \qquad \hat{p} = p + p'$$

If correlations in density fluctuations are ignored, then a time-averaged form of the Navier–Stokes equations is

$$\frac{\partial \rho u_i}{\partial x_i} = 0 \tag{2.9}$$

and if the correlation between fluctuations in density and velocity is small,

$$u_j \frac{\partial u_i}{\partial x_j} = -\frac{1}{\rho} \frac{\partial p}{\partial x_i} + F_i + \frac{1}{\rho} \frac{\partial}{\partial x_i} \left( \mu \frac{\partial u_i}{\partial x_j} \right) - \frac{\partial}{\partial x_j} \overline{u_i' u_j'} \qquad (2.10)$$

where the overbar denotes time-averaging and the primitive variables are also time-averaged, for instance,

$$u_i = \lim_{(t_1 - t_2) \to \infty} \frac{1}{t_1 - t_2} \int_{t_1}^{t_2} \hat{u}_i(x_1, x_2, x_3, t) \, dt$$

The introduction of turbulence, following the current approach, is characterized by the Reynolds stress term $\rho \, \overline{u_i' u_j'}$ in the momentum equations. This has, of necessity, to be redefined in terms of measurable or calculable quantities in order that (2.10) be amenable to analysis.

A corresponding time-averaging of the enthalpy balance or species equations leads to an expression of the form

$$u_j \frac{\partial \lambda}{\partial x_j} = S_\lambda + \frac{\partial}{\partial x_j} \left( D_\lambda \frac{\partial \lambda}{\partial x_j} \right) - \frac{\partial \overline{u_j' \lambda}}{\partial x_j} \qquad (2.11)$$

in which $\overline{u_j' \lambda}$ represents a heat or species mass flux. This expression must again be defined in an analogous manner to the momentum equation.

The Reynolds stress terms can be redefined by using the Boussinesq concept that

$$-\rho \overline{u_i' u_j'} = \nu_t \left( \frac{\partial u_i}{\partial x_j} + \frac{\partial u_j}{\partial x_i} \right) - \tfrac{2}{3} \delta_{ij} \, k \qquad (2.12)$$

which introduces the turbulent kinematic viscosity $\nu_t$, the Kronecker delta $\delta_{ij}$, and the mean turbulent kinetic energy $k$,

$$k = \tfrac{1}{2} \overline{u_i'^2}$$

If the instantaneous pressure is redefined as

$$P = p + \tfrac{2}{3} k$$

the generalized time-averaged momentum equation (2.10) can be represented in the form

$$u_j \frac{\partial u_i}{\partial x_j} = -\frac{1}{\rho} \frac{\partial P}{\partial x_i} + F_i + \frac{1}{\rho} \frac{\partial}{\partial x_j} \left[ \mu_e \left( \frac{\partial u_i}{\partial x_j} + \frac{\partial u_j}{\partial x_i} \right) \right] \qquad (2.13)$$

in which the effective viscosity $\mu_e$ is

$$\mu_e = \mu_t + \mu$$

It is immediately apparent that (2.13) requires a definition of the turbulent viscosity $\mu_t$. In the so-called zero-equation eddy-viscosity model this is effected by evaluating $\mu_t$ from

$$\mu_t = C_\mu l^2 \left( \frac{\partial u_i}{\partial x_j} + \frac{\partial u_j}{\partial x_i} \right)$$

where $C_\mu$ is considered constant and $l$, a length scale, is obtained from an algebraic problem-dependent formula.

In the "one-equation" model a further transport equation is introduced to describe the spatial variation in turbulent kinetic energy. One form of such an equation is [3, 4]

$$u_j \frac{\partial k}{\partial x_j} = \frac{1}{\rho} \frac{\partial}{\partial x_j} \left[ \left( \mu + \frac{\mu_t}{\sigma_k} \right) \frac{\partial k}{\partial x_j} \right] + \frac{\mu_t}{\rho} \frac{\partial u_i}{\partial x_j} \left( \frac{\partial u_i}{\partial x_j} + \frac{\partial u_j}{\partial x_i} \right) - C_D \rho \frac{k^{3/2}}{l} \tag{2.14}$$

in which $\sigma_k$ is, effectively, a Prandtl–Schmidt number and the "constant" $C_D$ is assumed known.

In this case, closure is obtained by evaluating $\nu_t$ from

$$\nu_t = C_\mu k^{3/2} l$$

and $k$ from (2.14) and $l$ from an algebraic expression which is again problem-dependent.

In the "two-equation" model, another transport equation is introduced [3, 4],

$$u_j \frac{\partial \varepsilon}{\partial x_j} = \frac{1}{\rho} \frac{\partial}{\partial x_j} \left[ \left( \mu + \frac{\mu_t}{\sigma_\varepsilon} \right) \frac{\partial \varepsilon}{\partial x_j} \right] + C_1 k \frac{\partial u_i}{\partial x_j} \left( \frac{\partial u_i}{\partial x_j} + \frac{\partial u_j}{\partial x_i} \right) - C_2 \frac{\varepsilon^2}{k} \tag{2.15}$$

for evaluating $\varepsilon = k^{3/2} / l$. Again $\sigma_\varepsilon$, $C_1$, and $C_2$ are assumed to be known and are usually taken to be spacewise constant. Closure is achieved by evaluating $\nu_t$ as before. In this case, both $k$ and $l$ are now obtained from the respective transport equations.

Coupling due to enthalpy or species magnitudes is effected via the body force $\hat{F}_i$. For example, in free convection, this is of prime importance and is, indeed, the principal forcing mechanism and constitutes a strong coupling. Once the velocity field has been resolved, then such coupling can be incorporated via a suitable iterative process. With forced convection, however, such terms are, except at very low velocity values, of little significance and can be ignored. Each problem must, therefore, be treated on its merit.

## 2.1 POTENTIAL FLOW

This section will consider only incompressible potential flow. In the case of compressible flow, a potential can also be defined and used for a finite-element solution, but consideration of this is deferred to a subsequent section.

### 2.1A Governing Equations

For irrotational flow, the vorticity $\boldsymbol{\omega}$ is zero, and

$$\boldsymbol{\omega} = \nabla \times \mathbf{v} = \mathbf{0} \tag{2.16}$$

From the vector identity

$$\nabla \times \nabla \phi \equiv \mathbf{0} \tag{2.17}$$

it is seen that (2.16) has the solution

$$\mathbf{v} = \nabla \phi \tag{2.18}$$

where $\phi$ is defined as the scalar potential. The continuity equation becomes, for incompressible flow,

$$\nabla \cdot \mathbf{v} = 0 \tag{2.19}$$

so that substitution of (2.18) in (2.19) shows that $\phi$ satisfies Laplace's equation

$$\nabla^2 \phi = 0 \tag{2.20}$$

Also for incompressible flow, it can be shown in the case of two dimensions that a stream function $\psi$ can be defined such that the velocity components $u$, $v$ in the $x$- and $y$-directions, respectively, are given by

$$u = \frac{\partial \psi}{\partial y} \qquad v = \frac{\partial \psi}{\partial x} \tag{2.21}$$

where $\psi$ satisfies the Laplace equation

$$\nabla^2 \psi = 0 \tag{2.22}$$

The common boundary conditions for (2.20) are Dirichlet

$$\phi = g \qquad \text{on } S_1 \tag{2.23}$$

and Cauchy

$$\frac{\partial \phi}{\partial n} + \alpha \phi + q = 0 \qquad \text{on } S_2 \tag{2.24}$$

where $S_1$ and $S_2$ comprise the boundary surface. The Neumann condition can be obtained from (2.24). The same form of boundary conditions are common for (2.22).

## 2.1B Finite-Element Formulations

The Laplace equations form the basis for variational, weighted-residual, and boundary finite-element methods. For the least-squares finite-element method, the cartesian component equations of the continuity equation (2.19) and the condition of irrotationality (2.16) are generally used.

For the variational finite-element method, it can be shown [5, 6] that the functional whose extremization yields the solution to (2.20), (2.23), and (2.24) is

$$I = \tfrac{1}{2} \int_D \nabla \phi \cdot \nabla \phi \, dD + \int_{S_2} (q\phi + \tfrac{1}{2}\alpha\phi^2) \, dS_2 \tag{2.25}$$

The same form, reduced to two dimensions, is the relevant functional for the stream-function problem. The standard variational finite-element approach applied to (2.25) yields a linear-system matrix equation for solution [5–7]. The Galerkin formulation is straightforward and leads [7] to the same system matrix equation as the variational approach. The boundary finite-element [8] and least-squares [9, 10] methods lead similarly to linear-system matrix equations. The least-squares method involves higher derivatives which, in general, will lead to a better convergence than the variational or Galerkin methods, but it has the disadvantage of requiring higher-order weighting functions [7]. The admissibility requirements for least squares are one order higher than simple inspection might indicate [10].

It is important to note that the Laplace equation governs many other field phenomena, as well as potential flow, and the finite-element approaches considered in this section can be used to solve problems in these areas. Among the problems which can be handled in this way [6] are those involving gravitation, electrostatics, electric and thermal conduction, magnetostatics, and fluid flow in uniform porous media.

## 2.1c  Applications

The earliest finite-element formulation for Laplace's equation was presented by Zienkiewicz and Cheung [11], but this did not indicate specific solutions for potential flow. The application of the finite-element method to problems in fluid dynamics and heat transfer was then considered by Fried [12], but it was Martin's conference paper [13] that made a large audience aware of the possibilities for potential flow. The problem which Martin solved was for two-dimensional flow around a cylinder in a channel, using the stream function and linear triangular elements. Other variational formulations by Argyris et al. [14], de Vries and Norrie [15, 16], and Fujino [17] quickly followed, using both straight and curvilinear triangles, including hermitian elements. The use of the higher-order triangles has been further detailed by Argyris et al. [18–20], Fujino [21], Isaacs [22], Harrison and Cheung [23], and others. The Harrison and Cheung publication derives the stiffness matrix in analytic form for a higher-order element for the quasi-harmonic equation (a special case of which is the Laplace equation).

Special consideration of the boundary conditions is required for multiple bodies and lifting bodies. An analysis for multiple bodies, with and without lift, was given by de Vries and Norrie [6, 24]. Single-lifting airfoils in both incompressible and compressible flow were subsequently considered by various investigators. Baker [5] and Baker and Manhardt [25], for example, have described in some detail the boundary-condition specification and method of enforcing the Kutta condition for the airfoil in compressible (potential) flow, and these can be also used for the incompressible potential flow. Thompson [26, 27] has shown how the repeating boundary condition or cyclic constraint which transforms an isolated airfoil in a flow into a cascade of airfoils can be imposed directly, allowing a noniterative solution. By use of isoparametric cubic elements, and both potential and stream-function formulations, this flow was obtained around ovals and airfoils and shown to agree well with competing methods.

Most of the previously cited finite-element solutions are of the displacement type. Schmidt [28] has described a force method for potential flow, electing to solve for the velocity potential by assuming velocity fields across the elements. A nonvariational approach was used, and the velocity fields were based on harmonic polynomials [29].

The Galerkin approach is now commonly used [7] for potential flow. Fletcher [30] systematically compared the efficiency of various isoparametric elements for potential flow around a cylinder and found that rectangular elements were more efficient than triangular ones and quadratic shape functions more effective than linear shape functions.

The boundary-element method has also been used for potential problems, and this approach is well-described by Brebbia [8, 252]. The least-squares finite-element method has been applied by de Vries et al. [9] and by Norrie and de Vries [10] to potential flow to obtain the velocity components directly. The admissibility requirements were shown to be one order higher than had been commonly supposed. Fifth-order polynomial elements were shown to satisfy these conditions and to give a major improvement in accuracy over the linear elements (which do not satisfy the admissibility requirements) for a given number of system unknowns.

Other finite-element approaches to potential flow have also been put forward. Doctors [31] has described what can be regarded as a subdomain variant of the weighted-residual formulation. Integral-equation solutions for potential flow have been presented by Washizu and Ikegawa [32, 33] and by Hashimoto et al. [34]. These use finite strips or finite elements with collocation to solve the flow around wings of various shapes. A mixed finite-element method for potential flow has been proposed by Meissner [251].

## 2.2 LAMINAR VISCOUS FLOW

The two-dimensional equations for incompressible laminar flow may be expressed in terms of (1) the "primitive-variables" velocity and pressure $(u, v, p)$, (2) stream function and vorticity $(\psi, \zeta)$, or (3) stream function alone $(\psi)$. Each of the three forms has its own advantages and disadvantages (see Ref. [35]). The primitive-variable formulation apparently is the simplest and has the most potential for extension to three dimensions, and is the approach which will be described in this chapter. Formulations using stream-function–vorticity variables or the stream function alone are especially useful for certain types of problems. In particular, the stream-function formulation using $C^1$-elements is probably the most accurate and efficient for steady, two-dimensional internal flows. There is a large literature on these formulations, and the interested reader should begin by looking at the text by Chung [36]. For three-dimensional solutions, see Refs. [37, 38].

### 2.2A Navier–Stokes Equations

Nondimensionalizing all variables with respect to a characteristic length $L$, a characteristic velocity $U$, and the kinematic viscosity of the fluid $\nu$, the Navier–Stokes momentum equations may be written as

$$\frac{\partial u_i}{\partial t} + u_j u_{i,j} = -p_{,i} + \frac{1}{\text{Re}}(u_{i,j} + u_{j,i})_{,j} \tag{2.26}$$

and the continuity equation $\qquad \nabla \cdot \mathbf{u} = u_{i,i} = 0 \tag{2.27}$

where $u_i$ $(i = 1, 2)$ are the velocity components in the $x$- and $y$-directions, respectively, $p$ is the pressure, and Re is the Reynolds number $UL/\nu$. By breaking the boundary $\Gamma$ of the domain $\Omega$ of the problem into two parts, namely, a kinematic part $\Gamma_u$, where the velocity is known, and a mechanical part $\Gamma_s$, where tractions are known (in principle, a mixed boundary can also be handled), the boundary conditions may be specified as

$$u_i = \bar{u}_i \qquad \text{on } \Gamma_u \tag{2.28a}$$

and

$$\left[ -p\delta_{ij} + \frac{1}{\text{Re}}(u_{i,j} + u_{j,i}) \right] n_j = \bar{S}_i \qquad \text{on } \Gamma_s \tag{2.28b}$$

where **n** is a unit vector normal to the boundary and **S** is the traction vector.

Equation (2.26) is often simplified by insertion of the continuity equation (2.27). Olson and Tuann [39] argue that this substitution should not be made a priori because the continuity equation is only satisfied in the limit with an infinite number of elements. Then equation (2.26) leads to a more consistent numerical model of the physical problem via Galerkin's method or a variational principle. In particular, the resulting matrix equations contain coupling of the *xy*-components of velocity and have incorporated in them the correct number (3) of rigid-flow modes.

The two main sources of difficulty in solving the Navier–Stokes equations are the nonlinear convective terms in Eq. (2.26) and the uncoupled nature of the incompressibility constraint, Eq. (2.27). The nonlinear terms are so predominant in all but the most trivial flow situations that quasi-linear iteration methods will not work and full nonlinear solution methods for unsymmetric matrices must be used, such as the Newton–Raphson method in steady problems. The uncoupled nature of the incompressibility constraint leads to zeros on the diagonal of the matrix equations, but this is no problem provided an appropriate solver for nonpositive-definite systems is used, such as gaussian elimination. However, there is a restriction on the allowable interpolation functions which can be used for velocities and pressure. In Ref. [39], it was shown that the interpolation for pressure *p* should not be higher than for the dilatation $u_x + v_y$ (subscripts denote differentiation). This effectively means that the pressure interpolation should be one order less than for the velocity components. If this restriction is violated, spurious rigid-flow modes will appear in the matrix equations for each element. These modes remain in the assembled equations for an assemblage of elements (thereby rendering them singular) and in general cannot be removed by velocity boundary conditions alone. The preceding has been verified more rigorously in Ref. [40].

## 2.2B  Variational Formulation

Although no variational principle in the classical sense can be constructed for the full Navier–Stokes equations, a restricted variational principle can be derived in the form

$$J(\mathbf{u}, p, \mathbf{u}^0) = \int \int_\Omega \left[ \frac{Du_i^0}{Dt} u_i - pu_{i,i} + \frac{1}{4\text{Re}}(u_{i,j} + u_{j,i})^2 \right] dA - \int_{\Gamma_s} \bar{S}_i u_i \, ds \tag{2.29}$$

When the first variation is taken, the $\mathbf{u}^0$ is held constant, and then is equated to **u** immediately thereafter. This process (after appropriate integration by parts) will then yield Eqs. (2.26) and (2.27) as Euler equations and Eqs. (2.28) and (2.29) as essential and natural boundary conditions, respectively. Hence Eq. (2.29) forms a pseudoextremal principle which may conveniently be used as a basis for deriving finite-element matrix equations.

Since Eq. (2.29) contains products of first derivatives of the velocity components, the interpolation fields for these must be $C^0$ for convergence. On the other hand, since the pressure appears without any derivatives, strictly speaking, its interpolation field need not be continuous.

***Penalty-Function Formulation***   Instead of using the functional (2.29) as the basis for a finite-element solution, it is possible to use a different functional in which the incompressibility is introduced via a penalty parameter $\pi$ [41, 42]. The functional of Eq. (2.29) is replaced by one embodying the square of the incompressibility constraint multiplied by a "penalty," a large positive number $\pi$. That is,

$$J(\mathbf{u}, p, \mathbf{u}^0) = \int\int_{\Omega} \left[ \frac{Du_i^0}{Dt} u_i + \pi(u_{i,i})^2 + \frac{1}{4\mathrm{Re}}(u_{i,j} + u_{j,i})^2 \right] dA - \int_{\Gamma_s} \bar{S}_i u_i \, ds \qquad (2.30)$$

where $-\pi(u_x + v_y)$ has been introduced to replace the pressure. Therefore, although the pressure has been eliminated to reduce the problem size, a sequence of $\pi$-values must be tested until the compressibility error $u_x + v_y$ is negligible over the whole domain. Moreover, as noted before in the $(u, v, p)$-approach where the pressure is to be "underinterpolated" by one order, a similar process must be taken, namely, the $\pi$-term should be "underintegrated" by one order less than that required for exact integration. Otherwise the element is overconstrained and the final assembled finite-element equations cannot be solved.

## 2.2c  Finite-Element Representation

For the substitution of finite-element interpolation fields, the functional of Eq. (2.29) is written in its full form as

$$\Pi = \int\int_{\Omega} \left\{ (u_t^0 + u^0 u_x^0 + v^0 u_y^0)u + (v_t^0 + u^0 v_x^0 + v^0 v_y^0)v - p(u_x + v_y) \right.$$
$$\left. + \frac{1}{\mathrm{Re}}[u_x^2 + v_y^2 + \tfrac{1}{2}(u_y + v_x)^2] \right\} dA - \int_{\Gamma_s} (\bar{X}u + \bar{Y}v) \, ds \qquad (2.31)$$

where $\bar{X}$, $\bar{Y}$ are the $xy$-components of the boundary traction $\bar{S}$ specified on the mechanical boundary $\Gamma_s$. The interpolation of each variable within an element in shape-function form is given as

$$u = \mathbf{N}^T\mathbf{U} \qquad v = \mathbf{N}^T\mathbf{V} \qquad p = \mathbf{L}^T\mathbf{P} \qquad (2.32)$$

where $\mathbf{U}$, $\mathbf{V}$, $\mathbf{P}$ are vectors of nodal variables for $u$, $v$, $p$, respectively, and $\mathbf{N}$, $\mathbf{L}$ are vectors of shape functions (of $x$ and $y$) for velocities and pressure, respectively. Note that the same shape functions are used for both the velocity components, but different ones for the pressure.

The matrix equations for the element are then obtained by substituting Eq. (2.32) into Eq. (2.31), carrying out the integrations, and then minimizing with respect to the nodal variables as per the restricted principle, giving

$$
\begin{bmatrix} \mathbf{M} & 0 & 0 \\ 0 & \mathbf{M} & 0 \\ 0 & 0 & 0 \end{bmatrix} \begin{Bmatrix} \dot{\mathbf{U}} \\ \dot{\mathbf{V}} \\ \dot{\mathbf{P}} \end{Bmatrix}
$$

$$
+ \begin{bmatrix} \dfrac{1}{Re}\mathbf{K}^{uu} + \mathbf{Q}^x\mathbf{U} & \dfrac{1}{Re}\mathbf{K}^{uv} + \mathbf{Q}^y\mathbf{U} & -\mathbf{P}^x \\ \dfrac{1}{Re}\mathbf{K}^{uvT} + \mathbf{Q}^x\mathbf{V} & \dfrac{1}{Re}\mathbf{K}^{vv} + \mathbf{Q}^y\mathbf{V} & -\mathbf{P}^y \\ -\mathbf{P}^{xT} & -\mathbf{P}^{yT} & 0 \end{bmatrix} \begin{Bmatrix} \mathbf{U} \\ \mathbf{V} \\ \mathbf{P} \end{Bmatrix} = \begin{Bmatrix} \mathbf{F}^u \\ \mathbf{F}^v \\ 0 \end{Bmatrix} \qquad (2.33)
$$

where

$$
\mathbf{M} = \iint \mathbf{N}^T\mathbf{N}\, dA \qquad \mathbf{K}^{uu} = \iint \left( 2\frac{\partial \mathbf{N}^T}{\partial x}\frac{\partial \mathbf{N}}{\partial x} + \frac{\partial \mathbf{N}^T}{\partial y}\frac{\partial \mathbf{N}}{\partial y} \right) dA \qquad (2.34a, b)
$$

$$
\mathbf{K}^{vv} = \iint \left( \frac{\partial \mathbf{N}^T}{\partial x}\frac{\partial \mathbf{N}}{\partial x} + 2\frac{\partial \mathbf{N}^T}{\partial y}\frac{\partial \mathbf{N}}{\partial y} \right) dA \qquad \mathbf{K}^{uv} = \iint \frac{\partial \mathbf{N}^T}{\partial y}\frac{\partial \mathbf{N}}{\partial x}\, dA \qquad (2.34c, d)
$$

$$
\mathbf{P}^x = \iint \frac{\partial \mathbf{N}^T}{\partial x}\mathbf{L}\, dA \qquad \mathbf{P}^y = \iint \frac{\partial \mathbf{N}^T}{\partial y}\mathbf{L}\, dA \qquad \mathbf{Q}^x = \iint \mathbf{N}^T\mathbf{N}\frac{\partial \mathbf{N}}{\partial x}\, dA \qquad (2.34e, f, g)
$$

$$
\mathbf{Q}^y = \iint \mathbf{N}^T\mathbf{N}\frac{\partial \mathbf{N}}{\partial y}\, dA \qquad \mathbf{F}^u = \int_1^2 \bar{X}\mathbf{N}^T\, ds \qquad \mathbf{F}^v = \int_1^2 \bar{Y}\mathbf{N}^T\, ds \qquad (2.34h, i, j)
$$

and where $\dot{\mathbf{U}}$, $\dot{\mathbf{V}}$ are time derivatives of $\mathbf{U}$, $\mathbf{V}$, respectively. Note that the boundary-integral terms $\mathbf{F}^u$, $\mathbf{F}^v$ need only be included for elements adjacent to the mechanical boundary $\Gamma_s$ and then only for the edge of the element actually on the boundary. Note that although Eqs. (2.33) and (2.34) were derived from a pseudovariational principle here, the Galerkin method yields exactly the same results.

In Eq. (2.33), the first square matrix is a type of mass matrix, and the second is a stiffness matrix. The mass matrix is constant and symmetric but has zero entries for the pressure terms. The stiffness matrix is not symmetric and is not constant in that it depends on the unknown pair $(\mathbf{U}, \mathbf{V})$. The global mass and stiffness matrices for a specific flow problem are assembled from the individual element matrices following standard finite-element procedures.

**Time-Dependent Problems**   For time-dependent problems, the system equations have to be solved by a numerical time-integration method. Many researchers have been working on this type of problem with a variety of approaches, none of which has proved completely successful in all cases. The problem is really very difficult because (1) the mass matrix is full rather than diagonal, and (2) for most problems the nonlinear terms are so significant that their effect must be included somehow in the time-integrator operator. Hence, the algorithm must be an implicit kind. For further details see Chung [36], Brooks and Hughes [43], and Gresho et al. [44].

***Steady Problems***   For steady problems, the time-derivative terms in the global system of equations are dropped, leaving a nonlinear set of algebraic equations which are most conveniently solved by the Newton–Raphson method. The equations have the form

$$R = [K]\{\delta\} - \{P\} = 0 \qquad (2.35)$$

where the stiffness matrix $[K]$ is a function of the unknown solution vector $\{\delta\}$, and $\{P\}$ is the load vector. If $\{\delta_0\}$ is an approximate solution, Eq. (2.35) is expanded by Taylor series to give

$$R(\delta) = R(\delta_0) + \left[\frac{\partial R}{\partial \delta}\right]_0 \Delta\delta \approx 0 \qquad (2.36)$$

Substitution from Eq. (2.35) then gives

$$\left[K + \frac{\partial K}{\partial \delta} \cdot \delta_0\right]_0 \Delta\delta = \{P\} - [K]_0\{\delta_0\} \qquad (2.37)$$

The subscript 0 means evaluated for the approximate solution $\delta_0$. The second term in the first bracket above is easily obtained from Eq. (2.33) as

$$\left[\frac{\partial K}{\partial \delta} \cdot \delta_0\right] = \begin{bmatrix} Q^x U_0 & Q^y V_0 & 0 \\ Q^x U_0 & Q^y V_0 & 0 \\ 0 & 0 & 0 \end{bmatrix} \qquad (2.38)$$

where $U_0$, $V_0$ are the $U$, $V$ parts of $\delta_0$.

The procedure for the Newton–Raphson iterations is the following: Assume an approximate solution $\delta_0$; separate $\delta_0$ into its parts for each element; evaluate Eq. (2.37) for each element; sum element contributions into a global set; solve for correction to solution $\Delta\delta$ and add to $\delta_0$; and repeat until convergence is obtained. It is usual to use the solution for a low Reynolds number as the approximate solution for the next higher Reynolds number and so on.

The stream function $\psi$ is often of interest, and this is best approximated by solving the Poisson's equation

$$\nabla^2 \psi = u_y - v_x = f \qquad (2.39)$$

A functional equivalent for Eq. (2.39) is easily obtained as

$$I = \int\int_\Omega [\tfrac{1}{2}(\psi_x^2 + \psi_y^2) + f\psi]\, dA - \int_{C_1} \frac{\overline{\partial\psi}}{\partial n}\, \psi\, ds \qquad (2.40)$$

where $C_1$ is that part of the boundary of the domain $\Omega$ on which the normal derivative $\partial\psi/\partial n$ is known. A finite-element representation is then easily derived, typically using the same element and shape functions as for the velocity components. Further, if the same grid is used as for the flow problem, the evaluation of the load terms from $f = u_y - v_x$ is very easy.

In some of the early work in this area, erratic pressure distributions were encountered in some problems even though the flow velocity fields were well-behaved. Further, as the Reynolds number increased, the calculations became unstable (for the same gridwork of elements). The upwind-differencing approach [35] was borrowed from the finite-difference area, and upwind finite elements were introduced as a solution for these difficulties. (See, for example, Zienkiewicz and Heinrich [45].) Subsequent investigations by Gartling [46], Gresho and Lee [47], and others have suggested that this is counterproductive and that the difficulties are more correctly eliminated by softening the boundary conditions (e.g., switch to natural rather than essential ones) and by refining the finite-element grids and/or the element interpolations themselves. Furthermore, low-order upwind differencing in the finite difference method has itself received considerable criticism because it introduces false numerical viscosity, and it has now been largely replaced by high-order central and/or upwind differences [48].

## 2.3 GENERALIZED NEWTONIAN FLOWS

### 2.3A The Generalized Newtonian Fluid

Shear-rate dependence of viscosity is widely observed in the flow of complex liquids such as polymer melts and solutions, suspensions of fine particles, pastes, emulsions, and metals under large deformation. Such behavior is frequently modeled isothermally as generalized newtonian flow as

$$s_{ij} = 2\mu d_{ij} \qquad \mu = \mu(\mathrm{II}_d) \tag{2.41}$$

where $s_{ij}$ is the deviatoric-stress tensor, $\mu$ is the viscosity, $d_{ij}$ is the rate-of-deformation tensor $\frac{1}{2}(u_{i,j} + u_{j,i})$, $u_i$ is the velocity vector, and $\mathrm{II}_d$ is the second invariant of the rate-of-deformation tensor, $\frac{1}{2}d_{ij}d_{ij}$. Strictly speaking, the generalized newtonian model should be applied only to steady shearing flows and the assumption of incompressibility is implicit. However, because of its relative simplicity it is applied much more widely and can often give useful results approximating the behavior of complex fluids.

### 2.3B Applications of Finite Elements to Generalized Newtonian Flows

Finite-element solutions for generalized newtonian flow were first applied to aspects of thermoplastics melt processing by Palit and Fenner [49, 50], using the isothermal power-law model

$$\mu = \mu^*(\sqrt{4\mathrm{II}_d})^{n-1} \tag{2.42}$$

where $\mu^*$ is the consistency coefficient and $n$ is the power-law exponent. Solutions for coupled flow and heat transfer were also obtained by Palit using an exponential temperature dependence of viscosity, but these were limited by difficulties in treating convective heat transfer [51, 52].

Further applications to polymer melt flow, using Eq. (2.41), were made by Kiparissides and Vlachopoulos [53]; Caswell and Tanner [54]; Fenner and Nadiri [55]; Chou, Hami, and

Pittman [56]; and Roylance [57]. More recently, with the development of effective means for treating convective heat transport, coupled flow and heat transfer in polymer melts have been studied, using the temperature-dependent power law (see Nakazawa et al. [58, 59], Mahmoudzadeh [60], Pittman and Mahmoudzadeh [61], and Nakazawa and Zienkiewicz [62]), with $\mu^*$ in Eq. (2.42) given by

$$\mu^* = \mu_0 \, e^{-b(T-T_0)} \tag{2.43}$$

where $\mu_0$ is the reference value of $\mu^*$ at temperature $T_0$, $b$ is the temperature coefficient of viscosity, and $T$ is the local temperature.

Three-dimensional applications have also been presented by Menges et al. [63] and Masberg and Menges [64], and free-surface power-law flow has been treated by Tanner, Nickell, and Bilger [65]. A fuller review of these polymer-processing applications is given in Pittman and Nakazawa [66], where further examples of coupled power-law flow and heat transfer are shown.

A second important area of application was opened up by the recognition that in metal forming, since plastic deformations are so much greater than elastic ones, the processes can be modeled as generalized newtonian flows. The basis for this type of formulation was provided by Prager [67], and the finite-element treatment was developed and unified with other "nonnewtonian" problems by Zienkiewicz and Godbole [68–70]. Finite yield stress is treated using the von Mises criterion:

$$\langle \phi(F) \rangle = 0 \qquad F < 0$$

$$\langle \phi(F) \rangle \equiv \phi(F) \qquad F \geqslant 0 \tag{2.44}$$

$$F = \sqrt{3\mathrm{II}_s} - \sigma_y$$

where $\phi$ is the potential function; $F$ is the yield function; $\mathrm{II}_s$ is the second invariant of the deviatoric-stress tensor, $\frac{1}{2}s_{ij}s_{ij}$; and $\sigma_y$ is the uniaxial yield stress. With $\phi(F)$ chosen as $F^m$, the deviatoric-stress–rate-of-deformation relationship is

$$d_{ij} = \frac{\gamma \langle F^m \rangle \sqrt{3} \, s_{ij}}{\sqrt{4\mathrm{II}_s}} \tag{2.45}$$

leading to a generalized Bingham plastic model with exponent $m$. Comparison with Eq. (2.41) yields

$$\mu = \frac{\sigma_y + (\sqrt{4\mathrm{II}_d}/\sqrt{3}\,\gamma)^{1/m}}{\sqrt{12\mathrm{II}_d}} \tag{2.46}$$

The finite yield stress is modeled using a continuously varying viscosity, going to infinity as $\mathrm{II}_d$ goes to zero. In practice $\mu$ is limited to some large value. In a development of this work Zienkiewicz, Jain, and Oñate [71] incorporated strain-hardening in a transient, stretch-forming example by making $\sigma_y$ a function of accumulated effective strain $\bar{\varepsilon}$, obtained by time integration of

$$\frac{D\bar{\varepsilon}}{Dt} = \sqrt{4\mathrm{II}_d} \tag{2.47}$$

where $D/Dt$ is the convected derivative $(\partial/\partial t + u_i\, \partial/\partial x_i)$. Temperature dependence of the parameters in Eq. (2.45) and the resultant coupling with the thermal problem have also been treated [71, 72]. A recent survey of applications in metal forming is provided in Ref. [73].

Further applications of finite-element methods to the solution of generalized newtonian flows are found, for example, in work on blood flow by Godbole, Nakazawa, and Zienkiewicz, using the Casson equation [74].

## 2.3c  Finite-Element Techniques

General considerations in the choice of formulation for flow problems are discussed elsewhere in this volume. The penalty-function method with selective reduced integration is found satisfactory, particularly if three-dimensional applications are considered. Here a number of points relevant particularly to the solution of generalized newtonian flows are considered. The nonlinearity of the problem requires an iterative solution, starting with a newtonian (constant-viscosity), creeping-flow solution. $II_d$ is evaluated from this at the (full) integration points and substituted into the constitutive equation to give local viscosities. The velocity solution is then repeated using these values, and so on. This successive substitution scheme is often preferred to higher-order methods. Convergence is usually achieved easily in less than 10 iterations [58, 59, 62, 70]. Implicit in the above technique is the use of an elimination method to solve the linearized equations. Gauss-Seidl iteration has, however, been used, with simultaneous periodic updating of viscosities [49, 50].

In solving the coupled-flow and thermal problem, successive substitution is again preferred, although in very highly nonlinear cases even this may not converge, and a damped scheme, in which the means of values from two previous iterations are substituted, has been found effective [75].

When the thermal problem includes significant viscous heat generation, the possibility of an inner iteration on temperature arises. Viscosity in the source term of the energy equation is updated using the latest temperature, and only when this has converged is a further solution of the velocity field carried out. The inner iteration may be programmed very economically, since only the right-hand-side ("nodal-force") vector changes on each cycle, and there is some evidence that the scheme is more efficient than the alternative [76].

Particularly when thermal coupling is combined with shear dependence, viscosity variations of orders of magnitude may occur within the solution domain, and in the penalty formulation, this can cause difficulties with incompressibility enforcement. Use of a weighted penalty parameter proportional to the local viscosity has been proposed, and has been shown to give improved solution capabilities [59]. The theoretical basis has been discussed in Ref. [62].

The treatment of work-hardening in metals, by allowing parameters in the rheological model to depend on material history, has been mentioned above [72]. Similar ideas are involved in dealing with other forms of time dependence (thixotropy, rheopexy) often exhibited by suspensions, pastes, etc. Evaluation of material history is straightforward in lagrangian formulations, less so in eulerian ones. The requirement to integrate along stream-lines (path lines in unsteady flow) also occurs in viscoelastic flow using memory integral rheological models. In this context, finite-element schemes involving streamline tracking have been described by Viriyayuthakorn and Caswell [77]; Caswell [78]; Bernstein, Kadivar, and Malkus [79]; and Bernstein and Malkus [80]. A simple alternative approach has been used by Thompson, Pittman, and Zienkiewicz [81]. A convective-transport equation such as Eq. (2.47) is discretized and solved directly as an initial-value problem by finite elements.

## 2.4 LAKE AND HARBOR MOTION

### 2.4A Waves

It is well known that the infinitesimal wave can be described by the Helmholz equation. The finite-element method for this has been presented by Taylor and Davis [82]. However, there are practical difficulties, such as (1) a great number of degrees of freedom must be used because the wave length is extremely short, and (2) the wave problem is usually defined by the infinite boundary conditions.

A review paper on the unbounded domain was published by Zienkiewicz et al. [83]. One of the most promising methods for the infinite boundary condition of the unbounded domain is "the marriage of finite elements and boundary integrals" (Zienkiewicz et al. [84]). The boundary-integral method is the extension of the classical methods, which have been discussed by Garrison and Rao [85], Garrison [86], Harms [87], Lee [88], and many others. For the analysis of the field far from the structure, the boundary-element method can be adapted to the radiation conditions. This approach has been presented by Zienkiewicz et al. [84, 89, 90] and Berkhoff [91], employing the indirect boundary-element method and the linear triangular finite-element method. Hara et al. [92] have considered the higher-order boundary-element method corresponding to the isoparametric finite-element method.

The hybrid-type finite-element method, which can be matched to the analytical solution for the outer domain, has been considered by Mei and Chen [93], Yue et al. [94], Liu [95], Houston [96], Seto [97], and others. Sakai [98] derived a useful variational theorem for the radiation condition and presented a finite-element method based on this. The infinite-element method discussed by Bettess [99, 100] and by Bettess and Zienkiewicz [101] is based on the concept that the exponentially decaying interpolation function can be adapted to the infinite-length finite element. Ganeba et al. [102] presented the finite-element solution for harbor resonance based on the Helmholz equation, with two sources of dissipation: (1) the outward radiation of energy from within the harbor, which is analyzed by the boundary-integral method, and (2) turbulence.

### 2.4B Tides

In shallow-water theory, the basic equations of the tide are derived from the Navier–Stokes equations assuming a hydrostatic pressure distribution in the direction of water depth. If $u_i$ and $\zeta$ are current velocity and water elevation, the resulting equations averaged over a turbulent time scale are as follows.

*Equation of motion*:

$$\frac{\partial u_i}{\partial t} + u_j u_{i,j} + g\zeta_{,i} - A_1(u_{i,j} + u_{j,i})_{,j} - \gamma_{ij}u_j + \tau_i^S - \tau_i^B = 0 \qquad (2.48)$$

*Equation of continuity:*

$$\frac{\partial \zeta}{\partial t} + \{(H + \zeta)u_i\}_{,i} = 0 \tag{2.49}$$

where $H$ is the water depth from the mean sea level, $g$ is the acceleration due to gravity, and $A_1$ is the turbulent viscosity. The Coriolis force is given by

$$\gamma_{ij} = \begin{cases} f(i = 1, j = 2) \\ -f(j = 2, j = 1) \end{cases} \qquad \text{otherwise zero}$$

The surface stress and bottom friction are given by

$$\tau_i^S = \frac{C_a \rho_a}{\rho(H + \zeta)} W_i \sqrt{(W_k W_k)} \tag{2.50}$$

$$\tau_i^B = \frac{C}{\rho(H + \zeta)} u_i \sqrt{(u_k u_k)} \tag{2.51}$$

where $W_i$ is the wind velocity, $C_a$ is the wind-velocity coefficient, $\rho_a$ is the air density, and $C$ is the bottom friction coefficient.

Where the velocity is given on a boundary $S_1$, the corresponding boundary condition is

$$u_i = \hat{u}_i \qquad \text{on } S_1 \tag{2.52}$$

where the velocity flux is known on a boundary $S_2$, the boundary condition is

$$\gamma_i = A_1(u_{i,j} + u_{j,i})n_j = \hat{\gamma}_i \qquad \text{on } S_2 \tag{2.53}$$

and, finally, where the water elevation is defined on a boundary $S_3$,

$$\zeta = \hat{\zeta} \qquad \text{on } S_3 \tag{2.54}$$

where the caret denotes the described value on the boundary.

The modeling of a tidal flow relates to the way in which the tidal elevation at the seaward boundary is specified (by the tidal periodic function of time). At the landward boundary, a "seawall boundary" is commonly used at which the normal velocity is assumed to be zero. Tidal-flat conditions with other boundary conditions have been examined by Kawahara [103], Herrling [104], and Holz and Nitsche [105]. Sometimes, on the boundary $S_2$, the following condition is used:

$$t_i = \{-g\zeta\delta_{ij} + A_1(u_{i,j} + u_{j,i})\}n_j = \hat{t}_i \qquad \text{on } S_2 \tag{2.55}$$

However, this condition can cause unreasonable numerical results with the water elevation at the boundary being forced to be almost zero (Kawahara [106]). Since this is often contrary to the actual phenomena, this type of boundary condition is not recommended. An alternative approach for the seaward boundary is to use the progressive wave condition in which the normal velocity $u$ to the boundary is specified by

$$u = \zeta \sqrt{\frac{g}{H + \zeta}} \tag{2.56}$$

This condition can be effectively used for problems in which waves are generated in an inner domain and propagate toward the outer sea domain, but it is recommended that it be used far from the land boundary.

With the Galerkin approach, the weighted-residual equations corresponding to (2.48) and (2.49) become

$$\int_V (u_i^* \dot{u}_i) \, dV + \int_V (u_i^* u_j u_{i,j}) \, dV + \int_V (u_i^* g\zeta_{,i}) \, dV$$

$$+ A_1 \int_V (u_{i,j}^* u_{i,j}) \, dV + A_1 \int_V (u_{i,j}^* u_{j,i}) \, dV + \int_V (u_i^* \tau_i^B) \, dV$$

$$= \int_V (u_i^* \tau_i^S) \, dV + \int_{S_2} (u_i^* \hat{\gamma}_i) \, dS \tag{2.57}$$

$$\int_V \left( \zeta^* \frac{\partial \zeta}{\partial t} \right) dV + \int_V \zeta^* \{(H + \zeta) u_i\}_{,i} \, dV = 0 \tag{2.58}$$

where $u_i^*$ and $\zeta^*$ represent weighting functions for the equations of momentum and continuity, respectively. Alternative weighted-residual equations can also be formulated (Kawahara [107]).

The tidal-flow field under consideration is assumed to be divided into finite elements in the usual way. By using an interpolation function $\Phi_\alpha$ for both velocity and water elevation, the element equations can be derived from (2.57) and (2.58) in the form

$$M_{\alpha\beta} \dot{u}_{\beta i} + K_{\alpha\beta\gamma j} u_{\beta j} u_{\gamma i} + N_{\alpha i\beta} \zeta_\beta + S_{\alpha i\beta j} u_{\beta j} = \Omega_{\alpha i} \tag{2.59}$$

$$M_{\alpha\beta} \dot{\zeta}_\beta + A_{\alpha\beta j\gamma} u_{\beta j} \zeta_\gamma + B_{\alpha\beta j} u_{\beta j} = 0 \tag{2.60}$$

where $u_{\beta j}$ is the velocity in the $j^{\text{th}}$ direction at node $\beta$ of a finite element and $\zeta_\gamma$ is the water elevation at node $\gamma$. Also,

$$M_{\alpha\beta} = \int_V (\Phi_\alpha \Phi_\beta) \, dV \tag{2.61a}$$

$$K_{\alpha\beta j\gamma} = \int_V (\Phi_\alpha \Phi_{\beta,j} \Phi_\gamma) \, dV \tag{2.61b}$$

$$N_{\alpha i\beta} = g \int_V (\Phi_\alpha \Phi_{\beta,i}) \, dV \tag{2.61c}$$

$$S_{\alpha i\beta j} = A_1 \int_V (\Phi_{\alpha,i} \Phi_{\beta,j}) \, dV + A_1 \int_V (\Phi_{\alpha,k} \Phi_{\beta,k}) \delta_{ij} \, dV$$

$$+ \frac{g}{C^2} \int_V (u_k u_k)^{1/2} \cdot (\Phi_\alpha \Phi_\beta) \delta_{ij} \, dV \tag{2.61d}$$

$$\Omega_{\alpha i} = \int_V (\Phi_\alpha \tau_i^S)\, dV + \int_{S_2} (\Phi_\alpha \hat{\gamma}_i)\, dS \tag{2.61e}$$

$$A_{\alpha\beta j\gamma} = \int_V (\Phi_{\alpha,j} \Phi_\beta \Phi_\gamma)\, dV \tag{2.61f}$$

$$B_{\alpha\beta j} = A_{\alpha\beta j\gamma} \cdot H_\gamma \tag{2.61g}$$

where the bottom friction term is linearized·and the water depth over each finite element is interpolated as

$$H = \Phi_\alpha H_\alpha \tag{2.61h}$$

where $H_\alpha$ is the water depth at each node of the element. By superposing Eqs. (2.59) and (2.60) for all nodes in the whole flow field, the final finite-element equation can be assembled as a nonlinear, first-order simultaneous-equation system

$$M_{\alpha\beta} \dot{V}_\beta + K_{\alpha\beta\gamma} V_\beta V_\gamma + N_{\alpha\beta} Z_\beta + S_{\alpha\beta} V_\beta = \hat{\Omega}_\alpha \tag{2.62}$$

$$M_{\alpha\beta} \dot{Z}_\beta + A_{\alpha\beta\gamma} V_\beta Z_\gamma + B_{\alpha\beta} Z_\beta = \hat{\Sigma}_\alpha \tag{2.63}$$

where $V_\beta$ and $Z_\beta$ represent the components of velocity and water elevation, respectively, for all nodes in the flow field. For convenience, Eqs. (2.62) and (2.63) can be written in the form

$$G_\alpha \equiv M_{\alpha\beta} \dot{U}_\beta + F_\alpha(U_\beta) - \hat{\Omega}_\alpha = 0 \tag{2.64}$$

In order to solve the equation systems (2.62) and (2.63) or (2.64), a numerical-integration scheme in time needs to be introduced. As is well known, tidal flow is comprised of periodic constituents, and is sometimes coupled with a long period flow (especially drift currents). By decomposing the tidal flow into constituents, the numerical-integration technique can be applied to each constituent. For drift and for periodical currents, suitable numerical methods have already been derived.

## 2.4c  Constituent Decomposition Method

The natural tide in the sea is characterized by its periodic motion. Assuming that the tide consists of a finite number of constituents, the Galerkin approach can be employed with the numerical integration in time using a trigonometric series as the interpolation function. In this quasi-steady flow analysis, mixed interpolation is introduced. If $\Phi_\alpha$ and $\psi_\lambda$ are the interpolation functions for velocity and water elevation, respectively, the element equations for the finite-element solution can be derived as in the previous section. Kawahara and Hasegawa [108, 109] employed a quadratic interpolation function based on the six-node triangular finite element for velocity and a linear interpolation function based on the three-node triangular finite element for water elevation. Pearson and Winters [110] and Jamart and Winters [111, 112] employed linear interpolation functions for both velocity and water elevation. In these papers, eddy-viscosity terms have been ignored and nonlinear-convection terms have been linearized. Because of the similarity to steady-flow analysis, mixed interpolation must be a more reasonable choice for the interpolation function. Warzee and Sterling

[113], Provost et al. [114], and Rahman [115] consider the finite-element solutions based on this concept.

By superposing the element equations for all nodes in the whole flow field, a nonlinear first-order simultaneous equation set can be derived in the same form as for Eqs. (2.62) and (2.63), and then rewritten as in Eq. (2.64). Let the given term $\hat{\Omega}_\alpha$ in the new equation of form (2.64) be expressed by the sum of trigonometric functions having a period $\omega$, i.e.,

$$\hat{\Omega}_\alpha = \hat{\Omega}_\alpha^{(0)} + \sum_{j=1}^{N} \hat{\Omega}_{\alpha s}^{(j)} \sin j\omega t + \sum_{j=1}^{N} \hat{\Omega}_{\alpha c}^{(j)} \cos j\omega t \qquad (2.65)$$

The trial function may be written in the form

$$U_\beta = U_\beta^{(0)} + \sum_{j=1}^{N} a_\beta^{(j)} \sin j\omega t + \sum_{j=1}^{N} b_\beta^{(j)} \cos j\omega t \qquad (2.66)$$

where $U_\beta^{(0)}$, $a_\beta^{(1)} \cdots a_\beta^{(N)}$, and $b_\beta^{(1)} \cdots b_\beta^{(N)}$ are the unknown vectors to be determined. With Eqs. (2.65) and (2.66), the concepts of Fourier analysis lead to the following weighted-residual equation

$$\int_0^{2\pi/\omega} G_\alpha(U_\beta^{(0)}) \, dt = 0 \qquad (2.67)$$

$$\int_0^{2\pi/\omega} \sin i\omega t \, G_\alpha(\omega) \, dt = 0 \qquad (2.68)$$

$$\int_0^{2\pi/\omega} \cos i\omega t \, G_\alpha(\omega) \, dt = 0 \qquad (2.69)$$

From Eqs. (2.67) to (2.69) the unknown vectors can be determined, and then from Eq. (2.66) the velocity and water elevation at any location can be computed. The numerical results obtained by this approach have been in good agreement with observed field data (Kawahara and Hasegawa [109]).

With the above method, problems of unsteady nonlinear but periodic flow can be solved by effectively superposing the constituent solutions. The use of the trigonometric interpolation function thus allows periodic equations to be solved in a manner similar to the steady-flow equation. Another approach to this problem using Laplace transforms has been reported by Young and Liggett [116].

## 2.4D Time-Marching Method

Of the many numerical-integration methods in time reported for unsteady-flow analysis by the finite-element method, the majority utilize the time-marching method. In this approach, the time period under consideration is divided into intervals $\Delta t$, and function values at every discrete time point used for the numerical integration. There are two classes of time-marching method, implicit schemes and explicit schemes. An implicit scheme is one that includes a computational procedure to solve either a linear or nonlinear algebraic simultaneous-equation system. In an explicit scheme the computational results at the $(n+1)^{\text{th}}$ time point are derived from the results at $n^{\text{th}}$ time point or earlier time points, and this does not require a solution procedure to solve a simultaneous-equation system. Selection of the interpolation equation, that is, selection of the finite-element type, depends on the kind of numerical integration in time used.

Table 2.1 lists interpolation functions employed in a number of finite-element analyses in the area considered. Both normal and mixed interpolations are commonly used. A normal interpolation has the same interpolation function for both velocity and water elevation. The standard normal interpolation function is the linear polynomial based on a triangular finite element. The isoparametric element family is also often employed for these kinds of analyses. In a mixed interpolation different functions are used for velocity and for water elevation. Normally, a higher-order polynomial is used for the interpolation of velocity than that of water elevation. The basic reason why mixed interpolation is employed in the time-marching method for the tidal-flow analysis is quite different from the reason why it is used in the analysis of steady flow. In tidal analysis, it is not a requirement that mixed interpolation be used, and normal interpolation can be selected without causing special problems. For lower-order normal interpolation, such as the linear polynomial based on the three-node triangular finite element, an explicit type of numerical integration in time can be effectively applied. For higher-order normal interpolation, such as a quadratic polynomial based on

**TABLE 2.1**   Interpolation Functions

| Interpolation function | Reference |
| --- | --- |
| Linear triangle | Grotkop [120] |
| | Cullen [122–126] |
| | Herrling [104, 127] |
| | Holz [128], Holz and Nitsche [105] |
| | Connor and Wang [129], Wang [130] |
| | Kawahara and Hasegawa [108], Kawahara et al. [121, 131] |
| | Koutitas and O'Connor [132] |
| | Tanaka et al. [133] |
| | Signorini [134] |
| | Praagman [135] |
| | Argintaru and Spraggs [136] |
| | Murakami and Morikawa [137] |
| Quadratic triangle | Partridge and Brebbia [138] |
| Bilinear quadrilateral | Hirsch [139] |
| | Su and Wang [140] |
| Quadratic quadrilateral | Staniforth and Daley [141], Staniforth and Mitchell [142, 143] |
| | Gray [144], Lynch and Gray [145] |
| | Taylor and Davis [146, 147] |
| | Laible [148] |
| | Matsunashi [149] |
| | Trösch [150] |
| Mixed interpolation | Walters and Cheng [151] |
| | King and Norton [152] |
| | MacArthur and Norton [153] |
| | King [154] |

isoparametric finite elements, an implicit type of numerical integration in time can be used. In the case of mixed interpolation, the implicit type of numerical integration is standard.

Numerical-integration schemes in time that have been used for finite-element analyses in this area are listed in Table 2.2. The standard implicit scheme is trapezoidal integration and related schemes. In general, computations using the implicit scheme are more stable than those using the explicit scheme, but the penalty is the extensive computation required to solve an algebraic simultaneous-equation system. The core storage requirement for a simultaneous-equation solution is comparatively large, and sometimes this exceeds the limitation of the available computer. An alternate-direction scheme based on a topologically regular finite-element arrangement has been developed by Baker et al. [117] and Baker and Soliman [118]. While this has some advantages, topologically regular arrangements do not always suit practical problems which have complicated boundary configurations.

It is often important in tidal flow to compute a secondary wave which has a higher frequency than that of the incident wave specified at the boundary. These higher modes originate from resonance in an embayment which has irregular boundary and bottom topography. For these problems, the use of the implicit scheme with large time increments (to reduce computation costs) means that the higher-frequency modes can be missed. In the explicit

**TABLE 2.2**  Numerical-Integration Schemes for Time

| Scheme | Reference |
|---|---|
| **Implicit Scheme:** | |
| Finite-element scheme in time | Grotkop [140], Taylor and Davis [146, 147], Herrling [104] |
| Trapezoidal-integration scheme | Taylor and Davis [146, 147], Partridge and Brebbia [138], Young et al. [155, 156], Walters and Cheng [151], Holz and Nitsche [105], Trösch [150] |
| Full implicit scheme | King and Norton [152, Cochet et al. [157, 158], MacArthur and Norton [153] |
| Semilinearized scheme | Argintaru and Spraggs [136], Tanaka et al. [133] |
| Staggered scheme | Koutitas and O'Connor [132] |
| Semi-implicit scheme | Staniforth and Mitchell [142, 143] |
| Alternate-direction scheme | Baker et al. [117] |
| **Explicit scheme:** | |
| Runge-Kutta scheme | Partridge and Brebbia [138] |
| Leapfrog scheme | Cullen [122–126], Gray [144], Lynch and Gray [145], Cheng [159], Matsunashi [149] |
| Time-split scheme | Wang [160] |
| Two-step scheme | Kawahara et al. [119, 121, 160] |
| Averaging scheme | Wang [161] |
| Upwind scheme | Kanayama and Ohtsuka [162], Murakami and Morikawa [137] |
| **Semianalytical scheme:** | |
| Matrix exponential scheme | Holz and Hennlich [163] |
| Laplace transform scheme | Young and Liggett [116] |

scheme, the time increments should be chosen much shorter than in the implicit scheme. This is possible since the computing time for each computational cycle in the explicit scheme is much shorter than in the implicit scheme. The computer core storage requirement for the explicit scheme is also much less than for the implicit scheme. It is not unexpected, therefore, that the explicit scheme is becoming more widely used in finite-element analyses in this area.

To avoid the time-consuming solution of a simultaneous equation and to acquire numerical stability, a lumping technique has been originated by Kawahara et al. [119, 121], which for the two-step scheme can be represented as

$$\bar{M}_{\alpha\beta} U_{\beta}^{n+1/2} = \tilde{M}_{\alpha\beta} U_{\beta}^{n} - \frac{\Delta t}{2} F_{\alpha}(U_{\beta}^{n}) + \frac{\Delta t}{2} \Omega_{\alpha}^{n} \tag{2.70}$$

$$\bar{M}_{\alpha\beta} U_{\beta}^{n+1} = \tilde{M}_{\alpha\beta} U_{\beta}^{n} - \Delta t F_{\alpha}(U_{\beta}^{n+1/2}) + \Delta t \Omega_{\alpha}^{n} \tag{2.71}$$

where $$\tilde{M}_{\alpha\beta} = e\bar{M}_{\alpha\beta} + (1-e) M_{\alpha\beta} \tag{2.72}$$

and where $\bar{M}_{\alpha\beta}$ denotes the lumped matrix. The parameter $e$ is referred to as the *selective lumping parameter*, which controls the numerical damping and numerical stability. If the equation system includes the viscosity terms, the parameter $e$ can be chosen to be 1.0.

The limitation on the time increment in the explicit scheme is

$$\Delta t \leqslant \frac{\alpha \cdot \Delta x}{\sqrt{gh}} \tag{2.73}$$

where $h$ is water depth and $\Delta x$ is the minimum length of the finite element. The parameter $\alpha$ is usually 0.1 to 0.5. It is desirable that the finite-element configuration be such that $\Delta x / \sqrt{gh}$ be constant throughout the whole domain.

## 2.4E Drift Current

*Drift current* means a steady flow which moves steadily in a certain direction. There are many origins for drift currents, such as wind at the surface of the sea, ocean currents far from the coastline, residual components of the tidal flow, and so on. The basic equation for the flow can be expressed as

$$u_j u_{i,j} + g\zeta_{,i} - A_1(u_{i,j} + u_{j,i})_{,j} - \gamma_{ij} u_j + \tau_i^s - \tau_i^B = 0 \tag{2.74}$$

$$\{(H+\zeta)u_i\}_{,i} = 0 \tag{2.75}$$

where the same notation is used as in Eqs. (2.48) and (2.49). The boundary conditions are the same as in Eqs. (2.52) to (2.58). In the computation of the wind drift current, the surface stress $\tau_i^s$ is specified as a function of wind velocity. In case of drift current accompanied by offshore ocean current, the velocity at the seaward boundary is specified. In tidal-flow computation where the tidal elevation is given by sinusoidal functions, sometimes the differences of water elevation on the boundaries induce the drift current. In this case, the water elevations need specifying.

For steady-state flow, there exists both a steady and an unsteady approach. The steady approach assumes the steady state throughout the analysis, whereas the unsteady approach obtains the steady state as the final state of an unsteady-flow computation. Since the unsteady approach is the same as that described in another section, only the steady approach will be explained here. The weighted-residual equation used can be obtained from Eqs. (2.57) and (2.58) by neglecting the time-derivative terms. Mixed interpolation will be used for velocity and water elevation. The standard Galerkin–finite-element method leads to the nonlinear simultaneous-equation system. For the solution of this equation, the Newton–Raphson method is commonly used.

The above is the most primitive method for the drift-current analysis and is not suitable for relatively high-velocity flow because convergence of the Newton–Raphson method is not always achieved. To cope with this problem, Kawahara and Hasegawa [109] introduced the stream function into the analysis. By considering Eq. (2.75) the stream function $\psi$ can be defined as

$$u_i = \frac{1}{H+\zeta}\varepsilon_{ij}\psi_{,j} \approx \frac{1}{H}\varepsilon_{ij}\psi_{,j} \tag{2.76}$$

If Eq. (2.76) is used, Eq. (2.75) is automatically satisfied. Kawahara and Hasegawa [108] have discussed the method precisely.

Cochet et al. [157, 158] have utilized the penalty-function approach for this type of flow, in which the water elevation $\zeta$ is assumed to be

$$\zeta = -\lambda M_{i,j} \tag{2.77}$$

where $$M_i = (H+\zeta)u_i$$

and $\zeta$ is the penalty parameter. If Eq. (2.77) is introduced into the weighted-residual equation, the finite-element equation can be obtained by assuming a suitable interpolation function. The penalty parameter $\lambda$ must be chosen large enough for the method to work. Nine-node quadrilateral elements with four integration points and six-node triangular elements with three integration points are considered by this author, and the method has been applied to the study of environmental impact due to a nuclear-station thermal discharge into the St. Lawrence River. Moult [164] has explored the upwind finite-element method for drift-current problems using stream and vorticity functions based on the triangular finite element. With finite-element methods such as these, almost all drift-current problems can be effectively analyzed.

## 2.4F Tsunami and Storm Surge

Both tsunami and storm surge are natural hazards and time-dependent transient phenomena. The tsunami is analogous to a shock wave propagating along the surface of the sea, caused by a sudden deformation of the sea bottom due, mostly, to earthquakes and, sometimes, to volcanos. The sudden rise or fall of the sea bottom generates the tsunami wave, which is propagated toward the coast. As it approaches the coast and enters a bay, the tsunami wave can be greatly amplified by the configuration and bottom topography. The tsunami wave is of special importance because of the great damage which is often caused.

The storm surge can also be considered like a shock wave which has a long characteristic period and is induced by the climatological upheaval of the sea surface. When a low-pressure

region associated with a tropical storm, hurricane, or typhoon, passes over the sea, the surface
will be raised by the pressure difference. The raised water elevation corresponds to a wave
with a rather long period. If the generated wave period is coincident with the characteristic
period of a bay, the wave can be unpredictably amplified.

The above phenomena can be considered to be problems in transient, long-period wave
propagation, and the governing equation will be the shallow-water equation. The modeling
of tsunami divides into three parts: generation, propagation, and run-up. Tsunami generation
can be modeled by the shallow-water equation, including the bottom deformation. Thus the
equation of motion is

$$\frac{\partial M_i}{\partial t} + (u_j M_i)_{,j} + g(H + \zeta - b)\zeta_{,i} = 0 \tag{2.78}$$

and the equation of continuity is

$$\frac{\partial}{\partial t}(\zeta - b) + M_{i,i} = 0 \tag{2.79}$$

where

$$M_i = H + \zeta - b \tag{2.80}$$

and $u_i$ is the velocity, $\zeta$ is the water elevation, $H$ is the water depth, $b$ is the bottom deformation
in the epicenter region, and $g$ is the acceleration due to gravity. Coriolis force, eddy viscosity,
and bottom friction are all ignored because they are insignificant for the tsunami problem.

When the tsunami approaches the coastal sea, the deformation of the sea bottom can be
excluded from the governing equation, which can be written in terms of velocity $u_i$ instead
of $M_i$. Thus the equation of motion becomes

$$\frac{\partial u_i}{\partial t} + u_j u_{i,j} + g\zeta_{,i} = 0 \tag{2.81}$$

and the equation of continuity becomes

$$\frac{\partial \zeta}{\partial t} + \{(H + \zeta)u_i\}_{,i} = 0 \tag{2.82}$$

By specifying the appropriate boundary and initial conditions, the finite-element method can
be applied to Eqs. (2.81) and (2.82) in almost the same manner as described previously. Since
the tsunami is a transient phenomenon, the analysis can be carried out by using the time-
marching method for the numerical integration in time.

The wave period of the tsunami usually ranges from 15 minutes to 2 hours. The corresponding wavelength is about 1 to 10 km depending on the water depth. To obtain reasonable
numerical results for one wave, it is necessary to have at least 10 nodal points interpolating
the wave. Thus, a relatively refined finite-element mesh should be used. To cope with the
number of nodal points, the explicit type of numerical-integration scheme can be efficiently
used. Kawahara et al. [119, 160] and Kawahara and Nakazawa [166] applied the two-step
explicit scheme, for example, to the analysis of the tsunamis resulting from the Tokachi-oki
and Kanto earthquakes. Houston [165] has presented the analyses for the tsunami in the
Hawaiian islands.

The run-up of the tsunami toward the land is modeled as follows, assuming the coastline topography is given. The run-up computation is carried out, after determination of whether the sea bottom is exposed or under water, by the use of the following criteria: (1) if $h = H + \zeta \geqslant 0$, the sea bottom is exposed; (2) if $h = H + \zeta < 0$, the sea bottom is under water; where $H$ and $\zeta$ are the water depth and water elevation, respectively, with both quantities measured from the mean sea level. Kawahara et al. [121] have applied the finite-element method based on the triangular finite element to the computation over intertidal flats. In this computation, the following procedure is used. For each nodal point $i$ of each finite element, the water depth $H_i$, water elevation $\zeta_i$, and both components of current velocity $u_i$, $v_i$ are computed. Following this, the total water depth $h_i = H_i + \zeta_i$ is obtained. Using $h_i$, each element is examined to see whether

1. All nodal values of $h_i$ are $h_i > 0$,
2. At least one value of $h_i$ is $h_i > 0$, and the rest of $h_i$ are $h_i < 0$, or
3. All values of $h_i$ are $h_i < 0$.

In case 1, the element under consideration is under water. In case 2, at the nodal point at which $h_i > 0$ the water elevation and current velocity will be computed, and at the nodal point at which $h_i < 0$ the water elevation will also be computed but the current velocity will be treated as zero. In case 3, the element is on the exposed sea bed, and will be omitted from the computation. Similar treatments are discussed by Herrling [104], Holz and Nitsche [105], and Tanaka et al. [133].

From storm surges shallow-water theory gives the equation of motion as

$$\frac{\partial u_i}{\partial t} + u_j u_{i,j} + g(\zeta - \zeta_a)_{,i} + \tau_i^B = \tau_i^s \tag{2.83}$$

and the equation of continuity as

$$\frac{\partial \zeta}{\partial t} + \{(H + \zeta)u_i\}_{,i} = 0 \tag{2.84}$$

where the notation is the same as for Eqs. (2.48) and (2.49). The Coriolis force and eddy viscosity are neglected because these terms are insignificant for the storm-surge phenomena. Appropriate boundary and initial conditions are also introduced. The main driving-force term is derived from the water elevation by the low-pressure decrease $\zeta_a$. The low-pressure region due to the storm has been modeled as

$$\zeta_a = \frac{1}{\rho g}(p_\infty - p) \tag{2.85}$$

$$p_\infty - p = \frac{a}{\sqrt{1 + (r/r_0)^2}} \tag{2.86}$$

where $\rho$, $g$, and $p_\infty$ express water density, gravity acceleration, and reference pressure, respectively, and

$$r = \sqrt{(x - x_c)^2 + (y - y_c)^2} \tag{2.87}$$

in which $(x_c, y_c)$ denote the coordinates of the storm center, and $r_0$ and $a$ are empirical constants. Kawahara et al. [121] have presented the finite-element method for this situation using the two-step explicit scheme for the numerical integration in time. Tanaka et al. [133] extended their method to include wave overtopping on a breakwater.

## 2.4G Density Flows

In estuarine and coastal waters, where fresh water from an inland river is flowing into salt water, there are complicated hydraulic phenomena that occur because the density of river water is different from that of seawater. The fresh water will flow above the salt water because its density is less. If the velocity of the flow is low, the flow will be clearly stratified, but if the velocity is high, there will be a well-mixed flow showing a three-dimensional distribution of density.

The governing equations for a density flow can be written as

$$\frac{\partial \rho}{\partial t} + (\rho u_i)_{,i} = 0 \tag{2.88}$$

$$\rho \frac{\partial u_i}{\partial t} + \rho u_j u_{i,j} + P_{,i} - \tau_{ij,j} = 0 \tag{2.89}$$

$$u_{i,i} = 0 \tag{2.90}$$

where $u_i$, $P$, $\rho$, $\tau_{ij}$ denote velocity, pressure, density, and viscous stress, respectively. The first two equations are conservation equations for density and momentum, and the third equation represents the equation of continuity if the density change is small.

King and Norton [152] and King [154] have presented a finite-element solution for three-dimensional stratified flow in reservoirs. In these analyses, the hydrostatic pressure distribution is assumed and density is considered to be a function of temperature. Mixed interpolation is used, namely, quadratic interpolation for velocity and temperature, and linear interpolation for pressure. Brick, triangular prism, pyramid and tetrahedral elements are utilized. For the numerical integration in time an implicit scheme is used. The computed velocity was found to be in good agreement with the experimental results.

A two-layer stratified-flow analysis is developed by assuming that the upper layer is fresh water and the lower layer is salt water. The basic equations can be derived by vertically integrating the three-dimensional Navier–Stokes equation to obtain, for the upper layer,

$$\dot{s} + \dot{d} + \{(s+d)u_i\}_{,i} = 0 \tag{2.91}$$

$$\dot{u}_i + u_j u_{i,j} + g s_{,i} - \frac{1}{s+d} \{A''(s+d)(u_{i,j} + u_{j,i})\}_{,j} + \gamma_{ij} u_j + \alpha_m (u_i - v_i) = 0 \tag{2.92}$$

and, for the lower layer, $\qquad \dot{d} + \{(d-b)v_i\}_{,i} = 0 \tag{2.93}$

$$\dot{v}_i + v_j v_{i,j} + g\{\varepsilon s_{,i} + (1-\varepsilon)d_{,i}\} - \gamma_{ij} v_j$$

$$- \frac{1}{b-d}[A'(b-d)(v_{i,j} + v_{j,i})]_{,j} - \beta_m(u_i - v_i) + \gamma_m v_i = 0 \tag{2.94}$$

where $u_i$ and $v_i$ denote the upper and lower velocity, respectively, and $s$ and $d$ represent surface and interface water elevation, respectively. The Coriolis parameter has value

$$\gamma_{ij} = \begin{cases} f(i=1, j=2) \\ -f(i=2, j=1) \end{cases} \quad \text{otherwise zero}$$

and the density ratio is given by 

$$\varepsilon = \frac{\rho^u}{\rho^1}$$

where $\rho^u$ and $\rho^1$ are the water densities in the upper and lower layers, respectively. Friction stresses are linearized, and the parameters $\alpha_m$, $\beta_m$, $\gamma_m$ have the following values:

$$\dot{\alpha}_m = \frac{f_m}{(s+d)\rho^u} \sqrt{(\tilde{U}_k \tilde{U}_k)} \tag{2.95}$$

$$\beta_m = \frac{f_m}{(b-d)\rho^1} \cdot \sqrt{(\tilde{U}_k \tilde{U}_k)} \tag{2.96}$$

$$\gamma_m = \frac{f_b}{(b-d)\rho^1} \cdot \sqrt{(\tilde{V}_k \tilde{V}_k)} \tag{2.97}$$

where 

$$\tilde{U}_k = u_k - v_k \tag{2.98}$$

and 

$$\tilde{V}_k = v_k \tag{2.99}$$

The friction coefficients at the interface and at the bottom of the coastal waters are $f_m$ and $f_b$, respectively; the eddy viscosities in the upper and lower layer are given by $A^u$ and $A^1$; and acceleration due to gravity is denoted by $g$. For the boundary conditions, the two components of velocity, the surface force and the water elevation, are specified on both layers, respectively.

Kawahara et al. [167] developed a finite-element method based on Eqs. (2.91) to (2.94). For the integration in time, the periodic Galerkin method using trigonometric constituent decomposition was used. Quadratic interpolation for velocity based on a six-node triangular finite element and linear interpolation based on a three-node triangular element for surface and interface elevations were adopted. For the same problem, Kasahara et al. [168] employed the two-step explicit method for the numerical integration in time, using the three-node triangular element for the spatial interpolation.

If density changes gradually and continuously through the flow, a multiple-level flow analysis must be carried out. Consider several horizontal levels in the flow and assume that the density of water is constant for each level. Then, by integrating vertically over the distance between levels, the basic equations of the multiple-level flow analysis can be obtained. Wang [161] and Wang and Conner [169] developed the finite-element method for this approach using a leapfrog scheme for the numerical integration in time. A two-step explicit scheme was employed by Kawahara et al. [121, 170] to analyze Akita Bay and Tokyo Bay. Signorini [134] used the implicit numerical-integration scheme, employing linear interpolation functions for velocity, water elevation, and density, based on the triangular finite element. Spraggs and Camateros [171] and Meissner et al. [172] presented finite-element solutions for density flow in impoundments and coastal sea areas. Tanaka et al. [173] described a finite-element analysis for thermal discharge from a power plant to the coastal sea. Techniques such as these allow the solution of many of the density-flow problems encountered in practice.

## 2.5 COASTAL AND ESTUARY FLOW

The main fluid effects in coastal and estuary flow are wave, or free-surface, effects, and viscous flow in three dimensions with circulation and separation. The Reynolds numbers are such that turbulence is important, and further associated effects are sediment transport, chemical effects such as flocculation, and stratified flow due to gradients of density, temperature, or salinity. A comprehensive model of all these effects is still beyond available finite-element models. In practice, two main areas have been developed: the wave aspect, ignoring viscosity, and vertically integrated shallow-water models.

### 2.5A Governing Equations

The governing equations are the vector equations of momentum balance and the scalar equation of mass conservation or continuity. Both these equations are vertically integrated, and the use of the Leibnitz rule with the first equation leads to

$$\rho\left(\frac{\partial u}{\partial t}+u\frac{\partial u}{\partial x}+v\frac{\partial u}{\partial y}-\Omega v\right)=-\rho g\frac{\partial \eta}{\partial x}-\frac{g\gamma u}{C^2 h}+\frac{f_x}{h}+\mu\left(\frac{\partial^2 u}{\partial x^2}+\frac{\partial^2 u}{\partial y^2}\right) \tag{2.100}$$

$$\rho\left(\frac{\partial v}{\partial t}+u\frac{\partial v}{\partial x}+v\frac{\partial v}{\partial y}+\Omega u\right)=-\rho g\frac{\partial \eta}{\partial y}-\frac{g\gamma v}{C^2 h}+\frac{f_y}{h}+\mu\left(\frac{\partial^2 v}{\partial x^2}+\frac{\partial^2 v}{\partial y^2}\right) \tag{2.101}$$

in which $u$ and $v$ are vertically integrated velocities, $\Omega$ is a Coriolis parameter, $h(x, y)$ is depth of water, $\eta(x, y)$ is water surface elevation, $\gamma=\sqrt{(u^2+v^2)}$, and $f_x$ and $f_y$ are wind shear stresses. The $xy$-plane is in the undisturbed surface of the water and $z$ is vertically upward. $\mu$ is viscosity, which may be real or may be based on an eddy viscosity, and $C$ is Chezy's constant for bed friction. Clearly both an eddy viscosity and Chezy's constant are crude methods for dealing with turbulent effects. Usually, however, sophisticated turbulence models are not feasible. These equations are seen in slightly different forms depending upon the assumptions made in their derivation. The continuity equation is

$$\frac{\partial \eta}{\partial t}=\frac{\partial}{\partial x}(uh)+\frac{\partial}{\partial y}(vh) \tag{2.102}$$

Equations (2.100) to (2.102) can be considered in different ways depending upon which features are of interest. The simplest case is that of wave action with no Coriolis, viscous, or bed friction effects. In this case $u$ and $v$ can be eliminated to give the shallow-water wave equation in terms of $\eta$ only. If, in addition, the time dependence is harmonic, so that $\eta(x, y, t)=\eta(x, y)\exp i\omega t$, where $\omega$ is angular frequency, the wave equation becomes

$$\frac{\omega^2 \eta}{g}+\frac{\partial}{\partial x}\left(h\frac{\partial \eta}{\partial x}\right)+\frac{\partial}{\partial y}\left(h\frac{\partial \eta}{\partial y}\right)=0 \tag{2.103}$$

It is sometimes desirable to retain a simplified model of bed friction, in which case the Chezy term is linearized, using a new parameter $M$, chosen so that in one wave cycle the same amount of energy is dissipated. The use of such a factor leads to

$$-\frac{\omega^2 \eta}{g} + i\omega M\eta = \frac{\partial}{\partial x}\left(h\frac{\partial \eta}{\partial x}\right) + \frac{\partial}{\partial y}\left(h\frac{\partial \eta}{\partial y}\right) \tag{2.104}$$

where $M = 8u_{\max}/3\pi C^2 h$, and $u_{\max}$ is the maximum velocity in a wave cycle.

## 2.5B  Boundary Conditions

**Fixed Walls**    There is no flow through a fixed wall and hence there is no velocity normal to the boundary. If viscous effects are included in the model, there is also a "no-slip" condition. These conditions are simply stated as

$$u_n = 0 \qquad \text{and} \qquad u_t = 0 \tag{2.105}$$

with $n$ denoting the normal direction and $t$ the tangential direction to the boundary. In the wave model, the zero-flow condition is

$$\frac{\partial \eta}{\partial n} = 0 \tag{2.106}$$

**Fixed Elevation**    The other type of boundary condition is where the water surface elevation $\eta$ is known. This occurs when an estuary is connected to a sea, and the values of $\eta$ would be obtained from tide tables or other sources. It is assumed that the local estuary effects cannot appreciably affect the levels in the sea.

**Radiation Boundary**    Another important boundary condition is that of the open boundary where wave effects are radiated away. The appropriate condition here is the Sommerfeld [174] radiation condition, which can be expressed for the harmonic case in terms of elevation as

$$\lim_{r\to\infty} \sqrt{r}\left(\frac{\partial \eta}{\partial r} - \frac{i\omega}{c}\eta\right) = 0 \tag{2.107}$$

where $r$ is the radius from the region of interest, $c$ is the wave speed, and $i$ is $\sqrt{-1}$. The detailed derivation of this condition is fairly complicated, as are the ways in which it is applied in numerical models. There are basically four main methods for dealing numerically with the radiation condition. These are dampers [175], linking to exterior series solutions [176], linking to exterior boundary integrals, and infinite elements [177]. A reasonably complete survey is given by Zienkiewicz, Bettess, and Kelly [178]. In addition to the radiation boundary described above, repeatability condition boundaries, or long-shore boundaries, may arise [179].

## 2.5c Solution Procedures

In the wave problem a Galerkin procedure can be applied to Eq. (2.103) to arrive at a finite-element form

$$(\mathbf{K} - \omega^2 \mathbf{M})\boldsymbol{\eta} = \mathbf{0} \tag{2.108}$$

where $\boldsymbol{\eta}$ is the vector of nodal values of wave elevation, $\omega$ is the frequency of oscillation, and $\mathbf{K}$ and $\mathbf{M}$ are stiffness and mass matrices, given by

$$\mathbf{K} = \sum_{\substack{\text{all} \\ \text{elements}}} \int \mathbf{B}^T \mathbf{D} \mathbf{B} \, d\Omega \qquad \mathbf{M} = \sum_{\substack{\text{all} \\ \text{elements}}} \int \mathbf{N}^T \frac{1}{g} \mathbf{N} \, d\Omega \tag{2.109}$$

where

$$\mathbf{B} = \begin{bmatrix} \dfrac{\partial \mathbf{N}}{\partial x} \\[2mm] \dfrac{\partial \mathbf{N}}{\partial y} \end{bmatrix} \qquad \mathbf{D} = \begin{bmatrix} h & 0 \\ 0 & h \end{bmatrix} \tag{2.110}$$

and $\mathbf{N}$ is the element shape function. This is a classical eigenvalue problem and can be solved for $\omega$, the set of eigenvalues, and the associated eigenvectors, $\boldsymbol{\eta}$. These give the frequencies of oscillation of the water and the associated mode shapes. Such an analysis was first carried out by C. Taylor et al. [180], who produced frequencies and mode shapes for rectangular and circular harbors (for which there are analytical solutions), and also for real, irregularly shaped harbors. A mode shape obtained in this work is illustrated in Fig. 2.1. This type of analysis was subsequently taken up by other workers [181]. It is important to note that the analysis is a considerable simplification because viscous effects (including bed friction and separation), wave nonlinearity and breaking, and energy radiation through the harbor entrance are neglected. Despite this, results from the method are very useful in harbor design.

If bed friction is included, the problem is now one of damped oscillation. If Eq. (2.104) is discretized, the finite-element equations are complex. The response can now be determined for a given excitation frequency by solving the complex equations. The results for $\eta$ are complex and therefore have a magnitude and a phase. The effect of introducing a numerical model of the exterior, as described earlier, is also to add damping to the system, because energy is radiated away and does not return. For such cases in which the exterior damping due to radiation is included there is a large range of numerical solutions (see Refs. [175–178]).

When the flow cannot be assumed inviscid and all or most of the terms in Eqs. (2.100) to (2.102) are retained, then no variables can be eliminated and the problem is solved in terms of the two velocities $u$, $v$ and the surface elevation $\eta$. The continuity equation (2.102) can, however, be eliminated if a penalty formulation is used in which the elevation $\eta$ is expressed in terms of $u$ and $v$. This procedure is popular with the closely analogous Navier–Stokes equations. However, it does necessitate an additional computation afterward to determine $\eta$, if required.

The first attempts to solve Eqs. (2.100) to (2.102) numerically, using finite elements, were by Taylor and Davis [182], Connor and Wang [183], and Grotkop [184]. None of these workers included horizontal viscosity. It was later included by Connor and Brebbia [185] and in a complicated model by Zienkiewicz and Heinrich [186]. Connor and Brebbia allowed

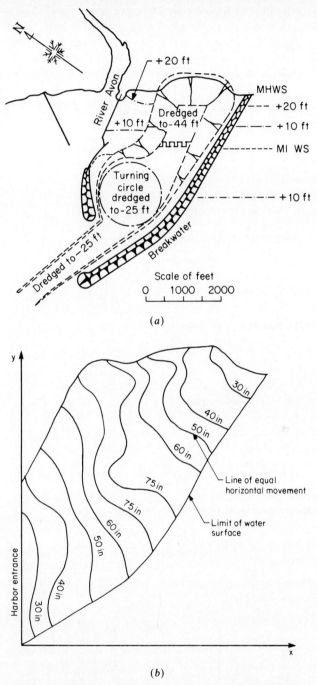

**FIG. 2.1** (*a*) Harbor layout for natural-frequency analysis [180]. (*b*) Horizontal movement for oscillation in harbor of Fig. 2.1*a* [180]. MWL = CD + 28 ft.

a tensor eddy viscosity in their formulation. Different workers tend to include or exclude certain terms and to deal with the terms which are present in different ways. The equations are nonlinear because of the presence of the convective-inertia terms and because of the Chezy bed friction term. In transient problems an explicit or implicit time-stepping solution procedure can be adopted. A large range of numerical models can be developed from Eqs. (2.100) to (2.102) and their variants. One particular formulation will now be developed which uses Galerkin weighting. Two separate shape functions will be adopted, for the interpolation on the velocities $u$, $v$ and on the surface elevation $\eta$; that is,

$$u = \mathbf{N}\mathbf{u} \qquad v = \mathbf{N}\mathbf{v} \qquad \eta = \mathbf{P}\boldsymbol{\eta} \tag{2.111}$$

This discretization is substituted into Eqs. (2.100) to (2.102), and Eqs. (2.100) and (2.101) are weighted with $\mathbf{N}^T$ and Eq. (2.102) is weighted with $\mathbf{P}^T$. This leads to the following matrices in which integration over the element domain is assumed.

- Mass matrix $\mathbf{M}$ from terms $\rho\,\partial u/\partial t$, $\rho\,\partial v/\partial t$, and $\partial\eta/\partial t$:

$$\mathbf{M} = \begin{bmatrix} \rho\mathbf{N}^T\mathbf{N} & 0 & 0 \\ 0 & \rho\mathbf{N}^T\mathbf{N} & 0 \\ 0 & 0 & \mathbf{P}^T\mathbf{P} \end{bmatrix} \tag{2.112}$$

- Convective-acceleration matrix $\mathbf{K}_1$ from

$$\rho\left(u\frac{\partial u}{\partial x} + v\frac{\partial u}{\partial y}\right) \qquad \rho\left(u\frac{\partial v}{\partial x} + v\frac{\partial v}{\partial y}\right)$$

$$\mathbf{K}_1 = \rho \begin{bmatrix} \mathbf{N}^T\mathbf{N}\dfrac{\partial\acute{u}}{\partial x} + \mathbf{N}^T\dfrac{\partial\mathbf{N}}{\partial x}\acute{u} + \mathbf{N}^T\dfrac{\partial\mathbf{N}}{\partial y}\acute{v} & \mathbf{N}^T\mathbf{N}\dfrac{\partial\acute{u}}{\partial y} \\ \mathbf{N}^T\mathbf{N}\dfrac{\partial\acute{v}}{\partial x} & \mathbf{N}^T\mathbf{N}\dfrac{\partial\acute{v}}{\partial y} + \mathbf{N}^T\dfrac{\partial\mathbf{N}}{\partial y}\acute{v} + \mathbf{N}^T\dfrac{\partial\mathbf{N}}{\partial x}\acute{u} \end{bmatrix} \tag{2.113}$$

where $\acute{u}$ and $\acute{v}$ are from the previous Newton–Raphson step and are given by $\acute{u} = \mathbf{N}\acute{\mathbf{u}}$ and $\acute{v} = \mathbf{N}\acute{\mathbf{v}}$.

- Coriolis acceleration matrix $\mathbf{K}_2$ from $-\rho\Omega v$ and $\rho\Omega u$:

$$\mathbf{K}_2 = \rho \begin{bmatrix} 0 & -\mathbf{N}^T\Omega\mathbf{N} \\ \mathbf{N}^T\Omega\mathbf{N} & 0 \end{bmatrix} \tag{2.114}$$

- Surface-gradient matrix $\mathbf{K}_3$, from $\rho g\,\partial\eta/\partial x$, $\rho g\,\partial\eta/\partial y$, and continuity-equation-velocity terms $\partial(hu)/\partial x$ and $\partial(hv)/\partial y$:

$$\mathbf{K}_3 = \begin{bmatrix} 0 & 0 & \mathbf{N}^T\rho g\dfrac{\partial\mathbf{P}}{\partial x} \\ 0 & 0 & \mathbf{N}^T\rho g\dfrac{\partial\mathbf{P}}{\partial y} \\ \dfrac{\partial\mathbf{P}^T}{\partial x}h\mathbf{N} & \dfrac{\partial\mathbf{P}^T}{\partial x}h\mathbf{N} & 0 \end{bmatrix} \tag{2.115}$$

- Atmospheric-pressure load matrix $\mathbf{f}_1$ from $\partial p_a/\partial x$ and $\partial p_a/\partial y$ [not included in Eqs. (2.100) and (2.101)]:

$$\mathbf{f}_1 = \begin{bmatrix} \mathbf{N}^T \dfrac{\partial p_a}{\partial x} \\[2ex] \mathbf{N}^T \dfrac{\partial p_a}{\partial y} \end{bmatrix} \tag{2.116}$$

- Viscous matrix $\mathbf{K}_4$ from $2\dfrac{\partial}{\partial x}\left(\mu\dfrac{\partial u}{\partial x}\right) - \dfrac{\partial}{\partial y}\left\{\mu\left(\dfrac{\partial u}{\partial y}+\dfrac{\partial v}{\partial x}\right)\right\}$, etc.:

$$\mathbf{K}_4 = \begin{bmatrix} 2\dfrac{\partial \mathbf{N}^T}{\partial x}\mu\dfrac{\partial \mathbf{N}}{\partial x}+\dfrac{\partial \mathbf{N}^T}{\partial y}\mu\dfrac{\partial \mathbf{N}}{\partial y} & \dfrac{\partial \mathbf{N}^T}{\partial y}\mu\dfrac{\partial \mathbf{N}}{\partial x} \\[3ex] \dfrac{\partial \mathbf{N}^T}{\partial x}\mu\dfrac{\partial \mathbf{N}}{\partial y} & \dfrac{\partial \mathbf{N}^T}{\partial x}\mu\dfrac{\partial \mathbf{N}}{\partial x}+2\dfrac{\partial \mathbf{N}^T}{\partial y}\mu\dfrac{\partial \mathbf{N}}{\partial y} \end{bmatrix} \tag{2.117}$$

- Surface-stress load matrix $\mathbf{f}_2$:

$$\mathbf{f}_2 = \begin{bmatrix} \mathbf{N}^T \dfrac{f_x}{h+\eta} \\[2ex] \mathbf{N}^T \dfrac{f_y}{h+\eta} \end{bmatrix} \tag{2.118}$$

- Chezy stress matrix $\mathbf{K}_5$. It is here assumed that $\gamma$ and $\eta$ in the Chezy term have been obtained from the velocities calculated in the previous iteration. Other more sophisticated approaches are, of course, possible.

$$\mathbf{K}_5 = \begin{bmatrix} \mathbf{N}^T \dfrac{\rho\gamma_x}{(h+\eta)C^2}\mathbf{N} & 0 \\[3ex] 0 & \mathbf{N}^T \dfrac{\rho\gamma_y}{(h+\eta)C^2}\mathbf{N} \end{bmatrix} \tag{2.119}$$

The complete tangent matrix is now obtained from

$$\mathbf{K} = \Sigma \mathbf{K}_i \quad \text{and} \quad \mathbf{f} = \Sigma \mathbf{f}_i \tag{2.120}$$

Now amalgamate all the variables into a single vector $\mathbf{z}$ and assume that the matrices have been summed over all elements. The Newton–Raphson algorithm can be written as

$$\frac{\partial F}{\partial z}\delta\mathbf{z} = F(\mathbf{z}) \tag{2.121}$$

and

$$\mathbf{z}_{n+1} = \mathbf{z}_n - \delta\mathbf{z} \tag{2.122}$$

where

$$F(\mathbf{z}) = \mathbf{K}(\mathbf{z})\mathbf{z} - \mathbf{f}$$

The variable $\eta$ and the continuity equation can be eliminated by using a penalty formulation, as was first done by Zienkiewicz and Godbole [187].

The expression for $\eta$ is now

$$\frac{\eta}{\lambda} = \frac{\partial}{\partial x}(hu) + \frac{\partial}{\partial y}(hv) \tag{2.123}$$

where $\lambda$ is a large "penalty" number [186]. This approach has not to date been applied to transient problems. It has, however, been used in steady-state problems. Such a solution was obtained by Bettess et al. [188], using a program developed by Heinrich [189], and is shown in Fig. 2.2. The problem is that of circulation in a region close to a harbor set in a coastline. The currents are generated by forcing terms from unbalanced radiation stresses caused by waves incident upon the coastline. Repeatability conditions have been applied at the ends of the model.

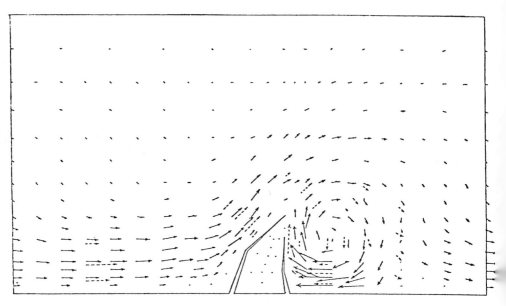

**FIG. 2.2**   Near-shore circulation pattern, constant viscosity (physical model pattern shown dotted) [188].

In many similar problems it is desirable to model the transient nature of the flow. In this case mass matrices, which were developed earlier, must be used. The governing equation is now of the form

$$\mathbf{M}\dot{\mathbf{z}} + \mathbf{K}(\mathbf{z})\mathbf{z} = \mathbf{f} \tag{2.124}$$

In solving such a set of equations it is necessary to have a time-integration scheme and a strategy to deal with the nonlinearity of the **K**-matrix. Many different time-stepping schemes are possible, and all cannot be described here. The simple choice is between explicit and implicit methods. If an explicit scheme is used the mass matrix should be "lumped" so as to become diagonal. The nonlinearity can be dealt with simply if the time step is sufficiently small, as the $z$-values from the previous iteration will be accurate enough. Implicit algorithms can in general use much larger time steps. They do need to solve nonlinear equations at each time step, however.

The time-stepping procedures which have been adopted in practice for these equations tend to be the trapezoidal rule and variants of the Runge-Kutta method. Some results obtained by Taylor and Davis [182] for flows in the southern North Sea are shown in Fig. 2.3.

**FIG. 2.3**   Finite-element solution for North Sea currents [182].

## 2.6 CONVECTION AND DISPERSION

### 2.6A Petrov–Galerkin and Galerkin Formulations

The relevant equations in advection form, using cartesian tensor notation, are

$$u_i \frac{\partial c}{\partial x_i} = \frac{\partial}{\partial x_i}\left(k_{ij}\frac{\partial c}{\partial x_j}\right)$$

(2.125)

where $u_i$ is the velocity in the direction of the $i^{\text{th}}$ unit vector, $\partial/\partial x_i$ is the partial derivative in the $x_i$-direction, $c$ is the concentration, and $k$ is the coefficient of dispersion.

The boundary conditions are generally of three types:

*Dirichlet*:
$$c = c_1 \qquad \text{on } S_1 \tag{2.126}$$

*Neumann*:
$$n_i k_{ij} \frac{\partial c}{\partial x_j} = f_2 \qquad \text{on } S_2 \tag{2.127}$$

*Robin*:
$$n_i k_{ij} \frac{\partial c}{\partial x_j} = h(c - c_3) \qquad \text{on } S_3 \tag{2.128}$$

The Dirichlet conditions are essential boundary conditions and must be satisfied by the trial function. The Neumann and Robin conditions can be combined with the differential equation and are natural boundary conditions.

In the Petrov–Galerkin method, a trial function $c = \sum c_1 N_1$ is inserted into the differential equation to form the residual and the weighted residual is set equal to zero, giving

$$\int_V W_J u_i \frac{\partial c}{\partial x_i} \, dV = \int_V W_J \frac{\partial}{\partial x_i} \left( k_{ij} \frac{\partial c}{\partial x_j} \right) dV \tag{2.129}$$

In the special case when the weighting function $W_J$ is the same as the trial function $N_J$, the Petrov–Galerkin method reduces to the Galerkin method. The dispersion terms can be integrated by parts and the boundary integrals can be combined with the boundary conditions, giving the Petrov–Galerkin formulation as

$$\int_V W_J u_i \frac{\partial c}{\partial x_i} \, dV = -\int_V k_{ij} \frac{\partial W_J}{\partial x_i} \frac{\partial c}{\partial x_j} \, dV + \int_{S_2} W_J f_2 \, dS + \int_{S_3} W_J h(c - c_3) \, dS \tag{2.130}$$

Hughes and Brooks [190] show why the natural boundary conditions are inappropriate at an outflow boundary if the convection terms are integrated by parts and, consequently, the convective term is not integrated by parts.

It is not appropriate to use an essential boundary condition at an outflow boundary when there is high convection, since there is no physical way to ensure that condition. The entire problem of the proper way to treat large convection arose in such a problem with an improper boundary condition [191], but Gartling [192] and Ben-Sabar and Caswell [193] indicated that the problem disappears if the essential boundary conditions are replaced by natural ones. Chang and Finlayson [194] showed that the problem also arose when the infinite domain of the original problem was truncated to a finite domain and an improper boundary condition was specified at the "infinite" end. Thus a natural boundary condition is always recommended at an outflow boundary.

The following sections present three solution methods in more detail in order of good, better, and best method.

## 2.6в "Upwind" Test Functions

Consider first the one-dimensional convective-diffusion equation with linear basis functions. The test functions are quadratic functions defined as follows. The weighting functions are

$$W_i = N_i + \alpha F(x) \qquad x_{i-1} \leqslant x \leqslant x_i \tag{2.131}$$

$$W_i = N_i - \alpha F(x) \qquad x_i \leqslant x \leqslant x_{i+1} \tag{2.132}$$

where $F(x)$ is given by

$$F(x) = -\frac{3}{h^2} x(x-h) \tag{2.133}$$

The optimal choice of $\alpha$ is

$$\alpha = \coth\frac{\gamma}{2} - \frac{2}{\gamma} \qquad \gamma = \mathrm{Pe} \tag{2.134}$$

where the term *optimal* refers to the fact that the exact solution is obtained at the nodes when using this value, provided the Peclet number Pe is constant and a uniform mesh size is used. The Peclet number is given by $uL/k$, where $L$ is the length.

In two-dimensional problems one can use either isoparametric elements or triangular elements [191, 195]. With isoparametric elements and linear basis functions, the basis functions are defined by tensor products of the basis functions in one dimension. For an isoparametric element with $-1 \leqslant \xi \leqslant 1$, $-1 \leqslant \eta \leqslant 1$, at the node $\xi = \eta = -1$:

$$N_i = \frac{1-\xi}{2}\frac{1-\eta}{2} = N_i(\xi)N_i(\eta) \tag{2.135}$$

Similarly, the weighting function is

$$W_i = W_i(\xi)W_i(\eta) \tag{2.136}$$

The one-dimensional weighting functions are

$$W_i(\xi) = N_i(\xi) + \alpha_{ij}\frac{3(1-\xi)(1+\xi)}{4} \tag{2.137}$$

in the $\xi$-direction and in the $\eta$-direction

$$W_i(\eta) = N_i(\eta) + \beta_{ij}\frac{3(1-\eta)(1+\eta)}{4} \tag{2.138}$$

The parameters $\alpha_{ij}$ and $\beta_{ij}$ are chosen by using the velocity

$$v = (\mathbf{V}_i + \mathbf{V}_j) \cdot \frac{\mathbf{l}_{ji}}{2} \tag{2.139}$$

where $\mathbf{l}_{ji}$ is a unit tangent to the boundary from node $i$ to node $j$. This velocity is used in Eq. (2.134) to determine the value of $\alpha_{ij}$ or $\beta_{ij}$, and the sign is taken to be the same as the sign of $v$. Equations for the other nodes can be obtained by symmetry and are listed in Huyakorn [195]. Huyakorn also gives the weighting functions for triangular elements using triangular coordinates. For quadratic trial functions the test function is a cubic polynomial. In one-dimensional problems the weighting functions are given in Ref. [190]. For eight- and nine-node elements the weighting functions are also listed in Ref. [196].

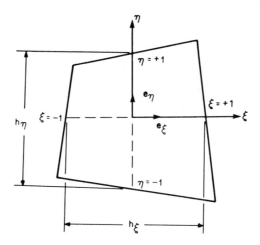

**FIG. 2.4** Four-node quadrilateral finite-element geometry.

### 2.6c Quadrature Upwind

One form of upwinding to eliminate oscillations is to use a reduced quadrature on the convective terms. We consider the approach of Hughes [197, 198] as illustrated in Fig. 2.4. The following quantities are evaluated:

$$u_\xi = \mathbf{e}_\xi \cdot \mathbf{u} \qquad u_\eta = \mathbf{e}_\xi \cdot \mathbf{u} \tag{2.140}$$

using the velocity at the center of the element. Then

$$\alpha_\xi = \frac{u_\xi h_\xi}{2k} \qquad \alpha_\eta = \frac{u_\eta h_\eta}{2k} \tag{2.141}$$

are evaluated using the value of the dispersion coefficient at the center of the element. (Here the material is isotropic and the dispersion coefficient is a scalar.) The value of the quadrature points is obtained from

$$\tilde{\xi} = \coth \alpha_\xi - \frac{1}{\alpha_\xi} \qquad \tilde{\eta} = \coth \alpha_\eta - \frac{1}{\alpha_\eta} \tag{2.142}$$

$$\tilde{\boldsymbol{\xi}} = (\tilde{\xi}, \tilde{\eta}) \tag{2.143}$$

The convective term in Eq. (2.130) is then replaced by the following expression:

$$\int_{v^e} N_J u_i \frac{\partial c}{\partial x_i} \, dV \equiv N_J^e(\tilde{\boldsymbol{\xi}}^e) u_i(\mathbf{O}^e) \Sigma C_I \frac{\partial N_I}{\partial x_i}(\tilde{\boldsymbol{\xi}}^e) j^e(\mathbf{O}^e) W \tag{2.144}$$

Here $\mathbf{O}^e$ is the origin of the $e^{\text{th}}$ element; $W$ is 2, 4, or 8 for one-, two-, or three-dimensional problems; and $j^e$ is the determinant of the jacobian, evaluated at the origin. For two-dimensional problems this is

$$j^e = \det \begin{bmatrix} \dfrac{\partial x^e}{\partial \xi} & \dfrac{\partial x^e}{\partial \eta} \\[2ex] \dfrac{\partial y^e}{\partial \xi} & \dfrac{\partial y^e}{\partial \eta} \end{bmatrix} \tag{2.145}$$

This procedure works quite well, but suffers from the disadvantage of excessive crosswind dispersion; i.e., there is more dispersion in a direction tangent to the flow direction than there should be, and the velocity in this direction is not large so that added dispersion is not needed.

A revision of the approach uses streamline upwind quadrature [190, 199]. In this method Eq. (2.130) is replaced by

$$\int_V W_J u_i \frac{\partial c}{\partial x_i} \, dV = -\int_V (k_{ij} + \tilde{k}_{ij}) \frac{\partial W_J}{\partial x_i} \frac{\partial c}{\partial x_j} \, dV + \int_{S_2} W_J f_2 \, dS + \int_{S_3} W_J h(c - c_3) \, dS \tag{2.146}$$

where

$$\tilde{k}_{ij} = \tilde{k} \hat{u}_i \hat{u}_j \tag{2.147}$$

$$\hat{u}_i = \frac{u_i}{\|\mathbf{u}\|} \qquad \|\mathbf{u}\| = (u_i u_i)^{1/2} \tag{2.148}$$

The $\tilde{k}$ is a scalar diffusivity defined by

$$\tilde{k} = \frac{\tilde{\xi} u_\xi h_\xi + \tilde{\eta} u_\eta h_\eta}{2} \tag{2.149}$$

Note that with this definition the extra diffusivity acts only in the direction of flow.

In practice it is easier to combine the added dispersion with the convection term.

$$\int \tilde{W}_J u_j \frac{\partial c}{\partial x_j} \, dV = -\int_V k_{ij} \frac{\partial W_J}{\partial x_i} \frac{\partial c}{\partial x_j} \, dV + \int_{S_2} W_J f_2 \, dS + \int_{S_3} W_J h(c - c_3) \, dS \tag{2.150}$$

$$\tilde{W}_J = W_J + \tilde{k} \hat{u}_i \frac{\partial W_J / \partial x_i}{\|\mathbf{u}\|} \tag{2.151}$$

In addition it is often efficient to replace the relation (2.142) by an approximation.

$$\tilde{\xi} = \begin{cases} \dfrac{\alpha}{3} & -3 \le \alpha \le 3 \\[2ex] \operatorname{sgn} \alpha & |\alpha| > 3 \end{cases} \tag{2.152}$$

The convection terms can be evaluated exactly or with one-point quadrature [190].

Payre et al. [200] move the integration nodes along the streamlines before they evaluate the convection terms, but they find this is an improvement only for cell Peclet numbers greater than 20.

## 2.6D Petrov–Galerkin Methods

In the Petrov-Galerkin method the weighting functions are not restricted to be the same as the basis functions, as in the Galerkin method. One choice of Petrov-Galerkin weighting functions are given above as upwind test functions. Another possibility is described here. One important difference is that these test functions are discontinuous across element boundaries, so that some minor changes must be made in the weighted residuals.

The weighted residual is taken as Eq. (2.129) but with a more general weighting function $\tilde{W}_J$ [190, 201]:

$$W_J = N_J + p_J \tag{2.153}$$

This time only part of the dispersion term is integrated by parts, namely, the part involving $N_J$, but not the part involving $p_J$, since $p_J$ is discontinuous across element boundaries. The boundary conditions are again utilized, giving as final equations in place of Eq. (2.130):

$$\int_V W_J u_i \frac{\partial c}{\partial x_i} \, dV = -\int_V k_{ij} \frac{\partial N_J}{\partial x_i} \frac{\partial c}{\partial x_j} + \sum_e \int_{V^e} p_J \frac{\partial}{\partial x_i} \left( k_{ij} \frac{\partial c}{\partial x_j} \right) dV$$

$$+ \int_{S_2} N_J f_2 \, dS + \int_{S_3} N_J h(c - c_3) \, dS \tag{2.154}$$

The additional weighting function is

$$p_J = \tau u_i \frac{\partial N_J}{\partial x_i} \tag{2.155}$$

where $\tau$ is chosen to achieve optimal accuracy in special problems. According to Hughes and Brooks [190] the following algorithm is recommended. It is optimal for one-dimensional problems and is the *ad hoc* generalization to multidimensional problems. The values of $\tilde{\xi}$ and $\tilde{\eta}$ are computed from Eqs. (2.140) to (2.142), as before, but then we use

$$\tau = \frac{\tilde{k}}{u_i u_i} \tag{2.156}$$

where
$$\tilde{k} = \frac{\tilde{\xi} u_\xi h_\xi + \tilde{\eta} u_\eta h_\eta}{2} \tag{2.157}$$

The same ideas have been generalized to systems of equations [201, 202].

## 2.6E Solution Oscillations

There are two philosophies for solving the problem of excessive oscillations in the solution. Gresho and Lee [203] argue that the oscillations tell the analyst that the model is inadequate. In some important region the mesh is not refined enough, the boundary conditions are inappropriate, or the problem is simply hard due to the parameter choices. If one uses upwind schemes, then both the solution and the physics are smoothed, and interpretation becomes difficult. They point out that the limitation on cell Peclet number is really a limitation on the cell Peclet number times the gradient of the solution, since the cell Peclet number limit can be exceeded without disastrous consequences provided the solution is not steep at the same place. Finally, they remind practitioners that the mass matrix should not be lumped because that causes excessive phase errors and may smooth the solution in time more than desired, but that explicit methods require mass lumping, which may be necessary for three-dimensional simulations.

In contrast, Brooks and Hughes [199] argue that central-difference (usual Galerkin) methods provide underdiffusion while upwind methods provide overdiffusion, and the optimal method is one that combines the two ideas to provide just the right amount of diffusion to dampen the oscillations but not to change the solution. They prefer to locate boundary layers with other means, and not depend on a "wiggle signal" to identify them. Sometimes it is not necessary to resolve the boundary layer to solve certain problems.

### 2.6F Summary

In summary, for ease of application, it is recommended that problems with large convection terms be solved by either (1) refining the mesh, (2) using upwind quadrature [Eq. (2.144)], (3) using streamline upwind quadrature [Eq. (2.150) or (2.153)], or (4) using a Petrov–Galerkin method [Eq. (2.154)].

## 2.7 ANALYSIS AND DESIGN OF SUBSONIC AND SUPERSONIC TURBOMACHINERY

This section covers the finite-element solution of subsonic and supersonic inviscid flows in turbomachines. The methods will be demonstrated for the blade-to-blade and the through-flow equations. Successful unchoked and choked solutions with shocks are obtained by use of the artificial-compressibility method.

### 2.7A Governing Equations

The Wu theory [204] has been the cornerstone of all quasi-3D turbomachinery calculations. The 3D flow in axial or centrifugal turbomachines is reasonably well approximated by the quasi-3D interactive solutions on a through-flow hub-to-shroud (S2) surface and on axisymmetric blade-to-blade (S1) surfaces (see Figs. 2.5 and 2.6).

The solution of the through-flow radial-equilibrium equation determines the shape (radius distribution and depth of stream tubes) of blade-to-blade surfaces as well as the boundary conditions at inlet and exit: flow angle $\beta$, Mach number $M$, and static pressure $p$. Solutions are then carried out on a selected number of these axisymmetric, but otherwise arbitrary, stream surfaces, determining new input parameters (intrablade distribution of work, blockage, and loss) for another through-flow analysis, and the loop is repeated to convergence.

We shall state the governing equations in terms of the stream function for both problems and in addition in terms of the velocity potential $\Phi$ for the S1 problem.

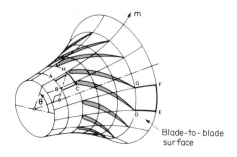

Blade-to-blade surface

CD: $\Psi = 0$                                    CD: $\delta\Phi/\delta n = 0$

HG: $\Psi = 1$                                    HG: $\delta\Phi/\delta n = 0$

BC: $\Psi(m) = \Psi_1(m)$; unknown                BC: $\Phi = \Phi_1(m)$

AH: $\Psi(m) = \Psi_1(m) + 1$                     AH: $\Phi = \Phi_1(m) + W_{\theta_1} \cdot r_1 \cdot s$

DE: $\Psi(m) = \Psi_2(m)$; unknown)               DE: $\Phi = \Phi_2(m)$

GF: $\Psi(m) = \Psi_2(m) + 1$                     GF: $\Phi = \Phi_2(m) + W_{\theta_2} \cdot r_2 \cdot s$

AB:                                               AB: $\Phi = W_{\theta_1} \cdot r \cdot \theta$

FE: $(\delta\Psi/\delta m) = (-\rho b/\dot{m}) W_\theta$   FE: $\delta\Phi/\delta m = W_{m_2}$

**FIG. 2.5**   Blade-to-blade surface of revolution and boundary conditions.

**Blade-to-Blade (S1) Problem**   Defining a velocity potential $\Phi$ satisfies the irrotationality condition identically, and the continuity equation yields

$$\frac{1}{r}(\rho b r \Phi_m)_m + \frac{1}{r}\left(\frac{\rho b}{r}\Phi_\theta\right)_\theta = b\Omega\frac{\partial\rho}{\partial\theta} \qquad W_m = \frac{\partial\Phi}{\partial m} \qquad W_\theta = \frac{1}{r}\frac{\partial\Phi}{\partial\theta} - \Omega r \qquad (2.158)$$

On the other hand, defining a stream function $\Psi$ satisfies mass continuity identically, and the vorticity definition yields

$$\frac{1}{r}\left(\frac{\dot{m}r}{\rho b}\Psi_m\right)_m + \frac{1}{r}\left(\frac{\dot{m}}{\rho b r}\Psi_\theta\right)_\theta = 2\Omega\frac{\partial r}{\partial m} - \omega_{m,\theta} \qquad W_m = \frac{\dot{m}}{\rho b r}\Psi_\theta \qquad W_\theta = \frac{-\dot{m}}{\rho b}\Psi_m \qquad (2.159)$$

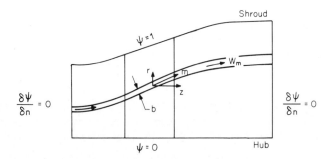

**FIG. 2.6**   Through-flow and boundary conditions.

where $m$ is the meridional distance along the blade-to-blade stream surface, $\theta$ is the circumferential direction, $r$ is the local radius of the stream surface $[r = r(m)]$, $b$ is the local depth of the stream tube $[b = b(m)]$, $\dot{m}$ is the mass flow rate, $W$ is the relative velocity ($W = V - \Omega r$, where $V$ is the absolute velocity), and $\omega$ is the vorticity.

The above illustrative analysis is applicable to stators and rotors.

**Hub-to-Shroud (S2) Problem**   The equation governing the through-flow is known as the *radial-equilibrium equation* and states:

$$\left(\frac{\Psi_r}{\rho r B}\right)_r + \left(\frac{\Psi_x}{\rho r B}\right)_x = -\omega \equiv \frac{-2\pi}{\dot{m} W_x}\left[\frac{W_\theta}{r}\frac{\partial}{\partial r}(rV_\theta) + T\frac{\partial s}{\partial r} - \frac{\partial I}{\partial r} + F_r\right] \qquad (2.160a)$$

$$W_x = \frac{\dot{m}}{2\pi\rho r B}\Psi_r, \qquad W_r = \frac{-\dot{m}}{2\pi\rho r B}\Psi_x \qquad (2.160b)$$

where $x$, $r$, $\theta$ are the axial, radial, and angular coordinates; $B$ is the blockage factor in the tangential direction; and $T$, $I$, $s$, $\omega$, $F_r$ are temperature, rothalpy, entropy, vorticity, and blade force, respectively.

Equation (2.160) can be used in two ways:

1. *Analysis Mode.*   The blade shape is specified; i.e., $W_\theta / W_x$ is known as a function of $(r, x)$.

2. *Design Mode.*   The desired work is specified; i.e., the distribution of $rV_\theta$ or an equivalent quantity, say pressure ratio, is known as a function of $(r, x)$.

Equations (2.158) to (2.160) are nonlinear since $\rho = F(\nabla\Phi)$ or $F(\nabla\Psi)$ and are of mixed type (elliptic-hyperbolic), as can be demonstrated by writing them in characteristic form [204]. It is shown that all three equations are elliptic where the relative Mach number remains subsonic and hyperbolic in the regions where it is supersonic. In addition, if Eq. (2.160) is used in a design mode, the above classification criteria are applicable in terms of the meridional Mach number, that is, $\sqrt{(W_x^2 + W_r^2)/a^2}$.

References [205–212] present finite-element subsonic and transonic solutions using the velocity-potential approach and subsonic solutions using the stream-function method. It is only recently [213] that transonic solutions have been possible with the stream function. References [214, 215] present reviews of turbomachinery methods.

## 2.7ʙ Finite-Element Discretization

The weak solution in the through-flow case, [Eq. (2.160), for example] can be written in the Galerkin–weighted-residual form:

$$\iint\limits_A N_i\left[\left(\frac{\Psi_r}{\rho r B}\right)_r + \left(\frac{\Psi_x}{\rho r B}\right)_x + \omega\right] dr\,dx = 0 \qquad (2.161)$$

where the test function is chosen to be $N_i$, the finite-element shape function. Upon integration by parts, assembling the contribution of all elements, and freezing the density at the previous iteration, one obtains a system of linear equations:

$$\mathbf{K}^n \mathbf{\Psi}^{n+1} = \mathbf{F}^n \tag{2.162}$$

where at element level $e$

$$k_{ij} = \iint_{A_e} \frac{1}{\rho r B} \left( \frac{\partial N_i}{\partial r} \frac{\partial N_j}{\partial r} + \frac{\partial N_i}{\partial x} \frac{\partial N_j}{\partial x} \right) dr \, dx \tag{2.163a}$$

$$f_i = \oint_c \frac{N_i}{\rho r B} \frac{\partial \Psi}{\partial n} \, dc + \iint_{A_e} N_i \omega \, dr \, dx \tag{2.163b}$$

$$\frac{\rho}{\rho_0} = \left( 1 - \frac{\gamma - 1}{2} \frac{V^2}{a_0^2} \right)^{1/(\gamma-1)} \tag{2.163c}$$

The contour integral $\oint_c$ exists only for elements having an edge on a flow boundary over which a nonzero-flux condition is specified. One should also note that $\rho_0$, $a_0$ denote local stagnation conditions which vary in a turbomachine with energy addition.

Efficient ways of developing the grids, with special capability of refinement near airfoil leading and trailing edges, are important, and some are described in Refs [207, 211]. In transonic computations, the bilinear element is most popular, but triangular (three-node) and quadratic (eight-node) elements have also been successfully used.

We note that for supersonic inlet Mach numbers in the blade-to-blade case, special boundary conditions are needed because of the phenomenon of unique incidence. Basically, the supersonic flow turning at the leading edge of a blade creates waves (expansion or compression) that propagate ahead of the cascade (for a subsonic axial inlet Mach number), changing the speed and angle of the incoming flow to the next blade. This phenomenon propagates from blade to blade and, because of periodicity, all channels ultimately sustain the same conditions. The net effect, therefore, is that neither the inlet Mach number nor the incoming flow angle is known a priori, but must be determined as part of the solution. Furthermore, in the presence of shocks, total pressure losses occur and the appropriate boundary condition at the exit is that of a specified static pressure (or a given pressure ratio across the cascade). In other words, for the supersonic inlet cascades, or even transonic cascades with losses, the exit flow angle is also not known a priori. A method based on a modified velocity potential is demonstrated in Ref. [216] for a potential solution of cascades for a supersonic inlet Mach number and is detailed in Sec. 2.7G, "Numerical Examples."

## 2.7c  Artificial Compressibility Method

As shown in Sec. 4.7 of Part 3, it is imperative in mixed elliptic-hyperbolic flow problems to introduce a "dissipation" in the supersonic (hyperbolic) region, if one exists, for the stability of calculations and shock capturing. This numerical dissipation can be introduced by the artificial-compressibility method [217]. The method is covered in Sec. 4.7 of Part 3 and can be summarized as replacing $\rho$ in Eqs. (2.158) to (2.160) by a density $\tilde{\rho}$, given by

$$\tilde{\rho} = \rho - \mu(\rho_e - \rho_{e-1}) \tag{2.164a}$$

$$\mu = \max\left(0, 1 - \frac{1}{M_e^2}, 1 - \frac{1}{M_{e-1}^2}\right) \tag{2.164b}$$

where $e$ is the element in question and $e - 1$ is the corresponding upstream element.

## 2.7D Transonic Iterative Methods

***Vertical-Line Successive Overrelaxation (VLSOR)*** The solution is obtained by marching station by station $(l)$ with the flow, assuming the solution at the preceding station $(l-1)$ and the following station $(l+1)$ to be given by the current iteration $(n+1)$ and the preceding iteration $(n)$, respectively. This results in a tridiagonal system of algebraic equations for the unknown $(\Phi$ or $\Psi)^{n+1}$ at the station $l$. The solution change $(\delta\Phi$ or $\delta\Psi)$ is then overrelaxed by a factor ranging from 1 to 2. The overrelaxation scheme has been shown to introduce transient terms in the iteration and can be recast in the time-dependent form [217]:

$$\alpha\Phi_{xt} + \gamma\Phi_{yyt} + \varepsilon\Phi_t = \mathbf{R} \tag{2.165a}$$

$$\Delta t\Phi_t = \delta\Phi_l^{n+1} \qquad \Delta x\,\Delta t\Phi_{xt} = \delta\Phi_l^{n+1} - \delta\Phi_{l-1}^{n+1} \tag{2.165b}$$

$$\mathbf{R} = \mathbf{K}\Phi - \mathbf{F} \tag{2.165c}$$

The $\Phi_{xt}$-term appearing in VLSOR has been shown to be necessary for iterative convergence [217] and has to be explicitly introduced in other schemes.

***Zebroid Scheme*** $(\Phi_z)$ The zebroid scheme is essentially a horizontal-line successive overrelaxation (HLSOR). Applied to each line, however, HLSOR produces an $\alpha\Phi_{yt}$-term of varying sign (similar to $\alpha\Phi_{xt}$ in Eq. (2.165)). To prevent this, the zebroid scheme is applied to alternate lines (black and white), and two sweeps are necessary to complete an iteration. A $\Phi_{xt}$-term can be added explicitly to the scheme to enhance convergence. The scheme has proved to be faster than VLSOR.

***First- and Second-Degree Implicit Methods*** $(\Phi_t$ and $\Phi_{tt})$ These implicit methods can be written, for example, for the velocity potential, as

$$\varepsilon\mathbf{L}\delta^2\Phi + \alpha\mathbf{L}\delta\Phi = -\beta\mathbf{R} \tag{2.166}$$

where $\varepsilon = 0$, 1 for first- $(\Phi_t\text{-})$ or second- $(\Phi_{tt}\text{-})$ degree methods, respectively; $\alpha$, $\beta$ are fixed- or variable-acceleration parameters; and $L$ is an operator approximating the compressible flow (possibly the laplacian operator). This implicit approach is attractive since many standard subsonic codes can be easily extended to produce a transonic capability. Again a $\Phi_{xt}$-term is necessary for iteration stability, rendering the matrix $\mathbf{L}$ asymmetric. However, to avoid repeated decomposition of the matrix, a laplacian can be used and the implicit procedure alternated with VLSOR. Alternatively, an asymmetric operator $\mathbf{L}$ can be constructed for the supersonic region as $\mathbf{L}_{ij} = \mathbf{L}_{ij} \cdot \mathbf{T}_{ij}$, where $\mathbf{T}_{ij}$ is an element transformation matrix zeroing out

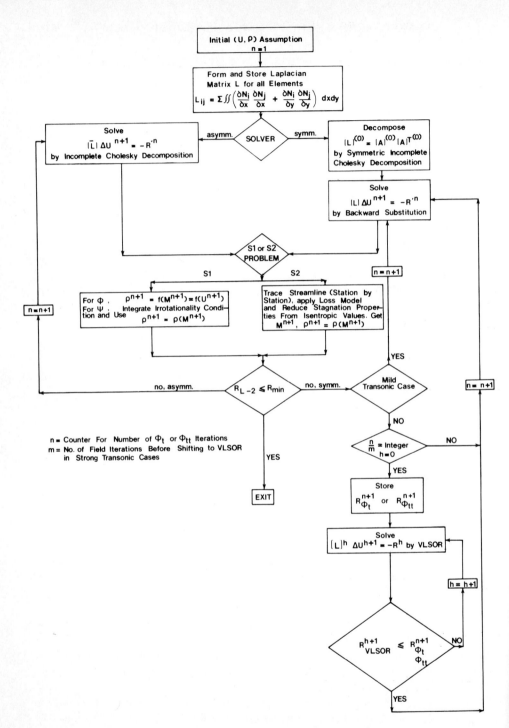

**FIG. 2.7** Flowchart of iterative procedures for transonic turbomachinery flows.

**3.112**

the contribution at a supersonic point from downstream nodes within the element while doubling the contribution to that node from the upstream nodes in the element on its left [218]. An exact *LU*-decomposition of this asymmetric operator can be used but an approximate *LU*-factorization (incomplete decomposition), where the zero pattern of the matrix is preserved, has been found to be more efficient [218].

Variable-acceleration parameters based on conjugate-gradient algorithms have also been tested. For $\varepsilon = 0$, and variable $\alpha$, the method of Eq. (2.165) reduces to the steepest-descent technique.

Figure 2.7 is a flowchart summarizing the procedures discussed above.

## 2.7E Updating the Thermodynamic Variables at Each Iteration

**Blade-to-Blade Flows**  For subsonic irrotational flows the density at each iteration is updated in terms of the speed from Eq. (2.163c). In the stream-function case, the classical difficulty of double-valuedness of the $\rho q$ versus Mach number in mixed-flow problems has only recently been resolved [213]. It is proposed to obtain the speed directly by integrating the vorticity equation when the streamline pattern is known. Once the speed is determined, the density can be uniquely updated. The vorticity (or irrotationality) equation in terms of speed is

$$\frac{1}{r}\frac{\partial V_m}{\partial \theta} - \frac{1}{r}\frac{\partial(rV_\theta)}{\partial m} = -\omega_{m,\theta} \qquad (2.167a)$$

or

$$\frac{1}{r}\frac{\partial W_m}{\partial \theta} - \frac{1}{r}\frac{\partial(rAW_m)}{\partial m} = 2\Omega\frac{\partial r}{\partial m} - \omega_{m,\theta} \qquad (2.167b)$$

where

$$A = \frac{W_\theta}{W_m} = -\frac{1/\rho b(\partial \Psi/\partial m)}{1/\rho br(\partial \Psi/\partial \theta)} = \tan \delta \qquad (2.168)$$

$\delta$ being the currently determined streamline slope.

With $\delta$ known everywhere, the first-order equation (2.167b) in $W_m$ is integrated by marching from an "initial" data curve crossing the characteristic direction of this equation. Such an integration can proceed line by line using a tridiagonal solver [213] and has been applied to transonic, unchoked flows.

**Hub-to-Shroud Flows**  Once a new iterative value of $\Psi$ has been established for the field, thermodynamic variables at every station can be calculated. First the flow velocities are determined everywhere by using the nodal-density values from the previous iteration [Eq. (2.160b)]. The thermodynamic calculation proceeds from inlet to exit by applying conservation laws along streamlines between adjacent stations; these are as follows.

| | | | |
|---|---|---|---|
| In a duct: | Angular momentum, | $rV_\theta$ = constant | (2.169a) |
| In a stator: | Total enthalpy, | $H_0$ = constant | (2.169b) |
| In a rotor: | Rothalpy $(H_0 - \Omega rV_\theta)$, | $I$ = constant | (2.169c) |

To carry this out, the streamline origin at each node of the current station needs to be traced back to the preceding station and a loss model (analytical or empirical) is applied. The presence of a loss is consistent with the assumption of an inviscid but rotational flow. Once the conserved quantity ($rV_\theta$, $H_0$, or $I$) has been determined at each node, the velocity triangle is complete and enough information is then available to calculate all quantities needed for terms on the right-hand side of Eq. (2.160$a$). The density is updated directly in terms of the static pressure and temperature from the ideal gas law.

## 2.7F Calculation of Losses Due to Shocks: The Modified Potential

In Sec. 2.7B, the boundary conditions for supersonic flows were discussed, and it was concluded that neither the inlet Mach number nor the flow angle can be imposed a priori, i.e., the inlet mass flow rate is unknown. In addition the exit flow angle is also unknown.

In Refs. [216, 219] the analogous situation, in a convergent-divergent nozzle with specified back pressure, is discussed. A Dirichlet boundary condition at the exit is used, where the value of $\Phi$ is updated iteratively to position the shock such that the imposed back pressure is recovered. References [216, 220] generalize the approach to cascades via a modified potential by virtue of which, while the flow is still irrotational, entropy changes across shocks are accounted for.

The general procedure consists of an inner and an outer iteration and is as follows.

An initial inlet Mach number ($M_I$) and flow angle ($\beta_I$) are chosen to achieve a certain tangential whirl component, $W_{\theta I} = q_I \sin \beta_I$, which is imposed by the through-flow solution. This whirl, which is kept constant during the entire iterative procedure, defines the distribution $\Phi_I(\theta)$ at the inlet. To initiate the outer loop an arbitrary initial value of $\Delta\Phi$ between an inlet point and an exit point is then chosen, as well as an initial total pressure loss. The exit flow angle $\beta_E$ [$\beta_E = f(M_I, \beta_I, M_E)$], and hence the distribution $\Phi_E(\theta)$ [$\Phi_E(\theta) = f(\Delta\Phi, M_E, \beta_E, \theta)$], are determined from the exit Mach number ($M_E$) corresponding to the desired static back pressure ($p_{SB}$) and the assumed total pressure. As the solution evolves, $M_I$ and $\beta_I$ change and the values of $\beta_E$ and the distribution $\Phi_E(\theta)$ are continuously recalculated. When a shock appears, the entropy generated across the shock is calculated from

$$\frac{\Delta S}{R} = \ln \frac{\left( \dfrac{2\gamma M_s^2}{\gamma+1} - \dfrac{\gamma-1}{\gamma+1} \right)^{1/(\gamma-1)}}{\left\{ \dfrac{[(\gamma+1)/2]M_s^2}{1+[(\gamma-1)/2]M_s^2} \right\}^{\gamma/(\gamma-1)}} \tag{2.170}$$

and is used to modify the stagnation density and total pressure behind the shock such that

$$p = \left( \frac{\rho^\gamma}{\gamma M_\infty^2} \right) e^{-\Delta s/R} \qquad \rho = \rho_i e^{-\Delta s/R} \tag{2.171}$$

where $\rho_i$ is as defined by Eq. (2.163$c$).

After a certain residual ($K\Phi - F$) convergence criterion is achieved, the inner loop is judged to have converged between $M_I$, $\beta_I$, and $\beta_E$ for the chosen $\Delta\Phi$. At this stage the numerical exit static pressure ($P_{SE}$) is checked against the desired back pressure ($P_{SB}$) and a new value of $\Delta\Phi$ imposed to adjust the back pressure. The outer iterative loop is completed when $P_{SE} = P_{SB}$. The mass flow rates at the inlet and exit and in the channel can be shown to differ during iteration and to correspond at convergence. This approach is also applicable to choked flows at subsonic and supersonic inlet Mach numbers.

## 2.7G Numerical Examples

Only two illustrative examples are shown here. In Fig. 2.8 the results (Mach number distribution) of calculations for a supersonic inlet cascade [216] by the modified-potential formulation are illustrated for two back pressures. The Mach number contours are shown in Fig. 2.9.

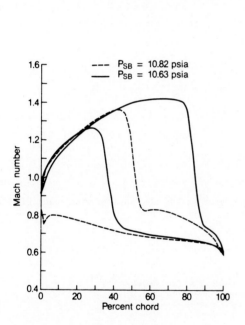

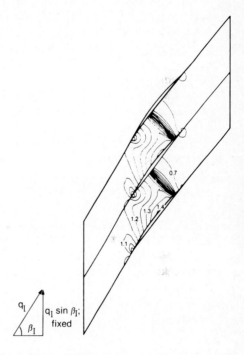

**FIG. 2.8**  Solution of supersonic flow in a cascade by the modified-potential method, 9.5% camber DCA blades, chord/pitch = 1.462. ($a$) For $p_{SB} = 10.82$ (unchoked), $M_I = 1.114$, $\beta_I = 59.04°$, $\Delta\Phi = 250$. ($b$) For $p_{SB} = 10.63$ (choked), $M_I = 1.126$, $\beta_I = 58.28°$, $\Delta\Phi = 264$.

**FIG. 2.9**  Mach number contours for case ($b$) of Fig. 2.8.

Figure 2.10 shows the supersonic leading-edge Mach number, coarse and fine grids used in the stream-function solution discretization of the through-flow of a supersonic inducer, and the converged streamline pattern [213]. The convergence history and the necessary stabilizing effect of the artificial compressibility are illustrated in Fig. 2.11.

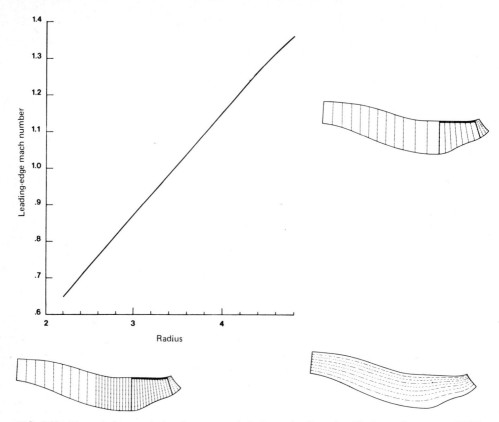

**FIG. 2.10** Through-flow analysis of a supersonic inducer: leading-edge Mach number, coarse FEM grid, fine FEM grid, and converged streamline pattern.

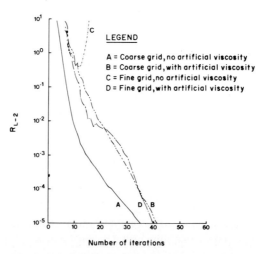

**FIG. 2.11** Stabilizing effect of artificial viscosity in supersonic through-flow analysis.

## 2.7H  Concluding Remarks

This section presents an effective finite-element treatment of subsonic and supersonic flows governed by the blade-to-blade and radial-equilibrium equations in turbomachinery. In particular, it demonstrates the proper methodology for solving supersonic inlet and choked cascades by a modified-potential formulation as well as the supersonic through-flow problem.


## 2.8  BOUNDARY-LAYER TURBULENT FLOW

Many situations occur, particularly in aerodynamic flows, wherein a simplification of the Navier–Stokes equations to the boundary-layer form [221] is appropriate and useful. Jaffe and Smith [222] report on the pioneering work of Smith and Clutter on numerical solution of the laminar-flow case; see also Blottner and Flugge-Lotz [223] and Blottner [224, 225]. Finite-difference numerical solution procedures for the time-averaged [226] boundary-layer equation set for turbulent flow were developed in the mid-1960s, with detailed comparisons with experimental data sets reported in the 1968 AFOSR Stanford Conference [227]. The development and examination of finite-element numerical algorithms for the boundary-layer equations are more recent. Popinski and Baker [228] reported in 1976 the first comparison between the linear-basis finite-element and Crank-Nicolson algorithms. Soliman and Baker [229] document the accuracy and convergence character of the linear, quadratic, and cubic finite-element algorithm applied to laminar boundary-layer flows with various pressure gradients. For turbulent boundary layers, Soliman and Baker [230] report on accuracy and convergence of the linear and quadratic finite-element algorithm, including algebraic and two-equation closure models.


### 2.8A  Governing-Equation System

It is required to determine the steady, two-dimensional time-averaged velocity and pressure distributions, $\mathbf{u}(x, y)$ and $\bar{p}(x, y)$ for a boundary-layer flow, where

$$\mathbf{u}(x, y) \equiv \bar{u}(x, y)\mathbf{i} + \bar{v}(x, y)\mathbf{j} \qquad (2.172)$$

Using the familiar ordering analysis [221], the time-averaged, steady-flow Navier–Stokes equations for an incompressible flow reduce to the nondimensional form.

$$L(\bar{\rho}) = \frac{\partial \bar{u}}{\partial x} + \frac{\partial \bar{v}}{\partial y} = 0 \qquad (2.173)$$

$$L(\bar{u}) = \bar{u}\frac{\partial \bar{u}}{\partial x} + \bar{v}\frac{\partial \bar{u}}{\partial y} - \frac{\partial}{\partial y}\left(\frac{\bar{\nu}}{\mathrm{Re}}\frac{\partial \bar{u}}{\partial y} - \overline{u'v'}\right) + \frac{1}{\bar{\rho}}\frac{d\bar{p}}{dx} = 0 \qquad (2.174)$$

$$L(\bar{v}) = \frac{\partial}{\partial y}(\bar{p} - \bar{\rho}\overline{v'v'}) = 0 \qquad (2.175)$$

The $x$-axis is aligned with the direction of predominant flow, and the $y$-coordinate traverses the boundary-layer thickness $\delta(x)$; see Fig. 2.12. In Eq. (2.174), $-\overline{u'v'}$ is the time-averaged (Reynolds) shear stress due to fluctuating velocity correlation.

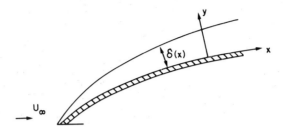

**FIG. 2.12**  The boundary-layer flow solution domain.

Equation (2.175) indicates that the pressure variation through $\delta(x)$ exactly balances the Reynolds transverse normal stress to first order. Hence,

$$\bar{p}(x, y) = p_1(x)[1 + \overline{\rho v' v'}(y)] \tag{2.176}$$

where $p_1(x)$ is the exterior inviscid-flow pressure distribution.

Equations (2.173) to (2.174) define a well-posed, initial boundary-value problem for $\mathbf{u}(x, y)$, upon identification of the Reynolds stress. Two closure models are available; the basis for each involves definition of a "turbulent" kinematic viscosity $\nu^t$ such that

$$-\overline{u'v'} \equiv \nu^t \left(\frac{\partial \bar{u}}{\partial y}\right) \tag{2.177}$$

Dimensional homogeneity dictates that $\nu^t$ be the linear product of a scale velocity and scale length,

$$\nu^t \equiv Ul \tag{2.178}$$

where $U$ and $l$ are measures on the scale of fluctuating velocity correlations. For the turbulence kinetic-energy (TKE) closure model, the velocity scale $U$ is defined as

$$U \equiv [\tfrac{1}{2}(\overline{u'u'} + \overline{v'v'} + \overline{w'w'})]^{1/2} \equiv k^{1/2} \tag{2.179}$$

i.e., the square root of the kinetic energy $(k)$ of the fluctuating velocity correlation. The corresponding length scale $l$ is the isotropic dissipation length scale $l_d$,

$$l \equiv \frac{\omega^b C k^{3/2}}{\varepsilon} \equiv l_d \tag{2.180}$$

where $\varepsilon$ is the isotropic turbulence dissipation function,

$$\varepsilon \equiv \frac{2\bar{\nu}}{3} \overline{\frac{\partial u_i'}{\partial x_j} \frac{\partial u_i'}{\partial x_k}} \delta_{jk} \tag{2.181}$$

$C_\nu$ is a correlation constant, and $\omega$ is a specified function of $y$ that accounts for wall-proximity damping effects on the length scale. Hence, Eq. (2.178) takes the form

$$\nu^t \equiv \omega^b C_\nu \left(\frac{k^2}{\varepsilon}\right) \tag{2.182}$$

For the Prandtl mixing-length turbulence (MLT) closure model, the length scale $l_m$ is defined as [226]

$$l_m \equiv \begin{cases} ky & 0 \le y \le \dfrac{\lambda\delta}{\kappa} \\ \lambda\delta & y > \dfrac{\lambda\delta}{\kappa} \end{cases} \qquad (2.183)$$

where $\delta(x)$ is the boundary-layer thickness, and $\kappa = 0.435$ and $\lambda = 0.09$ are constants. The scale velocity is proportional to the magnitude of mean-flow–strain rate; hence, Eq. (2.178) becomes

$$\nu^t \equiv (\omega l_m)^2 \left| \frac{\partial \bar{u}}{\partial y} \right| \qquad (2.184)$$

where $\omega$ is the van Driest damping function

$$\omega \equiv 1 - e^{-y/A} \qquad (2.185)$$

and $A$ is a defined function of wall shear and pressure gradient. Furthermore, Soliman and Baker [230] suggest Eq. (2.185) for Eq. (2.182) with $b \approx 2.0$.

Equation (2.182) or (2.184), coupled with Eq. (2.177), completes the closure. Defining the "effective viscosity" as

$$\nu^e \equiv \frac{\bar{\nu}}{\text{Re}} + \nu^t \qquad (2.186)$$

Eq. (2.174) takes the nonlinear parabolic form

$$L(\bar{u}) = \bar{u}\frac{\partial \bar{u}}{\partial x} + \bar{v}\frac{\partial \bar{u}}{\partial y} - \frac{\partial}{\partial y}\left(\nu^e \frac{\partial \bar{u}}{\partial y}\right) + \frac{1}{\bar{\rho}}\frac{d\bar{p}}{dx} = 0 \qquad (2.187)$$

The boundary-layer form of the additional differential equations for the TKE closure are also parabolic and of the form [231]

$$L(k) = \bar{u}\frac{\partial k}{\partial x} + \bar{v}\frac{\partial k}{\partial y} - \frac{\partial}{\partial y}\left(\frac{\nu^e}{C_k}\frac{\partial k}{\partial y}\right) - \nu^t\left(\frac{\partial \bar{u}}{\partial y}\right)^2 + \varepsilon = 0 \qquad (2.188)$$

$$L(\varepsilon) = \bar{u}\frac{\partial \varepsilon}{\partial x} + \bar{v}\frac{\partial \varepsilon}{\partial y} - \frac{\partial}{\partial y}\left(\frac{\nu^t}{C_\varepsilon}\frac{\partial \varepsilon}{\partial y}\right) - C_\varepsilon^1 \varepsilon k^{-1}\nu^t\left(\frac{\partial \bar{u}}{\partial y}\right)^2 + C_\varepsilon^2 \varepsilon^2 k^{-1} = 0 \qquad (2.189)$$

where the various $C_\beta^\alpha$ are model constants. The MLT closure requires no additional equations.

Since Eqs. (2.187) to (2.189) are parabolic, two boundary conditions and an initial distribution are required. The continuity equation (2.173) is purely an initial-value equation requiring only a wall specification $v_w$. Hence, for an impervious surface all variables vanish, yielding

$$\bar{u}(x, 0) = 0 = \bar{v}(x, 0) \qquad k(x, 0) = 0 = \varepsilon(x, 0) \qquad (2.190)$$

At the free stream, $y > \delta(x)$, all dependent variables merge smoothly with vanishing $y$-derivative into their free-stream levels; hence

$$\frac{\partial \bar{u}}{\partial y} = 0 = \frac{\partial k}{\partial y} = \frac{\partial \varepsilon}{\partial y} \qquad y > \delta \tag{2.191}$$

Initial distributions for $\bar{u}$, $k$, and $\varepsilon$ at $(x_0, y)$ are required to initialize Eqs. (2.187) to (2.189). In the absence of experimental data (the usual case), Cole's law [226] can be utilized to compute $\bar{u}(x_0, y < \delta)$ based upon $u_1(x_0)$ and $\delta(x_0)$. This is sufficient for initializing an MLT solution; see Eqs. (2.184) to (2.185). Further, should a TKE solution be required, the MLT computation of $\nu^t$ via Eq. (2.184) and Eqs. (2.182) and (2.180) can be employed to establish $k(x_0, y)$ and $\varepsilon(x_0, y)$, assuming a relationship exists between $l_d$ and $l_m$. Soliman and Baker [230] suggest

$$l_d \equiv C^{-1/2} \omega^a l_m \tag{2.192}$$

where $C$ and $a$ are model constants. Combining Eqs. (2.178) to (2.180) and (2.192),

$$k(x_0, y) = C\omega^{2(2-a)} l_m^2 \left| \frac{\partial \bar{u}}{\partial y} \right| \tag{2.193}$$

$$\varepsilon(x_0, y) = \frac{C^{1/2} \omega^{b-a} C_\nu k^{-3/2}}{l_m} \tag{2.194}$$

Equations (2.192) to (2.194) have been determined to yield initial distributions that converge to solutions of Eqs. (2.188) and (2.189), for a range of problem specifications. Suggested values for the model constants $\{a, b, C, C_\nu\}$ are $\{1.0, 2.0, 3.0, 0.068\}$.

As a final step, a coordinate transformation is usually employed to account for boundary-layer growth. A suitable elementary form is

$$\xi = x \tag{2.195}$$

$$\eta = \frac{y}{f(x)} \tag{2.196}$$

where $f(x) > \delta(x)$ is any convenient piecewise continuous function defining the solution domain. With $h \equiv f'/f$, where the prime indicates the ordinary derivative, the final form of Eqs. (2.173) and (2.187) to (2.189) for the description of the turbulent boundary-layer problem is

$$L(\bar{v}) = \left( \frac{\partial}{\partial \xi} - \eta h \frac{\partial}{\partial \eta} \right) \bar{u} + \frac{1}{f} \frac{\partial \bar{v}}{\partial \eta} = 0 \tag{2.197}$$

$$L(\bar{u}) = \bar{u} \left( \frac{\partial}{\partial \xi} - \eta h \frac{\partial}{\partial \eta} \right) \bar{u} + \frac{\bar{v}}{f} \frac{\partial \bar{u}}{\partial \eta} - \frac{1}{f} \frac{\partial}{\partial \eta} \left( \frac{\nu^e}{f} \frac{\partial \bar{u}}{\partial \eta} \right) + \frac{1}{\rho} \frac{dp_1}{d\xi} = 0 \tag{2.198}$$

$$L(k) = \bar{u} \left( \frac{\partial}{\partial \xi} - \eta h \frac{\partial}{\partial \eta} \right) k + \frac{\bar{v}}{f} \frac{\partial k}{\partial \eta} - \frac{1}{f} \frac{\partial}{\partial \eta} \left( \frac{\nu^e}{fC_k} \frac{\partial k}{\partial \eta} \right) - \frac{\nu^t}{f^2} \left( \frac{\partial \bar{u}}{\partial \eta} \right)^2 + \varepsilon = 0 \tag{2.199}$$

$$L(\varepsilon) = \bar{u} \left( \frac{\partial}{\partial \xi} - \eta h \frac{\partial}{\partial \eta} \right) \varepsilon + \frac{\bar{v}}{f} \frac{\partial \varepsilon}{\partial \eta} - \frac{1}{f} \frac{\partial}{\partial \eta} \left( \frac{\nu^t}{fC_\varepsilon} \frac{\partial \varepsilon}{\partial \eta} \right) - C_\varepsilon^1 \frac{\varepsilon \nu^t}{kf^2} \left( \frac{\partial \bar{u}}{\partial \eta} \right)^2 + C_\varepsilon^2 \frac{\varepsilon^2}{k} = 0 \tag{2.200}$$

## 2.8ʙ Finite-Element Solution Algorithm

The final-element algorithm is established on the discretization $\cup \Omega_e$ of the solution domain $\Omega \equiv \eta \times \xi \varepsilon y \times (x, x_0)$. The finite-element semidiscrete approximation $q_j^h$ to the true solution $q_j = \{\bar{u}, \bar{v}, k, \varepsilon\}$ is defined as

$$q_j(x, y) \approx q_j^h(\eta, \xi) \equiv \overset{M}{\underset{e=1}{\cup}} q_e^j(\eta, \xi) \tag{2.201}$$

where $M$ is the number of finite-element domains. The approximate-solution form for each variable and parameter, i.e., $k_e$, $\varepsilon_e$, $\bar{u}_e$, $\bar{v}_e$, and $\nu_e^t$, is

$$q_e(\eta, \xi) = \{N_k(\eta)\}^T \{Q(\xi)\}_e \tag{2.202}$$

The elements of $\{N_k\}$ are polynomials complete to degree $k$, while the elements of $\{Q\}_e$ are the to-be-determined expansion coefficients.

The finite-element algorithm employs the standard Galerkin–weighted-residual formulation [232] for $q_e$ representing each of $\bar{u}_e$, $k_e$, and $\varepsilon_e$, and if the standard matrix notation of Ref. [232, Chap. 6] is used, the matrix statement of the finite-element algorithm is

$$S_e[\Delta_e\{U\}_e^T[A3000]\{Q\}_e' - \Delta_e(\{U\}_e^T[A40010]h\{ETA\} - \{V\}_e^T[A3001])\{Q\}_e$$
$$+ \Delta_e f^{-1}\{XNUE\}_e^T[A3011]\{Q\}_e + \Delta_e\{SORCQ\}_e] \equiv \{0\} \tag{2.203}$$

For $q_e = u_e$, the source term in Eq. (2.203) is the pressure gradient, while for $q_e = k_e$,

$$\{SORCK\}_e = -\{XNUE\}_e^T([A40011]\{U\}_e)\{U\}_e + [A200]\{EPS\}_e \tag{2.204}$$

The source term for $q_e = \varepsilon_e$ is the scalar-element average factor $\varepsilon_e/k_e \equiv \overline{\varepsilon/k}$ times $\{SORCK\}_e$.

A Taylor series implicit-integration algorithm for Eq. (2.203) is

$$\{FQ\} = \{Q\}_{j+1} - \{Q\}_j - h[\Theta\{Q\}_{j+1}' + (1-\Theta)\{Q\}_j'] + \cdots = \{0\} \tag{2.205}$$

where $j$ is the $\xi$-step index, $h$ is the step size, and $\Theta = \frac{1}{2}$ yields the trapezoidal rule. Substituting (2.203) into (2.205) eliminates the derivative, and the Newton iteration solution algorithm is

$$[J(\{Q\}_{j+1}^p)]\{\delta Q\}_{j+1}^{p+1} = -F(\{Q\}_{j+1}^p) \tag{2.206}$$

where the dependent variable is the $(p+1)^{\text{st}}$ iteration vector

$$\{\delta Q\}_{j+1}^{p+1} \equiv \{Q\}_{j+1}^{p+1} - \{Q\}_{j+1}^p \tag{2.207}$$

## 2.8c Discussion and Results

Soliman and Baker [230] verify accuracy and convergence estimates for the finite-element algorithm for several turbulent boundary-layer flow cases. Numerical experiments document the use of nonuniform grids obtained by using a geometric progression ratio. Several test cases were selected from the experimental data sets reported in the Stanford Proceedings [227], among the most demanding of which is the Bradshaw relaxing-flow experiment (IDENT

2400). This case corresponds to evolution of a nonequilibrium incompressible boundary-layer flow induced by abrupt removal of a moderately adverse pressure gradient. Nominal free-stream velocity ($U_\infty$) is 33.5 m/s, wind-tunnel background turbulence level is less than 0.1%, and the reference unit Reynolds number is $2.38 \times 10^7$ m$^{-1}$. Discretizations containing at least $M = 30$ finite-element domains are required for adequate solution accuracy, using the linear ($k = 1$) algorithm. Figures 2.13 and 2.14 summarize computed solution accuracy of $k = 1$ compared with data for the Bradshaw experiment. The published $\bar{u}$-velocity profile at the first station ($x = 47$ inches) was curve-fit and interpolated at solution nodes to initialize $\{U\}$. If required, Eqs. (2.192) to (2.194) were employed to initialize $\{K\}$ and $\{EPS\}$. Using as the comparison basis the usual boundary-layer integral-parameter distributions, the solution agreement using the Prandtl mixing-length turbulence (MLT) closure model was improved for $\delta^*$ and $C_f$ by setting $\lambda = 0.11$ rather than the standard value $\lambda = 0.09$; see Eq. (2.183). It is not unexpected that an algebraic (point-function) model would experience some difficulty in describing nonequilibrium (path-function) phenomena. Figure 2.14 presents the same comparison, obtained using the turbulence kinetic-energy (TKE) closure model. The published standard-model constants were employed, i.e., $C_k = 1.0$, $C_\varepsilon = 1.3$, $C_\varepsilon^1 = 1.44$, and $C_\varepsilon^2 = 1.92$, and the initialization and low-turbulence Reynolds number model constants were $a = 1.0$, $b = 2.0$, and $C = 3.0$. Agreement is excellent on all comparison bases, except for a modest underprediction of growth in $\delta^*$ (hence $H$) in the initial solution region.

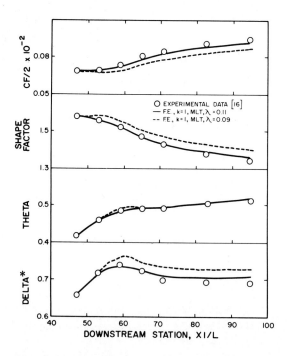

**FIG. 2.13** Boundary-layer parameter distributions for Bradshaw relaxing flow.

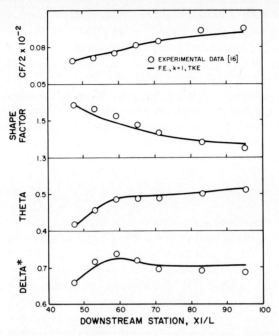

**FIG. 2.14** Boundary-layer parameter distributions for Bradshaw relaxing flow.

Additional results verifying the issue of accuracy and convergence are reported [230], the principal requirement being to confirm the exponent $2(k+1-m)=2k$ for convergence measured in the energy norm under the discretization refinement. Figure 2.15 summarizes predicted accuracy and convergence with discretization refinement in the energy norm $E(\varepsilon^h, \varepsilon^h)$, for the linear $(k=1)$ and quadratic $(k=2)$ algorithms. The solid lines, drawn at integer slopes of 2 and 4, essentially interpolate the numerical data, confirming the validity

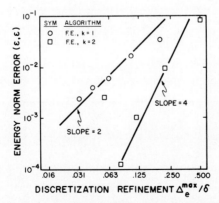

**FIG. 2.15** Accuracy and convergence for the linear and quadratic finite-element algorithms for turbulent boundary layer.

of the exponent $2k$. Both solutions illustrate coarse-grid accuracy superior to strict adherence to the convergence curve. Additional data are given in Ref. [230], including direct comparison to the familiar Crank–Nicolson finite-difference algorithm.

A finite-element solution algorithm has been derived and verified for the partial-differential-equation systems governing turbulent boundary-layer flow. A Galerkin–weighted-residual statement forms the theoretical basis, and implicit integration is employed for the resultant system of ordinary differential equations. The results of numerical experiments confirm accuracy and convergence estimates in the energy norm. This contribution is a condensation of Ref. [230].

## 2.9 TURBULENT FLOW

Although two-equation turbulence models have been in use for some time in finite-difference codes, few finite-element solutions of turbulent flow have yet been published [233–235]. These references all use the well-known $k\varepsilon$-turbulence model which, in the finite-element context, can lead to iterative convergence difficulties [236]. An alternative model is employed in the finite-element solution method [237] described in this section, the procedure best being illustrated by consideration of a particular flow problem. Turbulent flow through a sudden pipe expansion exemplifies most of the difficulties characterizing the numerical simulation of confined turbulent flow, as well as being of great practical importance. Figure 2.16 portrays the geometry and basic features of the particular problem selected for solution. A turbulent

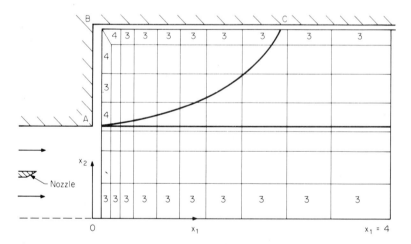

**FIG. 2.16**  Schematic of the flow and finite-element grid.

jet (coaxial with the pipe) emerges from a nozzle to mix with a turbulent but slower-moving annular stream. Subsequently the flow passes through a sudden expansion at the step $AB$, producing a shear layer spreading downstream from $A$ and a region of recirculation $ABC$ with reattachment at $C$. The expansion ratio (downstream-to-upstream pipe diameter) is 0.476, and the Reynolds number based on diameter $D$ and bulk velocity $U$ downstream of the step is 62,000. Experimental data for this arrangement is available in Ref. [238]. It will be assumed that the flow is incompressible, axisymmetric, and isothermal and that the mean flow field is stationary in time.

## 2.9A Governing Equations

If $u_1$, $u_2$ represent the mean velocity components in the axial and radial coordinate directions $x_1$, $x_2$, respectively, and if all variables are rendered dimensionless with respect to $U$ and $D$, the problem can be formulated as follows.

*Dynamic Equations*

$$u_m \frac{\partial u_n}{\partial x_m} + \frac{\partial p}{\partial x_n} - \frac{1}{x_2}\frac{\partial}{\partial x_m}(x_2 \tau_{mn}) + 2\frac{\mu_e}{\text{Re}}\frac{u_2}{x_2^2}\delta_{n2} = 0 \tag{2.208}$$

$$\frac{1}{x_2}\frac{\partial}{\partial x_m}(x_2 u_m) = 0 \tag{2.209}$$

$$\tau_{mn} = \frac{\mu_e}{\text{Re}}\left(\frac{\partial u_m}{\partial x_n} + \frac{\partial u_n}{\partial x_m}\right) \tag{2.210}$$

*Turbulence-Model Equations*

$$\mu_e = 1 + \mu_T = 1 + \text{Re}\,|q|l \tag{2.211}$$

where $q$ is the square root of turbulence kinetic energy $k$. Ignoring viscous effects, it is determined by the transport equation,

$$2u_m \frac{\partial q}{\partial x_m} - \frac{1}{x_2}\frac{\partial}{\partial x_m}\left(\frac{x_2 l}{\sigma_q}\frac{\partial q^2}{\partial x_m}\right) = P_q - D_q \tag{2.212}$$

where the source terms $P_q$ and $D_q$ are given by

$$P_q = l(S_u + S_q) \qquad D_q = \frac{C_\mu q^2}{l} \tag{2.213}$$

$$S_u = \left(\frac{\partial u_n}{\partial x_m} + \frac{\partial u_m}{\partial x_n}\right)\frac{\partial u_n}{\partial x_m} + 2\left(\frac{u_2}{x_2}\right)^2 \qquad S_q = \frac{2}{\sigma_q}\left(\frac{\partial q}{\partial x_m}\right)^2 \tag{2.214}$$

Equations (2.211) to (2.214) are formally equivalent to the well-known $kl$–one-equation model. Provided $l$ can be prescribed, these equations, together with Eqs. (2.208) to (2.210), suitable boundary conditions, and values for $C_\mu$ and $\sigma_q$, form a closed set. Otherwise, a further transport equation must be included. Usually a transport equation for the dissipation of turbulence energy $\varepsilon$ is selected [233–235]. However, for reasons which are elaborated in Refs. [238, 239], a transport equation for a frequency (or vorticity of the large-scale motions),

$f$ is preferred, $l$ then being derived from the equations

$$l = \frac{C_\mu |q|}{f} \tag{2.215}$$

$$u_m \frac{\partial f}{\partial x_m} - \frac{1}{x_2} \frac{\partial}{\partial x_m}\left(x_2 \frac{C_\mu}{2\sigma_f} q^2 \frac{\partial \ln f^2}{\partial x_m}\right) = P_f - D_f \tag{2.216}$$

where
$$P_f = C_{1f} S_u \qquad D_f = C_{2f} f^2 \tag{2.217}$$

### Boundary Conditions

### Nonwall Boundaries

*Inlet:*  $\qquad u_m = \hat{u}_m \qquad q = \hat{q} \qquad f = \hat{f} \qquad\qquad x_1 = 0 \qquad 0 \leqslant x_2 \leqslant 0.238 \qquad (2.218)$

where $\hat{u}_m$, $\hat{q}$, and $\hat{f}$ are experimentally prescribed functions (see Figs. 2.17 to 2.19 and Ref. [233]).

*Axis:*  $\qquad u_2 = 0 \qquad \dfrac{\partial u_1}{\partial x_2} = \dfrac{\partial q}{\partial x_2} = \dfrac{\partial f}{\partial x_2} = 0 \qquad\qquad x_2 = 0 \qquad 0 \leqslant x_1 \leqslant 4 \qquad (2.219)$

*Outlet:*  $\qquad -p + \tau_{11} = \tau_{12} = \dfrac{\partial q}{\partial x_1} = \dfrac{\partial f}{\partial x_2} = 0 \qquad\qquad x_1 = 4 \qquad 0 \leqslant x_2 \leqslant \tfrac{1}{2} \qquad (2.220)$

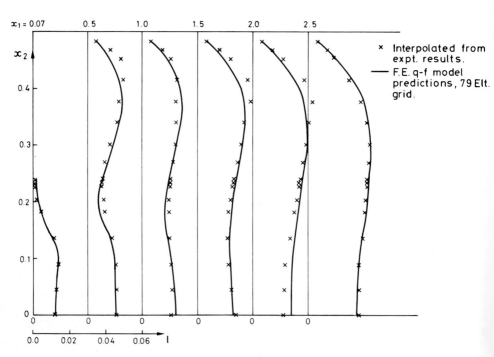

**FIG. 2.17**  Experimental length-scale profiles compared with $qf$-model predictions.

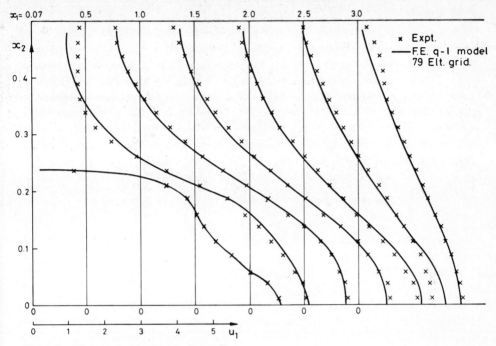

**FIG. 2.18**  One-equation model velocity profiles.

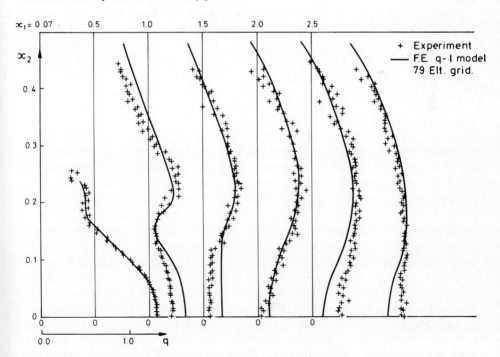

**FIG. 2.19**  One-equation model $q$-profiles compared with experiment.

*Wall Boundaries*

As a general rule, the velocity field in the vicinity of a wall exhibits very steep normal variations requiring an expensive concentration of nodes if the solution is to be extended to the physical boundary. Furthermore, the dissipation term $D_q$ has the simple form shown in Eq. (2.213) only when viscous effects are negligible. These pose serious difficulties in devising numerical wall procedures. Although finite-element solutions through to the wall have been achieved for parabolic flows [239], the more usual approach is to remove the mesh boundary a distance $\Delta h$ from the wall to a less problematic position where the flow is fully turbulent, and match the numerical solution to assumed analytical expressions describing the wall behavior of the dependent variables [233–235, 240]. Without loss of generality, consider the wall $x_2 = \frac{1}{2}$ and let $y$ represent distance normal to the wall. Then the behavior of the velocity field is [240]

$$u_1^+ = \frac{1}{\kappa} \ln y^+ + C \qquad y^+ \gtrsim 30 \tag{2.221}$$

$$u_2^+ = \frac{Q}{\mathrm{Re}} y^+ u_1^+ \tag{2.222}$$

where if $\tau_s$ is the wall shear stress, $Q$ denotes $d|\tau_s|^{-1/2}/dx$, and $u_1^+$ and $y^+$ are (usually) defined as $u_1/|\tau_s|^{1/2}$ and $y \,\mathrm{Re}\,|\tau_s|^{1/2}$, respectively. It is assumed that, close to the wall, $\partial q/\partial x_2$ is approximately zero. This is reasonable if the production and dissipation of $k$ are in balance [241], whereas when transport effects penetrate very close to the wall (e.g., near reattachment), it places the minimum restriction on the value of $q$. The behavior of the length scale is assumed to be [241]

$$l = C_\mu^{1/4} \kappa y \qquad y^+ \gtrsim 30 \tag{2.223}$$

which, in turn, yields $f$ via Eq. (2.215).

## 2.9ʙ Finite-Element Solution Procedure

*Discretization*   The mesh used is shown in Fig. 2.16. Unnumbered elements are of the eight-node quadratic-velocity linear-pressure type (type 2 elements). Those numbered 3 are of a special type (type 3) introduced in Ref. [242]. Their main distinguishing feature is the introduction of the normal derivatives of velocity as additional nodal variables at the boundary (so that the $u$-variation is cubic in the normal direction, pressure remaining bilinear). Elements numbered 4 (type 4) are essentially type 3 elements with the derivative parameters suppressed at one of the nodes [either because they are not required as at $B$ (Fig. 2.16) or in order to merge a type 3 with a type 2 element, e.g., point $A$] [242]. Each of these elements is regarded as type 2 as far as the $\mu_e$-variation is concerned. The dynamic equations [(2.208) to (2.210)] are discretized on this mesh by invoking the standard Galerkin procedure, continuity being handled by the PALM method [240] with a penalty parameter of unity. The discretization of the turbulence equations will be only briefly described, a fuller account being available in Ref. [239]. Consider Eq. (2.212). On each element, $q$ in the convective terms and $q^2$ in the diffusion terms are interpolated in the same way as $u$. The source terms $P_q$, $D_q$ and the diffusion coefficient $(1/\sigma_q)$ are all discretized with type 2 interpolation. An algebraic system of equations is then developed by weighting the residual with the "velocity" shape functions in the usual Galerkin fashion. The nodal values of $P_q$ and $D_q$ required in this discretization are generated by simply evaluating the right-hand sides of Eqs. (2.213) at each node (where the values of $S_u$ and $S_q$ at a node are taken as the area averages of these quantities over the elements sharing the node). Equation (2.216) is treated in a similar fashion [237]. Gaussian quadrature is then used to evaluate the resulting element matrices.

**Wall "Slip" Conditions**   The mesh boundary is displaced a distance $\Delta h = 0.07$ from the step (inlet is therefore at $x_1 = 0.07$ to coincide with a measurement station), and $\Delta h = 0.02$ from the pipe wall. Consider, once again without loss of generality, the $i^{\text{th}}$ node adjacent to the pipe wall, $x_2 = \frac{1}{2}$. If $\partial u_{i,m}$ denotes the normal derivative of $u_m$ at this node, then it is shown in Ref. [240] that

$$|\tau_s|^{1/2} = \kappa \, \Delta h \, |\partial u_{i,1}| \qquad \Delta h^+ \gtrsim 30 \qquad (2.224)$$

and the wall mesh-edge (or "slip") conditions for velocity are then given by

$$u_{i,1} = \kappa \, \Delta h \, \partial u_{i,1} \left( \frac{1}{\kappa} \ln \Delta h^+ + C \right) \qquad \Delta h^+ \gtrsim 30 \qquad (2.225)$$

$$u_{i,1} u_{i,2} = \Delta h (u_{i,1} \partial u_{i,2} - u_{i,2} \partial u_{i,1}) \qquad (2.226)$$

When type 3 wall elements are used (as in the present study), Eqs. (2.225) and (2.226) constitute proper and yet simple numerical boundary conditions for the velocity components. However, if more conventional elements are preferred, the velocity derivatives appearing are not explicitly available. Those appearing in Eq. (2.225) must be determined separately by differentiating the elemental variation, and Eq. (2.226) is usually replaced by $u_{i,2} = 0$ [234]. Alternatively, a slip equation for $u_{i,1}$ can be dispensed with, and Eq. (2.221) incorporated into a natural "traction" boundary condition [235].

At positions on the mesh edge where production and dissipation of $k$ are in balance (e.g., remote from reattachment) $|\tau_s|^{1/2} = C_\mu^{1/4} q$ [241]. Thus the definition of $\Delta h^+$ in Eqs. (2.225) can be replaced by $\Delta h^+ = C_\mu^{1/4} q \, \mathrm{Re} \, \Delta h$. It is convenient to employ this definition everywhere on the wall since it avoids $\Delta h^+$ becoming small near reattachment and Eq. (2.225) is then appropriate everywhere. The point $B$ (Fig. 2.16) is dealt with simply by setting $u_1$ and $u_2$ to zero. The above relation, $|\tau_s|^{1/2} = C_\mu^{1/4} q$, is often used to provide a boundary condition on $k^{1/2}$ [233–235]. However, in accordance with previous discussion, $q$ is left free at all wall adjacent nodes, the natural boundary condition $\partial q^2 / \partial y = 0$ then being approximated. Equations (2.223) and (2.215) provide values for $f$.

**Method of Solution**   Suppose approximations to $\underline{u}$, $\mu_T$, $l$ (and hence $q, f$) from Eqs. (2.211) and (2.215) are known. Then the procedure used to update these values is as follows:

**1.** With $\mu_T$ fixed, solve the dynamic equations to update $\underline{u}$, $p$.†

---

† The Newton–Raphson iterative method in conjunction with a frontal solver is used. As the overall solution is approached, one iteration proves sufficient.

**2.** With $\underline{u}$ fixed, update $\mu_T$ by solving the turbulence-model equations using the following sequence (repeated until $\mu_T$ converges).

    *a.* Two-equation model only. With $q$ fixed, solve the $f$-equation to update $l$ via Eq. (2.215).†

    *b.* With $l$ fixed, solve the $q$-equation to update $q$.†

Steps 1 and 2 are operated in sequence until overall convergence is achieved. It is found that the method converges reliably even from fairly poor initial guesses [237]. This robustness is due to the mathematical form of the $q$- and $f$-equations, the method of discretization employed, and the weak coupling between each equation system in the above steps (hence the preference over the $k\varepsilon$-form). The initial guess employed in the present analysis was $\underline{u} = 0$, $\mu_T$ constant, and (for the two-equation model) $l$ constant over the interior elements and equal to $C_\mu^{1/4}\kappa y$ in the wall elements.

## 2.9c Results

The model parameters $\kappa$, $C$, $C_\mu$, $\sigma_q$, $\sigma_f$, $C_{1f}$, $C_{2f}$ were set to the values 0.419, 5.45, 0.09, 1.0, 1.0, 0.052, 0.92, respectively, all except $C_{1f}$ and $\sigma_f$ being as recommended. (*Note*: The "tuned" value of $C_{1f}$ is strongly dependent upon the inlet profile of $f$ in which there is bound to be experimental uncertainty.) The one-equation ($ql$-) model predictions [$l$ prescribed experimentally in the interior (see Fig. 2.17) and by Eq. (2.223) at the wall edge] are compared with experiment in Figs. 2.18 and 2.19. Agreement is good, validating both the physical model and the discretization used. The calculations were repeated with the two-equation ($qf$-) model, and Fig. 2.17 compares the length scale thus predicted with that of experiment. It was confirmed that these solutions were grid-converged by repeating the calculations with 14 elements across the pipe.

## 2.9D Discussion

The computational model described above has much to recommend it for the type of problem considered. It is fairly robust and efficient and certainly does not appear to suffer the convergence problems encountered with Galerkin treatments of the $k\varepsilon$-equations [233, 235, 236]. Furthermore, as has been demonstrated, it can produce good agreement with experiment on fairly coarse meshes.

Of course, finite-element modeling of turbulent flow is a rapidly evolving subject, and many changes and improvements are sure to emerge. In particular, it remains to fully explore the $f$-equation, both theoretically and practically. It is also probable that for problems where wall effects exert a greater influence (e.g., flow with heat transfer) it will prove necessary to improve the wall treatment of the turbulence quantities. However, all such developments can be incorporated quite naturally into the computational framework presented here.

---

† The Newton–Raphson iterative method in conjunction with a frontal solver is used. As the overall solution is approached, one iteration proves sufficient.

## 2.10 TURBULENT HEAT TRANSFER

It is now possible to solve certain problems in turbulent heat transfer using the finite-element method. One of the more complex such problems involves the flow of liquid metal through nuclear-reactor rod bundles. Liquid-metal-cooled fast breeder reactors contain an array of closely packed cylindrical fuel rods of fissile material. For performance and safety reasons a prediction of the temperature distribution in the rods and interrod axially flowing coolant is essential. The current analogy is based on the subchannel approach in which a small part of the flow domain, bounded by a set of rod surfaces and lines connecting rod centerlines (the hatched area in Fig. 2.20), is considered for analysis. Near the containment boundaries such an assumption would involve different-type boundary conditions. These can be treated as special areas during the analysis and considered in isolation, and then be coupled with adjacent areas to give an overall flow–heat-transfer pattern.

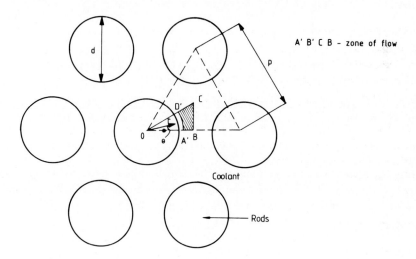

**FIG. 2.20**   Rod-bundle geometry.

The more recent finite-element approach for solving this type of problem is found in Refs. [243, 244]. Slager [244] used the one-equation model of turbulence to determine the velocity distribution and compared these with experimental results [245]. Both flow and heat transfer have also been analyzed [243], and again a favorable comparison with experimental results was obtained. The application of the finite-element method to analyze this type of problem is presented in the following sections.

### 2.10A Governing Equations for Turbulent Heat Transfer in Rod Bundles

The fluid flow between the rods is three-dimensional. However, generally, the secondary vortices in the plane parallel to the rod cross section are less than 5% of the bulk velocity [245] and can be ignored. This results in the velocities $u_1$, $u_2$ in this plane being set to zero as has been adopted previously. In addition, the flow can be considered to be fully developed such that

$$\frac{\partial Z}{\partial x_3} = 0 \qquad Z = u_i,\, k,\, \varepsilon \qquad \text{and} \qquad \frac{\partial p}{\partial x_3} = \text{constant}$$

where $p$ is the local pressure, $k$ is the mean turbulent kinetic energy, and $\varepsilon = k^{3/2}/l$, where $l$ is a length scale.

A set of equations for the present pseudo-three-dimensional problem is [246]

$$0 = \frac{\partial p}{\partial x_3} + \frac{\partial}{\partial x_1}\left[(\mu + \mu_t)\frac{\partial u_3}{\partial x_1}\right] + \frac{\partial}{\partial x_2}\left[(\mu + \mu_t)\frac{\partial u_3}{\partial x_2}\right] \tag{2.227}$$

$$0 = \frac{\partial}{\partial x_1}\left[\left(\mu + \frac{\mu_t}{\sigma_k}\right)\frac{\partial k}{\partial x_1}\right] + \frac{\partial}{\partial x_2}\left[\left(\mu + \frac{\mu_t}{\sigma_k}\right)\frac{\partial k}{\partial x_2}\right] + \mu_t\left[\left(\frac{\partial u_3}{\partial x_1}\right)^2 + \left(\frac{\partial u_3}{\partial x_2}\right)^2\right] - \sigma C_D \frac{k^{3/2}}{l} \tag{2.228}$$

for the one-equation model and an additional closure equation,

$$0 = \frac{\partial}{\partial x_1}\left[\left(\mu + \frac{\mu_t}{\sigma_\varepsilon}\right)\frac{\partial \varepsilon}{\partial x_1}\right] + \frac{\partial}{\partial x_2}\left[\left(\mu + \frac{\mu_t}{\sigma_\varepsilon}\right)\frac{\partial \varepsilon}{\partial x_2}\right] + C_1 \sigma k\left[\left(\frac{\partial u_3}{\partial x_1}\right)^2 + \left(\frac{\partial u_3}{\partial x_2}\right)^2\right] - \sigma C_D \frac{\varepsilon^2}{k} \tag{2.229}$$

when the two-equation model is invoked. Here, $\sigma_k$, $\sigma_\varepsilon$, $C_D$, $C_1$, and $C_2$ are taken to be spacewise constant, and the required turbulent viscosity $\mu_t$ is evaluated from

$$\mu_t = C_\mu \sigma k^{1/2} l \tag{2.230}$$

in which $C_\mu$ is assumed to be constant and the length scale is described in an algebraic manner [245] in terms of the radius $r$ and distance $\hat{r}$ to the location of maximum velocity, both measured from the rod center. The ratio $l/\hat{r}$ is given by

$$\frac{l}{\hat{r}} = \frac{r}{\hat{r}} \qquad 0 < \frac{r}{\hat{r}} < 0.44$$

$$\frac{l}{\hat{r}} = 0.44 + 0.066 \sin\frac{\pi(r/\hat{r} - 0.44)}{0.38} \qquad 0.44 < \frac{r}{\hat{r}} < 1$$

for the one-equation model and is evaluated from Eq. (2.229) for the two-equation model. The constants used in the current analysis are [246]

$$C_1 = 1.45 \qquad C_2 = 0.18 \qquad C_D = 0.38 \qquad C_\mu = 0.18 \qquad \sigma_k = 1.3 \qquad \sigma_\varepsilon = 1.0$$

A form of the energy equation used in the present analysis is

$$u_i \frac{\partial T}{\partial x_i} = \frac{1}{\rho}\frac{\partial}{\partial x_i}\left[\left(\frac{\mu}{\sigma} + \frac{\mu_t}{\sigma_t}\right)\frac{\partial T}{\partial x_i}\right] \tag{2.231}$$

in which the variables again take on a time-averaged meaning.

In the near-wall regions, wall functions are used to predict the variation in both the velocity and temperature. This obviates the need for an excessive mesh refinement near the wall, and thus the only requirement is that the first node of the finite-element mesh be placed within the fully turbulent zone. This avoids the necessity of making a provision for wall functions in the laminar and transition regions. The inclusion of such functions can be readily accommodated for the current application since the Reynolds numbers are large and there are no singular points where strains could become either zero or infinite. The particular wall functions used are [246]

$$u_3 = \frac{1}{K}\left(\frac{\tau_w}{\rho}\right)^{1/2} \ln Er_+ \qquad (2.232a)$$

$$T_+ = \sigma_t \left[ u_1 + P\left(\frac{\sigma}{\sigma_t}\right) \right] \qquad (2.232b)$$

$$k = \frac{C_\mu \tau_w}{K^2 \rho} \qquad (2.232c)$$

where $\quad r_+ = \left(\frac{r\rho}{\mu}\right)\left(\frac{\tau_w}{\rho}\right)^{1/2}$ $\qquad\qquad\qquad (2.232d)$

$$T_+ = (T - T_{\text{wall}}) \frac{(\rho\tau_w)^{1/2}}{\dot{T}} \qquad (2.232e)$$

$$\dot{T} = \frac{\mu_t}{\sigma_t} \cdot \frac{\partial T}{\partial x_2}$$

$$= \frac{C_\mu}{\sigma_t} \cdot \rho k^{1/2} x_2 \frac{\partial T}{\partial x_2} \qquad x_1 \text{ normal to wall, } x_2 \text{ parallel to wall} \qquad (2.232f)$$

$\tau_w$ is the wall shear and is given by

$$\tau_w = \mu \frac{\partial u_3}{\partial r}\bigg|_{\text{wall}} = (\mu + \mu_t)\frac{\partial u_3}{\partial r}\bigg|_{\text{near-wall node}}$$

and $P(\sigma/\sigma_\varepsilon)$ is the Spalding–Jayatalika function given by

$$P\left(\frac{\sigma}{\sigma_t}\right) = 9.24\left[\left(\frac{\sigma}{\sigma_t}\right)^{3/4} - 1\right]\left[1 - 0.28 \exp\left(-0.007\frac{\sigma}{\sigma_t}\right)\right]$$

## 2.10в  Solution Technique and Results

The results presented are restricted to the two-equation model with imposed boundary conditions as shown in Fig. 2.21. The flow equations were first solved, using an iterative approach [246], with the $\varepsilon$-equation uncoupled. Subsequently, the energy equation was solved with the velocity distributions known. A Galerkin–weighted-residual approach was adopted for the finite-element solution, and upwinding proved to be unnecessary. All variables were relaxed with a 0.5 relaxation factor and the necessary iterations repeated until the maximum relative change was less than 1%. The domains, both fluid and solid, were discretized using

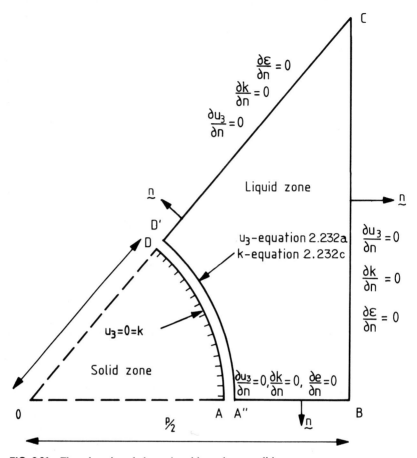

**FIG. 2.21**  Flow-domain subchannel and boundary conditions.

eight-node isoparametric elements. Typical stream-function plots are shown in Fig. 2.22 for a Reynolds number of 270,000.

When the temperature distribution was evaluated, the same mesh was retained in the fluid zone. Within the area of the rod a coarse mesh was found to be adequate. Again eight-node isoparametric elements were employed, and the dimensionless temperature contours are shown on Fig. 2.23.

Fuller details of the approach can be found in the cited references. Its main attribute is that for the solid-fluid system being analyzed a single domain is sufficient. A possible refinement of the method would be to reexamine the boundary-wall functions with a possible view to the redevelopment of special elements.

## 2.11 HYDRODYNAMIC LUBRICATION

Traditionally, most theoretical treatments of hydrodynamic lubrication in journal and thrust bearings used the finite-difference method to solve the Reynolds equation. The derivation of

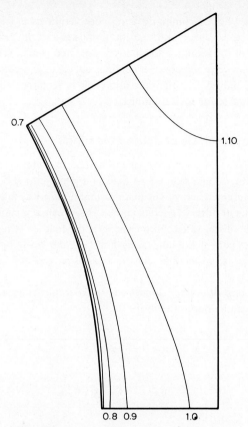

**FIG. 2.22** $u/\bar{u}$ contours. Re = 270,000, two-equation model.

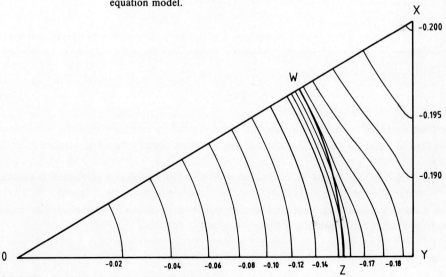

**FIG. 2.23** Dimensionless temperature contours.

this equation from the laws of continuity and conservation of momentum assumes that fluid-inertia terms can be neglected and that the flow is essentially two-dimensional. Consequently, the solution of the resulting Poisson-type equation is relatively easy and has been used to provide useful design predictions for bearings operating at medium loads and speeds. Under more extreme conditions, a rigorous approach is required, and the finite-element method has proved valuable for such solutions.

## 2.11A Finite-Element Analysis of Journal Bearings

To illustrate the application of the finite-element method to hydrodynamic lubrication, the analysis of the three-dimensional steady-flow field in a plain journal bearing with two inlet grooves (Fig. 2.24) is presented below. The main assumptions are as follows: fluid properties are constant, fluid-inertia or advection terms in the cross-stream direction only are neglected, and body forces may be disregarded. Furthermore, if the load-carrying part of the bearing exists in the convergent part of the lubricating film (i.e., the shaded portion of Fig. 2.24), then it is convenient to unwrap the film and use a cartesian grid as shown in Fig. 2.25.

*Governing Equations and Boundary Conditions*    Under the above assumptions, the fluid-momentum equations can be put in the form

$$u \cdot \nabla \cdot u = -\frac{1}{\rho}\frac{\partial p}{\partial x} + \nu \nabla \cdot \nabla \cdot u \tag{2.233}$$

$$0 = -\frac{1}{\rho}\frac{\partial p}{\partial y} + \nu \nabla \cdot \nabla \cdot v \tag{2.234}$$

$$u \cdot \nabla \cdot w = -\frac{1}{\rho}\frac{\partial p}{\partial z} + \nu \nabla \cdot \nabla \cdot w \tag{2.235}$$

where $u$, $v$, and $w$ are the velocity components in the $x$-, $y$-, and $z$-directions, respectively; $p$ is the pressure; and $\rho$ and $\nu$ are the lubricant density and kinematic viscosity, respectively.
   The continuity equation is

$$\nabla \cdot u = 0 \tag{2.236}$$

With the weighted-residual approach, the finite-element system matrix can be obtained as described in Ref. [247]. Standard 20-node isoparametric "brick" elements were used for the solution.
   The boundary conditions may be either prescribed or introduced conveniently through the boundary integral. However, since the momentum equations are ellipsoidal in nature, each requires the specification of six boundary conditions—a total of 18 in all. For a bearing symmetrical about its centerline the conditions are as follows:

In the $x$-direction:   $u = 0$    on $\Gamma_1$    for $x = 0$ $\tag{2.237a}$

$u = 0$    on $\Gamma_2$    for $y = 0$ $\tag{2.237b}$

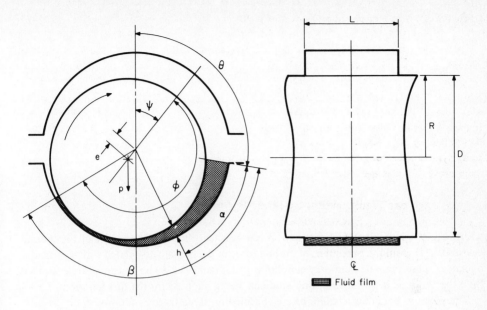

**FIG. 2.24**   Journal-bearing nomenclature.

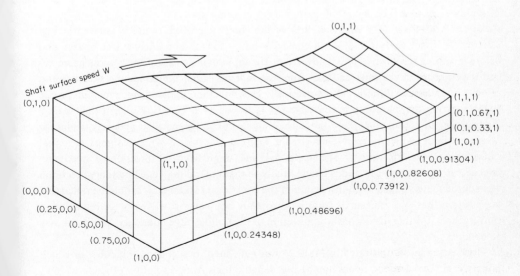

**FIG. 2.25**   Cartesian grid.

In the $y$-direction: $v = 0$    on $\Gamma_2$    for $y = 0$      (2.238a)

$$V = W \sin \frac{\partial h}{\partial z} \quad \text{on } \Gamma_2 \quad \text{for } y = h \qquad (2.238b)$$

$$\frac{\partial v}{\partial x} = 0 \quad \text{on } \Gamma_1 \quad \text{for } x = 0 \qquad (2.238c)$$

In the $z$-direction: $w = 0$    on $\Gamma_2$    for $y = 0$      (2.239a)

$$w = W \cos \frac{\partial h}{\partial z} \quad \text{on } \Gamma_2 \quad \text{for } y = h \qquad (2.239b)$$

$$\frac{\partial w}{\partial x} = 0 \quad \text{on } \Gamma_1 \quad \text{for } x = 0 \qquad (2.239c)$$

where $h$ is the local film thickness and $W$ the surface velocity of the shaft of the journal bearing. $\Gamma_1$, $\Gamma_2$, and $\Gamma_3$ are sections of the boundary of the domain associated with a particular boundary condition. The boundary conditions (2.238) and (2.239) on $\Gamma_1$ and $\Gamma_2$ are evaluated from the previous iteration field, null gradients being adopted for the first iteration.

The pressure boundary conditions are specified on three faces as follows:

$$p = 0 \quad \text{on } \Gamma_1 \quad \text{for } x = \frac{L}{2} \qquad (2.240a)$$

$$p = 0 \quad \text{on } \Gamma_3 \quad \text{for } z = z_1 \qquad (2.240b)$$

$$p = 0 \quad \text{on } \Gamma_3 \quad \text{for } z = z_2 \qquad (2.240c)$$

such that
$$\left( \frac{\partial p}{\partial z} \right)_{z_2} = 0 \qquad (2.240d)$$

**Solution Procedure** The main features of the solution procedure are illustrated in Fig. 2.26, where it can be seen that an inertialess solution for the film is always computed first before including the effects of fluid advection. The input data consist of the bearing geometry and the pressure at the inlet and exit from the lubricant film; the remaining pressure and velocity boundary conditions are automatically generated and updated since the film profile changes during the solution procedure according to Eqs. (2.237) to (2.240). For the bearing, the bush length and diameter and the journal diameter can be specified precisely, while the bearing attitude, which is represented by the angle $\psi$ (see Fig. 2.24), is assigned an initial value for an eccentric ratio $\varepsilon$. The angle $\phi$ is measured from the position of maximum thickness of the bearing gap and is fixed initially so that the trailing-edge boundary condition was approximately satisfied on inspection of the converged solution. (It should be noted that the position that $\phi$ is measured from is a dynamic one since $\psi$ will vary during solution convergence.) Further details of the application of the trailing-edge boundary conditions may be obtained from [248, 249].

The bearing mesh illustrated in Fig. 2.26 was generated by scaling a unit cube for which geometric subdivision and nodal numbering, suitable for a frontal solution procedure [250], was effected by the GENTOP program suite. Hence, the real mesh $x$-coordinates were simply

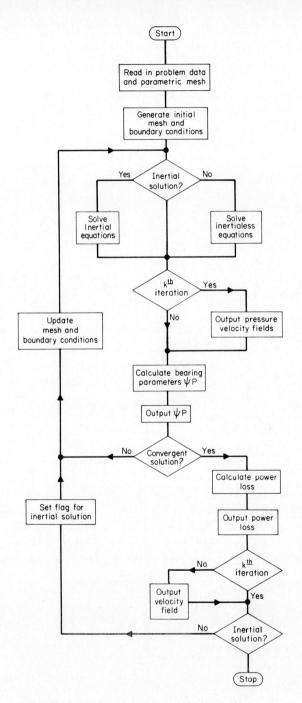

**FIG. 2.26** Main features of the solution procedure.

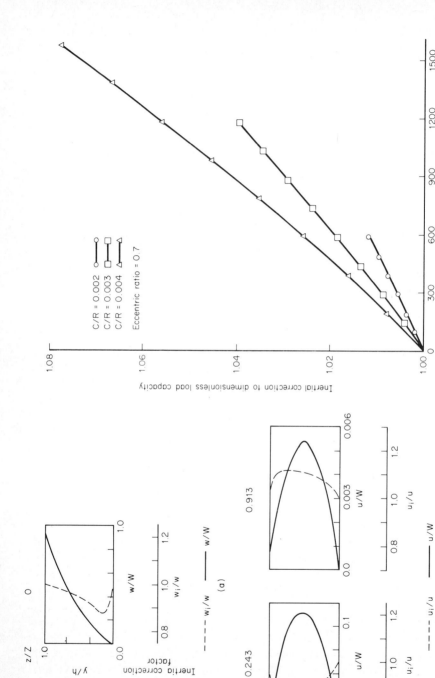

**FIG. 2.28** Effect of fluid advection on load capacity.

**FIG. 2.27** Velocity distributions. (a) Streamwise velocity distribution on bearing centerplane. (b) Axial velocity distributions on the plane $X/L = 0.25$. $C/R = 0.004$, $L/D = 0.5$, $Re = 589$, $\varepsilon = 0.7$.

obtained by multiplying the unit-cube coordinate by half the bearing width, $L/2$, with similar calculations for the $y$- and $z$-directions. Thus, written formally where the overbar denotes a fixed coordinate,

$$M(x, \bar{y}, \bar{z}) = P(\xi, \bar{\eta}, \bar{\zeta}) \cdot \frac{L}{2}$$

$$M(\bar{x}, y, \bar{z}) = P(\bar{\xi}, \eta, \bar{\zeta}) C [1 + \varepsilon \cos(\theta - \psi + \alpha)] \qquad (2.241)$$

$$M(\bar{x}, \bar{y}, z) = P(\bar{\xi}, \bar{\eta}, \zeta) R(\phi - \theta)$$

where $R$ is the journal radius and $C$ is the bearing clearance (i.e., the difference between the shaft and bush radii).

The initial solution of Eqs. (2.233) to (2.236) is now effected, with the exclusion of the fluid-advection terms in Eqs. (2.233) to (2.235), to yield velocity and pressure fields. Subsequent integration of the pressure field produces both the value of the load-carrying capacity of the bearing and the load direction, that is, $\psi$. The new value of $\psi$ is used as a new input parameter and the process repeated until convergence is obtained. It then remains to introduce the advection terms, and the whole sequence of events continues until the convergence of the velocity fields falls within satisfactory limits. The final velocity distributions at the film inlet and outlet may then be integrated and their difference taken to find the lubricant flow rate, while, as indicated earlier, integration of the pressure profiles yields the load-carrying capacity of the bearing. Also, the velocity derivatives $\partial v / \partial z$ and $\partial u / \partial y$ are evaluated at the bearing surface, summed, and multiplied by the dynamic viscosity to give $\tau_{yz}$. This stress provides a resistive torque to the journal shaft which may then be used to determine the power loss of the bearing.

## 2.11B  Results

The main feature of the finite-element approach to a hydrodynamic lubricating film lies in its ability to include cross-film velocities (i.e., a complete three-dimensional geometry) and to account for low fluid advection in the film without resorting to upwinding techniques. The method of presentation is intended to reflect this by comparing inertialess parameters with those which include inertia terms, the latter being denoted by the subscript $i$.

Figure 2.27 depicts the streamwise and axial components of velocity in the film which have been selected at positions in the bearing where fluid inertia will have the greatest influence. For the streamwise component, this occurs at $z/Z = 0$, where $Z$ is the unwound length of the bearing which coincides with the maximum lubricant-film thickness on the bearing centerplane. A similar argument applies to the axial component of velocity at $z/Z = 0.243$ at a plane located at $x/L = 0.25$. However, it can be seen that this component can be significantly affected by inertia at higher values of $z/Z$, which corresponds to a point near minimum film thickness where the lubricant flow is almost entirely lateral.

Such modifications of the velocity distribution may have severe consequences on any heat generation in the lubricant film.

Finally, the effect of fluid advection on the overall performance of the bearing can be demonstrated by considering its load-carrying capacity as shown in Fig. 2.28. As expected, the results at high bearing clearance ratios and Reynolds number (lubricant Reynolds number $= W\bar{h}/\nu$, where $\bar{h}$ is the average film thickness) are increasingly modified.

## 2.12 REFERENCES

1. Schlichting, H., *Boundary Layer Theory*, McGraw-Hill, New York, 1960.

2. Bradshaw, P., T. Cebeci, and J. H. Whitelaw, *Engineering Calculation Methods for Turbulent Flow*, Academic Press, New York, 1981.

3. Wolfshtein, M., "Some Solutions of the Plane Turbulent Impinging Jet," *Trans. ASME J. Basic Eng.*, 1970.

4. Wolfshtein, M., "Convection Processes in Turbulent Impinging Jet," Ph.D. thesis, University of London, London, 1967.

5. Baker, A. J., *Finite Element Computational Fluid Mechanics*, Hemisphere/McGraw-Hill, New York, 1983.

6. Norrie, D. H., and G. de Vries, *The Finite Element Method*, Academic Press, New York, 1973.

7. Chung, T. J., *Finite Element Analysis of Fluid Dynamics*, McGraw-Hill, New York, 1978.

8. Brebbia, C. A., *The Boundary Element Method for Engineers*, Pentech Press, London, Plymouth, 1978.

9. de Vries, G., T. Labrujere, and D. H. Norrie, "A Least-Squares Finite Element Solution for Potential Flow," Mech. Eng. Rep. 86, Department of Mechanical Engineering, University of Calgary, Calgary, Alta., December 1976.

10. Norrie, D. H., and G. de Vries, "Admissibility Requirements and the Least Squares Finite Element Solution for Potential Flow," *Proceedings of the Seventh Australasian Hydraulics and Fluid Mechanics Conference*, Institution of Engineers (Australia), Nat. Conf. Pub. 80/4, August 18–22, 1980, pp. 115–118.

11. Zienkiewicz, O. C., and Y. K. Cheung, "Finite Elements in the Solution of Field Problems," *Engineer*, 507–510 (September 24, 1965).

12. Fried, I., "Finite Element Method in Fluid Dynamics and Heat Transfer," Rep. 38, Institut für Statik und Dynamik der Luft und Raumfahrkonstructionen, University of Stuttgart, Stuttgart, April 1967.

13. Martin, H. C., "Finite Element Analysis of Fluid Flows," *Proc. 2nd Conf. Matrix Methods Struct. Eng.*, Wright-Patterson Air Force Base, Ohio, AFFDL-TR-68-150, 1968, pp. 517–538.

14. Argyris, J. H., G. Mareczek, and D. W. Scharpf, "Two and Three Dimensional Flow Using Finite Elements," *Aero. J. R. Aero. Soc.*, 73:961–964 (1969).

15. de Vries, G., and D. H. Norrie, "Application of the Finite Element Method to Potential Flow Problems: Part 1," Mech. Eng. Rep. 7, Department of Mechanical Engineering, University of Calgary, Calgary, Alta., August 1969.

16. de Vries, G., and D. H. Norrie, "Application of the Finite Element Technique to Potential Flow Problems: Part 2," Mech. Eng. Rep. 8, Department of Mechanical Engineering, University of Calgary, Calgary, Alta., July 1969.

17. Fujino, T., "Analysis of Hydrodynamic Problems by the Finite Element Method," *Japan–U.S. Seminar on Matrix Methods of Structural Analysis and Design*, Tokyo, August 25–30, 1969.

18. Argyris, J. H., G. Mareczek, and D. W. Sharpf, "Two and Three Dimensional Flow Analysis Using Finite Elements," *Nucl. Eng. Des.*, 11:230–236 (1970).

19. Argyris, J. H., "The Impact of the Digital Computer on Engineering Science (Part 1)," *Aero. J. R. Aero. Soc.*, 74:709, 13–41 (1970).

20. Argyris, J. H., and G. Mareczek, "Potential Flow Analysis by Finite Elements," *Ingenier-Archiv*, **42**(1):1–25 (1972).

21. Fujino, T., "Analyses of Hydrodynamic and Plate Structures by the Finite Element Methods," in R. H. Gallagher, Y. Yamada and J. T. Oden (eds.), *Recent Advances in Matrix Methods of Structural Analysis and Design*, University of Alabama Press, Huntsville, 1971, pp. 725–786.

22. Isaacs, L. T., "A Curved Cubic Triangular Finite Element for Potential Flow Problems," *Int. J. Numer. Meth. Eng.*, **7**(3):337–344 (1973).

23. Harrison, D. G., and Y. K. Cheung, "A Higher-Order Triangular Finite Element for the Solution of Field Problems in Orthotropic Media," *Int. J. Numer. Meth. Eng.*, **7**(3):287–295 (1973). (*Note*: There is a typographical error on p. 294. The first element of the $S_{y2}$-submatrix should read $10C_I^2 - 4C_{IH}C_{I-1}$; the printed version omits the exponent 2 in the first term.)

24. de Vries, G., and D. H. Norrie, "The Application of the Finite Element Technique to Potential Flow Problems," *Trans. ASME Ser. E, J. Appl. Mech.*, **38**:798–802 (1971).

25. Baker, A. J., and P. D. Manhardt, "Finite Element Analysis of Low Speed Viscous and Inviscid Aerodynamic Flows," NASA Rep. CR-2908, National Aeronautics and Space Administration, 1977.

26. Thompson, D. S., "Finite Element Analysis of the Flow Through a Cascade of Aerofoils," Rep. CUED/A Turbo/TR45 (ARC34412), Cambridge University Engineering Department, Cambridge, 1973.

27. Thompson, D. S., "Flow Through a Cascade of Aerofoils," in J. T. Oden, O. C. Zienkiewicz, R. H. Gallagher, and C. Taylor (eds.), *Finite Element Methods in Flow Problems*, University of Alabama Press, Huntsville, 1974, pp. 707–720.

28. Schmidt, G., "Incompressible Flow in Multiply Connected Regions," in C. A. Brebbia and J. J. Connor (eds.), *Numerical Methods in Fluid Dynamics*, Pentech Press, London, 1974, pp. 153–171 (*Proc. Int. Conf. Univ. Southampton, Southampton*, September 26–28, 1973).

29. Schmidt, G., "The Harmonic Finite Element for Use in Field Problems," Ph.D. thesis, University of Washington, Seattle, 1970.

30. Fletcher, C. A. J., "The Application of the Finite Element Method to Two-Dimensional Inviscid Flow," Rep. WRE-TN-1606 (WRYD), Weapons Research Establishment, Australian Defence Scientific Service, Salisbury, South Australia, May 1976.

31. Doctors, L. J., "An Application of the Finite Element Technique to Boundary Value Problems of Potential Flow," *Int. J. Numer. Meth. Eng.*, **2**:243–252 (1970).

32. Washizu, K., and M. Ikegawa, "Lifting Surface Problems Analysis," in Y. Yamada and R. H. Gallagher (eds.), *Theory and Practice in Finite Element Structural Analysis*, University of Tokyo Press, Tokyo, 1973, pp. 573–582.

33. Washizu, K., and M. Ikegawa, "Finite Element Technique in Lifting Surface Problems," in J. T. Oden, O. C. Zienkiewicz, R. H. Gallagher, and C. Taylor (eds.), *Finite Element Methods in Flow Problems*, University of Alabama Press, Huntsville, 1974, pp. 195–207.

34. Hashimoto, M., K. Washizu, and M. Ikegawa, "Application of the Finite Element Technique Combined with the Collection Method to Subsonic Lifting Surface Problems," *Proc. 2d Int. Symp. Finite Element Meth. Flow Prob.*, St. Margherita Ligure, Italy, June 14–18, 1976, pp. 149–158.

35. Tuann, S. Y., and M. D. Olson, "Review of Computing Methods for Recirculating Flows," *J. Comp. Phys.*, **29**(1):1–19 (1978).

36. Chung, T. J., *Finite Element Analysis in Fluid Dynamics*, McGraw-Hill, New York, 1978.

37. Gresho, P. M., G. D. Upson, S. T. Chan, and R. L. Lee, "Recent Progress in the Solution of the Time-Dependent Three-Dimensional Incompressible Navier–Stokes Equations," *Proc. 4th Int. Symp. Finite Elements Flow Prob.*, Tokyo, July 26–29, 1982.

38. Baker, A. J., "Research on a Finite Element Numerical Algorithm for the Three-Dimensional Navier–Stokes Equations," USAF Rep. AFWAL-TR-82-3012, Wright–Patterson Air Force Base, Ohio, April 1982.

39. Olson, M. D., and S. Y. Tuann, "Primitive Variables versus Stream Function Finite Element Solutions of the Navier–Stokes Equations," in R. H. Gallagher et al. (eds.), *Finite Elements in Fluids*, Wiley, New York, 1978.

40. Sani, R. L., P. M. Gresho, and R. L. Lee, "On the Spurious Pressures Generated by Certain GFEM Solutions of the Incompressible Navier–Stokes Equations," *Proc. 3d Int. Conf. Finite Elements Flow Prob.*, Banff, Alta., June 10–13, 1980.

41. Hughes, T. R., and W. K. Lui, "Review of the Finite Element Analysis of Incompressible Viscous Flows by the Penalty Function Formulation," *J. Comp. Phys.* **30**:1-60 (1979).

42. Reddy, J. N., "On Penalty Function Methods in the Finite-Element Analysis of Flow Problems," *Int. J. Numer. Meth. Fluids*, **2**(2):151-172 (1982).

43. Brooks, A., and T. J. R. Hughes, "Streamline Upwind Formulation for Navier–Stokes and Advection-Diffusion Equations," *Proc. 4th Int. Symp. Finite Element Meth. Flow Prob.*, Tokyo, July 26–29, 1982.

44. Gresho, P. M., R. L. Lee, and R. L. Sani, "On the Time-Dependent Solution of the Incompressible Navier–Stokes Equations in Two and Three Dimensions," C. Taylor (ed.), *Recent Advances in Numerical Methods in Fluids*, Pineridge Press, Swansea, Wales, 1980.

45. Zienkiewicz, O. C., and J. C. Heinrich, "The Finite Element Method and Convection Problems in Fluid Mechanics," in R. H. Gallagher et al. (eds.), *Finite Elements in Fluids*, Wiley, New York, 1978, vol. 3, pp. 1-23.

46. Gartling, D. K., "Some Comments on the Paper by Heinrich, Huyakorn, Zienkiewicz and Mitchell," *Int. J. Numer. Meth. Eng.*, **12**(1):187-190 (1978).

47. Gresho, P. M., and R. L. Lee, "Don't Suppress the Wiggles, They're Telling You Something," *Comput. Fluids*, **9**:223-240 (1981).

48. Leonard, B. P. "A Survey of Finite Differences with Upwinding for Numerical Modelling of the Incompressible Convective Diffusion Equation," in C. Taylor (ed.), *Recent Advances in Numerical Methods in Fluids*, Pineridge Press, Swansea, Wales, 1981.

49. Palit, K., and R. T. Fenner, "Finite Element Analysis of Slow Non-Newtonian Channel Flow," *A.I.Ch.E. J.*, **18**:628-633 (1972).

50. Palit, K., and R. T. Fenner, "Finite Element Analysis of Two-Dimensional Slow Non-Newtonian Flows," *A.I.Ch.E. J.*, **18**:1163-1170 (1972).

51. Palit, K., "Finite Element Analysis of Non-Isothermal Slow Non-Newtonian Channel Flow," Polymer Proc. Res. Rep. No. 2, Dept. Mech. Eng., Imperial College, London, 1974.

52. Palit, K., "Melt Flow in Polymer Processing Equipment," Ph.D. thesis, Dept. Mech. Eng., Imperial College, London, 1972.

53. Kiparissides, C., and J. Vlachopoulos, "Finite Element Analysis of Calendering," *Polymer Eng. Sci.*, **16**:712-719 (1976).

54. Caswell, B., and R. I. Tanner, "Wirecoating Die Design Using Finite Element Methods," *Polymer Eng. Sci.*, **18**:416-421 (1978).

55. Fenner, R. T., and F. Nadiri, "Finite Element Analysis of Polymer Melt Flow in Cable-Covering Crossheads," *Polymer Eng. Sci.*, **19**:203-209 (1979).

56. Choo, K. P., M. L. Hami, and J. F. T. Pittman, "Deep Channel Operating Characteristics of a Single Screw Extruder: Finite Element Predictions and Experimental Results for Isothermal Non-Newtonian Flow," *Polymer Eng. Sci.*, **21**:100-104 (1981).

57. Roylance, D., "Use of 'Penalty' Finite Elements in Analysis of Polymer Melt Processing," *Polymer Eng. Sci.*, **20**:1029-1034 (1980).

58. Nakazawa, S., J. F. T. Pittman, and O. C. Zienkiewicz, "Numerical Solution of the Flow and Heat Transfer of Polymer Melts," *Proceedings Third International Conference on Flow Problems*, Banff, Alta., June 10-13, 1980.

59. Nakazawa, S., J. F. T. Pittman, and O. C. Zienkiewicz, "Numerical Solution of Flow and Heat Transfer in Polymer Melts," in R. H. Gallagher et al. (eds.), *Finite Elements in Fluids*, Wiley, London, 1982, pp. 251-283.

60. Mahmoudzadeh, H., "An Analysis of Temperature Measurement Errors in Polymer Melts," M.Sc. thesis, Dept. Chem. Eng., University College of Swansea, Swansea, Wales, 1981.

61. Pittman, J. F. T., and H. Mahmoudzadeh, "The Performance of Melt Thermocouples: 1. The Flush-Mounted Type. 2. The Upstream Pointing Parallel to Flow Type," *Polymer Eng. Rev.*, **3**(1):63-74, 75-107 (Aug. 1983).

62. Nakazawa, S., and O. C. Zienkiewicz, "Finite Element Analysis of Flow and Coupled Heat Transfer in Polymeric Fluids," in E. Hinton et al. (eds.), *Proceedings of the International Conference on Numerical Methods for Coupled Problems*, Pineridge Press, Swansea, Wales, September 1981, pp. 851-859.

63. Menges, G., H. Cordes, and U. Masberg, "Flow Fields in Complex Flow Channels," *Kunststoffe* (Engl. Trans.), **70**:11-13 (1980).

64. Masberg, U., and G. Menges, "Calculation of Three-Dimensional Velocity and Temperature Fields in Flow Channels," *Proceedings of the Society of Plastic Engineers 38th Annual Technical Conference*, New York, 1980, pp. 96-99.

65. Tanner, R. I., R. E. Nickell, and R. W. Bilger, "Finite Element Methods for the Solution of Some Incompressible Non-Newtonian Fluid Mechanics Problems with Free Surfaces," *Comput. Meth. Appl. Mech. Eng.*, **6**:155-174 (1975).

66. Pittman, J. F. T., and S. Nakazawa, "Analysis of Melt Flow and Heat Transfer Using Finite Elements," *Polymer Eng. Rev.*, **4**(3):143-175 (July 1984).

67. Prager, W., *Introduction to Mechanics of Continua*, Ginn, Boston, 1961.

68. Zienkiewicz, O. C., and P. N. Godbole, "Flow of Plastic and Viscoplastic Solids with Special References to Extrusion and Forming Processes," *Int. J. Numer. Meth. Eng.*, **8**:3-16 (1974).

69. Zienkiewicz, O. C., and P. N. Godbole, "A Penalty Function Approach to Problems of Plastic Flow of Metals with Large Surface Deformation," *J. Strain Anal.*, **10**:180-185 (1975).

70. Zienkiewicz, O. C., and P. N. Godbole, "Viscous Incompressible Flow with Special Reference to Non-Newtonian (Plastic) Flow," in R. H. Gallagher et al. (eds.), *Finite Elements in Fluids*, Wiley, London, 1975, vol. 1, pp. 25-55.

71. Zienkiewicz, O. C., P. C. Jain, and E. Oñate, "Flow of Solids during Forming and Extrusion; Some Aspects of Numerical Solutions," *Int. J. Solids Struct.*, **14**:15-38 (1978).

72. Zienkiewicz, O. C., E. Oñate, and J. C. Heinrich, "Plastic Flow in Metal Forming: I. Coupled Thermal, II. Thin Sheet Forming," in H. Armen and R. F. Jones (eds.), *Proceedings of Winter Annual Meeting of ASME*, San Francisco, American Society of Mechanical Engineers, New York, 1978, pp. 107-120.

73. Pittman, J. F. T., R. D. Wood, J. M. Alexander, and O. C. Zienkiewicz (eds.), *Proceedings of the International Conference on Numerical Methods in Industrial Forming Processes*, Pineridge Press, Swansea, Wales, 1982.

74. Godbole, P. N., S. Nakazawa, and O. C. Zienkiewicz, "Blood Flow Analysis by the Finite Element Method," in B. R. Simon (ed.), *Proceedings of the First International Conference on Finite Elements in Biomechanics*, Tucson, Ariz., February 1980, pp. 277-293.

75. Nakazawa, S., and J. F. T. Pittman, "A Finite Element System for Analysis of Melt Flow and Heat Transfer in Polymer Processing," Ref. [73] above, 523-533 (1982).

76. Hami, M. L., "Finite Element Solutions for Flow in the Metering Section of a Single Screw Extruder," Ph.D. thesis, Dept. Chem. Eng., University College, Swansea, Wales, 1977.

77. Viriyayuthakorn, M., and B. Caswell, "Finite Element Simulation of Viscoelastic Flow," Rep. NSF ENG7800722/1, Div. Eng., Brown University, Providence, R.I., July 1979.

78. Caswell, B., "Finite Element Method for Fluids with Memory," *J. Non-Newtonian Fluid Mech.*, **5**:199 (1979).

79. Bernstein, B., M. K. Kadivar, and D. S. Malkus, "Steady Flow of Memory Fluids with Finite Elements; Two Test Problems," *Comput. Meth. Appl. Mech. Eng.*, **27**:279-302 (1981).

80. Bernstein, B., and D. S. Malkus, "Finite Elements for Steady Flows of Memory Fluids," Ref. [73] above, 611-619 (1982).

81. Thompson, E. G., J. F. T. Pittman, and O. C. Zienkiewicz, "Some Integration Techniques for the Analysis of Viscoelastic Flows," *Int. J. Numer. Fluids*, **3**:165-177 (1983).

82. Taylor, C., and J. M. Davis, "Tidal and Long Wave Propagation—A Finite Element Approach," *Comput. Fluid*, **3**:125-148 (1975a).

83. Zienkiewicz, O. C., P. Bettess, T. C. Chiam, and C. Emson, "Numerical Methods for Unbounded Field Problems and a New Infinite Element Formulation," *Proceedings of the ASME Winter Annual Meeting*, New York, 1981.

84. Zienkiewicz, O. C., D. W. Kelly, and P. Bettess, "Marriage a la Mode—The Best of Both Worlds (Finite Elements and Boundary Integrals)," in R. Glowinsky, E. Y. Rodin, and O. C. Zienkiewicz (eds.), *Energy Methods in Finite Element Analysis*, Wiley, New York, 1979, pp. 81-107.

85. Garrison, C. J., and V. S. Rao, "Interaction of Waves with Submerged Objects," *Proc. ASCE*, **97**(WW2):259-277 (1971).

86. Garrison, C. J., "Hydrodynamic Loading of Large Off-Shore Structures: Three Dimensional Source Distribution Methods," in O. C. Zienkiewicz, R. W. Lewis, and K. G. Stagg (eds.), *Numerical Methods in Off-shore Engineering*, Wiley, New York, 1978, pp. 87-140.

87. Harms, V. W., "Diffraction of Water Waves by Isolated Structures," *Proc. ASCE*, **105**(WW2):131-147 (1979).

88. Lee, J. W., "Wave-Induced Oscillations in Harbours of Arbitrary Geometry," *J. Fluid Mech.*, **45**(2):375-394 (1971).

89. Zienkiewicz, O. C., D. W. Kelly, and P. Bettess, "The Coupling of the Finite Element Method and Boundary Solution Procedures," *Int. J. Numer. Meth. Eng.*, **11**:355-375 (1977).

90. Zienkiewicz, O. C., P. Bettess, and D. W. Kelly, "The Finite Element Method for Determining Fluid Loading on Rigid Structures Two and Three Dimensional Formulations," in O. C. Zienkiewicz, R. W. Lewis and K. G. Stagg (eds.), *Numerical Methods in Off-Shore Engineering*, Wiley, New York, 1978, pp. 141-183.

91. Berkhoff, J. C. W., "Linear Wave Propagation Problems and the Finite Element Method," in R. H. Gallagher, J. T. Oden, C. Taylor, and O. C. Zienkiewicz (eds.), *Finite Elements in Fluids*, Wiley, New York, 1976, vol. 1, pp. 251-264.

92. Hara, H., O. C. Zienkiewicz, and P. Bettess, "Application of Finite Elements to Determination of Wave Effects on Off-Shore Structures," *2d Int. Conf. Behav. Off-Shore Struct.*, Imperial College, London, 1979, pp. 383-390.

93. Mei, C. C., and H. S. Chen, "A Hybrid Element Method for Steady Linearized Free-Surface Flows," *Int. J. Numer. Meth. Eng.*, **10**:1153-1175 (1976).

94. Yue, D. K. P., H. S. Chen, and C. C. Mei, "A Hybrid Element Method for Diffraction of Water Waves by Three-Dimensional Bodies," *Int. J. Numer. Meth. Eng.*, **12**:245-266 (1978).

95. Liu, P. L. F., "Finite Element and Boundary Integral Equation Methods in Water Wave Refraction and Diffraction," in S. Y. Wang et al. (eds.), *Finite Elements in Water Resources*, University of Mississippi Press, University, 1980, pp. 5.211-5.222.

96. Houston, J. R., "Modelling of Short Waves Using the Finite Element Method," in S. Y. Wang et al. (eds.), *Finite Elements in Water Resources*, University of Mississippi Press, University, 1980, pp. 5.181–5.195.

97. Seto, H., "New Hybrid Element Approach to Wave Hydrodynamic Loadings on Off-Shore Structure," in T. Kawai (ed.), *Finite Element Flow Analysis*, University of Tokyo Press, Tokyo, 1982, pp. 435–442.

98. Sakai, F., "Vibration Analysis of Fluid-Solid Systems," in J. F. Abel, T. Kawai, and S. F. Shen (eds.), *Interdisciplinary Finite Element Analysis*, Cornell University Press, Ithaca, N.Y., 1981, pp. 453–477.

99. Bettess, P., "Finite Elements," *Int. J. Numer. Meth. Eng.*, **11**:53–64 (1977).

100. Bettess, P., "More on Infinite Elements," *Int. J. Numer. Meth. Eng.*, **15**:1613–1629 (1980).

101. Bettess, P., and O. C. Zienkiewicz, "Diffraction and Refraction of Surface Waves Using Finite and Infinite Elements," *Int. J. Numer. Meth. Eng.*, **11**:1271–1290 (1977).

102. Ganeba, M. B., L. C. Wellford, Jr., and J. J. Lee, "Dissipative Finite Element Model for Harbour Resonance Problems," in T. Kawai (ed.), *Finite Element Flow Analysis*, University of Tokyo Press, Tokyo, 1982, pp. 451–459.

103. Kawahara, M., "Typhoon Surge Analysis by Selective Lumping Two Step Explicit Finite Element Method," in K. P. Holz et al. (eds.), *Finite Elements in Water Resources*, (Springer-Verlag, Hannover, 1982, pp. 6.13–6.21.

104. Herrling, B., "A Finite Element Model for Estuaries with Intertidal Flats," *Proc. 15th Coast. Eng. Conf. ASCE*, Honolulu, 1976, pp. 3.396–3.415.

105. Holz, K. P., and G. Nitsche, "Tidal Wave Analysis for Estuaries with Inter-Tidal Flats," in S. Y. Yang (ed.), *Finite Elements in Water Resources*, University of Mississippi Press, University, 1980, pp. 5.113–5.126.

106. Kawahara, M., "On Finite Element Methods in Shallow Water Long Wave Flow Analysis," in J. T. Oden (ed.), *Computational Methods in Non-Linear Mechanics*, North-Holland, Amsterdam, 1980, pp. 261–287.

107. Kawahara, M., "Finite Element Method in Two Layer and Multi-Leveled Flow Analysis," in S. Y. Wang et al. (eds.), *Finite Elements in Water Resources*, University of Mississippi Press, University, 1980, pp. 5.3–5.19.

108. Kawahara, M., and K. Hasegawa, "Finite Element Analysis of Two-Layered Tidal Flow," in L. C. Wellford, Jr. (ed.), *Applications of Computer Methods in Engineering*, University of Southern California, Los Angeles, 1977, pp. 1357–1366.

109. Kawahara, M., and K. Hasegawa, "Periodic Galerkin Finite Element Method of Tidal Flow," *Int. J. Numer. Meth. Eng.*, **12**:115–127 (1978).

110. Pearson, C. E. and D. F. Winters, "On the Calculation of Tidal Currents in Homogeneous Estuaries," *J. Phys. Ocean*, **7**(6):520–531 (1977).

111. Jamart, B. M., and D. F. Winters, "A New Approach to the Computation of Tidal Motions in Estuaries," in J. C. J. Nihoul (ed.), *Hydrodynamics of Estuaries and Fjords*, North-Holland, Amsterdam, 1978, pp. 261–281.

112. Jamart, B. M. and D. F. Winters, "Finite Element Solutions in Fourier Space, with Application to Knight Inlet, British Columbia," in D. H. Norrie et al. (eds.), *3d Int. Conf. Finite Element Meth. Flow Prob.*, 1980, pp. 103–112.

113. Warzee, G., and M. A. Sterling, "Application of the Finite Element Method to Periodic Tidal Computation," in S. Y. Wang et al. (eds.) *Finite Elements in Water Resources*, University of Mississippi Press, University, 1980, pp. 5.127–5.137.

114. Provost, C. L., A. Poncet, and G. Rougier, "Finite Element Computation of Some Tidal Spectral Components," in S. Y. Wang et al. (eds.), *Finite Elements in Water Resources*, University of Mississippi Press, University, 1980, pp. 5.128–5.168.

115. Rahman, M., "Tidal Propagation in a Rectangular Basin of the Bay of Fundy," in K. P. Holz et al. (eds.), *Finite Elements in Water Resources*, Springer-Verlag, Hannover, 1982, pp. 5-91-5-100.

116. Young, F. D. L., and J. A. Liggett, "Transient Finite Element Shallow Lake Circulation," *Proc. ASCE*, **103**(HY2):109-121 (1977).

117. Baker, A. J., M. O. Soliman, and D. W. Pepper, "A Time-Split Finite Element Algorithm for Environmental Release Prediction," in C. A. Brebbia et al. (eds.), *Proc. 2d Conf. Finite Elements Water Resources*, 1978, pp. 4.53-4.65.

118. Baker, A. J., and M. O. Soliman, "Analysis of a Finite Element Algorithm for Numerical Predictions in Water Resources Research," in S. Y. Wang et al. (eds.), *Finite Elements in Water Resources*, University of Mississippi Press, University, 1980, pp. 1.40-1.55.

119. Kawahara, M., N. Takeuchi, and T. Yoshida, "Two Step Explicit Finite Element Method for Tsunami Wave Propagation Analysis," *Int. J. Numer. Meth. Eng.*, **12**(2):331-351 (1978a).

120. Grotkop, G., "Finite Element Analysis of Long-Period Water Waves," *Comput. Meth. Appl. Mech. Eng.*, **2**:147-157 (1973).

121. Kawahara, M., H. Hirano, K. Tsubota, and K. Inagaki, "Selective Lumping Finite Element Method for Shallow Water Flow," *Int. J. Numer. Meth. Fluids*, **2**:89-112 (1982).

122. Cullen, M. J. P., "A Simple Finite Element Method for Meteorological Problems," *J. Inst. Math. Appl.*, **11**:15-31 (1973).

123. Cullen, M. J. P., "Integrations of the Primitive Equations on a Sphere Using the Finite Element Method," *Q.J.R. Meteor. Soc.*, **100**:555-562 (1974a).

124. Cullen, M. J. P., "A Finite Element Method for a Nonlinear Initial Value Problem," *J. Inst. Math. Appl.*, **13**:233-247 (1974b).

125. Cullen, M. J. P., "Application on Finite Element Methods to Meteorological Problems," in R. H. Gallagher et al. (eds.), *Finite Element Methods in Flow Problems*, I.C.C.A.D., St. Margherita, 1976a, pp. 759-767.

126. Cullen, M. J. P., "On the Use of Artificial Smoothing in Galerkin and Finite Difference Solutions of the Primitive Equations," *Q.J.R. Meteor. Soc.*, **102**:77-93 (1976b).

127. Herrling, B., "Tidal Computation in the Elbe Estuary with a Coupled FE Model," *Finite Elements in Water Resources*, in S. Y. Wang et al. (eds.), University of Mississippi Press, University, 1980, pp. 5.138-5.147.

128. Holz, K. P., "A Higher-Order Time Integration Scheme for Open Channel Flow," *Comput. Meth. Appl. Mech. Eng.*, **8**:117-124 (1976).

129. Connor, J. J., and J. Wang, "Finite Element Modelling of Hydrodynamic Circulation," in C. A. Brebbia and J. J. Connor (eds.), *Numerical Methods in Fluid Dynamics*, Pentech Press, Plymouth, 1977, pp. 355-387.

130. Wang, J. D., "Real Time Flow in Unstratified Shallow Water Flow," *Proc. ASCE*, **104**(WW1):53-68 (1978).

131. Kawahara, M., K. Hasegawa, and Y. Kawanago, "Periodic Tidal Flow Analysis by Finite Element Perturbation Method," *Comput. Fluid.*, **5**:175-189 (1977).

132. Koutitas, C., and B. O'Connor, "Finite Element-Fractional Step Solution of the 3-D Coastal Circulation Model," in S. Y. Wang et al. (eds.), *Finite Elements in Water Resources*, University of Mississippi Press, University, 1980, pp. 5.64-5.71.

133. Tanaka, T., Y. Ono, and T. Ishise, "The Open Boundary Value Problems in Ocean Dynamics by Finite Elements," in S. Y. Wang et al. (eds.), *Finite Elements in Water Resources*, University of Mississippi Press, University, 1980, pp. 5.47-5.63.

134. Signorini, S. R., "A Three Dimensional Numerical Model of Circulation and Diffusion-Advection Processes for Estuaries and Coastal Application by Finite Element Method," in T. Kawai (ed.), University of Tokyo Press, Tokyo, 1982, pp. 603-610.

135. Praagman, N., "Residual Currents During Changing Meteorological Circumstances," in K. P. Holz et al. (eds.), *Finite Elements in Water Resources*, Springer-Verlag, Hannover, 1982, pp. 6.39-6.48.

136. Agrintaru, V., and L. Spraggs, "A Time Integration Technique for Modelling of Small Amplitude Tidal Waves," in K. P. Holz et al. (eds.), *Finite Elements in Water Resources*, Springer-Verlag, Hannover, 1982, pp. 5.17-5.25.

137. Murakami, K., and M. Morikawa, "Tidal Current and Substance Dispersion by Finite Element Method Using Finite Difference Technique," in K. P. Holz et al. (eds.), *Finite Elements in Water Resources*, Springer-Verlag, Hannover, 1982, pp. 15.21-15.30.

138. Partridge, P. W., and C. A. Brebbia, "Quadratic Finite Elements in Shallow Water Problems," *Proc. ASCE*, **102**(HY9):1299-1313 (1976).

139. Hirsch, J. E., "The Finite Element Method Applied to Ocean Circulation Problems," in R. O. Reid et al. (eds.), *Numerical Models of Ocean Circulation*, National Academy of Science, Durham, 1975, pp. 340-346.

140. Su, T. Y., and S. Y. Wang, "Depth-Averaging Models of River Flow," in S. Y. Wang et al. (eds.), *Proc. 3d Int. Conf. Finite Elements Water Resources*, 1980, pp. 5.223-5.235.

141. Staniforth, A. N., and R. W. Daley, "A Finite-Element Formulation for the Vertical Discretization of Sigma-Coordinate Primitive Equation Model," *Month. Weath. Rev.*, **105**:1108-1118 (1977).

142. Staniforth, A. N., and H. L. Mitchell, "A Semi-Implicit Finite-Element Barotropic Model," *Month. Weath. Rev.*, **105**:154-169 (1977).

143. Staniforth, A. N., and H. L. Mitchell, "A Variable-Resolution Finite-Element Technique for Regional Forecasting with the Primitive Equation," *Month. Weath. Rev.*, **106**:439-447 (1978).

144. Gray, W. G., "An Efficient Finite Element Scheme for Two Dimensional Surface Water Computation," in G. F. Pinder et al. (eds.), *Finite Elements in Water Resources*, Pentech Press, Plymouth, 1977, pp. 433-449.

145. Lynch, D. R., and W. G. Gray, "Finite Element Simulation of Shallow Water Problems with Moving Boundaries," in C. A. Brebbia et al. (eds.), *Proc. 2d Conf. Finite Elements Water Resources*, 1978, pp. 2.23-2.42.

146. Taylor, C., and J. M. Davis, "Tidal and Long Wave Propagation—A Finite Element Approach," *Comput. Fluid.*, **3**:125-148 (1975a).

147. Taylor, C., and J. M. Davis, "Tidal Propagation and Dispersion in Estuaries," *Finite Elements in Fluids*, New York, 1975b, pp. 95-118.

148. Laible, J. P., "On the Behaviour of a Semi-Analytic and Layered Galerkin Model for 3D Flows in Lakes with Variable Eddy Viscosity," in T. Kawai (ed.), *Finite Element Flow Analysis*, University of Tokyo Press, Tokyo, 1982, pp. 535-545.

149. Matsunashi, J., "Two-Dimensional Time Dependent Simulations of Hydro-Mass Behaviour in the Sea of Harima," in T. Kawai (ed.), *Finite Element Flow Analysis*, University of Tokyo Press, Tokyo, 1982, pp. 555-562.

150. Trösch, J., "Three-Dimensional Finite Elements for the Calculation of Circulations in a Deep Lake," in T. Kawai (ed.), *Finite Element Flow Analysis*, University of Tokyo Press, Tokyo, 1982, pp. 529-534.

151. Walters, R. A., and R. T. Cheng, "A Two Dimensional Hydrodynamic Model of a Tidal Estuary," in C. A. Brebbia et al. (eds), *Proc. 2d Conf. Finite Elements Water Resources*, 1978, pp. 2.3-2.21.

152. King, I. P., and W. R. Norton, "Recent Application of RMA's Finite Element Models for Two Dimensional Hydrodynamics and Water Quality," in C. A. Brebbia et al. (eds.), *Proc. 2d Conf. Finite Elements Water Resources*, 1978, pp. 2.81-2.99.

153. MacArthur, R. C., and W. R. Norton, "Application of the Finite Element Method to Vertically Stratified Hydrodynamic Flow and Water Quality," in S. Y. Wang et al. (eds.), *Finite Elements in Water Resources*, University of Mississippi Press, University, 1980, pp. 5.92-5.102.

154. King, I. P., "A Three Dimensional Finite Element Model for Stratified Flow," in T. Kawai (ed.), *Finite Element Flow Analysis*, University of Tokyo Press, Tokyo, 1982, pp. 513–520.

155. Young, F. D. L., J. A. Liggett, and R. H. Gallagher, "Steady Stratified Circulation in a Cavity," *Proc. ASCE*, **102**(EM1):1–17 (1976a).

156. Young, F. D. L., J. A. Liggett, and R. H. Gallagher, "Unsteady Stratified Circulation in a Cavity," *Proc. ASCE*, **102**(EM6):1009–1023 (1976b).

157. Cochet, J. F., D. Dhatt, and G. Touzot, "Comparison of Explicit and Implicit Methods Applied to Finite Element Models of Tidal Problems," in D. H. Norrie et al. (eds.), *Proc. 3d Int. Conf. Finite Element Meth. Flow Prob.*, 1980, vol. II, pp. 113–122.

158. Cochet, J. F., D. Dhatt, G. Hubert, and G. Touzot, "River and Estuary Flow by a New Penalty Finite Element," in T. Kawai (ed.), *Finite Element Flow Analysis*, University of Tokyo Press, Tokyo, 1982, pp. 563–570.

159. Cheng, R. T., "Transient Three-Dimensional Circulation of Lakes," *Proc. ASCE*, **103**(EM1):17–34 (1977).

160. Kawahara, M., S. Nakazawa, S. Ohmori, and K. Hasegawa, "Tsunami Wave Propagation Analysis by the Finite Element Method," in C. A. Brebbia et al. (eds.), *Proc. 2d Conf. Finite Elements Water Resources*, 1978b, pp. 2.131–2.150.

161. Wang, H. P., "Multi-Level Finite Element Hydrodynamic Model of Block Island Sound," in G. F. Pinder et al. (eds.), *Finite Elements in Water Resources*, Pentech Press, Plymouth, 1975, pp. 469–493.

162. Kanayama, H., and K. Ohtsuka, "Finite Element Analysis on the Tidal Current and the COD Distribution of Mikawa Bay," *Proceedings of the IFAC Symposium on Environmental Systems Planning Design and Control*, Kyoto, Japan, August 1977.

163. Holz, K. P., and H. Hennlich, "Numerical Experiences from the Computation of Tidal Waves by the Finite Element Method," in G. F. Pinder et al. (eds.), *Finite Elements in Water Resources*, Pentech Press, Plymouth, 1976, pp. 419–431.

164. Moult, A., "An Upwind Finite Element Formulation for Convection or Buoyancy Dominated Flows in Rivers, Bays and Estuaries," in S. Y. Wang et al. (eds.), *Finite Elements in Water Resources*, University of Mississippi Press, University, 1980, pp. 5.103–5.112.

165. Houston, J. R., "Interaction of Tsunamis with the Hawaiian Islands Calculated by a Finite Element Model," *J. Phys. Ocean*, **8**(1):93–102 (1978).

166. Kawahara, M., and S. Nakazawa, "Finite Element Method for Unsteady Shallow Water Wave Equation," in J. F. Abel et al. (eds.), *U.S.-Japan Seminar on Interdisciplinary Finite Element Methods*, Cornell University Press, Ithaca, N.Y., 1979, pp. 267–283.

167. Kawahara, M., M. Morihira, S. Kataoka, and K. Hasegawa, "Periodic Finite Elements in Two-Layer Tidal Flow," *Int. J. Numer. Meth. Fluid.*, **1**:45–61 (1981).

168. Kasahara, K., H. Hara, W. Fujiwara, and M. Kawahara, "Two-Step Explicit Finite Element Method for Two-Layer Flow Analysis," in T. Kawai (ed.), *Finite Element Flow Analysis*, University of Tokyo Press, Tokyo, 1982, pp. 611–618.

169. Wang, J. D., and J. J. Connor, "Mathematical Modelling of Near Coastal Circulation," MIT Rep. No. 200, Massachusetts Institute of Technology, Cambridge, Mass., 1975.

170. Kawahara, M., S. Nakazawa, S. Ohmori, and T. Takagi, "Two Step Explicit Finite Element Method for Storm Surge Propagation Analysis," *Int. J. Numer. Meth. Eng.*, **15**:1129–1148 (1980).

171. Spraggs, L. D., and C. Camateros, "Modelling Impoundments During Winter Conditions," in T. Kawai (ed.), *Finite Element Flow Analysis*, University of Tokyo Press, Tokyo, 1982, pp. 587–593.

172. Meissner, U., M. Narten, and R. Ratke, "Numerical Models and Their Calibration for the Analysis of Flow and Heat Transport Problems in Rivers," in T. Kawai (ed.), *Finite Element Flow Analysis*, University of Tokyo Press, Tokyo, 1982, pp. 595–601.

173. Tanaka, T., Y. Ono, T. Ishise, and K. Nakata, "Simulation Analysis for Diffusion of Discharged Warm Water in the Bay by Finite Elements," in K. P. Holz et al. (eds.), *Finite Elements in Water Resources*, Springer-Verlag, Hannover, 1982, pp. 15.31–15.41.

174. Sommerfield, A., *Partial Differential Equations in Physics*, Academic Press, New York, 1949.

175. Bando, K., P. Bettess, and C. Emson, "The Effectiveness of Dampers for the Analysis of Exterior Scalar Wave Diffraction by Cylinders and Ellipsoids," *Int. J. Numer. Meth. Fluids*, 4(7):599–617 (July 1984).

176. Chen, H. S., and C. C. Mei, "Oscillations and Wave Forces in an Offshore Harbour," MIT Rep. No. 190, Ralph M. Parsons Laboratory for Water Resources and Hydrodynamics, Massachusetts Institute of Technology, Cambridge, Mass., August 1974.

177. Bettess, P., and O. C. Zienkiewicz, "Diffraction and Refraction of Surface Waves Using Finite and Infinite Elements," *Int. J. Numer. Meth. Eng.*, 11:1271–1290 (1977).

178. Zienkiewicz, O. C., P. Bettess, and D. W. Kelly, "The Finite Element Method for Determining Fluid Loading on Rigid Structures—Two- and Three-Dimensional Formulations," in O. C. Zienkiewicz et al. (ed.), *Numerical Methods in Offshore Engineering*, Wiley, New York, 1978, chap. 4, pp. 141–183.

179. Austin, D. I., and P. Bettess, "Longshore Boundary Conditions for Numerical Wave Models," *Int. J. Numer. Meth. Fluids*, 2:263–276 (1982).

180. Taylor, C., B. S. Patil, and O. C. Zienkiewicz, "Harbour Oscillation—a Numerical Treatment for Undamped Natural Modes," *Proc. Inst. Civ. Eng.*, 43:141–156 (1969).

181. Connor, J. J., and C. A. Brebbia, *Finite Element Techniques for Fluid Flow*, Newnes, Butterworth, London, 1976.

182. Taylor, C., and J. M. Davis, "Tidal Propagation and Dispersion in Estuaries," in R. H. Gallagher et al. (eds.), *Finite Elements in Fluids*, vol. 1: *Viscous Flow and Hydrodynamics*, Wiley, New York, 1975, chap. 5.

183. Connor, J. J., and J. Wang, "Finite Element Modelling of Hydrodynamic Circulation," in C. Brebbia and J. J. Connor (eds.), *Numerical Methods in Fluid Dynamics*, Pentech Press, Plymouth, 1974.

184. Grotkop, G., "Finite Element Analysis of Long-Period Water Waves," *Comput. Meth. Appl. Mech. Eng.*, 2:147–157 (1973).

185. Connor, J. J., and C. A. Brebbia, *Finite Element Techniques for Fluid Flow*, Newnes, Butterworth, London, 1976.

186. Zienkiewicz, O. C., and J. C. Heinrich, "A Unified Treatment of Steady-State Shallow Water and Two-Dimensional Navier–Stokes Equations—Finite Element Penalty Function Approach," *Comput. Meth. Appl. Mech. Eng.*, 17/18:673–698 (1979).

187. Zienkiewicz, O. C., and P. N. Godbole, "Viscous Incompressible Flow with Special Reference to Non-Newtonian (Plastic) Fluids," in R. H. Gallagher et al. (eds.), *Finite Elements in Fluids*, Wiley, New York, 1975, vol. 1, pp. 25–55.

188. Bettess, P., C. A. Fleming, J. C. Heinrich, O. C. Zienkiewicz, and D. I. Austin, "Longshore Currents Due to Surf Zone Barriers," *Proceedings of the Sixteenth Coastal Engineering Conference*, Hamburg, American Society of Mechanical Engineers, New York, 1978, vol. 1, pp. 776–790.

189. Heinrich, J. C., "SHANAL 1—A Finite Element Program for Solving the Vertically Integrated Two-Dimensional Steady-State Shallow Water Equations Using a Penalty Function Formulation," Rep. CNME/CR/92, Dept. of Civil Engineering, University College of Swansea, Swansea, Wales, 1978.

190. Hughes, T. J. R., and A. Brooks, "A Theoretical Framework for Petrov-Galerkin Methods with Discontinuous Weighting Functions: Application to the Streamline-Upwind Procedure," in R. H. Gallagher (ed.), *Finite Elements in Fluids*, Wiley, New York, vol. 4, 1975.

191. Heinrich, J. C., P. S. Huyakorn, O. C. Zienkiewicz, and A. R. Mitchell, "An 'Upwind' Finite Element Scheme for Two-Dimensional Convective Transport Equation," *Int. J. Numer. Meth. Eng.*, **11**:131–143 (1977).

192. Gartling, D. K., "Some Comments on the Paper by Heinrich, Huyakorn, Zienkiewicz, and Mitchell," *Int. J. Numer. Meth. Eng.*, **12**:187–190 (1978).

193. Ben-Sabar, E., and B. Caswell, "A Stable Finite Element Simulation of Convective Transport," *Int. J. Numer. Meth. Eng.*, **14**:545–565 (1979).

194. Chang, M. W., and B. A. Finlayson, "On the Proper Boundary Conditions for the Thermal Entry Problem," *Int. J. Numer. Meth. Eng.*, **15**:935–942 (1980).

195. Huyakorn, P. S., "Solution of Steady-State, Convective Transport Equation Using an Upwind Finite Element Scheme," *Appl. Math. Model.*, **1**:189–195 (1977).

196. Heinrich, J. D., and O. C. Zienkiewicz, "Quadratic-Finite Element Schemes for Two-Dimensional Convective-Transport Problems," *Int. J. Numer. Meth. Eng.*, **11**:1831–1844 (1977).

197. Hughes, T. J. R., and A. Brooks, "A Multi-Dimensional Upwind Scheme with No Crosswind Diffusion," in T. J. R. Hughes (ed.), *Finite Element Methods for Convection Dominated Flows*, American Society of Mechanical Engineers, New York, 1979, AMD vol. 34, pp. 19–35.

198. Hughes, T. J. R., "A Simple Scheme for Developing 'Upwind' Finite Elements," *Int. J. Numer. Meth. Eng.*, **12**:1359–1365 (1978).

199. Brooks, A. N., and T. J. R. Hughes, "Streamline Upwind/Petrov-Galerkin Formulations for Convection Dominated Flows with Particular Emphasis on the Incompressible Navier–Stokes Equations," *Comput. Meth. Appl. Mech. Eng.*, **32**:199–259 (1982).

200. Payre, G., M. de Broissia, and J. Bazinet, "An 'Upwind' Finite Element Method via Numerical Integration," *Int. J. Numer. Meth. Eng.*, **18**:381–396 (1982).

201. Hughes, T. J. R., T. E. Tezduyar, and A. N. Brooks, "Streamline Upwind Formulations for Advection-Diffusion Navier–Stokes, and First-Order Hyperbolic Equations," in T. Kawai (ed.), *Finite Element Flow Analysis*, University of Tokyo Press, Tokyo, 1982, pp. 97–104.

202. Tezduyar, T. E., and T. J. R. Hughes, "Development of Time-Accurate Finite Element Techniques for First-Order Hyperbolic Systems with Particular Emphasis on the Compressible Euler Equations," final report prepared under NASA–Ames University Consortium Interchange, No. NCA2-OR745-104, 1982.

203. Gresho, P. M., and R. L. Lee, "Don't Suppress the Wiggles—They're Telling You Something," in T. J. R. Hughes (ed.), *Finite Element Methods for Convection Dominated Flows*, American Society of Mechanical Engineers, New York, 1979, AMD vol. 34.

204. Wu, C. H., "A General Theory of Three-Dimensional Flow in Subsonic and Supersonic Turbomachines of Axial, Radial and Mixed Flow Type," NACA TN 2694, National Advisory Committee for Aeronautics, 1952.

205. Hirsch, Ch., and G. Warzee, "A Finite Element Method for Through-Flow Calculations in Turbomachines," *ASME J. Fluids Eng.*, **98**:403–421 (1976).

206. Hirsch, Ch., and G. Warzee, "An Integrated Quasi-3D Finite Element Calculation Program for Turbomachinery Flows," ASME Pap. 78-GT-56, American Society of Mechanical Engineers, New York, 1978.

207. Habashi, W. G., E. G. Dueck, and D. P. Kenny, "Finite-Element Approach to Compressor Blade-to-Blade Cascade Analysis," *AIAA J.*, **17**(7):693–698 (July 1979).

208. Habashi, W. G., and P. L. Kotiuga, "Numerical Solution of Subsonic and Transonic Cascade Flows," *Int. J. Numer. Meth. Fluids*, **2**:317–330 (December 1982).

209. Akay, H. U., and A. Ecer, "Transonic Flow Computations in Cascades Using Finite Element Method," *ASME J. Eng. Power*, **103**:657–664 (October 1981).

210. Deconinck, H., and Ch. Hirsch, "Finite Element Methods for Transonic Blade-to-Blade Calculation in Turbomachines," *ASME J. Eng. Power*, **103**:665–677 (October 1981).

211. Habashi, W. G., and G. G. Youngson, "A Transonic Quasi-3D Analysis for Gas Turbine Engines Including Split-Flow Capability for Turbofans," *Int. J. Numer. Meth. Fluids*, **3**(1):1–22 (January 1983).

212. Akay, H. U., and A. Ecer, "Finite Element Analysis of Transonic Flows in Highly Staggered Cascades," *AIAA J.*, **20**(2):410–416 (February 1982).

213. Habashi, W. G., and M. M. Hafez, "Finite Element Stream Function Solutions of Transonic Rotational Internal and External Flows," *Numerical Methods for Partial Differential Equations*, **2**:127–144 (1985), and "Finite Element Stream Function Solutions for Transonic Turbomachinery Flow," AIAA Pap. 82-1268, June 1982.

214. Habashi, W. G., "Numerical Methods for Turbomachinery," in C. Taylor and K. Morgan (eds.), *Recent Advances in Numerical Methods in Fluids*, Pineridge Press, Swansea, Wales, 1980, chap. 8, pp. 245–286.

215. Hirsch, Ch., and H. Deconinck, "A Survey of Finite Element Methods for Transonic Flows," in P. L. Roe (ed.), *Numerical Methods in Aeronautical Fluid Dynamics*, Academic Press, New York, 1982, pp. 143–188.

216. Habashi, W. G., M. M. Hafez, and P. L. Kotiuga, "Computation of Choked and Supersonic Turbomachinery Flows by a Modified Potential Method," *AIAA J.*, **23**(2):214–220 (February 1985), and "Finite Element Methods for Internal Flow Calculations," AIAA Pap. 83-1404.

217. Hafez, M. M., J. South, and E. Murman, "Artificial Compressibility Methods for Numerical Solutions of Transonic Full Potential Equation," *AIAA J.*, **17**(8):838–844 (August 1979).

218. Habashi, W. G., and M. M. Hafez, "Finite Element Solution of Transonic Flow Problems," *AIAA J.*, **20**(10):1368–1376 (October 1982).

219. Deconinck, H., and Ch. Hirsch, "Boundary Conditions for the Potential Equation in Transonic Internal Flow Calculations," ASME Pap. 83-GT-35, American Society of Mechanical Engineers, New York, 1983.

220. Habashi, W. G., and M. M. Hafez, "Finite Element Solutions of Transonic External and Internal Flows," Chapter 22 in W. G. Habashi (ed.), *Advances in Computational Transonics*, Pineridge Press, Swansea, Wales, 1985, pp. 671–701.

221. Schlichting, H., *Boundary Layer Theory*, McGraw-Hill, New York, 1968.

222. Jaffe, N. A., and A. M. O. Smith, "Calculation of Laminar Boundary Layers by Means of a Differential-Difference Method," *Prog. Aero. Sci.*, **12**:19 (1971).

223. Blottner, F. G., and I. Flugge-Lotz, "Finite Difference Computation of the Boundary Layer with Displacement Thickness Iteration," *J. Mecanique*, **2**(4):397–423 (1963).

224. Blottner, F. G., "Finite Difference Methods of Solution of the Boundary Layer Equations," *AIAA J.*, **8**(3):193–205 (1970).

225. Blottner, F. G., "Computational Techniques for Boundary Layers," *AGARD Lect. Notes*, **73** (1975).

226. Cebeci, T., and A. M. O. Smith, *Analysis of Turbulent Boundary Layers*, Academic Press, New York, 1974.

227. *AFOSR-IFP-Standard Conference on Computation of Turbulent Boundary Layers*, Vol. I, S. J. Kline, G. Sovran, M. R. Morkovan, D. J. Cockrell (eds.); Vol. II, D. A. Coles and E. A. Hirst (eds.), Thermosciences Division, Department of Mechanical Engineering, Stanford University, Stanford, Calif., 1969.

228. Popinski, Z., and A. J. Baker, "An Implicit Finite Element Algorithm for the Boundary Layer Equations," *J. Comp. Phys.*, **21**(1):55–84 (1976).

229. Soliman, M. O., and A. J. Baker, "Accuracy and Convergence of a Finite Element Algorithm for Laminar Boundary Layer Flow," *J. Comput. Fluids*, **9**:43–62 (1981).

230. Soliman, M. O., and A. J. Baker, "Accuracy and Convergence of a Finite Element Algorithm for Turbulent Boundary Layer Flow," *Comput. Meth. Appl. Mech. Eng.*, **28**:81–102 (1981).

231. Hanjalic, K., and B. E. Launder, "A Reynolds Stress Model of Turbulence and Its Application to Thin Shear Flows," *J. Fluid Mech.*, **52**:609–638 (1972).

232. Baker, A. J., *Finite Element Computational Fluid Mechanics*, McGraw-Hill/Hemisphere, New York, 1983.

233. Larock, B. E., and D. R. Schamber, "Approaches to the Finite Element Solution of Two-Dimensional Turbulent Flows," in C. Taylor and K. Morgan (eds.), *Computational Techniques in Transient and Turbulent Flow*, Pineridge Press, Swansea, Wales, 1981.

234. Taylor, C., C. E. Thomas, and K. Morgan, "Analysis of Turbulent Flow with Separation Using the Finite Element Method," in C. Taylor and K. Morgan (eds.), *Computational Techniques in Transient and Turbulent Flow*, Pineridge Press, Swansea, Wales, 1981.

235. Tong, G. D., "Computation of Turbulent Recirculating Flow," Ph.D. thesis, Dept. of Civil Engineering, University College of Swansea, Swansea, Wales, 1982.

236. Smith, R. M., "On the Finite-Element Calculation of Turbulent Flow Using the $(k\text{-}\varepsilon)$ Model," *Int. J. Numer. Meth. Fluids*, **4**:303–319, 1984.

237. Smith, R. M., "A Practical Method of Two-Equation Turbulence Modelling Using Finite Elements," *Int. J. Numer. Meth. Fluids*, **4**:321–336, 1984.

238. Freeman, A. R., and R. T. Szczepura, "Mean and Turbulent Velocity Measurements in an Abrupt Axi-Symmetric Pipe Expansion with Complex Inlet Geometry," *Proc. Int. Symp. Appl. Laser-Doppler Anemometry Fluid Mech.*, Lisbon, 1982.

239. Baker, A. J., and J. A. Orzechowski, "A continuity Constraint Finite Element Algorithm for Three-Dimensional Parabolic Flow Prediction," *Proceedings of ASME-AIAA Symposium on Computers in Flow Predictions and Fluid Dynamics Experiments*, Washington, D.C., 1981.

240. Hutton, A. G., and R. M. Smith, "On the Finite Element Simulation of Incompressible Turbulent Flow in General Two-Dimensional Geometries," in C. Taylor and B. A. Schrefler (eds.), *Numerical Methods in Laminar and Turbulent Flows*, Pineridge Press, Swansea, Wales, 1981.

241. Launder, B. E., and D. B. Spalding, *Lectures in Mathematical Models of Turbulence*, Academic Press, New York, 1972.

242. Hutton, A. G., "Finite Element Boundary Techniques for Improved Performance in Computing Navier–Stokes and Related Heat Transfer Problems," in R. H. Gallagher (ed.), *Finite Elements in Fluids*, Wiley, New York, 1982.

243. Taylor, C., C. E. Thomas, and K. Morgan, "Turbulent Heat Transfer via the Finite Element Method: Heat Transfer in Rod Bundles," *Int. J. Numer. Meth. Fluids*, **3**(4):363–375 (1983).

244. Slager, W., "Finite Element Solution of Axial Turbulent Flow in a Bare Rod Bundle Using a One Equation Turbulence Model," *Nucl. Sci. Eng.*, **82**:243–259 (1982).

245. Carajilescov, P., and N. E. Todreas, "Experimental and Analytical Study of Axial Turbulent Flows in an Interior Sub-channel of a Bare Rod Bundle," *Heat and Mass Transfer*, American Society of Mechanical Engineers, New York, 1976, pp. 262–268.

246. Thomas, C. E., "Analysis of Confined Turbulent Flows," Ph.D. thesis, University of Wales, 1982.

247. Hood, P., and C. Taylor, "Navier–Stokes Equations Using Mixed Interpolation," in O. C. Zienkiewicz, R. H. Gallagher, and C. Taylor (eds.), *Conf. Proc. Finite Element Meth. Flow Prob.*, 1974.

248. Dawson, D., and C. M. Taylor, "Fundamental Aspects on Cavitation in Bearings," *Proceedings of the First Leeds-Lyon Symposium on Tribology, Cavitation and Related Phenomena in Lubrication*, Mechanical Engineering Publications, Bury St. Edmunds, U.K. 1974.

249. Kvitnitsky, Y. I., N. F. Kirkatch, and Y. D. Poltovsky, "The Solution of Reynolds Equation Under Natural Boundary Conditions for Hydrodynamic Journal Bearings," *Wear*, **37**:217–231 (1976).

250. Hood, P., "Frontal Solution Program for Unsymmetric Matrices," *Int. J. Numer. Meth. Eng.*, **10**:379–399 (1974).

251. Meissner, U., "A Mixed Finite Element Model for Use in Potential Flow Problems," *Int. J. Numer. Meth. Eng.*, **6**:467–473 (1973).

252. Brebbia, C. A., and L. C. Wrobel, "Steady and Unsteady Potential Problems Using the Boundary Element Method," in C. Taylor and K. Morgan (eds.), *Recent Advances in Numerical Methods in Fluids*, Pineridge Press, London, 1980.

# CHAPTER 3
# GEOMECHANICS

Finite-element analyses have revolutionized many aspects of geotechnical engineering by providing the capability of analyzing, in a fairly routine manner, many difficult boundary-value problems such as stresses around excavations, seismic response of earth dams and deeply embedded structures, and the response of offshore platforms to wave and earthquake loading. These analyses are easily conducted while taking the natural variability of soil deposits into account. However, there are two major drawbacks to finite-element analyses: cost and the lack of a general stress-strain relation for soils which can model all the important characteristics of the response of soils to loads. These factors have a major impact on dynamic analysis but are less critical for static analysis.

High costs result from the large regions that must be analyzed and the iterative or incremental nature of the solutions of the equations of equilibrium or motion that are necessary because of the nonlinear response of soil to load. In dynamic analysis, the need for full solutions at each time increment add substantially to the cost.

The development of constitutive relations for soils has been one of the most active research areas in geotechnics in recent years, and a plethora of new models of soil behavior has evolved. However, these new models have had little impact on geotechnical engineering practice. The relatively simple models adopted in the late 1960s for static analysis and in the early 1970s for dynamic-response analysis still dominate engineering practice today, and no significant shift away from these models is yet evident. The only change is the slow shift toward true nonlinear dynamic-response analyses for offshore engineering problems from the predominant iterative elastic analyses.

Procedures for static and dynamic finite-element analysis of soil structures and soil-structure interaction problems are described in the next two sections. Primary emphasis is on the procedures which dominate engineering practice despite their rather obvious limitations. Recent innovations which show signs of making some impact on practice are also discussed, but in much less detail. Finite-element analyses in geotechnical engineering are remarkable for the fact that certain computer programs are used almost exclusively, especially in dynamic-response analyses. For this reason, the presentations are keyed directly to these programs, although the principles of analysis are, of course, of general application. The third section considers the very important area of flow through porous media. This is a rapidly developing area in which finite-element analysis has made great strides. Complex problems involving aquifer seepage are now routinely solved by this technique.

## 3.1 STATIC FINITE-ELEMENT ANALYSIS OF SOIL-STRUCTURE SYSTEMS

Static loading of soil may cause significant deformations and in the limit a shear failure of a soil mass. It is important to have an adequate factor of safety against such a failure, and this is commonly computed from a limit-equilibrium analysis in which the soil is assumed to be rigid perfectly plastic. Such an analysis does not address deformations; these are generally computed from a separate analysis.

A rigorous analysis of deformations requires an application of the laws of mechanics. These involve satisfying both equilibrium and compatibility conditions throughout the region for the appropriate stress–strain relations, and for the boundary conditions in question. In addition, because strains depend on effective stress rather than total stress, a rigorous analysis also requires an application of the laws of hydraulics. Until the development of high-speed computers and the finite-element method, such analyses were not computationally feasible, and instead, a simpler stress-path approach was, and still is, used.

The finite-element method is a very powerful analytical technique which is basically easy to use and will become more so in the future with the advance of interactive computer graphics. The accuracy of predictions from such a method depends upon a knowledge of (1) the geometry of the problem, (2) the loading, and (3) the stress-strain relations of the soil. In practice there will be considerable uncertainty concerning these items so that the real value of such analyses is in assisting the engineer to place bounds on likely response. The greatest uncertainty is associated with the stress-strain relations, and since these affect the finite-element development, they will be discussed first.

### 3.1A Stress–Strain Relations for Soil

The stress–strain relations of soil are highly complex, being nonlinear, inelastic, and stress-level–dependent. In addition, strains are dependent on effective stress rather than total stress so that changes in the pore-fluid pressure lead to deformation even though the total stress may remain constant. Various stress–strain models have been proposed to represent the behavior of soil. These range from very simple linear-elastic models to complex elastoplastic models, and these will be briefly examined.

***Linear-Elastic Stress–Strain Model***   At any point in a stressed body there are six components of effective stress and six components of strain. The simplest relation between these
components is a linear-elastic one involving a linking matrix **D** which comprises 36 elastic
constants. However, **D** is symmetric so that the 36 constants reduce to 21. If the material has
identical properties in all directions, it is said to be *isotropic* and the 21 elastic constants
further reduce to 2. The most commonly used two constants are Young's modulus $E$ and
Poisson's ratio $\nu$. The bulk modulus $B$ and the shear modulus $G$ are perhaps more fundamental
parameters, as they relate the volumetric strain to the mean normal effective stress, and the
shear strain to the shear stress.

Direct determination of the shear modulus $G$ requires special equipment, whereas both
the bulk modulus $B$ and Young's modulus $E$ can be determined from the commonly used
triaxial test. For this reason $E$ and $B$ are probably the most practical parameters to use.

For the plane-strain condition there are three components of stress and strain rather than
six, and these components are related through $E$ and $B$ as follows:

$$\begin{Bmatrix} \sigma'_x \\ \sigma'_y \\ \tau'_{xy} \end{Bmatrix} = \frac{3B}{9B-E} \begin{bmatrix} 3B+E & 3B-E & 0 \\ 3B-E & 3B+E & 0 \\ 0 & 0 & E \end{bmatrix} \begin{Bmatrix} \varepsilon_x \\ \varepsilon_y \\ \gamma_{xy} \end{Bmatrix} \qquad (3.1)$$

where $\sigma'$ = the normal effective stress
$\qquad \tau'$ = the shear stress
$\qquad \varepsilon$ = the normal strain
$\qquad \gamma$ = the shear strain

The subscripts $x$ and $y$ refer to the $xy$-coordinate system.

***Nonlinear-Elastic Model***   Soil is not, in fact, linear-elastic except perhaps at very low strains
so that $E$ and $B$ will vary with stress level. Two approaches can be used to handle this problem:

1. An incremental linear-elastic approach in which a tangent modulus is used. The appropriate
   tangent modulus depends on the stress level, varying from a maximum value when the
   shear stress is zero, to zero when the shear stress is a maximum.

2. An equivalent linear-elastic approach in which a secant modulus is used. The appropriate
   secant modulus depends on the stress level, and an iterative procedure is required to
   obtain it.

The appropriate $E$ and $B$ depend upon the level of stress and can be obtained from
laboratory tests. In the interpretation of such tests it is common to express the distortional
response in terms of modified hyperbolas and the volumetric response in exponential form.
In this way the appropriate Young's moduli, both tangent $E_t$ and secant $E_s$, are given by

$$E_t = \left[ 1 - \frac{R_F(1-\sin\phi)(\sigma'_1-\sigma'_3)}{2c\cos\phi+2\sigma'_3\sin\phi} \right]^2 k_E P_a \left( \frac{\sigma'_3}{P_a} \right)^n \qquad (3.2)$$

$$E_s = \left[ 1 - \frac{R_F(1-\sin\phi)(\sigma'_1-\sigma'_3)}{2c\cos\phi+2\sigma'_3\sin\phi} \right] k_E P_a \left( \frac{\sigma'_3}{P_a} \right)^n \qquad (3.3)$$

The bulk modulus $B$ is given by

$$B = k_B P_a \left( \frac{\sigma'_m}{P_a} \right)^m \tag{3.4}$$

The complete stress–strain behavior of the soil is therefore defined by two elastic soil parameters $E$ and $B$. These parameters in turn depend upon the type of soil and the level of stress within the soil and are specified in terms of seven soil constants:

$k_E$ = the Young's modulus number

$n$ = the Young's modulus exponent

$k_B$ = the bulk modulus number

$m$ = the bulk modulus exponent

$R_f$ = the failure ratio

*For sand*:     $\phi_1$ = the peak friction angle at a confining stress of 1 atm

$\Delta\phi$ = the decrease in friction angle for a 10-fold increase in confining stress

*For clay*:     $c$ = the cohesion intercept of the strength envelope

$\phi$ = the slope of the strength envelope

The method of obtaining these constants is described in detail by Duncan and Chang [1] and by Duncan et al. [2]. In addition, Duncan et al. present tables of computed soil constants for various soil types together with suggested soil constant values for compacted soils. Byrne and Eldridge [3] suggest an alternative method for obtaining the bulk modulus constants, and in addition present soil constants for sand. Byrne et al. [4] suggest values for saturated clay for undrained conditions.

Byrne et al. [4] also indicate that the undrained stress–strain relations of saturated clay soil are markedly affected both by the stress path followed during consolidation as well as the stress path followed during undrained shear and suggest a model to account for such behavior.

**Dilatant-Elastic Stress–Strain Model**   The two-parameter elastic model implies that volume changes are induced by changes in mean normal effective stress alone, while shear strains are induced by shear stress alone. In fact, soil does not behave in this manner except perhaps at very low levels of shear strain. Volumetric strains are induced by changes in shear stress as well as by changes in the mean normal stress. Simple shear-test data show that loose sands undergo significant volume contractions while dense sands undergo large volume expansions. The incremental shear-induced volume change, $\Delta\varepsilon_v$, can be expressed in terms of a tangent dilation parameter $\alpha_t$ as follows:

$$\Delta\varepsilon_v = -\alpha_t \, \Delta\gamma \tag{3.5}$$

in which $\Delta\gamma$ is the increment of maximum shear strain.

The dilation term $\alpha_t$ depends upon the stress level and the density of the sand and can be obtained from simple shear or triaxial tests as discussed by Byrne and Eldridge [3]. It can also be expressed in terms of a modified form of Rowe's stress dilatancy theory, and this is also described by Byrne and Eldridge.

The dilatant-elastic materials leads to a three-parameter stress–strain model in which the increments of volumetric and shear strain are related to the corresponding stress increments as follows:

$$\begin{Bmatrix} \Delta\varepsilon_\nu \\ \Delta\gamma \end{Bmatrix} = \begin{bmatrix} \dfrac{1}{B} & -\dfrac{\alpha_t}{G} \\ 0 & \dfrac{1}{G} \end{bmatrix} \begin{Bmatrix} \Delta\sigma_m \\ \Delta\tau \end{Bmatrix} \tag{3.6}$$

It is essentially an extension of the two-parameter nonlinear-elastic stress–strain model.

***Elastic–Plastic Stress–Strain Model*** A basic assumption of elastic models is that the unloading path is identical to the loading path. This is generally not true for soils where the recoverable strain upon unloading is generally small. The recoverable strain is considered to be elastic, while the nonrecoverable strain is considered to be plastic. The unloading curve can be modeled by an incremental elastic approach in which a different elastic modulus is used upon unloading as compared with loading, and such an approach has been used by many researchers including Duncan et al. [5]. However, there is a fundamental difference between elastic and plastic strains in terms of their directions, and this cannot be properly accounted for in an elastic model.

The first comprehensive elastoplastic model for soil was developed by Roscoe and his coworkers at Cambridge in the 1950s and 1960s. It is called CAM CLAY and is described in detail by Roscoe and Burland [6], Schofield and Wroth [7], and Atkinson and Bransby [8].

Basically, if the soil is normally consolidated, large plastic strains will occur, whereas if the soil is overconsolidated, the strains will be small and elastic. The elastic and plastic zones are shown in Fig. 3.1 for a soil consolidated to an effective stress $p_0$. They are separated by a curved line called a *yield locus* and bounded by a critical-state line with slope $M$. Provided the load increment is such that the stress state remains within the elastic zone (increment *AB*), the strains will be small and can be computed from an elastic model. If the load increment is such that the stress state crosses the yield locus (increment *AD*), then plastic as well as elastic strains occur during the loading portion *CD*. When the stress path crosses

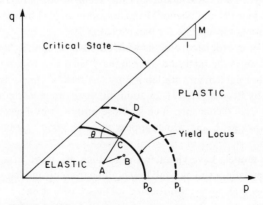

**FIG. 3.1**  Elastic and plastic zones.

the yield locus, it drags the yield locus with it, so that the new yield locus will be the dashed line shown in Fig. 3.1. This dashed line implies a new maximum past pressure $p_1$. Upon unloading, the yield locus does not move back but remains fixed unless a subsequent load increment causes it to move out again.

The shapes of the yield loci are based upon laboratory test results. Originally a log spiral was suggested and later an ellipse (Roscoe and Burland [6]). The plastic volume change, $\Delta\varepsilon_v^p$, associated with moving the yield locus from the solid to the dashed position is given by

$$\Delta\varepsilon_v^p = \frac{\lambda - k}{1 + e} \ln \frac{p_1}{p_0} \tag{3.7}$$

where $e$ = the void ratio of the soil
     $\lambda$ = the slope of the $e$ versus $\ln p$ line in the normally consolidated region
     $k$ = the slope of the $e$ versus $\ln p$ line in the overconsolidated region

The shear component of the plastic strain $\Delta\varepsilon_s^p$ is determined from the volumetric component and the shape of the yield locus. It is assumed that the resultant plastic strain $\Delta\varepsilon^p$ is normal to the yield locus (associated flow rule) as shown in Fig. 3.1. Hence if $\theta$ is the slope of the yield surface, $\Delta\varepsilon_s^p$ is given by

$$\Delta\varepsilon_s^p = \frac{1}{\tan\theta} \Delta\varepsilon_v^p \tag{3.8}$$

The plastic components of strain for a stress increment outside the yield locus are therefore given by Eqs. (3.7) and (3.8). For a stress increment within the yield locus, no plastic strains occur.

The elastic components of the strain occur for stress increments both within and outside the yield locus and depend upon the bulk modulus $B$ and the shear modulus $G$, and these can be obtained from unload or reload tests on the soil. In the elastic region, therefore, the strain increments can be specified by $B_t$ and $E_t$, while in the plastic region additional plastic strains also occur. Generally the plastic strains are an order of magnitude larger than the elastic strains.

The adaption of the CAM CLAY model for finite-element analyses is discussed in detail by Zienkiewicz and Naylor [9] and Naylor [10]. Duncan et al. [11] describe a modified form of the CAM CLAY model appropriate for compacted soils.

There are many other elastoplastic models which are based upon CAM CLAY concepts. A feature of these models is the inclusion of secondary yield loci within the "elastic" zone. Such models are in better agreement with laboratory test results. One of the more promising ones is that presented by Pender [12, 13]. In addition, there are many models which are not based upon the CAM CLAY concepts, such as those proposed by Prevost [14], Lade [15], and Nakai and Matsuoka [16], and which appear to be in good agreement with observed behavior.

While elastoplastic models have characteristics which are more in agreement with the observed laboratory behavior of soil, it is felt that nonlinear-elastic models currently represent the state of the art, and that more sophisticated models have not yet proved themselves in terms of field predictions.

## 3.1B Finite-Element Formulation

In the finite-element method of analysis the region is subdivided into discrete elements. A displacement pattern is assumed within the element, from which a stiffness matrix relating the element nodal forces and displacement can be determined from the principle of virtual work. This involves equating the work done by the internal stresses with that done by the nodal forces. The work done by the internal stresses depends upon the stress–strain relations of the soil. For an elastic material such stress–strain relations were presented earlier as follows:

$$\boldsymbol{\sigma}' = \mathbf{D}\boldsymbol{\varepsilon} \tag{3.9}$$

These stress–strain relations are in terms of effective stress. The total stress $\sigma$ and the effective stress $\sigma'$ are related as follows:

$$\boldsymbol{\sigma} = \boldsymbol{\sigma}' + \mathbf{u} \tag{3.10}$$

where $u$ = the pore-fluid pressure which acts only in the normal direction

When the pore-fluid pressure is introduced into the finite-element formulation, the element-nodal-force–displacement relationship is as follows:

$$\mathbf{k}\boldsymbol{\delta} = \mathbf{f} - k_w\mathbf{u} \tag{3.11}$$

where $\mathbf{k}$ = the element stiffness matrix based upon effective stress–strain relations
  $\boldsymbol{\delta}$ = the element nodal deflections
  $\mathbf{f}$ = the element nodal forces
  $k_w$ = the load vector associated with a unit pore-fluid pressure

If the contribution of each element is added in such a manner as to satisfy both equilibrium and compatibility at the nodes, the global system of equations to be solved is

$$\mathbf{K}\boldsymbol{\delta} = \mathbf{F} - K_w\mathbf{u} = \mathbf{F}' \tag{3.12}$$

where $\mathbf{K}$ = the global stiffness matrix
  $\boldsymbol{\delta}$ = the deflection vector
  $\mathbf{F}$ = the vector of total nodal forces
  $K_w$ = a matrix associated with pore-fluid pressure
  $\mathbf{u}$ = the vector of the element pore-fluid pressure
  $\mathbf{F}'$ = the vector of effective nodal forces

Equation (3.12) is then solved to yield the nodal displacements $\{\delta\}$, which are in turn used to determine the element strains and effective stresses.

The above formulation in terms of effective stress was first proposed by Christian [17] and has been used by Byrne [18] and by Byrne and Duncan [19]. For undrained conditions it is often desirable to work with total rather than effective stresses, in which case the pore-fluid pressure is set to zero and the appropriate $\mathbf{D}$ is obtained from tests evaluated in terms of total rather than effective stresses.

Until recently the type of finite element used in geotechnical engineering practice was thought not to be particularly important because of the uncertainty associated with the stress–strain relations. Many of the earlier programs use a constant-strain triangular element or a quadrilateral element comprised of four constant-strain triangles. However, recent studies by Sloan and Randolf [20] indicate that for highly constrained conditions that can occur near failure, such lower-order elements are not adequate and higher-order elements are required. More recent programs generally use an isoparametric formulation. Such elements offer a number of advantages, including efficient integration and differentiation and handling of curved and arbitrary geometric shapes. A detailed description of these elements is given by Desai and Abel [21].

The nonlinear nature of the soil can be handled by an equivalent elastic approach in which a secant modulus is used, or an incremental elastic approach in which a tangent modulus is used, as discussed earlier. The secant modulus approach is associated with single-step loading in which the total load and pore pressures acting on the system must be considered at all times. The response to an increment of load, $\Delta F'$, is obtained by subtracting the response of the system to two separate load vectors $F'$ and $F' + \Delta F'$, in which $F'$ is the original load acting on the system.

The tangent modulus approach is associated with incremental loading, in which case the stresses and forces in Eq. (3.12) are replaced by stress and force increments. Such a procedure allows the sequence of construction and loading to be simulated in an analysis. This is especially important in modeling strains and displacements during construction, for example, in earth dams. The tangent modulus approach can also consider the inelastic nature of soil by using a different modulus on unloading as compared with loading.

The tangent modulus approach may present problems with stress paths that involve unloading of normal stress. Such a problem can arise when the stress in an element reaches the strength envelope of the soil. For such a stress state, the shear modulus is set to zero, which means the shear stress in that element will not change for a further increment of loading. If the increment of load is such that the normal stress decreases, then, unless the strength envelope is horizontal, the predicted stress state will violate the failure criterion. A method of shedding such overstress to adjacent elements has been proposed by Zienkiewicz et al. [22] and Byrne and Janzen [23], and Hafez and Abdel-Sayed [24] have successfully used such an approach. Such a problem does not arise for the secant approach.

Both the undrained and subsequent response as drainage occurs can be determined from the solution of Eq. (3.12). The undrained response to a load increment can be obtained using a **K** based on $E_t$ and $B_t$ in terms of total stresses evaluated from undrained tests. The initial undrained pore pressures can be specified by using the Skempton pore-pressure parameters. The subsequent response as dissipation of these pore pressures occurs is obtained by switching to an effective-stress approach. This is achieved by using $E_t$ and $B_t$ based on effective stresses and reducing the pore pressure in Eq. (3.12) as dissipation proceeds. The rate at which dissipation occurs would require a solution of the consolidation or flow equation.

The stress and flow problems are actually coupled through volumetric compatibility and can be solved rigorously in terms of effective stresses by introducing an additional volumetric constraint as suggested by Christian [17] and Christian and Boehmer [25] or along the lines suggested by Sandu and Wilson [26].

For the dilatant-elastic model there is an additional shear-induced volume-change parameter, $\alpha_t$, which is analogous to the coefficient of thermal expansion in thermoelasticity and can be handled in the same manner. The stress and strain increments due to the load increment are first computed on the basis of an incremental elastic material using the parameters $E_t$ and $B_t$ only. With $\alpha_t$ and the shear-strain increment known, the dilatant volume changes in each element are then computed. The hydrostatic load vector to cause such volumetric increments is computed and applied to the system along with the load increment, and new stress and strain increments are computed. By analogy the method is referred to as *dilatant-elastic* and is described in detail by Byrne and Eldridge [3].

There are many computer programs available for two-dimensional nonlinear-elastic analysis of soil. Two such programs are SOILSTRESS, described by Byrne and Janzen [27], which uses an equivalent elastic approach, and FEADAM, described by Duncan et al. [8], which uses an incremental elastic approach.

## 3.1c Soil-Structure Systems and Interface Elements

When structural members rest upon soil or are buried within soil, their contribution to global stiffness is simply added to that of the soil elements in such a way as to satisfy both equilibrium and compatibility at the nodes.

A number of computer programs have been developed to model such behaviour. For three-dimensional analysis SAP IV [28], NONSAP [29], and ADINA [30] are commonly used. While these programs can also handle two-dimensional problems, a simpler two-dimensional program such as NLSSIP [19] can be used for such analyses.

When the contribution of soil and structural elements is added, it is generally assumed that no slip occurs at the interface. However, unless the structural member has a rough face, it is possible that slip will occur at the interface. In addition, where tensile stresses in the soil are involved, the soil may pull away and lose contact with the structural member. Such behavior can be accounted for by specifying two nodes rather than one node at points along the interface. One of the nodes is attached to the soil while the other is attached to the structural member. The nodes have the same initial coordinates. As loading proceeds, the nodes will basically move together until slip or a tension failure occurs, at which point they will move apart. Such behavior can be specified by an interface element having a stiffness matrix relating the forces and deflections at the interface nodes. The stiffness terms remain high, which prevents relative movement until the shear or tensile strength at the interface is reached, at which point the appropriate stiffness term drops essentially to zero, allowing movement to occur freely. Interface elements have been developed by many researchers, including Goodman et al. [31], Desai et al. [32], and Duncan et al. [11].

## 3.1d Application to an Arctic Offshore Platform

Oil-drilling requirements in arctic waters has recently led to some novel offshore-platform designs. An example of such a platform comprising a sand-filled steel square caisson is shown in Fig. 3.2. The caisson has dimensions $90 \times 90 \times 24$ m and is filled with dredged sand. The foundation conditions are comprised of a medium stiff clay underlain by sand, as shown in the figure. Ice loading is the critical design factor and amounts to 6000 kN per lineal meter. Important design considerations are (1) the failure modes of the system, (2) the deformations of the system, and (3) the forces on the structural members.

SOIL 1: Sand Above Water Table
SOIL 2: Sand Below Water Table
SOIL 3: Clay

NOTE: Soil and Steel Properties are listed in Table I.

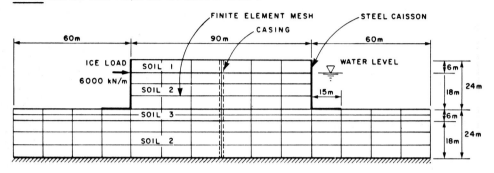

**FIG. 3.2**   Caisson-retained island.

The failure modes of the soil-structure system can be estimated reasonably well from conventional equilibrium methods, and this subject has been addressed by McCreath et al. [33]. However, the deformation patterns and forces on the structural members cannot be assessed from conventional geotechnical methods. The finite-element method of analysis is particularly useful in dealing with soil structures such as these for which there are no records of past performance.

The problem shown is three-dimensional, and a rigorous analysis would require a three-dimensional finite-element representation. However, a conservative estimate of the response of the system can be obtained from a two-dimensional analysis. Herein the plane-strain

**TABLE 3.1**   Soil and Structural-Member Properties

| | | | | | | | | | |
|---|---|---|---|---|---|---|---|---|---|
| | | | Soil properties | | | | | | |
| Soil type | Description | $c$, kN/m$^2$ | $\phi$, degrees | $\gamma$, kN/m$^3$ | $k_E$ | $n$ | $k_B$ | $m$ | $R_f$ |
| 1 | Loose sand above water table | 0 | 32 | 20 | 400 | 0.5 | 200 | 0.5 | 0.9 |
| 2 | Loose sand below water table | 0 | 32 | 20 | 400 | 0.5 | 200 | 0.5 | 0.9 |
| 3 | Clay | 60 | 0 | 20 | 200 | 0 | 2000 | 0 | 0.9 |

Steel-member properties

$E = 200 \times 10^6 \text{ kN/m}^2$
$A = 0.56 \text{ m}^2$
$I = 0.16 \text{ m}^4$
$\alpha = 0.007$

$\beta = 100$
$M_y = 11 \times 10^5 \text{ kN} \cdot \text{m}$
$M_p = 12 \times 10^5 \text{ kN} \cdot \text{m}$
$\sigma_y = 10 \times 10^5 \text{ kN/m}$

computer program NLSSIP was used to perform the analysis. This program considers the nonlinear nature of both the soil and structural elements and is described in detail by Byrne and Duncan [19]. The finite-element mesh and the arrangement of the structural members is shown in the figure. The soil and structural-member properties are listed in Table 3.1. Interface elements were not included in the analysis.

The construction procedure is modeled by assuming that the sand within the caisson is placed in four layers. The predicted horizontal effective stresses on the face of the caisson at the end of construction are shown in Fig. 3.3 and correspond closely to the at-rest pressure defined by $k_0 = 1 - \sin \phi$.

The ice load is applied in a number of steps. The predicted horizontal effective stresses on the left-hand face of the caisson for the 6000-kN ice load are also shown in Fig. 3.3. It may be seen that very high stresses occur in the region of the ice load and correspond approximately to the passive pressure at that depth.

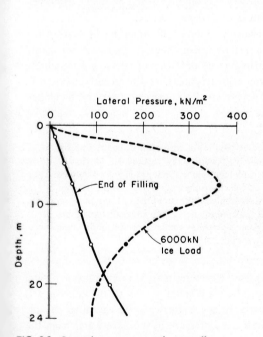

**FIG. 3.3** Lateral pressure on caisson wall.

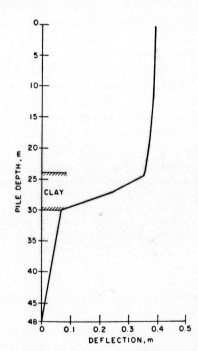

**FIG. 3.4** Horizontal deflection at location of casing.

The horizontal displacement profile at the location of a proposed drill casing (Fig. 3.2) is shown in Fig. 3.4. It may be seen that the maximum displacement is about 0.4 m, with most of the movement caused by shearing strains in the clay zone. These movements are a concern for such a casing. If the casing is flexible, it will essentially move or track with the soil and the induced forces and movements can be computed on that basis. However, if the casing is stiff, it will cut through the soil, and this can be accounted for by a secondary analysis similar to that used for laterally loaded piles, described by Byrne et al. [34].

## 3.2 DYNAMIC-RESPONSE ANALYSIS OF SOIL STRUCTURES

The dynamic response of soil structures is usually computed by using finite-element methods of analysis. In theory, such analyses can be conducted for a structure with arbitrary three-dimensional geometry. However, such a complete analysis is impracticable at present because of computer storage requirements and the cost of analysis. Furthermore, the lack of a good three-dimensional stress-strain relation for soils would make such an analysis of dubious value. Therefore, in present geotechnical engineering practice, dynamic-response analysis is limited to two dimensions and applied to axisymmetric structures or cross sections of more general structures such as earth dams. Such cross sections are assumed to deform in plane strain.

Dynamic response can be generated by earthquakes, explosions, ocean waves, and vibrating machinery. The most pervasive and difficult problem facing geotechnical engineers is the response to earthquake motions, and attention will be confined to this problem. However, the same basic principles apply to the other areas of dynamic response.

Since Newmark's classic paper [35] on seismically induced deformations in dams, it has been accepted in engineering practice that the seismic performance of soil structures should be evaluated in terms of deformations rather than in terms of factors of safety against stability failure. The state of the art for analyzing permanent deformations was recently assessed in a report on earthquake engineering research by the National Research Council of the United States [36]:

> Many problems in soil mechanics, such as safety studies of earth dams, require that the possible permanent deformations that would be produced by earthquake shaking of prescribed intensity and duration be evaluated. Where failure develops along well-defined failure planes, relatively simple elastoplastic models may suffice to calculate displacements. However, if the permanent deformations are distributed throughout the soil, the problem is much more complex, and practical, reliable methods of analysis are not available. Future progress will depend on development of suitable plasticity models for soil undergoing repetitive loading. This is currently an important area of research.

It is clear that the dynamic-response analysis of soil structures is still in a rudimentary state.

In the case of saturated soils, a decision must be made initially whether the analysis will be conducted in terms of total or effective stresses. Effective stresses are integranular stresses and are computed at any location by subtracting the pressure in the pore water from the total stresses. Deformations are controlled by effective stresses, and soil properties such as moduli and strength are functions of effective stress. Therefore, an effective-stress analysis is always preferable. However, such analyses are more difficult to perform and require pore-water pressure generation and dissipation models. Studies by Finn et al. [37] on the response of level, saturated sandy sites to seismic excitation show that effective-stress analyses are generally not necessary unless the pore-water pressures are likely to exceed 30% of the effective overburden pressure.

Dynamic-response analysis, as practiced today, had its origins in the pioneering attempts of Seed and his coworkers at the University of California at Berkeley to explain, in a quantitative way, the extensive liquefaction of saturated sands that occurred in 1964 during the earthquakes in Alaska and Niigata, Japan. Seed and Idriss [38] made the basic assumption that the nonlinear hysteretic stress–strain response of the sand could be determined by an equivalent linear-elastic method of analysis. The fundamental assumption of the equivalent linear method of analysis is that nonlinear response can be approximated satisfactorily by a damped linear-elastic model if the properties of that model are chosen appropriately. The method for one-dimensional analysis was incorporated in the computer program SHAKE by Schnabel et al. [39]. This program is widely used to predict the distribution of cyclic shear stresses for liquefaction studies and to provide input for soil-structure interaction analyses.

The decision in 1969 to model nonlinear soil by an equivalent linear-elastic model fixed the direction of development of dynamic-response analysis for about the next 10 years. The success of the one-dimensional model in explaining the response of level ground during earthquakes led to generalizations of the model to two and pseudo-three dimensions in the finite-element computer programs QUAD-4 [39], LUSH [41], and FLUSH [42]. These programs are the most frequently used for analysis of the seismic response of slopes and dams and for the solution of soil-structure interaction problems such as the response of deeply embedded nuclear-reactor structures to earthquake loading. Because it dominates current geotechnical engineering practice, the equivalent linear method of analysis and its associated computer programs will be discussed in considerable detail.

All these programs are formulated in terms of total stresses and treat nonlinear behavior by iterative linear-elastic procedures. Strong interest has developed in nonlinear effective-stress methods of analysis since 1976, when the first such method was proposed by Finn et al. [43]. Some of these developments which are now being applied in practice will also be described. They fall primarily into two categories: those based on nonlinear hysteretic stress-dependent stress–strain relations and those based on the concept of an elastic–plastic solid with combined isotropic and kinematic hardening.

## 3.2A Equivalent Linear Model

***Time-Domain Solutions for Soil Structures*** The equations of motion for a soil structure discretized into finite elements may be written in the time domain as

$$[M]\{\ddot{u}\} + [C]\{\dot{u}\} + [K]\{u\} = -\{m\}\ddot{y}(t) \qquad (3.13)$$

where $\{u\}$ = nodal-point displacements relative to the fixed base
$\{\ddot{u}\}, \{\dot{u}\}$ = corresponding accelerations and velocities
$[K]$ = stiffness matrix
$[C]$ = damping matrix
$[M]$ = mass matrix (lumped or consistent)
$\ddot{y}(t)$ = given input acceleration at the rigid base with horizontal and vertical components

$$h(t) = C_h \cdot \ddot{y}(t) \qquad v(t) = C_v \cdot \ddot{y}(t) \qquad (3.14)$$

where $C_h$, $C_v$ = scalar constants
$\{m\}$ = load vector corresponding to $\ddot{y} = 1$

The load vector is related to the mass matrix through

$$\{m\} = [M] \left( C_h \left\{ \begin{array}{c} 1 \\ 0 \\ 1 \\ 0 \\ \vdots \\ 1 \\ 0 \end{array} \right\} + C_v \left\{ \begin{array}{c} 0 \\ 1 \\ 0 \\ 1 \\ \vdots \\ 0 \\ 1 \end{array} \right\} \right) \tag{3.15}$$

The structure is assumed to be supported on a rigid base at which the earthquake accelerations are inputted. The solution of Eqs. (3.13) in the time domain is carried out using QUAD-4 [40].

The stress–strain properties of the soil are defined in each finite element by a constant Poisson ratio $\mu$ and by shear-strain–dependent shear moduli $G$ and equivalent viscous damping ratios $\lambda\%$. An equivalent modulus and damping ratio at any shear-strain level are defined by the slope of the major axis of the hysteresis loop corresponding to that strain (Fig. 3.5) and the area of the loop [44], respectively. Variations of shear moduli and damping

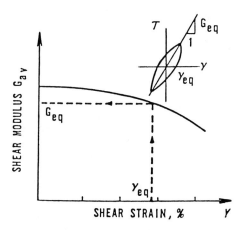

**FIG. 3.5**  Secant modulus versus shear strains.

ratios for sands and clays with shear strain are illustrated in Figs. 3.6 and 3.7 and tabulated for convenient use in finite-element programs in [39]. The tabulated values are frequently used in dynamic-response analyses in the absence of site-specific data. Maximum or low-shear-strain moduli $G_0$ may be determined in the field by using geophysical methods [45] or by appropriate laboratory tests on good-quality samples from the field [46].

Formulation of the stiffness matrix $[K]$ follows standard finite-element procedures [47]. The damping matrix $[C]$ is derived on the assumption that damping is of the Rayleigh type. The Rayleigh damping matrix is formulated for each finite element, and these matrices are summed appropriately to give the global matrix $[C]$.

The damping matrix for element $q$ is given by

$$[c]_q = \alpha_q [m]_q + \beta_q [k]_q \tag{3.16}$$

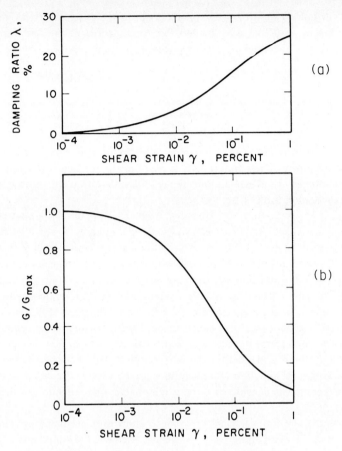

**FIG. 3.6** Shear moduli and damping ratios for sands [44].

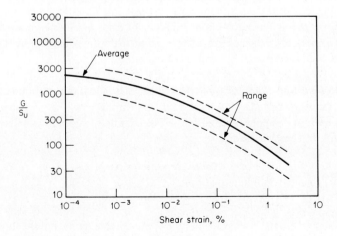

**FIG. 3.7** Shear moduli for clays [44].

in which $[c]_q$, $[m]_q$, and $[k]_q$ are the damping, mass, and stiffness submatrices, respectively, for element $q$; and $\alpha_q$ and $\beta_q$ are parameters that are functions of the damping value and stiffness characteristics of element $q$. The parameters $\alpha_q$ and $\beta_q$ are given by

$$\alpha_q = \lambda_q \cdot \omega_1 \qquad (3.17a)$$

$$\beta_q = \frac{\lambda_q}{\omega_1} \qquad (3.17b)$$

The value of $\lambda_q$, which represents the damping ratio for element $q$, is based on the strain developed in the element. The parameter $\omega_1$ is equal to the fundamental frequency of the system and is obtained from the solution of the eigenvalue problem associated with the free-undamped-vibration form of Eq. (3.13),

$$[K]\{\phi^n\} = \omega_n^2[m]\{\phi^n\} \qquad (3.18)$$

in which $\{\phi\}^n$ are the mode shapes associated with the natural frequencies $\omega_n$.

Initial values of moduli and damping ratios are selected corresponding to small shear-strain values ($\gamma = 10^{-4}\%$) or to strain levels judged appropriate for the anticipated earthquake loading, and an elastic analysis is carried out for the entire duration of the earthquake. An average or effective strain (usually assumed to be about 65% of the maximum value) is computed in each finite element, and moduli and damping ratios are selected compatible with these average strains and used for the next iteration. The procedure is repeated until no significant changes in moduli or damping ratios are necessary. The response determined during this last iteration is considered to be a reasonable approximation to the nonlinear response.

QUAD-4 was the first finite-element program to allow different damping ratios in each element. This was a very important advance because it allowed strain-compatible damping ratios to be developed at all locations in a structure. Rayleigh damping, however, is frequency-dependent, and as the frequency increases so does the damping. Therefore, the response to the higher frequencies of the input motion are damped out. This does not seem to be a very important concern in the dynamic-response analysis of dams or other large earth structures. The equations of motion are solved by direct integration in the time domain, and this procedure may introduce additional damping—numerical damping.

**Frequency-Domain Solutions for Soil Structures**    The equations of motion may also be solved in the frequency domain by using LUSH [41]. In this case, the viscous damping can be introduced by using complex moduli in the formulation of the stiffness matrix $[K]$. For example, the use of complex moduli

$$G^* = G(1 - 2\lambda^2 + 2i\lambda\sqrt{1 - \lambda^2}) \qquad (3.19a)$$

$$E^* = E(1 - 2\lambda^2 + 2i\lambda\sqrt{1 - \lambda^2}) \qquad (3.19b)$$

will lead to exactly the same response amplitudes of a simple damped oscillator as a modal analysis with uniform fraction of critical damping, $\lambda$, except for a slight unimportant error in phase. The equations of motion may then be written as

$$[M]\{\ddot{u}\} + [K]\{u\} = -\{m\}\ddot{y}(t) \tag{3.20}$$

where $[K]$ is now complex.

Complex-response analysis rests on the assumption that the input motion is harmonic with frequency $\omega$,

$$\ddot{y}(t) = \ddot{Y} \cdot e^{i\omega t} \tag{3.21}$$

in which $\ddot{Y}$ may be complex. The response will also be harmonic and of the form

$$\{u\} = \{U\} e^{i\omega t} \tag{3.22}$$

where $\{U\}$ is a constant, perhaps complex, vector. Substitution of Eq. (3.22) into Eq. (3.20) gives

$$[K] - \omega^2[M]\{U\} = -\ddot{Y} \cdot \{m\} \tag{3.23}$$

which is a set of linear equations in the unknowns $\{U\}$ which can be solved by gaussian elimination if $\omega$ is not a natural frequency of the system.

Earthquake motions are not harmonic. However, earthquake records for computational purposes are usually digitized with $N$ points at a constant time interval $\Delta t$. The digitized record can be decomposed into $0.5N + 1$ harmonics as

$$\ddot{y}(t) = \operatorname{Re} \sum_{s=0}^{N/2} \ddot{Y}_s \cdot e^{i\omega_s t} \tag{3.24}$$

in which

$$\omega_s = \frac{2\pi s}{N \cdot \Delta t} \qquad s = 0, 1, \ldots, \frac{N}{2} \tag{3.25}$$

The $\ddot{Y}_s$ are the complex amplitudes

$$\ddot{Y}_s = \begin{cases} \dfrac{1}{N} \sum\limits_{k=0}^{N-1} \ddot{y}_k \cdot e^{-i\omega_s k \Delta t} & \text{for } s = 0, s = \dfrac{N}{2} \\[4mm] \dfrac{2}{N} \sum\limits_{k=0}^{N-1} \ddot{y}_k \cdot e^{-i\omega_s k \Delta t} & \text{for } 1 \leqslant s < \dfrac{N}{2} \end{cases} \tag{3.26}$$

and

$$\ddot{y}_k = \ddot{y}(k \cdot \Delta t) \qquad k = 0, 1, \ldots, N-1 \tag{3.27}$$

are the digitized values of $\ddot{y}(t)$.

Solutions are not required at all possible frequencies. For soil-structure interaction problems, the highest frequency at which solutions are found is of the order of 20 Hz. For earth dams, 8 to 10 Hz is typical. This highest required frequency must be specified. The computational effort can be further reduced by solving the equations of motion for a limited number of frequencies in the domain and obtaining the solutions at other frequencies by interpolation. Typically, solutions are obtained directly for every fourth, eighth, or sixteenth frequency. In LUSH, the base need not be horizontal and the specified motions can have any direction in the plane of the model.

***Frequency-Domain Solutions for Soil-Structure Interaction Problems*** A major requirement of dynamic finite-element analysis of a soil structure is that the boundaries of the
finite-element model should be sufficiently removed from the structure so that the dynamic
response is not affected by wave reflection or trapped energy. For earth structures such as
dams with mainly free surfaces, except for the base which is usually assumed to be rigid,
this requirement is not prohibitive. However, for deeply embedded structures such as nuclear-
reactor containment structures, the requirement can lead to excessive computing costs. If
energy-transmitting boundaries are used so that the full effects of radiation damping can be
taken into account, the boundaries of the finite-element model can be brought much closer
to the structure. Obviously, some three-dimensional effects such as energy leakage at right
angles to plane-strain cross sections can also be included in this manner.

An extended and more efficient form of LUSH called FLUSH [42] has been developed
which includes energy-transmitting boundaries. A schematic view of a "three-dimensional"
model in which energy is transmitted only across the faces of the plane-strain sections is
shown in Fig. 3.8. Note the length of the model to minimize the effects of the rigid boundaries
at the ends. If energy-transmitting boundaries are placed at the ends, then the size of the
model can be drastically reduced, as shown in Fig. 3.9.

The presence of the transmitting boundaries leads to a modified form of Eq. (3.20):

$$[M]\{\ddot{u}\} + [K]\{u\} = -\{m\}\ddot{y} - \{V\} + \{F\} - \{T\} \tag{3.28}$$

The forces $\{V\}$ arise from the viscous boundaries on the planar sides of the slice. These
forces are

$$\{V\} = \frac{1}{L}[C](\{\dot{u}\} - \{\dot{u}\}_f) \tag{3.29}$$

where $L$ is the thickness of the slice, $[C]$ is a simple diagonal matrix which depends on the
properties of the free field, and $\{\dot{u}\}_f$ are the known free-field velocities [42].

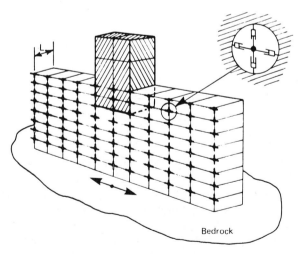

**FIG. 3.8** Schematic view of a simplified three-dimensional
model [42].

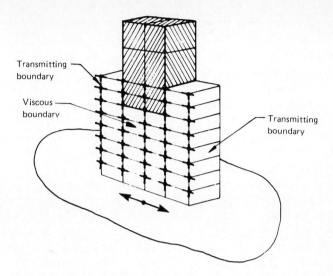

**FIG. 3.9** Schematic view of a simplified three-dimensional model with transmitting boundaries [42].

The forces $\{F\}$ act at the ends of the slice. They are merely the forces which act on a vertical plane in the free field, and they involve no horizontal transmission of wave energy. These forces are

$$\{F\} = [G]\{u\}_f \tag{3.30}$$

where $[G]$ is a simple frequency-independent stiffness matrix formed from the complex moduli in the free field [40].

The forces related to energy transmission are

$$\{T\} = ([R] + [L])(\{u\} - \{u\}_f) \tag{3.31}$$

where $[R]$ and $[L]$ are the frequency-dependent boundary stiffness matrices introduced by Lysmer and Drake [48] and Waas [49]. These matrices represent the exact dynamic effect of the soil outside the ends of the discretized domain in Fig. 3.9.

Solutions of Eqs. (3.28) are obtained in the frequency domain in the manner discussed earlier.

***Permanent-Deformation Analysis*** Since the final analysis with strain-compatible soil properties is purely elastic, the permanent deformations caused by earthquake shaking cannot be computed by this type of analysis. The computed strains may bear no relation to strains in the field and are used only for deriving the strain-compatible properties. However, the stresses derived from these strains are assumed to be representative of stresses in the ground. The accelerations are also assumed to be reasonably representative of field values. Finn et al. [43] have shown by comparison of the results of iterative-elastic and true nonlinear dynamic-response analyses of level ground that the above assumptions are reasonable for stable soils (Fig. 3.10), that is, for soils which do not develop significant pore-water pressures

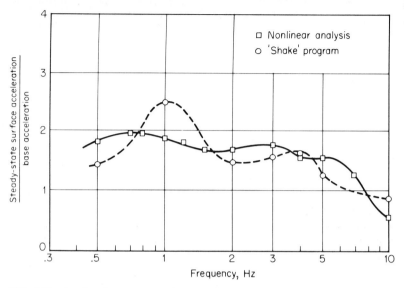

**FIG. 3.10** Acceleration responses for deep sandy site by nonlinear and equivalent linear analysis [43].

or significant nonlinear response during earthquake excitation and if pseudoresonance does not occur during the equivalent linear analysis.

### 3.2B Estimation of Permanent Deformations

Since deformations are not given directly by dynamic analysis based on the concept of the equivalent linear solid, they are estimated from static and seismic stresses with the aid of strain data from cyclic triaxial tests. In principle, the static and dynamic stresses in a given finite element are simulated as closely as possible on a sample in a cyclic triaxial test, and the resulting axial strain is assumed to be the strain potential of the finite element in the soil structure, for example, in an earth dam. In recent practice, this strain is converted to a shear-strain potential by multiplying by the factor $1 + \mu$, where $\mu$ is Poisson's ratio. The strain potential is defined as the strain that develops in an unconstrained soil element under specified loading. The finite elements in the dam are all interconnected, so obviously strains in the elements obtained by the above procedure are not the strains that will develop in the dam but are an indication of its potential for straining under the given seismic excitation.

Correspondence between the soil elements in the field and the triaxial samples is established by ensuring that the same initial static stresses exist on failure planes in the field and on failure planes in the triaxial samples. Because the seismic motions are assumed to be shear waves propagating vertically upward, horizontal planes in the dam are treated as potential failure planes. Seismic shear stresses $\tau$ on these planes are assumed to be the most significant in generating deformations; the cyclic normal stresses are neglected. The initial static-stress state is defined by the ratio, $\tau_{fc}/\bar{\sigma}_{fc} = \alpha$, where $\tau_{fc}$ = initial static shear stress and $\bar{\sigma}_{fc}$ = initial normal effective stress at each location on horizontal planes in the dam. These stresses can be created on the failure plane of a triaxial test by the proper selection of vertical and radial

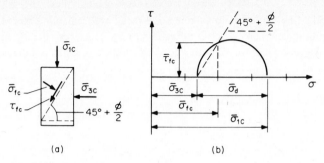

**FIG. 3.11** Simulation of initial field stresses ($\bar{\sigma}_{fc}$ and $\bar{\tau}_{fc}$) is triaxial test specimen.

effective consolidation stresses $\bar{\sigma}_{1c}$ and $\bar{\sigma}_{3c}$. The stresses and failure plane are shown in Fig. 3.11$a$, and the relationship between the stresses on the failure plane and the consolidation stresses may be deduced from the Mohr diagram in Fig. 3.11$b$ in the following form:

$$\tau_{fc} = \tfrac{1}{2}\bar{\sigma}_d \cos\phi \tag{3.32}$$

$$\bar{\sigma}_{fc} = \bar{\sigma}_{3c} + \bar{\sigma}_d \cos^2\left(45 + \frac{\phi}{2}\right) \tag{3.33}$$

$$\bar{\sigma}_d = (\bar{\sigma}_{1c} - \bar{\sigma}_{3c}) \tag{3.34}$$

from which $\bar{\sigma}_{1c}$ and $\bar{\sigma}_{3c}$ may be easily calculated.

　　Cyclic triaxial tests are conducted using uniform stress cycles. Therefore, in order to estimate the deformations caused by the seismic shear stresses from laboratory test data, the irregular time histories (Fig. 3.12$a$) of shear stresses must be converted into an equivalent number of uniform stress cycles (Fig. 3.12$b$). *Equivalent* here means that the cycles of uniform

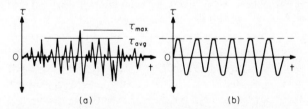

**FIG. 3.12** Irregular and equivalent uniform shear stresses.

shear stress have the same effect as the computed stresses. The number of equivalent cycles depends on the magnitude of the uniform shear stress and the weighting curve used to define equivalence. Generally, the magnitude of the uniform shear stress is taken to be $0.65\tau_{max}$, where $\tau_{max}$ = maximum shear stress in the time history. The liquefaction strength curve with or without the prior application of a factor of safety is usually selected as the weighting curve.

　　Procedures for converting the irregular shear-stress histories to cycles of uniform shear stress have been described by Lee and Chan [50], who used a weighting curve obtained by adjusting a liquefaction curve obtained by cyclic triaxial tests to field conditions. Seed et al.

[51] used a weighting curve obtained from large-scale, cyclic, simple shear tests. Because of a lack of information on many aspects of the weighting process, Seed et al. [51] have proposed a standard weighting curve for all soils under all conditions of likely interest. This curve is given in Fig. 3.13.

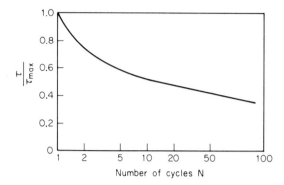

**FIG. 3.13** Standard weighting curve for stress equivalent [51].

It may be seen from the curve, for example, that 8 cycles of shear stress $\tau$, with $\tau/\tau_{max} = 0.55$, are equivalent to 3.0 cycles with $\tau/\tau_{max} = 0.65$; or each cycle of a shear stress with $\tau/\tau_{max} = 0.55$ is equivalent to 0.4 cycle with $\tau/\tau_{max} = 0.65$. By using the weighting curve in this manner, the cycles of shear stress of various amplitudes in the time history of shear stress can be converted to an equivalent number of cycles of uniform shear stress, $\tau_d$.

Laboratory test data on strength and deformation under cyclic loading are most conveniently specified for a given number of cycles of a uniform cyclic loading; 10 cycles is used often. Therefore, the equivalent uniform loading in each finite element of the dam is converted to 10 cycles of an appropriate shear-stress level, $\tau_d$, again using the weighting curve.

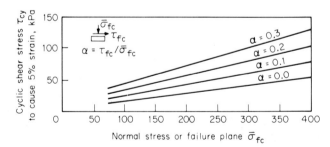

**FIG. 3.14** Typical test data from cyclic loading tests [52].

Typical cyclic triaxial test data are shown in Fig. 3.14, which gives the cyclic shear stress $\tau_{cy}$ required to cause 5% strain in 10 cycles of loading for various initial static-stress conditions specified by $\alpha$-values [52]. Similar plots may be drawn for other strain levels, such as 10, 15, and 20%. The cyclic shear stress is generated by the appropriate pulsating deviator stress $\sigma_{dp}$. The relationship between $\sigma_{dp}$ and $\tau_{cy}$ is defined in the Mohr diagram in Fig. 3.15. If the

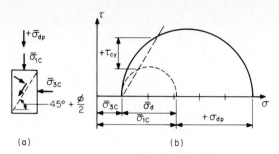

(a)                                          (b)

**FIG. 3.15**   Relationship between cyclic deviatoric stress and cyclic shear stress on the failure plane in a triaxial test.

initial static shear stress is zero at a given location in the dam, the corresponding failure plane in the triaxial specimen is taken (in conventional practice) at 45° to the principal stress direction (Fig. 3.16). The cyclic shear stress $\tau_{cy}$ (Fig. 3.16) in this case is multiplied by a correction factor [53] $C_r$, so that $\tau_d = C_r \tau_{cy}$.

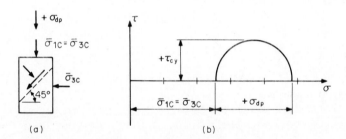

(a)                                          (b)

**FIG. 3.16**   Failure plane and corresponding stresses for isotropically consolidated triaxial specimen.

With test data such as those in Fig. 3.14 the cyclic shear stresses $\tau_j$ causing $j\%$ shear strain ($j = 5\%$, $10\%$, etc.) may be plotted for each horizontal plane as shown in Fig. 3.17 [54]. The uniform cyclic shear stresses $\tau_d$, 10 cycles of which are equivalent to the various seismically induced shear-stress–time histories, are also shown for the same horizontal plane. The resulting plot gives a convenient graphical representation of the strain potential for the horizontal row of finite elements resting on the plane.

Where the curve $\tau_d$ coincides with a shear-strain potential line $\tau_j$, the shear-strain potential is $j\%$. Intermediate values of strain potential are obtained by interpolation. By repeating this process for other horizontal planes in the dam, the strain potential in each finite element may be obtained as shown in Fig. 3.18 [52]. Contours of shear-strain potential may also be drawn to provide a more integrated picture of strain potential as shown in Fig. 3.19, which depicts the distribution of shear-strain potential in the Tsengwen Dam for a specified seismic event [54].

A simple approach was suggested by Seed et al. [52] to get a global estimate of dam deformations from strain potentials. The average shear strain in a section of the dam is multiplied by the average height of the section to provide an estimate of the horizontal

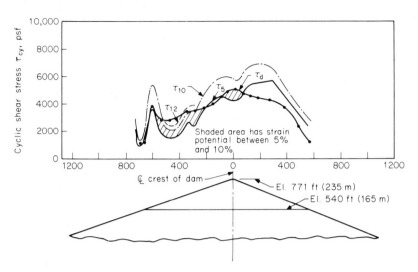

**FIG. 3.17** Strain potential along a horizontal plane [54].

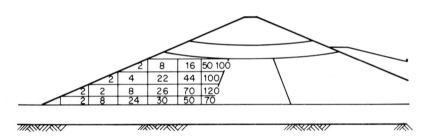

**FIG. 3.18** Shear-strain potentials in finite elements for lower San Fernando Dam [52].

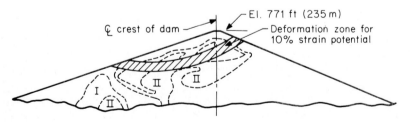

**FIG. 3.19** Contours of strain potential over dam cross section [54].

displacement. For the example shown in Fig. 3.18 the average shear strain is about 30% and the approximate height of fill is about 80 ft, giving a horizontal displacement of the top of the fill of about 24 ft—an unsatisfactory condition.

More recently, Serff et al. [55] and Seed [56] have proposed a procedure for converting the strain potentials to a set of compatible deformations. The shear stress corresponding to the strain potential in a finite element is determined from the *static* stress–strain curve (Fig. 3.20*a*). The shear stresses are converted to shear forces and applied to the nodes of the finite element (Fig. 3.20*b*). The deformations under these nodal forces are then determined by a

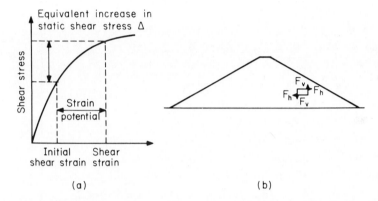

**FIG. 3.20**   Conversion of shear-strain potential to equivalent shear forces [56].

static analysis and are assumed to be a good approximation to the seismically induced permanent deformations. The degree of approximation in this procedure is not known. Although there is no theoretical justification for the procedure, it seems a very plausible approach to obtain practically useful estimates of deformations.

***Application to Seismic Response of Oroville Dam***   A 1979 study of the seismic response of the Oroville Dam [57] by the California Division of Water Resources will be used to illustrate some important aspects of seismic-response analysis. The Oroville Dam is located on the Feather River in the foothills of the Sierra Nevada above the Sacramento Valley and is about 8 km (5 miles) east of the city of Oroville. The embankment has a maximum height of 235 m (770 ft) and a crest length of 1707 m (5600 ft) from the gated spillway to the left abutment. The embankment is made up of a gravel-clay core with sand–gravel–cobble transitions and shells upstream and downstream.

On August 1, 1975, an earthquake of Richter magnitude 5.7 occurred about 12 km (7.5 miles) from the dam, which produced an acceleration of about 0.1$g$ at the base of the dam. The proximity of the earthquake indicated that active faults were very close to the dam, and this led to a review of the seismic stability of the embankment and associated structures. An earthquake with a Richter magnitude of 6.5 at a hypocentral distance of 5 km (3 miles) from the dam was selected as the design earthquake for dynamic-response analysis. The associated accelerations at the base of the dam were defined by the following characteristics: maximum acceleration = 0.6$g$, duration = 20 seconds, predominant period = 0.4 seconds; and the time history of accelerations was constructed from modified Pacoima and Taft earthquake acceleration records.

Acceleration-response spectra computed from crest accelerations recorded during the earthquake indicated that the dam had a fundamental period of 0.8 seconds (Fig. 3.21). The

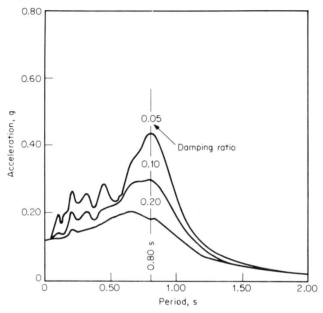

**FIG. 3.21**   Response spectra for Oroville Dam during earthquake, August 1, 1975 [57].

Oroville Dam has a crest-length–to–height ratio of approximately $L/H = 7$ and is situated in a triangular canyon. According to the work of Makdisi [58] on dams of triangular section and uniform properties, there is a significant three-dimensional effect on dynamic response even at $L/H = 7$. His results in Fig. 3.22 show that at $L/H = 7$ the ratio of the fundamental period computed in plane-strain two-dimensional response, $P_{2D}$, is 1.3 times the period calculated by three-dimensional analysis, $P_{3D}$. This indicates a period of about 1 second for the Oroville Dam in 2D plane-strain analysis.

Gravel shells occupy 90% of the embankment and were assumed to dominate the dynamic response. Therefore, while the properties of the clay core were selected from the data in Fig. 3.7, the dynamic properties of the shell material were measured in cyclic triaxial tests. Because of the large sizes in the shell, the tests were run on scalped material which modeled the gradation pattern of the shell material. The measured damping characteristics are given closely by the damping curve for sands in Fig. 3.6*a*. The measured strain-dependent shear moduli are shown in Fig. 3.23, and curves for other gravelly materials are shown for comparison. The data are shown in terms of the modulus parameter $K_2$, defined [44] as

$$G = 1000 K_2 (\sigma'_m)^{1/2} \tag{3.35}$$

in which $G$ is the shear modulus and $\sigma'_m$ is the mean effective normal stress in lb/ft$^2$. The

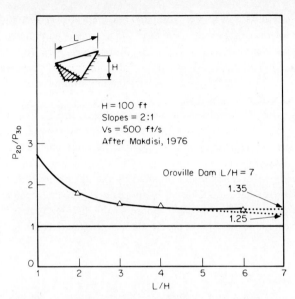

**FIG. 3.22** Relationship between fundamental periods of a dam in 2D and 3D response [57].

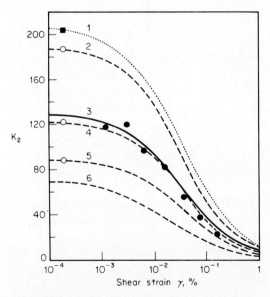

**FIG. 3.23** Shear modulus parameter $K_2$ for Oroville Dam and other selected sources [57]. (1) Estimated from recorded dynamic response during 1975 earthquakes. (2) Dense sand and gravel (California). (3) Triaxial test on modeled Oroville gravel. (4) Dense sand and gravel (Washington). (5) Sand and gravel (Venezuela). (6) Dense sand, $D_r \approx 90\%$.

value of $K_{2,max}$ required to generate a fundamental period of 1 second was obtained by dynamic analysis of the embankment for the 1975 recorded earthquake and shocks. The corresponding curve is shown in Fig. 3.23 also. The difference between this curve and the experimentally determined curve is a measure of the difficulty in determining the values of soil properties for dynamic analysis and indicates the importance of carrying out calibration studies of this kind whenever possible.

In order to simulate 3D response as much as possible by the 2D dynamic analysis, it was decided to assign pseudostiffness properties to the dam to achieve the 3D fundamental frequency of 0.8 second. This required a $K_{2,max} = 350$, a value obtained by a 2D parametric study, the results of which are shown in Fig. 3.24. It was assumed that if the period were accurately modeled, the accelerations computed by the 2D plane-strain analysis would be representative of these that would occur in the dam during the design earthquake. The procedure was tested by analyzing the response to the 1975 earthquake. The shapes and magnitudes in the computed patterns of accelerations were generally similar to those observed.

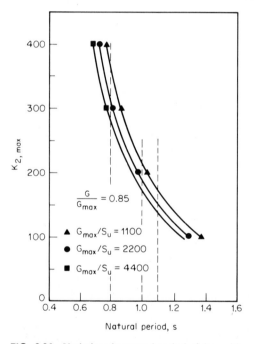

**FIG. 3.24** Variations in natural period of dam with soil stiffness [57].

The pseudo 3D analysis described above is assumed to model the kinematic characteristics of dynamic response but not the inertial characteristics. Therefore, it does not yield the correct dynamic shear stresses directly. The shear strains computed by the pseudo 3D analysis are assumed equal to the shear strains in the real dam. The shear stresses in the dam may then be obtained by multiplying the shear strains by the appropriate values of the field moduli, instead of using values of the pseudomoduli used to ensure correct kinematic modeling of the response of the dam. For example, if the field moduli are characterized by $K_{2,\max} = 205$, then the true dynamic shear stresses in the dam, $\tau_t$, are given by the equation

$$\tau_t = \frac{205\,\tau_{P3D}}{350} \qquad\qquad (3.36)$$

in which $\tau_{P3D}$ are the dynamic shear stresses determined by the pseudo 3D analysis.

It is interesting to compare the shear stresses computed in this manner with stresses $\tau_{2D}$ from a plane-strain 2D analysis, also using $K_{2,\max} = 205$. Contours of $\tau_{2D}/\tau_t$ are shown in Fig. 3.25. It is evident that the 3D effects of abutment restraint are very effective in reducing the shear stresses in the plane of the cross section, especially in the upper part of the dam where the stresses from the 2D analysis range from 140 to 200% of the estimated real stresses in the dam. The approach to the estimation of 3D dynamic shear stresses described above relies heavily on an intuitive understanding of dynamic-response characteristics and plausible assumptions, as do many other features of dynamic-response analysis today.

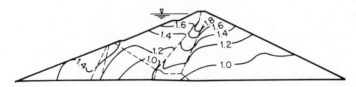

**FIG. 3.25**  Contours of ratios of maximum dynamic shear stresses from 2D and 3D analyses ($\tau_{2D}/\tau_{3D}$) [57].

### 3.2c NonLinear Effective-Stress Analysis

As discussed previously, there are two major limitations associated with equivalent linear analysis: the analysis is conducted in terms of total stresses so that the effects of pore-water pressures on soil properties cannot be taken into account, and permanent deformations cannot be computed directly. To overcome these limitations, researchers have been developing constitutive relations to model the nonlinear hysteretic stress–strain response of soil [59]. The models fall into two main categories: incremental elastic and those based on some form of plasticity theory. Two models, one of each type, that have found their way into engineering practice will be described in the following sections, to illustrate the present state of the art and the kinds of problems for which these more complex methods are appropriate.

### 3.2d Incremental Elastic Method

Finn, Lee, and Martin [43] developed a one-dimensional non-linear method of analysis for the response of level ground to seismic excitation. Following conventional engineering practice, they assumed seismic excitation to be due primarily to vertical propagation of shear waves, and they developed a shear model of soil response to predict field behavior. In this model, the behavior of soil in shear is assumed to be nonlinear and hysteretic.

The relationship between shear stress $\tau$ and shear strain $\gamma$ for the initial loading phase under either drained or undrained loading conditions is assumed to be hyperbolic and given by

$$\tau = f(\gamma) = \frac{G_{\max}\gamma}{(1+(G_{\max}/\tau_{\max})|\gamma|)} \tag{3.37}$$

in which $G_{\max}$ is the maximum shear modulus and $\tau_{\max}$ is the appropriate shear strength. This initial loading or skeleton curve is shown in Fig. 3.26a. The unloading-reloading has been modeled using the Masing [60] criterion. This implies that the equation for the unloading curve from a point $(\tau_r, \gamma_r)$ at which the loading reverses direction is given by

$$\frac{\tau - \tau_r}{2} = \frac{f(\gamma - \gamma_r)}{2} \tag{3.38a}$$

or

$$\frac{\tau - \tau_r}{2} = \frac{G_{\max}(\gamma - \gamma_r)/2}{1+(G_{\max}/2\tau_{\max})|\gamma - \gamma_r|} \tag{3.38b}$$

The shape of the unloading-reloading curve is shown in Fig. 3.26b.

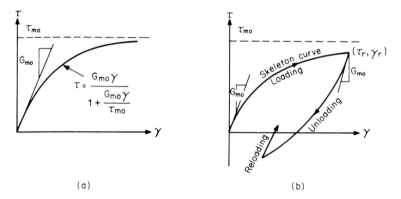

(a)                                        (b)

**FIG. 3.26** (a) Initial loading curve. (b) Masing stress-strain curves for unloading and reloading.

For one-dimensional analysis, the stiffness matrix $[K]$ in Eq. 3.13 is determined using the appropriate tangent shear modulus $G_t$ derived from Eq. 3.37 or 3.38. Dynamic response is then determined by solving Eq. 3.13 in the time domain and assuming that only horizontal shearing deformations are possible.

A pore-water pressure generation model developed by Martin, Finn, and Seed [61] was coupled with the nonlinear equations of motion to provide, for the first time, the option of performing nonlinear dynamic effective stress analysis. In this model, increments in pore-water pressure $\Delta u$ induced by increments in seismic loading are given by

$$\Delta u = \bar{E}_r \cdot \Delta\varepsilon_{vd} \tag{3.39}$$

in which $\bar{E}_r$ is the effective rebound modulus of the soil and $\Delta\varepsilon_{vd}$ is the increment in volumetric plastic strain. The latter is a function of the current shear strain and the total accumulated volumetric strain [43, 61].

Both transient and residual pore-water pressures are generated by seismic loading. The transient pressures result from elastic coupling between the soil skeleton and pore water. Residual pore water pressures result from plastic deformations of the soil skeleton and depend on both the intensity and duration of seismic loading and the drainage characteristics of the soil. Stability and stiffness during seismic loading are strongly influenced by residual pore-water pressures, whereas transient pore-water pressure effects tend to be neutralized by the corresponding changes in total normal stress and are therefore much less significant. For this reason, the Martin–Finn–Seed pore-water pressure model was developed to estimate residual pore-water pressures only. Therefore, it is not necessary to model coupled response of soil and water when using this model and the resulting dynamic analysis is considerably less complex and computationally cheaper.

The distribution of accumulated pore-water pressure at any time depends not only on the rate of generation but on the rates of internal diffusion and external drainage. Therefore, an equation describing simultaneous generation and diffusion of pore-water pressures is used with the equations of motion of the soil to describe the total response to seismic loading.

The shear modulus is dependent on the level of mean normal effective stress $\sigma'_m = \sigma_m - u$, in which $\sigma_m$ is the total mean normal stress and $u$ is the current seismically induced pore-water pressure. Therefore, as the pore-water pressure increases and reduces the mean effective stresses, these parameters must be adjusted accordingly. For example, it is commonly assumed that $G_{max} \propto \sigma_m^{1/2}$, therefore,

$$\frac{G}{G_{max}} = \left(\frac{\sigma'_m}{\sigma'_{mo}}\right)^{1/2} \tag{3.40}$$

where $G$ is the maximum shear modulus for the current cycle of loading.

If significant volumetric compaction occurs during seismic loading, the moduli should also be modified to reflect this strain hardening, following procedures outlined by Finn et al. [43]. The shear strength $\tau_{max}$, which is a linear function of the effective vertical stress $\sigma'_v$, is modified in similar fashion. The analysis continuously modifies the soil properties for the effects of pore-water pressures and dynamic and compaction strains.

The method of analysis is incorporated in two computer programs, DESRA-1 [62] and DESRA-2 [63]. The latter is an extension of DESRA-1 to include an energy-transmitting base. The programs contain various options regarding internal diffusion and external drainage of pore water. They may be operated in either total- or effective-stress modes. The total-stress mode is generally used for clay deposits, the effective-stress mode for saturated cohesionless materials.

The DESRA-2 program has been validated by Finn and Bhatia [64] using data from cyclic simple shear tests with regular and irregular stress-and-strain histories of loading. The program has also been used successfully to predict seismically induced accelerations and pore-water pressures in Owi Island in Tokyo Bay by Finn, Ishihara, and Iai [65]. DESRA-2 was used in 1985 by Iai, Tsuchida, and Finn [66] to simulate the response of six sites in Japan during the 1978 Miyagi-Ken-Oki earthquake as part of a detailed review of liquefaction during that earthquake by the Port and Harbor Research Institute of Japan.

The nonlinear programs CHARSOIL [67] and MASH [58] may be used to perform nonlinear total-stress analysis, and an iterative procedure has been developed to allow MASH to be used for effective-stress analysis [69]. Studies by Finn, Martin, and Lee [37] have shown that in total-stress mode DESRA-2 and CHARSOIL give similar results, and Martin and Seed [69] have shown that results from MASH and DESRA-2 are also compatible.

Programs to conduct nonlinear dynamic effective-stress analysis for level sites are readily available, are easy to use, are based on conventional soils data, have been well validated, and are recommended as preferable for site response analyses.

## 3.2ᴇ Nonlinear Dynamic Effective Stress: 2D

Siddharthan and Finn [70] extended the DESRA-2 analysis to two dimensions in the computer program TARA-2. The extension was accomplished by the addition of a model for the response of soil to hydrostatic stresses. Under hydrostatic stress, the soil response was assumed to be nonlinearly elastic and dependent on the mean normal effective stress. Hysteresis was neglected in the hydrostatic model. Response in the shear was modeled by the nonlinear hysteretic model in DESRA-2.

A modified and extended version of this program developed by Finn, Yogendrakumar, Yoshida, and Yoshida [71] is TARA-3, which has a number of additional options, such as energy-transmitting boundaries and the facility to conduct nonlinear consolidation analyses during seismic excitation.

An incrementally elastic approach was adopted in TARA-3 to model nonlinear behavior using tangent shear and bulk moduli $G_t$ and $B_t$, respectively. The incremental dynamic equilibrium forces $\{\Delta P\}$ are given by

$$[M]\{\Delta \ddot{x}\} + [C]\{\Delta \dot{x}\} + [K]\{\Delta x\} = \{\Delta P\} \qquad (3.41)$$

where $[M]$, $[C]$ and $[K]$ are the mass, damping, and stiffness matrices respectively, and $\{\Delta x\}$, $\{\Delta \dot{x}\}$, $\{\Delta \ddot{x}\}$ are the matrices of incremental relative displacements, velocities, and accelerations. The viscous damping is of the Rayleigh type, and the stiffness matrix is a function of the current tangent moduli. The use of shear and bulk moduli allows the elasticity matrix $[D]$ to be expressed as

$$[D] = B_t[Q_1] + G_t[Q_2] \qquad (3.42)$$

where $[Q_1]$ and $[Q_2]$ are constant matrices for the plane-strain conditions usually considered in analyses. This formulation reduces the computation time for formulating $[D]$ whenever $G_t$ and $B_t$ change in magnitude because of straining or pore-water pressure changes.

The tangent shear modulus at any time, $G_t$, is determined as described in the DESRA-2 analysis. The tangent bulk modulus $B_t$ is assumed to be given by

$$B_t = K_b P_a \left( \frac{\sigma'_m}{P_a} \right)^n \qquad (3.43)$$

in which $K_b$ is the bulk modulus, $P_a$ is atmospheric pressure, $\sigma'_m$ is the current mean normal effective stress, and $n$ is a constant for a given soil type.

$K_b$ and $n$ are experimentally determined by triaxial tests [1]. Both $G_t$ and $B_t$ are modified continuously for the effects of seismically induced pore-water pressures.

An important feature of soil–structure interaction response is the effect of slip between soil and structure. Slip may occur during very strong shaking or under moderate shaking if high pore-water pressures are developed under the structure. TARA-3 contains slip elements to allow for relative motion between structure and soil in both sliding and rocking modes during earthquake excitation. The elements are of the type presented by Goodman, Taylor, and Brekke [72].

A series of simulated earthquake tests on centrifugal models was conducted in the United Kingdom at the Cambridge University Geotechnical Centrifuge to establish a data base on the seismic response of soils and soil-structure interaction systems. The tests were sponsored by the U.S. Nuclear Regulatory Commission through the U.S. Army Corps of Engineers to enable verification of existing methods of seismic-response analysis. Details of some of these tests have been described by Finn et al. in [73, 74, 75] and Finn in [76, 77].

The results of some typical analyses of these model tests by TARA-3 are presented below to show the ability of nonlinear effective-stress methods to give a detailed and coherent picture of dynamic response.

A plane-strain model of a saturated submerged embankment is shown in Fig. 3.27. The model is 110 mm high with side slopes of 2.2 to 1.0 and a crest width of 236 mm. The centrifuge acceleration used was 80 g. The model, therefore, corresponds to a prototype 8.8 m high with a crest width of 18.8 m. The model was instrumented by eight DJB A23 piezoelectric accelerometers (ACC) and ten Druck PDCR 81 pore-pressure transducers (PPT). The locations of those instruments for which results will be presented are shown in Fig. 3.27.

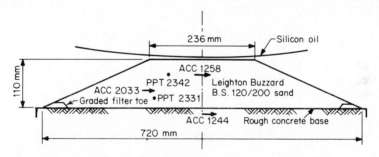

**FIG. 3.27**  Submerged model embankment showing instrumentation [77].

The embankment was constructed with Leighton Buzzard sand passing BSS No. 120 and retained on BSS No. 200. The liquefaction potential of the sand was determined by cyclic simple-shear tests using the University of British Columbia simple-shear device [78].

De-aired silicon oil was used as a pore fluid in order to model the drainage conditions in the prototype during the earthquake. If the linear scale factor between model and prototype is $N$, then excess pore-water pressure dissipates $N^2$ times faster in the model than in the prototype if the same fluid is used in both. The rate of loading by seismic excitation will be only $N$ times faster. Therefore, to model prototype drainage conditions during the earthquake, a pore fluid with a viscosity $N$ times the prototype viscosity must be used. This viscosity was achieved by an appropriate blending of commercial silicon oils.

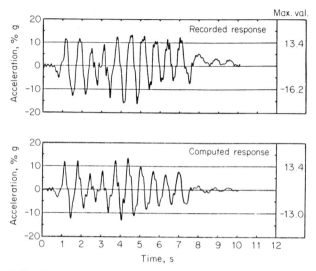

**FIG. 3.28**   Measured and computed accelerations for ACC 1258 [77].

The dynamic response of the model embankment was analyzed using TARA-3. Computed and measured accelerations are shown in Fig. 3.28 for ACC 1258 near the crest of the embankment and in Fig. 3.29 for ACC 2033 located in the lower half of the embankment. The computed and measured acceleration records are very similar in frequency content, and the peak accelerations are satisfactorily predicted.

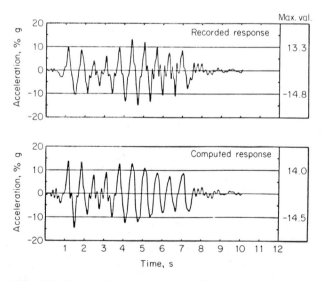

**FIG. 3.29**   Measured and computed accelerations for ACC 2033 [77].

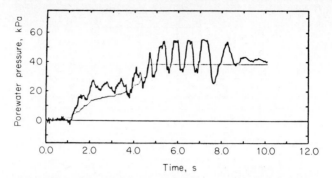

**FIG. 3.30** Measured and computed pore-water pressures at PPT 2331 (el. 19 m) [77].

The computed pore-water pressures for PPT 2331 located near accelerometer ACC 2033 are compared with the measured pore-water pressures in Fig. 3.30. Very good agreement is also found between the computed and measured pore-water pressures for the gauge PPT 2342 located in the vicinity of ACC 1258 (Fig. 3.31). That TARA-3 models the residual pore-water

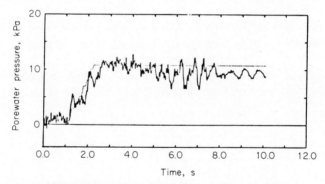

**FIG. 3.31** Measured and computed pore-water pressures at PPT 2342 (el. 73 m) [77].

pressure quite well may be seen by comparing the peak computed pore-water pressure with the measured pressure at the end of the earthquake. The elastic fluctuations in the pore-water pressure due to transient changes in the total mean normal stresses are not modeled. The stability and stiffness of the soil depends mostly on the level of residual pore-water pressures, and therefore the trouble it would take to model the complex fully coupled analysis that would be required to predict the transient fluctuations is not warranted.

It remains to investigate whether soil–structure interaction effects can be modeled adequately. A centrifugal model of an embedded structure and foundation is shown in Fig. 3.32. The foundation layer is 110 mm deep and width perpendicular to the plane of the figure is 480 mm. The foundation was constructed using Leighton Buzzard sand with a nominal relative density $D_r = 64\%$. The gravity structure was modeled by an aluminum cylinder 150 mm high embedded 30 mm in the dry foundation soil. Centrifugal acceleration was

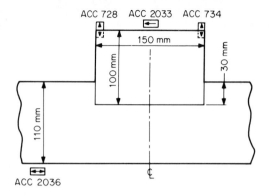

**FIG. 3.32** Centrifuge model of an embedded structure [77].

nominally 80 g. The model, therefore, simulated a structure approximately 8 m high and 12 m in diameter embedded to a depth of 2.4 m in the soil. Average contact pressure of the structure in the soil was 220 kPa.

The response of the structure was determined by using TARA-3 to analyze an equivalent 2D slice of the structure.

Since interest is primarily in whether TARA-3 can model interaction effects, the accelerations will be reported only for acclerometers mounted on the structure. Their locations are shown in Fig. 3.32. ACC 2033 measures horizontal acceleration and ACC 728 and 734 record vertical accelerations due to rocking. The computed and measured horizontal accelerations at the top of the structure at the location of ACC 2033 are shown in Fig. 3.33. They are very

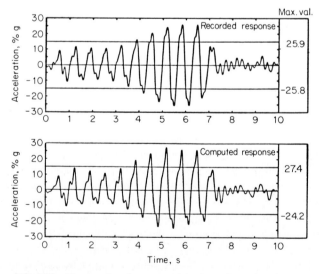

**FIG. 3.33** Measured and computed horizontal accelerations at top of embedded structure at ACC 2033 [77].

similar in frequency content, each corresponding to the frequency of the input motion at ACC 2036. The peak accelerations agree very closely.

The measured and computed vertical or rocking accelerations are shown in Fig. 3.34. Again the records are very similar and the peak accelerations are predicted very closely. Note that the frequency of oscillation is much higher than that of the horizontal accelerations at the top of the structure. This occurs because the foundation soils are much stiffer under normal compressive stresses due to rocking than under the shear stresses induced by the horizontal accelerations.

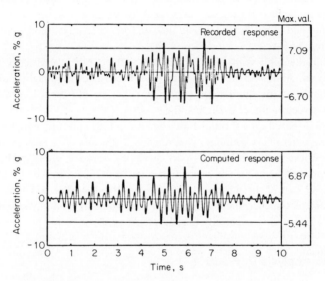

**FIG. 3.34**  Measured and computed vertical accelerations at top left-hand corner of embedded structure at ACC 728 [77].

On the evidence to date, it appears that TARA-3 can model 2D nonlinear dynamic effective-stress response reliably.

## 3.2F  Plasticity Analysis

There is increasing interest in the application of methods based on the theory of plasticity, especially the anisotropic (kinematic) theory of plasticity, to the problems of soil dynamics. Two particular formulations of the anisotropic theory of plasticity appear to have great potential for multidimensional analyses: the multi-yield surface model of Prevost [79, 80] and the two-surface model of Mroz, Norris, and Zienkiewicz [81] and Dafalias and Herrmann [82]. The models are still in the process of development, but progress to date has been impressive.

These models assume soil to be an inelastic porous skeleton coupled with a viscous pore fluid. The total pore-water pressure (the sum of the residual and elastic) is computed directly from the coupled equations of motion in the effective-stress mode of analysis. Total-stress versions of these models are also available.

An extensive review of these methods was conducted by Finn and Martin [83]. They concluded that both models represent the response of soils to static loading very well. Both have demonstrated the potential to model the phenomenological aspects of pseudostatic cyclic loading, but verification has been limited. None of the models has yet been verified for the case of strongly degrading clays or readily liquefiable sands under dynamic loading.

The Prevost model has been incorporated in the computer program DYNAFLOW [84]. The capabilities of the program have been critically reviewed by Ferrito and Nakamoto [85] using laboratory test data. They conclude that, at least for the simple stress conditions of the laboratory tests, the model behaves satisfactorily. However, verification under the complex stress conditions in the field is necessary to check fully the predictive capability of the model. An alternative method of verification would be data from centrifugal models similar to those used in validating TARA-3.

An example of the application of DYNAFLOW to the dynamic analysis of an earth dam is given by Prevost, Abdel-Ghaffer, and Lacy [86]. Prevost, Cuny, Hughes, and Scott [87] present an example of the quasi-static total-stress analysis of a centrifuged model of an offshore gravity structure under cyclic loading.

DYNAFLOW is based on a form of Biot's equations [88] and fully couples the response of soil and pore water. This coupling, combined with the use of a large number of yield surfaces to match the nonlinear stress–strain curve of a soil accurately, makes very heavy demands on computational time and capacity compared to the incremental elastic nonlinear models. The lower cost of the incremental models and the fact that they are based directly on familiar parameters, such as shear strength and shear and bulk moduli, make these methods more acceptable in practice, especially for parametric studies.

### 3.2G  Dynamic Analysis in Practice

Dynamic analysis in geotechnical engineering is still dominated by iterative elastic methods, but since about 1980 there has been a perceptible shift towards nonlinear analysis for certain classes of problems. This is especially true for site-response analyses to determine site-specific ground motions and design spectra. In the offshore, where many sites are underlain by soft saturated deposits and nonlinearity and pore-water pressures are likely to be important, nonlinear analyses of the DESRA type are becoming increasingly popular [89, 90, 91]. They have also been used at sites of critical facilities on land, such as compressor stations and sites for LNG tanks [92].

The assimilation of 2D and 3D nonlinear methods into engineering practice has only just begun because of the more recent availability of validated programs. Some applications to date have been to the soil–structure interaction analysis of an offshore gravity platform [93] and to tailings dams [94].

### 3.2H  Conclusions

Soil is a very complex material, and, in spite of the undoubtedly formidable potential of the theory of plasticity, it is probable that no one theory will be able to model all aspects of soil behavior. There will always be room for special models for particular kinds of problems. The equivalent linear methods of analysis appear to be particularly applicable to stable sites, whose soil properties do not degrade significantly during cyclic loading and where significant permanent deformations are unlikely. For approximately level ground conditions, the nonlinear hysteretic methods of analysis appear best. For two- and three-dimensional dynamic analyses, equivalent linear methods are still by far the most widely used methods.

As pointed out by the earthquake engineering research study [36], more sophisticated methods are required for deformation analyses in two and three dimensions. This is particularly so when soil properties degrade significantly during dynamic excitation. Extensions of successful 1D methods of nonlinear effective stress analysis such as TARA-3 appear to provide adequate and economical solutions. Plasticity methods incorporating very generalized stress–strain relations are much more complex, require much more computational time, and have not yet found favor in geotechnical engineering practice in the area of soil dynamics.

The search for a good constitutive model is not yet over. The development of such a model has been identified as one of the major research areas of soil dynamics for the next decade [36]. The prospects for success will be enhanced by close cooperation between researchers and practitioners. Such cooperation will facilitate verification of complex models in engineering practice.

## 3.3 POROUS MEDIA

This section is concerned with the simulation of four aspects of subsurface flow in porous media. The relatively straightforward problem of homogeneous, single-phase flow is discussed first, followed by a treatment of the more difficult concept of multiphase flow. Next the problem of convective-dispersive transport in nonhomogeneous fluids is addressed. Finally the challenging problem of nonisothermal multiphase flow is considered. The material presented here is drawn extensively from the work of Huyakorn and Pinder [95].

### 3.3A Simulation of Saturated Groundwater Flow in a Confined Aquifer

The movement of a homogeneous single-phase liquid in a groundwater reservoir is described by the equation

$$\nabla \cdot K \cdot \nabla h - S_s \frac{\partial h}{\partial t} = 0 \tag{3.44}$$

where $h(x, y, z, t)$ is the hydraulic head, $K(x, y, z)$ is the hydraulic conductivity, $S_s(x, y, z)$ is the specific storage, $t$ is time, and $\nabla(\cdot)$ is the gradient operator defined in the cartesian coordinates $(x, y, z)$. While this equation can be solved in a straightforward way using a finite-element approximation technique, it is often reduced in dimensionality by vertical integration because the vertical-flow component is relatively unimportant. When the groundwater reservoir is considered confined, that is, there is no free surface within the reservoir, the resulting two-dimensional equation reads

$$\nabla \cdot T \cdot \nabla \bar{h} - q - S \frac{\partial \bar{h}}{\partial t} = 0 \tag{3.45}$$

where, defining $b(x, y)$ as the reservoir thickness and denoting vertically average quantities by an overbar,

$$T(x, y) \equiv \bar{K}(x, y)b(x, y), \quad S(x, y) \equiv \bar{S}_s(x, y)b(x, y)$$

$q(x, y)$ is the net vertical leakage out of the groundwater reservoir, and $\nabla(\cdot)$ is now defined only over $x$ and $y$. The new coefficients $T(x, y)$ and $S(x, y)$ are known as the transmissivity and storage coefficient, respectively.

The ordinary differential equations generated through the application of the Galerkin-finite-element method in space to (3.45) are written

$$[A]\{h\} + [B]\left\{\frac{dh}{dt}\right\} = \{f\} \tag{3.46}$$

where
$$[A] = \sum_{e=1}^{m} [A]^e \quad [B] = \sum_{e=1}^{m} [B]^e \quad \{f\} = \sum_{e=1}^{m} \{f\}^e$$

$\{h\}$ contains the head values at the nodes, $e$ denotes an element-defined quantity, and $m$ is the number of elements used to approximate the domain of interest. Typical elements of matrices $[A]^e$, $[B]^e$, and $\{f\}^e$ are

$$A_{IJ}^e = \int_{R^e} \nabla N_I \cdot T \cdot \nabla N_J \, dR$$

$$B_{IJ}^e = \int_{R^e} S N_I N_J \, dR$$

$$f_I^e = \int_{B_2^e} \mathbf{n} \cdot (T \cdot \nabla \bar{h}) N_I \, dB - \int_{R^e} N_I q \, dR$$

where $B_2^e$ is that segment of the domain boundary $B$ coinciding with a side or sides of element $e$. The expression $\mathbf{n} \cdot (T \cdot \nabla \bar{h})$ is the inward-directed normal flux to the boundary $B_2^e$ and, when required computationally, is provided via Neumann boundary-condition information. Note that if the head at node $I$ is specified by a Dirichlet boundary condition, this specification replaces the equation obtained by weighting with respect to $N_I$. The problem parameters $T$ and $S$ are usually specified elementwise or as expansions in terms of the basis functions. The ordinary time derivative appearing in (3.46) is generally approximated using finite differences such as

$$\left(\theta[A] + \frac{1}{\Delta t}[B]\right)\{h\}^{k+1} = \left((\theta-1)[A] + \frac{1}{\Delta t}[B]\right)\{h\}^k + \theta\{f\}^{k+1} + (1-\theta)\{f\}^k \tag{3.47}$$

where $t = k \, \Delta t$ and $\theta$ is a time-weighting factor defined such that $0 \le \theta \le 1$, and $\theta = 0.5$ yields the second-order accurate Crank–Nicolson approximation.

## 3.3B Simulation of Saturated Groundwater Flow in an Unconfined Aquifer

The vertically integrated governing equation for essentially horizontal flow in an unconfined groundwater reservoir is generally written

$$\nabla \cdot \boldsymbol{T} \cdot \nabla \bar{h} - (S_s b + S_y)\frac{\partial \bar{h}}{\partial t} + I = 0 \tag{3.48}$$

where $b(x, y, t)$ is now the saturated thickness of the reservoir and $S_y$ is the specific yield. If $a$ is the elevation of the reservoir base defined with respect to the same datum as the head $\bar{h}$, then $b \equiv \bar{h} - a$. In defining $\bar{h}$, the vertical integration of Eq. (3.44) was performed over the interval $b(x, y, t)$. The transmissivity is now given by $\boldsymbol{T} = (\bar{h} - a)\boldsymbol{K} = b\boldsymbol{K}$. Because $\boldsymbol{T}$ is a function of $\bar{h}$, Eq. (3.48) is nonlinear. The term $I$ denotes flow into the saturated portion of the groundwater reservoir via leakage from below or net infiltration from above.

Employing a finite-element–Galerkin approximation in space and a backward-finite-difference approximation in time, one obtains the approximating algebraic equation

$$\left([A] + \frac{1}{\Delta t}[B]\right)\{h\}^{k+1} = \frac{1}{\Delta t}[B]\{h\}^k + \{f\}^{k+1} \tag{3.49}$$

where the matrices $[A]$, $[B]$, and $\{f\}$ are defined as before and typical entries in the element coefficient matrices are given by

$$A_{IJ}^e = \int_{R^e} \nabla N_I \cdot \boldsymbol{K}b \cdot \nabla N_J \, dR$$

$$B_{IJ}^e = \int_{R^e} (S_s b + S_y) N_I N_J \, dR$$

$$f_I^e = \int_{R^e} \mathbf{n} \cdot (\boldsymbol{K}b \cdot \nabla \bar{h}) N_I \, dB - \int_{R^e} N_I I \, dR$$

Because Eq. (3.49) is weakly nonlinear, a simple Picard-type iteration scheme is appropriate. This procedure is easily described by rewriting Eq. (3.49) using the iteration index $r$.

$$\left([A] + \frac{1}{\Delta t}[B]\right)_r \{h\}_{r+1}^{k+1} = \frac{1}{\Delta t}[B]_r\{h\}^k + \{f\}^{k+1} \tag{3.50}$$

The nonlinear matrices $[A]$ and $[B]$ are updated at iteration level $r+1$ using information derived from iteration $r$. Equation (3.50) is solved repeatedly until $\|\{h\}_{r+1}^{k+1} - \{h\}_r^{k+1}\|$ is within a specified tolerance. One then proceeds to time level $k+2$.

## 3.3c Sharp-Interface Simulation of Saltwater Intrusion

The simulation of areal groundwater flow in the neighborhood of a saltwater saturated segment of a reservoir is often achieved by assuming that a sharp interface separates the salt water and fresh water (see Fig. 3.35). The fluids are each considered homogeneous and each

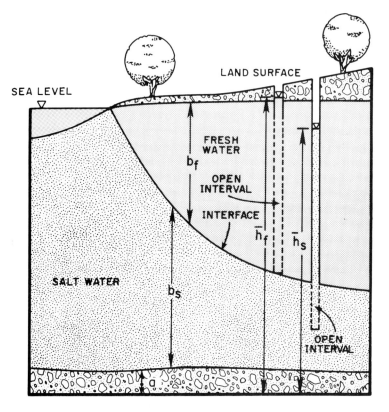

SEA LEVEL

LAND SURFACE

FRESH WATER

$b_f$

OPEN INTERVAL

INTERFACE

$\bar{h}_f$ $\bar{h}_s$

SALT WATER

$b_s$

OPEN INTERVAL

$a$

**FIG. 3.35** Saltwater–freshwater system separated by a sharp interface.

exhibits a vertically averaged head. Let us denote the vertically averaged freshwater head by $\bar{h}_f$ and the vertically averaged saltwater head by $\bar{h}_s$. When pressure continuity across the interface is assumed in an unconfined aquifer, the governing equations for the system may be written

$$\boldsymbol{\nabla} \cdot \boldsymbol{T}_f \cdot \boldsymbol{\nabla} \bar{h}_f - (S_y + \phi \rho_f^*)\frac{\partial \bar{h}_f}{\partial t} + \phi \rho_s^* \frac{\partial \bar{h}_s}{\partial t} + I = 0 \qquad (3.51a)$$

$$\boldsymbol{\nabla} \cdot \boldsymbol{T}_s \cdot \boldsymbol{\nabla} \bar{h}_s + \phi \rho_f^* \frac{\partial \bar{h}_f}{\partial t} - \phi \rho_s^* \frac{\partial \bar{h}_s}{\partial t} = 0 \qquad (3.51b)$$

where $\phi$ is the porosity, and we have neglected the specific yield and vertical flux from the lower boundary of the reservoir. The transmissivities are now defined as $T_f = b_f K_f$, $T_s = b_s K_s$, and $I$ is the net infiltration. The variables $\rho_f^*$ and $\rho_s^*$ are dimensionless densities defined as

$$\rho_s^* = \frac{\rho_s}{\rho_s - \rho_f} \qquad \text{and} \qquad \rho_f^* = \frac{\rho_f}{\rho_s - \rho_f}$$

Application of the Galerkin–finite-element procedure yields a set of nonlinear algebraic equations with two unknown head values per node, i.e.,

$$[A]\{h\}+[B]\left\{\frac{dh}{dt}\right\}=\{r\} \tag{3.52}$$

where $\qquad [A]=\sum_{e=1}^{m}[A]^e \qquad [B]=\sum_{e=1}^{m}[B]^e \qquad$ and $\qquad \{r\}=\sum_{e=1}^{m}\{r\}^e$

Typical elements of $[A]^e$, $[B]^e$, $\{r\}$, $\{h\}/\{dh/dt\}$, and $\{r\}^e$ are given by

$$[A_{IJ}]^e=\begin{bmatrix} \int_{R^e}\boldsymbol{\nabla}N_I\cdot T_f\cdot\boldsymbol{\nabla}N_J\,dR & 0 \\[2ex] 0 & \Omega\int_{R^e}\boldsymbol{\nabla}N_I\cdot T_s\cdot\boldsymbol{\nabla}N_J\,dR \end{bmatrix}$$

$$[B_{IJ}]^e=\begin{bmatrix} \int_{R^e}(S_y+\phi\rho_f^*)N_IN_J\,dR & \int_{R^e}-\phi\rho_f^*N_IN_J\,dR \\[2ex] \int_{R^e}-\phi\rho_s^*N_IN_J\,dR & \Omega\int_{R^e}\phi\rho_s^*N_IN_J\,dR \end{bmatrix}$$

$$\{h_I\}=\left\{\begin{array}{c}\bar{h}_{fI}\\ \bar{h}_{sI}\end{array}\right\} \qquad \left\{\frac{dh_I}{dt}\right\}=\left\{\begin{array}{c}\dfrac{dh_{fI}}{dt}\\[2ex] \dfrac{dh_{sI}}{dt}\end{array}\right\}$$

$$\{R_I\}^e=\left\{\begin{array}{c}\displaystyle\int_{B_2^e}\mathbf{n}\cdot T_f\cdot\boldsymbol{\nabla}\bar{h}_fN_I\,dB+\int_{R^e}IN_I\,dR\\[2ex] \Omega\displaystyle\int_{B_2^e}\mathbf{n}\cdot T_s\cdot\boldsymbol{\nabla}\bar{h}_sN_I\,dB\end{array}\right\}$$

The parameter $\Omega\equiv\rho_s^*/\rho_f^*$ is a scaling factor used only to generate symmetry in the coefficient matrix $[B]$. Use of a weighted-finite-difference approximation for the time derivative yields

$$\left([A]+\frac{1}{\Delta t}[B]\right)\{h\}^{k+1}=\frac{1}{\Delta t}[B]\{h\}^k+\{r\}^k \tag{3.53}$$

Because of difficulties associated with solving this system of nonlinear algebraic equations, a strategy such as the following is employed: For the first estimate at a new time level use

$$\{h\}^{k+1}=\{h\}^k+\sigma^*\frac{\Delta t}{\Delta t'}(\{h\}^k-\{h\}^{k-1}) \qquad 0\leqslant\sigma^*\leqslant 1 \tag{3.54}$$

where $\Delta t=t_{k+1}-t_k$, $\Delta t'=t_k-t_{k-1}$, and $\sigma^*$ is an extrapolation coefficient. For subsequent iterate levels use is made of the relation

$$\{h\}_{r+2}^{k+1}=\{h\}_{r+1}^{k+1}+(\omega-1)(\{h\}_{r+1}^{k+1}-\{h\}_r^{k+1}) \qquad 1\leqslant\omega<2 \tag{3.55}$$

# 3.200

PART THREE: FEM APPLICATIONS

where $\omega$ is an overrelaxation parameter. The use of $\sigma^* = 0.5$ and $\omega = 1.5$ has been found to be satisfactory.

## 3.3D Single-Phase Oil-Reservoir Simulation

The equation describing single-phase oil-reservoir flow behavior is written

$$\nabla \cdot \frac{k}{\mu} \cdot (\nabla p + \rho g \nabla z) - (\alpha + \phi\beta)\frac{\partial p}{\partial t} = 0 \tag{3.56}$$

where $k$ is permeability of the reservoir, $g$ is gravitational acceleration, $\rho$ is oil density, $p$ is oil pressure, $z$ is elevation, $\mu$ is oil viscosity, $\alpha$ is reservoir-skeleton compressibility, and $\beta$ is oil compressibility. Equation (3.56) is essentially the same as the saturated-groundwater flow equation, and its vertically integrated form is solved in the same manner as Eq. (3.45). However, one must be careful to allow in the well-discharge specification for the oil-volume change accompanying the transfer of oil from reservoir to surface conditions.

## 3.3E Variably Saturated Groundwater-Flow Simulation

The flow of water in a porous medium where air and water coexist can be described by the equation

$$\nabla \cdot K k_{rw} \cdot (\nabla \psi + \nabla z) - \phi \frac{\partial S_w}{\partial t} - S_w S_s \frac{\partial \psi}{\partial t} = 0 \tag{3.57}$$

where $K$ is, as earlier, the saturated hydraulic conductivity, $S_s$ is the specific storage, $S_w$ is the saturation of water and a function of the pressure head $\psi$, and $k_{rw}$ is the relative permeability, which is a function of the saturation $S_w$ and therefore the pressure head $\psi$. The pressure head is defined in terms of the water pressure $p_w$, the air pressure $p_a$, and the water density $\rho_w$ as $\psi = (p_w - p_a)/\rho_w g$. The third term in Eq. (3.57) is normally modified by using the chain rule of differentiation to yield

$$\frac{\partial S_w}{\partial t} = \frac{dS_w}{d\psi}\frac{\partial \psi}{\partial t} \equiv \frac{c}{\phi}\frac{\partial \psi}{\partial t} \tag{3.58}$$

where $c \equiv \phi(dS_w/d\psi)$ is called the *specific moisture capacity*. Typical experimentally determined curves for the nonlinear coefficients $k_{rw} = k_{rw}(\psi)$ and $S_w = S_w(\psi)$ are presented in Fig. 3.36. Differentiation of the curve $S_w = S_w(\psi)$ and multiplication by $\phi$ yield $c$. Combination of (3.57) and (3.58) under the assumption that $c \gg S_w S_s$ yields

$$\nabla \cdot K k_{rw} \cdot (\nabla \psi + \nabla z) - c\frac{\partial \psi}{\partial t} = 0 \tag{3.59}$$

Approximation of (3.59) using the Galerkin–finite-element method results in the following system of nonlinear algebraic equations

$$[A]\{\psi\} + [B]\left\{\frac{d\psi}{dt}\right\} = \{f\} \tag{3.60}$$

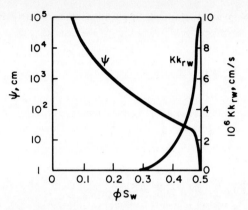

**FIG. 3.36**  Constitutive relations for yolo light clay.

where $\qquad [A]=\sum_{e=1}^{m} [A]^e \qquad [B]=\sum_{e=1}^{m} [B]^e \qquad$ and $\qquad \{f\}=\sum_{e=1}^{m} \{f\}^e$

Typical coefficients of the element coefficient matrix are

$$A_{IJ}^e = \int_{R^e} \boldsymbol{\nabla} N_I \cdot Kk_{rw} \cdot \boldsymbol{\nabla} N_J \, dR$$

$$B_{IJ}^e = \int_{R^e} cN_I N_J \, dR$$

$$f_I^e = -\int_{R^e} \boldsymbol{\nabla} N_I \cdot Kk_{rw} \cdot \boldsymbol{\nabla} z \, dR + \int_{B_2^e} \mathbf{n} \cdot Kk_{rw} \cdot (\boldsymbol{\nabla}\psi + \boldsymbol{\nabla} z) N_I \, dB$$

where the second term in $f_I^e$ represents the inward normal flux usually specified through a Neumann-type boundary condition. If $\psi_I$ is specified at node $I$, this specification replaces the above approximation. In this development the $[B]$-coefficient matrix is said to be formulated consistently if off-diagonal members are generated and retained in the integration process. However, an alternative approach using a lumped matrix is also possible. This diagonalizing procedure can be accommodated in several ways; one approach replaces the matrix $[B]$ with a matrix with elements

$$B_{II}^e = \int_{R^e} cN_I \, dR \qquad B_{IJ} = 0 \qquad I \ne J$$

The time derivative in (3.60) can be approximated using a weighted-finite-difference approach to yield

$$\left(\theta[A]^{k+\theta} + \frac{[B]^{k+\theta}}{\Delta t}\right)\{\psi\}^{k+1} = \{f\}^{k+\theta} + \left((\theta-1)[A]^{k+\theta} + \frac{[B]^{k+\theta}}{\Delta t}\right)\{\psi\}^k \qquad 0 \le \theta \le 1 \quad (3.61)$$

While Eq. (3.61) is often highly nonlinear, the Picard iteration procedure is generally the method employed in achieving a solution. The matrix coefficients are evaluated through linear interpolation. One approximates $\{\psi\}^{k+\theta}$ for this purpose using

$$\{\psi\}^{k+\theta} = \theta\{\psi\}^{k+1} + (1-\theta)\{\psi\}^{k} \tag{3.62}$$

where $\{\psi\}^{k+1}$ is the most recent iterative value. In solving (3.61) it is often advantageous to have both a head-value closure criterion and a mass-balance closure criterion. The backward-in-time approximation $\theta = 1$ provides a stable algorithm. However, improved accuracy can sometimes be achieved using values of $\theta$ over the interval $[1, 0.5]$.

## 3.3F Simulation of Immiscible Displacement in Oil Reservoirs

Simulation of the immiscible flow of oil requires an equation describing the dynamics of each phase occupying the reservoir. If the fluid and reservoir-skeleton compressibilities are assumed negligible, the governing equations for an oil-water system are .

$$\nabla \cdot [k\lambda_w \cdot (\nabla p_w + \rho_w g \nabla z)] - \phi\frac{\partial S_w}{\partial t} = 0 \tag{3.63a}$$

$$\nabla \cdot k\lambda_0 \cdot (\nabla p_0 + \rho_0 g \nabla z)] - \phi\frac{\partial S_0}{\partial t} = 0 \tag{3.63b}$$

where $\lambda_w \equiv k_{rw}/\mu_w$ and $\lambda_0 \equiv k_{ro}/\mu_o$ are the water and oil mobilities, respectively. Define $\Phi_w = p_w + \rho_w gz$ and $\Phi_o = p_o + \rho_o gz$. Equations (3.59) can now be written, assuming gradients in fluid density to be small, as

$$\nabla \cdot k\lambda_w \cdot \nabla\Phi_w - \phi\frac{\partial S_w}{\partial t} = 0 \tag{3.64a}$$

$$\nabla \cdot k\lambda_o \cdot \nabla\Phi_o + \phi\frac{\partial S_w}{\partial t} = 0 \tag{3.64b}$$

where the identity $S_w + S_o = 1$ has been used in modifying the right-hand side of Eq. (3.63b). Application of the Galerkin–finite-element method to (3.64) yields

$$[T_w]\{\Phi_w\} + [M]\left\{\frac{dS_w}{dt}\right\} = \{f_w\} \tag{3.65a}$$

$$[T_o]\{\Phi_o\} - [M]\left\{\frac{dS_w}{dt}\right\} = \{f_o\} \tag{3.65b}$$

where $\quad [T_i] = \sum_{e=1}^{m} [T_i]^e \quad [M] = \sum_{e=1}^{m} [M]^e \quad$ and $\quad \{f_i\} = \sum_{e=1}^{m} \{f_i\}^e \quad i = w, o$

Typical elements of $[T_i]^e$, $[M]^e$, and $\{f_i\}^e$ are

$$T_{iIJ}^e = \int_{R^e} \nabla W_I \cdot k\lambda_i \cdot \nabla N_J \, dR \approx \lambda_i k : \int_{R^e} \nabla W_I \nabla N_J \, dR \qquad i = w, o$$

$$M_{IJ}^e = \int_{R^e} \phi W_I N_J \, dR$$

$$f_{iI}^e = \int_{B_2^e} \mathbf{n} \cdot k\lambda_i \cdot \nabla \Phi_i W_I \, dB \qquad i = w, o$$

The time derivatives appearing in Eq. (3.65) can be approximated once again in a straightforward way using finite-difference methods. Note that the weighting function $W_I$ in this formulation has been selected such that it may be different from the basis function. It is well known that convergence to the correct solution in problems of this kind requires an asymmetric approximation favoring the upstream direction. In finite-difference theory this is called *upstream weighting*. In finite-element approximations this asymmetry is normally achieved using an asymmetric weighting or basis function. A description of this approach is detailed in Huyakorn and Pinder [96].

Experience suggests that the system of coupled highly nonlinear equations (3.65) is solved more efficiently using the Newton–Raphson or chord-slope iterative methods rather than Picard iteration. The application of Newton–Raphson and chord-slope methods to equations of this kind are rather straightforward and are described in Huyakorn and Pinder [95].

### 3.3G  Simulation of Solute and Energy Transport

The preceding sections have concentrated on the simulation of the behavior of homogeneous fluids. Now attention is turned to nonhomogeneous fluids such as encountered in flow fields characterized by concentration and temperature gradients. Such systems require governing equations not only for fluid flow but also for species and energy transport. As a first case, consider species and thermal transport in a saturated groundwater reservoir.

The chemical-species and thermal-transport equations for a single-phase fluid are of fundamentally the same form and can be written generically as

$$A\frac{\partial u}{\partial t} + \mathbf{B} \cdot \nabla u - \nabla \cdot (E \cdot \nabla u) + Fu - G = 0 \tag{3.66}$$

where for the case of mass transport with first-order reactions

$$A \equiv \Phi \kappa_k$$

$$\mathbf{B} \equiv \mathbf{V}$$

$$E \equiv \phi D$$

$$F \equiv \phi \lambda_k^* \kappa_k$$

$$G \equiv \sum_{m=1}^{M} \phi \xi_{km} \lambda_m^* \kappa_m c_m$$

and

$$u \equiv c_k$$

The parameters appearing above are defined as follows:

$\kappa_k$ = the retardation coefficient of species $k$

$\mathbf{V}$ = the specific discharge or superficial velocity

$\mathbf{D}$ = the dispersion coefficient

$\lambda_k^*$ = the decay constant for first order decay of species $k$

$\xi_{km}$ = the fraction of component $m$ transforming by first-order reaction into component $k$

$c_k$ = the mass concentration of species $k$ per unit volume of fluid phase

Equation (3.66) also may be used to describe energy transport in a single-phase fluid in the absence of phase change. In this instance, the appropriate definition of the parameters appearing in (3.62) is

$$A \equiv \phi \rho^l c_v^l + (1 - \phi) \rho^s c_v^s$$

$$\mathbf{B} \equiv \rho^l c_v^l \mathbf{V}^l$$

$$E \equiv \mathbf{K}$$

$$F \equiv 0$$

$$G \equiv [\phi \rho^l Q^l + (1 - \phi) \rho^s Q^s]$$

and

$$u \equiv T$$

where the superscripts $l$ and $s$ designate liquid and solid properties, respectively. Parameters appearing in these definitions and not appearing heretofore are

$c_v^m$ = the specific heat of phase $m$ at constant volume

$\mathbf{K}$ = the hydrodynamic thermal-dispersion tensor for the combined fluid-solid medium

$Q^m$ = the heat supply to phase $m$ from an external source

$T$ = the medium temperature

Solution of (3.66) requires that a velocity field for the flow be available. Because the fluid density is now dependent upon composition and temperature, the potential form of Darcy's expression is an inappropriate source for the velocity, and the more general form implicitly appearing in Eq. (3.56) must be used:

$$\mathbf{V}^l = -\frac{\mathbf{k}}{\mu} \cdot (\nabla p + \rho^l g \nabla z) \tag{3.67}$$

The retrieval of $\mathbf{V}^l$ from (3.67) implies a knowledge of the pressure $p$. This field may be computed from a slight variant on the continuity equation (3.56),

$$H \frac{\partial p}{\partial t} - \nabla \cdot [\mathbf{M} \cdot (\nabla p + \rho^l g \nabla z)] = 0 \tag{3.68}$$

where 

$$H \equiv \rho^l (\alpha + \phi \beta) \quad \text{and} \quad \mathbf{M} = \frac{\rho^l \mathbf{k}}{\mu}$$

No restrictions on fluid-density variability have thus far been imposed in writing Eqs. (3.67) and (3.68). However, to solve these equations, a constitutive relationship relating density to either species concentration or temperature is needed. A commonly used relationship is

$$\rho^l = \rho_0^l + \left(\frac{d\rho^l}{du}\right)_{u_0}(u - u_0) \qquad (3.69)$$

The term $d\rho^l/du$ is the thermal volume expansion in the case of energy transport and the concentration-dependent volume expansion for the case of species transport. For the important case of chloride transport where $\rho_0^l$ is the freshwater density, $d\rho^l/du \approx 0.7$ for concentrations of chloride ranging from zero up to that in seawater. In addition, in the case of energy transport, the temperature dependence of the viscosity may be important such that an appropriate constitutive relationship for this dependence is required.

The set of equations represented by (3.66) to (3.69) can be solved using two distinctly different strategies. One approach solves the equations sequentially. In the first step, the flow equation is solved for pressure. This solution is used in conjuction with Eq. (3.67) to obtain velocity, which is then used in Eq. (3.68) when solving for species concentration or temperature. Application of the Galerkin–finite-element approach yields the following set of ordinary differential equations in time:

$$[Q]\left\{\frac{du}{dt}\right\} + [S]\{u\} = \{f\} \qquad (3.70a)$$

$$[T]\left\{\frac{dp}{dt}\right\} + [Y]\{p\} = \{g\} \qquad (3.70b)$$

where 
$$[Q] = \sum_{e=1}^{m}[Q]^e \quad [S] = \sum_{e=1}^{m}[S]^e \quad [T] = \sum_{e=1}^{m}[T]^e \quad [Y] = \sum_{e=1}^{m}[Y]^e$$

$$\{f\} = \sum_{e=1}^{m}\{f\}^e \quad \text{and} \quad \{g\} = \sum_{e=1}^{m}\{g\}^e$$

Typical coefficients of the element coefficient matrices are

$$Q_{IJ}^e = \int_{R^e} A N_I N_J \, dR$$

$$S_{IJ}^e = \int_{R^e} \{\mathbf{B} \cdot \boldsymbol{\nabla} N_J N_I + \boldsymbol{\nabla} N_I \cdot \mathbf{E} \cdot \boldsymbol{\nabla} N_J + F N_J N_I\} \, dR$$

$$f_I^e = \int_{R^e} G N_I \, dR + \int_{B_2^e} \mathbf{n} \cdot \mathbf{E} \cdot \boldsymbol{\nabla} u N_I \, dB$$

$$T_{IJ}^e = \int_{R^e} H N_I N_J \, dR$$

$$Y_{IJ}^e = \int_{R^e} \boldsymbol{\nabla} N_I \cdot \mathbf{M} \cdot \boldsymbol{\nabla} N_J \, dR$$

and 
$$g_I^e = -\int_{R^e} \rho^l g \boldsymbol{\nabla} N_I \cdot \mathbf{M} \cdot \boldsymbol{\nabla} z \, dR + \int_{B_2^e} \mathbf{n} \cdot \mathbf{M} \cdot (\boldsymbol{\nabla} p + \rho^l g \boldsymbol{\nabla} z) N_I \, dB$$

The last term in the definition of $f_I$ and $g_I$ are fluxes which are normally specified in the problem statement when required algebraically.

The transport equation occasionally requires accommodation of third-type boundary conditions. In the context of Eq. (3.66) third-type boundary conditions are of the form

$$\mathbf{n} \cdot \mathbf{E} \cdot \nabla u = q(u - \tilde{u}) \tag{3.71}$$

where $\tilde{u}$ denotes the concentration of the fluid crossing the boundary with velocity $q$. To implement this condition one simply replaces the definition of $f_I^e$ by

$$f_I^e = \int_{R^e} GN_I \, dR + \int_{B_2^e} q(u - \tilde{u}) N_I \, dB \tag{3.72}$$

Then after $u$ in (3.72) is replaced by its approximating counterpart, this information is transferred to the left-hand side of (3.70a) by augmenting the matrix $[Q]$.

When an injection well is encountered, another modification of the governing equation is required. A term of the form $q(\tilde{u} - u)$ is added to the left-hand side of Eq. (3.66), where $q$ is now the well discharge. The usual procedure for incorporating well discharge in a model is to consider the well to be a point and write

$$q(\tilde{u} - u) = Q_w \delta(\mathbf{x} - \mathbf{x}_I)(\tilde{u} - u) \tag{3.73}$$

where $\delta(\cdot)$ is the Dirac delta function and $\mathbf{x}_I$ denotes the well coordinates. The new term in the approximating finite-element equation is

$$\int_{R^e} N_I q(\tilde{u} - u) \, dR = \int_{R^e} N_I Q_w \delta(\mathbf{x} - \mathbf{x}_I)(\tilde{u} - u) \, dR = Q_w(\tilde{u}_I - u_I) \tag{3.74}$$

Now $-Q_w$ must be incorporated into matrix $[S]$ and $-Q_w \tilde{u}_I$ is added to vector $\{f\}$.

The ordinary differential equations in time represented by Eq. (3.70) are reduced to a set of algebraic equations using a finite-difference approach, i.e.,

$$\frac{1}{\Delta t}[Q]^{k+\theta}(\{u\}^{k+1} - \{u\}^k) + \theta[S]^{k+1}\{u\}^{k+1} + (1-\theta)[S]^k\{u\}^k$$

$$= \theta\{f\}^{k+1} + (1-\theta)\{f\}^k \tag{3.75a}$$

$$\frac{1}{\Delta t}[T]^{k+\theta}(\{p\}^{k+1} - \{p\}^k) + \theta[Y]^{k+1}\{p\}^{k+1} + (1-\theta)[Y]^k\{p\}^k$$

$$= \theta\{g\}^{k+1} + (1-\theta)\{g\}^k \tag{3.75b}$$

Equations (3.75) are now solved sequentially using algebraic algorithms that take advantage of the special features of each coefficient matrix such as the symmetry of the matrix generated through the combination of $[T]$ and $[Y]$.

A second approach to the solution of the fluid-flow and transport equations is to solve them simultaneously. It is convenient in this formulation to replace the density in the body-force term of the flow equation with its constitutive representation. For example, for the case of chloride transport, the flow equation becomes

$$H\frac{\partial p}{\partial t} - \nabla \cdot M \cdot (\nabla p + \{\rho_0^l + 0.7u\}g\nabla z) = 0 \tag{3.76}$$

Equation (3.66) is approximated as before, and (3.76) is also approximated using the Galerkin–finite-element approach to yield the ordinary differential equations

$$[Q^*]\left\{\frac{du^*}{dt}\right\} + [S^*]\{u^*\} = \{f^*\} \tag{3.77}$$

where, as before,

$$[Q^*] = \sum_{e=1}^{m} [Q^*]^e \quad [S^*] = \sum_{e=1}^{m} [S^*]^e \quad \text{and} \quad \{f^*\} = \sum_{e=1}^{m} \{f^*\}^e$$

Typical entries of the element coefficient matrices obtained by simultaneous solution for $p$ and $u$ are

$$[Q^*]_{IJ}^e = \begin{bmatrix} \int_{R^e} AN_J N_I \, dR & 0 \\ 0 & \int_{R^e} HN_J N_I \, dR \end{bmatrix}$$

$$\left\{\frac{du^*}{dt}\right\}_I = \begin{Bmatrix} \dfrac{du_I}{dt} \\ \dfrac{dp_I}{dt} \end{Bmatrix}$$

$$[S^*]_{IJ}^e = \begin{bmatrix} \int_{R^e} (\boldsymbol{B} \cdot \nabla N_J N_I + \nabla N_I \cdot \boldsymbol{E} \cdot \nabla N_J + FN_J N_I) \, dR & 0 \\ \int_{R^e} \nabla N_I \cdot M \cdot (0.7g\nabla z) N_J \, dR & \int_{R^e} \nabla N_I \cdot M \cdot \nabla N_J \, dR \end{bmatrix}$$

$$\{f^*\}_I^e = \begin{bmatrix} \int_{R^e} GN_I \, dR + \int_{B_2^e} \mathbf{n} \cdot \boldsymbol{E} \cdot \nabla u N_I \, dB \\ -\int_{R^e} \nabla N_I \cdot M \cdot (\rho_0^l g\nabla z) \, dR + \int_{B_2^e} \mathbf{n} \cdot M \cdot (\nabla p + \rho^l g\nabla z) N_I \, dB \end{bmatrix}$$

Equation (3.77) is now discretized in time using a standard finite-difference algorithm, i.e.,

$$\frac{1}{\Delta t}[Q^*](\{u^*\}^{k+1} - \{u^*\}^k) + \theta\{u^*\}^{k+1} + (1-\theta)\{u^*\}^k = \theta\{f^*\}^{k+1} + (1-\theta)\{f^*\}^k \tag{3.78}$$

As written, Eq. (3.78) appears to be linear. However, the coefficient $\boldsymbol{B}$ in $S_{IJ}^{*e}$ is proportional to velocity and thus, via Darcy's law, is a function of fluid pressure. Unless $\boldsymbol{B}$ is approximated using earlier time levels, the system of algebraic equations represented by Eq. (3.78) is weakly nonlinear and a Picard-type iterative solution scheme should be employed.

It is well known that Eqs. (3.75) and (3.76) are difficult to solve for convection-dominated flows. As $|B|$ times grid spacing becomes large relative to $|E|$, numerical solutions begin to develop an oscillatory behavior. This behavior can be subdued only at the expense of numerical smearing of the sharp solution front via artificial diffusion or by the use of a finer finite-element discretization.

When one elects to use the approach of enhanced discretization, a rule of thumb is to select the element size such that the characteristic length of the element (e.g., max $\Delta x$) satisfies the constraint $|B||\Delta x|/|E| \leqslant 2$. Here the magnitudes of $B$ and $E$ are used to denote typical average element-level behavior.

If the problem under consideration is too large in scale to allow for the recommended level of discretization, artificial diffusion can be introduced in several ways. The most common approach is to "upstream-weight" the convective term (the term containing $B$), as was recommended earlier in the discussion of the multiphase oil-reservoir equations. Another approach that is suitable for problems wherein convection is not extraordinarily dominant is to select $\theta \approx \frac{2}{3}$. This decreases the order of accuracy of the time-derivative approximation leading to modest, but not excessive, numerical smearing of the front with its concomitant beneficial suppression of numerical oscillations.

### 3.3H  Simulation of Nonisothermal Multiphase Flow

In this section the focus is on the particular case of geothermal reservoir simulation. While there are several avenues of approach to the formulation of this problem, herein the strategy that employs pressure and enthalpy as the dependent variables is considered. The fluid-flow equation for the steam-water mixture is given by

$$\frac{\partial}{\partial t}(\phi\rho) + \nabla \cdot (\rho^g V^g + \rho^l V^l) = 0 \tag{3.79}$$

where the superscripts $g$, $l$, and $s$ denote the gas, liquid, and solid phases, respectively. The energy-balance equation is given by

$$(1-\theta)\rho^s\frac{\partial h^s}{\partial t} + \frac{\partial}{\partial t}(\phi\rho h) + \nabla \cdot (\rho^l h^l V^l) + \nabla \cdot (\rho^g h^g V^g) - \nabla \cdot \kappa \cdot \left[\frac{\partial T}{\partial h}\nabla h + \frac{\partial T}{\partial p}\nabla p\right] = 0 \tag{3.80}$$

where $h$ is enthalpy and $\kappa$ is the thermal conductivity of the fluid-filled reservoir. The new variables which appear in Eqs. (3.79) and (3.80) are defined by

$$\rho \equiv S^l\rho^l + S^g\rho^g \tag{3.81a}$$

$$h \equiv \frac{1}{\rho}[S^l\rho^l h^l + S^g\rho^g h^g] \tag{3.81b}$$

Equations (3.79) and (3.80) can be rewritten by making use of the relationship

$$V^m = \frac{-kk_r^m}{\mu^m}(\nabla p + \rho^m g\nabla z) \qquad m = l, g \tag{3.82}$$

to yield
$$\frac{\partial}{\partial t}(\phi\rho) - \nabla \cdot [\tau^g \cdot (\nabla p + \rho^g g \nabla z) + \tau^l \cdot (\nabla p + \rho^l g \nabla z)] = 0 \qquad (3.83)$$

where
$$\tau^m \equiv \frac{\rho^m k k_r}{\mu^m}$$

and
$$(1-\phi)\rho^s \frac{\partial h^s}{\partial t} + \frac{\partial}{\partial t}(\phi\rho h) - \nabla \cdot [\tau^l \cdot (\nabla p + \rho^l g \nabla z) h^l]$$

$$-\nabla \cdot [\tau^g \cdot (\nabla p + \rho^g g \nabla z) h^g] - \nabla \cdot \kappa \cdot \left(\frac{\partial T}{\partial h}\nabla h + \frac{\partial T}{\partial p}\nabla p\right) = 0 \qquad (3.84)$$

The liquid and gas phases are assumed to be at the same pressure. The notation used in writing Eqs. (3.83) and (3.84) may be condensed so that these equations become

$$\nabla \cdot (\tau \cdot \nabla p) + \nabla \cdot \mathbf{G} - \frac{\partial F}{\partial t} = 0 \qquad (3.85a)$$

$$\nabla \cdot (\lambda \cdot \nabla p) + \nabla \cdot (\beta \cdot \nabla h) + \nabla \cdot \mathbf{P} - \frac{\partial H}{\partial t} = 0 \qquad (3.85b)$$

where  $\tau \equiv \tau^l + \tau^g$

$F \equiv \phi\rho$

$H \equiv \phi\rho h + (1-\phi)\rho^s h^s$

$\lambda \equiv \kappa\frac{\partial T}{\partial p} + \tau^l h^l + \tau^g h^g \qquad h^l \leq h \leq h^g$ (two-phase region)

$\lambda \equiv \kappa\frac{\partial T}{\partial p} + \tau h \qquad h^l > h; \ h^g < h$ (single-phase region)

$\beta \equiv \kappa\frac{\partial T}{\partial h}$

$\mathbf{G} = (\rho^l g\tau^l + \rho^g g\tau^g) \cdot \nabla z$

$\mathbf{P} = (\rho^l h^l g\tau^l + \rho^g h^g g\tau^g) \cdot \nabla z$

The pressure-enthalpy relationship for water and steam is the remaining thermodynamic information needed to close the system of Eqs. (3.85). This information is put into computer-readable form via the steam tables or regression equations.

Application of the Galerkin–finite-element formulation yields a set of ordinary differential equations in time. A system of highly nonlinear algebraic equations results when the time derivative is approximated using a finite-difference representation. The Newton-Raphson iterative procedure can be used in solving these equations. If $r+1$ represents the current iteration level and the difference between successive iterations is denoted by

$$\Delta p_J \equiv p_J^{r+1,k+1} - p_J^{r,k+1} \qquad (3.86a)$$

and
$$\Delta h_J \equiv h_J^{r+1,k+1} - h_J^{r,k+1} \qquad (3.86b)$$

the resulting matrix equation can be written, using $W_I$ to denote an asymmetric weighting function, as

$$[A]\{u\} = \{f\} \tag{3.87}$$

where
$$[A] = \sum_{e=1}^{m} [A]^e \quad \text{and} \quad \{f\} = \sum_{e=1}^{m} \{f\}^e$$

Typical elements of $[A]^e$ and $\{f\}^e$ are

$$
[A]_{IJ}^e =
\begin{bmatrix}
\int_{R^e} \left[ \nabla W_I \cdot \left( \boldsymbol{\tau} \cdot \nabla N_J + \frac{\partial \boldsymbol{\tau}}{\partial p_J} \cdot \nabla p^{k+1,r} \right) - N^I \left( \frac{\partial \mathbf{G}}{\partial p} \right) \cdot \nabla N_J + \frac{N_I}{\Delta t} \frac{\partial F^{k+1,r}}{\partial p_J} \right] dR \\[2ex]
\int_{R^e} \Bigg[ \nabla W_I \cdot \left( \boldsymbol{\lambda} \cdot \nabla N_J + \frac{\partial \boldsymbol{\lambda}}{\partial p_J} \cdot \nabla p^{k+1,r} + \frac{\partial \boldsymbol{\beta}}{\partial p_J} \cdot \nabla h^{k+1,r} \right) \\[1ex]
\qquad - N_I \left( \frac{\partial \mathbf{G}}{\partial p} \right)_J \cdot \nabla N_J + \frac{N_I}{\Delta t} \frac{\partial H^{k+1,r}}{\partial p_J} \Bigg] dR
\end{bmatrix}
$$

$$
\begin{bmatrix}
\int_{R^e} \left[ \nabla W_I \cdot \frac{\partial \boldsymbol{\tau}}{\partial h_J} \cdot \nabla p^{k+1,r} - N_I \left( \frac{\partial \mathbf{G}}{\partial h} \right)_J \cdot \nabla N_J + \frac{N_I}{\Delta t} \frac{\partial F^{k+1,r}}{\partial h_J} \right] dR \\[2ex]
\int_{R^e} \Bigg[ \nabla W_I \cdot \left( \frac{\partial \boldsymbol{\lambda}}{\partial h_J} \cdot \nabla p^{k+1,r} + \boldsymbol{\beta} \cdot \nabla N_J + \frac{\partial \boldsymbol{\beta}}{\partial h_J} \cdot \nabla h^{k+1,r} \right) \\[1ex]
\qquad - N_I \left( \frac{\partial \mathbf{P}}{\partial h} \right)_J \cdot \nabla N_J + \frac{N_I}{\Delta t} \frac{\partial H^{k+1,r}}{\partial h_J} \Bigg] dR
\end{bmatrix}
$$

$$
\{u\}_I = \left\{ \begin{array}{c} \Delta p_I \\ \Delta h_I \end{array} \right\}
$$

$$
\{f\}_I^e = \left\{
\begin{array}{c}
\int_{R^e} \left[ \nabla W_I \cdot \boldsymbol{\tau} \cdot \nabla N_J p^{k+1,r} - N_I \nabla N_J \cdot \mathbf{G}_J^{k+1,r} + \frac{N_I (F^{k+1,r} - F^k)}{\Delta t} \right] dR \\[2ex]
\int_{R^e} \left[ \nabla W_I \cdot (\boldsymbol{\lambda} p_J^{k+1,r} \cdot \nabla N_J + \boldsymbol{\beta} h_J^r \cdot \nabla N_J) - N_I \nabla N_J p_J^{k+1,r} + \frac{N_I (H^{k+1,r} - H^k)}{\Delta t} \right] dR
\end{array}
\right\}
$$

The solution of Eq. (3.87) is used to update the nonlinear coefficients appearing in this equation and in the boundary terms which have not been explicitly presented herein. This iterative procedure is continued until such time as convergence is achieved using a suitable norm. Considerable difficulty may be encountered when the thermodynamic variables approach the two-phase boundary of the pressure-enthalpy diagram. To successfully cross this boundary a modification of the standard Newton–Raphson procedure is required. One approach is to calculate the thermodynamic derivatives with respect to pressure and enthalpy such that if the evaluation is to be made in the two-phase zone a negative-pressure and positive-enthalpy increment is used. If the evaluation is to be made in the single-phase zone, a positive-pressure and negative-enthalpy increment is employed.

## 3.3ı Summary

Within this short section on porous-media simulation, a considerable scope of material has been covered. Progression in difficulty has been from the relatively straightforward simulation of single-phase groundwater flow to the challenging problem of nonisothermal multiphase flow. This survey is nevertheless incomplete. Among the many interesting variations on the problems considered that could not be discussed herein because of space limitations are fractured media flow, flow in deformable reservoirs, and multiphase miscible transport.

## 3.4 REFERENCES

1. Duncan, J. M., and C.-Y. Chang, "Nonlinear Analysis of Stress and Strain in Soils," *J. Soil Mech. Found. Div. ASCE*, **96**(SM5):1629-1651 (September 1970).

2. Duncan, J. M., P. M. Byrne, K. S. Wong, and P. Mabry, "Strength Stress–Strain and Bulk Modulus Parameters for Finite Element Analyses of Stresses and Movements in Soil Masses," Rep. No. UCB/GT/78-02, Department of Civil Engineering, University of California, Berkeley, August 1980.

3. Byrne, P. M., and T. L. Eldridge, "A Three Parameter Dilatant Elastic Stress–Strain Model for Sand," *International Symposium on Numerical Models in Geomechanics*, Switzerland, September 1982, pp. 73-79.

4. Byrne, P. M., Y. P. Vaid, and L. Samarsekera, "Undrained Deformation Analysis Using Path Dependent Material Properties," *International Symposium on Numerical Models in Geomechanics*, Swiss Federal Institute of Technology, Zurich, Switzerland, September 13-17, 1982, pp. 294-332.

5. Duncan, J. M., S. Wong, and Y. Ozawa, "FEADAM: A Computer Program for Finite Element Analysis of Dams," Rep. No. UCB/GT/80-02, Department of Civil Engineering, University of California, Berkeley, December 1980.

6. Roscoe, K. H., and J. B. Bransby, "On the Generalized Stress–Strain Behaviour of 'Wet' Clay," in J. Heyman and F. A. Leckie (eds.), *Engineering Plasticity*, Cambridge University Press, Cambridge, 1968, pp. 535-609.

7. Schofield, A. N., and C. P. Wroth, *Critical State Soil Mechanics*, McGraw-Hill, London, 1968.

8. Atkinson, J. H., and P. L. Bransby, *The Mechanics of Soils: An Introduction to Critical State Soil Mechanics*, London, McGraw-Hill, 1975.

9. Zienkiewicz, O. C., and D. J. Naylor, "The Adaptation of Critical State Soil Mechanics Theory for Use in Finite Elements," *Proceedings of Roscoe Memorial Symposium*, Cambridge, 1972, pp. 537-547.

10. Naylor, D. J., "Stress–Strain Laws for Soil," in C. R. Scott (ed.), *Developments in Soil Mechanics*, Applied Science Publishers, London, 1978.

11. Duncan, J. M., T. B. D'Orazio, C.-S. Chang, K. S. Wong, and L. I. Namiq, "CON2D: A Finite Element Computer Program for Analysis of Consolidation," Rep. No. UCB/GT/81-01, U.S. Army Engineers Waterways Experiment Station, Vicksburg, Miss., Nikken-Sekkei, Japan, 1981.

12. Pender, M. J., "A Model for the Behaviour of Overconsolidated Soil," *Geotechnique*, **28**(1):1-25 (1978).

13. Pender, M. J., "A Unified Model for Soil Stress–Strain Behaviour," Spec. Sess. No. 9, "Constitutive Equations on Soil," *Proc. 9th ICMFE*, Tokyo, 1977.

14. Prevost, J.-H., "Plasticity Theory for Soil Stress–Strain Behaviour," *J. Eng. Mech. Div. ASCE*, **104**(EM5):1177-1194 (1978).

15. Lade, P. V., "Elasto-Plastic Stress–Strain Theory for Cohesionless Soil with Curved Yield Surfaces," *Int. J. Solids Struct.*, **13**:1019-1035 (1977).

16. Nakai, T., and H. Matsuoka, "Constitutive Equations for Soil Based on the Extended Concept of Spatially Mobilized Plane and its Application to Finite Element Analysis," *Soils and Foundations*, vol. 23, no. 4, December 1983.

17. Christian, J. T., "Undrained Stress Distribution by Numerical Methods," *J. Soil Mech. Found. Div. ASCE*, **94**(SM6) (1968).

18. Byrne, P. M., "Effective Stress Finite Element Slope Analysis," *Proc. 29th Can. Geotech. Conf.*, Vancouver, October 1976, vol. III, pp. 35-55.

19. Byrne, P. M., and J. M. Duncan, "NLSSIP—A Computer Programme for Nonlinear Analysis of Soil-Structure Interaction Problems," *Soil Mech. Ser.*, No. 41, University of British Columbia, Vancouver, July 1979.

20. Sloan, S. W., and M. F. Randolph, "Numerical Prediction of Collapse Loads Using Finite Element Methods," *Int. J. for Numer. and Analytical Meth. in Geomechanics*, **6**:41-46 (1982).

21. Desai, C. S., and J. F. Abel, *Introduction to the Finite Element Method*, Van Nostrand Reinhold, New York, 1972.

22. Zienkiewicz, O. C., S. Valliapan, and I. P. King, "Stress Analysis of Rock as a 'No Tension' Material," *Geotechnique*, **18**(1):56-66 (1968).

23. Byrne, P. M., and W. Janzen, "INCOIL: A Computer Program for Nonlinear Analysis of Stresses and Deformations in Oil Sand Masses," Rep. submitted to Oil Sands Technol. Res. Authority, Agreement No. 272, February 1983.

24. Hafez, H., and G. Abdel-Sayed, "Finite Element Analysis of Soil-Steel Structures," *Can. J. Civ. Eng.*, **10**(2):287-244 (1983).

25. Christian, J. T., and J. W. Boehmer, "Plane Strain Consolidation by Finite Elements," *J. Soil Mech. Found. Div. ASCE*, **96**:1435-1457 (1970).

26. Sandu, R. S., and E. L. Wilson, "Finite Element Analysis of Seepage in Elastic Media," *J. Eng. Mech. Div. ASCE*, **95**(EM3):641-652 (1969).

27. Byrne, P. M., and W. Janzen, "SOILSTRESS: A Computer Program for Nonlinear Analysis of Stresses and Deformation in Soil," *Soil Mech. Ser.*, No. 52, University of British Columbia, Vancouver, December 1981.

28. Bathe, K. J., E. L. Wilson, and F. E. Peterson, "SAP IV—A Structural Analysis Program for Static and Dynamic Response of Linear Systems," Rep. No. EERC 73-11, Earthquake Engineering Research Centre, University of California, Berkeley, June 1973, rev. April 1974.

29. Bathe, K. J., E. L. Wilson, and R. H. Iding, "NONSAP—A Structural Analysis Program for Static and Dynamic Response of Nonlinear Systems," Rep. No. UC-SESM 74-3, Structural Engineering Laboratory, Department of Civil Engineering, University of California, Berkeley, February 1974.

30. Bathe, K. J., "ADINA—A Finite Element Program for Automatic Dynamic Incremental Nonlinear Analysis," Rep. 82448-1, Acoustics and Vibration Lab., Mech. Eng. Dept., Massachusetts Institute of Technology, Cambridge, Mass., September 1975, rev. May 1977.

31. Goodman, R. E., R. L. Taylor, and T. L. Brekke, "A Model for the Mechanics of Jointed Rock," *J. Soil Mech. Found. Div. ASCE*, **94**(SM3) (1968).

32. Desai, C. S., M. M. Zaman, J. G. Lightner, and H. J. Siriwardane, "Thin-Layer Element for Interfaces and Joints," *Int. J. Numer. Anal. Meth. Geomech.* (to appear).

33. McCreath, D. R., W. E. Hodge, and A. G. Harrington, "Geotechnical Design Considerations for the Gulf Oil Mobile Arctic Caisson, Beaufort Sea," *Can. Geotech. J.* (to appear).

34. Byrne, P. M., D. L. Anderson, and W. Janzen, "Response of Pile and Casings to Horizontal Free-Field Soil Displacement," *36th Canadian Geotechnical Conference*, Vancouver, B.C., June 1983.

35. Newmark, N. M., "Effect of Earthquakes on Dams and Embankments," *Geotechnique*, **5**(2) (June 1965).

36. National Research Council, U.S.A., "Earthquake Engineering Research—1982," Report by Committee on Earthquake Engineering Research, National Academy Press, Washington, D.C., 1982.

37. Finn, W. D. Liam, G. R. Martin, and M. K. W. Lee, "Comparison of Dynamic Analyses for Saturated Sands," *Proceedings ASCE Geotechnical Engineering Division Specialty Conference*, Pasadena, Calif., June 19–21, 1978, pp. 472–491.

38. Seed, H. B., and I. M. Idriss, "Influence of Soil Conditions on Ground Motion during Earthquakes," Proc. Pap. 6347, *J. Soil Mech. Found. Div. ASCE*, **95**(SM1):99–137 (January 1969).

39. Schnabel, P. B., J. Lysmer, and H. B. Seed, "SHAKE: A Computer Program for Earthquake Response Analysis of Horizontally Layered Sites," Rep. No. EERC 72–12, Earthquake Engineering Research Centre, University of California, Berkeley, December 1972.

40. Idriss, I. M., J. Lysmer, R. Hwang, and H. B. Seed, "QUAD-4: A Computer Program for Evaluating the Seismic Response of Soil-Structures by Variable Damping Finite Element Procedures," Rep. No. EERC 73-16, Earthquake Engineering Research Centre, University of California, Berkeley, July 1973.

41. Lysmer, J., T. Udaka, H. B. Seed, and R. Hwang, "LUSH: A Computer Program for Complex Response Analysis of Soil-Structure System," Rep. No. EERC 74-4, Earthquake Engineering Research Centre, University of California, Berkeley, 1974.

42. Lysmer, J., T. Udaka, C. F. Tsai, and H. B. Seed, "FLUSH: A Computer Program for Approximate 3-D Analysis of Soil-Structure Interaction Problems," Rep. No. EERC 75-30, Earthquake Engineering Research Centre, University of California, Berkeley, 1975.

43. Finn, W. D. Liam, K. W. Lee, and G. R. Martin, "An Effective Stress Model for Liquefaction," Preprint 2752, *Proceedings ASCE Annual Convention and Exposition*, Philadelphia, Pa., Sept. 22–Oct. 1, 1976; also Proc. Pap. 13008, *J. Geotech. Eng. Div. ASCE*, **103**(GT6):517–533 (June 1977).

44. Seed, H. B., and I. M. Idriss, "Soil Moduli and Damping Factors for Dynamic Response Analyses," Rep. No. EERC 70-10, Earthquake Engineering Research Centre, University of California, Berkeley, December 1970.

45. Ballard, R. F., Jr., and F. G. McLean, "Seismic Field Methods for in Situ Moduli," Misc. Pap. S-75-10, April, U.S. Army Engineer Waterways Experiment Station, Vicksburg, Miss., 1975.

46. Hardin, B. O., and V. P. Drnevich, "Shear Modulus and Damping in Soils: Measurement and Parameter Effects," Proc. Pap. 8977, *J. Soil Mech. Found. Div. ASCE*, **98**(SM6) (June 1972).

47. Zienkiewicz, O. C., *The Finite Element Method*, McGraw-Hill, London, 1977.

48. Lysmer, J., and L. A. Drake, "A Finite Element Method for Seismology," *Methods of Computational Physics*, Academic Press, New York, 1972, vol. II, chap. 6.

49. Waas, G., "Earth Vibration Effects and Abatement for Military Facilities—Analysis Method for Footing Vibrations through Layered Media," Tech. Rep. S71-14, U.S. Army Engineer Waterways Experiment Station, Vicksburg, Miss., September 1972; also a doctoral dissertation entitled "Linear Two-Dimensional Analysis of Soil Dynamics Problems in Semi-Infinite Layered Media," University of California, Berkeley, 1972.

50. Lee, K. L., and K. Chan, "Number of Equivalent Significant Cycles in Strong Motion Earthquake," *Proc. Int. Conf. Microzonation*, Seattle, October 1972, vol. II, pp. 609–627.

51. Seed, H. B., I. M. Idriss, F. Makdisi, and N. Banerjee, "Representation of Irregular Stress Time Histories by Equivalent Uniform Stress Series in Liquefaction Analyses," Rep. No. EERC 75-29, Earthquake Engineering Research Centre, University of California, Berkeley, October 1975.

52. Seed, H. B., K. L. Lee, I. M. Idriss, and F. Makdisi, "Analysis of the Slides in the San Fernando Dams During the Earthquake of February 9, 1971," Rep. No. EERC 73-2, Earthquake Engineering Research Centre, University of California, Berkeley, June 1973.

53. Seed, H. B., "Evaluation of Soil Liquefaction Effects on Level Ground during Earthquakes," Preprint 2752, *ASCE Annual Meeting*, Philadelphia, Pa., October 1976, pp. 1–104.

54. Kramer, R. W., R. W. Macdonald, D. A. Tiedmann, and A. Viksne, "Dynamic Analysis of Tsengwen Dam, Taiwan, Republic of China," U.S. Department of the Interior, Bureau of Reclamation, 1975.

55. Serff, N., H. B. Seed, F. I. Makdisi, and D. K. Chang, "Earthquake Induced Deformation of Earthdam," Rep. No. EERC 76-4, Earthquake Engineering Research Centre, University of California, Berkeley, 1976.

56. Seed, H. B., "Considerations in the Earthquake-Resistant Design of Earth and Rockfill Dams," *Geotechnique*, **29**(3):215-263 (1979).

57. Bingham, E. G., (ed.), "The August 1, 1975 Oroville Earthquake Investigations," Department of Water Resources, State of California, chap. V by William D. Hammond and Leslie F. Harder, 1975, pp. 187-289.

58. Makdisi, F. I., "Performance and Analysis of Earth Dams during Strong Earthquakes," Ph.D. dissertation Graduate Division in Engineering, University of California, Berkeley, 1976.

59. Yong, R. N., and K. Hon-Yim (eds.), *Proc. of Workshop on Limit Equilibrium, Plasticity and Generalized Stress-Strain in Geotechnical Engineering*, McGill University, Montreal, Quebec, ASCE, New York, May 28-30, 1980.

60. Masing, G., "Eigenspannungen und Verfestigung beim Messing," *Proc. 2d Int. Congr. Appl. Mech.*, Zurich, Switzerland, 1926.

61. Martin, G. R., W. D. Liam Finn, and H. B. Seed, "Fundamentals of Liquefaction under Cyclic Loading," Rep. No. 23, *Soil Mech. Ser.*, Department of Civil Engineering, University of British Columbia, Vancouver; also Proc. Pap. 11284, *J. Geotech. Eng. Div. ASCE*, **101**(GT5):423-438 (May 1975).

62. Lee, M. K. W., and W. D. Liam Finn, "DESRA-1: Program for the Dynamic Effective Stress Response Analysis of Soil Deposits Including Liquefaction Evaluation," Rep. No. 36, *Soil Mech. Ser.*, Department of Civil Engineering, Unviersity of British Columbia, Vancouver, B.C., 1975.

63. Lee, M. K. W., and W. D. Liam Finn, "DESRA-2: Dynamic Effective Stress Response Analysis of Soil Deposits with Energy Transmitting Boundary Including Assessment of Liquefaction Potential," Rep. No. 38, *Soil Mech. Ser.*, Department of Civil Engineering, University of British Columbia, Vancouver, B.C., 1978.

64. Finn, W. D. Liam, and S. K. Bhatia, "Verification of Non-Linear Effective Stress Model in Simple Shear," *Proc. ASCE Fall Meeting*, Hollywood-by-the-Sea, Florida, October 1980.

65. Finn, W. D. Liam, S. Iai, and K. Ishihara, "Performance of Artificial Offshore Islands under Wave and Earthquake Loading: Field Data Analyses," OTC Paper 4220, *Proc. of Offshore Technology Conference*, Houston, Texas, May 1983.

66. Iai, S., H. Tsuchida, and W. D. Liam Finn, "An Effective Stress Analysis of Liquefaction at Ishinomaki Port during the 1978 Miyagi-Ken-Oki Earthquake," *Report of the Port and Harbour Research Institute*, vol. 24, no. 2, June 1985.

67. Streeter, V. L., E. B. Wylie, and F. E. Richart, "Soil Motion Computations by Characteristics Method," *J. Geotech. Eng. Div. ASCE*, **100**(GT3):247-263 (March 1974).

68. Martin, P. P., *Non-Linear Methods for Dynamic Analysis of Ground Response*, Ph.D. Dissertation, Department of Civil Engineering, University of California, Berkeley, California (1975).

69. Martin, P. P., and H. B. Seed, "Simplified Procedure for Effective Stress Analysis of Ground Response," Proc. Paper 14659, *J. Geotech. Eng. Div. ASCE*, **105**(GT6):739-758 (June 1979).

70. Siddharthan, R., and W. D. Liam Finn, "TARA: Two-Dimensional Non-Linear Static and Dynamic Response Analysis," Report to Ertec Western, Inc., Long Beach, California, 1981, pp. 1-168.

71. Finn, W. D. Liam, M. Yogendrakumar, N. Yoshida, and H. Yoshida, *TARA-3: A Program for Non-Linear Static and Dynamic Effective Stress Analysis*, Soil Dynamics Group, University of British Columbia, Vancouver, B.C., 1986.

72. Goodman, R. E., R. L. Taylor, and T. L. Brekke, "A Model for the Mechanics of Jointed Rock," *J. Soil Mech. and Foundation Div. ASCE*, **94**(SM3):637-659 (March 1968).

73. Finn, W. D. Liam, R. Siddharthan, F. Lee, and A. N. Schofield, "Seismic Response of Offshore Drilling Islands in a Centrifuge Including Soil-Structure Interaction," OTC Paper 4693, *Proc. 16th Annual Offshore Technology Conf.*, Houston, Texas, 1984.

74. Finn, W. D. Liam, R. S. Steedman, M. Yogendrakumar, and R. H. Ledbetter, "Seismic Response of Gravity Structures in a Centrifuge," OTC Paper 4885, *Proc. 17th Annual Offshore Technology Conf.*, Houston, Texas, 1985, 389–394.

75. Finn, W. D. Liam, R. Siddharthan, and R. H. Ledbetter, "Soil-Structure Interaction during Earthquakes," *Proc. 11th Int. Conf. of the Int. Soc. of Soil Mechanics and Foundation Engineers*, San Francisco, California, August 11–14, 1985.

76. Finn, W. D. Liam, "Dynamic Effective Stress Response of Soil Structures: Theory and Centrifugal Model Studies," *Proc. 5th Int. Conf. on Numer. Meth. in Geomechanics*, Nagoya, Japan, 1985, vol. 1, pp. 35–46.

77. Finn, W. D. Liam, "Estimating Liquefaction Potential by Analysis," *Proc., 2d Int. Conf. On Constitutive Laws for Engineering Materials*, University of Arizona, Tucson, Arizona, Jan. 5–10, 1987.

78. Finn, W. D. Liam, J. Pickering, and P. L. Bransby, "Sand Liquefaction in Triaxial and Simple Shear Test," Proc. Paper 8039, *J. Soil Mech. and Foundation Div. ASCE*, 97(SM4):639–659 (April 1971).

79. Prevost, J. H., "Anisotropic Undrained Stress-Strain Behaviour of Clays," Proc. Paper 13942, *J. Geotech. Eng. Div. ASCE*, 104(GT8):1075–1090 (August 1978).

80. Prevost, J. H., "Mathematical Modelling of Soil Stress-Strain Strength Behaviour," *Proc. 3d Int. Conf. Numer. Meth. Geomech.*, Aachen, Germany, April 2–6, 1979, pp. 347–361.

81. Mroz, Z., V. A. Narris, and O. C. Zienkiewicz, "Application of an Anisotropic Hardening Model in the Analysis of Elastoplastic Deformation of Soils," *Geotechnique*, 29(1):1–34 (1979).

82. Dafalias, Y. F., and L. R. Herrmann, "A Boundary Surface Soil Plasticity Model," *Proc. Int. Symp. Soils under Cyclic and Transient Loading*, Swansea, Wales, Jan. 7–11, 1980, vol. 1, pp. 335–345.

83. Finn, W. D. Liam, and G. R. Martin, "Soil as an Anisotropic Kinematic Hardening Solid," *Proc. ASCE Fall Meeting*, Hollywood-by-the-Sea, Florida, October 1980.

84. Prevost, J. H., *DYNAFLOW—A Nonlinear Transient Finite Element Analysis Program*, Rep. No. 81-SM-1, Princeton University, Princeton, N.J., January 1981.

85. Ferritto, J. M., and R. T. Nakamoto, *A Summary of the Prevost Effective Stress Soil Model*, Technical Report R-913, Naval Civil Engineering Laboratory, Port Hueneme, California, October 1984.

86. Prevost, J. H., A. M. Abdel-Ghaffar, and S. J. Lacy, "Nonlinear Dynamic Analyses of an Earth Dam," *J. Geotech. Eng. Div. ASCE*, 111(GT7):882–897 (July 1985).

87. Prevost, J. H., B. Cuny, T. J. R. Hughes, and R. F. Scott, "Offshore Gravity Structures: Analysis," *J. Geotech. Eng. Div. ASCE*, 107(GT2):143–165 (February 1981).

88. Biot, M. A., "General Theory of Three-Dimensional Consolidation," *J. Applied Physics*, 12:155, 1941.

89. Finn, W. D. Liam, *Review of Earthquake Criteria to the Balder Plateform*, Rep. to Exxon Production Research Co., Houston, Texas, 1981.

90. Finn, W. D. Liam, *Seismic Response of the Pescadeo B-1 Site*, Rep. to Exxon Production Research Co., Houston, Texas 1981.

91. Finn, W. D. Liam, *Seismic Response of Koakoak Tanker Island*, Rep. to Dome Petroleum Ltd., Calgary, Alberta, 1982.

92. Finn, W. D. Liam, *Site Specific Response Spectra for LNG Tank Site*, Rep. to Acres International Ltd., Toronto, 1985.

93. Finn, W. D. Liam, *Response of Gravity Platform to Wave and Earthquake Loading*, Rep. to Exxon Production Research Co., Houston, Texas, 1985.

94. Finn, W. D. Liam, *Preliminary Seismic Response Studies of Lornex Dam*, Rep. to Klohn Leonoff Consultants, Vancouver, B.C., 1986.

95. Huyakorn, P. S., and G. F. Pinder, *Computational Methods in Subsurface Flow*, Academic Press, New York, 1983.

96. Huyakorn, P. S., and G. F. Pinder, "Solution of Two-Phase Flow Using a New Finite Element Technique," in *Proceedings of the International Conference on Numerical Modeling*," University of Southampton, Southampton, 1977, pp. 375–390.

# CHAPTER 4
# AEROMECHANICS

This chapter is concerned with general discussions of compressible flows, transonics and shock waves, and atmospheric convection and diffusion. Applications of finite elements to aerodynamics began as an extension to fluid mechanics and as a result of knowledge achieved in finite-difference studies such as upwinding, artificial viscosity, artificial compressibility, shock capturing and shock fitting, etc. [1–4]. The literature on finite elements in compressible flows appeared during the 1970s [5–9], and extensive studies on transonics have been undertaken in recent years [10–29].

In most of the applications to aerodynamics, an inviscid compressible flow would be applicable. A comprehensive treatment of subsonic aerodynamics is presented in Ref. [9]. In dealing with compressible viscous flows such as in viscous shear layers and turbulence, a general method of solution is reported in Ref. [8]. A complete system of conservation equations is used in this approach. These topics are presented in Secs. 4.1 and 4.2.

For high-speed flows, shock waves are encountered in general, and there are various schemes which have been suggested to cope with shock discontinuities. These techniques are discussed in Secs. 4.3 to 4.8 by various authors, as briefly outlined below.

Bristeau, Glowinski, Periaux, Perrier, Pironneau, and Poirier present least-square finite-element formulations and solutions by conjugate gradients. These allow implementation of the entropy condition by upwinding the density in order to eliminate unphysical (expansion) shocks. The program has been used to simulate a trijet engine AMD/BA Falcon 50 with very impressive results. See Sec. 4.3 for details.

In Sec. 4.4, Chung discusses the discontinuous-function method. To model the shock discontinuity, quadratic isoparametric elements are used, with each element divided into four quadrants such that independent interpolations of the velocity potential are constructed for each quadrant. The shock discontinuity is allowed to develop freely at the center of the element as a result of the Lagrange multiplier matrix satisfying the Rankine–Hugoniot conditions. Although this method allows development of perfect shocks (without smearing), the computational time appears to be excessive.

Eberle presents the artificial compression method and solution by successive-line overrelaxation techniques. In this process, the mass flux is calculated at a point upstream of the central point under consideration via linear Taylor expansions. With the gradual grid refinement the number of iterations can be reduced significantly. This is particularly useful for modeling of the wing-body combination. More details are discussed in Sec. 4.5.

In Sec. 4.6, Ecer and Akay summarize their combined shock-capturing and shock-fitting techniques which expedite convergence of the shock calculations. To obtain a steady-state solution, a pseudo-unsteady formulation is combined with a damping matrix of the pseudo-time-dependent problem constructed for numerical stability.

Hafez and Habashi discuss the mixed-type iterative algorithm in Sec. 4.7. They show finite-element applications analogous to the finite-difference approach in which artificial compressibility is utilized for convergence. Discussions of rotational flow in terms of the stream function are also presented in this section.

Finally, in Sec. 4.8 Cullen presents convection and diffusion in the atmosphere [30–32], a subject which has not attracted as much attention as other areas of aeromechanics. He concludes that the finite-element method is less liable to nonlinear instability than finite-difference schemes. Although the fields tend to contain more small-scale roughness than in finite-difference models, it does not grow so fast after it appears. Cullen further comments that conclusions are not yet clear for dispersion models, since the choice of mathematical model and collection of data are much greater causes of error than the finite-element technique under consideration.

## 4.1 COMPRESSIBLE INVISCID FLOWS

This section considers the finite-element solution of subsonic flows. The governing equation is of elliptic type, and there is indeed an extremum principle. Existence and uniqueness of the solution are therefore guaranteed under rather general conditions. For reviews of this field see Shen [33–35] and Chung [36]. Emphasis here is directed toward field solvers for nonlinear problems.

### 4.1A Linearized Equations

For steady two-dimensional subsonic flows, the Prandtl-Glauert equation is a good approximation. In cartesian coordinates

$$(1 - M_\infty^2)\phi'_{xx} + \phi'_{yy} = 0 \tag{4.1a}$$

or

$$(1 - M_\infty^2)\psi'_{xx} + \psi'_{yy} = 0 \tag{4.1b}$$

where $\phi'$ is the perturbation potential, $\psi'$ the perturbation stream function, and $M_\infty$ the free-stream Mach number. The stream-function formulation calls for a Dirichlet boundary condition, namely, that the airfoil is a streamline; while the potential requires a Neumann boundary condition, namely, that no flux crosses the solid body. In both formulations a Kutta condition is necessary for lifting cases. In the far field the perturbation velocities must vanish.

**The Laplace Equation** Equations (4.1$a$) and (4.1$b$) can be recast in the "incompressible" form, upon a simple transformation of coordinates, as

$$\phi_{xx} + \phi_{yy} = 0 \qquad (4.2a)$$

$$\psi_{xx} - \psi_{yy} = 0 \qquad (4.2b)$$

A Green's function approach is usually used to solve the linear equations (4.2$a$) or (4.2$b$), for example,

$$\phi = \frac{1}{2\pi} \iint_{\partial\Omega} \left( \phi \frac{\partial G}{\partial n} - \frac{\partial \phi}{\partial n} \right) ds \qquad (4.3)$$

where $G$ is Green's function (source) and $\partial\Omega$ is the boundary (surface) of the airfoil. The relation of Green's function to singularity methods in two- and three-dimensional flows is well known [37]. A discretization of the integral equation (4.3) leads to a full matrix in terms of the unknown nodal values on the boundary line. Such a matrix is diagonally dominant and is usually inverted by gaussian elimination.

Alternatively, Eqs. (4.2$a$) and (4.2$b$) can be replaced by a variational formulation, namely (for the potential),

$$\min_{\phi} I = \iint_{\Omega} (\phi_x^2 + \phi_y^2) \, dx \, dy \qquad (4.4)$$

Upon finite-element discretization, Eq. (4.4) leads to a large, sparse-matrix equation which can be solved iteratively. In this case, the Galerkin–weighted-residual method will lead to the same matrix equation, as can be easily checked by applying the Gauss divergence theorem to (4.2$a$):

$$\iint_{\Omega} W(\phi_{xx} + \phi_{yy}) \, dx \, dy = 0 \qquad (4.5)$$

where $W$ is a weight function, identical to the shape function $N$ used for $\phi$-representation. In general, the resulting linear algebraic equations are of the form $\mathbf{K}\phi = \mathbf{f}$, where a typical element of the matrix $\mathbf{K}$ and vector $\mathbf{f}$ is

$$k_{ij} = \iint_{\Omega} \left( \frac{\partial N_i}{\partial x} \frac{\partial N_j}{\partial x} + \frac{\partial N_i}{\partial y} \frac{\partial N_j}{\partial y} \right) dx \, dy \qquad (4.6a)$$

$$f_i = \oint_c N_i \left( \frac{\partial \phi}{\partial n} \right) dc \qquad (4.6b)$$

For more details see Chung [36].

***Iterative Methods*** For large systems of equations direct methods are not efficient. Iterative methods exploiting some properties of the sparse matrix are recommended. In the present case, the matrix is symmetric and positive-definite, with a small bandwidth. Successive overrelaxation is applicable, but the rate of convergence depends on the choice of an optimum relaxation parameter. On the other hand, the conjugate-gradient method [38] is preferred since no estimation of any parameter is needed. Recently, improvement of the rate of convergence by several orders of magnitude has been achieved using approximate factorization procedures such as preconditioning. An approximate $LL^T$ which preserves the zero pattern of the original matrix has proved very efficient [39, 40]. Other preconditioning techniques, e.g., symmetric successive overrelaxation, are also useful. Another novel method is the multigrid method [41]. The only disadvantage is the programming complexity, especially if nonrectangular elements are used.

***The Poisson Equation*** If there is a source (vorticity) distribution in the field, Eqs. (4.2$a$) and (4.2$b$) become

$$\phi_{xx} + \phi_{yy} = S(x, y) \tag{4.7$a$}$$

$$\psi_{xx} + \psi_{yy} = -\omega(x, y) \tag{4.7$b$}$$

A field discretization is necessary even if Green's function (boundary-element method) is used. For the field solvers, the source $S$ or vortex $\omega$ will affect only the right-hand-side term of the matrix equation

$$f_i = \oint_c N_i \left( \frac{\partial \psi}{\partial n} \right) dc - \iint_\Omega N_i \omega \, dx \, dy \tag{4.7$c$}$$

The same comments made for the Laplace equation, regarding iterative methods, also apply to the Poisson equation.

It is obvious that if $S$ is not identically zero, a stream function cannot be easily defined [42]. Similarly, if $\omega$ does not vanish everywhere, the potential is not easily defined. The case where both $S$ and $\omega$ do not vanish will be discussed later.

## 4.1B Nonlinear Equations

***Homogeneous Equations*** Good results [43, 44] have been obtained in solving the nonlinear compressible equations

$$(\rho \Phi_x)_x + (\rho \Phi_y)_y = 0 \tag{4.8$a$}$$

or

$$\left( \frac{\Psi_x}{\rho} \right)_x + \left( \frac{\Psi_y}{\rho} \right)_y = 0 \tag{4.8$b$}$$

where

$$\rho = \left[ 1 - \frac{\gamma - 1}{2} (u^2 + v^2 - 1) \right]^{1/(\gamma - 1)} \tag{4.8$c$}$$

and

$$u = \Phi_x = \frac{\Psi_y}{\rho} \qquad v = \Phi_y = \frac{-\Psi_x}{\rho} \tag{4.8$d$}$$

Note that $\rho$ is a unique function of the speed $q^2 = u^2 + v^2$, but there are two values of $\rho$ for every mass flux $(\Psi_x^2 + \Psi_y^2)$; one corresponds to subsonic and the other to supersonic flow, with a square-root singularity in the density-mass flux relationship at the sonic speed. This classical difficulty is discussed in Ref. [45].

As long as the flow is purely subsonic, the problem is well-defined and Eq. (4.8a) or (4.8b) is elliptic. An extremum principle due to Bateman [43] states

$$\min_{\Phi} I = \int\int_{\Omega} p \, d\Omega \tag{4.9}$$

where

$$p = \frac{\rho^{\gamma}}{M_{\infty}^2}$$

Alternatively, $I$ can be replaced by a function of two variables $\Phi$ and $\rho$:

$$\max I(\Phi, \rho) = \int\int_{\Omega} [\rho(\Phi_x^2 + \Phi_y^2) + F(\rho)] \, d\Omega \tag{4.10a}$$

such that $I_{\Phi} = 0$ gives

$$(\rho\Phi_x)_x + (\rho\Phi_y)_y = 0 \tag{4.10b}$$

while $I_{\rho} = 0$ gives

$$\rho = \Phi_x^2 + \Phi_y^2 + F'(\rho) \tag{4.10c}$$

Hence $F(\rho)$ is chosen such that (4.10c) is consistent with Bernoulli's equation.

Similarly, for the stream-function formulation, Lin and Rubinov [46] show that the following functional has an extremum for subsonic flows:

$$\max I(\Psi, \rho) = \int\int_{\Omega} \left( C\rho - \frac{\rho^{\gamma}}{\gamma - 1} + \frac{1}{2} \frac{\Psi_x^2 + \Psi_y^2}{\rho^2} \right) d\Omega \tag{4.11a}$$

such that $I_{\Psi} = 0$ gives

$$\left(\frac{\Psi_x}{\rho}\right)_x + \left(\frac{\Psi_y}{\rho}\right)_y = 0 \tag{4.11b}$$

while $I_{\rho} = 0$ gives

$$C + \frac{\gamma\rho^{\gamma-1}}{\gamma - 1} - \frac{1}{2}\frac{\Psi_x^2 + \Psi_y^2}{\rho^2} = 0 \tag{4.11c}$$

Both $\Phi$- and $\Psi$-problems are nonlinear. Solutions are obtained by iteration; therefore the complete procedure consists of outer and inner iterations. Various outer-iteration strategies are discussed below.

### Outer Iterations

*Poisson Iteration*   The nonlinear equation is recast in the form

$$\Phi_{xx}^{n+1} + \Phi_{yy}^{n+1} = \frac{-(\rho_x^n\Phi_x^n + \rho_y^n\Phi_y^n)}{\rho^n} \tag{4.12a}$$

and

$$\Psi_{xx}^{n+1} + \Psi_{yy}^{n+1} = -\rho \left[ \Psi_x^n\left(\frac{1}{\rho^n}\right)_x + \Psi_y^n\left(\frac{1}{\rho^n}\right)_y \right] \tag{4.12b}$$

or, more generally,          $$\rho \mathbf{L} \delta \Phi = -\alpha \mathbf{R}^n \qquad \delta \Phi = \Phi^{n+1} - \Phi^n \tag{4.13a}$$

and                          $$\frac{1}{\rho} \mathbf{L} \delta \Psi = -\alpha \mathbf{R}^n \qquad \delta \Psi = \Psi^{n+1} - \Psi^n \tag{4.13b}$$

where $\mathbf{L}$ is the laplacian operator, $\mathbf{R}$ is the residual, and $\alpha$ is the acceleration parameter. Convergence is rapid as long as $\mathbf{L}$ (incompressible operator) is a good approximation to the nonlinear compressible operator. A scaled iteration using the Prandtl–Glauert factor is useful, namely,

$$\rho_\infty [(1 - M_\infty^2) \partial_{xx} + \partial_{yy}] \delta \Phi = -\alpha \mathbf{R}^n \tag{4.14a}$$

or

$$\frac{1}{\rho_\infty (1 - M_\infty^2)} [(1 - M_\infty^2) \partial_{xx} + \partial_{yy}] \delta \Psi = -\alpha \mathbf{R}^n \tag{4.14b}$$

The operator on the left-hand side is still independent of iteration.

***Taylor Iteration, Conservative Form*** A slightly different procedure, where the left-hand-side operator changes from iteration to iteration is

$$(\rho^n \Phi_x^{n+1})_x + (\rho^n \Phi_y^{n+1})_y = 0 \qquad \text{or} \qquad (\rho^n \delta \Phi_x)_x + (\rho^n \delta \Phi_y)_y = -\alpha R(\Phi^n) \tag{4.15a}$$

$$\left(\frac{\Psi_x^{n+1}}{\rho^n}\right)_x + \left(\frac{\Psi_y^{n+1}}{\rho^n}\right)_y = 0 \qquad \text{or} \qquad \left(\frac{\delta \Psi_x}{\rho^n}\right)_x + \left(\frac{\delta \Psi_y}{\rho^n}\right)_y = -\alpha R(\Psi^n) \tag{4.15b}$$

The matrix resulting from finite-element discretization has to be reassembled if the coefficients are updated at every iteration.

***Taylor Iteration, Nonconservative Form*** To account for the nonlinear compressibility effects in the left-hand-side operator, the equation can be written in nonconservative form, namely,

$$\rho^n \left[ \left(1 - \frac{u^2}{a^2}\right) \Phi_{xx}^{n+1} - 2\frac{uv}{a^2} \Phi_{xy}^{n+1} + \left(1 - \frac{v^2}{a^2}\right) \Phi_{yy}^{n+1} \right] = 0 \tag{4.16a}$$

and

$$\frac{1}{(1 - M^2)^n \rho^n} \left[ \left(1 - \frac{u^2}{a^2}\right) \Psi_{xx}^{n+1} - 2\frac{uv}{a^2} \Psi_{xy}^{n+1} + \left(1 - \frac{v^2}{a^2}\right) \Psi_{yy}^{n+1} \right] = 0 \tag{4.16b}$$

where the coefficients are evaluated on the basis of the previous iteration.

　　More work is done in every iteration, but the number of iterations required for convergence to a certain tolerance (hence the total computational effort) is less.

***Local Linearization Method*** In the local linearization [43, 47, 48] local coordinates $(\xi_e, \eta_e)$ are defined in each element, at each iteration, by the local velocity direction $(V_e)$ and the normal to it. Therefore

$$V_e^{(n+1)} = V_e^{(n)} + u'(\xi_e, \eta_e) \tag{4.17}$$

or

$$\Phi = V_e \xi_e + \Phi' \tag{4.18}$$

The perturbation potential is governed by

$$\rho_e \left[ (1 - M_e^2) \frac{\partial^2 \Phi'}{\partial \xi_e^2} + \frac{\partial^2 \Phi'}{\partial \eta_e^2} \right] = 0 \qquad (4.19)$$

The applicable variational integral can be written, after some manipulations, as

$$\delta I(\Phi) = \tfrac{1}{2}\delta \sum_{e=1}^{N} \rho_e \int\!\!\int_{A_e} [(1 - M_e^2)\Phi_{\xi_e}^2 + \Phi_{\eta_e}^2 + 2V_e M_e^2 \Phi_{\xi_e}] \, d\xi_e \, d\eta_e - \oint_c \rho \delta \Phi \left(\frac{\partial \Phi}{\partial n}\right) dc \qquad (4.20)$$

providing a basis for an iterative procedure where at each step new values of $V_e$, $M_e$, $\rho_e$ as well as new $(\xi_e, \eta_e)$-directions are obtained. The local linearization method is also applicable to the stream-function formulation; in that case the variational integral is

$$\delta I(\Psi) = \tfrac{1}{2}\delta \sum_{e=1}^{N} \frac{1}{\rho_e} \int\!\!\int_{A_e} [(1 - M_e^2)\Psi_{\xi_e}^2 + \Psi_{\eta_e}^2] \, d\xi_e \, d\eta_e - \oint_c \frac{1}{\rho} \delta \Psi \left(\frac{\partial \Psi}{\partial n}\right) dc \qquad (4.21)$$

Unlike the Taylor iteration for the nonconservative form, the local linearization can be used with constant-velocity triangular elements, as is clear from Eqs. (4.20) and (4.21).

**Newton's Method**   To guarantee second-order convergence, the jacobian of the nonlinear operator is calculated. At each iteration a linear problem, with variable coefficients, is solved:

$$J(\Phi^n)\delta\Phi = -R(\Phi^n) \qquad (4.22a)$$

and
$$J(\Psi^n)\delta\Psi = -R(\Psi^n) \qquad (4.22b)$$

where $J(\Phi^n)$ is

$$J(\Phi^n) = \left[ \rho\left(1 - \frac{u^2}{a^2}\right)\partial_x - \frac{\rho u v}{a^2}\partial_y \right]_x + \left[ \rho\left(1 - \frac{v^2}{a^2}\right)\partial_y - \frac{\rho u v}{a^2}\partial_x \right]_y \qquad (4.23a)$$

$$J(\Psi^n) = \left[ \frac{1}{\rho(1 - M^2)}\left(1 - \frac{u^2}{a^2}\right)\partial_x - \frac{u v}{\rho(1 - M^2)a^2}\partial_y \right]_x$$

$$+ \left[ \frac{1}{\rho(1 - M^2)}\left(1 - \frac{v^2}{a^2}\right)\partial_y - \frac{u v}{\rho(1 - M^2)a^2}\partial_x \right]_y \qquad (4.23b)$$

The difficulty in the stream-function formulation as $M$ approaches unity is pronounced in Eq. (4.23b). Equation (4.22) is complicated, but usually very few iterations are required. It is obvious that Poisson and Taylor methods are degenerate cases of Eq. (4.23).

**Nonhomogeneous Equations**   If there are sources, $S$, or vorticity, $\omega$, distributions in the field, the nonlinear compressible-flow equations become

$$(\rho u)_x + (\rho v)_y = S \qquad (4.24)$$

$$u_y - v_x = -\omega \qquad (4.25)$$

If $S = 0$, a stream function exists, while if $\omega = 0$, a potential function exists and Eqs. (4.24) and (4.25) are replaced by a single second-order, nonlinear, nonhomogeneous equation. For the general case when both $S$ and $\omega$ do not vanish the following methods are used.

***Velocity-Splitting Method***   The velocity is decomposed into irrotational and rotational parts, namely,

$$u = \Phi_x + u' \qquad v = \Phi_y + v' \tag{4.26}$$

Hence Eqs. (4.24) and (4.25) become

$$(\rho\Phi_x)_x + (\rho\Phi_y)_y = -(\rho u')_x - (\rho v')_y + S \tag{4.27}$$

$$u'_y - v'_x = -\omega \tag{4.28}$$

Furthermore, $u'$ and $v'$ can be chosen such that

$$u' = \psi'_y \qquad v' = -\psi'_x \tag{4.29}$$

Hence, Eq. (4.28) becomes $\qquad \psi'_{xx} + \psi'_{yy} = -\omega \tag{4.30}$

Consistent boundary conditions for $\Phi$ and $\psi'$ are $\Phi_n = 0$ and $\psi' = $ constant on the airfoil. A similar approach (vector potential) has been used in Ref. [49] for 3D flows in turbomachines.

***Weighted Least Squares***   Equations (4.24) and (4.25) can be written in the form

$$L\begin{pmatrix} u \\ v \end{pmatrix} = \begin{pmatrix} S \\ -\omega \end{pmatrix} \tag{4.31}$$

Define $\bar{\phi}$, $\bar{\varphi}$ such that

$$QL^*\begin{pmatrix} \bar{\Phi} \\ \bar{\psi} \end{pmatrix} = \begin{pmatrix} u \\ v \end{pmatrix}$$

where

$$Q = \begin{pmatrix} \dfrac{1}{\rho} & 0 \\ 0 & \dfrac{1}{\rho} \end{pmatrix}$$

that is, $\qquad -\rho\bar{\Phi}_x - \bar{\psi}_y = \rho u \qquad -\rho\bar{\Phi}_y + \bar{\psi}_x = \rho v \tag{4.32}$

Hence, Eqs. (4.24) and (4.25) become

$$LQL^*\begin{pmatrix} \bar{\Phi} \\ \bar{\psi} \end{pmatrix} = \begin{pmatrix} S \\ -\omega \end{pmatrix}$$

or

$$(\rho\bar{\Phi}_x)_x + (\rho\bar{\Phi}_y)_y = -S$$

$$\left(\frac{\bar{\psi}_x}{\rho}\right)_x + \left(\frac{\bar{\psi}_y}{\rho}\right)_y = +\omega \tag{4.33}$$

In this choice, both $\bar{\Phi}$ and $\bar{\psi}$ are governed by nonlinear equations similar to the potential and the stream-function equations. Both Eqs. (4.30) and (4.33) are suitable for finite-element discretization. Other splitting methods, for example, multiplicative correction, where the velocity is represented by $\vec{q} = \lambda\nabla\Phi$, leads to $(\lambda\Phi_x)_y - (\lambda\Phi_y)_x = -\omega$, where application of standard finite-elements is not straightforward.

### 4.1c  Euler Equations

The general governing equations of inviscid flows are the continuity, the momentum, and the energy equations. A least-square method to solve the primitive-variable equations is discussed in Refs. [50–52]. Another alternative is the Clebsch representation of the velocity field ($\vec{q} = \lambda\nabla\mu - \nabla\Phi$), which results in Hamilton's system for the four state variables $\Phi$, $\rho$, $\mu$, and $\rho\lambda$, as discussed in Ref. [53]. However, for steady two-dimensional (and axisymmetric) subsonic flows, the Euler equations can be replaced by stream-function and vorticity equations [45]. Two stream functions are needed for three-dimensional calculations.

### 4.1d  Numerical Examples

The finite-element discretization and the solution of incompressible flow around a Joukowsky airfoil, using a stream-function formulation and constant-velocity triangular elements, are given in Figs. 4.1 and 4.2. The result is in good agreement with theory. The surface Mach number distribution and the Mach number contours of flow over a NACA 0012 airfoil at $M_\infty = 0.72$ are shown in Figs. 4.3 and 4.4. These calculations have been obtained using Poisson and Taylor iterations, as well as local-linearization outer iterations with triangular elements, and are compared to published results [54]. It is found that the local-linearization procedure is generally fastest. The airfoil is represented by 20 points, and only four layers of elements

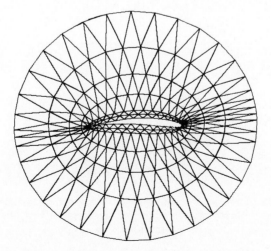

**FIG. 4.1**  Automated finite-element mesh generation around a Joukowsky airfoil.

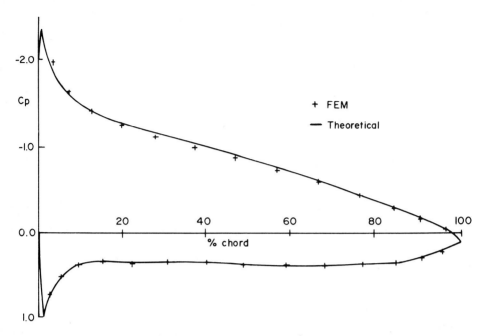

**FIG. 4.2** FEM results for incompressible flow over a Joukowsky airfoil (5% camber, 10% thickness, 5° angle of attack).

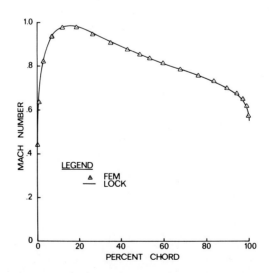

**FIG. 4.3** FEM result for compressible flow over a NACA 0012 airfoil at $M_\infty = 0.72$; triangular elements, polar coordinates.

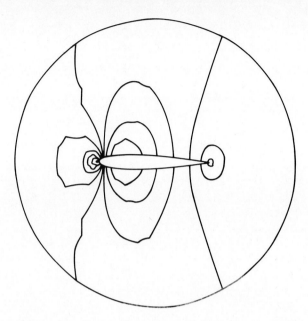

**FIG. 4.4**  Mach number contours for flow over NACA 0012
airfoil at $M_\infty = 0.72$

are used in the finite-element discretization. Although simple triangular elements are used,
methods are demonstrated in Refs. [43, 48, 55] for an effective representation of the far field
and for describing the geometry of the triangular elements in polar coordinates, for arbitrary
geometries. These two effects combined help reduce the solution-domain size and improve
accuracy considerably.

The rate of convergence of some iterative procedures is given in Fig. 4.5 on the basis of
bilinear elements. The zebroid algorithm is a horizontal successive-line overrelaxation (SLOR)
on alternate lines, while the first- and second-degree solvers are variants of the Poisson or
Taylor schemes. These schemes are detailed in Refs. [45, 56]. It should be mentioned that
Poisson, Taylor, and local-linearization iterative procedures do not converge for transonic
flows and indeed are restricted to subsonic Mach numbers. Finally, the same finite-element
techniques described in this chapter have also found wide application in turbomachinery
problems (see Sec. 2.8 in Part 3).

## 4.1E  Concluding Remarks

Calculations of steady, two-dimensional, subsonic flows by finite elements are reviewed.
Formulations in terms of potential and stream functions are studied. Iterative procedures for
the nonlinear equations are discussed. While the stream-function formulation has the advantage of using Dirichlet boundary conditions and representing rotational flows, the potential
function is used for three-dimensional and unsteady flows.

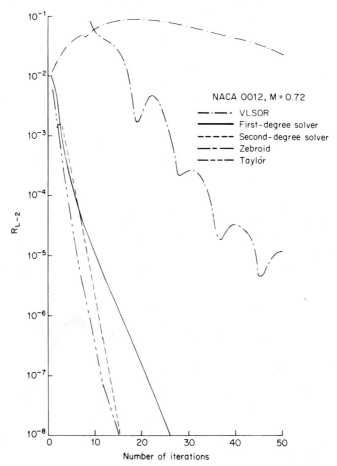

**FIG. 4.5**   Rate of convergence of several iterative procedures; bilinear element.

## 4.2 COMPRESSIBLE VISCOUS FLOWS

### 4.2A Finite Elements for Compressible Viscous Flows

In aerodynamics, one may safely assume that the field is compressible but inviscid. However, this assumption may not hold true when viscous shear layers or turbulence are of major concern. With this in mind, a system of governing equations containing all variables such as velocity, density, temperature, and pressure can be solved [57, 58].

The following conservation laws and equation of state apply:

$$\rho\frac{\partial \mathbf{u}}{\partial t} + \rho(\mathbf{u}\cdot\boldsymbol{\nabla})\mathbf{u} - \frac{\partial \sigma_{ij}}{\partial x_j}\mathbf{i}_i = 0 \tag{4.34}$$

$$\frac{\partial \rho}{\partial t} + \boldsymbol{\nabla}\cdot(\rho\mathbf{u}) = 0 \tag{4.35}$$

$$\rho \frac{\partial \varepsilon}{\partial t} + \rho (\mathbf{u} \cdot \mathbf{\nabla}) \varepsilon - \sigma_{ij} d_{ij} - \mathbf{\nabla} \cdot \mathbf{q} - Q = 0 \tag{4.36}$$

$$p = \rho R T \tag{4.37}$$

The finite-element approximations for the velocity $\mathbf{u}$, density $\rho$, temperature $T$, and pressure $p$, and use of the Galerkin approach and semidiscrete time-dependent method, lead to

$$\begin{bmatrix} \hat{A}_{\alpha\beta ij} & 0 & 0 & C_{\alpha i\beta} \\ 0 & \hat{B}_{\alpha\beta} & 0 & 0 \\ \hat{D}_{\alpha\beta} & 0 & \hat{L}_{\alpha\beta} & \hat{C}_{\alpha\beta} \\ 0 & 0 & 0 & E_{\alpha\beta} \end{bmatrix} \begin{bmatrix} V_{\beta j} \\ \rho_{\beta} \\ T_{\beta} \\ P_{\beta} \end{bmatrix}^{(n+1)} = \begin{bmatrix} \Delta t E_{\alpha i} \\ \Delta t G_{\alpha} \\ \Delta t Q_{\alpha} \\ F_{\alpha} \end{bmatrix}^{(n+1)} + \begin{bmatrix} \hat{E}_{\alpha i} \\ \hat{G}_{\alpha} \\ \hat{Q}_{\alpha} \\ 0 \end{bmatrix}^{(n)} \tag{4.38}$$

where $(n+1)$ indicates the unknown vector to be determined at the $(n+1)^{\text{th}}$ time step, marching in time until desired time increments are advanced. Note that a nonlinear equation solver such as Newton–Raphson techniques may be used for convergence within each time step. A compressible, thermal boundary-layer problem behind the shock wave was solved, using Eq. (4.38). Definitions of the notations used in Eqs. (4.34) to (4.38) above and further details of the approach are found in Refs. [57, 58].

# 4.3 TRANSONIC FLOW AND SHOCK WAVES: LEAST-SQUARES AND CONJUGATE-GRADIENT METHODS

This section describes a finite-element method to simulate transonic potential flows for compressible inviscid fluids modeled by the so-called full-potential equation, using the approach from Refs. [59, 60]. For other finite-element methods for transonic potential flows see, for example, Refs. [61–63]. Finite-difference methods have been extensively used for solving transonic-potential-flow problems; see references cited in Ref. [59].

## 4.3A The Physical Problem

The numerical simulation of transonic potential flows for compressible inviscid fluids is a nontrivial problem since:

1. The equations governing these flows are nonlinear and of changing type (elliptic in the subsonic-flow region, hyperbolic in the supersonic one);

2. Shocks may exist in these flows corresponding to discontinuities of velocity, pressure, and density; and

3. An entropy condition must be included in order to eliminate rarefaction shocks since they are not physical.

It is supposed that the fluids are compressible and inviscid and that their flows are potential and therefore quasi-isentropic, with weak shocks only. This is only an approximation since usually the flow is no longer potential after a shock (cf. Ref. [64]). For flows past bodies it is supposed that these bodies are sufficiently slender and parallel to the main flow in order not to create a wake in the outflow.

## 4.3B Mathematical Formulation

**Governing Equations**    If $\Omega$ is the flow region and $\Gamma$ its boundary, it follows from e.g., Ref. [64], that the flow is governed by

$$\nabla \cdot \rho\mathbf{u} = 0 \qquad (\textit{continuity equation}) \tag{4.39}$$

$$\rho = \rho_0\left(1 - \frac{\gamma-1}{\gamma+1}\frac{|\mathbf{u}^2|}{c_*^2}\right)^{1/(\gamma-1)} \tag{4.40}$$

$$\mathbf{u} = \nabla\phi \tag{4.41}$$

where $\phi$ is the velocity potential, $\rho$ is the density of the fluid, $\gamma$ is the ratio of specific heats ($\gamma = 1.4$ in air), and $c_*$ is the critical velocity.

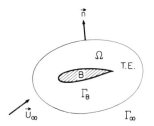

**FIG. 4.6**    Flow around an arbitrary airfoil.
T.E. = trailing edge.

**Boundary Conditions**    For an airfoil $B$ (see Fig. 4.6) the flow is assumed to be uniform on $\Gamma_\infty$ and tangential at $\Gamma_B$. One then has

$$\frac{\partial\phi}{\partial n} = \mathbf{u}_\infty \cdot \mathbf{n} \qquad \text{on } \Gamma_\infty \qquad\qquad \frac{\partial\phi}{\partial n} = 0 \qquad \text{on } \Gamma_B \tag{4.42}$$

Since only Neumann boundary conditions are involved, the potential $\phi$ is determined only to within an arbitrary constant. To remedy this, one can prescribe the value of $\phi$ at some point within $\Omega \cup \Gamma$ and, for example, one may use

$$\phi = 0 \qquad \text{at the trailing edge of } B \tag{4.43}$$

**Lifting Airfoils and the Kutta–Joukowsky Condition**    In fact, the Kutta–Joukowsky condition is not specific for transonic flows since it also occurs for incompressible inviscid flows and compressible subsonic flows (see Refs. [65–67] for more information on the numerical treatment of the Kutta–Joukowsky condition for two-dimensional and three-dimensional flows).

***Shock and Entropy Conditions***   Across a shock the flow must satisfy the Rankine–Hugoniot conditions

$$(\rho\mathbf{u} \cdot \mathbf{n})_+ = (\rho\mathbf{u} \cdot \mathbf{n})_- \qquad \text{where } \mathbf{n} \text{ is normal at the shockline or surface} \qquad (4.44)$$

$$\text{The tangential component of the velocity is continuous} \qquad (4.45)$$

A suitable weak formulation of (4.39) to (4.41) will take (4.44) and (4.45) into account. The entropy condition can be formulated as follows (for more details, see Ref. [64] and Sec. 4.3E on numerical implementation):

> Following the flow one cannot have a positive variation of velocity through a shock since this would imply a negative variation of entropy, which is an unphysical phenomenon. (4.46)

***On the nonuniqueness of Physical Solutions***   On the basis of numerical experiments (see, e.g., Ref. [68]), one has become recently aware of the possible existence of multiple physical solutions (i.e., those satisfying the Kutta–Joukowsky and entropy conditions) of Eqs. (4.39) to (4.45); this property is associated, actually, to flow instabilities. A specific example of multiple physical solutions is discussed in Sec. 4.3F.

## 4.3c  Least-Squares Formulation of the Continuous Problem

The practical implementation of the entropy condition (4.46) is not discussed in this section; we discuss only the variational formulation of Eqs. (4.39) to (4.42), (4.44), and (4.45) and of an associate nonlinear least-squares formulation. (For the properties of Sobolev spaces, refer to Chap. 2 of Part 1 and also to Refs. [69–71].)

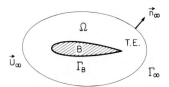

**FIG. 4.7**  Symmetric flow around a symmetric airfoil.  T.E. = trailing edge.

***A Variational Formulation of the Continuity Equation***   Consider Fig. 4.7, which shows a symmetric flow, subsonic at infinity, around a symmetric airfoil; thus the Kutta–Joukowsky condition is automatically satisfied. The airfoil is imbedded in a "large" domain, and with the previous notation, the continuity equation and the boundary conditions are, respectively,

$$\nabla \cdot \rho(\phi)\nabla\phi = 0 \quad \text{in } \Omega \quad \text{with} \quad \rho(\phi) = \rho_0\left(1 - \frac{\gamma - 1}{\gamma + 1}\frac{|\nabla\phi|^2}{c_*^2}\right)^{1/(\gamma - 1)} \qquad (4.47)$$

$$\rho\frac{\partial\phi}{\partial n} = 0 \quad \text{on } \Gamma_B \qquad \rho\frac{\partial\phi}{\partial n} = \rho_\infty\mathbf{u}_\infty \cdot \mathbf{n}_\infty \quad \text{on } \Gamma_\infty \qquad (4.48)$$

On $\Gamma$ $(=\Gamma_B \cup \Gamma_\infty)$ define $g$ by $g = 0$ on $\Gamma_B$, $g = \rho_\infty \mathbf{u}_\infty \cdot \mathbf{n}_\infty$ on $\Gamma_\infty$; then

$$\rho \frac{\partial \phi}{\partial n} = g \quad \text{on } \Gamma \quad \text{and} \quad \int_\Gamma g \, d\Gamma = 0 \tag{4.49}$$

An equivalent variational formulation of (4.47) and (4.49) is

$$\int_\Omega \rho(\phi) \nabla \phi \cdot \nabla v \, dx = \int_\Gamma g v \, d\Gamma \quad \forall v \in H^1(\Omega), \, \phi \in W^{1,\infty}(\Omega)/\mathbb{R} \tag{4.50}$$

where, for $1 \leqslant p \leqslant +\infty$, $W^{1,p}(\Omega)$ is the Sobolev functional space defined by

$$W^{1,p}(\Omega) = \left\{ v \,\middle|\, v \in L^p(\Omega), \frac{\partial v}{\partial x_i} \in L^p(\Omega), \forall i \right\}$$

[with $H^1(\Omega) = W^{1,2}(\Omega)$]; the function $\phi$ is determined only to within an arbitrary constant. Observe that the space $W^{1,\infty}(\Omega)$ is a natural choice for $\phi$ since physical flows require (among other properties) a positive density $\rho$; therefore [from (4.47)] $\phi$ must satisfy

$$|\nabla \phi| \leqslant \delta < \left( \frac{\gamma + 1}{\gamma - 1} \right)^{1/2} c_* \quad \text{on } \Omega$$

**Least-Squares Formulation of Eq. (4.50)**    For a genuine transonic flow, the problem specified by (4.50) is not equivalent to a standard problem of the calculus of variations (as is the case for purely subsonic flows). To remedy this situation a nonlinear least-squares formulation is introduced as follows: let $X$ be a set of feasible transonic-flow solutions; the least-squares problem is then

$$\min_{\xi \in X} J(\xi) \quad \text{with} \quad J(\xi) = \tfrac{1}{2} \int_\Omega |\nabla y(\xi)|^2 \, dx \tag{4.51}$$

where in (4.51), $y(\xi)$ $(=y)$ is a solution of the following linear variational problem:

$$\int_\Omega \nabla y \cdot \nabla v \, dx = \int_\Omega \rho(\xi) \nabla \xi \cdot \nabla v \, dx - \int_\Gamma g v \, d\Gamma \quad \forall v \in H^1(\Omega), \, y \in H^1(\Omega)/\mathbb{R} \tag{4.52}$$

If the transonic-flow problem (4.50) has solutions, these solve the least-squares problem (4.51) and give the value zero to the objective function $J$.

## 4.3D Finite-Element Approximation and Least-Squares Conjugate-Gradient Solution of the Approximate Problems

Only two-dimensional problems are considered here, but the following methods apply also to three-dimensional problems.

**Finite-Element Approximation of the Nonlinear Variational Problem (4.50)**    Consider the nonlifting situation at the beginning of Sec. 4.3C, "Least-Squares Formulation of the

Continuous Problem," once the flow region has been embedded in a large bounded domain $\Omega$. This latter domain is approximated by a polygonal domain $\Omega_h$; with $\mathcal{T}_h$ a standard triangulation of $\Omega_h$, $H^1(\Omega)$ [and in fact $W^{1,p}(\Omega)$, $\forall h, p \geq 1$] is approximated by

$$H^1_h = \{v_h \mid v_h \in C^0(\bar{\Omega}), \, v_h|_T \in P_1 \, \forall T \in \mathcal{T}_h\} \tag{4.53}$$

where, in (4.53), $P_1$ = space of polynomials in two variables of degree $\leq 1$. The value zero is prescribed for the potential at the trailing edge; this leads to

$$V_h = \{v_h \mid v_h \in H^1_h, \, v_h(\text{trailing edge}) = 0\} \tag{4.54}$$

Clearly dim $H^1_h = 1 +$ dim $V_h =$ number of vertices of $\mathcal{T}_h$. If we drop for simplicity the subscript $h$ from $\Omega_h$, the variational problem (4.50) is approximated by

$$\int_\Omega \rho(\phi_h)\nabla\phi_h \cdot \nabla v_h \, dx = \int_\Gamma g_h v_h \, d\Gamma \qquad \forall v_h \in V_h, \, \phi_h \in V_h \tag{4.55}$$

with $g_h$ an approximation of $g$ in (4.50). The above discrete variational formulation implies that $\rho(\partial\phi/\partial n)|_\Gamma = g$ is (approximately) automatically satisfied. Let $\mathcal{B}_h = \{w_i\}_{i=1}^{N_h}$ be a vector basis of $V_h$. Then problem (4.55) is equivalent to the nonlinear system in finite dimension

$$\int_\Omega \rho(\phi_h)\nabla\phi_h \cdot \nabla w_i \, dx = \int_\Gamma g_h w_i \, d\Gamma \qquad \forall i = 1, \ldots, N_h \, ; \, \phi_h = \sum_{j=1}^{N_h} \phi_j w_j \tag{4.56}$$

where $\phi_j = \phi_h(P_j)$, $\forall j = 1, \ldots, N_h$, assuming that $\{P_i\}_{i=1}^{N_h}$ is the set of the vertices of $\mathcal{T}_h$ different from the trailing edge (TE) and that $\mathcal{B}_h$ is defined by

$$w_i \in H^1_h \qquad \forall i = 1, \ldots, N_h \qquad w_i(P_i) = 1 \qquad w_i(P_j) = 0 \qquad \forall j \neq i \qquad w_i(\text{TE}) = 0$$

From the above choice for $H^1_h$ and $V_h$ there is no problem of numerical integration since, in (4.55) and (4.56), $\nabla\phi_h$, $\nabla v_h$ [and therefore $\rho(\phi_h)$] are piecewise constant.

**Least-Squares Formulation of the Discrete Problem (4.55), (4.56)** Combining the results of the previous sections leads to the following least-squares formulation of the approximate problem (4.55), (4.56):

$$\min_{\xi_h \in X_h} J_h(\xi_h) \qquad \text{with} \qquad J_h(\xi_h) = \tfrac{1}{2}\int_\Omega |\nabla y_h(\xi_h)|^2 \, dx \tag{4.57}$$

with $y_h(\xi_h)$ $(=y_h)$ the solution of the following linear variational problem:

$$\int_\Omega \nabla y_h \cdot \nabla v_h \, dx = \int_\Omega \rho(\xi_h)\nabla\xi_h \cdot \nabla v_h \, dx - \int_\Gamma g_h v_h \, d\Gamma \qquad \forall v_h \in V_h, \, y_h \in V_h \tag{4.58}$$

**Conjugate-Gradient Solution of the Least-Squares Problem (4.57), (4.58)** A preconditioned conjugate-gradient algorithm for solving the least-squares problem (4.57), (4.58), with $X_h = V_h$, is as follows (cf. [59, 65-67]).

***Step 0: Initialization***

Given

$$\phi_h^0 \in V_h \tag{4.59}$$

compute $g_h^0$ from

$$\int_\Omega \nabla g_h^0 \cdot \nabla v_h \, dx = \langle J'(\phi_h^0), v_h \rangle \qquad \forall v_h \in V_h, \, g_h^0 \in V_h \tag{4.60}$$

and set

$$z_h^0 = g_h^0 \tag{4.61}$$

Then for $n \geq 0$, assuming $\phi_h^n$, $g_h^n$, $z_h^n$ known, compute $\phi_h^{n+1}$, $g_h^{n+1}$, $z_h^{n+1}$ by the following steps.

***Step 1: Descent***

Compute

$$\lambda^n = \text{argument } \min_{\lambda \in \mathbb{R}} J_h(\phi_h^n - \lambda z_h^n)$$

and set

$$\phi_h^{n+1} = \phi_h^n - \lambda^n z_h^n \tag{4.62}$$

***Step 2: Construction of the New Descent Direction***

Define $g_h^{n+1}$ by

$$\int_\Omega \nabla g_h^{n+1} \cdot \nabla v_h \, dx = \langle J_h'(\phi_h^{n+1}), v_h \rangle \qquad \forall v_h \in V_h, \, g_h^{n+1} \in V_h \tag{4.63}$$

then

$$\gamma_{n+1} = \frac{\displaystyle\int_\Omega \nabla g_h^{n+1} \cdot \nabla(g_h^{n+1} - g_h^n) \, dx}{\displaystyle\int_\Omega |\nabla g_h^n|^2 \, dx} \tag{4.64}$$

$$z_h^{n+1} = g_h^{n+1} + \gamma_{n+1} z_h^n \tag{4.65}$$

Do $n = n+1$ and go to (4.62).

***Discussion***    The two nontrivial steps of algorithm (4.59) to (4.65) are:

1. The solution of the single-variable minimization problem in (4.62) where the corresponding line search can be done by a dichotomy or Fibonacci method (see Refs. [72–74]). One observes that each evaluation of $J_h(\xi_h)$, for a given argument $\xi_h$, requires the solution of the linear approximate Neumann problem (4.58) to obtain the corresponding $y_h$.

2. The calculation of $g_h^{n+1}$ from $\phi_h^{n+1}$, which requires the solution of two linear approximate Neumann problems [namely, (4.58), with $\xi_h = \phi_h^{n+1}$, and (4.63)].

***Calculation of $J_h'(\phi_h^n)$ and $g_h^n$***    It follows from Refs. [59, 60] that (if $\rho_0 = 1$), then $\forall \eta_h \in V_h$,

$$\langle J_h'(\xi_h), \eta_h \rangle = \int_\Omega \rho(\xi_h) \nabla y_h \cdot \nabla \eta_h \, dx - 2K\alpha \int_\Omega (\rho(\xi_h))^{2-\gamma} \nabla \xi_h \cdot \nabla y_h \nabla \xi_h \cdot \nabla \eta_h \, dx \tag{4.66}$$

with $K = (1/c_*^2)(\gamma - 1)/(\gamma + 1)$ and $\alpha = 1/(\gamma - 1)$. It is then quite easy to obtain $g_h^{n+1}$ from

$\phi_h^{n+1}$, using (4.63) and (4.66). It is clear that an efficient Poisson solver will be a basic tool if one uses the above algorithm to solve the discrete problem (4.55). As stopping criterion for algorithm (4.59) to (4.65) one may use either $J_h(\phi_h^n) \leq \varepsilon$ or $\int_\Omega |\nabla g_h^n|^2 \, dx \leq \varepsilon$, where $\varepsilon$ is a given "small" positive number.

***Numerical Solution of a Test Problem***   The above methods are applied to the numerical solution of a symmetric flow, uniform and subsonic at infinity, around a disk. From the symmetry, the Kutta–Joukowsky condition is automatically satisfied. If $|u_\infty|$ is sufficiently small, the flow is purely subsonic and a very good solution is obtained in quite a few iterations of algorithm (4.59) to (4.65) ($\sim$5 iterations). For greater values of $|u_\infty|$ a supersonic "pocket" appears. The computed† Mach distribution on the "skin" of the body as shown on Fig. 4.8 lets appear a rarefaction (or expansion) shock which is an unphysical phenomenon. The correct Mach distribution is shown on Fig. 4.9. From the above test, it appears that some dissipation has to be included in the above numerical process in order to avoid those unphysical shocks violating the entropy condition (4.46). This is done in the next section.

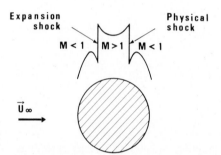

**FIG. 4.8**   Symmetric flow around a cylinder (computed solution).

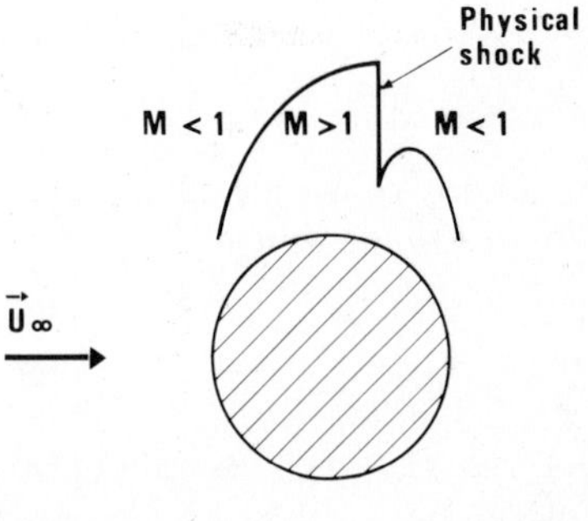

**FIG. 4.9**   Symmetric flow around a cylinder (true solution).

## 4.3E  Numerical Implementation of the Entropy Condition

***Generalities***   Several methods based on a penalty and/or artificial viscosity are discussed in Refs. [59, 60, 65–67]. There is described below a method based on upwinding of the density (as in, e.g., Refs. [59, 63, 75]). Actually, methods using an upwinding of the density have been extensively used (see the above references) to eliminate unphysical shocks. These methods have been quite effective, coupled to alternating-direction methods (implicit or semi-implicit (see [63, 75])) if the computational mesh is regular (finite-difference or regular finite-element grids). In particular, their application combined with finite-element techniques has been limited to quadrilateral elements on quasi-regular meshes (close, in fact, to finite-difference methods). The method discussed below can be used with simplicial finite elements (i.e., triangles in two dimensions, tetrahedra in three dimensions) and appears to be quite effective, as shown by numerical experiments.

---

† There is still a fast convergence ($\sim$10 iterations).

*A Modified, Discrete Continuity Equation by Upwinding the Density in the Flow Direction*  Following Refs. [76–81] (see also [59, 60]), the continuity equation (4.47) is written in the local coordinate system {s, n}, where (see Fig. 4.10), for a two-dimensional flow, s is the unit vector of the stream direction (that is, $s = u/|u|$ if $u \neq 0$) and n is the corresponding normal unit vector (conventionally oriented).

**FIG. 4.10**   Local coordinate system.

By using {s, n} and setting $k = (\gamma - 1)/(\gamma + 1)$, $\alpha = 1/(\gamma - 1)$, $U = |\nabla \phi|/c_*$ one may obtain from the continuity equation (4.47)

$$\rho \frac{\partial^2 \phi}{\partial n^2} + \rho \frac{1 - U^2}{1 - kU^2} \frac{\partial^2 \phi}{\partial s^2} = 0 \qquad (4.67)$$

which clearly shows the elliptic-hyperbolic aspect of the transonic-flow problem. Actually (4.67) can also be written

$$\rho \frac{\partial^2 \phi}{\partial n^2} + \frac{U^2 - 1}{2k\alpha U^2} \nabla \phi \cdot \nabla \rho = 0 \qquad (4.68)$$

with $1/2k\alpha = (\gamma + 1)/2$. By using (4.68) the discrete continuity equation (4.55) may be modified as follows:

Find $\phi_h \in V_h$ such that, $\forall v_h \in V_h$, one has

$$\int_\Omega \rho(\phi_h) \nabla \phi_h \cdot \nabla v_h \, dx + \frac{1}{2k\alpha} \int_\Omega \left( \frac{\partial}{\partial s} h_s (\bar{U}_h^2 - 1)^+ \nabla \phi_h \cdot \nabla \bar{\rho}_h \right)_h v_h \, dx = \int_\Omega g_h v_h \, d\Gamma \quad (4.69)$$

The approximate problem (4.69) is a finite-element variant of a finite-difference scheme due to T. Holst [75]. In (4.69), $h_s$ is a measure of the local size of the finite-element mesh in the flow direction; $(\partial/\partial s)_h$ is an approximation of $(\nabla \phi_h/|\nabla \phi_h|) \cdot \nabla$; and $\bar{U}_h$, $\bar{\rho}_h$ are upwinded approximations of $U$ and $\rho$, respectively. More precisely, the second integral in the left-hand side of (4.69) is written as follows:

$$\int_\Omega \left( \frac{\partial}{\partial s} h_s (\bar{U}_h^2 - 1)^+ \nabla \phi_h \cdot \nabla \bar{\rho}_h \right)_h v_h \, dx$$

$$= (-1) \sum_{P_i \in \Sigma_h} v_h(P_i) \sum_{j=1}^{2} u_{ji} \sum_{T \in \mathcal{T}_i} m(T) h_s(T) (\bar{U}_h^2 - 1)^+ \nabla \phi_h \cdot \nabla \bar{\rho}_h \frac{\partial w_i}{\partial x_j} \qquad (4.70)$$

where

1. $\Sigma_h = \{P_i\}_{i=1}^{N_h}$ is the set of the vertices of $\mathcal{T}_h$, with $P_0 =$ trailing edge.

**2.** $w_i$ is the basis function of $H_h^1$ [cf. (4.53)] associated to $P_i$ by

$$w_i \in H_h^1 \qquad \forall i = 0, 1, \ldots, N_h \qquad w_i(P_i) = 1 \qquad w_i(P_j) = 0 \qquad \forall j \neq i$$

**3.** $\mathcal{T}_i$ is the subset of $\mathcal{T}_h$ consisting of those triangles having $P_i$ as a common vertex; $m(T) = \text{meas } T$, where meas $T = $ area of triangle $T$.

**4.** $\{u_{ji}\}_{j=1}^2$ is the approximation of $(\nabla \phi_h / |\nabla \phi_h|)$ at vertex $P_i$, obtained for $j = 1, 2$, by the following averaging formulae (other averaging methods are possible):

$$\left( \frac{\partial \phi_h}{\partial x_j} \right)_i = \frac{\sum\limits_{T \in \mathcal{T}_i} (\partial \phi_h / \partial x_j)(|\partial w_i / \partial x_j|)}{\sum\limits_{T \in \mathcal{T}_i} |\partial w_i / \partial x_j|} \qquad u_{ji} = \frac{(\partial \phi_h / \partial x_j)_i}{\left[ \sum\limits_{l=1}^{2} (\partial \phi_h / \partial x_l)_i^2 \right]^{1/2}}$$

**5.** $h_s(T)$ is the length of $T$ in the s-direction; that is,

$$h_s(T) = \frac{2}{\sum\limits_{k=1}^{3} |\partial w_{kT} / \partial s|}$$

where $w_{kT}$, $k = 1, 2, 3$, are the basis functions associated with the vertices $P_{kT}$ of $T$. Actually

$$h_s(T) = \frac{2|\nabla \phi_h|_T}{\sum\limits_{k=1}^{3} |\nabla \phi_h \cdot \nabla w_{kT}|}$$

**6.** $\bar{U}_h^2$ is defined as follows: To each vertex $P_i$ of $\mathcal{T}_h$ one associates an inflow triangle $T_i$ which is the triangle of $\mathcal{T}_h$ having $P_i$ as a vertex and which is crossed by the vector

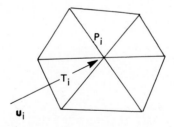

**FIG. 11**   Portion of finite-element mesh.

$\mathbf{u}_i = \{u_{ij}\}_{j=1}^2$ pointing to $P_i$ (as shown in Fig. 4.11). One then defines $U_i^2$ by $U_i^2 = (|\nabla \phi_h^2|^2 / c_*^2)|_{T_i}$, and for each triangle $T$ of $\mathcal{T}_h$,

$$\bar{U}_h^2 = \frac{\sum\limits_{k=1}^{3} U_{kT}^2 |\partial w_{kT} / \partial s|_T}{\sum\limits_{k=1}^{3} |\partial w_{kT} / \partial s|_T}$$

**7.** Finally there is obtained $\bar{\rho}_h \in H_h^1$ as follows: As for $U_i^2$, $\rho_i$ is defined by $\rho_i = \rho(\phi_h)|_{T_i}$, and then

$$\bar{\rho}_h = \sum_{i=0}^{N_h} \rho_i w_i$$

***Least-Squares Solution of the Approximate Problem (4.69)***   For solving the discrete, upwinded continuity equation (4.69) the following least-squares formulation can be used:

$$\min_{\xi_h \in V_h} J_h(\xi_h) \qquad \text{where} \qquad J_h(\xi_h) = \tfrac{1}{2} \int_\Omega |\nabla y_h(\xi_h)|^2 \, dx \qquad (4.71)$$

where $y_h(\xi_h)$ $(=y_h)$ is the solution of the following linear variational equation:

$$\int_\Omega \nabla y_h \cdot \nabla v_h \, dx = \int_\Omega \rho(\phi_h) \nabla \phi_h \cdot \nabla v_h \, dx - \int_\Gamma g_h v_h \, d\Gamma$$

$$+ \frac{1}{2k\alpha} \int_\Omega \left( \frac{\partial}{\partial s} h_s (\bar{U}_h^2 - 1)^+ \nabla \phi_h \cdot \nabla \rho_h \right)_h v_h \, dx \qquad \forall v_h \in V_h, \, y_h \in V_h \qquad (4.72)$$

Since $J_h$ is a nondifferentiable functional of $\phi_h$, to solve problem (4.71) and (4.72), there has been used, instead of algorithm (4.59) to (4.65), a generalization of the conjugate-gradient method, due to Lamaréchal [82, 83], which applies also to the minimization of nondifferentiable functionals.

## 4.3F Numerical Experiments

Some numerical results obtained using the above methods are described in this section.

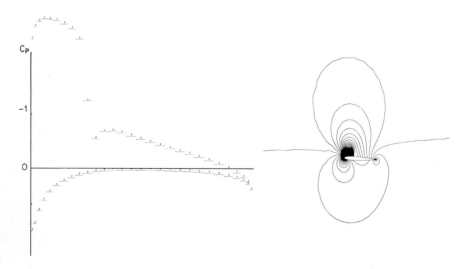

**FIG. 4.12**   Flow around NACA 0012 airfoil. $M_\infty = 0.6$, angle of attack $\alpha = 6°$.

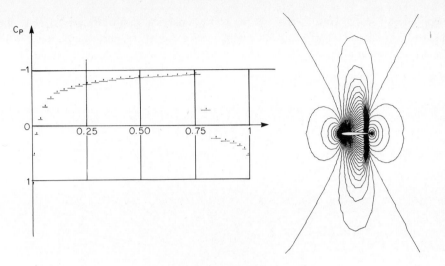

**FIG. 4.13**  Flow around NACA 0012 airfoil. $M_\infty = 0.85$, $\alpha = 0°$.

*Simulations of Flows Around a NACA 0012 Airfoil*   As a first example, consider flows around a NACA 0012 airfoil at various angles of attack and Mach number at infinity. The corresponding pressure distribution on the skin of the airfoil is shown in Figs. 4.12 to 4.14, on which also are shown the iso-Mach lines. It follows from these results that the physical shocks are well-defined and very neat, and also that the transition (without shock) from the subsonic region to the supersonic region is smoothly represented, implying that the entropy

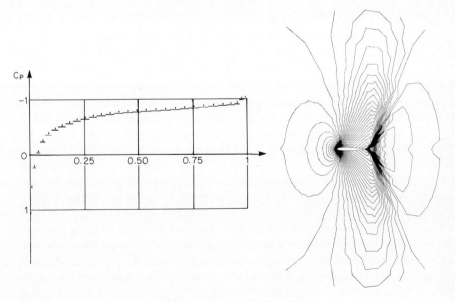

**FIG. 4.14**  Flow around NACA 0012 airfoil. $M_\infty = 0.90$, $\alpha = 0°$.

condition has been correctly satisfied. The above numerical results are very close to those obtained by various authors using finite-difference methods (see, particularly, Ref. [76]). In Fig. 4.15, a typical triangular mesh used to solve the above test problems is shown.

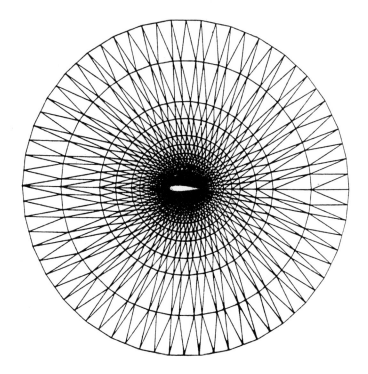

**FIG. 4.15** Typical finite-element mesh for airfoil test problems.

**Simulation of Flows Around a NACA 64006 Airfoil**    The main interest of this test problem is that it has (at least) *three* solutions satisfying the Rankine–Hugoniot, Kutta–Joukowsky, and entropy conditions. It corresponds to a NACA 64006 airfoil at $M_\infty = 0.89$ and $\alpha = 0°$. On Fig. 4.16 are shown the iso-Mach lines of the symmetric solution and on Fig. 4.17 the corresponding pressure distribution. Figure 4.18 shows the iso-Mach lines of a nonsymmetric solution (with a nonzero circulation), and Fig. 4.19 shows the corresponding pressure distribution on the upper and lower parts of the airfoil. There exists a third solution obtained from the second one by a symmetry with respect to the symmetry axis of the airfoil.

**A Three-Dimensional Industrial Application**    The methods described in the above sections have been used for the numerical simulation of the aerodynamical performances of a trijet engine AMD/BA Falcon 50. Figure 4.20 shows the trace on the aircraft of the tridimensional mesh used for the computation, and Fig. 4.21 shows the corresponding Mach distribution (dark: low Mach number; white: high Mach number). It will be seen that the flow is mostly supersonic on the upper part of the wings.

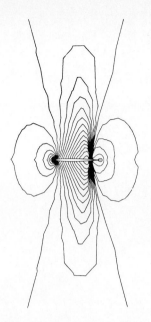

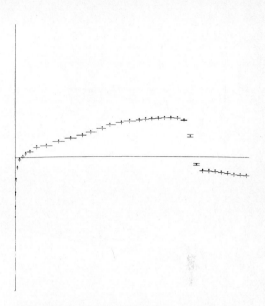

**FIG. 4.16** Iso-Mach lines for NACA 64006 airfoil at $M_\infty = 0.89$ and $\alpha = 0°$; symmetric solution.

**FIG. 4.17** Pressure distribution around NACA 64006 airfoil at $M_\infty = 0.89$ and $\alpha = 0°$; symmetric solution.

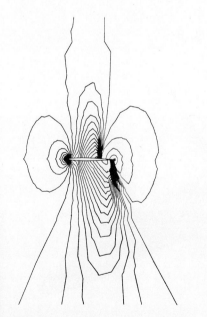

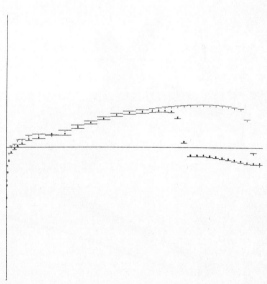

**FIG. 4.18** Iso-Mach lines for NACA 64006 airfoil at $M_\infty = 0.89$ and $\alpha = 0°$; non-symmetric solution.

**FIG. 4.19** Pressure distribution around NACA 64006 airfoil at $M_\infty = 0.89$ and $\alpha = 0°$; nonsymmetric solution.

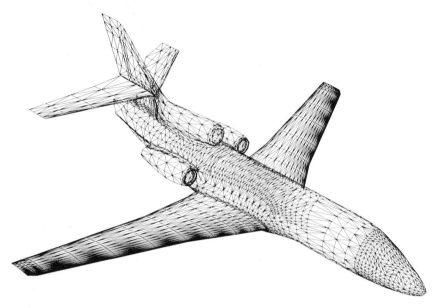

**FIG. 4.20** Finite-element mesh for AMD/BA Falcon 50 aircraft.

**FIG. 4.21** Computed Mach distribution for transonic-flow simulation, AMD/BA Falcon 50 aircraft, $M_\infty = 0.85$, $\alpha = 1°$.

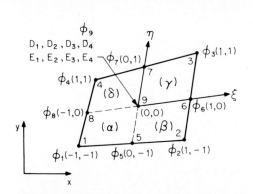

**FIG. 4.22** Element-discontinuity method for nine-node isoparametric element.

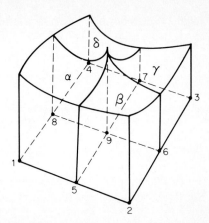

**FIG. 4.23** Discontinuous functional representation of velocity-potential surface within finite element.

## 4.4 TRANSONIC FLOW AND SHOCK WAVES: DISCONTINUOUS FUNCTIONS

Assume that the shock wave passes through an isoparametric element, causing an explicit discontinuity in pressure at the center of the element as depicted in Fig. 4.22. An independent interpolation of $\phi$ for each quadrant is given by (see Fig. 4.23)

$$\phi^{(\alpha)} = \alpha_1 + \alpha_2\xi + \alpha_3\eta + \alpha_4\xi\eta + \alpha_5\xi^2 + \alpha_6\eta^2 \tag{4.73a}$$

$$\phi^{(\beta)} = \beta_1 + \beta_2\xi + \beta_3\eta + \beta_4\xi\eta + \beta_5\xi^2 + \beta_6\eta^2 \tag{4.73b}$$

$$\phi^{(\gamma)} = \gamma_1 + \gamma_2\xi + \gamma_3\eta + \gamma_4\xi\eta + \gamma_5\xi^2 + \gamma_6\eta^2 \tag{4.73c}$$

$$\phi^{(\delta)} = \delta_1 + \delta_2\xi + \delta_3\eta + \delta_4\xi\eta + \delta_5\xi^2 + \delta_6\eta^2 \tag{4.73d}$$

There is thus a total of 24 constants to be determined uniquely. By means of (4.73) four equations can be written for $\phi$ at the corner nodes, eight equations at the midside nodes, and four equations at the center node, resulting in sixteen equations. Eight additional equations can be obtained from the difference between the slopes of $\phi$ and their rates of change at the center node. They are

$$D_1 = \frac{\partial\phi^{(\alpha)}}{\partial\xi} - \frac{\partial\phi^{(\beta)}}{\partial\xi} \qquad D_2 = \frac{\partial\phi^{(\beta)}}{\partial\eta} - \frac{\partial\phi^{(\gamma)}}{\partial\eta} \tag{4.74a, b}$$

$$D_3 = \frac{\partial\phi^{(\gamma)}}{\partial\xi} - \frac{\partial\phi^{(\delta)}}{\partial\xi} \qquad D_4 = \frac{\partial\phi^{(\delta)}}{\partial\eta} - \frac{\partial\delta^{(\alpha)}}{\partial\eta} \tag{4.74c, d}$$

$$E_1 = \frac{\partial^2\phi^{(\alpha)}}{\partial\xi^2} - \frac{\partial^2\phi^{(\beta)}}{\partial\xi^2} \qquad E_2 = \frac{\partial^2\phi^{(\beta)}}{\partial\eta^2} - \frac{\partial^2\phi^{(\gamma)}}{\partial\eta^2} \tag{4.74e, f}$$

$$E_3 = \frac{\partial^2\phi^{(\gamma)}}{\partial\xi^2} - \frac{\partial^2\phi^{(\delta)}}{\partial\xi^2} \qquad E_4 = \frac{\partial^2\phi^{(\delta)}}{\partial\eta^2} - \frac{\partial^2\phi^{(\alpha)}}{\partial\eta^2} \tag{4.74g, h}$$

With 24 equations now available, solving for the unknown constants in (4.73) gives

$$\phi^{(\alpha)} = \Phi_N^{(\alpha)}(\xi, \eta)\phi_N + F_r^{(\alpha)}(\xi, \eta)D_r + G_r^{(\alpha)}(\xi, \eta)E_r \tag{4.75a}$$

$$\phi^{(\beta)} = \Phi_N^{(\beta)}(\xi, \eta)\phi_N + F_r^{(\beta)}(\xi, \eta)D_r + G_r^{(\beta)}(\xi, \eta)E_r \tag{4.75b}$$

$$\phi^{(\gamma)} = \Phi_N^{(\gamma)}(\xi, \eta)\phi_N + F_r^{(\gamma)}(\xi, \eta)D_r + G_r^{(\gamma)}(\xi, \eta)E_r \tag{4.75c}$$

$$\phi^{(\delta)} = \Phi_N^{(\delta)}(\xi, \eta)\phi_N + F_r^{(\delta)}(\xi, \eta)D_r + G_r^{(\delta)}(\xi, \eta)E_r \tag{4.75d}$$

where $N = 1, 2, \ldots, 9$ and $r = 1, 2, 3, 4$. It is clear that $\phi_N$, $F_r$, and $G_r$ represent the interpolation functions for continuity of $\phi_N$ and discontinuities of $D_r$ and $E_r$, respectively.

To obtain the finite-element analogue of the full potential equation, an interpolation field for the velocity potential function is assumed in the form

$$\phi = \Psi_m Q_m \tag{4.76}$$

where the index (summation) convention is used here and in the following. Here $\Psi_m$ represents the continuous interpolation functions for $\phi$ and the discontinuous interpolation functions for derivatives of $\phi$ at the element nodes; $Q_m$ denotes the nodal values of $\phi$ plus its first- and second-order discontinuous derivatives. An orthogonal projection of the residuals of the potential equations onto the subspace spanned by both continuous and discontinuous interpolation fields leads to

$$\int_\Omega (\phi_{,ii} - G)\Psi_m \, d\Omega = 0 \tag{4.77}$$

Integrating by parts yields

$$A_{mn}Q_n = G_m + F_m + S_m \tag{4.78}$$

where

$$A_{mn} = \int_\Omega \Psi_{m,i}\Psi_{n,i} \, d\Omega \tag{4.79}$$

$$G_m = \int_\Omega \frac{1}{a^2}\Psi_{n,i}\Psi_{p,j}\Psi_{q,i}\Psi_{m,j} \, d\Omega \; Q_n Q_p Q_q \tag{4.80}$$

$$F_m = \int_{\Gamma_1} \phi_{,i}n_i\Psi_m^* \, d\Gamma \tag{4.81}$$

$$S_m = -\int_{\Gamma_2} \beta_j n_j \Psi_m^* \, d\Gamma \tag{4.82}$$

with $\beta_j = (1/a^2)\phi_{,i}\phi_{,j}\phi_{,i}$. The boundary conditions are given by $F_m$ representing the Neumann type of $\Gamma_1$, and $S_m$ denoting the surfaces of pressure discontinuity on $\Gamma_2$, as shown in Fig. 4.24. We introduce a notation for discontinuity given by (4.82)

$$S_m = (S_m)_1 - (S_m)_2 \tag{4.83}$$

where the subscripts 1 and 2 refer to the upstream and downstream values of $S_m$, respectively, at the surface of pressure discontinuity.

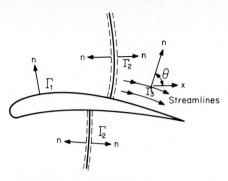

**FIG. 4.24**  Boundary surfaces.

From the element geometry (Fig. 4.22), a typical $17 \times 17$ shock-element-influence coefficient matrix $A_{mn}$ is found to have the form

$$A_{mn} = \int_{\Omega} \left( \frac{\partial \Psi_m}{\partial x} \frac{\partial \Psi_n}{\partial x} + \frac{\partial \Psi_m}{\partial y} \frac{\partial \Psi_n}{\partial y} \right) d\Omega$$

$$= \int_{-1}^{0} \int_{-1}^{0} \frac{\partial \Psi_m^{(\alpha)}}{\partial x} \frac{\partial \Psi_n^{(\alpha)}}{\partial x} |\mathbf{J}| \, d\xi \, d\eta + \int_{-1}^{0} \int_{0}^{1} \frac{\partial \Psi_m^{(\beta)}}{\partial x} \frac{\partial \Psi_n^{(\beta)}}{\partial x} |\mathbf{J}| \, d\xi \, d\eta$$

$$+ \int_{0}^{1} \int_{0}^{1} \frac{\partial \Psi_m^{(\gamma)}}{\partial x} \frac{\partial \Psi_n^{(\gamma)}}{\partial x} |\mathbf{J}| \, d\xi \, d\eta + \int_{0}^{1} \int_{-1}^{0} \frac{\partial \Psi_m^{(\delta)}}{\partial x} \frac{\partial \Psi_n^{(\delta)}}{\partial x} |\mathbf{J}| \, d\xi \, d\eta + \cdots$$

where $\qquad \dfrac{\partial \Psi_m^{(\alpha)}}{\partial x} = \dfrac{1}{|\mathbf{J}|} \left( \dfrac{\partial y}{\partial \eta} \dfrac{\partial \Psi_m^{(\alpha)}}{\partial \xi} - \dfrac{\partial y}{\partial \xi} \dfrac{\partial \Psi_m^{(\alpha)}}{\partial \eta} \right), \cdots \qquad$ with $\qquad x = \Lambda_N x_N, y = \Lambda_N y_N \qquad$ (4.84)

in which $\Lambda_N$ is the standard isoparametric interpolation function derived from

$$x, y = c_1 + c_2 \xi + c_3 \eta + c_4 \xi \eta + c_5 \xi^2 + c_6 \eta^2 + c_7 \xi^2 \eta + c_8 \xi \eta^2 + c_9 \xi^2 \eta^2$$

and $$|\mathbf{J}| = \frac{\partial x}{\partial \xi} \frac{\partial y}{\partial \eta} - \frac{\partial x}{\partial \eta} \frac{\partial y}{\partial \xi}$$

$$\Psi_m^{(\alpha)} = [\Phi_1 \Phi_2 \cdots \Phi_9 F_1 F_2 F_3 F_4 G_1 G_2 G_3 G_4]^{(\alpha)}$$

$$\Psi_m^{(\beta)} = [\Phi_1 \Phi_2 \cdots \Phi_9 F_1 F_2 F_2 F_4 G_1 G_2 G_3 G_4]^{(\beta)}$$

$$\Psi_m^{(\gamma)} = [\Phi_1 \Phi_2 \cdots \Phi_9 F_1 F_2 F_3 F_4 G_1 G_2 G_3 G_4]^{(\gamma)} \qquad (4.85)$$

$$\Psi_m^{(\delta)} = [\Phi_1 \Phi_2 \cdots \Phi_9 F_1 F_2 F_3 F_4 G_1 G_2 G_3 G_4]^{(\delta)}$$

$$Q_m = [\phi_1 \phi_2 \cdots \phi_9 D_1 D_2 D_3 D_4 E_1 E_2 E_3 E_4]^T$$

The gaussian quadrature integration of the type (4.84) is also performed on the nonlinear term $G_m$. Thus the globally assembled finite-element equations are written as

$$A_{\alpha\beta} Q_\beta = G_x + F_x + S_x \qquad (4.86)$$

Here the Neumann boundary conditions $F_x$ can be satisfied automatically, but special

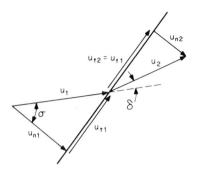

**FIG. 4.25**  Oblique shock wave.

treatment for the shock conditions $S_x$ is required, and direct applications of Rankine–Hugoniot conditions can be invoked (see Fig. 4.25) to obtain an equivalent form of $S_x$. The Rankine–Hugoniot conditions are

$$\rho_1 u_{n1} = \rho_2 u_{n2} \tag{4.87}$$

together with momentum normal and tangent to the wave,

$$\rho_1 u_{n1}^2 + P_1 = \rho_2 u_{n2}^2 + P_2$$

$$u_{t1} = u_{t2}$$

and the energy

$$H_1 + \tfrac{1}{2}u_1^2 = H_2 + \tfrac{1}{2}u_2^2 = \hat{H}$$

These equations, in view of the geometric relations and the appropriate equations of state, lead to

$$1 - \varepsilon = A$$

with

$$A = (1 - \varepsilon_1)(1 - d)$$

$$\varepsilon = \frac{u_{n2}}{u_{n1}} \qquad \varepsilon_1 = \frac{\gamma - 1}{\gamma + 1} + \frac{2}{(\gamma + 1)M_1^2} = \frac{a_*^2}{u_1^2}$$

$$d = \frac{\tan^2 \sigma}{M_1^2 - 1} \qquad a_*^2 = \frac{\gamma - 1}{\gamma + 1}\left[1 + \frac{2}{(\gamma - 1)M_\infty^2}\right]U^2$$

Thus the Rankine–Hugoniot condition results in

$$(1 - A)u_{n1} - u_{n2} = 0$$

or

$$\left[(1 - A)\cos \sigma - \frac{\sin \sigma}{\tan (\sigma + \delta)}\right]u_1 = 0 \tag{4.88a}$$

This can be easily recast in the form

$$q_{k\alpha}Q_\alpha = 0 \tag{4.88b}$$

Here $u_1$ is the resultant local velocity upstream of the oblique shock. The shock angle $\sigma$ is determined from the discontinuity values $D_r$ at the element center. Note that the downstream velocity $u_2$ is eliminated through the deflection angle $\delta$, which is determined between the tangential velocity $u_{12}$ and downstream velocity $u_2$. The shock-boundary-condition matrix (4.88$b$) is now equivalent to (4.83). The quantity $q_{kx}$ is called the *shock boundary matrix* with $k$ denoting the number of shock elements.

To enforce the shock boundary condition (4.88$b$), Lagrange multipliers $\lambda_k$ are introduced such that

$$\lambda_k q_{k\alpha} Q_\alpha = 0 \tag{4.89}$$

To replace $S_x$ in (4.86) through Lagrange multipliers, an energy functional in quadratic form is constructed as

$$\chi = \tfrac{1}{2} A_{\alpha\beta} Q_\alpha Q_\beta - R_\alpha Q_\alpha \tag{4.90}$$

where $R_x = G_x + G_x$. Adding (4.89) to (4.88) gives

$$\chi = \tfrac{1}{2} A_{\alpha\beta} Q_\alpha Q_\beta - R_\alpha Q_\alpha + \lambda_k q_{k\alpha} Q_\alpha \tag{4.91}$$

The objective is to seek an extremum of $\chi$ for the flow field satisfying the jump conditions with respect to every $Q_\alpha$ and $\lambda_k$:

$$\delta\chi = \frac{\partial\chi}{\partial Q_\alpha}\delta Q_\alpha + \frac{\partial\chi}{\partial\lambda_k}\delta\lambda_k = 0$$

For all arbitrary values of $\delta Q_\alpha$ and $\delta\chi_k$, we must have $\partial\chi/\partial Q_\alpha = 0$ and $\partial\chi/\partial\lambda_k = 0$, leading to

$$\begin{bmatrix} A_{\alpha\beta} & q_{k\alpha} \\ q_{k\beta} & 0 \end{bmatrix} \begin{bmatrix} Q_\beta \\ \lambda_k \end{bmatrix} = \begin{bmatrix} R_\alpha \\ 0 \end{bmatrix} \tag{4.92}$$

By writing Eq. (4.92) in a compact form

$$B_{ij} X_j = Y_i \tag{4.93}$$

and noting that $Y_i$ contains $R_\alpha$, which is nonlinear, Eq. (4.93) can be written in an iterative form

$$B_{ij} X_j^{(n+1)} = Y_i^{(n)}$$

Initially, we consider a shockless domain, with $R_\alpha = 0$:

$$A_{\alpha\beta} Q_\beta = 0 \tag{4.94}$$

If the solution (4.92) yields $Q_\beta$, indicating nonzero $D_r$, then (4.94) is replaced by the expression containing the jump condition (4.91) in the subsequent iterations. In this iterative scheme $R_\alpha$ will be kept updated. The magnitude of $D_r$ calculated at the center of an element signifies the strength of the shock. The direction of the shock is determined by connecting the centers of shock elements ($D_r \neq 0$). For multiple occurrences, interactions, and reflections of shocks, it is advisable to start with the shock-element influence coefficients applied to the entire domain. At each iterative cycle, the shock boundary matrix $q_{k\alpha}$ is removed when $D_r$ is found to be zero,

$$A_{\alpha\beta}Q_\beta = R_\alpha \qquad (4.95)$$

Using this approach a missile consisting of a 4-caliber tangent ogive and 9-caliber afterbody was solved. A comparison of the numerical results with the experimental work gave an excellent agreement. See Refs. [84, 85] for further details.

In conclusion, the discontinuous-function method is extremely rigorous, with shocks allowed to develop freely without any damping effect. Although the computer time is excessive, it is hoped that this can be remedied in the future.

## 4.5 TRANSONIC FLOW AND SHOCK WAVES: ARTIFICIAL COMPRESSIBILITY AND SUCCESSIVE-LINE OVERRELAXATION

The present simple finite-element scheme is proposed for transonic-flow predictions. Although designed with the least sophistication, pressure distributions past two- and three-dimensional aircraft components can be computed to engineering accuracy requirements using this approach.

### 4.5A Governing Equations

The fluid is taken to be a perfect gas and the flow is assumed to be irrotational. Then, the compressible flow is governed by the following three equations:

*Conservation of mass:* $\qquad\qquad \rho_t + (\rho u)_x + (\rho v)_y + (\rho w)_z = 0 \qquad (4.96)$

where $\qquad\qquad\qquad\qquad u = \phi_x \qquad v = \phi_y \qquad w = \phi_z$

*Bernoulli's equation:* $\qquad\qquad dp + \rho d\left(\phi_t + \dfrac{q^2}{2}\right) = 0 \qquad (4.97)$

*Isentropic equation of state:* $\qquad\qquad p = A\rho^\kappa \qquad (4.98)$

where $\rho$ is the density, $p$ is the static pressure, $q$ is the total velocity, $\kappa$ is the adiabatic exponent, $\phi$ is the velocity potential, $t$ is the time, and $u$, $v$, $w$ are the velocity components in cartesian coordinates $x$, $y$, $z$.

The density can be expressed as a function of the velocity, if the pressure defined by the equation of state is entered in Eq. (4.97), which is subsequently integrated to give

$$\rho = \left[\frac{\kappa - 1}{A\kappa}\left(B - \phi_t - \frac{q^2}{2}\right)\right]^{1/(\kappa - 1)} \qquad (4.99)$$

where the constants of integration can be removed by a suitable normalization of $\phi$ and $\rho$. To obtain the variational principle of potential theory, Bernoulli's equation is divided through by the potential differential $d\phi$ and integrated over the entire fluid volume $V$, giving

$$\iiint \left[ p_\phi + \rho \left( \phi_t + \frac{q^2}{2} \right)_\phi \right] dV = 0 \tag{4.100}$$

Integration by parts and use of Eqs. (4.96) and (4.100) allows the variational principle to be obtained as

$$\iiint [\rho(uu_\phi + vv_\phi + ww_\phi) - \rho_t] \, dV = 0 \tag{4.101}$$

## 4.5B Solution Procedure

For the numerical discretization of Eq. (4.101) the flow domain is subdivided into finite elements which piecewise approximate the potential by trilinear (bilinear) interpolation in 3D (2D) in between eight (four) neighboring nodal points each. Since the stationarity of the integral (4.101) is true everywhere, it is also true for each nodal point of the computational grid. Thus $\partial/\partial\phi$ can be replaced by $\partial/\partial\phi_i$ ($i = 1, \ldots, N$), where $N$ is the total number of grid points. The density and its time derivative are computed at cell centers and kept constant over the element. Space derivatives of the potential are found by the chain rule of differentiation together with the inverse jacobian matrix of the local isoparametric mapping function. Now after Eq. (4.101) has been discretized in the manner outlined above, a large sparse matrix for the unknown $\phi_i$'s is assembled and solved by successive-line overrelaxation.

In order to account for the proper domain of dependence at supersonic speeds, the mass flux $\rho q$ is calculated at a point $H$ placed a small distance upstream of the control point under consideration. This is most easily done by the linear Taylor expansion of the quantity

$$(\rho q)_H = \rho q + (\rho q)_s \, \Delta s = \rho q \left\{ 1 + [q^{-2} - \rho(\kappa p)^{-1}] \frac{\Delta q^2}{2} \right\}$$

which means that the first term of Eq. (4.101) has only to be multiplied by the switching function

$$a = 1 + \min\left[0, q^{-2} - \rho(\kappa p)^{-1}\right] \frac{\Delta q^2}{2}$$

where $\Delta q^2$ is the difference of the velocity square between the nearest upwind cell and the control point element.

## 4.5C Applications

*Unsteady Airfoil Flow*   For unsteady problems the variational principle (4.101) is modified to account for moving and eventually distorting the computational grid fixed to the airfoil, which, for example, may plunge, pitch, or vary its contour for flap simulation:

$$\iint \{\rho[(u - x_t)u_\phi + (w - z_t)w_\phi] - \rho_t - \rho(x_{tx} + z_{tz})\} \, dx \, dz = 0$$

$x_t$ and $z_t$ are the displacement velocity components of the mesh, which are represented by the same element interpolation as the potential. A high-reduced-frequency example for which the full potential formulation is justified is shown in Fig. 4.26.

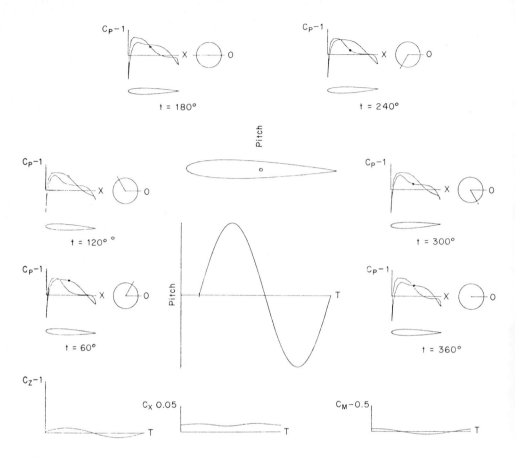

**FIG. 4.26**   Characteristics of pitching NACA 0012 airfoil. $M_\infty = 0.752$, $K = c/(u_\infty \Delta T) = 0.4$, $\delta = 2° \sin t$.

**Wings**   For a simplified modeling of the vortex sheet behind the trailing edge of the wing, the lifting-line theory is applied and a constant jump of the potential is introduced along the grid lines, leaving the trailing edge at its local bisector. A bound vortex is placed inside the wing with spanwise circulation proportional to the potential jump distribution along the trailing edge. From this vortex system a far-field potential is induced which, added to the undisturbed free-stream potential, is updated after each relaxation sweep at the points forming the perimeters of the computational grid. Element integration by the trapezoidal rule was sufficient for all cases computed so far.

    Figures 4.27 and 4.28 show pressure distributions past wings obtained with the present algorithm. With the fact known that neither a boundary-layer nor a wind-tunnel wall interference correction is applied, the agreement with experiments can be well-accepted for wing-design considerations.

**Wing-Body Combination**   In the present approach the quasi-two-dimensional topology of the isolated wing grid is retained by shifting and distorting the mesh such that the element

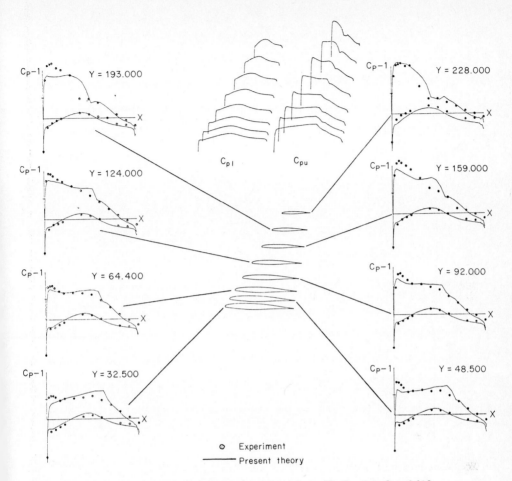

**FIG. 4.27**  Pressure distributions around test wing. $M_\infty = 0.8$, $\alpha = 2°$, $C_L = 0.4$, $C_D = 0.015$.

volumes are wrapped around the fuselage. Then a smoothing routine reshapes the input fuselage to a sufficiently continuous bump in the symmetry wall in order to avoid geometrical singularities.

From a crude grid with five subsequent grid refinements and potential-distribution interpolation, the result of Fig. 4.29 was obtained after not more than 18 equivalent iterations on the finest grid.

## 4.5D  Other Approaches

A nontrivial problem in finite-element methods is the sharp resolution of shocks if they are strong. In contrast to finite-difference schemes there is no sound theory yet for constructing a fully conservative shock operator for finite-element formulations. Despite this fact a growing number of authors suggest successfully working procedures for this problem. Habashi and Hafez [86] and Lucchi [87] extend the logic for the artificial density-switching function over

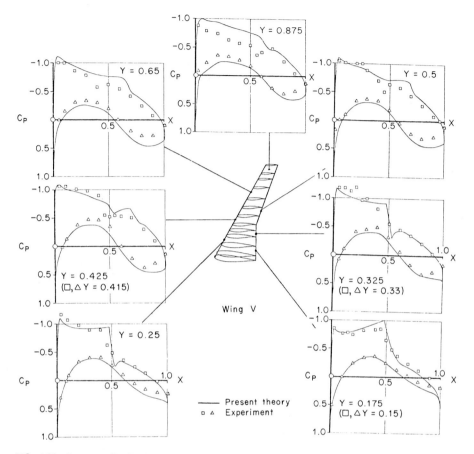

**FIG. 4.28**  Pressure distributions around test wing.  $M_\infty = 0.78$, $\alpha = 0.9°$.

two adjacent elements in streamwise direction. Fornasier [88] uses density upwinding along quasi-diagonal grid directions. Eberle [89] suggests a rotated-element arrangement with upwinding along grid lines. Ecer and Akay [90] introduce a least-square integral along grid lines coinciding with shock waves.

## 4.6 TRANSONIC FLOW AND SHOCK WAVES: COMBINED SHOCK CAPTURING AND SHOCK FITTING

### 4.6A Governing Equations

The solution of the full-potential equation for three-dimensional, steady, inviscid, and irrotational flows, expressed in the conservative form as follows, is considered:

$$(\rho\phi_{,x})_{,x} + (\rho\phi_{,y})_{,y} + (\rho\phi_{,z})_{,z} = 0 \qquad \text{in } \Omega \tag{4.102}$$

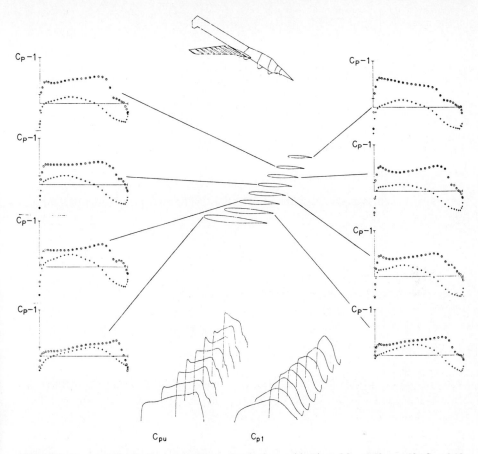

**FIG. 4.29** Pressure distribution around test wing-body combination. $M_\infty = 0.9°$, $\alpha = 0°$, $C_L = 0.32$, $C_D = 0.01$.

where $x$, $y$, $z$ are the cartesian coordinates, $\phi$ is the velocity potential, $\Omega$ is the solution domain, and $\rho$ is the mass density of the fluid. The general boundary conditions of Eq. (4.102) are

$$\phi = \phi_0 \qquad \text{on } S_1 \tag{4.103}$$

$$\rho\phi_{,n} = f \qquad \text{on } S_2 \tag{4.104}$$

where $\phi_0$ and $f$ are some specified quantities on the boundary $S = S_1 + S_2$, and $n$ is the outward normal on $S_2$. If flux-type boundary conditions are specified on all boundaries, $\phi$ must be specified at a single node for reference.

The finite-element treatment of this problem is outlined here for potential transonic flows [91-95]; an extension to full Euler equations can be found in Ref. [96].

By combining the isentropic equation of state with the Bernoulli equation, one obtains the relation

$$\rho = \text{const } (K^2 - q^2)^{1/(\gamma-1)} \tag{4.105}$$

for the mass density, where $\gamma$ is the ratio of specific heats,

$$K^2 = \frac{2a^2}{\gamma - 1} + q^2 \qquad (4.106)$$

and
$$q^2 = \phi_{,x}^2 + \phi_{,y}^2 + \phi_{,z}^2. \qquad (4.107)$$

In the above, $K$ is the maximum attainable speed which is constant throughout the flow, $a$ is the local speed of sound, and $q$ is the local flow speed.

## 4.6B Finite-Element Formulation

For a finite-element formulation of Eqs. (4.102) to (4.104), the Bateman's variational functional [97]

$$\pi = \int_{\Omega} p \, d\Omega + \int_{S_2} f\phi \, dS \qquad (4.108)$$

can be used, where for isentropic and perfect gases

$$p = \frac{\gamma - 1}{2\gamma} (\text{const}) \rho^{\gamma} \qquad (4.109)$$

is the pressure.

Expressing Eq. (4.108) for a finite element $e$, summing the contributions of all elements in the domain, and using the stationary values of the resulting expression yield the following variational statement

$$\delta\pi = \sum_e \left[ -\int_{\Omega_e} \rho_e (\phi_{,x}\delta\phi_{,x} + \phi_{,y}\delta\phi_{,y} + \phi_{,z}\delta\phi_{,z}) \, d\Omega + \int_{S_{2e}} f_e\delta\phi \, ds \right] = 0 \qquad (4.110)$$

Shape functions $N_i^e(x, y, z)$ with $C_0$-interelement continuities are chosen so that within each element the interpolation

$$\phi^e(x, y, z) = N_i^e(x, y, z)\phi_i^e = \mathbf{N}^T\boldsymbol{\phi}^e \qquad (i = 1, \dots, m) \qquad (4.111)$$

holds, where $\phi_i^e$ are the nodal values of the velocity potential and $m$ is the number of element nodal points. Substituting Eq. (4.111) into (4.110) yields the following system of equations:

$$\mathbf{K}\boldsymbol{\phi} = \mathbf{f} \qquad (4.112)$$

where
$$\mathbf{K} = \sum_e \int_{\Omega_e} \rho_e(\mathbf{N}_{,x}\mathbf{N}_{,x}^T + \mathbf{N}_{,y}\mathbf{N}_{,y}^T + \mathbf{N}_{,z}\mathbf{N}_{,z}^T) \, d\Omega \qquad (4.113)$$

$$\mathbf{f} = \sum_e \int_{S_{2e}} f_e\mathbf{N} \, dS \qquad (4.114)$$

$$\boldsymbol{\phi} = \sum_e \boldsymbol{\phi}^e \qquad (4.115)$$

When eight-node trilinear isoparametric elements are chosen for three-dimensional problems, a selective gaussian integration scheme is recommended in evaluating the element matrices in Eq. (4.113). In that case, the density $\rho_e$ can be evaluated only at the centroid of the elements, while a two-point gaussian quadrature per direction is utilized for the volume integration of the shape functions and their global derivatives. Since the local density in an element is nearly constant in the flow direction, very little sacrifice in accuracy is made. This, however, leads to significant saving in computations because the volume integrations of the global derivatives need be performed only once throughout the entire nonlinear iterations.

## 4.6c A Pseudo-Unsteady Formulation

To obtain a steady-state solution to the nonlinear equation (4.102) a pseudo-unsteady formulation is considered in the following form:

$$\frac{\Delta t}{\omega}(\rho\phi_{,xt})_{,x} + \frac{\Delta t}{\omega}(\rho\phi_{,yt})_{,y} + \frac{\Delta t}{\omega}(\rho\phi_{,zt})_{,z} + (\rho\phi_{,x})_{,x} + (\rho\phi_{,y})_{,y} + (\rho\phi_{,z})_{,z} = 0 \qquad (4.116)$$

where $t$ is the pseudo-time direction, $\Delta t$ is the time increment, and $\omega$ is a relaxation or a damping coefficient. The weak form of the above equation can be written as

$$\delta\pi = -\int_{\Omega} \rho\left(\frac{\Delta t}{\omega}\phi_{,xt}\delta\phi_{,x} + \frac{\Delta t}{\omega}\phi_{,yt}\delta\phi_{,y} + \frac{\Delta t}{\omega}\phi_{,zt}\delta\phi_{,z} + \phi_{,x}\delta\phi_{,x} + \phi_{,y}\delta\phi_{,y} + \phi_{,z}\delta\phi_{,z}\right) d\Omega$$

$$+ \int_{S_2} f\delta\phi \, dS = 0 \qquad (4.117)$$

where $f = \rho\phi_{,n}$ is the mass flux specified on the boundary $S_2$.

Finite-element discretization of Eq. (4.117) yields the following pseudo-unsteady system of nonlinear equations:

$$\Delta t \mathbf{C}\dot{\boldsymbol{\phi}} + \mathbf{K}\boldsymbol{\phi} = \mathbf{f} \qquad (4.118)$$

where

$$\mathbf{C} = \frac{\mathbf{K}}{\omega} \qquad (4.119)$$

is the damping matrix of the above pseudo-time-dependent problem. Here the relaxation factor $\omega$ is used to control the stability and convergence of the numerical integrations to be employed in obtaining steady-state solutions. Using finite differencing in time, the following step-by-step numerical-integration scheme for Eq. (4.118) can be obtained

$$\mathbf{K}^n \bar{\boldsymbol{\phi}}^{n+1} = \mathbf{f}^n \qquad (4.120)$$

with

$$\boldsymbol{\phi}^{n+1} = \omega\bar{\boldsymbol{\phi}}^{n+1} + (1 - \omega)\boldsymbol{\phi}^n \qquad (4.121)$$

where $n$ is the pseudo-time step. Starting with an initial guess for $\phi^0$, the step-by-step integrations are continued until a steady-state solution is reached at the $n^{\text{th}}$ step as

$$\boldsymbol{\phi}^{n+1} \approx \boldsymbol{\phi}^n \qquad (4.122)$$

Equation (4.120) is nonlinear since $\mathbf{K}^n = \mathbf{K}^n(\tilde{\rho}^n)$, where $\tilde{\rho}^n$ is the density to be evaluated between the $n^{\text{th}}$ and $(n+1)^{\text{th}}$ time steps. Therefore a "good" estimate of the coefficient matrix is necessary at each time step to assure the stability of the numerical integrations. An appropriate procedure for evaluating $\mathbf{K}^n$ and consequently $\mathbf{C}^n$ at a time step $n$ is to use

$$\tilde{\rho}_e^n \approx \rho_e^n \tag{4.123}$$

when the local flow is subsonic, and use

$$\tilde{\rho}_e^n \approx \rho_e^n - \alpha_e \, \Delta s_e \rho_{e,s}^n \tag{4.124}$$

when it is supersonic [91–93]. In the above equation, $s$ is the streamline direction, $\Delta s_e$ is the element size in the direction of $s$, and $\alpha_e$ is the coefficient of artificial viscosity.

The extrapolation scheme of Eq. (4.123) takes into account the elliptic nature of the equations in the subsonic region, whereas Eq. (4.124) considers the hyperbolic nature of the equations in the supersonic region. For sufficiently streamlined elements and uniform grids, Eq. (4.124) can further be expressed as follows

$$\tilde{\rho}_e^n \approx \alpha_e \rho_{eu}^n + (1 - \alpha_e)\rho_e^n \tag{4.125}$$

where $\rho_{eu}^n$ is the mass density of the nearest element located directly at the upstream side of $e$. This corresponds to the well-known "upwinding" techniques used in finite differences [98]. The amount of artificial viscosity $\alpha_e$ and the value of relaxation factor $\omega$ are determined according to the stability considerations of the numerical integrations.

## 4.6D Choice of the Artificial-Viscosity Distribution

One of the most important factors in determining the efficiency of the solution procedure has been the choice of the artificial-viscosity distribution. The finite-difference schemes have traditionally employed a fixed artificial-viscosity distribution for a particular grid. For each grid point, this distribution is determined only as a function of the local Mach number. Thus, while for rough grids the convergence is fast, for finer grids it slows down because of the reduction in the artificial viscosity.

The basic steps of the finite-element scheme proposed here are as follows: (1) choose a relatively high artificial viscosity, (2) obtain convergence to a steady state, (3) reduce the artificial viscosity, (4) repeat steps 1 to 4 until a solution with sufficiently small artificial viscosity is obtained. A nondimensional constant $\mu_e$ is employed throughout the supersonic region to control the amount of artificial viscosity. The coefficient of artificial viscosity in Eq. (4.125) is then calculated as [91–93]

$$\alpha_e = \mu_e\left(1 - \frac{1}{M_e^2}\right) \qquad \omega < \frac{1}{\alpha_e M_e^2} \qquad 0 < \omega \le 1 \tag{4.126}$$

where $e$ denotes the element and $M_e$ is the local Mach number in a particular element. Higher values of $\mu_e$ provide better convergence, but accuracy suffers owing to excessive artificial viscosity.

## 4.6E An Alternative Numerical-Integration Technique

The numerical-integration scheme based on a direct solution of the system defined in Eq. (4.120) has been employed with success for the solution of transonic-flow problems in Ref. [91]. However, since the left-hand side of Eq. (4.120) is nonlinear, a full decomposition of the coefficient matrix $\mathbf{K}^n$ is needed at each step, which makes the scheme computationally somewhat inefficient. For efficiency considerations the time integrations in Eq. (4.120) are modified as follows:

$$\mathbf{K}^0 \bar{\boldsymbol{\phi}}^{n+1} = \mathbf{f}^n + (\mathbf{K}^0 - \mathbf{K}^n)\boldsymbol{\phi}^n \tag{4.127}$$

with

$$\boldsymbol{\phi}^{n+1} = \omega \bar{\boldsymbol{\phi}}^{n+1} + (1 - \omega)\boldsymbol{\phi}^n \tag{4.128}$$

where

$$\mathbf{K}^0 = \mathbf{K}(\rho_\infty) \tag{4.129}$$

is constant for all time steps and $\mathbf{K}^n$ is evaluated using $\tilde{\rho}^n$ as given in Eqs. (4.123) and (4.124). Hence, the decomposition of $\mathbf{K}^0$ is needed only for the first time step, and the subsequent solutions can be obtained with relatively inexpensive forward and backward substitutions. Analytical as well as numerical stability analyses have shown that this constant-coefficient-matrix scheme has similar convergence characteristics as the variable-coefficient-matrix scheme of Eq. (4.120) and hence should be preferred [92].

## 4.6F Modeling of Shocks

Convergence and accuracy of the solutions in transonic flows strongly rely on the modeling of the shock. Most investigators have considered the shock as an area with high-pressure gradients where one has to provide sufficient grid refinement for accuracy. Mostly, however, the accurate modeling of the shock requires the proper treatment of a discontinuity rather than excessive local grid refinements. Also, it is always observed that the solution converges last at the shock since it is located farthest downstream at the shock.

The problems related to the treatment of the shock then are of two types: (1) inaccurate modeling of the shock discontinuity, which may provide artificial smearing, (2) insufficient artificial viscosity, which may cause numerical instabilities in the supersonic pocket, with shock as the most critical location.

To attain convergence and stability around the shock, the choice of the computational grid and the artificial-viscosity parameter requires considerable effort with either shock-capturing or shock-fitting methods which are commonly employed in treating the shocks.

Shock-capturing techniques are more popular because of the generality of locating the shock and the simplicity of the modeling. However, in order to obtain accuracy and stability around the shock, these techniques generally require special attention while artificial viscosity is being introduced. To stabilize the high-frequency oscillations in the vicinity of the shock, artificial viscosity is sometimes added even to the portions of the subsonic flow immediately following the shock [99]. On the other hand, if one attempts to use the shock-fitting procedure directly, convergence difficulties may be reduced considerably. However, in this case, one is faced with the basic problem of locating the shock accurately.

**Shock Capturing**   In the present formulation, the potential function $\phi$ is continuous across the element interfaces, but the derived quantities such as $\rho$, $p$, and $a$ are discontinuous. Since the supersonic elements are treated by adding artificial viscosity as discussed previously, when the flow is changing from supersonic to subsonic, the continuity of the mass flux is satisfied as a natural consequence of the variational formulation as follows:

$$\tilde{\rho}^{+}\phi_{,n}^{+} = \rho^{-}\phi_{,n}^{-} \tag{4.130}$$

where $+$ and $-$ denote the upstream and downstream sides of the interface, and $\tilde{\rho}$ is the modified density defined by Eq. (4.124). Hence, if the interfaces are sufficiently aligned with the shock lines, the shocks are allowed to appear between the elements, and the continuity of the actual mass flux

$$\rho^{+}\phi_{,n}^{+} = \rho^{-}\phi_{,n}^{-} \tag{4.131}$$

is satisfied in the limit, as the artificial-viscosity parameter approaches zero.

In this technique, commonly known as *shock capturing*, no modifications are made in the basic form of the finite-element equations. Although shocks can occur as discontinuities between the elements, some artificial smearing is present owing to the interaction between the subsonic and supersonic elements neighboring the shock.

**Shock Fitting**   In the proposed shock-fitting procedure, the shock is again assumed to occur at the element interfaces. However, when a shock is detected as a change from supersonic flow between two adjoining elements, these elements are uncoupled. This results in a physical separation of subsonic and supersonic regions of flow on the computational grid.

A natural boundary condition is imposed on the shock line of the supersonic element in the following form:

$$\tilde{f}_{e}^{n} = f_{e}^{n} - \alpha_{e}\,\Delta s_{e}\,f_{e,s}^{n} \tag{4.132}$$

$$f_{e}^{n} = (\rho_{e}^{+}\phi_{,n}^{+})^{n} \tag{4.133}$$

where $+$ indicates the upstream supersonic element. The value of $\phi_{i}$ at the shock points are in turn placed as forced boundary conditions on the nodes of the subsonic element $(-)$ downstream of the shock as follows:

$$\phi_{i}^{-} = \phi_{i}^{+} \tag{4.134}$$

Although this technique is computationally straightforward to implement, as in all other shock-fitting techniques, it relies strongly on the prior determination of the shock position. For this reason a combined version of shock-capturing and shock-fitting techniques is recommended.

## 4.6G The Combined Computational Procedure for Shocks

Since, as has been shown in Refs. [91–93], the scheme is uniformly convergent in a wider range of initial conditions for higher artificial viscosities, shock-capturing solutions are first obtained by selecting a large artificial-viscosity parameter $\alpha_{e}$. Following this, a series of shock-capturing solutions are obtained by gradually decreasing $\alpha_{e}$ until convergence difficulties are detected. With the previously converged shock-capturing solutions as an initial guess, an attempt at shock fitting is subsequently made to check the shock position. If the initial shock position is correct and the artificial-viscosity content is optimum, the influence from downstream to upstream at the shock is minimal in the shock capturing. Hence, both techniques yield essentially the same solution beyond which no further decrease in the artificial viscosity is possible.

If the the initial position of shock is incorrect, the shock moves to a different position after fitting, generally toward the downstream direction. The developed fitting scheme differs from the classical fitting procedures in which the position of the shock remains fixed. In the present case, however, when the conditions in Eqs. (4.132) and (4.134) are applied on a particular flow configuration, a new shock position is free to develop at each iteration. The computer code can automatically detect a new shock position with shock fitting. If a new shock position is actually so reached, then the shock capturing can again be employed by reducing the artificial viscosity. The above process is repeated until a unique solution is obtained. To improve efficiency and accuracy, at any point during the iterations, the solution procedure can be switched from one scheme to another without altering the computational grid.

## 4.7 TRANSONIC FLOW AND SHOCK WAVES: MIXED-TYPE ALGORITHMS

For transonic flows, the potential equation is of mixed elliptic-hyperbolic type and its solution admits a discontinuity: a shock wave. Discretization techniques (finite differences and finite elements) and iterative procedures to calculate transonic flows are discussed in this section, starting with the simple small-disturbance equation followed by the full-potential and stream-function formulations.

### 4.7A Transonic Small-Disturbance Theory and Finite-Difference Methods

For small disturbances, the linearized equation of compressible flow is given in terms of a perturbation potential $\phi$ by

$$(1 - M_\infty^2)\phi_{xx} + \phi_{yy} = 0 \qquad (4.135)$$

and the boundary condition is linearized to $\phi_y = \pm f'(x) - \alpha$, where $f(x)$ is the shape of the airfoil and $\alpha$ its angle of attack. Equation (4.135) is elliptic if $M_\infty^2 < 1$ and hyperbolic if $M_\infty^2 > 1$, and cannot represent a mixed flow. For $M_\infty^2 = 1$, the equation degenerates to $\phi_{yy} = 0$ and the linear theory breaks down for transonic flows.

Von Karman derived the nonlinear transonic equation

$$(1 - M^2)\phi_{xx} + \phi_{yy} = 0 \qquad 1 - M^2 \approx 1 - M_\infty^2 - (\gamma + 1)M_\infty^2 \phi_x \qquad (4.136)$$

This equation allows for the mixed nature of the transonic flows and the formation of shock waves. Because of nonlinearity, the characteristics

$$\frac{dy}{dx} = \pm \frac{1}{\sqrt{M^2 - 1}} \tag{4.137}$$

become complex for $M^2 < 1$; that is, in the subsonic region the equation is elliptic. Equation (4.136) can be written in a conservation form

$$[(1 - M_\infty^2)\phi_x - \tfrac{1}{2}(\gamma + 1)M_\infty^2\phi_x^2]_x + (\phi_y)_y = 0 \tag{4.138}$$

The shock-jump conditions are contained in Eq. (4.138), namely,

$$[(1 - M_\infty^2)\phi_x - \tfrac{1}{2}(\gamma + 1)M_\infty^2\phi_x^2] - \left(\frac{dx}{dy}\right)_s [\phi_y] = 0 \tag{4.139}$$

while the irrotationality condition

$$\phi_{yx} - \phi_{xy} = 0 \tag{4.140}$$

leads to

$$[\phi_x] + \left(\frac{dx}{dy}\right)_s [\phi_y] = 0 \quad \text{i.e.} \quad [\phi] = 0 \tag{4.141}$$

where $[a] = a^+ - a^-$ denotes the jump of a quantity $a$ across a shock $s$. Cole [100] pointed out that there are other forms which can be derived from Eq. (4.136). For example,

$$\left[\tfrac{1}{2}(1 - M_\infty^2)\phi_x^2 - \tfrac{1}{2}\phi_y^2 - \left(\frac{\gamma + 1}{3}\right)M_\infty^2\phi_x^3\right]_x + (\phi_x\phi_y)_y = 0 \tag{4.142}$$

Equation (4.142) is not conserved across a shock (as will be discussed below), and it is associated with the wave drag $D$ as follows:

$$\frac{D}{\gamma\rho_\infty} = \oint_c \left[\tfrac{1}{2}(1 - M_\infty^2)\phi_x^2 - \tfrac{1}{2}\phi_y^2 - \left(\frac{\gamma + 1}{3}\right)M_\infty^2\phi_x^3\right] dx$$

$$- \oint_c \phi_x\phi_y \, dx - \frac{\gamma + 1}{12}M_\infty^2 \int_s [\phi_x]^3 \, dy \tag{4.143}$$

Shrinking the contour $c$ to the airfoil, Eq. (4.143) becomes

$$\frac{D}{\gamma\rho_\infty} = -\oint_c \phi_x\phi_y \, dx \tag{4.144}$$

Another estimate of the drag is

$$\frac{D}{\gamma\rho_\infty} = -\frac{\gamma + 1}{12}M_\infty^2 \int_s [\phi_x]^3 \, dy \tag{4.145}$$

which is related to the entropy production due to the shock.

In 1970, Murman and Cole [101] introduced a type-dependent finite-difference scheme to solve Eq. (4.136). For subsonic points central differences are used for $x$-derivatives, while for supersonic points the $x$-derivative is approximated by backward differences. The $y$-derivatives are always central differences. Because of backward differences an artificial viscosity of the order of the grid size is introduced and the Murman–Cole scheme is an approximation of a modified equation of the form

$$(1 - M_\infty^2)\phi_{xx} + \phi_{yy} = -\varepsilon\phi_{xxx} \tag{4.146}$$

where $\varepsilon = \max\left[(M_\infty^2 - 1)\,\Delta x, 0\right]$.

A similar equation (with $\varepsilon$ as a constant) has been studied by Sichel [102] as a model for viscous transonic flows. The discretization leads to a system of nonlinear algebraic equations which is solved iteratively by a vertical-line successive overrelaxation (VLSOR) algorithm, marching with the flow. The development of the solution through iteration can be described by an artificial time-dependent equation which is similar to the unsteady, low-frequency transonic equation [103] (except for a damping term proportional to $\phi_t$):

$$\alpha\phi_{xt} = (1 - M^2)\phi_{xx} + \phi_{yy} \tag{4.147}$$

The $\phi_{xt}$-term is indispensable for the iterative solution of the mixed-type equation and is responsible for the convergence of the VLSOR algorithm for transonic-flow calculations. Other iterative algorithms, for example, horizontal-line successive overrelaxation (HLSOR), do not converge. In fact, VLSOR marching against the flow direction does not converge either.

To capture the right shock strength and position, Murman [104] introduced a conservative scheme with four operators, as shown in Fig. 4.30. With such discretization, mass is conserved and correct sharp shocks are produced.

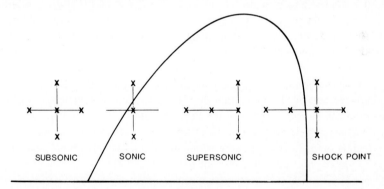

**FIG. 4.30** Murman's conservative schemes.

For one-dimensional flow, the Murman scheme is defective at the sonic point and admits nonphysical expansion shocks as a solution. Recently, Engquist and Osher [105] developed stable and positive entropy satisfying approximations for transonic-flow calculations where the following inequality is guaranteed:

$$\left[\tfrac{1}{2}(1 - M_\infty^2)\phi_x^2 - \tfrac{1}{2}\phi_y^2 - \tfrac{1}{3}(\gamma + 1)M_\infty^2\phi_x^3\right]_x + (\phi_x\phi_y)_y \geqslant 0 \tag{4.148}$$

The Engquist–Osher scheme can be interpreted as a Godunov-type scheme in which shocks are replaced by compression waves [106]. Recently, Hughes [107] introduced a shock-capturing finite-element scheme (for 1D conservation law and using a discontinuous weighting function) which is similar to the Engquist–Osher scheme.

## 4.7B Finite-Element Methods for the Transonic Small-Disturbance Equation

A variational formulation of the transonic small-disturbance equation is studied in Ref. [108] using the functional

$$I(\phi) = \int\int_\Omega \left[\tfrac{1}{2}(1 - M_\infty^2)\phi_x^2 + \tfrac{1}{2}\phi_y^2 - \tfrac{1}{6}M_\infty^2(\gamma+1)\phi_x^3\right] dx\,dy - \int_{\partial\Omega} f'(x)\phi\,ds \qquad (4.149)$$

The first variation of $I$ is

$$\delta I = \int\int_\Omega \{[(1 - M_\infty^2)\phi_x - \tfrac{1}{2}(\gamma+1)M_\infty^2\phi_x^2]_x + \phi_{yy}\}\delta\phi\,dx\,dy + \int_{\partial\Omega}\left(\frac{\partial\phi}{\partial n} - f'(x)\right)\delta\phi\,ds \qquad (4.150)$$

The matrix associated with the second variation $\delta^2 I$,

$$\begin{bmatrix} F\phi_x\phi_x & F\phi_x\phi_x \\ F\phi_y\phi_x & F\phi_{yy} \end{bmatrix} = \begin{bmatrix} (K - \phi_x) & 0 \\ 0 & 1 \end{bmatrix} \qquad (4.151)$$

where $F$ is the integrand in Eq. (4.149), indicates that the functional $I$ is not positive-definite.

A Galerkin–finite-element method is applied by Hafez et al. [109] using bilinear shape functions on rectangles. In subsonic regions, the nodal algebraic equation is identical to the nine-point finite-difference formula for elliptic equations. In the supersonic region, the governing equation is hyperbolic, where $x$ is the timelike direction. A nonstandard Galerkin projection technique for integrating initial-value problems is used where regularization terms representing artificial viscosity ($\varepsilon_1\phi_{yyx}$) and artificial inertia ($\varepsilon_2\phi_{xxyy}$) are introduced in a manner similar to that of Showalter and Ting [110]. For different choices of $\varepsilon_1$ and $\varepsilon_2$, the nodal equation can be made similar to the Lees scheme [111] or just Murman's supersonic operator. Two blending elements are needed, a sonic element between subsonic and supersonic regions, which is simply a Galerkin approximation of $\phi_{yy} = 0$, and a finite-element analogue of Murman's shock-point operator. The finite-element schemes are shown in Fig. 4.31. The system of nonlinear algebraic equations are solved iteratively by the VLSOR algorithm. In general, the accuracy and the efficiency of the calculations are similar to finite differences. In the one-dimensional case, the sonic operator is again defective. A finite-element analogue of the Engquist–Osher scheme is given in Ref. [112].

Another Galerkin–finite-element method for the transonic small-disturbance equation is based on a system of first-order equations [113]:

$$u_t = [(1 - M_\infty^2)u - \tfrac{1}{2}(\gamma+1)M_\infty^2 u^2]_x + v_y + (\varepsilon_1 u_x)_x + \varepsilon_2 u$$

$$v_t = u_y - v_x + \varepsilon_3 v \qquad (4.152)$$

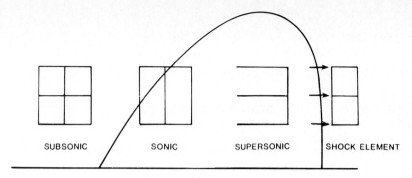

**FIG. 4.31**  Finite-element transonic schemes.

using Crank–Nicolson finite differences in time. The system of Eqs. (4.152) (with $\varepsilon_1 = 0$) is always hyperbolic in $t$. The $(\varepsilon_1 u_x)_x$ is representing the artificial viscosity which vanishes for $M^2 < 1$, while $\varepsilon_2 u$, $\varepsilon_3 v$ are damping terms to accelerate the convergence ($\varepsilon_2 u$, $\varepsilon_3 v$ vanish in the supersonic region at all times, while they vanish in the subsonic region only when the steady state is reached) [114].

So far the mixed-type and the time-dependent methods have been discussed. A third approach to transonic-flow calculations is the least-squares method. The order of the equation is doubled and the system becomes more ill-conditioned, which calls for very efficient iterative algorithms. Chan and Brashears [115] used higher-order shape functions with few elements and a direct inversion procedure at every iteration. Artificial viscosity is introduced implicitly by neglecting the contribution of downstream elements at each supersonic node. Shocks are smeared and do not satisfy the right jump conditions as observed usually with nonconservative calculations.

## 4.7c  The Full-Potential Equation and Finite-Difference Calculations

The small-disturbance equation is only a model which describes most of the interesting features of transonic flows. The simplified equation together with the linearized boundary condition is in some cases sufficient. For practical cases of complex geometry, the exact potential equation and the exact boundary conditions are required.

The extension is basically technical, following the main guidelines of the small-disturbance mixed-type method, namely:

1. The introduction of artificial viscosity (to construct stable supersonic schemes)
2. The use of conservative switching schemes (to capture the right shock without excessive smearing)
3. The use of consistent iterative algorithms (including the $\Phi_{xt}$-term for reliable convergence)

Following Jameson [116] the full-potential equation can be rearranged in the symbolic form

$$(1 - M^2)\Phi_{ss} + \Phi_{nn} = 0 \qquad (4.153)$$

where
$$\Phi_{ss} = \frac{u^2}{q^2}\Phi_{xx} + \frac{2uv}{q^2}\Phi_{xy} + \frac{v^2}{q^2}\Phi_{yy}$$

and
$$\Phi_{nn} = \frac{v^2}{q^2}\Phi_{xx} - \frac{2uv}{q^2}\Phi_{xy} + \frac{u^2}{q^2}\Phi_{yy}$$

Upwind differences are used to approximate the terms contributing to $\Phi_{ss}$, while the terms associated with $\Phi_{nn}$ are central-differenced. Many iterative schemes can be described by the following artificial time-dependent equation [117]:

$$\varepsilon\Phi_t + \delta\Phi_{tt} + 2\alpha\Phi_{st} + 2\beta\Phi_{nt} = (a^2 - q^2)\Phi_{ss} + a^2\Phi_{nn} \tag{4.154}$$

or
$$\varepsilon\Phi_T + \left(\delta + \frac{\alpha^2}{a^2 - q^2} + \frac{\beta^2}{a^2}\right)\Phi_{TT} = (a^2 - q^2)\Phi_{SS} + a^2\Phi_{NN}$$

where
$$T = t + \left(\frac{\alpha}{a^2 - q^2}\right)s + \left(\frac{\beta}{a^2}\right)n \qquad N = n \qquad S = s \tag{4.155}$$

For supersonic flows, the coefficient of $\Phi_{TT}$ must be negative in order to have a hyperbolic equation where $S$ is the timelike direction, i.e.,

$$\alpha^2 > (M^2 - 1)\beta^2 + \delta(q^2 - a^2) \tag{4.156}$$

The sign of $\alpha$ has to be chosen to guarantee the right domain of dependence. Moreover, a von Neumann analysis leads to

$$\varepsilon = 0 \qquad \text{for} \qquad M^2 > 1 \tag{4.157}$$

Equation (4.154) and conditions (4.156) are a slight generalization of Jameson's analysis of the two-level-line relaxation algorithm marching with the flow direction.

The upwind-difference approximation of $\Phi_{ss}$ introduces an artificial viscosity of the form $\varepsilon\Phi_{sss}$, or, more precisely,

$$(1 - M^2)\left[\left(\frac{u^2}{q^2}\Phi_{xxx} + \frac{uv}{q^2}\Phi_{yxx}\right)\Delta x + \left(\frac{uv}{q^2}\Phi_{xyy} + \frac{v^2}{q^2}\Phi_{yyy}\right)\Delta y\right] \tag{4.158}$$

Later Jameson [118] used a conservative form of Eqs. (4.153) and (4.158), i.e.,

$$(\rho\Phi_x)_x + (\rho\Phi_y)_y = \left[\rho(1 - M^2)\left(\frac{u^2}{q^2}\Phi_{xx} + \frac{uv}{q^2}\Phi_{yx}\right)\Delta x\right]_x$$

$$+ \left[\rho(1 - M^2)\left(\frac{uv}{q^2}\Phi_{xy} + \frac{v^2}{q^2}\Phi_{yy}\right)\Delta y\right]_y = 0 \tag{4.159}$$

For accurate treatments of boundary conditions, global transformations are used. Jameson and Caughey [119] have used local transformations, as in isoparametric elements, to calculate complex configurations in their so-called finite-volume method. For bilinear elements the finite-volume method based on balancing of fluxes across auxiliary faces leads to an odd–even decoupled system. Fourth-order terms are added to the system to avoid this problem. It should be mentioned, however, that in the case of triangles, the finite-element formulation and the flux-balancing approach produce identical nodal equations.

## 4.7D Finite-Element Methods for Full-Potential Equation

The variational formulation of potential flow is given by the Bateman principle, namely,

$$I = \int \int p \, dA \qquad \text{is stationary} \qquad (4.160)$$

Only for subsonic flows, $I$ has an extremum. For transonic flow, the Galerkin finite element can be applied to Eq. (4.159) (where $x$ and $y$ are of the order of the size of the element). Higher-order shape functions are required for the solution of Eq. (4.159). Moreover, a finite-element analogue of upwind differences is needed.

Recently a simple method has been used widely for both finite-difference and finite-element full-potential calculations, namely, the artificial compressibility, where the density is modified to introduce an effective dissipation [120–122]. The method is based on the observation that Eq. (4.159) can be rewritten in the form

$$(\rho \Phi_x)_x + (\rho \Phi_y)_y = (\mu u \rho_x \, \Delta x)_x + (\mu v \rho_y \, \Delta y)_y \qquad (4.161a)$$

or $\qquad (\rho_1 \Phi_x)_x + (\rho_2 \Phi_y)_y = 0 \qquad (4.161b)$

where $\qquad \rho_1 = \rho - \mu \rho_x \, \Delta x \qquad \rho_2 = \rho - \mu \rho_y \, \Delta y \qquad \mu = \max\left(0, 1 - \frac{1}{M^2}\right)$

A slightly different form, more amenable to finite-element discretization, is

$$(\tilde{\rho} \Phi_x)_x + (\tilde{\rho} \Phi_y)_y = 0 \qquad (4.162)$$

where $\qquad \tilde{\rho} = \rho - \mu \rho_s \, \Delta s \qquad \text{and} \qquad \rho_s \, \Delta s = \frac{u}{q} \rho_x \, \Delta x + \frac{v}{q} \rho_y \, \Delta y$

Using triangular or isoparametric bilinear elements and assuming $\tilde{\rho}$ is given, Eq. (4.162) results in a symmetric positive-definite matrix. Such a linearization, however, is inconsistent and bound to lead to convergence difficulties, since the nonlinearity is essential and responsible for the mixed-type nature of the equation. Results can be obtained, however, for moderate Mach numbers using an excessive artificial viscosity. For higher transonic Mach numbers, Taylor and Poisson iterations do not converge.

Equation (4.162) is equivalent to Eq. (4.153) (except in the shock region), and the VLSOR algorithm is suitable for the mixed-type equation. In finite-difference calculations, reliable convergence is guaranteed if the $\Phi_{xt}$-term is explicitly augmented in the VLSOR algorithm. The finite-element analogue is discussed in Ref. [123].

Fast iterative hybrid algorithms are developed for finite elements using Taylor or Poisson iteration as well as conjugate-gradient methods preconditioned by an approximate $LL^T$-factorization and, in all cases, alternated with the VLSOR algorithm [123]. Other first- and second-degree procedures, with necessary modifications for mixed-type equations (to account for a $\Phi_{xt}$-term), prove to be useful.

Alternatively, a hyperbolic system of first-order equations, similar to Eq. (4.152), is solved:

$$\frac{1}{2}\frac{\rho}{a^2}(u^2+v^2)_t = (\rho u)_x + (\rho v)_y + (\varepsilon_1 u_x + \varepsilon_2 v_x)_x + (\varepsilon_3 u_y + \varepsilon_4 v_y)_y + \varepsilon_5(u^2+v^2)$$

$$u^2\left(\frac{v}{u}\right)_t = u_y - v_x$$

(4.163)

with proper choices of the $\varepsilon$-coefficients.

The third approach, the least-squares method, has been successfully applied to the transonic full-potential equation by Glowinski and Pironneau [124] using a preconditioned conjugate gradient. To exclude nonphysical expansion shocks, an entropy inequality is imposed by using a penalty function and recently by using artificial viscosity and artificial density.

## 2.7E Rotational (Nonisentropic) Flows

For some practical problems, the irrotationality assumption is not justified and the potential function is not adequate to correctly describe the flow field. General steady inviscid flows are governed by a system of first-order equations (Euler) which is of mixed elliptic-hyperbolic type. Time-dependent methods have been traditionally used but convergence to the steady state is generally slow. Least-squares formulations of the steady equations are under investigation [125, 126].

Here, the Euler equations are replaced by a stream-function formulation:

$$\left(\frac{\Psi_x}{\tilde{\rho}}\right)_x + \left(\frac{\Psi_y}{\tilde{\rho}}\right)_y = -\omega \equiv p\frac{dS/R}{d\Psi} - \frac{dH}{d\Psi}$$

(4.164)

where $H$ is the total enthalpy, $S$ is the entropy, $p$ is the pressure, and $R$ is the gas constant. The density is given by

$$\rho = [(\gamma-1)M_\infty^2(H(\Psi)-\tfrac{1}{2}q^2)]^{1/\gamma+1} \cdot e^{-S(\Psi)/R}$$

(4.165)

The weak solution of Eq. (4.164) admits a shock across which the tangential momentum is conserved. Mass is automatically conserved. To conserve normal momentum, a correct jump in the entropy has to be imposed.

A traditional difficulty with this formulation is the density-mass flux relationship; namely, there is a subsonic and a supersonic branch with a square-root singularity at the sonic speed. Finite-difference solutions of Eqs. (4.164) and (4.165) are reported in Ref. [127] using the artificial-compressibility method. Finite-element solutions using similar procedures have been obtained by the authors [128, 129].

## 4.7F Numerical Examples

Some results based on the artificial-compressibility method are briefly presented. Finite-element results for a range of Mach numbers for a NACA 0012 airfoil are plotted in Fig.

4.32. In Fig. 4.33 the finite-element solutions of the irrotational velocity potential and irrotational stream-function equations for $M_\infty = 0.8385$ are presented. The nonisentropic (rotational) stream-function solution is also shown in the same figure. The rates of convergence of various iterative procedures are compared in Fig. 4.34 for $M_\infty = 0.85$. Details of the iterative procedures can be found in Refs. [121, 123, and 128].

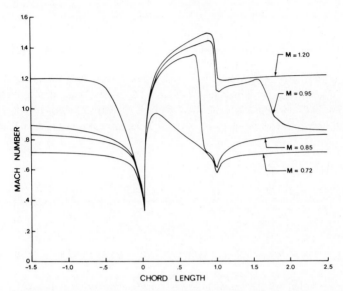

**FIG. 4.32**   FEM transonic results, NACA 0012, bilinear elements.

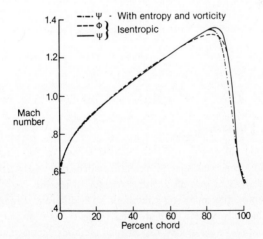

**FIG. 4.33**   Isentropic irrotational potential and stream-function solutions and nonisentropic, rotational stream-function solution of transonic flow ($M_\infty = 0.8385$) around a 4.2% circular bump placed in a channel of height/chord ratio of 2.

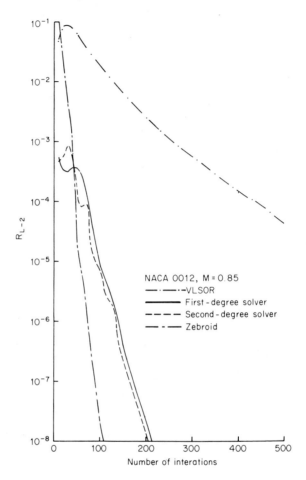

**FIG. 4.34** Rates of convergence of several iterative procedures.

### 4.7G Concluding Remarks

Steady transonic potential flows are governed by a second-order mixed elliptic-hyperbolic equation. The difficulty due to the mixed-type nature can be handled by using a time-dependent equation which is always hyperbolic in time and for which the steady-state solution is of interest. In this chapter, the mixed-type methods with different strategies in subsonic and supersonic regions are emphasized. The artificial viscosity, its form and magnitude, and the way it is implemented play an essential role in such methods. Consistent iterative algorithms are developed, resulting in efficient reliable conservative calculations.

For rotational nonisentropic flows the stream-function formulation is an alternative to the Euler primitive-variable equations. Such a formulation is very suitable for finite-element analysis, using the same efficient techniques developed for potential calculations.

# 4.8 CONVECTION AND DIFFUSION IN THE ATMOSPHERE

## 4.8A Definition of the Problems

This section discusses two numerical modeling problems in the atmosphere: the global modeling problem, where grid lengths of 150 km for 5-day forecasts, or 1500 km for multi-annual climate experiments, can be afforded with present computers; and the problem of dispersion, particularly in the boundary layer, with resolution of about 1 km and an integration time of a few hours.

**Forecast Problem**  The forecast problem is generally solved by using the three-dimensional compressible-flow equations with the hydrostatic assumption made. For a full discussion and scale analysis, see Ref. [130]. Since the grid length used has to be 150 km or greater, not all the motions which carry out important heat exchanges in the atmosphere can be represented explicitly. Extra parts have to be added to the models to describe vertical convective motions, which have a space scale of 0.1 to 10 km. In addition, the equations of motion only describe adiabatic processes, and representations of the effects of moisture and radiation have to be included. Most of the differences between different forecast models are concerned with different representations of these effects.

**Dispersion Problem**  The dispersion problem is mostly concerned with turbulent transfer in the atmospheric boundary layer. It is not possible to represent the turbulent motion explicitly, and it is therefore necessary to represent its bulk effect only. This is commonly done by introducing an exchange coefficient $K(z)$ and describing the effect of the mixing by equations of the form

$$\frac{\partial C}{\partial t} = \frac{\partial}{\partial z}\left[ K(z)\frac{\partial C}{\partial z}\right] \tag{4.166}$$

where $z$ is a vertical coordinate and $C$ can represent temperature, moisture, or momentum. The exchange coefficient has to depend on the static stability of the air through the Richardson number

$$\mathrm{Ri} = g\frac{\partial \theta}{\partial z}\left[ T\left(\frac{\partial u}{\partial z}\right)^2\right]^{-1} \tag{4.167}$$

where $\theta$ is the potential temperature, $u$ the wind speed, $T$ the temperature, and $g$ the acceleration due to gravity. An extensive review of how the coefficient $K(z)$ is chosen is given in Ref. [131]. Uncertainty in this choice is the main difficulty in solving this problem; the choice of numerical procedure for solving the problem is of secondary importance. The remainder of the equations used are the same as in forecast models. The hydrostatic assumption is often still made because the flows treated are usually slow.

## 4.8B Governing Equations

**Forecast Model**  The equations are written here in spherical polar coordinates $(\lambda, \theta)$, with vertical coordinate $\sigma = p/p_*$, where $p$ is pressure and $p_*$ is surface pressure. The earth's surface is represented by $\sigma = 1$ and the "top" of the atmosphere by $\sigma = 0$. Alternative choices are discussed in Ref. [130], but this system is the most commonly used. The wind components in the horizontal directions are written as $(u, v)$, and the vertical velocity can be written as $\dot{\sigma}$, which is defined as

$$\dot{\sigma} = \frac{D\sigma}{Dt} \equiv \frac{\partial \sigma}{\partial t} + \frac{u}{a \cos \theta} \frac{\partial \sigma}{\partial \lambda} + \frac{v}{a} \frac{\partial \sigma}{\partial \theta} \tag{4.168}$$

or

$$\omega = \frac{Dp}{Dt} \equiv \frac{\partial p}{\partial t} + \frac{u}{a \cos \theta} \frac{\partial p}{\partial \lambda} + \frac{v}{a} \frac{\partial p}{\partial \theta} \tag{4.169}$$

$\phi$ is the geopotential, $a$ is the radius of the earth, $T$ is the temperature, $q$ is the specific humidity, $(\tau_\lambda, \tau_\theta)$ is the horizontal surface stress, $H$ and $M$ are the vertical convective heat and moisture fluxes, $L$ is the latent heating, $P$ is the rate of precipitation, $\Omega$ is the angular velocity of the earth's rotation, with $f = 2\Omega \sin \theta$, $g$ is the acceleration due to gravity, and $Q$ is the diabatic heating. Write $(U, V)$ for $(p_* u, p_* v)$.

The equations are

$$\frac{\partial U}{\partial t} + \frac{1}{a \cos \theta} \left[ \frac{\partial}{\partial \lambda} (Uu) + \frac{\partial}{\partial \theta} (Vu \cos \theta) \right] + \frac{\partial}{\partial \sigma} (p_* \dot{\sigma} u)$$

$$- V \left( f + \frac{u \tan \theta}{a} \right) + \frac{1}{a \cos \theta} \left( p_* \frac{\partial \phi}{\partial \lambda} + RT \frac{\partial p_*}{\partial \lambda} \right) = K \nabla \cdot p_* \nabla u + g \frac{\partial \tau_\lambda}{\partial \sigma} \tag{4.170}$$

$$\frac{\partial V}{\partial t} + \frac{1}{a \cos \theta} \left[ \frac{\partial}{\partial \lambda} (Uv) + \frac{\partial}{\partial \theta} (Vv \cos \theta) \right] + \frac{\partial}{\partial \sigma} (p_* \dot{\sigma} v)$$

$$+ U \left( f + \frac{u \tan \theta}{a} \right) + \frac{1}{a} \left( p_* \frac{\partial \phi}{\partial \theta} + RT \frac{\partial p_*}{\partial \theta} \right) = K \nabla \cdot p_* \nabla v + g \frac{\partial \tau_\theta}{\partial \sigma} \tag{4.171}$$

$$\frac{\partial \phi}{\partial \sigma} + \frac{RT}{\sigma} = 0 \tag{4.172}$$

$$\frac{\partial p_*}{\partial t} + \frac{1}{a \cos \theta} \left[ \frac{\partial U}{\partial \lambda} + \frac{\partial}{\partial \theta} (V \cos \theta) \right] + \frac{\partial}{\partial \sigma} (p_* \dot{\sigma}) = 0 \tag{4.173}$$

$$\frac{\partial}{\partial t} (p_* T) + \frac{1}{a \cos \theta} \left[ \frac{\partial}{\partial \lambda} (UT) + \frac{\partial}{\partial \theta} (VT \cos \theta) \right] + \frac{\partial}{\partial \sigma} (p_* \dot{\sigma} T) - \frac{\kappa T \omega}{\sigma}$$

$$= K \nabla \cdot p_*^{\kappa+1} \nabla \frac{T}{p_*^\kappa} + \frac{g}{C_p} \frac{\partial H}{\partial \sigma} + \frac{p_*}{C_p} (\dot{Q} + L\dot{P}) \tag{4.174}$$

$$\frac{\partial}{\partial t} (p_* q) + \frac{1}{a \cos \theta} \left[ \frac{\partial}{\partial \lambda} (Uq) + \frac{\partial}{\partial \theta} (Vq \cos \theta) \right] + \frac{\partial}{\partial \sigma} (p_* \dot{\sigma} q) = K \nabla \cdot p_* \nabla q + g \frac{\partial M}{\partial \sigma} - p_* P \tag{4.175}$$

The boundary conditions are

$$\dot{\sigma} = 0 \qquad \text{at } \sigma = 0, 1$$

$$H, M \text{ specified at } \sigma = 1$$

These equations describe motions on many space and time scales. The largest terms are $p_* \, \partial\phi/\partial\lambda$ and $-fV$ in (4.170) and $p_* \, \partial\phi/\partial\theta$ and $fU$ in (4.171). These terms almost balance, leaving a small residual which acts as the forcing term for $\partial U/\partial t$. The horizontal advective terms, for instance, $(\partial/\partial\lambda)(Uu)$, are somewhat smaller. The terms associated with the spherical geometry, for instance $-(uV\tan\theta)/a$, are small correction terms. The terms multiplied by $K$ represent the effect of turbulent mixing and also act as artificial viscous terms. These are required because the equations with $K = 0$ would have discontinuous solutions. Solution of this system is expensive, and it is necessary to spend most of the effort in approximating the largest terms of the equations and using simpler procedures for the smaller terms.

**Dispersion Problem**   A subset of the equations is solved. The spherical geometry is ignored. The important parts of the model are the vertical exchange coefficients ($\tau_\lambda$, $\tau_\theta$) and the fluxes $H$ and $M$. The simplest theory ($K$-theory) assumes that terms of the form (4.166) are added to each equation.

### 4.8c  Solution Procedures

**Forecast Problem**   The solution procedure described below appears to be the most effective finite-element scheme for this problem. For further details and alternatives see Refs. [132–135]. In this procedure only horizontal variations are described by finite elements, with several thousand nodal parameters. The vertical structure is described by up to 15 layers, and finite differences are used to approximate vertical derivatives. Finite differences are also used to describe the time evolution. The system describes fast-moving waves with speeds of 300 m/s in addition to information propagating with the flow speed, typically less than 50 m/s. A mixed time-integration scheme is therefore used, represented symbolically below:

$$C_{t+\Delta t} = C_{t-\Delta t} + \Delta t(L_{t-\Delta t} + L_{t+\Delta t}) + 2\,\Delta t\, A_t + 2\,\Delta t\, D_{t-\Delta t} \qquad (4.176)$$

The advective increments are written as $A$, the diffusive increments as $D$, and the *linearized* increments due to the fast waves as $L$. A linear system therefore has to be solved at each time step.

The horizontal representation is chosen to ensure the accuracy of the balance between the largest terms in (4.170), (4.171). Therefore the vertical component of vorticity, $\zeta$, and the horizontal divergence $D$ are used as variables, and a differentiated form of (4.170), (4.171) is solved. It can be shown that this has similar advantages to using a staggered finite-difference mesh. The mesh is as regular as possible, since any variations in the mesh result in spurious noise generation and considerable loss in accuracy for smooth data. On a sphere this is difficult to achieve; either a quasi-regular grid can be used or else a regular latitude-longitude grid with special procedures near the poles [130]. This difficulty is exactly the same as that in finite-difference models. Either triangles or rectangles can be used, with linear or bilinear interpolation as appropriate. If triangles are used, they should be equilateral (or as nearly so as possible). Distorted quadrilaterals should not be used, nor should higher-order interpolation functions. All these alternatives are found to produce either spurious noise generation or wrong results for smooth data. Important nonlinear terms seem to be calculated most accurately using a two-stage method illustrated below. It is important not to calculate products of two piecewise constant quantities derived from derivatives of piecewise linear functions; this can result in nonlinear instability. The terms involving functions of $\theta$ vary very slowly, and the so-called product approximation is sufficiently accurate to represent them. Equations (4.170) to (4.175) can then be solved by a multistage Galerkin procedure, some of which is illustrated below for the advective form of Eq. (4.175).

*Analytic form*                       *Matrix form*

Given $\zeta$:

$$\nabla^2\psi = \zeta \qquad\qquad \mathbf{K}\psi = \mathbf{M}\zeta$$

$$u = \frac{1}{a\cos\theta}\frac{\partial\psi}{\partial\theta} \qquad\qquad \mathbf{M}\mathbf{u}_1 = \mathbf{Y}\psi$$

$$\mathbf{u} = \frac{\mathbf{u}_1}{a\cos\theta} \qquad (4.177)$$

$$q_1 = \frac{1}{a\cos\theta}\frac{\partial q}{\partial\lambda} \qquad\qquad \mathbf{M}\mathbf{q}_1 = \frac{\mathbf{X}\mathbf{q}}{a\cos\theta}$$

$$\frac{\partial q}{\partial t} = -uq_1 \qquad\qquad \mathbf{M}\frac{\partial\mathbf{q}}{\partial t} = -\mathbf{P}u\mathbf{q}_1$$

In this procedure all functions are regarded as piecewise (bi)linear, and piecewise (bi)linear representations are also calculated for various intermediate quantities. Slowly varying terms are approximated by multiplying nodal values. The procedure can easily be generalized to all the terms in (4.170) to (4.175); it is possible to economize considerably because certain intermediate quantities are used several times, and the calculated values can be reused. It can be seen that there are a large number of inversions of the mass matrix $\mathbf{M}$. An element of the matrix equation $\mathbf{Mu} = \mathbf{Ku}$ can be written as

$$m_0 u_0 + \sum_{i=1}^{n} m_i u_i = (\mathbf{Ku})_0 \qquad (4.178)$$

where the sum is taken over all nodes adjacent to node 0. This can be inverted using the obvious iteration

$$m_0 u_0^s = \alpha\left[(\mathbf{Ku})_0 - \sum_{i=1}^{n} m_i u_i^{s-1}\right] + (1-\alpha)m_0 u_0^{s-1} \qquad (4.179)$$

where $\alpha$ is an underrelaxation parameter. The right-hand-side vector $(\mathbf{Ku})_0$ is most accurate for slowly varying functions and least accurate for rapidly varying functions. Thus it is found that two to three iterations are sufficient to obtain adequate accuracy in practice. The linear system arising from the implicit time integration in (4.176) is solved by standard methods. If a latitude-longitude grid is used a fast Fourier transform method is very effective. Iterative methods can be used since the linear system is a discrete approximation to a Helmholz equation which gives no convergence problems.

***Dispersion Problem***   The main term which has to be evaluated is of the form (4.166). The finite-element representation is also used in the vertical in this case. Usually $K(z)$ varies rapidly with $z$. It can be represented either as an analytic formula or as a piecewise linear formulation. A multistage procedure should not be used but

$$-\int K(z)\frac{\partial C}{\partial z}\frac{\partial \phi_n}{\partial z}$$

formed directly, where $\phi_n$ are piecewise linear test functions. Integration by parts has been used. A two-stage procedure would give near-zero values if $C$ alternates in sign between nodes. The grid length can be varied to give maximum resolution near the boundary, since the spurious generation of noise is unlikely in a diffusion problem.

In both problems extra physical processes have to be represented. In this finite-element scheme the data is represented by a best-least-squares (bi)linear fit. Subroutines to handle these processes are most conveniently written in terms of area-averaged values. It is therefore necessary to extract these average values over suitable cells from the best linear fit, calculate

**FIG. 4.35**   500-mb chart for 2 June 1977.

**FIG. 4.36**   72-hour 500-mb chart for 5 June 1977.

increments due to the physical processes, and then invert to obtain a best linear fit to the increments.

## 4.8D Software and Hardware Requirements

Both problems require long integration times with the same program on a fixed grid. The need for optimization is only in the time-dependent code, not in the programs used to set up the grid. Note that in a problem of this size it is never possible to handle the problem as a matrix problem as in engineering applications. Each row of the matrix equation

$$\mathbf{M\dot{u} = Ku}$$

contains $n$ entries, where $n$ is the number of nodes adjacent to any given node. The storage requirement for coefficients is thus $nN$ on a general grid, if $N$ is the number of nodes, or just $n$ if the grid is regular.

**FIG. 4.37**   72-hour 500-mb forecast for 5 June 1977, spectral model.

## 4.8E  Applications

One sample result from the forecast problem is shown. Figure 4.35 shows initial data in the form of a 500-mb geopotential field for 2 June 1977, and Fig. 4.36 shows the same field 72 hours later. Figure 4.37 shows results from a model using global expansions in spherical harmonics, and Fig. 4.38 shows results from a finite-element model. The spherical harmonic model had 946 degrees of freedom, and the finite-element model had 1126 degrees of freedom in its horizontal representation of each field; each had five layers in the vertical.

The results show many deficiencies common to both models, for instance, over Scandinavia and the western Atlantic. Some of the larger-scale changes are correctly predicted, but most of the detail has been lost. The spherical harmonic model gives better results over Canada and the eastern Pacific. It is found that models with considerably higher resolution (9000 finite-difference points) can capture much of the detail. Models using different numerical techniques converge to essentially the same answer, but require a different number of degrees of freedom to do so. The most cost-effective methods appear to be fourth-order finite-difference

**FIG. 4.38**   72-hour 500-mb forecast for 5 June 1977, finite-element model.

methods on staggered grids, or spherical harmonic methods. The finite-element model is less liable to nonlinear instability than many finite-difference schemes, but the results contain more small-scale roughness.

## 4.9 REFERENCES

1. Sichel, M., "Structure of Weak Non-Hugoniot Shocks," *Phys. Fluids*, **6**:653–663 (May 1963).

2. Murman, E. M., and J. D. Cole, "Calculation of Plane Steady Transonic Flows," *AIAA J.*, **9**(1):114–121 (1971).

3. Murman, E. M., "Analysis of Embedded Shock Waves Calculated by Relaxation Methods," *AIAA J.*, **12**:626–633 (May 1973).

4. Jameson, A., "Transonic Potential Flow Calculation Using Conservation Form," *Proceedings AIAA Second Computational Fluid Dynamics Conference*, Hartford, Conn., June 1975, pp. 148–161.

5. Gelder, D., "Solution of the Compressible Flow Equations," *Int. J. Numer. Meth. Eng.*, **3**:35–43 (1971).

6. Periaux, J., "Three-Dimensional Analysis of Compressible Potential Flows with the Finite Element Method," *Int. J. Numer. Meth. Eng.*, **9**(4):775–831 (1975).

7. Shen, S. F., "An Aerodynamist Looks at the Finite Element Method," in R. H. Gallagher, J. T. Oden, C. Taylor, and O. C. Zienkiewicz (eds.), *Finite Elements in Fluids*, Wiley, London, 1975, vol. 2.

8. Chung, T. J., "Analysis of Unsteady Compressible Boundary Layer Flow via Finite Elements," *Int. J. Comput. Fluids*, **4**(1A):1–12 (1976).

9. Habashi, W. G., "A Finite Element Approach to Subsonic Aerodynamics," *Int. J. Numer. Meth. Eng.*, **14**:665–679 (1979).

10. Chung, T. J., *Finite Element Analysis in Fluid Dynamics*, McGraw-Hill, New York, 1978.

11. Glowinski, R., J. Periaux, and O. Pironneau, "Transonic Flow Simulation by the Finite Element Method via Optimal Control," *2d Int. Symp. Finite Element Meth. Flow Prob.*, ICCAD, Santa Margherita-Ligure, Italy, 1976.

12. Bristeau, M. O., R. Glowinski, J. Periaux, P. Perrier, O. Pironneau, and G. Poirier, "Applications of Optimal Control and Finite Element Methods to Calculation of Transonic Flows and Incompressible Viscous Flows," in B. Hunt (ed.), *Numerical Methods in Applied Fluid Dynamics*, Academic Press, London, 1980, pp. 203–312.

13. Periaux, J., *Résolution de Quelques Problèmes Non Linéaires en Aérodynamique par des Méthodes d'Elements Finis et de Moindres Carrés Fonctionnels*, Université Pierre et Marie Curie, Paris, June 1979.

14. Bristeau, M. O., R. Glowinski, J. Periaux, P. Perrier, and O. Pironneau, "On the Numerical Solution of Nonlinear Problems in Fluid Dynamics by Least Squares and Finite Element Methods: I. Least Square Formulations and Conjugate Gradient Solution of the Continuous Problems," *Comput. Meth. Appl. Mech. Eng.*, **17/18**:619–657 (1979).

15. Bristeau, M. O., "Application of Optimal Control Theory of Transonic Flow Computations by Finite Element Methods," in R. Glowinski and J. J. Lions (eds.), *Computing Methods in Applied Sciences and Engineering, Part II*, 1977, *Lecture Notes in Physics*, vol. 91, Springer-Verlag, Berlin, 1979, pp. 103–124.

16. Bristeau, M. O., "Application of a Finite Element Method to Transonic Flow Problems Using an Optimal Control Approach," in W. Kollmann (ed.), *Computational Fluid Dynamics*, Hemisphere Publications, Washington, D.C., 1980, pp. 281–328.

17. Glowinski, R., *Numerical Methods for Nonlinear Variational Problems*, 2d ed., Springer-Verlag, New York, 1983.

18. Bristeau, M. O., R. Glowinski, J. Periaux, P. Perrier, O. Pironneau, and G. Poirier, "Transonic Flow Simulations by Finite Element and Least-Square Methods," in R. H. Gallagher, D. H. Norrie, J. T. Oden, and O. C. Zienkiewicz (eds.), *Finite Elements in Fluids*, Wiley, London, 1982, vol. 4, pp. 453–482.

19. Eberle, A., "Evaluation of a Minimum Principle for Transonic Flow Computations by Finite Elements," *Notes on Numerical Fluid Mechanics*, vol. 2, Vieweg, Braunschweig, 1979.

20. Ecer, A., and H. U. Akay, "Investigation of Transonic Flow in a Cascade Using the Finite Element Method," *AIAA J.*, **19**(2):1174–1182 (1981).

21. Akay, H. U., and A. Ecer, "Transonic Flow Computations in Cascades Using Finite Element Method," *ASME J. Eng. Power*, **103**(4):657–664 (1981).

22. Ecer, A., and H. U. Akay, "Finite Element Analysis of Transonic Flows in Cascades—Importance of Computational Grids in Improving Accuracy and Convergence," NASA Contractor Rep. no. 3446, National Aeronautics and Space Administration, July 1981.

23. Ecer, A., H. U. Akay, and B. A. Bhutta, "Finite Element Computations of Three-Dimensional Transonic Flows," in K. N. Ghia, T. J. Mueller, and B. R. Patel (eds.), *Computers in Flow Predictions and Fluid Dynamics Experiments*, American Society of Mechanical Engineers, New York, 1981, pp. 171–179.

24. Akay, H. U., and A. Ecer, "Treatment of Transonic Flows with Shocks Using Finite Elements," in R. H. Gallagher, D. Norrie, J. T. Oden, and O. C. Zienkiewicz (eds.), *Finite Elements in Fluids*, Wiley, London, 1982, vol. 4, chap. 23.

25. Ecer, A., and H. U. Akay, "A Finite Element Formulation of Euler Equations for the Solution of Steady Transonic Flows," *AIAA 20th Aerospace Sciences Meeting*, Orlando, Fla., January 1982.

26. Wellford, L. C., and M. M. Hafez, "Mixed Finite Element Methods and Dual Iterative Algorithms for the Calculation of Transonic Flows," *2d Int. Symp. Finite Element Meth. Flow Prob.*, ICCAD, Santa Margherita-Ligure, Italy, June 1976.

27. Wellford, L. C., and M. M. Hafez, "A Finite Element First-Order Equation Formulation for the Small-Disturbance Transonic Flow Problem," *Comput. Meth. Appl. Mech. Eng.*, **22**:161-186 (1980).

28. Hafez, M. M., L. C. Wellford, C. L. Merkle, and E. M. Murman, "Numerical Computations of Fluid Flows by Finite Element and Finite Differences Methods," NASA-CR-3070, National Aeronautics and Space Administration, December 1978.

29. Habashi, W. G., and M. M. Hafez, "Finite Element Method for Transonic Cascade Flows," AIAA Pap. 81-1472, *17th Joint Propulsion Conference*, Colorado Springs, July 1981.

30. Cullen, M. J. P., "The Finite Element Method," GARP Publ. Ser. No. 17, *World Meteorological Organization*, Geneva, 1979, pp. 300-337.

31. Cullen, M. J. P., and C. D. Hall, "Forecast and General Circulation Results with Finite Element Models," *Q. J. R. Meteor. Soc. U.K.*, **105**:571-592 (1979).

32. Cullen, M. J., and K. W. Morton, "Analysis of Evolutionary Error in Finite Element and Other Methods," *J. Comp.*, **34**:245-267 (1980).

33. Shen, S. F., "An Aerodynamicist Looks at the Finite Element Method," in R. H. Gallagher et al. (eds.), *Finite Elements in Fluids*, Wiley, London, 1975, vol. 2, pp. 179-204.

34. Shen, S. F., "Finite Element Methods in Fluid Mechanics," *Annu. Rev. Fluid Mech.*, **9**:421-455 (1977).

35. Shen, S. F., "Transonic Aerodynamic Computation with Finite Element Method," in R. H. Gallagher et al. (eds.), *Finite Elements in Fluids*, Wiley, London, 1978, vol. 3, pp. 183-204.

36. Chung, T. J., *Finite Element Analysis in Fluid Dynamics*, McGraw-Hill, New York, 1978.

37. Argyris, J. H., and D. W. Scharpf, "Two and Three-Dimensional Potential Flow by the Method of Singularities," *Aero. J. R. Aero. Soc.*, **73**:956-961 (1969).

38. Wong, Y. S., and M. Hafez, "Application of Conjugate Gradient Methods to Transonic Finite Difference and Finite Element Calculations," *AIAA J.*, **20**:1526-1533 (September 1982).

39. Axelsson, O., "On Preconditioning and Convergence Acceleration in Sparse Matrix Problems," Rep. CERN 74-10, Geneva, 1974.

40. Meijerink, J. A., and H. A. van der Vorst, "An Iterative Solution Method for Linear Systems of Which the Coefficient Matrix is a Symmetric $M$-Matrix", *Math. Comput.*, **31**:48-162 (January 1977).

41. Deconinck, H., and Ch. Hirsch, "Finite Element Methods for Transonic Blade-to-Blade Calculation in Turbomachines," *J. Eng. Power*, **103**:665-677 (October 1981).

42. Hamed, A., and S. Abdallah, "Streamlike Function: A New Concept in Flow Problems Formulation," *J. Aircraft*, **16**:801-802 (December 1979).

43. Habashi, W. G., "A Finite Element Approach to Subsonic Aerodynamics," *Int. J. Numer. Meth. Eng.*, **14**:665-679 (1979).

44. Periaux, J., "Three-Dimensional Analysis of Compressible Potential Flows with the Finite Element Method," *Int. J. Numer. Meth. Eng.*, **9**(4) (1975).

45. Habashi, W. G., and M. M. Hafez, "Finite Element Stream Function Solutions for Transonic Turbomachinery Flows," AIAA Pap. 82-1268, June 1982.

46. Lin, C. C., and L. Rubinov, "On the Flow Behind Curved Shocks," *J. Math. Phys.*, **27**:105-129 (1948).

47. Shen, S. F., and W. G. Habashi, "Local Linearization of the Finite Element Method and Its Applications to Compressible Flows," *Int. J. Numer. Meth. Eng.*, **10**:565–577 (1974).

48. Habashi, W. G., "The Finite Element Method in Subsonic Aerodynamics," *Proceedings of the 1976 Heat Transfer and Fluid Mechanics Institute*, Stanford University Press, Stanford, 1976, pp. 374–389.

49. Lacor, C., and Ch. Hirsch, "Rotational Flow Calculations in Three-Dimensional Blade Passages," ASME Pap. 82-GT-316, 1982.

50. Fletcher, C. A. J., "Finite Element Formulation Suitable for Subsonic and Transonic Flows," *Lecture Notes in Physics*, vol. 90, Springer-Verlag, Berlin, 1979.

51. Glowinski, R., and O. Pironneau, "On the Computation of Transonic Flows," *France–Japanese Conference, Functional Analysis and Numerical Analysis*, Tokyo, Kyoto, September 1976.

52. Chattot, J. J., J. Gui-Roux, and J. Laminie, "Numerical Solution of a First Order Conservation Equation by a Least Square Method," *Int. J. Numer. Meth. Eng.*, **2**:209–219 (1982).

53. Akay, H. U., and A. Ecer, "Investigation of Rotational Transonic Flows Through Ducts Using a Finite Element Scheme," AIAA Pap. 82-1267, June 1982.

54. Lock, R. C., "Test Cases for Numerical Methods in Two-Dimensional Transonic Flows," AGARD Rep. no. 575, 1970.

55. Habashi, W. G., "Unbounded Two-Dimensional Potential Flows by the Finite Element Method," *Int. J. Numer. Meth. Eng.*, **14**:1347–1358 (1979).

56. Habashi, W. G., and M. M. Hafez, "Finite Element Solution of Transonic Flow Problems," *AIAA J.*, **20**(10):1368–1376 (October 1982).

57. Chung, T. J., "Analysis of Unsteady Compressible Boundary Layer Flow Via Finite Elements," *Int. J. Comput. Fluids*, **4**(1A):1–12 (1976).

58. Chung, T. J., *Finite Element Analysis in Fluid Dynamics*, McGraw-Hill, New York, 1978.

59. Glowinski, R., *Numerical Methods for Nonlinear Variational Problems*, Springer-Verlag, New York, 1984.

60. Bristeau, M. O., R. Glowinski, J. Periaux, P. Perrier, O. Pironneau, and G. Poirier, "Transonic Flow Simulations by Finite Element and Least-Square Methods," in R. H. Gallagher, D. H. Norrie, J. T. Oden, and O. C. Zienkiewicz (eds.), *Finite Elements in Fluids*, Wiley, London, 1982, vol. 4, pp. 453–482.

61. Amara, M., P. Joly, and J. M. Thomas, "A Mixed Finite Element Method for Solving Transonic Flow Equations," *Comput. Meth. Appl. Mech. Eng.*, **39**:1–19 (1983).

62. Eberle, A., "Finite Element Methods for the Solution of the Full Potential Equation in Transonic Steady and Unsteady Flow," in R. H. Gallagher, D. H. Norrie, J. T. Oden, and O. C. Zienkiewicz (eds.), *Finite Elements in Fluids*, Wiley, London, 1982, vol. 4, pp. 483–504.

63. Deconinck, H., and C. Hirsch, "Subsonic and Transonic Computation of Cascade Flows," in R. Glowinski and J. L. Lions (eds.), *Computing Methods in Applied Sciences and Engineering*, North-Holland, Amsterdam, 1980, pp. 175–195.

64. Landau, L., and L. Lifchitz, *Mécanique des Fluides*, Mir, Moscow, 1953.

65. Bristeau, M. O., R. Glowinski, J. Periaux, P. Perrier, O. Pironneau, and G. Poirier, "Applications of Optimal Control and Finite Element Methods to the Calculation of Transonic Flows and Incompressible Viscous Flows," in B. Hunt (ed.), *Numerical Methods in Applied Fluid Dynamics*, Academic Press, London, 1980, pp. 203–312.

66. Periaux, J., *Résolution de Quelques Problèmes Non Linéaires en Aérodynamique par des Méthodes d'Eléments Finis et de Moindres Carrés Fonctionnels*, Thèse de 3ème cycle, Université Pierre et Marie Curie, Paris, June 1979.

67. Bristeau, M. O., R. Glowinski, J. Periaux, P. Perrier, and O. Pironneau, "On the Numerical Solution of Nonlinear Problems in Fluid Dynamics by Least Squares and Finite Element Methods: I. Least

Square Formulations and Conjugate Gradient Solution of the Continuous Problems," *Comput. Meth. Appl. Mech. Eng.*, **17/18**:619–657 (1979).

68. Steinhoff, J., and A. Jameson, "Multiple Solutions of the Transonic Potential Flow Equation," *AIAA J.*, **20**(11):1521–1525 (1982).

69. Lions, J. L., *Problèmes aux Limites dans les Équations aux Dérivées Partielles*, Presses de l'Université de Montréal, Montréal, Que., 1962.

70. Adams, R. A., *Sobolev Spaces*, Academic Press, New York, 1975.

71. Necas, J., *Les Méthodes Directes en Théorie des Équations Élliptiques*, Masson, Paris, 1967.

72. Wilde, D. J., and C. S. Beightler, *Foundations of Optimization*, Prentice-Hall, Englewood Cliffs, N.J., 1967.

73. Polak, E., *Computational Methods in Optimization*, Academic Press, New York, 1971.

74. Brent, R., *Algorithms for Minimization without Derivatives*, Prentice-Hall, Englewood Cliffs, N.J., 1973.

75. Holst, T., "An Implicit Algorithm for the Transonic Full-Potential Equation in Conservative Form," in R. Glowinski and J. L. Lions (eds.), *Computing Methods in Applied Sciences and Engineering*, North-Holland, Amsterdam, 1980, pp. 157–174.

76. Jameson, A., "Transonic Flow Calculations," in H. J. Wirz and J. J. Smolderen (eds.), *Numerical Methods in Fluid Dynamics*, McGraw-Hill, New York, 1978, pp. 1–87.

77. Jameson, A., "Three-Dimensional Flows around Airfoils with Shocks," in R. Glowinski and J. L. Lions (eds.), *Computing Methods in Applied Sciences and Engineering, Part II, Lecture Notes in Computer Sciences*, vol. 11, Springer-Verlag, Berlin, 1974, pp. 185–221.

78. Jameson, A., "Iterative Solution of Transonic Flows over Airfoils and Wings Including Flows at Mach 1," *Comm. Pure Appl. Math.*, **27**:283–309 (1974).

79. Jameson, A., "Numerical Calculation of a Transonic Flow Past a Swept Wing by a Finite Volume Method," in R. Glowinski and J. L. Lions (eds.), *Computing Methods in Applied Sciences and Engineering, Part II*, 1977, *Lecture Notes in Physics*, vol. 91, Springer-Verlag, Berlin, 1979, pp. 125–139.

80. Bristeau, M. O., "Application of Optimal Control Theory to Transonic Flow Computations by Finite Element Methods," in R. Glowinski and J. L. Lions (eds.), *Computing Methods in Applied Sciences and Engineering, Part II*, 1977, *Lecture Notes in Physics*, vol. 91, Springer-Verlag, Berlin, 1979, pp. 103–124.

81. Bristeau, M. O., "Application of a Finite Element Method to Transonic Flow Problems Using an Optimal Control Approach," in W. Kollmann (ed.), *Computational Fluid Dynamics*, Hemisphere Publications, Washington, D.C., 1980, pp. 281–328.

82. Lemaréchal, C., "An extension of 'Davidon' Methods to Non-Differentiable Problems," in J. Balinski and P. Wolfe (eds.), *Mathematical Programming Study 3: Non-Differentiable Optimization*, North-Holland, Amsterdam, 1975, pp. 95–109.

83. Lemaréchal, C., "Extensions Diverses des Méthodes de Gradient et Applications," Thèse d'Etat, Université Paris IX, Paris, 1980.

84. Chung, T. J., and C. G. Hooks, "Discontinuous Functions in Transonic Flow," AIAA Pap. No. 76-329, 1976.

85. Chung, T. J., *Finite Element Analysis in Fluid Dynamics*, McGraw-Hill, New York, 1978.

86. Habashi, W. G., and M. M. Hafez, "Finite Element Method for Transonic Cascade Flows," AIAA Pap. 81-1472, July 1981.

87. Lucchi, C. W., "Subdomain Finite Element Method to Compute the Transonic Potential Flow Around a Profile or in a Cascade," MBB Rep. FE122/S/R/1508, 1980.

88. Fornasier, L., "A Rotated Artificial Density for FEM," MBB-UFE122-AERO-MT-489, 1980.

89. Eberle, A., "Evaluation of a Minimum Principle for Transonic Flow Computations by Finite Elements," *Notes on Numerical Fluid Mechanics*, Vieweg, Braunschweig, 1979, vol. 2, pp. 78-87.

90. Ecer, A., and H. U. Akay, "Finite Element Analysis of Transonic Flows in Cascades—Importance of Computational Grids in Improving Accuracy and Convergence," NASA Contractor Rep. 3446, National Aeronautics and Space Administration, 1981.

91. Ecer, A., and H. U. Akay, "Investigation of Transonic Flow in a Cascade Using the Finite Element Method," *AIAA J.*, **19**(9):1174-1182 (1981).

92. Akay, H. U., and A. Ecer, "Transonic Flow Computations in Cascades Using Finite Element Method," *ASME J. Eng. Power*, **103**(4):657-664 (1981).

93. Ecer, A., and H. U. Akay, "Finite Element Analysis of Transonic Flows in Cascades—Importance of Computational Grids in Improving Accuracy and Convergence," NASA Contractor Rep No. 3446, National Aeronautics and Space Administration, July 1981.

94. Ecer, A., H. U. Akay, and B. A. Bhutta, "Finite Element Computations of Three-Dimensional Transonic Flows," in K. N. Ghia, T. J. Mueller, and B. R. Patel (eds.), *Computers in Flow Predictions and Fluid Dynamics Experiments*, American Society of Mechanical Engineers, New York, 1981, pp. 171-179.

95. Akay, H. U., and A. Ecer, "Treatment of Transonic Flows with Shocks Using Finite Elements," in R. H. Gallagher, D. Norrie, J. T. Oden, and O. C. Zienkiewicz (eds.), *Finite Elements in Fluids*, Wiley, London, 1982, vol. 4, chap. 23.

96. Ecer, A., and H. U. Akay, "A Finite Element Formulation of Euler Equations for the Solution of Steady Transonic Flows," *AIAA 20th Aerospace Sciences Meeting*, Orlando, Fla., January 1982; *AIAA J.*, **21**(3):343-350 (1983).

97. Serrin, J., "Mathematical Principles of Classical Fluid Mechanics," *Handbuch der Physik*, Springer-Verlag, Berlin, 1959, vol. VIII, chap. I.

98. Hafez, M., J. South, and E. Murman, "Artificial Compressibility Methods for Numerical Solutions of Transonic Full Potential Equation," *AIAA J.*, **17**(8):838-844 (August 1979).

99. Jameson, A., "Acceleration of Transonic Potential Flow Calculations of Arbitrary Meshes by the Multiple Grid Method," *AIAA Computational Fluid Dynamics Conference*, Williamsburg, Va., July 1979, pp. 122-146.

100. Cole, J. D., "Twenty Years of Transonic Flow," Boeing Scientific Research Lab., Doc. DI-82-0878, 1969.

101. Murman, E. M., and J. D. Cole, "Calculation of Plane Steady Transonic Flows," *AIAA J.*, **9**(1):114-121 (1971).

102. Sichel, M., "Structure of Weak Non-Hugoniot Shocks," *Phys. Fluids*, **6**:653-663 (May 1963).

103. Ashley, H., and M. Landahl, *Aerodynamics of Wings and Bodies*, Addison-Wesley, Reading, Mass., 1965.

104. Murman, E. M., "Analysis of Embedded Shock Waves Calculated by Relaxation Methods," *AIAA J.*, **12**:626-633 (May 1973).

105. Engquist, B., and S. Osher, "Stable and Entropy-Satisfying Approximations for Transonic Flow Calculations," *Math. Comp.*, **34**(149):45-75 (January 1980).

106. Van Leer, B., "On the Relation between the Upwind Differencing Schemes of Godunov, Engquist, Osher and Roe," ICASE Rep. No. 81-11, 1981.

107. Hughes, T. J. R., "A Shock-Capturing Finite Element Method," (in preparation).

108. Wellford, L. C., and M. M. Hafez, "A Finite Element First-Order Equation Formulation for the Small-Disturbance Transonic Flow Problem," *Comput. Meth. Appl. Mech. Eng.*, **22**:161-186 (1980).

109. Hafez, M. M., L. C. Wellford, C. L. Merkle, and E. M. Murman, "Numerical Computations of Fluid Flows by Finite Element and Finite Differences Methods," NASA-CR-3070, National Aeronautics and Space Administration, December 1978.

110. Showalter, R. E., and P. W. Ting, "Pseudo-Parabolic Partial Differential Equations," *SIAM J. Math. Anal.*, **1**(1):1–26 (1970).

111. Lees, M., "Alternating Direction Methods for Hyperbolic Differential Equations," *J. Soc. Ind. Appl. Math.*, **10**:610–616 (1962).

112. Osher, S., "Approximations par Eléments Finis avec Décentrage pour des Lois de Conservation Hyperboliques Nonlinéaires Multidimensionelles," *C. R. Acad. Sci. Paris, Ser. A*, 819–821 (1980).

113. Wellford, L. C., and M. M. Hafez, "Mixed Finite Element Methods and Dual Iterative Algorithms for the Calculation of Transonic Flows," *2d Int. Symp. Finite Elements Meth. Flow Prob.*, Santa Margherita-Ligure, Italy, June 1976.

114. Wong, Y. S., and M. Hafez, "Applications of Conjugate Gradient Methods to Transonic Finite Difference and Finite Element Calculations," *AIAA J.*, **20**(11):1526–1533 (September 1982).

115. Chan, S. T. K., and M. R. Brashears, "Finite Element Analysis of Unsteady Transonic Flow," AIAA Pap. 75-875, 1975.

116. Jameson, A., "Iterative Solution of Transonic Flow over Airfoils and Wings," *Commun. Pure Appl. Math.*, **2**:283–309 (1974).

117. Hafez, M. M., and J. C. South, "Vectorization of Relaxation Methods for Solving Transonic Full Potential Equation," in *Numerical Methods for the Computation of Inviscid Transonic Flow with Shock Waves*, GAMM Workshop, Sweden, 1979.

118. Jameson, A., "Transonic Potential Flow Calculation Using Conservation Form," *Proceedings of the AIAA Computational Fluid Dynamics Conference*, Hartford, Conn., June 1975, pp. 148–161.

119. Jameson A., and D. A. Caughey, "Finite Volume Method for Transonic Potential Flow Calculations," *Proceedings of the AIAA Third Computational Fluid Dynamics Conference*, New Mexico, June 1977, pp. 35–54.

120. Eberle, A., "Transonic Potential Flow Computations by Finite Element: Airfoil and Wing Analysis, Airfoil Optimization," MBB-UFE 14280-DGLR 78-65, 1978.

121. Hafez, M., J. South, and E. Murman, "Artificial Compressibility Methods for Numerical Solutions of Transonic Full Potential Equation," *AIAA J.*, **17**(8):838–844 (August 1979).

122. Holst, T. L., "An Implicit Algorithm for the Conservative Transonic Full Potential Equation Using an Arbitrary Mesh," *AIAA J.*, **17**(10) (October 1979).

123. Habashi, W. G., and M. M. Hafez, "Finite Element Solution of Transonic Flow Problems," *AIAA J.*, **20**(10):1368–1376 (October 1982).

124. Glowinski, R., and O. Pironneau, "On the Computation of Transonic Flows," *France–Japanese Conference, Functional Analysis and Numerical Analysis*, Tokyo, Kyoto, September 1976.

125. Fletcher, C. A. J., "Finite Element Formulations Suitable for Subsonic and Transonic Flows," *6th International Conference on Numerical Methods in Fluids Dynamics*, U.S.S.R., 1978, in *Lecture Notes in Physics*, vol. 90, Springer-Verlag, Berlin, 1979.

126. Chattot, J. J., J. Gui-Roux, and J. Laminie, "Numerical Solution of a First-Order Conservation Equation by a Least Square Method," *Int. J. Numer. Meth. Fluids*, **2**:209–219 (1982).

127. Hafez, M. M., and D. Lovell, "Numerical Solution of Transonic Stream Function Equation," *AIAA J.*, **21**(3):327–335 (March 1983).

128. Habashi, W. G., and M. M. Hafez, "Finite Element Stream Function Solutions of Transonic Rotational Internal and External Flows," *Numerical Methods for Partial Differential Equations*, **2**:127–144, 1985, and "Finite Element Stream Function Solutions for Transonic Turbomachinery Flow," AIAA Pap. 82-1268, June 1982.

129. Habashi, W. G., M. M. Hafez, and P. L. Kotiuga, "Computation of Choked and Supersonic Turbomachinery Flows by a Modified Potential Method," *AIAA J.*, **23**(2):214–220 (February 1985), and "Finite Element Methods for Internal Flow Calculations," AIAA Pap. 83-1404, August 1983.

130. Kasahara, A., "Computational Aspects of Atmospheric Simulations," *Meth. Comput. Phys.*, **17**:1-66 (1977).

131. McBean, G. A. (ed.), "The Planetary Boundary Layer," Tech. Note No. 165, *World Meteorological Organization*, Geneva, 1979.

132. Cullen, M. J. P., "The Finite Element Method," GARP Publication Ser. No. 17, *World Meteorological Organization*, Geneva, 1979, pp. 300-337.

133. Cullen, M. J. P., and C. D. Hall, "Forecast and General Circulation Results with Finite Element Models," *Q. J. R. Meteor. Soc. U.K.*, **105**:571-592 (1979).

134. Cullen, M. J. P., and K. W. Morton, "Analysis of Evolutionary Error in Finite Element and Other Methods," *J. Comp. Phys.*, **34**:245-267 (1980).

135. Staniforth, A., and H. L. Mitchell, "A Variable Resolution Finite Element Technique for Regional Forecasting with the Primitive Equations," *U.S. Month. Weath. Rev.*, **106**:439-447 (1978).

# CHAPTER 5
# COUPLED SYSTEMS

All systems in engineering present certain amounts of interaction or coupling between structure, fluid, and soil parts or due to thermal and other effects. Fluids such as water, air, or lubricants may be interacting with structural elements such as buildings, dams, offshore structures, mechanical components, pressure vessels, etc. Surface structures interact with soil through their foundations, and the behavior of buried structures is coupled with their surrounding rock or soil strata. The simulation of each of these media can be defined as a system. In many cases engineers can assume that the effects of one system on the other does not occur concurrently for all practical purposes. Typical examples of this behavior are wind forces on stiff buildings or hydrodynamic forces on massive offshore platforms. In these cases the forces on the structures can be computed by assuming that they are rigid and neglecting their interaction with the fluid.

For structures such as flexible masts or compliant offshore structures, the systems representing solid and fluid may need to be considered at the same moment in time. Systems such as these are said to be coupled *concurrently*, as at any time the behavior of one influences the other and vice versa. Interaction may occur not only between systems of the same or different types (i.e., structure-structure or structure-soil) but also within the same body; e.g., the temperature and stress fields may be coupled in the same body.

Two methods of solution may be attempted when solving coupled problems:

1. They can be solved together by applying considerations of compatibility and equilibrium to join the different systems.

2. They can be analyzed separately, and then the equilibrium and compatibility conditions are used to link them together.

Method 1 is generally preferred since the main characteristic of coupled systems is that the processes are concurrent. Method 2 has, however, important applications, as many engineers nowadays have access to computer codes which can analyze a particular part of the whole system but cannot synthesize them into one general procedure.

The classification of a problem as *coupled* or *uncoupled* will depend on the characteristics of the different systems and on how they interact. Consider, for instance, the offshore structure shown in Fig. 5.1, which is acted upon by waves and is resting on the soil. If the solid

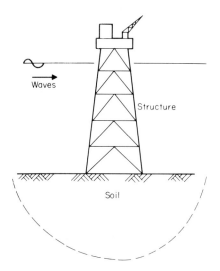

**FIG. 5.1** Fluid-soil-structure interaction problem.

structures are sufficiently stiff, the fluid forces can be considered to be acting on the undeformed platform all the time; otherwise the movements of the platform become important. Similarly, the relative rigidity of the soil versus the structure will determine if soil-structure coupling is required in the analysis. The ways in which interaction can occur for the fluid-structure-soil system are summarized in the diagram shown in Fig. 5.2, where the double arrows indicate

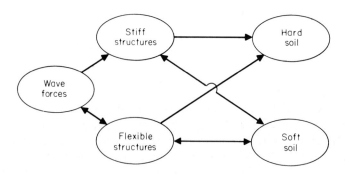

**FIG. 5.2** System interaction.

that coupling can occur. The interaction is indeed more complex than described above, as the fluid forces, for instance, will be different depending on the relative wavelength versus structural dimensions. The example serves to indicate the difficulties of defining in general what is a coupled system.

In what follows only interaction between fluid, structure, and soil will be considered. Coupling between thermal effects and structural response is a separate topic which has been partly described in Chap. 3 of Part 3. Within this context the interaction between two systems may be classified as follows;

1. *Structure-Structure Interaction.* Structure-structure interaction frequently occurs in structural analysis when two different structural forms are being combined or when the system is analyzed by using substructures.

2. *Structure-Fluid Interaction.* Structure-fluid interaction can be divided into two main types.
   *a. External Fluid Problems.* Cases for which the structure is surrounded by the fluid, such as water around a platform or wind action on buildings.
   *b. Internal Fluid Problems.* Cases for which the fluid is now contained within a solid, such as fluid in a reservoir or vessels or flow in ducts.

3. *Structure-Soil Interaction.* Structure-soil interaction problems can be divided into two types.
   *a. Buried Structures.* Cases in which the soil is surrounding the structure, such as tunnels, mines, or buried power plants.
   *b. Surface Structures.* Cases where the structure is resting on the soil, such as with foundations.

4. *Fluid-Fluid Interaction.* Fluid-fluid interaction problems occur with multiphase fluids or for cases involving different fluids, e.g., air and water in wind-induced waves.

5. *Fluid-Soil Interaction.* Fluid-soil interaction problems can be divided into two types.
   *a. Fluid-Dominated Cases.* Cases involving sedimentation and erosion, for example.
   *b. Soil-Dominated Cases.* Cases involving liquefaction and consolidation, for example.

6. *Soil-Soil Interaction.* Soil-soil interaction problems occur in multilayered media, rock-soil interaction, etc.

Finally the type of coupling can be static or dynamic. *Static* coupling occurs when dynamic forces are negligible; when the effect of inertia cannot be ignored, the coupling is said to be *dynamic.*

## 5.1 DIFFERENT TYPES OF ELEMENTS

Each of the systems to be combined in coupled problems can usually be associated with a physical region of the problem. The governing equations for each region can then be written in matrix form using finite elements, boundary elements, finite differences, etc., and then combined. When the region has some particular property such as extending to infinity, special formulations are sometimes used to take into consideration the radiation effect. This gives rise to different methods of solution for different parts of the problem and the subsequent need of combining all the parts. To carry out this combination properly we need to understand the differences between the analytical techniques employed. Special elements may also be required because of the necessity of representing more accurately certain states within the part of the continuum under study, such as in fracture mechanics. The most common analytical formulations used in computational mechanics are (1) finite elements, (2) special finite elements, (3) boundary elements, and (4) simplified boundary elements. These will be discussed below in that order.

## 5.1A Finite Elements

The finite-element theory is nowadays well understood by engineers. It is usually based on weak residual formulations which have two important properties: they reduce the order of the derivatives in the starting variational statements, and they require only approximate satisfaction of the natural boundary conditions of the problem. For example, in Laplace's equation, after substituting interpolation functions and integrating over elements, one can find the element matrices and assemble them together into the finite-element system matrices which can be represented by

$$\mathbf{KU} = \mathbf{F} \tag{5.1}$$

where $\mathbf{K}$ is the finite-element matrix for the whole system, $\mathbf{U}$ is the vector of nodal unknowns, and $\mathbf{F}$ is the right-hand-side vector containing the *nodal* values of the integrated fluxes.

Similar matrices are obtained for dynamic problems. Thus the finite-element system of equations for the scalar wave equation is

$$\mathbf{KU} + \mathbf{M\ddot{U}} = \mathbf{F} \tag{5.2}$$

where $\mathbf{M}$ is the inertia or mass matrix for the system.

Finally, if damping is included, Eq. (5.2) will become

$$\mathbf{KU} + \mathbf{C\dot{U}} + \mathbf{M\ddot{U}} = \mathbf{F} \tag{5.3}$$

The finite-element matrices obtained in this manner are symmetric because they are deduced from symmetric operators and the same basis functions are used for the approximation $u$ and the virtual or weighting function $u^*$.

## 5.1B Special Finite Elements

Applications of the above finite-element theory are usually restricted to closed, i.e., finite, domains and for a comparatively smooth variation of the interpolation functions. For problems involving fracture mechanics or those with infinite domains special elements need to be developed. These elements can simply be based on including appropriate singular functions (such as those of order $\sqrt{r}$ in fracture mechanics) or on developing infinite elements which can take energy radiation into consideration. Finite elements extending to infinity are especially important in coupled problems and have recently received a great deal of attention. Although they may be used instead of boundary elements (see Sec. 5.3), they are essentially different and are based on the classical finite-element approach. Assume, for instance, a potential problem, but instead of using the standard basis functions for $u$ and $u^*$ one now postulates decaying functions to model the behavior of the potential and flux when the domain $\Omega$ extends to infinity. This is better explained by considering the interface $\Gamma_I$ shown in Fig. 5.3. The dashed lines represent planes normal to the interface emanating from the corner of the element—which in this case is a triangular one with straight sides for simplicity; the $\zeta$-coordinate originated at the center of the element can be used as a reference axis.

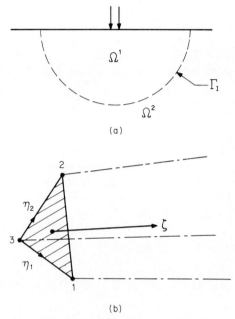

(a)

(b)

**FIG. 5.3** Infinite elements. ($a$) Two regions. ($b$) Triangular interface element.

The function for the potential may be postulated as

$$u(\zeta, \eta_1, \eta_2) = \hat{u}(\eta_1 \eta_2) f(\zeta) \tag{5.4}$$

where $\hat{u}(\eta_1 \eta_2)$ are the standard two-dimensional finite-element functions, with $\eta_1 \eta_2$ the homogeneous coordinates for triangular elements. The $f(\zeta)$-function instead is a decay function which reduces the magnitude of $u$ as $\zeta$ increases. This function in unity at $\zeta = 0$ and tends to zero at infinity. The function $f$ proposed by Ungless [1] is simply

$$f(\zeta) = \frac{1}{1 + \zeta / L} \tag{5.5}$$

We can now substitute this expression into Eq. (5.4) and work as usual with finite elements. The only difference is that the integration over $\Omega$ needs now to be carried out over the infinite domain of the element and resort must be made to numerical integration.

Instead of (5.5) Bettess [2] has proposed using exponential decay functions. His shape functions in the $\zeta$-direction are defined by Lagrange polynomials multiplied by exponential decay terms. In this case a set of internal nodes is needed because of the type of polynomials, the simplest of which is a linear function with two internal nodes.

The form of the solution will depend on the coefficients taken for the exponential decay, i.e., on the $\lambda$-parameter used in the following equation:

$$f(\zeta) = F(\zeta)\, e^{-\zeta/\lambda} \tag{5.6}$$

The advantage of infinite elements is that they can be used for a series of problems for which the fundamental solution required for boundary elements (see Sec. 5.3) may be difficult to determine. The method does not give an accurate indication of the behavior of the system toward infinity, but the effect of the far region on the domain of interest can be easily introduced.

### 5.1c Boundary Elements

Boundary elements are based on completely different principles than finite elements. While in classical finite elements the approximate and weighting functions belong to the same set, special types of functions are postulated in boundary elements for the weighting function $u^*$. They are such that they satisfy the equilibrium equations of the problem and are usually Green's type of functions in infinite or semi-infinite domains.

Under these conditions the potential at any point on the surface is related to the potential and fluxes at all the other points by the equation

$$\tfrac{1}{2}u + \int_{\Gamma_q} uq^*\, d\Gamma + \int_{\Gamma_u} \bar{u}q^*\, d\Gamma = \int_{\Gamma_q} \bar{q}u^*\, d\Gamma + \int_{\Gamma_u} qu^*\, d\Gamma \tag{5.7}$$

The $\tfrac{1}{2}$-coefficient is valid for smooth boundaries; for corner points the value of this coefficient is proportional to the solid angle. The bars over the $u$ and $q$ in (5.7) indicate that these values are known, i.e., are given boundary conditions. The total boundary is $\Gamma = \Gamma_u + \Gamma_q$.

If one applies the above equation at all points, a system of equations is formed which can be written in matrix form—before applying the boundary conditions—as

$$\mathbf{HU} = \mathbf{GQ} \tag{5.8}$$

After the boundary conditions on $\Gamma_u$ and $\Gamma_q$ have been taken into consideration, the columns of the above matrices can be rearranged to produce the following system,

$$\mathbf{AX} = \mathbf{B} \tag{5.9}$$

where $\mathbf{X}$ is now the vector of unknown $u$- and $q$-values.

Notice that the values of fluxes $(\mathbf{Q})$ in Eq. (5.8) are their actual values at the nodes. In finite elements these values instead are weighted and the *integrated fluxes* are concentrated at the nodes. These values are represented by the vector $\mathbf{F}$ of Eq. (5.1). It is now possible to relate the values of $\mathbf{F}$ and $\mathbf{Q}$ through a distribution matrix $\mathbf{N}$ whose terms represent the weighting of the boundary values of flux by the interpolation functions, i.e.,

$$F = NQ \qquad (5.10)$$

To combine the boundary-element region with the finite-element part (Fig. 5.4), one can deduce a matrix which can be easily implemented in finite-element codes. We start by

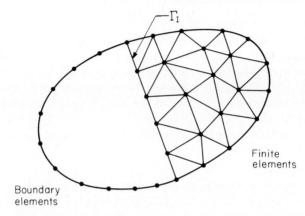

**FIG. 5.4** Domain divided into finite- and boundary-element regions.

transforming Eq. (5.8) by inverting $G$, i.e.,

$$G^{-1}(HU) = Q \qquad (5.11)$$

Next we premultiply both sides by the distribution on matrix $N$ to obtain the weighted flux vectors $F$ of finite elements, i.e.,

$$(NG^{-1}H)U = NQ \qquad (5.12)$$

which can be redefined using $\qquad K' = NG^{-1}H \qquad (5.13a)$

$$F' = NQ \qquad (5.13b)$$

Hence Eq. (5.12) has the following finite-element form:

$$K'U = F' \qquad (5.14)$$

The main discrepancy that now arises between the above formulation and finite elements is the fact that the matrix $K'$ is generally asymmetric. The asymmetry arises due to the approximation involved in the discretization process and the choice of the assumed solution. The matrix can be made symmetric by minimizing the square of the errors in the nonsymmetric off-diagonal terms, as the asymmetry is usually small. This gives a new matrix whose coefficients are defined by

$$K = \tfrac{1}{2}(K' + K'^{,T}) \qquad (5.15)$$

This matrix can now be assembled with the finite-element matrices as shown in Fig. 5.4 to give a global system of equations. The disadvantage of this technique is that the nodal equations within the boundary-element region are all coupled, which gives a full system of equations. Because of this it is sometimes preferable to use approximate boundary elements.

### 5.1D Approximate Boundary Elements

Approximate boundary elements are an approximation to the boundary elements developed in Sec. 5.3 and consequently require only boundary integration. Notice that by contrast the infinite elements developed in Sec. 5.2 are based on an integration in the domain.

The idea of approximating Green functions has practical interest in cases where the fundamental solution is difficult to obtain or cumbersome to use. The other advantage is that contrary to the boundary-element treatment of Sec. 5.3 each boundary node now relates only to its neighbors rather than to all the other nodes.

To illustrate the technique consider again the case of the Laplace equation, which can be represented as

$$\int_\Omega (\nabla^2 u^*) u \, d\Omega = \int_\Gamma u q^* \, d\Gamma - \int_\Gamma q u^* \, d\Gamma \tag{5.16}$$

(Notice that $\Gamma = \Gamma_u + \Gamma_q$; that is, we write the integrals in terms of the total boundary for simplicity.) Consider, for instance, that the above equation refers to the external region of Fig. 5.5, which extends to infinity. The fundamental solution for the three-dimensional

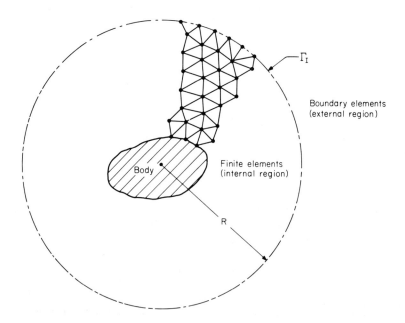

**FIG. 5.5**   Finite-element and external domains.

Laplace's equation, for instance, is

$$u^* = \frac{1}{4\pi r} \tag{5.17}$$

For any point in the *internal domain* (including those near but not on the $\Gamma_I$ interface) one can write

$$\int_{\Gamma_I} u q^* \, d\Gamma = \int_{\Gamma_I} q u^* \, d\Gamma \tag{5.18}$$

Notice that any boundary integrals on the $\Gamma$-domain at infinity will disappear when $r \to \infty$. Substitution of the fundamental solution into (5.18) leads to

$$\int_{\Gamma_I} \frac{1}{r} q \, d\Gamma = \int_{\Gamma_I} u \frac{\partial}{\partial n} \frac{1}{r} \, d\Gamma \tag{5.19}$$

The expression has been obtained by taking the reference point outside the external domain, i.e., in the inside finite-element region, and because of this Eq. (5.18) does not present the $\frac{1}{2}$-term of Eq. (5.7). The boundary values are still interrelated, resulting in nonbanded equations. We can, however, simplify this formulation if $\Gamma_I$ is considered to be a circle of sufficiently large radius $R$. Since $R$ is constant one can write $d\Gamma = R \, d\theta$ ($\theta$ is the angular coordinate). Notice also that $n \equiv r$. Hence Eq. (5.19) becomes

$$\int_0^\pi \left( \frac{1}{R} \frac{\partial u}{\partial R} + u \frac{1}{R^2} \right) d\theta = 0 \tag{5.20}$$

This is a special form of the Sommerfeld radiation condition, which can also be written approximately on $\Gamma_I$ as

$$\frac{\partial u}{\partial r} + \frac{1}{r} u = 0 \tag{5.21}$$

Equation (5.21) can be applied at each boundary node independently of the others, which gives a system of banded equations as in finite elements.

The importance of the above procedure is that it can be generalized to find approximate radiation conditions in cases where the fundamental solution is complex [3].

Consider, for instance, the case of the wave, or Helmholtz, equation

$$\nabla^2 u + \kappa^2 u = 0 \quad \text{in } \Omega \tag{5.22}$$

where $\kappa$ is the wave number and $u$ is the potential. In reference again to Fig. 5.5 the boundary-element region is assured to extend to infinity.

The fundamental solution for two dimensions is

$$u^* = \frac{1}{4i} H_0^{(2)}(\kappa r) \tag{5.23}$$

where $H$ is a Hankel function and $r$ is the distance from the point under consideration to any other point on $\Gamma_I$.

The inverse weighted-residual statement for (5.22) with similar boundary conditions as before (i.e., natural $q = \bar{q}$ and essential $u = \bar{u}$) is

$$\int_\Omega (\nabla^2 u^* + \kappa^2 u^*) u \, d\Omega = \int_{\Gamma_I} q^* u \, d\Gamma - \int_{\Gamma_I} u^* q \, d\Gamma \tag{5.24}$$

Since the function $u^*$ satisfies the Helmholtz equations, one can write, for any point external to the boundary of that region (i.e., just inside the finite-element part),

$$\int_{\Gamma_I} u^* q \, d\Gamma = \int_{\Gamma_I} q^* u \, d\Gamma \tag{5.25}$$

or, in terms of the fundamental solution,

$$\int_{\Gamma_I} H_0^{(2)}(\kappa r) q \, d\Gamma = \int_{\Gamma_I} \frac{H_0^{(2)}(\kappa r)}{\partial n} u \, d\Gamma \tag{5.26}$$

One can simplify this formulation if again the *observation* point is assumed to be far away from our region of interest. This means that one can use an asymptotic expansion for the Hankel function and its derivative (note $n = r$ over a circle). In addition, if $\Gamma_I$ is considered to be a circle of large radius $R$, one obtains

$$\sqrt{\frac{2}{\pi \kappa}} \, e^{i\pi/4} \int_{\Gamma_I} \frac{1}{\sqrt{R}} \left( \frac{\partial u}{\partial R} + i\kappa u \right) e^{-i\kappa R} \, d\Gamma = 0 \tag{5.27}$$

As $R$ is constant over $\Gamma$, we write $d\Gamma = R \, d\theta$; and

$$\int_0^{2\pi} \sqrt{R} \left( \frac{\partial u}{\partial R} + i\kappa u \right) d\theta = 0 \tag{5.28}$$

This is another form of the Sommerfeld condition, which can be written on $\Gamma_I$ as

$$\frac{\partial u}{\partial \kappa} + i\kappa u = 0 \tag{5.29}$$

Similarly, one can deduce the appropriate radiation condition for stress analysis, soil dynamics, fluid flow, and many other complex problems.


## 5.2 MATRIX PROCEDURE FOR COUPLED SYSTEMS

In coupled problems one frequently needs to combine two or more regions. This may be because one of the regions is a fluid and another is a solid, for instance. Consider for simplicity the case of a body divided into only two regions (Fig. 5.6) called $\Omega^1$ and $\Omega^2$. The interface between the two regions will be called $\Gamma_I$ as usual, and the external surfaces of regions $\Omega^1$ and $\Omega^2$ will be defined as $\Gamma_1$ and $\Gamma_2$, respectively. The potential function, its velocity, and the acceleration vectors over each region will be called $\mathbf{U}$, $\dot{\mathbf{U}}$, and $\ddot{\mathbf{U}}$, respectively. The fluxes

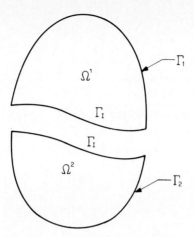

**FIG. 5.6** Coupling of two bodies.

at the nodes and their integrated values are designated by $\mathbf{Q}$ and $\mathbf{F}$. Hence $\mathbf{U}^1$, $\mathbf{Q}^1$, $\mathbf{F}^1$ will denote the function, fluxes, and integrated fluxes on the external surface of region 1 (i.e., on $\Gamma_1$) and $\mathbf{U}^2$, $\mathbf{Q}^2$, $\mathbf{F}^2$ the same values for the external surface of region 2 ($\Gamma_2$). $\mathbf{U}_I^1$, $\mathbf{Q}_I^1$, and $\mathbf{F}_I^1$ are similar quantities on the interface $\Gamma_I$ if it belongs to $\Omega^1$, and $\mathbf{U}_I^2$, $\mathbf{Q}_I^2$, and $\mathbf{F}_I^2$ are those values if $\Gamma_I$ belongs to $\Omega^2$. Notice that in the other case the normals are in opposite directions.

The conditions for coupling on the interface are compatibility and equilibrium, which can be expressed as follows.

**1.** *Compatibility.* $\mathbf{U}_I = \mathbf{U}_I^1 = \mathbf{U}_I^2$ or $\Gamma_I$, with the following additional conditions in dynamic problems:

$$\left. \begin{array}{l} \dot{\mathbf{U}}_I = \dot{\mathbf{U}}_I^1 = \dot{\mathbf{U}}_I^2 \\ \ddot{\mathbf{U}}_I = \ddot{\mathbf{U}}_I^1 = \ddot{\mathbf{U}}_I^2 \end{array} \right\} \quad \text{on } \Gamma_I \qquad (5.30)$$

and

**2.** *Equilibrium.* The equilibrium condition can be expressed in terms of nodal flux values as

$$\mathbf{Q}_I^1 + \mathbf{Q}_I^2 = 0 \quad \text{on } \Gamma_I \qquad (5.31)$$

or in terms of integrated values as

$$\mathbf{F}_I^1 + \mathbf{F}_I^2 = 0 \quad \text{on } \Gamma_I \qquad (5.32)$$

The first form is usually applied with boundary elements, the second with finite elements.

The systems of equations for dynamic equilibrium in the two regions can be written as follows. For region 1,

$$\begin{bmatrix} \mathbf{M}_{11}^1 & \mathbf{M}_{1I}^1 \\ \mathbf{M}_{I1}^1 & \ddot{\mathbf{U}}_{II}^1 \end{bmatrix} \begin{Bmatrix} \ddot{\mathbf{U}}^1 \\ \ddot{\mathbf{U}}_I^1 \end{Bmatrix} + \begin{bmatrix} \mathbf{C}_{11}^1 & \mathbf{C}_{1I}^1 \\ \mathbf{C}_{I1}^1 & \mathbf{C}_{II}^1 \end{bmatrix} \begin{Bmatrix} \dot{\mathbf{U}}^1 \\ \dot{\mathbf{U}}_I^1 \end{Bmatrix} + \begin{bmatrix} \mathbf{K}_{11}^1 & \mathbf{K}_{1I}^1 \\ \mathbf{K}_{I1}^1 & \mathbf{K}_{II}^1 \end{bmatrix} \begin{Bmatrix} \mathbf{U}^1 \\ \mathbf{U}_I^1 \end{Bmatrix} = \begin{Bmatrix} \mathbf{F}^1 \\ \mathbf{F}_I^1 \end{Bmatrix} \qquad (5.33)$$

and for region 2,

$$\begin{bmatrix} \mathbf{M}_{22}^2 & \mathbf{M}_{2I}^2 \\ \mathbf{M}_{I2}^2 & \mathbf{M}_{II}^2 \end{bmatrix} \begin{Bmatrix} \ddot{\mathbf{U}}^2 \\ \ddot{\mathbf{U}}_I^2 \end{Bmatrix} + \begin{bmatrix} \mathbf{C}_{22}^2 & \mathbf{C}_{2I}^2 \\ \mathbf{C}_{I2}^2 & \mathbf{C}_{II}^2 \end{bmatrix} \begin{Bmatrix} \dot{\mathbf{U}}^2 \\ \dot{\mathbf{U}}_I^2 \end{Bmatrix} + \begin{bmatrix} \mathbf{K}_{22}^2 & \mathbf{K}_{2I}^2 \\ \mathbf{K}_{I2}^2 & \mathbf{K}_{II}^2 \end{bmatrix} \begin{Bmatrix} \mathbf{U}^2 \\ \mathbf{U}_I^2 \end{Bmatrix} = \begin{Bmatrix} \mathbf{F}^2 \\ \mathbf{F}_I^2 \end{Bmatrix}$$

Introducing the equilibrium and compatibility conditions (5.30) and (5.32), leads to

$$\begin{bmatrix} \mathbf{M}_{11}^1 & \mathbf{M}_{1I}^1 & \mathbf{0} \\ \mathbf{M}_{I1}^1 & \mathbf{M}_{II}^1 + \mathbf{M}_{II}^2 & \mathbf{M}_{I2}^2 \\ \mathbf{0} & \mathbf{M}_{2I}^2 & \mathbf{M}_{22}^2 \end{bmatrix} \begin{Bmatrix} \ddot{\mathbf{U}}^1 \\ \ddot{\mathbf{U}}_I \\ \ddot{\mathbf{U}}^2 \end{Bmatrix} + \begin{bmatrix} \mathbf{C}_{11}^1 & \mathbf{C}_{1I}^1 & \mathbf{0} \\ \mathbf{C}_{I1}^1 & \mathbf{C}_{II}^1 + \mathbf{C}_{II}^2 & \mathbf{C}_{I2}^2 \\ \mathbf{0} & \mathbf{C}_2^2 & \mathbf{C}_{22}^2 \end{bmatrix} \begin{Bmatrix} \dot{\mathbf{U}}^1 \\ \dot{\mathbf{U}}_I \\ \dot{\mathbf{U}}^2 \end{Bmatrix}$$

$$+ \begin{bmatrix} \mathbf{K}_{11}^1 & \mathbf{K}_{1I}^1 & \mathbf{0} \\ \mathbf{K}_{I1}^1 & \mathbf{K}_{II}^1 + \mathbf{K}_{II}^2 & \mathbf{K}_{I2}^2 \\ \mathbf{0} & \mathbf{K}_{2I}^2 & \mathbf{K}_{22}^2 \end{bmatrix} \begin{Bmatrix} \mathbf{U}^1 \\ \mathbf{U}_I \\ \mathbf{U}^2 \end{Bmatrix} = \begin{Bmatrix} \mathbf{F}^1 \\ \mathbf{0} \\ \mathbf{F}^2 \end{Bmatrix} \qquad (5.34)$$

or, in general, 
$$\mathbf{M}\ddot{\mathbf{U}} + \mathbf{C}\dot{\mathbf{U}} + \mathbf{K}\mathbf{U} = \mathbf{F} \qquad (5.35)$$

An important special case of these equations is for steady-state problems, i.e., problems for which the functions and right-hand-side vector varies harmonically with time:

$$\mathbf{F} = \hat{\mathbf{F}} \, e^{i\omega t} \qquad \mathbf{U} = \hat{\mathbf{U}} \, e^{i\omega t} \qquad (5.36)$$

For this case Eq. (5.35) reduces to

$$(-\omega^2 \mathbf{M} + i\omega \mathbf{C} + \mathbf{K})\hat{\mathbf{U}} = \hat{\mathbf{F}} \qquad (5.37)$$

where $\omega$ is the exciting frequency. This equation governs a large range of engineering problems.


## 5.3 FLUID-STRUCTURE INTERACTION PROBLEMS

As previously discussed fluid-structure interaction problems can be divided into *external fluid problems*, such as wave forces on offshore structures, floating bodies, wind acting on buildings, bridges, etc., and *internal fluid problems*, such as when the fluid is contained inside a duct or vessel. Some systems, however, will fall in one or the other category depending on physical conditions. For instance, a dam in a reservoir is a closed system if the whole body of water is considered, but is an open system if the water is assumed to extend only up to a certain distance from the dam and then appropriate radiation boundary conditions are applied. Some examples are shown in Fig. 5.7.

    External fluid problems can be analyzed by dividing the fluid into a series of elements and extending the mesh sufficiently far from the body. If these are finite elements, the difficulty then lies in applying the right boundary conditions, but this can be achieved using the infinite elements, boundary elements, or the radiation-type conditions described earlier. The description of the fluid media using boundary elements is most attractive, especially when the boundary elements can be converted into equivalent finite-element matrices and combined with finite elements for the structural analysis part. Representing the fluid with finite elements does not present any special difficulties in most cases but requires working with a number of unwanted internal unknowns. This number can be very large in three-dimensional problems.

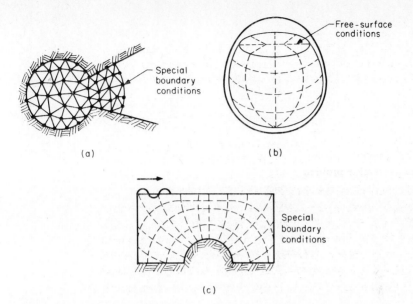

**FIG. 5.7**   Some infinite-element meshes for potential fluid flow. (*a*) Harbor divided into finite elements. (*b*) Fluid in container. (*c*) Obstruction at the bottom of the sea.

## 5.3A Wave Forces on Submerged Bodies

Consider the problem described in Fig. 5.8: a submerged cylindrical body under wave forces. The waves are assumed to be harmonic and linear—Airy type—in which case the wave potential can be decomposed into two parts: the incident and the scattered potentials. That is,

$$u = u_0 + u_s \qquad (5.38a)$$

where $u_s(x, y, t) = \hat{u}(x, y)\, e^{-i\omega t}$, $\omega$ is the frequency, and $\kappa = \omega/c$ is the wave number, with $c$ the wave celerity.

Within the $\Omega_1$-domain the following equation needs to be satisfied:

$$\nabla^2 u(x, y, t) = 0 \qquad \text{in } \Omega_1 \qquad (5.38b)$$

with the following boundary conditions:

1. *Bottom condition:* $\dfrac{\partial u}{\partial n} = 0 \qquad$ on $\Gamma_2$

2. *Free-surface condition:* $\dfrac{\partial^2 u}{\partial t^2} + g\dfrac{\partial u}{\partial y} = 0 \qquad$ on $\Gamma_4$

$$(5.38c)$$

3. *Obstruction condition:* $\dfrac{\partial u}{\partial n} = 0 \qquad$ on $\Gamma_1$

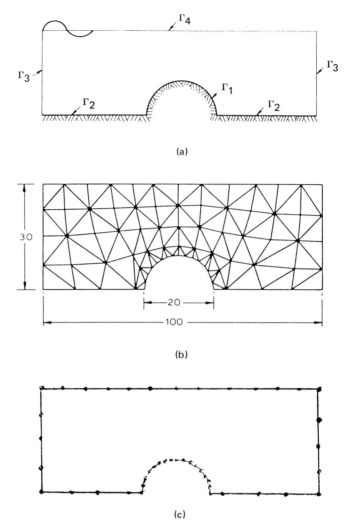

FIG. 5.8  Wave forces on a half cylinder. (a) Type of boundaries.
(b) Finite-element mesh. (c) Boundary-element mesh.

4. *Radiation condition in terms of scattered potential:*

$$\lim_{|x|\to\infty} \left\{ \frac{\partial u_s}{\partial n} + \frac{\kappa}{\omega} \frac{\partial u_s}{\partial t} \right\} = 0 \qquad \text{on } \Gamma_3$$

The $u_0$ solution for the incident wave will satisfy the first three boundary conditions and be defined by the wave theory of $\Gamma_3$ and be a harmonic function in $\omega$. Hence the problem can be expressed in terms of the time-independent scattered field. This gives

$$\nabla^2 \hat{u}(x, y) = 0 \qquad \text{on } \Omega_1 \tag{5.38d}$$

with

**1.** *Bottom condition:* $\dfrac{\partial \hat{u}}{\partial n} = 0$    on $\Gamma_2$

**2.** *Free-surface condition:* $\dfrac{\partial \hat{u}}{\partial n} - \dfrac{\omega^2}{g}\hat{u} = 0$    on $\Gamma_4$

**3.** *Obstruction condition:* $\dfrac{\partial \hat{u}}{\partial n} = -q_0$    on $\Gamma_1$     (5.38e)

where $q_0$ represents the velocities produced by the incident field.

**4.** *Radiation condition*:

$$\dfrac{\partial \hat{u}}{\partial n} - i\kappa\hat{u} = 0 \quad \text{on } \Gamma_3$$

The numerical solution for region $\Omega_1$ can be found in terms of boundary or finite elements as shown in Fig. 5.8b and c.

The *finite-element* formulation of the problem results in the following system of equations:

$$\left\{ \mathbf{K} + \left(i\kappa + \dfrac{\omega^2}{g}\right)\mathbf{M}\right\}\hat{\mathbf{U}} = \mathbf{F} \tag{5.38f}$$

The *boundary-element* formulation is based on the single, two-dimensional Green's function

$$u^* = \dfrac{1}{2\pi}\ln\dfrac{1}{r} + \text{constant}$$

and the following integral relationship:

$$c_i\hat{u}_i + \int_{\Gamma_1+\Gamma_2} \dfrac{\partial u^*}{\partial n}\hat{u}\,d\Gamma + \int_{\Gamma_3}\left(\dfrac{\partial u^*}{\partial n} - i\kappa u^*\right)u\,d\Gamma$$

$$+ \int_{\Gamma_4}\left(\dfrac{\partial u^*}{\partial n} - \dfrac{\omega^2}{g}u^*\right)u\,d\Gamma + \int_{\Gamma_1}u^*q_0\,d\Gamma = 0 \tag{5.38g}$$

where $c_i$ is a constant and is proportional to the solid angle at the boundary point $i$ (for smooth boundaries, $c_i = \tfrac{1}{2}$). We then need to propose a certain type of element to discretize the $\Gamma$ surface of the domain (Fig. 5.8c), carry out a series of analytical or numerical interpretations, and finally obtain the following system of equations:

$$\left(\mathbf{H} - i\kappa\mathbf{G}' - \dfrac{\omega^2}{g}\mathbf{G}''\right)\hat{\mathbf{U}} = -\mathbf{G}\mathbf{Q}_0 \tag{5.38h}$$

$\mathbf{G}'$ and $\mathbf{G}''$ are matrices which apply only on the $\Gamma_3$- and $\Gamma_4$-parts of the boundary. $\mathbf{G}$ corresponds to the $\Gamma_1$-part of the boundary.

Equation (5.38h) can be written in compact form as

$$A\hat{U} = B \tag{5.38i}$$

After Eq. (5.38i) has been solved, the potentials are known, and then the wave forces can be computed by first calculating the pressures using Bernoulli's equation. The dynamic pressure is given by

$$p(x, y, t) = -\rho \, \text{Re} \left\{ \frac{\partial u(x, y, t)}{\partial t} \right\} \tag{5.38j}$$

Once the pressures are known, we can integrate them over the obstruction to find the wave forces.

The forces on cylindrical obstructions of the type studied here were computed for a depth-to-radius ratio of $h/a = 3.0$ and for a range of wave numbers as shown in Figs. 5.9 and 5.10. Results obtained using different types of boundary elements were compared with

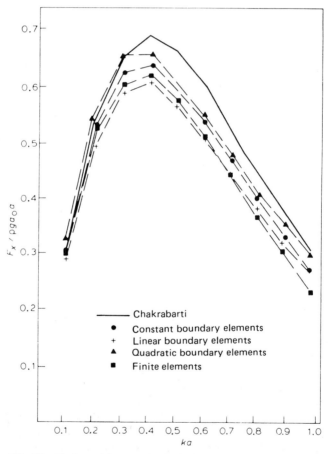

**FIG. 5.9**  Horizontal force on half cylinder.

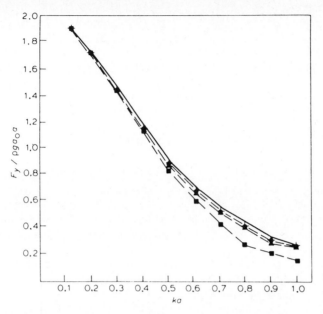

**FIG. 5.10**   Vertical force on half cylinder (key as in Fig. 5.9).

those produced by linear finite elements and the analytical results due to Chakrabarti and Naftzger [4, 5]. The constant boundary-element results for vertical and horizontal forces obtained using a mesh of 32 elements are shown in Figs. 5.9 and 5.10. To improve the results, two meshes, one consisting of 46 linear elements and the other of 8 quadratic elements, were employed. The results appear now to be in better agreement with those obtained by Chakrabarti and Naftzger. In particular, the quadratic elements seem to be better suited for this problem, as they can represent more accurately the geometry of the half cylinder, which was not possible when constants or linear elements were used.

Matrices obtained in this way can then be coupled to the structural matrices for the half-cylinder obstruction to study the effect of wave-structure interaction on the combined system.

## 5.3B  Added Mass and Damping Coefficients

A problem with important practical applications is the determination of the added mass and damping matrices for a fluid in order to combine their effect with structural matrices. Sometimes these values can be reduced to a single coefficient when one knows the geometry of the system. In Ref. [6] results are presented for the mass and damping coefficients of a heaving, half-submerged cylinder, starting from the governing equations for a floating body as shown in Fig. 5.11. The body is assumed to be rigid and subject to the three velocity components indicated in the figure, which can be written together in terms of a velocity vector $\dot{X}$. The problem can now be solved numerically by subdividing the fluid using a finite-element mesh as indicated in Ref. [7] and shown in Fig. 5.12, or by using the boundary-element grid of Fig. 5.13 [6]. The finite-element solution can be obtained as indicated in other chapters

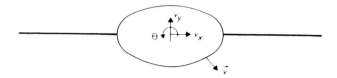

**FIG. 5.11** Rigid 2D motion.

of this handbook. Let us now assume that boundary elements are used. The starting matrix relationships—Eq. (5.8)—can be written as

$$\mathbf{A}\hat{\mathbf{U}} = \mathbf{G}\mathbf{Q}_0 \qquad (5.39a)$$

The matrix $\mathbf{A}$ is assumed to include the radiation and the surface boundary conditions, as shown in Eq. (5.38$h$) of Sec. 5.3A. The values of $\mathbf{Q}_0$ are functions of the velocities imposed on the rigid body and can be written as

$$\mathbf{Q}_0 = \mathbf{R}\dot{\mathbf{X}} \qquad (5.39b)$$

where each velocity component is assumed to be harmonic, that is, $q = q_0\, e^{-i\omega t}$. We can hence

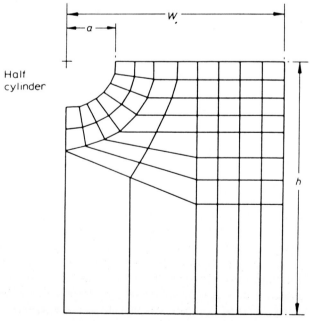

Half cylinder

**FIG. 5.12** Finite-element mesh (162 cubic elements, 359 nodes). $a = 10$, $h/a = 6$, $w/a = 5$.

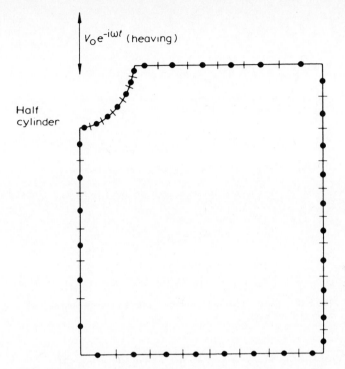

**FIG. 5.13**  Boundary-element mesh (61 constant elements). $a = 10$, $h/a = 6$, $w/a = 5$.

apply unit velocities in turn to represent surge, heave, and roll and solve for the potentials. Then we compute the pressures and the forces on the body as indicated in the preceding section. The forces on the floating body are represented by a vector **F**, and once this is done we can find the added mass and damping coefficients. If the total force is represented by $\vec{F}$, we can then write

$$c_m = -\omega M_H \, \text{Im} \, \{\vec{F}\}$$
$$c_d = \omega M_H \, \text{Re} \, \{\vec{F}\}$$

$(5.39c)$

where $c_m$ and $c_d$ are the added mass and damping coefficients for the rigid floating body, and $M_H$ is the mass of water displaced by the half cylinder.

For the case of the heaving motion of a half-submerged cylinder (Figs. 5.12 and 5.13), the boundary conditions on the symmetry axes can be taken to be $q = 0$. For simplicity, this is the only motion studied here. Numerical results were obtained by employing a 61-constant boundary-element mesh as shown in Fig. 5.13 and compared with results given by Newton [7] and Porter [8]; the agreement was found to be satisfactory. Notice that the boundary-element results presented in Fig. 5.14 achieved accuracy similar to that obtained with a much finer finite-element mesh consisting of 62 cubic elements with 359 nodes.

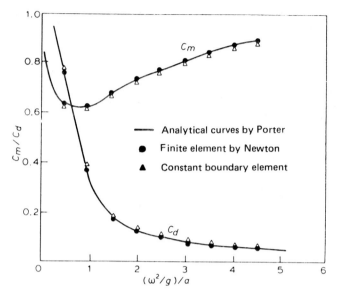

**FIG. 5.14**  Added mass and damping coefficients for a heaving half-submerged cylinder.

## 5.3c  Wave Diffraction around a Cylindrical Obstruction [3]

The case of a single vertical column subject to an incident harmonic wave was studied to determine how the application of the radiation condition affects the accuracy of the solution.

The column was surrounded by a finite-element mesh as shown in Fig. 5.15, and wave-diffraction results were found for different wavelengths, with the application of the radiation condition on the external boundary.

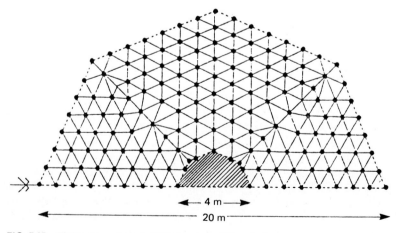

**FIG. 5.15**  Finite-element mesh (268 elements, 161 nodes).

As a test to determine the adequacy of the radiation condition in representing a train of plane harmonic waves, the case with no solid cylinder was studied first. For long waves [$\lambda$ (wavelength) $\approx 30$ m] the results were very accurate, within 3% of the exact solution. When the wavelength was reduced, the errors tended to increase, which was to be expected as the element mesh became too coarse. It was found that for linear elements such as the ones used here, ideally eight elements per wavelength should be used.

A further test was run to compare our results with those obtained by Mei [9] using a finite-element mesh and the Hankel-function formulation, i.e., the fundamental solution. The results are for an incident wavelength of $\lambda = 2\pi$ m and a unit incident surface elevation with frequency $\omega = 3.1321$. In Fig. 5.16 the results of the exact solution, the finite-element solution due to Mei, and the solution obtained in Ref. [3] are compared. The solution of Ref. [3] compares favorably in consideration of the coarseness of the mesh around the cylinder. Mei's solution, for instance, uses 18 elements around the cylinder and represents the geometry of the obstruction better.

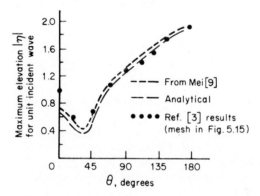

**FIG. 5.16** Results for maximum surface elevation round a circular cylinder, radius = 2 m, wavelength = $2\pi$ m.

## 5.3D Harbor Resonance [Eq. (3.15)]

As another example of the application of the radiation condition, we consider the harbor-resonance equation, i.e.,

$$\frac{\partial}{\partial x}\left(h\frac{\partial u}{\partial x}\right) + \frac{\partial}{\partial y}\left(h\frac{\partial u}{\partial y}\right) + \kappa^2 hu = 0 \tag{5.40a}$$

with boundary condition 
$$h\frac{\partial u}{\partial n} = q \qquad \text{on } \Gamma_2 \tag{5.40b}$$

where $u$ is now the wave elevation referred to the still-water level with in-plane coordinates $x$ and $y$, $h$ is the depth, $q$ is a given value of flux on $\Gamma_2$-boundaries, and $\kappa$ is the wave number.

We have the situation shown in Fig. 5.17. One needs to apply a boundary condition on the fictitious ocean boundary $\Gamma_1$, which will allow wave energy to pass across $\Gamma_1$ without

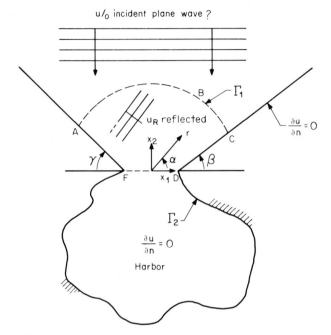

**FIG. 5.17**   Definition sketch for harbor oscillation problem.

distortion. To do this we need to split the wave elevation into three parts:

**1.** The incident field $u_0$.

**2.** The reflected field calculated from the plane-wave reflections by the coastline and called $u_R$ (see Fig. 5.17).

**3.** The scattered field $u_s$ originating from inside the harbor.

Hence the total wave field is $\qquad\qquad u = u_0 + u_r + u_s \qquad\qquad$ (5.40c)

with the incident field given by

$$u_0 = a \, \exp\left[-i\kappa r \cos\left(\theta - \alpha\right)\right] \qquad (5.40d)$$

We know that the scattered wave field $u_s$ will be traveling away from the harbor mouth on $\Gamma_1$. This effect is represented by the Sommerfeld boundary condition, which may be written

$$\lim_{r \to \infty}\left[\sqrt{r}\left(\frac{\partial u_s}{\partial r} + i\kappa u_s\right)\right] = 0 \qquad (5.40e)$$

or, approximately, $\qquad\qquad \dfrac{\partial u_s}{\partial r} + i\kappa u_s = 0 \qquad$ on $\Gamma_1 \qquad\qquad$ (5.40f)

Using (5.40f) we may write, for the total field $u$,

$$\frac{\partial u}{\partial r} + i\kappa u = \frac{\partial}{\partial r}(u_0 + u_R) + i\kappa(u_0 + u_R) = f \qquad (5.40g)$$

Note that the right-hand side is a known function $f$ of the horizontal coordinates, the angles determining the local geometry and the angle of incidence of the wave field $u_0$.

This boundary condition can now be incorporated into our variational-type statement to obtain

$$\int_\Omega \left[ \frac{\partial}{\partial x}\left(h\frac{\partial u}{\partial x}\right) + \frac{\partial}{\partial y}\left(h\frac{\partial u}{\partial y}\right) + \kappa^2 hu \right] u^* \, d\Omega = \int_{\Gamma_2} \left( h\frac{\partial u}{\partial n} - q \right) u^* \, d\Gamma$$

$$+ \int_{\Gamma_1} \left( h\frac{\partial u}{\partial n} + i\kappa u - f \right) u^* \, d\Gamma \qquad (5.40h)$$

which, after integration by parts, gives

$$\int_\Omega \left( h\frac{\partial u}{\partial x}\frac{\partial u^*}{\partial x} + h\frac{\partial u}{\partial y}\frac{\partial u^*}{\partial y} - \kappa^2 huu^* \right) d\Omega = \int_{\Gamma_2} qu^* \, d\Gamma + \int_{\Gamma_1} (hf - i\kappa hu)u^* \, d\Gamma \qquad (5.40i)$$

which is the starting expression for our finite-element formulation incorporating the boundary condition (5.40f) on $\Gamma_2$.

Numerical results with and without the use of the radiation condition were obtained for the classical case of the old Duncan Basin within Table Bay in South Africa.

To simulate deterministically the effect of waves entering the harbor we discretized it into finite elements (Fig. 5.18). Along the contour $ABCDEF$ we applied the usual zero normal-flux

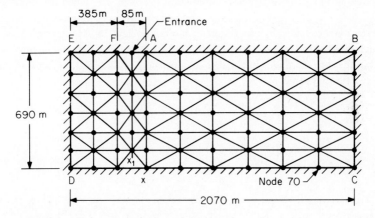

**FIG. 5.18**   Mesh for the old Duncan Basin.

condition $\partial u/\partial n = 0$. On the harbor entrance $AF$ we applied the radiation condition for an incident plane wave of unit amplitude entering the harbor in the negative $y$-direction, for the moment ignoring reflections from the neighboring coastline. The resulting elevations at node 70 for unit incident waves of different frequencies are plotted in Fig. 5.19. The first peaks occur at the same frequencies as those predicted by the harmonic analysis given by Brebbia and Adey [10]. For instance, the first peak represents the first significant period of about 11.45 minutes, which is the mode corresponding to water flowing in and out of the basin and is called the *pumping mode*. The second peak also corresponds to a simple motion,

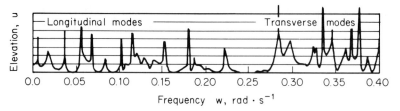

**FIG. 5.19**   Maximum surface elevation at node 70 with radiation.

the so-called *sloshing mode*. The results were plotted up to $\omega = 0.4$ rad/s, which is the lower bound of the wind-generated part of the wind spectrum.

It is interesting to note that after a series of mainly longitudinal modes, the transverse modes start to play a more significant part. The effect of these modes is considerable, especially from the probabilistic-response point of view. The application of the radiation condition on the harbor mouth adequately represents the input of wave energy into the system as well as energy passing out of the harbor. A more extensive discussion of this example can be found in Walker and Brebbia [11].

## 5.4 INTERNAL FLUID PROBLEMS

Consider now a type of fluid-structure interaction problem, i.e., when the fluid is enclosed within a vessel as represented in Fig. 5.20. The vessel may be represented by using standard finite elements and the fluid by using finite or boundary elements. It seems more appropriate for these types of problems to represent the fluid by boundary elements since one is not interested in the internal nodes but wishes to construct the fluid matrices and combine them with the structural system.

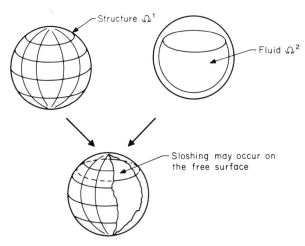

**FIG. 5.20**   Internal fluid problem.

Assume first that the fluid is incompressible and inviscid and that its behavior can be represented by a potential called $U$. The boundary-element influence matrices for this case can be written as

$$\mathbf{HU} = \mathbf{GQ} \tag{5.41}$$

where $\mathbf{U}$ and $\mathbf{Q}$ are the nodal potential and normal velocity vectors.

Consider for simplicity that the movement is harmonic. Hence the velocity at any point $k$ can be written in terms of the displacement $W_k$ as follows:

$$Q_i = i\omega W_k \tag{5.42}$$

The velocity potential can be related to the pressure $P_k$ through Bernoulli's equation. For harmonic motion, this gives

$$U_k = -\frac{1}{i\omega\rho} P_k \tag{5.43}$$

Here we can now write (5.41) as        $$\mathbf{HP} = \omega^2 \rho \mathbf{GW} \tag{5.44}$$

Inverting $\mathbf{H}$, we obtain        $$\mathbf{P} = \omega^2 \rho \mathbf{H}^{-1}\mathbf{GW} \tag{5.45}$$

To combine (5.45) with the finite-element system describing the structure we need to work in terms of equivalent nodal forces. The relationship between nodal pressures and equivalent forces can be written in terms of the distribution matrix $\mathbf{N}$ such that the nodal forces are

$$\mathbf{F} = \mathbf{NP} \tag{5.46}$$

Equation (5.46) now becomes

$$\mathbf{F} = \omega^2 \rho (\mathbf{NH}^{-1}\mathbf{G})\mathbf{W} = \mathbf{M}_F \mathbf{W} \tag{5.47}$$

The form of $\mathbf{M}_F$ is the same as for a finite-element formulation. Hence one can now superimpose it to the mass of the vessel and obtain the final matrices for the fluid-structure system. Notice that the $\mathbf{H}$- and $\mathbf{G}$-matrices of Eq. (5.41) have the same form as for a static-potential problem. $\mathbf{M}_F$ will generally be asymmetric but can be symmetrized by applying the procedure shown in Eq. (5.15).

## 5.4A Free-Surface Boundary Conditions

To represent sloshing on the free surface of the fluid, one needs to take into consideration the kinematic condition, i.e.,

$$\frac{\partial U}{\partial z} = -\frac{1}{g}\frac{\partial^2 U}{\partial t^2} \tag{5.48}$$

where $z$ is the normal to the free surface. Notice that $\partial U/\partial z$ is then the velocity of the fluid in the vertical direction.

For harmonic problems we can write

$$Q = \frac{\partial U}{\partial z} = \frac{\omega^2}{g} U$$

This normal velocity can be written in function of the $W$-displacements and the potential in function of the pressure as shown earlier; i.e., for any point $k$ we have

$$Q_k = i\omega W_k = -\frac{\omega}{g} \frac{1}{i\rho} P_k \qquad (5.49)$$

Thus,                              $$P_k = g\rho W_k \qquad (5.50)$$

Once again these pressures can be converted into equivalent nodal forces using the distribution matrix $\mathbf{N}$. The equivalent nodal forces $\mathbf{F}_s$ on the free surface are defined as

$$\mathbf{F}_s = g\rho \mathbf{N} \mathbf{W}_s \qquad (5.51)$$

where $F_s$ and $W_s$ represent the forces and displacements on the nodes of the sloshing or free surface. Relationship (5.51) applies only on the nodes on the free surface and can be included in the left-hand-side vector of Eq. (5.47). The nodes on the sloshing surface are then usually eliminated by a matrix-condensation technique since they are not directly related to the nodes of the structure.

### 5.4в Extension to Compressible Fluid

The extension of the above theory to compressible fluid has important applications in engineering as well as problems involving explosions inside pressure vessels, compressive wave propagation, and so on. Mathematically it follows the lines of the wave-diffraction problems already discussed. Compressibility of the fluid is important when the frequencies become higher but can usually be neglected at low frequencies [12].

The governing equation for compressible potential flow is

$$\nabla^2 u = \frac{1}{c^2} \frac{\partial^2 u}{\partial t^2} \qquad (5.52)$$

where $c$ is the speed of sound in the fluid. For harmonic motion Eq. (5.52) becomes

$$\nabla^2 u + \kappa^2 u = 0 \qquad (5.53)$$

where $\kappa$ is the wave number ($\kappa = \omega/c$).

The main difference between this formulation and the boundary-element point of view is that the Green's function corresponding to Eq. (5.30) is

$$u^* = \frac{1}{4i} H_0^{(2)}(\kappa r) \qquad \text{for the 2D case} \qquad (5.54)$$

and                       $$u^* = \frac{1}{4\pi r} \exp(-i\kappa r) \qquad \text{for the 3D case} \qquad (5.55)$$

The rest of the development follows the same lines as before.

**TABLE 5.1**  Nondimensional Frequencies of Sloshing in a Circular Cylindrical Tank ($\omega^2 R/g$; $H/R = 1.0$)

|  |  | Mesh | | | | Exact |
|---|---|---|---|---|---|---|
| $n$ | $m$ | $10 \times 10 \times 10$ | $15 \times 15 \times 15$ | $20 \times 20 \times 20$ | $25 \times 25 \times 25$ | (5.22) |
| 0 | 1 | 3.86 | 3.85 | 3.84 | 3.84 | 3.83 |
|  | 2 | 7.07 | 7.08 | 7.07 | 7.06 | 7.02 |
|  | 3 | 10.19 | 10.27 | 10.27 | 10.25 | 10.17 |
| 1 | 1 | 1.81 | 1.79 | 1.77 | 1.76 | 1.75 |
|  | 2 | 5.48 | 5.43 | 5.39 | 5.38 | 5.33 |
|  | 3 | 8.84 | 8.74 | 8.69 | 8.65 | 8.54 |
| 2 | 1 | 3.16 | 3.12 | 3.09 | 3.07 | 3.04 |
|  | 2 | 6.95 | 6.85 | 6.81 | 6.78 | 6.71 |
|  | 3 | 10.42 | 10.25 | 10.17 | 10.13 | 9.97 |
| 3 | 1 | 4.40 | 4.32 | 4.27 | 4.25 | 4.20 |
|  | 2 | 8.39 | 8.23 | 8.16 | 8.12 | 8.02 |
|  | 3 | 12.02 | 11.74 | 11.61 | 11.55 | 11.35 |

### 5.4c  Sloshing in a Rigid Container

Komatsu [16] has considered several interesting examples involving sloshing, starting with a fluid in a rigid container. In this case the equations of motion under harmonic vibrations can be written as

$$(\mathbf{K} - \omega^2 \mathbf{M})\mathbf{W} = \mathbf{0}$$

where the **K**-matrix is due to the contribution of the free-surface sloshing only and **M** is the fluid mass matrix. The **W**-vector applies to the free-surface nodes only. By varying the eigenvalues the corresponding eigenvectors can be found.

Table 5.1 presents the sloshing eigenvalues for the fluid in a rigid circular cylindrical container with a flat bottom. The results were obtained using a ring boundary element and different meshes. The $10 \times 10 \times 10$ mesh in the table (see Fig. 5.20), for instance, represents 10 elements each for the bottom, wall, and free surface. The eigenvalues are compared against an exact solution [17] and are found to be in close agreement.

## 5.5  SOIL-STRUCTURE INTERACTION PROBLEMS

Soil-structure interaction problems are becoming increasingly important in engineering, and it is necessary in many cases to be able to predict the coupled behavior of large structures or structures subject to considerable environmental loads. In many of these applications the dynamic response of the system is of primary importance.

These types of coupled problems can be divided into the following two classes:

1. *Surface-Structure Systems.*  Systems such as buildings, dams, offshore platforms, and others, most of which are subject to dynamic forces.

**2.** *Buried-Structure Systems.* Systems such as tunnels, underground shelters, and galleries, all of which are surrounded by a soil region extending to infinity.

The main difficulty with these types of interaction problems is the characterization of the soil itself, which presents a complex, nonlinear behavior. In some cases this behavior can be approximated by an equivalent hysteretic damping. Some solutions for surface foundations are available which use the half-space theory; most of them have the disadvantage of being valid only for homogeneous elastic soils, for which no material damping occurs [13]. Recent studies allow the extension of the theory to account for damping, but the results are not in tabulated form [14]. In addition, it has been found that layered media behave in a different way than a homogeneous medium, resulting in a stronger frequency depending on the radiation damping [15].

In many cases soils can be conveniently represented using finite elements because of their nonlinear and inhomogeneous behavior. However, although finite elements allow for a better representation for the soil properties, they tend to model radiation damping inaccurately and have numerical problems related to mesh resolution. Radiation damping is very significant in soil dynamics, but finite elements are unable to represent this properly because they require domain integration. It is then necessary to use some of the special elements described earlier or apply appropriate radiation conditions on the boundary. In addition, it is important to discretize the region of interest with a finite-element mesh that is fine enough not to produce artificial damping of frequencies during wave propagation. The mesh size should be a function of the wave celerity and related to the wavelength $\lambda$; that is, $\lambda = Tc$, where $T$ is the period of the exciting frequency and $c$ is the velocity of propagation of the wave. The typical mesh size should be approximately $\lambda/10$ to $\lambda/4$ if one is using linear or quadratic elements, respectively. It is easy to see that discretization problems will frequently arise when studying processes with very short periods, such as earthquakes.

It is now generally accepted that soil-foundation interaction effects are important and should be taken into consideration especially when computing the dynamic response of a system. Their relative importance will depend on the particular soil and structure under consideration. For hard soils the interaction effects become less significant, and, similarly, for large structural masses coupling is less important. Soil coefficients for evaluating the interaction effects can be obtained by considering the foundation to be a rigid circular base and using the half-space solution (for tables, see Ref. [15]). Flexible foundations, however, will behave differently, and we will need to carry out some form of numerical analysis. The need for a realistic computational technique is reinforced by the fact that in dynamics the interaction coefficients can be considered of equal importance to the static coefficients and need to vary with frequency.

An important consideration in any numerical analysis is that it should be able to represent the radiation damping, which is usually of a higher order of magnitude than the structural damping. Because of this the use of boundary elements to represent the soil has now become widespread. The advantages of using boundary elements in soil mechanics are obvious, as the number of unknowns reduces only to those required at the finite boundaries of the region under consideration (Fig. 5.21). Recent advances in boundary elements allow for the efficient representation of elastoplastic [18] or elastic-viscoplastic materials [19], nontension materials [20], and other types of nonlinearities [21, 28].

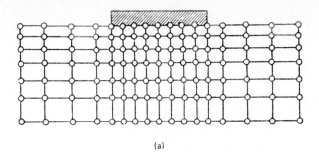

(a)

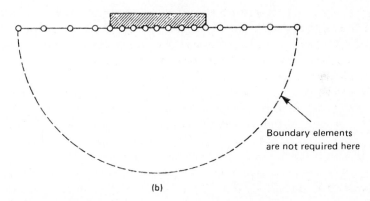

Boundary elements
are not required here

(b)

**FIG. 5.21**   Representation of soil by (*a*) finite-element and (*b*) boundary-element mesh.

## 5.5A Static Interaction [21]

Consider the example of a building standing on an infinite half space representing the soil (Fig. 5.22). The finite-element domain represents the structure, and the infinite half space is represented by a boundary-element region. Notice that since the plane representing the soil extends to infinity, it is in principle necessary to introduce an infinite number of boundary elements. This difficulty can be eliminated in practice in either of two ways:

1. Truncate the plane at a finite distance (approximate method), as shown in Fig. 5.22 and used in the present example. Notice that in the present case the domain has been closed with a few large boundary elements. These are not generally needed but have been used here to better compare the boundary-element solution with a finite-element solution obtained with the same closed domain.

2. Use a fundamental solution appropriate to the half-space problem rather than a free-space Green's function. With this approach, boundary elements are required only at the interface between the structure and the soil; yet the remainder of the soil domain is rigorously taken into account if the soil is homogeneous, isotropic, and elastic (for other cases more complex types of fundamental solutions are required).

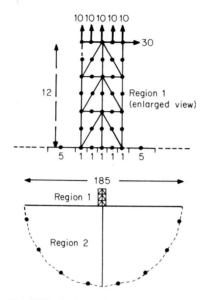

**FIG. 5.22** Finite-element and boundary-element combination mesh.

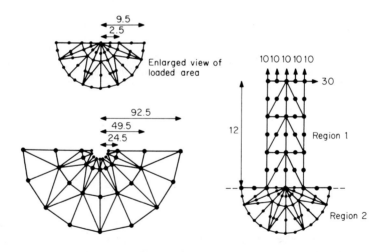

| FE solution | Combination solution |
|---|---|
| −339 | −355 |
| −97 | −105 |
| 135 | 135 |
| 361 | 370 |
| 600 | 617 |

**FIG. 5.23** Finite-element mesh. Table shows vertical displacements along loaded top ×10⁻⁶.

Regions 1 and 2 shown in Fig. 5.22 were then combined, where region 2 could be a boundary element (type 1 above) or a finite-element domain (Fig. 5.23). The combination of the boundary-element region 2 with the finite-element region 1 was carried out by finding the equivalent symmetric stiffness matrix for the boundary-element domain [see Eq. (3.15)]. Five concentrated vertical loads along the top and an additional horizontal load acting at a corner were considered. The results obtained are shown in the table of Fig. 5.23.

The combination solution is in good agreement with the results obtained using finite elements for the whole domain, but it is interesting to note that the foundation was adequately represented using only 37 boundary-element nodes as opposed to 163 for the finite-element case. Savings are more pronounced for three-dimensional applications.

## 5.5B Dynamic Soil-Structure Interaction

Dominguez and Alarcon [29] have studied the dynamic soil-structure interaction problem. They have computed the dynamic stiffness of two and three-dimensional foundations. They simulate the viscous properties of the soil by introducing a complex value of the shear modulus. This is equivalent to a hysteretic or Voigt-type model.

They employ the boundary-element method with the fundamental (Kelvin) solution for the complete space. The boundary to be discretized is then the soil-foundation interface and the free surface (Fig. 5.24). They show that only a small amount of free field around the foundation needs to be discretized in order to obtain accurate results.

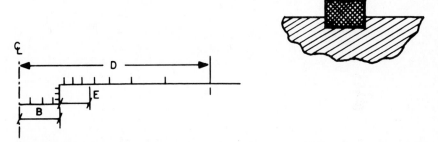

**FIG. 5.24**   Boundary-element discretization for embedded foundation. $D$ = distance from the extreme of the last element to the central line.

In Fig. 5.25, the influence of the amount of discretized free field is shown for an embedded foundation. First, the rocking stiffness is represented for the same case as Fig. 5.24 but with an embedment ratio $E/B = 0.5$. Here, the extent of free field discretized has an important influence until it reaches $D = 2B$. In Figs. 5.15b and 5.28c the same curves are plotted for the horizontal stiffness and two values of the dimensionless frequency $a_0$. The amount of free field that has to be discretized to obtain good results increases with the embedment ratio.

Figure 5.26 shows the amplitude of the free-surface motion when a unit harmonic motion of frequency $a_0 = 0.5$ is applied to a surface or embedded massless foundation. In the work by Dominguez and Alarcon [30] the reader can find plots of the variation of the stiffness components with frequency for foundations on the surface or embedded in an elastic half space with no damping.

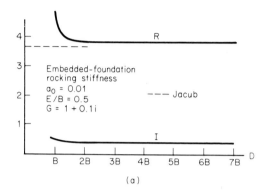

(a)

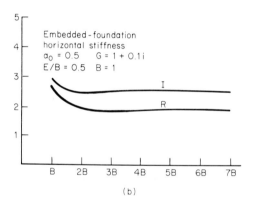

(b)

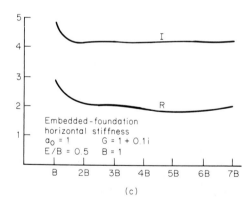

(c)

**FIG. 5.25** Influence of the amount of discretized free field. $a_0 = \omega B / c_s$, $G =$ shear modulus.

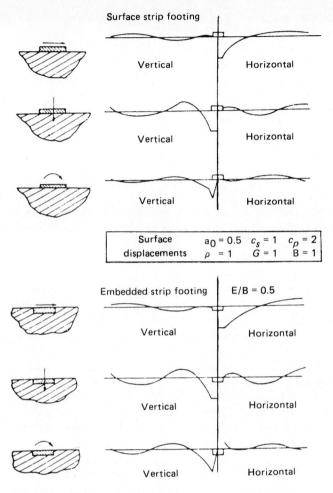

**FIG. 5.26** Amplitude of free-surface motion. $c_s$ = celerity shear wave, $c_p$ = celerity pressure wave, $\rho$ = material density.

# 5.6 REFERENCES

1. Ungless, R. F., "An Infinite Finite Element," M.Sc. thesis, Department of Civil Engineering, University of British Columbia, Vancouver, 1973.

2. Bettess, P., "Infinite Elements," *Int. J. Numer. Meth. Eng.*, **2**:53–64 (1977).

3. Brebbia, C. A., and S. Walker, "Simplified Boundary Elements for Radiation Problems," *Res. Note Appl. Math. Model.*, **2**(2) (June 1978).

4. Chakrabarti, S. K., and R. A. Naftzger, "Non-Linear, Wave Forces on Half Cylinder and Hemisphere," *J. Waterways, Harbours and Coastal Eng. Dev. ASCE*, **189** (August 1974).

5. Naftzger, R., and S. Chakrabarti, "Scattering of Waves by Two-Dimensional Circular Obstacles in Finite Water Depth," *J. Ship Res.*, **23**(1) (March 1979).

6. Au, M. C., and C. A. Brebbia, "Numerical Prediction of Wave Forces Using the Boundary Element Method," *Appl. Math. Model.*, **6**(4) (August 1982).

7. Newton, R. E., "Finite Element Analysis for Two-Dimensional Added Mass and Damping," in *Finite Elements in Fluids*, Wiley, New York, vol. 1, chap. 11.

8. Porter, W. R., "Pressure Distribution, Added-Mass and Damping Coefficients for Cylinders Oscillating in a Free Surface," Rep. Ser. 82, Iss. 16, Institute of Engineering Research, University of California, Berkeley, 1960.

9. Mei, C., "Oscillations and Wave Forces in a Man-Made Harbour in the Open Sea," *Proc. 10th Symp. Naval Hydrodynamics*, London, 1975.

10. Brebbia, C. A., and R. A. Adey, "Circulation Problems," *Proc. Finite Element Symp.*, Atlas Computer Laboratory, Didcot, U.K., HMSO, March 26–28, 1975.

11. Walker, S., and C. Brebbia, "Harbour Resource Problems Using Finite Elements," *Adv. Water Resources*, **1**(3) (June 1978).

12. Walker, S., "Boundary Elements in Fluid/Structure Interaction Problems," in C. Brebbia (ed.), *New Developments in Boundary Element Methods*, Computational Mechanics, Southampton, England, 1980.

13. Veletsos, A. S., and Y. T. Wei, "Lateral and Rocking Vibration of Footings," *Proc. ASCE Soil Mech. Div.*, **97** (September 1971).

14. Luco, J. E., "Independence Function for a Rigid Foundation in a Medium," *Nucl. Eng. Design*, **31**:204–207 (1974).

15. Brebbia, C. A., and S. Walker, *Dynamics of Offshore Structures*, Butterworth, London, 1980.

16. Komatsu, K., "Fluid-Structure Interaction," in *Progress in Boundary Element Methods*, Pentech Press, London, Wiley, New York, 1982, vol. 1.

17. Abramson, H. N. (ed.) "The Dynamic Behavior of Fluids in Mooring Containers," NASA-SP-106, National Aeronautics and Space Administration, 1966.

18. Telles, J., and C. A. Brebbia, "Plasticity," in C. A. Brebbia (ed.), *Progress in Boundary Element Methods*, Pentech Press, London, Wiley, New York, 1981, vol. 2.

19. Telles, J., and C. A. Brebbia, "Viscoplasticity and Creep," in C. Brebbia (ed.), *Progress in Boundary Element Methods*, Pentech Press, London, 1983.

20. Venturini, W. S., and C. A. Brebbia, "The Boundary Element Method for the Solution of No-Tension Materials," in C. Brebbia, (ed.), *Boundary Element Methods*, Springer-Verlag, Berlin, 1981.

21. Brebbia, C. A., J. Telles, and L. Wrobel, *Boundary Element Techniques—Theory and Applications in Engineering*, Springer, Berlin, 1984.

22. Brebbia, C. A. (ed.), "Boundary Element Methods," *Proc. 3rd Int. Conf. Boundary Element Meth. Eng.*, Irvine, Calif., July 1982, Springer-Verlag, Berlin, 1981.

23. Brebbia, C. A. (ed.), "Boundary Element Methods in Engineering," *Proc. 4th Int. Conf. Boundary Element Meth. Eng.*, Southampton, September, 1982 Springer-Verlag, Berlin, 1982.

24. Brebbia, C. A., et al. (eds.), "Boundary Elements V," *Proc. of the 5th Int. Cong. on Boundary Element Methods*, Hiroshima, Japan, Springer, Berlin, 1983.

25. Brebbia, C. A. (ed.), "Boundary Elements VI," *Proc. of the 6th Int. Conf. on Boundary Element Methods*, held on board the QEII from Southampton to New York, 1984, Springer, Berlin, 1984.

26. Brebbia, C. A., and G. Maier (eds.), "Boundary Elements VII," *Proc. of the 7th Int. Conf. on Boundary Element Methods*, Villa Olivo, Italy, 1985, Springer, Berlin, 1985.

27. Brebbia, C. A., and M. Tanaka (eds.), "Boundary Elements VIII," *Proc. of the 8th Int. Conf. on Boundary Element Methods*, Tokyo, Japan, 1986, Springer, Berlin, 1986.

28. Connor, J. J., and C. A. Brebbia (eds.), "Brebbia/86," *Proc. of the Boundary Element Technology Conference*, MIT, Cambridge, Massachusetts, 1986, Springer, Berlin, 1986.

29. Dominguez, J., and E. Alarcon, "Elastodynamics," in C. Brebbia (ed.), *Progress in Boundary Element Methods*, Pentech Press, London, Wiley, New York, 1981, vol. 2.

30. Dominguez, J., and E. Alarcon, "Dynamic Stiffness of Foundations," *2d Int. Conf. Innovative Numer. Anal.*, École Polytechnique, Montreal, 1980.

31. Brebbia, C. A., *Boundary Element Methods for Engineers*, Pentech Press, London, Computational Mechanics, Boston, 1978. Reprinted 1984.

# CHAPTER 6
# BIOMECHANICS

Biomechanics is the study of the motion and effect of forces on mechanical and functional behaviors of biological bodies. The body organs are the primary concern of biomechanics, but since the introduction of modern prostheses [1], the scope of biomechanics has expanded to include consideration of the interaction of living systems with human-made materials as well. In order to help the medical physicians diagnose diseases and make remedial decisions, the objective of biomechanical studies is to continually gain improved knowledge about the dynamic behavior of the living organs under normal and altered conditions.

For historical background and the theoretical and experimental development of bio-mechanics, all researchers interested in the field should consult the publication by Fung [2] for its lucid, detailed presentation and extensive references. For analytical studies, idealized models have been proposed to help depict the mechanical properties of the constituent materials of body organs. Use of simplified geometry has also enabled the nonlinear, finite deformation of living structures to be analyzed with adoption of appropriate strain-energy functions. Such elegant approaches are workable in theorizing the fundamentals of bio-mechanics and are indeed necessary for categorizing the characteristics of the constituent biological materials; the real-world, applied problems involving complex biological systems, unfortunately, are amenable only to approximate numerical solutions.

Finite-element analysis renders its service for treating practical biomechanics problems, where the true, complicated geometric shape and material properties of the living systems with or without augmentation of prosthetic components have to be dealt with. As far as the data acquisition of true dynamic geometry of body organs is concerned, the modern utilization of x-ray, gamma-ray, optical, and ultrasound energy [3] has enabled the body content to be accurately scanned by application of computer-aided tomographic techniques. Some organs which undergo rapid shape changes in time, such as the heart and lung, must be scanned by a more sophisticated device, such as the dynamic spatial reconstructor [4], to achieve the required high resolution both spatially and temporally.

Biological materials vary widely in stiffnesses. For instance, bone has an elastic modulus of order $10^{10}$ Pa, whereas muscle is of order $10^4$ Pa. Hence, small-deformation theory may be adequate for analysis of bone, but, in most cases, muscle must be investigated by application of finite-deformation theory. Unlike human-made materials, which can be extensively tested to determine their properties, biological materials tested *in vitro* often produce nonrepeatable results, attributable largely to variation in preconditioning of the specimen. Furthermore, whether or not the results obtained by *in vitro* tests are applicable to *in vivo* situations remains controversial [5]. Yamada's book [6] offers a wealth of information on the material properties of body organs. However, for furthering meaningful biomechanical research, a great deal of both *in vitro* and *in vivo* testings of biological materials still need to be conducted to substantiate the already available data. Implanting markers onto organs and tracing them by scanning appear to be a potential means for achieving valid *in vivo* tests; this technique [7], nevertheless, remains to be perfected by extensive trial applications.

There are numerous biomechanical studies, ranging from the skin [8], which is a membranous tissue covering the body, to the heart [9], which is the most vital and best-protected organ of the body. In the ensuing subsections, areas of biomechanics where major applications of finite-element analyses have been made in recent years will be delineated. The invited contributors present an up-to-date review of their respective, specialized fields and point out the currently active and potential research subjects. An extensive list of references covering subjects in solid biomechanics, fluid biomechanics, and thermal biomechanics is provided at end of this section.

For biomechanical studies, both commercially available and in-house finite-element computer programs, preprocessors, and postprocessors are in constant use. Besides geometric distinction in finite-element analyses of biological structures, significantly different from one application to another are the preparatory work of input data for defining the loadings and boundary conditions, and the computational procedure involving various underlying theories and material properties. As the complexity of the biomechanical system increases, the inevitable problem of excessive computer time and storage requirements has also been encountered. Use of advanced hardware such as the supercomputer Cray 1 [10] and its newer generations, and special software algorithms [11], becomes increasingly frequent.

Along with the finite-element method, finite-difference and other methods have also contributed and will continue to play important roles in solving problems in biomechanics [12]. It can also be expected that other utilizations of the finite-element concept, such as for nonhomogeneous anthropometric scaling of biological regions [13], will also find their place in biomechanical studies.

## 6.1 CRASH-INJURY STUDIES

Crash-injury studies are motivated by staggering societal losses. In 1980, the U.S. National Research Council reported in "Accident Facts" that the cost of 51,900 traffic fatalities and

2 million injuries was $35.8 billion. The object is to delineate injury mechanics, tolerance to impact and protection. Injuries are caused by a collision of the body with a stationary or moving object. High forces of short duration (5 to 100 milliseconds) are created over small areas, exciting a transient response. Crash-injury studies relied initially on experimental work. Finite-element (FE) models were not attempted until the early 1970s. Suitable dynamic codes are now available. For example, a research-oriented, general-purpose finite-element program [14] has been developed for dynamic analysis of contact and impact problems.

A model should closely simulate the geometry, material properties, and dynamic characteristics of the prototype. Compliance with these requirements for biological models can be challenging. One must ascertain model accuracy and limitations by validation against experimental data. Absolute validation, however, is very difficult. Often a model can be used to assess the efficacy of protective equipment, even though it cannot predict responses for all impact conditions. In this exposition finite-element models for four body regions are briefly discussed: head, thorax, spine, and femur. More details are provided in Ref. [15].

## 6.1A Head Models

The head has received enormous attention because of its high susceptibility to injury. Simple 2D plane strain [16] and layered axisymmetric models (spherical and oval) [17], simulating scalp, skull, and brain were developed, along with a 3D empty-skull [18] model. These were followed by a 3D brain model, including dura folds and ventricles [19], and a 3D skull-brain model excluding dura [16]. Finally, there was a 3D skull-brain-cervical-spine model, including dura folds and cord [20].

All models were linear, using elastic or viscoelastic homogeneous and isotropic properties. Cranial-bone properties have been identified with a reasonable degree of confidence. By contrast, soft-tissue properties, particularly those of the living brain, are not well known. The brain was assumed to be nearly incompressible with a bulk modulus differing by a factor of over 100 [16, 19]. The models were subject to a traction boundary condition simulating direct impact or an acceleration pulse representing inertial loading. Response parameters such as skull strains, brain pressure gradients, and shear strains were used to explain skull fractures and brain-injury mechanisms. However, injuries to blood vessels, cells, and cell membranes could not be handled by existing macro models. Perhaps future micro models can combine mechanical principles and biomechanical laws to investigate intracellular energy transfer and cell damage.

Model validations have been attempted [16, 19]. Large discrepancies in skull strains and brain pressures were not surprising because of the many approximations and assumptions made. Model resonances in Refs. [16, 19] are lower than those of the human head [21] by more than an order of magnitude, because of the coarseness of the mesh. Also, large-impedance differentials [20] on the order of $10^5$ between various head layers would erroneously attenuate the impact pulse. The selected material representation may be inadequate for living biological systems. To vary material properties until an agreement was achieved [19] is a curve-fitting procedure which is subjective and unscientific. Head models developed thus far must be regarded as crude replicas of an extremely complex living biological system. However, they are useful for assessing relative impact severity and speculation of injury mechanisms. As yet, they should not be used to predict injury.

## 6.1B Thoracic Models

Several thoracic finite-element models simulating frontal-impact response of the rib cage were developed. Early linear models used beam elements to represent the ribs, sternum, spine, and clavicles [22, 23]. They were three-dimensional and symmetric about the midsagittal plane, and the input forces were in the anteroposterior direction. Bone and cartilage were linearly viscoelastic. The thoracic viscera were considered as part of the chest wall. Global geometric characteristics and cross-sectional properties were based on previously published data.

These early models were not rigorously validated and were accepted if the displacement configuration of the ribs was "reasonable." The results of Ref. [22] showed good agreement with experimental data for chest deflection and potential fracture sites. This model was extended [24] to simulate the response of a child's thorax, using anatomical data from a 9-year-old male cadaver.

Another model [25] has used large deformations to predict rib stresses with a small number of degrees of freedom. An elastic element represented the flexural and torsional resistance of the rib by a curved, nonprismatic bar. Three elements of equal length were used to represent a typical half rib. The sternum and vertebrae were rigid bodies and the intervertebral disks were viscoelastic beams. The model was validated by using a single rib to simulate blunt frontal sternal impact. The run was 30 milliseconds in duration for a 32-millisecond input pulse. An explicit integration scheme was used, requiring small time steps which were governed by the minimum wave transit time along the element. Additional results of rib-cage response to shoulder harness and air-bag loading are given in Ref. 14 of Ref. [25]. In each case the computation was terminated at 70 milliseconds or sooner for input pulses which were approximately twice as long. Excessive computer cost was the presumed reason for early termination of computation.

## 6.1C Vertebral Models

Dynamic models of vertebrae were motivated by the pilot-ejection problem plaguing military aircraft designers. A detailed three-dimensional finite-element model [26] was developed to simulate a lumbar vertebra. The spongy bone of the vertebral body was represented by 51 brick elements, while the cortex and end plates were simulated by 48 thin-shell elements. The posterior structure was composed of 11 brick brick elements to model the pedicle, laminae, and the articular facets. The processes were modeled by four plate elements. Facet geometry was defined to permit articulation if two identical vertebrae were stacked together. Material properties were taken from the literature, while the input loads were estimated from experimental data [27]. Static and dynamic runs were made, and in spite of the large variation in cortical-bone thickness, there was generally good çorrelation in cortical strain.

## 6.1D Femoral Models

The femur is basically a cylindrical shaft with two enlarged extremities. However, its geometry is complex, having evolved to fulfill physiological and mechanical functions. Variability in fracture loads and sites were found [28]. Modeling of the impact response of the femur is not as common as that of orthopedic applications treated elsewhere in this chapter. The dynamic response of an anteroposterior femoral midsection was investigated [29] using a plane-strain model. Elastic, homogeneous, and isotropic material properties were assumed for both compact and cancellous bone. Loads of varying duration (3 to 75 milliseconds) were applied at the lateral and medial condyles. The response was dependent upon impact duration, which could excite the lower vibrational modes. A reasonable agreement was noted between model predictions of fracture loads and experimental data. Future models should be three-dimensional and account for bone anisotropy.

## 6.2 ORTHOPEDIC AND JOINT MECHANICS

The use of finite-element analysis (FEA) in orthopedic biomechanics started after the method had been well established in traditional engineering applications. Rybicki et al. [30] and Brekelmans et al. [31] were probably among the first to use FEA for stress calculation in the femur. Since their two-dimensional analysis was made, enormous progress has been made in the last decade to apply the finite-element method to bone and joint mechanics with a high degree of sophistication.

The structural elements that are subjected to analysis include bone, articular cartilage, and the intervertebral disk. These biological materials are inhomogeneous, anisotropic, and biphasic with time-dependent nonlinear behaviors. In bone-fracture fixation and prosthetic joint replacement, metals, ceramic, graphite, and polymers are commonly used. To fix joint implants to bone, polymethylmethacrylate is used as a grouting agent (bone cement). Because of the structural and material complexities, simplified assumptions must be made to obtain practical solutions.

The most common stress analysis in orthopedic biomechanics concerns the traditional boundary-value problem where body and surface forces or displacements are well-defined. In elastodynamic problems, the ill-defined energy function associated with nonlinear material properties has created new challenges to finite-element application in orthopedic bio-mechanics. In the field of joint prosthetics, interface loosening has been a significant problem. Unknown boundary conditions and the associated failure criteria require innovative modeling and computational methods. Simple two-dimensional models, using either the effective-modulus technique or reinforcing-side-plate (spanning-element) approach, were tried to solve the three-dimensional problem. Axisymmetric models using ring elements have proved useful for selected geometric shapes. The truly three-dimensional model appears to be most attractive, but its benefit must be carefully weighted against the escalated costs involved.

### 6.2A Bone Modeling and Fracture Fixation

It is important to quantitate stress distribution in bone, since its biological remodeling appears to be related to the local state of stress [32, 33]. The femur has been studied extensively because of its common involvement in joint disease and total-hip replacement. Both two- and three-dimensional finite-element models were used [30, 31, 34–37]. A very sophisticated model containing 1950 three-dimensional solid elements has been developed with experimental validation [36] (see Fig. 6.1).

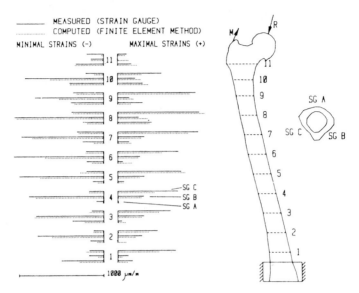

**FIG. 6.1** Principal strains on femur surface—comparison between the measured (strain gauge) and calculated (3D FEA) strains at different levels along the bone. (From Rohlmann et al., 1982 [36].)

Similar analyses were also performed on other load-bearing bones [38, 39] and for the investigation of bone properties and stress-related remodeling [40–42]. Correlation between von Mises effective stress with trabecular-bone density and orientation was conducted to establish the quantitative basis of Wolff's law [33, 43]. Stresses in canine femur predicted by FEA agreed favorably with *in vivo* measurements using strain gauges on living bone [44].

Bone-fracture fixation using metal plates and screws has been a popular model for FEA. Fracture-fixation rigidity and stress-shielding effects were thoroughly studied [45–48]. Structural stiffness of an external fracture fixator was analyzed using beam elements [49]. Bone stresses at the pin-bone interface in such a fixator were calculated using both two- and three-dimensional finite-element models [50]. Results from these studies have greatly improved the design of these devices and their clinical application.

### 6.2B Analysis of Prosthetic Joint Systems

Joint prostheses lend themselves well to FEA owing to their well-defined geometrical and material properties. However, these devices are implanted in the bone, and they must be analyzed as a system of composite structures. Total-hip prosthesis has been investigated most widely because of its enormous clinical volume. Two-dimensional finite-element models with varying degrees of sophistication were first attempted [51–54]. Axisymmetric models were developed later to analyze the stem portion of the femoral component [55, 56]. A significant amount of information has been established in a three-dimensional fashion. A similar model was used by the author in the design of a proximal-femur prosthesis for the replacement of the entire bone and joint section necessitated by tumor resection (Fig. 6.2). True three-dimensional models using either 8-node tetrahedral or 20-node isoparametric elements have

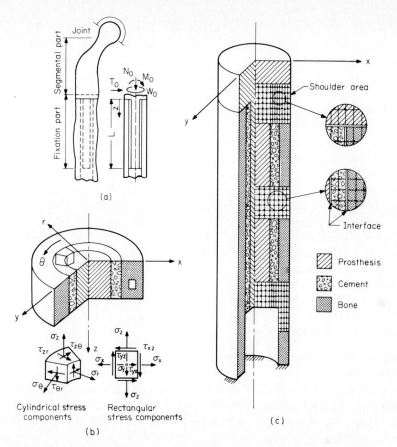

**FIG. 6.2** Finite-element analysis of a segmental prosthesis used to replace the proximal femur and hip joint after tumor resection. (*a*) Schematic diagram of the prosthetic system with the joint loads transferred to the proximal-stem portion. (*b*) Comparison of the rectangular stress components (axisymmetric finite-element model using ring elements) and the cylindrical stress components (true 3D model). (*c*) Mesh density and the interface (including prosthesis-bone shoulder contact) nodal-point separation in the axisymmetric finite-element model to study the stresses in the stem, cement, and bone. (From Chao et al., 1981, unpublished data.)

become more popular in analyzing the entire-hip prosthetic system [36, 57–60]. The real justification for such complex models must be carefully assessed in the light of the uncertainties in material properties and boundary and joint loading conditions.

Although planar models have been tried for knee-joint prostheses, three-dimensional FEA would be more desirable because of the irregular geometry of the system [61–64]. Other types of orthopedic implants are beginning to utilize this powerful analytic method. Artificial finger joints [65], a ceramic-proximal-humerus prosthesis using extracortical fixation [44], and the resurfacing prostheses for the hip [66] are only a few examples. Following the current trend, it is safe to predict that such applications will grow substantially in the future. Hopefully, the quality of the analyses will also improve as the investigators begin to gain more insight into the method as well as into the problems to be solved.

## 6.2c Cartilage Mechanics and Other Applications

Articular cartilage is an important connective tissue with its known mechanical functions of lubrication, load bearing, and shock absorption. The finite-element method was used to characterize the elastic response of its solid phase on the basis of contact stress analysis [67]. A semianalytic finite-element model was used to study the electromechanical property of human articulating cartilage on the basis of the contemporary mixture theory [68]. Under the assumption that cartilage is a nonporous compliant material with a layer of bone base and is covered by synovial fluid, the squeeze-film lubrication theory was studied [69]. Under the assumption that cartilage is elastic and the synovial fluid is newtonian, a minimization algorithm was used to solve the dynamic boundary-value problem using FEA.

In the analysis of intervertebral-disk mechanics, the model is generally divided into three regions: vertebral body and end plates, annulus fibrosus, and nucleus pulposus. Disk material is usually considered linear-elastic but inhomogeneous and anisotropic. Three-dimensional models were used, but axisymmetry and plane-symmetry conditions were assumed [70–73]. Application of FEA to other areas of orthopedic biomechanics has been relatively rare. Since such formulations are particularly effective in handling heat transfer and kinetic problems of deformable linkage systems, more applications of this nature are expected [56, 74].

## 6.2d Discussion and Remarks

Irregular geometry, complex material behavior, and the sophisticated boundary conditions made FEA an ideal method for solving many mechanically oriented problems in human skeletal-joint systems. However, the qualitative nature of the biological behavior and the highly variable clinical parameters involved in the system may require gross assumptions and thus decrease the validity of FEA. A clear perception of the nature of the problem is a prerequisite, and it forms the basis on which practical and realistic goals can be established for the analysis. In design-oriented problems where geometry becomes the key variable, the use of FEA will face its challenge in balancing the modeling and computational costs with the usefulness of results produced.

Although simpler models based on compound-beam and beam-on-elastic foundation theories are less exact in matching geometric shapes of the biological system and are unable to calculate certain stress components, their readily available closed-form solution is particularly valuable in conducting parametric analysis and design optimization [75, 76] (Fig. 6.3). In studying the interface-loosening problem, the use of a complete finite-element model may be difficult because of unknown failure criteria of interface bonding, as well as the cost involved in performing the required iterative computation [77]. In this respect, either a simpler model with an available closed-form solution [78] or a refined finite-element model restricted only to the localized region of the interface between dissimilar materials would seem more practical. The stresses obtained on the basis of idealized interface conditions in a simpler model can be used as the boundary condition for the refined analysis.

The value of using FEA in orthopedic biomechanics should not be judged by the sophistication of the model used. Although certain two-dimensional analyses were considered incorrect theoretically, the use of more expensive three-dimensional elements does not guarantee the validity of such studies. Even if the need for three-dimensional analysis is indicated, effort

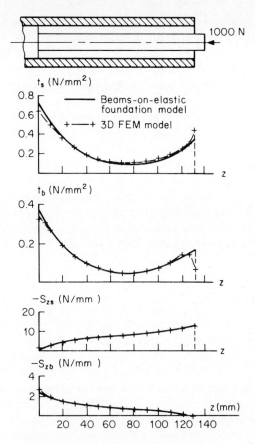

**FIG. 6.3** Comparison of axial-stem stress ($S_{zs}$),
bone stress ($S_{zb}$), stem-cement interface shear
stress ($t_s$), and bone-cement interface shear stress
($t_b$) under axial loading (1000 N) as calculated
with the FEA model and the beams-on-elastic-
foundation model. (From Huiskes, 1980 [56].)

must be made to utilize the benefits of geometric symmetry. It is more ideal to use simpler
models for parametric analysis. A more refined system can then be developed to verify the
results and provide localized stress distributions at the most critical regions where simple
models cannot provide reliable results. Since the basic bone configurations are similar, sharing
the basic model geometry should be considered in the future. Certain benchmark testing
between different finite-element models would be desirable to clarify the limitations inherent
to each analysis.

In many orthopedic problems, useful information is best provided on a relative basis.
Very rarely is an absolute solution either needed or possible because of many unknown
conditions of the biological system. The question concerning the effects of material nonlinearity and anisotropy on stress distribution should also be investigated by following the
same guidelines. Although FEA has been a powerful tool for engineers in the past decade,

its validity and efficacy in biomechanical application can only be assured with a comprehensive knowledge of orthopedic practice and its clinical implications.

Finally, orthopedic surgery is a pragmatic branch of medicine, and the clinical application of biomechanical findings has frequently been a direct response based on much diluted information. In many ways, FEA is especially attractive to the clinicians with only a rudimentary knowledge of mechanics, since the rather dramatic mechanical failures of implants can now be related to material selection and design weaknesses. In this respect, the visibility of finite-element analysis with its marvelous three-dimensional pictorial presentation can be a motivating force for, as well as an obstacle to, the collaborative efforts between engineers and surgeons. On one hand, the capability of FEA provided physicians with unprecedented knowledge for relating visible failures of their practice with the seemingly apparent weaknesses of an implant. On the other hand, the multiple assumptions made during the course of analysis can obscure and misplace important clinical and biological factors. There is no question that FEA will offer great potential in orthopedic application, but it would be ill-advised to overly emphasize the value of such analysis.

## 6.3 DENTAL MECHANICS

Experimental stress-analysis techniques have been used to study dental structures since 1950, and a review of those related to single restorations and fixed bridges was published by Craig and Farah in 1977 [79]. The application of finite-element method in dental research started in the early 1970s, and it has been used to study two-dimensional [80–85], axisymmetric [86–91], and three-dimensional problems [92–96] and thermal gradients and stresses [97, 98].

Wright and Yettram [85] determined the reactive-force distributions for teeth loaded singly and when used as fixed-bridge abutments; the model for the latter is shown in Fig. 6.4a. Appropriate physical constants for gold and the anatomical structures were used and linear-elastic behavior was assumed. A finite-element model of a buccolingual section of a lower bicuspid with three levels of alveolar bone support was loaded vertically, obliquely, and horizontally on the buccal cusp and the forces around the root were determined. A decrease in alveolar height resulted in a decrease in tooth support and an increase in the force in the periodontal membrane; the forces were much greater for nonaxial loading. The force distributions around the roots for the three loading conditions, Fig. 6.4b, were determined for teeth: (1) not connected, (2) rigidly splinted, and (3) minimal splinting (only the center element used). Maximum forces occurred at the alveolar crest and the root apex, and oblique and horizontal loading should be minimized. Two tooth abutments should be rigidly splinted when a cantilever fixed bridge is used to avoid high forces and to reduce bone resorption.

The optimum design of a full gold crown for a first molar was studied by Farah, Craig, and Sikarskie [86], using an idealized axisymmetric model (Fig. 6.5). This type of restoration is luted to the tooth with zinc phosphate cement with low tensile and shear strength, and clinical failure is usually in the cement at the margin of the restoration. Emphasis was placed on the effect of marginal geometry on the stresses at the margin. Four geometries were studied: (1) knife (KN), (2) chamfer (CH), (3) flat shoulder with rounded angle (FS), and (4) flat shoulder with a bevel (SB). The radial and axial stresses were determined with axial loading and under the assumption of elastic behavior. The maximum shear stresses compared favorably

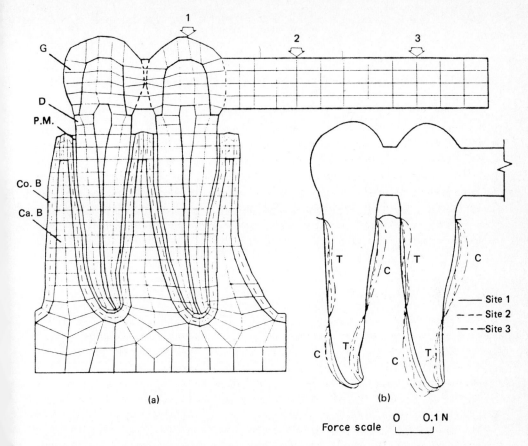

**FIG. 6.4**  (*a*) Two-dimensional finite-element model of first and second lower bicuspids with a fixed bridge loaded at three positions G = gold, P.M. = periodontal membrane, CO.B. = cortical bone, CA.B. = cancellous bone, D = dentin. Lines in CØ.B. show assumed principal stiffness direction. (*b*) Nodal force around roots at force of 0.294 N and rigid splinting. Site 1 ——, site 2 - - -, site - · -; T and C = tensile and compressive forces (from [85]).

to those determined from three-dimensional photoelastic models. Plots of axial radial and shear stresses through the lines, indicated in Fig. 6.5 (A–B, C–D, etc.), showed that the geometry that resulted in minimum chance of failure of the cement was CH, followed by FS, SB, and KN.

Three-dimensional finite-element analysis was used by Cook et al. [92] to determine the optimum material and design of a dental blade implant in the mandible. The model is shown in Fig. 6.6*a*, and the principal stress profiles in the lingual cortical plate adjacent to the implant are plotted for an axial load of 450 N on the pontic of a three-unit fixed bridge, on the free-standing implant and on the tooth, in Fig. 6.6*b*. The model represented a section of a baboon mandible and LTI (vitreous) carbon, $Al_2O_3$, and carbon-coated $Al_2O_3$ blade implants of identical geometry were used. Loading was axial on the tooth, pontic, or implant. Mechanical and histological analyses of implants in baboons showed good correlation with

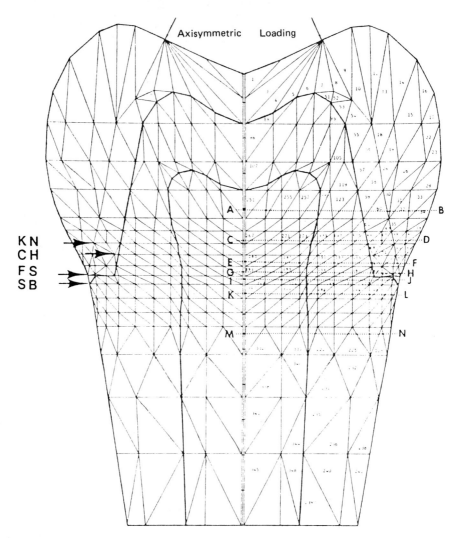

**FIG. 6.5** Axisymmetric finite-element model of restored first molar with a gold crown having the following shoulder geometry: KN = knife, CH = chamfer, FS = shoulder, and SB = bevel, and loaded at 444 N (from [86]).

the finite-element data. Compressive stresses were three times lower in the crestal region for $Al_2O_3$ versus LTI-carbon implants. The use of the implant as part of a three-unit bridge significantly reduced the stress levels. Reduction of the elastic modulus of the interfacial tissue layer substantially reduced stresses around implants regardless of the implant material.

Temperature gradients and thermal stresses in teeth during cutting were determined by Brown, Christensen, and Lloyd [97] using axisymmetric finite-element analysis. A model of a lower second molar is shown in Fig. 6.7$a$, and the temperature distribution after 1 second of simulated dry cutting of enamel is given in Fig. 6.7$b$. Temperatures for dry cutting and

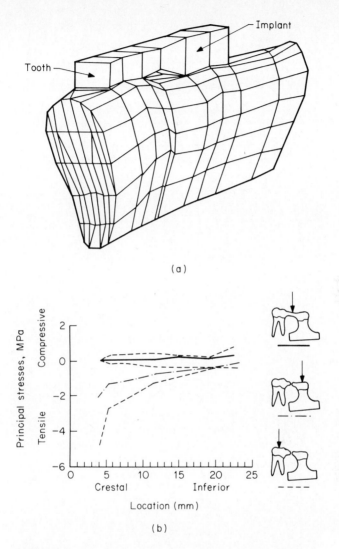

**FIG. 6.6**  (*a*) Three-dimensional finite-element model of a section of the mandible of a baboon for blade implants. (*b*) Principal stresses in the lingual cortical plate from crestal to inferior border adjacent to the vitreous (glassy) carbon blade implant when a load of 450 N was applied to the natural tooth – – –, free standing implant – · – ·, and to the pontic of the fixed 3-unit bridge —— (from [92]).

with coolants verified the calculations. The results supported the accepted recommendations to use water cooling; these data also showed that a water stream is a better coolant than an air-water spray. Calculations indicated that dry cutting of enamel can cause fractures from high thermal stresses, and in dry cutting of dentin can cause pulpal damage if the cutting is 1 to 2 mm from the pulp.

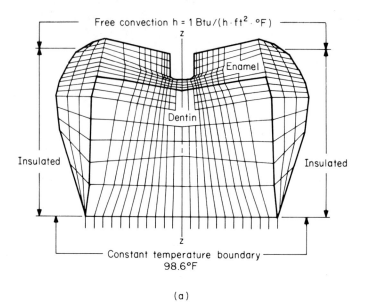

(a)

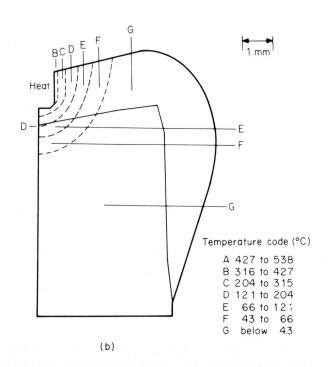

Temperature code (°C)

A 427 to 538
B 316 to 427
C 204 to 315
D 121 to 204
E  66 to 121
F  43 to 66
G below 43

(b)

**FIG. 6.7** (*a*) Axisymmetric finite-element differential temperature grid for a molar. (*b*) Temperature distribution after 1 second of dry cutting of enamel (energy deposition of 0.44 cal/s) (from [97]).

## 6.4 CARDIOMECHANICAL STUDIES

Since the left ventricle is the main pumping chamber of the heart, which propels fresh blood to circulate and thereby provides oxygen as an energy source for the entire body, it has been and continues to be the center of research in cardiomechanics. Various idealized models, mostly of axisymmetric shapes, have been proposed for two-dimensional finite-element stress and functional analyses of the left ventricle. To account for the finite deformation of the heart chambers during cardiac cycles, use of the strain-energy functions has also been suggested, but the method of solution is only tractable for some idealized geometries. Without use of the true geometry of the ventricle, the validity of the results so obtained is highly debatable. On cardiac analyses, the handbook on cardiovascular systems edited by Berne et al. [99] contains a collection of authoritative review chapters providing extensive lists of pertinent literatures. In particular, on finite-element applications to cardiac analyses, the review article by Pao [9] has delineated the historical development up to 1979.

The true three-dimensional shape of the heart has been accurately reconstructed since 1977 by application of computer-aided tomographic techniques [3], and three-dimensional finite-element analyses of isolated left ventricle and connected left and right ventricles have consequently been realized [9, 100]. Figure 6.8 illustrates reconstruction of the true shape and dimensions of a canine left ventricle at several selected cardiac instants by stacking of the basal-to-apical cross sections obtained by use of an x-ray scanner. In-house finite-element computer programs are available to partition the reconstructed three-dimensional shape into a desired number of tetrahedral elements, carry out the incremental-loading analysis, and consequently display or plot either the principal stresses on the epicardial and endocardial surfaces or the cross-sectional stresses of the left ventricle as shown in Fig. 6.9 [9].

Now that the scanning technique has been advanced to a fine resolution of 1 mm spatially and 1/60 second temporally [4], the extent to which finite-element analysis can be fully and justifiably utilized for cardiomechanical studies is limited only by the readiness of efficient numerical procedures and the economic feasibility of adopting an effective computer. As in other finite-element applications, the problems plaguing cardiomechanics include the need of (1) more precise definition of loading and boundary conditions, (2) more detailed specification of cardiac material properties, and (3) improved speedier numerical methods and computers to reduce computer cost for finite-deformation analyses. At present, a three-dimensional shape such as the one shown in Fig. 6.8b partitioned by use of 1200 nodes results in a stiffness matrix of order $3600 \times 360$, arranged in rectangular form [11], which requires computer time of approximately 1 to 3 hours on an IBM 360/370 computer or 5 to 10 minutes on a Cray 1 computer [10], depending on the step size used in the incremental-loading analysis and also on the degree of nonhomogeneity of the materials involved.

Valvular analysis is one among many considerations which should be incorporated into ventricular analysis for refinement of the boundary conditions. On natural and prosthetic cardiac valves, Christie and Medland [101] have presented a series of elaborated studies. From their work, more pertinent references on valvular studies can be found. As far as the loadings for ventricular analyses are concerned, only normal internal pressure has hitherto been considered. The blood flow in the chamber is known to have a significant shear effect on the ventricular wall [102]. Apparently, further research on the loading conditions for ventricular analyses is mandatory.

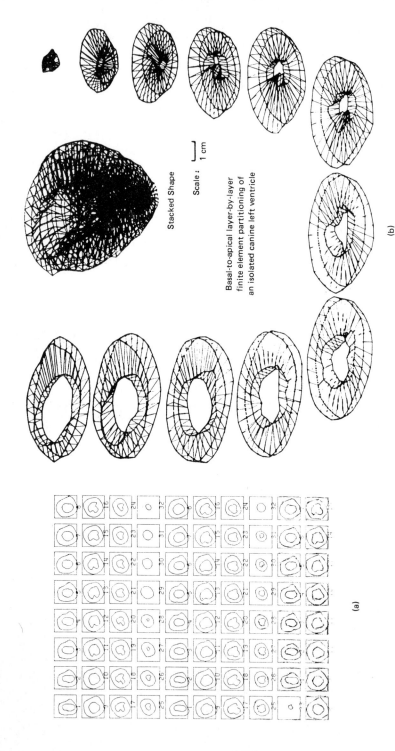

**FIG. 6.8** (*a*) Sample reconstructed basal-to-apical cross-sectional shapes of an isolated, working left ventricle by application of computer-aided tomography at various instants of a cardiac cycle. First instant's shapes are numbered 1 to 32, whereas the second instant needs 33 shapes for describing the slightly extended left ventricle. (*b*) Stacking of the basal-to-apical cross-sectional shapes and partitioning of the three-dimensional, true shape of the left ventricle into parallel layers which are to be further divided into tetrahedral elements for finite-element analysis.

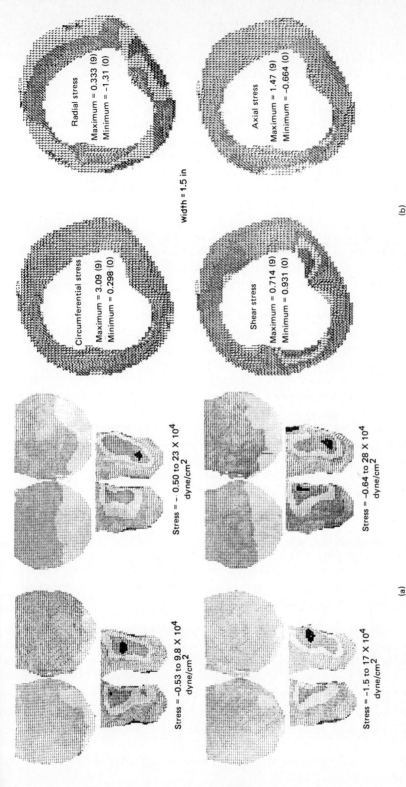

Radial stress

Maximum = 0.333 (9)
Minimum = −1.31 (0)

Axial stress

Maximum = 1.47 (9)
Minimum = −0.664 (0)

width = 1.5 in

(b)

Circumferential stress

Maximum = 3.09 (9)
Minimum = 0.298 (0)

Shear stress

Maximum = 0.714 (9)
Minimum = 0.931 (0)

Stress = −0.50 to 23 × 10⁴ dyne/cm²

Stress = −0.64 to 28 × 10⁴ dyne/cm²

Stress = −0.53 to 9.8 × 10⁴ dyne/cm²

Stress = −1.5 to 17 × 10⁴ dyne/cm²

(a)

**FIG. 6.9** (*a*) Computer contour plot of principal stresses on the epicardial (outside) and endocardial (inside) surfaces of the left ventricle at four different cardiac instants. The ranges of the stresses are indicated. The maximum principal stresses are found on the endocardial surface, in the darkened regions. (*b*) Postprocessor of plotting the circumferential, radial, shear, and axial stress contours is also available. Shown here are the results for the first number 22 cross section of Fig. 6.8*a*.

3.337

Papillary muscles and myocardial-wall strips excised from ventricles have been extensively tested to determine cardiac material properties [99, 103]. Treating the ventricular wall as a layered laminate of unidirectional fiber-reinforced material with fiber orientation varying across the wall thickness, its stress-dependent elastic modulus has been quantified and utilized in finite-element analyses of the left ventricle. By implanting radiopaque markers on ventricular walls and scanning their dynamic displacements during cardiac cycles, regional myocardial volume changes as high as 30% have been calculated at end-diastolic and end-systolic instants [7]. If the myocardium is indeed incompressible, the regional volume changes must then be attributed totally to the blood-volume changes in the ventricular wall. Hence, it suggests that a myocardium-blood composite model would be more appropriate for ventricular stress and functional analyses. The blood flow in the coronary artery affects the infusion in the ventricular walls. Stein [102] has pointed out that the branching, tapering, and variation in cross-sectional shapes of coronary artery all significantly alter the blood-flow velocity distributions. Hence, finite-element analyses can again be expected to play an important role in numerical solution of the coronary-arterial-flow problems and in resolving the problem of atherosclerosis, which is of acute concern to cardiologists and physiologists.

Incorporations of elaborated loading and boundary conditions and detailed material characteristics will further increase the complexity of finite-element cardiac analyses. This complexity results in increased use of the array processors for matrix manipulation [10] and the resumable segmented method of numerical solution on a time-sharing computer [11]. Rather than investigate the entire ventricle, researchers are expected to shift the emphasis to regional cardiac analyses on hypertrophy and infarction by use of implanted markers [104]. The markers identify a particular investigated cardiac region which makes finite-element analysis economically feasible because of the limited number of elements involved. Moreover, tracing of the dynamic displacements of these implanted markers by scanning enable the stretching and contraction of myocardial fibers to be measured in vivo during cardiac cycles. Ascertaining these basic passive and active characteristics of myocardium are prerequisite for assessment of cardiac functional status and reserve.

## 6.5 LUNG-PARENCHYMA ANALYSIS

The finite-element method in lung-parenchyma analysis has been an extremely useful tool in the study of the regional behavior in the lung in recent years. Some typical characteristics of the lung parenchyma are as follows.

1. *Nonlinear Large Deformation.* Lung tissue, like other soft tissues, behaves nonlinearly in its force versus deformation relationship, with maximum extension ratios as large as 200%. Typically, the tissue may be regarded as incompressible. However, the lung parenchyma which consists of spatial arrangement of tissue membranes and air sacs must be modeled as a compressible continuum.

2. *Hysteresis.* All soft tissue, including lung tissue, contains largely fluids. Further, the deformational responses of the tissue are dependent on the transport and electronic and biochemical characteristics of its cellular and molecular constituents. These factors are believed to be responsible for the loading-path and rate-dependent nature of the tissue.

Thus far, most finite-element modeling efforts have not seriously taken into consideration these features.

3. *Homogeneity and Isotropy.* To date, lung-parenchyma analysis has categorically used the assumption that the continuum is homogeneous and initially isotropic. This assumption is justified if one is interested only in obtaining qualitatively the distortion behavior of the lung under gravity and other kinematically prescribed boundary conditions. This assumption, however, puts many limits on the scope of the study.

4. *Active-Feedback System.* So far, most experimental evidence on the mechanical properties of lung parenchyma relates to passive behaviors. The role of the smooth muscles on the mechanical properties of the lung tissue may be important, but this topic has not been addressed seriously in the past.

## 6.5A Some Recent Finite-Element Analyses of Lung Parenchyma

Within the framework of a passive conservative system for the lung parenchyma, several studies have been carried out. Some typical ones are outlined briefly below.

An averaged lung unit enclosed by alveolar walls has been treated as a representative sample of the continuum of lung parenchyma [105]. The mechanical properties of the lung parenchyma are then computed on the basis of this averaged alveolus by the finite-element approach. The mechanical properties of the parenchyma so obtained are validated by experimental data on lung-tissue cubes [106, 107]. This "averaged-alveolus" approach provides constitutive relationships of the lung parenchyma for finite-element studies of the lung. There are several other analytical approaches that have also resulted in various strain-energy density functions for the lung parenchyma [108, 109].

Stresses and deformation analysis of the entire lung have been reported in several publications. To date, the finite-element method has been the only feasible approach in dealing with the problem [110–118]. A more detailed review may be found in Ref. [119]. Typically, the lung is modeled by solid tetrahedral elements. At the boundaries, the direction of the reactions (pleural pressure) is assumed to be normal to the lung surface with no shear components, and the displacements are prescribed (mixed boundary conditions). A typical loading used is the body force due to gravity. In all cases a reference state of the lung has been presumed. Some used the resting configuration, while others referred to the maximum lung capacity. A typical finite-element solution is shown in Fig. 6.10.

## 6.5B Summary

Finite-element analysis has a significant role in lung-parenchyma analysis, particularly when it is coordinated with experimental research. In general, the experimental data available are limited. Even for those that are available, there are often more questions than answers in the conditions and limitations of the data. In most cases the difficulties of experimental observations overwhelm the desirability of the form of data for analytical purposes. In finite-element analysis for very large deformations, approximations are often required. They are difficult to generalize because of their dependence on available experimental evidence.

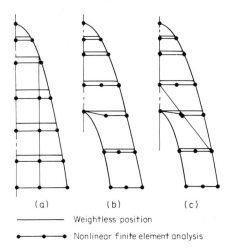

(a)                (b)                (c)

——————— Weightless position

●———●———● Nonlinear finite element analysis

**FIG. 6.10** Lung-tissue displacements from their uniform weightless expansion state at functional residual capacity as predicted by nonlinear finite-element analysis are shown for (a) lung as a solid mass of paraboloid, (b) lungs with mediastinal cavity and hilar support constraint, and (c) lungs with fissure, mediastinal cavity, and hilar support. The reduction of distortional displacements may be seen in the order of (a) to (c). This illustrates the importance of these structural characteristics of the lung in reducing the nonuniformity of regional deformation due to gravitational distortion.

## 6.6 INTESTINAL FLOW

The intestine, one component of the alimentary canal, is a long tubular organ which accomplishes several fluid-mechanical functions by means of flows induced by movements of its wall. Usually such movements are described in terms of patterns which have been seen in early observations of the viscera exposed by surgery or through fluoroscopic visualization of radiopaque fluids along the intestinal lumen. Such patterns have been called *peristalsis*, *segmentation*, and *pendular movements*. Since movements of the intestinal wall are due to contractions of muscle cells over given segments, it appears better to refer to contractions—longitudinal contractions when only the longitudinal muscle layer is active, transverse or ring contractions when only the circular muscle layer is active. Of course, combinations of the two basic contractions may occur, leading to very complicated patterns [120].

The fundamental problem of intestinal flow is to determine the flow of chyme—the luminal fluid—which is induced by contractions of different kind. In investigations of intestinal flow due to transverse contractions of finite length and amplitude, the finite-element method has been found extremely useful. In this section, an application of finite elements to flow in the small intestine is summarized.

In the fed state, the contractions of the small intestine occur at random in space and time; they appear as organized movements only over relatively short segments. Since the exact shape of the inner surface of the small intestine during contractions is not well known, and it surely does not conform to a single geometry, it was assumed to be of a rather simple type, as illustrated in Fig. 6.11a. Essential features are, however, retained, especially the propagative nature of the contraction. It was considered that a two-dimensional model would provide the basic knowledge desired. The case of axisymmetric flow was left for further investigations. An estimate has indicated that axisymmetric contractions would be nearly one-third more effective in pumping than equivalent two-dimensional contractions.

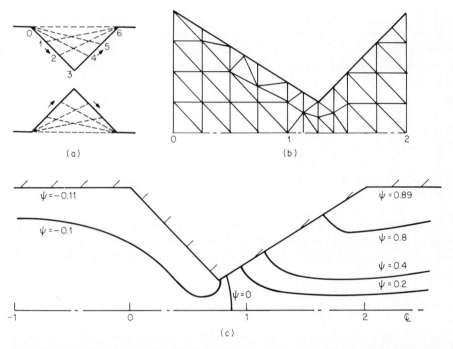

**FIG. 6.11**  (a) Simplified model of propagative transverse contraction in the small intestine. (b) Subdivision in triangular elements for one position of the wall. (c) Instantaneous streamlines.

The fluid was assumed to be newtonian since very little is known about the rheology of chyme in the small intenstine, except for some crude measurements of viscosity. With the data available, both the Reynolds number and the Strouhal number were found to be small. The assumption of creeping flow was then adopted. The following governing equation was used:

$$\iint_A \left( \frac{\partial^2 \psi}{\partial x^2} \frac{\partial^2 \delta\psi}{\partial x^2} + 2\frac{\partial^2 \psi}{\partial x\,\partial y} \frac{\partial^2 \delta\psi}{\partial x\,\partial y} + \frac{\partial^2 \psi}{\partial y^2} \frac{\partial^2 \delta\psi}{\partial y^2} \right) dx\,dy$$

$$= \phi_s \frac{\partial^2 \psi}{\partial n^2} \frac{\partial \delta\psi}{\partial n}\,ds - \phi_s \frac{\partial}{\partial n}\left( \frac{\partial^2 \psi}{\partial n^2} + \frac{\partial^2 \psi}{\partial s^2} \right) \delta\psi\,ds \qquad (6.1)$$

where $\psi$ is the stream function; $x$, $y$ are the cartesian coordinates; and $n$, $s$ are the normal-tangential coordinates. The above equation results from a Galerkin–weighted-residual statement. To solve this equation for moving boundaries, a triangular element was used. The global numbering system was set up so that the system matrix would have the smallest bandwidth possible. In the choice of the approximation function, it was important to consider that in the Poiseuille flow—expected at the ends of the conduit—the stream function is a cubic. A higher order was deemed necessary, and thus a quintic was adopted after introducing some improvements with respect to previous uses of a fifth-degree function. To illustrate the subdivision of the region of flow, one of the several geometries used is shown in Fig. 6.11*b* (see Ref. [121] for other figures). The element used in the analysis was an 18-degree-of-freedom triangle on which two major improvements were achieved: (1) by the use of an oblique coordinate system, the element matrix was given explicitly and there was no need to invert any matrix; (2) through interpretation of boundary relations rather than boundary conditions, important errors in higher derivatives were eliminated [122].

For the internal flow due to the contractions, the only natural boundary condition was a zero-shear stress along the line of symmetry. The essential boundary conditions are those for the stream function and its first derivatives. A detailed discussion of the boundary conditions can be found in Ref. [122].

Once the stream function was determined through calculation with an IBM 360 computer, the streamlines for each wall position were determined. One example, showing the streamlines, is given in Fig. 6.11*c*. A dividing streamline always appears, since the flow is that in which no pressure difference exists between the ends of the conduit.

The streamlines give a detailed view of the flow at each instant, but determinations of the changes of material lines are necessary to shed light on the convective mixing due to the contractions. Lines which were originally perpendicular to the walls are shown in Fig. 6.12*a* after three successive contractions.

To test the accuracy of the calculations, the method was used to compute the stream function of a Poiseuille flow; agreement was up to the sixth digits. Since an analytical solution was obtained for longitudinal contractions [122], the finite element was used in the same case and results were reproduced with differences only in the fourth digit of values of the second derivatives.

The pumping capacity of transverse contractions is demonstrated by the values of the stream function at the conduit wall in Fig. 6.11*c*. By a collection of values for different positions of the moving segment of the wall, the diagram shown in Fig. 6.12*b* was obtained. Integration of this diagram yields a volume which is the volume transported by each contraction.

The conclusions refer to the flow induced by finite-length and finite-amplitude transverse movements of the wall of a conduit, otherwise at rest, as a model of flow in the small intestine. From the fluid-mechanical point of view, it was determined that a progressive, finite-length contraction induces irreversible creeping flow. This means that it can pump effectively and lead to convective mixing. For these effects to be obtained, the contraction need not be occlusive. From the point of view of the finite-element method, an 18-degree-of-freedom finite element was found to be an excellent tool for investigating intestinal flow, after some improvements were introduced.

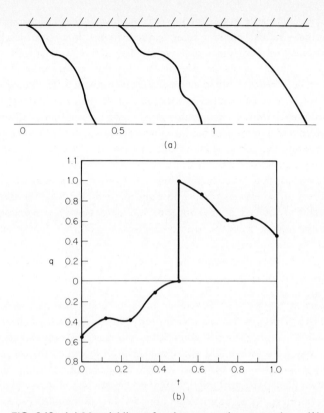

**FIG. 6.12** (*a*) Material lines after three successive contractions. (*b*) Flow rate generated by one contraction as a function of time.

## 6.7 BLOOD FLOW

There are two kinds of blood-flow problems for which finite-element methods have been used. Firstly, in the large arteries the blood may be treated as an incompressible newtonian fluid flowing at moderate Reynolds number so that the full Navier–Stokes equation must be used. Secondly, in the capillaries the acceleration terms may be neglected, but blood may no longer be considered as a newtonian fluid. The individual blood cells must be treated as discrete particles nearly filling the capillary. The suspending fluid is the blood plasma which can be considered a newtonian incompressible fluid having a slow viscous flow.

In capillary blood flow the walls of the vessel are usually assumed to be fixed, which is a good approximation because such a small-diameter tube through solid tissue is relatively stiff. The motion of the blood plasma is governed by Stokes equations and the continuity equation

$$\nabla p = \mu \nabla^2 \mathbf{u} \qquad\qquad (6.2)$$

$$\nabla \cdot \mathbf{u} = 0 \qquad\qquad (6.3)$$

where **u** is velocity and $p$ is pressure. The slow viscous flow of the plasma may also be treated in two-dimensional and axisymmetric cases by the use of a stream function and a vorticity vector or by the use of stream function alone. The use of the primitive variables of velocity and pressure is advantageous in the case of capillary flow because the velocity boundary condition on the surface of the blood cells is easily incorporated. The blood cells must also obey equations of motion and continuity. They are incompressible but may be elastic. Red blood cells consist of a thin elastic membrane filled with a solution of hemoglobin, which may also be considered a newtonian fluid. In low-Reynolds-number flow the cells must obey a so-called zero-drag condition, which means that the net force and net moment on any particle suspended in a Stokes flow should both be zero. The blood cells may be deformed by the viscous flow, in which case the final shape must be found as part of the solution. The combined problem of the viscous plasma flow and the red-blood-cell deformation are conveniently treated by use of a variational principle $\delta D_m = 0$, where $D_m$ is a modified dissipation function given by

$$D_m = 2\mu \int_V e_{ij}^2 \, dV - 2 \int_V p e_{kk} \, dV - 2 \int_S \tau_i u_i \, dA + 2 \int_S T \, d\dot{A} + 2 \int_S \dot{W} \, dA \qquad (6.4)$$

where $\mu$ is a viscosity, $e_{ij}$ is the strain-rate tensor, $\tau_i$ are given boundary stress components, $T$ is an isotropic tension in the cell membrane, and $\dot{W}$ is the time rate of change of the strain energy of the cell membrane. The red-blood-cell membrane is like a two-dimensional incompressible fluid, and its surface area is constant. This is enforced by the isotropic tension $T$. The strain energy $W$ of the cell membrane is taken to be that of a thin shell in bending and in shear in its own plane. The final grid for an axisymmetric red-blood-cell flow in a circular capillary is shown in Fig. 6.13. The grid is deformed as the computation proceeds. The nodes on the cell boundary locate the membrane and serve as well as boundary nodes of the plasma.

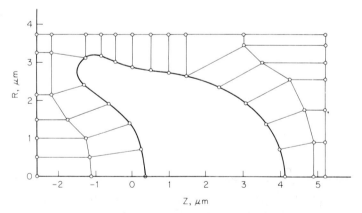

**FIG. 6.13** Finite-element grid for an axisymmetrically deformed red cell flowing in a capillary blood vessel. The motion is from left to right. The Z-axis of rotational symmetry and only half the cell (heavy line) is shown. The interior of the cell is fluid at constant pressure and uniform velocity, so no grid is required inside the cell. The segment shown is repeated in the Z-direction to represent a line of cells in a capillary.

The fluid elements are curved isoparametric quadrilaterals. Velocity and pressure are used as the nodal variables at corner nodes, and velocity only is specified at side nodes so that in local coordinates the approximation of the velocity is quadratic and that of the pressure is linear. By running the model for a range of pressure drops and diameter ratios, the variation of the apparent viscosity in capillary flow has been determined [123].

Examples of capillary-flow computation using the stream function have been given by Tong and Fung [124] and by Gupta et al. [125]. In these computations the blood cells are assumed to be rigid. The stream-function approach has also been used by Vawter et al. [126] to study flow in a right-angle bifurcation.

Another blood-cell problem which has been treated by finite-element methods is the flow of white blood cells in capillaries [127]. In contrast to red blood cells, the white blood cells are viscoelastic and are treated as solid spheres. The cell cytoplasm is treated as incompressible, and the primary variables are nodal displacements and an isotropic pressure.

In the large arteries and veins blood flow takes place in a pulsating manner at the heart rate, and there is a wave propagation accompanying the flow. The vessel walls must be considered elastic in order to produce the propagating wave pulses of pressure and flow. There has been a relatively large literature of wave-propagation studies in blood flow (see [128]) but only a few studies have used the finite-element method. A recent treatment using a finite-element modeling of one-dimensional pulsatile-flow equations in flexible tubes is given by Rooz et al. [129]. Other finite-element analyses of pulsatile blood flow were given by Davids and Mani [130] and Wille [131].

Finite-element analysis has also been used in arterial flows to study the flow patterns at bifurcations. In these treatments the arterial walls are assumed to be rigid for simplicity, but the geometry may be represented quite accurately. Such computations have been usually two-dimensional. Examples may be found in Gokhale et al. [132] and Subbaraj and Patil [133]. Some of the main points of interest in these computations are the magnitude of the wall shear stress and the location of zones of separation which are thought to have bearing on the development of atherosclerosis.

Finite-element methods have also been used in describing tissue blood flow. In this case the field equations are those of heat conduction modified by the effects of the blood flow. An example may be found in Sekins [134]. The blood flow is treated essentially as a heat sink in this problem, the field equations being those of heat conduction.


## 6.8 REFERENCES

1. Hench, L. L., "Biomaterials," *Science*, **208**:826–831 (1980).

2. Fung, Y. C., *Biomechanics, Mechanical Properties of Living Tissues*, Springer-Verlag, New York, 1981.

3. Johnson, S. A., R. A. Robb, E. L. Ritman, B. K. Gilbert, J. F. Greenleaf, L. D. Harris, M. J. Berggren, R. Sturm, P. A. Chevalier, R. M. Heethaar, E. H. Wood, G. T. Herman, and Y. C. Pao, "Bioimage Synthesis and Analysis from x-Ray, Gamma, Optical and Ultrasound Energy," in K. Preston Jr. and M. Onoe (eds.), *Digital Processing of Biomedical Image*, Plenum Press, New York, 1976, pp. 203–226.

4. Ritman, E. L., J. H. Kinsey, R. A. Robb, B. K. Gilbert, L. D. Harris, and E. H. Wood, "Three-Dimensional Imaging of Heart, Lungs and Circulation," *Science*, **210**:273–380 (1980).

5. Elzingo, G., and N. Westerhof, "How to Quantify Pump Function of the Heart," *Circ. Res.*, **44**:303–308 (1979).

6. Yamada, H., *Strength of Biological Materials*, Williams & Wilkins, Baltimore, 1970.

7. Pao, Y. C., P. A. Chevalier, and E. L. Ritman, "Quantification of Regional Heart Muscle Contraction in Intact Thorax," *Biomechanics Symposium*, American Society of Mechanical Engineers, 1981, pp. 27–30.

8. Hayes, L. J., and K. R. Diller, "A Finite Element Model for the Exposure of a Composite Man with Distributed Internal Heat Generation to a Convective Subfreezing Environment," *Advances in Bioengineering*, American Society of Mechanical Engineers, 1981, pp. 225–228.

9. Pao, Y. C., "Finite Elements in Stress Analysis and Estimation of Mechanical Properties of Working Heart," chap. 8 in R. H. Gallagher, B. R. Simon, P. C. Johnson, and J. F. Gross (eds.), *Finite Elements in Biomechanics*, Wiley, New York, 1982, pp. 127–152.

10. Russel, R. M., "The Cray-1 Computer System," *Comm. ACM*, **21**:63–72 (1978).

11. Pao, Y. C., "Solving Large Structural Stiffness Matrix Equations by Resumable Segments," *Comput. Struct.*, **14**:247–254 (1981).

12. Liou, R. J., M. E. Clark, J. M. Robertson, and L. C. Cheng, "Three-Dimensional Simulation of Steady Flow Past a Partial Stenosis," *J. Biomech.*, **14**:325–337 (1981).

13. Lewis, J. L., W. D. Lew, and J. R. Zimmerman, "A Nonhomogeneous Anthropometric Scaling Method Based on Finite Element Principles," *J. Biomech.*, **13**: 815–824 (1980).

14. Taylor, R. L., and J. L. Sackman, Rep. No. DOT-HS-805-630, NTIS, Springfield, Va., 1980, vols. I, II.

15. King, A. I., and C. C. Chou, "Mathematical Modelling, Simulation and Experimental Testing of Biomechanical System Crash Response," *J. Biomech.*, **9**:301–307 (1976).

16. Shugar, T. A., "A Finite Element Head Injury Model," Rep. No. DOT-HS 803-211, NTIS, Springfield, Va., 1977, vol. 1.

17. Khalil, T. B., and R. P. Hubbard, "Parametric Study of Head Response by Finite Element Modelling," *J. Biomech.*, **10**:119–132 (1977).

18. Nickell, R. E., and P. V. Marcal, "In-Vacuo Modal Dynamic Response of the Human Skull," *Trans. ASME Eng. Ind.*, **96**:490–494 (1974).

19. Ward, C. C., "Analytical Brain Models for Head Impact," *Proc. Int. Conf. Biomech. Trauma* (*IRCOBI*), Berlin, 1977, pp. 389–398.

20. Hosey, R. R., and Y. K. Liu, "A Homeomorphic Finite-Element Model of Impact Head and Neck Injury," *Biomechanics Symposium*, American Society of Mechanical Engineers, New York, 1980, pp. 851–870.

21. Kahlil, T. B., D. C. Viano, and D. L. Smith, "Experimental Analysis of the Vibrational Characteristics of the Human Skull," *Sound Vibration*, **63**:351–376 (1979).

22. Chen, P. H., and S. B. Roberts, "Dynamic Response of the Human Thoracic Skeleton to Impact," UCLA Pap. ENG-0274, School of Engineering and Applied Science, University of California, Los Angeles, 1974.

23. Kazemieslamian, M., "A Mathematical Model of the Human Ribcage," Ph.D. dissertation, Wayne State University, Detroit, 1973.

24. Roberts, S. B., and P. H. Chen, "Global Geometric Characteristics of Typical Human Ribs," *J. Biomech.*, **5**:191–201 (1972).

25. Reddi, M. M., H. C. Tsai, and L. Ovenshire, "Computer Simulation of Human Thoracic Skeletal Response," *Biomechanics Symposium*, American Society of Mechanical Engineers, New York, 1980, pp. 871–888.

26. Hakim, N. S., and A. I. King, "A Three-Dimensional Finite Element Dynamic Response Analysis of a Vertebra with Experimental Verification," *J. Biomech.*, **12**:279–292 (1979).

27. Hakim, N. S., and A. I. King, "Study of the Strain Distribution over the Cortical Surface of Lumbar Vertebrae," *Proc. 23d Int. Instrumentation Symp.*, Las Vegas, Nevada, 1977, pp. 145-153.

28. Viano, D. C., and R. L. Stalnaker, "Mechanisms of Femoral Fracture," *J. Biomech.*, **13**:701-717 (1980).

29. Viano, D. C., and T. B. Khalil, "Investigation of Impact Response and Fracture of the Human Femur by Finite Element Modeling," *Proceedings Modeling-Biodynamic Response to Impact*, SAE Publ. SP-412, 1976, pp. 53-61.

30. Rybicki, E. F., F. A. Simonen, and E. B. Weiss, "On the Mathematical Analysis of Stress in the Human Femur," *J. Biomech.*, **5**:203-215 (1972).

31. Brekelmans, W. A. M., H. W. Poort, and T. J. J. H. Slooff, "A New Method to Analyze the Mechanical Behavior of Skeletal Parts," *Acta Orthop. Belg.*, Suppl. **1**:3-24 (1972).

32. Koch, J. C., "The Laws of Bone Architecture," *Am. J. Anat.*, **21**:177-298 (1917).

33. Wolff, J., "Über die Innere Architecture der Knochen und ihre Bedentung für die Frage vom Knochenwachtstum," *Virch. Arch. Pathol. Anat. Physiol.*, **50**:389 (1870).

34. Brown, T. D., M. E. Way, and A. B. Ferguson, "Stress Distribution Changes in Adult Femoral Heads Altered by Avascular Necrosis," *Biomechanics Symposium*, American Society of Mechanical Engineers, New York, 1980, pp. 147-167.

35. Olofsson, H., "Three-Dimensional FEM Calculation of Elastic Stress Field in Human Femur," Inst. Technol., Uppsala, University of Uppsala, Sweden, 1976.

36. Rohlmann, A., G. Bergmann, and R. Köelbel, "The Relevance of Stress Computation in the Femur with and without Endoprostheses," in R. H. Gallagher, B. R. Simon, P. C. Johnson, and J. F. Gross (eds.), *Finite Elements in Biomechanics*, Wiley, New York, 1982, chap. 17, pp. 361-377.

37. Valliappan, S., N. L. Svensson, and R. D. Wood, "Three-Dimensional Stress Analysis of the Human Femur," *Comput. Biol. Med.*, **7**:253-264 (1977).

38. Goel, V. K., S. Valliappan, and N. L. Svensson, "Stresses in the Normal Pelvis," *Comput. Biol. Med.*, **8**:91-104 (1978).

39. Hayes, W. C., L. W. Swanson, and D. J. Schurman, "Axisymmetric Finite Element Analysis of the Lateral Tibial Plateau," *J. Biomech.*, **11**:21-33 (1978).

40. Carter, D. R., R. Vasu, D. M. Spengler, and R. T. Dueland, "Stress Fields in the Unplated and Plated Canine Femur Calculated from In Vivo Strain Measurement," *J. Biomech.*, **14**:63-70 (1981).

41. Hassler, C. R., E. Y. Rybicki, K. D. Cummings, and L. D. Clark, "Quantification of Bone Stresses During Remodeling," *J. Biomech.*, **13**:185-190 (1980).

42. Vichnin, H. H., W. C. Hayes, and S. C. Batterman, "Finite Element Analysis of Multiaxial Strength Experiments for Compact Bone," *Biomechanics Symposium*, American Society of Mechanical Engineers, New York, 1977, pp. 147-150.

43. Hayes, W. C., and B. Snyder, "Toward a Quantitative Formulation of Wolff's Law in Trabecular Bone," AMD 45, *Mechanical Properties of Bone*, American Society of Mechanical Engineers, New York, 1981, pp. 43-68.

44. Chao, E. Y., "Mechanics of Bioceramic Endoprostheses Using Conical Cone Fixation without Bone Cement," *Advances in Bioengineering*, American Society of Mechanical Engineers, New York, 1980, pp. 89-92.

45. Levine, D. L., and J. E. Stoneking, "A Three-Dimensional Finite Element Based Study of an Orthopaedic Bone Plate," *Biomechanics Symposium*, American Society of Mechanical Engineers, New York, 1980, pp. 713-728.

46. Rybicki, E. F., F. A. Simonen, E. J. Mills, C. R. Hasseler, P. Scoles, D. Milne, and E. G. Weiss, "Mathematical and Experimental Studies on the Mechanics of Plated Transverse Fracture," *J. Biomech.*, **7**:377-387 (1974).

47. Rybicki, E. F., and F. A. Simonen, "Mechanics of Oblique Fracture Fixation Using a Finite Element Model," *J. Biomech.*, **10**:141-148 (1977).

48. Simon, B. R., S. L. Y. Woo, G. M. Stanley, S. R. Olmstead, M. P. McCarthy, G. F. Hermott, and W. H. Akeson, "Evaluation of One-, Two-, and Three-Dimensional Finite Element and Experimental Models of Internal Fixation Plates," *J. Biomech.*, **10**:79-86 (1977).

49. Chao, E. Y., and K. N. An, "Stress and Rigidity Analysis of External Fracture Fixation Devices," *Biomechanics Symposium*, American Society of Mechanical Engineers, New York, 1980, pp. 691-711.

50. Crippen, T. E., R. Huiskes, and E. Y. Chao, "Axisymmetric Analysis of Pin-Bone Interface Stresses of External Fixation Devices," *Biomechanics Symposium*, American Society of Mechanical Engineers, New York, 1981, pp. 247-250.

51. Andriacchi, T. P., J. O. Galante, T. B. Belytschko, and S. Hampton, "A Stress Analysis of the Femoral Stem in Total Hip Prostheses," *J. Bone Joint Surg.*, **58A**:618-624 (1976).

52. Kwak, B. M., O. K. Lim, Y. Y. Kim, and K. Rim, "An Investigation of the Effect of Cement Thickness on an Implant by Finite Element Stress Analysis," *Int. Orthop.* (*SICOT*), **2**:315-319 (1979).

53. McNeice, G. M., and H. C. Amstutz, "Finite Element Studies in Hip Reconstruction," in P. V. Komi (ed.), *Biomechanics: Proceedings of the Fiftieth International Congress of Biomechanics*, Baltimore, 1976, pp. 394-405.

54. Svensson, N. L., S. Valliapann, and R. D. Woods," "Stress Analysis of Human Femur with Implanted Charnley Prosthesis," *J. Biomech.*, **10**:581-588 (1977).

55. Ducheyne, P., E. Aernoudt, P. DeMeester, M. Martens, J. C. Mulier, and D. Van Leeuwen, "Factors Governing the Mechanical Behavior of the Implant-Porous Coating Trabecular-Bone Interface," *J. Biomech.*, **11**:297-307 (1978).

56. Huiskes, R., "Some Fundamental Aspects of Human Joint Replacement," *Acta Orthop. Scand.*, Suppl. **185** (1980).

57. Crowninshield, R. D., R. A. Brand, R. C. Johnston, and J. C. Milroy, "An Analysis of Femoral Component Stem Design in Total Hip Arthroplasty," *J. Bone Joint Surg.*, **62A**:68-78 (1980).

58. Hampton, S. J., T. P. Andriacchi, and J. O. Galante, "Three-Dimensional Stress Analysis of the Femoral Stem of a Total Hip Prosthesis," *J. Biomech.*, **13**:443-448 (1980).

59. Tarr, R., J. Lewis, F. Ghassemi, A. Sarmiento, I. Clark, and V. Weingarten, "Anatomic Three-Dimensional Finite Element Model of the Proximal Femur with Total Hip Prosthesis," *Biomechanics Symposium*, American Society of Mechanical Engineers, New York, 1980, pp. 511-525.

60. Valliapann, S., S. Kjellberg, and N. L. Svensson, "Finite Element Analysis of Total Hip Prosthesis", *Biomechanics Symposium*, American Society of Mechanical Engineers, New York, 1980, pp. 527-558.

61. Chao, E. Y., H. W. Wong, W. E. Frain, and M. G. Coventry, "Stress Analysis of the Geometric Knee under Static Loading," ASME Publ. No. 77-Bio-6, American Society of Mechanical Engineers, New York, 1977.

62. Hayes, W. C., "Theoretical Modeling and Design of Implant Systems," *Proceedings of the Workshop on Mechanical Failure of Total Joint Replacement*, American Academy of Orthopedic Surgeons, Chicago, Illinois, 1978, pp. 159-175.

63. Pissinou, G. I., and P. A. Brooke, "Stress Analysis of a Freeman-Swanson Knee Prosthesis," *Biomechanics Symposium*, American Society of Mechanical Engineers, New York, 1980, pp. 567-580.

64. Röhrle, H., R. Scholten, and W. Sollback, "Analysis of Stress Distribution in Natural and Artificial Knee Joint on the Femur Side Using the Finite Element Method," *Biomechanics Symposium*, American Society of Mechanical Engineers, New York, 1980, pp. 781-794.

65. Huisekes, R., J. Van Heck, P. S. Walker, D. J. Green, and D. Nunamaker, "A Three-Dimensional Stress Analysis of a New Finger-Joint Prosthesis Fixation Systems," *Biomechanics Symposium*, American Society of Mechanical Engineers, New York, 1980, pp. 749-762.

66. Shybut, G. T., M. J. Askew, R. Y. Hori, and S. D. Stulberg, "Theoretical and Experimental Studies of Femoral Stresses Following Surface Replacement Hip Arthroplasty," *The Hip*, Mosby, St. Louis, 1980, chap. 10, pp. 192–224.

67. Roth, V., and V. C. Mow, "Finite Element Analysis of Contact Problems for Indentation of Articular Cartilage," *Advances in Bioengineering*, American Society of Mechanical Engineers, New York, 1977, pp. 47–48.

68. Swenson, L. W., R. L. Piziali, and D. J. Schurman, "An Electromechanical Model for Human Articular Cartilage," *Advances in Bioengineering*, American Society of Mechanical Engineers, New York, 1979, pp. 105–108.

69. Rybicki, E. F., W. A. Glaeser, J. S. Strenkowski, and M. A. Tamm, "Effects of Cartilage Stiffness and Viscosity on a Nonporous Compliant Bearing Lubrication Model for Living Joints," *J. Biomech.*, **12**:403–409 (1979).

70. Belytschko, T., R. Kulak, A. Schultz, and J. Galante, "Finite Element Stress Analysis of an Intervertebral Disc," *J. Biomech.*, **7**:277–285 (1976).

71. Fulak, R. F., T. B. Belytschko, and A. B. Schultz, "Nonlinear Behavior of the Human Intervertebral Disc under Axial Load," *J. Biomech.*, **9**:377–386 (1976).

72. Lin, N. S., Y. K. Liu, R. Gautam, and P. Nikravesh, "Systems Identification for Material Properties of the Intervertebral Joint," *J. Biomech.*, **11**:1–14 (1978).

73. Spilker, R. L., "Mechanical Behavior of a Simple Model of an Intervertebral Disk under Compressive Loading," *J. Biomech.*, **13**:895–901 (1980).

74. Hight, T. K., R. L. Piziali, and D. A. Nagel, "A Dynamic Nonlinear Finite Element Model of Human Leg," *J. Biomech. Eng.*, **101**:176–184 (1979).

75. Bartel, D. L., "Theoretical Modeling—Stress Analysis Effect of Geometry," *Proceedings of the Workshop on Mechanical Failure of Total Joint Replacement*, American Academy of Orthopedic Surgeons, Chicago, Illinois, 1978, pp. 141–157.

76. Huiskes, R., T. E. Crippen, J. E. Bechtold, and E. Y. Chao, "Analytic Guidelines for Optimal Stem Designs of Custom-Made Joint Prostheses," *Biomechanics Symposium*, American Society of Mechanical Engineers, New York, 1981, pp. 221–224.

77. Hampton, S. J., and T. P. Andriacchi, "An Analytical Representation of the Nonlinear Interface Condition in a Bone-Cement-Prosthesis System," *Biomechanics Symposium*, American Society of Mechanical Engineers, New York, 1980, pp. 193–206.

78. Huiskes, R., and R. Y. Schouten, "The Effect of Interface Loosening on the Stress Distribution in Intramedullary Fixed Artificial Joints," *Advances in Bioengineering*, American Society of Mechanical Engineering, New York, 1980, pp. 213–216.

79. Craig, R. G., and J. W. Farah, "Stress Analysis and Design of Single Restorations and Fixed Bridges," *Oral Sci. Rev.*, **10**:45–74 (1977).

80. Anusavice, K. J., P. H. Dehoff, and C. W. Fairhurst, "Comparative Evaluation of Ceramic-Metal Bond Tests Using Finite Element Stress Analysis," *J. Dent. Res.*, **59**:608–613 (1980).

81. Atmaram, G. H., and H. Mohammed, "Estimation of Physiological Stresses with a Natural Tooth Considering Fibrous PDL Structure," *J. Dent. Res.*, **60**:873–877 (1981).

82. Craig, R. G., and J. W. Farah, "Stresses from Loading Distal-Extension Removable-Partial Dentures," *J. Prosth. Dent.*, **39**:274–277 (1978).

83. Takahashi, N., T. Kitagami, and T. Komori, "Analysis of Stress on a Fixed Partial Denture with a Blade-Vent Implant Abutment," *J. Prosth. Dent.*, **40**:186–191 (1978).

84. Tesk, J. A., and O. Widera, "Stress Distribution in Bone Arising from Loading on Endosteal Dental Implants," *J. Biomed. Mater. Res. Symp.* **4**(7):251–261 (1973).

85. Wright, K. W. J., and A. L. Yettram, "Reactive Force Distributions for Teeth When Loaded Singly and When Used as Fixed Partial Denture Abutments," *J. Prosth. Dent.*, **42**:411–416 (1979).

86. Farah, J. W., R. G. Craig, and D. L. Sikarskie, "Photoelastic and Finite Element Stress Analysis of a Restored Axisymmetric First Molar," *J. Biomech.*, **6**:511–520 (1973).

87. Farah, J. W., J. M. Powers, J. B. Dennison, R. G. Craig, and J. Spencer, "Effects of Cement Bases on the Stress and Deflections in Composite Restorations," *J. Dent. Res.*, **55**:115–120 (1976).

88. Farah, J. W., J. B. Dennison, and J. M. Powers, "Effects of Design on Stress Distribution of Intracoronal Gold Restorations," *J. Am. Dent. Assoc.*, **94**:1151–1154 (1977).

89. Selna, L. G., H. T. Shillingburg, Jr., and P. A. Kerr, "Finite Element Analysis of Dental Structures—Axisymmetric and Plane-Stress Idealizations," *J. Biomed Mater. Res.*, **9**:237–252 (1975).

90. Widera, G. E. O., J. A. Tesk, and E. Privitzer, "Interaction Effects among Cortical Bone, Cancellous Bone, and Periodontal Membrane of Natural Teeth and Implants," *J. Biomed. Mater. Res. Symp.*, **7**(10):613–623 (1976).

91. Wright, K. W. J., and A. L. Yettram, "Finite Element Stress and Analysis of a Class I Amalgam Restoration Subjected to Setting and Thermal Expansion," *J. Dent. Res.*, **57**:715–723 (1978).

92. Cook, S. D., J. J. Klawitter, A. M. Weinstein, and C. J. Lavernia, "The Design and Evaluation of Dental Implants with Finite Element Analysis," *Biomechanics Symposium*, American Society of Mechanical Engineers, New York, 1980, pp. 169–192.

93. DeFranco, J. C., H. A. Koenig, and C. J. Burstone, "Three-Dimensional Large Displacement Analysis of Orthodontic Appliances," *J. Biomech.*, **9**:793–801 (1976).

94. Gupta, K. K., A. C. Knoell, and D. E. Grenoble, "Mathematical Modeling and Structural Analysis of the Mandible," *Biomater. Med. Devices Artif. Organs*, **1**:469–479 (1973).

95. Knoell, A. C., "A Mathematical Model of an In Vitro Human Mandible," *J. Biomech.*, **10**:159–166 (1977).

96. Weinstein, A. M., J. J. Klawitter, and S. D. Cook, "Implant-Bone Interface Characteristics of Bioglass Dental Implants," *J. Biomed. Mater. Res.*, **14**:23–29 (1980).

97. Brown, W. S., D. O. Christensen, and B. A. Lloyd, "Numerical and Experimental Evaluation of Energy Inputs, Temperature Gradients, and Thermal Stresses during Restorative Procedures," *J. Am. Dent. Assoc.*, **96**:451–458 (1978).

98. Takahashi, N., T. Kitagami, and T. Komori, "Evaluation of Thermal Change in Pulp Chamber," *J. Dent. Res.*, **56**:1480 (1977).

99. Berne, R. M., N. Sperelakis, and S. K. Geiger (eds.), *Handbook of Physiology*, sec. 2: *The Cardiovascular System*, American Physiology Society, Bethesda, Md., 1979.

100. Pao, Y. C., "Discussion on 'Geometric Modeling of the Human Left Ventricle,'" *J. Biomech. Eng.*, **102**:274–275 (1980).

101. Christie, G. W., and I. C. Medland, "The Effects of Tissue Anisotropy on the Mechanics of Bioprosthetic Heart Valves," *Biomechanics Symposium*, American Society of Mechanical Engineers, New York, 1981, pp. 11–14.

102. Stein, P. D., "Relation of Fluid Dynamics to Cardiovascular Pathophysiology," *Advances in Bioengineering*, American Society of Mechanical Engineers, New York, 1981, pp. 71–76.

103. Pao, Y. C., G. K. Nagendra, R. Padiyar, and E. L. Ritman, "Derivation of Myocardial Fiber Stiffness Equation Based on Theory of Laminated Composite," *J. Biomech. Eng.*, **102**:252–257 (1980).

104. Pao, Y. C., G. K. Nagendra, and E. I. Ritman, "Isoparametric Finite-Element Analysis of Heart Wall Muscle as Layered Composite," *Advances in Bioengineering*, American Society of Mechanical Engineers, New York, 1981, pp. 139–142.

105. Fung, Y. C., "A Theory of Elasticity of the Lung," *J. Appl. Mech.*, **41**:8–14 (1974).

106. Hoppin, F. G., G. C. Lee, and S. V. Dawson, "Properties of Lung Parenchyma in Distortion," *J. Appl. Physiol.*, **39**:742–751 (1975).

107. Lee, G. C., and A. Frankus, "Elasticity Properties of Lung Parenchyma Derived from Experimental Distortion Data," *Biophys. J.*, **15**:481–493 (1975).

108. Frankus, A., and G. C. Lee, "A Theory for Distortion Studies of Lung Parenchyma Based on Alveolar Membrane Properties," *J. Biomech.*, 7:101–107 (1974).

109. Fung, Y. C., P. Tong, and P. Patitucci, "Stress and Strain on the Lung," *J. Eng. Mech.*, **104**(EM1):201–224 (1978).

110. Karakaplan, A. D., M. P. Bieniek, and R. Skalak, "Finite Element Analysis of Lung Parenchyma," *Biomechanics Symposium*, American Society of Mechanical Engineers, New York, 1980, pp. 409–428.

111. Lee, G. C., R. C. Tai, and N. T. Tseng, "Finite Deformation Modeling of Regional Behavior in Lungs," *Proc. 1st Int. Conf. Mech. Med. Biol.*, Aachen, Germany, 1978.

112. Liu, J. T., and G. C. Lee, "Static Finite Deformation Analysis of the Lung," *J. Eng. Mech. Div.*, **EM1**:225–238 (1978).

113. Matthews, F. L., and J. B. West, "Finite Element Displacement Analysis of a Lung," *J. Biomech.*, **5**:591–600 (1972).

114. Pao, Y. C., P. A. Chevalier, J. R. Rodarte, and L. D. Harris, "Finite-Element Analysis of the Strain Variations in Excised Lobe of Canine Lung," *J. Biomech.*, **11**:91–100 (1978).

115. Vawter, D. L., Y. C. Fung, and J. B. West, "Constitutive Equations of Lung Tissue Elasticity," *J. Biomech. Eng.*, **101**:38–45 (1978).

116. Vawter, D. L., and W. H. Shields, "The Effect of Surface Tension and Regional Expansion in the Lung," *Biomechanics Symposium*, American Society of Mechanical Engineers, New York, 1980, pp. 369–388.

117. Vawter, D. L., "A Finite Element Model of Macroscopic Deformation of the Lung," *Biomechanics Symposium*, American Society of Mechanical Engineers, New York, 1980, pp. 389–408.

118. West, J. B., and F. L. Matthews, "Stresses, Strains and Surface Pressures in the Lung Caused by Its Weight," *J. Appl. Physiol.*, **32**:332–345 (1972).

119. Lee, G. C., "Finite Element Analysis in Soft Tissue Mechanics," *Biomechanics Symposium*, American Society of Mechanical Engineers, New York, 1980, pp. 27–42.

120. Macagno, E. O., and J. Christensen, "Fluid Mechanics of the Duodenum," *Annu. Rev. Fluid Mech.*, **12**:139–158 (1980).

121. Stavistsky, D., E. O. Macagno, and J. Christensen, "Finite-Element Analysis of Flow Induced by Contractions Like Those of the Intestine," *J. Biomech.*, **14**:183–193 (1981).

122. Stavitsky, D., "Flow and Mixing in a Contracting Channel with Applications to the Human Intestine," Ph.D. thesis, University of Iowa, Iowa City, 1979.

123. Zarda, P. R., S. Chien, and R. Skalak, "Interaction of a Viscous Incompressible Fluid with an Elastic Body," in T. Belytschko and T. L. Geers (eds.), *Computational Methods for Fluid-Structure Interaction Problems*, AMD 26, American Society of Mechanical Engineers, New York, 1977, pp. 65–82.

124. Tong, P., and Y. C. Fung, "Slow Particulate Viscous Flow in Channels and Tubes—Application in Biomechanics," *J. Appl. Mech.*, **93**:721–728 (1971).

125. Gupta, B. B., R. Natarajan, and V. Seshadri, "Analysis of Blood Flow in Capillaries by Finite Element Method," *Microvasc. Res.*, **12**:91–100 (1976).

126. Vawter, D. L., Y. C. Fung, and B. W. Zweifach, "Distribution of Blood Flow and Pressure from a Microvessel into a Branch," *Microvasc. Res.*, **8**:44–52 (1974).

127. Tozeren, H., "Flow of Elastic and Viscoelastic Spheres in Tubes," Ph.D. thesis, Columbia University, New York, 1980.

128. Skalak, R., S. R. Keller, and T. W. Secomb, "Mechanics of Blood Flow," *J. Biomech. Eng.*, **103**:102–115 (1981).

129. Rooz, E., D. F. Young, and T. R. Rogge, "Finite-Element Modeling of Pulsatile Flow in Flexible Tubes," *Advances in Bioengineering*, American Society of Mechanical Engineers, New York, 1980, pp. 169–172.

130. Davids, N., and M. K. Mani, "A Finite Element Analysis of Endothelial Flow," *Biol. Rheol.,* **11**:137–147 (1974).

131. Wille, S. O., "Pressure and Flow Patterns in the Vicinity of an Arterial Stenosis," *Biomechanics Symposium,* American Society of Mechanical Engineers, New York, 1980, pp. 295–314.

132. Gokhale, V. V., R. I. Tanner, and K. B. Bischoff, "Finite Element Solution of the Navier-Stokes Equations for Two-Dimensional Steady Flow through a Section of Canine Aorta Model," *J. Biomech.,* **11**:241–249 (1978).

133. Subbaraj, K., and M. Patil, "Finite Element Analysis of Fluid Flow at Branching Sites," *Biomechanics Symposium,* American Society of Mechanical Engineers, New York, 1980, pp. 329–345.

134. Sekins, K. M., A. F. Emery, J. F. Lehmann, and J. A. MacDougall, "Determination of the Perfusion Field During Local Hyperthermia with the Aid of Finite Element Thermal Models," *Advances in Bioengineering,* American Society of Mechanical Engineers, New York, 1981, pp. 113–116.

# CHAPTER 7
# FURTHER FINITE-ELEMENT APPLICATIONS

Although it originated in structural engineering, the finite-element method has developed beyond this field to become a standard computational tool in science and technology. Some of the many areas in which the finite-element method has been applied are aircraft, automotive, and ship structures; steel and reinforced-concrete bridges and buildings; earthquake response of multistory structures and reservoir-dam systems; rock mechanics; plasticity design; fracture mechanics; dynamics of semisubmerged (offshore) structures; fibrous composites; viscous, subsonic, and supersonic flows; oscillating airfoils; sonar transducers; acoustic and electromagnetic fields; magnet design; plasma flows; nuclear-reactor flux computation; glacier-ice flow; tectonic plate motion; seepage and groundwater flow; oil- and gas-reservoir engineering; biomechanics; pollutant dispersion in the atmosphere, lakes, and tidal estuaries; surface waves; ignition and combustion; and statistics. It is clearly impossible even in a large handbook such as this to cover every field in detail. The aim is to present the underlying mathematical principles, the fundamental formulations, and the more important and better-developed applications to guide both the practitioner and the newcomer to the finite-element method. In the preceding chapters of Part 3, many major areas of application have been described in some depth. The present chapter presents selected applications, which although perhaps less well known, illustrate the generality and the power of the finite-element method.

## 7.1 CHEMICAL REACTIONS

The inclusion of chemical reactions in finite-element simulations can lead to quantitative and qualitative differences. Oftentimes the equations that need to be solved with chemical reactions are one-dimensional in character so that the ability to handle irregular geometries may not play so major a role. There may be many different time scales in the problem: time scales for diffusion may be very different from time scales for reaction, and there may be several, widely different time scales for reaction. The problems are thus stiff, and require methods suited for stiff initial-value problems. The reaction-rate expression is frequently highly non-linear so that iterative schemes that work for diffusion problems may not work for reaction problems. None of these differences poses insurmountable difficulties, so that the finite-element method can be applied to problems with chemical reactions.

## 7.1A Governing Equations

A typical problem is to model diffusion and reaction of species in a porous catalyst pellet. The nondimensional form of the equations is [1]

$$\nabla^2 c = \phi^2 R(c, T) \tag{7.1}$$

$$\left.\begin{array}{l}\quad\end{array}\right\} \quad \text{in } V$$

$$\nabla^2 T = -\beta \phi^2 R(c, T) \tag{7.2}$$

$$-\mathbf{n} \cdot \nabla c = \text{Bi}_m (c - c_B) \tag{7.3}$$

$$\left.\begin{array}{l}\quad\end{array}\right\} \quad \text{on } S$$

$$-\mathbf{n} \cdot \nabla T = \text{Bi}(T - T_B) \tag{7.4}$$

where $\phi$ is the Thiele modulus, $c$ is the concentration, Bi is the Biot number, $R$ is the reaction rate, and the other symbols have the usual meaning. The subscript $B$ indicates the boundary. There may be more than one chemical species involved, but the equations are similar, except that the chemical-reaction-rate term depends on all the concentrations and temperature. Usually there is no interaction between the species in the diffusion term, although in certain cases the diffusion coefficient $\alpha$ depends on concentration $c$. Then a typical equation is

$$\nabla \cdot (D(c)\nabla c) = \phi^2 R(c) \tag{7.5}$$

When the region of physical space can be approximated by one-dimensional problems, and the temperature is constant, the equations reduce to

$$\frac{1}{x^{a-1}} \frac{d}{dx}\left(x^{a-1}\frac{dc}{dx}\right) = \phi^2 R(c(x)) \tag{7.6}$$

$$\frac{dc}{dx} = 0 \quad \text{at } x = 0 \tag{7.7}$$

$$-\frac{dc}{dx} = \text{Bi}_m(c - c_B) \quad \text{at } x = 1 \tag{7.8}$$

These equations (and their modifications) are referred to as the *reaction-diffusion problem.* There are no typical solutions; for some parameters the solution is smooth, whereas for other parameters the solution has very large gradients. When the solution is smooth, only a few elements are necessary; even one high-order element often suffices. When the solution has large gradients, the finite-element method is needed because the mesh must be refined with small elements in the region of the large gradients.

Another situation with chemical reaction is the flow of a reacting fluid in a packed bed or empty tube. In a typical case the equations model flow in the axial direction and dispersion in the radial direction of a cylindrical vessel.

$$\frac{\partial c}{\partial z} = \alpha \nabla^2 c - \mathrm{Da_I} R(c, T) \tag{7.9}$$

$$\frac{\partial T}{\partial z} = \alpha' \nabla^2 T + \mathrm{Da_{III}} R(c, T) \tag{7.10}$$

$$\frac{\partial c}{\partial r} = 0 \qquad \frac{\partial T}{\partial r} = 0 \qquad \text{at } r = 0 \tag{7.11}$$

$$\frac{\partial c}{\partial r} = 0 \qquad -\frac{\partial T}{\partial r} = \mathrm{Bi}_w(T - T_B) \qquad \text{at } r = 1 \tag{7.12}$$

$$c(r, z) = c_0(r) \qquad T(r, z) = T_0(r) \qquad \text{at } z = 0 \tag{7.13}$$

where $\alpha$ is the dimensionless diffusion coefficient, $\mathrm{Da_I}$ is the Damköler group I, and $\mathrm{Da_{III}}$ is the Damköler group III. Frequently, there are large gradients in the axial direction, which has an initial-value character. The gradients in the radial direction are frequently small and only a few elements are needed, or a single high-order element may be used. In the axial direction, however, an initial-value method is recommended, which could be a finite-element method. If the axial term includes diffusion and conduction

$$\nabla^2 c = \frac{1}{r} \frac{\partial}{\partial r} \left( r \frac{\partial c}{\partial r} \right) + \frac{\partial^2 c}{\partial z^2} \tag{7.14}$$

then the finite-element method is required in the axial direction to handle the steep gradients.

Another case with chemical reaction is the spontaneous ignition of a solid. The dimensionless equation for heat conduction with a reaction that is zeroth-order is

$$\frac{\partial T}{\partial t} = \nabla^2 T + \mathrm{Da_{III}} R(T) \tag{7.15}$$

$$R(T) = \exp\left(-\frac{\gamma}{T}\right) \tag{7.16}$$

$$T = T_B \qquad \text{on } S_1 \tag{7.17}$$

$$-\mathbf{n} \cdot \nabla T = \mathrm{Bi}_w(T - T_B) \qquad \text{on } S_2 \tag{7.18}$$

where $\gamma$ is the dimensionless activation energy. The Frank–Kamenetskii approximation [2] leads to a simpler equation,

$$\nabla^2 \phi + \delta \, e^{\phi} = 0 \tag{7.19}$$

$$\delta = \mathrm{Da_{III}} \exp\left(-\frac{\gamma}{T_B}\right) \tag{7.20}$$

$$\phi = 1 \qquad \text{on } S_1 \tag{7.21}$$

$$-\mathbf{n} \cdot \nabla \phi = \mathrm{Bi}_w(\phi - 1) \qquad \text{on } S_2 \tag{7.22}$$

which leads to a critical value of the parameter $\delta$. This problem is then an eigenvalue problem. This problem, too, leads to solutions with large gradients in some regions, and the finite-element method is an ideal way to solve the problem since the space can be discretized finely in the region of large gradients.

## 7.1B Galerkin–Finite-Element Method

The Galerkin method can be applied directly to the equations involving chemical reaction, but it is of interest to know when a variational principle exists [3]. The complication of fluid flow is treated elsewhere; here we consider Eq. (7.1) involving only diffusion and reaction when the temperature is constant.

$$\nabla^2 c = \phi^2 R(c) \tag{7.23}$$

$$c = c_1 \qquad \text{on } S_1 \tag{7.24}$$

$$-\mathbf{n} \cdot \nabla c = q_2 \qquad \text{on } S_2 \tag{7.25}$$

$$-\mathbf{n} \cdot \nabla c = \mathrm{Bi}_m(c - c_3) \qquad \text{on } S_3 \tag{7.26}$$

The variational integral corresponding to Eqs. (7.23) to (7.26) is

$$\Phi(c) = \tfrac{1}{2} \int_V \nabla c \cdot \nabla c \, dV + \int_V \int_0^c R(z) \, dz \, dV + \int_{S_2} q_2 c \, dS + \tfrac{1}{2} \mathrm{Bi}_m \int_{S_3} (c - c_3)^2 \, dS \tag{7.27}$$

A variation of this integral gives (with $v = c$)

$$\int_V \nabla v \cdot \nabla c \, dV + \int_V v R(c) \, dV + \int_{S_2} q_2 v \, dS + \mathrm{Bi}_m \int_{S_3} v(c - c_3) \, dS = 0 \tag{7.28}$$

Integration by parts reveals the Euler equation

$$\int_V v(-\nabla^2 c + R(c)) \, dV = 0 \tag{7.29}$$

and the following boundary conditions:
*Essential*:

$$c = c_1 \qquad \text{on } S_1 \tag{7.30}$$

*Natural*:

$$\int_{S_2} v(q_2 + \mathbf{n} \cdot \nabla c) \, dS = 0 \tag{7.31}$$

$$\int_{S_3} v(\mathrm{Bi}_m(c - c_3) + \mathbf{n} \cdot \nabla c) \, dS = 0 \tag{7.32}$$

Clearly the Galerkin method leads to the same equation, (7.28).

When the finite-element method is illustrated for these equations, Eq. (7.6) is used to obtain

$$\mathbf{Jc} - \mathbf{F} = 0 \tag{7.33}$$

The element integrals are defined as

$$J_{ij}^e = \int_e \frac{\partial N_i}{\partial x} \frac{\partial N_j}{\partial x} x^{a-1} \, dx + \mathrm{Bi}_m N_i N_j|_{x=1} \tag{7.34}$$

$$F_i^e = -\phi^2 \int_e N_i R(c(x)) x^{a-1} \, dx + \mathrm{Bi}_m N_i c_B|_{x=1} \tag{7.35}$$

Here the reaction-rate term depends on concentration so that there is a nonlinear set of equations. These can be solved using an iterative method; successive substitution works if the reaction rate is slow. Let the superscript $s$ denote the value at the $s^{\underline{\mathrm{th}}}$ iteration.

$$\mathbf{Jc}^{s+1} = \mathbf{F}^s \tag{7.36}$$

For more severe cases the Newton–Raphson method is required.

$$\mathbf{Jc}^{s+1} = \mathbf{F}^s + \frac{\partial \mathbf{F}^s}{\partial \mathbf{c}} (\mathbf{c}^{s+1} - \mathbf{c}^s) \tag{7.37}$$

In this case the element integrals are more complicated.

$$\mathbf{J}_1^s \mathbf{c}^{s+1} = \mathbf{F}_1^s \tag{7.38}$$

$$\mathbf{J}_1^s = \mathbf{J} - \frac{\partial \mathbf{F}^s}{\partial \mathbf{c}} \tag{7.39}$$

$$\mathbf{F}_1^s = \mathbf{F}^s - \frac{\partial \mathbf{F}^s}{\partial \mathbf{c}} \mathbf{c}^s \tag{7.40}$$

Since the reaction-rate term may vary drastically throughout the element, it may be necessary to use a higher-order gaussian integration scheme than is necessary for the diffusion terms.

If the diffusion coefficient also depends on concentration [Eq. (7.5)], then the Galerkin method is still applicable. Oftentimes a successive-substitution method is suitable for the concentration dependence of the diffusion coefficient:

$$J_{ij}^{e,s} = \int_e D(c^s) \nabla N_i \cdot \nabla N_j \, dV \tag{7.41}$$

The reaction-diffusion problem in Eqs. (7.6) to (7.8) can also be transient, in which case the equations are like Eqs. (7.9) to (7.10) with different boundary conditions (7.7) to (7.8). In such cases initial-value methods can be used in time while finite-element methods are used in space. Cavendish and Oh [4] apply such a method when the material properties (diffusion coefficient and reaction-rate constants) are discontinuous functions of position corresponding to different layers of catalyst.

Problems involving spontaneous ignition are frequently two- and three-dimensional. For Eq. (7.19), the element and system equations become

$$J_{ij}^e = \int_e \nabla N_i \cdot \nabla N_j \, dV + \text{Bi}_m \int N_i N_j \, dS \tag{7.42}$$

$$F_i^e = \delta \int_e N_i e^\phi \, dV + \text{Bi}_m \int N_i \, dS \tag{7.43}$$

$$\mathbf{J}\boldsymbol{\phi} = \mathbf{F} \tag{7.44}$$

Since solutions exist only for certain values of the parameter $\delta$, it is necessary to iterate carefully. Anderson and Zienkiewicz [5] suggest using a quasi-Newton method in which the element jacobian matrix is

$$J_{ij}^{e,s} = \int_e \nabla N_i \cdot \nabla N_j \, dV - \delta \int_e N_i N_j \, e^{\phi^s} \, dV + \text{Bi}_m \int_{S_3} N_i N_j \, dS \tag{7.45}$$

$$F_i^{e,s} = \delta \int_e N_i \, e^{\phi^s}(-1 + \phi^s) \, dV + \text{Bi}_m \int_{S_3} N_i \, dS \tag{7.46}$$

and the full equations are then     $$\mathbf{J}^s \boldsymbol{\phi}^{s+1} - \mathbf{F}^s = \mathbf{0} \tag{7.47}$$

They suggest a strategy to find the critical value of $\delta$, and later references on bifurcation theory give even better ones [6].

### 7.1c  Collocation on Finite Elements

The collocation method is attractive for chemically reacting systems because it avoids the evaluation of the reaction rate at many gaussian quadrature points. There are two ways to apply the orthogonal collocation method. In the original method [7] lagrangian elements are used and the first derivatives are made continuous between elements. In the other method hermitian elements are used and the continuity between the elements is satisfied automatically. The second method is more economical when the coefficients are smooth, but does lead to a nonlumped-mass matrix in time-dependent problems. The first method leads to a lumped-mass matrix and is applicable if the coefficients (such as diffusivity) have discontinuities between elements.

Here the method is illustrated for the one-dimensional problem, Eq. (7.7). First the equation is transferred onto a single element

$$u = \frac{(x - x_e)}{\Delta x_e}, \qquad \Delta x_e = x_{e+1} - x_e \tag{7.48}$$

$$\frac{1}{\Delta x_e^2} \frac{d^2 c}{du^2} + \frac{a-1}{x_e + u \, \Delta x_e} \frac{1}{\Delta x_e} \frac{dc}{du} = \phi^2 R(c(u)) \tag{7.49}$$

$$\frac{1}{\Delta x_1} \frac{dc}{du}\bigg|_{u=0} = 0 \tag{7.50}$$

$$-\frac{1}{\Delta x_{NE}}\frac{dc}{du}\bigg|_{u=1} = \mathrm{Bi}_m(c-1) \qquad \text{at } u=1, e=NE \tag{7.51}$$

The collocation method is applied (see the section on collocation) to give

$$\mathbf{Bc}+\mathbf{Ac}=\mathbf{F} \tag{7.52}$$

which is a large-banded matrix problem, easily solved [7, 8].

Hermite cubic polynomials can also be used with the collocation method (see Section 6.2 in Part 2 on collocation). The collocation and Galerkin methods can be combined to form a $C^0$-method. The equation governing the continuity of slope between elements is replaced by a Galerkin condition [9].

## 7.2 NEUTRON FLUX

### 7.2A Transport and Diffusion Equations

Neutron-flux calculations are usually divided into calculations involving radiation shielding (source problems) and reactor core (eigenvalue problems). In both cases the particle transport is described by a linearized version of the Boltzmann transport equation. Typical derivations of the basic equations can be found in the literature [10–13]. In general, the neutron flux depends on seven variables: three space variables, two angular variables, energy, and time. Usually this number of variables has to be reduced considerably to treat practical problems. Up to five variables are treated simultaneously in the open literature with present numerical and computer techniques. Depending on the variables of interest, different approximations of the general transport equation are used. Three classifications are most popular:

1. Omission of the angular variables results in the transient-diffusion theory approximation.
2. Omission of the time and one space dimension results in two-dimensional stationary transport approximations.
3. Omission of two space variables results in the one-dimensional transient transport equation.

The following will concentrate on the transient-diffusion theory approximation, and the basic equations will be given in the so-called multigroup form. This form is obtained by dividing the energy space into subspaces called *energy groups*. Material data and solution values are considered as independent of energy in each group. A diffusion equation exists for each group and is called the *group equation*. The group equations are connected by terms describing the scattering from one group to any other group. Thus the multigroup formalism can be viewed as a hypermatrix representation of the total discretized problem. The group diffusion equation for the neutron flux $\phi^g$ in group $g$ with coordinate vector $\mathbf{r}$ and time $t$ reads

$$\frac{1}{v_g}\frac{\partial \phi^g}{\partial t}(\mathbf{r},t)=\nabla D^g(\mathbf{r},t)\nabla \phi^g(\mathbf{r},t)-\Sigma_a^g(\mathbf{r},t)\phi^g(\mathbf{r},t)$$

$$+\sum_{\substack{g'=1\\g'\neq g}}^{G}\Sigma_s^{g'g}(\mathbf{r},t)\phi^{g'}(\mathbf{r},t)+\chi^g(1-\beta)\sum_{g'=1}^{G}\nu\Sigma_f^{g'}(\mathbf{r},t)\phi^{g'}(\mathbf{r},t)$$

$$+\sum_{k=1}^{K}\chi^{kg}\cdot\lambda^k\cdot C^k(\mathbf{r},t) \qquad g=1,2,\ldots,G \tag{7.53}$$

The group index $g$ ranges from 1 to $G$. $v_g$ is the velocity of the neutrons in group $g$, while $C^k(\mathbf{r}, t)$ denotes the concentration of delayed fission sources in group $k$ ranging from 1 to $K$. All the other quantities describe material properties. These include the diffusion coefficient ($D^g$), the absorption cross section ($\Sigma_a^g$), the scattering cross section from group $g'$ into group $g$ ($\Sigma_s^{g'g}$), the fission cross section ($\Sigma_f^g$), the number of neutrons per fission ($\nu$), the fractions of fission and delayed neutrons ($\chi^g$ and $\chi^{kg}$), the total and individual relative contributions of delayed neutrons ($\beta$ and $\beta^k$), and the decay constant of the delayed neutron family $k$($\lambda^k$).

Boundary conditions have to be added (with $\alpha^g$ the boundary constant of group $g$):

$$\phi^g(\mathbf{r}) = \phi^g(\mathbf{r}) \qquad \text{on } \Gamma_1 \tag{7.54}$$

and

$$D^g(\mathbf{r}, t)\frac{\partial}{\partial \vec{n}}\phi^g(\mathbf{r}, t) = -\alpha^g\phi^g(\mathbf{r}, t) \qquad \text{on } \Gamma_2 \tag{7.55}$$

The fission source $C^k$ due to the delayed neutrons in group $k$ is determined from the equation

$$\frac{\partial C^k}{\partial t}(\mathbf{r}, t) = -\lambda^k C^k(\mathbf{r}, t) + \beta^k \sum_{g'=1}^{G} \nu\Sigma_f^{g'}(\mathbf{r}, t)\phi^{g'}(\mathbf{r}, t) \qquad k = 1, 2, \ldots, K \tag{7.56}$$

and the initial conditions are

$$\phi^g(\mathbf{r}, t=0) = \phi_0^g(\mathbf{r}) \qquad g = 1, 2, \ldots, G \tag{7.57}$$

$$C^k(\mathbf{r}, t=0) = C_0^k(\mathbf{r}) \qquad k = 1, 2, \ldots, K \tag{7.58}$$

where $\phi_0^g(\mathbf{r})$ is the stationary neutron distribution and $C_0^k(\mathbf{r})$ is the stationary distribution of the delayed fission sources according to

$$C_0^k(\mathbf{r}) = \frac{\beta^k}{\lambda^k} \sum_{g'=1}^{G} \nu\Sigma_f^{g'}(\mathbf{r}, t=0)\phi_0^{g'}(\mathbf{r}) \tag{7.59}$$

A similar set of equations holds for each energy group. Sophisticated techniques were developed in reactor physics to determine the group-averaged cross sections from basic experimental data. The experimental data cover an energy range of approximately 10 decades. The number of groups varies between one and several hundred. Therefore the averaged data depend on both problem and problem discretization. The dependence on these data limits the efficient use of the finite-element method in neutron-flux calculations.

## 7.2B Numerical Methods of Reactor Physics

The finite-element method (FEM) was introduced into reactor physics only in the early seventies [14–19]. At that time other powerful methods were established or already under development in reactor physics. The basic advantages and disadvantages of these methods have to be understood if one wants to judge the role of the FEM in neutron-flux calculations.

Most reactor-physics problems can be described by regular or orthogonal geometries, and thus finite-difference methods are usually most suitable for the discretization of space. Finite-difference discretizations result in matrices which are easy to handle and which behave well with various iterative equation solvers. Thus reactor physicists are used to programs which are easy to handle and which provide solutions in an effective and reliable way. In a manner similar to the space variable, the angular variable was approximated by discretized values. The discretized equations are known as *discrete ordinate equations*, and they are programmed in highly optimized production codes. There is one major disadvantage of the discrete ordinate equations, the so-called ray effect, which means that neutron transport is performed primarily in the discrete directions, thus resulting in strange angular distributions. There are various ways to circumvent this effect, and finite-element approximations are among the more promising.

A linear discretization is usually used for the time variable. With finite-difference approximations in space, one usually gets a diagonal matrix for the time operator. There is therefore a broad spectrum of advanced methods available for the time integration.

Among the commonly used codes for reactor physics are RSYST [20] or AMPX [21] for cross-section generation, problem formulation, and data management; VENTURE [22] and PDQ [23] for the solution of the diffusion equation; ANISN [24] and DOT [25] for the solution of the discrete ordinate equations; and IQSBOX [26] for the solution of transient-diffusion problems.

## 7.2c Finite-Element Discretization in Neutron-Flux Calculations

The following features of the FEM make it attractive for reactor-physics engineers:

- FEM is an integral method, thus it reduces the number of unknowns.

- FEM uses general trial functions and does not require special element shapes.

- FEM has the potential to treat problems of great geometric complexity.

- FEM offers continuous solutions over the element space. This allows the engineer to determine local flux values and to avoid discretization problems like the ray effect.

These advantages are not of equal importance for all the variables. With the present multigroup concept there is no sense in a higher-order coupling of the energy variable with any of the other variables. Thus all major finite-element programs in reactor physics start with an integral formulation of the system of group equations. Various methods exist to derive such a formulation, and the most popular is the Galerkin procedure.

If the solution in an element $m$ is approximated by shape functions $\xi_i$,

$$\phi(x, y, z) \approx \sum_{i=1}^{I} \phi_i \xi_i(x, y, z) \tag{7.60}$$

there is obtained from Eqs. (7.53) to (7.56) as the contribution of this element to the solution point $i$ in group $g$

$$\sum_{i=1}^{I} \int_V \xi_i \xi_j \, dV \frac{\partial}{\partial t} \phi_i^g = -v^g \left\{ D_m^g \sum_{i=1}^{I} \int_V \nabla \xi_i \, \nabla \xi_j \, dV \right.$$

$$- [\omega^g + \Sigma_{am}^g - \chi^g (1-\beta) \nu \Sigma_{fm}^g] \sum_{i=1}^{I} \int_V \xi_i \xi_j \, dV \Bigg\} \phi_i^g$$

$$+ v^g \lambda^g (1-\beta) \sum_{\substack{g'=1 \\ g' \neq g}}^{G} \nu \Sigma_{fm}^{g'} \sum_{i=1}^{I} \int_V \xi_i \xi_j \, dV \phi_i^g$$

$$+ v^g \sum_{\substack{g'=1 \\ g' \neq g}}^{G} \Sigma_{sm}^{g'g} \sum_{i=1}^{I} \int_V \xi_i \xi_j \, dV \phi_i^g + v^g \sum_{k=1}^{K} \chi^{kg} \lambda^k \sum_{i=1}^{I} \int_V \xi_i \xi_j \, dV C_i^k$$

$$- v^g \alpha^g \sum_{i=1}^{I} \int^{\Gamma} \xi_i \xi_j \, d\Gamma \qquad j=1,2,\ldots,I; \; g=1,2,\ldots,G \qquad (7.61)$$

and

$$\sum_{I=1}^{I} \int_V \xi_i \xi_j \, dV \frac{\partial}{\partial t} C_i^k = -\lambda^k \sum_{i=1}^{I} \int_V \xi_i \xi_j \, dV C_i^k$$

$$+ \beta_k \sum_{g'=1}^{G} \nu \Sigma_{fm}^{g'} \sum_{i=1}^{I} \int_V \xi_i \xi_j \, dV \phi_i \qquad k=1,2,\ldots,K \qquad (7.62)$$

Using conventional finite-element procedures leads to a semidiscrete transient system of equations:

$$\mathbf{T} \frac{\partial}{\partial t} \boldsymbol{\phi}^g = \mathbf{K}^g \boldsymbol{\phi}^g + v^g \lambda^g (1-\beta) \sum_{g'=1}^{G} \mathbf{F}^{g'} \boldsymbol{\phi}^{g'} + v^g \sum_{\substack{g'=1 \\ g' \neq g}}^{G} \mathbf{S}^{g'g} \boldsymbol{\phi}^{g'}$$

$$+ v^g \sum_{k=1}^{K} \chi^{kg} \lambda^k \, \mathbf{T} \mathbf{C}^k, \qquad g=1,2,\ldots,G \qquad (7.63)$$

$$\mathbf{T} \frac{\partial}{\partial t} \mathbf{C}^k = -\lambda^k \mathbf{T} \mathbf{C}^k + \beta_k \sum_{g'=1}^{G} \mathbf{F}^{g'} \boldsymbol{\phi}^{g'}, \qquad k=1,2,\ldots,K \qquad (7.64)$$

where $\mathbf{T}$ is the mass matrix, and the other matrices are combinations of the mass matrix and cross sections or in the case of $\mathbf{K}$ of the mass matrix, the stiffness matrix, and material data.

In addition, local cross-section variations over the finite-element space may be taken into account, as, for instance, in depletion calculations [27]. As indicated, time is usually treated separately. However, because of the first-order time derivative at least two time steps have to be coupled. This leads in finite elements to complex time-integration schemes with nondiagonal capacity matrices (implicit in terms of complexity). Reference [28] reports the most popular approximations and applications, and it will be seen that space and angle variables are usually discretized separately. For the angular-domain zeroth-order polynomials (discrete ordinate formulation), first-order polynomials or spherical-harmonics expansions are used most frequently. Quadrilaterals representing equal solid angles are most natural.

Special attention is given to the discretization of the space variable. Triangles and quadrilaterals are used in two-dimensional calculations, while three-dimensional codes prefer prisms and sometimes tetrahedra. The order of the trial functions is restricted by the angular-flux singularities or by material inhomogeneities. Thus first-order approximations are used in transport theory, while first- and second-order approximations can be found in diffusion calculations. (For a more detailed discussion, see Ref. [29].)

Among the element shapes, the triangles are most popular. In general they give satisfactory results. For symmetrical problems, however, they tend to introduce a slight bias as soon as the discretization does not reflect the symmetry conditions. For practical purposes this seems to have little effect. Very unsatisfactory for reactor physicists is the occurrence of negative flux values at nodes near boundaries. Negative fluxes are not reasonable from a physical point of view. In finite elements, however, they may occur because of the integral formulation of the problem. Often a mesh refinement will solve the problem. Unfortunately, the use of quadrilaterals does not result in considerable improvements, as one may expect, owing to the higher-order terms in the trial functions.

Once the diffusion (transport) equation is discretized, one usually assembles elementary matrices to system matrices. Because of the nature of the multigroup diffusion equation and the algorithms used for matrix inversion, an explicit assembling of the system and source matrices seems to be the most economic.

The solution process is divided into two phases. First, one solves the group equations. Second, one determines the smallest eigenvalue of the multigroup system or performs the time integration. The solution of the group equations is often called the *inner iteration*. Various techniques have been developed and tried for this iteration. There are many reasons for this. The most important ones can be found in the structure of the system matrices. These matrices can be characterized as being more irregular and more dense than those known from finite-difference discretizations. Also the condition number which determines the numerical behavior of a matrix is higher than in finite differences. In structural mechanics, therefore, direct inversion algorithms are often applied. This was true for the early versions of most finite-element programs in reactor physics too. However, the need to have fast and efficient programs forced the shift to iterative procedures, at least for 3D programs. The described nature of the matrices lead to conjugate-gradient methods (DIFGEN) [30] or block iterative methods (TRIDENT [31] and FEM-BABEL [32]). The conjugate-gradient method is most effective with preconditioning. Good preconditioning methods are the incomplete Cholesky-conjugate-gradient method [33, 34], and the incomplete inverse–conjugate-gradient method [35]. However, frequently a simple scaling of the system matrices results in a similar improvement of the performance of the equation solver.

The eigenvalue determination is called *outer iteration*. Usually the power-iteration method is applied. Various techniques can be tried to speed up the convergence of the iteration process. They are all well known from finite-difference programs and seem to work with finite elements as well as with finite differences. However, in judging the various methods, one has to take into account that in finite-element calculations all the scatter and fission matrices have the same structure as the system matrix. Thus for multigroup problems with many scattering contributions the calculation of the source vectors may become very expensive.

Lumping techniques for the scatter matrix have been investigated at several installations [36, 37].

The time integration of transient problems is performed by applying a rational Padé approximation. In reactor physics fast and stable algorithms which rely on the diagonal form of the capacity matrix (time derivation) and on the regular structure of finite-difference matrices are available to solve the transient problem [38]. In finite elements, all matrix structures are irregular, and therefore, in order to compete with standard transient programs in reactor physics new time-integration techniques have to be developed for transient finite-element programs. Schmidt and Fremd [28] propose an alternative-direction explicit method which is based on a matrix-splitting method developed by Saul'ev and modified by Trujillo and Busby [39]. This method requires a diagonal (lumped) capacity matrix but no regular node numbering.

As in other finite-element applications, sound software techniques are necessary to solve reactor-physics equations by the FEM in a satisfactory way. As stated in Ref. [28] such techniques include (1) modular program design—in particular, net generators from structural-mechanics programs should be connectable; (2) elaborated data-management techniques, with effective data transfer and automatic-restart possibilities; (3) skillful preprocessors which allow an easy problem description in terms familiar to the engineer and offer extensive debugging information for the input data; and (4) powerful postprocessors which help to analyze and interpret the results, especially in nonorthogonal geometries.

For a more updated discussion of the FE discretization in neutron flux (including consistency and convergence considerations), see Refs. [29] and [40].

## 7.2D Finite-Element Applications in Neutron-Flux Calculations

The finite-element method is used in practice to solve stationary and transient reactor-physics equations. Both diffusion and transport problems are treated, and the range of applications includes all the major neutron-flux problems such as shielding, eigenvalue, or depletion calculations. Production-type programs exist for the solution of diffusion-theory problems [30–32]. However, the full power of the FEM can be used only very rarely. Often only special variables are discretized by the FEM. The performance of finite-element codes in reactor physics is comparable to other reactor-physics programs. Such comparisons tend to be favorable for the FEM in problems with nonorthogonal geometries [41]. Also problems which show significant ray effects can be solved with finite-element programs satisfactorily [28]. Finally it should be mentioned that the wide area of problems where radiation physics and structural mechanics are coupled (for instance, to determine the radiation damage of pressure vessels) still remains to be investigated. The status of the FEM in neutron-flux calculations is such that calculations of this type are now becoming performable.

## 7.3 PLASMAS

The plasma state of matter consists of charged particles interacting predominantly through long-range coulomb force to behave as an electrically neutral statistical entity in which the random energy of the particles is large enough to escape neutral atom formation. There are two major categories of plasma modeling: (1) macroscopic dynamics and stability of the plasma obtained by solving a set of continuum equations describing a radiative, conducting, and viscous fluid in the presence of electric and magnetic fields; (2) microscopic plasma studies through the constituent particle-particle and particle-field interactions and their effects taken into account statistically and phenomenologically.

The use of finite-element method in plasma research started in the seventies, especially in multidimensional calculations. Akin and Wooten [42] calculated the axisymmetric tokamak-plasma equilibria within the Galerkin formulation in the ideal magnetohydrodynamic (MHD) limit. Gupta et al. [43] determined the magnetic pressure surfaces surrounding spherical plasma balls of varying sizes in a spherical pinch for a qualitative understanding of the device. Bakker and van den Berg [44] developed a finite-element program to calculate the mass separation of gaseous mixtures in plasma centrifuges.

Blum et al. [45] developed a code, SCED, to study plasma equilibria self-consistently with the diffusion phenomena for a realistic tokamak machine. Anderson and Barnes [46] used the finite elements with bicubic-spline basis functions to accurately calculate the axisymmetric equilibria and their stability in the plasmas confined in the field-reversed devices. Anderson et al. [47] calculated the 3D mirror equilibria using the tricubic splines in a finite-element vector-potential formulation of the guiding-center MHD theory [48].

Ohta et al. [49] and Takeda et al. [50] used the power of the finite-element method to model complex geometries in the analysis of magnetohydrodynamic instabilities of a circular-cylindrical current-carrying plasma in a strong axial magnetic field. Boyd et al. [51] used the Japanese approach for studying a linear pinch upon modifying the treatment of the vacuum potential energy. Appert et al. [52, 53] applied the finite-element approach to the eigenmode analysis of fixed-boundary magnetohydrodynamics stability of cylindrical homogeneous plasma and studied the dependence of the solution on the choice of local basis functions. Dewar et al. [54], Grimm et al. [55], and Grimm and Johnson [56] studied the magneto-dynamics of tokamak plasmas of arbitrary cross sections using the Galerkin method with a combination of Fourier-Bessel and finite-element expansion functions. Upon finding that the weakly growing internal instability modes are difficult to calculate in the tokamak MHD equilibria when the standard finite-element method is used [57], Gruber [58] proposed a "hybrid finite-element" method in which a function and its derivatives were expanded in terms of different basis functions and obtained considerably improved results.

On the basis of above findings, three major finite-element codes, PEST [55], ERATO [59], and GATO [60], have evolved to study the stability of confined plasmas in the ideal MHD limit. The application of these codes (PEST [61–63], ERATO [64–69], GATO [70–73]) has mainly been for axisymmetric toroidal geometries, but helically symmetric geometries have also been considered by an extension of ERATO [65, 67]. Subsequently, resistive MHD equations have been used to calculate the nonlinear evolution of tearing modes in tokamak discharges [74–76]. A 2D numerical simulation of plasma diffusion using triangular finite elements has been reported by Hennart et al. [77] for a multipole plasma-confinement machine.

In recent years the use of finite-element method has made possible realistic plasma simulation using particles. On the basis of the variational algorithms proposed by Lewis [78–79], Godfrey [80] was able to show that replacing the finite-difference method in an existing 2D code with the finite-element method improved the stability and accuracy of the code while reducing the computer time and memory requirements. Okuda and Cheng [81] and Okuda et al. [82] reported success in reducing the spatial grid effect in plasma simulation by using higher-order multipoles and splines as the local interpolation functions. On the basis of this study the electrostatic and magnetostatic 3D particle-simulation models have been developed and applied to a magnetically confined plasma near thermal equilibrium [83]. Buneman [84] and Buneman et al. [85] showed that it was possible to do meaningful 3D electromagnetic-particle plasma simulations when tetrahedral finite elements [86] are used. A variational formulation of Poisson's equation using isoparametric finite elements has been employed by Wooten et al. [87] to solve 3D Poisson and Vlasov equations for the modeling of ion extraction from a plasma. The problem of anomalous skin effect in a plasma column has been solved by Tran and Troyon [88] by finite-element numerical integration of coupled Vlasov and Maxwell equations. The solution of Fokker–Planck equations has been addressed by Mehlhorn and Duderstadt [89] and Fyfe et al. [90].

### 7.3A Ideal MHD Plasma Equilibria

The governing fluid and Maxwell's equations relating magnetic field **B**, current **J**, and plasma-pressure tensor **P** are

$$\mathbf{J} \times \mathbf{B} = \nabla \cdot \mathbf{P} \tag{7.65}$$

$$\nabla \times \mathbf{B} = \mu \mathbf{J} \tag{7.66}$$

$$\nabla \cdot \mathbf{B} = 0 \tag{7.67}$$

which neglect electrostatic field and plasma motion. A simple model for the equilibrium fields is obtained by assuming an isotropic plasma pressure and axially symmetric configurations in cylindrical coordinates $r$, $z$, $\theta$. Upon separating **B** into the toroidal and poloidal fluxes

$$\mathbf{B} = \frac{\mu F(\psi)\hat{\boldsymbol{\theta}} - \hat{\boldsymbol{\theta}} \times \nabla \psi}{r} \tag{7.68}$$

and noting that

$$J_\theta = r \frac{dP}{d\psi} + \mu \frac{F}{r} \frac{dF}{d\psi} \tag{7.69}$$

Eqs. (7.65) to (7.67) may be combined with (7.68) and (7.69) to yield the Grad–Shafranov equation [91].

$$\frac{\partial^2 \psi}{\partial r^2} - \frac{1}{r} \frac{\partial \psi}{\partial r} + \frac{\partial^2 \psi}{\partial z^2} = \mu r^2 \frac{dp}{d\psi} - \mu^2 F \frac{dF}{d\psi} \tag{7.70}$$

Here $\hat{\boldsymbol{\theta}}$ is the unit vector in the $\theta$-direction, $F$ is the flux function of the poloidal plasma currents, and $\psi$ is the stream function defining the surface of constant magnetic pressure through $\psi = $ constant. By approximating the right-hand side of Eq. (7.70) as $g\psi + h$, by defining a differential operator for it as

$$D = \frac{\partial}{\partial r}\left(\frac{1}{r}\frac{\partial \psi}{\partial r}\right) + \frac{1}{r}\frac{\partial^2 \psi}{\partial z^2} - \frac{1}{r}g\psi - \frac{1}{r}h \tag{7.71}$$

and by applying the Galerkin criterion

$$\iint_\Omega \psi D \, dr \, dz = 0$$

the desired variational form is obtained [42]:

$$I = \iint_\Omega \left\{ \left( \frac{1}{2} \left[ \left( \frac{\partial \psi}{\partial r} \right)^2 + \left( \frac{\partial \psi}{\partial z} \right)^2 + g\psi^2 \right] + h\psi \right\} \frac{1}{r} \, dr \, dz$$

This can be solved by the standard finite-element procedure subject to the appropriate boundary conditions and further simplifications if any. If $h$ is nonzero, the resulting equations are nonlinear and must be solved by iteration methods. The boundary conditions are (1) $\partial \psi / \partial n = 0$ in the plane of symmetry normal to the axis of symmetry; (2) $\psi = $ constant in the inner surface of the conductor containing plasma and $\psi = $ constant + sources due to external conductor currents [42], or $\psi$ to be determined to give the desired shape for the plasma surface.

## 7.3в MHD Stability of Plasmas

The magnetohydrodynamic stability problem of a toroidal system is essentially that of finding eigenvalues $\omega^2$ and eigenfunction $\boldsymbol{\xi}$ such that the lagrangian

$$L = \omega^2 K(\boldsymbol{\xi}^* \boldsymbol{\xi}) - \delta W(\boldsymbol{\xi}^*, \boldsymbol{\xi}) \tag{7.72}$$

is stationary against variation in $\boldsymbol{\xi}$. Here the real part of $\boldsymbol{\xi}(\mathbf{r}t) \equiv \boldsymbol{\xi}(\mathbf{r}) \exp{(-i\omega t)}$ is the plasma displacement at $\mathbf{r}$, and $\omega^2 K$ and $\delta W$ are the kinetic- and potential-energy functionals:

$$K = \frac{1}{2} \int_{\text{plasma}} \rho |\xi|^2 \, d\tau \tag{7.73}$$

$$\delta W = \frac{1}{2} \int_{\text{plasma}} \left[ \frac{\mathbf{Q} - \mathbf{B}(\boldsymbol{\xi} \cdot \boldsymbol{\nabla} P)}{B^2} + \left( \mathbf{J} \cdot \frac{\mathbf{B}}{B^2} \right) \mathbf{B} \times \boldsymbol{\xi}^* \cdot \mathbf{Q} \right.$$

$$\left. - 2\boldsymbol{\xi} \cdot \boldsymbol{\nabla} P \boldsymbol{\xi}^* \cdot \boldsymbol{\chi} + \gamma P |\boldsymbol{\nabla} \cdot \boldsymbol{\xi}|^2 \right] d\tau + \frac{1}{2} \int_{\text{vacuum}} |\boldsymbol{\nabla} \times \mathbf{A}|^2 \, d\tau \tag{7.74}$$

where $d\tau$ is the volume element, $\rho$ is the plasma density, $\mathbf{Q}$ is the perturbed magnetic field, $\chi$ is the local magnetic-field-line curvature, $\gamma$ is the ratio of specific heats, and $A$ is the vector potential corresponding to $Q$ in vacuum. Only those eigensolutions are acceptable which give a fixed $K$ (the kinetic-energy norm), and have the magnetic field vanishing normal to the confining conductor and continuous across the plasma-vacuum interface.

Approximating
$$\boldsymbol{\xi} = \sum_m \mathbf{a}_m \boldsymbol{\Phi}_{m'}$$

the application of Galerkin method to Eq. (7.72) yields the matrix eigenvalue problem

$$\Sigma(\omega^2 \langle \boldsymbol{\Phi}_m | K | \boldsymbol{\Phi}_m \rangle - \langle \boldsymbol{\Phi}_m | \delta W | \boldsymbol{\Phi}_m \rangle) \mathbf{a}_m = 0$$

It is convenient to split the displacement into suitable components which reflect the symmetry of the problem and take into consideration the boundary conditions in a natural way [49–73]. The finite-element discretization is straightforward, but a successful and meaningful solution of a problem depends on the choice of elements and interpolation functions [56, 58, 64, 92, 93].


## 7.4 ACOUSTICS

The acoustic field equations are derived from the continuity, momentum, energy, and state equations for nonviscous compressible flow without body forces [94]. The acoustic approximation is introduced by considering a steady mean flow $V_0$, $p_0$, $\rho_0$ upon which there are small perturbations $V$, $p$, $\rho$. $V_0$, $V$, $p_0$, $p$, $\rho_0$, $\rho$ are the fluid velocity, pressure, and density, nondimensionalized respectively with suitable reference quantities $c_r$, $\rho_r c_r^2$, and $\rho_r$. $c_r$ is the reference speed of sound. If spatial coordinates are nondimensionalized with respect to a reference length $L$ and the time by $L/c_r$ and if harmonic perturbations proportional to $\exp{(i\eta_r t)}$, where $\eta_r = \omega L / c_r$ and $\omega$ rad/s is the dimensional excitation frequency, are assumed, the acoustic field equations can be written

$$(i\eta_r + V_0 \cdot \nabla)V + \frac{1}{\rho_0}\nabla p + (V \cdot \nabla)V_0 - \frac{\nabla p_0}{\gamma p_0 \rho_0}p = 0 \tag{7.75}$$

$$(i\eta_r + V_0 \cdot \nabla)p + \gamma p_0 \nabla \cdot V + V \cdot \nabla p_0 + \gamma(\nabla \cdot V_0)p = 0 \tag{7.76}$$

Equation (7.75), a vector equation, is the linearized momentum equation, and Eq. (7.76) is the linearized energy (or, equivalently, continuity) equation. These are valid if the mean flow $V_0$ is rotational or irrotational. If the mean flow field and the acoustic perturbations are irrotational, a velocity-potential formulation is appropriate [95].

A wide range of boundary conditions can accompany the field equations. The simplest one, and the one used in examples in this section, in the absence of mean flow, requires that at a solid surface the normal component (direction $n$) of acoustic particle velocity, or equivalently the normal pressure derivative, must vanish; that is,

$$V \cdot n = 0 \qquad \text{or} \qquad \frac{\partial p}{\partial n} = 0 \qquad \text{on solid boundaries} \tag{7.77}$$

More complicated boundary conditions involving mean flow and normally reacting walls are discussed in Ref. [96]. In some cases the boundary motion may be specified, and in others it may be implied by additional field equations. The former case would include the problem of the specified motion of a piston, while the latter would include acoustic transmission through an elastic wall.


### 7.4A Special Cases

The simplest and most common use of finite-element methods in acoustics deals with applications to propagation in a quiescent medium. In these cases $V_0 = 0$ and $\nabla p_0 = 0$ and

Eqs. (7.75) and (7.76) combine to the Helmholtz equation

$$\nabla^2 p + \eta_r^2 p = 0 \tag{7.78}$$

This field equation arises in connection with the acoustics of enclosures [97–101] and ducts and mufflers with no mean flow [102–104].

If the mean-flow-field velocity is uniform, $\mathbf{V}_0 = M\mathbf{e}_x$, and $\nabla p_0 = 0$, Eqs. (7.75) and (7.76) combine to a "convected" Helmholtz equation (note $M$ = mean flow Mach number)

$$\nabla^2 p - \left( i\eta_r + M\frac{\partial}{\partial x} \right)^2 p = 0 \tag{7.79}$$

This field equation arises in connection with the transmission of sound in uniform ducts with uniform flow. If the mean flow is sheared so that $\mathbf{V}_0 = M(r)\mathbf{e}_x$, where $r$ is a transverse coordinate in a two-dimensional or cylindrical coordinate system, and $\nabla p_0 = 0$, then Eqs. (7.75) and (7.76) reduce to

$$\left( i\eta_r + M\frac{\partial}{\partial x} \right)\mathbf{V} + \frac{1}{\rho_0}\nabla p + u_r \frac{\partial M}{\partial r}\mathbf{e}_x = 0 \tag{7.80}$$

$$\left( i\eta_r + M\frac{\partial}{\partial x} \right)p + \gamma p_0 \nabla \cdot \mathbf{V} = 0 \tag{7.81}$$

These field equations, and a single equivalent one (given here in cylindrical coordinates),

$$\frac{d^2 p}{dr^2} + \left[ \frac{2k_x\,(\partial M/\partial r)}{\eta_r - k_x M} + \frac{1}{r} \right]\frac{dp}{dr} + \left[ (\eta_r - k_x M)^2 - k_x^2 - \frac{m^2}{r^2} \right]p = 0 \tag{7.82}$$

obtained when assuming $p(x, r, \theta) = P(r)\exp(-ik_x x)\exp(-im\theta)$, form the basis for studies of acoustics in axially uniform ducts carrying a sheared mean flow [105, 106].

Equations (7.75) and (7.76) in essentially their complete form are required for studies of sound transmission in nonuniform ducts and the radiation from ducts to the far field [107, 108].

## 7.4b Finite-Element Formulation

In acoustics several principles can be used to produce the linear algebraic equations in the unknown nodal variables. Those most frequently employed are variational methods based on Hamilton's principle [102], the Galerkin method [107], and the residual least-squares method [109]. In the following examples these three approaches are utilized.

## 7.4c Applications

The potential uses of finite-element methods in problems in acoustics are many. Attention here is limited to two examples, the acoustics of irregular rigid enclosures and the one-dimensional propagation of sound in ducts with a mean flow. While among the simplest applications these problems provide considerable insight.

### 7.4D The Natural Frequencies of Enclosures

The Helmholtz equation, Eq. (7.78), is now considered subject to appropriate boundary conditions. Within the context of enclosures are included rooms and vehicle enclosures. While forced response is usually the final goal, the calculation of natural frequencies plays an important role and provides a convenient demonstration of the finite-element application. Reference [99] provides a review of the problem as well as a survey of the literature. References [97–101] provide more details on the following discussion.

The Helmholtz equation, with the boundary condition of $\partial P/\partial n = 0$ at the boundary, represents the Euler equation and natural boundary condition of the variational problem over the volume $\forall$:

$$\delta \frac{1}{2} \int \int \int_\forall (\nabla p \cdot \nabla p - \eta_r^2 p^2)\, d\forall = 0$$

Use of conventional finite-element procedures leads to an eigenvalue problem

$$(\mathbf{K} - \eta_r^2 \mathbf{M})\mathbf{P} = 0$$

where

$$\mathbf{K} = \int \int \int_\forall \mathbf{N}_x^T \mathbf{N}_x + \mathbf{N}_y^T \mathbf{N}_y + \mathbf{N}_z^T \mathbf{N}_z\, d\forall$$

$$\mathbf{M} = \int \int \int_\forall \mathbf{N}^T \mathbf{N}\, d\forall$$

and $\mathbf{N}$ is the global shape-function matrix which is known explicitly within each element. The matrices $\mathbf{M}$ and $\mathbf{K}$, obviously analogous to mass and stiffness matrices in vibration analysis, are formed by integration at the element level and assembly by conventional means.

The enclosure problem is three-dimensional and consideration of elements and shape functions is important to ensure economical calculation while maintaining required accuracy. Craggs [99] has studied the use of several types of elements including a 32-DOF cuboid element using the pressure and its three first partial derivatives at each corner as the nodal variables, an 8-DOF cuboid with lagrangian (or equivalently, serendipity) shape functions [109, 110] and a 4-DOF tetrahedral element with linear shape function. Petyt, Lea, and Koopmann used a 20-DOF isoparametric cuboid [100], and Craggs considered the isoparametric version of the 8-DOF cuboid [99]. These are all fully three-dimensional elements, although only the tetrahedral element and the isoparametric elements can be used to fit complicated boundaries.

Craggs [99] has presented comparisons of the performance of the 32-DOF "hermitian" element and the 8-DOF and 20-DOF cuboid isoparametric elements for the case of a cuboid enclosure with a single element width- and heightwise and an increasing number lengthwise. The 32-DOF cuboid is impressive in its performance but of limited value since it is not used as isoparametric. The two isoparametric elements are the most useful, and convergence is best with an increasing number of elements for the 20-DOF version; however, one can argue that on the basis of the number of assembled degrees of freedom the 8-DOF version is better.

Petyt, Lea, and Koopmann [100] have made calculations and comparisons with experiment for the 20-DOF isoparametric element in the simulation of the acoustic characteristics of a

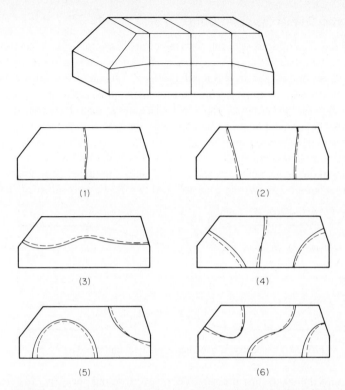

**FIG. 7.1**   Finite-element grid in model van (symmetric with respect to vertical midplane) and first six symmetric and antisymmetric mode-shape nodal curves [100]. (Reproduced by permission of the author and Academic Press.)

light van. For the enclosure shown in Fig. 7.1 a finite-element model with 16 elements was used. Because of the prismatic shape of the van, symmetry arguments can be used to reduce the actual calculations to 8 elements arranged as shown. From the comparison of experiment and theory for the first six symmetric and antisymmetric modes one must conclude that this element performs well in this type of problem. The 8-DOF isoparametric element may also be quite satisfactory. Craggs [99] has tested the 8-DOF and 20-DOF elements in a cylindrical geometry, and if one compares them on the basis of total number of degrees of freedom, the two elements are comparable.

When the enclosure is prismatic (in the shape of a right prism) an analytic solution in the direction of the axis of the prism can be obtained by separation of variables [97, 101]. The problem remaining after this separation is two-dimensional and of a greatly reduced number of degrees of freedom. In connection with this approach examples of the use of triangular 9-DOF elements [97] and triangular 6-DOF elements [101] are available.

In summary, the finite-element method is well suited to problems of resonance in enclosures. The formulation in terms of Hamilton's principle is appropriate and the element choice is not clearly indicated. For high-frequency modes, mesh requirements create dimensionality problems.

## 7.4E Acoustic Transmission in Ducts

Modeling of acoustic transmission in ducts is important in internal-combustion-engine muffler design, noise control in air-handling systems, and noise suppression in turbofan aircraft engines. Problems of this type are governed by Eqs. (7.75) and (7.76) with suitable boundary conditions. In general, the pressure and acoustic particle velocity field in the duct is two- or three-dimensional. However, at suitably low frequencies in ducts with area variations which are not severe the acoustic field can be approximated well with a greatly simplified model which recognizes that the acoustic propagation is in the form of plane waves traveling axially [108]. The governing field equations can be derived directly from the equations of unsteady one-dimensional gas dynamics or from Eq. (7.75) and a modified "one-dimensional" form of Eq. (7.76). Figure 7.2 shows the geometry with which we are concerned. The mean flow

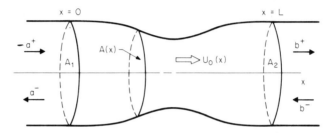

**FIG. 7.2**   Geometry of one-dimensional nonuniform duct.

velocity $U_0$ and the mean flow pressure, density, and sound speed $p_0$, $\rho_0$, $c_0$ are assumed known from the steady one-dimensional gas dynamic equations. The governing field equations are

$$i\eta_r u + U_0 \frac{du}{dx} + u \frac{dU_0}{dx} + \frac{\gamma - 2}{\rho_0^2} \frac{dp_0}{dx} \rho + \frac{c_0^2}{\rho_0} \frac{d\rho}{dx} = 0 \tag{7.83}$$

$$i\eta_r \rho + \frac{1}{A} \frac{d}{dx} (AU_0 \rho + A\rho_0 u) = 0 \tag{7.84}$$

Equations (7.83) and (7.84) are a generalized form of Webster's horn equation with mean flow induced. No wall boundary conditions can be specified so that only hard walls are considered. The required boundary conditions are a combination of a source model and radiation condition at the ends $x = 0$ and $x = 1$ (the nonuniformity length $L$ is the length scale).

At $x = 0$ and $x = 1$, $u$ and $\rho$ are specified as the sum of right- and left-propagating plane waves [94]. Since for plane waves $p = \pm \rho_0 c_0 u$, it follows that at $x = 0$,

$$\left\{ \begin{matrix} \rho \\ u \end{matrix} \right\}_{x=0} = \begin{bmatrix} 1 & 1 \\ \dfrac{c_0}{\rho_0} & -\dfrac{c_0}{\rho_0} \end{bmatrix} \left\{ \begin{matrix} a^+ \\ a^- \end{matrix} \right\} \tag{7.85}$$

and at $x = 1$,
$$\left\{ \begin{matrix} \rho \\ u \end{matrix} \right\}_{x=1} = \begin{bmatrix} 1 & 1 \\ \dfrac{c_0}{\rho_0} & -\dfrac{c_0}{\rho_0} \end{bmatrix} \begin{bmatrix} e^{-ik^+L} & \\ & e^{-ik^-L} \end{bmatrix} \left\{ \begin{matrix} b^+ \\ b^- \end{matrix} \right\} \tag{7.86}$$

where $k^+$ and $k^-$, the axial wave numbers of right-running and left-running plane waves, are given by

$$k^{\pm} L = \frac{\eta_r}{U_0 \pm c_0}$$

and $U_0$, $c_0$ are evaluated at $x = 1$. An infinite duct $x > 1$ corresponds to $b^- = 0$. This is assumed in the following. The source amplitude is given by $a^+$. The reflection coefficient is $R = b^+/a^+$ and the transmission coefficient is $T = a^-/a^+$. The problem is to find the pressure field in $0 \leqslant x \leqslant 1$ and to calculate the reflection coefficient $R$ and transmission coefficient $T$.

This model has been considered in detail by Astley and Eversman [108] to test various aspects of the application of the finite-element method to duct acoustics. While one-dimensional, it retains all features of more complicated problems. In Ref. [108] the weighted-residual method and the residual least-squares method of formulation were tested. Both the Galerkin method and the residual least-squares method were used with three-node lagrangian elements and two-node hermitian elements.

The solution vector is approximated according to

$$\left\{ \begin{matrix} \rho \\ u \end{matrix} \right\} \approx \left\{ \begin{matrix} \tilde{\rho} \\ \tilde{u} \end{matrix} \right\} = \{ \tilde{f} \} = [ N_i \quad N_0 \quad N_1 ] \left\{ \begin{matrix} \delta_i \\ \delta_0 \\ \delta_1 \end{matrix} \right\} \tag{7.87}$$

where $[ N_i \, N_0 \, N_1 ]$ is a global shape-function matrix which implicitly interpolates the solution field in terms of nodal values of $\tilde{p}$ and $\tilde{u}$ (and derivatives for hermitian elements) in the interior, given by the vector $\delta_i$, and nodal values of $\tilde{\rho}$ and $\tilde{u}$ (and derivatives for hermitian elements) at the endpoints of the region ($x = 0$ and $x = 1$), given by the vectors $\delta_0$ and $\delta_1$. If either lagrangian or hermitian elements are used, Eqs. (7.85) and (7.86) allow $\delta_0$ and $\delta_1$ to be represented in the form

$$\delta_0 = \mathbf{T}_0 \mathbf{a} \qquad \delta_1 = \mathbf{T}_1 \mathbf{b} \tag{7.88}$$

where $\mathbf{T}_0$ and $\mathbf{T}_1$ are $2 \times 2$ for lagrangian elements and $4 \times 2$ for hermitian elements. The global shape function is then written

$$\tilde{\mathbf{f}} = [ N_i \quad N_0 T_0 \quad N_1 T_1 ] \left\{ \begin{matrix} \delta_i \\ a \\ b \end{matrix} \right\} = \mathbf{N}' \boldsymbol{\Delta} \tag{7.89}$$

The nodal variables now include interior values of density and velocity (and derivatives for hermitian elements) and modal amplitudes at the end nodes.

Equations (7.83) and (7.84) are written

$$\mathbf{L} \left( \begin{matrix} \boldsymbol{\rho} \\ \mathbf{u} \end{matrix} \right) = \mathbf{0}$$

where $\mathbf{L}$ is a $2 \times 2$ linear matrix differential operation. A conventional application of the finite-element method using the weighted-residual method yields the algebraic equations

$$\mathbf{K}_G \boldsymbol{\Delta} = \mathbf{0} \qquad \text{where} \qquad \mathbf{K}_G = \int_0^1 \mathbf{N}'^T \mathbf{L} \mathbf{N}' A \, dx \tag{7.90}$$

while application of the residual least-squares (RLS) method yields

$$\mathbf{K}_{LS}\mathbf{\Delta} = \mathbf{0} \qquad \text{where} \qquad \mathbf{K}_{LS} = \int_{0}^{1} (\mathbf{N}^{*\prime})^{T}(\mathbf{L}^{*})^{T}\mathbf{L}\mathbf{N}^{\prime}A\, dx \qquad (7.91)$$

In specific solutions some components of $\mathbf{\Delta}$ will be specified (e.g., $a^{+}$ given and $b^{-} = 0$) and will create inhomogeneous terms for the right-hand side of Eqs. (7.90) and (7.91). The corresponding rows are deleted as not representing permissible variations. A complete set of equations for the unknown modal coefficients and internal nodal variables results.

Of particular interest is the performance of the four formulations of the finite-element method. A first test considers the number of degrees of freedom required to achieve a given level of accuracy. A measure of this can be obtained by considering a uniform duct for which an exact solution is known and comparing the computed transmission coefficient $T$ with the exact value. This is done in Figs. 7.3 and 7.4, where the error $\varepsilon$ is defined as the absolute

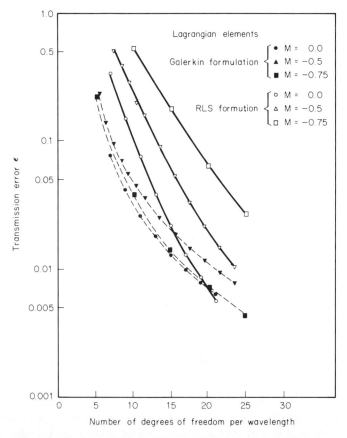

**FIG. 7.3** Error in transmission coefficient for uniform duct with lagrangian elements used in Galerkin and residual-least-squares formulations. Plotted as function of number of degrees of freedom per dependent variable per wavelength.

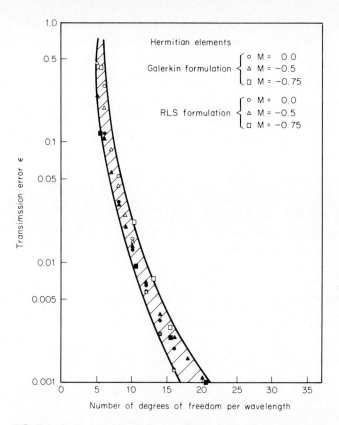

**FIG. 7.4**  Error in transmission coefficient for uniform duct with hermitian elements used in Galerkin and residual-least-squares formulations. Plotted as function of number of degrees of freedom per dependent variable per wavelength.

value of the difference between the computed transmission coefficient $T_c$ and the exact $T_e$,

$$\varepsilon = |T_c - T_e|$$

Three duct-flow Mach numbers, directed toward the source, are considered to effectively alter the number of acoustic wavelengths in the duct length $L$. For $M = 0$, $\lambda/L = 1$; for $M = -0.5$, $\lambda/L = 2$; and for $M = -0.75$, $\lambda/L = 4$. The abscissa of these figures is the number of degrees of freedom per dependent variable (two dependent variables in this problem) per wavelength. This normalization permits comparison of accuracy on the basis of equivalent resolution independent of the effective wavelength. Figure 7.3 shows the error for lagrangian elements, and Fig. 7.4 shows the error for hermitian elements. From Fig. 7.3 it is noted that the lagrangian RLS scheme gives a degeneration of accuracy with increasing Mach number (reduction in wavelength), indicating an undesirable trend toward cumulative errors in the numerical solution. The Galerkin scheme, although showing considerable variation with Mach number, is in fact bounded above (the curve for $M = -0.5$ is close to the upper bound). The lagrangian RLS scheme is judged to be unsatisfactory for this type of problem.

From Fig. 7.4 it is seen that the accuracy is better for both the Galerkin and RLS schemes when hermitian elements are used, and, perhaps most important, the accuracy is nearly unaffected by a change in the Mach number, as all results lie within the shaded band. The conclusion drawn is that hermitian elements are superior if they are judged on the basis of accuracy for a given number of degrees of freedom. With hermitian elements both the Galerkin and RLS schemes perform well. The Galerkin scheme with lagrangian elements is, however, still capable of producing good results. The ease with which isoparametric lagrangian elements in two and three dimensions can be formulated is an important consideration in more complicated problems.

When the duct is nonuniform, there will normally exist regions of relatively low Mach number and regions of high Mach number with the possibility of severe mean flow gradients. There may exist disparate requirements on the finite-element mesh. Failure to meet these requirements may cause local lack of resolution to create inaccuracies throughout the solution region. One expects Galerkin schemes to be particularly susceptible on the basis of the uniform-duct results presented above. This was illustrated in Ref. [108] with numerical results for a converging-diverging duct with the shape of a quartic polynomial with a contraction ratio of 0.5, a nondimensional frequency $\eta_r = 2.16$, an inlet Mach number of $-0.3$, and a throat Mach number of $-0.86$. The effective wavelengths at the inlet and throat are approximately $\lambda/L = 2\pi/3$ and $\lambda/L = 2\pi/15$, respectively.

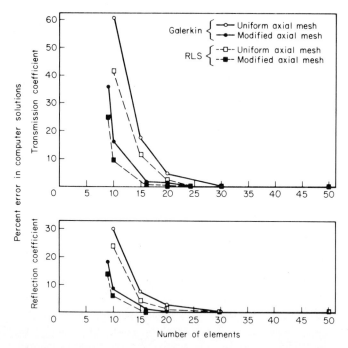

**FIG. 7.5** Convergence trends for the transmission and reflection coefficients for a quartic duct with contraction ratio of 0.5, nondimensional frequency $\eta_r = 2\cdot16$, inlet Mach number $M_1 = -0.3$, and throat Mach number $M_E = -0.86$.

Figure 7.5 shows the convergence of the transmission coefficient and reflection coefficient as a percent error from a final converged value obtained with a large number of elements. Only hermitian elements are used with both the Galerkin and RLS schemes. Two mesh-spacing schemes, always with an equal number of elements, were used. One used equal elements and the second used smaller elements near the throat. It is first noted that convergence occurs much more rapidly with the refined mesh-spacing algorithm. In addition, as expected, the RLS scheme produces a slightly more rapid convergence than the Galerkin scheme, particularly initially.

The following conclusions are drawn in Ref. [108]. The hermitian Galerkin scheme is the most suitable scheme for full-scale implementation. The hermitian RLS scheme, shown to be of comparable accuracy in the cases cited here, exhibits a slight tendency to cumulative errors (see Ref. [108] for more details). Both lagrangian element schemes are inferior to the hermitian schemes. This is particularly true of the lagrangian RLS scheme.

## 7.5 FINITE ELEMENTS FOR ELECTRIC AND MAGNETIC FIELDS

Partial differential equations (PDEs) occur in modeling electromagnetic and electrostatic field problems [111–113], fluid flow [114], heat transfer [115], structural and continuum mechanics [116], and other boundary-value problems. The techniques that are in vogue for solving these equations satisfying specified boundary conditions are (1) closed-form (analytical) solutions [117], (2) analog methods [118], and (3) numerical techniques [119–121].

The finite-element method [122] is a numerical technique for solving boundary-value problems. In this method, the partial differential equations modeling the field are transformed into energy-related expressions called *functionals*. Approximate solutions to the field problem are then sought which extremize (or minimize) these functionals. By this procedure, a detailed modeling of the solution is possible and results can be obtained within the desired limits of accuracy. Alternative procedures such as the weighted-residual or the weak Galerkin formulation [123] are also possible. The present discussion will, however, be restricted to the variational form only.

The advantages of the finite-element method are that the technique is versatile and flexible for modeling complex geometries, yields accurate and stable solutions, incorporates the natural boundary conditions within the functional formulation, and is well suited to handling material nonlinearities and eddy currents.

### 7.5A The Finite-Element Procedure

The steps involved in the solution of electric and magnetic field problems by the finite-element method are as follows:

1. Define the boundary-value problems by a partial differential equation or a set of equations.
2. Obtain a variational formulation for the PDE in terms of an energy-related expression called the functional.
3. Subdivide the field region into subregions (finite elements).

4. Choose a trial solution in terms of nodal values of the potential weighted by interpolation functions.

5. Minimize the functional with respect to each of the nodal potentials.

6. Solve the algebraic equations.

7. Convert the potential solution to useful design parameters.

The general expression for an energy-related functional for the partial differential equation representing the field distribution

$$\mathbf{D}\mathbf{A} = \mathbf{f} \tag{7.92}$$

is given by

$$F = \int_v [\mathbf{A}^T \mathbf{D}\mathbf{A} - 2\mathbf{A}^T \mathbf{f}]\, dv \tag{7.93}$$

## 7.5B Some Partial Differential Equations and Their Functionals

In the following sections, some partial differential equations for electric and magnetic field problems and their respective variational formulations in terms of energy-related functional expressions are described.

*Scalar Poisson Equation*   For magnetostatic fields, where time-varying fields are absent, the current density and the vector potential are related by

$$\nu \nabla^2 \mathbf{A} = -\mathbf{J} \tag{7.94}$$

where $\mathbf{A}$ = a single component vector directed along the $z$-direction
$J$ = the time-invariant source current density ($z$-directed)
$\nu$ = the inverse permeability, which may be both position- and field-dependent

The associated functional expression will be of the form

$$F = \frac{\nu}{2} \int_v (\text{grad } \mathbf{A})^2 \, dv - \int_v \mathbf{J} \cdot \mathbf{A} \, dv - \oint_s A \, \text{grad } \mathbf{A} \cdot \mathbf{ds} \tag{7.95}$$

Similar expressions to the above may be obtained for electrostatic field problems in terms of a scalar-potential function in place of the single-component vector function $\mathbf{A}$, and a volumetric charge density in place of the current density $J$. Otherwise, the formulation of the differential equation and the functional expression are the same as for Eqs. (7.94) and (7.95), respectively.

*Eddy-Current Diffusion Equation*   The steady-state linear diffusion equation defined in terms of a single-component vector potential $\mathbf{A}$, with the source and response functions assumed to be periodic in time, may be expressed by

$$\nu \nabla^2 \mathbf{A} = j\omega\sigma\mathbf{A} - \mathbf{J} \tag{7.96}$$

The relevant functional expression for this problem is given by

$$F = \frac{\nu}{2}\int_\Omega |\nabla A|^2 \, d\Omega + \frac{j\omega\sigma}{2}\int_\Omega \mathbf{A}^2 \, d\Omega - \int_\Omega \mathbf{J} \cdot \mathbf{A} \, d\Omega - \oint_s A \, \text{grad} \, \mathbf{A} \cdot \mathbf{ds} \qquad (7.97)$$

***Curl Curl Equations for Vector Field Problems***   The magnetostatic field problem with time-invariant fields and sources may be described by the curl curl equation in terms of a generalized vector-potential function $A$ such that

$$\nabla \times \nu \, \nabla \times \mathbf{A} = \mathbf{J} \qquad (7.98)$$

The energy-related functional expression for (7.98) is given by

$$F = \frac{\nu}{2}\int_v (\text{curl } \mathbf{A})^2 \, dv - \int_v \mathbf{J} \cdot \mathbf{A} \, dv - \oint_s \mathbf{A} \times \nu \, \text{curl } \mathbf{A} \cdot \mathbf{ds} \qquad (7.99)$$

***Scalar Helmholtz Equation***   Many homogeneous waveguide problems require a scalar Helmholtz equation to be solved in terms of a scalar-potential function of the form

$$(\nabla^2 + \lambda^2)\phi = 0 \qquad (7.100)$$

where $\lambda$ is the wave number and $\phi$ is the scalar-potential function. The related functional expression is given by

$$F = \frac{1}{2}\int\int (|\text{grad } \phi|^2 - \lambda^2\phi^2) \, dx \, dy - \oint_s \phi \, \text{grad } \boldsymbol{\phi} \cdot \mathbf{ds} \qquad (7.101)$$

## 7.5c  Approximate Field Solution and Functional Minimization

Subdividing the field region into triangular elements, one may define the approximate solution in a typical element with nodes $i, j, m$ in terms of the nodal values of the unknown potential and weighting functions such that

$$\mathbf{A} = \Sigma \zeta_k A_k \qquad (7.102a)$$

or

$$\phi = \Sigma \zeta_k \phi_k \qquad (7.102b)$$

where $\zeta_k$ is the weighting function. For first-order triangular finite elements, the weighting functions will be of the form

$$\zeta_k = \frac{a_k + b_k x + c_k y}{2\Delta} \qquad k = i, j, \text{ or } m \qquad (7.103)$$

where

$$a_k = x_j y_m - x_m y_j$$

$$b_k = y_j - y_m$$

$$c_k = x_m - x_j \qquad \text{in cyclic modulo 3}$$

$$\Delta = \text{triangle area}$$

From variational calculus [124], it is known that the approximate solution which renders the functional stationary is the required solution to the field problem. This is achieved by setting the first derivative of the functional with respect to each of the nodal potentials to zero. Formally this is described as

$$\frac{\partial F}{\partial A_k} = 0 \quad \text{or} \quad \frac{\partial F}{\partial \phi_k} = 0 \tag{7.104}$$

When this procedure is carried over all the finite elements and the resulting element matrices are appropriately combined, a global-matrix equation results, of the form

$$\mathbf{SA} = \mathbf{R} \quad \text{or} \quad \mathbf{S\phi} = \mathbf{T} \tag{7.105}$$

where $\mathbf{S}$ = the stiffness or coefficient matrix, which may be
          linear or nonlinear depending upon the material characteristics
          associated with each finite-element region
$\mathbf{A}$ and $\mathbf{\phi}$ = potential functions
$\mathbf{R}$ and $\mathbf{T}$ = forcing functions

It must be noted that in the functional minimization process described above, one sets the boundary integrals of Eqs. (7.95), (7.97), (7.99), and (7.100) to zero. This implies that Dirichlet (applied-potential) boundary conditions or homogeneous Neumann (flux-normal) boundary conditions are specified in the problem. If the boundary conditions are other than these, then they must be explicitly included in the analysis.

## 7.5D Applications to Electrical Machinery and Devices

The efficacy of the finite-element method is now illustrated by selected two- and three-dimensional applications. These include the nonlinear field distribution in electrical machine cross sections, eddy-current analysis for nondestructive evaluation of flaws in metallic objects, electrostatic applications, modeling of permanent-magnet machines, and the analysis of a homogeneous waveguide. This list of applications is by no means comprehensive or complete, and each item must be regarded only as an illustration of the method.

*Nonlinear Field Distribution in Electrical Machinery*   A general topologically unrestricted variational formulation of the electromagnetic field problem in electrical machines has been given in Refs. [125–131]. The nonlinear partial differential equation (7.94) which defines the field problem, when specialized to two dimensions, yields

$$\frac{\partial}{\partial x}\left(\nu\frac{\partial \mathbf{A}}{\partial x}\right) + \frac{\partial}{\partial y}\left(\nu\frac{\partial \mathbf{A}}{\partial y}\right) = -\mathbf{J} \tag{7.106}$$

The corresponding functional of (7.95) may also be specialized to this case, so that

$$F = \iint\left(\int_0^B \nu B\, dB - \mathbf{J}\cdot\mathbf{A}\right) dx\, dy - \oint \mathbf{A}\cdot\frac{\partial \mathbf{A}}{\partial n}\, ds \tag{7.107}$$

where the flux density

$$B = \sqrt{\left(\frac{\partial A}{\partial x}\right)^2 + \left(\frac{\partial A}{\partial y}\right)^2} \qquad (7.108)$$

Minimization of (7.107) with respect to the nodal potentials of a first-order triangular element yields

$$\frac{\partial F}{\partial A_K}\bigg|_{k=i,j,m} = \sum_{k=i}^{m} \sum_{l=i}^{m} (b_k b_l + C_k C_l)A_K - J\left(\frac{\partial A}{\partial A_K}\right) = 0 \qquad (7.109)$$

When the procedure described in (7.109) is carried over all triangles in the region, one obtains the global-matrix equation

$$\mathbf{SA} = \mathbf{T} \qquad (7.110)$$

Matrix **S** is a nonlinear, symmetric, sparse, and band-structured. The nonlinear equation (7.110) must, therefore, be quasi-linearized by a Newton-Raphson (N-R) algorithm, and the resulting set of equations solved by a direct or iterative procedure. Each nonlinear iteration updates the reluctivity with respect to the B-H magnetization characteristic of the material. The N-R algorithm and the solution of the linearized equations described in Ref. [125] are as follows.

The $k^{\text{th}}$ iterate of the vector potential yields the $(k+1)^{\text{th}}$ iterate, following the relation

$$A^{k+1} = A^k - [\mathscr{J}]^{-1} \cdot [S \cdot A^k - T] \qquad (7.111)$$

where $[\mathscr{J}]$ is the jacobian matrix of partial derivatives of the iteration function

$$[S \cdot A^k - T] \qquad (7.112)$$

The set of linearized equations resulting from Eq. (7.111) reduces to a matrix equation, whose coefficient or stiffness matrix is also sparse, symmetric, and band-structured. Gaussian elimination [132] or the preconditioned conjugate-gradient method [133] may be employed to yield a stable, accurate, and speedy solution.

The B-H characteristic is usually modeled by cubic-spline interpolation [134] to ensure slope continuity. This has general applications to material characteristics in different regions and is more accurate than the simple piecewise linear interpolation technique.

Figure 7.6 shows the magnetic field plot obtained in Ref. [112] for a 50 MVA turbine generator on load. The solution obtained for a four-pole dc machine on load is described in Ref. [135]. It must be noted that the flux distribution in both the aforesaid cases are nonsymmetric about the direct or quadrature axis. The representation of this magnetic state is accomplished by applying a "periodic boundary condition" to the field problem. This boundary condition is based on the fact that the flux entering one pole leaves the other and, therefore, the vector potentials along the axis of the first pole are equal but of opposite sign to that of the next.

Application of the nonlinear analysis to a quarter section of a single-phase transformer is described in Ref. [125]. From the resulting vector-potential solution, the voltage induced in the winding is evaluated from energy considerations. The results of this analysis were compared with search-coil test data, and the waveform of the magnetizing current was estimated and compared against the test data.

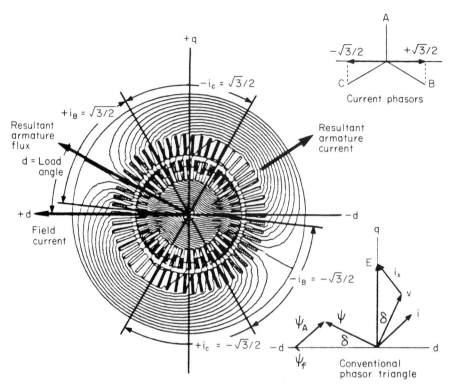

**FIG. 7.6**  Magnetic field plot for a 50-MVA turbine generator on load.

***Analysis of the Steady-State Eddy-Current Diffusion Problem***  The governing partial differential equation and functional expression shown in Eqs. (7.96) and (7.97) specialized to the two-dimensional cartesian system yield the following, as described in Refs. [136] and [137].

$$\frac{\partial^2 A}{\partial x^2} + \frac{\partial^2 A}{\partial y^2} = \frac{j\omega\mu\mu_0 A}{p} - J_s \tag{7.113}$$

$$F = \int\int \frac{1}{2}\left[\left(\frac{\partial A}{\partial x}\right)^2 + \left(\frac{\partial A}{\partial y}\right)^2\right] dx\,dy + \frac{j\omega\mu\mu_0}{2\rho}\int\int A^2\,dx\,dy - \int\int J_s \cdot A\,dx\,dy \tag{7.114}$$

Minimization of (7.114) for first-order triangular elements leads to a complex matrix equation

$$SA + CA = T \tag{7.115}$$

The application of the steady-state diffusion-equation solution described above to the nondestructive evaluation of a crack in a bar of aluminum is illustrated in Fig. 7.7a and b.

Another application of the steady-state eddy-current diffusion method to a utility generator for obtaining its operational impedances was described in Ref. [138]. The flux plots obtained at a 0.1-Hz frequency of the excitation current were also illustrated.

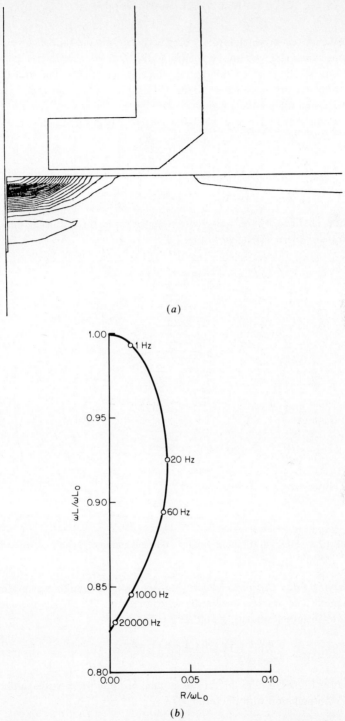

(a)

(b)

**FIG. 7.7** (*a*) Eddy-current distribution in a bar of aluminum with a crack. (*b*) Normalized impedance plane diagram for a bar of aluminum with a crack.

The skin-effect problem which involves both eddy-current and source-current distribution in a power-line conductor was solved in Ref. [139] by an integrodifferential formulation. This formulation results from combining the diffusion equation (7.96) with the constraint condition that the integral of the current-density distribution in the conductor yields the total current $I$. The partial differential equation describing the steady-state skin-effect problem in terms of the vector potential $A$ and the source current $I$ is given as

$$\nu \nabla^2 \mathbf{A} - j\omega\sigma \mathbf{A} = -\frac{I + j\omega\sigma \displaystyle\iint \mathbf{A} \cdot \mathbf{ds}}{\displaystyle\iint ds} \qquad (7.116)$$

The solution obtained by the weighted-residual method for a transmission-line bundle conductor arrangement is illustrated in Fig. 7.8.

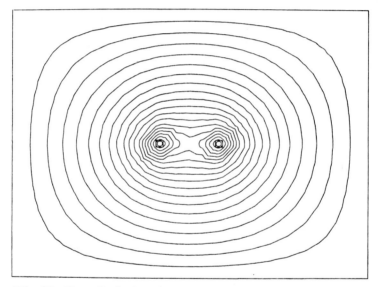

**FIG. 7.8** Flux distribution for a transmission-line bundle conductor arrangement.

**The Time-Varying Eddy-Current Problem**   In Ref. [140], a solution was presented for the saturated magnetic field problem in a linear induction motor. The partial differential equation was modified to include a velocity $V$ so that

$$\frac{\partial}{\partial x}\left(\frac{1}{\mu}\frac{\partial A}{\partial x}\right) + \frac{\partial}{\partial y}\left(\frac{1}{\mu}\frac{\partial A}{\partial y}\right) = \frac{1}{\rho}\left(\frac{\partial A}{\partial t} + V\frac{\partial A}{\partial x}\right) \qquad (7.117)$$

An alternative formulation to the functional minimization process was applied using the weak Galerkin formulation with the result

$$\int_\Omega \left(\frac{\partial A}{\partial t} + V\frac{\partial A}{\partial x}\right)\phi(x, y)\, dx\, dy + \int_\Omega \rho\nu\left(\frac{\partial A}{\partial x}\cdot\frac{\partial W}{\partial x} + \frac{\partial A}{\partial y}\cdot\frac{\partial W}{\partial y}\right) dx\, dy = 0 \qquad (7.118)$$

where $\phi$ is required to vanish wherever essential boundary conditions apply on $A$ on the boundary. Substituting the finite-element approximation on $A$ in (7.118) yields the time-dependent matrix equation

$$\mathbf{M}\frac{d}{dt}\mathbf{A}+\mathbf{NA}=0 \tag{7.119}$$

which is solved by a time-integration technique.

*A Two-Dimensional Microwave Application*   In the previous sections, finite-element analysis of dc and low-frequency problems were illustrated. The first application of the finite-element procedure to a homogeneous waveguide problem was described in Ref. [141].

In the design of microwave devices, it is desirable to employ waveguides with arbitrarily shaped cross sections (often, other than rectangular, circular, or elliptic cross sections). To analyze the behavior of such devices, one needs to solve the eigenvalue problem of the scalar Helmholtz equation described in Eq. (7.100), subject to homogeneous Dirichlet or Neumann-type boundary conditions as described previously. The functional for this PDE is given by Eq. (7.101). Discretization of the field region into finite elements with functional minimization as earlier described yields the matrix equation

$$\mathbf{S}\boldsymbol{\phi} = k^2\mathbf{T}\boldsymbol{\phi} \tag{7.120}$$

The solution of Eq. (7.120) obained for a T-septate-vaned rectangular waveguide is illustrated by the dominant odd-symmetry H-mode in the above reference.

## 7.5E  Three-Dimensional Finite-Element Solution

In the following section, three-dimensional applications of the electrostatic and magnetic field problems will be illustrated. These include both scalar and vector solutions obtained for sample problems.

*The Electrostatic Problem*   Steady-state electrostatic fields may be described by the three-dimensional scalar Poisson equation in terms of potential function $V$, the volumetric charge density $\rho$, and permittivities $\nu_x$, $\nu_y$, $\nu_z$:

$$\nu_x\frac{\partial^2 V}{\partial x^2}+\nu_y\frac{\partial^2 V}{\partial y^2}+\nu_z\frac{\partial^2 V}{\partial z^2}=\rho \tag{7.121}$$

The functional expression for Eq. (7.123) is of the form

$$F=\int_{\text{vol}}\left(\frac{\nu}{2}|\nabla V|^2+\rho V\right)d\,\text{vol} \tag{7.122}$$

One may consider first-order triangular-prism elements shown in Ref. [143] for the description of the field region. The approximation to the potential solution may then be expressed as a linear combination of unknown nodal potentials weighted by interpolation functions $\zeta_k$ such that

$$v = \sum_{k=1,2,\ldots,n} \zeta_k v_k \tag{7.123}$$

where

$$\zeta_k = \lambda_k \left( \frac{1 + p\tau}{2} \right) \tag{7.124}$$

with $k = 1, 2, \ldots, 6$ (nodes)

$p = 1$, for $k = 1, 2, 3$

$p = -1$, for $k = 4, 5, 6$

and $\lambda_k$ are the area coordinates defined by Eq. (7.103). Once the field solution is obtained by the functional minimization process, the electric field is obtained from the relationship

$$\mathbf{E} = -\text{grad } V \tag{7.125}$$

The application of this solution to an octant of a single-phase transformer for the evaluation of the electric field distribution is shown in Fig. 7.9. From this solution, one may determine the capacitance $C$ of the device from the energy due to the electrostatic field.

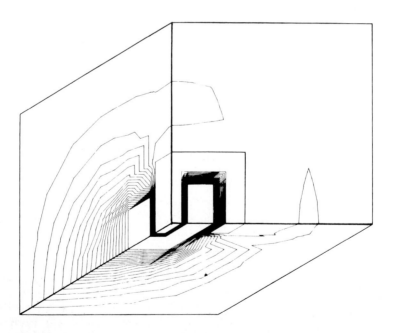

**FIG. 7.9** Electrostatic-potential distribution in a three-dimensional slice of a single-phase transformer.

The energy stored in the system is first computed following the relation

$$w = \tfrac{1}{2}\mathbf{V}^T\mathbf{S}\mathbf{V} \tag{7.126}$$

Also the energy is related to the capacitance by the integral expression

$$w = \tfrac{1}{2}\int_{\text{vol}} CV^2 \, d \text{ vol} \tag{7.127}$$

If Eqs. (7.128) and (7.129) are combined, the capacitance is obtained as

$$C = \frac{\mathbf{V}^T\mathbf{S}\mathbf{V}}{\mathbf{V}^T\mathbf{V}} \tag{7.128}$$

**Permanent-Magnet Device Analysis**   It is convenient to choose a scalar-potential function for solving permanent-magnet fields which satisfies the relationship between the magnetic field $H$ and the potential function such that

$$\mathbf{H} = -\text{grad } \phi \tag{7.129}$$

Using the relationships $\qquad \text{div } \mathbf{B} = 0 \qquad \mathbf{B} = \mu_r \mu_0 \mathbf{H} \tag{7.130}$

the differential equation, the corresponding functional, and the expression for its minimization are obtained by substituting $\phi$ for $A$ and the divergence of the magnetic moment $M_0$ (the intrinsic magnetization in the preferred direction) in Eqs. (7.94) and (7.95) so that

$$\text{div } \frac{1}{\nu} \text{ grad } \phi - \text{div } \frac{\nu}{\nu_0}\mathbf{M}_0 = 0 \tag{7.131}$$

$$F = \int \frac{1}{\nu}(\text{grad } \phi)^2 \, dv - 2\int \phi \frac{\nu}{\nu_0}\mathbf{M}_0 \cdot \mathbf{ds} \tag{7.132}$$

$$\frac{\partial F}{\partial \phi_k} = \int \frac{1}{\nu} \text{ grad } \zeta_k \cdot \text{grad } \zeta_1 \, dv - \int \zeta_k \frac{\nu}{\nu_0}\mathbf{M}_0 \cdot \mathbf{ds} \tag{7.133}$$

It may be noted that the divergence of $\mathbf{M}_0$ in the magnet is zero in the entire volume except on the magnet edges, say, along the $y$ direction. The details of this derivation have been shown in Ref. [142]. Equation (7.133) yields a set of nonlinear equations for each element, and when the element contributions are added together, a global-matrix equation is obtained of the form

$$\mathbf{S}\boldsymbol{\phi} = \mathbf{0} \tag{7.134}$$

The above magnetic scalar potential solution was applied to determine the flux distribution in the pole of a disk-type permanent-magnet dc motor. The vector plot of flux densities and the comparison of numerical values obtained with test results are illustrated in Fig. 7.10$a$ and $b$.

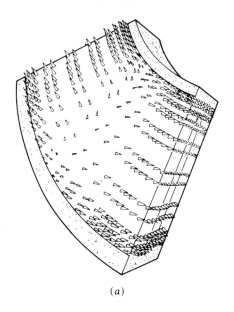

(a)

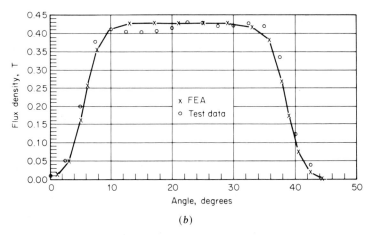

(b)

**FIG. 7.10**  (a) Vector plot of flux densities in the pole of a disk-type permanent magnet dc motor. (b) Comparison of computed flux densities with test results in the pole of a disk-type permanent magnet dc motor.

**Application of the Curl Curl Equation**   In many machinery applications, the scalar-potential solution described in the previous section is not convenient, since currents can only be represented indirectly. This may be observed from the following.

If we substitute for $H$ the gradient of a scalar-potential function of Eq. (7.1.29) in the first Maxwell's equation

$$\operatorname{curl} \mathbf{H} = \mathbf{J}_s \tag{7.135}$$

it is seen that an inconsistency arises, since

$$\text{curl } \mathbf{H} = \text{curl } (-\text{grad } \phi) = 0 \tag{7.136}$$

Equation (7.136) indicates that the scalar representation of the magnetic field $H$ does not hold in the source-current region. Therefore, source currents must be expressed by a line- or surface-current density in terms of the discontinuity of the tangential component of the magnetic field at the interface. Thus

$$\mathbf{H}_{t1} - \mathbf{H}_{t2} = \mathbf{J} \tag{7.137}$$

Equation (7.137) implies that the source current can only be expressed as a current sheet. In a practical electric machine, however, current-carrying conductors are discrete and are embedded in iron slots. Therefore a scalar representation is not only inconvenient but also inaccurate. In such cases, a vector representation of the field in terms of the curl curl equation (7.98) is most appropriate. If the functional of (7.99) is minimized in the three-dimensional region and the resulting set of equations is solved, one obtains the required vector-potential solution to the field problem. Such a procedure was applied to the determination of flux densities in a laboratory model of an air-gap winding generator. The equipotential plot of $A$ and comparison of calculated and tested values of flux densities are shown on the next page in Fig. 7.11$a$ and $b$, respectively.

## 7.5F Hybrid Finite-Element Methods

Since complete scalar solutions are not always suitable for modeling electromagnetic field problems with source currents, owing to the requirement of thin-sheet representation of sources, vector-potential solutions had become attractive. However, total vector-potential solutions are not only cumbersome, but expensive to implement in practical field geometries of electrical apparatus. This had spurred interest in hybrid techniques which couple the scalar and vector solutions. The first of these methods is the so-called reduced-scalar-potential method described in Ref. [144]. The second is the integral-equation technique [145]. The third method described is the $T$ omega method [146].

Practical magnetic field problems usually involve current sources, so that it is convenient to express the total field $H$ as the sum of the field due to the sources, $H_s$, and the field due to the induced magnetization, $H_m$, so that

$$\mathbf{H} = \mathbf{H}_m + \mathbf{H}_s \tag{7.138}$$

Since curl $\mathbf{H}_m = 0$, a scalar potential can be introduced such that

$$\mathbf{H}_m = -\text{grad } \phi \tag{7.139}$$

Also since
$$\text{div } \mathbf{B} = 0 \tag{7.140}$$

and
$$\mathbf{B} = \mu_r \mu_0 \mathbf{H} \tag{7.141}$$

one obtains, by combining Eqs. (7.138) through (7.142), the nonlinear partial differential

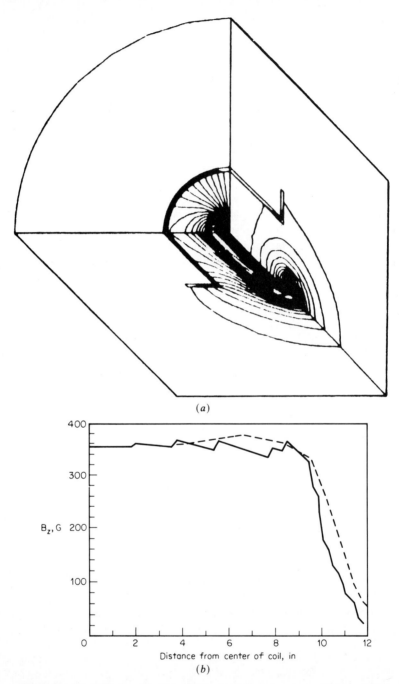

(a)

B_z, G

Distance from center of coil, in

(b)

**FIG. 7.11** (a) Equipotential plot of the magnetic vector potential in a three-dimensional model of an air-gap winding generator. (b) Comparison of calculated and measured flux densities in a three-dimensional model of an air-gap winding generator.

3.390

equation of the Poisson type

$$\text{div } \mu \text{ grad } \phi = \text{div } \mu \, H_s \tag{7.142}$$

The potential $\phi$ is subject to the boundary condition $\phi = 0$ at infinity and satisfies the continuity conditions

$$\phi_1 = \phi_2 \tag{7.143}$$

$$\mu_1 \left( \frac{\partial \phi}{\partial n} \right)_1 - \mu_2 \left( \frac{\partial \phi}{\partial n} \right)_2 = (\mu_1 - \mu_2) H_s \tag{7.144}$$

at the interface between two regions of different materials.

The above method is the basis for both the differential form of finite-element representation and the integral formulation as described in Refs. [144] and [145], respectively.

***Integral-Equation Solution***   The method described in this section using an integral-equation formulation is based on the reduced-scalar-potential technique described in the previous section.

If a magnetization vector **M** is defined such that

$$\mathbf{M} = \frac{1}{\mu_0} \mathbf{B} - \mathbf{H} = \chi(\mathbf{H})\mathbf{H} \tag{7.145}$$

where $\chi$ is the susceptibility, then we can evaluate the scalar-potential function $\phi$ of (7.139) in terms of this magnetization, and finally evaluate $H_m$. The scalar-potential function $\phi$ may be expressed by the integral relations

$$\phi = \frac{1}{4\pi} \int_{v'} M(r') \text{ grad } \frac{1}{r - r'} \, dv' \tag{7.146}$$

where $r$ and $r'$ are position vectors of the field and source points, respectively. The integration of Eq. (7.146) is taken over the volume of all iron regions present in the problem. The component of $H$ derived from the sources, namely, $H_s$ in Eq. (7.138), may be evaluated from the source-current density $J$ using the Biot–Savart law. Therefore,

$$\mathbf{H}_s = \frac{1}{4\pi} \int \frac{\mathbf{J} \times (r - r')}{|r - r'|^3} \, dv' \tag{7.147}$$

The integral for the unknown magnetization in (7.147) is then obtained by combining (7.139), (7.145), (7.146), and (7.147), which after some algebraic manipulation yields

$$M(r) = \chi(r) \left[ H_0(r) - \frac{1}{4\pi} \text{ grad } \int_{v'} M(r') \text{ grad } \frac{1}{|r - r'|} \, dv' \right] \tag{7.148}$$

The kernels in the integral equation may be modeled by pulse functions, or Green's functions in the traditional finite-element manner, described in Ref. [145].

***The T-Omega Method***   With the *T*-omega method a gauge is defined on the magnetic field *H* in terms of a vector **T** and a scalar-potential function $\Omega$ such that

$$\mathbf{H} = \mathbf{T} - \text{grad } \Omega \tag{7.149}$$

The $\Omega$ in this formulation is not related to the magnetic scalar potential in any way, and is defined by the zero divergence on *H* only. Thus one obtains

$$\text{div } \mathbf{B} = \text{div } \mu(\mathbf{T} - \text{grad } \Omega) = 0 \tag{7.150}$$

Also the vector **T** is related to the source-current density such that

$$\mathbf{J} = \text{curl } \mathbf{T} \tag{7.151}$$

It is evident that the choice of *T* is not unique and, therefore, other constraint conditions must be imposed to obtain a unique solution to the field problem. For the case of a finite-length solenoid or for a single coil of arbitrary cross section, the choice of *T* is simple and can be expressed as ampere turns per unit height of coil. If the core of the solenoid is air or consists

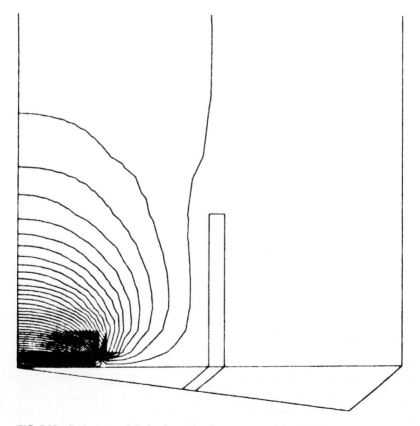

**FIG. 7.12**   Scalar-potential plot for a circular current-carrying conductor.

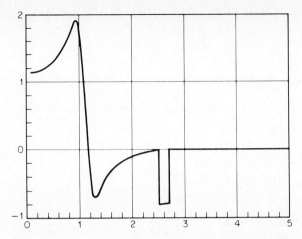

**FIG. 7.13** Comparison of the axial flux density along the x-direction for circular coil obtained by the T-omega method with a finite element axisymmetric solution.

of nonmagnetic material, $T$ and grad $\Omega$ are separable. The functional expression for the differential equation (7.150) is then obtained as

$$F = \int_v \mu (\mathrm{grad}\,\Omega)^2\, dv - \int_v \bar{T} \cdot \mu\, \mathrm{grad}\,\Omega\, dv + \oint_s \mu \Omega (T - \mathrm{grad}\,\Omega) \cdot \overline{ds} \qquad (7.152)$$

The solution obtained by the $T$-omega method for a single circular conductor is shown by the scalar plot of Fig. 7.12. The comparison of the axial flux density along the x-direction for this conductor with a finite-element axisymmetric solution is illustrated in Fig. 7.13.

## 7.6 REFERENCES

1. Finlayson, B. A., "Orthogonal Collocation in Chemical Reaction Engineering," *Cat. Rev. Sci. Eng.*, **10**:69–138 (1974).

2. Frank-Kamenetskii, D. A., *Diffusion and Heat Transfer in Chemical Kinetics*, Plenum Press, New York, 1969.

3. Finlayson, B. A., *The Method of Weighted Residuals and Variational Principles*, Academic Press, New York, 1972.

4. Cavendish, J. C., and S. H. Oh, "A Computationally Efficient Galerkin Technique for Approximating Transient Diffusion-Reaction Equations in Composite Media," *Chem. Eng. J.*, **17**:41–54 (1979).

5. Anderson, C. A., and O. C. Zienkiewicz, "Spontaneous Ignition: Finite Element Solutions for Steady and Transient Conditions," *Trans. ASME J. Heat. Transfer*, **96**:398–404 (1974).

6. Chan, T. F. C., and H. B. Keller, "Arc-Length Continuation and Multi-Grid Techniques for Nonlinear Elliptic Eigenvalue Problems," *SIAM J. Sci. Stat. Comput.*, **3**:173–194 (1982).

7. Carey, G. F., and B. A. Finlayson, "Orthogonal Collocation on Finite Elements," *Chem. Eng. Sci.*, **30**:587–596 (1975).

8. Finlayson, B. A., *Nonlinear Analysis in Chemical Engineering*, McGraw-Hill, New York, 1980.

9. Carey, G. F., D. Humphrey, and M. F. Wheeler, "Galerkin and Collocation-Galerkin Methods with Superconvergence and Optimal Fluxes," *Int. J. Numer. Meth. Eng.*, **17**:939–950 (1981).

10. Case, K. M., F. de Hoffman, and G. Placzek, "Introduction to the Theory of Neutron Diffusion", U.S. Government Printing Office, Washington, D.C., 1953.

11. Henry, A. F., "Refinements in Accuracy of Coarse Mesh Finite Difference Solution of the Group Diffusion Equations," IAEA/SM-154/21, *Seminar on Numerical Reactor Calculations*, Vienna, 1972.

12. Duderstadt, J. J., and W. R. Martin, *Transport Theory*, Wiley, New York, 1979.

13. Sanchez, R., and N. J. McCormic, "A Review of Neutron Transport Approximations," *Nucl. Sci. Eng.*, **80**:481 (1982).

14. Onishi, T., "Application of the Finite Element Solution Technique to the Neutron Diffusion and Transport Equations," *Proceedings of the Conference on New Developments in Reactor Mathematics and Application*, Idaho Falls, March 1971.

15. Semenza, L. A., E. E. Lewis, and B. C. Rossow, "The Application of the FEM to the Multigroup Diffusion Equation," *Nucl. Sci. Eng.*, **47**:302 (1972).

16. Kaper, H. G., G. K. Leaf, and A. J. Lindeman, "Application of Finite Element Methods in Reactor Mathematics: Numerical Solution of the Neutron Diffusion Equation," USAEC Rep. ANL-7925, Argonne Nat. Lab., Argonne, Illinois, 1972.

17. Kang, C. M., and K. F. Hansen, "Finite Element Methods for Reactor Analysis," *Nucl. Sci. Eng.*, **51**:456 (1972).

18. Franke, H. P., and F. A. R. Schmidt, "FEM2D, ein Program zur Lösung der zweidimensionalen Diffusionsgleichung nach der Methode der Finiten Elemente," IKE 4-25, Institut für Kernenergetik und Energiesysteme, Universität Stuttgart, 1974. (See also Franke, H. P. and F. A. R. Schmidt, "FEM2D, a Program for Solving the Two-Dimensional Diffusion Equation by The Method of Finite Elements," NTIS-ORNL-TR-2971, July, 1974.)

19. Kavenoky, A., "NEPTUNE: A Modular System for the Calculation of Light Water Reactors," *Conf. 750413*, Charleston, 1975, vol. II, p. V-27.

20. Rühle, R., "RSYST, ein integriertes Modulsystem mit Datenbasis zur automatisierten Berechnung von Kernreaktoren," IKE 4-12, Institut für Kernenergetik und Energiesysteme, Universität Stuttgart, 1972.

21. "AMPX-II, Modular Code System for Generating Coupled Multigroup Neutron-Gamma-Ray Cross Section Libraries from Data in ENDF Format," Radiation Shielding Information Center PSR-63, Dept. of Nuclear Engineering, Pennsylvania State University, State College, Pennsylvania, 1978.

22. Vondy, D. R., T. B. Fowler, and G. W. Cunningham, III, "The BOLD VENTURE Computation System for Nuclear Reactor Core Analysis," Version III, ORNL-5711, Oak Ridge National Laboratory, Oak Ridge, Tenn., 1981.

23. Pfeifer, C. J., "PDQ-7 Reference Manual II," USAEC WAPD-TM-947 (L), Bettis Atomic Power Lab., Westinghouse Electric Corp., Pittsburgh, Pennsylvania, 1971.

24. Engle, W. W., Jr., "ANISN, A One-Dimensional Discrete Ordinates Transport Code with Anisotropic Scattering," K-1693, Oak Ridge Gaseous Diffusion Plant, Oak Ridge, Tennessee, March 1967.

25. Rhoades, W. A., et al., "The DOT IV Twodimensional Discrete Ordinates Transport Code with Space-Dependent Mesh and Quadrature," ORNL-TM-6529, Oak Ridge National Laboratory, Oak Ridge, Tenn., 1979.

26. Finnemann, H., "Nodal Expansion Method for the Analysis of Space-time Effects in LWRs," *NEACRP Specialist's Meeting on Calculation of 3D Rating Distributions in Operating Reactors*, Paris, November 1979.

27. Kavenoky, A., and J. Lautard, "A Finite Element Depletion Diffusion Calculation Method with Space-Dependent Cross Sections," *Nucl. Sci. Eng.*, **64**:563 (1977).

28. Schmidt, F., and R. Fremd, "Experience in Using the Finite Element Method for Reactor Calculations," in M. M. R. Williams and A. J. H. Goddard (eds.), *Finite Element Methods in Radiation Physics, Ann. Nucl. Energy,* **8**(11/12) (1981).

**Selected Papers on Diffusion Theory**
a. Schmidt, F., and R. Fremd, "Experience in Using the Finite Element Method for Reactor Calculations."
b. Grenfell, D. T., "The Application of the Finite Element Method to the Solution of Radiation-Shielding Problems."
c. Estiot, J. C., D. Honde, G. Palmiotti, and M. Salvatores, "Comparison of Finite Differences and Finite Elements in the Case of a Large Fast Power Reactor."

**Selected Papers on Transport Theory**
d. Ackroyd, R. T., "The Why and How of Finite Elements."
e. Martin, W. R., et al., "Phase-Space Finite Element Methods Applied to the First-Order Form of the Transport Equation."
f. Mordant, M., "Some Efficient Lagrangian Mesh Finite Elements Encoded in ZEPHYR for Two-Dimensional Transport Calculations."
g. Lewis, E. E., and H. A. Ozgener, "The Constrained Finite Element Approach to Coarse-Mesh Transport Computations."

29. Schmidt, F., "The Finite Element Method in Reactor Physics," University of Stuttgart, in preparation at the time of publication.

30. Schmidt, F. A. R., R. Fremd, and D. Wörner, "DIFGEN—ein Programmpaket zur Lösung der Diffusionsgleichung nach der Methode der Finiten Elemente," IKE 4-75, Institut für Kernenergetik und Energiesysteme, Universität Stuttgart, 1978.

31. Kavenoky, A., et al., "NEPTUNE: Les Modules ELECTRE et CRONOS pour les Calculs Stationaires et Transitoires de Distribution de Puissance avec Prise en Compte des Contre-reactions Thermohydraulics," *NEACRP Specialists Meeting on Calculation of 3D Rating Distributions in Operating Reactors,* Paris, November 1979.

32. Ise, T., T. Yamazaki, and Y. Nakahara, "FEM-BABEL: A Computer Program for Three-Dimensional Neutron Diffusion Equation by the FEM," JAERI 1256, Japan Atomic Research Institute, Tokyo, November 1977.

33. Meijerink, J. A., and H. A. Van der Vorst, "An Iterative Solution Method for Linear Systems of Which the Coefficient Matrix is a Symmetric M Matrix," *Math. Comput.,* **31**:148 (1977).

34. Kershaw, D. S., "The Incomplete Cholesky Conjugate Gradient Method for the Iterative Solution of Systems of Linear Equations," UCRL-78333, University of California, Livermore, 1979.

35. Johnson, O. G., and G. Paul, "Optimal Parametrized Incomplete Inverse Preconditioning for Conjugate Gradient Calculation," IBM Res. Rep. No. RC 8644, IBM Watson Research Center, Yorktown Heights, New York, 1981.

36. Fremd, R., "Die Lösung der reaktorkinetischen Gleichungen in zwei und drei Dimensionen mit der Methode der Finiten Elemente," Dissertation, Institut für Kernenergetik und Energiesysteme der Universität Stuttgart, Stuttgart, 1981.

37. Lautard, J. J., "New Finite Element Representation for 3D Reactor Calculations," *Proc. Topl. Mtg. Adv. Math. Meth. Solution Nucl. Eng. Prob.,* Munich, April 1981.

38. Werner, W., "Kinetics of Nuclear System: Solution Methods for the Space-Time Dependent Neutron Diffusion Equation," *Adv. Nucl. Sci. Technol.,* **10** (1978).

39. Trujillo, D. M., and H. R. Busby, "Finite Element Nonlinear Heat Transfer Analysis Using a Stable Explicit Method," *Nucl. Eng. Des.,* **44**:227 (1977).

40. Gado, J., and F. Schmidt, "Solution of the Neutron Diffusion Equation in Hexagonal Geometries," submitted to *Annals of Nucl. Energy* (1986).

41. Buckel, G., et al., "Summary of Results Obtained for the Static Neutronic LMFBR Benchmark Problem," *TANSAO,* **39**:484 (1981).

42. Akin, J. E., and J. W. Wooten, "Tokamak Plasma Equilibria by Finite Elements," in R. H. Gallagher et al. (eds.), *Finite Elements in Fluids*, Wiley, New York, 1978, vol. 3, pp. 351–361.

43. Gupta, R. P., E. Panarella, and P. Silvester, "A Finite Element Analysis of the Plasmas Pinched in Three Dimensions," in R. H. Gallagher et al. (eds.), *Finite Elements in Fluids*, Wiley, New York, 1982, vol. 4, pp. 551–572.

44. Bakker, M., and M. S. Van den Berg, "A Program to Solve Rotating Plasma Problems," *Comp. Phys. Commun.*, **20**:429–439 (1980).

45. Blum, J., J. Le Foll, and B. Thooris, "The Self-Consistent Equilibrium and Diffusion Code SCED," *Comp. Phys. Commun.*, **24**:235–254 (1981).

46. Anderson, D. V., and D. C. Barnes, "Accurate Calculations of Field-Reversed Axisymmetric Equilibria and Their MHD Stability Properties," *J. Comp. Phys.*, **42**:288–308 (1981).

47. Anderson, D. V., J. Breazeal, and C. B. Sharp, "Calculations of 3D Mirror Equilibria Using a Finite Element Vector Potential Representation," *J. Comp. Phys.*, **46**:189–214 (1982).

48. Hall, L. S., and B. McNamara, "3-Dimensional Equilibrium of Anisotropic, Finite-Pressure Guiding-Centre Plasma-Theory of Magnetic Plasma," *Phys. Fluids*, **18**:552–565 (1975).

49. Ohta, M., Y. Shimomura, and T. Takeda, "Analysis of Hydromagnetic Plasma Stability by the Finite-Element Method," *Nucl. Fusion*, **12**:271–274 (1972).

50. Takeda, T., Y. Shimomura, M. Ohta, and M. Yoshikawa, "Numerical Analysis of Magnetohydrodynamic Instabilities by the Finite Element Method," *Phys. Fluids*, **15**:2193–2201 (1972).

51. Boyd, T. J. M., G. A. Gardner, and L. R. T. Gardner, "Numerical Study of Hydromagnetic Stability Using the Finite-Element Method," *Nucl. Fusion*, **13**:764–766 (1973).

52. Appert, K., D. Berger, R. Gruber, and F. Troyon, "Studium der Eigenschwingungen eines zylindrischen Plasmas mit der Methode der finiten Elemente," *Z. Angew. Math. Phys.*, **25**:229–240 (1974).

53. Appert, K., D. Berger, R. Gruber, and J. Rappaz, "A New Finite Element Approach to the Normal Mode Analysis in Magnetohydrodynamics," *J. Comp. Phys.*, **18**:284–299 (1975).

54. Dewar, R. L., J. M. Greene, R. C. Grimm, and J. L. Johnson, "Numerical Study of the Magnetohydrodynamic Spectra in Tokamaks Using Galerkin's Method," *J. Comp. Phys.*, **18**:132–153 (1975).

55. Grimm, R. C., J. M. Greene, and J. L. Johnson, "Computation of the Magnetohydrodynamic Spectrum in Axisymmetric Toroidal Confinement Systems," *Meth. Comp. Phys.*, **16**:253–280 (1976).

56. Grimm, R. C., and J. L. Johnson, "Recent Developments in the Computational Aspects of MHD Stability," *Comp. Phys. Commun.*, **12**:45–52 (1976).

57. Berger, D., R. Gruber, and F. Troyon, "A Finite Element Approach to the Computation of the MHD Spectrum of Straight Noncircular Plasma Equilibrium," *Comp. Phys. Commun.*, **11**:313-323 (1976).

58. Gruber, R., "Finite Hybrid Elements to Compute the Ideal Magnetohydrodynamic Spectrum of an Axisymmetric Plasma," *J. Comp. Phys.*, **26**:379–389 (1978).

59. Gruber, R., F. Troyon, D. Berger, L. C. Bernard, S. Rousset, R. Schreiber, W. Kerner, W. Schneider, and K. V. Roberts, "ERATO Stability Code," *Comp. Phys. Commun.*, **21**:323–371 (1981).

60. Moore, R. W., L. C. Bernard, V. S. Chan, R. H. Davidson, D. R. Dobrott, F. J. Helton, R. L. Miller, W. W. Pfeiffer, R. E. Waltz, and T. S. Wang, "Optimization and Control of Plasma Shape and Current Profile in Non-circular Cross-Section Tokamaks," in *Plasma Physics and Controlled Nuclear Fusion Research, Proc. 8th Int. Conf.*, Brussels, 1980, IAEA, Vienna, 1981, vol. 1, pp. 355–361.

61. Manickam, J., R. C. Grimm, and R. L. Dewar, "The Linear Stability Analysis of MHD Models in Axisymmetric Toroidal Geometry," *Comp. Phys. Commun.*, **24**:355–361 (1981).

62. Jardin, S. C., "Ideal Magnetohydrodynamic Stability of the Spheromak Configuration," *Nucl. Fusion*, **22**:629–642 (1982).

63. Munro, J. K., Jr., L. A. Charlton, D. J. Strickler, W. A. Cooper, J. T. Hogan, and D. W. Swain, "Ideal MHD Analysis of the Stability of ISX-B High-Beta Plasmas," *Nucl. Fusion*, **22**:599–610 (1982).

64. Tsunematsu, T., T. Takeda, T. Matsuura, G Kurita, and M. Azumi, "Convergence of Solution of the MHD Stability Code ERATO," *Comp. Phys. Commun.*, **19**:179-183 (1980).

65. Gruber, R., S. Semenzato, F. Troyon, T. Tsunematsu, W. Kerner, P. Merkel, and W. Schneider, "HERA and Other Extensions of ERATO," *Comp. Phys. Commun.*, **24**:363-376 (1981).

66. Gruber, R., Ch. Pfersisch, S. Semenzato, F. Troyon, and T. Tsunematsu, "On the Numerical Determination of Ideal MHD Limits of Stability of Axisymmetric Toroidal Configurations," *Comp. Phys. Commun.*, **24**:381-387 (1981).

67. Gruber, R., W. Kerner, P. Merkel, J. Nuhrenberg, W. Schneider, and F. Troyon, "Stability-Beta Limit of Helical Equilibria," *Comp. Phys. Commun.*, **24**:389-398 (1981).

68. Kerner, W., and H. Tasso, "Tearing Mode Stability in 1D and 2D," *Comp. Phys. Commun.*, **24**:407-411 (1981).

69. Tokuda, S., T. Tsunematsu, M. Azumi, T. Takizuka, and T. Takeda, "Second Stability Region Against the Internal Kink Mode in a Tokamak," *Nucl. Fusion*, **22**:661-664 (1982).

70. Miller, R. L., "Stability of EBT in Guiding-Centre Fluid Theory," *Nucl. Fusion*, **21**:1249-1257 (1981).

71. Bernard, L. C., F. J. Helton, and R. W. Moore, "GATO: An MHD Stability for Axisymmetric Plasmas with Internal Separtrices," *Comp. Phys. Commun.*, **24**:377-380 (1981).

72. Chu, M. S., F. J. Helton, J. K. Lee, R. W. Moore, J. M. Greene, and T. H. Jensen, "Current-Driven Nonideal Instability in a Force-Free Toroidal Plasma," *Comp. Phys. Commun.*, **24**:399-406 (1981).

73. Hellesten, T., "Stabilization of Free-Boundary Modes by a Magnetic Separatrix," *Nucl. Fusion*, **22**:565-567 (1982).

74. Tasso, H., and J. T. Virtamo, "Energy Principle for 3-D Resistive Instabilities in Shaped Cross Section Tokamaks," *Plasma Phys.*, **22**:1003-1013 (1980).

75. Kerner, W., and H. Tasso, "Tearing Mode Stability for Arbitrary Current Distribution," *Plasma Phys.*, **24**:97-107 (1982).

76. Ederly, D., R. Pellat, and J. L. Soulé, "Effects of Toroidal Coupling on the Non-Linear Evolution of Tearing Modes and on Stochastisation of the Magnetic field Topology in Plasmas," *Comp. Phys. Commun.*, **24**:427-436 (1981).

77. Hennart, J. P., R. England, J. G. Martin, and L. Melendez, "A Finite Element Model for Plasma Simulation in Multipoles," *Int. J. Numer. Meth. Eng.*, **14**:1449-1460 (1979).

78. Lewis, H. R., "Variational Algorithms for Numerical Simulation of Collisionless Plasma with Point Particles Including Electromagnetic Interactions," *J. Comp. Phys.*, **10**:400-419 (1972).

79. Lewis, H. R., "Application of Hamilton's Principle to the Numerical Analysis of Vlasov Plasmas," *Meth. Comp. Phys.*, **9**:307-333 (1970).

80. Godfrey, B. B., "A Galerkin Algorithm for Multidimensional Plasma Simulation Codes," Los Alamos Laboratory Report LA-7687-MS, Los Alamos, 1979.

81. Okuda, H., and C. Z. Cheng, "Higher Order Multipoles and Splines in Plasma Simulations," *Comp. Phys. Commun.*, **14**:169-176 (1978).

82. Okuda, H., A. T. Lin, C. C. Lin, and J. M. Dawson, "Splines and High Order Interpolation in Plasma Simulation," *Comp. Phys. Commun.*, **17**:227-231 (1979).

83. Okuda, H., W. W. Lee, and C. Z. Cheng, "Electrostatic and Magnetostatic Particle Simulation Models in Three Dimensions," *Comp. Phys. Commun.*, **17**:233-238 (1979).

84. Buneman, O., "The Advance from 2D Electrostatic to 3D Electromagnetic Particle Simulation," *Comp. Phys. Commun.*, **12**:21-31 (1976).

85. Buneman, O., C. W. Barnes, J. C. Green, and D. E. Nielsen, "Principles and Capabilities of 3-D, E-M Particle Simulations," *J. Comp. Phys.*, **38**:1-44 (1980).

86. Buneman, O., "Tetrahedral Finite Elements for Interpolation," *SIAM J. Sci. Stat. Comput.*, **1**:223-248 (1980).

87. Wooten, J. W., J. H. Wheaton, D. H. McCollough, R. W. McGaffey, J. E. Akin, and L. J. Drooks, "Ion Extraction and Optics in 3D," *J. Comp. Phys.*, **43**:95–110 (1981).

88. Tran, T. M., and F. Troyon, "Finite Element Calculation of the Anomalous Skin Effect in a Homogeneous, Unmagnetized Cylindrical Plasma Column," *Comp. Phys. Commun.*, **16**:51–56 (1978).

89. Mehlhorn, T. A., and J. J. Duderstadt, "A Discrete Ordinate Solution of Fokker–Planck Equation Characterizing Charged Particle Transport," *J. Comp. Phys.*, **38**:86–106 (1980).

90. Fyfe, D., A. Weiser, I. Bernstein, S. Eisenstat, and M. Schultz, "A Finite Element Solution of a Reduced Fokker-Planck Equation," *J. Comp. Phys.*, **42**:327–336 (1981).

91. Callen, J. D., and R. A. Dory, "Magnetohydrodynamic Equilibria in Sharply Curved Axisymmetric Devices," *Phys. Fluids*, **15**:1523–1528 (1972).

92. Rappaz, J., "Approximation of the Spectrum of a Non-Compact Operator Given by the Magnetohydrodynamic Stability of a Plasma," *Numer. Math.*, **28**:15–24 (1977).

93. Evegnoz, H., and Y. Jaccard, "A Nonconforming Finite Element Method to Compute the Spectrum of an Operator Relative to the Stability of a Plasma in Toroidal Geometry," *Numer. Math.*, **36**:455–465 (1981).

94. Peirce, A. D., *Acoustics: An Introduction to its Physical Principles and Applications*, McGraw-Hill, New York, 1981, pp. 6–20, 400–402.

95. Horowitz, S. J., R. K. Sigman, and B. T. Zinn, "An Iterative Finite Element—Integral Technique for Predicting Sound Radiation from Turbofan Inlets in Steady Flight," Pap. 82-0124, American Institute of Aeronautics and Astronautics, 1982.

96. Myers, M. K., "On the Acoustic Boundary Condition in the Presence of Flow," *J. Sound Vibration*, **71**(3):429–434 (1980).

97. Shuku, T., and K. Ishihara, "The Analysis of the Acoustic Field in Irregularly Shaped Rooms by the Finite Element Method," *J. Sound Vibration*, **29**(1):67–76 (1973).

98. Craggs, A., "The Use of Simple Three-Dimensional Acoustic Finite Elements for Determining the Natural Modes and Frequencies of Complex Shaped Enclosures," *J. Sound Vibration*, **23**(3):331–339 (1972).

99. Craggs, A., "The Application of Acoustic and Absorption Finite Elements to Sound Fields in Small Enclosures," in M. M. Kamal and J. A. Wolf, Jr. (eds.), *Finite Element Applications in Acoustics*, American Society of Mechanical Engineers, New York, 1981, pp. 1–19.

100. Petyt, M., J. Lea, and G. H. Koopmann, "A Finite Method for Determining the Acoustic Modes of Irregular Shaped Cavities," *J. Sound Vibration*, **45**(4):495–502 (1976).

101. Richards, T. L., and S. K. Jha, "A Simplified Finite Element Method for Studying Acoustic Characteristics Inside a Car Cavity," *J. Sound Vibration*, **63**(1):61–72 (1979).

102. Craggs, A., "A Finite Element Method for Modelling Dissipative Mufflers with a Locally Reacting Liner," *J. Sound Vibration*, **54**(2):285–296 (1977).

103. Kagawa, Y., T. Yamabuchi, and A. Mori, "Finite Element Simulation of an Axisymmetric Acoustic Transmission System with a Sound Absorbing Wall," *J. Sound Vibration*, **53**(3):357–374 (1977).

104. Astley, R. J., and W. Eversman, "A Finite Element Method for Transmission in Non-Uniform Ducts without Flow: Comparison with the Method of Weighted Residuals," *J. Sound Vibration*, **57**(3):367–388 (1978).

105. Astley, R. J., and W. Eversman, "The Finite Element Duct Eigenvalue Problem: An Improved Formulation with Hermitian Elements and No-Flow Condensation," *J. Sound Vibration*, **69**(1):13–25 (1980).

106. Dong, S. B., C. Y. Liu, and V. Aronessian, "Sound Propagation in a Non-Uniform Moving Medium Contained in a Cylindrical Duct," in M. M. Kamal and J. A. Wolf, Jr. (eds.), *Finite Element Applications in Acoustics*, American Society of Mechanical Engineers, New York, 1981, pp. 111–120.

107. Astley, R. J., and W. Eversman, "Acoustic Transmission in Non-Uniform Ducts with Mean Flow: II. The Finite Element Method," *J. Sound Vibration*, **74**(1):103-121 (1981).

108. Astley, R. J., and W. Eversman, "Accuracy and Stability of Finite Element Schemes for the Duct Transmission," Pap. 81-2015, American Institute of Aeronautics and Astronautics, 1981.

109. Norrie, D. H., and G. de Vries, *An Introduction to Finite Element Analysis*, Academic Press, New York, 1978, pp. 31-56, 152-165, 181-219, 276-279.

110. Zienkiewicz, D. C., *The Finite Element Method*, McGraw-Hill, New York, 1977, pp. 148-177, 261-262.

111. Carter, G. W., "The Electro-Magnetic Field in Its Engineering Aspects," Longmans, Green, London, 1954.

112. Bewley, L. V., *Two-Dimensional Fields in Electrical Engineering*, Dover, New York, 1963.

113. Binns, K. J., and P. J. Lawrenson, *Analysis and Computation of Electric and Magnetic Field Problems*, Pergamon Press, Oxford, 1962.

114. Gallagher, R. H., J. T. Oden, and O. C. Zienkiewicz (eds.), *Finite Element in Fluids*, Wiley, London, 1975, vols. 1, 2.

115. Armor, A. F., and M. V. K. Chari, "Heat Flow in the Stator Core of Large Turbine-Generators by the Method of Three-Dimensional Finite Elements," pts. 1, 2, *IEEE Trans.*, **PAS-95** (September-October 1976).

116. Levy, S., and J. P. D. Wilkinson, *The Component Element Method in Dynamics*, McGraw-Hill, New York, 1976.

117. Stratton, J. A., *Electromagnetic Theory*, McGraw-Hill, New York, 1941.

118. Benedikt, O., *The Nomographic Computation of Complicated and Highly Saturated Magnetic Circuits*, Pergamon Press, London, 1964.

119. Erdelyi, E. A., M. S. Sarma, and S. S. Coleman, "Magnetic Fields in Nonlinear Salient Pole Alternators," *IEEE Trans.*, **PAS-87**(10) (October 1968).

120. Muller, W., and W. Wolff, "Numerische Berechnung dreidimensionaler Magnet Felder fur grosse Turbogenerator en bei Feldabhangiger Permeabilitat und Beliebiger Strondichte Verteilung," *ETZ-A*, **94**:276-282 (1973).

121. Turner, M. J., R. W. Clough, H. C. Martin, and L. J. Topp, "Stiffness and Deflection Analysis of Complex Structures," *J. Aero. Sci.*, **23**:805-823 (1956).

122. Zienkiewicz, O. C., and Y. K. Cheung, *The Finite Element Method in Structural and Continuum Mechanics*, McGraw-Hill, London, 1967.

123. Stakgold, I., *Green's Functions and Boundary Value Problems*, Wiley, New York, 1979.

124. Hildebrand, F. B., *Advanced Calculus or Applications*, Prentice-Hall, Englewood Cliffs, N.J., 1948.

125. Silvester, P., and M. V. K. Chair, "Finite Element Solution of Saturable Magnetic Field Problems," *IEEE Trans.*, **PAS-89**(7):1642-1651 (1970).

126. Andersen, O. W., "Iterative Solution of Finite Element Equations in Magnetic Field Problems," Pap. T-72, IEEE Power Engineering Society, 1972, pp. 411-417.

127. Csendes, Z. J., "The High Order Polynomial Finite Element Method in Electromagnetic Field Computation," *Finite Elements in Electric and Magnetic Field Problems*, Wiley, Chichester, 1980, chap. 7.

128. Konrad, A., and P. Silvester, "Triangular Finite Elements for the Generalized Bessel Equation of Order m," *Int. J. Numer. Meth. Eng.*, **7**:43-55 (1973).

129. Silvester, P., H. S. Cabayan, B. T. Browne, "Efficient Techniques for Finite Element Analysis of Electric Machines," *IEEE Trans.*, **PAS-92**(4) (1973).

130. Brandl, P., K. Reichert, and W. Vogt, "Simulation of Turbogenerators on Steady State Load," *Brown Boveri Rev.*, **9** (1975).

131. Minnich, S. H., Z. J. Csendes, M. V. K. Chari, S. C. Tandon, and J. F. Berkery, "Load Characteristics of Synchronous Generators by the Finite Element Method," F 80 206-3, *IEEE PES Winter Meeting*, New York, N.Y., February 1980.

132. Fox, L., *An Introduction to Numerical Linear Algebra*, Clarendon Press, Oxford, 1964.

133. Hestenes, M. R., and E. Stiefel, "Method of Conjugate Gradients for Solving Linear Systems," Rep. No. 1659, National Bureau of Standards, Washington, D.C., 1952.

134. Stoer, J., and R. Bulirsch, *Introduction to Numerical Analysis*, Springer-Verlag, New York, 1980.

135. Chari, M. V. K., and P. Silvester, "Finite Element Analysis of Magnetically Saturated D.C. Machines," IEEE Pap. 71 TP 3-WR, *Winter Meeting*, February 1971.

136. Silvester, P., and C. R. S. Haslam, "Magnetotelluric Modelling by the Finite Element Method," *Geophys. Prospecting*, **20**:872–891 (1972).

137. Chari, M. V. K., "Finite Element Solution of the Eddy Current Problem in Magnetic Structures," *IEEE Trans.*, **PAS-93**(1) (1973).

138. Minnich, S. H., J. W. Dougherty, and D. K. Sharma, "Calculation of Generator Simulation—Model Constants—Using Finite Element Analysis," *ICEM*, Budapest, September 1982.

139. Konrad, A., and M. V. K. Chari, "Power Loss and Forces Due to Skin Effect in Transmission Lines and Busbars," *IEEE Canadian Communications Energy Conference*, Oct. 13–15, Montreal, 1982.

140. Foggia, A., J. C. Sabonnadiere, and P. Silvester, "Finite Element Solution of Saturated Travelling Magnetic Field Problems," *IEEE Trans.*, **PAS-94**(3) (1975).

141. Silvester, P., "A General High-Order Finite-Element Waveguide Analysis Program," *IEEE Trans.*, **MTT-17**(4) (1969).

142. Chari, M. V. K. and J. D'Angelo, "Finite Element Analysis of Magneto Mechanical Devices," *Proceedings of the 5th International Workshop on Rare-Earth Cobalt Magnets and Their Applications*, Roanoke, Va., June 7–10, 1981, pp. 237–257.

143. Chari, M. V. K., A. Konrad, M. A. Palmo, and J. D'Angelo, "Three-Dimensional Analysis for Machine Field Problems," *COMPUMAG Conference*, Chicago, 1981.

144. Simkin, J., and C. W. Trowbridge, "On the Use of the Total Scalar Potential in the Numerical Solution of Field Problems in Electromagnetics," *Int. J. Numer. Meth. Eng.*, **1**:423–440 (1979).

145. Simkin, J., and C. W. Trowbridge, "Application of Integral Equation Methods for the Numerical Solution of Magnetostatic and Eddy Current Problems," Rutherford Laboratory Rep. RL-76-041, England.

146. Carpenter, C. J., and D. Locke, "Numerical Models of 3-Dimensional End-Winding Arrays," *Conference on Computation of Magnetic Fields*, Oxford, 1976, pp. 47–55.

# CHAPTER 8
# ACCURATE FINITE-ELEMENT ANALYSIS

Selection of a numerical-analysis model involves picking the computer manipulation error and devising error-management strategies for the finite-element discretization. The principal decisions regarding manipulation error concern selection of the arithmetic mode (precision, rounding, or truncation), the sequence of arithmetic operations, and error detection and recovery logic. The principal decisions regarding finite-element discretization involve the choice of the mesh: the finite-element models to be used and their allocation; and the number, type, and disposition of general and displacement coordinates throughout the system being modeled. These decisions are the focus of this chapter.

Section 8.1 presents a precise classification and the state of the art of knowledge of the errors associated with finite-element numerical models. Section 8.2 seeks to define principles for selecting a mesh-design strategy. Together, these two sections indirectly address the environment the analyst encounters in wrestling with the questions of accuracy and efficiency of the finite-element analysis.

## 8.1 SOLUTION ERRORS IN FINITE-ELEMENT ANALYSIS

The development of the finite-element analysis so far indicates that it is a discretization technique especially suited for positive-definite, self-adjoint systems, or systems with such components. The application of the method leads to discretized equations in the form of $\dot{\mathbf{u}} = \mathbf{f}(\mathbf{u})$, where $\mathbf{u}$ lists the response of the discretized system at $n$ preselected points called *nodes*. Instead of explicit expressions, the vector function $\mathbf{f}$ and its jacobian $\mathbf{f}_{,u}$ are available only numerically for a numerically given $\mathbf{u}$. The solution of $\dot{\mathbf{u}} = \mathbf{f}(\mathbf{u})$ is usually obtained by a digital computer. Because of the finiteness of the computer wordlength, the numerical solution $\mathbf{u}_c$ is in general different from $\mathbf{u}$. Let $\mathbf{u}(\mathbf{x}, t)$ denote the actual response of the system in continuum at points corresponding to those of $\mathbf{u}$. In the literature $\mathbf{u}(\mathbf{x}, t) - \mathbf{u}$ is called the *discretization error*, $\mathbf{u} - \mathbf{u}_c$ is called the *round-off error*, and the sum of the two, that is, $\mathbf{u}(\mathbf{x}, t) - \mathbf{u}_c$, *is called the solution error*. In this section, a state-of-the-art survey is given on the identification, growth, relative magnitudes, estimation, and control of the components of the solution errors [78, 79].

## 8.1A Introduction

In this subsection the definitions of the notation and the terminology used in the section are given, and the scope and the organization of the material discussed are outlined.

***Notation*** Matrices with more than one column are denoted by roman uppercase boldface letters. If the matrix is a single column, lowercase boldface letters are used. For example, an $n \times m$ matrix may be denoted as $\mathbf{A}$, its $j^{\text{th}}$ column as $\mathbf{a}_j$, its $(i, j)$ element as $a_{ij}$. The time derivatives are shown with dots above, and other derivatives are denoted by a comma in the subscript. For example, $\phi = \phi(x_1, x_2, \ldots, x_n, t)$ may be denoted as $\phi(\mathbf{x}, t)$, its derivative with respect to time $t$ as $\dot{\phi}$, the derivative with respect to $x_i$ as $\phi_{,x_i}$. The jacobian of $\phi$ with respect to the components of $\mathbf{x}$ may be shown as $\phi_{,\mathbf{x}}$, and its hessian may be shown as $\phi_{,\mathbf{xx}}$.

***Finite-Element Method*** The finite-element method was first introduced by structural engineers in solving the boundary-value problems of elasticity; here it is assumed that the method is a discretization technique for *positive-definite, self-adjoint,* and *elliptic* systems for which an equivalent *variational formulation* is available. Then the finite-element method is a *Rayleigh–Ritz* method using an *admissible trial solution* where the *undetermined parameters* are the local values of the response at preselected finite number of points (nodes), and the *coordinate functions* are the suitably chosen *generalized pyramid functions* [1] of class $p$, where $p \geq m - 1$ and $m$ is the highest order of differentiation appearing in the *functional of the variational formulation* [2, 3]. Unless otherwise stated, these definitions will be used in this section.

Let $\mathbf{x}$ denote the coordinates of a point in the spatial solution domain, and let $u(\mathbf{x}, t)$ denote the actual-response quantity at this point at time $t$. Let $\mathbf{x}_i$, $i = 1, 2, \ldots, n$, denote the coordinates of the nodes. The list of actual responses at these nodes at time $t$ is denoted by $\mathbf{u}(\mathbf{x}, t) = [u(\mathbf{x}_1, t), u(\mathbf{x}_2, t), \ldots, u(\mathbf{x}_n, t)]^T$. Let $\mathbf{u}(t) = [u_1(t), u_2(t), \ldots, u_n(t)]^T$ denote the finite-element approximation of $\mathbf{u}(\mathbf{x}, t)$, i.e., undetermined parameters. Let $\boldsymbol{\psi}(\mathbf{x}) = [\psi_1(\mathbf{x}), \psi_2(\mathbf{x}), \ldots, \psi_n(\mathbf{x})]^T$ denote the chosen generalized pyramid functions. Since for the pyramid function $\psi_i(\mathbf{x}_j) = \delta_{ij}$, where $\delta_{ij}$ is the Kronecker delta, then $\Psi(\mathbf{x}, t) = \mathbf{u}(t)^T \boldsymbol{\psi}(\mathbf{x})$ is a trial function such that $\Psi(\mathbf{x}_j, t)$ is an approximation of $u(\mathbf{x}_j, t)$. Suppose $\boldsymbol{\psi}(\mathbf{x})$ is such that the *essential boundary conditions* are satisfied by $\Psi(\mathbf{x}, t)$ for any $\mathbf{u}(t)$; then $\Psi$ is *admissible*. Let $\Phi$ denote the variational functional. The use of $\Psi$ in $\Phi$ and the application of the Rayleigh–Ritz procedure leads to

$$\dot{\mathbf{u}} = \mathbf{f}(\mathbf{u}) \tag{8.1}$$

Consider the power-series expansion of $\mathbf{f}$ about point $\mathbf{u}_0$:

$$\mathbf{f}(\mathbf{u}) = \mathbf{f}(\mathbf{u}_0) + \mathbf{f}_{,\mathbf{u}}(\mathbf{u}_0)(\mathbf{u} - \mathbf{u}_0) + \cdots \tag{8.2}$$

The algorithms of the finite-element method are such that, given the numerical value of $\mathbf{u}_0$, the numerical values of the vector function $\mathbf{f}$ and its jacobian $\mathbf{f}_{,\mathbf{u}}$, that is, $\mathbf{f}(\mathbf{u}_0)$ and $\mathbf{f}_{,\mathbf{u}}(\mathbf{u}_0)$, are readily available, perhaps, after considerable computations.

In the case of time-independent boundary-value problems with system loads $\mathbf{p}$, in Eqs. (8.1) and (8.2): $\mathbf{u} = \mathbf{0}$, $\mathbf{u}_0 = \mathbf{0}$, $\mathbf{f}(0) = -\mathbf{p}$, and $\mathbf{f}_{,\mathbf{u}} = \mathbf{K} + \lambda \mathbf{G}$, where $\mathbf{K}$ is the *stiffness matrix due to material*, $G$ is *stiffness matrix due to initial stresses*, and $\lambda$ is the scalar representing the scalar of the initial-stress magnitudes (or some similar quantity). With these, from Eqs. (8.1) and (8.2), the response of the discretized system may be formally written as $\mathbf{u} = [\mathbf{K} + \lambda \mathbf{G}]^{-1}\mathbf{p}$, so long as the problem is a linear one. The formal solution implies that further numerical operations are needed to obtain the solution numerically. In general, in the finite-element method, given the initial conditions, the solution of Eq. (8.1) may be obtained numerically. Owing to the finiteness of the computer wordlength, the numerical solution $\mathbf{u}_c(t)$ of Eq. (8.1) is different from its exact solution $\mathbf{u}(t)$.

**Terminology of Error Kinds** Consider the actual physical system for which the numerical solution $\mathbf{u}_c(t)$ is obtained. Suppose one makes very accurate measurements of the response quantities in the actual system. Let $\mathbf{e}$ represent the difference between the measured quantities and the corresponding computed quantities $\mathbf{u}_c(t)$ at a given time. Vector $\mathbf{e}$ is called the *total error*, and its $i^{\text{th}}$ component $e_i$ is the $i^{\text{th}}$ total error at time $t$. The total error is the sum of various errors defined below.

**Mathematical Modeling Error** The analysis which yielded $\mathbf{u}_c(t)$ is based on a mathematical formulation abstracted from the actual physical system. During this abstraction, for the sake of numerical convenience, many simplifying assumptions are made relative to the geometry of the solution domain, system parameters, and functional structure and magnitude of the response quantities. The quantity $\mathbf{u}(\mathbf{x}, t)$, defined previously as the actual response at the nodes at time $t$, is the response of the mathematical model. The difference between the measured quantities of the physical system and the corresponding $\mathbf{u}(\mathbf{x}, t)$ at a given time is the mathematical modeling error at that time. Newtonian mechanics, beam theory, and thin-shell theory are examples of mathematical models of actual physical systems. Very little mathematical modeling errors result, if the assumptions of the mathematical model are reasonable for the actual system represented by that model. Otherwise the modeling errors may be unacceptably large. For example, in order to use newtonian mechanics, the velocities should be far smaller than the relativistic values. Likewise, for the beam theory the height-to-span ratio, and for the thin-shell theory the thickness-times-curvature values, must be sufficiently small. In this section it is assumed that the mathematical modeling errors are negligible.

**Discretization Errors** Discretization errors are caused by representing the infinitely many degrees of freedom of the mathematical model by the finite number of degrees of freedom in the discretized system. With the notation defined earlier, the discretization error at time $t$ is $\mathbf{u}(t) - \mathbf{u}(\mathbf{x}, t)$ [4].

***Round-off Errors***   Round-off errors are caused by the limitation of digital computers in representing real numbers. Owing to the finiteness of the computer wordlengths, only a finite subset of the infinitely many real numbers can be represented in these machines. None of the irrational numbers and very few of the rational numbers can be represented. With the notation defined earlier, the round-off error at time $t$ is $\mathbf{u}_c(t) - \mathbf{u}(t)$ [4].

***Solution Errors***   The total error less the mathematical modeling error is the solution error. In fact, these errors are the sum of the discretization and round-off errors; that is $\mathbf{u}_c(t) - \mathbf{u}(\mathbf{x}, t)$ constitutes the solution errors at time $t$ [4].

***Terminology of Error Analysis***   From an analytical point of view, the errors defined above may be further identified by their simpler constituents.

***Equation Errors***   The discretized equations, i.e., those in Eq. (8.1), are in fact the approximations of the governing equations of the mathematical model at specific points (the nodes) at time $t$. In fact, the equation sign in Eq. (8.1) indicates only an approximation. Let $\mathbf{r}$ denote the residue to make the equation an exact equation, such that Eq. (8.1) may be rewritten as

$$\dot{\mathbf{u}}(\mathbf{x}, t) = \mathbf{f}(\mathbf{u}(\mathbf{x}, t)) - \mathbf{r} \tag{8.3}$$

Vector $\mathbf{r}$ is called the *equation error* at time $t$. There are three basic components of the equation error: $\mathbf{r}_d$, $\mathbf{r}_r$, and $\mathbf{r}_i$. Vector $\mathbf{r}_d$ is called the *equation discretization error*, and it represents all errors in representing the governing equations at the nodes by means of the finite elements. Vector $\mathbf{r}_r$ is called the *equation round-off error*, and it lists all errors caused by representing the discrete equations only by the numbers available to the digital computer. Vector $\mathbf{r}_i$ is called the *inherited errors* at time $t$, and it represents the effects of all equation errors of the earlier times [4].

***Solution Errors***   The definition of solution error is given above. In terms of the equation errors, the solution errors at time $\tau$ may be redefined as the sum of the effects of all equation errors at times $t < \tau$, and the *manipulation errors* (see below).

***System's Intrinsic Characteristics***   Note that Eq. (8.3) is basically a set of ordinary differential equations which may or may not have stable solutions. In a nonstable system, errors such as $\mathbf{r}$ propagate with ever-increasing magnitudes, whereas in a stable system they propagate with decreasing magnitudes. The stability is an intrinsic characteristic of the system. The eigenvalues of the jacobian of $\mathbf{f}$, i.e., those of $\mathbf{f}_{,u}$, represent such characteristics—a fact which has been known for a long time [5]. With the eigenvalues of $\mathbf{f}_{,u}$, it is possible to predict the manner in which the equation errors are transformed into the solution errors.

***Manipulation Errors***   As stated earlier for Eq. (8.1), the solution of Eq. (8.3) is likewise obtained numerically by using one of the many solution algorithms and a digital computer. During the solution process, depending upon the solution algorithm, not only are an unpredictable amount of round-off errors committed but also the intrinsic characteristics of the system may be altered. The effect of these factors in the solution error is called the manipulation error [6]. It is possible to have large manipulation errors in an intrinsically stable system owing to a wrong choice of the solution algorithm.

***Terminology of Error Measures***   As discussed earlier, in the finite-element method, one is interested in the accuracy of the computed-response quantities $\mathbf{u}_c(t)$ at the nodes at any time $t$. In terms of the actual response of the mathematical model at the same nodes and time, $\mathbf{u}(\mathbf{x}, t)$, the solution error $\mathbf{e}$ may be expressed as

$$\mathbf{e} = \mathbf{e}(t) = \mathbf{u}(\mathbf{x}, t) - \mathbf{u}_c(t) \tag{8.4}$$

The knowledge of $\mathbf{e}$ enables one to compute the actual response $\mathbf{u}(\mathbf{x}, t)$ from the computed response $\mathbf{u}_c(t)$. Since $\mathbf{u}(\mathbf{x}, t)$ is not available in general, the computation of $\mathbf{e}$ by other means is necessary. This is a very difficult proposition. In practice, rather than $\mathbf{e}$, an estimate of $\mathbf{e}$ or of a related quantity is sought. Some of the related quantities are defined below.

***Local Errors***   In an $n$-node discrete system

$$\mathbf{e} = [e_1, e_2, \ldots, e_n]^T \tag{8.5}$$

where the $j^{\text{th}}$ component, $e_j$, is the error in the computed response at node $j$. This quantity, i.e., $e_j$, is called the *local error* at node $j$.

***Error Magnitudes***   Many times, especially in the case of round-off errors, the magnitude of an error is easier to compute than its actual value. The magnitude of the $j^{\text{th}}$ local error $e_j$ is shown by $|e_j|$. The vector listing the magnitudes of the components of $\mathbf{e}$ is shown by $|\mathbf{e}|$, namely,

$$|\mathbf{e}| = [|e_1|, |e_2|, \ldots, |e_n|]^T \tag{8.6}$$

***Error Norms***   Often, instead of $\mathbf{e}$, one attempts to compute some norm of $\mathbf{e}$ which is shown as $\|\mathbf{e}\|$ and is a positive scalar. There are various ways of defining the norm of $\mathbf{e}$; however, each must obey the following rules: the *positivity* rule (that is, $\|\mathbf{e}\| > 0$, and $\|\mathbf{e}\| = 0$ only if $\mathbf{e} = \mathbf{0}$), the *homogeneity* rule (that is, for any scalar $\lambda$, $\|\lambda\mathbf{e}\| = |\lambda|\,\|\mathbf{e}\|$), and the *triangle inequality* (that is, if $\mathbf{e} = \mathbf{e}_1 + \mathbf{e}_2$, then $\|\mathbf{e}_1\| + \|\mathbf{e}_2\| \geq \|\mathbf{e}\|$). The most widely used norms are the *p-norms*:

$$\|\mathbf{e}\|_p = (|e_1|^p + |e_2|^p + \cdots + |e_n|^p)^{1/p} \qquad \text{for } p = 1, 2, \text{ or } \infty \tag{8.7}$$

Also used are the *Euclid norm,*

$$\|\mathbf{e}\|_E = \|\mathbf{e}\|_2 \tag{8.8}$$

and the *positive-definite-quadratic-form norm,*

$$\|\mathbf{e}\|_q = (\tfrac{1}{2}\mathbf{e}^T\mathbf{A}\mathbf{e})^{1/2} \tag{8.9}$$

where $\mathbf{A}$ is a constant $n^{\text{th}}$-order real, symmetric, and positive-definite matrix. From the definitions of the norms, it can be shown that

$$|e_j| \leq \|\mathbf{e}\| \qquad \text{for any } j \tag{8.10}$$

Therefore, any norm of the solution error can be used as an upper bound for the magnitude of any of its local errors [if Eq. (8.9) is used, $\mathbf{A}$ is such that $a_{jj} > 1$].

***Absolute Error***   The quantity defined in Eq. (8.4) is also called the *absolute solution error.* Sometimes, it may be more feasible to deal with the relative errors (defined below) than the absolute errors.

***Relative Error***   In those systems where the response appears to be growing with ever-increasing magnitudes, it may be more meaningful to deal with the ratio of the error to the response. Let $e_j$ denote the $j^{\text{th}}$ local solution error, and let $u_{c_j}$ denote the computed response at the same point. The quantity $e_{r_j}$ is defined as

$$e_{r_j} = \frac{e_j}{u_{c_j}} \qquad u_{c_j} \neq 0 \qquad \text{for any } j = 1, 2, \ldots, n \tag{8.11}$$

and it is called the $j^{\text{th}}$ *relative local error.* Similarly, the quantity $\|\mathbf{e}\|/\|\mathbf{u}_c\|$, $(\mathbf{u}_c \neq \mathbf{0})$, is called the *relative-solution-error norm.*

***Scope***   Many of the concepts defined in this subsection are common in all discretization techniques. In the discussions of this section these concepts are used to the extent that they are useful in explaining the errors in the finite-element solutions. Naturally, the ones which play a more important role in the finite-element method are emphasized. The scope of the discussions is thus limited by the relevance to the finite-element method. The objective is to survey the state of the art of various aspects of the error phenomena, such as the quantification of its basic components, the understanding of their propagation, and the estimation of the errors present in the computed response. The problem of how to select the mesh and the interpolation functions to minimize the errors is discussed in Sec. 8.2.

***Organization***   With the notation and the terminology having been defined in this section, the equation errors are studied, the factors affecting their magnitudes are reviewed, their relative importance is discussed, and their quantification is given in the Sec. 8.1B. Section 8.1C deals with the role of the intrinsic-system properties in transmitting the equation errors into the solution errors. Manipulation errors are discussed in Sec. 8.1D, and current research is surveyed in Sec. 8.1E. Section 8.1F discusses the state of the art of practical error estimation. Finally, Sec. 8.1G presents the conclusions deduced from the discussions of this section. The list of references includes publications relevant to this section, and it is by no means complete.

## 8.1B Equation Errors

The application of the finite-element method to the mathematical model of the actual physical system yields the discrete equations of the type of Eq. (8.1), which only approximates the conditions of the mathematical model at the nodes. The sources of the approximation are the use of the finite set of real numbers representable in a digital computer, the use of a finite number of nodal points, and the application of the finite-element method not to the mathematical model but to an approximation of it. In Sec. 8.1A the errors caused by these sources are defined as the round-off errors, the discretization errors, and the inherited errors, respectively. Only after adding these error quantities to the equations does Eq. (8.1) become an exact equation, as shown in Eq. (8.3). In the following paragraphs these errors are studied, the factors affecting their magnitudes are reviewed, and their relative importance is discussed.

***Equation Round-off Errors*** As discussed earlier, the finite-element method provides, instead of the explicit expressions for Eq. (8.1), the numerical values of $\mathbf{f}(\mathbf{u}_0)$ and $\mathbf{f}_{,\mathbf{u}}(\mathbf{u}_0)$, i.e., the numerical values of the vector function $\mathbf{f}$ and its jacobian $\mathbf{f}_{,\mathbf{u}}$ at $\mathbf{u} = \mathbf{u}_0$. For example, in the equilibrium problems of elasticity, when $\mathbf{u}_0$ is a geometrically compatible deflection state, $\mathbf{f}(\mathbf{u}_0)$ is the list of unbalanced forces at the nodes, and $\mathbf{f}_{,\mathbf{u}}(\mathbf{u}_0)$ is the stiffness matrix associated with the directions of the components of $\mathbf{u}_0$. In order to obtain $\mathbf{f}(\mathbf{u}_0)$ and $\mathbf{f}_{,\mathbf{u}}(\mathbf{u}_0)$, the elemental matrices are calculated and assembled in a digital computer, always using the finite real number set of the digital computer during the arithmetic operations. Obviously, the computed matrices are different from the intended $\mathbf{f}(\mathbf{u}_0)$ and $\mathbf{f}_{,\mathbf{u}}(\mathbf{u}_0)$, and the effect of the difference on Eq. (8.1) is the equation round-off error. The exact computation of this error is not possible; however, with the following rules, an estimate can be made.

Most of the modern digital computers use *floating-point arithmetic*, and the numbers used in this arithmetic are represented as floating-point numbers. The representation of a floating-point number consists of an *exponent* and a *mantissa* of $l$ number of binary bits long. The exponent is such that the mantissa is a quantity between 0.5 and 1.0; therefore, the exponent portion may be taken as the upper-bound estimate of the magnitude of the actual number. Let $a_1$ denote the actual number, $|a_1|$ its magnitude, and $fl(a_1)$ its machine representation; then the round-off error $\varepsilon$ involved in the representation may be expressed as

$$\varepsilon = fl(a_1) - a_1 \qquad \text{with} \qquad |\varepsilon| \leqslant |a_1| 2^{-l} \tag{8.12}$$

where $l$ is the number of the binary bits assigned for the mantissa. Let $a_1$ and $b_1$ denote two real numbers, $a_1 + b_1$ and $a_1 b_1$ their actual sum and product, and $fl(a_1 + b_1)$ and $fl(a_1 b_1)$ the corresponding machine results. It can be shown that the following hold:

$$\varepsilon = fl(a_1 + b_1) - (a_1 + b_1) \qquad \text{with} \qquad |\varepsilon| \leqslant (|a_1| + |b_1|) 2^{-l} \tag{8.13}$$

and $\qquad \varepsilon = fl(a_1 b_1) - a_1 b_1 \qquad \text{with} \qquad |\varepsilon| \leqslant |a_1||b_1| 2^{-l} \tag{8.14}$

Similar inequalities may be written for the round-off errors in matrix operations. Let $\mathbf{a}$ and $\mathbf{b}$ denote two vectors of order $n$, and $fl(\mathbf{a}^T\mathbf{b})$ denote the result of $\mathbf{a}^T\mathbf{b}$ product carried out in an $l$-bit mantissa machine. Then

$$\varepsilon = fl(\mathbf{a}^T\mathbf{b}) - \mathbf{a}^T\mathbf{b} \qquad \text{with} \qquad |\varepsilon| \leqslant n\|\mathbf{a}\|\,\|\mathbf{b}\| 2^{-l} \tag{8.15}$$

Similarly, if $\mathbf{A}$ and $\mathbf{B}$ denote two $p \times n$ and $n \times q$ matrices, and $fl(\mathbf{AB})$ is the result obtained for the $\mathbf{AB}$ product in an $l$-bit mantissa machine, one may write

$$\mathbf{F} = fl(\mathbf{AB}) - \mathbf{AB} \qquad \text{with} \qquad \|\mathbf{F}\| \leqslant \|\mathbf{A}\|\,\|\mathbf{B}\| n 2^{-l} \tag{8.16}$$

where $\|\mathbf{A}\|$, $\|\mathbf{B}\|$, and $\|\mathbf{F}\|$ are the *Euclid norms* or *subordinate matrix norms* of $\mathbf{A}$, $\mathbf{B}$, and $\mathbf{F}$, respectively [7].

From these it is clear that in order to minimize the equation round-off errors one should use large $l$ (i.e., machines with longer wordlength, or double-precision arithmetic), smaller-magnitude quantities (so that the norms appearing in the definitions of $|\varepsilon|$ be small), and smaller-size matrices (so that $n$ appearing in the definitions of $|\varepsilon|$ be small).

If Eq. (8.13) is used with $a_1 > 0$, and $b_1 = -c_1$ with $c_1 > 0$, the relative error in the computed quantity $fl(a_1 - c_1)$ may be expressed as

$$\frac{|\varepsilon|}{fl(a_1 - c_1)} \leqslant 2^{-l}\frac{|a_1| + |a_1|}{fl(a_1 - c_1)} \tag{8.17}$$

which shows that the computed quantity $fl(a_1 - c_1)$ may be overwhelmed by the round-off errors if $|a_1 - c_1|$ is sufficiently small. Unfortunately, in the finite-element method, this type of differencing occurs very often, such as in computing the differences (and in the case of shells, the differences of the differences) of the nodal coordinates of element vertices. It is clear that, given a machine (i.e., given a mantissa length $l$), there is always a limit to the mesh refinement beyond which the computed quantities may be 100% erroneous.

The equation round-off errors, $r_r$, may be held negligibly small by using sufficiently large $l$ (i.e., longer-wordlength machines and double-precision arithmetic), with not-too-refined finite-element meshes. This is the current practice in the finite-element technology.

**Equation Discretization Errors**   As shown in the previous subsection, in the finite-element method the actual response $u(\mathbf{x}, t)$ is approximated by the trial solution $\Psi(\mathbf{x}, t)$, which is

$$\Psi(\mathbf{x}, t) = \mathbf{u}(t)^T\boldsymbol{\psi}(\mathbf{x}) \tag{8.18}$$

where
$$\boldsymbol{\psi}(\mathbf{x}) = [\psi_1(\mathbf{x}), \psi_2(\mathbf{x}), \dots, \psi_n(\mathbf{x})]^T \tag{8.19}$$

and
$$\mathbf{u}(t) = [u_1(t), u_2(t), \dots, u_n(t)]^T \tag{8.20}$$

where $u_j(t)$ is to represent $u(\mathbf{x}_j, t)$, i.e., the response at the $j^{\text{th}}$ node at time $t$, and $\psi_j(\mathbf{x})$ is the $j^{\text{th}}$ pyramid function. Note that Eq. (8.18) implies, that, for the pyramid functions,

$$\psi_i(\mathbf{x}_j) = \delta_{ij} \qquad \text{(Kronecker delta: } \delta_{ii} = 1, \text{ and } \delta_{ij} = 0 \text{ if } i \neq j) \tag{8.21}$$

Let $\mathcal{D}_j$ denote the spatial domain defined by the finite elements meeting at node $j$. The $j^{\text{th}}$ generalized pyramid function is such that

$$\psi_j(\mathbf{x}) = 0 \qquad \text{if } \mathbf{x} \text{ is on or outside the boundary of domain } \mathcal{D}_j \tag{8.22}$$

and $\psi_j(\mathbf{x})$ is a known interpolated value such that

$$|\psi_j(\mathbf{x})| \leqslant 1 \qquad \text{if } \mathbf{x} \text{ is inside the domain } \mathcal{D}_j \tag{8.23}$$

Let $\Delta\Psi = \Delta\Psi(\mathbf{x}) = \Delta\Psi(\mathbf{x}, t)$ denote the difference between the actual and the assumed responses; that is,

$$\Delta\Psi = u(\mathbf{x}, t) - \Psi(\mathbf{x}, t) \tag{8.24}$$

In the finite-element method the pyramid functions are selected such that $\Psi(\mathbf{x}, t)$ is of *class* $p \geqslant m - 1$, $m$ being the highest-order differentiation appearing in the functional $\Phi$ of the variational formulation of the problem, and

$$\lim_{n \to \infty} \Delta\Psi \to 0 \qquad \text{for all } \mathbf{x} \text{ in the solution domain} \tag{8.25}$$

is guaranteed [which means that, given $t$, $\Psi(\mathbf{x}, t)$ is the power-series expansion of $u(\mathbf{x}, t)$ about $\mathbf{x}$, up to a selected order].

The functional $\Phi$ of the variational formulation involves the derivatives of $u(\mathbf{x}, t)$ up to order $m$, and integrals in the solution domain. Formally one may write

$$\Phi[u(\mathbf{x}, t)] = \Phi[\Psi(\mathbf{x}, t) + \Delta\Psi(\mathbf{x}, t)] + \Delta\Phi[\Psi(\mathbf{x}, t) + \Delta\Psi(\mathbf{x}, t)] \tag{8.26}$$

where $\Delta\Phi$ represents the errors caused by the possibilities that (1) the sum of the spatial domains represented by the finite elements may be different than the actual spatial domain, (2) the essential boundary conditions of the problem may not be satisfied by $\Psi(\mathbf{x}, t)$ at points which are not nodal boundary points, and (3) the additional boundary conditions of the problem, if there are any, may not be satisfied by $\Psi(\mathbf{x}, t)$ at all. Because of $\Delta\Phi$ and $\Delta\Psi$, the application of the Rayleigh–Ritz procedure to $\Phi[u(\mathbf{x}, t)]$ and $\Phi[\Psi(\mathbf{x}, t)]$ will, in general, yield different equations of the type of Eq. (8.1). The ones obtained from $\Phi[u(\mathbf{x}, t)]$ would be the exact ones, and the ones obtained from $\Phi[\Psi(\mathbf{x}, t)]$ would be the approximate ones. Let the difference between these two sets of equations be denoted by $\mathbf{r}_d$. The vector $\mathbf{r}_d$ constitutes the equation discretization errors. Note that

$$\lim_{n\to\infty} \mathbf{r}_d \to \mathbf{0} \tag{8.27}$$

For a given $n$, it is possible to express $\mathbf{r}_d$ in terms of the higher-order derivatives of the response and the mesh sizes, by taking advantage of the *remainder theorem* of the power-series expansions. If the response of the actual system is sufficiently smooth (that is, if the higher-order derivatives are not varying rapidly in the finite elements), by using the approximate solution itself, $\mathbf{r}_d$ may be approximately evaluated by such expressions. This is being done in the *finite-difference* methods [8, 9]. Its extension to the finite-element method is proposed [10, 11]. From these expressions it is possible to obtain relations such as

$$\|\mathbf{r}_d\| = O(h^p) \tag{8.28}$$

where $h$ is the typical mesh size of the mesh used, and $p$ is a power usually larger than 1. Such expressions are useful in assessing the rate with which the equation discretization errors will vanish with decreasing mesh size. The power $p$ is related with the degree of the interpolation rule used in the pyramid functions [see the comment in brackets below Eq. (8.25)].

There has been some interest among investigators to express the equation discretization errors [12, 13] or their components in the element level [14, 15].

From the above discussion, it is clear that the equation discretization errors decrease with decreasing mesh size, and the rate with which the reduction takes place increases by the use of higher-order interpolation rules, i.e., higher-order elements.

**Inherited Errors in the Equations**   As discussed earlier, instead of the explicit expressions for Eq. (8.1), the finite-element method provides the numerical values of $\mathbf{f}(\mathbf{u}_0)$ and $\mathbf{f}_{,\mathbf{u}}(\mathbf{u}_0)$ at a given $\mathbf{u} = \mathbf{u}_0$. If $\mathbf{u}_0$ is a prescribed state (such as the initial state), then in $\mathbf{f}(\mathbf{u}_0)$ and $\mathbf{f}_{,\mathbf{u}}(\mathbf{u}_0)$ only the effects of the round-off and the equation discretization errors exist. However, in many problems, such as the nonlinear equilibrium problems, and linear or nonlinear propagation problems, one needs the computation of the response at many time stations. In such problems, $\mathbf{u}_0$ is the computed response (at one of the time stations), and, therefore, it contains errors inherited from the preceding analysis. Let $\mathbf{r}_i$ represent the effect of such inherited errors present in $\mathbf{u}_0$ on the discrete equations. Vector $\mathbf{r}_i$ is called the *equation inherited errors*. The magnitude of the equation inherited errors depends on the magnitude of the inherited errors in $\mathbf{u}_0$. The inherited errors in $\mathbf{u}_0$ are the sum of the effects of all earlier discretizations and round-off errors. Depending upon the intrinsic system characteristics and also the manipulation techniques used in the analysis, the earlier discretization and round-off errors may contribute to the errors in $\mathbf{u}_0$ with increasing or decreasing magnitudes. If they contribute with increasing magnitudes, the inherited errors $\mathbf{r}_i$ in the discrete equations may easily overwhelm the other two error components, i.e., $\mathbf{r}_d$ and $\mathbf{r}_r$, discussed earlier.

To control the inherited equation errors, one must first control the equation round-off errors and the equation discretization errors, and then control the propagation of their effects in the response. Given the equation errors, the computation of their effects in the solution and the propagation of such effects are discussed in the next two subsections. From such discussions it is clear that one may do very little other than select appropriate solution algorithms to control the error propagation. Therefore the crux of the matter in controlling the inherited errors is to minimize, as much as possible, the equation round-off and the equation discretization errors.

## 8.1c  Solution Errors Due to Equation Errors

Consider the exact discretized equations given Eq. (8.3). In the previous section the constituents of the equation errors, $\mathbf{r}$, are discussed. Let $\mathbf{u}'(t)$ denote the exact solution of Eq. (8.3) in the absence of $\mathbf{r}$, i.e., the solution of Eq. (8.3) when $\mathbf{r} = 0$. The quantity $\mathbf{h}$, defined as

$$\mathbf{h} = \mathbf{u}'(t) - \mathbf{u}(\mathbf{x}, t) \tag{8.29}$$

is the effect of the equation errors on the response. In fact, $\mathbf{h}$ is the solution error in the absence of the manipulation errors, and it may be considered as the transformation of the equation errors as the solution errors. In this subsection the relationships between $\mathbf{r}$ and $\mathbf{h}$ are discussed, and the role of the intrinsic system characteristics in these relationships is shown.

Let $\mathbf{u}(\mathbf{x}, t_0) = \mathbf{u}'(t_0) = \mathbf{u}_0$ denote the response at time $t_0$. Noting that the equation error $\mathbf{r}$ is also a function of response $\mathbf{u}$, the power-series expansion of the right-hand side of Eq. (8.3) about $\mathbf{u}_0$ may be written as

$$\mathbf{f}(\mathbf{u}(\mathbf{x}, t_0)) - \mathbf{r} = \{\mathbf{f}(\mathbf{u}_0) - \mathbf{r}(\mathbf{u}_0)\} + [\mathbf{f}_{,u}(\mathbf{u}_0) - \mathbf{r}_{,u}(\mathbf{u}_0)]\{\mathbf{u}(\mathbf{x}, t_0) - \mathbf{u}_0\} + \mathbf{t}_f + \mathbf{t}_r \tag{8.30}$$

where $\mathbf{t}_f$ and $\mathbf{t}_r$ are the remainders of the expansions of $\mathbf{f}$ and $\mathbf{r}$, respectively. Defining

$$\mathbf{f}(\mathbf{u}_0) - \mathbf{r}(\mathbf{u}_0) = -\mathbf{p} \qquad \mathbf{f}_{,u}(\mathbf{u}_0) - \mathbf{r}_{,u}(\mathbf{u}_0) = \mathbf{K} \qquad \mathbf{u}(\mathbf{x}, t_0) - \mathbf{u}_0 = \Delta\mathbf{u} \tag{8.31-8.33}$$

and

$$\delta\mathbf{p} = -\mathbf{r}(\mathbf{u}_0) \qquad \delta\mathbf{K} = \mathbf{r}_{,u}(\mathbf{u}_0) \qquad \Delta\mathbf{u}' = \mathbf{u}' - \mathbf{u}_0 \tag{8.34-8.36}$$

one may write

$$\mathbf{f}(\mathbf{u}_0) = -(\mathbf{p} + \delta\mathbf{p}) \qquad \mathbf{f}_{,u}(\mathbf{u}_0) = \mathbf{K} + \delta\mathbf{K} \qquad \mathbf{u}' = \Delta\mathbf{u} + \mathbf{h} \tag{8.37-8.39}$$

where **h** is as defined in Eq. (8.29). In the finite-element method one computes numerically the vector function **f** and its jacobian at $\mathbf{u}_0$ (i.e., the unbalanced forces and the stiffness matrix). Namely, $\mathbf{p} + \delta\mathbf{p}$ and $\mathbf{K} + \delta\mathbf{K}$ are computed instead of their true values **p** and **K**, respectively. As a result, instead of true incremental response $\Delta\mathbf{u}$, one computes $\Delta\mathbf{u} + \mathbf{h}$, where **h** represents the induced errors.

***Effect of System Characteristics in Equilibrium Problems***   For equilibrium problems with no time-dependent system components, $\dot{\mathbf{u}}$ is absent in the governing equations; thus Eq. (8.3) becomes, for $t = t_0$,

$$0 = \mathbf{f}(\mathbf{u}(\mathbf{x}, t_0)) - \mathbf{r} \tag{8.40}$$

Using the expansion given in Eq. (8.30), this may be rewritten as

$$[\mathbf{f}_{,u}(\mathbf{u}_0) - \mathbf{r}_{,u}(\mathbf{u}_0)]\{\mathbf{u}(\mathbf{x}, t_0) - \mathbf{u}_0\} = -\{\mathbf{f}(\mathbf{u}_0) - \mathbf{r}(\mathbf{u}_0)\} - \mathbf{t}_f \tag{8.41}$$

where it is assumed that $\mathbf{t}_r = \mathbf{0}$ (i.e., the equation errors are varying linearly with the response at the vicinity of $\mathbf{u}_0$). By using the definitions in Eqs. (8.31) to (8.33) this becomes

$$\mathbf{K}\,\Delta\mathbf{u} = \mathbf{p} - \mathbf{t}_f \tag{8.42}$$

In the finite-element method, since the equation errors are not numerically available, instead of **K** and **p**, one uses $\mathbf{K} + \delta\mathbf{K}$ and $\mathbf{p} + \delta\mathbf{p}$ in Eq. (8.42), and as a result, $\Delta\mathbf{u}$ becomes $\Delta\mathbf{u} + \mathbf{h}$:

$$[\mathbf{K} + \delta\mathbf{K}]\{\Delta\mathbf{u} + \mathbf{h}\} = \{\mathbf{p} + \delta\mathbf{p}\} - \mathbf{t}_f \tag{8.43}$$

In Eqs. (8.42) and (8.43), **K** and $\mathbf{K} + \delta\mathbf{K}$ represent the actual and the approximate systems, **p** and $\mathbf{p} + \delta\mathbf{p}$ represent the actual and the approximate system loads, and the $\mathbf{t}_f$ represent the nonlinear terms of the system.

***Effect of System Characteristics in Linear Equilibrium Problems***   In linear equilibrium problems, because of the linearity of the vector function **f** with respect to the response **u**, one has

$$\mathbf{t}_f = \mathbf{0} \tag{8.44}$$

With this, Eqs. (8.42) and (8.43) become

$$\mathbf{K}\,\Delta\mathbf{u} = \mathbf{p} \quad \text{and} \quad [\mathbf{K} + \delta\mathbf{K}]\{\Delta\mathbf{u} + \mathbf{h}\} = \{\mathbf{p} + \delta\mathbf{p}\} \tag{8.45, 8.46}$$

Subtracting side by side and then formally solving for **h** leads to

$$\mathbf{h} = [\mathbf{K} + \delta\mathbf{K}]^{-1}\{\delta\mathbf{p} - \delta\mathbf{K}\,\Delta\mathbf{u}\} \tag{8.47}$$

which is the relation showing how the errors in the equations transform into the errors in the solution. Here, the errors are the absolute errors, and $\mathbf{K} + \delta\mathbf{K}$ stands for the system characteristics.

One gains more insight if one seeks to answer the following question: Given some norm of the relative errors in the equations, what is the corresponding relative error in the solution?

Through manipulation of Eqs. (8.45), and (8.46), the following may be obtained [16]:

$$\frac{\|\mathbf{h}\|}{\|\Delta\mathbf{u}\|} \leq \|\mathbf{K}\| \|\mathbf{K}^{-1}\| \left[ \frac{\|\delta\mathbf{p}\|}{\|\mathbf{p}\|} + \alpha\left( \frac{\|\delta\mathbf{K}\|}{\|\mathbf{K}\|} \right) \right] \tag{8.48}$$

where

$$\alpha = \left( 1 - \|\mathbf{K}\| \|\mathbf{K}^{-1}\| \frac{\|\delta\mathbf{K}\|}{\|\mathbf{K}\|} \right)^{-1} \tag{8.49}$$

In these equations $\|\mathbf{h}\|/\|\Delta\mathbf{u}\|$ is the norm of the relative errors in the incremental response, and $\|\delta\mathbf{p}\|/\|\mathbf{p}\|$ and $\|\delta\mathbf{K}\|/\|\mathbf{K}\|$ are the norms of the relative errors in the equations. The factor $\|\mathbf{K}\| \|\mathbf{K}^{-1}\|$ is the *conditioning number* of the system, which is a system property as shown below. Using $p = 2$ subordinate vector norms for the matrices, it can be shown that [17]

$$\|K\| \|K^{-1}\| = \frac{\lambda_1}{\lambda_n} \tag{8.50}$$

where $\lambda_1$ is the largest and $\lambda_n$ is the smallest eigenvalue of $[\mathbf{K}^H\mathbf{K}]^{1/2}$ (here, $H$ shows the *Hermitian transpose*). It can be shown that the eigenvalues of $\mathbf{K}$ and $[\mathbf{K}^H\mathbf{K}]^{1/2}$ are identical when $\mathbf{K}$ is real-symmetric and positive-definite. Clearly, the transformation of the equation errors into solution errors depends on the system eigenvalues. When $\lambda_1/\lambda_n$ is a large number, one should try to reduce the equation errors more vigorously. For example, in the linear equilibrium problems of cantilevered structures it can be shown that $\lambda_1/\lambda_2$ is very large, and, therefore, one must have very small equation errors to have acceptably accurate solutions.

***Effect of System Characteristics in Eigenvalue Problems***   In eigenvalue problems, in addition to Eq. (8.44), there are no system loads. Therefore

$$\mathbf{p} = \delta\mathbf{p} = \mathbf{0} \quad \text{and} \quad \mathbf{K} = \mathbf{A} - \lambda\mathbf{B} \quad \delta\mathbf{K} = \delta\mathbf{A} - \lambda\,\delta\mathbf{B} \tag{8.51–8.53}$$

where $\lambda$ is a system parameter. In elasticity problems, $\lambda$ may be a constant showing the scale factor of initial stress magnitudes at the $\mathbf{u}_0$-state, or it may be a constant related with the free vibrational frequencies. With Eqs. (8.51) to (8.53), Eqs. (8.42) and (8.43) become

$$\mathbf{A}\,\Delta\mathbf{u} = \lambda\mathbf{B}\,\Delta\mathbf{u} \quad \text{and} \quad [\mathbf{A} + \delta\mathbf{A}]\{\Delta\mathbf{u} + \mathbf{h}\} = \lambda[\mathbf{B} + \delta\mathbf{B}]\{\Delta\mathbf{u} + \mathbf{h}\} \tag{8.54, 8.55}$$

Because of the equation errors $\delta\mathbf{A}$ and $\delta\mathbf{B}$, the eigenvalues and the eigenvectors of the exact equations of Eq. (8.54) are different from those of Eq. (8.55). The difference is the solution errors corresponding to the equation errors $\delta\mathbf{A}$ and $\delta\mathbf{B}$. The relationship between $\mathbf{A}$ and $\mathbf{B}$, and the errors in the eigenvalues and the eigenvectors, are extensively discussed in Ref. [18]. As an example, consider the case where both $\mathbf{A}$ and $\mathbf{B}$, and $\mathbf{A} + \delta\mathbf{A}$ and $\mathbf{B} + \delta\mathbf{B}$, are real and symmetric, and $\mathbf{B}$ and $\mathbf{B} + \delta\mathbf{B}$ are positive-definite (which is the case in most of the problems of linear structural mechanics). Then, both the eigenvalue problems defined in Eqs. (8.54) and (8.55) are nondefective, and they possess real eigenvalues. Let $(\lambda_i, \mathbf{v}_i)$, $i = 1, \ldots, n$, denote the eigenpairs of the exact system in Eq. (8.54). Let $(\mu, \mathbf{s})$ denote an eigenpair of the approximate problem in Eq. (8.55). Suppose $\mathbf{v}_i$, for all $i$, are normalized with $\mathbf{B}$ such that $\mathbf{V}^{-1}\mathbf{B}\mathbf{V} = \mathbf{I}$; then from Eq. (8.54) one writes that $\mathbf{A} = \mathbf{V}\,\text{diag}\,(\lambda_i)\mathbf{V}^{-1}$. From Eq. (8.55), noting that $(\mu, \mathbf{s})$ is an eigenpair, one writes

$$[\mathbf{A} - \mu \mathbf{B}]\mathbf{s} = \mathbf{d} \qquad \text{where} \qquad \mathbf{d} = [\mu\,\delta\mathbf{B} - \delta\mathbf{A}]\mathbf{s} \qquad (8.56)$$

The use of $\mathbf{A} = \mathbf{V}\,\text{diag}\,(\lambda_i)\mathbf{V}^{-1}$ and $\mathbf{B} = \mathbf{V}\mathbf{V}^{-1}$ in Eq. (8.56), after some manipulations, yields [19]

$$\min\,(\lambda_i - \mu) \le \kappa \frac{\|\mathbf{d}\|}{\|\mathbf{s}\|} \qquad \text{where} \qquad \kappa = \|\mathbf{V}\|\,\|\mathbf{V}^{-1}\| \qquad (8.57)$$

which establishes an upper bound for the error in the computed eigenvalue $\mu$ in terms of the system characteristics and the equation errors. Similar bounds may be computed for the errors in the computed eigenvectors and Rayleigh (or Schwarz) quotients [18].

***Effect of System Characteristics in Nonlinear Equilibrium Problems*** The exact and the approximate discrete equations of nonlinear equilibrium problems are as in Eqs. (8.42) and (8.43). Given the numerical values of $\mathbf{u}$, the finite-element method provides $\mathbf{f}(\mathbf{u})$ and $\mathbf{f}_{,\mathbf{u}}$ numerically. This, therefore, naturally leads to the use of the *Newton–Raphson methods* for the solution of Eq. (8.40); since, in these methods, one only needs the evaluation of $\mathbf{f}$ and its jacobian $\mathbf{f}_{,\mathbf{u}}$ at the successive estimates of the equilibrium state $\mathbf{u} = \mathbf{u}_0 + \Delta\mathbf{u}$, that is, at states $\mathbf{u}_1$, $\mathbf{u}_2, \ldots, \mathbf{u}_k \approx \mathbf{u}$ (for sufficiently large $k$). The recurrence formula defining the estimates of the successive states may be obtained from Eq. (8.41) as

$$\mathbf{u}_{k+1} = \mathbf{u}_k - [\mathbf{f}_{,\mathbf{u}}(\mathbf{u}_k) - \mathbf{r}_{,\mathbf{u}}(\mathbf{u}_k)]^{-1}\{\mathbf{f}(\mathbf{u}_k) - \mathbf{r}(\mathbf{u}_k)\} \qquad \text{for } k = 0, 1, \ldots \qquad (8.58)$$

with $\mathbf{u}_0$ known. Defining

$$\mathbf{f}_{,\mathbf{u}}(\mathbf{u}_k) = [\mathbf{K} + \delta\mathbf{K}]_k \qquad \mathbf{f}(\mathbf{u}_k) = -\{\mathbf{p} + \delta\mathbf{p}\}_k \qquad (8.59)$$

and noting that, in general, the equation error $\mathbf{r}$ is not available, and the finite-element method provides only $[\mathbf{K} + \delta\mathbf{K})_k$ and $\{\mathbf{p} + \delta\mathbf{p}\}_k$, Eq. (8.58) becomes

$$\mathbf{u}'_{k+1} = \mathbf{u}_k + \mathbf{h}_{k+1} = \mathbf{u}_k + [\mathbf{K} + \delta\mathbf{K}]^{-1}\{\mathbf{p} + \delta\mathbf{p}\}_k \qquad \text{for } k = 0, 1, \ldots \qquad (8.60)$$

with $\mathbf{h}_0 = \mathbf{0}$ and $\mathbf{u}_0$ known. Vector $\mathbf{h}_{k+1}$ represent the solution errors due to the equation errors $[\delta\mathbf{K}]_k$ and $\{\delta\mathbf{p}\}_k$ defined as

$$[\delta\mathbf{K}]_k = -\mathbf{r}_{,\mathbf{u}}(\mathbf{u}_k) \qquad \text{and} \qquad \{\delta\mathbf{p}\}_k = -\mathbf{r}(\mathbf{u}_k) \qquad (8.61)$$

Suppose when $k = m$, $\{\mathbf{p} + \delta\mathbf{p}\}_m$ is acceptably small so that $\mathbf{u}'_m$ can be used as an approximation of the true equilibrium state $\mathbf{u}_m = \mathbf{u} + \Delta\mathbf{u}$. Then, for $k = m$, using the definitions in Eqs. (8.59) to (8.61), one may write from Eqs. (8.58) and (8.60)

$$\mathbf{u}_m = \mathbf{u}_{m-1} + [\mathbf{K}]^{-1}_{m-1}\{\mathbf{p}\}_{m-1} \qquad \text{and} \qquad \mathbf{u}_m + \mathbf{h}_m = \mathbf{u}_{m-1} + [\mathbf{K} + \delta\mathbf{K}]^{-1}_{m-1}\{\mathbf{p} + \delta\mathbf{p}\}_{m-1}$$

$$(8.62, 8.63)$$

Subtracting side by side, one may write

$$\mathbf{h}_m = [\mathbf{K} + \delta\mathbf{K}]^{-1}_{m-1}\{\mathbf{p} + \delta\mathbf{p}\}_{m-1} - [\mathbf{K}]^{-1}_{m-1}\{\mathbf{p}\}_{m-1} \qquad (8.64)$$

which indicates that the solution error in the $m^{\text{th}}$ estimate is caused by $\delta\mathbf{K}$ and $\delta\mathbf{p}$ of the

$(m-1)^{\underline{\text{th}}}$ step, and it is of the type of Eq. (8.47). Thus, the discussions for the linear equilibrium problems given in this subsection apply also for the nonlinear equilibrium problems.

***Effect of System Characteristics in Propagation Problems*** The governing exact discrete equations of these problems are as in Eq. (8.3) for which the following holds:

$$\mathbf{u}(\mathbf{x}, t_0) = \mathbf{u}_0 \qquad \text{known}$$

The power-series expansion of the right-hand side of Eq. (8.3) as in Eq. (8.30) leads to

$$\{\dot{\mathbf{u}}(\mathbf{x}, t) - \dot{\mathbf{u}}_0\} = [\mathbf{f}_{,\mathbf{u}} - \mathbf{r}_{,\mathbf{u}}]_{\mathbf{u}_0}\{\mathbf{u}(\mathbf{x}, t) - \mathbf{u}_0\} + \mathbf{t}_f \tag{8.65}$$

where it is assumed that $\mathbf{t}_r = 0$, and the use is made of $\mathbf{u}(\mathbf{x}, t_0) = \mathbf{u}_0$, $0 = \mathbf{f}(\mathbf{u}_0) - \mathbf{r}(\mathbf{u}_0)$. The initial conditions for this propagation problem of $\mathbf{u}(\mathbf{x}, t) - \mathbf{u}_0$ are

$$\{\mathbf{u}(\mathbf{x}, t) - \mathbf{u}_0\}_{t=t_0} = 0 \tag{8.65a}$$

In the finite-element method, in the case of the absence of the equation errors $\mathbf{r}$, Eq. (8.65) becomes

$$\{\dot{\mathbf{u}}'(t) - \dot{\mathbf{u}}_0\} = [\mathbf{f}_{,\mathbf{u}}]_{\mathbf{u}_0}\{\mathbf{u}'(t) - \mathbf{u}_0\} + \mathbf{t}_f \tag{8.66}$$

and the initial conditions of the propagation problem of $\mathbf{u}'(t) - \mathbf{u}_0$ are

$$\{\mathbf{u}'(t) - \mathbf{u}_0\}_{t=t_0} = \mathbf{h}_0 \tag{8.67}$$

where the relationship between $\mathbf{u}(\mathbf{x}, t)$ and $\mathbf{u}'(t)$ is as in Eq. (8.29). In Eq. (8.67) $\mathbf{h}_0$ may be interpreted as the inherited error at time $t_0$. At times $t$ in the immediate vicinity of $t_0$, vector $\mathbf{t}_f$ is of second order, and it may be neglected in Eq. (8.66) in order to linearize the problem. Let $\mathbf{v}(t) \approx \mathbf{u}'(t) - \mathbf{u}_0$ denote the dependent variable of the linearized problem. Then for Eqs. (8.66) and (8.67) one may write

$$\dot{\mathbf{v}} = [\mathbf{K} + \delta\mathbf{K}]_0 \mathbf{v} \qquad \text{with} \qquad \mathbf{v}(t_0) = \mathbf{h}_0 \tag{8.68}$$

where $[\mathbf{K} + \delta\mathbf{K}]_0 = [\mathbf{f}_{,\mathbf{u}}]_{\mathbf{u}_0}$ is the coefficient matrix provided by the finite-element method. From Eq. (8.68), it may be seen that the propagation of the inherited error $\mathbf{h}_0$ is a function of the eigenvalues of $[\mathbf{K} + \delta\mathbf{K}]_0$. If all the eigenvalues are with negative real parts, then $\mathbf{h}_0$ will propagate with decreasing magnitudes. However, even one eigenvalue with a positive real part will cause the propagation of the inherited error $\mathbf{h}_0$ with increasing magnitudes. When $[\mathbf{K} + \delta\mathbf{K}]_0$ is real and symmetric, then all the eigenvalues are real and there are $n$ mutually orthogonal eigenvectors. Let $(\mu_i, \mathbf{s}_i)$, $i = 1, \ldots, n$, denote the eigenpairs of $[\mathbf{K} + \delta\mathbf{K}]_0$. Suppose the eigenvectors are normalized such that $\mathbf{S}^T\mathbf{S} = \mathbf{I}$. Then one can also write that $[\mathbf{K} + \delta\mathbf{K}]_0 = A = \mathbf{S}^T \text{diag}(\mu_i)\mathbf{S}$. By consideration of the transformation $\mathbf{v} = \mathbf{S}\boldsymbol{\xi}$, the problem in Eq. (8.68) may be rewritten as $\dot{\boldsymbol{\xi}} = \text{diag}(\mu_i)\boldsymbol{\xi}$ with the initial conditions of $\boldsymbol{\xi}(t_0) = \mathbf{S}^T\mathbf{h}_0$; the solution of which is $\boldsymbol{\xi} = \text{diag}(e^{\mu_i t})\mathbf{S}^T\mathbf{h}_0$. By transforming back one may write for the solution of Eq. (8.68) $\mathbf{v} = \mathbf{S}\,\text{diag}(e^{\mu_i t})\mathbf{S}^T\mathbf{h}_0$. This shows clearly that the positive real parts in the eigenvalues $\mu_i$ will cause the propagation of $\mathbf{h}_0$ with increasing magnitudes. This, of course, has been known for a long time, as a result of studies dealing with system stabilities [5].

In an intrinsically unstable system, the errors will tend to grow like the response itself. In such cases, rather than the absolute error, the relative error is a more meaningful quantity. In other words, for unstable systems, instead of **h**, one may consider $[h_1/u'_1, h_2/u'_2, \ldots, h_n/u'_n]^T$, provided that $u'_i \neq 0$, $i = 1, \ldots, n$.

From the above discussion, it is clear that the system characteristics play a very important role, especially in propagation problems, in the growth of the errors.

## 8.1D  Manipulation Errors

In Sec. 8.1C the manner in which the equation errors **r** are transformed into the solution errors and the effect of the intrinsic system characteristics on this transformation are discussed, under the assumption that no further errors are incorporated into the response as the discrete equations, Eqs. (8.1), are solved numerically. Since in the finite-element method the solution of Eq. (8.1) is obtained in a digital computer by means of some *solution algorithm*, unfortunately additional errors are incorporated into the solution. These additional errors are defined as the manipulation errors (see Sec. 8.1A).

There are two sources of the manipulation errors: finiteness of the computer wordlengths and the solution algorithms. The first causes further round-off errors during manipulations, and the second may cause the alteration of the growth patterns of the equation errors. Let **g** denote the manipulation errors; then

$$\mathbf{g} = \mathbf{u}_c(t) - \mathbf{u}'(t) \tag{8.69}$$

where $\mathbf{u}_c(t)$ is the computed response, and $\mathbf{u}'(t)$ is the exact solution of the approximate equations (8.1). Denoting the exact solution of the mathematical model by $\mathbf{u}(\mathbf{x}, t)$ and using Eq. (8.25), one may write

$$\mathbf{u}(\mathbf{x}, t) - \mathbf{u}_c(t) = \mathbf{g} + \mathbf{h} \tag{8.70}$$

which is the *total solution error.*

In this subsection, the manipulation errors are discussed for each class of problem dealt with in Sect. 8.1C.

***Effect of Manipulation Errors in Equilibrium Problems***   In equilibrium problems, since $\dot{\mathbf{u}}$ does not exist in the equations, the approximate discrete Eqs. (8.1) become

$$\mathbf{f}(\mathbf{u}') = \mathbf{0} \tag{8.71}$$

The power-series expansion of **f** about $\mathbf{u}_0$ may be written as

$$\mathbf{0} = \mathbf{f}(\mathbf{u}_0) + [\mathbf{f}_{,\mathbf{u}}(\mathbf{u}_0)]\{\mathbf{u}' - \mathbf{u}_0\} + \mathbf{t}_f \tag{8.72}$$

where $\mathbf{t}_f$ represents the remainder of the expansion. Given the numerical values of $\mathbf{u}_0$, the finite-element method provides the numerical values of $\mathbf{f}(\mathbf{u}_0)$ and $\mathbf{f}_{,\mathbf{u}}(\mathbf{u}_0)$ as

$$\mathbf{f}(\mathbf{u}_0) = -\{\mathbf{p} + \delta\mathbf{p}\}_0 \quad\text{and}\quad \mathbf{f}_{,\mathbf{u}}(\mathbf{u}_0) = [\mathbf{K} + \delta\mathbf{K}]_0 \tag{8.73, 8.74}$$

where the components $\delta\mathbf{p}$ and $\delta\mathbf{K}$ are the unknown equation errors already present in the computed matrices.

*Effect of Manipulation in Linear Equilibrium Problems*   In linear equilibrium problems the remainder term $\mathbf{t}_f$ in the power-series expansion is zero; then from Eqs. (8.72) to (8.74) one may write

$$[\mathbf{K} + \delta\mathbf{K}]_0\{\mathbf{u}' - \mathbf{u}_0\} = \{\mathbf{p} + \delta\mathbf{p}\}_0 \qquad (8.75)$$

where $\mathbf{u}_0$, $[\mathbf{K} + \delta\mathbf{K}]_0$, and $\{\mathbf{p} + \delta\mathbf{p}\}_0$ are known, and $\mathbf{u}'$ is unknown. One may obtain the solution of Eq. (8.75) in a digital computer by using one of the available algorithms. The solution algorithms for this problem may be classified as the *direct methods* (i.e., the *factorization techniques*), where the number of arithmetic operations is known a priori, and the *indirect methods* (i.e., the *iteration techniques*), where the number of arithmetic operations is not known a priori. In the finite-element method the factorization techniques are being used more often.

In the factorization techniques, one first finds the factors of $[\mathbf{K} + \delta\mathbf{K}]_0$ as either LU, where L is *unit lower triangular* and U is *upper triangular*, or as QR, where Q is *unitary* and R is upper triangular. In the finite-element method, usually the LU-algorithms are preferred (since, generally, $[\mathbf{K} + \delta\mathbf{K}]_0$ is real, symmetric, and banded, for which the factorization leads to $\mathbf{U}^T\mathbf{U}$ with banded U):

$$[\mathbf{K} + \delta\mathbf{K}]_0 = \mathbf{LU} \qquad (8.76)$$

This is called the *factorization* phase of the algorithm. With Eq. (8.76), Eq. (8.75) may be rewritten as

$$\mathbf{LU}\{\mathbf{u}' - \mathbf{u}_0\} = \{\mathbf{p} + \delta\mathbf{p}\}_0 \qquad (8.77)$$

Then, in the *forward-pass* phase of the algorithm, from

$$\mathbf{Lz} = \{\mathbf{p} + \delta\mathbf{p}\}_0 \qquad (8.78)$$

the auxiliary quantities $\mathbf{z}$ are easily solved owing to the special structure of L. Finally in the *backward-pass* phase, from

$$\mathbf{U}\{\mathbf{u}' - \mathbf{u}_0\} = \mathbf{z} \qquad (8.79)$$

the solution of Eq. (8.75), $\mathbf{u}' - \mathbf{u}_0$, is easily obtained with the special structure of U. However, at every phase of the algorithm, the round-off errors are introduced into the computed quantities. In actuality, instead of Eqs. (8.76), (8.78), (8.79), and (8.75), one has respectively,

$$[\mathbf{K} + \delta\mathbf{K}]_0 = \mathbf{LU} - \Delta\mathbf{K} \qquad \mathbf{Lz} = \{\mathbf{p} + \delta\mathbf{p}\}_0 + \mathbf{b} \qquad \mathbf{U}\{\mathbf{u}_c - \mathbf{u}_0\} = \mathbf{z} - \mathbf{c} \qquad (8.80\text{-}8.82)$$

and $\qquad ([\mathbf{K} + \delta\mathbf{K}]_0 + \Delta\mathbf{K})(\mathbf{u}_c - \mathbf{u}_0) = \{\mathbf{p} + \delta\mathbf{p}\}_0 + \Delta\mathbf{p} \qquad$ where $\qquad \Delta\mathbf{p} = \mathbf{b} + \mathbf{Lc} \qquad (8.83)$

In these equations $\Delta\mathbf{K}$, $\mathbf{b}$, and $\mathbf{c}$ are the round-off error effects associated with the factorization, the forward pass, and the backward pass, respectively. It may be observed from Eq. (8.83) that $\Delta\mathbf{K}$ and $\Delta\mathbf{p}$ are the counterparts of $\delta\mathbf{K}$ and $\delta\mathbf{p}$, and they are caused by the manipulation. The contribution of $\Delta\mathbf{K}$ and $\Delta\mathbf{p}$ on the solution $\mathbf{u}_c$ is the manipulation error $\mathbf{g}$. Note that the transformation of $\Delta\mathbf{K}$ and $\Delta\mathbf{p}$ into $\mathbf{g}$ is as the transformation of $\delta\mathbf{K}$ and $\delta\mathbf{p}$ into $\mathbf{h}$. This type of transformation is discussed in Sec. 8.1C.

Among the iterative methods, the *Gauss–Seidel iteration* (with *overrelaxation* and *underrelaxation* options) is most often used. In this method, Eq. (8.75) is first scaled with diag $[(k_{ii} + \delta k_{ii})^{-1}]$ such that

$$\text{diag}\,[(k_{ii} + \delta k_{ii})^{-1}][\mathbf{K} + \delta \mathbf{K}]_0 = -\mathbf{L} + \mathbf{I} - \mathbf{U} \qquad (8.84)$$

and
$$\text{diag}\,[(k_{ii} + \delta k_{ii})^{-1}]\{\mathbf{p} + \delta \mathbf{p}\}_0 = \mathbf{q} \qquad (8.85)$$

where $\mathbf{L}$ and $\mathbf{U}$ are the zero-lower-triangular and the zero-upper-triangular matrices, respectively. Defining

$$\mathbf{v}' = \mathbf{u}' - \mathbf{u}_0 \qquad (8.86)$$

Eq. (8.75) may be rewritten as

$$\mathbf{v}' = \mathbf{q} + \mathbf{L}\mathbf{v}' + \mathbf{U}\mathbf{v}' \qquad (8.87)$$

and the Gauss–Seidel iteration without relaxation is

$$\mathbf{v}'_{k+1} = \mathbf{q} + \mathbf{L}\mathbf{v}'_{k+1} + \mathbf{U}\mathbf{v}'_k \qquad \text{for } k = 0, 1, \dots, \qquad \text{with } \mathbf{v}'_0 = \mathbf{0} \qquad (8.88)$$

In actuality, due to the round-off errors during the manipulation, instead of Eqs. (8.84) to (8.86) and (8.88), one has, respectively,

$$\text{diag}\,[(k_{ii} + \delta k_{ii})^{-1}][\mathbf{K} + \delta \mathbf{K}]_0 = -\mathbf{L} + \mathbf{I} - \mathbf{U} - \text{diag}\,[(k_{ii} + \delta k_{ii})^{-1}]\,\Delta \mathbf{K} \qquad (8.89)$$

$$\text{diag}\,[(k_{ii} + \delta k_{ii})^{-1}]\{\mathbf{p} + \delta \mathbf{p}\}_0 = \mathbf{q} + \mathbf{d} \qquad (8.90)$$

$$\mathbf{v} = \mathbf{u}_c - \mathbf{u}_0 \qquad (8.91)$$

$$\mathbf{v} = \mathbf{q} + \mathbf{d} + \mathbf{L}\mathbf{v} + \mathbf{U}\mathbf{v} - \text{diag}\,[(k_{ii} + \delta k_{ii})^{-1}]\,\Delta \mathbf{K}\,\mathbf{v} \qquad (8.92)$$

and
$$\mathbf{v}_{k+1} = \mathbf{q} + \mathbf{d} + \mathbf{L}\mathbf{v}_{k+1} + \mathbf{U}\mathbf{v}_k + \mathbf{d}_k \qquad \text{for } k = 0, 1, \dots, \qquad \text{with } \mathbf{v}_0 = \mathbf{0} \qquad (8.93)$$

By back substitution one may write for (8.75)

$$([\mathbf{K} + \delta \mathbf{K}]_0 + \Delta \mathbf{K})(\mathbf{u}_c - \mathbf{u}_0) = \{\mathbf{p} + \delta \mathbf{p}\}_0 + \Delta \mathbf{p} \qquad (8.94)$$

where
$$\Delta \mathbf{p} = \text{diag}\,(k_{ii} + \delta k_{ii})\left(\mathbf{d} + \sum_k \mathbf{d}_k\right) \qquad (8.95)$$

In Eq. (8.74) $\Delta \mathbf{K}$ and $\Delta \mathbf{p}$ represent the errors caused by the manipulation (their effect in the computed response $\mathbf{u}_c$, that is, $\mathbf{g}$, is the manipulation error). The transformation of $\Delta \mathbf{K}$ and $\Delta \mathbf{p}$ into $\mathbf{g}$ is the same as the transformation of $\delta \mathbf{K}$ and $\delta \mathbf{p}$ into $\mathbf{h}$. This has already been discussed in Sec. 8.1C.

The approximate solution obtained for Eq. (8.75) by means of a digital computer and a solution algorithm is essentially the exact solution of Eq. (8.83) or (8.94). Thus, the knowledge of $\Delta \mathbf{K}$ and $\Delta \mathbf{p}$ would enable one to obtain the exact solution $\mathbf{u}'$ of Eq. (8.75) by Eq. (8.69), just as the knowledge of $\delta \mathbf{K}$ and $\delta \mathbf{p}$ would enable one to obtain the exact solution $\mathbf{u}(\mathbf{x}, t)$ of Eq. (8.40) by Eq. (8.29). However, the computation of $\Delta \mathbf{K}$ and $\Delta \mathbf{p}$ is a much harder problem than the computation of $\delta \mathbf{K}$ and $\delta \mathbf{p}$. The main difficulty is in the apparent randomness of the rounding-off processes. Other factors determining the magnitudes of $\Delta\mathbf{K}$ and $\Delta\mathbf{p}$ are those discussed for Eqs. (8.12) to (8.17), and also the type of the algorithm. A good account of possibilities and difficulties for the most-used algorithms is given in Ref. [19]. In general, the magnitudes of $\Delta\mathbf{K}$ and $\Delta\mathbf{p}$ are smaller if $[\mathbf{K} + \delta\mathbf{K}]_0$ is of small order, banded, symmetric, and positive-definite, and has a small conditioning number. Obviously, the algorithms which take advantage of these properties, when they exist, produce smaller-magnitude $\Delta\mathbf{K}$ and $\Delta\mathbf{p}$.

***Effect of Manipulation in Eigenvalue Problems***   Eigenvalue problems are the special case of the linear equilibrium problems discussed in the preceding subsection. For this class of problems, in Eq. (8.72),

$$\mathbf{t}_f = 0 \qquad \mathbf{f}(\mathbf{u}_0) = 0 \qquad [\mathbf{f}_{,u}(\mathbf{u}_0)] = [\mathbf{A} + \delta\mathbf{A}] - \lambda[\mathbf{B} + \delta\mathbf{B}] \qquad (8.96\text{-}8.98)$$

and thus it becomes

$$[\mathbf{A} + \delta\mathbf{A}]\{\mathbf{u}' - \mathbf{u}_0\} = \lambda[\mathbf{B} + \delta\mathbf{B}]\{\mathbf{u}' - \mathbf{u}_0\} \qquad (8.99)$$

which is a general algebraic eigenvalue problem. In Eq. (8.99), $\delta\mathbf{A}$ and $\delta\mathbf{B}$ represent the equation errors, and the finite-element method produces the numerical values of $[\mathbf{A} + \delta\mathbf{A}]$ and $[\mathbf{B} + \delta\mathbf{B}]$.

Since usually $n > 4$, the solution of these problems is essentially obtained by a digital computer and iterative solution algorithms. During the iterations, many round-off errors take place, and the solutions thus obtained are approximate for Eq. (8.99) but basically exact for a modified problem such as

$$[\mathbf{A} + \delta\mathbf{A} + \Delta\mathbf{A}]\{\mathbf{u}_c - \mathbf{u}_0\} = \lambda[\mathbf{B} + \delta\mathbf{B} + \Delta\mathbf{B}]\{\mathbf{u}_c - \mathbf{u}_0\} \qquad (8.100)$$

where $\Delta\mathbf{A}$ and $\Delta\mathbf{B}$ represent the modifications caused by the manipulations. The effect of $\Delta\mathbf{A}$ and $\Delta\mathbf{B}$ on the computed eigenvalues and eigenvectors are the manipulation errors. Note that in Eq. (8.100) $\Delta\mathbf{A}$ and $\Delta\mathbf{B}$ play the same role as $\delta\mathbf{A}$ and $\delta\mathbf{B}$. Therefore, the discussions of the previous section related with the effects of $\delta\mathbf{A}$ and $\delta\mathbf{B}$ on the computed eigenpairs also apply to those of $\Delta\mathbf{A}$ and $\Delta\mathbf{B}$. The problem of quantifying $\Delta\mathbf{A}$ and $\Delta\mathbf{B}$ is usually a harder problem than quantifying $\delta\mathbf{A}$ and $\delta\mathbf{B}$. The main difficulty lies again in the apparent randomness of the rounding-off processes. Other factors determining the magnitudes of $\Delta\mathbf{A}$ and $\Delta\mathbf{B}$ are those discussed for Eqs. (8.12) to (8.17), and also the type of the solution algorithm. A good account of possibilities and difficulties for more-often used algorithms is given in Ref. [19]. In general, the magnitudes of $\Delta\mathbf{A}$ and $\Delta\mathbf{B}$ are smaller if $[\mathbf{A} + \delta\mathbf{A}]$ and $[\mathbf{B} + \delta\mathbf{B}]$ are of small order, banded, real, symmetric, and positive-definite. Obviously, the algorithms which take advantage of these, when they exist, produce smaller-magnitude $\Delta\mathbf{A}$ and $\Delta\mathbf{B}$.

***Effect of Manipulation in Nonlinear Equilibrium Problems***   The discrete governing equations and their power-series expansions for these problems are as in Eqs. (8.71) and (8.72). In these problems the remainder in Eq. (8.72) is not zero. The usual method of solving these problems is the Newton–Raphson iteration as given in Eq. (8.60), since, given a $\mathbf{u}_k$, the finite-element method provides $\mathbf{f}(\mathbf{u}_k)$ and $\mathbf{f}_{,u}(\mathbf{u}_k)$ as $-\{\mathbf{p} + \delta\mathbf{p}\}_k$ and $[\mathbf{K} + \delta\mathbf{K}]_k$, respectively. One may see from Eq. (8.60) that, to obtain the response at the $(k+1)^{\text{th}}$ step, one has to solve a set of linear equations of the type of Eq. (8.75). This indicates that the computed response contains also the manipulation errors; it is essentially the exact solution of a set of modified equations as in Eq. (8.94). Let $\mathbf{u}'_k$ denote the response at step $k$ without the manipulation errors, $\mathbf{g}_k$ denote the manipulation errors such that $\mathbf{u}'_k + \mathbf{g}_k$ is the computed response $\mathbf{u}_{c,k}$, and $[\Delta \mathbf{K}]_k$ and $\{\Delta \mathbf{p}\}_k$ denote the modifications caused in the equations by the manipulation. Thus, instead of

$$\mathbf{u}'_{k+1} = \mathbf{u}'_k + [\mathbf{K} + \delta \mathbf{K}]_k^{-1}\{\mathbf{p} + \delta \mathbf{p}\}_k \qquad \text{for } k = 0, 1, \ldots, \qquad \text{with } \mathbf{u}'_0 = \mathbf{0} \qquad (8.101)$$

one has

$$\mathbf{u}'_{k+1} + \mathbf{g}_{k+1} = \mathbf{u}'_k + [\mathbf{K} + \delta \mathbf{K} + \Delta \mathbf{K}]_k^{-1}\{\mathbf{p} + \delta \mathbf{p} + \Delta \mathbf{p}\}_k \qquad k = 0, 1, \ldots, \qquad \text{with } \mathbf{u}'_0 = \mathbf{0} \quad (8.102)$$

Suppose when $k = m$, the residue $\{\mathbf{p} + \delta \mathbf{p}\}_m$ is sufficiently small so that $\mathbf{u}_{c,k+1} = u_{k+1} + \mathbf{g}_{k+1}$ can be used as the solution representing the equilibrium state. Then, subtracting Eq. (8.101) and Eq. (8.102) side by side, and using $m$ for $k+1$, one may write

$$\mathbf{g}_m = [\mathbf{K} + \delta \mathbf{K} + \Delta \mathbf{K}]_{m-1}^{-1}\{\mathbf{p} + \delta \mathbf{p} + \Delta \mathbf{p}\}_{m-1} - [\mathbf{K} + \delta \mathbf{K}]_{m-1}^{-1}\{\mathbf{p} + \delta \mathbf{p}\}_{m-1} \qquad (8.103)$$

which indicates that the manipulation error at the $m^{\text{th}}$ step is caused by $\Delta \mathbf{K}$ and $\Delta \mathbf{p}$ of the $(m-1)^{\text{th}}$ step, and the relationship is of the type of Eq. (8.63). Thus, it is established that the manipulation errors have a similar effect on the solution as the discretization. It is important to note that the manipulation errors of steps preceding the $(m-1)^{\text{th}}$ step reflect on the solution as inherited errors, and their effects are in $\delta \mathbf{K}$ and $\delta \mathbf{p}$.

There are various variants of the basic Newton–Raphson algorithm, and they are all being widely used. As the algorithm changes, the quantities $\Delta \mathbf{K}$, $\Delta \mathbf{p}$, and $m$ all change. In other words, the manipulation errors are very much algorithm-dependent. The assessment of $\Delta \mathbf{K}$ and $\Delta \mathbf{p}$ is very difficult mainly because of the apparent randomness of the rounding-off processes. The factors discussed for Eqs. (8.12) to (8.17) also directly affect the magnitudes of $\Delta \mathbf{K}$ and $\Delta \mathbf{p}$.

**Effect of Manipulation in Propagation Problems**   In propagation problems the equations are as in Eq. (8.1), with the known initial conditions $\mathbf{u}(\mathbf{x}, t_0)$, i.e.,

$$\dot{\mathbf{u}}'(t) = \mathbf{f}(\mathbf{u}'(t)) \qquad \text{for } t > t_0 \qquad (8.104)$$

and

$$\mathbf{u}(\mathbf{x}, t_0) = \mathbf{u}'_0 \qquad \text{known at} \qquad t = t_0 \qquad (8.105)$$

In the numerical solutions of these equations, the time variable $t$ is considered by its discrete values $t_k$ such that

$$t_{k+1} = t_k + \hbar_k \qquad k = 0, 1, \ldots \qquad (8.106)$$

where $t_k$ is the time at the $k^{\text{th}}$ discrete station, and $\hbar_k$ is the time increment in station $k$. In many algorithms $\hbar_k$ is taken as constant, that is,

$$\hbar_k = \hbar \qquad k = 0, 1, \ldots \qquad (8.107)$$

and in many other algorithms it can be varied from station to station. The numerical solutions provide the values of the response only at the discrete time stations, chronologically, starting with $\mathbf{u}_0'$ as $\mathbf{u}_c(t_k)$, $k = 0, 1, \ldots$, instead of $\mathbf{u}'(t_k)$, $k = 0, 1, \ldots$. The difference $\mathbf{g}_k = \mathbf{g}(t_k)$, $k = 0, 1, \ldots$, defined as

$$\mathbf{g}_k = \mathbf{u}_c(t_k) - \mathbf{u}'(t_k) \tag{8.108}$$

is due to the manipulations with a finite machine and an approximate algorithm. Of course, at the $k^{\text{th}}$ station, one also has the solution errors due to discretization, $\mathbf{h}(t_k) = \mathbf{h}_k$:

$$\mathbf{h}_k = \mathbf{u}'(t_k) - \mathbf{u}(\mathbf{x}, t_k) \tag{8.109}$$

Suppose the solution of Eq. (8.104) is already marched out up to the $k^{\text{th}}$ station, and the response for station $k+1$ is to be computed. As far as this computation is concerned, the quantity $\mathbf{e}_k$ defined as

$$\mathbf{e}_k = \mathbf{h}_k + \mathbf{g}_k \tag{8.110}$$

(i.e., the *total solution error* at station $k$) is the inherited error. The numerical solution at time station $k+1$, i.e., $\mathbf{u}_c(t_{k+1})$, will contain not only the propagated version of the inherited error $\mathbf{e}_k$, but also the round-off errors $\mathbf{e}_k^r$ of the arithmetic operations of the step and the truncation errors $\mathbf{e}_k^t$ of the step due to the approximate nature of the algorithm. Let $\mathbf{A}_k$ denote the mechanism by which the inherited errors $\mathbf{e}_k$ at the time $t_k$ propagate to time $t_{k+1}$. With this, one may write

$$\mathbf{e}_{k+1} = \mathbf{A}_k \mathbf{e}_k + \mathbf{e}_k^r + \mathbf{e}_k^t \tag{8.111}$$

Clearly, $\mathbf{e}_k^r$ and $\mathbf{e}_k^t$ are algorithm-dependent. It is shown below that $\mathbf{A}_k$ is also algorithm-dependent. Therefore, $\mathbf{A}_k$, $\mathbf{e}_k^t$, and $\mathbf{e}_k^r$, $k = 0, 1, \ldots$, represent the effect of the manipulations.

In the finite-element method, given $\mathbf{u}_c(t_k)$, one has the numerical values of the vector function $\mathbf{f}$ and its jacobian $\mathbf{f}_{,\mathbf{u}}$ for $\mathbf{u}_c(t_k)$, rather than the explicit expressions of the equations in Eq. (8.104). Let $\mathbf{f}_k$ and $\mathbf{f}_{,k}$ denote the values of $\mathbf{f}$ and $\mathbf{f}_{,\mathbf{u}}$ at $\mathbf{u}_c(t_k)$. Namely,

$$\mathbf{f}_k = \mathbf{f}(\mathbf{u}_c(t_k)) = -\{\mathbf{p} + \delta\mathbf{p}\}_{t=t_k} \quad \text{and} \quad \mathbf{f}_{,k} = \mathbf{f}_{,\mathbf{u}}(\mathbf{u}_c(t_k)) = [\mathbf{K} + \delta\mathbf{K}]_{t=t_k} \tag{8.112, 8.113}$$

Many of the algorithms with which one may march out the numerical solution may be expressed as

$$\mathbf{u}_c(t_{k+1}) = \mathbf{u}_c(t_{k-q}) + (q+1)\hbar \, (\text{weighted average of } \mathbf{f}_i, \ i = k, \ldots) \tag{8.114}$$

where $q$ is a nonnegative integer and $\hbar$ is the time increment (if the time increments are variable, $\hbar$ represents some averaged value). If $q = 0$, and $\mathbf{f}_i$-values used in the "weighted average" are for $\mathbf{u}_c(t)$ with $t_k \leq t \leq t_{k+1}$, the algorithms are called the *single-step methods* (such as the Euler method and the Runge–Kutta methods), whereas, if $q > 0$, and $\mathbf{f}_i$-values used in the "weighted average" are those of the time stations, the algorithms are called the *multistep methods* (various predictor and predictor-corrector methods). For multistep methods, Eq. (8.114) may be rewritten as

$$\mathbf{u}_c(t_{k+1}) = \mathbf{u}_c(t_{k-q}) + (q+1)\hbar \sum_{i=0}^{r} \beta_i \mathbf{f}_{k+s-i} \tag{8.115}$$

where $s$ is either 0 or 1, and $r \geqslant 0$. If $s = 0$, the methods are called *open-type* or *predictor* methods. If $s = 1$, the methods are called *closed-type* or *corrector* methods. It may be observed that the multistep methods are not *self-starting* (i.e., initially one needs the response at several time stations in order to use them), and the corrector methods require the use of a predictor [since the corrector requires $\mathbf{f}_{k+1}$ for the prediction of $\mathbf{u}_c(t_{k+1})$].

Each of the above methods employs different amounts of arithmetic operations, and each has different truncation errors. One may compute different responses $\mathbf{u}_c(t_{k+1})$ for the $(k+1)^{\text{th}}$ station by using different methods, all using the same data at the $k^{\text{th}}$ station. The derivation of the equations of the type of (8.114) for various methods is such that, as a by-product, one also obtains expressions for their truncation errors (basically, by matching the interpolating polynomials with the power-series expansions, and using the remainder theorem). The expressions for the truncation errors are of the type

$$\mathbf{e}_r^t = \boldsymbol{\rho} O(\hbar^p) \qquad (8.116)$$

where $\boldsymbol{\rho}$ lists the values of the higher-order derivatives at some unknown time, $\hbar$ is the time increment at station $k$, and $p$ is a positive integer. The expressions for the truncation errors indicate concisely how fast the truncation errors will vanish with decreasing size of time increments. Unfortunately, the expressions for round-off errors cannot be expressed as easily, although some upper-bound values may be stated for the components of $\mathbf{e}_k^r$. It is interesting to note that, as $p$ increases in Eq. (8.116), the truncation errors of the method vanish rapidly with decreasing mesh size; however, meanwhile, the magnitudes of the round-off errors grow. The methods with large $p$ are called *higher-order methods*.

As mentioned in the discussion of Eq. (8.111), the third element of the manipulation errors, i.e., matrix $\mathbf{A}_k$, is method-dependent and also depends on the intrinsic properties of the system as represented by the jacobian matrix $\mathbf{f}_{,k}$. This can be shown by a simple example. Suppose a single-step method is being used and $\hbar$ is sufficiently small. Then Eq. (8.114) may be rewritten as

$$\mathbf{u}_c(t_{k+1}) \approx \mathbf{u}_c(t_k) + \hbar \mathbf{f}_{,k} \mathbf{u}_c(t_k) \qquad (8.117)$$

where it is assumed that $\mathbf{f}_i$-values in the interval of $t_k - t_{k+1}$ do not change, and they may be approximated by $\mathbf{f}_i \approx f_{,i} \mathbf{u}_c(t_i)$ [see the discussions leading to the linearized Eqs. (8.68)]. One may rewrite Eqs. (8.117) as

$$\mathbf{u}_c(t_{k+1}) \approx \mathbf{A}_k \mathbf{u}_c(t_k) \qquad \text{where} \qquad \mathbf{A}_k = \mathbf{I} + \hbar \mathbf{f}_{,k} = \mathbf{I} + \hbar[\mathbf{K} + \delta\mathbf{K}]_{t=t_k} \qquad (8.118, 8.119)$$

Since Eq. (8.118) shows the propagation of the solution at $t_k$ into that of $t_{k+1}$, matrix $\mathbf{A}_k$ in Eq. (8.118) is the same as the one in Eq. (8.111). Matrix $\mathbf{A}_k$ is clearly system-dependent through the jacobian $\mathbf{f}_{,k}$, and algorithm-dependent through the time increment $\hbar$ and the way it is related to $\mathbf{f}_{,k}$. One may observe from Eq. (8.118) that, if the eigenvalues of $\mathbf{A}_k$ are inside the unit circle centered at the origin of the complex plane, the propagation process will be with decreasing magnitudes; otherwise, it will be with increasing magnitudes. Matrix $\mathbf{A}_k$ is a *matrix polynomial* of the jacobian $\mathbf{f}_{,k}$; therefore, the eigenvalues of $\mathbf{A}_k$ are 1 plus the $\hbar$-multiple of those of $\mathbf{f}_{,k}$. From this, it can be shown that, if $\mathbf{f}_{,k}$ is such that the system is unstable, i.e., there is at least one eigenvalue of $\mathbf{f}_{,k}$ with a positive real part, then there will be at least one eigenvalue of $\mathbf{A}_k$ outside the unit circle, regardless of the value of the time increment $k$. On the other hand, even if the system is stable, i.e., none of the eigenvalues of $\mathbf{f}_{,k}$ is with real positive part, by improper choice of the time increment $k$, one may have some of the eigenvalues of $\mathbf{A}_k$ fall outside the unit circle. In other words, the algorithm may change a stable system into an unstable one.

In the multistep methods, the structure of $\mathbf{A}_k$ depends on the algorithm more than in the single-step methods. Here, too, $\mathbf{A}_k$ is a matrix polynomial of $\mathbf{f}_{,k}$, where the degree of the polynomial is greater than 1, and the polynomial coefficients depend on not only $k$ but also $\beta_i$, $i = 0, 1, \ldots$, the coefficients of the algorithm. Let $p(\mathbf{f}_{,k}) = \mathbf{A}_k$ denote the matrix polynomial. If the eigenvalues of $\mathbf{f}_{,k}$ are $\mu_i$, $i = 1, 2, \ldots, n$, then the eigenvalues of $\mathbf{A}_k$ are $p(\mu_i)$, $i = 1, 2, \ldots, n$. Clearly even if all $\mu_i$ are with negative real parts, i.e., the system is stable, $p(\mu_i)$ may be such that they may fall outside the unit circle centered at the origin of the complex plane either by the wrong choice of $k$ or by the wrong choice of the algorithm, or both, and thus may cause instabilities by enlarging the magnitudes of the inherited errors without bound.

## 8.1E  Current Research on Error Prediction

In the preceding sections, various errors which may take place in the finite-element analysis are defined, and the factors affecting their magnitudes and growth are discussed. The finite-element method, in essence, is the computation of the vector function $\mathbf{f}$ and its jacobian $\mathbf{f}_{,u}$, related to Eq. (8.1). The errors in the computed response, in one way or another, are all associated with the errors in the numerical values of $\mathbf{f}$ and $\mathbf{f}_{,u}$. These errors are essentially due to discretization and manipulation, since the inherited errors are the propagated versions of the discretization and manipulation errors committed earlier. In other words, the building blocks of the solution errors are the errors in the numerical values of the jacobian $\mathbf{f}_{,u}$, that is, $\delta\mathbf{K}^d$, $\delta\mathbf{K}^r$, $\Delta\mathbf{K}$, and in the numerical values of the vector function $\mathbf{f}$, that is, $-\delta\mathbf{p}^d$, $-\delta\mathbf{p}^r$, $\Delta\mathbf{p}$ where $d$ and $r$ refer to discretization and round-off, and $\delta$ to equation phase and $\Delta$ to solution phase). In the finite-element method, instead of $\mathbf{f}$ and $\mathbf{f}_{,u}$, one deals with $\mathbf{f} - \delta\mathbf{p} - \delta\mathbf{p}^d - \delta\mathbf{p}^r - \Delta\mathbf{p}$ and $\mathbf{f}_{,u} + \delta\mathbf{K}^d + \delta\mathbf{K}^r + \Delta\mathbf{K}$ ($\delta\mathbf{p}$ representing the inherited error). The knowledge of the blocks enables one to compute the solution error.

In the following paragraphs, a short review of the published works on the solution errors in the finite-element method is given. The references are only to indicate the trends, and are by no means complete.

*Computation of the Equation Round-off Errors*   The quantities $\delta\mathbf{p}^r$, $\delta\mathbf{p}$, $\delta\mathbf{K}^r$, and $\Delta\mathbf{K}$ are the basic blocks of the manipulation error analysis. Yet in the recent finite-element literature almost no work is available dealing with either a priori or *a posteriori* evaluation of these quantities. Probably this is owing partly to the difficult nature of the problem, and partly to the existence of a rather easy and yet effective measure for controlling the magnitudes of the round-off errors (discussed in the next section). However, in the finite-difference literature one may find many interesting investigations on this matter [2]. Once these equation errors are evaluated, the computation of their effects in both the equilibrium and the propagation problems can easily be done as outlined earlier. The methods of such computations have been extensively studied in the texts of numerical analysis [19–21].

*Computation of the Equation Discretization Errors*   The quantities $\delta\mathbf{K}^d$ and $\delta\mathbf{p}^d$ are the basic blocks of discretization error analysis. Once they are numerically available, the computation of their effects in the response can easily be computed as discussed earlier. The methods of such computations have been extensively studied in the texts of numerical analysis [19–22]. The adaptation of these methods for the finite-element analysis has been proposed [10, 11].

**A Priori Computation of $\delta\mathbf{K}^d$ and $\delta\mathbf{p}^d$**    The quantities $\delta\mathbf{K}^d$ and $\delta\mathbf{p}^d$ are governed essentially by the remainder theorem of the power-series expansions. Since the evaluation of the higher-order derivatives of the response quantities at unknown points is required for their definition, a priori estimation of these quantities is impossible unless the response is such that the higher-order derivatives appearing in the expressions for $\delta\mathbf{K}^d$ and $\delta\mathbf{p}^d$ are all zero. There have been few efforts in the finite-element literature dealing with the expressions for these quantities [12–15].

**A Posteriori Computation of $\delta\mathbf{K}^d$ and $\delta\mathbf{p}^d$**    A *posteriori* computation of the equation discretization errors $\delta\mathbf{K}^d$ and $\delta\mathbf{p}^d$ is quite possible [10, 11]. This has been done in the finite-difference method for a long time [21, 22]. In the finite-element method, investigators have been looking into this problem only recently [14, 15, 23, 24].

*Computation of Some Norm of the Solution Discretization Error*    In the recent literature, this is the most active area in the error problem of the finite-element method. Most work has been confined to the linear equilibrium problems with positive-definite and self-adjoint operators. Many investigators, motivated by the problem of convergence in the finite-element method, tried to obtain an upper-bound value for some norm of the solution discretization errors in the form of $K\hbar^p$, where $K$ and $p$ are constants, and $\hbar$ is a typical mesh size. The true solution of the discretized problem, $\Psi(\mathbf{x}, t)$, is as defined in Eq. (8.18). The true solution of the mathematical model is $u(\mathbf{x}, t)$. Let $D$ denote the spatial domain of the problem. Then, for the Euclid norm of the solution discretization error at time $t$, $\pi_E(t)$, may be expressed as

$$\pi_E(t) = \|u(\mathbf{x}, t) - \Psi(\mathbf{x}, t)\|_E = \sqrt{\int_D (u(\mathbf{x}, t) - \Psi(\mathbf{x}, t))^2 \, dD} \qquad (8.120)$$

Let $\pi$ denote any norm of the solution discretization error at time $t$. Given a mesh with typical mesh size $\hbar$, if one writes

$$\pi \leqslant K\hbar^p \qquad (8.121)$$

what is the minimum value of $p$ for which Eq. (8.121) is true? Is $K$ a true constant? The answers to these questions may be found in Refs. [25–36].

In the linear elasticity problems, many investigators dealt with the *energy norms* [i.e., the positive-definite-quadratic-form norm as in Eq. (8.9), defined over domain $D$] of the finite-element solutions. They showed that, depending upon the type of functional used, the energy norms may constitute a *minimizing* or *maximizing sequence* with mesh refinement [1, 3, 20, 37, 38]. The fact that, by changing the functional, one can obtain the upper and lower bounds of the energy norms is important especially in the eigenvalue problems, where the energy norms are quite closely related with the eigenvalues, and in the equilibrium problems with a single concentrated load, where the energy norms are the scaled values of the displacement in the direction of the single concentrated load.

The studies dealing with bounding the norms of the discretization errors have no doubt shed light on the convergence problem of the finite-element method. However, they are of limited help in assessing the errors in the computed-response quantities $u_c(t)$.

## 8.1F State of the Art of Error Estimation

Because of the difficulties in quantitative estimation through numerical analysis, the current practice in assessing the solution errors in the computed-response quantities is through computer experimentation, and it is mostly confined to the linear equilibrium problems. In these experiments, the same problem is solved repeatedly, each time halving the mesh size. Then for each point (or for selected mesh points) in the crude mesh the response is plotted against the mesh size. The study of these plots enables one to assess the errors as discussed below.

*State of the Art of Estimation for Solution Errors Due to Manipulation*   Because of their apparently random character, the effect of round-off errors is reflected erratically on the response–mesh-size curves. These curves assume a randomly oscillating form when the solution errors due to round-off are large (Fig. 2.41 of Ref. [39] is a good example). Once such a behavior is identified, the errors can be controlled by using larger mesh sizes, or longer mantissa lengths, or both.

Algorithmic portions of the manipulation errors usually manifest themselves by extremely large computed-response quantities. When they are identified, their control is first attempted by varying the parameters of the algorithm (such as decreasing the time increment in propagation problems or readjusting the relaxation parameter in the iterative methods). If this fails, one usually changes the algorithm, hoping that the new one will work.

*State of the Art of Estimation for Solution Errors Due to Discretization*   Since discretization errors decrease with decreasing mesh size, the response–mesh-size curves assume a converging appearance with decreasing mesh size, if no other error exists in the response quantities. If the convergence is *monotonic*, one may use *Richardson's extrapolation technique* to find the value of the response corresponding to zero mesh size [40–43]. This technique is based on two assumptions: (1) the error is caused by only the discretization; (2) the discretization error decreases monotonically with decreasing mesh size. The assumptions are valid assumptions if the manipulation errors are rendered negligible as discussed above, and if the finite-element representations are as defined in Sect. 8.1A. The application of Richardson's extrapolation techniques for the finite-element method has already appeared in the literature [28, 44, 45].

In Richardson's extrapolation, at a point, one assumes

$$u_c - u = K\hbar^p \tag{8.122}$$

where $u_c$ is the computed response, $u$ is its value without discretization errors, $\hbar$ is the typical mesh size, and $K$ and $p$ are constants to be determined as a result of computer experimentation. Since Eq. (8.112) contains three values to be determined (that is, $u$, $K$, and $p$), one needs at least three experiments with typical mesh sizes $\hbar_1$, $\hbar_2$, and $\hbar_3$ to yield the responses at the points $u_{c_1}$, $u_{c_2}$, and $u_{c_3}$, respectively. By writing Eq. (8.122) for $(u_{c_i}, \hbar_i)$, $i = 1, 2, 3$, one obtains three equations from which $K$, $p$, and $u$ may be obtained.

## 8.1G Conclusions

From the discussions in this section, the following conclusions may be drawn:

1. The errors in the computed results originate from two sources: the round-off errors in the numerical representations, and the discretization errors caused by representing the infinite-degree-of-freedom response by finite degrees of freedom. These errors may be represented as the equation errors.

2. Depending upon the system characteristics, the equation errors reflect on the solution by changing their magnitudes.

3. The algorithms used in obtaining the solution from the equations contribute further to the solution errors in two ways: by causing more round-off errors and by altering the system characteristics.

4. The combined system-algorithm characteristics play a very important role in the error propagation, especially in the propagation problems.

5. The jacobian $\mathbf{f}_{,\mathbf{u}}$ computed by means of the finite-element method possesses very favorable system characteristics (such as symmetry, positive-definiteness, and bandedness) for error reduction, provided that one uses those solution algorithms which take advantage of these favorable properties.

6. Very little has been done in assessing the equation errors in the finite-element method, although the mechanisms by which these reflect on the solution are very well understood.

7. The studies trying to obtain bounds for the norms of the discretization errors in terms of typical mesh sizes are very useful in understanding the convergence problem, but they are of limited help in assessing the errors in a meaningful way.

8. Although it is possible to handle the error problem, no components exist in the present finite-element software to do so.

9. In order to assess the errors by computer experiments, the same problem should be solved at least three times by gradually refining the finite-element mesh. Then, the response–mesh-size plots should be produced for each mesh point of the crudest mesh, if possible.

10. In the response–mesh-size plots the erratic appearance signals the presence of excessive round-off errors.

11. Richardson's extrapolation technique may be applied successfully to the response–mesh-size curves to find the response for infinitely small mesh size, if the discretization is the only reason for the errors, and if the results are obtained by means of the conforming elements.

## 8.2 PRINCIPLES FOR DESIGN OF FINITE-ELEMENT MESHES

### 8.2A Introduction

The goal of mesh design is to select the number and location of finite-element nodes and element types so that the associated analyses will be accurate enough. For the "best" mesh, accuracy is attained by using least resources for the design and analysis processes [78].

The best mesh is characterized by economy, simplicity, and discipline. Because it involves fewer degrees of freedom and lower-degree element types, this mesh requires fewer calculations for the analysis [46]. Since the mesh avoids disparate nodal spacing and extreme element geometrics, extra calculations to control the manipulation errors associated with these irregularities are avoided [47, 48]. Since the grid is fine enough to furnish reliable measures of discretization error [49, 50], excessively fine meshes are excluded.

Data on meshing abound in the literature. Much of this data has as its primary value the building of credibility of the accuracy of proposed element models as a function of grid refinement. Of more direct interest are the citations that appear in the reference section at the end of this chapter. This bibliography, compiled by Dave Turcke (and updated for this chapter), is the most complete bibliography of papers on finite-element meshing known to the authors.

Notable among previous work are the studies of Ebner, Case and Mason, Mallett, and Key [51]. These studies expose the complexity of mesh designing and provide some guidelines covering problems of idealization and discretization.

Research studies on nodal arrangement and refinement provide a narrower and deeper understanding of the mesh-design problem. The importance, theorems, and pragmatics of optimum nodal siting have been researched by McNeice and Marcal [49], Turcke and McNeice [52], Carroll and Barker [53], and Babuska and Rheinboldt [54], among others. The importance, theorems, and sensors for focused grid refinements have been the fruit of investigations by Melosh and Killian [55], Babuska [56], Szabo and Mehta [57], Shephard [58], and others. Study of a design strategy in which both element type and grid refinement are treated as design variables is a recent development [57], suggesting that mesh-design technology is still evolving.

This chapter reviews principles of good mesh design using results of an extensive study of the torsion problem. Thereby, it provides a context within which observations of all researchers can be placed. It addresses errors in replacing the continuum by discrete elements in linear finite-element analysis. (Research in meshing for nonlinear problems is just beginning and will involve more extensive study.)

The chapter proceeds from definitions through mesh-refinement strategy. The next section defines the mesh-design problem and terminology. Subsequent sections introduce the principles of mesh arrangement and evolution. The last section cites generalizations for mesh designing.

Throughout the chapter, mesh-design principles are set off as single-numbered items. Proven principles are italicized. Principles which are confirmed, without exception, by numerical experiments are not italicized.

The authors wish to express their appreciation to Dr. Ivo Babuska for his careful review of this chapter and the suggestions he made to strengthen it.


## 8.2B  Definitions

Given the mathematical idealization of an engineering system and the subset of finite-element models that may be used in the analysis, then the mesh-design problem is to establish an acceptable discretization. The discretization is particularized by selecting the number of nodes and elements and the arrangement of nodes and element types so the associated analysis produces response predictions of adequate accuracy.

For a structural system, the idealization is established by selection of mathematical models of the geometry, material behavior, and boundary conditions. The subset of element types may include any of the large number of element types described in the literature. For a membrane, for example, available shapes include triangular, quadrilateral, and pentagonal, and behavior variables include displacements and displacement derivatives as generalized coordinates. For structures, typical responses of interest are deflections, stresses, stiffnesses, vibration modes, and stability limits.

We may visualize the design as a point in the three-dimensional design space of Fig. 8.1. The primary coordinates of the point are the number of nodes and the element type (or types). These are primary in the sense that varying either coordinate independently is sufficient to develop an acceptable mesh for most grids an analyst might select. The secondary coordinate is mesh arrangement: the siting of nodes and the disposition of element types. Varying mesh arrangement has an impact upon efficiency of the analysis.

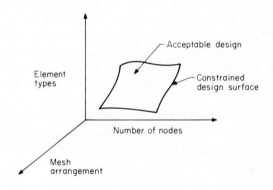

| Design variables | | |
| --- | --- | --- |
| Nodal | Element type | Arrangement |
| Displacement components | Trial functions | Nodal spacing |
| | Nodal pattern | Element shape |
| Displacement continuity | Formulation basis | Connectivity of nodes |
| Displacement B.C. models | Strain-disp. model | Allocation of element types |
| Equivalent-load models | Material-behavior constraints | Allocation of B.C. models |

**FIG. 8.1**   Mesh-design space.

Constraints on mesh designs consist of limitations on computer resources and arrangements. Resource constraints are important: they make it impossible to find an acceptable mesh. In examining design principles, however, they can be ignored. Constraints on mesh arrangement limit nodal spacing and element shapes. (The elements must fill the space; extreme element geometrics must be avoided; relatively closely spaced nodes are inadmissible; symmetric structures must have symmetric meshes; etc.) These constraints may be viewed as limiting the design point to particular surfaces in the design space.

Among all meshes which are acceptable, we seek the mesh which minimizes the resources required for the design and analysis processes. This complicates discussion of mathematical error bounds and convergence rates with a discussion of actual accuracy, effective convergence rates, and the efficiency of design and solution algorithms and software.

We consider four types of meshes: optimum, regular, focused, and undisciplined.

In an optimum mesh, the nodal coordinates are selected so that the potential is minimized with respect to the nodal coordinates as well as the nodal-response variables. This defines the "extended finite-element analysis method" [61].

A regular mesh is one in which the elemental-equation discretization error bound for the element is the same for every element of the grid. In the simplest regular grid, every element is the same type, shape, and size.

Focused grids are irregular meshes in which the elemental-equation discretization error is reduced in one or more local regions by spatial concentration of generalized coordinates. These meshes are developed from a parent mesh by considering inefficiencies of the parent mesh in estimating system responses. In a sequence of focused meshes, the originating parent is the "root parent," or "root."

Undisciplined meshes are irregular, have no parent, and are nonoptimum.

These mesh-arrangement policies can be embedded in a mesh-evolution policy. The policy may be an $h$, a $p$, or a mixed policy. In an $h$-policy successive meshes involve only decreases in grid interval. In a $p$-policy, element trial functions are replaced by higher-degree functions by each successor. Either the number of generalized displacements at an element node or the number of nodes per element is increased to reduce discretization error. A mixed policy involves changes in grid size and trial-function degree in successive meshes.

## 8.2c Illustrative Problem

The test problem of this chapter is the problem of determining the torsional rigidity of a square shaft [78]. The shaft is fixed at one end, free to warp along its length, and twisted by a torque exerted at its free end. Sokolnikoff [59] recites the analytic solution to this problem. The warping response is reproduced in successive octants of the cross section, with alternating sign.

For the numerical analyses, finite-element models are formulated in terms of the warping values at the nodes [60]. All models are constructed so the finite-element analysis constitutes a Ritz analysis of the shaft. Thus, all numerical solutions overestimate the torsional constant.

Each analysis uses one of four element types for all elements of the mesh. These element types are designated by the degree of the warping function. Thus the *linear element* (simplex element) assumes warping modeled by all terms of a polynomial through those linear in the $x$-, $y$-coordinates of the cross section [60]. The *hyperbolic-element* warping function includes, in addition, the *xy*-term. The *superquadratic element* uses a polynomial which is complete through all second-degree terms and includes some of the third degree. The *reduced-integration element* uses the superquadratic function, but performs numerical integrations of strain-energy density using only four Gauss points.

Since all analyses are rectangular grid modules, special boundary conditions are introduced to imply antisymmetric response across the octant radial lines. Since all elements which cross the diagonals of the square shaft must be square to imply antisymmetric warping responses, all grid intervals along the *x*-axis match those along the *y*-axis and all grids are $N \times N$ grids, where $N$ is the number of grid intervals along an axis.

We define accuracy by

$$d = -\log \frac{J_e - J_n}{J_e} \qquad (8.123)$$

where     $d$ = the number of digits of accuracy of the solution
            $J$ = the solution strain energy
   $e$ and $n$ = subscripts denoting the exact and numerical solutions of the problem

Convergence rate is the change in error per unit change in the grid interval or the number of degrees of freedom of the analysis. Accordingly, the effective convergence rate is the change in error per unit change in computer time.

To avoid the diversity of discussion caused by considering a variety of computer codes, let us define the resource needs as the computer time required by an in-core computer code which uses the usual steps of finite-element analysis: mesh generation, element-matrix generation, matrix assembly, equation solution, and stress recovery. This will provide the measure of resources for all comparisons of this chapter. The values of this measure will change with computer cycle time and the efficiency of the computer software. Thus, all experimental data given here used the same computer (IBM 5100) and computer code.

## 8.2D Mesh Arrangements

Mesh-arrangement decisions include where to locate nodes and each type of element. This section examines the relation between those decisions and the accuracy and efficiency of the analyses. It includes design principles for optimum-grid arrangements.

Figure 8.2 shows results of a sequence of optimum-grid solutions of the test problem using the linear element. The ordinate of the curve is the logarithm of the number of active degrees of freedom in the analysis. The abscissa is the number of digits of accuracy in the estimate of strain energy. Thus, the scales are log-log scales.

Studies leading to this curve illustrate the following principles of grid arrangement:

1. *The extended-element method leads to uniquely defined nodal siting whenever the potential is sensitive to nodal positions.*

Babuska [56] proves that this hypothesis is a theorem for the two-point boundary-value problem. The search for the optimum grid in the test problem suggests the proof may be extended to torsion. The fact that torsion, membrane, and three-dimensional stress problems

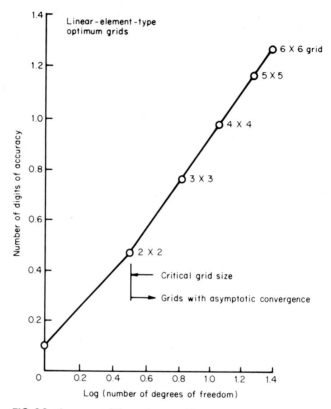

**FIG. 8.2**   Accuracy of the optimum-grid sequence.

may involve Laplace's equation indicates that a theorem may be developed for a broad class of problems in linear elastostatics.

This hypothesis means that the total potential is a convex function of the nodal coordinates and the unknowns. This fact justifies limiting the search for an optimum grid to finding a single optimum. (It also suggests the advantage of using a search algorithm such as that of Fletcher and Reeves [62] to implement search for the optimum.)

**2.** *The sequence of optimum-grid solutions provides a monotonically convergent sequence in the energy norm.*

This statement follows from statement 1 and the fact that elements fulfill requirements for monotonic convergence [63, 64]. It is reflected in the fact that the curve of Fig. 8.2 is single-valued with respect to the parameters.

This statement ensures that analysis of a finer grid cannot yield a worse estimate of strain energy. Pragmatically, this means that results of two successively finer grids can yield a measure of the discretization error in the analysis.

**3.** *There is a critical number of degrees of freedom above which convergence is a power of the interval size.*

This rate of convergence is a consequence of the use of polynomial trial functions complete up to some degree of the polynomial. Since about 98% of available element models are based on polynomials, this theorem can be regarded as a practical generalization. The existence of a critical level of refinement was observed first by Babuska and Rheinboldt [65].

This theorem is reflected in Fig. 8.2. The sequence of solutions defines a straight line when the grid is finer than $1 \times 1$.

Figure 8.3 shows the envelope which embraces all possible grid arrangements of the test problem using the linear element. The ordinate of this curve, and of most of the rest of the curves of this chapter, is the logarithm of the computer time (in seconds) to perform the finite-element analysis.

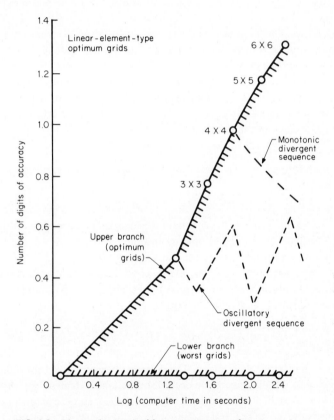

**FIG. 8.3**   Linear element: grid-arrangement envelope.

The upper branch of the envelope represents data for the optimum-grid solutions of Fig. 8.2. The points on this branch do not include the calculation time to find the optimum arrangement. As Turcke and Carroll note [67, 76], the extended finite-element method requires solving a set of nonlinear simultaneous equations even for the engineering system which behaves linearly. In general, the extended FEM severely penalizes the calculations. Turcke [66] notes a case in which optimization of a particular grid penalized the analysis time by a factor of 40. In the torsion studies of this chapter almost 85% of the computer resources were used in just locating the optimum grids (to two digits of accuracy).

Babuska and Rheinboldt [54] cite a theorem defining the quadratic character of the design surface in the neighborhood of the optimum grid. They indicate that the curvature is low, lending mathematical rationale to the Carroll principle:

4. *The practical goal of grid-arrangement optimization is a set of near-optimum values of the nodal coordinates.*

The lower branch of the envelope of Fig. 8.3 defines results of the analysis for a sequence of meshes associated with worst-grid arrangements. Worst grids involve nodes which are so close together that constraint equations must be introduced to eliminate computer manipulation errors.

When this is done, the accuracy of the analysis is that of the coarsest possible grid. Calculation times are slightly increased over those of comparable optimum-grid arrangements in imposing kinematic constraints.

The sequence of worst-grid arrangements is easily identified. For all practical purposes each grid is uniquely identified. The sequence provides a monotonic sequence of results in the energy norm. Since the effective rate of convergence is zero, the set is of interest only in defining the lower branch of the envelope.

Studying the envelope leads to two additional principles:

5. *The optimum grid associates with least computer time to attain a particular accuracy in the energy norm.*

This principle follows from the basis of the extended method and the fact that the number of calculations for an analysis is independent of the location of the nodes. Recalling that the data of Fig. 8.3 exclude the computer time to find the optimum, we observe that principle 5 identifies optimum-grid results as ideal limiting results.

It follows from this principle and the existence of a worst grid that the advantage of optimizing grid arrangement can be measured by the difference in the number of digits of accuracy between results of analyses of the grids.

6. *Fixing the grid-arrangement parameter is essential in guaranteeing convergence in finite-element analysis.*

Proof of this statement is by exception. The dotted curves of Fig. 8.3 show that oscillating divergence and monotonic divergence can occur for the simplex element by particular choices of successive grid arrangements. Thus even though the element model can satisfy completeness requirements, convergence to the exact solution does not occur.

In the introduction (Sec. 8.2A) it was noted that grid arrangement primarily affects solution efficiency. Principle 6 indicates that implicit in this conclusion is the assumption that an adequate grid-arrangement policy is used. Optimum, regular, and focused arrangement policies are adequate.

Principle 6 reflects the fact that the envelope of Fig. 8.3 enlarges as calculation time approaches infinity. Another consequence of this fact is that meshes of a particular element type which yield the same accuracy can differ in calculation time by orders of magnitude depending upon grid arrangements.

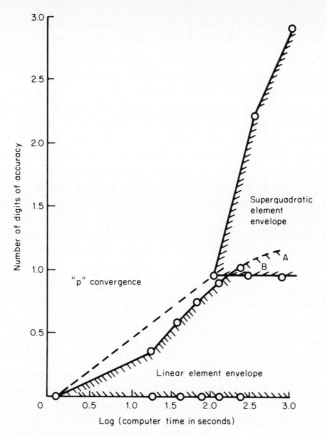

**FIG. 8.4**   Grid-arrangement envelopes.

## 8.2E  Accuracy versus Element Type

Figure 8.4 shows grid-arrangement envelopes for linear and superquadratic element analyses of the test problem. Comparing these envelopes leads to the following conclusions:

**7.** *A lower-degree element type has the potential for meeting low-accuracy requirements more efficiently than a higher degree, when accuracy is sensitive to element type.*

In terms of Fig. 8.4, this principle means that a disjoint region must exist in the neighborhood of the junctures of the upper and lower branches of the grid-arrangement envelopes.

Proof of this principle depends on two considerations. First, the higher-degree element model contains the behavior states of the lower as a subset. Therefore, its juncture point must lie above that of the lower degree when accuracy is element-type–sensitive. Second, the higher-degree element analysis must involve more computer time than the lower for the same grid. Therefore, the higher-degree juncture point must fall to the right of the lower on plots such as that of Fig. 8.4. Accordingly, there exist accuracy levels, and grid arrangements and refinements, for which the lower-degree element is better.

**8.** *A higher-degree element type has the potential for meeting high-accuracy requirements more efficiently than a lower degree, when accuracy is sensitive to element type.*

In terms of Fig. 8.4, this principle asserts that a disjoint region of higher-degree solutions must exist above the optimum solution branch of the lower degree.

The principle is a consequence of three considerations. First, each branch of the envelope must exhibit monotonic convergence and is therefore single-valued in the computer time and accuracy coordinates. Second, disregarding manipulation error, the upper branch of the grid-arrangement envelope extends to infinity in the number of digits of accuracy that can be attained. Third, the convergence rate (slope) along the upper branch must decrease monotonically (because the convergence becomes exponential and the number of calculations increases from a linear up to a cubic function of the number of degrees of freedom in the analysis as the grid is refined), with the higher-degree element associating with a higher effective convergence rate.

These arguments also lead to the conclusion that the grid-arrangement envelopes of a higher- and lower-degree element share an intersection. Thus, we have the following principle.

**9.** *Analyses using lower-degree elements can produce greater accuracy in less computer time than those using higher-degree elements, and conversely, when different grid arrangements are used for each.*

This principle is illustrated by the types A and B analysis points in Fig. 8.4. Here the type A analysis is based on the hyperbolic torsion model and the type B analysis on the superquadratic model.

Principles 7 to 9 can serve to improve the perspective on the selection of element type. Without qualifying observations with a specification of grid arrangement, the claim that a higher-degree element is always more efficient than a lower is invalid. The better element type to use depends on the grid arrangement to be used, the analysis accuracy required, characteristics of the implementing computer code, and the problem of interest.

A similar comparison between envelopes of the superquadratic and reduced-integration superquadratic models furnishes additional principles. Figure 8.5 shows these grid-arrangement envelopes.

**10.** *Reduced-integration elements of type A have the potential for meeting higher-accuracy requirements more efficiently than fully integrated ones, when accuracy is sensitive to this element distinction.*

**11.** *Analysis using fully integrated elements can produce higher accuracy more efficiently than analysis using reduced-integration elements of type A, and conversely, when different grid arrangements are used for each.*

The proof of these statements follows the arguments supporting principles 8 and 9. However, these principles must be qualified by limiting the reduced-integration elements to be of type A, i.e., to be guaranteed to produce estimates of strain energy which are greater than or equal to the exact value.

Unfortunately, a number of reduced-integration elements available to the analyst are not of type A, are only of type A for limited geometries, or have not been examined with respect to this characteristic. The authors believe use of these elements in production analyses should await further research.

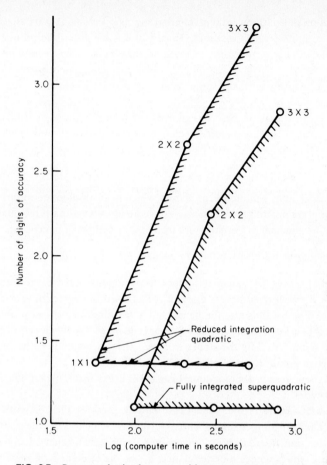

**FIG. 8.5**    Superquadratic elements: grid-arrangement envelope.

On the other hand, use of a reduced-integration element of type A is advisable compared with use of its fully integrated counterpart. Principle 10 and lack of a principle like principle 7 recommend this guideline.

## 8.2F Mesh Evolution

A mesh-evolution strategy is a set of rules by which meshes are redesigned to arrive at an acceptable mesh. In this section, we evaluate the effectiveness of existing strategies.

The common process of mesh evolution involves (1) performing a finite-element analysis of the system using a relatively coarse mesh and the favored element type; (2) evaluating the quality of the solution to determine if the mesh is acceptable; (3) accepting the solution, or, if the solution is unacceptable, repeating tasks 1 and 2 using a refined mesh.

Thus, mesh evolution requires sensors which estimate the accuracy and efficiency associated with a given mesh and criteria for mesh redesign.

The goal of mesh evolution is the minimum computer time to identify an acceptable mesh and perform its finite-element analyses. Thus, it is desirable that the process define where, how, and by how much a given mesh should be changed so it will nearly be a best mesh.

Current technology partially supports this goal. It includes sensors to identify accuracy and efficiency of a given mesh and some experience with indicated mesh changes on solution accuracy [50, 55, 58, 61, 67, 74, 78].

Besides the constraints of mesh design, mesh refinement usually is subject to additional constraints [55, 61, 72]. These supplemental constraints establish policies on the following questions: (1) Will the grid interval be reduced, the element degree increased, or both? (2) Will refinement allow the introduction of irregular elements? (3) Will the refinement be global or local?

The next paragraphs summarize principles which bear on these questions.

Recent literature demonstrates superior convergence rates using $p$-refinement rather than the venerable $h$-refinement. The literature leads to the following conclusion.

**12.** *The asymptotic convergence rate of a p-refinement policy is twice that of an h-strategy.*

Babuska [65] proves the statement under the assumption that the grid interval is reduced everywhere in $h$-meshing and every element is increased in degree for $p$-meshing.

The data of Fig. 8.4 illustrate the benefits of $p$-meshing for the test problem. The upper branch of the grid envelopes show results from $h$-sequences. The two junction points represent results of a $p$-sequence. Only the slopes in $h$-sequences near the juncture points are higher than the effective $p$-convergence indicated by the dotted line.

Figure 8.6 shows results of optimum-grid analyses using linear, hyperbolic, and superquadratic element types.

The continuous curve is the result of a "pony-express" policy of mesh refinement. In this strategy, analyses are performed with a particular element type (the pony) with increasingly finer grids, until the effective convergence degrades efficiency so much that the next higher element type becomes a better choice. Then, the element type (new pony) and grid are changed together.

The importance of this policy resides in the following principle.

**13.** *A pony-express policy is the best policy for mesh refinement.*

Since this policy can produce either $h$- or $p$-meshes, convergence of its analysis results cannot be inferior to either mesh-refinement strategy. Though implementation of this policy may double the computer time for the analysis, because there are two competing meshes at any stage, it avoids the large computer-time penalties that can arise with a pure $h$- or $p$-strategy, as seen in Fig. 8.4.

Using a regular mesh policy, all grids would be regular or regular in subregions. The policy is advantageous because it caters to reducing computer time by replicating rather than generating element matrices.

Figure 8.7 facilitates the assessment of this policy. The figure shows pony-express policy results using optimum grids and pony-express curves from regular grids. The lower curve disregards replication computer-time savings. The middle curve includes them. The upper curve includes them and exploits extrapolatability of regular-grid sequences.

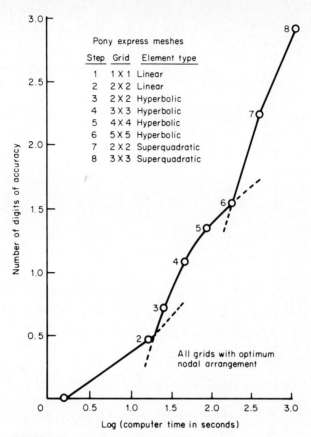

**FIG. 8.6**  Pony-express optimum meshes.

Examining this data, we conclude the following.

**14.** *The sequence of regular grids produces a monotonically convergent sequence of the energy norm.*

This is a theorem when each mesh includes the model of its predecessor as a subset. In general, however, it would require some qualifications on the problem characteristics (i.e., the relation between solution smoothness and the element degree). We observe that it is true for the torsion test problem by inspecting Fig. 8.7.

**15.** *The sequence of regular grids produces a convergent sequence of the energy norm with error a power of the interval size for polynomial trial-function elements.*

This theorem on $h$-convergence of regular grids is proved in the finite-element context by Babuska and Rheinboldt [50, 54]. They also suggest that the convergence rate is independent of the problem.

One of the practical uses of principle 15 is extrapolation of analysis results. This theorem points to use of Richardson's extrapolation. The importance of this powerful device is reflected

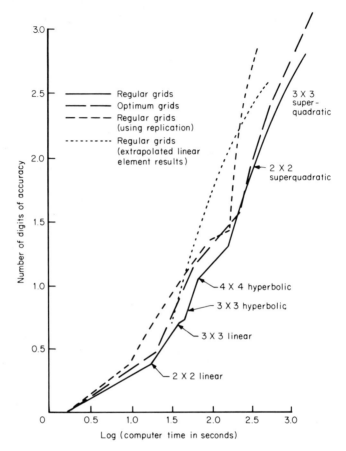

**FIG. 8.7**   Regular and irregular mesh results.

in the upper (dotted) curve of Fig. 8.7. The computer time plotted is the time required to perform the two finite-element analyses that furnish the extrapolated result.

The efficiency of extrapolation analysis is dramatically better than the results produced by any single analysis. Since it is far better than direct use of optimum meshes (the results of which are amenable neither to extrapolation nor replication), we conclude the following.

**16.** *Extrapolation can provide compelling reasons for use of regular meshes.*

The compulsion is a consequence of the high efficiency of analysis and the few calculations required for extrapolation. The torsion-analysis experiments indicate that when more than two analyses are required to attain the desired accuracy, extrapolation makes regular meshes more efficient than development of the results by any mesh. This conclusion is valid even if the "wrong" element has been chosen to attain the accuracy desired.

The generality of principle 16 reflects the need for further research in extrapolation. The idea was shown to be effective for finite-element analyses in 1958 but, on the basis of its use in current production analyses, it is still not considered viable for practical use.

Comparing the middle curve of the regular grid of Fig. 8.7 with the lower curve leads to the following conclusion.

**17.** *Analysis economics associated with replication of element matrices become decreasingly important as the grid interval diminishes.*

This conclusion is a consequence of the fact that as the grid gets finer, the number of calculations is increasingly dominated by the equation-solving process.

The conclusion is manifest in experiments on the test problem. As Fig. 8.7 shows, regular grids are more efficient than optimum grids for simplex-element grids up to $6 \times 6$. However, the relatively small advantage of the regular meshes over the irregular meshes (in this case, optimum grid), does not justify their use except when the ratio of the number of replicated elements to degrees of freedom is high and the number of degrees of freedom is small.

Figure 8.8 provides data for comparing pony-express results for focused and optimum grids using the linear, hyperbolic, and superquadratic element types.

The lowest curve in the figure shows results for a focused mesh when the same implementing computer code is used as for the optimum grids. These results illustrate the following principle.

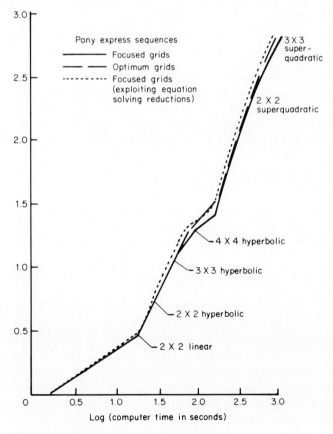

**FIG. 8.8** Global and focused refinement results.

**18.** *The sequence of focused grids produces a monotonically convergent sequence of the energy norm.*

Proof of this statement follows from the definition of the pony-express policy and the fact that the element types used in analyses satisfy the sufficiency requirements of monotonicity [63, 64].

**19.** *The focusing policy results in grids which are near-optimum arrangements.*

As Fig. 8.8 shows, when a focused grid is very close to the optimum-grid curve, the rate of convergence tends to be less than the optimum grid convergence, and conversely. Thereby, the sequence of focused grid seeks the optimum-grid configuration without violating principles 5 and 18.

Statement 19 is confirmed for each of the element types of this study as well as for the pony-express policy.

The dotted curve of Fig. 8.8 describes the accuracy–calculation-time relation when the finite-element analysis process is modified to exploit the fact that local subdivision changes only a small part of the system stiffness matrix. As a consequence, superposition can be used to reduce the number of calculations in solving the simultaneous equations. The dotted curve illustrates the following principle.

**20.** *The analysis economics of a focused-grid policy become increasingly important as grid refinement increases.*

This statement is a consequence of the monotonically rising importance in calculation time of the equation solution as the number of equilibrium equations increases.

Because of this principle and principles 18 and 19, there must exist a grid size smaller than that for which the calculation time is less for the focused than for optimum grids (still ignoring optimum-grid search time). Figure 8.7 shows that this occurs with the linear element when the grid size is greater than $1 \times 1$.

Comparing the data in Figs. 8.7 and 8.8, we conclude that the focused-grid policy will result in more efficient meshes than the regular or optimum grid if calculation economics are exploited.

### 8.2G  Conclusions

On the basis of the state of the art as condensed into statements 1 to 20, we highlight the following generalizations on mesh design:

**1.** The pony-express policy, in which both grid size and element type are changeable during mesh refinement, is the ideal mesh-evolution policy. It cannot be inferior to either an *h*- or a *p*-policy and avoids the inordinate penalties that may occur with either of these.

**2.** The most efficient element model to use for a particular analysis varies with accuracy requirements, number of degrees of freedom, and computer implementation. Usually, higher-degree elements should be selected when accuracy requirements are high and lower-degree elements when accuracy requirements are low. Reduced-integration elements, whenever they are guaranteed to be of type A, should be preferred over the corresponding fully integrated element.

3. The most efficient grid arrangement varies with the analysis purpose, computer code, and accuracy required. Generally, optimized grids should be used for studies of element characteristics, focused grids for production analyses of complex systems, and regular grids when extrapolation can be exploited. Use of successive grids which lack the discipline of an optimum, focused, or regular arrangement can lead to an acceptable mesh design. However, it could also incur exorbitant time penalties to attain the required accuracy or lead to an oscillatory or divergent sequence of results.

Considerable research has been completed on the problem of mesh design. In addition to the references already cited, further information can be found in [68–71] and [73]. Much is known about optimum grids and the development of adaptive grids and their relation to particular element types and problems. The rash of recent additions to the literature and the wealth of unanswered questions suggest that the technology is still in an era of rapid change.

## 8.3 REFERENCES

1. Synge, J. L., *The Hypercircle Method in Mathematical Physics*, Cambridge University Press, Cambridge, 1957.

2. Melosh, R. J., "Basis for Derivation of Matrices for Direct Stiffness Method," *AIAA J.*, **1**(7):1631-1637 (July 1963) pp. 1631-1633.

3. Utku, S., "Stiffness Matrices for Thin Triangular Elements of Nonzero Gaussian Curvature," *AIAA J.*, **5**(9):1659-1667 (September 1967).

4. Crandall, S. H., *Engineering Analysis, A Survey of Numerical Procedures*, McGraw-Hill, New York, 1956, chap. 3.

5. Poincaré, H., "Sur l'équilibre d'une Mass Fluide Animée d'un Movement de Rotation," *Acta Math.*, 7:259-380 (September 1985), in *Oeuvre de Henri Poincaré*, Gauthier-Villars, Paris, 1951, vol. 7, pp. 40-140.

6. Melosh, R. J., "Inherited Error in Finite Element Analyses of Structures," *Computers and Structures*, Pergamon Press, New York, 1973, vol. 3, pp. 1205-1217.

7. Wilkinson, J. H., *The Algebraic Eigenvalue Problem*, Clarendon Press, Oxford, 1965, pp. 56-58.

8. Collatz, L., *The Numerical Treatment of Differential Equations*, 3d ed., Springer-Verlag, New York, 1966 (1st ed., 1951, in German), pp. 348-353.

9. Crandall, S. H., *Engineering Analysis: A Survey of Numerical Procedures*, McGraw-Hill, New York, 1956, pp. 163-171, 265-269.

10. Utku, S., "Error Computation in Numerical Solutions of Linear Boundary Value Problems," *Proceedings of the Second International Conference on Mathematical Modeling*, University of Missouri, Rolla, July 1979, pp. 285-294.

11. Utku, S., and M. M. El-Essawi, "Error Computation in Finite Element Methods," *Proceedings of the Seventh Conference on Electronic Computation*, ASCE, New York, August 1979, pp. 584-592.

12. Walz, J. E., R. E. Fulton, and N. J. Cyrus, "Accuracy and Convergence of Finite Element Approximations," AFFDL-TR-68-150, Wright–Patterson Air Force Base, Ohio, 1968, pp. 995-1027.

13. Walz, J. E., R. E. Fulton, N. J. Cyrus, and R. T. Eppink, *Accuracy of Finite Element Approximations to Structural Problems*, TN-D-5728, National Aeronautics and Space Administration, Washington, D.C., March 1970, pp. 1-53.

14. Gray, W. G., and G. F. Pinder, "On the Relationship Between the Finite Element and Finite Difference Methods," *Int. J. Numer. Meth. Eng.*, **10**:893-923 (1976).

15. Jamet, P., "Estimation of the Interpolation Error for Quadrilateral Finite Elements Which Can Degenerate into Triangles," *SIAM J. Numer. Anal.*, **14**(5):925–930 (October 1977).

16. Wilkinson, J. H., *The Algebraic Eigenvalue Problem*, Clarendon Press, Oxford, 1965, pp. 189–191.

17. Wilkinson, J. H., *The Algebraic Eigenvalue Problem*, Clarendon Press, Oxford, 1965, pp. 87–89.

18. Wilkinson, J. H., *The Algebraic Eigenvalue Problem*, Clarendon Press, Oxford, 1965, chap. 3.

19. Wilkinson, J. H., *The Algebraic Eigenvalue Problem*, Clarendon Press, Oxford, 1965.

20. Crandall, S. H., *Engineering Analysis: A Survey of Numerical Procedures*, McGraw-Hill, New York, 1956.

21. Carnahan, B., H. A. Luther, and J. O. Wilkes, *Applied Numerical Methods*, Wiley, New York, 1969.

22. Collatz, L., *The Numerical Treatment of Differential Equations*, 3d ed., Springer-Verlag, New York, 1966 (1st ed., 1951, in German).

23. Babuska, I., and W. C. Rheinboldt, "Error Estimates for Adaptive Finite Element Computations," *SIAM J. Numer. Anal.*, **15**(4):736–754 (August 1978).

24. Babuska, I., and W. C. Rheinboldt, "On the Reliability and Optimality of the Finite Element Method," *Comput. Struct.*, **10**:87–94 (1979).

25. McLay, R. W., "Completeness and Convergence Properties of Finite Element Displacement Functions—A General Treatment," AIAA Pap. No. 6-143, *AIAA 5th Aerospace Sciences Meeting*, New York, January 1967.

26. Tong, P., and T. H. H. Pian, "The Convergence of Finite Element Method in Solving Linear Elastic Problems," *Int. J. Solids Struct.*, **3**:865–879 (1967).

27. Johnson, M. W., and R. W. McLay, "Convergence of the Finite Element Method in the Theory of Elasticity," *Trans. ASME*, June 1968, pp. 274–278.

28. Lynn, P. P., and A. P. Boresi, "Kinds of Convergence and Improved Convergence of Conforming Finite Element Solutions in Plate Bending," *Nucl. Eng. Design*, **11**:159–176 (1970).

29. Fix, G., and G. Strang, "Fourier Analysis of the Finite Element Method in Ritz–Galerkin Theory," *Stud. Appl. Math.*, **48**(3):265–273 (1969).

30. Fried, I., "Accuracy of Finite Element Eigenproblems," *J. Sound Vibration*, **18**(2):289–295 (1971).

31. Schultz, M. H., "$L^2$ Error Bounds for the Rayleigh Ritz Galerkin Method," *SIAM J. Numer. Anal.*, **8**(4):737–749 (December 1971).

32. Babuska, I., "Error Bounds for Finite Element Method," *Numer. Math.*, **16**:322–333 (1971).

33. Zlamal, M., "Some Recent Advances in the Mathematics of Finite Elements," in J. R. Whiteman (ed.), *The Mathematics of Finite Elements and Applications*, Academic Press, New York, 1973, pp. 59–81.

34. Barnhill, R. E., and J. R. Whiteman, "Error Analysis of Finite Element Methods with Triangles for Elliptic Boundary Value Problems," in J. R. Whiteman (ed.), *The Mathematics of Finite Elements and Applications*, Academic Press, New York, 1973, pp. 83–112.

35. Ciarlet, P. G., "Orders of Convergence in Finite Element Methods," in J. R. Whiteman (ed.), *The Mathematics of Finite Elements and Applications*, Academic Press, New York, 1973, pp. 113–129.

36. Babuska, I., and R. B. Kellogg, Nonuniform Error Estimates for the Finite Element Method," *SIAM J. Numer. Anal.*, **12**(6):868–875 (1975).

37. Prager, W., and J. L. Synge, "Approximations in Elasticity Based on the Concept of Function Spaces," *Q. Appl. Math.*, **5**:241–269 (1947).

38. Fraeijs de Veubeke, B. M., *Matrix Methods of Structural Analysis*, Pergamon Press, Oxford, 1964.

39. Utku, S., *Instructor's Manual* for Norris, Wilbur, and S. Utku, *Elementary Structural Analysis*, 3d ed., McGraw-Hill, New York, 1976, pt. II, pp. 91–97.

40. Richardson, L. F., "The Approximate Arithmetic Solution by Finite Differences of Physical Problems," *Trans. R. Soc. London*, **A210**:307–357 (1910).

41. Richardson, L. F., and J. A. Gaunt, "The Deferred Approach to the Limit," *Trans. R. Soc. London,* **A226**:299–361 (1927).

42. Crandall, S. H., *Engineering Analysis: A Survey of Numerical Procedures,* McGraw-Hill, New York, 1956, pp. 171–173, 269–270.

43. Carnahan, B., H. A. Luther, and J. O. Wilkes, *Applied Numerical Methods,* Wiley, New York, 1969, pp. 78, 90, 364.

44. Lynn, P. P., and B. S. Dhillon, "Convergence of Eigenvalue Solutions in Conforming Plate Bending Finite Elements," *Int. J. Numer. Meth. Eng.,* **4**:217–234 (1972).

45. Ramey, G. E., and N. Krishnamurthy, "Error Estimates for Conforming Finite Element Solutions," *Comput. Struct.,* **4**:1207–1222 (1974).

46. Melosh, R. J., "Design Principles for Finite Element Meshing," *NASA-ICASE Symp. Math. Model.,* Langley Research Center, Hampton, Va., October 24, 1979.

47. Melosh, R. J., "Manipulation Errors in Computer Solution of Critical Size Structural Equations," NASA CR-1784, National Aeronautics and Space Administration, Washington, D.C., June 1971.

48. Melosh, R. J., "Characteristics of Manipulation Errors in Solving Load-Deflection Equations," *On General Purpose Finite Element Computer Programs,* American Society of Mechanical Engineers, New York, 1970, pp. 123–142.

49. McNeice, G. M., and P. V. Marcal, "Optimization of Finite Element Grids Based on Minimum Potential Energy," Trans. No. 7, Brown University, Providence, R.I., 1971.

50. Babuska, I., and W. C. Rheinboldt, "A-Posteriori Error Estimates for the Finite Element Method," *Int. J. Numer. Meth. Eng.,* **12**:1597–1615 (1978).

51. Ebner, A., (ed.), "Guidelines for Finite Element Idealization," Preprint 2504, ASCE National Convention, New Orleans, April 1975.

52. Turcke, D. J., and G. M. McNeice, "A Variational Approach to Grid Optimization in the Finite Element Method," *Conference on Variational Methods in Engineering,* Southampton University, Southampton, September 1972.

53. Carroll, W. E., and R. M. Barker, "A Theorem for Optimum Finite Element Idealization," *Int. J. Solids Struct.,* **9**:883–895 (1973).

54. Babuska, I., and W. C. Rheinboldt, "Analysis of Optimal Finite Element Meshes in $R^1$," *Math. Comput.,* **33**(146):435–463 (April 1978).

55. Melosh, R. J., and D. E. Killian, "Finite Element Analysis to Attain a Prespecified Accuracy," *Proceedings 2d National Congress on Computing in Structures,* Washington, D.C., 1976.

56. Babuska, I., "The Self-Adaptive Approach in the Finite Element Method," *The Mathematics of Finite Element Applications II,* Academic Press, New York, 1976.

57. Szabo, B. A., and A. K. Mehta, "*P*-Convergent Finite Element Approximations in Fracture Mechanics," *Int. J. Numer. Meth. Eng.,* **12**:551–560 (1978).

58. Shephard, M. S., "Finite Element Grid Optimization with Interactive Graphics," Ph.D. thesis, Department of Structural Engineering, Cornell University, Ithaca, N.Y., June 1979.

59. Sokolnikoff, I. S., *Mathematical Theory of Elasticity,* McGraw-Hill, New York, 1956.

60. Herrmann, L. R., "Elastic Torsion Analysis of Irregular Shapes," *Proc. ASCE Conf.,* **91**(EM6):11–19 (1965).

61. Carroll, W. E., "Inclusive Criteria for Optimum Grid Generation in the Discrete Analysis Technique," *Comput. Struct.,* **6**, 1976.

62. Fletcher, R., and C. M. Reeves, "Function Minimization by Conjugate Gradients," *Comput. J.,* **1964**:149–154 (1964).

63. Melosh, R. J., "Basis for Derivation of Matrices for the Direct Stiffness Method," *AIAA J.,* **1**:1631–1637 (July 1963).

64. Melosh, R. J., and D. W. Lobitz, "On a Numerical Sufficiency Test for Monotoxic Convergence of Finite Element Models," *AIAA J.*, **13**(5):675–678 (May 1975).

65. Babuska, I., and W. C. Rheinboldt, "Reliable Error Estimation and Mesh Adaptation for the Finite Element Method," Note Bull. 910, University of Maryland, College Park, April 1979.

66. Turcke, D. J., "Optimum Mesh Configuration in the Finite Element Method," Ph.D. thesis, Department of Civil Engineering, University of Waterloo, Waterloo, Ont., July 1974.

67. Babuska, I., A. Miller, and M. Vogelius, "Mathematical Problems of Discrete Modeling and a-Posteriori Reliability Estimates," *Symposium on Mathematical Modeling in Structural Engineering*, NASA-Langley and George Washington University, Hampton, Va., October 1979.

68. de Arandes, O., "Optimization of Finite Element Solutions," AFFDL-TR-71-160, *Proceedings Third Conference on Matrix Methods in Structural Mechanics*, Wright–Patterson Air Force Base, Dayton, December 1973, pp. 423–446.

69. Carey, G. F., and D. L. Humphrey, "Residuals, Adaptive Refinement and Non-Linear Iterations for Finite Element Computations," in M. Shephard and R. Gallagher (eds.), *Finite Element Grid Optimization*, ASME Publ. PVP-38, American Society of Mechanical Engineers, New York, 1979.

70. Peano, A., R. Riccioni, A. Pasini, and L. Sardella, "Adaptive Approximation in Finite Element Structural Analysis," in A. K. Noor and H. G. McComb (eds.), *Trends in Computerized Structural Analysis and Synthesis*, 1978.

71. Killian, D. E., "Selective Refinement of a Finite Element Mesh for Improved Accuracy," Master's thesis, Virginia Polytechnic Institute and State University, Blacksburg, 1975.

72. Szabo, B. A., P. K. Busu, and M. F. Rossow, "Adaptive Finite Element Analysis Based on P-Convergence," NASA Conf. Publ. 2059, 1978, pp. 43–50.

73. Melosh, R. J., and P. V. Marcal, "An Energy Basic for Mesh Refinement of Structural Continua," *Int. J. Numer. Meth. Eng.*, **11**:1083–1091 (August 1977).

74. Molmari, G., and A. Viviani, "Grid Iteration for Finite Element Grid Optimization," in M. S. Shephard and R. H. Gallagher (eds.), *Finite Element Grid Optimization*, ASME Publ. PVP-38, American Society of Mechanical Engineers, New York, 1979.

75. Turcke, D. J., "Finite Element Mesh Configurations Using Isoenergetics and Equalized Energy Levels," *Symposium on Future Trends in Computerized Structural Analyses and Synthesis*, Washington, D.C., November 1978.

76. Carroll, W. E., "Recent Developments Dealing with Optimum Finite Element Analysis Techniques," in M. S. and R. H. Gallagher (eds.), *Finite Element Grid Optimization*, ASME Publ. PVP-38, American Society of Mechanical Engineers, New York, 1979.

77. Sobieszczanski, J., "Matrix Algorithm for Structural Modification Based upon the Parallel Element Concept," *AIAA J.*, 7, 1969.

78. Noor, A. K., and W. D. Pilkey (eds.), *State-of-the-Art Surveys on Finite Element Technology*, AMD, American Society of Mechanical Engineers, New York, 1983, chaps. 3, 9.

79. Utku, S., and R. J. Melosh, "Solution Errors in Finite Element Analysis," *Comput. Struct.*, **18**:379–395 (1984).

# FEM
# COMPUTATIONS

# CHAPTER 1
# SOLUTION METHODS

The progressive development of the finite-element method in static and dynamic analysis of structures leads to larger and larger systems of equations that need to be solved. Thus, much research effort has gone toward increasing the performance of numerical solution algorithms with regard to aspects such as the nature and inherent complexity of the physical problems to be treated, the size of the associated equation systems to be solved, and the computational speed.

Most of the problems that the structural analyst must solve lead to the numerical solution of a system of equations which falls into one of the following categories:

1. Linear system of equations associated with a static problem, written in terms of a symmetric stiffness matrix

$$\mathbf{Kq} = \mathbf{g}$$

2. Linear eigenvalue problem giving the free-vibration eigenfrequencies of a structure according to the equation

$$\mathbf{Kx} = \omega^2 \mathbf{Mx}$$

3. Nonlinear system of equations associated with an equilibrium written in the form of a residual equation

$$\mathbf{r(q)} = \mathbf{0}$$

**4.** Transient response of a linear or nonlinear structure:

$$\mathbf{M\ddot{q}} + \mathbf{f(q, \dot{q})} = \mathbf{g(q, t)} \qquad \mathbf{q}_0, \dot{\mathbf{q}}_0 \text{ given}$$

With respect to the size of problems to be solved, the requirements have changed considerably with time. During the early period of the use of the finite-element method, solving a linear static problem of order 100 was considered in many cases to be a challenge. Currently, eigenvalue problems of order 10,000 are solved on an everyday basis, and the nonlinear transient response of a structure can be predicted without much difficulty with models having about 10,000 unknowns.

The associated computing time depends on numerous factors. Of course, it depends to some extent on the choice of the method and, to a larger extent, on the available computing power, but it is also much influenced by implementation aspects such as the organization of the central processing unit (CPU) and input/output (I/O) operation, the matrix-storage schemes used, and the ways in which sparsity is exploited, the specific iteration procedures adopted, the use of numerical conditioning and scaling, and the definition of convergence criteria.

In most cases, the numerical solution of problems of types 2 to 4 is organized around the solution of a linearized system of equations of type 1. For example, the efficient solution of free-vibration problems relies almost always on the power-iteration scheme, which can be regarded as a sequence of linear static problems with different load vectors. The efficient solution of static linear problems is thus of paramount importance in the development of FEM software.

The present discussion of FEM solution algorithms has been limited to structural applications and has been divided into three parts.

In the first part, linear static and free-vibration problems have been considered simultaneously because the most efficient eigenvalue extraction methods for large systems are vector-iteration algorithms and are thus organized as a sequence of linear static problems. Beginning with a review of the main direct methods for solving linear problems (Gauss elimination, Choleski factorization), the chapter proceeds with a brief description of the methods available for storing and solving sparse matrices (band memorization schemes, frontal and substructure methods, hypermatrices, and element-by-element memorization). The rest of the section is devoted to aspects of eigenvalue calculation such as specific algorithms (Lanczos method), elimination of rigid-body modes, and calculation of error bounds.

The second part presents an overview of the most common methods for extracting eigensolutions. Some background is provided for the matrix analysis essential for understanding eigensolution algorithms.

The third part deals with the iterative solution of nonlinear systems of equations. Classical methods such as Newton algorithms, conjugate gradients, and quasi-Newton updates are reviewed, and a brief outline is given of the available methods for tracing structural response beyond critical points.

The fourth part describes some of the classical methods for time integration of dynamic equations and discusses important features such as their accuracy, stability, adequacy for solving specific problems, and computer implementation.

# 1.1 SOLUTION ALGORITHMS FOR STATIC AND EIGENVALUE PROBLEMS

## 1.1A General Considerations

***Static Problems*** Essentially, there are two different classes of methods for solving linear systems of equations: direct solution techniques and iterative methods.

It is interesting to note that during the early development of the finite-element method, iterative solution algorithms such as the Gauss–Seidel method were used extensively, and much research was done to improve them. Their computer implementation is very straightforward since the matrix of the system does not need to be assembled; all matrix multiplications are carried out at the element level. This method suffers from a very basic disadvantage, however. The solution time can only be estimated and is very much problem-dependent because the number of iterations required for convergence depends mainly on the condition number of the matrix to be solved. It is now recognized that iterative methods are generally not competitive except in some specific problem areas such as reanalysis, optimization, and the solution of very large 3D problems.

In a direct solution, the system of equations is solved using a number of steps and operations which are predetermined in an exact manner. Unlike iterative methods, the number of operations is not sensitive to the condition number of the matrices to be solved; only the accuracy of the solution can be affected by ill-conditioning.

Direct methods such as Gauss elimination and Choleski factorization proceed in two steps: an elimination phase and a solution phase. They are thus very attractive for solving the same system of equations with several right-hand sides, since elimination is performed only once. Very efficient variants of them have been proposed which take account of sparsity in an optimum manner and reduce the number of operations accordingly.

***Eigenvalue Problems*** The finite-element method applied to structural-vibration problems generally leads to an eigenvalue problem in standard form

$$\mathbf{K}\mathbf{x} = \omega^2 \mathbf{M}\mathbf{x} \tag{1.1}$$

where $\mathbf{K}$ and $\mathbf{M}$, the stiffness and mass matrices, are both symmetric. The mass matrix is positive-definite, if one excepts the case of degrees of freedom (DOF) with zero mass. Normally, the stiffness matrix is also positive-definite, except in the occurrence of rigid-body modes and/or linear constraints between degrees of freedom which are introduced by lagrangian multipliers. The eigensolutions of Eq. (1.1) may thus be supposed ordered in the form

$$0 \leqslant \omega_1^2 \leqslant \omega_2^2 \cdots \leqslant \omega_n^2 \qquad \mathbf{x}_{(1)}, \mathbf{x}_{(2)}, \ldots, \mathbf{x}_{(n)}$$

In practice, the choice of an eigenvalue extraction method to solve Eq. (1.1) is guided mostly by the number of degrees of freedom. The following cases of problems may be defined according to their size:

$$\text{I.} \qquad 0 < n \leqslant 10$$

$$\text{II.} \qquad 10 < n \leqslant 250$$

> III.    $250 < n \leqslant 1000$
>
> IV.   $1000 < n < 10,000$
>
> V.         $n > 10,000$

where $n$ is the number of degrees of freedom. Obviously, this classification is only approximate, and may be modified somewhat according to the topology of the structural stiffness and mass matrices.

The eigenvalue algorithms applicable to class I problems, with few DOF, present no interest in a finite-element context. They are generally based on a direct expansion of the characteristic equation.

The eigenvalue equation of class II problems can often be solved entirely in core memory. Problems falling in this range may use all the standard methods for which the numerical accuracy does not deteriorate too much with an increasing number of DOF. Also of interest are [1–7]:

- The Jacobi method for reduction to diagonal form
- The Givens and Householder methods for reduction to tridiagonal form, followed by a Sturm sequence algorithm to solve the tridiagonal matrix
- The power-iteration algorithm and its derived versions (Wielandt's inverse iteration with or without shift, subspace iteration, Lanczos method)

For structural eigenvalue problems falling into class III, one can still operate into core memory as long as the bandwidth, or, more generally, the population of $\mathbf{K}$ and $\mathbf{M}$, is such that no auxiliary memory is needed. If their size exceeds the available space, a condensation algorithm may be used to reduce the initial number of DOF in order to fit into core memory with the reduced problem.

Most of the current eigenvalue problems corresponding to finite-element applications fall into class IV. Solving the final eigenvalue problem entirely in core memory is not possible. The choice of a practical method is limited, and its efficiency is largely dependent on the technique used to memorize the stiffness and mass matrices. Most of the methods applicable to this category of problems are derived forms of the power-iteration law, and are thus organized around a linear equation solver for large sparse matrices.

Beyond this limit, which will probably be raised somewhat due to the availability of supercomputers, it is often hazardous to solve the eigenvalue problem [Eq. (1.1)] in one step. Multilevel solution techniques based on substructuring (such as the well-known component-mode approach of Refs. [36, 37]) exist which allow one to obtain the eigensolution of the total problem from a synthesis of the results of separate analyses. This structural-synthesis approach is often used with success in the framework of large projects, such as vehicles and aircraft engines, in which every contractor performs the dynamic analysis of the component(s) under his or her responsibility. The synthesis of the final eigenvalue problem implies introducing into the model two kinds of structural modes characteristic of each component: boundary modes which represent the coupling with adjacent substructures, and internal-vibration modes which reproduce the dynamic behavior of the concerned element. The synthesis technique is also successfully applied in projects involving experimental vibration analysis of some of the components.

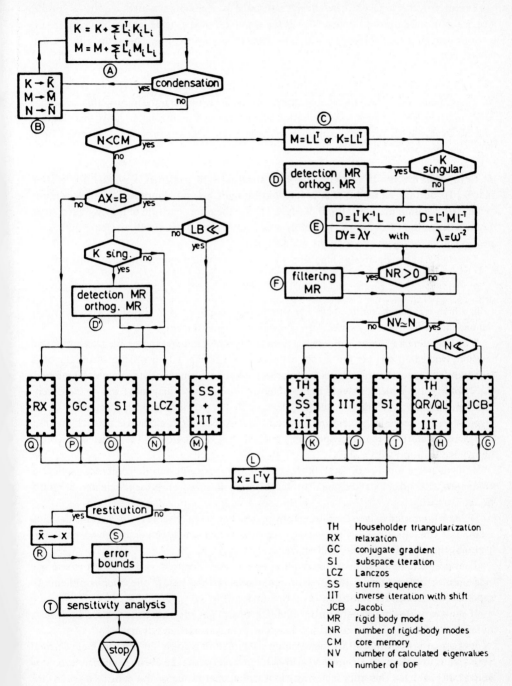

**FIG. 1.1** Solution of $\mathbf{Kx} = \omega^2 \mathbf{Mx}$.

TH  Householder triangularization
RX  relaxation
GC  conjugate gradient
SI  subspace iteration
LCZ  Lanczos
SS  sturm sequence
IIT  inverse iteration with shift
JCB  Jacobi
MR  rigid body mode
NR  number of rigid-body modes
CM  core memory
NV  number of calculated eigenvalues
N  number of DOF

Except for the case of these structural-synthesis techniques which require a specific organization (often project-dependent) of the computational scheme, one can summarize the various strategies available for vibration analysis of large structures. This is done in Fig. 1.1, where $N$ denotes the number of DOF.

**Preliminary Operations**   Using the initial eigenvalue problem [Eq. (1.1)], with the stiffness and mass matrices in the unassembled form of Fig. 1.1a, one can decide whether to reduce the number of DOF using a condensation algorithm such as in Fig. 1.1b. At this stage, **K** and **M** are available for the eigenvalue analysis. Even after condensation they may not fit into core memory (CM).

**In-Core Algorithms**   If $N < \text{CM}$, the best strategy is to construct a symmetric iteration matrix. To do this, either **M** or **K** is factored by the Choleski algorithm, and the resulting symmetric iteration matrices (Eq. E of Fig. 1.1) have the eigenspectrum of the original system. In both cases, the existence of rigid-body modes (RM), is automatically detected during the process of factoring or inverting the stiffness matrix.

The choice of the eigenvalue algorithm to solve the resulting symmetric eigenvalue problem

$$\mathbf{D}\mathbf{y} = \lambda \mathbf{y} \tag{1.2}$$

from which rigid-body modes have been previously removed (Eq. F of Fig. 1.1), is largely dependent on the relative number of eigenvalues to be extracted.

If one is interested in the entire eigenspectrum, it is best to use a successive-transformation method. One can use either the Jacobi method, Eq. G of Fig. 1.1, in which the initial matrix is reduced to diagonal form by successive orthogonal transformations, or a combined method, Eq. H of Fig. 1.1, which proceeds in three steps: reduction to tridiagonal form by the Givens and Householder methods (the second, denoted T. H., performs better); calculation of the eigenvalues by successively factoring the tridiagonal ($QR$- and $QL$-methods), which is possibly improved by shift on the eigenspectrum; and, finally, calculation of the eigenvectors from an inverse iteration with a shift.

The larger the number of DOF of the system, the more efficient the combined method is compared with Jacobi's algorithm. The Jacobi method, however, presents greater computational simplicity.

If one is interested only in the lower eigenfrequencies, it is advisable to use a vector-iteration method of von Mises type. It is generally recognized that subspace iteration, version I (Fig. 1.1), has the highest reliability and efficiency.

The subspace-iteration algorithm requires one to periodically solve a so-called interaction eigenvalue problem having a size significantly smaller than that of the initial problem. To solve it, one uses either algorithm G or H shown in Fig. 1.1.

If the available core memory is too limited, one might prefer the more classical inverse iteration with spectral shift (algorithm J) rather than subspace iteration.

If the goal is to extract all the eigenvalues contained in a given interval, the most efficient approach is to isolate the eigenvalues within the interval using the Sturm sequence technique (Eq. K of Fig. 1.1). This approach involves a tridiagonalization of the matrix $(\mathbf{K} - \mu\mathbf{M})$ for each value of the frequency shift $\mu$. After extraction of the eigenvalues, the corresponding eigenvectors are calculated by inverse iteration with shift (Eq. K of Fig. 1.1).

The iteration matrix (Eq. E of Fig. 1.1) was made symmetrical as the base transformation on eigenvectors. The eigenvectors in the initial DOF are recovered by the inverse transformation (Eq. L of Fig. 1.1).

***Out-of-Core Algorithms*** Let us next consider the second part of the flowchart which corresponds to problems for which an out-of-core solution is needed. Most of the algorithms are based on the repetitive use of a linear solution algorithm.

A choice that was popular in the past was to take advantage of the band form of the stiffness and mass matrices. In this process, the most appropriate eigenvalue extraction method is probably to locate the zeros of $\det (\mathbf{K} - \mu \mathbf{M})$ by the Sturm sequence technique (Eq. M of Fig. 1.1). The eigenmodes are found next by inverse iteration with spectral shift.

If one exploits the sparsity of the system rather than of its bandwidth, there are other matrix-handling schemes (such as the frontal method) which take full advantage of the topology of the finite-element mesh. The linear solution scheme for $\mathbf{Kq} = \mathbf{g}$ is then organized for an easy solution of an arbitrarily large sequence of right-hand sides, and the eigenvalue extraction method is necessarily based on the vector-iteration concept. At the very first iteration, either a gaussian elimination or a Choleski factorization of the stiffness matrix is performed, during which the occurrence of rigid-body modes is detected. If rigid-body modes are present, an orthogonalization scheme is constructed which will allow convergence to the elastic modes by appropriate filtering in the iteration process (Eq. D' of Fig. 1.1).

The iteration algorithm on eigenvectors, which is generally used to gather most of the desirable qualities such as fast convergence, numerical stability, satisfactory frequency resolution, and good performance in CPU time, is the inverse subspace iteration (Eq. O of Fig. 1.1). Its frequency resolution is linked to that of the algorithm used to solve the interaction problem, which has a size equal to the number of trial vectors. For this purpose, the algorithm generally retained is the combined method mentioned in Eq. H of Fig. 1.1. One may also use the Jacobi method (Eq. G of Fig. 1.1). The main inconvenience of the subspace-iteration algorithm is the need to handle simultaneously all the trial vectors (possibly using auxiliary memory), which reduces the advantage of the method when a large number of eigenvalues is required.

The Lanczos algorithm (Eq. N of Fig. 1.1), because of its great simplicity and remarkable property of requiring a minimal number of iterations, has received much attention from numerical analysts since its discovery [8]. For a long time, however, the numerical results achieved with it were disappointing. The failure of the algorithm, even for relatively small systems, was attributed to rounding error propagation. The observation [19] that the cause of failure of the Lanczos method is a progressive deterioration of the trial vector because of extremely rapid disappearance of its lower frequency, and not because of a rapid loss of accuracy, has renewed interest in the method. Recent experiments have shown that appropriate modifications of the algorithm, including truncation of the iteration process, reorthogonalization, and a restart procedure, lead to a highly reliable and remarkably fast eigenvalue extraction method. Its lower storage requirements and its computational simplicity make it even more attractive now than subspace-iteration methods.

Finally, let us also mention for completeness that some methods exist which allow a direct extraction of the eigenspectrum without requiring any linear system solution. They are based upon a direct minimization of the Rayleigh quotient, either by mathematical programming techniques such as the conjugate gradient (Eq. P of Fig. 1.1) or by coordinate relaxation (Eq Q of Fig. 1.1). Despite their numerous advantages such as computational simplicity, easy implementation, and necessity of assembling structural matrices, these methods are very seldom used, owing to the deterioration of convergence properties with an increasing number of DOF.

*A Posteriori Calculations*  In case an initial reduction of the system has been achieved, the eigenmodes are determined only in terms of the retained DOF. A restitution of the full set of DOF is then necessary (Eq. R of Fig. 1.1).

The next operation, which is of special interest when a condensation of the number of DOF has been performed, is to calculate error bounds to the computed eigenspectrum (Eq. S of Fig. 1.1).

The last step is often very useful from an engineering point of view, especially when the vibration analysis of the structure has been performed at a preliminary design stage. The sensitivity analysis (Eq. T of Fig. 1.1) allows an easy prediction of eigenfrequency and eigenmode changes due to elementary mass and stiffness modifications.

The flowchart of Fig. 1.1 covers reasonably well all the aspects and methods to be considered in finite-element software for vibration analysis of large structures. Describing in detail all the methods and algorithms would require a textbook in itself.

Most eigenvalue extraction methods are considered to be classical. The algorithms and their numerical properties (required number of operations, numerical conditioning, convergence, etc.) are described in Refs. [1-37], but most of the information is contained in Refs. [1, 2]. The only eigenvalue extraction method that will be analyzed in detail in this section is the Lanczos iteration algorithm.

The following presentation will be limited to some less classical aspects of the finite-element method applied to static and vibration analysis of large structures, namely:

- Organization of the linear solution algorithms which are directly applicable to static problems and form, at the same time, the basis for vector-iteration methods in eigenvalue analysis

- Memorization schemes for the stiffness and mass matrices according to the method of solution

- Numerical properties of the Lanczos method for eigenvalue extraction and its computer implementation

- Calculation of error bounds to the numerically exact frequencies of the model

- Sensitivity analysis of the eigensolution with respect to elementary stiffness and mass modifications

## 1.1B Solution of the Static Problem $Ax = b$ by the Direct Method

The flowchart of Fig. 1.1 shows clearly that most of the eigenvalue extraction methods applicable to large systems rely upon the availability of an efficient linear equation solver for a symmetric matrix of large dimension.

The algorithm must be applicable, in a repetitive way, to a large number of right-hand sides. Therefore, iterative methods are a priori discarded.

Among the direct methods, the most used are those based on triangulation of the initial matrix because they allow one to take account of the sparsity of the initial matrix, their computer implementation is straightforward, and they perform well in terms of both accuracy and CPU cost.

**The Gauss Elimination Method for a Symmetric Matrix**    Starting from the system of equations

$$\mathbf{Ax} = \mathbf{b}$$

with $\mathbf{A}$ symmetric, the Gauss elimination method proceeds in two steps.

1. *Reduction of $\mathbf{A}$ to Triangular Form.*    Elementary operations are performed on the successive rows in order to transform $\mathbf{A}$ into upper triangular form. The product of the successive transformation matrices is a lower triangular matrix with a unit diagonal. Formally, one can write

$$\mathbf{LA} = \mathbf{U} \qquad \text{or} \qquad \mathbf{A} = \mathbf{L}^{-1}\mathbf{U}$$

The matrix $\mathbf{U}$ is constructed explicitly, but the transformation matrix $\mathbf{L}$ is not. The associated linear system becomes

$$\mathbf{LB} = \mathbf{y} \qquad \text{with} \qquad \mathbf{y} = \mathbf{Ux}$$

*The Algorithm*    In order to preserve the symmetry of the initial matrix, the successive pivots are selected along the diagonal.

At step $r$, the pivot $a_{ii}^{(r-1)}$ ($i^{\text{th}}$ diagonal element) is selected, generally according to its largest module. Rows and columns $i$ and $r$ are next permuted so that $a_{ii}^{(r-1)}$ becomes $a_{rr}^{(r-1)}$. Elimination of this pivot is then performed in order to produce zeros under the diagonal term.

The following terms are not affected by the transformation

$$a_{ij}^{(r)} = a_{ij}^{(r-1)} \qquad i = 1, \ldots, r; j = i, \ldots, n$$

$$a_{ij}^{(r)} = 0 \qquad j = 1, \ldots, r-1; i = j+1, \ldots, n \qquad (1.3)$$

$$b_i^{(r)} = b_i^{(r-1)} \qquad i = 1, \ldots, r$$

while the remaining terms are transformed according to

$$a_{ir}^{(r)} = 0 \qquad\qquad\qquad i = r+1, \ldots, n$$

$$a_{ij}^{(r)} = a_{ij}^{(r-1)} - \frac{a_{ir}^{(r-1)}}{a_{rr}^{(r)}} a_{rj}^{(r)} \qquad \begin{matrix} i = r+1, \ldots, n \\ j = r+1, \ldots, n \end{matrix} \qquad (1.4)$$

$$b_{ir}^{(r)} = b_i^{(r-1)} - \frac{a_{ir}^{(r-1)}}{a_{rr}^{(r)}} b_r^{(r)} \qquad i = r+1, \ldots, n$$

If step $r = 1$ corresponds to the initial matrix $\mathbf{A}$, the triangular form is obtained at step $n - 1$, and the determinant of $\mathbf{A}$, if needed, can be calculated by forming the product of the successive pivots

$$\det \mathbf{A} = \prod_{r=1}^{n} a_{rr}^{(r)}$$

**2.** *Back Substitution.* The initial unknowns are restored by

$$\mathbf{Ux} = \mathbf{y}$$

The back substitution is performed by

$$x_i = \frac{1}{u_{ii}}\left( y_i - \sum_{r=i+1}^{n} u_{ir} x_r \right) \qquad i = n, n-1, \ldots, 1$$

***Equivalence with the Static-Condensation Algorithm***  Let us consider the linear static problem $\mathbf{Kq} = \mathbf{g}$ in the partitioned form

$$\begin{bmatrix} \mathbf{K}_{CC} & \mathbf{K}_{CR} \\ \mathbf{K}_{RC} & \mathbf{K}_{RR} \end{bmatrix} \begin{bmatrix} \mathbf{q}_C \\ \mathbf{q}_R \end{bmatrix} = \begin{bmatrix} \mathbf{g}_C \\ \mathbf{g}_R \end{bmatrix} \tag{1.5}$$

If the $\mathbf{q}_C$ are eliminated in favor of the $\mathbf{q}_R$ using Eq. (1.5), then

$$\mathbf{q}_C = \mathbf{K}_{CC}^{-1}[\mathbf{g}_C - \mathbf{K}_{CR}\mathbf{q}_R] \tag{1.6}$$

Substitution into Eq. (1.5) yields

$$\mathbf{K}_{RR}\mathbf{q}_R = \bar{\mathbf{g}}_R \tag{1.7}$$

with the reduced stiffness matrix

$$\bar{\mathbf{K}}_{RR} = \mathbf{K}_{RR} - \mathbf{K}_{RC}\mathbf{K}_{CC}^{-1}\mathbf{K}_{CR}$$

and the reduced loads    $\bar{\mathbf{g}}_R = \mathbf{g}_R - \mathbf{K}_{RC}\mathbf{K}_{CC}^{-1}\mathbf{g}_C \tag{1.8}$

This condensation is equivalent to a block triangulation of the stiffness matrix by the Gauss elimination algorithm

$$\begin{bmatrix} \mathbf{I} & 0 \\ \mathbf{L}_{RC} & \mathbf{I} \end{bmatrix} \begin{bmatrix} \mathbf{K}_{CC} & \mathbf{K}_{CR} \\ \mathbf{K}_{RC} & \mathbf{K}_{RR} \end{bmatrix} = \begin{bmatrix} \mathbf{U}_{CC} & \mathbf{U}_{CR} \\ 0 & \mathbf{U}_{RR} \end{bmatrix}$$

with the following submatrices

$$\mathbf{U}_{CC} = \mathbf{K}_{CC}$$

$$\mathbf{L}_{RC} = -\mathbf{K}_{RC}\mathbf{K}_{CC}^{-1}$$

$$\mathbf{U}_{CR} = \mathbf{K}_{CR}$$

$$\mathbf{U}_{RR} = \bar{\mathbf{K}}_{RR} \qquad \text{the condensed stiffness matrix}$$

An elegant and efficient method which takes account of the topology of the stiffness matrix is to organize the Gauss elimination in block form according to Eqs. (1.5) to (1.8). This corresponds to the frontal concept introduced by Irons [42]. As the frontal concept is closely linked to the memorization scheme of the structural matrices, it will be considered again from the point of view of matrix partitioning in the next sction.

***Automatic Detection of Rigid-Body Modes by the Gauss Elimination Algorithm [38–41]***     Consider an unrestrained structure, capable of undergoing rigid-body displacements. The stiffness matrix is no longer positive-definite, since the system

$$\mathbf{Kq} = 0$$

has $r$ nontrivial solutions.

Suppose, first, that the degrees of freedom are partitioned

$$\mathbf{q} = \begin{bmatrix} \mathbf{q}_1 \\ \mathbf{q}_2 \end{bmatrix} \begin{matrix} n-r \\ r \end{matrix}$$

in such a way that fixation of the $r$ degrees of freedom $\mathbf{q}_2$ locks the kinematic modes of the structure. Let us next partition the stiffness matrix in the same way, and eliminate by the Gauss algorithm the $n - r$ degrees of freedom $\mathbf{q}_2$. The resulting matrix equation is

$$\begin{bmatrix} \mathbf{L}_{11} & 0 \\ \mathbf{L}_{21} & \mathbf{I} \end{bmatrix} \begin{bmatrix} \mathbf{K}_{11} & \mathbf{K}_{12} \\ \mathbf{K}_{21} & \mathbf{K}_{22} \end{bmatrix} \begin{bmatrix} \mathbf{q}_1 \\ \mathbf{q}_2 \end{bmatrix} = \begin{bmatrix} \mathbf{U}_{11} & \mathbf{U}_{12} \\ 0 & \mathbf{U}_{22} \end{bmatrix} \begin{bmatrix} \mathbf{q}_1 \\ \mathbf{q}_2 \end{bmatrix} = 0 \qquad (1.9)$$

The system (1.9) has $r$ nontrivial solutions $\mathbf{q}_2 \neq 0$ under the condition that $\mathbf{U}_{22} = 0$. The elimination process degenerates, and the rigid-body modes are calculated in terms of arbitrary values given to $\mathbf{q}_2$ by

$$\mathbf{U}_{11}\mathbf{q}_1 = -\mathbf{U}_{12}\mathbf{q}_2 \qquad (1.10)$$

If, with the Gauss elimination algorithm, the selection criterion of the successive pivots on the diagonal is the largest module, the detection of rigid-body and, more generally, kinematic modes becomes automatic. After $n - r$ elimination steps, one is left with zero remaining pivots: the corresponding DOF are the $\mathbf{q}_2$. The simplest way to obtain the explicit expression of rigid-body modes is to give a unit value to each of the $\mathbf{q}_2$ successively. The matrix of rigid-body modes is obtained by solving (1.10) with $\mathbf{q}_2 = \mathbf{I}$.

$$\begin{bmatrix} \mathbf{q}_1 \\ \mathbf{q}_2 \end{bmatrix} = \begin{bmatrix} -\mathbf{U}_{11}^{-1}\mathbf{U}_{12} \\ \mathbf{I} \end{bmatrix}$$

***Occurrence of Linear Constraints in the Gauss Elimination Method***     In many cases, the solution of the static problem

$$\mathbf{Kq} = \mathbf{g}$$

is subjected to linear constraints, expressed in the form

$$\mathbf{Cq} = 0$$

where $\mathbf{C}$ is a rectangular matrix $(p \times n)$. This is equivalent to locating the minimum of the quadratic problem

$$\min_{(\mathbf{q},\boldsymbol{\lambda})} \tfrac{1}{2}\mathbf{q}^T\mathbf{K}\mathbf{q} - \mathbf{q}^T\mathbf{g} + \boldsymbol{\lambda}^T\mathbf{C}\mathbf{q}$$

where $\boldsymbol{\lambda}$ are $p$ lagrangian multipliers associated with the constraints. The resulting matrix equation is

$$\begin{bmatrix} \mathbf{K} & \mathbf{C}^T \\ \mathbf{C} & \mathbf{0} \end{bmatrix}\begin{bmatrix} \mathbf{q} \\ \boldsymbol{\lambda} \end{bmatrix} = \begin{bmatrix} \mathbf{g} \\ \mathbf{0} \end{bmatrix} \tag{1.11}$$

and involves an extended stiffness matrix which is still symmetric but no longer positive-definite.

   Provided that the Gauss elimination algorithm is implemented with a maximum pivot strategy, systems of type (1.11) may easily be solved; each linear constraint gives rise to a negative pivot, but the positive-definite property of the extended strain energy

$$\tfrac{1}{2}\mathbf{q}^T\mathbf{K}\mathbf{q} + \boldsymbol{\lambda}^T\mathbf{C}\mathbf{q}$$

is still preserved by the solution.

**Choleski Triangular Decomposition**   In the indefinite case, the symmetric matrix $\mathbf{A}$ may be decomposed in the form

$$\mathbf{A} = \mathbf{L}\mathbf{D}\mathbf{L}^T$$

where $\mathbf{L}$ is a triangular matrix with unit diagonal, and $\mathbf{D}$ is the diagonal matrix with pivot elements. The equations giving rise to the successive elements of $\mathbf{L}$ are

$$\sum_{r=1}^{\min(i,j)} d_{rr}l_{ri}l_{rj} = a_{ij}$$

**The Algorithm**   Starting with $d_{11} = a_{11}$, one obtains $n(n+1)/2$ equations resulting from the following decomposition:

$$d_{11} = a_{11}$$

$$l_{j1} = \frac{a_{j1}}{d_{11}} \qquad j = 2, \ldots, n$$

$$\left.\begin{array}{l} d_{ii} = a_{ii} - \displaystyle\sum_{r=1}^{i-1} d_{rr}l_{ri}^2 \\[2ex] l_{ji} = \dfrac{1}{d_{ii}}\left(a_{ij} - \displaystyle\sum_{r=1}^{i-1} d_{rr}l_{ri}l_{rj}\right) \qquad j = i+1, \ldots, n \end{array}\right\} \begin{array}{l} \\ i = r, \ldots, n \end{array} \tag{1.12}$$

The determinant of the initial matrix is obtained by finding the product

$$\det \mathbf{A} = \prod_{i=1}^{n} d_{ii}$$

In this form the Choleski algorithm is used to calculate eigenvalues by the Sturm sequence technique [18].

***The Positive-semidefinite Case*** When factoring is applied directly to the structural mass or stiffness matrix, their positive-semidefinite properties permit the decomposition to take the form

$$\mathbf{A} = \mathbf{L}\mathbf{L}^T$$

To solve the associated linear system, one proceeds in solving successively the two triangular systems

$$\mathbf{L}\mathbf{y} = \mathbf{b} \quad \text{and} \quad \mathbf{L}^T\mathbf{x} = \mathbf{y}$$

***The Occurrence of Linear Constraints*** The main limitation of the Choleski decomposition algorithm for finite-element applications is its failure when applied to systems of type (1.11).

***Automatic Detection of Rigid-Body Modes by the Choleski Algorithm [38–41]*** Let us suppose, as before, that the sequence of generalized displacements is partitioned in the form

$$\mathbf{q} = \begin{bmatrix} \mathbf{q}_1 \\ \mathbf{q}_2 \end{bmatrix}$$

The $\mathbf{K}_{11}$-matrix being singular, the triangular decomposition is pursued up to step $n - r$:

$$\begin{bmatrix} \mathbf{K}_{11} & \mathbf{K}_{12} \\ \mathbf{K}_{21} & \mathbf{K}_{22} \end{bmatrix} = \begin{bmatrix} \mathbf{L}_{11} & \mathbf{0} \\ \mathbf{U} & \mathbf{V} \end{bmatrix} \begin{bmatrix} \mathbf{L}_{11}^T & \mathbf{U}^T \\ \mathbf{0} & \mathbf{I} \end{bmatrix} \qquad (1.13)$$

with

$$\mathbf{U} = \mathbf{K}_{21}\mathbf{L}_{11}^{-T}$$

$$\mathbf{V} = \mathbf{K}_{22} - \mathbf{U}\mathbf{U}^T = \mathbf{K}_{22} - \mathbf{K}_{21}\mathbf{K}_{11}^{-1}\mathbf{K}_{12}$$

The singularity of the stiffness matrix is concentrated in the kernel $\mathbf{V}$ which vanishes identically. The rigid-body modes are obtained as before by giving a unit value to each of the $\mathbf{q}_2$ successively. One obtains

$$\begin{bmatrix} \mathbf{q}_1 \\ \mathbf{q}_2 \end{bmatrix} = \begin{bmatrix} -\mathbf{L}_{11}^{-T}\mathbf{U}^T \\ \mathbf{I} \end{bmatrix}$$

If, as with Gauss elimination, the successive rows are selected according to the largest pivot criterion, the triangulation process is stopped when all the remaining diagonal terms have vanished. The associated DOF are then collected in $\mathbf{q}_2$.

The major drawback of the Choleski decomposition in comparison with the Gauss elimination, when applied to rigid-body detection, is the requirement of a row and column permutation according to the choice of successive pivots.

## 1.1c  Matrix Memorization and Handling Schemes for Sparse Structural Stiffness and Mass Matrices

***Constant-Bandwidth Matrices*** The symmetric structural matrices that result from a finite-element discretization with appropriate numbering of DOF often present a banded form. It means that a constant $b \ll n$ exists such that

$$a_{ij} = 0 \qquad \begin{cases} i - j > b \\ i = 1, \ldots, n \\ j = 1, \ldots, i \end{cases}$$

Owing to the symmetry of the matrix, only its upper (or lower) triangular part must be stored. The memory space required is

$$\tfrac{1}{2}(b+1)(2n-b)$$

where the quantity $(b+1)$ is the half bandwidth of the matrix. Figure 1.2 shows a typical banded matrix: the part to be stored is limited to the shaded area.

x    initial terms
●    fill-in terms
----   skyline of the matrix

Ⓐ   pivot
Ⓑ   terms used
Ⓒ   terms modified by elimination or factorization

Ⓓ   pivot for Gauss elimination
Ⓔ   pivot for Choleski triangularization
Ⓕ   active area

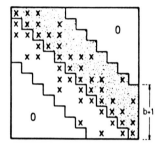

**FIG. 1.2**   A typical banded matrix, constant bandwidth.

*Gauss Elimination*    Equations (1.3) and (1.4) defining the Gauss elimination algorithm show that its application to a banded matrix does not alter its topology. For a certain pivot element, only the terms lying between the row of the pivot and the diagonal are modified (Fig. 1.3a, hatched area).

Figure 1.3b shows the topology of the upper triangular part of the matrix after Gauss elimination of all the DOF. The only additional nonzero terms, or "fill-in" terms, appear between the diagonal and the last nonzero term of each column. As a result, the band stored in memory is not necessarily filled at the end of the process. The fill-in is limited to the area between the diagonal and the "skyline" of the matrix (Fig. 1.3).

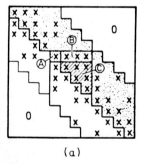

(a)

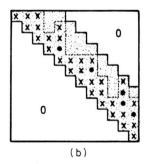

(b)

**FIG. 1.3**   Banded matrix for Gauss elimination. (*a*) Before. (*b*) After.

***Choleski Decomposition***   The situation arising with the Choleski decomposition algorithm is quite similar. As shown by Fig. 1.4, which diagrams Eq. (1.2), the active area is the triangular area located above the current pivot. The terms affected by the decomposition are located in the hatched area. The fill-in terms appear in the same places as in Gauss elimination.

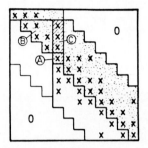

**FIG. 1.4**   Choleski triangularization.

***Band Memorization Schemes***   A constant-bandwidth matrix may be stored in two ways:

1. If a sufficiently large memory core is available, the main diagonal and the successive subdiagonals can be stored in sequence. This requires a working space of $(b+1)(2n-b)/2$ words.

2. Figure 1.5 shows that this memorization is not very efficient since at each elimination or decomposition step the active area does not exceed a triangle of size $(b+1)(b+2)/2$. A more economical scheme is to store the matrix row by row or column by column in order to work simultaneously only on the $b+1$ active lines. This procedure limits to $(b+1)^2$ the necessary working space.

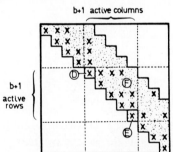

**FIG.  1.5**   Banded   matrix   for   rowwise memorization.

The ordering of the linear equations and the numbering of the finite-element model determine the bandwidth. The banded structure of a matrix can be optimized through a simple renumbering of the nodes, as seen in Fig. 1.6, which is an elementary example of a simply connected domain.

However, determining the optimal node sequence through a single inspection of the matrix is very difficult. Numerous algorithms have been defined which automate this task with

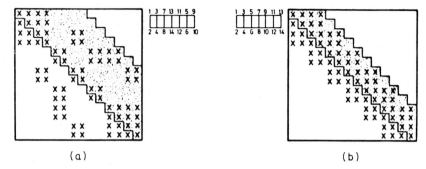

**FIG. 1.6** Simply connected domain. (*a*) Nonoptimal node numbering. (*b*) Optimal node numbering.

variable success. They are based on the minimum-bandwidth criterion, which does not necessarily imply a minimum number of arithmetic operations.

It is also worthwhile noticing that for multiply connected domains the constant-bandwidth concept loses most of its interest. Figure 1.7 shows that even for a very sparse matrix, the half bandwidth can reach the order of the system in the most unfavorable case.

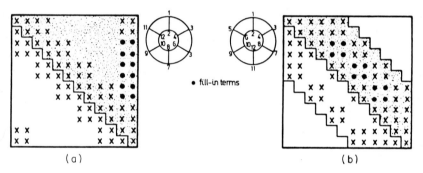

**FIG. 1.7** Multiply connected domain. (*a*) Bandwidth = number of degrees of freedom. (*b*) Minimum bandwidth.

***Variable-Bandwidth Matrices*** The weakness of the bandwidth can be reduced somewhat by introducing the variable-bandwith concept, in which one stores the matrix column after column. The handling of zero terms within the band is avoided by limiting the storage of the matrix to its skyline. In this case, the bandwidth varies from column to column (Fig. 1.8), and each column corresponds to a variable-length record containing

- The column number $n_c$
- The row number of the last nonzero term of the column, $n_r$
- The numerical values of the $(n_c - n_r + 1)$ nonzero terms

If an automatic row-and-column reordering algorithm is applied, the performance criterion to be adopted corresponds to minimum fill-in of the matrix. In contrast to the case of constant bandwidth, this criterion leads to a minimum of arithmetic operations.

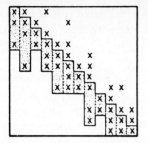

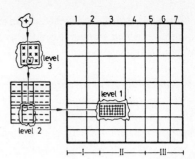

**FIG. 1.8**  Band matrix: locally variable band-width.

**FIG. 1.9**  Multilevel addressing scheme.

***Multilevel Addressing and Hypermatrix Concept***  The hypermatrix concept [43] requires splitting the initial matrix into submatrices which are handled in the same way as the scalar elements of an ordinary matrix.

In a hypermatrix memorization scheme the addressing process is as follows (Fig. 1.9):

1. The submatrices which result from partitioning the initial matrix define the addressing level 1. Their size is adapted to fit into core memory and corresponds to a logical record length giving maximum performance in terms of I/O cost. Normally, the presence of zero terms in the submatrices is taken into account in the method of memorization of the submatrix.

2. The addresses of the submatrices are stored in an address matrix (level 2). The role of this address matrix is twofold:
   *a.* To take advantage of the sparsity of the initial matrix by omitting the null submatrices to which a zero address is simply affected.
   *b.* To provide easy addressing of submatrices.

3. In case the address matrix itself is too large, it can be split into submatrices, giving rise to a level 3 address matrix, and so on.

The main advantages of such a multilevel address scheme are:

• It allows for easy handling of matrices of almost unlimited sizes, in contrast to other memorization schemes which have upper limits.

• It is not specialized to a particular solution method since any matrix operation (addition, product, triangular decomposition, etc.) defined at the single-term level has corresponding operations between submatrices.

In particular, Gauss elimination and Choleski decomposition are easy to implement in terms of hypermatrices. The same remark holds, of course, for block relaxation methods.

This flexibility of the hypermatrix memorization concept is obtained at the following cost:

• The machine dependence of the corresponding software

• The complexity of the addressing scheme

• The relatively poor CPU performance

*The Frontal Method*  In its original form, the Irons method is an elegant variant of Gauss elimination in which all operations involving zero terms, even within the band of the matrix, are automatically avoided.

*The Frontal Method in Its Original Form [42]*  Eliminating one row of the stiffness matrix leads to a modification of the subsequent rows according to Eqs. (1.3) and (1.4). It is obvious that the transformation affects only the terms $k_{ij}$ such that $k_{ir}$, $k_{rj} \neq 0$.

The basic concept of the frontal method is to update, at each elimination step, a triangular array which contains only the elements affected by the current transformation. The size of this working array is generally much smaller than the half bandwidth of the matrix. The frontal method becomes particularly advantageous when the population of the system is such that the band itself remains too sparse.

The active DOF, that is, the DOF which are involved in the elimination step under way, form the equation front of the system (Fig. 1.10a). The triangular array containing the active DOF remains, in general, much smaller in size than with any other method.

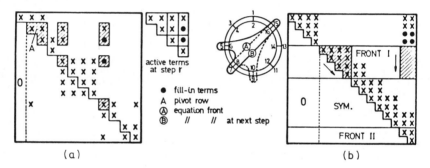

FIG. 1.10  Frontal method. (*a*) Simply connected domain. (*b*) Multiply connected domain.

The computational strategy is as follows:

1. A given DOF is introduced in the equation front as soon as a nonzero element of the corresponding column is involved in the elimination process.

2. A given row is eliminated as soon as all the DOF of the intersecting columns have disappeared from the equation front.

The superiority of the frontal method over the band concept is particularly obvious in the case of multiply connected domains.

Figure 1.10b shows such an example. At the step considered, the DOF associated with node 5 are eliminated. Eliminating nodes 3 and 4 produces coupling terms between both pairs of nodes (5, 6) and (15, 16). The DOF 5, 6, 7, 8, 15, and 16 form the equation front, which splits into two disconnected parts as shown by Fig. 4.10b. At the next step, node 6 is eliminated and no new DOF enters the equation front.

The main feature of the frontal method lies in the fact that the elimination sequence must correspond to the assembling sequence of the structural elements in the finite-element model. Indeed, a given node of the finite-element mesh can be eliminated as soon as it is no longer involved in a further connection. Hence, in the frontal method, the assembling and elimination sequences on the stiffness matrix are intimately connected. The assembling of the total matrix is not performed explicitly, and the need for a complex addressing scheme is completely avoided.

To summarize, it is the order in which elements are assembled which defines the elimination sequence. The optimal ordering of the elements corresponds to a continuous progression of the equation front through the structure with minimum size. Reordering algorithms exist which provide the optimal finite-element sequence automatically.

**The Method of Substructures [44]**  The method of substructures is a variant of Irons frontal method in which the elimination is no longer performed row after row, but is done simultaneously on a block of equations, the size of which depends both on available space in core memory and CPU performance of the algorithm. The substructuring process adopted is based on the concept of substructures in series. It is a recursive procedure in which a substructure is defined (see Fig. 1.11) as the result of the assembling to the previous substructure of a certain number of elements. A DOF attached to the substructure can be eliminated if it is not involved in other element connections.

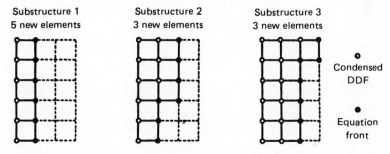

**FIG. 1.11**  Organization in substructures.

*The Assembling Process*  Before condensation, the stiffness matrix of each substructure results from the assembling of the previous substructure stiffness matrix together with the stiffness matrices of $n_e$ new elements. Formally, this assembling operation may be written in the form

$$\mathbf{K}_S = \mathbf{L}_{S-1}^T \mathbf{K}_{S-1} \mathbf{L}_{S-1} + \sum_{ne} \mathbf{l}_e^T \mathbf{k}_e \mathbf{l}_e$$

where $\mathbf{L}_{S-1}$ is the localization operator of the previous substructure, and $\mathbf{l}_e$ are the localization operators of the new elements to be assembled.

*The Static-Condensation Process*  The DOF of the substructure are partitioned into two groups

$$\mathbf{q} = \begin{bmatrix} \mathbf{q}_C \\ \mathbf{q}_R \end{bmatrix}$$

where the $\mathbf{q}_C$ are condensed DOF and the $\mathbf{q}_R$ are retained. Elimination of the $\mathbf{q}_C$ is made according to Eqs. (1.5) to (1.8) and reduces the initial size $(n_R + n_C)$ of the matrix to the size

$n_R$. The submatrices $\mathbf{K}_{CC}^{-1}$ and $\mathbf{K}_{CC}^{-1}\mathbf{K}_{CR}$ are stored on auxiliary memory to allow condensation of the other load vectors and back calculation of eliminated DOF.

**The Memorization Process [43, 45, 46]** The normal technique is to assemble the stiffness matrix (1.5) of the substructure into core memory. The required space is

$$\tfrac{1}{2}(n_R+1)(n_R+2) \qquad \text{for } \mathbf{K}_{RR}$$

$$\tfrac{1}{2}(n_C+1)(n_C+2) \qquad \text{for } \mathbf{K}_{CC} \text{ and } \mathbf{K}_{CC}^{-1}$$

$$n_R n_C \qquad \text{for } \mathbf{K}_{RC} \text{ and } \mathbf{K}_{CC}^{-1}\mathbf{K}_{CR}$$

where $n_R$ is the dimension of the equation front, and is thus imposed by the topology of the system. $n_C$ depends on the number of elements assembled in the substructure and may be adjusted according to two criteria:

- CPU and I/O costs
- Available core memory

The practice acquired with the SAMCEF code [48] shows that the optimal choice is

$$30 < n_{C,\text{opt}} < 50$$

for moderate frontwidth ($n_R < 200$), but tends to increase with the frontwidth $n_R$.

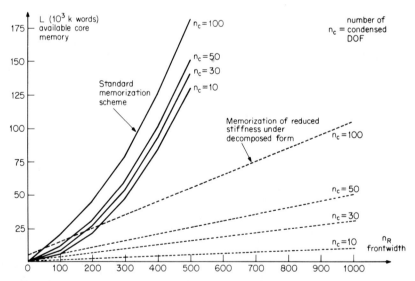

**FIG. 1.12** Method of substructures: memory requirements.

Figure 1.12 shows the minimum core space required to solve a problem with given frontwidth $n_R$ as a function of the number $n_C$ of condensed DOF. It clearly shows that solving problems with a frontwidth larger than 500 or 600 is hopeless, even when advantage is taken of the virtual-memory concept. This limitation may be overcome in two ways:

1. By storing the matrices $\mathbf{K}_{RR}$, $\mathbf{K}_{RC}$, and $\mathbf{K}_{CC}$ according to the hypermatrix concept, in which case the assembling sequence is complicated considerably.

2. By observing that the reduced matrices $\mathbf{K}_{RR}$ [Eq. (1.7)] do not need to be constructed explicitly [46]; they may instead be expressed in the form of a sum of elementary contributions

$$\bar{\mathbf{K}}_{RR} = \sum_{ne} \mathbf{l}_{Re}^{T} \mathbf{K}_{e} \mathbf{l}_{Re} - \sum_{nS} \mathbf{L}_{RS}^{T}(\mathbf{K}_{RC}\mathbf{K}_{CC}^{-1}\mathbf{K}_{CR})\mathbf{L}_{RS} \tag{1.14}$$

where the first term represents the contribution of the substructure currently assembled and the second term contains the contribution of the DOF condensed in the previous substructures.

Figure 1.12 shows the decisive benefit that can be gained from the use of the decomposed form (1.14) of the successive reduced stiffness matrices. Systems with a frontwidth of 2000 DOF can be solved easily in a core memory of 200 Kbytes. The penalty of the method is the increased complexity of the assembling procedure for $\mathbf{K}_{RC}$ and $\mathbf{K}_{CC}$, which, however, does not detract from the performance of the algorithm. This matrix-handling scheme has been used experimentally for several years in the finite-element system SAMCEF [48].

***The Method of Substructures for Dynamic Condensation [25, 35]***   In dynamic problems, the method of substructures may be used in two ways, as suggested by the flowchart of Fig. 1.1. On the one hand, when using vector-iteration eigenvalue algorithms such as subspace iteration and the Lanczos method, the method of substructures provides an efficient tool for solving the static problem $\mathbf{Kq} = \mathbf{g}$. Its solution has to be organized in order to minimize the cost of subsequent linear solutions with next right-hand sides corresponding to actualized inertia forces. The alternative way of taking advantage of the substructure concept is to achieve a simultaneous reduction of the mass matrix using the following reasoning.

One knows from engineering experience that the fundamental vibration modes of a structure are not complicated in shape and can thus be represented with reasonable accuracy with a few point loads adequately located. Thus, these modes will not be affected too much if the associated consistent load due to inertia loads

$$\mathbf{g} = \omega^{2}\mathbf{Mq} \tag{1.15}$$

is redistributed in a statically equivalent manner on a reduced number of DOF.

Let the $\mathbf{q}_{R}$ denote the DOF contained in the equation front augmented by the DOF retained to represent the fundamental mode shapes. The reduced static problem takes the form

$$\begin{bmatrix} \mathbf{K}_{RR} & \mathbf{K}_{RC} \\ \mathbf{K}_{CR} & \mathbf{K}_{CC} \end{bmatrix} \begin{bmatrix} \mathbf{q}_{R} \\ \mathbf{q}_{C} \end{bmatrix} = \begin{bmatrix} \bar{\mathbf{g}}_{R} \\ \mathbf{0} \end{bmatrix} \tag{1.16}$$

where $\mathbf{g}_{R}$ denotes the statically equivalent load to (1.15).

The second equation corresponds to static condensation

$$\mathbf{q}_{C} = -\mathbf{K}_{CC}^{-1}\mathbf{K}_{CR}\mathbf{q}_{R} \tag{1.17}$$

which, when substituted into (1.16), gives the reduced static problem

$$\bar{\mathbf{K}}_{RR}\mathbf{q}_{R} = \bar{\mathbf{g}}_{R}$$

The reduced inertia load is obtained from a virtual-work conservation equation

$$\mathbf{q}_R^T \bar{\mathbf{g}}_R = \mathbf{q}^T \mathbf{g} = \omega^2 [\mathbf{q}_R \quad \mathbf{q}_C]^T \begin{bmatrix} \mathbf{M}_{RR} & \mathbf{M}_{RC} \\ \mathbf{M}_{CR} & \mathbf{M}_{CC} \end{bmatrix} \begin{bmatrix} \mathbf{q}_R \\ \mathbf{q}_C \end{bmatrix}$$

which, owing to (1.17), becomes

$$\mathbf{q}_R^T \bar{\mathbf{g}}_R = \omega^2 \mathbf{q}_R^T \bar{\mathbf{M}}_{RR} \mathbf{q}_R$$

with the condensed stiffness matrix

$$\bar{\mathbf{M}}_{RR} = \mathbf{M}_{RR} - \mathbf{K}_{RC} \mathbf{K}_{CC}^{-1} \mathbf{M}_{CR} - \mathbf{M}_{RC} \mathbf{K}_{CC}^{-1} \mathbf{K}_{CR} + \mathbf{K}_{RC} \mathbf{K}_{CC}^{-1} \mathbf{M}_{CC} \mathbf{K}_{CC}^{-1} \mathbf{K}_{CR} \qquad (1.18)$$

The initial eigenvalue problem is thus reduced to the form proposed almost simultaneously by Guyan and Irons [33, 34]:

$$\bar{\mathbf{K}}_{RR} \mathbf{q}_R = \omega^2 \bar{\mathbf{M}}_{RR} \mathbf{q}_R \qquad (1.19)$$

A full and comprehensive discussion of the algorithm applied to vibration and stability problems has been made in Refs. [31, 35, and 40]. It is shown that:

- The range of validity of the approximation (1.19) is that for which the inequality

$$\varepsilon = \frac{\omega_i^2}{\mu_i^2} \ll 1 \qquad (1.20)$$

holds, where $\mu_i^2$ is the lower eigenfrequency of the internal eigenvalue problem

$$\mathbf{K}_{CC} \mathbf{q}_C = \mu^2 \mathbf{M}_{CC} \mathbf{q}_C$$

The inequality provides a guide for the choice of the $\mathbf{q}_C$ since it indicates that the condensed variables should be chosen in order to maximize the lower frequency $\mu_1$ of the internal eigenvalue problem.

- The exact eigenvalues can be expanded in terms of the reduced solution in the form

$$\omega^2 = \bar{\omega}^2 \left[ 1 - \frac{\Delta \mathbf{q}_C^T \mathbf{K}_{CC} \Delta \mathbf{q}_C}{\mathbf{q}_R^T \mathbf{K}_{RR} \mathbf{q}_R} \right] + 0(\Delta^2)$$

where $\Delta \mathbf{q}_C$ is the first-order correction to the $\mathbf{q}_C$. This result shows that the eigenfrequencies are systematically increased by the condensation process.

The condensation of the mass matrix according to Eq. (1.17) is a relatively costly operation since it involves twice the number of arithmetic operations necessary to reduce $\mathbf{K}$.

Let us finally note that this mass condensation algorithm is very useful in all dynamic problems which are solved by a multilevel condensation using the superelement concept or parallel substructures [48].

***Element-by-Element Memorization***   When first-order iterative methods such as the conjugate-gradient algorithm [17] are used to solve the eigenvalue problem (1.1) there is no need to assemble physically the structural matrices $\mathbf{K}$ and $\mathbf{M}$.

Let us consider the problem of minimizing the Rayleigh quotient

$$R(\mathbf{q}) = \frac{\mathbf{q}^T \mathbf{K} \mathbf{q}}{\mathbf{q}^T \mathbf{M} \mathbf{q}} \tag{1.21}$$

which is equivalent to solving the eigenvalue problem (1.1). In order to converge to higher eigenmodes, the minimization is subject to the additional orthogonality constraints

$$\mathbf{a}^T \mathbf{M} x_{(j)} = 0 \qquad j = 1, \ldots, r-1$$

The quadratic expressions involved in (1.21) are, except for a normalizing factor, the potential and kinetic energies of the structure. They may be expressed in the form of elementary contributions

$$V = \tfrac{1}{2} \sum_e \mathbf{q}_e^T \mathbf{k}_e \mathbf{q}_e \qquad T = \frac{\omega^2}{2} \sum_e \mathbf{q}_e^T \mathbf{m}_e \mathbf{q}_e$$

where the displacements $\mathbf{q}_e$ at element level are extracted from the structural displacement vector $\mathbf{q}$ by a localization operation (boolean)

$$\mathbf{q}_e = \mathbf{l}_e \mathbf{q}$$

The functional (1.21) can thus be written in the form

$$R(\mathbf{q}) = \frac{\sum_e (\mathbf{l}_e \mathbf{q})^T \mathbf{k}_e (\mathbf{l}_e \mathbf{q})}{\sum_e (\mathbf{l}_e \mathbf{q})^T \mathbf{m}_e (\mathbf{l}_e \mathbf{q})}$$

and its evaluation involves the elementary matrices $\mathbf{k}_e$ and $\mathbf{m}_e$ together with the boolean operator $\mathbf{l}_e$.

The first-order schemes require also the evaluation of the gradient vector

$$g(\mathbf{q}) = \frac{\partial R}{\partial \mathbf{q}} = \frac{\mathbf{K} \mathbf{q} - R(\mathbf{q}) \mathbf{M} \mathbf{q}}{\mathbf{q}^T \mathbf{M} \mathbf{q}}$$

which, written in the form     $$g(\mathbf{q}) = \frac{\sum_e \mathbf{l}_e^T (\mathbf{k}_e - R(\mathbf{q}) \mathbf{m}_e) \mathbf{l}_e \mathbf{q}}{\sum_e (\mathbf{l}_e \mathbf{q})^T \mathbf{m}_e (\mathbf{l}_e \mathbf{q})}$$

does not imply a physical assembling of $\mathbf{K}$ and $\mathbf{M}$.

One will note, however, that the eigenvalue algorithms based on the Rayleigh quotient minimization, despite their easy computer implementation and their low memory requirements, tend to become obsolete [25]. This is due to the following drawbacks:

● Their rate of convergence is affected not only by the conditioning number of the problem, but also by the number of DOF.

● Their CPU cost is high in comparison with other algorithms.

● When applied to static problems, they solve one load case at a time, and do not allow an imposed-displacement type of loading.

Let us finally note that with vector-iteration algorithms organized out of core, the calculation of inertial forces, which implies simply a matrix-vector product with **M**, may also be achieved using an element-by-element memorization of the mass matrix.

### 1.1D An Efficient Eigenvalue Solver: The Lanczos Biorthogonal Algorithm

The Lanczos method for eigenvalue extraction is a method that is increasing in popularity in structural-vibration applications [15, 27, 28, 30–32] owing to its ability to extract a given number of eigenvalues of system (1.1) in a minimum number of iterations.

Here, we will concentrate on the case where both matrices **K** and **M** are symmetric and positive-semidefinite. In some problems, however, it is convenient to introduce linear constraints between DOF, in which case the extended eigenvalue problem takes the form derived from (1.11):

$$\begin{bmatrix} \mathbf{K} & \mathbf{C}^T \\ \mathbf{C} & \mathbf{0} \end{bmatrix} \begin{bmatrix} \mathbf{x} \\ \boldsymbol{\lambda} \end{bmatrix} = \omega^2 \begin{bmatrix} \mathbf{M} & \mathbf{0} \\ \mathbf{0} & \mathbf{0} \end{bmatrix} \begin{bmatrix} \mathbf{x} \\ \boldsymbol{\lambda} \end{bmatrix} \tag{1.22}$$

The extended stiffness matrix is no longer positive-definite, but the positive character of the generalized stiffnesses and masses is still preserved by the eigensolutions. The method may also be extended to structural-stability problems such as in Ref. [32], but the following presentation will be limited to positive eigenvalues.

The main drawback of the Lanczos method is the rapid loss of orthogonality that occurs in the building-up sequence of conjugate directions. This can be overcome to some extent by using reorthogonalization schemes such as proposed in Refs. [19, 27, 28]; nevertheless, a safe application of the method requires one to calculate *a posteriori* bounds in order to appreciate the loss of accuracy.

Another difficulty of the method is the occurrence of coincident eigenvalues. The Lanczos method does not fail by lack of convergence as does the ordinary power method, but it provides only one eigenmode for each multiple eigenvalue; thus, an appropriate remedy is a restart procedure with orthogonal trial vectors.

Despite these difficulties, the Lanczos method, if implemented in a convenient way, probably remains the most powerful algorithm to extract eigenvalues, not because of its computational simplicity and low storage requirements, but because of its property of requiring a minimum number of iterations per eigenvalue to be extracted. In the following sections the algorithm will be described and some aspects of its computer implementation will be discussed in depth.

***The Biorthogonal Lanczos Algorithm for Symmetric Matrices***   The eigenvalue problem (1.1) involves symmetric matrices, and only its lower eigenvalues are generally useful for engineering purposes. The Lanczos method is a variant of the power method, in which the successive iterates of a starting vector $\mathbf{x}_0$ are calculated by

$$\mathbf{y}_r = \mathbf{M}\mathbf{x}_r$$
$$\mathbf{x}_{r+1} = \mathbf{K}^{-1}\mathbf{y}_r \tag{1.23}$$

The matrix $\mathbf{K}^{-1}$ is the inverse of $\mathbf{K}$ or, possibly, if rigid-body and kinematic modes occur, its pseudoinverse. Biorthogonality is maintained between both sequences

$$\mathbf{x}_{r+1}^T\mathbf{y}_i = 0 \qquad \mathbf{y}_{r+1}^T\mathbf{x}_i = 0 \qquad i \le r \tag{1.24}$$

by modifying (1.23) into

$$\mathbf{x}_{r+1}^* = \mathbf{K}^{-1}\mathbf{y}_r - \boldsymbol{\alpha}_r\mathbf{x}_r - \boldsymbol{\beta}_{r-1}\mathbf{x}_{r-1}$$
$$\mathbf{y}_{r+1}^* = \mathbf{M}\mathbf{x}_{r+1}^* \tag{1.25}$$

followed by a normalization of the new iterates

$$\mathbf{x}_{r+1} = \frac{\mathbf{x}_{r+1}^*}{\gamma_{r+1}} \qquad \mathbf{y}_{r+1} = \frac{\mathbf{y}_{r+1}^*}{\gamma_{r+1}}$$

The coefficients in (1.25) are obtained as follows:

$$\boldsymbol{\alpha}_r = \mathbf{y}_r^T\mathbf{K}^{-1}\mathbf{y}_r$$
$$\boldsymbol{\beta}_{r-1} = \mathbf{y}_{r-1}^T\mathbf{K}^{-1}\mathbf{y}_r = \mathbf{x}_r^{*T}\mathbf{y}_r = \gamma_r$$

The recurrence relations (1.25) can be written in the matrix form

$$\mathbf{K}^{-1}\mathbf{M}[\mathbf{x}_0 \ \ \mathbf{x}_1 \ \ \cdots \ \ \mathbf{x}_r] = [\mathbf{x}_0 \ \cdots \ \mathbf{x}_r]\mathbf{T}_r + [\mathbf{0} \ \cdots \ \mathbf{x}_{r+1}^*] \tag{1.26}$$

with the tridiagonal matrix

$$\mathbf{T}_r = \begin{bmatrix} \alpha_0 & \beta_0 & & & & 0 \\ \gamma_1 & \alpha_1 & \beta_1 & & & \\ & \gamma_1 & \alpha_2 & \cdot & & \\ & & \cdot & \cdot & \cdot & \\ & & & \cdot & \cdot & \cdot \\ & & & & \cdot & \cdot & \beta_{r-1} \\ & 0 & & & & \gamma_{r-1} & \alpha_r \end{bmatrix} \tag{1.27}$$

To obtain the interaction eigenvalue problem, we premultiply Eq. (1.26) at step $r$ by the orthogonal sequence $[\mathbf{y}_0 \ \mathbf{y}_1 \ \cdots \ \mathbf{y}_r]^T$. If Eqs. (1.24) are used, the matrix equation obtained is

$$[\mathbf{y}_0 \ \ \mathbf{y}_1 \ \ \cdots \ \ \mathbf{y}_r]^T\mathbf{K}^{-1}\mathbf{M}[\mathbf{x}_0 \ \cdots \ \mathbf{x}_r] = [\mathbf{y}_0 \ \ \mathbf{y}_1 \ \ \cdots \ \ \mathbf{y}_r]^T[\mathbf{x}_0 \ \ \mathbf{x}_1 \ \ \cdots \ \ \mathbf{x}_r]\mathbf{T}_r \tag{1.28}$$

Let us next denote by $z$ an eigenvector of $\mathbf{T}_r$ associated with the eigenvalue $\mu$. With the definition of two successive iterations

$$\mathbf{v}_0 = [\mathbf{x}_0 \ \ \mathbf{x}_1 \ \ \cdots \ \ \mathbf{x}_r]\mathbf{z}$$
$$\mathbf{v}_1 = \mathbf{K}^{-1}\mathbf{M}\mathbf{v}_0$$

Eq. (1.28) yields $\qquad\qquad\qquad \mu = \dfrac{\mathbf{v}_1^T\mathbf{M}\mathbf{v}_0}{\mathbf{v}_0^T\mathbf{M}\mathbf{v}_0} = \dfrac{1}{\omega^2}$

Therefore, the eigenvalues of $\mathbf{T}_r$ are the Schwartz quotients [40] that can be constructed in the orthogonal subspace spanned by the vectors $[\mathbf{x}_0\ \mathbf{x}_1\ \cdots\ \mathbf{x}_r]$. They are thus expected to converge rapidly to the eigenvalues of (1.1).

**Reorthogonalization**    When the foregoing algorithm is applied in its crude form, a rapid loss of orthogonality is observed between the two sequences of vectors $\mathbf{x}_r$ and $\mathbf{y}_r$. As observed by Golub et al. [19], departure from orthogonality is the result of cancellation in the computation of $\mathbf{x}_{r+1}$ and $\mathbf{y}_{r+1}$ from (1.25) rather than a consequence of rounding-error accumulation.

In order to be certain of obtaining the full set of eigensolutions it is necessary to ensure that the computed $\mathbf{q}_r$ are orthogonal to working accuracy. The conventional way of restoring orthogonality with all previously computed vectors is the well-known Schmidt process. Two passes are generally sufficient: the iterative Schmidt process proposed by Ojalvo [27] does not seem necessary.

An alternative to the Schmidt process has been proposed by Golub et al. [19] in the symmetric case and generalized to the unsymmetric case in Ref. [28]. It consists of using elementary hermitian matrices to transform the iteration vectors $[\mathbf{x}_0\ \mathbf{x}_1\ \cdots\ \mathbf{x}_r]$ into a basis of unit vectors. This second procedure, although computationally efficient in most situations, may lead to difficulties in the presence of linear constraints in the stiffness matrix since all the unit vectors can no longer be considered as independent.

**Restart Procedure**    When coincident eigenvalues occur, the iteration scheme (1.25) gives only one eigenmode for each multiple eigenvalue. Indeed, in the initial trial vector $\mathbf{q}_0$, the eigenmodes associated with the same eigenvalue are represented through one linear combination which does not change from iteration to iteration. Separation of multiple eigenmodes is thus impossible as long as only one starting vector is used.

In order to avoid this drawback, Golub and Underwood [29] proposed a block Lanczos algorithm in which the trial vector $\mathbf{x}_0$ is replaced by a set of independent trial vectors. Then, each iteration (1.25) yields a set of vectors, and orthogonality is kept between the set of vectors within the same iteration. This process yields to a block tridiagonal matrix.

A more economical solution is to develop a restart procedure after a given number of iterations have been performed on the initial trial vector $\mathbf{x}_0$. A new trial vector $\mathbf{x}_{n+1}$ is chosen orthogonal to the first sequence

$$\mathbf{y}_i^T\mathbf{x}_{n+1}' = 0 \qquad i = 1,\ldots,n$$

and the recurrence relation is modified into ($p > n$)

$$\gamma_{p+1}\mathbf{x}_{p+1} = \mathbf{K}^{-1}\mathbf{y}_p - \alpha_p\mathbf{x}_p - \beta_{p-1}\mathbf{x}_{p-1} - \varepsilon_{pn}\mathbf{x}_n \qquad (1.29)$$

with $\gamma_{p+1}$, $\alpha_p$, and $\beta_{p-1}$ calculated as before and

$$\varepsilon_{pn} = \mathbf{y}_p^T\mathbf{x}_{n+1} = \mathbf{y}_p^T\mathbf{K}^{-1}\mathbf{y}_n$$

Let us next gather the recurrence relations (1.25) and (1.29) into one matrix equation and denote by

$$\mathbf{x}_p = [\mathbf{x}_0\ \cdots\ \mathbf{x}_n\mathbf{x}_{n+1}\ \cdots\ \mathbf{x}_p]$$

the set of vectors at iteration $p$

$$\mathbf{K}^{-1}\mathbf{M}\mathbf{X}_p = \mathbf{X}_p\mathbf{H}_p + [0 \quad \cdots \quad \mathbf{x}_{n+1}^* \quad 0 \quad \cdots \quad \mathbf{x}_{p+1}^*] \tag{1.30}$$

The matrix $\mathbf{H}_p$ is tridiagonal except for the line $n$ containing $\varepsilon_{pn}$

$$\mathbf{H}_p = \begin{bmatrix} \mathbf{T}_n & 0 \\ \hline 0 & \mathbf{T}_{p-n} \end{bmatrix} \leftarrow [\varepsilon_{pn}]$$

To obtain the interaction matrix, we premultiply (1.30) by $\mathbf{X}_p^T\mathbf{M}$:

$$\mathbf{X}_p^T\mathbf{M}\mathbf{K}^{-1}\mathbf{M}\mathbf{X}_p = \mathbf{X}_p^T\mathbf{M}\mathbf{X}_p\mathbf{H}_p + \mathbf{Y}_p^T[0 \quad \cdots \quad \mathbf{x}_{n+1}^* \quad 0 \quad \cdots \quad \mathbf{x}_{p+1}^*]$$

The last term is zero, except for the row $n$ which contains $\varepsilon_{pn}$. The result is the interaction equation

$$\mathbf{X}_p^T\mathbf{M}\mathbf{K}^{-1}\mathbf{M}\mathbf{X}_p = \mathbf{S}_p \tag{1.31}$$

with the symmetric interaction matrix

$$\mathbf{S}_p = \begin{bmatrix} \mathbf{T}_n & \mathbf{0} \\ \hline \mathbf{0} & \mathbf{T}_{p-n} \end{bmatrix} \leftarrow [\varepsilon_{pn}]$$

$$\uparrow$$
$$\varepsilon_{pn}$$

This restart procedure can be employed several times, and the developments discussed in following subsections can be easily generalized to give an interaction matrix of almost tridiagonal form by the Householder transformation and then solved as before, using a method such as the *QR*-method or the Sturm sequence with bisection.

***Choice of Starting Vectors*** The number of independent modes in the system designated by Eq. (1.22) is limited by the presence of linear constraints and possibly also by the rank of the mass matrix (cases occur where some DOF have no attached mass), so that a random starting vector may not be used to initiate the exact eigenvector search. Therefore, in order to restrict the complete space to the appropriate one, the arbitrary starting vector $\mathbf{x}_0^*$ is transformed by using

$$\mathbf{x}_0 = \mathbf{K}^{-1}\mathbf{M}\mathbf{x}_0^*$$

$$\mathbf{y}_0 = \mathbf{M}\mathbf{x}_0$$

The same procedure must be employed for each restarting vector. If only the eigenvalues are required and not the eigenmodes, this starting procedure is not necessary since it does not affect the coefficients of the interaction matrix.

***Convergence Strategy*** In the classical Lanczos algorithm, the sequence (1.25) is continued until $\mathbf{y}_r^T\mathbf{x}_r = 0$ (breakdown) or $r = N - 1$ (normal termination), where $N$ is the effective number of DOF. In case of breakdown, the corresponding coefficients $\gamma_r$ vanish. The pattern of the tridiagonal matrix (1.27) then shows that a complete subspace of vectors $[\mathbf{x}_0 \; \cdots \; \mathbf{x}_{r-1}]$ has been isolated if either $\mathbf{x}_r$ or both vectors are zero. The dead-end breakdown corresponding to $(\mathbf{x}_r^T \mathbf{y}_r = 0, \; \mathbf{y}_r \neq 0, \; \mathbf{x}_r \neq 0 \text{ for } r < N-1)$ occurs only if $\mathbf{M}$ is not positive-definite and is thus unlikely to occur in vibration analysis.

Generally, the number of required eigenvalues is much lower than $N$, and the Lanczos sequence is truncated well before the occurrence of either normal termination or breakdown. The convergence criterion is based on the eigenvalues of the interaction matrix (1.31)

$$\mathbf{Sa} = \mu \mathbf{a} \tag{1.32}$$

Let $\mu_1^{(r)} \geqslant \mu_2^{(r)} \geqslant \cdots \mu_r^{(r)}$ and $[\mathbf{a}_{(1)} \; \mathbf{a}_{(2)} \; \cdots \; \mathbf{a}_{(r)}]$ be the eigensolutions obtained at step $r$. Convergence of the Lanczos sequence is reached when

$$|\mu_k^{(r+1)} - \mu_k^{(r)}| < \varepsilon \mu_k^{(r)} \qquad k = 1, \dots, s \tag{1.33}$$

where $\varepsilon$ denotes the precision required on the eigenvalues. This simple criterion does not require the calculation of the eigenmodes at each step, but has been proved to be efficient. A more elaborate criterion which involves the eigenmodes $\mathbf{a}_{(i)}$ also may be found in Refs. [27, 28].

Let us assume that the criterion (1.33) is satisfied after $n_1$ iterations using (1.25). The restart procedure is then employed to investigate the possibility of coincident eigenvalues. The iteration process (1.29) is continued until (1.33) is satisfied for an additional eigenvalue $s+1$. If no multiple eigenvalues appear in the eigenspectrum, the Lanczos iteration is stopped and the eigenvectors are calculated as described below. Otherwise, a new starting vector is constructed and $n_2$ iterations are performed.

For each starting vector, a maximum number of iterations $n_1, n_2, \dots,$ can be defined. The following choice is usually found to give satisfactory results.

$$n_1 = 3s + 5 \qquad n_i = 5 \qquad i > 2 \tag{1.34}$$

For some ill-conditioned problems, the number of iterations in (1.34) may not be sufficient to ensure satisfaction of the convergence criterion (1.33). In the case of nearly coincident eigenvalues, however, the restarting procedure is expected to improve the rate of convergence of the algorithm.

***Calculation of Eigenmodes***   Once the eigenvalues $(\mu_1, \dots, \mu_s)$ of $\mathbf{S}$ have been determined, inverse iteration with shift provides an efficient algorithm for computing the associated eigenvectors $\mathbf{a}_{(k)}$ (cf. [2], procedure TINVIT). To restore the eigenvectors of the initial problem (1.1), we return to Eq. (1.31), from which we deduce that the approximation to $\mathbf{x}_{(k)}$ contained in the subspace $\mathbf{X}$ is

$$\mathbf{x}_{(k)} = \mathbf{X} \mathbf{a}_{(k)}$$

If error bounds to the initial problem (1.1) are needed, they can be obtained from the bracketing algorithm described in Sec. 1.1F. This error-analysis procedure is rendered straightforward by the fact that the Lanczos algorithm provides directly the Schwarz quotients associated with the approximate eigenvectors.

## 1.1E Vector Iteration in Presence of Rigid-Body Modes
### [39, 41, 49]

***Separation into Rigid-Body and Elastic Modes***   Earlier in this chapter (Sec. 1.1B), in the discussion of linear solution methods, it was shown that rigid-body and kinematic modes may be extracted automatically during Gauss elimination or triangulation of the stiffness matrix. The $r$ nontrivial solutions of $\mathbf{Ku} = 0$ are thus available at this stage, and they are taken to be collected in a rigid-body matrix

$$\mathbf{U} = [\mathbf{u}_{(1)} \quad \cdots \quad \mathbf{u}_{(r)}]$$

after orthogonalization with respect to the mass matrix. On the other hand, let us suppose that the elastic vibration modes from the elastic modal matrix

$$\mathbf{X} = [\mathbf{x}_{(1)} \quad \cdots \quad \mathbf{x}_{(r)}]$$

They obey the orthonormality relations

$$\mathbf{X}^T \mathbf{KX} = \mathbf{\Omega}^2 \qquad \mathbf{X}^T \mathbf{MX} = \mathbf{I}_n$$
$$\mathbf{X}^T \mathbf{MU} = 0 \qquad \mathbf{U}^T \mathbf{MU} = \mathbf{I}_r \tag{1.35}$$

where $\mathbf{\Omega}^2$ is the diagonal matrix of eigenvalues, and $\mathbf{I}_n$, $\mathbf{I}_r$ are identity matrices of dimension $n$ and $r$, respectively. The modal matrix $\mathbf{UX}$ forms a complete basis to express an arbitrary displacement vector

$$\mathbf{x} = \mathbf{Ua} + \mathbf{Xb} \tag{1.36}$$

with coefficients $\qquad \mathbf{a} = \mathbf{U}^T \mathbf{Mx} \qquad$ and $\qquad \mathbf{X}^T \mathbf{Mx}$

Similarly, the matrix $[\mathbf{MU} \quad \mathbf{MX}]$ of inertia forces forms a natural basis to expand an arbitrary load vector

$$\mathbf{p} = \mathbf{MUc} + \mathbf{MXd} \tag{1.37}$$

with $\qquad \mathbf{c} = \mathbf{U}^T \mathbf{p} \qquad$ and $\qquad \mathbf{d} = \mathbf{X}^T \mathbf{p}$

***Modification of Vector-Iteration Algorithms***   The generalization of the vector-iteration law

$$\mathbf{Kx}_{p+1} = \mathbf{Mx}_p \tag{1.38}$$

relies upon the following property of the associated static problem, namely, that the linear system $\mathbf{Kx} = \mathbf{p}$ admits a solution under the necessary and sufficient condition that the applied external force is orthogonal to the rigid-body modes, which means static equilibrium

$$\mathbf{U}^T \mathbf{p} = 0 \tag{1.39}$$

Starting from an arbitrary load $\mathbf{p}$, it can always be transformed into a modified load

$$\hat{\mathbf{p}} = \mathbf{A}^T \mathbf{p}$$

with the filtering operator $\qquad \mathbf{A} = \mathbf{I} - \mathbf{UU}^T \mathbf{M}$

which has the property of extracting the rigid-body part in the developments (1.36) and (1.37)

$$\mathbf{Ax} = \mathbf{Xb} \qquad \text{and} \qquad \mathbf{A}^T\mathbf{p} = \mathbf{MXd}$$

The initial static problem $\mathbf{Kq} = \mathbf{g}$ is thus replaced by

$$\mathbf{Kq} = \mathbf{A}^T\mathbf{g} \qquad (1.40)$$

and the power-iteration law is modified accordingly:

$$\mathbf{Kx}_{p+1} = \mathbf{A}^T\mathbf{Mx}_p \qquad (1.41)$$

Its solution is not unique, since to a particular solution $\mathbf{x}'_{p+1}$ a general solution of the homogeneous equation may always be added:

$$\mathbf{x}_{p+1} = \mathbf{x}'_{p+1} + \mathbf{Ur}$$

The unity of the solution is thus ensured by imposing orthogonality with respect to rigid-body modes.

The iteration law (1.41) is generalized as follows:

$$\mathbf{Kx}'_{p+1} = \mathbf{A}^T\mathbf{Mx}_p$$
$$\mathbf{x}_{p+1} = \mathbf{Ax}'_{p+1} \qquad (1.42)$$

It extends all the eigenvalue extraction methods based on power iteration (inverse iteration, subspace iteration, Lanczos method, etc.) to hypostatic structures.

***Method of Temporary Links***   Obtaining a solution to the modified static problem (1.40) raises no difficulty, in practice. Imagine that a set of $r$ temporary supports constrains the structure in an isostatic manner. As the applied load $\hat{\mathbf{g}} = \mathbf{A}^T\mathbf{g}$ is self-equilibrated, no reaction appears at the support and the temporary fixations have the effect only of positioning the structure geometrically. As the linear solution algorithms (Gauss elimination and Choleski triangulation; see Sec. 1.1B) lead to an automatic solution of $r$ degrees of freedom associated with the singularities of $\mathbf{K}$, an appropriate choice to lock the rigid-body modes is to adopt these as temporary fixations. If one sets $\mathbf{q}_2 = 0$, the static problem for the isostatic structure with self-equilibrated load is replaced by

$$\begin{bmatrix} \mathbf{K}_{11} & 0 \\ 0 & \mathbf{K}_{22} \end{bmatrix} \begin{bmatrix} \mathbf{q}_1 \\ \mathbf{q}_2 \end{bmatrix} = \begin{bmatrix} \mathbf{p}_1 \\ \mathbf{p}_2 \end{bmatrix}$$

in which the remaining DOF are calculated by

$$\mathbf{q}_1 = \mathbf{K}_{11}^{-1}\mathbf{p}_1$$

If an inverse matrix of the isostatic structure is needed such that

$$\mathbf{q} = \mathbf{G}_{\text{iso}}\hat{\mathbf{g}} = \mathbf{G}_{\text{iso}}\mathbf{A}^T\mathbf{g}$$

it can thus be written in the form

$$G_{iso} = \begin{bmatrix} K_{11}^{-1} & 0 \\ 0 & 0 \end{bmatrix}$$

and the associated matrix

$$F_0 = G_{iso}A^T \qquad \text{such that} \qquad q = F_0 g$$

is a pseudoinverse to $K$ which verifies the pseudoinversion relation [50]

$$K_0 F = A^T$$

The final form of the vector-iteration algorithm is

$$y_{p+1} = A^T M x_p$$
$$x'_{p+1} = G_{iso} y_{p+1} \qquad\qquad (1.43)$$
$$x_{p+1} = A x'_{p+1}$$

When used in conjunction with the Lanczos method, the projection operations involved in (1.43) may be combined with the other projection operations. Therefore, the eigenvalue extraction procedure is not significantly complicated by the occurrence of kinematic modes.

## 1.1F Error Bounds of Eigenfrequencies [25, 31, 35, 40]

The possibility of obtaining error bounds on calculated eigenfrequencies (in particular, using the Guyan–Irons condensation algorithm) relies upon the availability of the first iterate $x_1$ of an arbitrary vector $x_0$

$$x_1 = K^{-1} M x_0$$

and of the associated Rayleigh and Schwarz quotients

$$\rho_0 = \frac{x_0^T K x_0}{x_0^T M x_0} \qquad \rho_1 = \frac{x_0^T M x_0}{x_0^T M x_1} \qquad\qquad (1.44)$$

which verify the well-known inequality relationship

$$\rho_0 \geq \rho_1 \geq 0$$

The bound algorithms proposed below result from the properties of the bilinear form

$$A(\alpha, \beta) = \frac{(x_0 - \alpha x_1)^T K (x_0 - \beta x_1)}{x_1^T K x_1} \qquad\qquad (1.45)$$

which can be rewritten in terms of the quotients (1.44)

$$A(\alpha, \beta) = \rho_0 \rho_1 - (\alpha + \beta)\rho_1 + \alpha\beta \qquad\qquad (1.46)$$

In particular, $A(\alpha, \alpha)$ is positive-definite and its minimum occurs for $\alpha = \rho_1$. On the other hand, the spectral expansion of (1.45) is constructed by developing $\mathbf{x}_0$ and $\mathbf{x}_1$ in terms of eigenvectors

$$\mathbf{x}_0 = \sum_n \alpha_n \mathbf{x}_{(n)} \qquad \mathbf{x}_1 = \sum_n \frac{\alpha_n}{\omega_n^2} \mathbf{x}_{(n)}$$

The result of the substitution is

$$A(\alpha, \beta) = \frac{\sum\limits_n \alpha_n^2 (\omega_n^2 - \alpha)(\omega_n^2 - \beta)}{\sum\limits_n \alpha_n^2} \tag{1.47}$$

***Krylov and Bogoliubov Bounds***   A first set of bounds is obtained by setting $\alpha = \beta$ in (1.46) and (1.47) under the condition that $\mathbf{x}_0$ is sufficiently close to an eigenmode $\mathbf{x}_{(j)}$ so that

$$A(\alpha, \alpha) = \rho_0 \rho_1 - 2\alpha \rho_1 + \alpha^2$$

$$= \frac{\sum\limits_n \alpha_n^2 (\omega_n^2 - \alpha)^2}{\sum\limits_n \alpha_n^2} \geq \min_n \, (\omega_n^2 - \alpha)^2 = (\omega_j^2 - \alpha)^2$$

the inequality being the tightest for $\alpha = \rho_1$. Depending on whether $\alpha = \rho_0$ or $\alpha = \rho_1$, one obtains the set of bounds

$$\rho_0 - \sqrt{\rho_0^2 - \rho_0 \rho_1} \leq \omega_j^2 \leq \rho_0 + \sqrt{\rho_0^2 - \rho_0 \rho_1}$$
$$\rho_1 - \sqrt{\rho_1 \rho_0 - \rho_1^2} \leq \omega_j^2 \leq \rho_1 + \sqrt{\rho_0 \rho_1 - \rho_1^2} \tag{1.48}$$

which provides an uncertainty interval on the eigenvalue $\omega_j^2$ which is the closest to $\rho_0$ and $\rho_1$.

***Temple and Kato Bounds***   A second bound algorithm, attributed to Temple and Kato, depends on the property of the bilinear form (1.45) to remain positive-definite in an $[\alpha, \beta]$-interval in which no eigenvalue is contained. Its application is thus restricted to the case of a specified eigenvalue $\omega_i^2$, and conditioned to the availability of two numbers $\mu$ and $\nu$ such that

$$\omega_{i-1}^2 \leq \mu < \rho_1 < \rho_0 < \nu \leq \omega_{i+1}^2 \tag{1.49}$$

where $\mu$ and $\nu$ are, respectively, an upper bound to $\omega_{i-1}$ and a lower bound to $\omega_{i+1}^2$ which in most cases can be obtained from the application of the previous bound algorithm (1.48).
   By successively making

$$\alpha = \omega_i^2 \qquad \text{and} \qquad \alpha = \mu$$
$$\beta = \nu \qquad\qquad\qquad \beta = \omega_i^2$$

in (1.46) and also taking account of (1.49), the following lower and upper bounds to $\omega_i^2$ are obtained:

$$\rho_1 \frac{\nu - \rho_0}{\nu - \rho_1} \leq \omega_i^2 \leq \rho_1 \frac{\rho_0 - \mu}{\rho_1 - \mu} \tag{1.50}$$

In most cases they provide a much better bracketing of the exact eigenvalues of (1.1) than the bounds (1.48). Of course, the use of (1.50) is conditioned to the fact that the bounds $\mu$ and $\nu$ calculated by the previous bound algorithm are accurate enough to respect the condition (1.49).

In practice, the bound algorithms (1.48) and (1.50) are very useful tools for calculating the loss of accuracy due to condensation in the use of the Guyan-Irons algorithm, for controlling the convergence of all the vector-iteration methods, and for detecting the occurrence of parasitic solutions as may happen with Lanczos iteration.

***Sensitivity Analysis***   In many cases, the structural engineer is faced with the problem of obtaining information about the influence of a mass or stiffness modification on the vibration characteristics of a structure. To this end, an elementary modification of the structural model is defined in the form

$$(\mathbf{K} + \gamma \mathbf{l}\mathbf{k}\mathbf{l}^T)\mathbf{y} = \omega^2(\mathbf{M} + \mu \mathbf{l}\mathbf{m}\mathbf{l}^T)\mathbf{y} \tag{1.51}$$

where $\mathbf{k}$ and $\mathbf{m}$ are stiffness and mass "kernels." In particular, the formula (1.51) allows the representation of change in the characteristics of a specified element, in which case $\mathbf{k}$ and $\mathbf{m}$ are its stiffness and mass matrices for unit transverse dimension (section, thickness), and $\gamma$ and $\mu$ are proportionality constants. In the case of lumped stiffness and mass, $\mathbf{k} = \mathbf{m} = 1$. $\mathbf{l}$ is an incidence matrix involving the DOF concerned by the structural modification. In the case of the modification of a given finite element, $\mathbf{l}$ is its localization operator.

Expand the solution of the modified system (1.51) in terms of eigenmodes of the initial system (1.1):

$$\mathbf{y} = \Sigma \alpha_r \mathbf{x}_{(r)}$$

By setting $\mathbf{b}_r = \mathbf{l}^T \mathbf{x}_{(r)}$ and noting that $\mathbf{K}\mathbf{x}_{(r)} = \omega_r^2 \mathbf{M}\mathbf{x}_{(r)}$, one obtains

$$\sum_r \alpha_r(\omega_r^2 - \omega^2)\mathbf{M}\mathbf{x}_{(r)} + (\gamma \mathbf{l}\mathbf{k} - \omega^2 \mu \mathbf{l}\mathbf{m}) \sum_r \alpha_r \beta_r = 0 \tag{1.52}$$

Next, premultiply (1.52) by a mode $\mathbf{x}_{(m)}$ and take account of orthonormality. The homogeneous linear system in the $\alpha_m$ variables follows

$$\alpha_m(\omega_m^2 - \omega^2) + \sum_j \alpha_j(\gamma \gamma_{mj} - \omega^2 \mu \mu_{mj}) = 0 \tag{1.53}$$

with the definition of the modal stiffness and mass contributions to the elementary modification

$$\gamma_{mr} = \mathbf{b}_m^T \mathbf{k}\mathbf{b}_r, \qquad \mu_{mr} = \mathbf{b}_m^T \mathbf{m}\mathbf{b}_r$$

The sensitivity analysis results from the hypothesis of small perturbations. The approximations to the eigensolutions

$$\left. \begin{matrix} \mathbf{y}_{(r)} \\ \hat{\omega}_r^2 \end{matrix} \right\} = \mathbf{x}_{(r)} + \sum_{j \neq r} \alpha_j \mathbf{x}_{(j)}$$

are obtained from (1.53) by assuming $|\alpha_m| \ll 1$, and are found to be

$$\hat{\omega}_r^2 = \frac{\omega_r^2 + \gamma\gamma_{rr}}{1 + \mu\mu_{rr}} \qquad \alpha_m = \frac{\gamma\gamma_{mr} - \hat{\omega}_r^2\mu\mu_{mr}}{\omega\omega_m^2 - \hat{\omega}_r^2} \tag{1.54}$$

They allow for an easy evaluation of changes in eigenfrequencies and eigenmodes due to an elementary stiffness and mass modification, in particular, when changing the characteristics of a given element.

The approximations (1.54) are of primary importance in the framework of structural optimization methods in the presence of constraints on the eigenspectrum. They are also very useful in the process of adjusting a numerical model to experimentally measure modal data.


## 1.2 EIGENSOLUTION EXTRACTION METHODS

This section presents methods for extracting eigenvalues and eigenvectors. With the exception of the Lanczos method, which was described in the previous section, most of the major methods are outlined.


### 1.2A Eigenvalue Problems in Engineering Simulations

Eigenvalue problems occur in three main areas of engineering analysis. The most common area is the vibration of structures. The remaining two areas include linearized buckling analysis and heat-transfer analysis. The buckling analysis is described by the system of equations

$$-\mathbf{K}_G\boldsymbol{\phi} = \lambda\,\mathbf{K}\boldsymbol{\phi} \tag{1.55}$$

where $\mathbf{K}_G$ is the nonlinear-strain stiffness matrix, $\mathbf{K}$ is the linear-strain matrix, and $\lambda$ are buckling loads. The heat-transfer analysis eigenproblem is defined by the system of equations

$$\mathbf{K}\boldsymbol{\phi} = \lambda\,\mathbf{C}\boldsymbol{\phi} \tag{1.56}$$

where $\mathbf{K}$ is the heat-conductivity matrix, $\mathbf{C}$ is the heat-capacity matrix, and $\lambda$ and $\boldsymbol{\phi}$ represent thermal "frequencies" and mode shapes.

The structural-vibration eigenproblem is typically divided into several special types depending on various properties of the system's mass, damping, and stiffness matrices. The following sections list several types of structural eigenproblems and contain the orthogonality conditions which the eigenvectors satisfy. Proofs of the orthogonality relations may be found in Refs. [1, 52–55].

***Undamped Symmetric Systems***   The undamped system with symmetric $\mathbf{M}$- and $\mathbf{K}$-matrices is the most common case encountered in structural simulation.

*Eigenvalue problem*:

$$(-\Omega_k^2\mathbf{M} + \mathbf{K})\boldsymbol{\phi}_k = \mathbf{0} \qquad (N \times 1) \tag{1.57}$$

*Modal matrix*:

$$\mathbf{\Phi} = [\boldsymbol{\phi}_1 \mid \boldsymbol{\phi}_2 \mid \cdots \mid \boldsymbol{\phi}_L] \qquad (N \times L) \tag{1.58}$$

*Orthogonality conditions*:

$$\boldsymbol{\phi}_i^T \mathbf{M} \boldsymbol{\phi}_j = \hat{\delta}_{ij} \bar{m}_i \qquad \boldsymbol{\phi}_i^T \mathbf{K} \boldsymbol{\phi}_j = \hat{\delta}_{ij} \bar{m}_i \Omega_i^2 \tag{1.59}$$

where                    $\hat{\delta}_{ij} = $ Kronecker delta

**Proportionately Damped Systems**    The classical damping model of proportional damping is very popular in structural-forced-response studies since it results in real mode shapes and uncoupled equations of motion.

*Eigenvalue problem*:

$$(\alpha_k^2 \mathbf{M} + \alpha_k \mathbf{C} + \mathbf{K}) \boldsymbol{\Lambda}_k = \mathbf{0} \qquad (N \times 1) \tag{1.60}$$

*Relation to undamped symmetric systems*:

$$\alpha_k = -\zeta_k \Omega_k \pm i \Omega_k \sqrt{1 - \zeta_k^2}$$
$$\boldsymbol{\Lambda}_k = \boldsymbol{\phi}_k \tag{1.61}$$

*Orthogonality conditions*:

$$\boldsymbol{\phi}_i^T \mathbf{C} \boldsymbol{\phi}_j = \hat{\delta}_{ij} 2 \zeta_i \Omega_i \bar{m}_i \tag{1.62}$$

and Eq. (1.59).

**General Damped Systems**    General damped systems are frequently encountered in simulating rotating structures or machinery components [56] and systems with active dampers or discrete vibration isolators.

*Eigenvalue problem (quadratic form)*:

$$(\alpha_k^2 \mathbf{M} + \alpha_k \mathbf{C} + \mathbf{K}) \boldsymbol{\Lambda}_k = \mathbf{0} \qquad (N \times 1) \tag{1.63}$$

*Adjoint eigenvalue problem (quadratic form)*:

$$(\alpha_k^2 \mathbf{M}^T + \alpha_k \mathbf{C}^T + \mathbf{K}^T) \boldsymbol{\delta}_k = \mathbf{0} \qquad (N \times 1) \tag{1.64}$$

*Eigenvalue problem (generalized form)*:

$$(\alpha_k \mathbf{A}_1 + \mathbf{B}_1) \boldsymbol{\Gamma}_k = \mathbf{0} \qquad \text{or} \qquad (\alpha_k \mathbf{A}_2 + \mathbf{B}_2) \boldsymbol{\Gamma}_k = \mathbf{0} \qquad (2N \times 1) \tag{1.65}$$

*Adjoint eigenvalue problem (generalized form)*:

$$(\alpha_k \mathbf{A}_1^T + \mathbf{B}_1^T) \boldsymbol{\gamma}_k = \mathbf{0} \qquad \text{or} \qquad (\alpha_k \mathbf{A}_2^T + \mathbf{B}_2^T) \boldsymbol{\gamma}_k = \mathbf{0} \qquad (2N \times 1) \tag{1.66}$$

*Eigenvalue problem (standard form)*:

**M, K** nonsingular:        $\left( \dfrac{1}{\alpha_k} \mathbf{I}_{2N} - \mathbf{D}^{-1} \right) \boldsymbol{\Gamma}_k = \mathbf{0} \qquad (2N \times 1) \tag{1.67}$

**M** nonsingular:        $(\alpha_k \mathbf{I}_{2N} - \mathbf{D}) \boldsymbol{\Gamma}_k = \mathbf{0} \qquad (2N \times 1) \tag{1.68}$

*Adjoint eigenvalue problem (standard form):*

**M, K** nonsingular:
$$\left(\frac{1}{\alpha_k}\mathbf{I}_{2N} - (\mathbf{D}^{-1})^T\right)\boldsymbol{\beta}_k = \mathbf{0} \qquad (2N \times 1) \qquad (1.69)$$

**M** nonsingular:
$$(\alpha_k \mathbf{I}_{2N} - \mathbf{D}^T)\boldsymbol{\beta}_k = \mathbf{0} \qquad (2N \times 1) \qquad (1.70)$$

*Definitions:*

$$\mathbf{A}_1 = \left[\begin{array}{c:c} \mathbf{M} & \mathbf{0} \\ \hdashline \mathbf{0} & -\mathbf{K} \end{array}\right] \qquad \mathbf{B}_1 = \left[\begin{array}{c:c} \mathbf{C} & \mathbf{K} \\ \hdashline \mathbf{K} & \mathbf{0} \end{array}\right] \qquad (2N \times 2N)$$

$$\mathbf{A}_2 = \left[\begin{array}{c:c} \mathbf{0} & \mathbf{M} \\ \hdashline \mathbf{M} & \mathbf{C} \end{array}\right] \qquad \mathbf{B}_2 = \left[\begin{array}{c:c} -\mathbf{M} & \mathbf{0} \\ \hdashline \mathbf{0} & \mathbf{K} \end{array}\right] \qquad (2N \times 2N)$$

$$\mathbf{D} = -\mathbf{A}_1^{-1}\mathbf{B}_1 = -\mathbf{A}_2^{-1}\mathbf{B}_2 = \left[\begin{array}{c:c} -\mathbf{M}^{-1}\mathbf{C} & -\mathbf{M}^{-1}\mathbf{K} \\ \hdashline \mathbf{I}_N & \mathbf{0} \end{array}\right]$$

$$\mathbf{D}^{-1} = \left[\begin{array}{c:c} \mathbf{0} & \mathbf{I}_N \\ \hdashline -\mathbf{K}^{-1}\mathbf{M} & -\mathbf{K}^{-1}\mathbf{C} \end{array}\right]$$

$$\boldsymbol{\Gamma}_i = \left[\begin{array}{c} \alpha_i\boldsymbol{\Lambda}_i \\ \hline \boldsymbol{\Lambda}_i \end{array}\right] \qquad \boldsymbol{\gamma}_i = \left[\begin{array}{c} \alpha_i\boldsymbol{\delta}_i \\ \hline \boldsymbol{\delta}_i \end{array}\right] \qquad (2N \times 1)$$

**M, K** nonsingular:                $\boldsymbol{\beta}_i = \mathbf{A}_1^T \boldsymbol{\gamma}_i$

**M** nonsingular:                   $\boldsymbol{\beta}_i = \mathbf{A}_2^T \boldsymbol{\gamma}_i$         (1.71)

*Orthogonality conditions:*

$$\boldsymbol{\gamma}_i^T \mathbf{A}_1 \boldsymbol{\Gamma}_j = \boldsymbol{\delta}_i^T(\alpha_i\alpha_j \mathbf{M} - \mathbf{K})\boldsymbol{\Lambda}_j$$
$$= \hat{\delta}_{ij}\boldsymbol{\delta}_i^T(\alpha_i^2 \mathbf{M} - \mathbf{K})\boldsymbol{\Lambda}_i = \hat{\delta}_{ij}a_{1i}$$

$$\boldsymbol{\gamma}_i^T \mathbf{B}_1 \boldsymbol{\Gamma}_j = \boldsymbol{\delta}_i^T(\alpha_i\alpha_j \mathbf{C} + (\alpha_i + \alpha_j)\mathbf{K})\boldsymbol{\Lambda}_j$$
$$= \hat{\delta}_{ij}\boldsymbol{\delta}_i^T(\alpha_i^2 \mathbf{C} + 2\alpha_i\mathbf{K})\boldsymbol{\Lambda}_i = -\hat{\delta}_{ij}a_{1i}\alpha_i$$

$$\boldsymbol{\gamma}_i^T \mathbf{A}_2 \boldsymbol{\Gamma}_j = \boldsymbol{\delta}_i^T((\alpha_i + \alpha_j)\mathbf{M} + \mathbf{C})\boldsymbol{\Lambda}_j \qquad (1.72)$$
$$= \hat{\delta}_{ij}\boldsymbol{\delta}_i^T(2\alpha_i \mathbf{M} + \mathbf{C})\boldsymbol{\Lambda}_i = \hat{\delta}_{ij}a_{2i}$$

$$\boldsymbol{\gamma}_i^T \mathbf{B}_2 \boldsymbol{\Gamma}_j = \boldsymbol{\delta}_i^T(-\alpha_i\alpha_j \mathbf{M} + \mathbf{K})\boldsymbol{\Lambda}_j$$
$$= \hat{\delta}_{ij}\boldsymbol{\delta}_i^T(-\alpha_i^2 \mathbf{M} + \mathbf{K})\boldsymbol{\Lambda}_i = -\hat{\delta}_{ij}a_{2i}\alpha_i$$

**M, K** nonsingular: $\boldsymbol{\beta}_i^T\boldsymbol{\Gamma}_j = \hat{\delta}_{ij}a_{1i}$       $\boldsymbol{\beta}_i^T\mathbf{D}\boldsymbol{\Gamma}_j = \hat{\delta}_{ij}a_{1i}\alpha_i$

**M** nonsingular: $\boldsymbol{\beta}_i^T\boldsymbol{\Gamma}_j = \hat{\delta}_{ij}a_{2i}$       $\boldsymbol{\beta}_i^T\mathbf{D}\boldsymbol{\Gamma}_j = \hat{\delta}_{ij}a_{2i}\alpha_i$

where                         $\hat{\delta}_{ij}$ = Kronecker delta

$$a_{2i} = \frac{a_{1i}}{\alpha_i} \qquad \alpha_i \neq 0$$

**Symmetric Damped Systems** This type of system represents the special case of general damped systems when $\mathbf{M}$ is symmetric and positive-definite, and $\mathbf{C}$ and $\mathbf{K}$ are both symmetric and positive-semidefinite. The eigenvectors of the previous section now satisfy

$$\boldsymbol{\delta}_k = \boldsymbol{\Lambda}_k \qquad \boldsymbol{\gamma}_k = \boldsymbol{\Gamma}_k$$

The eigenvalues satisfy $\qquad$ $\text{Re}\,(\alpha_k) \leqslant 0$ $\qquad\qquad$ (1.73)

where the equality holds only if (1) $\mathbf{C}$ is positive-semidefinite or (2) $\mathbf{K}$ is positive-semidefinite or (3) $\mathbf{C} = 0$.

**Systems with Structural Damping** Structural or hysteretic damping is used to account for the frequency-independent energy dissipation which occurs within the material of a structure. A brief mathematical description of the free vibration problem is as follows:

*Eigenvalue problem*:

$$(\alpha_k^2 \mathbf{M} + (\mathbf{K}_1 + i\mathbf{K}_2))\boldsymbol{\Lambda}_k = \mathbf{0}$$
$$\mathbf{M} = \mathbf{M}^T \qquad \mathbf{K}_1 = \mathbf{K}_1^T \qquad \mathbf{K}_2 = \mathbf{K}_2^T \tag{1.74}$$

*Orthogonality conditions*:

$$\boldsymbol{\Lambda}_j^T \mathbf{M} \boldsymbol{\Lambda}_k = \hat{\delta}_{jk}\bar{m}_j \qquad \boldsymbol{\Lambda}_j^T(\mathbf{K}_1 + i\mathbf{K}_2)\boldsymbol{\Lambda}_k = \hat{\delta}_{jk}\bar{m}_j \alpha_j^2 \tag{1.75}$$

**Gyroscopic Systems** Conservative gyroscopic systems are frequently encountered in simulation models of spinning structures or machinery components [52]. If damping is neglected, this system type exhibits the following characteristics:

*System property matrices*:

$$\mathbf{M} > 0 \qquad \mathbf{K} \geqslant 0 \qquad \mathbf{C}^T = -\mathbf{C} \tag{1.76}$$

*Regular eigenvalue problem*:

$$(\alpha_k^2 \mathbf{M} + \alpha_k \mathbf{C} + \mathbf{K})\boldsymbol{\Lambda}_k = \mathbf{0} \qquad (N \times 1) \tag{1.77}$$

*Adjoint eigenvalue problems*:

$$(\alpha_k^2 \mathbf{M}^T + \alpha_k \mathbf{C}^T + \mathbf{K}^T)\boldsymbol{\delta}_k = \mathbf{0} \tag{1.78}$$

*Modal properties*:

$$\text{Re}\,(\alpha_k) = 0 \qquad \boldsymbol{\delta}_k = \bar{\boldsymbol{\Lambda}}_k \qquad \text{(complex conjugate)} \tag{1.79}$$

## 1.2B Preliminary Theorems Related to Eigenvalue Extraction

All eigenvalue extraction methods rely on certain characteristic properties drawn from matrix theory. This section contains a list of these properties. The interested reader can obtain the related proofs in Refs. [54–56].

### Eigenvalue Shifting

**1.** The eigensolutions of
$$\lambda_i \mathbf{M} \boldsymbol{\phi}_i = \mathbf{K} \boldsymbol{\phi}_i \tag{1.80}$$

are related to the eigensolutions of

$$\mu_i \mathbf{M} \boldsymbol{\psi}_i = (\mathbf{K} - \rho \mathbf{M}) \boldsymbol{\psi}_i \tag{1.81}$$

by
$$\mu_i = \lambda_i - \rho \qquad \boldsymbol{\psi}_i = \boldsymbol{\phi}_i \tag{1.82}$$

**2.** The eigensolutions of
$$\lambda_i \boldsymbol{\phi}_i = \mathbf{D} \boldsymbol{\phi}_i \tag{1.83}$$

are related to the eigensolutions of

$$\mu_i \boldsymbol{\psi}_i = (\mathbf{D} - \rho \mathbf{I}) \boldsymbol{\psi}_i \tag{1.84}$$

by
$$\mu_i = \lambda_i - \rho \qquad \boldsymbol{\psi}_i = \boldsymbol{\phi}_i \tag{1.85}$$

### Similarity Transformations

**1.** Two matrices $\mathbf{A}$ and $\mathbf{B}$ are said to be similar if there exists some matrix $\mathbf{T}$ such that

$$\mathbf{T}^{-1} \mathbf{A} \mathbf{T} = \mathbf{B} \tag{1.86}$$

**2.** Similar matrices have the same eigenvalues with the same multiplicities.

**3.** Any real symmetric matrix is similar to a unique diagonal matrix.

**Eigenvalues of Diagonal and Triangular Matrices**    The eigenvalues of a diagonal or triangular matrix are equal to the elements contained on the main diagonal of the matrix.

### Orthogonal Matrices

**1.** A matrix $\mathbf{T}$ is said to be orthogonal if

$$\mathbf{T}^{-1} = \mathbf{T}^T \qquad \text{(transpose)} \tag{1.87}$$

**2.** If $\mathbf{P}_1, \mathbf{P}_2, \ldots, \mathbf{P}_n$ are orthogonal, then the product $\mathbf{P}_1, \mathbf{P}_2, \ldots, \mathbf{P}_n$ is also orthogonal.

**3.** The transpose of an orthogonal matrix is itself orthogonal.

### Determinants

**1.** Matrix products:

$$\det (\mathbf{A}_1, \mathbf{A}_2 \cdots \mathbf{A}_n) = \det (\mathbf{A}_1) \cdot \det (\mathbf{A}_2) \cdots \det (\mathbf{A}_n) \tag{1.88}$$

**2.** Matrix transpose:

$$\det (\mathbf{A}^T) = \det (\mathbf{A}) \tag{1.89}$$

### Matrix Factorization

1. Let $A$ be a general matrix of dimension $n \times n$. Then $A$ may be factored as

$$A = LR \qquad (1.90)$$

where $L$ is left triangular with 1s on the diagonal, and $R$ is right triangular with nonzero diagonal elements if

$$\mathbf{a}_{11} \neq 0 \qquad \det \begin{bmatrix} a_{11} & a_{12} \\ a_{21} & a_{22} \end{bmatrix} \neq 0 \qquad \cdots \qquad \det \begin{bmatrix} a_n & \cdots & a_{1n} \\ \vdots & \ddots & \vdots \\ a_{n1} & \cdots & a_{nn} \end{bmatrix} \neq 0 \qquad (1.91)$$

This factorization, if it is possible, is unique.

2. If $A$ is symmetric, the factorization in Eq. (1.90) reduces to

$$A = LDL^T \qquad (1.92)$$

where $L$ is left triangular with ones on the main diagonal and $D$ is diagonal. The condition in (1.91) must still be true for this factorization to exist.

3. If $A$ is symmetric and positive-definite, that is, if the inequality signs in (1.91) can be replaced by greater-than signs, $A$ has a Choleski factorization of the form

$$A = TT^T \qquad (1.93)$$

where $T$ is a lower triangular matrix.

### Sturm Sequence Property

Let $M$ and $K$ represent the symmetric mass and stiffness matrices, respectively. Then the number of eigenvalues of

$$\lambda_i M \phi_i = K \phi_i$$

that are smaller than some number $\mu$ is equal to the number of negative elements in $D$, where

$$K - \mu M = LDL^T \qquad (1.94)$$

This factorization is described in (1.92). An interesting proof of this theorem is provided in the excellent text by Bathe [57].

### Reduction to Hessenberg and Tridiagonal Forms

1. If $a_{ij} = 0$ for all $i$ and $j$ such that $|i - j| > 1$, then $A$ is said to be a tridiagonal matrix:

$$A = \begin{bmatrix} a_{11} & a_{12} & 0 & 0 & \cdots & 0 \\ a_{21} & a_{22} & a_{23} & 0 & \cdots & 0 \\ 0 & a_{32} & a_{33} & a_{34} & \cdots & 0 \\ \vdots & & & & & \vdots \\ 0 \cdots\cdots\cdots\cdots\cdots\cdots\cdots\cdots\cdots a_{NN} \end{bmatrix} \qquad (1.95)$$

If $a_{ij} = 0$ for all $i$ and $j$ such that $i > j+1$, then $\mathbf{A}$ is an upper Hessenberg matrix:

$$\mathbf{A} = \begin{bmatrix} a_{11} & a_{12} & a_{13} & \cdots & a_{1N} \\ a_{21} & a_{22} & a_{23} & \cdots & a_{2N} \\ 0 & a_{32} & a_{33} & \cdots & a_{3N} \\ 0 & 0 & a_{43} & \cdots & a_{4N} \\ \vdots & \vdots & \vdots & & \vdots \\ 0 & 0 & 0 & \cdots & a_{NN} \end{bmatrix} \tag{1.96}$$

**2.** *Householder's Method.* Given some vector $\mathbf{V}$ of dimension $N$, a Householder matrix $\mathbf{Q}$ may be defined such that if

$$\mathbf{W} = \mathbf{QV} \qquad (N \times 1) \tag{1.97}$$

then

$$W_i = 0 \qquad i = 2, 3, \ldots, N \tag{1.98}$$

The matrix $\mathbf{Q}$ is calculated from

$$\mathbf{Q} = \mathbf{I} - \frac{1}{K} \mathbf{X X}^T$$

$$X_i = V_i \qquad i = 2, 3, \ldots, N$$

$$X_1 = V_1 + \beta \sqrt{V_1^2 + V_2^2 + \cdots + V_N^2} \tag{1.99}$$

$$\beta = \operatorname{sgn}(V_1) = +1 \text{ or } -1$$

$$K = \tfrac{1}{2} \mathbf{X}^T \mathbf{X}$$

A symmetric $N \times N$ matrix $\mathbf{A}$ may be reduced to tridiagonal form by a series of $N-2$ consecutive pre- and postmultiplications with Householder matrices. Each operation annihilates a portion of a single row and column of the matrix until the tridiagonal form is achieved. This process may be described by

$$\mathbf{A}_{R+1} = \mathbf{P}_R^T \mathbf{A}_R \mathbf{P}_R \tag{1.100}$$

where

$$\mathbf{P}_R = \left[ \begin{array}{c|c} \mathbf{I}_R & \mathbf{0} \\ \hline \mathbf{0} & \mathbf{Q}_R \end{array} \right] \tag{1.101}$$

$$\mathbf{I}_R = R \times R \text{ unit matrix}$$
$$\mathbf{Q}_R = \text{Householder matrix}$$

It can easily be shown that $\mathbf{Q}_R$ and $\mathbf{P}_R$ are orthogonal matrices. If $\mathbf{A}$ is nonsymmetric, the same series of $N-2$ operations described above will reduce $\mathbf{A}$ to upper Hessenberg form.

**3.** *Givens Method.* The Givens method reduces an $N \times N$ symmetric matrix to tridiagonal form making use of plane rotations. Unlike the Householder approach, where an entire column and row are reduced during each major operation, the Givens approach zeros one element at a time. It takes approximately twice as many arithmetic operations to reduce a matrix to tridiagonal form by Givens method as by Householder's method.

**4.** *The Elementary Transformation Method.* The three elementary row operations may be performed on a matrix by premultiplying it by the corresponding elementary matrix, i.e., interchange of rows $i$ and $j$; premultiply by

$$
{}^{(1)}\mathbf{E}_{ij} =
\begin{bmatrix}
1 & 0 & \cdots & & \cdots & & \cdots & 0 \\
0 & 1 & & \vdots & & \vdots & & 0 \\
 & & \ddots & & & & & \\
 & & & 1 & & & & \vdots \\
 & & & 0 & \cdots & 1 & \cdots & \\
\vdots & & & \vdots & 1 & & & \vdots \\
 & & & & & \ddots & & \\
 & & & & & & 1 & \\
 & & & 1 & \cdots & 0 & \cdots & \\
 & & & & & 1 & & \\
 & & & & & & \ddots & \vdots \\
0 & \cdots\cdots\cdots\cdots\cdots\cdots\cdots\cdots\cdots\cdots\cdots & 1
\end{bmatrix}
\begin{matrix} \\ \\ \\ \\ \leftarrow i \\ \\ \\ \\ \leftarrow j \\ \\ \\ \end{matrix}
\qquad (1.102)
$$

For multiplication of row $i$ by a nonzero constant $a$, premultiply by

$$
{}^{(2)}\mathbf{E}_{ij} =
\begin{bmatrix}
1 & & & & & & \\
 & 1 & & & \vdots & \mathbf{0} & \\
 & & \ddots & & \vdots & & \\
 & & & 1 & & & \\
 & & & & a & \cdots & \\
 & & & & 1 & & \\
 & \mathbf{0} & & & & \ddots & \\
 & & & & & & 1
\end{bmatrix}
\begin{matrix} \\ \\ \\ \\ \leftarrow i \\ \\ \\ \end{matrix}
\qquad (1.103)
$$

For addition of a constant multiple ($a$) of row $i$ to row $j$, premultiply by

$$
{}^{(3)}\mathbf{E}_{ij} =
\begin{bmatrix}
1 & 0 & \cdots & & \cdots & & \cdots & 0 \\
0 & 1 & & \vdots & & \vdots & & \vdots \\
 & & \ddots & & & & & \\
\vdots & & & 1 & \cdots & 0 & & \vdots \\
 & & & \vdots & \ddots & \vdots & & \\
 & & & a & \cdots & 1 & \cdots & \\
 & & & & & & \ddots & \vdots \\
0 & \cdots\cdots\cdots\cdots\cdots\cdots\cdots\cdots & 1
\end{bmatrix}
\begin{matrix} \\ \\ \\ \leftarrow i \\ \\ \leftarrow j \\ \\ \end{matrix}
\qquad (1.104)
$$

These matrices have very simple inverses given by

$$^{(1)}\mathbf{E}_{ij}^{-1} = {}^{(1)}\mathbf{E}_{ij}$$

$$
{}^{(2)}\mathbf{E}_{ij}^{-1} =
\begin{bmatrix}
1 & & & & & & & & \\
& 1 & & & & \vdots & & \mathbf{0} & \\
& & \ddots & & & \vdots & & & \\
& & & 1 & & \vdots & & & \\
& & & & \frac{1}{a} & \cdots & & & \leftarrow i \\
& & & & & 1 & & & \\
& \mathbf{0} & & & & & \ddots & \\
& & & & & & & 1
\end{bmatrix}
\quad \leftarrow i
$$

$$(1.105)$$

$$
{}^{(3)}\mathbf{E}_{ij}^{-1} =
\begin{bmatrix}
1 & 0 & \cdots & & \cdots & & \cdots & 0 \\
0 & 1 & & \vdots & & \vdots & & \vdots \\
& & \ddots & & & & & \\
\vdots & & & 1 & \cdots & 0 & \cdots & & \leftarrow i \\
& & & \vdots & \ddots & \vdots & & \vdots \\
& & (-a) & \cdots & & 1 & \cdots & & \leftarrow j \\
& & & & & & \ddots & \vdots \\
0 & \cdots & \cdots & \cdots & \cdots & \cdots & \cdots & 1
\end{bmatrix}
\quad
$$

Note that:

- Postmultiplying a matrix by $^{(1)}\mathbf{E}_{ij}^{-1}$ has the effect of interchanging columns $i$ and $j$.
- Postmultiplying a matrix by $^{(2)}\mathbf{E}_{ij}^{-1}$ has the effect of dividing each element of column $i$ by $a$.
- Postmultiplying a matrix by $^{(3)}\mathbf{E}_{ij}^{-1}$ has the effect of subtracting $(a)$ times column $j$ from column $i$.

A real $n \times n$ matrix can be reduced to upper Hessenberg form by repeated pre- and postmultiplication of the matrix by elementary matrices and their inverses. A sequence of $N - 2$ of these similarity transformations is required to reduce the matrix $\mathbf{A}$ to Hessenberg form, i.e.,

$$\mathbf{A}_{\text{Hess}} = \mathbf{E}_{N-2}\mathbf{E}_{N-3} \cdots \mathbf{E}_1\mathbf{A}\mathbf{E}_1^{-1}\mathbf{E}_2^{-1} \cdots \mathbf{E}_{N-2}^{-1} \qquad (1.106)$$

Note that $\mathbf{A}_{\text{Hess}}$ and $\mathbf{A}$ are similar matrices by Eq. (1.86).

## 1.2c Reduction to Standard Form

In general, three forms of the eigenvalue problem appear in the literature:

$$(\lambda^2\mathbf{M} + \lambda\mathbf{C} + \mathbf{K})\boldsymbol{\psi} = \mathbf{0} \qquad (N \times 1) \qquad (1.107)$$

$$(\lambda^2 \mathbf{M} + \mathbf{K})\boldsymbol{\psi} = \mathbf{0} \qquad (N \times 1) \tag{1.108}$$

$$(\lambda^2 \mathbf{I} + \mathbf{D})\boldsymbol{\psi} = \mathbf{0} \qquad (N \times 1) \tag{1.109}$$

These are typically referred to as the quadratic eigenvalue problem, the generalized eigenvalue problem, and the standard eigenvalue problem.

Most of the eigenvalue extraction algorithms apply only to the standard eigenvalue problem. Hence, the two remaining formulations must first be transformed into the standard form before iterative extraction of the eigenvalues can proceed. The quadratic-matrix eigenvalue problem can be transformed into a standard form as shown by Eqs. (1.67) to (1.72). The resulting matrix $\mathbf{D}$ is both unsymmetric and of dimension $2N \times 2N$. The generalized eigenvalue problem can also be easily transformed into standard form as

$$(\alpha^2 \mathbf{I} + \mathbf{D})\boldsymbol{\psi} = \mathbf{0} \tag{1.110}$$

where $\qquad \mathbf{D} = \mathbf{K}^{-1}\mathbf{M} \qquad$ and $\qquad \alpha = \dfrac{1}{\lambda} \tag{1.111}$

This transformation leads to an unsymmetric matrix $\mathbf{D}$ which in many cases cannot be directly substituted into an eigenvalue algorithm.

There are three ways to transform the generalized eigenvalue problem into a standard one containing a symmetric matrix.

**Case 1: M *Diagonal and All* $M_{ii} > 0$**   In this case set

$$\boldsymbol{\psi} = \mathbf{M}^{-1/2}\boldsymbol{\zeta} \tag{1.112}$$

and premultiply (1.108) by $\mathbf{M}^{-1/2}$, where

$$\mathbf{M}^{-1/2} = \text{diag}\,(M_{ii}^{-1/2}) \tag{1.113}$$

The results are

$$\begin{aligned} (\lambda^2 \mathbf{I} + \mathbf{M}^{-1/2}\mathbf{K}\mathbf{M}^{-1/2})\boldsymbol{\zeta} &= \mathbf{0} \\ (\lambda^2 \mathbf{I} + \hat{\mathbf{K}})\boldsymbol{\zeta} &= \mathbf{0} \end{aligned} \tag{1.114}$$

which has a symmetric matrix $(\hat{\mathbf{K}})$ if $\mathbf{K}$ is symmetric.

**Case 2: *Choleski Factorization***   Equation (1.93) shows that if either the mass or stiffness matrix is positive-definite, both matrices can be represented by the Choleski factorizations:

$$\begin{aligned} \mathbf{K} &= \mathbf{T}_K \mathbf{T}_K^T \\ \mathbf{M} &= \mathbf{T}_M \mathbf{T}_M^T \end{aligned} \tag{1.115}$$

where $\mathbf{T}_K$ and $\mathbf{T}_M$ are lower triangular matrices.

Substituting (1.115) into (1.108) yields

$$(\alpha^2 \mathbf{I} + \mathbf{T}_K^{-1} \mathbf{M} (\mathbf{T}_K^{-1})^T) \boldsymbol{\zeta} = \mathbf{0} \quad \text{or} \quad (\alpha^2 \mathbf{I} + \hat{\mathbf{K}}) \boldsymbol{\zeta} = \mathbf{0} \quad \alpha = \frac{1}{\lambda}$$

$$\boldsymbol{\psi} = (\mathbf{T}_K^T)^{-1} \boldsymbol{\zeta} = (\mathbf{T}_K^{-1})^T \boldsymbol{\zeta} \tag{1.116}$$

for factorization of the **K**-matrix, or

$$(\lambda^2 \mathbf{I} + \mathbf{T}_M^{-1} \mathbf{K} (\mathbf{T}_M^{-1})^T) \boldsymbol{\zeta} = \mathbf{0} \quad \text{or} \quad (\lambda^2 \mathbf{I} + \hat{\mathbf{K}}) \boldsymbol{\zeta} = \mathbf{0}$$

$$\boldsymbol{\psi} = (\mathbf{T}_M^T) \boldsymbol{\zeta} = (\mathbf{T}_M^{-1})^T \boldsymbol{\zeta} \tag{1.117}$$

for factorization of the **M**-matrix. Note that either formulation leads to the standard form with a symmetric matrix ($\hat{\mathbf{K}}$).

**Case 3: Eigensolutions of Mass Matrix**   Let the matrix **T** contain the eigenvectors ($\mathbf{T}_i$) of the mass matrix as columns. Assuming that these eigenvectors have been normalized such that

$$\mathbf{T}_i^T \mathbf{T}_i = 1 \tag{1.118}$$

It may be easily shown that

$$\mathbf{T}^T \mathbf{M} \mathbf{T} = \text{diag} (V_i) \tag{1.119}$$

where $V_i$ are the eigenvalues of the mass matrix. Utilizing (1.119) in (1.108) yields

$$(\lambda^2 \mathbf{I} + \text{diag} (V_i^{-1/2}) \mathbf{T}^T \mathbf{K} \mathbf{T} \, \text{diag} (V_i^{-1/2})) \boldsymbol{\zeta} = \mathbf{0} \quad \text{or} \quad (\lambda^2 \mathbf{I} + \hat{\mathbf{K}}) \boldsymbol{\zeta} = \mathbf{0}$$

$$\boldsymbol{\psi} = \mathbf{T} \, \text{diag} (V_i^{-1/2}) \boldsymbol{\zeta} \tag{1.120}$$

Equation (1.120) represents a standard eigenvalue problem with a symmetric matrix ($\hat{\mathbf{K}}$).

## 1.2D Eigenvalue Extraction Algorithms for Undamped Systems with Symmetric K and M

The following sections discuss various algorithms which are currently used to extract eigen-solutions. All the algorithms are iterative in nature since in essence extraction of eigenvalues represents solving for the roots of the polynomial equation

$$p(\lambda) = \det (\mathbf{A} - \lambda \mathbf{I}) = \sum_{i=1}^{2N} a_i \lambda^i = 0 \tag{1.121}$$

**Forward Iteration**   The forward-iteration calculation scheme is summarized by the following equations:

$$(\mathbf{K} - \lambda_i \mathbf{M}) \boldsymbol{\phi}_i = \mathbf{0} \quad (N \times 1)$$

$$\mathbf{M} \bar{\mathbf{X}}_{k+1} = \mathbf{K} \mathbf{X}_k \tag{1.122}$$

$$\mathbf{X}_{k+1} = \bar{\mathbf{X}}_{k+1} \cdot (\bar{\mathbf{X}}_{k+1}^T \mathbf{M} \bar{\mathbf{X}}_{k+1})^{-1/2}$$

This will converge to

$$\mathbf{X}_{k+1} \to \boldsymbol{\phi}_N \qquad \text{as } k \to \infty$$

$$\mathbf{X}_{k+1}^T \mathbf{K} \mathbf{X}_{k+1} \to \lambda_N \qquad \text{as } k \to \infty \tag{1.123}$$

provided that the initial guess vector $\mathbf{X}_1$ does not satisfy

$$\mathbf{X}_1^T \mathbf{M} \boldsymbol{\phi}_N = \mathbf{0} \tag{1.124}$$

Note that this iterative scheme converges to the largest eigenvalue.

**Inverse Iteration**    The inverse-iteration computations are summarized as follows:

$$(\mathbf{K} - \lambda_i \mathbf{M}) \boldsymbol{\phi}_i = \mathbf{0}$$

$$\mathbf{K} \bar{\mathbf{X}}_{k+1} = \mathbf{M} \mathbf{X}_k \tag{1.125}$$

$$\mathbf{X}_{k+1} = \bar{\mathbf{X}}_{k+1} \cdot (\bar{\mathbf{X}}_{k+1}^T \mathbf{M} \bar{\mathbf{X}}_{k+1})^{-1/2}$$

This will converge to

$$\mathbf{X}_{k+1} \to \boldsymbol{\phi}_1 \qquad \text{as } k \to \infty$$

$$\mathbf{X}_{k+1}^T \mathbf{K} \mathbf{X}_{k+1} \to \lambda_1 \qquad \text{as } k \to \infty \tag{1.126}$$

provided that the initial guess vector $\mathbf{X}_1$ does not satisfy

$$\mathbf{X}_1^T \mathbf{M} \boldsymbol{\phi}_1 = 0 \tag{1.127}$$

This iterative scheme converges to the smallest eigenvalue.

**Gram–Schmidt Orthogonalization**    Forward and inverse iteration can be made to converge to successively lower and higher eigenvalues, respectively, by Gram–Schmidt orthogonalization of the initial guess vectors. If the largest $M$-eigenvalues have been obtained by forward iteration, the next smallest eigenvalue may be obtained by utilizing the revised initial starting vector

$$\tilde{\mathbf{X}}_1 = \mathbf{X}_1 - \sum_{i=N-M+1}^{N} \alpha_i \boldsymbol{\phi}_i \tag{1.128}$$

where $\mathbf{X}_1$ is an arbitrarily selected initial starting vector satisfying

$$\mathbf{X}_1^T \mathbf{M} \boldsymbol{\phi}_{N-M} \neq 0 \tag{1.129}$$

and

$$\alpha_i = \frac{(\boldsymbol{\phi}_i^T \mathbf{M} \mathbf{X}_1)}{(\boldsymbol{\phi}_i^T \mathbf{M} \boldsymbol{\phi}_i)} \tag{1.130}$$

If the smallest $M$-eigenvalues have been obtained by inverse iteration, the next largest eigenvalue may be obtained by utilizing the revised initial starting vector

$$\tilde{\mathbf{X}}_1 = \mathbf{X}_1 - \sum_{i=1}^{M} \alpha_i \boldsymbol{\phi}_i \tag{1.131}$$

where $\mathbf{X}_1$ is an arbitrarily selected initial starting vector satisfying

$$\mathbf{X}_1^T \mathbf{M} \boldsymbol{\phi}_{M+1} \neq 0 \tag{1.132}$$

and

$$\alpha_i = \frac{(\boldsymbol{\phi}_i^T \mathbf{M} \mathbf{X}_1)}{(\boldsymbol{\phi}_i^T \mathbf{M} \boldsymbol{\phi}_i)} \tag{1.133}$$

These formulae follow from the fact that any vector may be represented by

$$\mathbf{X} = \sum_{i=1}^{N} C_i \boldsymbol{\phi}_i \tag{1.134}$$

where

$$C_i = \frac{(\boldsymbol{\phi}_i^T \mathbf{M} \mathbf{X})}{(\boldsymbol{\phi}_i^T \mathbf{M} \boldsymbol{\phi}_i)} \tag{1.135}$$

and from

$$\boldsymbol{\phi}_i^T \mathbf{M} \boldsymbol{\phi}_j = 0 \qquad \text{if } i \neq j$$

$$\mathbf{K}^{-1} \mathbf{M} \boldsymbol{\phi}_i = \left(\frac{1}{\lambda_i}\right) \boldsymbol{\phi}_i \tag{1.136}$$

$$\mathbf{M}^{-1} \mathbf{K} \boldsymbol{\phi}_i = \lambda_i \boldsymbol{\phi}_i$$

**Vector Iteration with Shifting**    Utilizing the results of Sec. 1.2B on eigenvalue shifting, it can be easily seen that if

$$\lambda_i \mathbf{M} \boldsymbol{\phi}_i = \mathbf{K} \boldsymbol{\phi}_i \tag{1.137}$$

then inverse iteration on

$$\mu_i \mathbf{M} \boldsymbol{\psi}_i = (\mathbf{K} - \rho \mathbf{M}) \boldsymbol{\psi}_i \tag{1.138}$$

will yield the eigenvalue of (1.138) with the smallest absolute magnitude and will therefore also yield the eigenvalue of (1.137) which is closest to the shift $\rho$, since

$$|\mu_i| = |\lambda_i - \rho| \tag{1.139}$$

**Polynomial Iteration**    The eigenvalues of

$$\lambda \mathbf{M} \boldsymbol{\phi}_i = \mathbf{K} \boldsymbol{\phi}_i \tag{1.140}$$

may be determined by solving the characteristic equation

$$p(\lambda) = \det(\lambda \mathbf{M} - \mathbf{K}) = 0 \tag{1.141}$$

The explicit method of solving (1.141) is to determine the coefficients of the characteristic polynomial (i.e., by Leverier's algorithm)

$$p(\lambda) = \sum_{i=0}^{2N} C_i \lambda^i = 0 \tag{1.142}$$

and then to determine the zeros of $p(\lambda)$ by a Newton–Raphson or bisection procedure.

The implicit method consists of factoring the matrix

$$\lambda \mathbf{M} - \mathbf{K} = \mathbf{L}(\lambda)\mathbf{R}(\lambda) \tag{1.143}$$

from which
$$p(\lambda) = \prod_{i=1}^{N} R_{ii}(\lambda) \tag{1.144}$$

as can be seen by reviewing Eq. (1.88) and the properties for general-matrix factorization which follow it. Equations (1.143) and (1.144) are repeated for each new guess of $\lambda$ which is determined from a bisection scheme or secant-iteration method:

$$\lambda_{k+1} = \lambda_k - p(\lambda_k) \cdot (\lambda_k - \lambda_{k-1}) \cdot (p(\lambda_k) - p(\lambda_{k-1}))^{-1} \tag{1.145}$$

A modified form of $p(\lambda)$ must be constructed after each eigenvalue is located to avoid reconvergence to the eigenvalue. The deflated form of the characteristic equation is given by

$$\tilde{p}(\lambda) = \frac{p(\lambda)}{\displaystyle\prod_{j=1}^{M} (\lambda - \lambda^{(j)})} \tag{1.146}$$

where $\lambda^{(1)}, \lambda^{(2)}, \ldots, \lambda^{(M)}$ are eigenvalues which have already been located.

**Sturm Sequence Iteration**    This eigenvalue extraction method relies on the Sturm sequence property discussed in Sec. 1.2B. The algorithm is most effectively used if the eigenvalue problem has been transformed to standard form and further reduced to tridiagonal form utilizing Householder's method or the Givens method, both of which are also discussed in Sect. 1.2B. The Sturm sequence property implies that the number of eigenvalues that occurs between two guesses $\mu_i$ and $\mu_j$ is simply the difference between the number of negative elements in $\mathbf{D}_i$ and $\mathbf{D}_j$, where

$$\mathbf{K} - \mu_i \mathbf{M} = \mathbf{L}_i \mathbf{D}_i \mathbf{L}_i^T$$
$$\mathbf{K} - \mu_j \mathbf{M} = \mathbf{L}_j \mathbf{D}_j \mathbf{L}_j^T \tag{1.147}$$

This property can be utilized in a bisection scheme to isolate each eigenvalue in a frequency range of interest. The eigenvalues and eigenvectors may then be calculated by using inverse iteration with shifts equal to the approximate eigenvalues calculated from the Sturm sequence bisection. Recall that inverse iteration will converge to the eigenvalue closest to the shift as discussed with Eqs. (1.137) to (1.139).

**Jacobi and Generalized Jacobi Methods**    The Jacobi method assumes that the generalized eigenvalue problem has been transformed into a standard form with a symmetric matrix as discussed in Sec. 1.2C:

$$\hat{\mathbf{K}}\boldsymbol{\zeta} = \lambda \boldsymbol{\zeta} \tag{1.148}$$

The objective of the Jacobi method is to determine a diagonal matrix which is similar to $\hat{\mathbf{K}}$. Due to the properties of similarity transformations and the eigenvalues of diagonal matrices, the diagonal elements of this matrix are the eigenvalues of $\hat{\mathbf{K}}$. The determination of the diagonal matrix proceeds iteratively via the recursion formula

$$\hat{\mathbf{K}}_{k+1} = \mathbf{P}_k^T \hat{\mathbf{K}}_k \mathbf{P}_k$$

$$\hat{\mathbf{K}}_1 = \hat{\mathbf{K}} \tag{1.149}$$

where $\mathbf{P}_k$ is the orthogonal "rotation" matrix defined by

$$\mathbf{P}_k = \begin{bmatrix} 1 & & & & & & & & & & 0 \\ & \ddots & & \vdots & & & \vdots & & & & \\ & & 1 & & & & & & & & \\ & \cdots & & \cos\theta & \cdots & & -\sin\theta & \cdots & & & \leftarrow i \\ & & & & 1 & & & & & & \\ & & & \vdots & & \ddots & \vdots & & & & \\ & & & & & 1 & & & & & \\ & \cdots & & \sin\theta & \cdots & & \cos\theta & \cdots & & & \leftarrow j \\ & & & & & & & 1 & & & \\ & & & & & & & & \ddots & & \\ 0 & \cdots & & & & & & & \cdots & 1 \end{bmatrix} \tag{1.150}$$

and $\theta$ is determined by the condition that the $(i, j)$-element of $\hat{\mathbf{K}}_{k+1}$ is zero. This implies that

$$\tan(2\theta) = \frac{2\hat{K}_{ij}^{(k)}}{\hat{K}_{ii}^{(k)} - \hat{K}_{jj}^{(k)}} \qquad \text{for} \qquad \hat{K}_{ii}^{(k)} \neq \hat{K}_{jj}^{(k)} \tag{1.151}$$

and

$$\theta = \pm\frac{\pi}{4} \qquad \text{for} \qquad \hat{K}_{ii}^{(k)} = \hat{K}_{jj}^{(k)} \tag{1.152}$$

The $\pm$ sign in (1.152) is determined according to the sign of $\hat{K}_{ij}^{(k)}$. The element that is annihilated for any given iteration may be chosen in several ways. The most effective method is to select the off-diagonal element of the maximum modulus in the current $\hat{\mathbf{K}}_k$-matrix. This can be done since the sum of the squares of the off-diagonal elements is reduced by twice the value of the square of the annihilated element for any given iteration.

As $K$ approaches infinity in (1.149), $\hat{\mathbf{K}}_k$ will approach the diagonal matrix containing the eigenvalues of $\hat{\mathbf{K}}$ and

$$\mathbf{P} = \mathbf{P}_1 \mathbf{P}_2 \cdots \mathbf{P}_k \tag{1.153}$$

will approach the modal matrix of $\hat{\mathbf{K}}$, containing its eigenvectors as columns.

The generalized Jacobi method proceeds in an almost identical fashion; however, the iteration is performed simultaneously on $\mathbf{M}$ and $\mathbf{K}$, which eliminates the requirement of reducing the generalized eigenvalue problem to standard form prior to Jacobi iteration. An excellent description of this method is provided in Ref. [57].

**QR-Algorithm**    Similar to the Jacobi method, the QR-method seeks to determine a diagonal matrix which is similar to the original matrix and, hence, has the same eigenvalues. The

$QR$-method assumes that the eigenvalue problem has been transformed to the standard form

$$\hat{\mathbf{K}}\boldsymbol{\zeta} = \lambda\boldsymbol{\zeta} \tag{1.154}$$

The matrix $\hat{\mathbf{K}}$ is first reduced to tridiagonal form ($\hat{\mathbf{S}}$) utilizing Householder matrices. The tridiagonal form provides a much more efficient means for applying the $QR$-iteration. Equation (1.154) becomes

$$\hat{\mathbf{S}}\boldsymbol{\eta} = \lambda\boldsymbol{\eta} \tag{1.155}$$

where

$$\hat{\mathbf{S}} = \mathbf{P}^T\hat{\mathbf{K}}\mathbf{P} \tag{1.156}$$

$$\boldsymbol{\eta} = \mathbf{P}^T\boldsymbol{\zeta} \tag{1.157}$$

Note that $\hat{\mathbf{S}}$ and $\hat{\mathbf{K}}$ have the same eigenvalues since the product ($\mathbf{P}$) of orthogonal Householder matrices is also orthogonal [see Eq. (1.100)].

The $QR$-algorithm is summarized by the following set of equations:

$$\hat{\mathbf{S}}_1 = \hat{\mathbf{S}} \tag{1.158}$$

$${}^1\mathbf{P}^T_{n,n-1}\,{}^1\mathbf{P}^T_{n-1,n-2}\cdots {}^1\mathbf{P}^T_{3,2}\,{}^1\mathbf{P}^T_{2,1}\hat{\mathbf{S}}_1 = \mathbf{R}_1 \tag{1.159}$$

or

$$\mathbf{Q}^T_1\hat{\mathbf{S}}_1 = \mathbf{R}_1 \tag{1.160}$$

Set

$$\hat{\mathbf{S}}_2 = \mathbf{R}_1\mathbf{Q}_1 = \mathbf{Q}^T_1\hat{\mathbf{S}}_1\mathbf{Q}_1 \tag{1.161}$$

$${}^2\mathbf{P}^T_{n,n-1}\,{}^2\mathbf{P}^T_{n-1,n-2}\cdots {}^2\mathbf{P}^T_{3,2}\,{}^2\mathbf{P}^T_{2,1}\hat{\mathbf{S}}_2 = \mathbf{R}_2 \tag{1.162}$$

or

$$\mathbf{Q}^T_2\hat{\mathbf{S}}_2 = \mathbf{R}_2 \tag{1.163}$$

Set

$$\hat{\mathbf{S}}_3 = \mathbf{R}_2\mathbf{Q}_2 = \mathbf{Q}^T_2\mathbf{Q}^T_1\hat{\mathbf{S}}_1\mathbf{Q}_1\mathbf{Q}_2 \tag{1.164}$$

and so on.

Equations (1.159) and (1.162) represent the reduction of $\hat{\mathbf{S}}_1$ and $\hat{\mathbf{S}}_2$ respectively, to right-triangular form. This is accomplished by repeated premultiplication with Jacobi rotation matrices. The products ($\mathbf{Q}_1, \mathbf{Q}_2$) of the rotation matrices are orthogonal matrices which possess an upper Hessenberg form. This ensures that the matrices $\hat{\mathbf{S}}_1$, $\hat{\mathbf{S}}_2$, etc., are also of upper Hessenberg form, and can therefore be readily reduced to triangular form with the Jacobi rotation matrices. Since the $\mathbf{Q}_i$-matrices are orthogonal, the matrix $\hat{\mathbf{S}}_i$ is always similar to $\hat{\mathbf{S}}$, as can be seen by Eqs. (1.161) and (1.164). Therefore, when the matrix $\hat{\mathbf{S}}_i$ converges to a diagonal matrix, the diagonal elements are the eigenvalues of $\hat{\mathbf{S}}$, and the matrix

$$\mathbf{Q} = \mathbf{Q}_1\mathbf{Q}_2\cdots\mathbf{Q}_k \tag{1.165}$$

converges to the modal matrix of $\hat{\mathbf{S}}$ containing its eigenvectors as columns. The $QR$-algorithm is frequently utilized with inverse iteration to obtain higher accuracy of the computed eigenvectors and eigenvalues. In this case, the approximate eigenvalues from the $QR$-iteration are used as shifts [Eq. (1.138)] so that the inverse iteration will converge to a more accurate estimate of each eigenvalue. Usually only two inverse iterations are required to yield satisfactory results.

**Subspace Iteration**  The subspace-iteration method is very similar to the inverse-iteration method; however, multiple eigensolutions are simultaneously extracted. The algorithm is summarized by the following equations:

$$\underset{N\times N}{\mathbf{K}}\ \underset{N\times q}{\mathbf{\Phi}} = \underset{N\times N}{\mathbf{M}}\ \underset{N\times q}{\mathbf{\Phi}}\ \underset{q\times q}{\mathbf{\Lambda}} \qquad (N\times q)$$

$$\mathbf{\Phi}=[\phi_1\,|\,\phi_2\,|\cdots|\,\phi_q] \qquad (N\times q)$$

$$\mathbf{\Lambda}=\mathrm{diag}\,(\lambda_i) \qquad (q\times q) \tag{1.166}$$

The process is as follows:

1. Solve

$$\mathbf{K}\bar{\mathbf{X}}_{k+1}=\mathbf{M}\mathbf{X}_k \qquad (N\times q) \tag{1.167}$$

by factorization of **K** and back substitution.

2. Form

$$\mathbf{K}_{k+1}=\bar{\mathbf{X}}_{k+1}^T\mathbf{K}\bar{\mathbf{X}}_{k+1} \qquad (q\times q)$$

$$\mathbf{M}_{k+1}=\bar{\mathbf{X}}_{k+1}^T\mathbf{M}\bar{\mathbf{X}}_{k+1} \qquad (q\times q) \tag{1.168}$$

3. Solve

$$\mathbf{K}_{k+1}\mathbf{Q}_{k+1}=\mathbf{M}_{k+1}\mathbf{Q}_{k+1}\mathbf{\Lambda}_{k+1} \qquad (q\times q) \tag{1.169}$$

by any of the eigenvalue extraction techniques discussed previously.

4. Form

$$\mathbf{X}_{k+1}=\bar{\mathbf{X}}_{k+1}\mathbf{Q}_{k+1} \tag{1.170}$$

The iteration in steps 1 to 4 is started by utilizing an $N\times q$ matrix $\mathbf{X}_1$ containing initial guesses for the lowest $q$-eigenvectors as columns. The iteration proceeds by repeating steps 1 to 4 until the eigenvalue ($\mathbf{\Lambda}$) and eigenvector ($\mathbf{Q}$) matrices converge:

$$\mathbf{\Lambda}_k\to\mathbf{\Lambda} \qquad (q\times q)$$

$$\mathbf{X}_k\to\mathbf{\Phi} \qquad (N\times q) \tag{1.171}$$

A popular means for starting the iteration is to let the first column of $\mathbf{MX}_1$ be the main diagonal of **M** and the remaining columns be unit vectors

$$\mathbf{e}_i=(0\quad 0\quad\cdots\quad 0\quad 1\quad\cdots\quad 0)^T$$

where $i=1, 2,\ldots, q-1$ correspond to the smallest $q-1$ ratios of $K_{ii}/M_{ii}$.

In order to accelerate convergence, the number $q$ is usually selected to satisfy

$$q=\min\,\{2p, p+8\} \tag{1.172}$$

where only the $p$-lowest eigensolutions are actually sought. Note that the size of the eigenvalue problem in Eq. (1.169) is usually much smaller than that in (1.165).

To verify all eigenvalues have been determined in the frequency range of interest, it is recommended that a Sturm sequence check be made by utilizing

$$p(\mu) = \det (\mathbf{K} - \mu\mathbf{M}) = \mathbf{LDL}^T$$

where $\mu$ is chosen slightly to the right of $\lambda_p$, as determined from the subspace iteration. The number of negative elements in $\mathbf{D}$ should be equal to $p$.

## 1.2E Eigenvalue Extraction Algorithms for Systems with Nonproportional Damping and General M, K, and C

Systems of this variety are frequently encountered in the analysis of spinning structures or machinery components, and in systems with discrete dampers. The main difference between this case and the undamped, symmetric-matrix case, is that here complex eigenvalues and eigenvectors result. Several popular schemes for extracting the eigensolutions are discussed below.

**Complex Determinant Search**  This method is very similar to polynomial iteration relying on repeated matrix factorization of

$$\lambda^2\mathbf{M} + \lambda\mathbf{C} + \mathbf{K} \tag{1.173}$$

to evaluate its determinant for each guess of $\lambda$. The zeros of

$$p(\lambda) = \det (\lambda^2\mathbf{M} + \lambda\mathbf{C} + \mathbf{K}) = 0 \tag{1.174}$$

are eigenvalues of the problem

$$(\lambda^2\mathbf{M} + \lambda\mathbf{C} + \mathbf{K})\boldsymbol{\psi} = \mathbf{0} \tag{1.175}$$

The search is guided by the Muller algorithm as discussed in Ref. [58].

**QR-Algorithm**  The $QR$-algorithm may be applied to the $2N$-order form of the quadratic eigenvalue problem as defined by Eqs. (1.67) and (1.68). The matrix is first transformed to Hessenberg form utilizing elementary similarity transformations (see the discussion of the elementary transformation method in Sec. 1.2B). The $QR$-algorithm as discussed in Sec. 1.2D is then applied to the transformed matrix to extract its eigenvalues. These eigenvalues are then substituted into a complex inverse-iteration algorithm which computes the eigenvectors and more accurate estimates of the eigenvalues. The extraction of complex eigensolutions by the $QR$-method is discussed in the excellent text by Wilkinson [1].

**Complex Vector Iteration**  Forward- and inverse-iteration schemes exist for computing complex eigenvalues and eigenvectors. Sweeping or Gram–Schmidt orthogonalization procedures are also available to avoid reconvergence to modes which have been previously located. References [59] and [60] contain detailed descriptions of these vector-iteration algorithms, utilizing the $2N$-standard form of the eigenvalue problem of (1.175) as given by Eqs. (1.67) and (1.68).

### 1.2F. Rayleigh–Ritz Techniques

The size of a matrix eigenvalue problem may be reduced by restricting the eigenvectors to a subspace spanned by a reduced number of "assumed modes." This can be easily seen by the following transformations:

$$\lambda \underset{N \times N}{\mathbf{M}} \underset{N \times 1}{\boldsymbol{\phi}} = \underset{N \times N}{\mathbf{K}} \underset{N \times 1}{\boldsymbol{\phi}} \tag{1.176}$$

Let

$$\underset{N \times 1}{\boldsymbol{\phi}} = \underset{N \times r}{\mathbf{T}} \underset{r \times 1}{\boldsymbol{\zeta}} \tag{1.177}$$

Then Eq. (1.176) becomes

$$\lambda \underset{r \times r}{\bar{\mathbf{M}}} \underset{r \times 1}{\boldsymbol{\zeta}} = \underset{r \times r}{\bar{\mathbf{K}}} \underset{r \times 1}{\boldsymbol{\zeta}}$$

where

$$\bar{\mathbf{M}} = \mathbf{T}^T \mathbf{M} \mathbf{T} \qquad \bar{\mathbf{K}} = \mathbf{T}^T \mathbf{K} \mathbf{T} \tag{1.178}$$

Note that if $r \ll N$ the matrix eigenvalue problem has been greatly reduced in size at the expense of producing only approximate eigenvalues and eigenvectors. A very popular transformation matrix $\mathbf{T}$ is

$$\mathbf{T} = \left[ \begin{array}{c} \mathbf{I}_m \\ \hline -\mathbf{K}_{ss}^{-1} \mathbf{K}_{sm} \end{array} \right] \qquad (N \times m) \tag{1.179}$$

where the $\mathbf{K}$-matrix is partitioned into master $(m)$ and slave $(s)$ degrees of freedom as follows:

$$\mathbf{K} = \left[ \begin{array}{c|c} \mathbf{K}_{mm} & \mathbf{K}_{ms} \\ {\scriptstyle m \times m} & {\scriptstyle m \times s} \\ \hline \mathbf{K}_{sm} & \mathbf{K}_{ss} \\ {\scriptstyle s \times m} & {\scriptstyle s \times s} \end{array} \right] \qquad (N \times N) \tag{1.180}$$

The $i^{\underline{\text{th}}}$ column in $\mathbf{T}$ represents the deflection of the structure if all master degrees of freedom ($m$DOF) are held fixed, except for $m$DOF $i$, which is given a unit displacement. It can easily be shown that the reduced stiffness and mass matrices in Eq. (1.178) become

$$\bar{\mathbf{K}} = \mathbf{K}_{mm} - \mathbf{K}_{ms} \mathbf{K}_{ss}^{-1} \mathbf{K}_{sm}$$

$$\bar{\mathbf{M}} = \mathbf{M}_{mm} - \mathbf{M}_{ms} \mathbf{K}_{ss}^{-1} \mathbf{K}_{sm} - \mathbf{K}_{ms} \mathbf{K}_{ss}^{-1} \mathbf{M}_{sm} + \mathbf{K}_{ms} \mathbf{K}_{ss}^{-1} \mathbf{M}_{ss} \mathbf{K}_{ss}^{-1} \mathbf{K}_{sm} \tag{1.181}$$

This procedure is referred to as *Guyan reduction* or *static condensation*.

Another very popular transformation matrix used in Eq. (1.177) is to make the column vectors of $\mathbf{T}$ equal to the eigenvectors from the analysis of a related structural system. This is frequently encountered in iterative design procedures where small changes are made to the simulation model, after which the eigensolutions of the modified system must be recalculated.

## 1.3 SOLVING SYSTEMS OF NONLINEAR EQUATIONS

Two main difficulties arise in the numerical solution of large systems of nonlinear finite-element equations encountered in structural analysis: finding appropriate solution algorithms to solve the nonlinear system for a given load level, and defining appropriate incrementation procedures to follow the load path of the structure.

The former aspect can be envisaged without making reference to structural applications. Most of the algorithms commonly used to solve nonlinear systems of equations have some relationship with the problem of minimizing an arbitrary function [61], and better understanding of properties such as convergence may be deduced from their application to a local quadratic approximation of the function. The first part of this section reviews most of the classical methods, such as standard Newton iteration, conjugate gradients, quasi-Newton updates, and secant Newton iteration, starting from the point of view of function minimization. Specific aspects of the methods proposed, such as the influence of accurate line search and appropriate scaling on convergence, and their computer implementation, are discussed later.

The latter part of the section deals with incremental procedures for continuously varying the increment size as the iteration proceeds, and methods of tracing nonlinear responses beyond critical points. Although postcritical states are usually not tolerated in structural design, the knowledge of this range provides better insight into nonlinear structural behavior such as the sensitivity to initial geometric imperfections. Among the various strategies that have been proposed to trace nonlinear responses beyond critical points, the most effective ones are the displacement control technique [62, 63] and the constant-arc-length method of Riks [64] and Wempner [65]. The latter is a generalization of the former, which leads to efficient and quite simple iteration techniques. The discussion of the incremental loading procedures will thus be limited to these two methods, which can be easily combined with the nonlinear iteration schemes proposed in Sec. 1.3A.

### 1.3A Nonlinear Solution Algorithms

#### Newton Methods for Solving Nonlinear Systems of Equations

*Principle of the Method*   Consider the problem of finding a solution to the system of equations

$$\mathbf{r}(\mathbf{q}) = \mathbf{0} \tag{1.182}$$

where $\mathbf{r}$ and $\mathbf{q}$ are $n$-dimensional vectors.

Newton's method of solution can be derived by assuming that we have an approximation $\tilde{\mathbf{q}}$ to $\mathbf{q}$, and that in the neighborhood of $\tilde{\mathbf{q}}$ the linear mapping

$$\mathbf{r}_L(\mathbf{q}) = \mathbf{r}(\tilde{\mathbf{q}}) + \frac{\partial \mathbf{r}(\tilde{\mathbf{q}})}{\partial \mathbf{q}} (\mathbf{q} - \tilde{\mathbf{q}}) \tag{1.183}$$

is a good approximation to $\mathbf{r}(\mathbf{q})$. A presumably better approximation to $\mathbf{q}$ can then be obtained by equating (1.183) to zero. Thus, Newton's method takes an initial approximation $\mathbf{q}_0$ to $\mathbf{q}$, and attempts to improve it iteratively by

$$\mathbf{q}_{k+1} = \mathbf{q}_k - \mathbf{S}_k^{-1} \mathbf{r}_k \qquad k = 0, 1, \ldots \tag{1.184}$$

taking $\mathbf{r}_k = \mathbf{r}(\mathbf{q}_k)$ and with the definition of the jacobian matrix

$$\mathbf{S} = \frac{\partial \mathbf{r}(\tilde{\mathbf{q}})}{\partial \mathbf{q}} \tag{1.185}$$

***Relationship with Function Minimization [61, 66]*** Further insight may be obtained into the concept of Newton's method if reference is made to the existence of a function $f(\mathbf{q})$ which admits as a local minimum the solution of Eq. (1.182), and for which the Taylor expansion around $\mathbf{q}_k$ is

$$f(\mathbf{q}_k+\mathbf{s}) = f(\mathbf{q}_k)+\mathbf{r}_k^T\mathbf{s}+\tfrac{1}{2}\mathbf{s}^T\mathbf{S}_k\mathbf{s}+O(\mathbf{s}^3)$$

$$= g(\mathbf{s})+O(\mathbf{s}^3) \tag{1.186}$$

where $g(\mathbf{s})$ is the quadratic local approximation of $f(\mathbf{q})$ at $\mathbf{q}=\mathbf{q}_k$:

$$g(\mathbf{s}) = f(\mathbf{q}_k)+\mathbf{r}_k^T\mathbf{s}+\tfrac{1}{2}\mathbf{s}^T\mathbf{S}_k\mathbf{s} \tag{1.187}$$

Let us choose $\mathbf{s}$ as the solution of the local quadratic minimum problem

$$\min_{\mathbf{s}} g(\mathbf{s})$$

The gradient of (1.187) is $\mathbf{r}_k+\mathbf{S}_k\mathbf{s}$, and the minimum occurs at a point $\mathbf{s}_k$ satisfying Eq. (1.184) rewritten in the form

$$\mathbf{S}_k\mathbf{s}_k = -\mathbf{r}_k \tag{1.188}$$

Provided that the local jacobian matrix is positive-definite, we have

$$\mathbf{r}_k^T\mathbf{s}_k = -\mathbf{s}_k^T\mathbf{S}_k\mathbf{s}_k < 0$$

which results in

$$f(\mathbf{q}_k+\mathbf{s}_k)-f(\mathbf{q}_k) = -\tfrac{1}{2}\mathbf{s}_k^T\mathbf{S}_k\mathbf{s}_k+O(\mathbf{s}^3) \tag{1.189}$$

Equation (1.189) shows that the function $f(\mathbf{q})$ decreases if the approximation in the vicinity of $\mathbf{q}_k$ [Eq. (1.187)] is good enough, and if the jacobian matrix is positive-definite.

It is a simple matter to show that if the sequence $\mathbf{q}_k$ generated from the algorithm converges to the solution $\mathbf{q}^*$, then its order of convergence is 2 and the method is, therefore, quadratically convergent.

From (1.184) and using the fact that $\mathbf{r}(\mathbf{q}^*)=\mathbf{0}$, we have

$$\mathbf{q}_{k+1}-\mathbf{q}^* = \mathbf{S}_k^{-1}[\mathbf{S}_k(\mathbf{q}_k-\mathbf{q}^*)+\mathbf{r}(\mathbf{q}^*)-\mathbf{r}(\mathbf{q}_k)] \tag{1.190}$$

and a Taylor expansion of the right-hand side gives

$$\mathbf{S}_k(\mathbf{q}_k-\mathbf{q}^*)+\mathbf{r}(\mathbf{q}^*)-\mathbf{r}(\mathbf{q}_k) = -\tfrac{1}{2}(\mathbf{q}_k-\mathbf{q}^*)^T\frac{\partial\mathbf{S}}{\partial q}(\bar{\mathbf{q}})(\mathbf{q}_k-\mathbf{q}^*) \tag{1.191}$$

where $\bar{\mathbf{q}} = \theta\mathbf{q}_k+(1-\theta)\mathbf{q}^*$, $\theta\in[0,1]$. Substituting (1.191) into (1.190) yields the inequality

$$\|\mathbf{q}_{k+1}-\mathbf{q}^*\| < c\|\mathbf{q}_k-\mathbf{q}^*\|^2 \tag{1.192}$$

where $c$ depends on the jacobian and its derivatives.

This result ensures that under very reasonable conditions the sequence generated from Newton's algorithm converges to the solution $\mathbf{q}^*$ of (1.182) if $\mathbf{q}_0$ is sufficiently close to $\mathbf{q}^*$, in which case the order of convergence is at least 2.

Unfortunately, however, a sufficiently good estimate of $\mathbf{q}^*$ is often not available. It is then helpful to examine the principal causes of failure of Newton's method and to incorporate into the method devices which reduce the probability of divergence.

To this end, let us regard Newton's method as a special case of the descent algorithm with the search direction defined in the metric of the jacobian matrix by Eq. (1.188). Then, an optimal step length can be adopted which verifies the requirement

$$f(\mathbf{q}_{k+1}) = \min_{\alpha} f(\mathbf{q}_k + \alpha \mathbf{s})$$

or
$$= \min_{\alpha} \left\{ f(\mathbf{q}_k) + \alpha \mathbf{s}^T \mathbf{r}_k + \frac{\alpha^2}{2} \mathbf{s}^T \mathbf{S}_k \mathbf{s} + O(\alpha^3 \mathbf{s}^3) \right\} \tag{1.193}$$

which yields the line-search equation

$$\mathbf{s}^T \mathbf{r}_k + \alpha \mathbf{s}^T \mathbf{S}_k \mathbf{s} + O(\alpha^2 \mathbf{s}^3) = 0 \tag{1.194}$$

With the particular choice (1.188) of the search direction, (1.194) becomes

$$(\alpha - 1) \mathbf{r}_k^T \mathbf{S}_k \mathbf{r}_k + O(\alpha^2 \mathbf{s}^3) = 0$$

It shows that the step length $\alpha = 1$ may not give a good estimate of $\mathbf{q}^*$ if the quadratic approximation is not accurate enough in the vicinity of $\mathbf{q}_k$.

Therefore, it may happen that $f_{k+1} > f_k$ with Newton's standard algorithm for one of the following reasons:

1. $\mathbf{S}_k^{-1}$ exists and is positive-definite, but $\mathbf{s}_k$ is so large that $f_{k+1} > f_k$.

2. $\mathbf{S}_k^{-1}$ exists but is not positive-definite, so that we may have $\mathbf{s}^T \mathbf{r}_k < 0$. This means that $\mathbf{s}$ is no longer downhill, and again it may happen that $f_{k+1} > f_k$.

3. $\mathbf{S}^T \mathbf{r}_k = 0$ is a limiting case of the preceding case, and corresponds to orthogonality between the search direction and the gradient. It cannot occur if $\mathbf{S}_k$ is positive-definite.

4. If $\mathbf{S}_k$ is singular, then $\mathbf{s}$ is not even defined, so that if further progress is to be made, one needs an alternative means to construct $\mathbf{s}$.

### Remedies against Failure

1. *Line Search: Generalized Newton's Method.*    If $\mathbf{S}_k^{-1}$ remains positive-definite, the expansion (1.193) shows that condition $f_{k+1} < f_k$, or in terms of the residual vector

$$\mathbf{s}^T \mathbf{r}(\mathbf{q}_k + \alpha \mathbf{s}) = 0 \tag{1.195}$$

may always be fulfilled if a line search is adopted. The original Newton algorithm may thus be modified by adding a line search before the progression step.

2. *Remedies against Positive-Definiteness.*
   *a.* Both failure due to orthogonality of the search direction with the gradient and failure due to the singularity of the jacobian matrix can be overcome by replacing the Newton step by a steepest-descent iteration.

***b.*** Failure due to the fact that the search direction is uphill can be avoided by reversing the search direction.

Modifications ***a*** and ***b*** lead to a safeguarded Newton algorithm defined by the flowchart in Fig. 1.13.

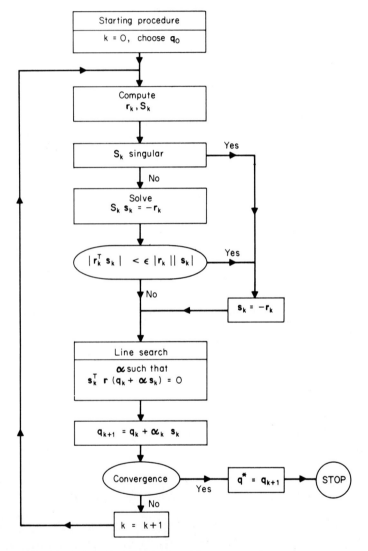

**FIG. 1.13**  Safeguarded Newton algorithm.

***c.*** An alternative method against failure due to nonpositive-definiteness of the jacobian matrix is to modify the jacobian matrix by adding to it a positive diagonal matrix which preserves its positive-definite character. The iteration scheme (1.184) is then replaced by

$$\mathbf{q}_{k+1} = \mathbf{q}_k - [\mathbf{S}_k + \mu \mathbf{D}]^{-1}\mathbf{r}_k$$

where $\mathbf{D}$ is a diagonal matrix with element $d_i > 0$, and $\mu$ is a scalar with $0 < \mu < 1$.

From the point of view of nonlinear structural mechanics, the modification may be regarded as the addition of linear springs to restrain the structure. Applications of this safeguarding technique have been reported in Ref. [67].

***Application to Nonlinear Finite-Element Equations [68, 69]*** The finite-element discretization of static nonlinear structural problems leads to systems of type (1.182) with

$$\mathbf{r}(q) = \mathbf{K}(\mathbf{q})\mathbf{q} - \mathbf{g} = 0 \tag{1.196}$$

where $\mathbf{q}$ is the vector of the unknown displacements and $\mathbf{g}$ is the vector of applied nodal loads.

Nonlinearities arise, in general, from material behavior or adaptation of the geometry; they are implicitly contained in the internal forces $\mathbf{K}(\mathbf{q})\mathbf{q}$ which result from the spatial integration of the internal stresses $\boldsymbol{\sigma}$

$$\mathbf{K}(\mathbf{q})\mathbf{q} = \int_V \mathbf{B}^T \boldsymbol{\sigma}\, dV \tag{1.197}$$

where $\mathbf{K}(\mathbf{q})$ is the structural stiffness matrix. In this case, the jacobian matrix (1.185) is the tangent-stiffness matrix

$$\mathbf{S}(\mathbf{q}) = \mathbf{K}^t(\mathbf{q}) = \frac{\partial}{\partial \mathbf{q}}[\mathbf{K}(\mathbf{q})\mathbf{q}] \tag{1.198}$$

plus a contribution of the external forces $\partial \mathbf{g}/\partial \mathbf{q}$ if these forces are dependent on geometry changes. This latter term is generally omitted to preserve the symmetry of the jacobian matrix.

In nonlinear structural dynamics, the effective loads in (1.196) are the difference between externally applied loads and the inertia forces, so that the spatially discretized system reads

$$\mathbf{r}(\mathbf{q}) = \mathbf{K}(\mathbf{q})\mathbf{q}(t) + \mathbf{M}\ddot{\mathbf{q}}(t) - \mathbf{g}(t) = 0 \tag{1.199}$$

The jacobian matrix of Newton's method is thus not only a function of the tangent-stiffness matrix $\mathbf{K}^t$ but also of the temporal-integration scheme used in the response. If such schemes are limited to those contained in Newmark's formula

$$\dot{\mathbf{q}}_{n+1} = \dot{\mathbf{q}}_n + (1 - \gamma)h\ddot{\mathbf{q}}_n + \gamma h\ddot{\mathbf{q}}_{n+1}$$
$$\mathbf{q}_{n+1} = \mathbf{q}_n + h\dot{\mathbf{q}}_n + (\tfrac{1}{2} - \beta)h^2\ddot{\mathbf{q}}_n + \beta h^2\ddot{\mathbf{q}}_{n+1} \tag{1.200}$$

where the subscript $n$ denotes the $n^{\underline{th}}$ time-integration step, $h$ the time-step size, and $(\beta, \gamma)$ the Newmark's parameters, the jacobian matrix becomes

$$\mathbf{S}(\mathbf{q}) = \mathbf{K}^t(\mathbf{q}) + \frac{1}{\beta h^2}\mathbf{M} + \frac{\partial \mathbf{g}}{\partial \mathbf{q}} \tag{1.201}$$

The last term appears only for geometry-dependent external forces and again is usually omitted for the purpose of symmetry. On the other hand, the mass-matrix term in Eq. (1.201) is dominant for sufficiently small step sizes and guarantees the positive-definite property of the jacobian matrix.

In problems involving viscous incompressible flow, the system of discretized nonlinear equations of motion reads

$$\mathbf{r}(\mathbf{q}) = [\mathbf{K} + \mathbf{C}(\mathbf{q})]\mathbf{q} - \mathbf{g} = 0 \qquad (1.202)$$

where $\mathbf{K}$ and $\mathbf{C}(\mathbf{q})$ are the diffusive and convective matrices, $\mathbf{q}$ is the vector of unknown nodal velocities and pressures, and $\mathbf{g}$ is the vector representing "virtual-work" equivalent body forces and surface tractions. Note that only $\mathbf{K}$ is symmetrical and unknown-independent, so that the jacobian matrix

$$\mathbf{S}(\mathbf{q}) = \mathbf{K} + \frac{\partial}{\partial \mathbf{q}}[\mathbf{C}(\mathbf{q})\mathbf{q}] \qquad (1.203)$$

is always unsymmetrical.

*Modified Newton Method*   In applying the Newton method to large systems of nonlinear finite-element equations, the costly operations of the numerical process are the evaluation of the jacobian matrix (1.185), the solution of the associated linear system (1.188), and the line search (1.195).

In order to minimize the cost of the linear solution, the Newton method is modified by keeping the jacobian matrix constant for a certain number of iterations of steps (see Fig. 1.14 for a comparison of standard and modified Newton methods in the one-dimensional case).

$$\mathbf{q}_{k+1} = \mathbf{q}_k - \mathbf{S}_i^{-1}\mathbf{r}_k \qquad k \geq i \qquad (1.204)$$

The reevaluation may either follow the user's own strategy or it can be resorted to only when the convergence criterion $\|\mathbf{r}_k\| < \varepsilon$ is on its way to being satisfied.

The corresponding number of iterations needed to achieve convergence is obviously greater in the modified Newton method since the property of the quadratic convergence is lost.

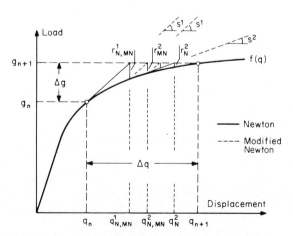

**FIG. 1.14**   Newton and modified Newton methods, 1D.

However, iterations using equations of the type of (1.204) are much cheaper since they involve only computation of the current residual vector $\mathbf{r}_k$.

***Approximate Line-Search Techniques***   As we have shown, the convergence of Newton-type procedures becomes strongly dependent on the step length along the search direction **s** when the starting approximation $\mathbf{q}_0$ is not contained in the neighborhood of the solution. On the other hand, line searches are expensive since one search may involve numerous evaluations of the residual vector to satisfy (1.195), which we restate here for convenience

$$\mathbf{s}^T\mathbf{r}(\mathbf{q}_k + \alpha\mathbf{s}) = 0 \qquad (1.195)$$

with great accuracy. Therefore, the line-search technique should be used with care and only when strictly necessary. Numerical experiments made by various authors lead to the conclusion that statement (1.195) can be replaced by

$$|\mathbf{s}^T\mathbf{r}(\mathbf{q}_k + \alpha\mathbf{s})| < \eta|\mathbf{s}^T\mathbf{r}_k| \qquad (1.205)$$

when $\eta$ is an appropriate threshold to be adjusted according to the class of nonlinear problem to be solved and the iteration method used. It has been observed that a range of $\eta$ from 0.25 to 0.5 is appropriate for most static and dynamic structural applications using the Newton method. In particular, no line search is attempted if (1.205) is satisfied with $\alpha = 1$.

### Conjugate-Gradient Methods

***Principle of the Method [61]***   The conjugate-gradient method, originally developed for minimization of quadratic functions, is a special case of the general conjugate-direction algorithm in which the set of conjugate directions is obtained from the orthogonalization of the successive gradients. Its advantage over the Newton method lies in the fact that it does not require explicit construction and inversion of the jacobian matrix.

The principle of the method consists of giving an iterative change $\alpha_k\mathbf{s}_k$ to the displacement vector so that

$$\mathbf{q}_{k+1} = \mathbf{q}_k + \alpha_k\mathbf{s}_k \qquad (1.206)$$

where
$$\mathbf{s}_k = -\mathbf{r}_k + \beta_k\mathbf{s}_{k-1} \qquad (1.207)$$

For a quadratic function

$$f = f_0 - \mathbf{q}^T\mathbf{p} + \tfrac{1}{2}\mathbf{q}^T\mathbf{S}\mathbf{q} \qquad (1.208)$$

the gradient vector, which is identical to the residual vector, is

$$\mathbf{r}_k = \mathbf{S}\mathbf{q}_k - \mathbf{p}$$

and $\beta_k$ is chosen so that
$$\mathbf{s}_{k-1}^T\mathbf{S}\mathbf{s}_k = 0 \qquad (1.209)$$

This gives the coefficient
$$\beta_k = \frac{\mathbf{s}_{k-1}^T\mathbf{S}\mathbf{r}_k}{\mathbf{s}_{k-1}^T\mathbf{S}\mathbf{s}_{k-1}}$$

or, if use is made of the fact that $\mathbf{Ss}_{k-1} = \mathbf{r}_k - \mathbf{r}_{k-1}$,

$$\beta_k = \frac{\mathbf{r}_k^T(\mathbf{r}_k - \mathbf{r}_{k-1})}{\mathbf{s}_{k-1}^T(\mathbf{r}_k - \mathbf{r}_{k-1})} \tag{1.210}$$

The line search is exact if $\alpha_k$ is chosen so that

$$\alpha_k \rightarrow \mathbf{s}_k^T \mathbf{r}_{k+1} = 0 \tag{1.211}$$

Various simplifications are proposed in the formula for $\beta_k$ according to the following situations:

1. The line search along $\mathbf{s}_k$ is exact.
2. The function to be minimized is quadratic.
3. The line search along $\mathbf{s}_{k-1}$ is also exact.

If hypotheses 1, 2, and 3 were simultaneously valid, one would obtain the widely used Fletcher–Reeves formula

$$\beta_k = \frac{\mathbf{r}_k^T \mathbf{r}_k}{\mathbf{r}_{k-1}^T \mathbf{r}_{k-1}} \tag{1.212}$$

while the Polak–Ribière formula

$$\beta_k = \frac{\mathbf{r}_k^T(\mathbf{r}_k - \mathbf{r}_{k-1})}{\mathbf{r}_{k-1}^T \mathbf{r}_{k-1}} \tag{1.213}$$

implies simply that exact line searches are used. The latter is thus generally considered to be more successful for nonquadratic functions. If inexact line searches are used, it is recommended to use rather the original formula (1.210). The algorithm may be organized as described by Fig. 1.15.

*Scaling and Conjugate Newton Methods*   The detailed theory of conjugate-gradient methods reveals their strong sensitivity to the ellipticity of the local jacobian matrix, a measure of which is its conditioning number [70]. Appropriate scaling of the algorithm is thus necessary to improve its convergence properties. Let $\mathbf{S}_a$ be some matrix that approximates the local jacobian $\mathbf{S}_k$, and let $\mathbf{L}$ and $\mathbf{L}^T$ be the Choleski factors of $\mathbf{S}_a = \mathbf{LL}^T$. The transformed matrix

$$\bar{\mathbf{S}}_k = \mathbf{L}^{-1}\mathbf{S}_k\mathbf{L}^{-T}$$

is then approximately a unit matrix and has nearly equal eigenvalues. Displacement and residual vectors are transformed accordingly:

$$\bar{\mathbf{q}}_k = \mathbf{L}^T\mathbf{q}_k \qquad \bar{\mathbf{r}}_k = \mathbf{L}^{-1}\mathbf{r}_k \tag{1.214}$$

As a consequence of the transformations (1.214), Eq. (1.207) is replaced by

$$\mathbf{s}_k = -\mathbf{S}_a^{-1}\mathbf{r}_k + \beta_k \mathbf{s}_{k-1} \tag{1.215}$$

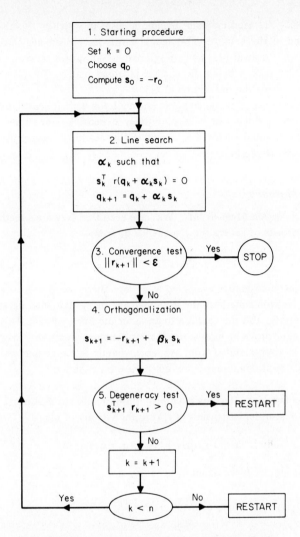

**FIG. 1.15**  Flowchart of the conjugate-gradient method.

and the orthogonalizing coefficient (1.210) is transformed into

$$\beta_k = \frac{\mathbf{r}_k(\mathbf{g}_k - \mathbf{g}_{k-1})}{\mathbf{s}_{k-1}^T(\mathbf{g}_k - \mathbf{g}_{k-1})} \tag{1.216}$$

where
$$\mathbf{g}_k = \mathbf{S}_a^{-1}\mathbf{r}_k$$

corresponds to the search direction in the standard modified Newton iteration. Clearly, the transformations implied in Eq. (1.214) do not have to be explicitly formed.

For linear equations, Fox and Stanton [70] proposed a very simple scaling procedure in which $\mathbf{S}_a$ is simply the diagonal matrix containing the diagonal terms of the stiffness matrix.

Jenning and Malik [71] used a similar technique also, in which $S_a$ is the original stiffness matrix after some of the extreme off-diagonal terms have been neglected. For nonlinear problems, Irons and Elsawaf [72] have developed a "conjugate Newton" procedure which satisfies Eq. (1.209) with $S$ being the current jacobian matrix. To this end, they use the information gained from the line search (1.211).

One of the drawbacks of conjugate-gradient methods is their sensitivity to the accuracy of the line searches, which can be prohibitively expensive, since they require frequent evaluations of the residual vector. For adequate line-search strategies using interpolation, consult, for example, Ref. [61].

### Quasi-Newton Methods

***Principle of Quasi-Newton Methods [61]*** We have seen that Newton's method for solving a system $r(q) = 0$ consists of generating a sequence $q_k$ from

$$q_{k+1} = q_k - S_k^{-1} r_k$$

where $S_k$ is the jacobian matrix evaluated at $q = q_k$. There are, however, a certain number of objections to Newton's method, the principal one being that each iteration requires the direct evaluation of $S_k$ and the solution to an associate linear system. This main drawback of Newton's method provides motivation for constructing algorithms in which the inverse jacobian matrix is approximated from available quantities rather than calculated directly. The basis for such approximations is the quasi-Newton equation.

***The Quasi-Newton Equation*** To obtain a direct approximation to the inverse jacobian matrix, let us consider a first-order expansion of $r(q)$ in the vicinity of $q_{k+1}$

$$r(q_k) = r(q_{k+1}) + S_{k+1}(q_k - q_{k+1}) + \Delta$$

where $\Delta \to 0$ as $q_k \to q_{k+1}$. If we define

$$y_k = r_{k+1} - r_k$$

$$s_k = q_{k+1} - q_k$$

and neglect the second-order term $\Delta$, we obtain

$$y_k = S_{k+1} s_k \tag{1.217}$$

Or, in inverse form      $G_{k+1} y_k = s_k$    with    $G_{k+1} = S_{k+1}^{-1}$        (1.218)

which is called the *Quasi-Newton equation*. Note that Eq. (1.217) is exact if $r$ derives from a quadratic functional and is nearly exact in a sufficiently small neighborhood of the solution if the functional is not quadratic but strictly convex.

The matrix $G_{k+1}$ is easily computable from $G_k$ if it is obtained by adding to $G_k$ a correction term $C_k$ which depends only on $G_k$, $y_k$, and $s_k$:

$$G_{k+1} = G_k + C_k \tag{1.219}$$

At the same time, the correction $\mathbf{C}_k$ should be constructed to preserve the symmetry and the positive-definiteness of the jacobian matrix.

***Quasi-Newton Algorithms***   With the ideas described above, the general quasi-Newton method for solving a nonlinear system is illustrated in the flow diagram in Fig. 1.16. The various quasi-Newton algorithms will differ only by the choice of the matrix-updating formula.

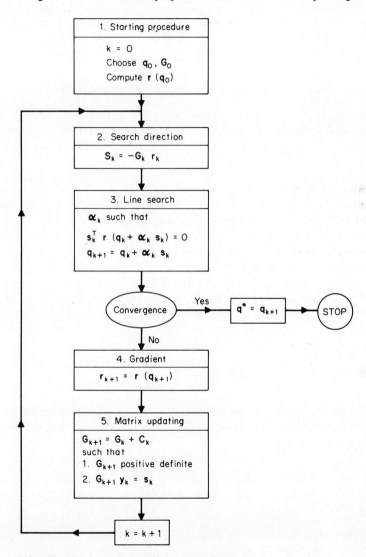

**FIG. 1.16**   The general quasi-Newton algorithm.

***One-Dimensional Interpretation of the Quasi-Newton Concept***   Dennis and More [74] noted that the quasi-Newton methods are the natural $n$-dimensional inheritors of the efficient one-dimensional secant procedure, as shown in Fig. 1.17.

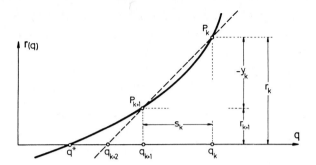

**FIG. 1.17** One-dimensional interpretation of quasi-Newton method.

Two successive points are utilized to calculate an approximation of the local tangent to $\mathbf{r}(\mathbf{q})$.

***Rank-1 Updates of the Inverse Jacobian Matrix***   To obtain the simplest correction (1.219), we investigate a correction in the form of a rank-1 update:

$$\mathbf{G}_{k+1}^{R1} = \mathbf{G}_k^{R1} + \mathbf{z}_k \mathbf{u}_k^T \tag{1.220}$$

where the vector $\mathbf{z}_k$ is selected to satisfy (1.218):

$$\mathbf{G}_{k+1}^{R1}\mathbf{y}_k = \mathbf{G}_k^{R1}\mathbf{y}_k + \mathbf{z}_k \mathbf{u}_k^T \mathbf{y}_k = \mathbf{s}_k$$

This yields

$$\mathbf{z}_k = \frac{\mathbf{s}_k - \mathbf{G}_k^{R1}\mathbf{y}_k}{\mathbf{u}_k^T \mathbf{y}_k} \tag{1.221}$$

and the correction formula

$$\mathbf{G}_{k+1}^{R1} = \mathbf{G}_k^{R1} + \frac{(\mathbf{s}_k - \mathbf{G}_k^{R1}\mathbf{y}_k)\mathbf{u}_k^T}{\mathbf{u}_k^T \mathbf{y}_k} \tag{1.222}$$

where $\mathbf{u}_k$ is an arbitrary vector but one such that $\mathbf{u}_k^T \mathbf{y}_k \neq 0$. Several rank-1 updates are possible. Obviously, it is highly desirable for $\mathbf{u}_k$ to depend only on $\mathbf{s}_k$, $\mathbf{S}_k$, and $\mathbf{y}_k$. Broyden [73] proposes $\mathbf{u}_k^T = \mathbf{y}_k^T \mathbf{G}_k^B$ so that

$$\mathbf{G}_{k+1}^B = \mathbf{G}_k^B + \frac{(\mathbf{s}_k - \mathbf{G}_k^B \mathbf{y}_k)\mathbf{y}_k^T \mathbf{G}_k^B}{\mathbf{y}_k^T \mathbf{G}_k^B \mathbf{y}_k} \tag{1.223}$$

It has been shown that in this way $\mathbf{G}_{k+1}^B$ is the "closest" to $\mathbf{S}_{k+1}^{-1}$ when the distance is measured by the Frobenius norm [74]. Note that Broyden's update is unsymmetric and hence does not preserve the eventual symmetry of $\mathbf{S}_{k+1}$.

For symmetric systems of equations, Davidson suggests the use of direction $\mathbf{u}_k = \mathbf{s}_k - \mathbf{G}_k \mathbf{y}_k$. The new correction matrix becomes

$$\mathbf{G}_{k+1}^D = \mathbf{G}_k^D + \frac{(\mathbf{s}_k - \mathbf{G}_k^D \mathbf{y}_k)(\mathbf{s}_k - \mathbf{G}_k^D \mathbf{y}_k)^T}{(\mathbf{s}_k - \mathbf{G}_k^D \mathbf{y}_k)^T \mathbf{y}_k} \tag{1.224}$$

The inverse formulae to (1.223) and (1.224), which correspond to the updating of the jacobian itself rather than its inverse, are trivial. They are simply obtained by exchanging the roles of the vectors $\mathbf{y}_k$ and $\mathbf{s}_k$. It is worthwhile noticing that the quasi-Newton algorithm with the rank-1 update (1.220), when applied to a quadratic function, does not involve any line search. It is thus expected that its application to nonquadratic cases will also dispense with an accurate line search, which makes it very attractive.

Unfortunately, the positive-definite character of the jacobian matrix is lost in the iteration process. This may lead to a breakdown of the algorithm if it is not safeguarded. Therefore, the rank-2 updates which may be constructed in order to preserve the positive-definiteness of $\mathbf{S}_k$ are generally preferred.

*A First Rank-2 Update: The Davidon–Fletcher–Powell (DFP) Formula*   In the DFP method [61], the updating formula is constructed in the symmetric form

$$\mathbf{G}_{k+1}^{\mathrm{DFP}} = \mathbf{G}_k^{\mathrm{DFP}} + \beta \mathbf{s}_k \mathbf{s}_k^T + \gamma [\mathbf{G}_k^{\mathrm{DFP}} \mathbf{y}_k][\mathbf{G}_k^{\mathrm{DFP}} \mathbf{y}_k]^T \tag{1.225}$$

and has to verify the quasi-Newton equation

$$\mathbf{G}_{k+1}^{\mathrm{DFP}} \mathbf{y}_k = \mathbf{s}_k$$
$$= \mathbf{G}_k^{\mathrm{DFP}} \mathbf{y}_k + \beta \mathbf{s}_k \mathbf{s}_k^T \mathbf{y}_k + \gamma [\mathbf{G}_k^{\mathrm{DFP}} \mathbf{y}_k] \mathbf{y}_k^T \mathbf{G}_k^{\mathrm{DFP}} \mathbf{y}_k$$

The equality above holds for the particular choice of coefficients $\beta$ and $\gamma$ which yield the DFP-updating formula

$$\mathbf{G}_{k+1}^{\mathrm{DFP}} = \mathbf{G}_k^{\mathrm{DFP}} + \frac{\mathbf{s}_k \mathbf{s}_k^T}{\mathbf{s}_k^T \mathbf{y}_k} - \frac{[\mathbf{G}_k^{\mathrm{DFP}} \mathbf{y}_k][\mathbf{G}_k^{\mathrm{DFP}} \mathbf{y}_k]^T}{\mathbf{y}_k^T \mathbf{G}_k^{\mathrm{DFP}} \mathbf{y}_k} \tag{1.226}$$

By making reference to the problem of minimizing a quadratic function, it can be proved that:

- If $\mathbf{G}_k^{\mathrm{DFP}}$ is positive-definite, and if a line search is made to determine the optimal step length, then $\mathbf{G}_{k+1}^{\mathrm{DFP}}$ is also positive-definite;

- If the line search is exact, the DFP method generates conjugate directions and has thus quadratic convergence. In particular, if the initial matrix $\mathbf{G}_0$ is the identity matrix, the method becomes the conjugate-gradient method.

It is also simple to show that the updating formula (1.226) may be inverted to approximate the jacobian matrix itself rather than its inverse. The resulting matrix

$$\mathbf{S}_{k+1}^{\mathrm{DFP}} = [\mathbf{G}_{k+1}^{\mathrm{DFP}}]^{-1}$$

is calculated by the updating formula

$$\mathbf{S}_{k+1}^{\mathrm{DFP}} = \left( \mathbf{I} - \frac{\mathbf{y}_k \mathbf{s}_k^T}{\mathbf{y}_k^T \mathbf{s}_k} \right) \mathbf{S}_k^{\mathrm{DFP}} \left( \mathbf{I} - \frac{\mathbf{s}_k \mathbf{y}_k^T}{\mathbf{y}_k^T \mathbf{s}_k} \right) + \frac{\mathbf{y}_k \mathbf{y}_k^T}{\mathbf{y}_k^T \mathbf{s}_k} \tag{1.227}$$

*Complementary Rank-2 Updates: The Broyden–Fletcher–Goldfarb–Shanno (BFGS) formulae*   Complementary updates to (1.226) and (1.227) are easily obtained by adopting for $\mathbf{S}_k$ an updating formula analogous to (1.225) which verifies the quasi-Newton equation written in the form of (1.217). It is directly obtained from the DFP formula (1.226) by inverting the role of $\mathbf{s}_k$ and $\mathbf{y}_k$:

$$\mathbf{S}_{k+1}^{\text{BFGS}} = \mathbf{S}_k^{\text{BFGS}} + \frac{\mathbf{y}_k \mathbf{y}_k^T}{\mathbf{s}_k^T \mathbf{y}_k} - \frac{[\mathbf{S}_k^{\text{BFGS}} \mathbf{s}_k][\mathbf{S}_k^{\text{BFGS}} \mathbf{y}_k]^T}{\mathbf{s}_k^T \mathbf{S}_k^{\text{BFGS}} \mathbf{s}_k} \tag{1.228}$$

Its inverse form is similarly obtained from the DFP formula (1.227):

$$\mathbf{G}_{k+1}^{\text{BFGS}} = \left( \mathbf{I} - \frac{\mathbf{s}_k \mathbf{y}_k^T}{\mathbf{s}_k^T \mathbf{y}_k} \right) \mathbf{G}_k^{\text{BFGS}} \left( \mathbf{I} - \frac{\mathbf{y}_k \mathbf{s}_k^T}{\mathbf{s}_k^T \mathbf{y}_k} \right) + \frac{\mathbf{s}_k \mathbf{s}_k^T}{\mathbf{y}_k^T \mathbf{s}_k} \tag{1.229}$$

According to several authors [74–76], there is growing evidence that the BFGS update is the best current formula for use in unconstrained minimization and solution of nonlinear problems with a positive-definite jacobian matrix.

***Computational Implementation of Quasi-Newton Updates*** The major disadvantage of the quasi-Newton concept, when it is applied in the form implied by the various updates above, is the destruction of the banded nature of the initial jacobian matrix. Various attempts have been made to develop special updates which preserve the sparsity of the finite-element system [77, 78]. However, all these methods appear somewhat cumbersome.

The most efficient way of performing the quasi-Newton corrections is, indeed, as proposed by Mathies and Strang [75], to apply the correction in the direction of search instead of modifying the approximate jacobian. In fact, using the inverse update as described by Eq. (1.223) at the $k^{\underline{\text{th}}}$ iteration, $\mathbf{G}_k$ can be written (for a single-rank symmetric update) as

$$\mathbf{G}_k = \mathbf{G}_0 + \sum_{i=0}^{k} \beta_i \mathbf{v}_i \mathbf{v}_i^T \tag{1.230}$$

For instance, for Davidon's update with line search, we have $\mathbf{v}_i = \alpha_i \mathbf{s}_i - \mathbf{G}_i \mathbf{y}_i$ and $\beta_i = [(\alpha_i \mathbf{s}_i - \mathbf{G}_i \mathbf{y}_i)^T \mathbf{y}_i]^{-1}$. If at each iteration, the correction vector $\mathbf{v}_i$ and coefficient $\beta_i$ are stored on auxiliary memory, the $(k+1)^{\underline{\text{th}}}$ direction of the search can be obtained from (1.230) as

$$\mathbf{s}_k = -\left( \mathbf{G}_0 + \sum_{i=0}^{k-1} \beta_i \mathbf{v}_i \mathbf{v}_i^T \right) \mathbf{r}_k \tag{1.231}$$

The new correction vector for Davidon's update is then

$$\mathbf{v}_k = \alpha_k \mathbf{s}_k - \mathbf{G}_0 \mathbf{r}_k - \sum_{i=0}^{k-1} \beta_i \mathbf{v}_i \mathbf{v}_i^T \mathbf{r}_k \tag{1.232}$$

Computational efficiency of this updating technique stems from the fact that, if an initial sparse jacobian $\mathbf{S}_0$ is given, it may be triangularized and stored only once, yielding the successive products $\mathbf{G}_0 \mathbf{r}_k$ and $\mathbf{G}_0 \mathbf{r}_{k+1}$ needed in Eqs. (1.231) and (1.232). In this manner, only the nonzero elements of $\mathbf{G}_0$ after gaussian elimination, the vectors $\mathbf{v}_i$, and the coefficients $\beta_i$ have to be stored. When the number of correction vectors becomes too large, the algorithm may be restarted with the initial matrix $\mathbf{G}_0$.

A last observation is about the theoretical difference that one can expect between the cost of Newton iteration and other iteration techniques. In the Newton method, the computation and triangularization of $\mathbf{S}_k$ requires $O(n^3)$ arithmetic operations. In the quasi-Newton method, for every iteration after the second one this is reduced to $O(n^2)$ operations; in a modified Newton iteration, the order is the same but the coefficient is lower since only one back substitution per iteration is needed.

*Memoryless Quasi-Newton Methods: Secant–Newton Algorithms* In Ref. [79], Crisfield developed a "faster modified Newton method" which resembles the conjugate-gradient method by having a form similar to that of Eq. (1.206), but differs in satisfying the secant relationship of Eq. (1.218) instead of verifying the orthogonality condition of Eq. (1.209). The principle behind the secant-Newton method is the substitution into one of the quasi-Newton updates of

$$\mathbf{G}_k = \mathbf{S}_a^{-1}$$

where $\mathbf{S}_a$ is an approximate jacobian matrix. They are thus memoryless versions of the quasi-Newton updates. The different updates so obtained can all be expressed in the form

$$\mathbf{s}_{k+1} = \beta \mathbf{S}_a^{-1} \mathbf{r}_{k+1} + \gamma \alpha_k \mathbf{s}_k + \delta \mathbf{S}_a^{-1} \mathbf{r}_k \qquad (1.233)$$

where $\beta$, $\gamma$, and $\delta$ are parameters dependent on the formula used, and $\alpha_k$ is the step length of the line search. For example, with Davidon's update, one obtains

$$\gamma = -\frac{\mathbf{r}_{k+1}^T(\alpha_k \mathbf{s}_k - \mathbf{S}_a^{-1}\mathbf{r}_k)}{\mathbf{y}_k^T(\alpha_k \mathbf{s}_k - \mathbf{S}_a^{-1}\mathbf{y}_k)} \qquad \beta = -(1+\gamma), \, \delta = \gamma \qquad (1.234)$$

Crisfield [80] points out that in contrast to conjugate-gradient and conjugate Newton approaches, the secant-Newton method expressed as Eq. (1.233) involves a scalar that differs from unity multiplying the vector $\mathbf{S}_a^{-1}\mathbf{r}_{k+1}$. Consequently, an approximate line search has already been introduced into the formula which might dispense of a more precise line search.

A more complete discussion of the method can be found in Refs. [79, 80].

## 1.3B Methods for Tracing Structural Response beyond Critical Points

*Displacement Control* The displacement control method is very effective for controlling the stop size in an incrementation procedure and for tracing the postcritical response, and it has been proposed by numerous authors [62, 63, 81–83]. It can be implemented in several ways according to the symmetry of the system to be solved and the number of load cases to be considered, but the most efficient procedure is probably that described in Ref. [83].

Let us consider the stiffness equation (1.196) in which incrementation of the load $\mathbf{g}$ is governed by some parameter $\lambda$, which means that the loading is increased in a proportional manner. If the load is incremented from $\lambda \mathbf{g}$ to $(\lambda + \Delta \lambda)\mathbf{g}$, starting from an approximation $\mathbf{q}$ to the solution at load level $\lambda$, the residual equation at load level $\lambda + \Delta \lambda$ is

$$\mathbf{r}(\bar{\mathbf{q}} + \Delta \mathbf{q}) = \mathbf{K}(\bar{\mathbf{q}} + \Delta \mathbf{q})(\bar{\mathbf{q}} + \Delta \mathbf{q}) - (\lambda + \Delta \lambda)\mathbf{g} = \mathbf{0}$$

and its first-order expansion yields the displacement increment

$$\mathbf{S}\,\Delta\mathbf{q} = \mathbf{r}(\bar{\mathbf{q}}) + \Delta\lambda\,\mathbf{g} \tag{1.235}$$

with
$$\mathbf{r}(\bar{\mathbf{q}}) = \lambda\mathbf{g} - \mathbf{K}(\bar{\mathbf{q}})\mathbf{q}$$

Equation (1.235) provides the generalization to the iteration formula (1.184) for nonconstant proportional loading

$$\mathbf{S}\,\Delta\mathbf{q}_k = \mathbf{r}_k + \Delta\lambda_k\,\mathbf{g} \tag{1.236}$$

Let us next assume that incrementation is performed in such a way that the $j^{\text{th}}$ component of the displacement vector is maintained at a constant value $\bar{u}$,

$$\mathbf{q}_{k,j} = \bar{u}$$

in which case
$$\Delta\mathbf{q}_{k,j} = 0 \tag{1.237}$$
This condition may be fulfilled by separating the solution to (1.237) into two loading cases.

1. $\Delta\mathbf{q}_{\mathrm{I}}$ is the contribution to the solution which verifies the residual equation at constant load level

$$\mathbf{S}_k\,\Delta\mathbf{q}_{\mathrm{I}} = \mathbf{r}_k \tag{1.238}$$

2. $\mathbf{q}_{\mathrm{II}}$ is the solution to the linear problem for a unit load level $\mathbf{g}$

$$\mathbf{S}_k\mathbf{q}_{\mathrm{II}} = \mathbf{g} \tag{1.239}$$

The solution to (1.236) provides the displacement increment in the form of a linear combination of (1.238) and (1.239),

$$\Delta\mathbf{q}_k = \Delta\mathbf{q}_{\mathrm{I}} + \Delta\lambda\,\mathbf{q}_{\mathrm{II}}$$

and displacement control is achieved by assuming that

$$\Delta\mathbf{q}_{k,j} = 0 \rightarrow \Delta\lambda = -\frac{\Delta q_{\mathrm{I},j}}{q_{\mathrm{II},j}} \tag{1.240}$$

The new approximation to the displacement solution is then

$$\mathbf{q} = \bar{\mathbf{q}} + \Delta\mathbf{q}_{\mathrm{I}} + \Delta\lambda\cdot\mathbf{q}_{\mathrm{II}} \tag{1.241}$$

The main advantage of this strategy is that no modification is implied in the gaussian elimination of the jacobian matrix, and that symmetry is preserved. The cost for it is an extra loading case to solve. This displacement control method is easy to combine with any one of the iteration schemes detailed in the first part of the section.

***The Arc-Length Method***   The drawback of the displacement control method remains the need to specify which displacement component must be used to perform the control. This can easily be circumvented, as suggested by Riks [64] and Wempner [65], by assuming in the $(n+1)$-dimensional space $(\mathbf{q}, \lambda)$ a specified length to the progression along the load curve. In this case each correction increment $\Delta\mathbf{q}_k$ is a solution of a linear problem with a nonlinear constraint

$$\mathbf{S}_k\,\Delta\mathbf{q}_k = \mathbf{r}_k + \Delta\lambda_k \cdot \mathbf{g}$$
$$\Delta\mathbf{q}_k^T\,\Delta\mathbf{q}_k + \Delta\lambda_k^2 = \Delta l^2 \qquad (1.242)$$

The solution to (1.243) is easily obtained using the procedure proposed by Batoz and Dhatt [84], except that $\Delta\lambda_k$ is now a solution of a second-degree equation, as described in Ref. [79]. The geometric interpretation of the iteration method is given in Fig. 1.18a.

An alternative procedure is to approximate the circular arc by its tangent $n$ which verifies the constraint equation

$$\mathbf{t} \cdot \mathbf{n} = \Delta\mathbf{q}_1^T\,\Delta\mathbf{q}_k + \Delta\lambda_1 \cdot \Delta\lambda_k = 0$$

as illustrated in Fig. 1.18b.

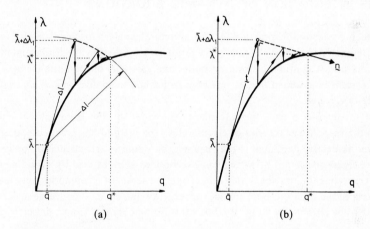

**FIG. 1.18**   (a) Original constant-arc-length method. (b) Modified constant-arc-length method.

The resulting system of equations

$$\mathbf{S}_k\,\Delta\mathbf{q}_k = \mathbf{r}_k + \Delta\lambda_k \cdot \mathbf{g}$$
$$\Delta\mathbf{q}_1^T\,\Delta\mathbf{q}_k + \Delta\lambda_1 \cdot \Delta\lambda_k = 0 \qquad (1.243)$$

is then linear in $(\Delta\mathbf{q}_k, \Delta\lambda_k)$ and can again be solved by considering two separate loading cases:

**1.** $\Delta\mathbf{q}_I$ is the solution of the residual equation

$$\mathbf{S}_k\,\Delta\mathbf{q}_I = \mathbf{r}_k \qquad (1.244)$$

**2.** $\mathbf{q}_{II}$ verifies the linear stiffness equation with unit load $\mathbf{g}$

$$\mathbf{S}_k\mathbf{q}_{II} = \mathbf{g} \qquad (1.245)$$

$\Delta\mathbf{q}_k$ is expressed as a linear combination of $\Delta\mathbf{q}_I$ and $\mathbf{q}_{II}$

$$\Delta\mathbf{q}_k = \Delta\mathbf{q}_I + \Delta\lambda_k \cdot \mathbf{q}_{II} \tag{1.246}$$

with $\Delta\lambda_k$ verifying the constraint (1.243). The load-increment factor is thus

$$\Delta\lambda_k = -\frac{\Delta\mathbf{q}_I^T \cdot \Delta\mathbf{q}_1}{\mathbf{q}_{II}^T \Delta\mathbf{q} + \Delta\lambda_1} \tag{1.247}$$

Equation (1.247) is equivalent to Eq. (1.240) but contains all displacement components in an integral sense.

A more comprehensive presentation of both methods, together with a discussion of some numerical applications, can be found in Ref. [85].

## 1.4 TIME INTEGRATION OF DYNAMIC EQUATIONS

It has become a common practice for the structural analyst to calculate the response of structural systems to transient loads. The result is a prediction of displacement, velocity, acceleration, and stress-time histories at nodes and elements of the finite-element model.

If the system is assumed linear, two approaches are available: *modal superposition* and *direct time integration.*

Modal superposition uses the information provided by the linear modal analysis and expresses the response as a series of eigenmodes. The method has great computer efficiency if the lower modes are dominant in the response, but requires the calculation of an important part of the eigenspectrum if high-frequency components are excited by a loading such as an impact. It also has the drawback that truncating the series of eigenmodes may lead to large inaccuracies in the solution. Both spatial convergence and spectral convergence of the modal series have to be checked in order to validate a solution obtained from a modal superposition method.

The limitations of modal superposition methods are easily overcome by using direct time-integration methods. If implemented and used in the proper way, time-integration algorithms are not limited to linear systems and have the capability of taking into account the higher-frequency content of the eigenspectrum.

However, the time-integration methods cannot be used simply as black boxes. Choosing a given operator and adjusting its parameters must be done with respect to accuracy and stability requirements while controlling the damping in the numerical solution.

The basis for direct time integration is the use of a difference equation in time. It plays the role of a digital filter to the solution, and the time step used in the time-marching process is thus of paramount importance. Its size is related not only to the frequency content of the excitation, but also to the spatial discretization in order to be consistent with the wave-propagation speed in the finite-element mesh.

For the last 20 years, direct time integration has been one of the most challenging fields of research in structural analysis. Numerous schemes have been proposed which differ by their type (implicit versus explicit) and their adequacy to solve specific classes of problems.

In terms of computer resources, time integration is a very consuming method of analysis and much attention is thus paid to its computer implementation. In particular, partitioned methods of solutions have been found to be a convenient way to take advantage of the specific nature of coupled fields but will not be covered here.

Indeed the present chapter will be limited to the fundamental aspects of time integration, namely:

- The concept of implicit and explicit methods of solution
- A brief description of the main classes of time-integration schemes
- A brief discussion of the accuracy and stability properties of time-integration schemes

Reference [86], in particular, constitutes an excellent source of information for a more advanced analysis of the subject.

## 1.4A Essential Features of Linear and Nonlinear Structural-Dynamics Problems

Let us consider the semidiscretized problem of transient response of a nonlinear structure, written in the form of a matrix dynamic-equilibrium equation

$$\mathbf{M}\ddot{\mathbf{q}} + \mathbf{f}(\mathbf{q}, \dot{\mathbf{q}}) = \mathbf{g}(\mathbf{q}, t) \qquad \mathbf{q}_0, \dot{\mathbf{q}}_0 \text{ given} \tag{1.248}$$

where

$\mathbf{q}(t), \dot{\mathbf{q}}(t), \ddot{\mathbf{q}}(t) =$ the $n$-dimensional time-dependent vectors of displacements, velocities, and accelerations

$\mathbf{M} =$ the mass matrix of the structure, symmetric and positive-definite

$\mathbf{f}(\mathbf{q}, \dot{\mathbf{q}}) =$ the internal resisting forces in the structure, which may depend on displacements and velocities

$\mathbf{q}(\mathbf{q}, t) =$ the external forces, which vary in general with time, but which may also depend on the displacements

$\mathbf{q}_0, \dot{\mathbf{q}}_0 =$ the initial values of displacements and velocities

The term $\mathbf{f}(\mathbf{q}, \dot{\mathbf{q}})$ describing the internal forces includes in fact two contributions: one corresponds to elastic restoring forces and the second represents internal dissipation.

Nonlinearities arise in general from inelastic material behavior and/or from adaptation of the geometry to the loading; they may affect both the external forces $\mathbf{q}(\mathbf{q}, t)$ and the internal forces $\mathbf{f}(\mathbf{q}, \dot{\mathbf{q}})$, which result from the volume integration of the stress distributions $\boldsymbol{\sigma}(\boldsymbol{\varepsilon}, \dot{\boldsymbol{\varepsilon}})$ implied by the nonlinear state. At the finite-element level the latter ones are calculated by

$$\mathbf{f}_e(\mathbf{q}, \dot{\mathbf{q}}) = \int \mathbf{B}_e^T \boldsymbol{\sigma}(\boldsymbol{\varepsilon}, \dot{\boldsymbol{\varepsilon}}) \, dV \tag{1.249}$$

In Eq. (1.249), $\boldsymbol{\varepsilon}$ and $\dot{\boldsymbol{\varepsilon}}$ denote, respectively, the strains and strain rates in the material, and $\mathbf{B}_e$ is the appropriate finite-element matrix yielding the strains in terms of nodal displacements.

If linearity is assumed with respect to displacements and velocities, the internal forces take the classical linear form

$$\mathbf{f}(\mathbf{q}, \dot{\mathbf{q}}) = \mathbf{K}\mathbf{q}(t) + \mathbf{C}\dot{\mathbf{q}}(t) \tag{1.250}$$

where $\mathbf{K}$ and $\mathbf{C}$, the constant stiffness and viscous damping matrices, are both symmetric and positive-definite in the absence of rigid-body modes.

When nonlinearities are present in the system, it is sometimes rewarding to split (1.249) into linear and nonlinear contributions

$$\mathbf{f}(\mathbf{q}, \dot{\mathbf{q}}) = \mathbf{Kq} + \mathbf{C\dot{q}} + \mathbf{b}(\mathbf{q}) + \mathbf{d}(\mathbf{q}, \dot{\mathbf{q}}) \qquad (1.251)$$

where $\mathbf{b}$ and $\mathbf{d}$ are the nonlinear stiffness and damping operators which include the *path-dependent* behavior contained in the constitutive law.

Obviously, the task of integrating in time the dynamic response requires a thorough understanding of the behavior of Eq. (1.248). The response consists of widely different oscillatory components with amplitudes which continually change due to instantaneous loading conditions and/or nonlinearities. Therefore, some components of the solution vector $\mathbf{q}(t)$ oscillate very rapidly while others may oscillate very slowly.

When the response is primarily dominated by the high-frequency components, Eq. (1.248) describes a problem of wave-propagation type, whereas it corresponds to a structural-dynamics problem when the low-frequency components are dominant.

In many situations, however, the response is of mixed type in the sense that both low- and high-frequency components are present in a nonnegligible manner. For example, the response of a structure to a shock is initially governed by high-frequency components, but the low-frequency ones gradually begin to dominate the response as time proceeds.

In order to capture these dominant features of structural systems by a direct integration method, it is essential to understand the role played by its *characteristic roots* on the selection of integration formulae. These roots result from the eigenvalue analysis of the homogeneous linear (or linearized) equations

$$\mathbf{M\ddot{q}} + \mathbf{C\dot{q}} + \mathbf{Kq} = \mathbf{0} \qquad (1.252)$$

Let us assume that $\mathbf{C}$ is an arbitrary symmetric positive-definite damping matrix, and define the matrices

$$\mathbf{\Omega}^2 = \text{diag}\,(\omega_1^2 \cdots \omega_n^2) \qquad \mathbf{X} = [\mathbf{x}_{(1)} \cdots \mathbf{x}_{(n)}]$$

collecting the eigensolutions of the undamped eigenvalue problem associated with (1.252)

$$\mathbf{Kx} = \omega^2 \mathbf{Mx} \qquad (1.253)$$

The transformed damping matrix

$$\mathbf{C}^* = \mathbf{X}^T \mathbf{CX} \qquad (1.254)$$

is also positive-definite, and we suppose its eigenvalues $\zeta_i$ to be ranged in order of increasing values

$$0 \le \zeta_1 \le \zeta_2 \cdots \le \zeta_n \qquad (1.255)$$

Assuming a solution to (1.252) of the form

$$\mathbf{q} = \mathbf{x}\,e^{\lambda t} \qquad (1.256)$$

and with the change of variables

$$x = Xa \tag{1.257}$$

where $X$ verifies the orthogonality relations $X^T K X = \Omega^2$ and $X^T M X = I$, Eq. (1.252) is transformed into a quadratic eigenvalue problem

$$[\Omega^2 + \lambda C^* + \lambda^2 I]a = 0 \tag{1.258}$$

An extensive discussion of matrix pencils of type (1.258) can be found in Refs. [87–89].

Let $a_{(j)}$ be an eigenvector of (1.258) associated with $\lambda_j$. These vectors are either real or arise in complex-conjugate pairs, according to the fact that the corresponding roots are respectively real or complex-conjugate. We may also suppose, without loss of generality, that

$$\bar{a}_{(i)}^T a_{(j)} = \delta_{ij} \tag{1.259}$$

Then premultiplying (1.258) by $\bar{a}_{(j)}^T$ we obtain

$$c_j^2 + b_j \lambda_j + \lambda_j^2 = 0 \tag{1.260}$$

with the positive coefficients

$$c_j^2 = \bar{a}_{(j)}^T \Omega^2 a_{(j)} \quad \text{and} \quad b_j = \bar{a}_{(j)}^T C^* a_{(j)} \tag{1.261}$$

The rate of decay and frequency of the complex roots

$$\lambda_j = \mu_j + i\nu_j \tag{1.262}$$

are related to them by

$$\mu_j = -\frac{b_j}{2} \quad \text{and} \quad c_j^2 = |\lambda_j^2| = \mu_j^2 + \nu_j^2 \tag{1.263}$$

By applying the Courant-Fisher theorem on variational characterization of eigenvalues to both bilinear forms (1.261), we obtain

$$\zeta_1 \leq b_j \leq \zeta_n \quad \text{and} \quad \omega_1^2 \leq c_j^2 \leq \omega_n^2 \tag{1.264}$$

and thus

$$-\frac{\zeta_n}{2} \leq \mu_j \leq -\frac{\zeta_1}{2} \quad \text{and} \quad \omega_1^2 < |\lambda_j^2| \leq \omega_n^2 \tag{1.265}$$

The latter inequality implies that all complex roots $\lambda_j$ lie in an annulus of the $\lambda$-plane. The former one defines a vertical strip which must also contain all the complex roots.

The assumption of positive damping implies $\zeta_i \geq 0$ so that all the roots are contained in the left-hand complex plane. It is easily seen that if we have $2\omega_n < \zeta_i$ all the roots are real, while if $2\omega_1 > \zeta_n$ all the roots are complex. An intermediate case is represented in Fig. 1.19.

It is obvious that in the undamped case, all the characteristic roots lie on the imaginary axis. It will be seen that this is a severe restriction on the choice of an integration formula.

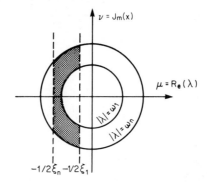

**FIG. 1.19**   Location of characteristic roots in the complex plane $\lambda = \mu + i\nu$ for a structural system with arbitrary positive damping.

As shown by Jensen [90], a root-locus form may also be given to the characteristic roots of Eq. (1.260) when proportional damping is assumed in the form

$$\mathbf{C} = \alpha\mathbf{M} + \beta\mathbf{K} \tag{1.266}$$

Thus, the transformed damping matrix also becomes diagonal

$$\mathbf{C}^* = \alpha\mathbf{I} + \beta\boldsymbol{\Omega}^2 \tag{1.267}$$

and Eq. (1.260) is replaced by

$$\omega_j^2 + (\alpha + \beta\omega_j^2)\lambda_j + \lambda_j^2 = 0 \tag{1.268}$$

If, for brevity, we drop the subscript $j$, a typical characteristic root is

$$\lambda(\alpha, \beta, \omega) = -\tfrac{1}{2}(\alpha + \beta\omega^2) \pm i\sqrt{\omega^2 - [\tfrac{1}{2}(\alpha + \beta\omega^2)]^2} \tag{1.269}$$

Letting

$$\mu = -\frac{\alpha + \beta\omega^2}{2}$$

we have

$$\omega^2 = -\frac{2\mu + \alpha}{\beta}$$

and substitution into Eq. (1.269) yields

$$\lambda = \mu \pm i\sqrt{r^2 - \left(\mu + \frac{1}{\beta}\right)^2} \tag{1.270}$$

where

$$r = \frac{\sqrt{1 - \alpha\beta}}{\beta}$$

Thus, we see that for all $\mu$ such that the radicand of (1.270) is positive, the locus of $\lambda$ is simply an upper circle of radius $r$ centered at $\mu = -1/\beta$. Its graphical representation is given

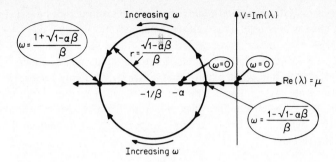

**FIG. 1.20** Root locus for a structural system with proportional damping.

by Fig. 1.20. Four physically important cases result from the examination of this root locus [91]:

1. *Undamped Case* $(\alpha = \beta = 0)$. The root locus of $\lambda$ lies strictly on the imaginary axis and coincides with the undamped eigenfrequencies.

2. *Mass-Proportional Damping* $(\alpha \neq 0, \beta = 0)$. The root locus of $\lambda$ starts at the origin $(0, 0)$ and at $(-\alpha h, 0)$ for $\omega = 0$. It coalesces at $\lambda = \alpha/2$. As the frequency $\omega$ is further increased, the root locus becomes a straight vertical line.

3. *Stiffness-Proportional Damping* $(\alpha = 0, \beta \neq 0)$. The root locus becomes a circle with radius $r = 1/\beta$ centered at $(-1/\beta, 0)$. Thus, the locus passes the real axis at the origin $(0, 0)$ for $\omega = 0$ and at $(-2h/\beta, 0)$ for $\omega = 1/\beta$. If $\omega$ is further increased, one root approaches the origin and the other one goes to $-\infty$.

4. *Rayleigh Damping* $(\alpha, \beta \neq 0)$. The root locus is again shown in Fig. 1.20. At both low and high $\omega$-values, the equations are heavily damped, whereas at an intermediate $\omega$ the equations are underdamped. This is in contrast to stiffness-proportional damping which introduces damping increasing with frequency. On the other hand, the mass-proportional damping case starts with a heavy damping which is decreased as $\omega$ increases.

As will be seen in the stability analysis of integration operators, the above analysis of the characteristic roots of structural-dynamics equations is essential to the choice of time-integration formulae. Confronting the physical behavior of Eq. (1.252) with the stability region of the various integration formulae provides the stability margins on which the selection of specific formulae may be based.

## 1.4B Essential Features of Integration Formulae

There is a large number of integration formulae available for solving systems of ordinary differential equations such as (1.248). The main classes of methods are:

- Runge–Kutta methods
- Exponentially fitted methods
- Series-expansion methods
- Linear multistep methods

We will not review all these methods, but rather will concentrate on the last two categories, which are the most widely used by structural dynamicists.

For each class of methods, two alternatives exist: *explicit* and *implicit* formulae. They differ mainly by the fact that implicit formulae imply the solution of a system of simultaneous equations at each time step while explicit methods involve simply vector calculations if a diagonal mass matrix is used. Besides the fact that implicit methods are thus much more complex to implement when nonlinearities are present in the system, a second important factor of selection between implicit- and explicit-integration algorithms lies in their stability and accuracy properties.

**A Numerical Example**   To have a better perception of the differences that can occur in the stability and accuracy properties of different integration formulae, let us consider the simple problem of a single-degree-of-freedom oscillator submitted to a nonzero initial displacement

$$\ddot{x} + \omega_0^2 x = 0 \qquad \omega_0 = \pi \text{ rad/s}$$
$$x(0) = 1 \qquad \dot{x}(0) = 0 \tag{1.271}$$

The exact solution to (1.271) is $x(t) = \cos \omega_0 t$. The response can be calculated numerically using first-order time-integration operators by recasting the system in first canonical form (using $y = \dot{x}$)

$$\dot{\mathbf{u}} = \mathbf{A}\mathbf{u} \tag{1.272}$$

with the state vector $\mathbf{u}^T = [x \ y]$, the initial condition $\mathbf{u}_{(0)}^T = [1 \ 0]$, and the system matrix

$$\mathbf{A} = \begin{bmatrix} 0 & 1 \\ -\omega_0^2 & 0 \end{bmatrix}$$

Let us apply to Eqs. (1.272) the three elementary integration formulae:

1. *Euler forward* (*explicit*): $\qquad \mathbf{u}_{n+1} = \mathbf{u}_n + h\dot{\mathbf{u}}_n \tag{1.273}$

2. *Euler backward* (*implicit*): $\qquad \mathbf{u}_{n+1} = \mathbf{u}_n + h\dot{\mathbf{u}}_{n+1} \tag{1.274}$

3. *Trapezoidal rule* (*implicit*): $\quad \mathbf{u}_{n+1} = \mathbf{u}_n + \dfrac{h}{2}(\dot{\mathbf{u}}_n + \dot{\mathbf{u}}_{n+1}) \tag{1.275}$

The three numerical solutions obtained after $T = 3$ seconds with a time-step size $h = T/32$ are compared to the exact solution in Fig. 1.21.

One observes that:

1. The numerical solution given by the trapezoidal rule is the most accurate one in the sense that it preserves the amplitude of the exact solution while it elongates slightly the period.

2. The Euler-backward formula produces a significantly larger elongation of the period and gives rise to a very strong numerical damping. It is thus numerically stable but inaccurate.

3. The Euler-forward formula produces the same elongation period as the implicit Euler scheme, but gives rise to an unstable response due to negative numerical damping. It is thus inaccurate and numerically unstable.

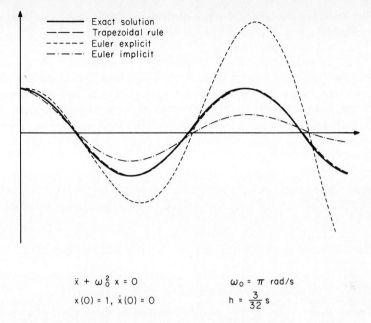

$$\ddot{x} + \omega_0^2 x = 0 \qquad\qquad \omega_0 = \pi \text{ rad/s}$$

$$x(0) = 1,\ \dot{x}(0) = 0 \qquad\qquad h = \frac{3}{32}\text{ s}$$

**FIG. 1.21**  Numerical integration of a single-DOF oscillator with different integration formulae.

***Characteristic Equation and Stability Region of Time-Integration Operators***  The behavior of the various time-integration formulae when applied to a specific system of linear differential equations may be explained by considering their characteristic equation obtained as follows [91].

Let us apply to the system of linear differential equations (1.272) a linear multistep formula in the general form

$$\mathbf{u}_n = \sum_{j=1}^{m} \alpha_j \mathbf{u}_{n-j} - h \sum_{j=0}^{m} \beta_j \dot{\mathbf{u}}_{n-j} \qquad (1.276)$$

where $\alpha_j$ and $\beta_j$ are real formula-dependent coefficients. After substitution of (1.272) into (1.276), the following difference equation is obtained:

$$\sum_{j=0}^{m} [\alpha_j - \beta_j h \mathbf{A}] \mathbf{u}_{n-j} = \mathbf{0} \qquad (1.277)$$

where $\alpha_0 = -1$ is assumed.

Let us next denote by $\mathbf{\Lambda} = \text{diag}\,(\mu_r)$ the matrix of eigenvalues of $\mathbf{A}$ and by $\mathbf{X}$ the associated eigenvector matrix. The characteristic equation associated with (1.277) can then be obtained by seeking a solution in the form

$$\mathbf{u}_n = \lambda^k \mathbf{X} \mathbf{x}_{n-k} \qquad (1.278)$$

where $\lambda$ is the solution-amplification factor. By combining Eqs. (1.277) and (1.278), and using the orthogonality property $\mathbf{X}^T\mathbf{X} = \mathbf{I}$, one obtains the characteristic equations associated with an eigenvalue $\mu_r$,

$$\sum_{j=0}^{m} (\alpha_j - \beta_j h\mu_r)\lambda^{m-j} = 0 \qquad (1.279)$$

From (1.278) one observes that the numerical solution to (1.272) by the linear multistep formula (1.276) remains bounded only if $|\lambda^j| \leq 1$, $j = 1, \ldots, m$. In particular, the case $|\lambda| = 1$ determines the boundary at which the solution neither grows nor decays. Therefore, the stability boundary is the mapping of the unit circle ($\lambda = e^{i\theta}$, $0 \leq \theta \leq 2\pi$) on the $\mu h$-plane and verifies the equation

$$\mu h = \frac{\displaystyle\sum_{j=0}^{m} \alpha_j e^{i(m-j)\theta}}{\displaystyle\sum_{j=0}^{m} \beta_j e^{i(m-j)\theta}} \qquad (1.280)$$

In particular, the single-step schemes (1.273) to (1.275) yield (see Fig. 1.22):

1. *Euler Explicit*: $\mu h = e^{i\theta} - 1$.   The stability boundary is a circle of unit radius centered at $\text{Re}(\mu h) = -1$. The solution is unstable everywhere but in the circle.

2. *Euler Implicit*: $\mu h = 1 - e^{-i\theta}$.   The stability boundary is also a circle of unit radius, but centered at $\text{Re}(\mu h) = +1$. The solution is stable everywhere except inside the circle.

3. *Trapezoidal Rule*: $\mu h = i \sin \theta (1 + \cos \theta)$.   The stability boundary is the imaginary axis, and the numerical solution is stable in the entire left-hand plane.

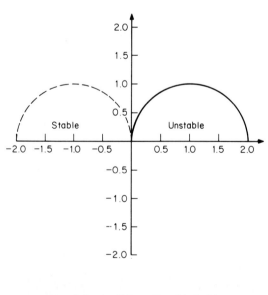

|  |  |
|---|---|
| —————— Euler implicit | Unstable inside |
| – – – – – Euler explicit | Unstable outside |

**FIG. 1.22**   Stability limits for Euler implicit and explicit methods.

Note that for the single-DOF system, the eigenvalues are $\mu = \pm i\omega_0$. The roots $\mu h$ are thus located in the stable region of the Euler-backward formula, in the unstable region of the Euler-forward formula, and right on the stability boundary of the trapezoidal rule.

This explains why the amplitude of the trapezoidal-rule solution is preserved, and why one observes a decay for the Euler implicit formula and an amplification for the explicit one.

Most of the implicit methods that are commonly used (trapezoidal rule, Newmark, Houbolt, Wilson, and others) are stable for the entire left-hand complex plane. This property is referred to as *A-stability* by mathematicians [92, 93] and as unconditional stability by structural engineers [94–96]. On the other hand, all the explicit formulae that are available are stable only inside a subdomain of the left-hand plane. It is shown in the next section that, from the computational viewpoint, the price paid for the unconditional stability of implicit formulae is to solve simultaneous systems of equations at each time step whereas the limited stability of explicit formulae is compensated by their computational simplicity since they involve only vector calculations.

The combined observations that we have just made on the eigenvalues of the structural-dynamic equations and on the stability domain of integration formulae provide us with the necessary tools for evaluating the numerical stability for all classes of time-integration methods.

**Implicit and Explicit Time-Integration Formulae**   The implicit character of a time-integration operator is defined in a general manner as follows. Assuming that displacements and velocities at time $t_{n+1}$ are approximated by using linear-difference formulae, a time-integration operator applicable to (1.248) may always be written in the form

$$\dot{\mathbf{q}}_{n+1} = \frac{\alpha}{h}\ddot{\mathbf{q}}_{n+1} + \mathbf{l}(\dot{\mathbf{q}}_n, \ddot{\mathbf{q}}_n, \ldots)$$

$$\mathbf{q}_{n+1} = \frac{\beta}{h^2}\ddot{\mathbf{q}}_{n+1} + \mathbf{m}(\mathbf{q}_n, \dot{\mathbf{q}}_n, \ddot{\mathbf{q}}_n, \ldots) \tag{1.281}$$

where $h$ is the time-step size, and where $\alpha$ and $\beta$ are specific coefficients of the difference formulae. The first term in Eq. (1.281) represents the implicit dependence of the interpolation formula with the solution at the current time step. The second term describes its dependence on the solution at previous time stations.

**Explicit Formulae**   If both coefficients $\alpha = \beta = 0$, then Eqs. (1.281) are called *explicit* and may be used to predict displacements and velocities $\mathbf{q}_{n+1}$ and $\dot{\mathbf{q}}_{n+1}$ from known quantities at instants $t_n, t_{n-1}, \ldots$.

These predictions become

$$\dot{\mathbf{q}}_{n+1} = \mathbf{l}(\dot{\mathbf{q}}_n, \ddot{\mathbf{q}}_n, \ldots)$$

$$\mathbf{q}_{n+1} = \mathbf{m}(\mathbf{q}_n, \dot{\mathbf{q}}_n, \ddot{\mathbf{q}}_n, \ldots) \tag{1.282}$$

and can be computed directly from solution at previous instants. The equilibrium equations may then be solved in the form

$$\ddot{\mathbf{q}}_{n+1} = \mathbf{M}^{-1}[\mathbf{g}(\mathbf{q}_{n+1}, t) - \mathbf{f}(\mathbf{q}_{n+1}, \dot{\mathbf{q}}_{n+1})] \tag{1.283}$$

in order to determine the accelerations.

It is readily seen from the above procedure that explicit integration is essentially a noniterative technique, and that it involves two main operations:

- Evaluating the balance between applied and resisting forces

$$\mathbf{g}(\mathbf{q}_{n+1}, t) - \mathbf{f}(\mathbf{q}_{n+1}, \dot{\mathbf{q}}_{n+1}) \tag{1.284}$$

- Solving a linear system associated with the mass matrix, an operation which is computationally trivial if the mass matrix exhibits diagonal form.

Unfortunately, this advantage of computational simplicity that characterizes explicit methods is reduced to a large extent by the limitations that are encountered in their application. As we have already seen, the step size that can be allowed in the time-marching process is strongly limited by the stability region of the formula, and special situations such as the occurrence of algebraic constraints between degrees of freedom are not easily dealt with.

*Implicit formulae* The displacements, velocities, and accelerations appearing in the equilibrium equations (1.248) are not independent quantities. Therefore, the spatially discretized system to be solved at each time $t$ may be written in the form of an equation for the displacement vector $\mathbf{q}(t)$

$$\mathbf{r}(\mathbf{q}) = \mathbf{M}\ddot{\mathbf{q}}(t) + \mathbf{f}(\mathbf{q}, \dot{\mathbf{q}}) - \mathbf{g}(\mathbf{q}, t) = \mathbf{0} \tag{1.285}$$

where $\mathbf{r}$ is the $n$-dimensional residual vector.

Since in the implicit case both coefficients $\alpha$ and $\beta$ take nonzero values in (1.281), accelerations and velocities become functions of $\mathbf{q}_{n+1}$,

$$\ddot{\mathbf{q}}_{n+1} = \frac{h^2}{\beta}[\mathbf{q}_{n+1} - \mathbf{m}(\mathbf{q}_n, \dot{\mathbf{q}}_n, \ddot{\mathbf{q}}_n, \ldots)]$$

$$\dot{\mathbf{q}}_{n+1} = \frac{\alpha h}{\beta}[\mathbf{q}_{n+1} - \mathbf{m}(\mathbf{q}_n, \dot{\mathbf{q}}_n, \ddot{\mathbf{q}}_n, \ldots)] + \mathbf{l}(\dot{\mathbf{q}}_n, \ddot{\mathbf{q}}_n, \ldots) \tag{1.286}$$

and after substitution of (1.286) into (1.285) the residual vector becomes a function of $\mathbf{q}_{n+1}$ only:

$$\mathbf{r}(\mathbf{q}_{n+1}) = \mathbf{0} \tag{1.287}$$

In order for the displacements $\mathbf{q}_{n+1}$ to satisfy fully the discretized equations (1.287), an equilibrium-iteration sequence is usually required if the equations are nonlinear. Most common solution techniques for such systems of simultaneous nonlinear equations imply a certain type of linearization: assuming an approximation $\mathbf{q}_{n+1}^k (k = 0, 1, \ldots)$ to $\mathbf{q}_{n+1}$, we admit, for instance, that in its neighborhood the linear mapping

$$\mathbf{r}_L(\mathbf{q}_{n+1}^{k+1}) = \mathbf{r}(\mathbf{q}_{n+1}^{k+1}) + \mathbf{S}(\mathbf{q}_{n+1}^k)(\mathbf{q}_{n+1}^{k+1} - \mathbf{q}_{n+1}^k) \tag{1.288}$$

is a good approximation to (1.287), with the definition of the iteration (jacobian) matrix

$$\mathbf{S}(\mathbf{q}_{n+1}^k) = \left[\frac{\partial \mathbf{r}}{\partial \mathbf{q}}\right]_{\mathbf{q}_{n+1}^k} \tag{1.289}$$

which reads in the present case

$$S(q) = \frac{\partial f}{\partial q} + \frac{\partial f}{\partial \dot{q}} \frac{\partial \dot{q}}{\partial q} + M \frac{\partial \ddot{q}}{\partial q} - \frac{\partial g}{\partial q} \qquad (1.290)$$

The different terms in the jacobian matrix (1.290) may be interpreted as follows:

$\partial f / \partial q$ represents the variation of internal loads with displacements, and is thus the tangent-stiffness matrix $K^t$

$\partial f / \partial \dot{q}$ describes the variation of internal loads with velocities and has thus the meaning of a tangent-damping matrix $C^t$

$\partial g / \partial q$ describes the dependence of external loads with geometry

Unlike the two preceding terms, the last one is nonsymmetric and is usually omitted to preserve the symmetrical character of the jacobian matrix (1.290). With the above definition the latter reads

$$S(q) = K^t(q) + C^t(q) \frac{\partial \dot{q}}{\partial q} + M \frac{\partial \ddot{q}}{\partial q} - \frac{\partial g}{\partial q} \qquad (1.291)$$

When linearity is assumed, the last term in Eq. (1.291) vanishes and the tangent matrices $K^t$ and $C^t$ reduce respectively to the constant stiffness and viscous damping matrices $K$ and $C$, yielding the constant jacobian

$$S_0 = K + C \frac{\partial \dot{q}}{\partial q} + M \frac{\partial \ddot{q}}{\partial q} \qquad (1.292)$$

### 1.4c  One-Step Linear Integration Formulae

One-step methods are characterized by the fact that the state of the system (i.e., displacements and velocities) at time $t_{n+1}$ is calculated as a function of the system state at the former time step $t_n$ only:

$$\dot{q}_{n+1} = \frac{\alpha}{h} \ddot{q}_{n+1} + l(\dot{q}_n, \ddot{q}_n)$$

$$\qquad (1.293)$$

$$q_{n+1} = \frac{\beta}{h^2} \ddot{q}_{n+1} + m(q_n, \dot{q}_n, \ddot{q}_n)$$

Their implicit character arises from the dependence on the acceleration at the current time step. By comparison with multistep linear formulae, which will be discussed later, they benefit from two advantages:

**1.** They are self-starting.

**2.** They allow for an easy change in step size during the time-marching process.

***Newmark's Method [97]***    In Newmark's method a Taylor series expansion of displacements and velocities is used to construct linear relationships of type (1.293). They are limited to second derivatives.

$$\mathbf{q}_{n+1} = \mathbf{q}_n + h\dot{\mathbf{q}}_n \int_{t_n}^{t_{n+1}} (t_{n+1} - \tau)\ddot{\mathbf{q}}(\tau)\,d\tau \qquad t_n < \tau < t_{n+1}$$

$$\dot{\mathbf{q}}_{n+1} = \dot{\mathbf{q}}_n + \int_{t_n}^{t_{n+1}} \ddot{\mathbf{q}}(\tau)\,d\tau$$

(1.294)

The approximation in Newmark's scheme consists of evaluating the integrals in (1.294) by a quadrature formula

$$\int_{t_{n+1}}^{t_{n+1}} (t_{n+1} - \tau)\ddot{\mathbf{q}}(\tau)\,d\tau = (\tfrac{1}{2} - \beta)h^2\ddot{\mathbf{q}}_n + \beta h^2\ddot{\mathbf{q}}_{n+1} + \mathbf{R}_n$$

$$\int_{t_n}^{t_{n+1}} \ddot{\mathbf{q}}(\tau)\,d\tau = (1 - \gamma)h\ddot{\mathbf{q}}_n + \gamma h\ddot{\mathbf{q}}_{n+1} + \mathbf{R}'_n$$

(1.295)

$\beta$ and $\gamma$ are the free parameters of Newmark's method: their choice results from a compromise between computational simplicity and stability and accuracy requirements. The remainder terms are given by

$$\mathbf{R}_n = (\beta - \tfrac{1}{6})h^3\mathbf{q}^{(3)}(\tau) + O[h^4 \quad \mathbf{q}^{(4)}]$$

$$\mathbf{R}'_n = (\gamma - \tfrac{1}{2})h^2\mathbf{q}^{(3)}(\tau) + O[h^3 \quad \mathbf{q}^{(4)}]$$

(1.296)

and show that maximal accuracy is obtained when $\gamma = \tfrac{1}{2}$ and $\beta = \tfrac{1}{6}$. It can be verified that this choice corresponds to a linear interpolation of accelerations over the time interval $(t_n, t_{n+1})$.

The substitution of the approximations (1.295) into (1.294) yield the difference equations

$$\mathbf{q}_{n+1} = \mathbf{q}_n + h\dot{\mathbf{q}}_n + (\tfrac{1}{2} - \beta)h^2\ddot{\mathbf{q}}_n + \beta h^2\ddot{\mathbf{q}}_{n+1}$$

$$\dot{\mathbf{q}}_{n+1} = \dot{\mathbf{q}}_n + (1 - \gamma)h\ddot{\mathbf{q}}_n + \gamma h\ddot{\mathbf{q}}_{n+1}$$

(1.297)

which have to be combined with the equilibrium equation $\mathbf{r}(\mathbf{q}_{n+1}) = 0$ to obtain the solution at $t_{n+1}$.

**Stability Analysis of the Newmark Method** Let us apply the Newmark formulae (1.297) to the undamped oscillator (1.271). After elimination of acceleration terms, the numerical solution of the system can be recast in the form of the matrix equation

$$\mathbf{B}\mathbf{u}_{n+1} = \mathbf{A}\mathbf{u}_n$$

(1.298)

where $\mathbf{u}_n^T = [\mathbf{x}_n^T \dot{\mathbf{x}}_n^T]$ is the state vector of the system and $\mathbf{A}$ and $\mathbf{B}$ are the matrices

$$\mathbf{B} = \begin{bmatrix} 1 + \beta h^2\omega_0^2 & 0 \\ \gamma h\omega^2 & I \end{bmatrix} \qquad \mathbf{A} = \begin{bmatrix} 1 - (\tfrac{1}{2} - \beta)h^2\omega_0^2 & h \\ -(1 - \gamma)h\omega_0^2 & 1 \end{bmatrix}$$

If the solution to (1.298) is assumed to be in the form of

$$\mathbf{u}_n = \lambda^k\mathbf{u}_{n-k}$$

(1.299)

the characteristic equation of the system

$$\det(\mathbf{A} - \lambda\mathbf{B}) = 0$$

(1.300)

takes the form of a quadratic polynomial in $\lambda$,

$$\lambda^2 - \lambda[2 - (\gamma + \tfrac{1}{2})r^2] + 1 - (\gamma - \tfrac{1}{2})r^2 = 0 \tag{1.301}$$

with

$$r^2 = \frac{\omega_0^2 h^2}{1 + \beta \omega_0^2 h^2}$$

Equation (1.301) admits a pair of complex-conjugate eigenvalues (corresponding to oscillatory motion) when

$$[(\gamma + \tfrac{1}{2})r^2] \leqslant 4 \quad \text{or} \quad (\gamma + \tfrac{1}{2})^2 - 4\beta \leqslant \frac{4}{\omega_0^2 h^2} \tag{1.302}$$

in which case these roots may expressed in exponential form

$$\lambda = \rho \, e^{i\theta} \tag{1.303}$$

with

$$\rho = [1 - (\gamma - \tfrac{1}{2})r^2]^{1/2} \qquad \theta = \tan^{-1} \frac{r[4 - (\gamma + \tfrac{1}{2})^2 r^2]^{1/2}}{2 - (\gamma + \tfrac{1}{2})r^2} \tag{1.304}$$

Whatever the step size $h$ is, the numerical solution will be stable only if $\rho \leqslant 1$. This implies that any Newmark algorithm has to fulfill the condition

$$\gamma \geqslant \tfrac{1}{2}$$

On the other hand, the maximum step size which preserves the oscillatory nature of the motion is obtained from (1.302). Unconditional stability is thus governed by the simultaneous conditions

$$\gamma \geqslant \tfrac{1}{2} \quad \text{and} \quad \beta \geqslant \tfrac{1}{4}(\gamma + \tfrac{1}{2})^2 \tag{1.305}$$

To obtain, at the same time, a measure of accuracy of the numerical solution, let us compare the exact and numerical solutions to (1.298) written in the form

$$\mathbf{u}_{n+1}^* = e^{i\omega_0 h} \mathbf{u}_n \quad \text{and} \quad \mathbf{u}_{n+1} = \rho \, e^{i\theta} \mathbf{u}_n \tag{1.306}$$

The error to the solution is

$$\mathbf{u}_{n+1} - \mathbf{u}_{n+1}^* = [\rho \, e^{i(\theta - \omega_0 h)} - 1] \, e^{i\omega_0 h} \mathbf{u}_n \tag{1.307}$$

and thus may be measured by

- The *amplification* error

$$A = \rho - 1 = -(\gamma - \tfrac{1}{2})\omega_0^2 h^2 + O(h^4) \tag{1.308}$$

- The *periodicity* error

$$\frac{\Delta T}{T} = \frac{\omega_0 h}{\theta} - 1 = \tfrac{1}{2}(\beta - \tfrac{1}{12})\omega_0^2 h^2 + O(h^3) \tag{1.309}$$

The stability and accuracy properties of the Newmark's family of algorithms that are discussed above are given in Table 1.1.

**TABLE 1.1**   Stability and Accuracy Properties of Newmark's Family Algorithms

| Algorithm | $\gamma$ | $\beta$ | Stability limit $\omega_0 h$ | Amplification error | Periodicity error $\Delta T/T$ |
|---|---|---|---|---|---|
| Purely explicit | 0 | 0 | 0 | $\dfrac{\omega_0^2 h^2}{2}$ | |
| Central difference | $\frac{1}{2}$ | 0 | 2 | 0 | $-\dfrac{\omega_0^2 h^2}{24}$ |
| Fox and Goodwin | $\frac{1}{2}$ | $\frac{1}{12}$ | 2.45 | 0 | $O(h^3)$ |
| Linear acceleration | $\frac{1}{2}$ | $\frac{1}{6}$ | 3.46 | 0 | $\dfrac{\omega_0^2 h^2}{24}$ |
| Average constant acceleration | $\frac{1}{2}$ | $\frac{1}{4}$ | $\infty$ | 0 | $\dfrac{\omega_0^2 h^2}{12}$ |

***Explicit Newmark's Scheme*** $(\beta = \gamma = 0)$   Equation (1.304) shows that an explicit prediction of both displacements and velocities gives necessarily an unstable numerical solution as long as there is no physical damping in the system. At least an implicit correction of velocities (with $\gamma \geq \frac{1}{2}$) is required to stabilize the solution.

***Central-Difference Scheme*** $(\beta = 0,\ \gamma = \frac{1}{2})$   It is easy to verify that the one-step explicit scheme so obtained

$$\mathbf{q}_{n+1} = \mathbf{q}_n + h\dot{\mathbf{q}}_n + \frac{h^2}{2}\ddot{\mathbf{q}}_n$$

$$\dot{\mathbf{q}}_{n+1} = \dot{\mathbf{q}}_n + \frac{h}{2}(\ddot{\mathbf{q}}_n + \ddot{\mathbf{q}}_{n+1})$$

(1.310)

does not differ from the well-known central-difference algorithm

$$\ddot{\mathbf{q}}_n = \frac{1}{h^2}(\mathbf{q}_{n+1} - 2\mathbf{q}_n + \mathbf{q}_{n-1})$$

(1.311)

which, because of its two-step form, does not involve velocities explicitly. Equation (1.302) shows that the step size is limited by the condition

$$\omega_0 h \leq 2$$

(1.312)

If the constitutive law is velocity-dependent, an explicit prediction of velocity has to be made in order to calculate the internal loads.

In order to minimize round-off error propagation [98], it is usually advised to restate the system of difference equations (1.310) in a sequence which uses velocities at midinterval but avoids calculating terms in $h^2$. The resulting time-marching sequence is given by Fig. 1.23. It has remarkable simplicity, and the cost of the equilibrium solution becomes negligible

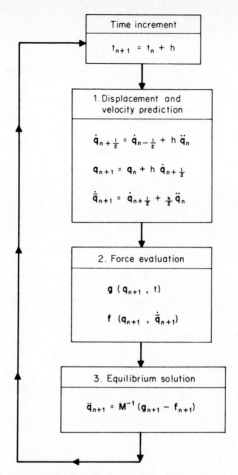

**FIG. 1.23**  Computational sequence for one-step explicit scheme.

when a diagonal mass matrix is used. It has thus been the basis for numerous explicit codes in structural dynamics.

A further advantage of a diagonal mass matrix lies in the fact that it depresses the eigenspectrum of the system. The use of a diagonal mass matrix enlarges thus the stability domain of the algorithm (1.312) and, at the same time, compensates for the period shortening $\Delta T/T = -1/24\omega_0^2 h^2$ that characterizes the central-difference scheme.

***Fox and Goodwin Scheme*** $(\gamma = \frac{1}{2}, \beta = \frac{1}{12})$   Equations (1.308) and (1.309) show that the implicit time-integration algorithm obtained with the choice $(\gamma = \frac{1}{2}, \beta = \frac{1}{12})$ has a zero amplification error together with a periodicity error of third order. Despite its implicit form, the algorithm is limited in stability by the condition $\omega_0^2 h^2 < 6$.

***Linear Acceleration Scheme*** $(\gamma = \frac{1}{2}, \beta = \frac{1}{6})$   The linear acceleration scheme is also an implicit algorithm with limited stability $(\omega_0^2 h^2 < 12)$, and its periodicity error is $\Delta T/T = \omega_0^2 h^2/24$.

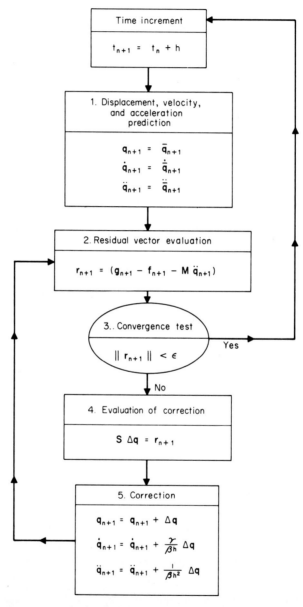

**FIG. 1.24** Computational iterative sequence for Newmark implicit scheme.

*Average Constant-Acceleration Scheme* ($\gamma = \frac{1}{2}$, $\beta = \frac{1}{4}$)  For linear applications, this choice corresponds to the best integration scheme with unconditional stability. It has a zero amplification error and its periodicity error is $\Delta T / T = \omega_0^2 h^2 / 12$.

*Computer Implementation of Newmark Implicit Algorithms [99]*  The basic computational sequence for Newmark implicit algorithms ($\beta \neq 0$) is described in Fig. 1.24, about which the following comments should be made.

1. The possible predictors are given by Table 1.2. In general, it is found that predictor $B$ has a tendency to generate instability for strongly nonlinear systems. Predictors $A$ and $C$ are thus recommended rather than predictor $B$.

2. When the problem remains linear, convergence occurs in one step and is not influenced by the choice of the predictor.

3. The convergence test for nonlinear problems may be achieved either on the residual vector itself or on the displacement correction. In both cases, an accuracy threshold has to be calculated which is a measure of either force or displacement amplitudes in the system.

4. The linear system from which the correction is obtained involves the jacobian matrix computed from Eq. (1.290).

$$S = \left[ K^t + \frac{\gamma}{\beta h} C^t + \frac{1}{\beta h^2} M - \frac{\partial g}{\partial q} \right]_{\bar{q}_{n+1}} \tag{1.313}$$

Various approximations to $S$ may be used according to the nonlinear solution method which is applied to the system $r(q_{n+1}) = 0$. For this specific aspect of nonlinear iteration, the reader is referred to Sec. 1.3. Roughly speaking, each time increment has to be solved as a load increment in a static problem. One main difference arises, however, from the fact that the iteration matrix remains generally positive-definite since, for sufficiently small $h$, the mass-matrix term becomes dominant in Eq. (1.313).

**TABLE 1.2**  Possible Predictors for Newmark Implicit-Integration Schemes

| | Predictor type | Predictor formulae |
|---|---|---|
| $A$ | Purely implicit: $\bar{q}_{n+1} = q_n$ | $\bar{\ddot{q}}_{n+1} = -\frac{1}{\beta h^2} [h\dot{q}_n + (\frac{1}{2} - \beta) h^2 \ddot{q}_n]$ <br><br> $\bar{\dot{q}}_{n+1} = \dot{q}_n + (1 - \gamma) h \ddot{q}_n + \gamma h \bar{\ddot{q}}_{n+1}$ |
| $B$ | Purely explicit: $\bar{\ddot{q}}_{n+1} = \ddot{q}_n$ | $\bar{q}_{n+1} = q_n + h\dot{q}_n + \frac{h^2}{2} \ddot{q}_h$ <br><br> $\bar{\dot{q}}_{n+1} = \dot{q}_n + h\ddot{q}_n$ |
| $C$ | Zero acceleration: $\bar{\ddot{q}}_{n+1} = 0$ | $\bar{q}_{n+1} = q_n + h\dot{q}_n + (\frac{1}{2} - \beta) h^2 \ddot{q}_n$ <br><br> $\bar{\dot{q}}_{n+1} = \dot{q}_n + (1 - \gamma) h\ddot{q}_n$ |

***Wilson's θ-Method***   Wilson's $\theta$-method [100] is a modification of Newmark's algorithm in which a linear variation of acceleration is assumed within a time step

$$\ddot{\mathbf{q}}(\tau) = \ddot{\mathbf{q}}_n + \theta(\ddot{\mathbf{q}}_{n+1} - \ddot{\mathbf{q}}_n) \qquad \theta = \frac{\tau - \tau_n}{h} > 0$$

Displacements and velocities are calculated at time $t_{n+1}$ using the Newmark difference formulae (1.297), with $(\beta = \frac{1}{6}, \beta = \frac{1}{2})$, but the stability of the method is obtained by expressing equilibrium at a later time $t_{n+\theta}$ $(\theta > 1)$ using the extrapolation formula

$$\mathbf{r}(\mathbf{q}_{n+\theta}) = \mathbf{0}$$

The stability equation of Wilson's method is found to be a cubic. It has two complex-conjugate roots which provide the representation of oscillatory motion and one spurious real root. Its numerical solution shows that a value $\theta > 1.37$ provides unconditional stability of the solution while keeping to a large extent the accuracy of the linear acceleration method.

The computational procedure is somewhat similar to that of Newmark's method and is given by Fig. 1.25. The associated tangent matrix is that evaluated at time $t_{n+\theta}$

$$\mathbf{S} = \left[ \mathbf{K}^t + \frac{3}{\theta h} \mathbf{C}^t + \frac{6}{\theta^2 h^2} \mathbf{M} - \frac{\partial \mathbf{g}}{\partial \mathbf{q}} \right]_{\bar{\mathbf{q}}_{n+1}}$$

***Hilber–Hughes–Taylor (HHT) α-Method [101, 102]***   Hilber, Hughes, and Taylor have proposed an elegant way to introduce damping in the Newmark method without degrading the order of accuracy. It consists of keeping the Newmark's formulae (1.297), whereas the time-discrete equations are modified in the form

$$\mathbf{M}\ddot{\mathbf{q}}_{n+1} + (1-\alpha)\mathbf{f}(\mathbf{q}_{n+1}, \dot{\mathbf{q}}_{n+1}) + \alpha\mathbf{f}(\mathbf{q}_n, \dot{\mathbf{q}}_n) = (1-\alpha)\mathbf{g}(\mathbf{q}_{n+1}, t) + \alpha\mathbf{g}(\mathbf{q}_n, t) \qquad (1.314)$$

Clearly, if $\alpha = 0$ the HHT method reduces to Newmark's scheme. If the parameters are picked such that $\alpha \in [0, \frac{1}{3}]$, $\gamma = \frac{1}{2} + \alpha$, $\beta = \frac{1}{4}(1+\alpha)^2$, the result is an unconditionally stable second-order scheme. The computational procedure is again similar to that of Newmark's algorithm so that the HHT $\alpha$-method is a logical replacement to it for nonlinear problems where controlling the numerical damping in the integration scheme is necessary. The associated tangent matrix is

$$\mathbf{S} = \left[ (1-\alpha)\mathbf{K}^t + \frac{(1-\alpha)\gamma}{\beta h} \mathbf{C}^t + \frac{1}{\beta h^2} \mathbf{M} - \frac{\partial \mathbf{g}}{\partial \mathbf{q}} \right]_{\bar{\mathbf{q}}_{n+1}}$$

## 1.4D  Multistep Linear-Integration Formulae

Various multistep integration schemes can be obtained using difference formulae operating on local values of displacements, velocities, and accelerations at several successive time steps. One has already seen that for velocities, linear-difference formulae may be written in the form

$$\sum_{j=0}^{m} [\alpha_j \mathbf{q}_{n-j} - \beta_j h \dot{\mathbf{q}}_{n-j}] = c_{p+1} h^{p+1} \mathbf{q}^{(p+1)}(t) \qquad (1.315)$$

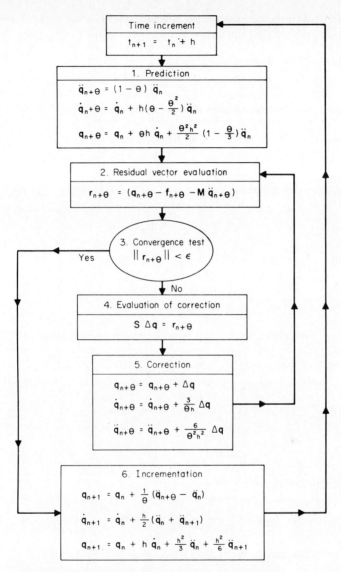

**FIG. 1.25**  Computational scheme for Wilson's $\theta$-method.

where $p$ is the consistency order of the formula. The approximation consists in equating the right-hand side of Eq. (1.315) to zero.

In order to construct multistep integration formulae applicable to the equilibrium equations (1.248) of structural dynamics, two distinct approaches may be adopted [95, 103]:

• The equilibrium equations may be rewritten in the form of a system of first-order equations, in which case Eq. (1.315) is directly applicable.

- Linear-difference formulae specialized to second-order systems may be constructed in a form similar to that of Eq. (1.315).

Both techniques will be briefly reviewed below.

**Multistep Equations Applicable to First-Order Systems [90]**   The initial residual equation (1.285) is primarily rewritten in first-order form using velocities as extra variables:

$$\mathbf{r}(\mathbf{q}, \mathbf{v}) = \mathbf{M}\ddot{\mathbf{q}} + \mathbf{f}(\mathbf{q}, \mathbf{v}) - \mathbf{g}(\mathbf{q}, t) = \mathbf{0} \tag{1.316}$$

$$\dot{\mathbf{q}} - \mathbf{v} = \mathbf{0} \tag{1.317}$$

Applying the first-order difference formula (1.315) to (1.317) yields

$$\sum_{j=0}^{m} [\alpha_j \mathbf{q}_{n-j} - h\beta_j \mathbf{v}_{n-j}] = \mathbf{0} \tag{1.318}$$

from which the velocity at time $t_n$ is expressed in the form

$$\mathbf{v}_n = \frac{\alpha_0}{\beta_0 h} \mathbf{q}_n + \frac{1}{\beta_0 h} \sum_{j=0}^{m} [\alpha_j \mathbf{q}_{n-j} - \beta_j h \mathbf{v}_{n-j}] \tag{1.319}$$

Similarly, Eq. (1.316) allows defining the linear combination of residuals

$$\mathbf{r}^*(\mathbf{q}, \mathbf{v}) = \frac{1}{\beta_0} \sum_{j=0}^{m} \beta_j \mathbf{r}(\mathbf{q}_{n-j}, \mathbf{v}_{n-j}) = \mathbf{0}$$

or, making use of (1.316) and (1.318) applied to velocities,

$$\mathbf{r}^*(\mathbf{q}, \mathbf{v}) = \frac{1}{\beta_0 h} \sum_{j=0}^{m} [\beta_j h(\mathbf{f}_{n-j} - \mathbf{g}_{n-j}) + \alpha_j \mathbf{M} \mathbf{v}_{n-j}] = \mathbf{0} \tag{1.320}$$

The resultant tangent-iteration matrix is

$$\mathbf{S}(\mathbf{q}_n) = \frac{\partial \mathbf{r}^*}{\partial \mathbf{q}} = \left[ \frac{\partial \mathbf{f}}{\partial \mathbf{q}} - \frac{\partial \mathbf{g}}{\partial \mathbf{q}} + \left( \frac{\alpha_0}{\beta_0 h} \mathbf{M} + \frac{\partial \mathbf{f}}{\partial \mathbf{v}} \right) \frac{\partial \mathbf{v}}{\partial \mathbf{q}} \right]_{\mathbf{q}_n}$$

and, with the previous definitions (1.290), it becomes

$$\mathbf{S}_n = \left[ \mathbf{K}^t + \frac{\alpha_0}{\beta_0 h} \mathbf{C}^t + \frac{\alpha_0^2}{\beta_0^2 h^2} \mathbf{M} - \frac{\partial \mathbf{g}}{\partial \mathbf{q}} \right]_{\mathbf{q}_n} \tag{1.321}$$

In the linear case, it reduces to

$$\mathbf{S}_0 = \mathbf{K} + \frac{\alpha_0}{\beta_0 h} \mathbf{C} + \frac{\alpha_0^2}{\beta_0^2 h^2} \mathbf{M}$$

**Implementation of Implicit Multistep Methods in First-Order Form**   The implementation of implicit multistep methods is very similar to the one-step case, except that it is based on the iterative solution of the modified residual equation (1.320).

The most convenient choice of the predictor formulae to initiate the iteration process is

$$\bar{\mathbf{q}}_n = \mathbf{0}$$

$$\bar{\mathbf{v}}_n = \frac{1}{\beta_0 h} \sum_{j=1}^{m} [\alpha_j \mathbf{q}_{n-j} - \beta_j h \mathbf{v}_{n-j}]$$

and the corrections to the displacements are solutions of

$$\mathbf{S}_n \Delta \mathbf{q} = \mathbf{r}^*(\bar{\mathbf{q}}_n, \bar{\mathbf{v}}_n)$$

They are next applied to displacements and velocities in the form

$$\mathbf{q}_n = \bar{\mathbf{q}}_n + \Delta \mathbf{q}$$

$$\mathbf{v}_n = \bar{\mathbf{v}}_n + \frac{\alpha_0}{\beta_0 h} \Delta \mathbf{q}$$

The main drawback of multistep methods in comparison with one-step algorithms lies in the need to keep track of the solution at extra time instants in order to calculate the residual vector (1.320). Besides, the time-stepping procedure is not self-starting, and thus requires using a one-step scheme to initiate the procedure.

*Park's Formula* Park [104] has suggested an integration formula of type (1.315) which exhibits very interesting stability properties when applied to problems of structural dynamics. It results from the composition of Gear's two- and three-step formulas

$$\mathbf{v}_{n+1} = \frac{1}{6h} [10\mathbf{q}_{n+1} - 15\mathbf{q}_n + 6\mathbf{q}_{n-1} - \mathbf{q}_{n-2}] \tag{1.322}$$

Thus, it corresponds to the following choice of coefficients

$$\beta_0 = 6 \qquad \beta_i = 0 \qquad (i = 1, 2, 3)$$

$$\alpha_0 = +10 \qquad \alpha_1 = -15 \qquad \alpha_2 = +6 \qquad \alpha_3 = -1$$

*Stability Analysis* The stability properties of the first-order multistep methods have already been discussed in application to an undamped linear system. The stability is governed by the characteristic equations associated to the successive eigenvalues $\mu_k = \pm i\omega_k$,

$$\sum_{j=0}^{m} (\alpha_j - \beta_j h \mu_k) \lambda^{m-j} = 0 \tag{1.323}$$

and the stability boundary is calculated by Eq. (1.181). A comparison of the stability-boundary algorithms is given in Fig. 1.26. Park's is stable everywhere except in a portion of the right-hand plane. The fact that the imaginary axis is well inside the stability region of the formula provides it with excellent stability properties.

*Multistep Equations Specialized to Second-Order Systems [95, 103]* Let us use a difference equation analogous to (1.315) and with the same order of consistency to calculate

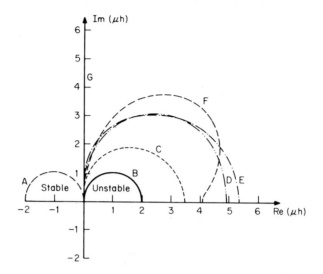

A = Explicit Euler                                           Stable inside
B = Implicit Euler
C = Park
D = Wilson, $\theta$ = 1.5                                   Unstable inside
E = Houbolt
F = Hilber-Hughes-Taylor (HHT), $\alpha$ = 0.1
G = Newmark, $\gamma = \frac{1}{2}$, $\beta = \frac{1}{4}$   Unstable in
                                                             right-hand plane

**FIG. 1.26** Comparison of stability boundaries for various algorithms in multistep forms.

accelerations:

$$\sum_{j=0}^{m} \left( \gamma_j \mathbf{q}_{n-j} - h^2 \delta_j \ddot{\mathbf{q}}_{n-j} \right) = D_{p+1} h^{p+1} \mathbf{q}^{(p+1)}(t) \tag{1.324}$$

and let us construct a linear combination of the residual equations (1.285) in the form

$$\mathbf{r}^*(\mathbf{q}) = \frac{1}{\delta_0} \sum_{j=0}^{m} \delta_j \mathbf{r}(\mathbf{q}_{n-j})$$

$$= \frac{1}{\delta_0} \sum_{j=0}^{m} \delta_j (\mathbf{M}\ddot{\mathbf{q}}_{n-j} + \mathbf{f}_{n-j} - \mathbf{g}_{n-j}) = \mathbf{0} \tag{1.325}$$

According to (1.324), accelerations are easily eliminated to yield an expression involving only displacements and, implicitly, velocities:

$$\mathbf{r}^*(\mathbf{q}) = \frac{1}{\delta_0} \sum_{j=0}^{m} \left[ \frac{\gamma_j}{h^2} \mathbf{M}\mathbf{q}_{n-j} + (\mathbf{f} - \mathbf{g})_{n-j} \right]$$

The associated tangent-iteration matrix is

$$S_n = \frac{\partial \mathbf{r}^*}{\partial \mathbf{q}_n} = \mathbf{K}^t + \left(\frac{\partial \dot{\mathbf{q}}}{\partial \mathbf{q}}\right)_n \mathbf{C}^t + \frac{\gamma_0}{\delta_0 h^2} \mathbf{M} - \left(\frac{\partial \mathbf{g}}{\partial \mathbf{q}}\right)_n$$

Use is made next of the difference equation (1.315) to calculate the velocity

$$\dot{\mathbf{q}}_n = \frac{\alpha_0}{\beta_0 h} \mathbf{q}_n + \frac{1}{\beta_0 h} \sum_{j=1}^{m} (\alpha_j \mathbf{q}_{n-j} - \beta_j h \dot{\mathbf{q}}_{n-j})$$

which gives the derivative

$$\left(\frac{\partial \dot{\mathbf{q}}}{\partial \mathbf{q}}\right)_n = \frac{\alpha_0}{\beta_0 h}$$

The final expression of the iteration matrix is

$$S_n = \left[ \mathbf{K}^t + \frac{\alpha_0}{\beta_0 h} \mathbf{C}^t + \frac{\gamma_0}{\delta_0 h^2} \mathbf{M} - \frac{\partial \mathbf{g}}{\partial \mathbf{q}} \right]_{\mathbf{q}_n} \tag{1.326}$$

The computer implementation of the iteration procedure is exactly the same as in the first-order case.

**Stability Analysis**  When applied to the undamped linear system

$$\mathbf{Kq} + \mathbf{M}\ddot{\mathbf{q}} = 0$$

the second-order approximation (1.324) leads to the stability equation

$$\sum_{j=0}^{m} (\gamma_j + \omega_k^2 h^2 \delta_j) \lambda^{m-j} = 0$$

and, in the complex plane, its stability boundary is thus given by

$$\mu h = \left( \frac{\displaystyle\sum_{j=0}^{m} \gamma_j\, e^{i(m-j)\theta}}{\displaystyle\sum_{j=0}^{m} \gamma\delta_j\, e^{i(m-j)\theta}} \right)^{1/2} \tag{1.327}$$

The formulae (1.280) and (1.327) thus allow for a comparison between first-order and second-order integration schemes from the point of view of their stability.

**Two-Step Second-Order Schemes**  The family of two-step schemes with consistency order equal to 2 (which is the minimum for second-order problems) may be written in general form as follows [95]:

$$\mathbf{q}_n - 2\mathbf{q}_{n-1} + \mathbf{q}_{n-2} - h^2 \left[ \left(\frac{1}{6} + \frac{\alpha}{2} + \phi\right)\ddot{\mathbf{q}}_n + \left(\tfrac{2}{3} - 2\phi\right)\ddot{\mathbf{q}}_{n-1} + \left(\frac{1}{6} - \frac{\alpha}{2} + \phi\right)\ddot{\mathbf{q}}_{n-2} \right] = 0 \tag{1.328}$$

$$\mathbf{q}_n(\tfrac{1}{2} + \alpha) - 2\alpha\mathbf{q}_{n-1} + \mathbf{q}_{n-2}(\alpha - \tfrac{1}{2}) - h\left[ \left(\frac{1}{6} + \frac{\alpha}{2} + \phi\right)\dot{\mathbf{q}}_n + \left(\tfrac{2}{3} - 2\phi\right)\dot{\mathbf{q}}_{n-1} + \left(\frac{1}{6} - \frac{\alpha}{2} + \phi\right)\dot{\mathbf{q}}_{n-2} \right] = 0$$
$$\tag{1.329}$$

in which case the consistency coefficients are found to be

$$C_3 = \phi \qquad D_3 = \alpha$$

The free parameters $\phi$ and $\alpha$ play the same role as the free parameters in Newmark's scheme.

As a matter of fact, it has been shown [95, 103] that Eqs. (1.328) and (1.329) are an equivalent multistep form of Newmark's schemes with the following equality between parameters:

$$\gamma = \frac{1}{2} + \alpha \qquad \beta = \frac{1}{6} + \frac{\alpha}{2} + \phi$$

Equation (1.329) thus provides a means for determining the stability boundary of Newmark's method.

### Three-Step Second-Order Schemes

*Houbolt's Method [105]* Houbolt's scheme is the best-known integration scheme pertaining to the category of second-order multistep formulas. It uses four-point backward-difference formulae for velocities and accelerations:

$$\dot{\mathbf{q}}_n = \frac{11\mathbf{q}_n - 18\mathbf{q}_{n-1} + 9\mathbf{q}_{n-2} - 2\mathbf{q}_{n-3}}{6h} \tag{1.330}$$

$$\ddot{\mathbf{q}}_n = \frac{2\mathbf{q}_n - 5\mathbf{q}_{n-1} + 4\mathbf{q}_{n-2} - \mathbf{q}_{n-3}}{h^2} \tag{1.331}$$

Thus, the solution requires the knowledge of three previous displacements but not of their derivatives. It corresponds to the general formulae (1.315) and (1.329) with the particular choices:

$$\alpha_0 = 1 \qquad \beta_0 = 6 \qquad \gamma_0 = 2 \qquad \delta_0 = 1$$

$$\alpha_1 = -18 \qquad \beta_i = 0 \quad i > 0 \qquad \gamma_1 = -5 \qquad \delta_i = 0 \quad i > 0$$

$$\alpha_2 = 9 \qquad \qquad \gamma_2 = 4$$

$$\alpha_3 = -2 \qquad \qquad \gamma_3 = -1$$

Like Park's method, Houbolt's algorithm exhibits very interesting stability properties as illustrated in Fig. 1.26. Its unstable region is fairly narrow and is contained entirely in the right-hand plane of the axis.

*Hilber–Hughes–Taylor $\alpha$-Method* The result of combining the modified residual equation (1.314) with Newmark's second-order scheme in the form (1.329) is a three-step formula with three free parameters. Although it is inefficient from a computational point of view, the three-step form of the HHT method helps to determine the stability boundary of the algorithm. Figure 1.27 shows its evolution when $\alpha$ is increased from 0.1 to 0.25.

*Wilson's $\theta$-Method* It has also been shown [103] that Wilson's $\theta$-method may be recast in the form of a three-step formula with one free parameter. The corresponding coefficients are

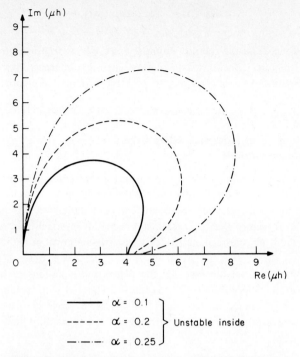

**FIG. 1.27** Stability boundaries of Hilber-Hughes-Taylor (HHT) scheme.

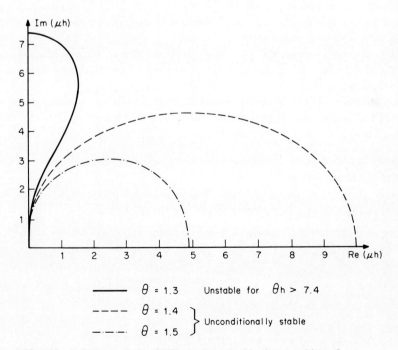

**FIG. 1.28** Stability analysis of Wilson's $\theta$-method in linear multistep form.

given in the reference, and the stability boundary of the algorithm may thus be determined from Eq. (1.327). Figure 1.28 shows its evolution when $\theta$ is increased from 1.3 to 1.5. From a computational point of view, however, the one-step form of the algorithm is much more efficient.

## 1.4E Error Control and Adaptive Step Size for Integration Formulae

Stability and accuracy requirements developed in the preceding sections demonstrate the importance of the control of error in the time-marching schemes, as well as the appropriate selection of the time-step size. Many researchers have addressed this problem, but it is recognized in the literature that no satisfactory general approach is available. Strategies implemented in the structural-response codes are mostly empirical or dedicated to particular situations.

The difficulty stems from the fact that the discretized equations of motion cannot be considered as mere ordinary differential equations integrated with variable-order formulae and truncation-error–based step-size control strategies, because of the purely oscillatory response characteristic which imposes restrictions related to stability limits.

*Explicit Formulae*   Accuracy and stability requirements govern in a concurrent manner the selection of step size for explicit formulae. Accuracy requirements dominate in the initial stage of the response when high-frequency components participate strongly, whereas stability requirements are of concern for the long-time solution when low-frequency components gradually become dominant and allow for larger time steps from the accuracy viewpoint.

Experience indicates that the truncation-error criterion cannot be used to determine stability limits in this case since it is a measure of local accuracy, whereas effective numerical instability is detected only after several tenths of steps of unstable integration (at least in linear situations).

The most reliable and efficient strategy appears to be the one based on the system-response frequency characteristics [108, 109]. It makes use of two different concepts to control stability and accuracy:

1. Stability is related to the so-called maximum perturbed apparent frequency of the multi-degree-of-freedom system

$$(\omega_a)_{max} = \max\left[(\omega_a)_1, \ldots, (\omega_a)_N\right] \tag{1.332}$$

where $(\omega_a)_i$ denotes the apparent frequencies of the individual degrees of freedom:

$$(\omega_a^2)_i \approx \frac{|\ddot{\mathbf{q}}_n - \ddot{\mathbf{q}}_{n-1}|_i}{|\mathbf{q}_n - \mathbf{q}_{n-1}|_i} \tag{1.333}$$

2. Accuracy is based on the dominant frquency calculated by

$$\omega_d = \left[\frac{\dot{\mathbf{q}}^T \mathbf{K} \dot{\mathbf{q}}}{\dot{\mathbf{q}}^T \mathbf{M} \dot{\mathbf{q}}}\right]_n^{1/2} \tag{1.334}$$

where velocities are used in the quadratic forms since they appear naturally in the explicit formula. The step size to be used is then

$$h \leqslant \min\left(\frac{c}{\omega_d}, \frac{2}{(\omega_a)_{\max}}\right) \tag{1.335}$$

where $c$ is a constant such that acceptable numerical damping and frequency distortion are achieved (e.g., 0.01 to 0.50).

Another way of looking at numerical instability is by monitoring energy balance throughout the transient response [98, 110]. Loss of energy balance is due to generation of spurious energy associated with unstable calculations and thus provides a sound way of checking the stability of an explicit calculation. This is particularly useful for nonlinear situations where instabilities may not be as obvious as in linear cases since computations can either regain stability after instability due to eigenvalue changes or dissipate locally a large amount of energy.

Energy balance can be computed as follows. Let us define

$$T_{n+1/2} = \tfrac{1}{2}\dot{\mathbf{q}}_{n+1/2}^T \mathbf{M}\dot{\mathbf{q}}_{n+1/2} \qquad T_n = \tfrac{1}{2}(T_{n-1/2} + T_{n+1/2}) \tag{1.336}$$

$$\Delta U_n = U_{n+1} - U_n = \frac{1}{2}\sum_e \int_{V_e} (\mathbf{B}_e^T)_{n+1/2}(\boldsymbol{\sigma}_n + \boldsymbol{\sigma}_{n+1})\, dV \tag{1.337}$$

$$\Delta W_n = W_{n+1} - W_n = \tfrac{1}{2}\Delta t_n \dot{\mathbf{q}}_{n+1/2}^T(\mathbf{g}_n + \mathbf{g}_{n+1}) \tag{1.338}$$

which are, respectively, the discrete values of the kinetic energy, the variations of the internal energy, and the variations of the work performed by the external forces. Hence, it is required that

$$|U_n + T_n - W_n| \leqslant \delta E \tag{1.339}$$

where $\delta$ is an appropriate tolerance and $E$ is some norm of the total energy, e.g.,

$$E = |U_n| + |T_n| + |W_n| \tag{1.340}$$

Obviously, a coherent conjugate measure of strain and stress must be used in the internal-energy computation (1.337) in nonlinear situations. Belytschko [110] suggests a $\delta$-value of 0.01 as being a suitable and realistic threshold. Satisfaction of (1.339) with $\delta$ of the order of 0.05 already suggests instabilities in the response that can lead to severe errors in nonlinear computations for parts of the mesh where numerical dissipation takes place.

***Implicit Formulae*** Error control aims mainly at accuracy for implicit formulae since the implicit way of solving the dynamic-equilibrium equations is seldom used with conditionally stable schemes. The problem of stating necessary and sufficient stability conditions is solved only in the linear case. The concept of stability for the nonlinear regime will not be discussed here; Ref. [102] contains a thorough discussion of the question. Classical stability concepts provide sufficient stability conditions in nonlinear cases if the response is accurately discretized by the time step chosen.

A variety of error-control criteria can be found in the literature; they differ by the concept on which they are based and by the cost of their implementation:

- The most reliable and clearly the most expensive error-control criterion is based on the difference between the two-half-step solution and the one-full-step solution [1].

- For small-scale problems, the residual-error criterion appears to be reliable, but since it works by evaluating the difference between the interpolated and the evaluated residual error at the midpoint, it requires one additional calculation of stiffness and damping terms per step [112].

- The criteria based on the energy balance for explicit operators are also popular and satisfy the necessary conditions for a bounded solution [98].

## 1.4F Some Special Problems and How to Deal with Them

***Starting Procedure for the Time Integration of Transient Responses***   Three distinct situations may arise for the prescribed initial conditions of a response.

**1.** The most frequent case corresponds to prescribed initial displacements and velocities [see Eq. (1.248)]; initial equilibrium is thus achieved by calculating accelerations such that

$$\mathbf{M}\ddot{\mathbf{q}}_0 = \mathbf{g}_0 - \mathbf{f}(\mathbf{q}_0, \dot{\mathbf{q}}_0) \tag{1.341}$$

This implies a standard solution in an explicit code and the solution of a linear system with the mass matrix as the system matrix in an implicit code; in the latter case, this initial-equilibrium computation is performed as the first iteration of the first time step of the response with vanishing stiffness and damping terms in the iteration matrix (1.165).

Again, solving (1.341) is trivial if the mass matrix is diagonal. This is a must in explicit programs; in implicit codes, $\mathbf{M}$ might be kept in its consistent form, in which case one uses the same elimination solution scheme as for the standard iteration matrix.

**2.** A second possible situation corresponds to establishing the dynamic response from a (given) static state of equilibrium. This is, for instance, the case for the transient response of flexible cable nets under disturbing forces. In such situations, velocities and accelerations initially vanish. The initial displacements are usually unknown and thus are solutions of a nonlinear static equation

$$\mathbf{f}(\mathbf{q}_0) = \mathbf{g}_0 \tag{1.342}$$

This cannot be dealt with in a standard explicit program, whereas implicit codes treat this problem easily as a special solution path with an iteration matrix identical to the initial tangent-stiffness matrix $\mathbf{K}_0^t$, which is eventually corrected by the dependence of external loads on the geometry, which is the last term in eq. (1.290).

**3.** The third case corresponds to the continuation of a response previously interrupted. If displacements, velocities, and accelerations are available for the last retrieved time station, restarting the analysis raises no difficulty.

***Impulsive and Step Loadings***   There are two important limiting cases of dynamic loading with steep variations in time: shock loads (impulse), and suddenly applied loads (step loading).

It is known that an impulsive loading applied to a mechanical system does not affect instantaneously either its displacement or its acceleration fields, whereas the velocity increases suddenly, as reflected by the momentum equation

$$\mathbf{M} \, \Delta\dot{\mathbf{q}} = \mathbf{p} \tag{1.343}$$

where

$$\Delta\dot{\mathbf{q}} = \dot{\mathbf{q}}_{t^+} - \dot{\mathbf{q}}_{t^-} \tag{1.344}$$

and

$$\mathbf{p} = \int_{t^-}^{t^+} \mathbf{g}(t) \, dt \tag{1.345}$$

is the momentum of the impulse.

Similarly, step loading does not instantaneously modify displacements and velocities of a system, but the acceleration varies according to the dynamic-equilibrium statement

$$\mathbf{M} \, \Delta\ddot{\mathbf{q}} = \Delta\mathbf{g} \tag{1.346}$$

where

$$\Delta\ddot{\mathbf{q}} = \ddot{\mathbf{q}}_{t^+} - \ddot{\mathbf{q}}_{t^-} \tag{1.347}$$

and

$$\Delta\mathbf{g} = \mathbf{g}(t^+) - \mathbf{g}(t^-) \tag{1.348}$$

Both particular systems (1.343) and (1.346) are treated as (1.341) by solving a linear system with the mass matrix as the system matrix. They are handled equally well by explicit or implicit codes, with the same remark regarding the lumped or consistent character of the system matrix.

The present way of treating loading discontinuities, in contrast with approximate representations such as sharp piecewise variations, remarkably does not introduce restrictions on the step size for the time integration in the vicinity of the discontinuity.

**Nonlinear Constraints**  Numerous practical problems of transient response can imply holonomic constraints on part of the degrees of freedom of a mechanical system. This is, for instance, the case for systems involving some kind of mechanism. These constraints are, in general, nonlinear, and each of them may be put in the form

$$c(\mathbf{q}, t) = 0 \tag{1.349}$$

The complete set of nonlinear equations for dynamic motion is then the set of Eq. (1.348) that may be recast in the form

$$\mathbf{M}\ddot{\mathbf{q}} = \mathbf{h}(\mathbf{q}, \dot{\mathbf{q}}, t) \tag{1.350}$$

plus $n_c$ equations like Eq. (1.349).

For each equation a virtual displacement $\delta\mathbf{q}$ will also verify the constraint so that

$$c(\mathbf{q} + \delta\mathbf{q}) = c(\mathbf{q}) + \left(\frac{\partial c}{\partial \mathbf{q}}\right)^T \delta\mathbf{q} = 0$$

and by virtue of (1.349)

$$\left(\frac{\partial c}{\partial \mathbf{q}}\right)^T \delta\mathbf{q} = 0 \tag{1.351}$$

Thus, a set of $n_c$ lagrangian multipliers $\lambda_i$ may be introduced which transforms the constraint problem into the augmented set of $n + n_c$ equations

$$\mathbf{M}\ddot{\mathbf{q}} = \mathbf{h}(\mathbf{q}, \dot{\mathbf{q}}, t) - \frac{\partial \mathbf{c}^T}{\partial \mathbf{q}} \boldsymbol{\lambda}$$

$$\mathbf{c}(\mathbf{q}, t) = \mathbf{0} \tag{1.352}$$

where $\boldsymbol{\lambda}$ and $\mathbf{c}$ collect the different multipliers and constraint statements, respectively.

At this point we have to remember that the standard way of integrating (1.352) explicitly is by predicting displacements and velocities in order to compute accelerations. Hence, the constraints themselves should be substituted for their second time derivative and the complete system with constraints should be written in the form

$$\begin{bmatrix} \mathbf{M} & \dfrac{\partial \mathbf{c}^T}{\partial \mathbf{q}} \\[2mm] \dfrac{\partial \mathbf{c}}{\partial \mathbf{q}} & \mathbf{0} \end{bmatrix} \begin{bmatrix} \ddot{\mathbf{q}} \\[1mm] \boldsymbol{\lambda} \end{bmatrix} = \begin{bmatrix} \mathbf{h}(\mathbf{q}, \dot{\mathbf{q}}, t) \\[1mm] \mathbf{s}(\mathbf{q}, \dot{\mathbf{q}}, t) \end{bmatrix} \tag{1.353}$$

where

$$\mathbf{s} = -\frac{\partial^2 \mathbf{c}}{\partial \mathbf{q}^2} \dot{\mathbf{q}}^2 - \frac{\partial^2 \mathbf{c}}{\partial \mathbf{q} \, \partial t} \dot{\mathbf{q}} - \frac{\partial^2 \mathbf{c}}{\partial t^2} \tag{1.354}$$

The effect of shift introduced by considering only the second derivative of the constraint can be limited to some extent by prescribing an oscillatory behaviour such as

$$\ddot{\mathbf{c}} + 2\mu \dot{\mathbf{c}} + \nu^2 \mathbf{c} = \mathbf{0} \tag{1.355}$$

where $\mu$ and $\nu$ are appropriate parameters (e.g., those yielding the critical damping). However, it is, in fact, more convenient to deal with such constraints in an implicit way.

Thus, system (1.352) is written

$$\mathbf{r}(\mathbf{q}, t) + \frac{\partial \mathbf{c}^T}{\partial \mathbf{q}} \boldsymbol{\lambda} = \mathbf{0}$$

$$\mathbf{c}(\mathbf{q}, t) = \mathbf{0} \tag{1.356}$$

and solved incrementally using the constraints themselves. By assuming a predicted solution $(\bar{\mathbf{q}}, \bar{\boldsymbol{\lambda}})$, an improved solution $(\bar{\mathbf{q}} + \Delta\mathbf{q}, \bar{\boldsymbol{\lambda}} + \Delta\boldsymbol{\lambda})$ is sought using the first-order approximation to (1.356):

$$\mathbf{r}(\bar{\mathbf{q}}, t) + \frac{\partial \mathbf{r}}{\partial \mathbf{q}}\bigg|_{\bar{\mathbf{q}}} \Delta\mathbf{q} + \frac{\partial \mathbf{c}^T}{\partial \mathbf{q}}\bigg|_{\bar{\mathbf{q}}} \bar{\boldsymbol{\lambda}} + \bar{\boldsymbol{\lambda}}^T \frac{\partial^2 \mathbf{c}}{\partial \mathbf{q}^2}\bigg|_{\bar{\mathbf{q}}} \Delta\mathbf{q} + \frac{\partial \mathbf{c}^T}{\partial \mathbf{q}}\bigg|_{\bar{\mathbf{q}}} \Delta\boldsymbol{\lambda} = \mathbf{0}$$

$$\mathbf{c}(\bar{\mathbf{q}}, t) + \frac{\partial \mathbf{c}}{\partial \mathbf{q}}\bigg|_{\bar{\mathbf{q}}} \Delta\mathbf{q} = \mathbf{0} \tag{1.357}$$

The correction vector $[\Delta\mathbf{q} \ \ \Delta\boldsymbol{\lambda}]^T$ is thus the solution of the augmented linear system

$$\mathbf{S}(\bar{\mathbf{q}}, \bar{\boldsymbol{\lambda}}) \begin{bmatrix} \Delta\mathbf{q} \\ \Delta\boldsymbol{\lambda} \end{bmatrix} = -\mathbf{l}(\bar{\mathbf{q}}, \bar{\boldsymbol{\lambda}}) \tag{1.358}$$

with the modified tangent-iteration matrix **S** and the extended residual vector **l**

$$S = \begin{bmatrix} \dfrac{\partial \mathbf{r}}{\partial \mathbf{q}} + \bar{\boldsymbol{\lambda}}^T \dfrac{\partial^2 \mathbf{c}}{\partial \mathbf{q}^2} & \dfrac{\partial \mathbf{c}^T}{\partial \mathbf{q}} \\[2ex] \dfrac{\partial \mathbf{c}}{\partial \mathbf{q}} & 0 \end{bmatrix} \qquad \mathbf{l} = \begin{bmatrix} \mathbf{r} + \dfrac{\partial \mathbf{c}^T}{\partial \mathbf{q}} \boldsymbol{\lambda} \\[2ex] \mathbf{c} \end{bmatrix} \qquad (1.359)$$

Hence, the implicit solution not only deals with the constraints themselves, but also treats the lagrangian multipliers as ordinary unknowns.

## 1.5 REFERENCES

1. Wilkinson, J. H., *The Algebraic Eigenvalue Problem*, Clarendon Press, Oxford, 1965.

2. Wilkinson, J. H., and C. Reinsch, *Handbook for Automatic Computation*, pt. II: *Linear Algebra*, Springer-Verlag, Berlin, 1971.

3. Schwarz, H. R., and H. Rutishauser, *Numerical Analysis of Symmetric Matrices*, English ed., Prentice-Hall, Englewood Cliffs, N.J., 1973.

4. Fadeev, D. K., and V. N. Fadeeva, *Computational Methods of Linear Algebra*, Freeman, San Francisco, 1963.

5. Ralston, A., and H. S. Wilf, *Mathematical Methods for Digital Computers*, Wiley, New York, 1967, vols. I, II.

6. Young, D. M., *Iterative Solution of Large Linear Systems*, Academic Press, London, 1971.

7. Wielandt, H., "Das Iterations Verfahren bei nicht selbstadjungierten linearen Eigenwertaufgaben," *Math. Z*, **50**:93–143 (1944).

8. Lanczos, C., "An Iterative Method for the Solution of the Eigenvalue Problem of Linear Differential and Integral Operators," *J. Res. Nat. But. Stand.*, **B45**:255–282 (1950).

9. Hestenes, M. R., and W. Karush, "A Method of Gradient for the Calculation of the Characteristic Roots and Vectors of a Real Symmetric Matrix," *J. Res. Nat. Bur. Stand.*, **47**:45–61 (1951).

10. Jennings, A., "A Direct Iteration Method of Obtaining Latent Roots and Vectors of a Symmetric Matrix," *Proc. Cambridge Philos. Soc.*, **63**:755 (1967).

11. Bronlund, O. E., "Eigenvalues of Large Matrices," *Symposium on Finite Element Techniques*, University of Stuttgart, Stuttgart, June 10–12, 1969.

12. Rutishauser, H., "Computational Aspects of F. L. Bauer's Simultaneous Iteration," *Numer. Math.*, **13**:4–13 (1969).

13. Rutishauser, H., "Simultaneous Iteration Method for Symmetric Matrices," *Numer. Math.*, **16**:205–223 (1970).

14. Clint, M., and A. Jennings, "The Evaluation of Eigenvalues and Eigenvectors of Real Symmetric Matrices by Simultaneous Iteration," *Comput. J.*, **13**(1) (1970).

15. Ojalvo, I. U., and M. Newman, "Vibration Modes of Large Structures by an Automatic Reduction Method," *AIAA J.*, **8**(7):1234–1239 (1970).

16. Martin, R. S., G. Peters, and J. H. Wilkinson, "The QR Algorithm for Real Hessenberg Matrices," *Numer. Math.*, **14**:219–231 (1970).

17. Geradin, M., "The Computational Efficiency of a New Minimization Algorithm for Eigenvalue Analysis," *J. Sound Vibration*, **19**(3) (1971).

18. Bathe, K. J., "Solution Methods for Large Generalized Eigenvalue Problems in Structural Engineering," SESM Rep. 71-20, Civ. Eng. Dept., University of California, Berkeley, 1971.

19. Golub, G. H., R. Underwood, and J. H. Wilkinson, "The Lanczos Algorithm for the Symmetric $Ax - \lambda Bx$ Problem," STAN-CS-72-270, Computer Science Dept., Stanford University, Stanford, Calif., 1972.

20. Jensen, P. S., "The Solution of Large Symmetric Eigenproblems by Sectioning," *SIAM J. Numer. Anal.*, **9**(4) (1972).

21. Gupta, K. K., "Eigenproblem Solution by a Combined Sturm Sequence and Inverse Iteration Technique," *Int. J. Numer. Meth. Eng.*, **7**:17–42 (1973).

22. Ruhe, A., "SOR Methods for the Eigenvalue Problem," Rep. UMINF-37, University of Umea, Sweden, 1973.

23. Bathe, K. J., and E. L. Wilson, "Solution Methods for Eigenvalue Problems in Structural Mechanics," *Int. J. Numer. Meth. Eng.*, **6**:213–226 (1973).

24. Corr, B. R., and A. Jennings, "Implementation of Simultaneous Iteration for Vibration Analysis," *Comput. Struct.*, **4**:497–507 (1973).

25. Geradin, M., "Analyse Dynamique Duale des Structures par la Méthode des Éléments Finis," *Coll. Publ. Fac. Sci. Appl., Liège*, **36** (1973).

26. Schwarz, H. R., "The Eigenvalue Problem $(A - \lambda B)x = 0$ for Symmetric Matrices of High Order," *Comput. Meth. Appl. Mech. Eng.*, **3**:11–28 (1974).

27. Ojalvo, I. U., "ALAPM, a Highly Efficient Eigenvalue Extraction Routine for Very Large Matrices," *Shock Vibration Dig.*, **7**(12) (1975).

28. Geradin, M., "Application of the Biorthogonal Lanczos Algorithm," LTAS Rep. VA-17, University of Liège, Liège, 1976.

29. Golub, G. H., and R. Underwood, *The Block Lanczos Method for Computing Eigenvalues*, Mathematical Software 3, Academic Press, New York, 1977, pp. 361–377.

30. Geradin, M., "On the Lanczos Method for Solving Large Structural Eigenvalue Problems," *ZAMM*, **59**:T127–129 (1979).

31. Geradin, M., and E. Carnoy, "On the Practical Use of Eigenvalue Bracketing in Finite Element Applications to Vibration and Stability Problems," Euromech 112, Hungarian Academy of Sciences, 1979, pp. 151–171.

32. Geradin, M., and E. Carnoy, "On the Practical Use of the Lanczos Algorithm in Finite Element Applications to Vibration and Bifurcation Problems," *Lecture Notes in Mathematics*, Springer-Verlag, New York, 1982.

33. Guyan, R. J., "Reduction of Stiffness and Mass Matrices," *AIAA J.*, **3**(2) (1965).

34. Irons, B. M., "Structural Eigenvalue Problems: Elimination of Unwanted Variables," *AIAA J.*, **3**(5):961–962 (1965).

35. Geradin, M., "Error Bounds for Eigenvalue Analysis by Elimination of Variables," *J. Sound Vibration*, **19**(1) (1971).

36. Hurty, W. C., "Dynamic Analysis of Structural Systems Using Component Modes," *AIAA J.*, **3**(4):678–685 (1965).

37. Craig, R., and M. Bampton, "Coupling of Substructures for Dynamic Analyses," *AIAA J.*, **6**(7):1313–1319 (1968).

38. Fraeijs de Veubeke, B., "Iteration in Semi-Definite Eigenvalue Problems," *J.A.S.*, **22**(10):710–720 (1955).

39. Craig, R., and M. C. Bampton, "On the Iterative Solution of Semi-Definite Eigenvalue Problems," *J. R. Aero. Soc.*, **75**:287–290 (1971).

40. Fraeijs de Veubeke, B., M. Geradin, and A. Huck, *Structural Dynamics*, CISM Udine, Lecture Series, no. 126, Springer-Verlag, New York, 1972.

41. Geradin, M., "Eigenvalue Analysis by Matrix Iteration in the Presence of Kinematic Modes," *Shock Vibration Dig.*, **6**(3) (1974).

42. Irons, B. M., "A Frontal Solution for Finite Element Analysis," *Int. J. Numer. Meth. Eng.*, **2**:5-32 (1970).

43. Schrem, E., "Computer Implementation of the Finite Element Procedure," *ONR Symposium*, University of Illinois, Urbana, 1971.

44. Sander, G., "Application de la Méthode des Éléments Finis à la Flexion des Plaques," *Coll. Publ. Fac. Sci. Appl.*, *Liège*, 1969.

45. Beckers, P., and G. Sander, "Improvement of the Frontal Solution Technique," LTAS Rep. SA-72, University of Liège, Liège, 1979.

46. Geradin, M., "Une Étude Comparative des Méthodes Numériques en Analyse Dynamique des Structures," ATMA, Sess. 1978, pp. 167-197.

47. Tewarson, R. P., *Sparse Matrices*, Academic Press, New York, 1973.

48. *SAMCEF Système d'Analyse des Milieux Continus par Éléments Finis*, Manuels LTAS, University of Liège, Liège.

49. Ericsson, T., and A. Ruhe, "The Spectral Transformation Lanczos Method for the Numerical Solution of Large Sparse Generalized Symmetric Eigenvalue Problems," *Math. Comput.* **35**(152) (1980).

50. Penrose, R., "A Generalized Inverse for Matrices," *Proc. Cambridge Philos. Soc.*, **51**:406-413 (1951).

51. Fraeijs de Veubeke, B., *On Frequency Shifting by Elementary Modifications of Inertia and Stiffness*, Van der Neut's Anniversary volume, Brokhuis, Rotterdam, 1972.

52. Frazer, R. A., W. J. Duncan, and A. R. Collar, *Elementary Matrices*, 1st ed., Macmillan, New York, 1947.

53. Lancaster, P., *Lambda Matrices and Vibrating Systems*, 1st ed., Pergamon Press, Toronto, 1966.

53a. Wilkinson, J. H., *The Algebraic Eigenvalue Problem*, Clarendon Press, Oxford, 1965.

54. Goult, R. J., R. F. Hoskins, J. A. Milner, and M. J. Pratt, *Computational Methods in Linear Algebra*, Wiley, New York, 1974.

55. Franklin, J. N., *Matrix Theory*, Prentice-Hall, Englewood Cliffs, N.J., 1968.

56. Palazzolo, A. B., B. P. Wang, and W. D. Pilkey, "Eigensolution Reanalysis of Rotor Dynamic Systems by the Generalized Receptance Method," *ASME J. Eng. Power*, **105**:543-550 (July 1983).

57. Bathe, K. J., *Finite Element Procedures in Engineering Analysis*, Prentice-Hall, Englewood Cliffs, N.J., 1982.

58. Atkinson, K. E., *An Introduction to Numerical Analysis*, 1st ed., Wiley, New York, 1978.

59. Hurty, W. C., and M. F. Rubinstein, *Dynamics of Structures*, Prentice-Hall, Englewood Cliffs, N.J., 1964.

60. Meirovitch, L., *Analytical Methods in Vibrations*, Macmillan, London, 1967.

61. Wolfe, M. A., *Numerical Methods for Unconstrained Optimization—An Introduction*, Van Nostrand Rheinhold, New York, 1978.

62. Pian, T. H. H., and P. Tong, "Variational Formulations of Finite Displacement Analysis," *IUTAM Symposium: High Speed Computing of Elastic Structures*, Liège, 1970, pp. 43-63.

63. Batoz, J. L., and G. Dhatt, "Incremental Displacement Algorithms for Nonlinear Problems," *Int. J. Numer. Meth. Eng.*, **14**:1262-1267 (1979).

64. Riks, E., "An Incremental Approach to the Solution of Snapping and Buckling Problems," *Int. J. Solids Struct.*, **15**:529-551 (1979).

65. Wempner, G. A., "The Application of Newton's Method to the Problem of Elastic Stability," *J. Appl. Mech.*, **39**:1060-1066 (1972).

66. Geradin, M., and C. Fleury, "Unconstrained and Linearly Constrained Minimization," in A. J. Morris (ed.), *Foundations of Structural Optimization: A Unified Approach*, Wiley, New York, 1982, chap. 8.

67. Schmidt, W. F., "Extending the Convergence Domain of the Newton–Raphson Method in Structural Analysis," *Comput. Struct.*, **9**:265–272 (1978).

68. Geradin, M., S. Idelsohn, and M. Hogge, "Computational Strategies for the Solution of Large Nonlinear Problems via Quasi-Newton Methods," *Comput. Struct.*, **13**:73–81 (1981).

69. Geradin, M., M. Hogge, and S. Idelsohn, in T. Belytschko and T. Hughes (eds.), "Implicit Finite Element Methods," *Computational Methods for Transient Analysis*, North-Holland, Amsterdam, 1983, chap. 4, pp. 417–471.

70. Fox, R. L., and E. L. Stanton, "Developments in Structural Analysis by Direct Energy Minimization," *AIAA J.*, **6**(6):1036–1042 (1968).

71. Jennings, A., and G. M. Malik, "The Solution of Sparse Linear Equations by the Conjugate Gradient Method," *Int. J. Numer. Meth. Eng.*, **12**:141–258 (1978).

72. Irons, B. M., and A. Elsawaf, "The Conjugate Newton Algorithm for Solving Finite Element Equations," in K. J. Bathe, J. T. Oden, and W. Wunderlich (eds.), *Proceedings U.S. German Symposium on Formulations and Algorithms in Finite Element Analysis*, Massachusetts Institute of Technology, Cambridge, Mass., 1977, pp. 656–672.

73. Dennis, J. E., "On Some Methods Based on Broyden's Secant: Approximation to the Hessian," F. A. Lootsma (ed.), *Numerical Methods for Nonlinear Optimization*, Academic Press, New York, 1972.

74. Dennis, J. E., and J. J. More, "Quasi-Newton Methods, Motivation and Theory," *SIAM Rev.*, **19**(1):46–89 (1977).

75. Mathies, H., and G. Strang, "The Solution of Nonlinear Finite Element Equations," *Int. J. Numer. Meth. Eng.*, **14**:1613–1626 (1979).

76. Bathe, K. J., and A. Cimento, "Some Practical Procedures for the Solution of Nonlinear Finite Element Equations," *Comput. Meth. Appl. Mech. Eng.*, **22**:59–85 (1980).

77. Geradin, M., S. Idelsohn, and M. Hogge, "Nonlinear Structural Dynamics via Newton and Quasi-Newton Methods," *Nucl. Eng. Des.*, **54**:339–348 (1980).

78. Schubert, L. K., "Modification of a Quasi-Newton Method for Nonlinear Equations with a Sparse Jacobian," *Math. Comp.*, **24**:27–30 (1970).

79. Crisfield, M. A., "Solution Procedures for Nonlinear Structural Analysis," in E. Hinton, D. R. J. Owen, and C. Taylor (eds.), *Recent Advances in Nonlinear Computational Mechanics*, Pineridge Press, Swansea, Wales, 1982, chap. 1.

80. Crisfield, M. A., "A Faster Modified Newton–Raphson Iteration," *Comput. Meth. Appl. Mech. Eng.*, **20**:267–278 (1979).

81. Argyris, J. H., "Continua and discontinua," *Proc. 1st Conf. Matrix Meth. Struct. Mech.*, Wright-Patterson Air Force Base, Ohio, 1965, pp. 11–189.

82. Haisler, W., J. Stricklin, and J. Key, "Displacement Incrementation in Nonlinear Structural Analysis by the Self-Correcting Methods," *Int. J. Numer. Meth. Eng.*, **11**:3–10 (1977).

83. Zienkiewicz, O. C., "Incremental Displacement in Nonlinear Analysis," *Int. J. Numer. Meth. Eng.*, **3**:587–588 (1971).

84. Batoz, J. L., and G. Dhatt, "Une Évaluation des Méthodes du Type Newton–Raphson Imposant l'Accroissement d'un Déplacement," Rapport Université Technologique de Compiègne, 1978.

85. Ramm, E., "The Riks–Wempner Approach—An Extension of the Displacement Control Method in Nonlinear Analyses," in E. Hinton, D. R. J. Owen, and C. Taylor (eds.), *Recent Advances in Nonlinear Computational Mechanics*, Pineridge Press, Swansea, Wales, 1982, chap. 3.

86. Belytschko, T., and T. J. R. Rughes (eds.), *Computational Methods for Transient Analysis*, Elsevier, New York, 1983.

87. Gantmatcher, F., *The Theory of Matrices*, Chelsea, New York, 1959, vol 2.

88. Lancaster, P., "Lambda-Matrices and Vibrating Systems," *Int. Ser. Mon. Pure Appl. Math.*, **94**, Pergamon Press, New York, 1966.

89. Courant, R., and D. Hilbert, *Methods of Mathematical Physics*, Interscience, New York, 1931, English ed., 1953.

90. Jensen, P. S., "Transient Analysis of Structures by Stiffly Stable Methods," *Comput. Struct.*, 4:615–626 (1974).

91. Park, K. C., "Time Integration of Structural Dynamics Equations: A Survey," *Pressure Vessels and Piping—A Decade of Progress*, American Society of Mechanical Engineers, New York, 1982, pp. 277–291.

92. Dahlquist, G. G., "A Special Stability Problem for Linear Multistep Methods," *BIT*, 3:27–43 (1963).

93. Gear, C. W., *Numerical Initial Value Problems in Ordinary Differential Equations*, Prentice-Hall, Englewood Cliffs, N.J., 1971.

94. Bathe, K. J., and E. L. Wilson, "Stability and Accuracy Analysis of Direct Integration Methods," *Int. J. Earthquake Eng. Struct. Dynam.*, 1:283–291 (1973).

95. Geradin, M., "A Classification and Discussion of Integration Operators for Transient Structural Response," AIAA Pap. 74-105, *AIAA 12th Aerospace Sciences Meeting*, Washington, D.C., Jan. 30–Feb. 1, 1974.

96. Goudreau, G. L., and R. L. Taylor, "Evaluation of Numerical Methods in Elasto-Dynamics," *Comput. Meth. Appl. Mech. Eng.*, 2:69–97 (1973).

97. Newmark, N. M., "A Method of Computation for Structural Dynamics," *J. Eng. Mech. Div.*, ASCE, 85:67–94 (1959).

98. Key, S. W., "Transient Response by Time Integration: Review of Implicit and Explicit Operators," in J. Donea (ed.), *Advanced Structural Dynamics*, Applied Science, London, 1978.

99. Geradin, M., M. Hogge, and S. Idelsohn, "Implicit Finite Element Methods," in T. Belytschko and T. Hughes (eds.), *Computational Methods for Transient Analysis*, North-Holland, Amsterdam, 1983, pp. 417–471.

100. Wilson, E. L., L. Farhoomand, and K. J. Bathe, "Nonlinear Dynamic Analysis of Complex Structures," *Earthquake Eng. Struct. Dynam.*, 1:241–252 (1973).

101. Hilber, H. M., T. J. R. Hughes, and R. L. Taylor, "Improved Numerical Dissipation for Time Integration Algorithms in Structural Dynamics," *Earthquake Eng. Struct. Dynam.*, 5:283–292 (1977).

102. Hughes, T. J. R., "Analysis of Transient Algorithms with Particular Reference to Stability Behavior," in T. Belytschko and T. J. R. Hughes (eds.), *Computational Methods for Transient Analysis*, North-Holland, Amsterdam, 1983, pp. 67–155.

103. Geradin, M., "Multistep Integration Methods for Transient Problems," *Shock Vibration Dig.*, 7(9):3–20 (1975).

104. Park, K. C., "An Improved Stiffly Stable Method for Direct Integration of Nonlinear Structural Dynamics Equations," *J. Appl. Mech.*, 42:464–470 (1975).

105. Park, K. C., "Evaluating Time Integration Methods for Nonlinear Dynamic Analysis," in T. Belytschko et al. (eds.), *Finite Element Analysis of Transient Nonlinear Structural Behavior*, ASME Appl. Mech. Symp. AMD, 14:35–58 (1975).

106. Felippa, C. A., and K. C. Park, "Direct Time Integration Methods in Nonlinear Structural Dynamics," *PENOMECH 1978 Conference*, Universität Stuttgart, Stuttgart, Aug. 30–Sept. 1, 1978.

107. Houbolt, J. C., "A Recurrence Matrix Solution for the Dynamic Response of an Elastic Aircraft," *J. Aero. Sci.*, 17:540–550 (1950).

108. Park, K. C., and P. G. Underwood, "A Variable Step Central Difference Method for Structural Dynamic Analysis: Theoretical Aspects," *Comput. Meth. Appl. Mech. Eng.*, 22:241–258 (1980).

109. Underwood, P. G., and K. C. Park, "A Variable Step Central Difference Method for Structural Dynamic Analysis: Implementation and Performance Evaluation," *Comput. Meth. Appl. Mech. Eng.*, 23:259–279 (1980).

110. Belytschko, T., "An Overview of Semi-Discretization and Time Integration Procedures," in T. Belytschko and T. J. R. Hughes (eds.), *Computational Methods for Transient Analysis*, Elsevier, New York, 1983, pp. 1–65.

111. Lindberg, B., "Error Estimates and Step Size Strategy for the Implicit Midpoint Rule with Smoothing and Extrapolation," Rep. NA-7259, Royal Institute of Technology, Stockholm, 1972.

112. Hibbit, H. D., and B. I. Karlsonn, "Analysis of Pipe Whip," Pap. 79-PVP-122, American Society of Mechanical Engineers, New York, 1979.

# CHAPTER 2
# SPECIAL ANALYSIS PROCEDURES

## 2.1 REANALYSIS

The basic objective of reanalysis methods is to compute system response as a function of design parameters without a complete structural analysis for each design modification. The usual approach is to use information about system response for an initial set of design variables to derive a reduced problem whose solution gives the response for a trial design. The resulting reduction in computing time allows repetitive analyses of large-scale finite-element models.

Modifications to the original system may be of small magnitude over a large portion of the structure, or of relatively large magnitude confined to a small portion of the structure. For computational efficiency, the former case is best treated by an approximate reanalysis technique. For accuracy, the latter case, i.e., local modifications, should be handled by an exact reanalysis method. Both approximate and exact reanalysis methods will be discussed in this chapter.

Because of the intimate connection between reanalysis of structures after modifications and structural optimization, the reanalysis technique should not only compute the modified response efficiently but also provide the design sensitivity information required in structural-optimization calculations. This sensitivity information is usually expressed in terms of derivatives of response with respect to design variables. A number of relatively recent technical papers deal exclusively with this aspect of the problem [1].

Most structural problems requiring static reanalysis involve changes in the coefficient matrix and the right-hand-side vector of a system of linear algebraic equations. For example, if the equilibrium equations are written as

$$\mathbf{Ku} = \mathbf{f} \tag{2.1}$$

where $\mathbf{K}$ is the stiffness matrix, $\mathbf{f}$ the external load vector, and $\mathbf{u}$ the vector of displacements, reanalysis methods are applied to study the variations in $\mathbf{u}$ as elements of $\mathbf{K}$ and $\mathbf{f}$ undergo changes. Reanalysis applied to frequency-response equations of the form

$$\mathbf{Z}(\omega)\mathbf{u} = \mathbf{f} \tag{2.2}$$

where $\omega$ is the excitation frequency and $\mathbf{Z}$ the impedance matrix, is also referred to as *static reanalysis* since the algebra of Eqs. (2.1) and (2.2) is similar for a fixed $\omega$. The term *dynamic reanalysis* is used when transient behavior is being investigated.

## 2.1A Static-Reanalysis Methods

The algebraic question associated with the reanalysis of systems described by Eqs. (2.1) and (2.2) asks for the change in the inverse of a matrix caused by changes in the elements of the original matrix. An early paper by Sherman and Morrison [2] provides the answer when only a single row or column of the matrix is to be modified. A generalization of this result was given by Woodbury, who derived the formula [3, 4]

$$(\mathbf{K} + \mathbf{ECF}^T)^{-1} = \mathbf{K}^{-1} - \mathbf{K}^{-1}\mathbf{E}(\mathbf{C}^{-1} + \mathbf{F}^T\mathbf{K}^{-1}\mathbf{E})^{-1}\mathbf{F}^T\mathbf{K}^{-1} \tag{2.3}$$

Another generalization was developed by Bartlett [5], who used a modification matrix of rank 1

$$\mathbf{\Delta K} = \mathbf{ab}^T \tag{2.4}$$

where $\mathbf{a}$ and $\mathbf{b}$ are $N \times 1$ and gave the result

$$(\mathbf{K} + \mathbf{ab}^T)^{-1} = \mathbf{K}^{-1} - \frac{(\mathbf{K}^{-1}\mathbf{a})(\mathbf{b}^T\mathbf{K}^{-1})}{1 + \mathbf{b}^T\mathbf{K}^{-1}\mathbf{a}} \tag{2.5}$$

Further results in this vein were introduced by Householder [6, 7].

*Exact Methods*  The purely algebraic results mentioned above serve as a basis for several exact reanalysis methods. For example, the successive-modification method developed by Kavlie and Powell [8] uses Eq. (2.5). This method treats arbitrary modifications $\mathbf{\Delta K}$ to the stiffness matrix $\mathbf{K}$ one nonzero column at a time. Let the static-equilibrium equations, before and after structural changes, be

$$\mathbf{Ku} = \mathbf{f} \tag{2.6}$$

$$(\mathbf{K} + \mathbf{\Delta K})\bar{\mathbf{u}} = \mathbf{f} \tag{2.7}$$

and consider the special case when just column $j$ of $\mathbf{\Delta K}$ is nonzero. Let $\mathbf{a}$ designate this nonzero column. Then

$$\Delta \mathbf{K} = \mathbf{a}\mathbf{b}^T \tag{2.8}$$

$$\mathbf{b}^T = [0 \quad 0 \quad \cdots \quad \underset{\underset{\text{column } j}{\uparrow}}{1} \quad \cdots \quad 0 \quad 0 \quad 0] \tag{2.9}$$

and Eq. (2.5) implies

$$(\mathbf{K} + \Delta \mathbf{K})^{-1} = \mathbf{K}^{-1} - \frac{\mathbf{K}^{-1}\mathbf{a}\mathbf{b}^T\mathbf{K}^{-1}}{1 + \mathbf{b}^T\mathbf{K}^{-1}\mathbf{a}} \tag{2.10}$$

which, in turn, gives the modified-system response $\bar{\mathbf{u}}$ in terms of the original response $\mathbf{u}$

$$\bar{\mathbf{u}} = \mathbf{u} - \frac{\mathbf{w}\mathbf{b}^T\mathbf{u}}{1 + \mathbf{b}^T\mathbf{w}} \tag{2.11}$$

where

$$\mathbf{K}\mathbf{w} = \mathbf{a} \tag{2.12}$$

If more than one column of $\mathbf{K}$ is to be modified, the procedure given above is applied successively to all the columns involved.

The direct modification method developed by Argyris et al. [9] is based on the Woodbury formula (2.3). This method is applicable to arbitrary changes in $\mathbf{K}$. To follow the computational approach, let the $N_c$ nonzero columns of $\Delta \mathbf{K}$ be placed in the columns of the $N \times N_c$ matrix $\overline{\Delta \mathbf{K}}$ and let the nonzero columns of $\Delta \mathbf{K}$ be designated by the set of ascending integers

$$j_1, j_2, \ldots, j_{N_c} \tag{2.13}$$

Then the $i^{\text{th}}$ row of the $N_c \times N$ boolean matrix $\mathbf{B}^T$ which expands $\overline{\Delta \mathbf{K}}$ into $\Delta \mathbf{K}$ has zero elements everywhere except in column $j_i$, and its $(i, j_i)$-element is 1. The stiffness modification matrix $\Delta \mathbf{K}$ is given by

$$\Delta \mathbf{K} = \overline{\Delta \mathbf{K}}\mathbf{B}^T \tag{2.14}$$

In the usual cases of structural modifications the nonzero columns of $\Delta \mathbf{K}$ are also the nonzero rows of $\Delta \mathbf{K}$. Then we may further condense $\overline{\Delta \mathbf{K}}$ into the $N_c \times N_c$ matrix $\overline{\overline{\Delta \mathbf{K}}}$ and write

$$\Delta \mathbf{K} = \mathbf{B}\overline{\overline{\Delta \mathbf{K}}}\mathbf{B}^T \tag{2.15}$$

Now, in Eq. (2.3), set

$$\mathbf{B} = \mathbf{E} \qquad \mathbf{B}^T = \mathbf{F}^T \qquad \mathbf{C} = \Delta \mathbf{K} \tag{2.16}$$

so that

$$(\mathbf{K} + \Delta \mathbf{K})^{-1} = \mathbf{K}^{-1} - \mathbf{K}^{-1}\mathbf{B}(\overline{\overline{\Delta \mathbf{K}}}^{-1} + \mathbf{B}^T\mathbf{K}^{-1}\mathbf{B})^{-1}\mathbf{B}^T\mathbf{K}^{-1} \tag{2.17}$$

The response of the modified system can then be expressed in terms of that of the original system

$$\bar{\mathbf{u}} = \mathbf{u} - (\mathbf{L}^T)^{-1}\mathbf{Z}\mathbf{Q}^{-1}(\mathbf{Q}^{-1} + \overline{\overline{\Delta \mathbf{K}}})^{-1}\overline{\overline{\Delta \mathbf{K}}}\mathbf{B}^T\mathbf{u} \tag{2.18}$$

where $\mathbf{L}$ is the lower triangular matrix in the Choleski factorization of the stiffness matrix

$$\mathbf{K} = \mathbf{L}\mathbf{L}^T \tag{2.19}$$

and

$$\mathbf{L}\mathbf{Z} = \mathbf{B} \tag{2.20}$$

$$\mathbf{Q} = \mathbf{Z}^T\mathbf{Z} \tag{2.21}$$

The pseudo-load method [10] is similar to the direct modification method. From Eqs. (2.7) and (2.14), the modified-system equations can be put into the form

$$(\mathbf{K} + \overline{\mathbf{\Delta K}}\mathbf{B}^T)\bar{\mathbf{u}} = \mathbf{f} \tag{2.22}$$

so that

$$\bar{\mathbf{u}} = \mathbf{u} - \mathbf{K}^{-1}\overline{\mathbf{\Delta K}}\mathbf{B}^T\bar{\mathbf{u}} \tag{2.23}$$

The boolean matrix $\mathbf{B}^T$ condenses $\bar{\mathbf{u}}$ to a vector containing only the coordinates that correspond to the nonzero columns of $\mathbf{\Delta K}$

$$\hat{\bar{\mathbf{u}}} = \mathbf{B}^T\bar{\mathbf{u}} \tag{2.24}$$

so that $\mathbf{u}$ has entries $u_{j_i}$, $1 \leq i \leq N_c$. Using the notation

$$\mathbf{KW} = \overline{\mathbf{\Delta K}} \tag{2.25}$$

and shifting the rows $j_i$, $1 \leq i \leq N_c$, to the top in Eq. (2.23), we see that

$$\begin{bmatrix} \hat{\bar{\mathbf{u}}} \\ \bar{\mathbf{u}}_r \end{bmatrix} = \begin{bmatrix} \hat{\mathbf{u}} \\ \mathbf{u}_r \end{bmatrix} - \begin{bmatrix} \hat{\mathbf{W}} \\ \mathbf{W}_r \end{bmatrix} \hat{\bar{\mathbf{u}}} \tag{2.26}$$

where $\hat{\bar{\mathbf{u}}}$, $\hat{\mathbf{u}}$ are $N_c \times 1$; $\bar{\mathbf{u}}_r$, $\mathbf{u}_r$ are $(N - N_c) \times 1$; $\hat{\mathbf{W}}$ is $N_c \times N_c$; and $\mathbf{W}_r$ is $(N - N_c) \times N_c$. The condensed displacement vector $\hat{\bar{\mathbf{u}}}$ can then be obtained by solving the $N_c \times N_c$ system of linear equations

$$(\mathbf{I} + \hat{\mathbf{W}})\hat{\bar{\mathbf{u}}} = \hat{\mathbf{u}} \tag{2.27}$$

where $\mathbf{I}$ is the $N_c \times N_c$ identity matrix. The remaining displacements are found by using the lower half of Eq. (2.26) once $\hat{\bar{\mathbf{u}}}$ is known

$$\bar{\mathbf{u}}_r - \mathbf{u}_r - \mathbf{W}_r\hat{\bar{\mathbf{u}}} \tag{2.28}$$

The three methods presented above are all exact in the sense that they give the same results as a complete analysis based on inversion of the modified stiffness matrix. Other exact reanalysis methods have appeared in the literature. Kirsch and Rubinstein [11] introduced several matrix-inverse adjustment methods suitable for structures modified in one isolated zone. Przemieniecki [12] used the Householder extension [6, 7] of the Woodbury formula (2.3) to reanalyze structures with local nonscattered alterations as in Ref. [11].

Some other contributions to the literature on exact static-reanalysis methods are contained in the papers by Melosh and Ruik [13]; Fenves and Erias [14]; Sack, Carpenter, and Hatch [15]; Argyris and Roy [16]; and Kosko [17].

**Approximate Methods**    Among the available techniques for approximate static reanalysis, the simplest is based on a Taylor series expansion. The elements of the stiffness matrix are functions of the design parameters denoted by $x_1, x_2, \ldots, x_s$. Thus, a truncated Taylor series can be written for the response of the modified system as

$$\bar{\mathbf{u}} = \mathbf{u} + \sum_{i=1}^{s} \frac{\partial \mathbf{u}}{\partial x_i} \Delta x_i + \sum_{\substack{i=1 \\ j=1}}^{s} \frac{\partial^2 \mathbf{u}}{\partial x_i \, \partial x_j} \Delta x_i \Delta x_j \tag{2.29}$$

where the derivatives are evaluated at the values of $x_i$ which define the original system. Differentiation of Eq. (2.1) gives

$$\frac{\partial \mathbf{u}}{\partial x_i} = -\mathbf{K}^{-1} \frac{\partial \mathbf{K}}{\partial x_i} \mathbf{u} \tag{2.30}$$

$$\frac{\partial^2 \mathbf{u}}{\partial x_i \, \partial x_j} = -\mathbf{K}^{-1} \left( \frac{\partial^2 \mathbf{K}}{\partial x_i \, \partial x_j} \mathbf{u} + \frac{\partial \mathbf{K}}{\partial x_i} \frac{\partial \mathbf{u}}{\partial x_j} + \frac{\partial \mathbf{K}}{\partial x_j} \frac{\partial \mathbf{u}}{\partial x_i} \right) \tag{2.31}$$

An example of the application of this method to a large-scale structure is given by Storaasli and Sobieszczanski [18].

Noor [19] applied the Taylor series expansion approach to the mixed method of structural analysis. When this method is used, static equilibrium is expressed by

$$\mathbf{G}\mathbf{y} = \mathbf{p} \tag{2.32}$$

where $\mathbf{G}$ is a generalized stiffness matrix, $\mathbf{y}$ is a response vector of forces and displacements, and $\mathbf{p}$ contains external loads. In this formulation, the nondiagonal elements of $\mathbf{G}$ are either linear in the design variables or constant. Consequently, the derivative matrices $\partial \mathbf{G}/\partial x_i$ are sparse and the efficiency of the reanalysis procedure is increased.

A perturbation approach given in Ref. [20] is applicable to static reanalysis. With the notation

$$\mathbf{K}_0 \mathbf{x} = \mathbf{f}_0 \tag{2.33}$$

$$\mathbf{K} = \mathbf{K}_0 + \mathbf{\Delta K} = \mathbf{K}_0 + \varepsilon \mathbf{K}_1 \tag{2.34}$$

$$\mathbf{f} = \mathbf{f}_0 + \mathbf{\Delta f} = \mathbf{f}_0 + \varepsilon \mathbf{f}_1 \tag{2.35}$$

$$\mathbf{K}\mathbf{y} = \mathbf{f} \tag{2.36}$$

the modified-system displacement vector $\mathbf{y}$ is written as a Maclaurin series in the perturbation parameter $\varepsilon$

$$\mathbf{y}(\varepsilon) = \mathbf{x} + \sum_{i=1}^{\infty} \varepsilon^i \mathbf{y}_i \tag{2.37}$$

where

$$\mathbf{K}_0 \mathbf{y}_1 = \mathbf{f}_1 - \mathbf{K}_1 \mathbf{x} \tag{2.38}$$

$$\mathbf{K}_0 \mathbf{y}_i = -\mathbf{K}_1 \mathbf{y}_{i-1} \qquad \text{for } i \geq 2 \tag{2.39}$$

A sufficient condition for convergence of this method is that any norm of $\varepsilon \mathbf{K}_0^{-1} \mathbf{K}_1$ be less than 1.

Another approximate approach to static reanalysis is the reduced-basis method. This method decreases the dimension of the system of equations to be solved by forcing the approximation to the response to lie in a selected subspace of $N$-vectors. The vector in this subspace minimizing the total potential energy is chosen to be the best approximation. Thus, restricting the displacement vector $\mathbf{u}$ to be a linear combination of $r$-vectors, $r < N$, we write

$$\mathbf{u} = \sum_{i=1}^{r} h_i \mathbf{y}_i = \mathbf{V}\mathbf{h} \tag{2.40}$$

where $\mathbf{V}$ is the $N \times r$ matrix

$$\mathbf{V} = [\mathbf{v}_1 \quad \mathbf{v}_2 \quad \mathbf{v}_r] \tag{2.41}$$

and $\mathbf{h}$ is the $r$-vector $\qquad \mathbf{h} = (h_1, h_2, \ldots, h_r)^T \tag{2.42}$

The total potential energy $E$ is given by

$$E = \tfrac{1}{2}\mathbf{u}^T \mathbf{K} \mathbf{u} - \mathbf{u}^T \mathbf{f} = \tfrac{1}{2}\mathbf{h}^T \bar{\mathbf{K}} \mathbf{h} - \mathbf{h}^T \bar{\mathbf{f}} \tag{2.43}$$

where $\bar{\mathbf{K}}$ is the $r \times r$ matrix defined by

$$\bar{\mathbf{K}} = \mathbf{V}^T \mathbf{K} \mathbf{V} \tag{2.44}$$

and $\bar{\mathbf{f}}$ is the $r$-vector $\qquad \bar{\mathbf{f}} = \mathbf{V}^T \mathbf{f} \tag{2.45}$

When the partial derivative of $E$ with respect to each $h_i$, $1 \leq i \leq r$, is set equal to zero, it is seen that

$$\bar{\mathbf{K}} \mathbf{h} = \bar{\mathbf{f}} \tag{2.46}$$

Thus, once the $r$-dimensional subspace has been selected, the reduced-basis method can proceed as follows

1. Form $\bar{\mathbf{K}}$, $\bar{\mathbf{f}}$ using Eqs. (2.44) and (2.45).
2. Solve for $\mathbf{h}$ in Eq. (2.46).
3. Compute the approximate response vector using Eq. (2.40).

In practice, the choice of an appropriate set of basis vectors presents the most serious difficulty in applying the reduced-basis method to realistic problems. An intuitively appealing, though not systematic, approach is proposed by Fox and Miura [21], who use basis vectors that are exact solutions of the equilibrium equations corresponding to typical or potential designs. Noor and Lowder [22] give a systematic approach for choosing the basis vectors $\mathbf{v}_k$, $1 \leq k \leq r$,

$$\mathbf{v}_1 = \mathbf{y}_0 \tag{2.47}$$

$$\mathbf{v}_{i+1} = \frac{\partial \mathbf{y}}{\partial x_i} \qquad i = 1, 2, \ldots, r-1 \tag{2.48}$$

where $\mathbf{y}_0$ is the displacement vector for the original structure and $\mathbf{y}$ is the displacement vector after modification. The dimension $r$ of the subspace chosen is the number $s$ of design variables plus 1. Another systematic approach, that of Sobieszczanski-Sobienski and Hajela [23], uses eigenvectors of the original-system stiffness matrix. The authors select the number of modes to be used as basis vectors according to the contribution of this set of modes to the total internal-strain energy of the original system.

Approximate reanalysis can also be carried out by iterative methods. From the equilibrium equation

$$\mathbf{K}\bar{\mathbf{u}} = \mathbf{f} - \Delta \mathbf{K}\bar{\mathbf{u}} \tag{2.49}$$

for the modified system, an iterative solution algorithm in the following recursive form is derived:

$$\mathbf{K}\bar{\mathbf{u}}^{(i)} = \mathbf{f} - \Delta\mathbf{K}\bar{\mathbf{u}}^{(i-1)} \qquad (2.50)$$

A natural starting vector is the displacement vector for the original system

$$\bar{\mathbf{u}}^0 = \mathbf{u} \qquad (2.51)$$

Noor and Lowder [22] combine the Taylor series expansion and iteration formulae. Their choice of $\bar{\mathbf{u}}^{(0)}$ is

$$\bar{\mathbf{u}}^{(0)} = \mathbf{u} + \sum_{i=1}^{s} \frac{\partial\mathbf{u}}{\partial x_i}\Delta x_i \qquad (2.52)$$

This initial vector is used to begin the iterative procedure of Eq. (2.50). Two other references on iterative methods are [24] and [25]. The latter paper gives a summary of iterative static-reanalysis methods, including Jacobi and block Gauss–Seidel iteration.

## 2.1B Free and Forced Vibration

***Eigensolution Reanalysis***   For forced vibration, the replacement of the stiffness matrix $\mathbf{K}$ with the impedance matrix $\mathbf{Z}(\omega)$ in the static-reanalysis methods of the previous section leads to frequency-response reanalysis methods. Here

$$\mathbf{Z}(\omega) = -\omega^2\mathbf{M} + i\omega\mathbf{C} + \mathbf{K} \qquad (2.53)$$

where $\mathbf{M}$ and $\mathbf{C}$ are mass and damping matrices, $i$ is the imaginary unit, and $\omega$ is the excitation frequency. One complication introduced by this replacement is that, when a broad band of frequencies is of interest, the number of static reanalyses required for each modification becomes large. Another difficulty is that, when damping is present, $\mathbf{Z}(\omega)$ is complex and all computations will normally have to be done with complex arithmetic.

The extension of static-reanalysis techniques to vibratory-system reanalysis indicated in the previous paragraph is simple and direct but sometimes cumbersome. Therefore, the eigenproblem approach is more commonly used. The undamped eigenvalue problem associated with the vibration problem defined by Eqs. (2.2) and (2.53) is

$$(\mathbf{K} - \omega^2\mathbf{M})\psi = 0 \qquad (2.54)$$

where $\psi$ is the eigenvector corresponding to the eigenvalue $\omega$. The damped eigenvalue problem, less frequently solved, can be written in the form

$$(\mathbf{K} + \lambda\mathbf{C} + \lambda^2\mathbf{M})\psi = 0 \qquad (2.55)$$

where $\mathbf{C}$ is the viscous damping matrix.

The fundamental problem in eigensolution reanalysis is to determine the eigenvalues and eigenvectors of the modified system without having to solve the $N \times N$ modified problem

$$(\mathbf{K} + \Delta\mathbf{K} - \omega^2\mathbf{M} - \omega^2\Delta\mathbf{M})\bar{\psi} = 0 \qquad (2.56)$$

or its damped counterpart in which damping-matrix elements may be modified, as can the mass and stiffness elements,

$$(\mathbf{K}+\lambda\mathbf{C}+\lambda^2\mathbf{M}+\Delta\mathbf{K}+\lambda\,\Delta\mathbf{C}+\lambda^2\,\Delta\mathbf{M})\bar{\mathbf{\psi}}=\mathbf{0} \tag{2.57}$$

Reanalysis methods usually rely upon the availability of a full solution for the eigenproperties of the original system to obtain a simpler problem, preferably of smaller dimension, whose solution approximates the eigenproperties of the modified system.

One commonly used eigensolution-reanalysis technique is the assumed-modes method. The basic approach is explained in books by Meirovitch [26], Clough and Penzien [27], Hurty and Rubinstein [28], and Bisplinghoff, Ashley, and Halfman [29]. For reanalysis, the eigenvectors of the modified system are written as a linear combination of a chosen subset of the eigenvectors of the original system. Thus, if $\mathbf{\rho}_k$, $1 \leq k \leq N$, are the original eigenvectors, the $n^{\text{th}}$ eigenvector $\mathbf{\psi}_n$ of the modified system is expressed by

$$\mathbf{\psi}_n = \sum_{i=1}^{L} \zeta_{in}\mathbf{\rho}_i \tag{2.58}$$

where $L < N$. If the original system is undamped, then the modified-system equations become

$$[\lambda_n^2(\mathbf{M}+\Delta\mathbf{M})+\lambda_n\,\Delta\mathbf{C}+\mathbf{K}+\Delta\mathbf{K}]\mathbf{\psi}_n = \mathbf{0} \tag{2.59}$$

It is convenient to rewrite Eq. (2.58) as

$$\mathbf{\psi}_n = \mathbf{\Phi}\mathbf{\zeta}_n \tag{2.60}$$

where $\mathbf{\Phi}$ is the matrix whose $k^{\text{th}}$ column is the original eigenvector $\mathbf{\rho}_k$ and $\mathbf{\zeta}_n$ is the vector whose $i^{\text{th}}$ entry is the coefficient $\zeta_{in}$ in Eq. (2.58). The orthogonality conditions for the original undamped system give

$$\mathbf{\rho}_i^T\mathbf{M}\mathbf{\rho}_j = \delta_{ij}\bar{m}_i \tag{2.61}$$

$$\mathbf{\rho}_i^T\mathbf{K}\mathbf{\rho}_j = \delta_{ij}\bar{m}_i\Omega_i^2 \tag{2.62}$$

in which $\delta_{ij}$ is the delta, $\Omega_i$ is the $i^{\text{th}}$ natural frequency, and $\bar{m}_i$ is the $i^{\text{th}}$ generalized mass. If Eq. (2.59) is multiplied by $\mathbf{\Phi}^T$ and Eqs. (2.60) to (2.62) are invoked, the following $2L \times 2L$ eigenvalue problem is obtained

$$\left(\lambda_n\begin{bmatrix} 0 & \begin{matrix}\text{diag}\,(\bar{m}_i) \\ +\mathbf{\Phi}^T\,\Delta\mathbf{M}\,\mathbf{\Phi}\end{matrix} \\ \hline \begin{matrix}\text{diag}\,(\bar{m}_i) \\ +\mathbf{\Phi}^T\,\Delta\mathbf{M}\,\mathbf{\Phi}\end{matrix} & \mathbf{\Phi}^T\,\Delta\mathbf{C}\,\mathbf{\Phi} \end{bmatrix} + \begin{bmatrix} \begin{matrix}-\text{diag}\,(\bar{m}_i) \\ -\mathbf{\Phi}^T\,\Delta\mathbf{M}\,\mathbf{\Phi}\end{matrix} & 0 \\ \hline 0 & \begin{matrix}\text{diag}\,(\bar{m}_i\Omega_i^2) \\ +\mathbf{\Phi}^T\,\Delta\mathbf{K}\,\mathbf{\Phi}\end{matrix} \end{bmatrix}\right)\begin{bmatrix}\lambda_n\mathbf{\zeta}_n \\ \hline \mathbf{\zeta}_n\end{bmatrix} = \mathbf{0} \tag{2.63}$$

Usually, the order $2L$ of the eigenvalue problem (2.63) is assumed to be much smaller than $2N$. Gunter et al. [30] have applied this method to compute the complex eigenvalues of nonconservative rotor bearings. Reference [20] gives a comparison of the assumed-modes approach with several other reanalysis methods used to solve problems dealing with elastic stability of columns.

The assumed-modes method can be applied to reanalysis problems with modification matrices of the form

$$\mu \mathbf{pq}^T \tag{2.64}$$

where $\mu$ is the modification magnitude and the vectors $\mathbf{p}$ and $\mathbf{q}$ locate the modification. This form of the modification is of practical importance. Applications have been discussed by Weissenburger [31, 32], Wilkinson [33], Pomazal [34, 35], and Hallquist [36, 37]. An extension of the basic approach by Vilmann and Snyder [38] treats line modifications such as spring line supports for a continuous member. A major advantage of modifications expressed in the form of Eq. (2.64) is that the resulting characteristic equation for the modified system, as well as the modified eigenvectors, can be written in closed form. For example, if the original system is undamped and symmetric, with stiffness and mass changes given by

$$\mathbf{\Delta K} = \mu_k \mathbf{pp}^T \tag{2.65}$$

$$\mathbf{\Delta M} = \mu_m \mathbf{pp}^T \tag{2.66}$$

then the characteristic equation for the modified system is

$$g(\omega_n) = \frac{1}{\mu_k - \mu_m \omega_n^2} + \sum_{i=1}^{L} \frac{(\boldsymbol{\varphi}_i^T \mathbf{p})^2}{\bar{m}_i(\Omega_i^2 - \omega_n^2)} = 0 \tag{2.67}$$

and the $n^{\underline{th}}$ eigenvector of the modified system is given by

$$\boldsymbol{\theta}_n = \sum_{i=1}^{L} \frac{(\boldsymbol{\varphi}_i^T \mathbf{p})}{\bar{m}_i(\Omega_i^2 - \omega_n^2)} \boldsymbol{\varphi}_i \tag{2.68}$$

The use of receptances in eigensolution reanalysis, proposed by Hirai, Yoshimura, and Takamura [39], has been developed by Wang, Palazzolo, and Pilkey [10] for initially proportionally damped systems undergoing arbitrary damping, stiffness, and mass modifications. Other applications of the approach can be found in Done and Hughes [40] and Done, Hughes, and Webby [41]. The classic reference on the use of receptances in vibration analysis is the textbook by Bishop and Johnson [42]. The receptance coefficient $G_{ij}(\omega)$ is defined to be the response at degree of freedom (DOF) $i$ due to a unit harmonic force of frequency $\omega$ applied at DOF $j$. For an undamped system

$$G_{ij}(\omega) = (\mathbf{K} - \omega^2 \mathbf{M})^{-1} = \sum_{k=1}^{N} \frac{\varphi_{ik}\varphi_{jk}}{\bar{m}_k(\Omega_k^2 - \omega^2)} \tag{2.69}$$

whenever $\omega^2 \neq \Omega_k^2$. In Eq. (2.69) $\varphi_{ik}$ is the $i^{\underline{th}}$ element of the $k^{\underline{th}}$ eigenvector $\boldsymbol{\varphi}_k$. In case damping is present the receptance matrix is given by

$$\mathbf{F}(\lambda) = [\mathbf{F}_1 \ \vdots \ \mathbf{F}_2 \ \vdots \ \cdots \ \vdots \ \mathbf{F}_N] = (\lambda^2 \mathbf{M} + \lambda \mathbf{C} + \mathbf{K})^{-1} \tag{2.70}$$

Equation (2.57) for the modified system can be rewritten as

$$(\mathbf{I}_N + \mathbf{S}(\lambda)\mathbf{F}(\lambda))\boldsymbol{\zeta} = \mathbf{0} \tag{2.71}$$

where $$\mathbf{S}(\lambda) = \lambda^2 \mathbf{\Delta M} + \lambda \mathbf{\Delta C} + \mathbf{\Delta K} \tag{2.72}$$

$$\boldsymbol{\psi} = \mathbf{F}(\lambda)\boldsymbol{\zeta} \tag{2.73}$$

and $\mathbf{I}_N$ is the $N \times N$ identity matrix. The modification matrix $\mathbf{S}(\lambda)$ is usually sparse. Let the nonzero rows (columns) of $\mathbf{S}(\lambda)$ be designated by the ascending integers $j_1, j_2, \ldots, j_p$. Then it follows from Eq. (2.71) that

$$\zeta_k = 0 \qquad k \neq j_m \qquad 1 \leq m \leq p \tag{2.74}$$

Now it is possible to condense the eigenvalue problem (2.71) and replace it by the $p \times p$ system

$$(\mathbf{I}_p + \hat{\mathbf{S}}(\lambda)\hat{\mathbf{F}}(\lambda))\hat{\boldsymbol{\zeta}} = \mathbf{0} \tag{2.75}$$

$$\hat{\mathbf{S}}(\lambda) = \lambda^2 \widehat{\Delta \mathbf{M}} + \lambda \widehat{\Delta \mathbf{C}} + \widehat{\Delta \mathbf{K}} \tag{2.76}$$

where

$$\hat{\zeta}_k = \zeta_{j_k} \qquad 1 \leq k \leq p \tag{2.77}$$

$$\widehat{\Delta M}_{m,n} = \Delta M_{j_m, j_n} \qquad 1 \leq m, n \leq p \tag{2.78}$$

$$\hat{F}_{m,n} = F_{j_m, j_n} \qquad 1 \leq m, n \leq p \tag{2.79}$$

The modified-system characteristic equation is

$$g(\lambda) = \det (\mathbf{I}_p + \hat{\mathbf{S}}(\lambda)\hat{\mathbf{F}}(\lambda)) = 0 \tag{2.80}$$

Once the condensed transformed vector $\hat{\boldsymbol{\zeta}}$ is found, the modified-system eigenvectors can be computed by

$$\boldsymbol{\psi}_n = [\mathbf{F}_{j_1} \vdots \mathbf{F}_{j_2} \vdots \cdots \vdots \mathbf{F}_{j_p}]\hat{\boldsymbol{\zeta}}_n \tag{2.81}$$

for $1 \leq n \leq N$. Note that the condensed problem (2.75) is not in the standard form of the eigenvalue problem; in fact, the presence of $\mathbf{F}(\lambda)$ makes it highly nonlinear.

Perturbation methods can also be used in eigensolution reanalysis. For example, if the modifications are small enough to justify the assumption that eigensolution changes will be of first order, then a Rayleigh's quotient [26] approximation gives

$$\omega_n^2 = \Omega_n^2 + \Delta(\Omega_n^2) = \frac{\bar{m}_n \Omega_n^2 + \boldsymbol{\varphi}_n^T \Delta \mathbf{K} \, \boldsymbol{\varphi}_n}{\bar{m}_n + \boldsymbol{\varphi}_n^T \Delta \mathbf{M} \, \boldsymbol{\varphi}_n} \tag{2.82}$$

Additional results of this kind are derived and discussed by Stetson and Palma [43], Franklin [44], Lund [45], Lancaster [46], Aubrun [47], Meirovitch and Ryland [48], and Romstad, Hutchinson, and Runge [20].

The use of the Taylor series in eigensolution reanalysis becomes possible when formulae for derivatives of the system-property matrices with respect to the design parameters are available. This approach has been applied to undamped symmetric systems by Fox and Kapoor [49]. With the normalization convention $m_n = 1$, Fox and Kapoor give the following equation for the natural frequencies of the modified system:

$$\omega_n^2 = \Omega_n^2 + \frac{\partial(\Omega_n^2)}{\partial x_1} \Delta x_1 + \cdots + \frac{\partial(\Omega_n^2)}{\partial x_s} \Delta x_s \tag{2.83}$$

$$\frac{\partial(\Omega_n^2)}{\partial x_k} = \boldsymbol{\varphi}_n^T \left( \frac{\partial \mathbf{K}}{\partial x_k} - \Omega_n^2 \frac{\partial \mathbf{M}}{\partial x_k} \right) \boldsymbol{\varphi}_n \tag{2.84}$$

where $x_k$, $1 \leq k \leq s$, are design variables and all derivatives are evaluated using their values for the initial system. The formula for the $n^{\text{th}}$ modified eigenvector is

$$\boldsymbol{\theta}_n = \boldsymbol{\varphi}_n + \frac{\partial \boldsymbol{\varphi}_n}{\partial x_1} \Delta x_1 + \cdots + \frac{\partial \boldsymbol{\varphi}_n}{\partial x_s} \Delta x_s \tag{2.85}$$

in which

$$\frac{\partial \boldsymbol{\varphi}_n}{\partial x_k} = -(\mathbf{W}_n^2 + 2\mathbf{M}\boldsymbol{\varphi}_n \boldsymbol{\varphi}_n^T \mathbf{M})^{-1} \left( \mathbf{W}_n \frac{\partial \mathbf{W}_n}{\partial x_k} + \mathbf{M}\boldsymbol{\varphi}_n \boldsymbol{\varphi}_n^T \frac{\partial \mathbf{M}}{\partial x_k} \right) \boldsymbol{\varphi}_n \tag{2.86}$$

$$\mathbf{W}_n = \Omega_n^2 \mathbf{M} - \mathbf{K} \tag{2.87}$$

$$\frac{\partial \mathbf{W}_n}{\partial x_k} = \mathbf{M} \frac{\partial (\Omega_n^2)}{\partial x_k} + \Omega_n^2 \frac{\partial \mathbf{M}}{\partial x_k} - \frac{\partial \mathbf{K}}{\partial x_k} \tag{2.88}$$

Equations (2.83) and (2.85) are first-order Taylor expansions. Rudisill [50] gives second-order formulae for symmetric undamped systems. For general damped systems, the reader is referred to Plaut [51], Rogers [52], and Garg [53].

**Transient Response**   The dynamic response of a linear damped structure is governed by the differential equations

$$\mathbf{M\ddot{u}} + \mathbf{C\dot{u}} + \mathbf{Ku} = \mathbf{f}(t) \tag{2.89}$$

Step-by-step numerical-integration methods for solving Eq. (2.89) provide algebraic formulae for response at time step $t_{k+1}$ in terms of known data for time step $t_k$ [54, 55]. Consequently, the static-reanalysis methods described above can be applied directly to step-by-step methods of integration simply by keeping the time fixed. This coupled static-reanalysis and numerical-integration scheme can become too cumbersome, however, when a large number of time steps is necessary. The modal formulation described below is an attractive alternative.

When the dynamic response is expressed by modal superposition [26, 56], the eigenproperties of the modified system appear in the formulae giving the response. Thus, the eigensolution-reanalysis methods of the previous section are applicable to time-response reanalysis. In this approach, the integration over time is separated from the effects of structural modification. Once the eigenvalues and eigenvectors of the modified system have been determined, modal superposition formulae contain them as constants and the integration over time can be carried out with any step size without further reanalysis computations.

## 2.1c Computational Aspects

The major objective of reanalysis methods is to reduce significantly the computational cost of the repeated analysis of a structure. The cost comparison is usually against the cost of a complete analysis for each modification carried out without recourse to the reanalysis methods described above. Thus, a particular reanalysis method is considered efficient when the number of arithmetic operations it requires is much lower than the number of operations in a complete analysis. The usual definition of an arithmetic operation is a multiplication or division followed by an addition or subtraction. Operation counts for standard matrix computations such as Choleski factorization, forward substitution, and back substitution are given in the textbook by Franklin [44]. Operation counts for reanalysis methods are given by relatively few authors [8, 9]. Another basis for measuring the speed and efficiency of a reanalysis method is, of course, actual computation times for complete analysis versus reanalysis for chosen test cases. Although this provides a less precise measure than an operations count, it is easier to apply and is, therefore, more commonly used.

## 2.1D Uses of Reanalysis

The most straightforward application of reanalysis methods is to parametric studies of structural response. When one or more parameters defining the system-property matrices are varied over a physically meaningful range, the resulting variation of response components of interest can be computed using the methods described above. Such studies are often not an end in themselves but are used as part of a design procedure to obtain intermediate results.

Since most practical structural-optimization techniques are interactive and require a large number of trial designs before an optimum structure emerges, reanalysis techniques are used within the repetitive-analysis portion of optimization algorithms. This application of reanalysis requires that the method chosen be able to provide the design sensitivity information [1] needed in optimization in addition to the modified-response data.

Another area of application for reanalysis methods is modification of the mathematical model to match test data. If experimental data are available for an existing structure and the mathematical modeling is believed to be deficient for certain parts of the system, the data for those parts can be repetitively modified until test data are closely matched by the model.

Finally, some design problems may be solved as inverse-reanalysis problems. The design may require certain responses to certain excitation inputs, and the question is to find what modifications to an initial design will give the desired characteristics. This question may sometimes be answered by observing the response for a number of possible modifications. In more complex situations, the approach may become indistinguishable from optimization. The goal of design may also be to construct a system with prescribed eigenvectors and eigenvalues. More information on prescribed eigensolution design is given in [10, 43, 45, 57].

## 2.2 MODAL SYNTHESIS

Major components of large and complex structures are often designed (and produced) by several different organizations. When data for these substructures of the complete system are available, the determination of the characteristics of the system is a task for the vibration analyst. In some instances, the system may have so many degrees of freedom that the structure is artificially subdivided into components and analysis is done on these components to obtain results for the full system. Finally, the design analysis of the structure may reach a stage which requires only a few substructures to be modified, while the rest of the system retains fixed properties. In all these types of analysis, methods of modal synthesis have been found very useful. These methods provide practical ways of computing modal data for the system from component modal information.

Since the publication of the pioneering work by Hurty [56] in 1960, on a generalized component-mode synthesis method, many variations of the method have appeared in the literature. Some of these will be described in the following sections. A number of others can be found in the references.

To simplify the notation, the description will be for a system made up of two components. In practice, the method is applied with any number of components coupled together. In addition, only undamped systems are treated here. Most of the available literature deals with such systems, but several methods have been developed for systems with damping [57, 58].

## 2.2A Selection of Component Modes

In this section, the various types of component modes commonly used in modal synthesis will be defined. Component normal modes, obtained by solving the eigenvalue problem

$$(\mathbf{K} - \omega^2 \mathbf{M})\boldsymbol{\psi} = \mathbf{0} \tag{2.90}$$

are called *fixed-interface*, *free-interface*, or *hybrid-interface* normal modes, depending on whether all, none, or some of the interface coordinates are assumed to be fixed in space. It is convenient to normalize these eigenvectors with respect to the mass matrix $\mathbf{M}$ so that

$$\boldsymbol{\Phi}^T \mathbf{M} \boldsymbol{\Phi} = \mathbf{I} \tag{2.91}$$

$$\boldsymbol{\Phi}^T \mathbf{K} \boldsymbol{\Phi} = \text{diag}\,(\omega_r^2) \tag{2.92}$$

where $\boldsymbol{\Phi}$ is a matrix whose columns are component normal modes. The complete normal-mode set is usually truncated to a set of $k$ normal modes, $k < n$.

If the physical displacement vector $\mathbf{u}$ is partitioned into two parts, one containing a set of coordinates denoted by $C$ (the constraint set), and the other containing the remaining set of coordinates denoted by $R$, then the statics of the structure can be cast into the form

$$\begin{bmatrix} \mathbf{K}_{RR} & \mathbf{K}_{RC} \\ \mathbf{K}_{CR} & \mathbf{K}_{CC} \end{bmatrix} \begin{bmatrix} \mathbf{u}_R \\ \mathbf{u}_C \end{bmatrix} = \begin{bmatrix} \mathbf{f}_R \\ \mathbf{f}_C \end{bmatrix} \tag{2.93}$$

A *constraint mode* is defined as the static-displacement vector resulting from the unit static displacement of one coordinate in the set $C$ while all remaining coordinates in the set $C$ are fixed. In terms of the partitions in Eq. (2.93), the constraint-mode matrix, i.e., the matrix whose columns are the constraint modes, is given by

$$\boldsymbol{\psi}_C = \begin{bmatrix} \mathbf{K}_{RR}^{-1} & \mathbf{K}_{RC} \\ & \mathbf{I}_{CC} \end{bmatrix} \tag{2.94}$$

where $\mathbf{I}_{CC}$ is the identity matrix with an order equal to the number of elements of $C$. The set $C$ must be such that rigid-body motion is prevented and $\mathbf{K}_{RR}$ is invertible.

An *attachment mode* is defined as the static deflection of the component resulting from the application of a unit force at one coordinate in a set $A$ of coordinates (attachment set), while the remaining coordinates in $A$ are force-free. If $S$ denotes the set of coordinates not in $A$, then, in the absence of rigid-body motion, the attachment modes are the columns of the flexibility matrix $\mathbf{G} = \mathbf{K}^{-1}$ and the attachment mode matrix $\boldsymbol{\psi}_A$ is given by

$$\boldsymbol{\psi}_A = \begin{bmatrix} \mathbf{G}_{SA} \\ \mathbf{G}_{AA} \end{bmatrix} \tag{2.95}$$

In case rigid-body modes are present, the coordinates may be partitioned into three sets, $R$, $A$, and $S$, where $R$ is a statically determinate constraint set which restrains the body against rigid-body motion, $A$ is the set of coordinates to which unit forces are to be applied to obtain the attachment modes, and $S$ is the set of coordinates not in $A$ or $R$. Then the attachment modes are defined by

$$\begin{bmatrix} \mathbf{K}_{SS} & \mathbf{K}_{SA} & \mathbf{K}_{SR} \\ \mathbf{K}_{AS} & \mathbf{K}_{AA} & \mathbf{K}_{AR} \\ \mathbf{K}_{RS} & \mathbf{K}_{RA} & \mathbf{K}_{RR} \end{bmatrix} \begin{bmatrix} \boldsymbol{\psi}_{SA} \\ \boldsymbol{\psi}_{AA} \\ \mathbf{O}_{RA} \end{bmatrix} = \begin{bmatrix} \mathbf{O}_{SA} \\ \mathbf{I}_{AA} \\ \mathbf{f}_{RA} \end{bmatrix} \tag{2.96}$$

so that
$$\boldsymbol{\psi}_A = \begin{bmatrix} \boldsymbol{\psi}_{SA} \\ \boldsymbol{\psi}_{AA} \\ \mathbf{O}_{RA} \end{bmatrix} = \begin{bmatrix} -\mathbf{K}_{SS}^{-1}\mathbf{K}_{SA}(\mathbf{K}_{AA} - \mathbf{K}_{AS}\mathbf{K}_{SS}^{-1}\mathbf{K}_{SA})^{-1} \\ (\mathbf{K}_{AA} - \mathbf{K}_{AS}\mathbf{K}_{SS}^{-1}\mathbf{K}_{SA})^{-1} \\ \mathbf{O}_{RA} \end{bmatrix} \tag{2.97}$$

Another set of attachment modes, called *inertia-relief modes*, has been defined and used by MacNeal [59] and Rubin [60] for components with rigid-body freedom. Inertia-relief modes are obtained by applying the load $\mathbf{f}'$ to the component, where $\mathbf{f}'$ is defined by

$$\mathbf{f}' = \mathbf{f} - \mathbf{M}\ddot{\mathbf{u}}_R \tag{2.98}$$

in which $\mathbf{f}$ is the external force and $\mathbf{u}_r$ is the vector of rigid-body displacements due to $\mathbf{f}$. Thus, $\mathbf{u}_R$ can be written as a linear combination of rigid-body modes,

$$\mathbf{u}_R = \boldsymbol{\psi}_R \mathbf{q} \tag{2.99}$$

and the differential equation for the rigid-body displacements due to $\mathbf{f}$ is

$$\boldsymbol{\psi}_R^T \mathbf{M} \boldsymbol{\psi}_R \ddot{\mathbf{q}} = \boldsymbol{\psi}_R^T \mathbf{f} \tag{2.100}$$

If the rigid-body modes $\boldsymbol{\psi}_R$ are normalized so that

$$\boldsymbol{\psi}_R^T \mathbf{M} \boldsymbol{\psi}_R = \mathbf{I} \tag{2.101}$$

then
$$\mathbf{f}' = \mathbf{f} - \mathbf{M}\boldsymbol{\psi}_R \boldsymbol{\psi}_R^T \mathbf{f} = \mathbf{P}\mathbf{f} \tag{2.102}$$

The equation defining the attachment modes $\bar{\boldsymbol{\psi}}_A$ is obtained from Eq. (2.96) by replacing the right-hand side by $\mathbf{f}'$:

$$\begin{bmatrix} \mathbf{K}_{SS} & \mathbf{K}_{SA} & \mathbf{K}_{SR} \\ \mathbf{K}_{AS} & \mathbf{K}_{AA} & \mathbf{K}_{AR} \\ \mathbf{K}_{RS} & \mathbf{K}_{RA} & \mathbf{K}_{RR} \end{bmatrix} \begin{bmatrix} \bar{\boldsymbol{\psi}}_{SA} \\ \bar{\boldsymbol{\psi}}_{AA} \\ \mathbf{O}_{RA} \end{bmatrix} = \begin{bmatrix} \mathbf{P}_{SS} & \mathbf{P}_{SA} & \mathbf{P}_{SR} \\ \mathbf{P}_{AS} & \mathbf{P}_{AA} & \mathbf{P}_{AR} \\ \mathbf{P}_{RS} & \mathbf{P}_{RA} & \mathbf{P}_{RR} \end{bmatrix} \begin{bmatrix} \mathbf{O}_{SA} \\ \mathbf{I}_{AA} \\ \mathbf{O}_{RA} \end{bmatrix} \tag{2.103}$$

The attachment modes $\bar{\boldsymbol{\psi}}_A$ differ from the desired modes $\boldsymbol{\psi}_A$ by certain rigid-body displacements. $\boldsymbol{\psi}_A$ can therefore be written as

$$\boldsymbol{\psi}_A = \bar{\boldsymbol{\psi}}_A + \boldsymbol{\psi}_R \mathbf{C}_R \tag{2.104}$$

The requirement that $\boldsymbol{\psi}_A$ be free of rigid-body contributions is met if $\boldsymbol{\psi}_A$ is orthogonal to the rigid-body modes, i.e.,

$$\boldsymbol{\psi}_R^T \mathbf{M}(\bar{\boldsymbol{\psi}}_A + \boldsymbol{\psi}_R \mathbf{C}_R) = 0 \tag{2.105}$$

When Eq. (2.105) is solved for $\mathbf{C}_R$ and the result substituted in Eq. (2.104), it is seen that

$$\boldsymbol{\psi}_A = (\mathbf{I} - \boldsymbol{\psi}_R \boldsymbol{\psi}_R^T \mathbf{M})\bar{\boldsymbol{\psi}}_A \tag{2.106}$$

or, since the matrix in the parentheses is $\mathbf{P}^T$,

$$\boldsymbol{\psi}_A = \mathbf{P}^T \bar{\boldsymbol{\psi}}_A \tag{2.107}$$

If we define a special flexibility matrix $\mathbf{G}_C$ such that

$$\bar{\boldsymbol{\psi}}_A = \mathbf{G}_C \mathbf{P} \mathbf{F}_A \tag{2.108}$$

where $\mathbf{F}_A$ is the matrix on the right-hand side of Eq. (2.103), then Eq. (2.107) can be put into the form

$$\boldsymbol{\psi}_A = \mathbf{P}^T \mathbf{G}_C \mathbf{P} \mathbf{F}_A \tag{2.109}$$

The attachment modes defined by Eq. (2.107) or Eq. (2.109) are referred to as *inertia-relief attachment modes*. The motivation for introducing these modes is their use with the mode-acceleration methods [56, 60] to improve convergence.

## 2.2B  A Generalized Modal-Synthesis Method

All methods of modal synthesis are conceptually similar, but differ in the types of component modes used. The common goal of these methods is to provide an accurate representation of system dynamics with the fewest number of substructure modes. Some methods are more suitable for certain applications than others, but no one approach is generally preferred over another. In this section, a generalized modal-synthesis formulation applicable to undamped free vibration is presented for systems with no rigid-body modes. This general procedure illustrates the basic philosophy of modal synthesis and can be extended to damped structures or to forced-vibration problems. The specialized formulations that are normally used in practice will be described briefly in the next section.

The system discussed is made up of two components, designated by superscripts 1 and 2, which share certain interface coordinates. If the displacement vectors $\mathbf{u}^1$ and $\mathbf{u}^2$ of the components are measured in the same frame of reference, then the physical displacements at the interface (junction coordinates) are related by

$$\mathbf{u}_J^1 = \mathbf{u}_J^2 \tag{2.110}$$

and the interface forces are equal and opposite:

$$\mathbf{f}_J^1 + \mathbf{f}_J^2 = \mathbf{0} \tag{2.111}$$

The displacement vectors $\mathbf{u}^k$ are written as linear combinations of preselected component modes $\boldsymbol{\psi}^k$

$$\mathbf{u}^k = \boldsymbol{\psi}^k \mathbf{p}^k \qquad k = 1, 2 \tag{2.112}$$

where $\boldsymbol{\psi}^k$ contains the kinds of modes defined in the previous section or other kinds that may be defined to suit the needs of the application at hand. The generalized coordinates $\mathbf{p}^k$ are functions of time.

The constraint equations (2.110) make the generalized coordinates a dependent set, and, therefore, it is convenient to derive the system equations of motion using Lagrange's equations with undetermined multipliers. The total kinetic energy $T$ and the total potential energy are given by

$$T = \tfrac{1}{2}\dot{\mathbf{p}}^{1^T} \bar{\mathbf{M}}^1 \dot{\mathbf{p}}^1 + \tfrac{1}{2}\dot{\mathbf{p}}^{2^T} \bar{\mathbf{M}}^2 \dot{\mathbf{p}}^2 \tag{2.113}$$

$$V = \tfrac{1}{2}\mathbf{p}^{1^T} \bar{\mathbf{K}}^1 \mathbf{p}^1 + \tfrac{1}{2}\mathbf{p}^{2^T} \bar{\mathbf{K}}^2 \mathbf{p}^2 \tag{2.114}$$

where

$$\bar{\mathbf{M}}^k = \boldsymbol{\psi}^{k^T} \mathbf{M}^k \boldsymbol{\psi}^k \qquad k = 1, 2 \tag{2.115}$$

$$\bar{\mathbf{K}}^k = \boldsymbol{\psi}^{k^T} \mathbf{K}^k \boldsymbol{\psi}^k \qquad k = 1, 2 \tag{2.116}$$

With the definitions

$$\bar{\mathbf{M}} = \begin{bmatrix} \bar{\mathbf{M}}^1 & 0 \\ 0 & \bar{\mathbf{M}}^2 \end{bmatrix} \tag{2.117}$$

$$\bar{\mathbf{K}} = \begin{bmatrix} \bar{\mathbf{K}}^1 & 0 \\ 0 & \bar{\mathbf{K}}^2 \end{bmatrix} \tag{2.118}$$

$$\mathbf{p} = \begin{bmatrix} \mathbf{p}^1 \\ \mathbf{p}^2 \end{bmatrix} \tag{2.119}$$

it is possible to rewrite Eqs. (2.113) and (2.114) in the compact form

$$T = \tfrac{1}{2}\dot{\mathbf{p}}^T \bar{\mathbf{M}} \dot{\mathbf{p}} \tag{2.120}$$

$$V = \tfrac{1}{2}\mathbf{p}^T \bar{\mathbf{K}} \mathbf{p} \tag{2.121}$$

The constraint equations (2.110) can be written in matrix form in terms of the generalized coordinates $\mathbf{p}$

$$\mathbf{Hp} = 0 \tag{2.122}$$

The lagrangian for the system is

$$L = T - V + \boldsymbol{\alpha}^T \mathbf{Hp} \tag{2.123}$$

where $\boldsymbol{\alpha}$ is a vector of Lagrange multipliers. For the free-vibration problem, forces are exerted at the component interfaces, so that the virtual work $\delta W$ vanishes,

$$\delta W = (\delta \mathbf{u}_j^1)^T \mathbf{f}_j^1 + (\delta \mathbf{u}_j^2)^T \mathbf{f}_j^2 = (\delta \mathbf{u}_j^1)^T (\mathbf{f}_j^1 + \mathbf{f}_j^2) = 0 \tag{2.124}$$

where Eqs. (2.110) and (2.111) have been used. Thus, Lagrange's equations take the form

$$\frac{d}{dt}\frac{\partial L}{\partial \dot{z}_i} - \frac{\partial L}{\partial z_i} = 0 \tag{2.125}$$

where $z_i$ is either $p_i$ or $\alpha_i$. Combining Eqs. (2.120), (2.121), (2.123), and (2.125), we obtain the system equations of motion

$$\bar{\mathbf{M}}\ddot{\mathbf{p}} + \bar{\mathbf{K}}\mathbf{p} = \mathbf{H}^T\boldsymbol{\alpha} \qquad (2.126)$$

which are to be solved subject to the constraints imposed on the $\mathbf{p}_k$ by Eq. (2.122). The order of Eq. (2.126) is equal to the total number of modes kept in the linear combination (2.112). But this equation is written in terms of the coordinates $\mathbf{p}_i$, which contain a certain number of redundant elements. This redundancy is expressed by Eq. (2.122). If the vector $\mathbf{p}$ has dimension $m$ and there are $c$ constraints, then the number of independent generalized coordinates is $n = m - c$, where $n$ is the total number of degrees of freedom of the composite-system model. Let $\mathbf{q}$ denote the $n$-vector of independent coordinates. Then the relation between $\mathbf{p}$ and $\mathbf{q}$ can be expressed by

$$\mathbf{p} = \mathbf{S}\mathbf{q} \qquad (2.127)$$

where $\mathbf{S}$ is an $m \times n$ transformation matrix which depends on the constraints of Eqs. (2.122). Then Eq. (2.126) is transformed into equations governing the behavior of $\mathbf{q}(t)$,

$$\hat{\mathbf{M}}\ddot{\mathbf{q}} + \hat{\mathbf{K}}\mathbf{q} = \mathbf{S}^T\mathbf{H}^T\boldsymbol{\alpha} \qquad (2.128)$$

where
$$\hat{\mathbf{M}} = \mathbf{S}^T\bar{\mathbf{M}}\mathbf{S} \qquad (2.129)$$

$$\hat{\mathbf{K}} = \mathbf{S}^T\bar{\mathbf{K}}\mathbf{S} \qquad (2.130)$$

To determine the transformation matrix $\mathbf{S}$, let the $c \times m$ constraint matrix $\mathbf{H}$ be partitioned as follows:

$$\mathbf{H} = [\mathbf{H}_1 \; \vdots \; \mathbf{H}_2] \qquad (2.131)$$

where $\mathbf{H}_1$ is $n \times c$ and $\mathbf{H}_2$ is $c \times c$, so that Eq. (2.122) can be written as

$$\mathbf{H}_1\mathbf{q} + \mathbf{H}_2\mathbf{p}_d = \mathbf{0} \qquad (2.132)$$

where $\mathbf{p}_d$ is the $c$-dimensional vector of dependent coordinates in the vector $\mathbf{p}$. Thus, a partition of $\mathbf{p}$ is given by

$$\mathbf{P} = \begin{bmatrix} \mathbf{q} \\ \mathbf{p}_d \end{bmatrix} \qquad (2.133)$$

Since the $p_{di}$ are linear combinations of the $q_k$, the matrix $\mathbf{H}_2$ must be invertible. Hence,

$$\mathbf{p}_d = -\mathbf{H}_2^{-1}\mathbf{H}_1\mathbf{q} \qquad (2.134)$$

$$\mathbf{P} = \begin{bmatrix} \mathbf{q} \\ \mathbf{p}_d \end{bmatrix} = \begin{bmatrix} \mathbf{I} \\ -\mathbf{H}_2^{-1}\mathbf{H}_1 \end{bmatrix}\mathbf{q} \qquad (2.135)$$

and therefore the transformation matrix $\mathbf{S}$ is

$$\mathbf{S} = \begin{bmatrix} \mathbf{I} \\ -\mathbf{H}_2^{-1}\mathbf{H}_1 \end{bmatrix} \qquad (2.136)$$

It follows that $\mathbf{HS} = \mathbf{0}$ and Eq. (2.128) becomes

$$\hat{\mathbf{M}}\ddot{\mathbf{q}} + \hat{\mathbf{K}}\mathbf{q} = \mathbf{0} \tag{2.137}$$

Equation (2.137) is the desired system equation of motion for undamped free vibration. The associated eigenvalue problem is

$$(-\omega^2\hat{\mathbf{M}} + \hat{\mathbf{K}})\hat{\boldsymbol{\psi}} = \mathbf{0} \tag{2.138}$$

where $\omega$ is the natural frequency corresponding to the eigenvector $\hat{\boldsymbol{\psi}}$. This eigenvector is transformed to match the original generalized coordinate vector $\mathbf{p}$ by multiplying it by the matrix $\mathbf{S}$:

$$\boldsymbol{\psi} = \mathbf{S}\hat{\boldsymbol{\psi}} \tag{2.139}$$

The extension of this formulation to damped systems undergoing forced vibration is, in principle, straightforward. Instead of Eq. (2.137), we obtain

$$\hat{\mathbf{M}}\ddot{\mathbf{q}} + \hat{\mathbf{C}}\dot{\mathbf{q}} + \hat{\mathbf{K}}\mathbf{q} = \mathbf{f} \tag{2.140}$$

where $\hat{\mathbf{C}}$ is the viscous damping matrix given by

$$\hat{\mathbf{C}} = \mathbf{S}^T\bar{\mathbf{C}}\mathbf{S} \tag{2.141}$$

and $\mathbf{f}$ is a forcing function. Equation (2.140) may be solved directly for $\mathbf{q}$, or the associated eigenvalue problem may be solved for the (complex-) system modes.

## 2.2c Some Particular Formulations

In this section, some of the more commonly used modal-synthesis methods are briefly reviewed. A large number of references are cited so that the reader may find the details necessary to use these methods in specific applications.

***Hurty's Method***   The original approach of Hurty [56, 61–63] is applicable to redundantly connected complex structures. In this method, component modes are determined by fixing all interface coordinates of the component under consideration. The motion of each component is expressed as a linear combination of rigid-body modes, fixed-constraint elastic-vibration modes, and redundant constraint modes. These fixed-constraint modes are well-conditioned so that truncation error due to omission of higher modes is minimal, but the constraint modes introduce additional computational complexity. In addition, when a large number of interface coordinates is required, the order of the eigenvalue problem is also large. Hurty's method is one of the simplest of all modal-synthesis methods and has good convergence properties. Hurty has derived a measure of eigenvalue error based on a linear perturbation of the initial solution.

***The Craig–Bampton Method***   The Craig–Bampton method [64] differs only slightly from Hurty's method and gives the same numerical results. The authors dispense with the separate identification of rigid-body modes in the synthesis process and treat all constraints as boundary constraints. A comparison of this method with other synthesis methods is given in Refs. [65, 66]. A numerical example can be found in Ref. [64]. Bajan and Feng [67] describe a similar modification of Hurty's method.

**Method Using Free–Free Component Modes** Goldman [68] presents a method which uses only the rigid-body and normal modes to solve the interconnection problem. The normal modes are of the free–free vibration type rather than of Hurty's fixed-constraint type, so that the need for the separate constraint analysis used by Hurty is obviated. This may, however, introduce some ill-conditioning and convergence problems. The method requires a certain amount of good judgment on the part of the analyst. In particular, the number and range of the mode shapes and frequencies for each component have to be selected such that they contain the necessary properties to allow accurate synthesis of the modes of the composite structure. Hou [69] develops another method using free–free component modes. The connection problem requires a specific selection of as many component modes as there are connections. Because an improper selection of component modes may lead to ill-conditioning problems with this method, success depends on good judgment in this selection.

**Component-Mode Substitution Method** The method of Benfield and Hruda [10] uses either constrained or free–free component modes. It does not require that the coordinates of the static-constraint modes appear in the final analysis of the system modes. This results in considerable savings in computational effort for structures with a large number of interface coordinates. To describe the method, consider two components $a$ and $b$ sharing an interface. Let $\hat{\mathbf{q}}_a$, $\hat{\mathbf{q}}_b$ denote the interior coordinates, and $\bar{\mathbf{q}}_a$, $\bar{\mathbf{q}}_b$ the interface coordinates belonging to components $a$ and $b$, respectively. Then the component-displacement vectors are

$$\mathbf{q}_a^T = [\bar{\mathbf{q}}_a^T \ \vdots \ \hat{\mathbf{q}}_a^T] \tag{2.142}$$

$$\mathbf{q}_b^T = [\bar{\mathbf{q}}_b^T \ \vdots \ \hat{\mathbf{q}}_b^T] \tag{2.143}$$

Let the associated force vectors be denoted by $\bar{\mathbf{f}}_a$, $\hat{\mathbf{f}}_a$, $\bar{\mathbf{f}}_b$, $\hat{\mathbf{f}}_b$:

$$\mathbf{f}_a^T = [\bar{\mathbf{f}}_a^T \ \vdots \ \hat{\mathbf{f}}_a^T] \quad \text{and} \quad \mathbf{f}_b^T = [\bar{\mathbf{f}}_b^T \ \vdots \ \hat{\mathbf{f}}_b^T] \tag{2.144}$$

The static relationship between the forces and the displacements for component $b$ may be written using a stiffness matrix $\mathbf{K}_b$ as

$$\mathbf{f}_b = \mathbf{K}_b \mathbf{q}_b \tag{2.145}$$

Let the coordinates of component $b$ be partitioned into two sets, one set consisting of interface coordinates connecting it to component $a$ and the other set consisting of coordinates interior to component $b$. In partitioned form, Eq. (2.145) becomes

$$\begin{bmatrix} \bar{\mathbf{f}}_b \\ \hat{\mathbf{f}}_b \end{bmatrix} = \begin{bmatrix} \mathbf{K}_{JJ}^b & \mathbf{K}_{JI}^b \\ \mathbf{K}_{IJ}^b & \mathbf{K}_{II}^b \end{bmatrix} \begin{bmatrix} \bar{\mathbf{q}}_b \\ \hat{\mathbf{q}}_b \end{bmatrix} \tag{2.146}$$

The interface-loaded component modes are interior displacements of the component due to the displacements of its interface coordinates. Thus, no external forces act at the interior coordinates:

$$\hat{\mathbf{f}}_b = \mathbf{0} \tag{2.147}$$

Then the constrained interior displacement of component $b$, denoted $\hat{\mathbf{q}}_{cb}$ is given by

$$\hat{\mathbf{q}}_{cb} = \mathbf{T}_{cb}\bar{\mathbf{q}}_c = -(\mathbf{K}_{II}^b)^{-1}\mathbf{K}_{IJ}^b\bar{\mathbf{q}}_b \tag{2.148}$$

Thus
$$\mathbf{q}_b = \mathbf{T}_{rb}\bar{\mathbf{q}}_b = \begin{bmatrix} \mathbf{I} \\ \mathbf{T}_{cb} \end{bmatrix}\bar{\mathbf{q}}_b \tag{2.149}$$

The potential energy of component $b$ is

$$V_b = \tfrac{1}{2}\mathbf{q}_b^T\mathbf{K}_b\mathbf{q}_b \tag{2.150}$$

so that the potential energy corresponding to the constrained displacements given by Eq. (2.149) takes the form

$$V_{bc} = \tfrac{1}{2}\bar{\mathbf{q}}_b^T\bar{\mathbf{K}}_b\bar{\mathbf{q}}_b \tag{2.151}$$

where
$$\bar{\mathbf{K}}_b = \mathbf{T}_{rb}^T\mathbf{K}_b\mathbf{T}_{rb} \tag{2.152}$$

is called the *reduced stiffness matrix*. Similarly, the kinetic energy of component $b$ is

$$T_b = \tfrac{1}{2}\dot{\mathbf{q}}_b^T\mathbf{M}_b\dot{\mathbf{q}}_b \tag{2.153}$$

so that the constrained kinetic energy can be expressed as

$$T_{bc} = \tfrac{1}{2}\dot{\bar{\mathbf{q}}}_b^T\bar{\mathbf{M}}_b\dot{\bar{\mathbf{q}}}_b \tag{2.154}$$

where
$$\bar{\mathbf{M}}_b = \mathbf{T}_{rb}^T\mathbf{M}_b\mathbf{T}_{rb} \tag{2.155}$$

is called the *reduced mass matrix*.

Since components $a$ and $b$ are coupled together, the interface coordinates of component $b$ are identical to the corresponding interface coordinates of component $a$:

$$\bar{\mathbf{q}}_b = \bar{\mathbf{q}}_a \tag{2.156}$$

which may be rewritten
$$\bar{\mathbf{q}}_b = \mathbf{T}_L\mathbf{q}_a = [\mathbf{I} \ \vdots \ \mathbf{0}]\begin{bmatrix} \bar{\mathbf{q}}_a \\ \hat{\mathbf{q}}_a \end{bmatrix} \tag{2.157}$$

The total potential energy of the constrained system is given by

$$V_T = V_a + V_{bc} \tag{2.158}$$

or
$$V_T = \tfrac{1}{2}\mathbf{q}_a^T\bar{\mathbf{K}}\mathbf{q}_a \tag{2.159}$$

where
$$\bar{\mathbf{K}} = \mathbf{K}_a + \mathbf{T}_L^T\bar{\mathbf{K}}_b\mathbf{T}_L \tag{2.160}$$

The total kinetic energy of the constrained system is

$$T_T = \tfrac{1}{2}\dot{\mathbf{q}}_a^T\bar{\mathbf{M}}\dot{\mathbf{q}}_a \tag{2.161}$$

where
$$\bar{\mathbf{M}} = \mathbf{M}_a + \mathbf{T}_L^T\bar{\mathbf{M}}_b\mathbf{T}_L \tag{2.162}$$

The dynamics of the undamped constrained system is described by Lagrange's equations, which take the form

$$\bar{\mathbf{M}}\ddot{\mathbf{q}}_a + \bar{\mathbf{K}}\mathbf{q}_a = \mathbf{0} \tag{2.163}$$

Let $\boldsymbol{\Phi}_a$ be the matrix whose columns are the eigenvectors of the system found from the eigenvalue problem associated with the dynamic equation (2.163). Then the displacement vector $\mathbf{q}_a(t)$ is a linear combination of these eigenvectors

$$\mathbf{q}_a(t) = \boldsymbol{\Phi}_a \boldsymbol{\zeta}_a(t) = \begin{bmatrix} \bar{\boldsymbol{\Phi}}_a \\ \hat{\boldsymbol{\Phi}}_a \end{bmatrix} \boldsymbol{\zeta}_a(t) \tag{2.164}$$

The eigenvectors obtained from the eigenvalue problem associated with Eq. (2.163) represent the modes of component $a$, and include approximate dynamic effects from component $b$. Component modes determined in this way improve the accuracy of the system results.

Next, a procedure for computing system modes using constrained-component branch modes will be presented. In the Benfield–Hruda method, one component is selected as the main body and all other components are designated as branch components. The coordinates of each branch are then transformed into main-body coordinates. Component-branch modes are determined with the interface between the branch and the main body fixed.

The constraint modes are defined as the elastic and rigid-body displacements of the interior coordinates $\hat{\mathbf{q}}$ due to unit displacements of the interface coordinates $\bar{\mathbf{q}}$ due to unit displacements of the interface coordinates $\bar{\mathbf{q}}$. This is the definition of $\hat{\mathbf{q}}_{cb}$ in Eq. (2.148) so that the columns of matrix $\mathbf{T}_{cb}$ defined in Eq. (2.148) are the constraint modes. The fixed-constraint-mode displacements $\hat{\mathbf{q}}_i$ are the elastic displacements of the interior coordinates $\mathbf{q}$ relative to the fixed interface coordinates. The interface displacements of component $b$ are expressed as a superposition of constraint-mode and fixed-constraint-mode displacements

$$\hat{\mathbf{q}}_b = \hat{\mathbf{q}}_{cb} + \hat{\mathbf{q}}_{ib} \tag{2.165}$$

Then, using Eq. (2.148), the constraint-mode transformation $\mathbf{T}_1^c$ is obtained as

$$\begin{bmatrix} \mathbf{q}_a \\ \mathbf{q}_b \end{bmatrix} = \mathbf{T}_1^c \begin{bmatrix} \bar{\mathbf{q}}_a \\ \hat{\mathbf{q}}_a \\ \bar{\mathbf{q}}_b \\ \hat{\mathbf{q}}_{ib} \end{bmatrix} \tag{2.166}$$

where

$$\mathbf{T}_1^c = \begin{bmatrix} \mathbf{I} & 0 & 0 & 0 \\ 0 & \mathbf{I} & 0 & 0 \\ 0 & 0 & \mathbf{I} & 0 \\ 0 & 0 & \mathbf{T}_{cb} & \mathbf{I} \end{bmatrix} \tag{2.167}$$

Next, using Eq. (2.157), a coupling transformation between components $a$ and $b$ is written as

$$\begin{bmatrix} \bar{\mathbf{q}}_a \\ \hat{\mathbf{q}}_a \\ \bar{\mathbf{q}}_b \\ \hat{\mathbf{q}}_{ib} \end{bmatrix} = \mathbf{T}_2^c \begin{bmatrix} \bar{\mathbf{q}}_a \\ \hat{\mathbf{q}}_a \\ \hat{\mathbf{q}}_{ib} \end{bmatrix} \tag{2.168}$$

where

$$\mathbf{T}_2^c = \begin{bmatrix} \mathbf{I} & 0 & 0 \\ 0 & \mathbf{I} & 0 \\ \mathbf{I} & 0 & 0 \\ 0 & 0 & \mathbf{I} \end{bmatrix} \tag{2.169}$$

Equation (2.166) then takes the form

$$\begin{bmatrix} \mathbf{q}_a \\ \mathbf{q}_b \end{bmatrix} = \mathbf{T}_1^c \mathbf{T}_2^c \begin{bmatrix} \bar{\mathbf{q}}_a \\ \hat{\mathbf{q}}_a \\ \hat{\mathbf{q}}_{ib} \end{bmatrix} \tag{2.170}$$

This equation defines the displacements of components $a$ and $b$ in terms of the displacements of component $a$ and the fixed-constraint modes of component $b$.

When the interface between components $a$ and $b$ is fixed, that is, $\bar{\mathbf{q}}_b = 0$, $\ddot{\mathbf{q}}_b = 0$, the equations of motion for component $b$, written in terms of the partitions of stiffness and mass matrices indicated in Eq. (2.146), are

$$\mathbf{M}_{II}^b \ddot{\mathbf{q}}_b + \mathbf{K}_{II}^b \hat{\mathbf{q}}_b = \mathbf{0} \tag{2.171}$$

which has the solution

$$\hat{\mathbf{q}}_b = \hat{\mathbf{q}}_{ib}(t) = \hat{\mathbf{\Phi}}_b^c \boldsymbol{\zeta}_b^c(t) \tag{2.172}$$

in which the modal matrix $\hat{\mathbf{\Phi}}_b^c$ is obtained by solving the eigenvalue problem corresponding to Eq. (2.171). From Eqs. (2.164) and (2.172), the following transformation is obtained:

$$\begin{bmatrix} \bar{\mathbf{q}}_a \\ \hat{\mathbf{q}}_a \\ \hat{\mathbf{q}}_{ib} \end{bmatrix} = \begin{bmatrix} \bar{\mathbf{\Phi}}_a & 0 \\ \hat{\mathbf{\Phi}}_a & 0 \\ 0 & \hat{\mathbf{\Phi}}_b^c \end{bmatrix} \begin{bmatrix} \boldsymbol{\zeta}_a(t) \\ \boldsymbol{\zeta}_b^c(t) \end{bmatrix} \tag{2.173}$$

The component displacements are related to the generalized coordinate vectors $\boldsymbol{\zeta}_a$ and $\boldsymbol{\zeta}_b^c$ as

$$\begin{bmatrix} \mathbf{q}_a \\ \mathbf{q}_b \end{bmatrix} = \mathbf{T}_3^c \begin{bmatrix} \boldsymbol{\zeta}_a \\ \boldsymbol{\zeta}_b^c \end{bmatrix} \tag{2.174}$$

where

$$\mathbf{T}_3^c = \mathbf{T}_1^c \mathbf{T}_2^c \begin{bmatrix} \bar{\mathbf{\Phi}}_a & 0 \\ \hat{\mathbf{\Phi}}_a & 0 \\ 0 & \hat{\mathbf{\Phi}}_b^c \end{bmatrix} \tag{2.175}$$

This transformation is obtained by combining Eqs. (2.170) and (2.173). Now, in order to derive the system modes, the potential energy is written as

$$V_T = \frac{1}{2} \begin{bmatrix} \mathbf{q}_a \\ \mathbf{q}_b \end{bmatrix}^T \begin{bmatrix} \mathbf{K}_a & 0 \\ 0 & \mathbf{K}_b \end{bmatrix} \begin{bmatrix} \mathbf{q}_a \\ \mathbf{q}_b \end{bmatrix} \tag{2.176}$$

or, in terms of the generalized coordinates, as

$$V_{ab} = \frac{1}{2} \begin{bmatrix} \boldsymbol{\zeta}_a \\ \boldsymbol{\zeta}_b^c \end{bmatrix}^T \mathbf{K}^c \begin{bmatrix} \boldsymbol{\zeta}_a \\ \boldsymbol{\zeta}_b^c \end{bmatrix} \tag{2.177}$$

where
$$\mathbf{K}^c = (\mathbf{T}_3^c)^T \begin{bmatrix} \mathbf{K}_a & 0 \\ 0 & \mathbf{K}_b \end{bmatrix} \mathbf{T}_3^c \qquad (2.178)$$

Similarly, the kinetic energy of the coupled system is

$$T_{ab} = \frac{1}{2} \begin{bmatrix} \dot{\boldsymbol{\zeta}}_a \\ \dot{\boldsymbol{\zeta}}_b^c \end{bmatrix}^T \mathbf{M}^c \begin{bmatrix} \dot{\boldsymbol{\zeta}}_a \\ \dot{\boldsymbol{\zeta}}_b^c \end{bmatrix} \qquad (2.179)$$

where
$$\mathbf{M}^c = (\mathbf{T}_3^c)^T \begin{bmatrix} \mathbf{M}_a & 0 \\ 0 & \mathbf{M}_b \end{bmatrix} \mathbf{T}_3^c \qquad (2.180)$$

Finally, the system modal matrix $\boldsymbol{\Phi}_a^c$ is obtained by solving the eigenvalue problem

$$\mathbf{K}^c \boldsymbol{\Phi}_m^c = \mathbf{M}^c \boldsymbol{\Phi}_m^c \boldsymbol{\Lambda}_m^c \qquad (2.181)$$

where $\boldsymbol{\Lambda}_m^c$ is the diagonal matrix of natural frequencies squared.

The Benfield–Hruda method [70] described above is called the *component-mode substitution method.* In an earlier related method, known as branch-mode analysis [71], the systems to be synthesized are chainlike, with each component connected to two other components, one on each side. The components are grouped into classes called *branches.* The dynamics of each branch is represented by branch modes. The approach is the same as the generalized component-mode synthesis method described in the previous section. The differences are in the selection of modes, which are obtained by solving branch eigenvalue problems.

***Rubin's Method*** Rubin's method [60] of component-mode representation achieves more accuracy by accounting for the contribution of neglected (residual) modes. This method uses the inertia-relief attachment modes defined in Eqs. (2.107) and (2.109). It is a significant refinement and extension of an earlier approach credited to MacNeal [59] and is closely related to the Craig–Chang method [66]. Rubin's method is not based on a Rayleigh–Ritz approach. Instead, a two-step approximation to dynamic response is used. The first step requires the solution of a statics problem, and the second step adds the inertial and damping forces corresponding to the approximate response obtained in the first step. Then the effect of the modes not retained in the calculations is determined without knowledge of those modes. Finally, a stiffness-matrix formulation for the equations of motion of the structural component, including the residual effects, is obtained and applied to modal synthesis.

To describe the first two steps of Rubin's method, let the physical displacement vector due to rigid-body motion be

$$\mathbf{u}_R = \boldsymbol{\psi}_R \mathbf{q}_R \qquad (2.182)$$

as in Eq. (2.99). The differential equation for the rigid-body displacements due to an external force $\mathbf{f}$ is

$$\mathbf{M}_R \ddot{\mathbf{q}}_R = \boldsymbol{\psi}_R^T \mathbf{f} \qquad (2.183)$$

where
$$\mathbf{M}_R = \boldsymbol{\psi}_R^T \mathbf{M} \boldsymbol{\psi}_R \qquad (2.184)$$

as in Eq. (2.100). Let the load vector $\mathbf{f}'$ be defined by Eq. (2.98). Then, the first-order statics problem for the constrained body can be stated in the form

$$\mathbf{u}_c^{(1)} = \mathbf{G}_c \mathbf{f}' = \mathbf{G}_c \mathbf{P} \mathbf{f} \tag{2.185}$$

in which Eq. (2.102) has been used. The matrix $\mathbf{G}_c$ is the flexibility matrix for the constrained body with enough conditions imposed on the body to prevent rigid-body motion. The actual static-elastic displacement $\mathbf{u}_e^{(1)}$ differs from $\mathbf{u}_c^{(1)}$ by certain rigid-body displacements

$$\mathbf{u}_e^{(1)} = \mathbf{u}_c^{(1)} + \boldsymbol{\psi}_R \mathbf{c}_R \tag{2.186}$$

Since $\mathbf{u}_e^{(1)}$ is free of rigid-body contributions, it is orthogonal to the rigid-body modes

$$\boldsymbol{\psi}_R^T \mathbf{M}(\mathbf{u}_c^{(1)} + \boldsymbol{\psi}_R \mathbf{c}_R) = \mathbf{0} \tag{2.187}$$

which implies
$$\mathbf{c}_R = -\boldsymbol{\psi}_R^T \mathbf{M} \mathbf{u}_c^{(1)} \tag{2.188}$$

where the normalization Eq. (2.101) has been used. Thus, the first-order approximation to elastic displacements is given by

$$\mathbf{u}_e^{(1)} = (\mathbf{I} - \boldsymbol{\psi}_R \boldsymbol{\psi}_R^T \mathbf{M}) \mathbf{u}_c^{(1)} \tag{2.189}$$

or
$$\mathbf{u}_e^{(1)} = \mathbf{P}^T \mathbf{G}_c \mathbf{P} \mathbf{f} = \mathbf{G} \mathbf{f} \tag{2.190}$$

which is obtained by combining Eqs. (2.185) and (2.189). The flexibility matrix $\mathbf{G}$ defined in Eq. (2.190) is symmetric but singular whenever the system has rigid-body modes.

The second-order approximation to the dynamic response is calculated by adding to the external forces the inertial and damping forces resulting from the first-order displacements. From Eq. (2.185), this approximation is found to be

$$\mathbf{u}_c^{(2)} = \mathbf{G}_c \mathbf{P}(\mathbf{f} - \mathbf{M} \ddot{\mathbf{u}}_e^{(1)} - \mathbf{C} \dot{\mathbf{u}}_e^{(1)}) \tag{2.191}$$

where $\mathbf{C}$ is the viscous damping matrix. As before, the rigid-body contribution can be reduced by multiplying $\mathbf{u}_c^{(2)}$ by $\mathbf{P}^T$:

$$\mathbf{u}_e^{(2)} = \mathbf{P}^T \mathbf{u}_c^{(2)} \tag{2.192}$$

The velocity and acceleration terms in Eq. (2.191) are obtained by differentiating Eq. (2.190) with respect to time. Then, if Eqs. (2.191) and (2.192) are combined, it is seen that

$$\mathbf{u}_e^{(2)} = \mathbf{G} \mathbf{f} - \mathbf{H} \ddot{\mathbf{f}} - \mathbf{B} \dot{\mathbf{f}} \tag{2.193}$$

where
$$\mathbf{H} = \mathbf{G} \mathbf{M} \mathbf{G} \tag{2.194}$$

$$\mathbf{B} = \mathbf{G} \mathbf{C} \mathbf{G} \tag{2.195}$$

Suppose, now, that a certain number of modes are to be retained in the calculations. Then, if $\mathbf{u}_{er}^{(1)}$ denotes the static residual displacement of the body after rigid-body contributions have been filtered out,

$$\mathbf{u}_{er}^{(1)} = \mathbf{G}_r \mathbf{f} \tag{2.196}$$

$$\mathbf{G}_r = \mathbf{G} - \mathbf{G}_N \tag{2.197}$$

$$\mathbf{G}_N = \boldsymbol{\psi}_N \mathbf{K}_N^{-1} \boldsymbol{\psi}_N^T \tag{2.198}$$

where $\boldsymbol{\psi}_N$ and $\mathbf{K}_N$ are the modal matrix and the generalized stiffness matrix, respectively, containing only the set of retained modes. Similarly, the second-order residual contribution to elastic displacements is given by

$$\mathbf{u}_{er}^{(2)} = \mathbf{G}_r \mathbf{f} - \mathbf{H}_r \ddot{\mathbf{f}} - \mathbf{B}_r \dot{\mathbf{f}} \tag{2.199}$$

$$\mathbf{H}_r = \mathbf{H} - \mathbf{H}_N \qquad \mathbf{H}_N = \mathbf{G}_N \mathbf{M} \mathbf{G}_N \tag{2.200}$$

$$\mathbf{B}_r = \mathbf{B} - \mathbf{B}_N \qquad \mathbf{B}_N = \mathbf{G}_N \mathbf{C} \mathbf{G}_N \tag{2.201}$$

Equations (2.196) to (2.201) give the residual contribution of the neglected modes without explicit specification of these modes, provided that the flexibility matrix $\mathbf{G}$ is known. The complete set of physical displacements $\mathbf{u}$ is then found by adding the residual contribution to the displacement obtained from the retained set of modes

$$\mathbf{u} = \boldsymbol{\psi}\mathbf{q} + (\mathbf{G}_r - \mathbf{H}_r s^2 - \mathbf{B}_r s)\mathbf{f} \tag{2.202}$$

where $s$ is the Laplace variable.

To apply the foregoing component-mode representation to modal synthesis, a stiffness formulation can be used. Since the applied forces occur only at interfaces with other components, a subset of Eq. (2.202) corresponding to interface displacements is

$$\mathbf{u}_I = \boldsymbol{\psi}_I \mathbf{q} + (\mathbf{G}_r - \mathbf{H}_r s^2 - \mathbf{B}_r s)\mathbf{f}_I \tag{2.203}$$

from which the following expression for $\mathbf{f}_I$ may be extracted:

$$\mathbf{f}_I = \mathbf{Z}\mathbf{u}_I - \mathbf{Z}\boldsymbol{\psi}_I \mathbf{q} \tag{2.204}$$

where
$$\mathbf{Z} = (\mathbf{G}_r - \mathbf{H}_r s^2 - \mathbf{B}_r s)^{-1} \tag{2.205}$$

The equations of motion governing $\mathbf{q}$ are in the form

$$(\mathbf{M}_Q s^2 + \mathbf{C}_Q s + \mathbf{K}_Q)\mathbf{q} = \boldsymbol{\psi}_I^T \mathbf{f}_I \tag{2.206}$$

The combination of Eqs. (2.204) and (2.206) gives the desired matrix formulation

$$\begin{bmatrix} \mathbf{Z}_{11} & \mathbf{Z}_{12} \\ \mathbf{Z}_{21} & \mathbf{Z}_{22} \end{bmatrix} \begin{bmatrix} \mathbf{q} \\ \mathbf{u}_I \end{bmatrix} = \begin{bmatrix} \mathbf{0} \\ \mathbf{f}_I \end{bmatrix} \tag{2.207}$$

where
$$\mathbf{Z}_{11} = \mathbf{M}_Q s^2 + \mathbf{C}_Q s + \mathbf{K} + \boldsymbol{\psi}_I^T \mathbf{Z} \boldsymbol{\psi}_I \tag{2.208}$$

$$\mathbf{Z}_{12} = -\boldsymbol{\psi}_I^T \mathbf{Z} \tag{2.209}$$

$$\mathbf{Z}_{22} = \mathbf{Z} \tag{2.210}$$

$$\mathbf{Z}_{21} = -\mathbf{Z}\boldsymbol{\psi}_I \tag{2.211}$$

This stiffness formulation is used in the standard way as described above, as a generalized modal-synthesis method. A major advantage of Rubin's formulation is that the modal respresentation involved can be based on test data. The test results needed are free-interface normal modes and the dynamic flexibility matrix for the interface points. In addition, the method has been found to be computationally efficient and accurate.

***Dynamic Transformation Method***   Kuhar and Stahle [72] developed a dynamic transformation method that can be used with any modal-synthesis formulation to reduce truncation error over a selected frequency range. Instead of completely omitting higher-frequency substructure modes from the equation of motion, this method includes all modes by using a transformation that relates the reduced modes not contained explicitly in the solution to the modes that are kept. If $\Omega$ is an exact natural frequency of the system, the undamped eigenvalue problem can be written in the partitioned form

$$\Omega^2 \begin{bmatrix} \mathbf{M}_{KK} & \mathbf{M}_{KR} \\ \mathbf{M}_{RK} & \mathbf{M}_{RR} \end{bmatrix} \begin{bmatrix} \mathbf{q}_K \\ \mathbf{q}_R \end{bmatrix} = \begin{bmatrix} \mathbf{K}_{KK} & \mathbf{K}_{KR} \\ \mathbf{K}_{RK} & \mathbf{K}_{RR} \end{bmatrix} \begin{bmatrix} \mathbf{q}_K \\ \mathbf{q}_R \end{bmatrix} \tag{2.212}$$

For a general frequency $\omega$, the reduced coordinate vector $\mathbf{q}_R$ in terms of the kept coordinate vector $\mathbf{q}_K$ is given from Eq. (2.212) by

$$\mathbf{q}_R = -(\mathbf{K}_{RR} - \omega^2 \mathbf{M}_{RR})^{-1}(\mathbf{K}_{RK} - \omega^2 \mathbf{M}_{RK})\mathbf{q}_K \tag{2.213}$$

The dynamic transformation matrix $\mathbf{T}(\omega)$ is defined as

$$\mathbf{T}(\omega) = \begin{bmatrix} \mathbf{I} \\ \mathbf{R}(\omega) \end{bmatrix} \tag{2.214}$$

with

$$\mathbf{R}(\omega) = -(\mathbf{K}_{RR} - \omega^2 \mathbf{M}_{RR})^{-1}(\mathbf{K}_{RK} - \omega^2 \mathbf{M}_{RK}) \tag{2.215}$$

Then the reduced equation of motion is obtained by substituting the coordinate transformation

$$\mathbf{q} = \begin{bmatrix} \mathbf{q}_K \\ \mathbf{q}_R \end{bmatrix} = \mathbf{T}(\omega)\mathbf{q}_K \tag{2.216}$$

into Eq. (2.212) and multiplying by the transpose of $\mathbf{T}$. Thus, the reduced set of equations becomes

$$\Omega^2 \mathbf{T}^T \mathbf{M} \mathbf{q}_K = \mathbf{T}^T \mathbf{K} \mathbf{q}_K \tag{2.217}$$

This eigenvalue problem is solved for a set of frequencies $\Omega_j^K$, $1 \le j \le m$, and a corresponding set of eigenvectors $\boldsymbol{\rho}_j^K$. The eigenvectors of the system (2.212) are then given by

$$\boldsymbol{\rho}_j = \mathbf{T}\boldsymbol{\rho}_j^K \tag{2.218}$$

This solution is approximate except when the reduction frequency $\omega$ used to evaluate $\mathbf{T}$ in Eqs. (2.214) and when (2.215) coincides with $\Omega_j^K$.

As an example of the use of the dynamic transformation method, its application to the Craig–Bampton modal synthesis [64] will be described. In this approach, the physical displacement vector $\mathbf{u}_j$ is related to modal coordinate $\boldsymbol{\eta}_j$ by

$$\mathbf{u}_j = \begin{bmatrix} \mathbf{I} & \mathbf{0} \\ \boldsymbol{\Phi}_c & \boldsymbol{\Phi}_n \end{bmatrix} \boldsymbol{\eta}_j \tag{2.219}$$

where $\boldsymbol{\Phi}_c$ is the matrix of constraint modes and $\boldsymbol{\Phi}_n$ is the matrix of component normal modes determined with all attachment coordinates fixed. The uncoupled modal coordinates $\boldsymbol{\eta}$ for the system obtained by putting together the component vectors $\boldsymbol{\eta}_j$ is related to the coupled-system coordinates vector $\mathbf{q}$ by a transformation

$$\boldsymbol{\eta} = \mathbf{Sq} \qquad (2.220)$$

The uncoupled equations of motion for two components are

$$\begin{bmatrix} \mathbf{M}_1 & \mathbf{0} \\ \mathbf{0} & \mathbf{M}_2 \end{bmatrix} \begin{bmatrix} \ddot{\mathbf{u}}_1 \\ \ddot{\mathbf{u}}_2 \end{bmatrix} + \begin{bmatrix} \mathbf{K}_1 & \mathbf{0} \\ \mathbf{0} & \mathbf{K}_2 \end{bmatrix} \begin{bmatrix} \mathbf{u}_1 \\ \mathbf{u}_2 \end{bmatrix} = \mathbf{0} \qquad (2.221)$$

The transformations (2.219) and (2.220) used with (2.221) yield the final mass and stiffness matrices

$$\mathbf{M} = \begin{bmatrix} \mathbf{M}_{JJ} & \mathbf{M}_{JI}^1 & \mathbf{M}_{IJ}^2 \\ \mathbf{M}_{IJ}^1 & \mathbf{I} & \mathbf{0} \\ \mathbf{M}_{IJ}^2 & \mathbf{0} & \mathbf{I} \end{bmatrix} \qquad (2.222)$$

$$\mathbf{K} = \begin{bmatrix} \mathbf{K}_{JJ} & \mathbf{0} & \mathbf{0} \\ \mathbf{0} & \text{diag}(\omega_1^2) & \mathbf{0} \\ \mathbf{0} & \mathbf{0} & \text{diag}(\omega_2^2) \end{bmatrix} \qquad (2.223)$$

where the subscript $I$ indicates interior and the subscript $J$ indicates junction (interface) coordinates. With these mass and stiffness matrices the transformation matrix $\mathbf{R}(\omega)$ takes the form

$$\mathbf{R}(\omega) = \omega^2 [\mathbf{K}_{RR} - \omega^2 \mathbf{I}]^{-1} \mathbf{M}_{RK} \qquad (2.224)$$

If all interface coordinates are included in the kept coordinates vector $\mathbf{q}_k$, then $\mathbf{R}(\omega)$ becomes simple to calculate because $\mathbf{K}_{RR} - \omega^2 \mathbf{I}$ will be a diagonal matrix. The reduced mass and stiffness matrices are given by

$$\mathbf{M}_K = \mathbf{M}_{KK} + 2\mathbf{R}^T \mathbf{M}_{RK} + \mathbf{R}^T \mathbf{R} \qquad (2.225)$$

$$\mathbf{K}_K = \mathbf{K}_{KK} + \mathbf{R}^T \mathbf{K}_{RR} \mathbf{R} \qquad (2.226)$$

**Lagrange Multiplier Approaches**   Dowell [73, 74] develops a free-vibration analysis for structures with arbitrary support conditions. In this method, free–free normal component modes are used and the constraint or continuity conditions between components is enforced by means of Lagrange multipliers. Unlike conventional approaches that eliminate the Lagrange multipliers and perform the subsequent analysis in terms of generalized coordinates, Dowell's method eliminates the generalized coordinates and retains the Lagrange multipliers in the analysis. These multipliers are physically interpreted as forces of constraint. The paper by Edge, Mayer, and Pierce [75], which gives a technique for dynamic analysis of space frames, also uses a Lagrangian multiplier approach. The authors eliminate the multipliers in favor of the generalized coordinates.

**Modal Synthesis Using Complex Modes**   A modal-synthesis method using complex modes has been developed by Hasselman and Kaplan [57] to include linear, autonomous, holonomic dynamical systems in general. This formulation is an extension of the usual synthesis procedure for such systems as vehicles, railroad cars, liquid-fueled rockets, and systems with feedback control. Such systems, in general, do not yield symmetric coefficient matrices. In these cases, a general eigenproblem is formed, leading to complex eigenvalues and eigenvectors. The authors also present frequency-response function formulae and applications to railcar dynamics.

**Other Methods**    A rank-1 tie-matrix method proposed by Hallquist and Snyder [76, 77] is an alternative approach to modal synthesis. This method sequentially connects coordinates of uncoupled components with springs, rigid links, or dashpots. Palazzolo, Wang, and Pilkey [10] use the receptance approach described as a reanalysis method to treat modal-synthesis problems. Meirovitch and Oz [78] apply modal synthesis to the active control of structures. Convergence and modal truncation problems are discussed by Hintz [79] and Hasselman and Hart [80]. Other references for modal-synthesis methods are Bajan, Feng, and Jaszlics [81], Hale and Meirovitch [82], Jensen [83], Meirovitch [84, 85], Meirovitch and Hale [86–88], Klosterman [89], Goldenberg and Shapiro [90], Klosterman and McClelland [91], Kana and Huzar [92, 93], Hasselman [94], Neubert and Raney [95], Hurty [96], Craig and Chang [97], Craig [98], Kung and Hohenemser [99], Leung [100], and Craig [101].

### 2.2D Comparison of Modal Synthesis with Dynamic Substructuring

Dynamic-substructuring methods are used to solve the eigenvalue problem for large complex structures whenever it is possible to increase computational efficiency by obtaining system eigenproperties from the eigenproperties of the structures that make up the system. The required fundamental equations for the given structure are derived such that substructure equations set up for individual substructures satisfy the boundary conditions of the adjacent substructures. Thus, the adjacent substructures have almost the same advantages and disadvantages insofar as substructure connection is concerned. For instance, the cost of computation depends largely on the number of nodes at the connecting interface between the substructures and the number of component modes retained in the calculations. Note that in the process of connecting the substructures the quantities associated with internal nodes in the substructures are eliminated. Computational accuracy is associated with the relationship between the eigenvalues of the substructures and the eigenvalues of the entire structure. Therefore, the type of fundamental equation for the given structure depends upon the type of substructure equations.

Modal-synthesis equations are generally of the standard form

$$\mathbf{AX} = \omega^2 \mathbf{BX} \qquad (2.227)$$

For this type of equation many convenient solution methods have been developed, as shown in Sec. 1.1 of Part 4 on eigensolutions.

In general, modal synthesis has the following advantages:

1. Iteration methods such as the inverse-power method including eigenvalue shifts are used when **A** and **B** are of large order.

**2.** The dynamic contribution of each substructure to the total system can be investigated in the design process.

**3.** Dynamic characteristics of the modified substructures are predicted from the eigensolutions of the unmodified substructures in designing the complete structure to meet design requirements.

Modal synthesis needs an extra procedure to transform modal coordinates to physical coordinates when the eigenvalue problem is formulated for the total structure.

The techniques introduced in Sec. 5.3 of Part 4 as substructuring techniques for dynamic condensation may also be called mathematical substructuring procedures [102, 103]. One of them, Guyan reduction, derives Eq. (2.227) under the assumption that internal-node displacements of substructures are statically related to boundary-node displacements. The exact equations, without this assumption, take the form

$$\mathbf{D}(\omega^2)\mathbf{X} = 0 \tag{2.228}$$

where the matrix $\mathbf{D}(\omega^2)$ includes $\omega^2$ in the form

$$\omega^2(\omega_n^2 - \omega^2)^{-1} \tag{2.229}$$

where $\omega_n^2$ is the $n^{\text{th}}$ eigenvalue of the substructure. For this case, the frequency equations will be

$$\det \mathbf{D}(\omega^2) = 0 \tag{2.230}$$

The required eigenvalues, $\omega_m^2$ $(m = 1, 2, 3, \ldots)$, are found by trial and error. A convenient method to find $\omega_m^2$ is in Ref. [104]. If the order of $\mathbf{D}(\omega^2)$ is very large, a numerical calculation may be troublesome. It should be mentioned that when the dynamic flexibility matrix $\mathbf{f}_D = (\mathbf{K} - \omega^2\mathbf{M})^{-1}$ is found, the elements in $\mathbf{f}_D$ include $\omega^2$ in the form $(\omega_n^2 - \omega^2)^{-1}$. Therefore, Eq. (2.228) should be evaluated and compared against analytical results as in Refs. [105, 106, 108], which use the dynamic flexibility matrix.

## 2.2E Modal Synthesis of Damped Systems

The modal-synthesis techniques shown in the preceding sections are limited to undamped structures. Application of modal synthesis to nonproportionally damped structures is discussed in this section. According to the modal-synthesis principle for damped structures, the damped-structure eigensolutions are required [109, 110]. Since the eigenvalue equations of damped structures can be transformed to standard eigenvalue equations [15], modal synthesis is applicable to damped structures [112].

The fundamental equations of a damped structure are given by

$$(\lambda^2\mathbf{M} + \lambda\mathbf{C} + \mathbf{K})\mathbf{X} = 0 \tag{2.231}$$

where $\mathbf{C}$ is the damping matrix.

In standard form, Eq. (2.231) is written as

$$\mu \mathbf{A}\mathbf{Y} = \mathbf{B}\mathbf{Y} \tag{2.232}$$

where
$$Y = \begin{bmatrix} \mu X \\ X \end{bmatrix} \qquad A = \begin{bmatrix} 0 & M \\ M & C \end{bmatrix} \qquad B = \begin{bmatrix} M & 0 \\ 0 & -K \end{bmatrix} \tag{2.233}$$

Once Eq. (2.231) is transformed into Eq. (2.232), the modal-synthesis method for undamped structures can be applied to the damped-system equations (2.232).

Many numerical-solution techniques have been developed for Eq. (2.232). However, it should be mentioned that the order of matrices in Eq. (2.232) is $2N$, whereas the order of the matrices in Eq. (2.231) is $N$. So, if the size of $M$ or $K$ is very large, computers with limited core memory would be inadequate to carry out the numerical calculations. In addition, Eq. (2.232) cannot utilize the advantage of the banded-matrix forms of $M$ and $K$, which often appear in structural analysis. Therefore, for large matrix equations, modal-synthesis methods are not as useful for damped structures as for undamped structures.

If modal synthesis is interpreted as a technique for obtaining system modes from the dynamic characteristics of individual substructures, structural-analysis methods which use receptances $(\lambda^2 M + \lambda C + K)^{-1}$ of the substructures (as in Ref. [106]) may also be considered a modal-synthesis method. In this case, the fundamental equations obtained are represented in the form of Eq. (2.228) and are solved by using an iterative method.

Once the eigensolutions of a damped structure are found, its dynamic response is easily obtained by modal analysis [113, 114]. For local modification of a damped structure, reanalysis techniques will be necessary (see Sec. 2.1). Note that the transient response of a locally modified structure can be calculated using unmodified structural-response data [107].

## 2.3 STATIC CONDENSATION AND SUBSTRUCTURING

### 2.3A Static Condensation

Static condensation, or simply condensation, is a process by which some of the degrees of freedom (DOF) are eliminated from the overall equilibrium equations prior to continuing with other phases of the solution. In the finite-element method, the terminology often refers to the elimination of elemental DOF that are not involved in satisfying interelement compatibility, before the element is assembled into the overall stiffness matrix of the structure. The technique of condensation, however, can effectively be applied in a variety of situations to reduce the size of equations. Quite generally, then, condensation is a procedure for eliminating some of the unknowns from a system of simultaneous equations by substitution into the remainder of the equations.

To establish the equations used in condensation, consider the stiffness matrix $K$, and the corresponding displacement and force vectors, $\delta$ and $P$, to be partitioned as

$$\begin{bmatrix} K_{ii} & K_{ib} \\ \hline K_{bi} & K_{bb} \end{bmatrix} \begin{Bmatrix} \delta_i \\ \delta_b \end{Bmatrix} = \begin{Bmatrix} P_i \\ P_b \end{Bmatrix} \tag{2.234}$$

where the $i$ DOF are to be condensed and the $b$ DOF are to be retained. The notations $i$ and $b$ have been selected to reflect common structural applications of the technique, where *internal* DOF are eliminated and *boundary* DOF remain. Although stiffness nomenclature has been used, (2.234) could represent any set of algebraic equations, with a square coefficient matrix $K$, a vector of unknowns $\delta$, and a vector of specified quantities $P$.

The upper part of Eq. (2.234) can be solved for $\boldsymbol{\delta}_i$ as

$$\boldsymbol{\delta}_i = \mathbf{K}_{ii}^{-1}\mathbf{P}_i - \mathbf{K}_{ii}^{-1}\mathbf{K}_{ib}\boldsymbol{\delta}_b \qquad (2.235)$$

When this equation is substituted into the lower part of Eq. (2.234) for $\boldsymbol{\delta}_i$ and the terms are collected, the remaining equations for $\boldsymbol{\delta}_b$ can be written as

$$\bar{\mathbf{K}}_{bb}\boldsymbol{\delta}_b = \bar{\mathbf{P}}_b \qquad (2.236)$$

where the reduced stiffness matrix $\bar{\mathbf{K}}_{bb}$ is

$$\bar{\mathbf{K}}_{bb} = \mathbf{K}_{bb} - \mathbf{K}_{bi}\mathbf{K}_{ii}^{-1}\mathbf{K}_{ib} \qquad (2.237)$$

and the reduced force vector $\bar{\mathbf{P}}_b$ is given by

$$\bar{\mathbf{P}}_b = \mathbf{P}_b - \mathbf{K}_{bi}\mathbf{K}_{ii}^{-1}\mathbf{P}_i \qquad (2.238)$$

The reduced equations (2.236) can now be used in some other solution process; e.g., they can be combined with other equations to form and solve a new system of equations. The reduced stiffness matrix and force vector formed at the boundaries are mathematically equivalent to the original quantities. Condensation frees the interior DOF to move as dictated by the boundary DOF according to the physical properties of the system. Once the unknowns $\boldsymbol{\delta}_b$ have been computed, then the condensed unknowns $\boldsymbol{\delta}_i$ can be recovered from Eq. (2.235).

Instead of carrying out the matrix operations of Eqs. (2.234) to (2.238), condensation algorithms are often written to eliminate the DOF one at a time. Each time a DOF, say $s$, is eliminated, the remaining coefficients of the matrix $\mathbf{K}$ and force vector $\mathbf{P}$ are modified according to

$$k_{ij} = k_{ij} - \frac{k_{si}k_{sj}}{k_{ss}} \qquad (2.239)$$

$$p_i = p_i - \frac{k_{si}p_s}{k_{ss}} \qquad (2.240)$$

These equations are the same as Eqs. (2.237) and (2.238) if the condensed set $b$ consists of only one DOF. When multiple DOF are to be condensed, the procedure is applied repeatedly, with the coefficient matrix being reduced in size by 1 each time. Each of the eliminated equations $s$ must be saved in order to recover $\boldsymbol{\delta}_s$ once the other unknowns have been determined.

The foregoing procedure is the same as gaussian elimination, and if continued for all unknowns in the system, it would allow a complete solution of the equations to be obtained. Hence, condensation is a partial gaussian elimination.

***Uses of Condensation*** Condensation is often used to eliminate DOF associated with an individual finite element before the element is assembled into the overall system equations. These DOF are generally internal to an element and hence are not involved in satisfying interelement compatibility. The internal DOF may be actual nodal displacements that result when simple elements are combined to form complex elements, or they may be generalized coordinates that are used to improve the accuracy of the element by adding more terms to the assumed-displacement field. In either case, the introduction of the internal DOF serves to increase the accuracy of calculations within an element.

A simple example is shown in Fig. 2.1a, where, for ease of modeling, four constant-strain triangles are combined to form a quadrilateral, which is more convenient in modeling. The stiffness matrix of the quadrilateral assemblage is $10 \times 10$, which can be reduced to $8 \times 8$ by condensing the displacement DOF associated with the internal node. The motivation for the condensation on the element level is to reduce the total number of equations and the bandwidth in the assembled equations. The number of computations, however, is exactly the same as when the internal DOF are carried into the assemblage and then solved. Savings in computational effort would result only if identical elements occurred in the model. Then the same element stiffness could be used a number of times without having to repeat the condensation.

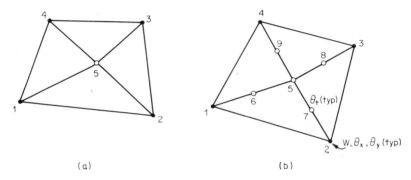

(a)                                    (b)

**FIG. 2.1**   Elements constructed from subelements. (a) Membrane. (b) Bending.

A similar example is afforded by the formulation of a compatible plate-bending element [116] shown in Fig. 2.1b. In this instance, the triangles contain different DOF at the interior midside nodes than at the corners. If these DOF were carried into the system equations, complications would result in codes that do not allow special DOF, or variable numbers of DOF at nodes. Reference [116] can also be consulted for another application of condensation, namely, for the inclusion of shearing deformations in bending elements.

The concept of eliminating internal DOF can be carried further, to where any assembly of elements can be condensed to yield an equivalent stiffness associated only with the nodes on its boundary. This leads to the method of substructures, which is discussed in Sec. 2.3B.

In various solution procedures, it is efficient to employ condensation at a certain stage to eliminate variables that do not directly participate in the rest of the solution. A common example occurs in structural-dynamics problems, where the number of assigned dynamic DOF is often smaller than the number of static DOF. This situation may arise because the only significant masses in the problem are actually concentrated at a few locations, or it may be due to a deliberate modeling strategy to reduce the size of the more costly dynamic solution. In either case the stiffness matrix can be condensed to eliminate the massless DOF, prior to solving the dynamics, or eigenvalue, problem.

Another example occurs in interaction problems, such as a structure submerged in, or in contact with, a fluid. Since the coupling of the structure and fluid occurs only at the wetted surface of the structure, it is often possible to describe one or both models in terms of selected variables on this boundary. Condensation can again be used to effect the reduction.

**Computational Aspects** Static condensation can be performed with any of the direct solution algorithms in common use, all of which are variants of gaussian elimination. The solution methods are presented in detail in Chap. 1 of Part 4.

**Condensation with Decomposition Methods** Methods such as those of Choleski or Crout solve a symmetric set of equations

$$\mathbf{K}\boldsymbol{\delta} = \mathbf{P} \tag{2.241}$$

by first factoring the coefficient matrix $\mathbf{K}$ into

$$\mathbf{K} = \mathbf{U}^*\mathbf{D}\mathbf{U} \tag{2.242}$$

where $\mathbf{U}$ is upper triangular and $\mathbf{D}$ is diagonal. The solution for $\boldsymbol{\delta}$ is then obtained by successively solving the systems

$$\mathbf{U}^*\mathbf{y} = \mathbf{P} \qquad \mathbf{D}\mathbf{z} = \mathbf{y} \qquad \mathbf{U}\boldsymbol{\delta} = \mathbf{z} \tag{2.243}$$

Condensation is effected by setting the coefficient matrix $\mathbf{K}$ equal to $\mathbf{K}_{ii}$ from the partitioned equations (2.234) and by letting the right-hand-side $\mathbf{P}$ be equal to $\mathbf{K}_{ib}$ and $\mathbf{P}_i$, in turn. The solutions

$$\boldsymbol{\delta} = \mathbf{K}_{ii}^{-1}\mathbf{K}_{ib} \qquad \text{and} \qquad \boldsymbol{\delta} = \mathbf{K}_{ii}^{-1}\mathbf{P}_i \tag{2.244}$$

provide the product matrices needed in Eqs. (2.236) to (2.238).

Various other algorithms have been proposed [117–119] which attempt to improve the efficiency of condensation by minimizing the number of operations, accounting for sparsity, etc. All these methods operate on the partitioned equations (2.234) and in some form continue the decomposition procedure into the boundary DOF to arrive at the required matrices.

**Condensation with the Frontal Solver** The frontal solution method [120] is a form of gaussian elimination that alternates the assembly and elimination phases of solving finite-element equations. It is an element-based algorithm in which the entire set of assembled equations is never available at one time. Only the unreduced equations pertaining to elements that have already been processed remain active and constitute the "front." As a new element is assembled, new DOF become active in the front, but as soon as one of them has received all its elemental contributions, it is eliminated.

In order to perform condensation with a frontal algorithm [121], it is merely necessary to tag the boundary DOF such that they will never be eliminated. The stiffness coefficients remaining in the front after all elements have been processed constitute the desired boundary stiffness.

**Condensation through a Transformation** It is sometimes useful to view the process of condensation as a transformation of the total DOF to the DOF remaining after condensation. This transformation, for example, is the basis for the well-known algorithm for reducing DOF in dynamics problems [122, 123]. Retaining the notation of $i$ for internal, or condensed, DOF and $b$ for the boundary, or remaining, DOF, the relationship between the two is given by the second term of Eq. (2.235). The desired transformation of total to remaining DOF can then be written as

$$\left\{ \frac{\boldsymbol{\delta}_i}{\boldsymbol{\delta}_b} \right\} = \left[ \frac{-\mathbf{K}_{ii}^{-1}\mathbf{K}_{ib}}{\mathbf{I}} \right] \boldsymbol{\delta}_b = \mathbf{T}\boldsymbol{\delta}_b \qquad (2.245)$$

where $\mathbf{I}$ is a unit matrix.

The forces are related by Eq. (2.238), or

$$\bar{\mathbf{P}}_b = \mathbf{T}^* \left\{ \frac{\mathbf{P}_i}{\mathbf{P}_b} \right\} \qquad (2.246)$$

Applying these transformations to the partitioned Eq. (2.234) yields

$$\bar{\mathbf{P}}_b = \mathbf{T}^*\mathbf{K}\mathbf{T}\boldsymbol{\delta}_b = \bar{\mathbf{K}}_{bb}\boldsymbol{\delta}_b \qquad (2.247)$$

where $\bar{\mathbf{K}}_{bb}$ is the same as in Eq. (2.237).

### 2.3B Substructuring

Substructuring is a method for solving a large complex structure by subdividing it into smaller, more manageable pieces [124, 125]. Each piece, or substructure, is modeled independently and its DOF are reduced by static condensation. The reduced substructure matrices are then reassembled and solved to obtain the solution of the original problem. Generally, the DOF of individual substructures are reduced to those on the boundaries since these are needed for satisfying continuity conditions with adjacent substructures.

In static analysis, the solution obtained by using substructures is exactly the same as would have been obtained had the structure been solved in one piece. Also, there is no savings in the number of computations performed unless repeated substructures occur in the model. The matrices solved for each of the substructures, however, are much smaller than for the entire structure, resulting in shorter solution times and smaller computer storage requirements at each stage of the solution. On the other hand, the method requires multiple computer runs and increases the bookkeeping requirements. With properly designed software, substructuring can be used to advantage in many applications.

*Uses of Substructuring*   Substructuring was originally developed to overcome computer memory limitations. With advances in both computer hardware and software, these limitations have, for all practical purposes, been removed. Today's general-purpose finite-element codes, with their out-of-core solvers, are capable of solving virtually any problem without resorting to substructuring. However, the cost of such solutions can be very high. With substructuring, smaller matrices are handled at each stage with correspondingly shorter computer runs. This reduces the chances of encountering computer failure, increases the efficiency of the solution by performing a larger portion of the calculations in core, and limits the losses to the particular stage being executed. Other reasons for substructuring are as follows.

*Management of Large Analyses*   Very large, complex structural models, such as those developed in airplane or ship designs, are efficiently analyzed with substructuring. Such models are created over long periods of time with numerous engineers working on different parts of the structure. Substructuring allows each part to be modeled and solved independently until the final assembly stage and, hence, provides for a systematic and orderly procedure for managing the project. Also, it allows subassemblies to be modeled in more detail than would be possible in one overall model.

***Repeated Substructures***   The computational efficiency of the method can be greatly increased if one substructure can be used several times in a given model. The creation of the model, the computation of the stiffness matrix, and the static condensation all need to be performed only once. Not all the effort can be saved, however. Eventually, the substructure needs to be renumbered and assembled into the overall model. Generally, the substructures also need to be rotated to their appropriate orientations in the global assemblage. These operations can negate any savings unless efficient software is available for this purpose. In certain applications it is possible that standard subassemblies, once modeled and condensed, can be saved and used again in completely new structural models. Special techniques have been developed for structures that possess cyclic symmetry [126]. Although not a general substructuring technique, this method is very efficient for structures that can be generated from one cyclic segment.

***Planned Reanalysis***   Substructuring can be useful in cases where reanalysis of one or more parts of a structure is contemplated. This might occur during the evaluation of alternative design concepts for a component or a region of a model. Only the modified substructures then need to be remodeled and assembled with the rest of the previously reduced substructures to obtain a new solution. This procedure can be carried a step further by invoking structural-optimization methods in conjunction with substructuring [127] to obtain a solution. Similar procedures can be followed when mesh refinements are planned in fracture or stress-concentration problems by isolating such areas into one substructure.

***Unplanned Reanalysis***   It is rare indeed when everything in an analysis goes smoothly and the design is proved adequate under all design loads. More likely, errors will be discovered in the model, some details of the design will be altered, or some areas of the structure will be overstressed. Just as in planned reanalysis, if the areas requiring remodeling or redesigning occur in isolated substructures, then only those portions of the work need to be redone.

***Nonlinear Analysis***   The substructuring technique can be applied to separate regions of structures which are subject to linear and nonlinear behavior simultaneously. Such a separation can be done by introducing interface conditions between the regions. Once the nonlinear region is isolated from the rest of the system, more efficient analysis of that region can be done using specific methods and codes designed for nonlinear analysis [128].

***Phases of Substructure Analysis***   A detailed derivation of the equations for the method of substructures may be found in several texts. It is convenient, however, to consider substructures as being merely complex finite elements whose internal degrees of freedom have been condensed according to the method presented in Sec. 2.3A. Assembly and solution procedures are then identical to those used in the finite-element method. Nevertheless, it is still useful to consider substructures analysis as consisting of the three following traditional distinct phases.

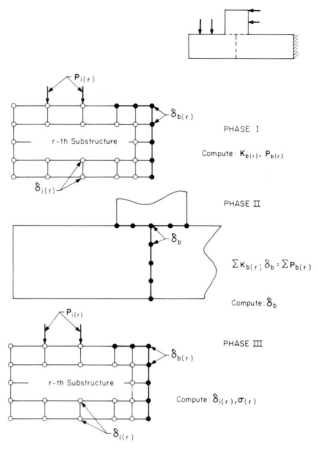

**FIG. 2.2**   Substructures method.

***Phase I: Generation of Substructure Matrices***   Once the overall structure has been divided
into several substructures and the common boundaries between them have been identified,
a phase I reduction to generate equivalent boundary stiffnesses and loads is performed
separately for each substructure. For this purpose the equations for the $r^{\text{th}}$ substructure,
shown in Fig. 2.2, can be partitioned as

$$\begin{bmatrix} \mathbf{K}_{ii} & \mathbf{K}_{ib} \\ \mathbf{K}_{bi} & \mathbf{K}_{bb} \end{bmatrix}_{(r)} \begin{Bmatrix} \boldsymbol{\delta}_i \\ \boldsymbol{\delta}_b \end{Bmatrix}_{(r)} = \begin{Bmatrix} \mathbf{P}_i \\ \mathbf{P}_b \end{Bmatrix}_{(r)} \qquad (2.248)$$

where $i$ refers to internal and $b$ to boundary DOF. The boundary DOF must include all
connections to adjacent substructures, but other DOF may be included in the $b$ set if desired.
Constraints on internal DOF can be applied in this phase, or it might be advantageous to
place the constraint points into the $b$-set (for example, when several sets of constraints are
to be considered) and hence defer the application of boundary conditions until phase II.
Static condensation is then used to eliminate the internal DOF to yield an equivalent, reduced

stiffness and load for substructure $r$:

$$\mathbf{K}_{bb(r)} = \mathbf{K}_{bb} - \mathbf{K}_{bi}\mathbf{K}_{ii}^{-1}\mathbf{K}_{ib} \qquad (2.249)$$

$$\mathbf{P}_{b(r)} = \mathbf{P}_b - \mathbf{K}_{bi}\mathbf{K}_{ii}^{-1}\mathbf{P}_i \qquad (2.250)$$

***Phase II: Solution for Boundary Displacements***   The substructure matrices from phase I are combined to form the overall boundary stiffness and load vector of the structure

$$\mathbf{K}_b\boldsymbol{\delta}_b = \mathbf{P}_b \qquad (2.251)$$

where $\mathbf{K}_b = \Sigma\,\mathbf{K}_{bb(r)}$ and $\mathbf{P}_b = \Sigma\,\mathbf{P}_{b(r)}$. The summation over the $r$ substructures denotes the usual finite-element assembly procedure and requires connectivity information for each substructure with respect to an overall boundary-node numbering scheme. Also it is assumed that all the substructures have been transformed into a global coordinate system. Additional boundary conditions and loads can now be applied to the boundary DOF, and the resulting equations are solved to obtain the boundary displacements $\boldsymbol{\delta}_b$.

***Phase III: Recovery of Internal Displacements***   The boundary displacements of the $r^{\text{th}}$ substructures $\boldsymbol{\delta}_{b(r)}$ are extracted from the overall boundary displacements $\boldsymbol{\delta}_b$, for which a solution was obtained in phase II. Using matrices saved in phase I allows the internal displacements to be recovered from

$$\boldsymbol{\delta}_{i(r)} = \mathbf{K}_{ii}^{-1}\mathbf{P}_i - \mathbf{K}_{ii}^{-1}\mathbf{K}_{ib}\boldsymbol{\delta}_{b(r)} \qquad (2.252)$$

The entire solution to substructure $r$ is now available for the calculation of stresses and forces. A separate phase III analysis is executed for each substructure for which internal displacements and stresses are desired.

***Implementation of Substructuring***   A part of the implementation of substructuring involves the development of efficient numerical algorithms for partitioning, manipulating, and solving the equations. Some of these approaches are discussed in Sec. 2.3A, and further information may be found in Refs. [117-121]. Of equal importance to the user is the development of software that facilitates the bookkeeping and data-management tasks associated with substructuring. Without adequate provisions for automating these tasks, users quickly become discouraged from using substructuring techniques, except when it becomes absolutely necessary to solve very large structures.

Probably the most important feature that differentiates the single-level substructuring codes of the 1960s from the present-day multilevel superelement codes is the data base [129]. The data base is a random-access file on which all substructure information and generated matrices are stored. Under the control of a data-base manager and a user command language, data are stored, retrieved, and updated continuously as the substructuring analysis proceeds through the various phases. This capability greatly eases the burden on the analyst.

Other features to be found in present-day substructuring software include:

1. Local coordinate systems and independent node numbering of individual substructures.
2. Ability to create new substructures through reflection or rotation of previously created substructures.

3. Automated identification and numbering of nodes on substructure interfaces.

4. Ability to combine substructures or superelements with regular finite elements.

5. Condensation of dynamic as well as static degrees of freedom.

6. Capabilities for performing nonlinear analysis by specifying linear and nonlinear substructures.

7. Multilevel substructuring, where several substructures can be combined and condensed to form a new substructure, which in turn can be used to form a higher-level substructure, and so on.

Another useful technique is called *constrained substructuring* [130]. This method circumvents the need for having matching meshes at substructure interfaces, as is usually required in order to satisfy compatibility. This requirement is often difficult to satisfy when one of the substructures requires a fine mesh, especially when three-dimensional solid elements are used. In such instances, irregular meshes generally result, as shown in Fig. 2.3*a*. Constrained substructuring allows a regular fine mesh to be continued to the boundary as shown in Fig. 2.3*b*. Only a reduced set of "master" nodes is retained at the boundary, and suitable shape

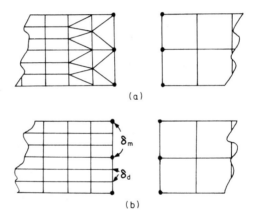

**FIG. 2.3**  Constrained substructures. (*a*) Conventional boundaries. (*b*) Constrained boundary.

functions are used to constrain the response of the other nodes to these masters. The constraint is imposed by writing relationships between the dependent (*d*) and master (*m*) nodes and constructing a transformation such as

$$\left\{ \begin{matrix} \delta_m \\ \delta_d \end{matrix} \right\} = \left[ \frac{\mathbf{I}}{\mathbf{T}} \right] \delta_m \tag{2.253}$$

This transformation is used to reduce the boundary stiffness of the substructure to contain only master nodes such as in Eq. (2.247).

Finally, one should be aware that although substructuring is often used as a means of reducing problem size and computation cost, it often has the opposite effect. Condensed substructure stiffnesses tend to be full. Hence, care must be taken in the selection of substructure boundaries; otherwise, very large bandwidths can result. This is especially true in models composed of three-dimensional elements. Generally, substructuring must be done between regions with few interconnections, e.g., the intersection of wing and fuselage or the intersection between two pipes forming a tee.

## 2.4 REFERENCES

1. Arora, J. S., "Survey of Structural Reanalysis Techniques," *ASCE J. Struct. Div.*, **112**:783–788 (April 1976).

2. Sherman, J., and W. J. Morrison, "Adjustment of an Inverse Matrix Corresponding to Changes in the Elements of a Given Column or a Given Row of the Original Matrix," *Ann. Math. Stat.*, **20**:621 (1949).

3. Woodbury, M., "Inverting Modified Matrices," Memorandum Report 42, S.R.G., Princeton, N.J., 1950.

4. Householder, A. S., *The Theory of Matrices in Numerical Analysis*, 1st ed., Dover, New York, 1964.

5. Bartlett, M. S., "An Inverse Matrix Adjustment Arising in Discriminant Analysis," *Ann. Math. Stat.*, **22**:107–111 (1951).

6. Householder, A. S., *Principles of Numerical Analysis*, McGraw-Hill, New York, 1953, p. 79.

7. Householder, A. S., "A Survey of Some Closed Methods for Inverting Matrices," *SIAM J.*, **5**(1):155–169 (September 1957).

8. Kavlie, D., and Powell, G., "Efficient Reanalysis of Modified Structures," *ASCE J. Struct. Div.*, **97**(ST1):377–392 (January 1971).

9. Argyris, J. H., O. E. Bronlund, and J. R. Roy, "A Direct Modification Procedure for the Displacement Method," *AIAA J.*, **9**(9):1861–1864 (September 1971).

10. Wang, B. P., A. B. Palazzolo, and W. D. Pilkey, "Reanalysis, Modal Synthesis and Dynamic Design," in A. Noor and W. Pilkey (eds.), *State-of-the-Art Finite Element Technology*, American Society of Mechanical Engineers, New York, 1983, chap. 8, pp. 225–229.

11. Kirch, U., and M. P. Rubinstein, "Reanalysis for Limited Structural Design Modifications," *ASCE J. Engr. Mech. Div.*, **98**(EM1):61–70 (February 1972).

12. Przemieniecki, J. S., *Theory of Matrix Structural Analysis*, McGraw-Hill, New York, 1968, pp. 426–427.

13. Melosh, R. J., and R. Luik, "Multiple Configuration Analysis of Structures," *ASCE J. Struct. Div.*, **ST11**:2581–2596 (November 1968).

14. Fenves, S. T., and R. Erias, "Multiple Configuration Analysis of Structures," *ASCE J. Struct. Div.*, **95**(ST7):1586–1615 (July 1969).

15. Sack, R. L., W. C. Carpenter, and G. L. Hatch, "Modification of Elements in the Displacement Method," *AIAA J.*, **5**(9):1708–1717 (September 1967).

16. Argyris, J. H., and J. R. Roy, "General Treatment of Structural Modifications," *ASCE J. Struct. Div.*, **98**(ST2):4645–4692 (February 1972).

17. Kosko, E., "Effect of Local Modifications in Redundant Structures," *J. Aero. Sci.*, 206–207 (March 1954).

18. Storaasli, O. O., and J. Sobieszczanski, "On the Accuracy of the Taylor Approximation for Structure Resizing," *AIAA J.*, **12**(2):231–233 (February 1974).

19. Noor, A., "Multiple Configuration Analysis via Mixed Methods," *ASCE J. Struct. Div.*, **ST9**:1991–1997 (September 1974).

20. Romstad, K. M., J. R. Hutchinson, and K. H. Runge, "Design Parameter Variation and Structural Response," *Int. J. Numer. Meth. Eng.*, **5**:337–349 (1973).

21. Fox, R. L., and H. Miura, "An Approximate Analysis Technique for Design Calculations," *AIAA J.*, **9**(1):177–179 (January 1971).

22. Noor, A. K., and H. E. Lowder, "Approximate Techniques of Structural Reanalysis," *Int. J. Comput. Struct.*, **4**(4):801–812 (1974).

23. Sobieszczanski-Sobienski, J., and P. Hajela, "Accuracy of an Approximate Static Structural Analysis Technique Based on Stiffness Matrix Eigenmodes," *AIAA/ASME/ASCE/AHS 20th Struct. Dynam. Mater. Conf.*, St. Louis, Apr. 4–6, 1979.

24. Kirsch, U., and M. F. Rubinstein, "Structural Reanalysis by Iteration," *Comput. Struct.*, **2**:497–510 (1972).

25. Phansalkar, S. R., "Matrix Iterative Methods for Structural Reanalysis," *Comput. Struct.*, **4**:779–800 (1974).

26. Meirovitch, L., *Analytical Methods in Vibrations*, 1st ed., Macmillan, New York, 1967.

27. Clough, R. W., and J. Penzien, *Dynamics of Structures*, 1st ed., McGraw-Hill, New York, 1975.

28. Hurty, W. C., and M. F. Rubinstein, *Dynamics of Structures*, 1st ed., Prentice-Hall, Englewood Cliffs, N.J., 1964.

29. Bisplinghoff, R. L., H. Ashley, and R. L. Halfman, *Aero-elasticity*, Addison-Wesley, Reading, Mass., 1955.

30. Gunter, E. J., K. C. Choy, and P. E. Allaire, "Modal Analysis of Turborotors Using Planar Modes-Theory," *J. Franklin Inst.*, **305**(4):221–243 (1978).

31. Weissenburger, J. T., "The Effects of Local Modifications on the Eigenvalues and Eigenvectors of Linear Systems," Ph.D. dissertation, U.M. 6607529, Sever Institute of Technology, Washington University, St. Louis, 1966.

32. Weissenburger, J. T., "Effect of Local Modifications on the Vibration Characteristics of Linear Systems," *J. Appl. Mech. Trans. ASME*, **35**:327–332 (1968).

33. Wilkinson, J. H., *The Algebraic Eigenvalue Problem*, 1st ed., Clarendon Press, Oxford, 1965.

34. Pomazal, R. J., "The Effect of Local Modifications on the Eigenvalues and Eigenvectors of Damped Linear Systems," Ph.D. Dissertation, U.M. 7013559, Michigan Technological University, Houghton, 1969.

35. Pomazal, R. J., "Local Modifications of Damped Linear Systems," *AIAA J.*, **9**(11):2216–2221 (1971).

36. Hallquist, J. O., "Modification and Synthesis of Large Dynamic Structural Systems," Ph.D. dissertation, U.M. 7514397, Michigan Technological University, Houghton, 1974.

37. Hallquist, J. O., "An Efficient Method for Determining the Effects of Mass Modifications in Damped Systems," *J. Sound Vibration*, **44**(3):449–459 (1976).

38. Vilmann, C. R., and V. W. Snyder, "Line Modification of Continuous Vibratory Systems." *J. Struct. Div. ASCE*, **104**(ST12):1819–1826 (December 1978).

39. Hirai, I., T. Yoshimura, and K. Takamura, "On a Direct Eigenvalue Analysis for Locally Modified Structures," *Int. J. Numer. Meth. Eng.*, **6**:441–442 (1973).

40. Done, G. T. S., and A. D. Hughes, "The Response of a Vibrating Structure as a Function of Structural Parameters," *J. Sound Vibration*, **38**(2):255–266 (1975).

41. Done, G. T. S., A. D. Hughes, and J. Webby, "The Response of a Vibrating Structure as a Function of Structural Parameters—Application and Experiment," *J. Sound Vibration*, **49**(2):149–159 (1976).

42. Bishop, R. E. D., *The Mechanics of Vibration*, 1st ed., Cambridge University Press, Cambridge, 1960.

43. Stetson, K. A., and G. E. Palma, "Inversion of First Order Perturbation Theory and Its Application to Structural Design," *AIAA J.*, **14**(4):454–460 (April 1976).

44. Franklin, J. N., *Matrix Theory*, 1st ed., Prentice-Hall, Englewood Cliffs, N.J., 1968.

45. Lund, J. W., "Sensitivity of the Critical Speeds of a Rotor to Changes in the Design," *J. Mech. Des. Trans. ASME*, **102**:115–121 (January 1980).

46. Lancaster, P., "Free Vibrations of Lightly Damped Systems by Perturbation Methods," *Q. J. Mech. Appl. Math.*, **13**:138–155 (1960).

47. Aubrun, J. N., "Theory of the Control of Structures by Low Authority Controllers," pap. no. 78-1689, *AIAA Conference on Large Space Platforms: Future Needs and Capabilities*, Los Angeles, Calif., Sept. 27–29, 1978.

48. Meirovitch, L., and G. Ryland II, "Response of Slightly Damped Gyroscopic Systems," *J. Sound Vibration*, **67**(1):1–19 (1979).

49. Fox, R. L., and M. P. Kapoor, "Rates of Change of Eigenvalues and Eigenvectors," *AIAA J.*, **6**(12):2426–2429 (1968).

50. Rudisill, C. S., "Derivatives of Eigenvalues and Eigenvectors for a General Matrix," *AIAA J.*, **12**(5):721–722 (May 1974).

51. Plaut, R. H., "Derivatives of Eigenvalues and Eigenvectors in Non-Self Adjoint Systems," *AIAA J.*, **11**(2):250–251 (February 1973).

52. Rogers, L. C., "Derivatives of Eigenvalues and Eigenvectors," *AIAA J.*, **8**(5):943–944 (May 1970).

53. Garg, S., "Derivatives of Eigensolutions for a General Matrix," *AIAA J.*, **11**(8):1191–1194 (August 1973).

54. Hilber, H. M., T. J. R. Hughes, and R. L. Taylor, "Improved Numerical Dissipation for Time Integration Algorithms in Structural Dynamics," *Earthquake Eng. Struct. Dynam.*, **5**:283–292 (1977).

55. Bathe, K.-J., and E. L. Wilson, *Numerical Methods in Finite Element Analysis*, Prentice-Hall, Englewood Cliffs, N.J., 1976.

56. Hurty, W. C., "Vibration of Structural Systems by Component Mode Synthesis," *Proc. ASCE*, **85**(4):51–69 (August 1960).

57. Hasselman, T. K., and A. Kaplan, "Dynamic Analysis of Large Systems by Complex Mode Synthesis," *J. Dynam. System, Measurement, Control, Trans. ASME*, Ser. G, **96**:327–333 (September 1974).

58. Meirovitch, L., *Computational Methods in Structural Dynamics*, Sijthoff and Noordhoff, Rockville, Maryland, 1980.

59. NacNeal, R. H., "A Hybrid Method of Component Mode Synthesis," *J. Comput. Struct.*, **1**(4):581–601 (December 1971).

60. Rubin, S., "An Improved Component-Mode Representation for Structural Dynamic Analysis," *AIAA J.*, **13**(8):995–1005 (August 1975).

61. Hurty, W. C., "Dynamic Analysis of Structural Systems Using Component Modes," *AIAA J.*, **3**:678–685 (April 1965).

62. Hurty, W. C., "Introduction to Modal Synthesis Techniques," *Synthesis of Vibrating Systems Colloquium, ASME 1971 Winter Annual Meeting*, Washington, D.C., November 1971, pp. 1–13.

63. Hurty, W. C., "A Criterion for Selecting Realistic Natural Modes of a Structure," TM 33-364, Jet Propulsion Lab., Pasadena, Calif., November 1967.

64. Craig, R. R., Jr., and M. C. C. Bampton, "Coupling of Substructures for Dynamic Analyses," *AIAA J.*, **6**(7):1313–1319 (July 1968).

65. Benfield, W. A., C. S. Bodley, and G. Morosow, "Modal Synthesis Methods," *Symposium on Substructure Testing and Synthesis*, NASA, Washington, D.C., August 1972.

66. Craig, R. R., and C.-J. Chang, "On the Use of Attachment Modes in Substructure Coupling for Dynamic Analysis," Pap. 77-405, *AIAA/ASME 18th Struct., Struct. Dynam., Mater. Conf.*, San Diego, Calif., 1977.

67. Bajan, R. L., and C. C. Feng, "Free Vibration Analysis by the Modal Substitution Method," *AAS Symposium on Space Projections from the Rocky Mountain Region*, American Astronautical Society pap. no. 68-8-1, Denver, Colo., July 1968.

68. Goldman, R. L., "Vibration Analysis by Dynamic Partitioning," *AIAA J.*, 7(6):1152–1154 (June 1969).

69. Hou, S., "Review of Modal Synthesis Techniques and a New Approach," in *The Shock and Vibration Bulletin*, Naval Research Laboratory, Washington, D.C., December 1969, no. 40, pt. 4, pp. 25–39.

70. Benfield, W. A., and R. F. Hruda, "Vibration Analysis of Structures by Component Mode Substitution," *AIAA J.*, 9(7):1255–1261 (July 1971).

71. Gladwell, G. M. L., "Branch Mode Analysis of Vibrating Systems," *J. Sound Vibration*, 1:41–59 (1964).

72. Kuhar, E. J., and C. V. Stahle, "A Dynamic Transformation Method for Modal Synthesis," *AIAA J.*, 12(5):672–678 (1974).

73. Dowell, E. H., "Free Vibrations of an Arbitrary Structure in Terms of Component Modes," *J. Appl. Mech.*, 39(3):727–732 (1972).

74. Dowell, E. H., "Free Vibrations of a Linear Structure with Arbitrary Support Conditions," *J. Appl. Mech.*, 39:595–600 (September 1971).

75. Edge, B. L., P. G. Mayer, and G. A. Pierce, "An Analysis Technique for Composite Structures Subject to Dynamic Loads," *J. Appl. Mech.*, 38, *Trans. ASME*, 93, ser. E: 118–124 (1971).

76. Hallquist, J. O., and V. Snyder, "Synthesis of Two Discrete Vibratory Systems Using Eigenvalue Modification," *AIAA J.*, 12(2):247–249 (February 1973).

77. Hallquist, J. O., and V. W. Snyder, "On the Connection of Viscously Damped Continuous Vibratory Systems," *J. Sound Vibration*, 32(1):131–142 (1974).

78. Meirovitch, L., and H. Oz, "Active Control of Structures by Modal Synthesis," in H. H. E. Leipholz (ed.), *Structural Control*, North-Holland, Amsterdam, 1980.

79. Hintz, R. M., "Analytical Methods in Component Modal Synthesis," *AIAA J.*, 13(8):2007–2016 (August 1975).

80. Hasselman, T. K., and G. C. Hart, "A Minimization Method for Treating Convergence in Modal Synthesis," *AIAA J.*, 12(3):316–323 (March 1974).

81. Bajan, R. L., C. C. Feng, and I. J. Jaszlics, "Vibration Analysis of Complex Structural Systems by Modal Substitution," *Proceedings of the 30th Shock and Vibration Symposium*, Monterey, Calif., October 1968.

82. Hale, A. L., and L. Meirovitch, "A General Substructure Synthesis Method for the Dynamic Simulation of Complex Structures," *J. Sound Vibration*, 69(2):309–326 (1980).

83. Jensen, P. S., "The Solution of Large Symmetric Eigenproblems by Sectioning," *SIAM J. Numer. Anal.*, 9(4):534–545 (1972).

84. Meirovitch, L., "A Modal Analysis for the Response of Linear Gyroscopic Systems," *J. Appl. Mech.*, 42(2):446–450 (1975).

85. Meirovitch, L., "A Stationarity Principle for the Eigenvalue Problem for Rotating Structures," *AIAA J.*, 14(10):1387–1394 (1976).

86. Meirovitch, L., and A. L. Hale, "Synthesis and Dynamic Characteristics of Large Structures with Rotating Substructures," in K. Magnus (ed.), *Proceedings of the IUTAM Symposium on the Dynamics of Multibody Systems*, Springer-Verlag, Berlin, 1978, pp. 231–244.

87. Meirovitch, L., and A. L. Hale, "A General Dynamic Synthesis for Structures with Discrete Substructures," Pap. No. 80-0798, *AIAA/ASME/ASCE/AHS 21st Struct., Struct. Dynam. Mater. Conf.*, Seattle, Wash., May 12–14, 1980.

88. Meirovitch, L., and A. L. Hale, "On the Substructure Synthesis Method," *An International Conference on Recent Advances in Structural Dynamics*, Southampton, England, July 7–11, 1980.

89. Klosterman, A. L., "On the Experimental Determination and Use of Modal Representations of Dynamic Characteristics," Ph.D. dissertation, University of Cincinnati, Cincinnati, 1971.

90. Goldenberg, S., and M. Shapiro, "A Study of Modal Coupling Procedures," NASA CR-1152252, Grumman Aerospace Corp., NASA Contract No. NAS-10535-8, 1972.

91. Klosterman, A. L., and W. A. McClelland, "Combining Experimental and Analytical Techniques for Dynamic System Analysis," *Tokyo Seminar on Finite Element Analysis*, Tokyo, November 1973.

92. Kana, D. D., and S. Huzar, "Synthesis of Shuttle Vehicle Damping Using Substructure Test Results," Interim Rep. for NASA Contract No. NAS8-27569, Southwest Research Institute, San Antonio, Tex., June 1972.

93. Kana, D. D., and S. Huzar, "Synthesis of Shuttle Vehicle Damping Using Substructure Test Results," *Journal of Spacecraft and Rockets*, **10**(12):790–797 (December 1973).

94. Hasselman, T. K., "Damping Synthesis from Substructure Tests," *AIAA/ASME/SAE 15th Struct., Struct. Dynam., Mater. Conf.*, AIAA Pap. No. 74-387, Las Vegas, Nev., April 1974.

95. Neubert, V. H., and J. P. Raney (eds.), *Synthesis of Vibrating Systems*, American Society of Mechanical Engineers, New York, November 1971, Bk. No. H00072.

96. Hurty, W. C., "Introduction to Modal Synthesis Techniques," in V. H. Neubert and J. P. Raney (eds.), *Synthesis of Vibrating Systems*, American Society of Mechanical Engineers, New York, November 1971.

97. Craig, R. R., and C. J. Chang, "A Review of Substructure Coupling Methods for Dynamic Analysis," NASA CP-2001, vol. 2, pp. 292–407.

98. Craig, R. R., "Methods of Component Mode Synthesis," *Shock Vibration Dig.*, **9**(11) (November 1977).

99. Kung, W. C., and K. H. Hohenemser, "Eigenvalue Analysis for Coupled Large Linear Damped Structures," *Comput. Meth. Appl. Mech. Eng.*, **12**:69–75 (1977).

100. Leung, Y. T., "An Accurate Method of Dynamic Substructuring with Simplified Computation," *Int. J. Numer. Meth. Eng.*, **14**:1241–1256 (1979).

101. Craig, R. R., "Substructure Coupling for Dynamic Analysis," *Advances in Civil Engineering Through Engineering Mechanics*, American Society of Chemical Engineers, New York, 1977, pp. 389–392.

102. Guyan, R. J., "Reduction of Stiffness and Mass Matrices," *AIAA J.*, **3**(2):380 (1965).

103. Leung, Y.-T., "An Accurate Method of Dynamic Substructuring with Simplified Computation," *Int. J. Numer. Meth. Eng.*, **14**:1241–1256 (1979).

104. Wittrick, W. H., and F. W. Williams, "A General Algorithm for Computing Natural Frequencies of Elastic Structures," *Q. J. Mech. Appl. Math.*, **24**:263–284 (1971).

105. Hirai, I., T. Yoshimura, and K. Takamura, "On a Direct Eigenvalue Analysis for Locally Modified Structures," *Int. J. Numer. Meth. Eng.*, **6**:441–442 (1973).

106. Palazzolo, A. B., "Vibrations of Locally Modified Mechanical and Structural Systems," Ph.D. dissertation, University of Virginia, Charlottesville, January 1981.

107. Kukreti, A. R., and C. C. Feng, "Dynamic Substructuring for Alternating Subsystems," *Proc. ASCE*, **EM5**:1113–1129 (1978).

108. Kubomura, K., "A Theory of Substructure Modal Synthesis," *J. Appl. Mech.*, **49**:903–908 (1982).

109. Pomazal, R. J., and V. W. Snyder, "Local Modifications of Damped Linear Systems," *AIAA J.*, **9**:2216–2221 (1971).

110. Hallquist, J. O., and V. W. Snyder, "Synthesis of Two Discrete Vibratory Systems Using Eigenvalue Modification," *AIAA J.*, **11**:247–249 (1973).

111. Hallquist, J. O., and V. W. Snyder, "On the Connection of Viscously Damped Continuous Vibratory Systems," *J. Sound Vibration*, **32**:131–142 (1974).

112. Hasselman, T. K., "Dynamic Analysis of Large Systems by Complex Mode Synthesis," *J. Dynam. Systems, Measurement, Control, ASME*, Ser. G, **96**:327–333 (September 1974).

113. Gutierrez, J. A., and A. K. Chopra, "A Substructure Method for Earthquake Analysis of Structures Including Structure-Soil Interaction," *Earthquake Eng. Struct. Dynam.*, **6**:51–69 (1978).

114. Takemiya, H., and K. Kawano, "Substructure Method for Earthquake Response of High-Elevated Multi-Span Continuous Bridge," *Proc. 7th World Conf. Earthquake Eng.*, 1980, vol. 5, pp. 459–466.

115. Foss, K. A., "Coordinates Which Uncouple the Equations of Motion of Damped Linear Dynamic Systems," *J. Appl. Mech.*, **25**:361–364 (1958).

116. Clough, R. W., and C. A. Felippa, "A Refined Quadrilateral Element for Analysis of Plate Bending," AFFDL-TR-68-150, *Proc. 2d Conf. Matrix Meth. Struct. Mech.*, Wright–Patterson Airforce Base, Ohio, December 1969, pp. 399–439.

117. Rosen, R., and M. F. Rubinstein, "Substructure Analysis by Matrix Decomposition," *J. Struct. Div. ASCE*, **96**(ST3) (March 1970).

118. Mondkar, D. P., and G. H. Powell, "Towards Optimal In-Core Equation Solving," *Int. J. Comput. Struct.*, **4**:531–548 (1974).

119. Felippa, C. A., "Solution of Linear Equations with Skyline-Stored Symmetric Matrix," *Int. J. Comput. Struct.*, **5**:13–30 (1975).

120. Irons, B. M., "A Frontal Solution Program," *Int. J. Numer. Meth. Eng.*, **2**:5–32 (1970).

121. Alizadeh, A., and G. T. Will, "A Substructured Frontal Solver and its Application to Localized Material Non-Linearity," *Int. J. Comput. Struct.*, **10**:225–231 (1979).

122. Guyan, R. J., "Reduction of Stiffness and Mass Matrices," *J. AIAA*, **3**:380 (1965).

123. Irons, B. M., "Structural Eigenvalue Problems: Elimination of Unwanted Variables," *J. AIAA*, **3**:961 (1965).

124. Przemieniecki, J. S., *Theory of Matrix Structural Analysis*, McGraw-Hill, New York, 1968.

125. Kardestuncer, H., *Elementary Matrix Analysis of Structures*, McGraw-Hill, New York, 1974, chap. 10.

126. "The NASTRAN Theoretical Manual" (Level 17.5), National Aeronautics and Space Administration, Washington, D.C., December 1980, sec. 4.5.

127. Arora, J. S., and A. K. Govil, "Design Sensitivity Analysis with Substructuring," *J. Eng. Div. ASCE*, **EM4**:537–548 (1977).

128. Dodds, R. H., Jr., and L. A. Lopez, "Substructuring in Linear and Nonlinear Analysis," *Int. J. Numer. Meth. Eng.*, **15**:583–597 (1980).

129. Jacobsen, K. P., "Fully Integrated Superelements: A Database Approach to Finite Element Analysis," *Int. J. Comput. Struct.*, **16**:307–315 (1983).

130. Kamel, H. A., D. Liu, and E. I. White, "The Computer in Ship Structure Design," in S. J. Fenves et al. (eds.), *Numerical and Computer Methods in Structural Mechanics*, Academic Press, New York, 1973, pp. 643–668.

# CHAPTER 3
# FEM MODELING
# AND PREPROCESSING

The subject of finite-element modeling has long been of critical importance to the practicing designer-analyst who is often faced with obtaining an accurate and cost-effective stress or vibration analysis of a particular design. Typically these two goals are in conflict. The purpose of this chapter on finite-element modeling is to assemble topics which are significant for the practicing modeler.

In the subsection on modeling requirements, several limitations of the finite-element method are discussed with regard to element technology and its effect on modeling considerations. Several general guidelines for finite-element modeling are also discussed. One must be aware that guidelines may not apply in all cases. It is also important to note that modeling techniques are different for vibration or nonlinear analyses than they are for simple static-stress or deflection analyses. Several unique aspects of nonlinear modeling are also discussed. The construction of a model is dependent on the expected response, whether it is contained plasticity, as in the case of a stress concentration, or overall structural yielding.

The importance of finite-element node-point sequencing and the use of planes of structural symmetry in the finite-element modeling and analysis process are discussed next. Considerable computational time may be realized for a particular finite-element model by making the proper use of node-point sequencing and structural symmetry, if it exists. Most commercially available finite-element computer programs provide node-point sequencing of a form which is optimum for the type of equation solution algorithms used in their programs (i.e., band or wave solvers).

The concluding section discusses automatic mesh generation and adaptive analysis. A historical as well as present and future look at this important subject is presented. Automatic mesh generation coupled with adaptive-reanalysis techniques and optimization potentially offer major productivity improvements to designers. A problem with these methods gaining widespread acceptance has been their propensity to generate "oddly" shaped finite elements and the fear that these elements would yield unreasonable results. This is still a valid concern. Several techniques which may be used to minimize this difficulty are discussed.


## 3.1 MODELING IN STRUCTURAL MECHANICS

*Modeling* is defined as a simulation of a system or structure. This definition infers artistic as well as functional simulation. The artistic part of modeling is not the "art form" that has been associated with finite elements; rather, finite-element modeling is a simulation of functional form. The "art" involved in finite elements is the expert use of engineering theory and judgment.

There are many factors involved in simulating a system. For finite elements or any analytical technique, there is more involved than matching the physical structure. There are additional factors, such as time and budget, which affect the type of models that are created. Such nonengineering limits temper the engineer's approach to modeling. Nevertheless, models must be practical and meet all the limits, engineering or otherwise.

This section is limited to presenting engineering constraints in finite-element modeling. These must then be weighted with the other limits in creating the final model.


### 3.1A Modeling for Problem Solving

Problem solving can be said to involve three steps. First, there is a review and definition of the problem. Second, one must create a practical approach to simulate the system. Finally, the solution is attempted. The definition step *affects* the modeling; however, modeling is the process of simulation.

When the approach to the solution is a finite-element analysis, then the first step of problem solving involves defining a geometry, support system, materials, and loadings. It is necessary to have this physical information to create models; however, other data are also required. Part of the definition step involves prescribing the type of solution needed to answer the questions concerning a design. These may involve requests for deflections, strength (stress and strain), fatigue life, or natural frequencies of vibration. The type of model created is influenced by the way the problem has been defined. The model is obviously affected by the prescribed geometric properties and by the type of results requested.

For a simple pipe tee (Fig. 3.1), the geometry is prescribed and the loading and support locations are indicated. However, there are many different finite-element models that may be used for just a simple linear static analysis. The type of model used is governed by the type of result requested, e.g., a basic check for flexibility and design stresses. A model for this type of problem would use strength-of-materials approximations of the joint. In this theory, all cross sections are limited to linear bending stresses; uncoupled joint flexibility and stress concentrations are also assumed to be known. These assumptions may limit the possible choices for the finite-element model. The joint could be modeled by using connecting beam elements, connecting straight pipe elements, or a specialty element for pipe tee joints.

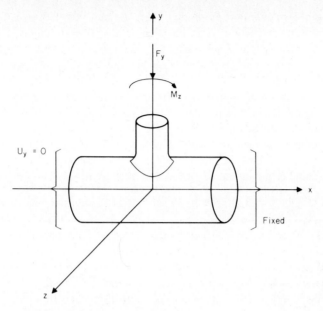

**FIG. 3.1** Pipe-tee loads and supports.

If a more detailed stress distribution is required at the branch to the main-run junction, a totally different model must be used. One detailed model, for example, may use all shell elements; a second model may use all 3D solid elements; a third possibility is a mixture of solids and shell elements. Each of these three possible models has a different theoretical basis and potential cost. The "best" model is the one that accurately answers the questions involved with a minimum of time and cost.

## 3.1B Element Selection

Choosing the right element is one step in modeling [1]. The finite-element codes offer a large selection of elements; the element families described in Chap. 4 of Part 2 are commonly found in commercial programs. For the proper choice of elements in structural mechanics, the following characteristics should be considered.

***Geometry and Theory***   The most fundamental geometric construct is a line. In structural mechanics, for instance, a line element may be an axial bar, slender beam, pipe, curved pipe, curved beam, cable, spring, etc.

The next level of geometry is the surface of revolution. Axisymmetric thin-shell and thick-ring elements exist for various loadings. There is also a large family of elements available for general surfaces. These are either flat-shell or curved-shell elements which accommodate membrane effects, plane-stress and plane-strain theories, bending theory of plates, shallow-shell theory, membrane plus bending, curved and layered shell theories, etc.

The two- and three-dimensional elements are the final geometric types. In some cases, 2D solid elements are expanded to have axisymmetric ring capabilities.

*Geometry and Displacement Function*  There are different element categories related to types of displacement functions (e.g., Lagrange family, Hermite family, serendipity family of elements [2]). There is, however, a broader form of classification which includes both the displacement function and geometry; these are the classes of isoparametric and non-isoparametric elements.

Modeling curved external boundaries with higher-order isoparametric elements is common; however, modeling studies [3] have shown that edges of those elements should remain straight within the plane of the element (see Fig. 3.2). For solid or planar elements, only the element edges on boundary surfaces should be curved, while for three-dimensional shell surfaces, element edges should follow the shell curvature but should not curve in the plane of the shell (Fig. 3.2). Internal edges should be curved only if they are parallel to the lines of constant stress in the given region.

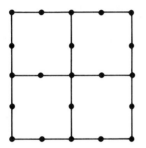
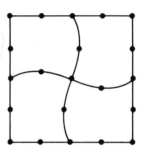

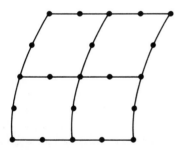
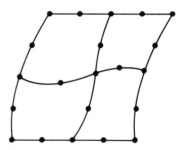

**FIG. 3.2**  Curved element boundaries.

Another class of elements is referred to as incompatible or nonconforming [4]. These may be formulated in parametric space or in the general element coordinate system. Their displacement functions have additional terms beyond those normally associated with element nodal degrees of freedom, and these terms impart extra flexibility to the element. The elements are incompatible because the extra shape functions allow edges of adjacent elements to gap or overlap within a structure (Fig. 3.3).

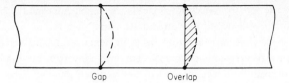

**FIG. 3.3**   Gapping and overlapping.

Elements with assumed displacement functions are generally stiff. Incompatible elements, on the other hand, are more flexible than the conforming elements of the same order (degrees of freedom). For coarse meshes the displacement and stress solutions for incompatible elements are quite accurate and solution for refined meshes converge to the same result. An example of an incompatible element is a simple linear element with the bilinear displacement function (Fig. 3.4). This element cannot "bend" properly for an applied in-plane moment, although with the addition of the extra quadratic terms in $u$ and $v$, it can be made to bend. It has the same number of nodes and degrees of freedom as a simple linear element. However, it does simulate a quadratic deflection and linear bending state.

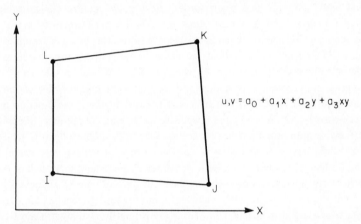

**FIG. 3.4**   Bilinear displacement element.

There are limitations to the incompatible elements: the bounded nature of the solution is lost; a displacement solution cannot be guaranteed to converge from below; and elements can become dependent upon values of Poisson's ratio. Incompatible elements may also violate the "patch test" for constant strain. It should be noted that element distortions are more critical in coarse meshes since the errors diminish as the mesh is refined. Finally, for incompatible shape functions, the generalized coefficients on opposite sides are equal. The functions are fine if the elements are parallelograms, but when the elements have sides of unequal length, opposite sides must have unequal curvatures.

**Stress Field**   The variations of stresses and strains are of lower order than displacements within the elements. Therefore, a model which gives an accurate displacement solution may not give as accurate a stress solution. For this reason, the potential variation of stress within an element is a criterion for selecting elements. A model must match both the potential deformations and stress distributions within a structure.

The constant-stress element is the most basic element and satisfies the basic convergence criteria for elements. As a mesh is refined, the solution converges, but because stress in each element is constant, equilibrium cannot be satisfied between elements except in regions where stress does not actually vary. For problems with high-stress gradients, an exceptionally fine mesh is required for an accurate solution.

Linear-stress field elements are currently the most commonly used. Almost all families (by geometry and theory) of elements have linear-stress capabilities. These types of elements are found in beams, plates, shells, and solids. Most design problems require a good linear-stress solution (sometimes called *primary stresses*), and design codes are based upon limiting these primary stresses [9].

In areas of discontinuities, high thermal gradients, fatigue studies, or nonlinear material problems, there is an interest in evaluating more than just a linear-stress state. Even then, a piecewise linear approximation of stress from multiple linear elements gives excellent results with relatively coarse meshes. Models can use local refinements for these maximum-stress states (Fig. 3.5).

Elements with quadratic and higher-order stress fields require cubic or higher-order displacement functions, and they have either more nodes per element or more degrees of freedom per node, which makes them inherently more expensive elements. Complex structures require relatively fine meshes to model the geometry and stress discontinuities properly; higher-order elements are practical only when relatively coarse meshes can be used for high-stress gradient problems. Even then, the quadratic of higher-order fit may over- or underestimate the stresses at the free surfaces. The order of the stress function must match the gradient properly, which is why the linear-stress elements are popular. In complex stress fields, a piecewise approximation is easy to visualize and, mathematically, relatively well-behaved for fitting higher-order curves. Final limitations for the higher-order elements are their potential incompatibilities with the lower-order elements and their lack of full families of elements. Many structures cannot be modeled using one type of element since special transition elements are required when both high- and low-order elements are used together.

Elements which use displacement functions are primarily available in most commercial codes. The selection processes above are related to these elements. Other types of elements are based on stress functions and on hybrid and mixed formulations [5].

### 3.1c Guidelines for Element Usage

Selection of the proper element is the important first step in modeling. Proper use involves distorting elements from ideal shapes, creating transitions in element patterns, using symmetry planes, etc.

Elements have ideal shapes, which involve little or no error in the numerical computation of individual stiffness matrices. It would be convenient if triangles could always be equilateral, quadrilaterals always be squares, and hexahedra always be cubes. However, it is almost impossible to model complex systems with a mesh of ideally shaped elements. Therefore, it is always wise to match the mesh refinement to the stress gradients and deformation patterns. This means that elements must vary in size, have unequal side lengths, and, possibly, be

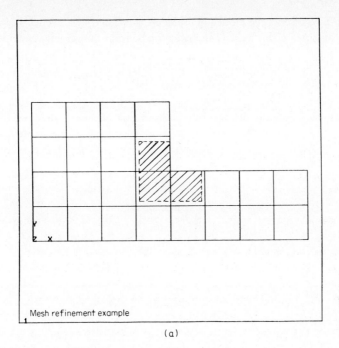

Mesh refinement example

(a)

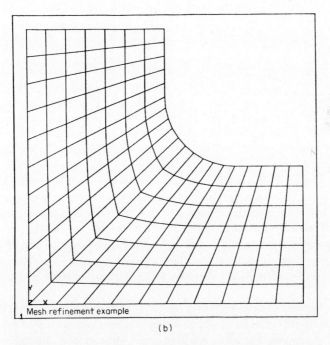

Mesh refinement example

(b)

**FIG. 3.5** Refinements for high-stress gradients. (*a*) Corner and surrounding area (shown cross-hatched) where refinement of mesh is required. (*b*) Refined mesh in corner region.

distorted. We now discuss the modeling problems associated with elements having unequal side lengths, distorted elements, and transitioning patterns for varying refinements.

**Aspect Ratio**    The element aspect ratio is the ratio between the longest and shortest element dimensions (Fig. 3.6). Acceptable ranges for aspect ratio are element- and problem-dependent, but users are normally given fixed numerical limits such as 3:1 for stresses and 10:1 for deflections. There is no hard and fast rule governing all elements. The limit to aspect ratio is affected by the order of the element displacement function, the numerical-integration pattern for stiffness, the material behavior (linear versus nonlinear), and even the resulting deflection and stress solution patterns.

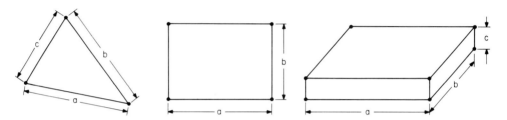

**FIG. 3.6**    Aspect ratio.

Elements with higher-order displacement functions and higher-order numerical quadratures for a given displacement function are less sensitive to large aspect ratios. Elements in regions of material nonlinearities are more sensitive to changes in aspect ratio than those in linear regions.

The best gauge for aspect-ratio limits is the ability of the element to simulate the deflection and stress gradient of the given problem. In a general stress field with gradients in all directions, most elements should have aspect ratios near 1:1. Since no particular direction dominates, the mesh refinement must be nearly equal in all directions. If a problem has a deflection or stress gradient dominant in a single direction, elements may have relatively high (10:1) aspect ratios, provided the shortest element dimension is in the direction of the maximum gradient.

Since an element's sensitivity to aspect ratio is dependent upon both element development and actual problem limits, general tests and problem-dependent checks must be implemented before using any of the elements. Simple "patch tests" for constant stress and similar tests under linear or other stress gradients can be run for each element type. The element evaluation studies proposed by Robinson [1] could be one source of such testing. However, a user should also create simple models with loadings to simulate expected problem distortions and stresses. The problemlike tests are necessary to develop cost-effective and accurate models.

**Distortions**    Skewing of elements or their out-of-plane warping are important considerations. *Skewing* is usually defined as the variation of element vertex angles from 90° for quadrilaterals and from 60° for triangles (Fig. 3.7a). Warpage occurs when all the nodes of three-dimensional plates and shells do not lie on the same plane or when the nodes on a single face of a solid deviate from a single plane (Fig. 3.7b).

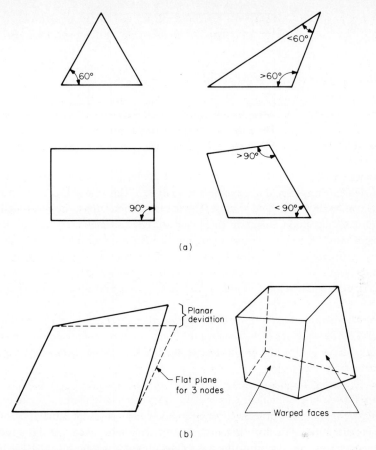

(a)

(b)

**FIG. 3.7**   (*a*) Skewed elements. (*b*) Warped elements.

***Transitioning***   There are two types of transition. One is the change in *element density* in the direction of the stress gradient (Fig. 3.8), in which the greatest refinement is in the region of the highest gradient. The second is transverse transitioning, which is used between *element patterns* with different densities across a transverse plane (Fig. 3.9).

The modeling criteria for transitions as shown in Fig. 3.8 are based upon the adjacent element sizes, which are relative lengths for line elements, areas for 2D or planar elements,

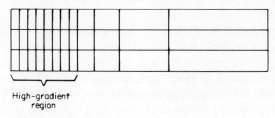

High-gradient
region

11015          **FIG. 3.8**   Transitions—element size changes.

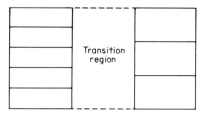

**FIG. 3.9**  Transitions—element pattern changes.

and volumes for 3D elements. In the creation of models, a common rule of thumb is that adjacent element sizes should not exceed a ratio of 2:1. This rule of thumb is actually based upon element strain energy and strain-energy density calculations, the ideal model being a mesh with constant strain energy in each element. For constant strain energy of elements, the volumes must be relatively small in regions of high stress or strain and large in regions of low stress or strain. This is also the exact pattern required to properly match stress and deformation gradients in a system. The energy criterion is used to generate optimum models. An initial model can be modified after each solution to create a mesh with nearly constant energy.

If a model requires transverse transition regions, they should be used only in the low-stress gradient, *never* near regions of maximum stress, deflection, or other regions of interest. These transition patterns involve the use of degenerate or distorted elements which can introduce errors in the transition region.

***Boundary Conditions***   Simulating forces and stress patterns is another special topic related to boundary conditions. A process common to many analyses is the simulation of moments as force couples, but, as in any other analysis, care should be taken that this approximation is far removed from the region of interest. Simulating stress states at model boundaries is not as common as approximating forces. However, given a prescribed planar stress (constant, linear, or other variation), an edge or surface pressure distribution can be employed to approximate the stress state. This is a potential alternative to applying axial forces or bending moments to shell or solid models of such structures as nozzles, cylinders, and piping systems. These simple stress distributions can be applied as normal or edge pressures to the solid and shell models (Fig. 3.10).

If a structure is axisymmetric but the loadings are nonsymmetric, three possible models can be used. One contains 2D axisymmetric elements in which the loads are approximated by a Fourier series representation (Fourier decomposition in the circumferential direction), and each harmonic term is one loading. The total response is the sum of all harmonics. This method is well-documented in finite-element texts and was prevalent in the late 1960s and early 1970s because it avoided large-scale 3D models which were difficult to create and expensive to run.

The second possibility is a 3D model with planes of symmetry. Actual loads are applied to this type of model. The harmonic procedure remains cost-effective when the number of terms required to approximate the loadings is relatively small. The actual break-even point is problem-dependent but usually lies somewhere between five and ten harmonic terms. Thus,

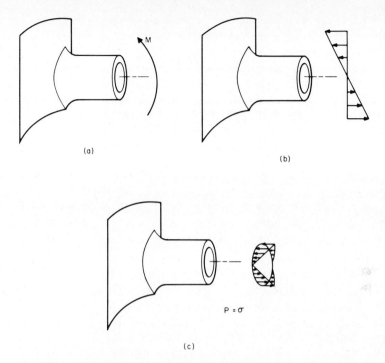

(a)

(b)

(c)

P = σ

**FIG. 3.10**  Stress distribution modeled as end pressure. (*a*) Nozzle with end moment. (*b*) Assumed linear bending stress. (*c*) Normal pressure distribution simulating stress.

for example, simulation of simple bending moments, shear forces, torsion, and soil loadings is performed economically with harmonic loadings because it (the simulation) requires only one to three harmonic terms per loading.

The third possibility employs cyclic symmetry [6] and is discussed in Sec. 3.3.

There are systems which require evaluating combinations of a set of loadings. In such systems, the individual component loadings are known but the combination of loadings giving the "worst-case" response (maximum stress, deflection, fatigue) must be found.

The most cost-effective procedure for satisfying loading combinations is the use of unit loadings. For linear-elastic structures, the superposition principle is valid, and a combined response gives the same result as the application of all loads simultaneously. If the number of loading cases is less than the number of combinations required, a unit load analysis can be cost-effective and computer calculation costs will decrease. Data storage and engineering costs, however, may be high.

***Discontinuities***  Cracks, holes, abrupt changes in sections, grillages, intersections of structures, reinforcements, and multiple materials can all be classified as creating discontinuous stress patterns. Relatively coarse, global-response models and detailed local-microresponse models exist for such problems. The global model, for example, ensures that the load path simulates overall response and provides adequate stress results away from the discontinuity.

A local model, on the other hand, provides detailed maximum stresses even in the region of discontinuity and are usually generated only to study nonlinear material behavior, cyclic response, or other failure modes.

Most structural models ignore potential flaws (like cracks). These are not generally designed into a system. If a flaw is detected during inspection, its impact on the structure must be evaluated. The types of models for simulating cracks are normally one of three types. First, the actual flaw can be modeled in fine detail. The region of the flaw would have an exceptionally fine grid. Second, midside nodes of quadratic isoparametric elements can be moved to the $\frac{1}{4}$- or $\frac{3}{4}$-side-length position to create singularities in those elements. Finally, there are specially formulated elements that include the effects of a crack. A good survey of linear-fracture procedures in finite elements can be found in Ref. [7].

Holes or openings in systems may be modeled for global or local response. The type of model required depends upon the level of detail requested. If the global-system response alone is the goal, a model need only approximate the stiffness of the regions with holes or cutouts. Two common modeling methods are used for this general response. The first uses a coarse mesh around the hole, the hole boundary being crudely approximated. The second model ignores the hole but places an element (or elements) at the hole location. The material properties (e.g., elastic modulus, density) of the element or elements at the hole location are set equal to zero or nearly zero. Attention must be paid to avoid singularities or ill-conditioned matrices. Note also that some commercial codes do not accept a zero elastic modulus.

There are two basic methods for detailed modeling of stresses near regions with holes and cutouts. The first involves using a refined mesh so that the peak stresses at the holes can be computed [8]. This entails several transitions of elements, thereby complicating the total analysis, and usually the mesh must be refined several times near the holes to prove convergence of the solutions, a process which can be expensive and time-consuming.

The second method models the system for an accurate primary stress pattern just outside the region of the holes. In the computation of the maximum-stress state, the stress-concentration factor $K_T$ should be applied to the primary stress. $K_T$ may be found in handbooks, experimental data, or detailed analyses of the region immediately surrounding the hole. The primary stress value should include all gross structural effects but should not include any local effects from the hole.

Modeling of local discontinuities or abrupt changes of section is similar to modeling holes and cutouts; yet there are no techniques for reducing the number of properties involved. The choice is thus between creating a refined mesh at the discontinuity or applying a stress-concentration factor to stresses from a linearized solution.

Models for reinforcements and intersections of structures can be quite involved, although if the detailed stresses of attachment and interaction are not important, the models are less involved. The most basic models require a reasonable mechanism for load transfer and calculation of linear-stress states. A ring-stiffened shell, for example, is a structure with reinforcements. This type of system can be modeled if one assumes that the stresses are primarily those of a membrane shell with some bending. The stiffeners can then be treated as open-section beams with loads offset from the shear center. Such a model produces good design stresses for the shell and for the stiffeners. In cases where cyclic loadings induce fatigue problems when the shell stress is near design limits or when the stiffener attachment design requires evaluation, the models must include considerable detail.

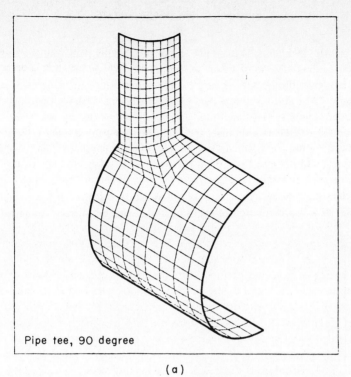

Pipe tee, 90 degree

(a)

Pipe tee, 90 degree

(b)

**FIG. 3.11** (*a*) Shell model for a pipe tee. (*b*) Local region of the model.

Another problem of interest is the modeling of intersecting plates, shells, and reinforcements of intersections. The most common approaches for thin-shell structures use plate and/or shell elements throughout the model while reinforced sections are merely thick-shell elements. Figure 3.11*a* and *b* shows a possible shell-element mesh for the pipe-tee problem discussed earlier (Fig. 3.1). The shell model properly represents the loads and deflections throughout, and shell elements simulate the shell-theory response quite well. Stress results are good in both the branch and main run; however, in the region of the intersection of the branch to the main run (Fig. 3.11*b*), there is potential for relatively high error in the stress calculations.

First, the thin-shell model connects only the midsurface planes of the elements. Figure 3.12 shows the poor representation of shell junctions with midsurface connections. This is

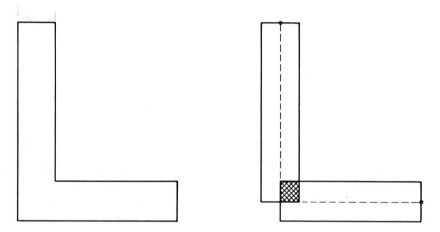

**FIG. 3.12**   Shell-to-shell intersection.

not a proper representation of the juncture or reinforcements. Second, the displacement-function flat-plate or -shell elements of commercial codes are of different order for membrane and bending action. The membrane (in-plane) displacement functions are linear, bilinear, or incomplete quadratics, while the bending (lateral) displacements are usually of cubic or incomplete quartic order. When two such elements are connected, the displacements (hence, forces and stresses) can be highly incompatible along the edge boundaries. This happens when the elements do not lie in the same plane. Only the nodal deflections and forces are compatible for all cases.

For intersecting shell structures, the plate and/or shell models are not completely satisfactory but are good if the stresses at the line of intersection are not important. In other cases, complete stress patterns, including concentrations, may be required. If so, the system requires a full 3D model (Fig. 3.13) or a combined shell and solid model (Fig. 3.14). The combination of shell and solid elements requires special modeling [9]. Shells have six degrees of freedom (DOF) per node: three translations and three rotations. Solids have only three DOF, all translations. Special linear-constraint equations may be imposed upon the common nodes to couple rotation of the shell to differential translation of the solid. Another technique for combining degrees of freedom involves the use of additional shell elements across the

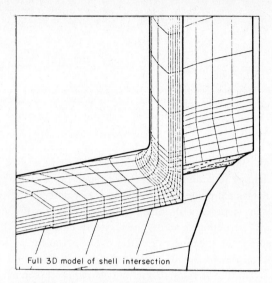

Full 3D model of shell intersection

**FIG. 3.13**   3D solid model for a pipe tee.

perpendicular free faces of the solids. These shell elements share the same nodes as the solids and must be very stiff in bending and flexible in membrane to connect to the solids. Equating the elastic modulus of the shells to a small number while prescribing an artificially large element thickness creates just such a response. As in other special techniques, this shell-to-solid intersection should be created sufficiently far from the region of interest for stress.

For each type of discontinuity presented here, certain cases require detailed modeling. In most design problems, the first models are relatively coarse, but computations inevitably are

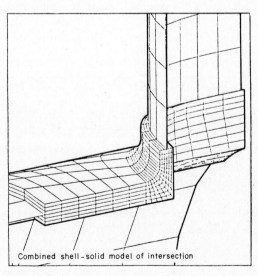

Combined shell-solid model of intersection

**FIG. 3.14**   Combined shell and solid model for a pipe tee.

needed in local regions. Local modeling [10] can be applied to any of those local stress problems.

Local modeling involves the evaluation of the system using a model which provides the correct total response and a correct representation of stresses away from any discontinuities. Therefore, the local-region models can be relatively coarse, and total-response analysis is then cost-effective. Only the local regions have refined meshes, and these models include only displacement boundary effects computed from the total response. The discontinuity alone is modeled. For the previous pipe-tee model, the global analysis would use the shell elements (Fig. 3.12), while the local model would use only the three-dimensional refinement region of Fig. 3.14. The shell displacement field is imposed on the solid-model boundaries.

Abrupt material changes (cladding or liners) also require special modeling consideration. In these cases, a finite-element model can also be coarse or refined. The coarse model would give a good total system response and proper load transfer across the material boundaries. The actual stresses are discontinuous across the region of change and, therefore, would not be accurate for separation of shearing calculations. The nodal forces across the boundary could be used in special design formulae to check for separation, but refined models are needed to compute separation stresses. These models require exceptionally fine meshes at the discontinuity.

### 3.1D Modeling for Geometric Nonlinearities

The previous discussion primarily involved modeling for linear static problems, but most of the data are also applicable to nonlinear problems. There are, however, some special considerations for nonlinearities. Nonlinearities are commonly classified as either geometric or material. Among the former are large deflections, stress stiffening, contacting surfaces, and buckling. Plasticity, creep, and nonlinear-elastic behavior are forms of material nonlinearities. This section will be limited to a discussion of geometric nonlinearities [11]. The common factors in problems such as these are the requirements for iterative solutions and the subsequent higher costs in comparison with linear problems. The following are some of the problems which fall into this category.

**Stress Stiffening**   Stress stiffening is also known as geometric or incremental stiffening [12] and was addressed during the early 1960s as a part of an incremental approach to large-deflection analyses [13]. Physically, it represents the coupling between the in-plane and transverse deflections. This coupling is the mechanism used by thin flexible structures to carry lateral loads. As the in-plane tension stresses increase, the capacity of the system to carry lateral loads also increases. Examples of structures that exhibit an increase in transverse stiffening are guy wires, undersea cables, inflatable shell structures, thin pressurized cylinders, tennis rackets, and bicycle wheels. All rely on pretensioning to increase lateral stiffness. This stiffening effect is known as the geometric stiffness matrix $\mathbf{K}^S$ and is added to the elastic (linear) stiffness matrix $\mathbf{K}$ of the system

$$(\mathbf{K} + \mathbf{K}^S)\mathbf{u} = \mathbf{P}$$

Since matrix $\mathbf{K}^S$ is a function of displacement, one linear-elastic solution must be calculated initially before $\mathbf{K}^S$ can be determined. Some problems require only two iterations to converge the solution for a single loading case. If stresses change considerably from one iteration to the next, more iterations are required.

**Buckling**   Linear-buckling analyses are generally used for predicting the elastic stability of systems [14, 15]. The standard procedure employs **K**- and $\mathbf{K}^S$-matrices developed for stress stiffening. Use of only these matrices provides for the in-plane and transverse coupling but ignores the pure bending contribution to the stability of systems. To fully describe the system's behavior with flexure, another stiffness matrix, $\mathbf{K}_{NL}$, is required. This new matrix is a quadratic function of displacement.

When only **K** and $\mathbf{K}^S$ are included in the buckling solution, the results are valid only for certain special structures, such as perfectly straight beams under axial loadings or spheres under pressure loads. These systems are subject to in-plane stresses which make $\mathbf{K}_{NL} = 0$. For all other problems this linear-buckling solution is an approximate analysis.

**Large Deflections**   Large deflections are commonly referred to as those which exceed a nominal structural dimension such as shell thickness or beam depth [16, 17]. Large rotations are commonly defined as those that exceed 10°, which is the case when the sine function of the deflection angle starts to differ significantly from the angle itself. Many theories have been advanced for large-deflection finite-element analyses to account for large deformations [18], but most do not include rotational-strain corrections. This limits their applicability to problems with small-rotation deformation when bending effects are dominant. For those methods which do account for rotation, convergence can be much faster.

Three general classes among the many techniques developed for solving large-deflection-large-rotation problems are those using direct numerical minimization of potential energy, linearized incremental procedures, and nonlinear iterative procedures. The incremental and nonlinear iterative procedures are those in common use for commercial codes. More information on large deflections can be found in Chap. 7 of Part 2.

**Contact Problems**   The evaluation of contacting surfaces is a special class of nonlinear problems. These problems are solved either by using contact elements between nodes on adjacent surfaces or by automatic coupling of node-point motion when differential movement shows contact.

Flanged structures, threaded connections, gear-tooth contacts, and impact of bodies are several examples of structures requiring contact evaluations. When friction is included in a contact problem, the analysis is also nonconservative, which means that it is dependent upon the load sequence. Any problem involving friction, then, must be solved as a series of load increments which follow the actual load history; otherwise the solution may not converge or, worse, converge to the incorrect answer.

If any of these nonlinearities induce higher-stress gradients in a section, the models match the gradient. Some nonlinear models may be coarse. Buckling problems are primarily deflection-dominated for gross structural motion; thus, models used to predict first buckling modes need not be exceptionally refined. Stress-stiffening models, on the other hand, do require accurate membrane stresses, and large-deflection or contact problems use coarse meshes only when load transfer and gross motion are important. The large-deflection and contact problems are quite likely to require refinements and are most likely to generate local high-stress gradients.

### 3.1ᴇ Modeling for Material Nonlinearities

Just as for an elastic analysis, constructing a finite-element grid for an inelastic analysis is based on the expected response. Since the inelastic response will, in general, be more complex (nonlinear) than its elastic counterpart, the finite-element grid must be adjusted as discussed earlier. An alternative approach is to allow the inelastic strain within an element to be of higher order than the total kinematic strain. This can be accomplished by allowing user-selected sets of "stress" points (also called *inelastic-integration points* for reasons which will be explained later) within each element, rather than the traditional approach of requiring a fixed number of stress points, such as centroids or nodes of Gauss points. This will require changes in the finite-element code, which can easily be accomplished [19]. With this accomplished, it can be shown that the construction of a finite-element grid need only account for the total kinematic-strain variation. The sets of element stress points will then be chosen to account for the inelastic-strain variation. This will result in the use of a minimum number of degrees of freedom for a given inelastic analysis, as the finite-element grid need not be made more complex to account for the inelastic strains and associated stresses. This is a considerable factor in the cost of an inelastic finite-element analysis. In addition, once we are satisfied that the finite-element grid is adequate to describe the total kinematic-strain response, we can test for convergence of the inelastic strains by changing the choice of stress points rather than follow the costly process of altering the finite-element grid. The corresponding cost of monitoring additional stress points is minimal compared with the cost of increasing the number of degrees of freedom. Two sample problems will be shown to demonstrate the use of inelastic-integration points. The first, involving plastic behavior, is the collapse of a simply supported beam, and the second, involving creep, is the thermal-stress relaxation of a plate.

A brief description of the construction and use of variable sets of stress points (inelastic-integration points) will follow. For a detailed description see Refs. [19, 20].

Consistent with small-strain theory, the total strain vector $\mathbf{e}$ is the linear sum

$$\mathbf{e} = \boldsymbol{\varepsilon}^e + \boldsymbol{\varepsilon}^i + \boldsymbol{\varepsilon}^0$$

where $\boldsymbol{\varepsilon}^e$, $\boldsymbol{\varepsilon}^i$, and $\boldsymbol{\varepsilon}^0$ are the elastic, inelastic, and initial (e.g., thermal) strain vectors, respectively. The resulting stress-strain relation is given by

$$\boldsymbol{\sigma} = \mathbf{E}(\mathbf{e} - \boldsymbol{\varepsilon}^i - \boldsymbol{\varepsilon}^0) \tag{3.1}$$

where $\mathbf{E}$ is a symmetric elastic matrix and $\boldsymbol{\sigma}$ is the stress vector. If we consider the incremental initial-strain approach to inelastic behavior, we arrive at the incremental equilibrium equation

$$\mathbf{K}\,\Delta\mathbf{u} = \Delta\mathbf{F} + \Delta\mathbf{Q}$$

where $\mathbf{K}$ is the stiffness matrix, $\Delta\mathbf{u}$ is the vector of incremental displacements, $\Delta\mathbf{F}$ is the vector of incremental external forces, and $\Delta\mathbf{Q}$ is the "pseudoload" vector defined by

$$\Delta\mathbf{Q} = \int_v \mathbf{B}^T \mathbf{E}\,\Delta\varepsilon^i\,dv \tag{3.2a}$$

for plastic behavior or

$$\Delta\mathbf{Q} = \int_v \mathbf{B}^T \mathbf{E}\,\Delta\varepsilon^i\,dv \cdot \Delta t \tag{3.2b}$$

for creep behavior, where **B** comes from the strain-displacement equation

$$e = Bu \qquad (3.3)$$

and $\Delta\varepsilon^i$ is the incremental inelastic-strain rate.

We will now confine our remarks to isoparametric elements, although similar comments are applicable for other types of elements. The stiffness matrix is obtained by the usual method of gaussian integration where the order of integration depends on the element shape function and geometry. However, the inelastic pseudoload vector described in Eqs. (3.2a and b) can be numerically integrated to as high an order as needed to account for the variation of inelastic strain or strain rate. The greater the nonlinearity of the inelastic strain, the higher the order of integration. The idea of allowing an arbitrary inelastic-strain distribution within an element was first used in shell theory, e.g., by Levine et al. [21], in which the plastic strain was confined to be linear in-plane and allowed to vary arbitrarily through the thickness using a scheme according to Simpson's rule of integration. This idea can be extended to using gaussian and Lobatto integration schemes in all directions [19]. A Lobatto integration scheme is especially useful when it is important to monitor element boundary points.

Two sample problems will be presented to demonstrate the use of variable inelastic-integration points. The first problem is a simply supported beam uniformly loaded to collapse.

The model, shown in Fig. 3.15, is idealized with eight 20-node isoparametric finite elements in the axial direction. This allows for an accurate description of the total strains, which are

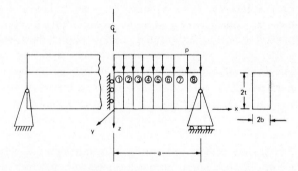

**FIG. 3.15**  Finite-element representation of simply supported beam under uniform loading.

linear through the depth. The number of integration points within each element is allowed to vary to account for the inelastic-strain variation and to determine the best choice of integration points. Figure 3.16 shows the comparison between Lobatto point and Gauss point schemes as well as the influence of variable sets of Lobatto points. An eight–Lobatto point scheme through the depth yields results which agree to within 2% of the beam solution presented in Ref. [22]. Lobatto point schemes appear to yield more accurate results than gaussian schemes with the same number of points. This is because the Lobatto point scheme includes the outer fibers and hence more accurately predicts initial yield. These results indicate that an eight-point scheme will yield accurate results for a bending problem. It is of interest to note that if too few points are chosen the analysis may go unstable. This is because the

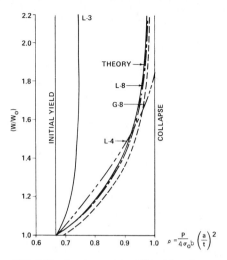

**FIG. 3.16** Load versus nondimensional center deflection of simply supported beam, under uniform pressure, for various numbers ($n$) of Lobatto (L-$n$) and Gauss (G-$n$) points through the depth. $W_0$ represents the center deflection at initial yield and $\sigma_0$ represents the yield stress.

plastic region is taken to be much greater than it actually is. In the present problem for the three-point Lobatto scheme, when the two outer fibers go plastic, then the plastic region is taken across the entire depth. To obtain the same accuracy as the L-8 case, using nodal stresses, an idealization with approximately eight elements through the depth would be needed if stresses were computed at the centroids, or four elements if stresses were computed at a $2 \times 2$ array of Gauss points. The latter case would require approximately three times the number of degrees of freedom with a considerable increase in computer cost.

The second sample problem is one of thermal stress relaxation involving creep alone. An infinite plate of width $2c$ is subjected to a steady-state temperature distribution across the width, as shown in Fig. 3.17. Secondary creep is assumed with the creep rate given as

$$\dot{\varepsilon}^c = 3 \times 10^{-24} \sigma^4 \, \text{sgn} \, \sigma$$

This problem is discussed by Mendelson et al. [23]. The solution to it can be found by

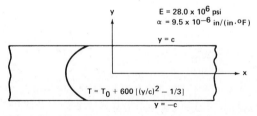

**FIG. 3.17** Infinite plate subjected to steady-state temperature distribution across width.

substituting

$$\sigma = E(\varepsilon - \varepsilon^c) \tag{3.4}$$

into the above equation, yielding

$$\frac{d\varepsilon^c}{(\varepsilon - \varepsilon^c)^4} = 3 \times 10^{-24} E^4 \, dt \tag{3.5a}$$

along with

$$\varepsilon = -0.0057(y^2 - \tfrac{1}{3}) + \int_0^1 \varepsilon^c \, dy \tag{3.5b}$$

where $\varepsilon = e - \alpha \Delta T$.

If $\varepsilon$ were constant, then Eq. (3.5a) would be the stress-relaxation equation and integrable directly. As it is, a numerical procedure must be used to integrate Eqs. (3.5a) and (3.5b).

One eight-node quadrilateral element is sufficient since the element used allows for a quadratic thermal strain distribution across the width. The creep strain will vary through the element depending on the choice of inelastic-integration points as well as the allowable stress distribution from Eq. (3.4).

The finite-element solution is found for various Lobatto point schemes across the width. The creep-strain distribution at various times is shown in Fig. 3.18. As the number of Lobatto

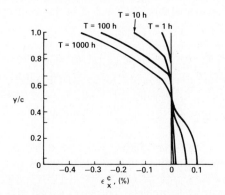

**FIG. 3.18** Creep-strain profile across width based on $1 \times 9$ Lobatto point scheme.

points is increased across the width, the creep-strain profile is represented more accurately, resulting in a better approximation of the integration performed in Eq. (3.5b). A single eight-node element is sufficient to represent the exact kinematic-strain distribution. The inelastic part of the total strain is found more accurately as the number of inelastic-strain integration points is increased. Figure 3.19 shows the total axial strain (uniform across the width) for various Lobatto point schemes. A nine–Lobatto point scheme appears necessary for this problem (up to 1000 hours) as shown. Thus accurate representation of the creep-strain distribution with an element can be obtained with the use of a variable set of inelastic-integration points, eliminating the need for a finer idealization.

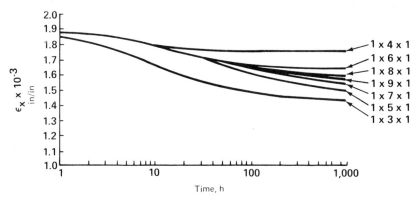

**FIG. 3.19**   Axial strain versus time for various Lobatto schemes.

## 3.1F Modeling for Structural Dynamics

Dynamics models have three possible categories, the first of which, having the least refinement, is used only for mode-frequency calculations. The other two are similar to static models, one giving better displacements, the other being for stress computations.

*Mode-Frequency Models*   The mode-frequency calculations involve solving the equation

$$|\mathbf{K} - \omega_i^2 \mathbf{M}|\mathbf{u} = 0 \quad i = 1, \ldots, n$$

where $\omega_i$ is the $i^{\text{th}}$ natural frequency of the system.

There are $n$ natural frequencies and modes for an $n$-DOF system. The eigenvalue solution produces the frequencies and the eigenvector modes are the relative distortions for each frequency. A model should only approximate the stiffness and mass to compute these natural frequencies.

The type of model to be used is dependent upon the simulations of mode shapes [24]. Low-frequency modes correspond to large-amplitude structural motions. In many design problems, however, only the few lowest modes are of interest while the higher-frequency modes are generally associated with problems like noise (acoustical) studies. The lower-mode-frequency models are usually coarse approximations to the system, but higher-frequency response models must be refined enough to simulate local deformation patterns. For example, a beam model is sufficient to represent the lowest longitudinal mode for a cylindrical tank, as shown in Fig. 3.20. The beam's physical properties, such as area and moment of inertia, are those of a cylinder. The beam is assumed to lie along the centerline of the actual cylinder. Beam cross-sectional constants would have to be modified so that the beam mass correctly approximates the mass of the cylinder. If the cylinder were filled with fluid, the mass of the fluid could be computed by hand and applied as lumped masses at each of the nodes.

This same problem may require an entirely different model to simulate higher-frequency modes. If circumferential modes of the tank were of interest, the model could use either axisymmetric elements with harmonic loading capability or 3D shell elements (Fig. 3.21). A contained fluid would be modeled as using equivalent lumped masses or even contained

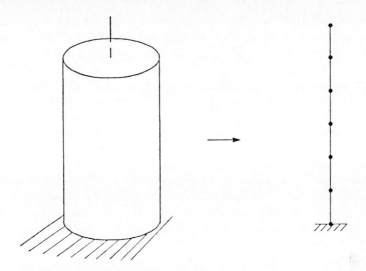

**FIG. 3.20**   Cylindrical tank—beam model.

"fluid" elements with stiffness and mass. Only the shell models physically resemble the cylinder. All three models produce, with acceptable approximations, the natural frequencies and mode shapes.

***Dynamic Reduction***   With the present graphics generation of models and constantly dropping computer costs, it is becoming less costly to create 3D models and to apply reduction techniques to minimize computations for transient analysis [25, 26]. The reduction processes involve condensing the original stiffness and mass matrices to equivalent stiffness and mass

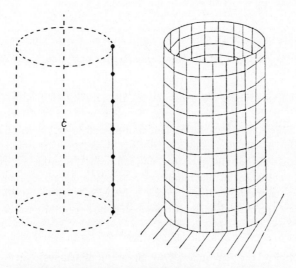

**FIG. 3.21**   Cylindrical tank—shell models.

matrices for a system. Both matrices are condensed to specified "master" locations and directions within the total model. These retained degrees of freedom are commonly called *dynamic degrees of freedom* (DDOF). The stiffness-matrix condensation gives a rather exact representation. The only errors in the reduced stiffness are those from arithmetic computer operations. The mass-matrix condensation is generally an approximation. The most commonly used mass-reduction technique, *Guyan reduction* [27], is an approximation in which mass is redistributed by using the relative stiffness between nodes. For Guyan reduction, the reduced mass can be lower or higher than the original mass. Therefore, the location and total number of DDOF have significant effects on the reduced-mass calculations.

There are certain advantages to using the reduction techniques, in which case more refined original models can be used for static analyses. Combined static and dynamic studies remain compatible with each other. If dynamic-stress calculations were required, models would not require any change. A drawback, however, is the need to select the number and location of DDOF in addition to the requirement of back substitution to compute the total deflection and/or stresses. This can reduce the cost advantages if many modes or transient time points are needed.

There are commercial codes with automatic DDOF-selection procedures, but the number of modes of interest or total DDOF required still must be specified by users. The automated procedures are based on retaining only the DDOF with the lowest ratio of diagonal stiffness and mass $(K/M)$ values [28]. This procedure is valid for creating a reduced model for the lowest frequencies. This is equivalent to an engineer's choosing the lower-stiffness and higher-mass regions of a model to represent low-frequency modes.

For selection of DDOF, the basic guidelines are as follows:

1. Include DDOF at points of high mass.
2. Choose only lateral DDOF to represent bending modes.
3. Ignore stretching (in-plane) DDOF if low frequencies are required.
4. Place DDOF at all points of interest in the design.
5. Place DDOF at all points with applied forces and nonzero applied displacements.
6. Use at least twice as many DDOF as the number of modes of interest.
7. Retain enough DDOF so that the loss (or gain) in mass does not exceed 10% of the original mass.

If one wishes to evaluate higher-frequency modes, then the automatically selected DDOF of the DDOF chosen by the above criteria must be augmented by DDOF that simulate high-frequency modes. These may include in-plane motion and more lateral DDOF.

The reduced matrices can also be used for linear-transient and harmonic-response analyses. In all three analysis cases (modal, transient, and harmonic), the reduced matrices are much less expensive to use because the total number of computations is greatly reduced as compared with using the original matrices. This is true only for calculating the displacement response at DDOF. If stresses and displacements are computed, however, the costs rise, but they never equal the cost of using the original matrix.

**Transient Response**   Transient analyses, linear and nonlinear, also involve simulating the forcing function. The structural model (stiffness and mass) must be able to approximate response frequencies up to specified limits. These models are usually checked by performing modal analyses to evaluate frequency content. The forcing functions (displacement, acceleration, force, pressure, etc.) must then have a small enough time step to excite the frequencies of interest properly. The general rule of thumb for time-step selection is to have 20 to 30 time points for the period of the highest frequency of interest. For example, if the maximum frequency of interest is 100 cps, the integration time step should be between 0.0003 and 0.0005 second. This time-step criterion minimizes the numerical damping or period elongation induced by the numerical integration of transient equations.

Two general classes of numerical-integration schemes are used for transient analyses (see Sec. 1.3 in Part 4). Explicit methods are those for which the current displacement response depends only on the past history while implicit methods are those for which the current displacement response depends upon the past and current response. Explicit solutions can become unstable if the time-step size is too large. All modes of a system must be excited for stable explicit solutions. Implicit solutions, on the other hand, are inherently stable. This is because a solution for a given time-step size excites only those modes with frequencies whose periods are 20 to 30 times greater than the step size. Only the inclusion of nonlinearities creates possible stability problems with implicit solutions.

### 3.1G  Summary

The finite-element method is a powerful numerical tool but, as with any method, it can give incorrect or misleading results when improperly used. Creating models for finite-element analyses involves the use of a great deal of engineering judgment [29]. An early attempt was made to eastablish modeling rules [30]. For this, a potential set of guidelines was first circulated for comment, and, later, additional guidelines were created. The basic consensus of reviewers was that these guidelines could not be stated as "rules" because they all had potential exceptions. Thus, correct models would have to be justified outside a set of rules, and all problems should be approached carefully. Basic assumptions should be checked with small test problems which may save reruns of an entire project.

## 3.2  GRID-POINT SEQUENCING

A key numerical problem which arises throughout finite-element analysis (whether linear or nonlinear, static or dynamic) is that of the solution of large sets of linear algebraic equations such as, in matrix form,

$$\mathbf{A}\mathbf{x} = \mathbf{b} \tag{3.6}$$

where the vector $\mathbf{b}$ and the square matrix $\mathbf{A}$ are known, and the unknown vector $\mathbf{x}$ is sought. In linear static analysis, for example, $\mathbf{A}$ is the system stiffness matrix (or its equivalent for nonstructural applications). For dynamic analysis, $\mathbf{A}$ is some linear combination of the system stiffness, mass, and damping matrices.

In finite-element applications, $\mathbf{A}$ contains mostly zeros (and is thus said to be *sparse* or *sparsely populated*) since the procedure under which finite-element matrices are assembled dictates that the off-diagonal matrix terms coupling any two degrees of freedom to each other are zero unless those degrees of freedom are common to the same finite element [2]. It also follows that the locations of the nonzero elements of the matrix **A** depend solely on the ordering of the unknowns. In finite-element applications, the ordering of the unknowns corresponds to the selection of grid-point (or joint) labels for the mesh points. It is thus possible to choose an ordering for sparse matrices so that the nonzeros are located to allow subsequent matrix operations such as equation solving or eigenvalue extraction. A good ordering is essential to the finite-element user since virtually all finite-element computer programs contain equation solution and eigenvalue routines which have been written expressly to operate efficiently on matrices possessing small bandwidth, profile, or wavefront. (All these terms will be defined precisely in the next section; in general, a banded matrix has all its nonzero entries clustered about the main diagonal.)

Efficiency in equation solving is obtained by avoiding arithmetic operations (multiplications and additions) on matrix terms that are known in advance to be zero. The computer execution time for most equation solvers and triangular factorization routines is proportional to the order $N$ of the matrix. More important, however, is that the execution time is also proportional to the *square* of some other matrix characteristic such as bandwidth $B$, profile $P$, or root-mean-square wavefront $W_{rms}$, depending on the specific type of equation solver. For a given finite-element model of a structure, $N$ is fixed, but $B$, $P$, and $W_{rms}$ depend on the ordering of the grid points. Clearly, in this case, it is desirable to make these quantities as small as possible.

First we will define the various terms encountered in connection with grid-point sequencing in finite-element analysis. Next, we will describe briefly the relationship between finite-element meshes and the matrices which result. Finally, we will discuss algorithms which have been developed to automate the grid-point sequencing problem.

### 3.2A Definitions

Although the definitions given here are reasonably standard, at least in finite-element circles, uniformity of definitions and notation among the various workers in the field does not yet exist.

Given a symmetric square matrix **A** of order $N$, we define a *row bandwidth* $b_i$ for row $i$ as the number of columns from the first nonzero in the row to the diagonal, inclusive. Numerically, $b_i$ exceeds by unity the difference between $i$ and the column index of the first nonzero entry of row $i$ of **A**. Then the matrix *semibandwidth* $B$ and *profile* $P$ are defined as

$$B = \max_{i \leqslant N} b_i \tag{3.7}$$

$$P = \sum_{i=1}^{N} b_i \tag{3.8}$$

Let $c_i$ denote the number of *active columns* in row $i$. By definition, a column $j$ is active in row $i$ if $j \geqslant i$ and there is a nonzero entry in that column in any row with index $k \leqslant i$. The *matrix wavefront* $W$ is then defined as

$$W = \max_{i \leqslant N} c_i \tag{3.9}$$

Sometimes $c_i$ is referred to as the *row wavefront* for row $i$. Since the matrix $\mathbf{A}$ is symmetric,

$$P = \sum_{i=1}^{N} b_i = \sum_{i=1}^{N} c_i \qquad (3.10)$$

The wavefront $W$ is sometimes called the *maximum wavefront* $W_{\max}$ to distinguish it from the *average wavefront* $W_{\mathrm{av}}$ and *root-mean-square wavefront* $W_{\mathrm{rms}}$ defined as

$$W_{\mathrm{av}} = \frac{1}{N} \sum_{i=1}^{N} c_i = \frac{P}{N} \qquad (3.11)$$

$$W_{\mathrm{rms}} = \sqrt{\frac{1}{N} \sum_{i=1}^{N} c_i^2} \qquad (3.12)$$

Thus, for symmetric matrices the average wavefront and average semibandwidth are equal. From these definitions, it follows that for a given matrix

$$W_{\mathrm{av}} \leqslant W_{\mathrm{rms}} \leqslant W_{\max} \leqslant B \leqslant N \qquad (3.13)$$

The first two inequalities would be equalities only for uninteresting special cases such as diagonal matrices.

The *degree* $d_i$ of grid point $i$ is defined as the number of other grid points (or nodes) to which it is "connected." In the finite-element context, two grid points are said to be *connected* if they are common to the same finite element. The rationale behind this definition is that two grid points common to the same finite element are generally coupled to each other by a nonzero off-diagonal term in the stiffness matrix. For a finite-element mesh having only one degree of freedom (DOF) per mesh point, $d_i$ is also the number of nonzero off-diagonal terms in row $i$ of matrix $\mathbf{A}$. The *maximum nodal degree M* is

$$M = \max_{i \leqslant N} d_i \qquad (3.14)$$

The *number of unique edges E* in a finite-element mesh is defined as the total number of unique connections in the mesh. Thus, for a mesh having one DOF per grid point, $E$ is equal to the number of nonzero off-diagonal matrix terms above the diagonal. Hence, for a symmetric matrix,

$$E = \sum_{i=1}^{N} \frac{d_i}{2} \qquad (3.15)$$

Thus the total number of nonzeros in $\mathbf{A}$ is $2E + N$, and the density $\rho$ of the matrix $\mathbf{A}$ is

$$\rho = \frac{2E + N}{N^2} \qquad (3.16)$$

Note that, in these definitions, the diagonal entries of the matrix $\mathbf{A}$ are included in $b_i$ and $c_i$ (and hence in $B$, $P$, $W_{\max}$, $W_{\mathrm{av}}$, and $W_{\mathrm{rms}}$). These definitions make it easy to convert the various parameters from one convention (including the diagonal) to the other (not including the diagonal).

Also, note that in this context, the order $N$ of the matrix $\mathbf{A}$ is sometimes taken to be the same as the number of nodes. In general finite-element usage, however, each node (grid point) has several degrees of freedom, not just one. For meshes having, say, six degrees of freedom per node, the actual values of $B$, $W_{max}$, $W_{av}$, or $W_{rms}$ would be, in the absence of constraints, six times their corresponding values computed for one degree of freedom per point.

These definitions can be illustrated by the following simple example. Figure 3.22 shows a matrix of order 6 in which $X$ denotes a nonzero entry. In each row and column a line is

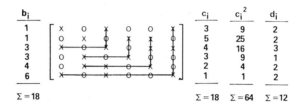

$$\Sigma = 18 \qquad\qquad \Sigma = 18 \quad \Sigma = 64 \quad \Sigma = 12$$

**FIG. 3.22**  Example illustrating definitions of matrix bandwidth, profile, and wavefront.

drawn from the first nonzero to the diagonal. Thus $b_i$ is the number of columns traversed by the solid line in row $i$ to the left of and including the diagonal. Similarly, the number of active columns $c_i$ in row $i$ is the number of vertical lines in row $i$ to the right of and including the diagonal. Thus, from the definitions, $B = 6$, $W_{max} = 5$, $P = 18$, $W_{av} = 3.0$, $W_{rms} = 3.3$, $M = 3$, $E = 6$, and $\rho = 50.0\%$. For large matrices arising out of realistic applications, the matrix density is usually below 5% [31].

## 3.2B The Relationship between Meshes and Matrices

Consider the one-dimensional, six-DOF system of six scalar springs shown in Fig. 3.23. For the grid-point numbering (labeling) indicated in that figure, the $6 \times 6$ system stiffness matrix looks like

$$\mathbf{K} = \begin{bmatrix} X & X & & X & & \\ X & X & X & & & \\ & X & X & X & & \\ X & & X & X & X & \\ & & & X & X & X \\ & & & & X & X \end{bmatrix} \tag{3.17}$$

where $X$ indicates the location of a nonzero entry. From Eq. (3.17) and the definition of Eq. (3.7), the matrix bandwidth $B$ is 4. For consecutively numbered structures, the bandwidth can also be obtained directly from the structure (Fig. 3.23) by adding unity to the maximum

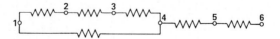

**FIG. 3.23**  Six-degree-of-freedom spring system.

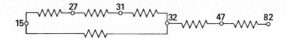

**FIG. 3.24** Six-degree-of-freedom spring system with non-consecutive grid labels.

numerical difference between connected node numbers (where node 1 is connected to node 4). The same bandwidth is also obtained for the numbering of Fig. 3.24, since the ordering of the mesh points is the same. From the point of view of the matrix connectivity, there is no difference between the structures in Figs. 3.23 and 3.24. Some finite-element programs allow the user to specify nonconsecutive grid-point numbers as in Fig. 3.24, rather than requiring consecutive numbering. The matrix bandwidth cannot be computed directly from the mesh by looking at the maximum numerical difference between connected node numbers when the nodes are not numbered consecutively. Instead, Fig. 3.24 must first be simplified to Fig. 3.23.

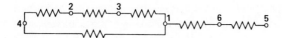

**FIG. 3.25** Six-degree-of-freedom system with poor mesh labeling.

To illustrate the difference that sequencing makes, consider the numbering of Fig. 3.25. Here, the bandwidth is 6, so that the ordering of Fig. 3.23 is to be preferred over that of Fig. 3.25. However, a still better sequence (i.e., one with a smaller bandwidth) is shown in Fig. 3.26, where $B = 3$.

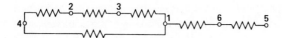

**FIG. 3.26** Six-degree-of-freedom system with good mesh labeling.

The same concepts can also be applied to two- and three-dimensional meshes. For example, consider the plate in Fig. 3.27 modeled with a $2 \times 4$ array of quadrilateral elements. Since all nodes common to the same finite element are "connected" to each other, the grid-point bandwidth is 7. A better sequence (i.e., one with a smaller bandwidth) would number first across the "short" direction (in the sense of number of nodes rather than actual distance), as in Fig. 3.28. With this sequence, the grid-point bandwidth is now 5.

**FIG. 3.27** A 2D mesh.

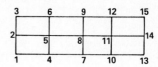

**FIG. 3.28** 2D mesh with good grid-point labeling.

In general, the plates of Figs. 3.27 and 3.28 have more than one DOF per node. Thus, although it generally suffices to consider only grid-point bandwidth when choosing an ordering, the actual bandwidth which the equation solver encounters would be much larger. For example, structures having six DOF per node and a grid-point bandwidth of $B$ would have a DOF bandwidth of $6B$.

Although the above discussion was written from the point of view of matrix bandwidth, similar comments could be made from the point of view of matrix profile or wavefront. Some finite-element codes, for instance, have matrix decomposition routines which operate fastest on those matrices having the smallest rms wavefront.

### 3.2c Automatic Resequencing Algorithms

So far, we have defined the relevant terms and indicated how a finite-element mesh might be resequenced to reduce the resulting matrix bandwidth. In general, however, it is very difficult for the finite-element practitioner to know how to sequence a given mesh to effect a good numbering, particularly for large, complicated meshes or those generated automatically on a computer. Even if a good sequence is known, it may be tedious to implement for large meshes. To overcome this problem, a large number of algorithms have been developed to automate the assignment of grid-point labels, given the connectivity of the mesh. Since it is clearly impractical to check each of the $N!$ possible sequences associated with a given matrix $\mathbf{A}$ of order $N$, each algorithm uses some presumably rational strategy to arrive quickly at a good grid-point sequence.

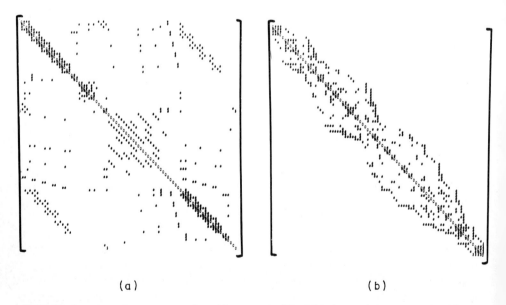

(a)                                      (b)

**FIG. 3.29**   Locations of nonzero terms in a stiffness matrix ($N = 87$) before and after automatic grid-point reordering. (a) Before: $B = 64$, $W_{max} = 43$, $P = 2336$, $W_{av} = 26.9$, $W_{rms} = 29.4$. (b) After: $B = 18$, $W_{max} = 13$, $P = 685$, $W_{av} = 7.9$, $W_{rms} = 8.3$; CYBER 74 computer time required = 0.6 second.

No attempt will be made here to review the various resequencing algorithms. An extensive bibliography of available algorithms is included in Ref. [31].

One excellent resequencing algorithm which is widely used was developed by Gibbs, Poole, and Stockmeyer[32]. This algorithm, known as the GPS algorithm, is both exceptionally fast and consistently reliable for the reduction of matrix bandwidth, profile, and wavefront. Lewis[33] has recently developed some improvements to the GPS scheme.

The GPS strategy can be summarized in general terms. First, it selects a single starting node (the node assigned the label 1 in the new sequence) to be an endpoint of a pseudodiameter of the finite-element mesh. The *diameter* of a mesh is the shortest path (in terms of number of edges) connecting any two grid points of maximal distance apart. A *pseudodiameter* locates points at nearly maximal distance apart. Second, the mesh is numbered using a procedure which is similar to the Cuthill–McKee (CM) numbering algorithm [34], in which the new labels 2 through $N$ are assigned by numbering the unnumbered nodes connected to new label $I$ in order of increasing degree, starting with $I = 1$ and continuing with increasing $I$ until all nodes are sequenced. This basic ordering strategy generally works well and has been used in several algorithms.

An example of a finite-element stiffness matrix before and after resequencing by an automatic program is shown in Fig. 3.29 for a small structure having 87 grid points.

## 3.3 SYMMETRY

The finite-element analysis of engineering problems with complex geometry is tedious at best. However, for problems with symmetry, it is possible to gain some information about the solutions from the symmetry alone [35–41]. Moreover, with symmetry present, the analyst needs to model only a portion of the overall region of interest, thereby saving both the analyst's time and the computer's time, the former generally being the more valuable. For example, a structure possessing one plane of mirror symmetry can be analyzed by modeling only one-half the structure, whether the loads are symmetric or not. Nonsymmetric loads, for which case the half structure must be analyzed twice, still have benefits, since a half structure generally costs much less than half as much to analyze as the complete structure would cost. For a half structure, the total number of degrees of freedom $N$ in the model is about half that of an equivalent full model, and the model's matrix bandwidth $B$ (either maximum or average) is also usually reduced, sometimes by as much as 50%. The overall computer solution involves equation solving (for which the computer time is proportional to $NB^2$) and numerous other operations (for which the time is roughly proportional to $N$) [2].

To be useful, symmetry must be exploited systematically and with confidence. This section reviews and summarizes the basic concepts involved in the systematic application of symmetry in finite-element analysis, where *symmetry* refers to objects rather than physical laws [42] or materials. In general, group theory is the mathematical language for discussions of symmetry (particularly in quantum mechanics), but such an approach is not necessary for finite-element applications and will not be used here. This discussion will, at times, emphasize structural applications since most finite-element analyses are in that area; however, the same concepts carry over into other areas.

## 3.3A Types of Symmetry and Definitions

In engineering applications, the most commonly encountered types of symmetry are reflective (or mirror) symmetry, rotational (or axial) symmetry, and inversion symmetry [39]. Examples of these three types are shown in Fig. 3.30.

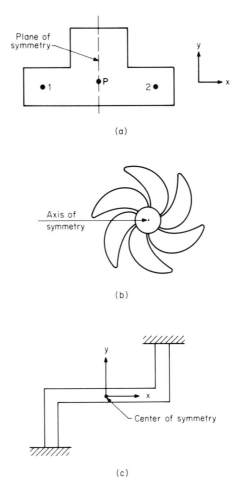

**FIG. 3.30**  Examples of different types of symmetry: (*a*) Reflective symmetry. (*b*) Rotational symmetry. (*c*) Inversion symmetry.

An object possesses symmetry if the application to the object of some operation (such as a reflection, rotation, or inversion) transforms the object into an equivalent configuration. For engineering applications, this characterization of symmetry requires not only geometrical symmetry, but also symmetry with respect to material properties and restraints. For example, in Fig. 3.30*b*, if one propeller blade were made of aluminum and another of bronze (an unlikely situation), there would be no symmetry to exploit. In some situations, other properties may also play a role in deciding the presence of symmetry; for example, thermal radiation problems require symmetry with respect to color. Symmetry can normally be identified by inspection.

The characterization of symmetry in a particular situation is not necessarily unique. For example, the symmetry of Fig. 3.30c can also be characterized as a sequence of two reflections, one in the $yz$-plane followed by one in the $xz$-plane, or vice versa. The same structure could also serve as an example of a structure with rotational symmetry (with a rotation angle of 180°).

In general, reflective symmetry is viewed as the fundamental type of symmetry, since it can be shown that all symmetric transformations of finite figures in three dimensions reduce to successive reflections in not more than three planes (which might not even be planes of symmetry) [43].

Once the symmetry properties of a structure are identified, the loads can be addressed. The question of whether a given system of loads is symmetric depends on the structure to which that system is applied. Specifically, a system of loads, when applied to a structure possessing certain symmetry, is defined as *symmetric* if it is transformed into an equivalent configuration by the symmetry operations of the structure [39]. The system of loads is defined as *antisymmetric* if the symmetry operations plus a negation of signs of all loads transform them into an equivalent configuration. For example, the loads in Fig. 3.31 are symmetric when applied to that structure, whose symmetry is characterized by the sequence of two reflections indicated above.

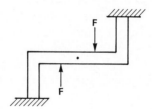

**FIG. 3.31**   A structure with symmetric loads.

## 3.3B The Guiding Principle

The principle on which all applications of symmetry are based is that "equivalent causes produce equivalent effects," or, more generally, "the effect is at least as symmetric as the cause" [35, 39]. In the context of structural mechanics, the practical effect of this principle is that symmetric loads produce symmetric effects (displacements, stresses, etc.) and antisymmetric loads produce antisymmetric effects.

## 3.3c Boundary Conditions

When only a portion of a symmetric structure is modeled, the basic principle provides the tool for systematically deriving the symmetric or antisymmetric boundary conditions which must be applied at artificial boundaries introduced because of symmetry. Emphasis in this section will be restricted to planes of symmetry, since reflective symmetry has already been identified as the fundamental type of symmetry.

Consider, for example, the symmetric region shown in Fig. 3.30$a$, where $P$ denotes a typical point in the plane of symmetry. Define a cartesian coordinate system with the $x$-direction normal to the plane of symmetry and the $yz$-plane parallel to the plane of symmetry. To derive the symmetric and antisymmetric boundary conditions to be applied at $P$ if only half the region is modeled, (1) consider in turn each displacement component at that point, (2) apply to that component (assumed to be nonzero) the symmetry (or antisymmetry) operations characterizing the structure, and (3) observe whether or not the component is transformed into itself. If it is not transformed into itself, the component must vanish in order not to violate symmetry. The relevant symmetry operation is a reflection onto the $yz$-plane containing point $P$. The antisymmetry operations consist of the same reflection followed by a negation of sign. For example, assume that $u_x$, the $x$-component of displacement, is nonzero at $P$. The reflection produces an image of $u_x$ with the opposite orientation. The additional negation of sign (for antisymmetry) yields a result coinciding with the original configuration. Therefore, $u_x$ must vanish at $P$ in order not to violate symmetry, but $u_x$ may be nonzero for antisymmetric behavior. Similarly, we find that $u_y$ and $u_z$ vanish at $P$ for antisymmetric behavior and may be nonzero for symmetric behavior.

Rotational degrees of freedom, if present, require slightly different treatment. Let points 1 and 2 in Fig. 3.30$a$ be image points of each other. Symmetric moments applied to these points must have opposite signs. For example, if the moment $M_z = 10 \, \text{lb} \cdot \text{in}$ is applied at point 2, its symmetric counterpart is the moment $M_z = -10 \, \text{lb} \cdot \text{in}$ at point 1. In other words, the reflection of an axial vector (a rotation or moment) onto a plane requires an additional negation of sign compared with the way true vectors reflect [39]. The mathematical basis for this result is that reflection is an improper orthogonal transformation.

The application of the symmetry operation (reflection) to the rotational components $R_x$, $R_y$, and $R_z$ at point $P$ in Fig. 3.30$a$ indicates that for symmetric behavior, $R_y$ and $R_z$ must vanish in order not to violate symmetry, and $R_x = 0$ for antisymmetry. To summarize, the boundary conditions to impose at point $P$ are

$$u_x = R_y = R_z = 0 \qquad \text{for symmetry}$$

$$R_x = u_y = u_z = 0 \qquad \text{for antisymmetry}$$

(3.18)

The results expressed in these equations may be generalized as follows: Points lying in a plane of *symmetry* can suffer no translation out of the plane and no rotation about in-plane lines. For *antisymmetry* the complementary set of degrees of freedom is constrained. The complementary nature of the symmetric and antisymmetric boundary conditions is a general result which follows from the observation that the only distinction between antisymmetry and symmetry is the additional negation in the symmetry operations.

When higher-order derivatives are used as degrees of freedom, additional symmetric and antisymmetric constraints are also required. Such constraints are most easily derived from the observations that $u_x$, the translational component of displacement normal to a symmetry plane, is either an odd or an even function of $x$, depending on whether the behavior is symmetric or antisymmetric, respectively. Similarly, the translational components of displacement parallel to a symmetric plane are even and odd in $x$ for symmetric and antisymmetric behavior, respectively [44]. For even functions of $x$, the odd-order derivatives with respect to $x$ must vanish for symmetry, and the even-order derivatives with respect to $x$ vanish for antisymmetry. Conversely, for odd functions of $x$, the even- and odd-order derivatives with respect to $x$ vanish for symmetry and antisymmetry, respectively. As before, the set of degrees of freedom constrained as a consequence of symmetry is complementary to the set which is constrained as a consequence of antisymmetry; i.e., whichever freedoms are constrained for symmetry will be free for antisymmetry, and vice versa. This follows directly from the definitions, since the only real distinction between symmetry and antisymmetry is the additional negation that distinguishes even from odd functions. Thus, if one can determine for some problem the (correct) symmetric boundary conditions, the antisymmetric conditions consist of the complementary set of degrees of freedom. One consequence of this property is that the total number of degrees of freedom arising from symmetric and antisymmetric models of a structure must equal the original number of degrees of freedom for the entire structure, disregarding symmetry.

The symmetric conditions for scalar field problems (e.g., heat conduction or potential fluid flow) are obtained as special cases of the preceding development. At a plane of symmetry, the normal derivative of the field variable vanishes; this is a natural boundary condition in finite-element analysis. For antisymmetry, the function itself must vanish at a plane of symmetry.

## 3.3D Nonsymmetric Loads

In general, most load systems applied to structures are neither symmetric nor antisymmetric, but nonsymmetric. However, any nonsymmetric system can always be uniquely decomposed into the sum of a symmetric and an antisymmetric system of loads [45, 46], as, for example,

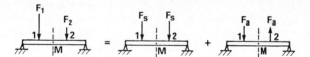

**FIG. 3.32**   Decomposition of nonsymmetric loads.

in Fig. 3.32. Given arbitrary loads $F_1$ and $F_2$ at a point 1 and its image, point 2, the symmetric part of the load $F_s$ and the antisymmetric part $F_a$ are given by

$$F_s = \frac{F_1 + F_2}{2}$$

$$F_a = \frac{F_1 - F_2}{2}$$

(3.19)

In linear problems, to which the principle of superposition applies, only half the problem shown in Fig. 3.32 needs to be modeled. The analyst would model the left half, say, and solve the problem in two steps: (1) the symmetric part of the load is applied along with symmetric boundary conditions at the middle $M$, and (2) the antisymmetric part of the load is applied along with antisymmetric boundary conditions imposed at $M$. Thus, we have Fig. 3.33$a$, for which the symmetric ($S$) and antisymmetric ($A$) boundary conditions are given in Eq. 3.18. Adding the two solutions in Fig. 3.33$a$ yields the solution of the original problem

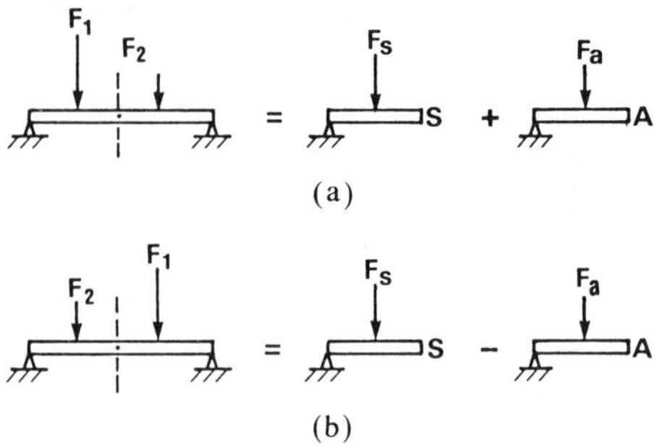

**FIG. 3.33**  Superposition of symmetric and antisymmetric solutions. (*a*) Modeled side. (*b*) Unmodeled side.

only for the left side of the structure (the modeled side). To obtain the solution for the right side (the unmodeled side), the two solutions can be subtracted, as indicated in Fig. 3.33*b*. Taking the difference of the symmetric and antisymmetric solutions has the practical effect of reversing the role played by the left and right sides. Thus, even though only the left side is modeled, the entire solution can be obtained.

### 3.3E  Multiple Planes of Symmetry

The rectangular region shown in Fig. 3.34 possesses two planes of symmetry (*xz* and *yz*); hence the problem can be decomposed into four parts, as shown. Any quadrant can be chosen to be modeled, and the four combinations of symmetric and antisymmetric boundary conditions (*SS*, *SA*, *AS*, and *AA*) imposed on the points lying in the two planes of symmetry. The four solutions can be combined in various ways to yield the solutions in all four quadrants [41, 46].

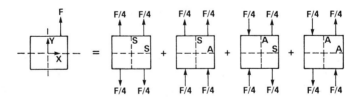

**FIG. 3.34**  Multiple planes of symmetry.

### 3.3F  Free Vibrations

The foregoing discussion has been devoted exclusively to statics problems, but free-vibration problems (eigenvalue problems) can also exploit symmetry. The calculation of all natural frequencies and mode shapes of a symmetric structure would require one eigenvalue analysis for each unique combination of symmetric and antisymmetric boundary conditions. For example, the natural frequencies of the region of Fig. 3.34, which has two orthogonal planes of symmetry, can be obtained by modeling only one quadrant and applying, in turn, each of the four combinations of boundary conditions.

The total number of degrees of freedom involved in the four component problems of Fig. 3.34 exactly equals the original number of DOF contained in the complete problem [44, 47]. This follows as a direct consequence of the symmetric and antisymmetric boundary conditions involving complementary sets of DOF. Thus we have "conservation of DOF." If this were not so, we would have the disturbing situation in which the mere application of symmetry would result in the creation or destruction of DOF. The purpose of applying symmetry is, of course, to solve a problem with less effort rather than to create a different one.

### 3.3G Time-Dependent Problems

All the preceding results for statics problems also apply to linear transient (time-dependent) situations, except that the entire history of time-dependent loads must be decomposed into symmetric and antisymmetric parts. This decomposition has been illustrated in the context of underwater shock response, for example, by Everstine [48].

### 3.3H Finite Elements in Planes of Symmetry

Special consideration is necessary to treat the situation in which elements lie entirely in the plane of symmetry (i.e., the grid points which define the element lie entirely in the plane). For example, in the stiffened plate shown in Fig. 3.35, the beam stiffener (modeled with beam

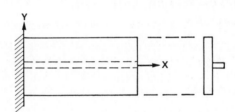

**FIG. 3.35**   An example of a symmetry plane containing a finite element.

elements) lies entirely in the xz-plane, which is a plane of structural symmetry. Although the symmetric boundary conditions are unaffected by this situation, care must be exercised in computing the geometrical properties of a beam element lying in the plane of symmetry. In particular, the properties for each "half element" should be specified so that the half element receives one-half the total *stiffness* rather than one-half the cross section. For example, properties such as area $A$, cross-sectional moments of inertia $I_1$, $I_2$, and $I_{12}$, and torsional constant $J$ are first computed for the full cross section before entering one-half of those values. (Note that $J$ and either $I_1$ or $I_2$ do not depend linearly on individual cross-sectional dimensions.)

To prove the validity of this approach, we need only treat each half the symmetric structure as a "superelement" involving many grid points. Then, if the two sides are recombined using the usual rules of matrix assembly, the resulting stiffness matrix would have to be the correct stiffness matrix for the entire structure. Thus, when an element is cut in half by a plane of symmetry, each side receives one-half the total stiffness.

### 3.3ı Cyclic Symmetry

Many structures, including turbine and pump impellers, rotating machines, space antennas, and propellers, exhibit rotational symmetry such as that shown in Fig. 3.30*b*. Such structures are made up of identical segments arranged symmetrically with respect to an axis. Because of symmetry, the only portion of the structure that must be modeled and analyzed is the smallest repeating segment.

Although several contributions have been made to various aspects of the problem [6, 36, 49–57], the most general treatments are those of Hussey [54], MacNeal, Harder, and Mason [6], and Thomas [55]. In the work by MacNeal, Harder, and Mason, an automated procedure was developed for both simple rotational symmetry and dihedral symmetry, a special case in which each segment has a plane of reflective symmetry. The theoretical approach, which is too lengthy to be repeated here, is based on a finite Fourier series transformation in the azimuthal coordinate. Nonsymmetric loads can also be handled. Irons and Ahmad include a good discussion of cyclic symmetry (referred to as *sectorial symmetry*) [58].

A special case of cyclic symmetry occurs with axially symmetric structures (bodies of revolution) for which the geometry is completely independent of the azimuthal coordinate. Nonsymmetric loads for such situations are often handled for linear problems by expanding the loads and all solution variables in a truncated Fourier series in the azimuthal coordinate.

## 3.4 AUTOMATIC MESH GENERATION AND ADAPTIVE ANALYSIS

Traditionally, the need to generate element meshes has been a drawback of using the finite-element method. However, there are a number of software packages and methods available today to aid in the generation of finite-element meshes. This is not to say that the generation of the element mesh is no longer a major bottleneck, but the situation today is substantially better than it was. Maybe more important than those improvements gained to date is the maturing of the meshing techniques that are needed to consider automated finite-element model generation. The meshing approaches that are currently available to generate finite-element models are discussed here, and how the current and new capabilities may be combined in the future are indicated.

In addition to the development of stand-alone finite-element preprocessors (see Sec. 3.1), there is a substantial amount of effort under way to link these capabilities directly with geometric design systems. The direct linking of these capabilities gives the analyst immediate use of the problem's geometry in the definition of an element mesh instead of requiring its redefinition during mesh generation. As the geometric design systems move toward the use of solid modeling techniques, the advantages obtainable by the direct linking to finite-element mesh generators become more important. This is because the unambiguous representations employed in solid modeling techniques can be used to automate many of the discretization steps carried out by the user in current preprocessing systems. In fact, it is only through the use of proper solid modeling techniques that completely automatic, three-dimensional mesh generation will be possible.

To many, *automatic mesh generation* means the generation of element meshes by any means in which the user does not have to type in each node-point coordinate and element connectivity. For purposes of this discussion, those techinques that can generate subregions of node points and element connectivities with only a limited amount of geometric and meshing information are termed *mesh generators*. Only those mesh generators that can generate the entire mesh for an object given only its overall geometry will be referred to as *automatic mesh generators*. It is this group of mesh-generating techniques that is of particular interest if the goal of automatically generating a three-dimensional finite-element mesh for solid objects is to be met.

Although automatic mesh generators linked to a solid modeler will make it possible to carry out a finite-element analysis without the user seeing an element mesh, there must still be control exercised on the gradation of that mesh if acceptable results are to be obtained. As will be demonstrated later in this section, it is possible to do this with automatic mesh generators by specifying mesh-density attribute information to the problem geometry. However, the appropriate method for dealing with the accuracy problem is to use an adaptive analysis program which employs *a posteriori* error estimates to measure the solution accuracy. An adaptive finite-element processor is a program which iteratively performs a finite-element analysis, determines the areas of the mesh where the solution is not sufficiently accurate, and improves the discretization in those areas until a prespecified degree of accuracy is obtained. In addition to those features of a standard finite-element program, the two key features needed in an adaptive program are the *a posteriori* error estimators and a method to improve the element mesh. The available methods to improve an element discretization adaptively are covered in this subsection.

## 3.4A Mesh-Generating Techniques

Since early in the 1970s, investigators have been developing methods to generate element meshes. These procedures afford the user a method to create a large number of elements quickly. Although these procedures drastically reduce the amount of effort required to lay out a mesh, the user must interact with the programs to ensure that a valid mesh of properly graded elements is obtained.

The various methods of mesh generation available can be classified into one of the following techniques:

1. Coordinate transformation [59–62]
2. Blending function [63–68]
3. Automatic triangulation [69–79]

Although some mesh-generating techniques are generally better than others, none has proved superior, or even entirely satisfactory, for all applications. In most cases mesh generators are used by first partitioning the domain of interest into a series of regions with nodes placed on the region boundaries. The desired mesh generators are then involved in each of the regions.

Smoothing algorithms [62, 80, 81] are often employed to determine the final locations of node points on the interior of a mesh. They normally operate by modifying the locations of nodes by the iterative application of a specific difference equation. The most popular such approach is the laplacian [62] method, which places the node at the centroid of the nodes to which it is connected. Other smoothing algorithms are based on potential functions [80, 81].

Coordinate-transformation techniques normally produce well-conditioned meshes, but are commonly the most restrictive mesh generators. The most popular such approach is based on isoparametric coordinates [59, 62] and requires that each of the prespecified number of region edges be represented by a specific-order polynomial. These mesh generators are often implemented in a manner such that opposite sides have the same number of element edges. These methods are quite dependable and are used frequently.

Blending functions in the form of transfinite mappings [63–68] suffer from the same general restrictions as the isoparametric mappings and produce very similar meshes. However, the blending-function mesh generators are much more flexible because the definition of what constitutes a region side is more general. These methods employ projectors which map a true surface to an approximate surface that matches the true surface at a nondenumerable number of points. These methods are extremely powerful for both two- and three-dimensional meshes, and the reader is referred to the references by Barnhill et al. [66] and Gordon and Hall [65] for details on the mathematics of these methods. As an indication of the power of these

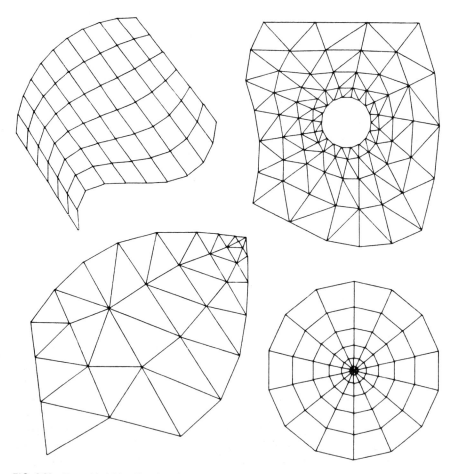

**FIG. 3.36**  Two-sided blending-function mesh-patch examples.

methods, Fig. 3.36 shows four single, two-sided mesh patches. It is possible with blending functions to generate an invalid mesh in some highly distorted cases. Therefore, there is some danger in the use of these methods. However, when placed in a highly interactive graphics preprocessor, these methods prove to be superior to isoparametric mappings because they can mesh and patch all cases that isoparametric mappings can mesh, plus many others that must be multiply patched with isoparametric mapping. For coupling of these mesh generators with interactive-graphics techniques, see Sec. 4.3B in this Part. These procedures may also be extended to three-dimensional surface meshes (Fig. 3.37) and solid meshes (Fig. 3.38).

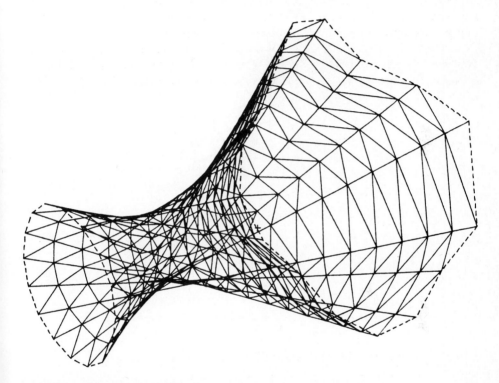

**FIG. 3.37**   Shell blending-function mesh.

Each of the mesh-generating approaches outlined above can be used to develop a starting mesh for an adaptive meshing procedure. Any of the basic mesh-enrichment schemes to be discussed could be used to improve that discretization until a solution of sufficient accuracy is obtained. However, of all the mesh-generating approaches possible, the only techniques available for automatically generating an element mesh without user input except that of the original geometry are the triangulation techniques [69–79]. These procedures have not proved extremely popular in the past because they (1) required as much input as other methods, (2) are computationally more expensive than other methods, (3) often produced poorly graded meshes of poorly shaped elements, and (4) on occasion, failed to generate a valid mesh in some regions. Recent improvements in these techniques, along with the fact that only a valid

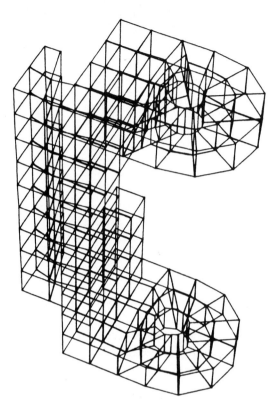

**FIG. 3.38**   Solid blending-function mesh.

mesh, not a "well-graded" mesh, is required for an adaptive analysis program, indicate that it may be possible to let the computer take care of all the mesh-generation efforts.

### 3.4ʙ Fully Automatic Mesh-Generation Approaches

There are a number of two-dimensional triangulation algorithms that have been developed [69–74]. Efforts to develop fully automatic three-dimensional mesh generators are more recent [75–79]. There are several different approaches used in the automatic triangulation algorithms. In most approaches the first step is to discretize the domain's boundary curves into a number of element edges. From that point, some techniques [71, 72] triangulate on the basis of the boundary polygon created by the element edges placed along the boundary. Elements are generated in the areas defined by cutting sharp corners off the polygon and replacing selected points of the polygon with new points on the interior of the domain. One such approach [71] first removes each polygon vertex with an angle less than 90°, which creates one triangular element for each vertex removed. With all vertices less than 90° removed, the algorithm then selects a vertex with an angle less than 180° and replaces that vertex with a new point on the interior of the domain, the coordinates of which are calculated on the basis of the coordinates of the removed vertex and its two neighbors. The area removed is broken into two triangles.

If one of the three modified vertex angles is less than 90°, it is removed, along with any others caused by this removal, until all acute angles have again been removed. This process of introducing new points and cutting off acute angles is continued until the polygon contains only three vertices which define the last triangle. A procedure of this type is referred to as an outside-in approach because it starts with only a boundary definition and works into the interior.

In other approaches [69, 70], additional interior information is incorporated into the triangulation algorithm. For example, Bykat's algorithm [70] first breaks the domain of interest into simple convex subregions and then triangulates each of these subregions into elements. Cavendish's algorithm [69], on the other hand, places node points throughout the interior of the domain and then proceeds to triangulate the domain using the boundary points and the interior points. These algorithms could be classified as outside-inside procedures because they are based on boundary information plus additional interior information.

Other algorithms might be based on an inside-out approach in which primary control is based on interior information. Such approaches [82, 83] have been used for area and volume encoding schemes, but their direct application to finite-element mesh generation is doubtful [74, 78]. An alternative to an inside-out approach is an inside-outside approach in which an area or volume encoding scheme is the basis of interior discretization; however, particular concern must be given to ensure proper representation of the boundary. Figure 3.39 shows a mesh automatically generated by an inside-outside approach [74]. The input to this mesh generator consists of the boundary curves and tolerance information applied to the curves (Fig. 3.39a).

It is common to apply one of the smoothing procedures [62, 80, 81] to the meshes generated by the triangulation procedures to improve the shape of the resulting elements.

The approaches being taken to fully automate three-dimensional mesh generation can proceed as extensions of two-dimensional algorithms. For example, a triangulation algorithm can be extended to a solid mesh by first triangulating the surfaces, defining interior surfaces until they are one layer of elements in from the original surface, triangulating those surfaces, and then forming solid elements between the surfaces. The algorithm used in Ref. [76], although substantially more complex than the triangulation algorithm just defined, is similar to it. The triangulated surfaces can also be used as starting points for the definition of solid elements that are defined one at a time by removal of those elements [79]. An outside-inside approach can also be taken in which the volume is tetrahedronized using a surface triangulation and a number of interior points placed inside the solid [77]. Cavendish et al. [7] have developed an outside-inside approach based on a given set of points and volume triangulation techniques. The use of an inside-outside approach based on a modified volume encoding scheme is currently being considered [78]. The mesh shown in Fig. 3.40 was generated using the modified-octree technique [78]. Progress on fully automatic mesh generators for three-dimensional solids has advanced to the point that they are being interfaced to commercial systems.

## 3.4c  Adaptive Mesh Improvements

After an initial element mesh has been generated, a first analysis run, and the areas of the mesh requiring improvement identified, one must improve the element discretization in those

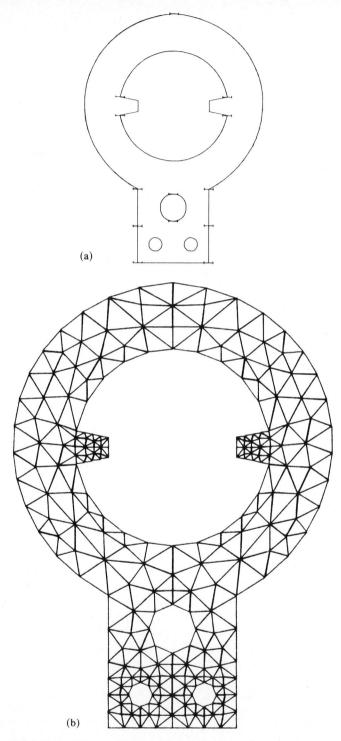

(a)

(b)

**FIG. 3.39** Mesh automatically generated by the modified–quadtree technique. (*a*) Boundary curves. (*b*) Final mesh.

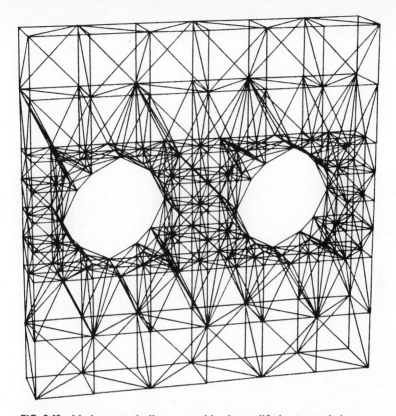

**FIG. 3.40**  Mesh automatically generated by the modified-octree technique.

areas. A number of methods have been proposed and tested for making improvements in the finite-element discretization. Some procedures retain the original mesh and improve the discretization in the areas of selected elements [84–91], while others reconfigure the mesh while maintaining the same element topology [92–96] or define an entirely new mesh [97, 98].

Two approaches can be taken to improve the discretization within the area of a selected element. The first is to subdivide the element into a number of smaller elements of the same type [84–88]. This approach is referred to as an *h*-version enrichment scheme because the discretization is improved by reducing the element size (often measured in terms of a side length *h*). The other approach is to leave the element geometry unaltered but to increase the polynomial order of selected elements. This approach is commonly referred to as a *p*-version approach [88–91].

When a selected element is subdivided, the new elements should not have an element aspect ratio† greater than that of the original element. Otherwise, as element subdivision

---

† The *element aspect ratio* is a measure of the shape of an element. It is often defined simply as the ratio of the length of the longest element side to the length of the shortest element side. The importance of this measure is that numerical ill-conditioning of the element stiffness matrix may result when an element becomes too elongated and/or the vertex angles become too small or too large. The degree of sensitivity to aspect ratio is a function of the element type and number of digits of accuracy available.

continues for a number of iterations, repeated subdivision in a given area will produce unacceptably shaped elements. One scheme that will ensure this for quadrilateral elements is shown in Fig. 3.41a. Figure 3.41b shows a scheme for triangles. In each scheme a single element is subdivided into four new elements. Referring to Fig. 3.41b, one can see that the

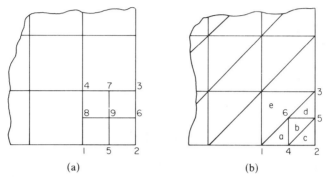

(a)                                    (b)

**FIG. 3.41**   Element subdivision schemes. (a) Scheme for quadrilateral element. (b) Scheme for triangular elements.

original triangular element with nodes 1, 2, 3 has been replaced by elements a, b, c, and d and the new nodes 4, 5, and 6 introduced at the midsides of the original element. Care must be exercised when adding these new nodes; for example, node 6 is along a side of element e and must be linearly constrained to nodes 1 and 3 if displacement continuity of the mesh is to be retained. These linear constraints can be handled by writing global constraint equations and enforced via static condensation [99], Lagrange multipliers [99], or other techniques [100]. In addition, they could be applied at an elemental level [84] and the constrained degrees of freedom removed via static condensation [99] in a manner similar to substructuring. The same basic subdivision schemes can be applied to higher-order elements [86, 101], with the caution that the constraint equation for a node on an edge between a subdivided and an unsubdivided element must reflect the quadratic or higher-order displacement field of the unsubdivided element.

There is a reasonable computing cost associated with the application of constraint equations which can be decreased by reducing the number of constraint equations. One method of doing this is to subdivide elements that have several subdivided elements of a smaller size along their edge. Although this introduces additional degrees of freedom to be solved, the improved accuracy and the elimination of the constraint equations often outweighs the cost of the additional degrees of freedom. By the appropriate combination of program-data structure and refinement strategy [88] such a procedure can be implemented. In fact, it is possible to carry out selective refinement of triangles without the use of constraint equations with a specific refinement strategy [88] that would always subdivide neighboring elements with either more than one subdivided neighbor or any subdivided neighbors two levels lower, plus the introduction of a temporary split subdivision. Figure 3.42 depicts the temporary split subdivision that takes element $e$ to $e_1$ and $e_2$. Although this reduces the aspect ratio, only the original and permanently subdivided elements are considered for further subdivision on the subsequent step. Thus, the degradation of aspect ratio is always limited to that caused by the bisection of a side of an element.

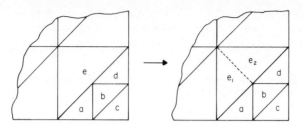

**FIG. 3.42**   Use of a temporary split subdivision to eliminate the need to constrain a node.

Nodes 4 and 5 that are introduced along the exterior edges in Fig. 3.42*b* need not be linearly constrained; however, other considerations arise for new exterior nodes. One consideration is the specification of loads and boundary conditions to be applied to the new node. If an edge is restrained or subjected to some distributed loading, this information should be reflected in the definition of problem input for the refined element mesh. The other consideration is related to the placement of the new node. If the actual domain boundary between nodes 2 and 3 in Fig. 3.42*b* is curved, then node 5 should not be placed at the midpoint of the straight line between them, but should be placed at the half arc length of the boundary curve between them. This point becomes particularly important when considering three-dimensional problems such as thin-shell structures idealized by planar elements. It is not possible to properly address these considerations if the adaptive processor's input is based on an initial finite-element mesh only.

An obvious advantage of a *p*-version approach to improving an element mesh is that it does not require the definition of additional elements. A problem that does remain is retaining displacement continuity between elements of different polynomial order. This problem can be overcome with the use of hierarchical finite elements [89–91, 102–106]. A property of hierarchical elements is that the degrees of freedom and stiffness matrix of an element of order $p$ are a subset of those for the element of polynomial order $p+1$. Continuity for these elements can be retained by forcing the values of the hierarchical variables along common edges between elements to be the same [105]. Thus, if elements having different polynomial orders share an edge, the hierarchical variables along that edge associated with the polynomial terms of higher order than that common to both elements are set equal to zero. There are also a number of other possible advantages to using hierarchical elements in an adaptive program because of improved convergence rates and efficiencies offered by using precomputed arrays [89, 107, 108].

Although the convergence rate of the *p*-version hierarchical elements for uniform refinements is superior to that of *h*-version uniform refinements for singular problems [107, 108], there is currently no such proof for the case of selective mesh improvements, such as would be performed by an adaptive-analysis program. It has been demonstrated [98] that the best possible convergence rates can be obtained by combining the two methods into a procedure that, in a given iteration, will use the method that gives the best result in that step. Such an approach is referred to as a "pony-express policy" [109].

The earliest methods for improving finite-element discretizations were based on moving nodal positions while retaining the same element topology [95, 96]. Because the element topology of such an approach is fixed, the methods allow only a limited amount of mesh improvement before element shapes degrade to an unacceptable point. Although they are no longer popular for steady-state problems [95, 96], these methods have been effectively used for time-dependent problems [92–94] in which the area requiring the most refined mesh changes with time. Figure 3.43 depicts a uniform mesh that adapts to the shape of a traveling shock wave in order to better track its motion.

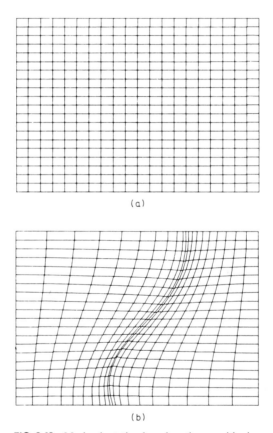

(a)

(b)

**FIG. 3.43**  Mesh adaptation based on the repositioning of nodal locations. (*a*) Original uniform mesh. (*b*) Adapting mesh accounting for a shock wave.

Methods in which a new mesh is defined in each step have the advantage of being able to make large improvements in the mesh configuration in a single iteration. A major disadvantage of such approaches is the amount of effort required to define a new mesh in each step. A technique that can make such approaches more attractive is to incorporate interactive computer graphics into a software system that displays information indicating how to set up a better mesh and giving the user the ability to interactively break up the domain into elements using interactive options and flexible mesh generators. The most common approach taken to indicate how the user should define a new mesh is to display a set of contours in the domain that gives an indication of where elements should be concentrated and the general mesh layout that should be used [97, 98]. Experience with such approaches indicates that they are useful for a first step but of questionable use for subsequent steps [97].

It is also possible to combine approaches. For example, it may prove useful to use an interactive approach for the first step and to use an adaptive processor for the subsequent steps. Procedures can also be combined with other special techniques. For example, problems with singularities could be attacked with the combination of a step of interactive mesh improvement plus singular elements at the location of the singularity [101].

## 3.4D Design of an Automated Finite-Element Modeler

It is assumed here that the finite-element modeling process begins after the complete definition of the problem geometry and attributes [110]. Thus, the first requirement of an automatic finite-element modeling processor is to possess a data base that can accept a geometric definition of a model instead of a particular finite-element mesh. This represents a substantial departure from the data structures of current finite-element programs. The use of a general data base will make it possible to design the automated meshing procedure so that as the discretization is improved in selected areas, the geometric approximation in those areas can also be improved and the edge loads and boundary conditions can be properly assigned.

The first function to be performed by an automated modeling process is to define an initial finite-element mesh. The only requirement placed on this mesh is that it be a valid mesh having acceptably shaped elements. It is not critical for this initial mesh to be well-graded since the adaptive-analysis portion of the program will ensure that the final mesh is sufficiently accurate. Thus any automatic mesh generator that can create a mesh meeting these requirements and can work for general geometries is satisfactory. It would also be advantageous if the data structure used to store the mesh were flexible enough to efficiently account for the mesh modifications that occur during the adaptive-analysis portion of the program.

In addition to generating an initial mesh and performing a finite-element analysis, the automatic finite-element modeling program must be able to measure local errors and to improve the discretization in selected areas. It must also be able to perform as many iterations of analysis, error estimation, and mesh improvement as required to ensure the desired degree of accuracy. Since the emphasis of this section is on mesh generation and improvement schemes, the question of error estimators is not being discussed. However, the development of dependable error estimators in meaningful norms is a critical facet of this process that is currently being investigated.

Since an automatic finite-element modeler must iteratively perform finite-element analysis and calculate error estimators, the computational efficiency of the process is important. A large amount of the effort in such a procedure is spent in data manipulation; thus it is important that efficient data structures which allow for quick scanning for specific information are used. Since the element discretization will be improved in each step by increasing the polynomial order and/or subdivision of selected elements, the finite-element data base must be capable of efficient expansion and modification.

The solution of the sets of global stiffness equations is an area where computational efficiency must be addressed. The equation solution process must take full account of the system sparseness, even when the new degrees of freedom are added. Since several solutions to similar discretizations of the problem will be obtained during the process, reanalysis [111] or iterative solution techniques [112] will play a key role in reducing equation solution times.

Computational efficiency can also be addressed by reducing the number of iterations required to obtain the required accuracy. The proper use of a pony-express policy [109], as mentioned above, is one possibility. Another is to perform multiple subdivisions or increases of polynomial order of selected elements with particularly high error estimates [112]. Improvements in the efficiency of the process can also be obtained by making adaptive improvements to the formulation by changing weighting functions [113].

Since it is computationally efficient to solve multiple-load-case problems by a single triangulation and one back substitution per load case, a single-element mesh should be employed for all load cases. However, it is well known that the optimum mesh is different for each load case. Therefore, techniques for defining a single, near-optimum mesh for multiple-load-case problems should be used [114] in an automated finite-element modeling program.

Currently, a number of investigators are working on the development of the various pieces needed for an automated finite-element modeling program that can handle cases such as static-elasticity problems in which there is little difficulty in specifying the basic class of element (i.e., plane or three-dimensional elasticity elements). In addition, some prototype software systems having many of the features mentioned above are under development. In particular, the FEARS program [115–119], based on $h$-version refinement, and the COMET-X program [89–91, 102–105], based on $p$-version refinement, are two examples.

## 3.5 REFERENCES

1. Robinson, J., "Element Evaluation—A Set of Assessment Points and Standard Tests," In J. Robinson (ed.), *Finite Element Methods in the Commercial Environment*, Robinson and Associates, Vicarage Rd., Verwood, Dorset, England, 1978.

2. Zienkiewicz, O. C., *The Finite Element Method*, 3d ed., McGraw-Hill, New York, 1977.

3. Thomas, K., "Effects of Geometric Distortion on the Accuracy of Plane Quadratic Isoparametric Elements," in A. M. Ebner (ed.), *Guidelines for Finite Element Idealization*, ASCE Preprint 2504, American Society of Chemical Engineers, New York, 1975.

4. Wilson, E. L., R. L. Taylor, W. P. Doherty, and J. Ghaboussi, "Incompatible Displacement Models," in S. Fenves, N. Perrone, A. Robinson, and W. Schnobrich (eds.), *Numerical and Computer Methods in Structural Mechanics*, Academic Press, New York, 1973.

5. Pian, T. H. H., "Derivation of Element Stiffness Matrices by Assumed Stress Distributions," *AIAA J.*, **2** (1964).

6. MacNeal, R. H., R. L. Harder, and J. B. Mason, "NASTRAN Cyclic Symmetry Capability," *NASTRAN: Users' Experiences*, NASA TM X-2893, National Aeronautics and Space Administration, Washington, D.C., 1973.

7. Apostal, M. C., "Finite Element Techniques for Postulated Flaws in Shell Structures," EPRI SR-22, Special Report, August 1975.

8. Segerlind, L. J., *Applied Finite Element Analysis*, Wiley, New York, 1975.

9. Feld, D. J., and J. G. Soudry, "Modeling the Interface Between Shell and Solid Elements," *MSC/NASTRAN User's Conference Proceedings*, MacNeal-Schwendler Corp., Los Angeles, California, March 1983.

10. Kelley, F. S., "Mesh Requirements for the Analysis of Stress Concentration by the Specified Boundary Displacement Method," *Proc. 2d Int. Comput. Eng. Conf.*, American Society of Mechanical Engineers, New York, August 1982.

11. Dietrich, D. E., "Geometric Nonlinearities," *ANSYS News*, 1 (1981).

12. Gallagher, R. H., "Geometrically Nonlinear Finite Element Analysis," *Finite Element Methods in Civil Engineering*, Engineering Institute of Canada, Montreal, 1972.

13. Oden, J. T., "Calculation of Geometric Stiffness Matrices for Complex Structures," *AIAA J.*, 4(8): 1480-1482 (1966).

14. Gallagher, R. H., and J. Padlog, "Discrete Element Approach to Structural Instability Analysis," *AIAA J.*, 1(6):1437-1439 (1963).

15. Przemienicki, J. S., "Stability Analysis of Complex Structures Using Discrete Element Techniques," *Symposium on Structural Stability Optimization*, London, 1967.

16. Biot, M. A., *Mechanics of Incremental Deformations*, Wiley, New York, 1965.

17. Novozhelov, V. U., *Foundations of the Nonlinear Theory of Elasticity*, Graylock Press, Rochester, N.Y., 1953.

18. Oden, J. T., *Finite Elements of Nonlinear Continua*, McGraw-HIll, New York, 1972.

19. Levy, A., "Inelastic Finite Element Modeling through User Selected Inelastic Integration Points," Grumman Research and Development Center Rep. RE-619, Grumman Aerospace Corp., Bethpage, New York, February 1981.

20. Levy, A., and A. B. Pifko, "On Computational Strategies for Problems Involving Plasticity and Creep," *Int. J. Numer. Meth. Eng.*, 17:747-771 (1981).

21. Levine, H. S., H. Armen, Jr., R. Winter, and A. B. Pifko, "Nonlinear Behavior of Shells of Revolution Under Cyclic Loading," *Comput. Struct.*, 13:589-617 (1973).

22. Prager, W., and P. G. Hodge, *Theory of Perfect Plastic Solids*, Wiley, New York, 1951, p. 501.

23. Mendelson, A., M. H. Hirschberg, and S. S. Manson, "A General Approach to the Practical Solution of Creep Problems," *J. Bas. Eng.* 18:585-593 (1959).

24. Steele, J. M., and T. C. T. Lam, "Introduction to Dynamic Finite Element Analysis with ANSYS," in D. Dietrich (ed.), *ANSYS Conference Proceedings*, Swanson Analysis Systems, 1983.

25. Nelson, M. F., "The Use of Condensation Technique for Solving Dynamics Problems," *Proc. Int. Conf. Vehicle Struct. Mech.*, Detroit, 1974.

26. Miller, C. A., "Dynamic Reduction of Structural Models," *J. Struct. Div. ASCE*, 106:(ST10) (October 1980).

27. Guyan, R. J., "Reduction of Stiffness and Mass Matrices," *AIAA J.*, 3(2) (February 1965).

28. Henshall, R. D., and J. H. Ong, "Automatic Masters for Eigenvalue Economization," *Earthquake Eng. Struct. Dynam.*, 3, 1975.

29. Dietrich, D. E. course coordinator, *Finite Element Concepts: Modeling Methods and Applications*, Ext. Short Course, with J. F. Abel, R. D. Cook, D. E. Dietrich, and J. A. Swanson (lecturers), University of Wisconsin, Madison, 1984.

30. Ebner, A. M., ed., "Guidelines for Finite Element Evaluation," ASCE Meeting Preprint 2504, *ASCE National Structural Engineering Convention*, April 1975.

31. Everstine, G. C., "A Comparison of Three Resequencing Algorithms for the Reduction of Matrix Profile and Wavefront," *Int. J. Numer. Meth. Eng.*, 14:837-853 (1979).

32. Gibbs, N. E., W. G. Poole, Jr., and P. K. Stockmeyer, "An Algorithm for Reducing the Bandwidth and Profile of a Sparse Matrix," *SIAM J. Numer. Anal.*, 13:236-250 (1976).

33. Lewis, J. G., "Implementation of the Gibbs-Poole-Stockmeyer and Gibbs-King Algorithms," *ACM Trans. Math. Software* 8:180-189 (1982).

34. Cuthill, E., and J. M. McKee, "Reducing the Bandwidth of Sparse Symmetric Matrices," *Proc. 24th Nat. Conf. Assoc. Comput. Mach.*, ACM Pub. P69, New York, 1969, pp. 157–172.

35. Rosen, J., *Symmetry Discovered*, Cambridge University Press, Cambridge, 1975.

36. Miller, A. G., "Application of Group Representation Theory to Symmetric Structures," *Appl. Math. Model.*, **5**:290–294 (1981).

37. Rosen, J., "Symmetry: An Introduction to Its Theory and Application in Physics (A Resource Article for Teachers)," Rep. TAUP-307-72, Department of Physics and Astronomy, Tel-Aviv University, Tel-Aviv, 1972.

38. Rosen, J., *A Symmetry Primer for Scientists*, Wiley, New York, 1982.

39. Glockner, P. G., "Symmetry in Structural Mechanics," *J. Struct. Div. ASCE*, **99**(ST1):71–89 (1973); discussion by K. R. Leimbach and D. Franz, **99**(ST8):1792–1794 (1973).

40. Renton, J. D., "On the Stability Analysis of Symmetrical Frameworks," *Q. J. Mech. Appl. Math.*, **17**(2):175–197 (1964).

41. Kardestuncer, H., and K. Berg, "Matrix Analysis of Large Symmetric Skeletal Systems," in P. G. Glockner and M. C. Singh (eds.), *Symmetry, Singularity and Group Theoretic Methods in Mechanics*, Calgary, Alta., 1974.

42. Smith, C. L., "Symmetry and the Laws of Nature," *New Sci.*, **92**(1274):94–97 (Oct. 8, 1981).

43. Shubnikov, A. V., and V. A. Koptik, *Symmetry in Science and Art*, Plenum Press, New York, 1974.

44. Everstine, G. C., "Comment on 'On Symmetries and Antisymmetries in Solving Vibration Problems Using High Precision Finite Elements,' " *J. Sound Vibration*, **52**(1):143–144 (1977).

45. Newell, J. S., "Symmetric and Anti-Symmetric Loadings," *Civ. Eng.* **9**(4):249–251 (1939).

46. Butler, T. G., "Using NASTRAN to Solve Symmetric Structures with Nonsymmetric Loads," *Tenth NASTRAN Users' Colloquium*, NASA CP-2249, National Aeronautics and Space Administration, Washington, D.C., 1982, pp. 216–232.

47. Everstine, G. C., "The Application of Structural Symmetry in Finite Element Analysis," TM-184-77-05, David Taylor Naval Ship Research and Development Center, Bethesda, Md., 1977.

48. Everstine, G. C., "A NASTRAN Implementation of the Doubly Asymptotic Approximation for Underwater Shock Response," *NASTRAN: Users' Experiences*, NASA TM X-3428, National Aeronautics and Space Adminstration, Washington, D.C., 1976, pp. 207–228.

49. Zienkiewicz, O. C., and F. C. Scott, "On the Principle of Repeatability and Its Application in Analysis of Turbine and Pump Impellers," *Int. J. Numer. Meth. Eng.*, **4**(3):445–448 (1972).

50. Noor, A. K., and R. A. Camin, "Symmetry Considerations for Anisotropic Shells," *Comput. Meth. Appl. Mech. Eng.*, **9**:317–335 (1976).

51. Noor, A. K., M. D. Mathers, and M. S. Anderson, "Exploiting Symmetries for Efficient Postbuckling Analysis of Composite Plates," *AIAA J.*, **15**(1):24–32 (1977).

52. Mangalgiri, P. D., B. Dattaguru, and T. S. Ramamurthy, "Specification of Skew Conditions in Finite Element Formulation," *Int. J. Numer. Meth. Eng.*, **12**(6):1037–1041 (1978).

53. Evensen, D. A., "Vibration Analysis of Multi-Symmetric Structures," *AIAA J.*, **14**(4):446–453 (1976).

54. Hussey, M. J. L., "General Theory of Cyclically Symmetric Frames," *J. Struct. Div. ASCE*, **93**(ST2):163–176 (1967).

55. Thomas, D. L., "Dynamics of Rotationally Periodic Structures," *Int. J. Numer. Meth. Eng.*, **14**(1):81–102 (1979).

56. Melvin, M. A., and S. Edwards, Jr., "Group Theory of Vibrations of Symmetric Molecules, Membranes, and Plates," *J. Acoust. Soc. Am.*, **28**(2):201–216 (1956).

57. Zheng, X., G. Bao, and S. Sun, "Applications of Group Theory to Vibrational Analysis of Shell Structure with Space Rotation Symmetry," in H. Guangqian and Y. K. Cheung (eds.), *Proceedings of the International Conference on Finite Element Methods*, Science Press, Beijing, China, Gordon and Breach, New York, 1982.

58. Irons, B., and S. Ahmad, *Techniques of Finite Elements*, Ellis Horwood, Wiley, Chichester, 1980.

59. Zienkiewicz, O. C., and D. V. Phillips, "An Automatic Mesh Generation Scheme for Plane and Curves Surface by Isoparametric Co-ordinates," *Int. J. Numer. Meth. Eng.*, 3:519–528 (1971).

60. Brown, P. R., "A Non-Interactive Method for the Automatic Generation of Finite Element Meshes Using the Schwarz-Christoffel Transformation," *Comput. Meth. Appl. Mech. Eng.*, 25:101–126 (1981).

61. Brown, P. R., and D. R. Hayhurst, "The Use of the Schwarz-Christoffel Transformation in Mesh Generation for the Solution of Two-Dimensional Problems," *Comput. Eng. ASME*, 3:1–7 (1982).

62. Hermann, L. R., "Laplacian-Isoparametric Grid Generation Scheme," *J. Eng. Mech. Div. ASCE*, 102:749–756 (1976).

63. Cook, W. A., "Body Oriented (Natural) Co-ordinates for Generating Three-Dimensional Meshes," *Int. J. Numer. Meth. Eng.*, 8:27–43 (1974).

64. Cook, W. A., and W. R. Oakes, "A Mapping Method for Generating Three-Dimensional Meshes: Past and Present," *Comput. Eng. ASME*, 3:9–16 (1982).

65. Gordon, W. J., and C. A. Hall, "Construction of Curvilinear Co-ordinates Systems and Applications to Mesh Generation," *Int. J. Numer. Meth. Eng.*, 7:461–477 (1973).

66. Barnhill, E. E., T. Birkhoff, and W. J. Gordon, "Smooth Interpolation in Triangles," *J. Approximation Theory*, 8:114–128 (1973).

67. Haber, R. B., M. S. Shephard, J. F. Abel, R. H. Gallagher, and D. P. Greenberg, "A General Two-Dimensional Finite Element Preprocessor Utilizing Discrete Transfinite Mappings," *Int. J. Numer. Meth. Eng.*, 16:1015–1044 (1981).

68. Haber, R. B., and J. F. Abel, "Discrete Transfinite Mappings for the Description and Meshing of Three-Dimensional Surfaces Using Interactive Computer Graphics," *Int. J. Numer. Meth. Eng.*, 18:41–66 (1982).

69. Cavendish, J. C., "Automatic Triangulation of Arbitrary Planar Domains for the Finite Element Method." *Int. J. Numer. Meth. Eng.*, 8:679–697 (1974).

70. Bykat, A., "Automatic Generation of Triangular Grid: I. Subdivision of General Polygon into Convex Subregions; II. Triangulation of Convex Polygons," *Int. J. Numer. Meth. Eng.*, 10:1329–1342 (1976).

71. Tracy, F. T., "Graphics Pre- and Post-Processor for Two-Dimensional Finite Element Programs," *SIGGRAPH 77'*, 11(2):8–12 (1977).

72. Sadek, E. A., "A Scheme for the Automatic Generation of Triangular Finite Elements," *Int. J. Numer. Meth. Eng.*, 15:1813–1822 (1980).

73. Schoofs, A. J. G., L. H. TH. M. Van Beukering, and M. L. C. Sluiter, "TRIQUAMESH Gebruiker-shandleiding: Rapport WE 78-01," Technische Hogeschool Eindhoven, Afdeling der Wertuigbouwkunde, 1978.

74. Yerry, M. A., and M. S. Shephard, "Finite Element Mesh Generation Based on a Modified-Quadtree Approach," *IEEE Comput. Graphics Appl.*, 3(1):39–46 (1983).

75. Cavendish, J. C., D. A. Field and W. H. Frey, "An Approach to Automatic Three-Dimensional Finite Element Mesh Generation," *Int. J. Numer. Meth. Eng.*, 21:329–348 (1985).

76. Sluiter, M. L. C., and D. L. Hansen, "A General Purpose Automatic Mesh Generator for Shell and Solid Finite Elements," *Comput. Eng. ASME*, 3:29–34 (1982).

77. Nguyen, N. Ph., "Automatic Mesh Generation with Tetrahedron Elements," *Int. J. Numer. Meth. Eng.*, 18:273–280 (1982).

78. Yerry, M. A., and M. S. Shephard, "Automatic Three-Dimensional Mesh Generation by the Modified-Octree Technique," *Int. J. Numer. Meth. Eng.*, 20:1965–1990 (1984).

79. Wordenweber, B., "Volume-Triangulation," CAD Group Document No. 110, Computer Laboratory, University of Cambridge, Cambridge, 1980.

80. Lorensen, W., "Grid Generation Tools for the Finite Element Analyst," in J. H. Conway (ed.), *First Chautaugua on Finite Element Modeling*, Wallace Press, Milford, New Hampshire, 1980, pp. 119–136.

81. Winslow, A. M., "Equipotential Zoning of Two-Dimensional Meshes," Lawrence Radiation Lab. Rep. UCRL 7312, University of California, Berkeley, 1963.

82. Klinger, A., and C. R. Dyer, "Experiments on Picture Representation Using Regular Decomposition," *Comput. Graphics Image Processing*, **5**:68–105 (1976).

83. Doctor, L. J., and J. G. Torborg, "Display Techniques for Octree-Encoded Objectives," *IEEE Comput. Graphics Appl.*, **1**:29–38 (July 1981).

84. Carey, G. F., "A Mesh-Refinement Scheme for Finite Element Computations," *Comput. Meth. Appl. Mech. Eng.*, **7**:93–105 (1976).

85. Melosh, R. J., and D. Killian, "Finite Element Analysis to Attain Prespecified Accuracy," *2d Nat. Symp. Computerized Struct. Anal. Des.*, Washington University, St. Louis, March 1976.

86. Melosh, R. J., and P. V. Marcal, "An Energy Basis for Mesh Refinement of Structural Continua," *Int. J. Numer. Meth. Eng.*, **11**(7):1083–1092 (1977).

87. Babuska, I., "The Self-Adaptive Approach in the Finite Element Method," *The Mathematics of Finite Elements and Applications II*, MAFELAP 1975, Academic Press, New York, 1976.

88. Bank, R. E., A. H. Sherman, and A. Waiser, "Refinement Algorithms and Data Structures for Regular Local Refinement," in R. S. Stepleman (ed.), *Scientific Computing: Applications of Mathematics and Computing to the Physical Sciences*, North-Holland, Amsterdam, 1983, pp. 3–17.

89. Peano, A., R. Riccioni, A. Pasini, and L. Sardella, "Adaptive Approximations in Finite Element Structural Analysis," *Comput. Struct.*, **10**:333–342 (1979).

90. Szabo B. A., P. K. Basu, and M. P. Rossow, "Adaptive Finite Element Analysis Based on *P*-Convergence," *Research in Computerized Structural Analysis and Synthesis*, NASA Conf. Pub. 2059, 1978, pp. 43–50.

91. Szabo, B. A., and D. A. Dunavant, "An Adaptive Procedure Based on the *P*-Version of the Finite Element Method," in I. Babuska (ed.), *Finite Element Workshop*, Lab. Numer. Anal., Inst. Phys. Sci. Technol., University of Maryland, College Park, 1980, pp. 142–155.

92. Miller, K., "Alternate Modes to Control the Nodes in the Moving Finite Element Method," in I. Babuska, J. Chandra, and J. E. Flaherty (eds.), *Adaptive Computational Methods for Partial Differential Equations*, SIAM, 1983.

93. Albert, M. R., and K. O'Neill, "The Use of Transfinite Mappings with Finite Elements on a Moving Mesh for Two-Dimensional Phase Change," in I. Babuska, J. Chandra, and J. E. Flaherty (eds.), *Adaptive Computational Methods for Partial Differential Equations*, SIAM, 1983.

94. Dwyer, H. A., "The Use of Adaptive Gridding," in I. Babuska, J. Chandra, and J. E. Flaherty (eds.), *Adaptive Computational Methods for Partial Differential Equations*, SIAM, 1983.

95. Fillipa, C. A., "Optimization of Finite Element Grids by Direct Energy Search," *Appl. Math. Modelling*, **1**:93–96 (September 1976).

96. Turcke, D. J., and G. M. McNeice, "Guidelines for Selecting Finite Element Grids Based on an Optimization Study," *Comput. Struct.*, **4**:499–519 (1974).

97. Shephard, M. S., R. H. Gallagher, and J. F. Abel, "Synthesis of Near-Optimum Finite Element Grids with Interactive Computer Graphics," *Int. J. Numer. Meth. Eng.*, **15**:1021–1039 (1980).

98. Molinari, G., and A. Viviani, "Grid Iteration for Finite Element Grid Optimization," in M. S. Shephard and R. H. Gallagher (eds.), *Finite Element Grid Optimization*, ASME Pub. PVP-38, American Society of Mechanical Engineers, New York, 1979.

99. Gallagher, R. H., *Finite Element Analysis: Fundamentals*, Prentice-Hall, Englewood Cliffs, N.J., 1975.

100. Abel, J. F., and M. S. Shephard, "An Algorithm for Multipoint Constraints in Finite Element Analysis," *Int. J. Numer. Meth. Eng.*, **14**:464–467 (1979).

101. Shephard, M. S., R. H. Gallagher, and J. F. Abel, "Finite Element Solutions to Point-Load Problems," *J. Eng. Mech. Div. ASCE*, **107** (EM5):839–850 (October 1981).

102. Rossow, M. P., and I. R. Katz, "Hierarchal Finite Elements and Precomputed Arrays," *Int. J. Numer. Meth. Eng.*, **12**(6):977–1000 (1978).

103. Szabo, B. A., and A. K. Mehta, "*P*-Convergent Finite Element Approximations in Fracture Mechnics," *Int. J. Numer. Meth. Eng.*, **12**:551–560 (1978).

104. Szabo, B. A., and A. G. Peano, "Hierarchic Finite Elements," Rep. WU/CCM-83/1, Center for Computational Mechanics, Washington University, St. Louis, March 1983.

105. Basu, P. K., B. A. Szabo, and B. D. Taylor, "Theoretical Manual and Users' Guide for Comet-XA," Rep. WU/CCM-79/2, Center for Computational Mechanics, Washington University, St. Louis, 1979.

106. Zienkiewicz, O. C., D. W. Kelly, J. Gago, and I. Babuska, "Hierarchical Finite Element Approaches, Error Estimates and Adaptive Refinement," *MAFELAP*, Brunel University, Uxbridge, Middlesex, United Kingdom, 1981.

107. Babuska, I., B. A. Szabo, and I. N. Katz, "The *P*-Version of the Finite Element Method," *SIAM J. Numer. Anal.*, **18**, 1981.

108. Babuska, I., and B. A. Szabo, "On the Rates of Convergence of the Finite Element Method," *Int. J. Numer. Meth. Eng.*, **18**:323–341 (1982).

109. Melosh, R. J., and S. Utku, "Principles for Design of Finite Element Meshes," in W. D. Pilkey and A. K. Noor (eds.), *State of the Art of Computational Mechanics*, American Society of Mechanical Engineers, New York, 1983.

110. Shephard, M. S., "The Finite Element Modeling Process—Will it be Automated?," in J. Robinson (ed.), *New and Future Development in Commercial Finite Element Methods*, Robinson and Associates, Dorset, England, 1981, pp. 451–468.

111. Law, K. H., and S. J. Fenves, "Sparse Matrices, Graph Theory, and Reanalysis," *Proc. First Int. Conf. Computation Civ. Eng.*, American Society of Chemical Engineers, New York, 1981, pp. 234–249.

112. Carey, G. F., and D. L. Humphrey, "Mesh Refinement and Iterative Solution Methods for Finite Element Computations," *Int. J. Numer. Meth. Eng.*, **17**:1717–1734 (1981).

113. Babuska, I., *Seminar for RPI Mathematics Department*, July 20, 1983; also Lab. Numer. Anal., Inst. Phys. Sci. Technol., University of Maryland report, College Park, 1983.

114. Shephard, M. S., "An Algorithm for Defining a Single Near-Optimum Mesh for Multiple-Load-Case Problems," *Int. J. Numer. Meth. Eng.*, **15**:617–625 (1980).

115. Babuska, I., and W. C. Rheinboldt, "A-Posteriori Error Estimates for the Finite Element Method," *Int. J. Numer. Meth. Eng.*, **12**:1597–1615 (1978).

116. Babuska, I., and W. C. Rheinboldt, "On a System for Adaptive Parallel Finite Element Computations," *Proceedings 1978 Annual Conference of ACM*, Washington, D.C., December 1978, Vol. 1, pp. 480–489.

117. Rheinboldt, W. C., and C. K. Mesztenyi, "On a Data Structure for Adaptive Finite Element Mesh Refinements," *ACM Trans. Math. Software*, **6**(2):166–187 (June 1980).

118. Rheinboldt, W. C., "Adaptive Mesh Refinement Processes for Finite Element Solutions, *Int. J. Numer. Meth. Eng.*, **17**:649–662 (1981).

119. Zare, P., and W. C. Rheinboldt, "Design of an Adaptive, Parallel Finite-Element System," *ACM Trans. Math. Software*, **5**(1):1–17 (1979).

# CHAPTER 4
# FEM HARDWARE
# AND POSTPROCESSING

## 4.1 MODERN COMPUTING SYSTEMS

The last two decades have witnessed an explosive growth in computer technology. This growth shows no sign of abating; all the indications are that the changes during the next decades will prove to be even greater, particularly with the introduction of novel forms of machine architecture (e.g., vector, array, and multiprocessor systems). The computer hardware developments are most noticeable at the two extremes of the spectrum. At one end, the large, expensive computer systems, usually referred to as *supersystems*, such as CRAY X-MP, CRAY-2, and CDC CYBER 205, have radically different and novel architectures resulting in very high performance [computational speed of the order of 100 million floating-point operations per second (100 MFLOPS) or more]. At the other end of the spectrum are the various types of minicomputers, engineering workstations (microcomputers, or micros), microprocessors, and handheld computers.

The introduction of these new computing systems has made a strong impact on finite-element technology. The supersystems have made possible new levels of sophistication in finite-element modeling as well as in problem depth and scope which were not possible before. More important, however, is that the new supersystems have opened up a view of the next steps to be taken in the development of finite-element analysis software and hardware systems. In order to realize the full potential of the supersystems in finite-element computation, special parallel numerical algorithms, programming strategies, and programming languages need to be developed.

The small, low-cost computer systems (minis, micros, and engineering workstations) provide a high degree of interactivity and free the finite-element analysts from the constraints that are often imposed on them by large, centralized computation centers. However, the effectiveness of the small computers for solving large-scale finite-element problems is limited. The combination of a fast attached processor with a mini (or micro) to make a dual-processor system can extend the range of finite-element problems that can effectively be solved by the minicomputer. In recent years, several general-purpose finite-element programs have been made operational on the minicomputers, and new finite element software is currently being developed for microcomputers.

This chapter discusses key finite-element requirements placed on evolving computer technology, summarizes some of the developments in computing systems during recent past and near-term future and relates these developments to finite-element technology, and outlines the likely directions of finite-element software and hardware systems.

A number of previous attempts have been made to predict the characteristics of future finite-element systems and the impact of the advances in computing systems on finite-element analysis (see, for example, Refs. [1–7]). The discussion presented here is much more detailed than that given in the cited references.

## 4.1A Technical Needs for Engineering Computations

The driving force for future developments in engineering computations will continue to be the need for improved productivity and cost-effective engineering systems. To achieve this goal, the following sets of technical needs can be identified:

1. Expanding the scope of engineering problems considered. This includes examination of more complex physical phenomena (e.g., progressive failure of fibrous composite structures), study of interaction phenomena (as would be required in the hydrodynamic-structural coupling in deep-sea mining and the thermal-control-structural coupling in space exploration), and the prediction of the reliability of the model's performance to uncertainties in its input parameters. Such reliability-based analysis can help in making rational design decisions and in achieving realistic cost-performance trade-offs.

2. Development of a hierarchy of models, algorithms, and procedures for engineering systems. Simplified and specialized models and algorithms are appropriate for use in the preliminary and conceptual design phases and more sophisticated models are used in the detailed design phase.

3. Development of effective integrated design, synthesis, and evaluation tools to support all phases of product development, including the design, management, and manufacturing cycle.

4. Continued reduction of cost and/or time for obtaining solutions to engineering design and analysis problems.

The hardware and software requirements to meet the aforementioned technical needs include:

1. A spectrum of available computer capabilities ranging from high-performance computing systems for large, complex problems to low-cost workstations which provide convenient computer capabilities at the engineer's desk.

**2.** Distributed asynchronous processors which carry out several different calculations in parallel using the same or different code and referencing the same or different data bases.

**3.** User-friendly hardware interfaces or engineering workstations with the following capabilities: high-speed graphics; high-speed, long-distance communication; and verbal (audio) as well as visual interfaces.

**4.** Artificial-intelligence-based expert systems, incorporating the experience and expertise of practitioners, to aid in the modeling of the engineering system, the adaptive refinement of the model, and the selection of the appropriate algorithm and procedure used in the solution.

**5.** Powerful engineering data-base management systems.

**6.** Turnkey engineering-application software systems which have advanced modeling and analysis capabilities and are easy to learn and to use.

The implication of these requirements on finite-element technology along with a scenario of future finite-element systems are discussed in another section. An assessment of future computer system needs for large-scale computation in a number of technical areas has been summarized in Ref. [8].

## 4.1B Review of Current and Projected Advances in Computer Technology

The major computer technology developments have been, and continue to be, focused on improvements of cost, size, power consumption, speed, and reliability of electrical components. These developments can be classified into two general areas: the hardware components and the computer architecture and system design methods [9]. The most notable advances in hardware components in the last two decades have occurred as a result of developments in microelectronics. Instead of connecting discrete components together by wires to produce a circuit, complete circuit patterns, components, and interconnections are placed on a small chip of semiconductor material (usually silicon); see Fig. 4.1. The principal

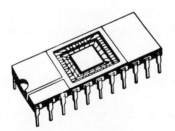

**FIG. 4.1**  Silicon chip.

advantages of microelectronic circuits are their reliability, low cost, and low power consumption. The ever-increasing number of devices packaged on a chip has given rise to the acronyms SSI, MSI, LSI, VLSI, and ULSI, which stand for small-scale, medium-scale, large-scale, very large-scale, and ultralarge-scale integration, respectively. Since 1960 the number of

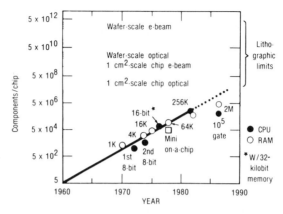

**FIG. 4.2** Digital logic capability commercially available on a single chip (based on a report by A. C. Haussmann, Lawrence Livermore National Laboratory).

components on a chip has increased continuously. For the case when no differentiation is made between logic and memory, the progression of development is shown in Fig. 4.2.

The full range of hardware components (computer building blocks) are now available on microelectronic chips; these include memory units, addressing units (i.e., counters and decoders), complete central processing units (CPUs) called *microprocessors*, and even complete microcomputers (which include the CPU, memory, and input/output functions all residing on a single chip).

The net effect of the aforementioned developments has been a significant decrease in the cost of performing computations. This is illustrated in Fig. 4.3, where it can be seen that the cost of performing a given calculation has decreased by a factor of 10 every 8 years [10].

The major advances in hardware components are reviewed here and some of the new computing systems are briefly described. The survey given here is by no means complete or exhaustive; the intention is to concentrate primarily on those developments which have had, or promise to have, the greatest impact on the manner in which finite-element computations are performed. Discussion is focused on semiconductor technology and processor speed, memory organization and secondary storage devices, access facilities and user interface, and networking.

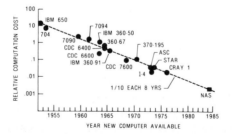

**FIG. 4.3** Trend of relative computation cost [10].

***Semiconductor Technology***   The predominant semiconductor material in use to date is silicon. Better understanding of this material as well as better processing, tooling, and packaging techniques enabled the design of fast dense circuitry. Current semiconductor technologies fall into two categories [11]:

*Logic made from bipolar transistors* which are current-controlled. Three classes of logic can be identified in this category, namely, transistor-transistor logic (TTL), emitter-coupled logic (ECL), and integrated injection logic ($I^2L$). The first is used in SSI and MSI. The second is suitable for LSI, and the third is good for VLSI.

*Logic made from field-effect transistors (FET)* which are voltage-controlled. A number of classes can be distinguished within this group, including metal-oxide semiconductor (MOS); complementary MOS, usually referred to as CMOS; and MOS devices fabricated in silicon grown on sapphire, referred to as SOS/MOS. The logic-circuit integration level attainable by each of the aforementioned technologies is depicted in Fig. 4.4.

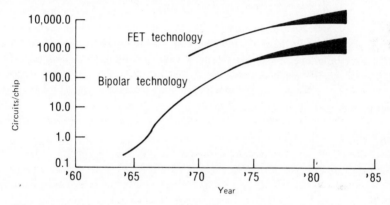

**FIG. 4.4**   Large circuits integration level [9].

Current research is directed toward (1) shrinking of conductor and device dimensions (scaling) to micron and submicron dimensions [12], and (2) increasing the speed of logic circuits (to achieve a machine cycle time of the order of 1 nanosecond ($1 \times 10^{-9}$ second) [13]).

The first objective can be accomplished by using recent and improved lithography tools [including optical, electron beams, ultraviolet (UV) optics, direct-write electron beam, x-ray, and ion-beam techniques]. Two candidate technologies are likely to achieve the second objective of ultrafast logic circuits. These technologies are (1) FET technology using gallium arsenide (GaAs), a component semiconductor material instead of silicon, and (2) three-dimensional integrated-circuit design.

***Memory***   Memory is the most rapidly advancing technology in microelectronics. Recent progress includes development of an entire hierarchy of addressable memories, and of high-speed, random-access memory chips with many bits of data. Each level in the hierarchy represents an order-of-magnitude decrease in access speed, and several-orders-of-magnitude increase in capacity, for the same cost. The techniques of splitting and interleaving among various types of memory hierarchies in individual systems have changed some of the basic concepts of computing itself. Instead of just a few registers in the CPU and a single-level memory, a typical machine may now have:

1. A number of high-speed, general-purpose registers
2. A cache memory for very rapid access to small amounts of data or instructions
3. Standard central or equivalent memory
4. Extended memory, directly addressable, but at a lower speed
5. Hardware-implemented virtual memory, extending the amount of addressable space

Initially, memories were based on bipolar transistor technology. However, by 1980, MOS technology accounted for over 80% of the semiconductor memory market. CMOS devices are becoming increasingly important because of their lower power requirements.

There are several types of semiconductor memories. These include random-access and read-only memories. In random-access memory (RAM), data can be written into or read out of any storage location in random fashion without regard to its physical location relative to other storage locations. Read-only memory (ROM) contains a permanent data pattern stored during the manufacture of the semiconductor chip in the form of transistors at each storage location that are either operable or inoperable. RAM can be either static or dynamic. Dynamic RAM (DRAM) requires constant refreshing to maintain its data, while static RAM (SRAM) does not. However, advances in DRAM permit double the amount of RAM at about the same cost as static RAM, so DRAM is used more frequently.

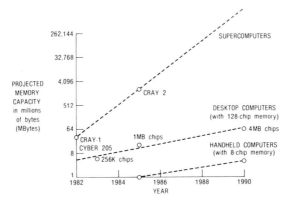

**FIG. 4.5** Projected computer memory based on chip-density increases.

Figure 4.5 shows the projected increase in the density of DRAM chips from their current value of 1 Mbyte ($8 \times 10^6$ bits) to 4 Mbytes ($32 \times 10^6$ bits) in 1990 on roughly a linear scale. These improvements take place by factors of 4 merely by halving the linear dimensions in each direction, which results in one-quarter the area with an added benefit of reduced power requirements.

The increase in the RAM chip's density from the current value of 1 Mbyte to the projected value of 4 Mbytes in 1990 can be exploited either by reducing the number of chips on the memory board, or, more likely, by increasing the user-memory capacity. The increase in the memory capacity is depicted in Fig. 4.5 for handheld computers with 8-chip memory boards and desktop computers with 128-chip memory boards. For the sake of comparison, the memory capacities of the current and planned supersystems are also shown in Fig. 4.5. The data presented in Fig. 4.5 are based on projections made in the current electronics literature. The impact of increased memory for finite-element analysis is quite significant, since memory capacity directly translates to increased-problem-size capability. Developments with low-power complementary metal-oxide semiconductor (CMOS) memory and higher speeds obtained by using gallium arsenide instead of silicon promise additional benefits for special-ized applications. However, for most applications, dynamic RAM in high densities is expected to be a major benefit to finite-element analysts since it will permit larger problems to be solved at reduced cost.

**Processor Speed and New Architectures**    The advances in microprocessor miniaturization currently allow several dozen layers (like floors in miniature buildings) in a single micropro-cessor CPU chip with hundreds of thousands of equivalent transistors on each layer. In addition to more compact CPU chips, the speed at which they are capable of operating will continue to increase. This is important to finite-element computations since the clock speed at which microprocessors can operate is directly proportional to the number of floating-point operations possible per second (the speed of computation). Early microprocessors had a clock speed of 1 MHz, which increased to 16 MHz in current microprocessors, and on the basis of current projections in the electronics literature, future speeds of over 50 MHz are expected (Fig. 4.6). The increase in the clock speed, measured in megahertz, directly affects

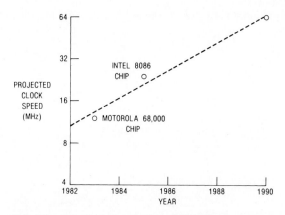

**FIG. 4.6**    Projected clock speed of CPU chips.

the throughput of engineering calculations measured in terms of the number of floating-point operations per second (FLOPS). The use of new materials such as gallium arsenide circuits in CPU chips is also expected to increase the CPU speed significantly. The impact of VLSI is likely to continue to play the most dominant role for immediate application in new products, while research on Josephson Junction devices requiring "supercool" environments may find application to some special-purpose computers where floating-point operations in the nanosecond range may be achievable.

Developments in the near future include very high-speed integrated circuits (VHSIC) and very high-performance integrated circuits (VHPIC) [14, 15].

In addition to increasing the speed of single processors in a control-flow architecture (conventional computers), two design options for faster processing exist. The two options are based on (1) using a few very fast processors and enhancing the control-flow architecture with pipelines (operating in an assembly-line manner) and some specialized processors, and (2) using a large number of fast or medium-speed off-the-shelf processors to form highly parallel systems. Examples of computing systems based on these two design options will be given in the succeeding section. See also Ref. [17].

Many of the new computers (from supercomputers to micros) contain more than one processor for improved performance. This trend is likely to continue as processors become easier to design and more compact. Before microprocessor CPUs were invented, the most laborious part of developing new computers was the signal back plane and digital-component wiring of a multiboard CPU. Now that the CPU is on a VLSI chip and associated chips are available for memory management, input/output and other functions which formerly used one or more boards, as well as the entire CPU and associated functions, are being condensed to one board, allowing additional boards for memory. In the case of microcomputers, all functions, including memory, are reduced to a single board. It is expected that the majority of computers in the future will be single-board computers, and if additional boards are required, they will be for memory or peripheral controller functions only.

**Secondary Storage Devices**   Significant advances are taking place in secondary storage technology. The advances reported in the literature for disk technology are depicted in Fig. 4.7. While the conventional hard disks (Winchester disks) are increasing in storage density

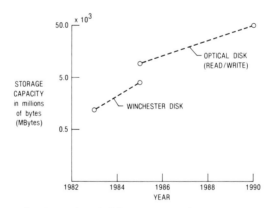

**FIG. 4.7**   Projected disk-storage capacity.

[currently in excess of 1 Gbyte $(1 \times 10^9$ bytes)] and floppy disks are exceeding 1 Mbyte, the optical disk promises to make the most dramatic impact on computer secondary storage. For example, the capability to read and to write rapidly and inexpensively 20 Gbytes (i.e., 20 billion characters) of data (equivalent to the contents of the *Encyclopaedia Britannica*) promises to provide an attractive and cost-effective storage for large volumes of data in relatively long-term project files typically used for multidisciplinary design projects. The future architectures promise to offer specialized hardware (e.g., chips) for fast floating-point calculations, interactive graphics, algebraic manipulation, input/output processing, and most other standard procedures, eventually including finite-element analysis on silicon or gallium arsenide chips.

***User-Interface Hardware and Software***   Great efforts are now aimed at improving the productivity of the analyst by developing user-friendly software and hardware interfaces. More finite-element software systems are becoming "turnkey" systems with defaults built in and with simple menu options. Future menu options are likely to be multiwindowed (one window for each task) and to be controlled by lightpen, voice, or mouse (which is an advanced user-friendly capability for accessing the system). The finite-element model can be generated by using either one of the geometric modeling software packages or a CAD system.

***Distributed Computing and Networking***   The first large-scale computer network, the ARPANET (Advanced Research Projects Area Network), was initiated in the midsixties. The major objective of this network was to explore the possibilities and implications of large-scale distributed computing, where the analyst at one location could have direct access to several computing facilities and/or data bases at a variety of remote locations. This initial work has pointed the way to the feasibility and practicality of distributed computing; however, a tremendous amount of work remains to be done in developing uniform protocols, standard control structures, and uniform data-description standards before distributed computing can be done routinely on a large scale. When these problems are solved, as they undoubtedly will be, many applications and extensions of distributed computing will take place. For example, distributed computing can be recursively applied to component subtasks according to a number of criteria.

Two recent developments will greatly enhance distributed computing. The first is the wide availability of engineering workstations (personal and desktop computers), and the second is new communication technology based on packet switching. In this technology, information is transmitted in packets, typically a few hundred bytes. This is the first communication technology geared to data transmission and is likely to permit economical implementation of distributed computing. The coupling of digital networking with the existing telephone and PBX exchange systems into integrated-services digital networks (ISDNs) promises to offer access to a wide range of data and central computers via desktop workstations.

## 4.1c  Major Features of Modern Computing Systems

Because of the rapid progress made in recent years in semiconductor technology, a number of novel forms of computer architectures have emerged. In order to put the new computer architectures in proper perspective, a classification of computing systems is needed. Several classifications have been proposed in the literature based on the mode of processing instructions and data and on the mode of interaction between different processors (see, for example, Ref. [11]). One of the earliest and most commonly used classifications is that introduced by Flynn [16], which is based on how the machine relates its instructions to the data being processed. A *stream* is defined as a sequence of items (instructions or data) as executed or operated on by a processor.

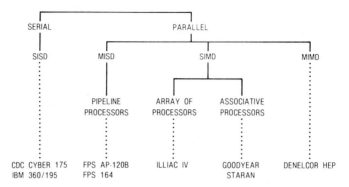

**FIG. 4.8**   Classification of computing systems.

Four broad classes can be identified according to whether the instruction or data streams are single or multiple (Fig. 4.8):

1. *Single-Instruction-Stream, Single-Data-Stream (SISD) Machines.*   These machines include the conventional serial computers which execute instructions sequentially, one at a time.

2. *Single-Instruction-Stream, Multiple-Data-Stream (SIMD) Machines.*   These are computers that have a single control unit, a collection of identical processors (or processing elements), a memory or memories, and an interconnection network which allows processors to exchange data. An example of an SIMD machine is depicted in Fig. 4.9. During execution

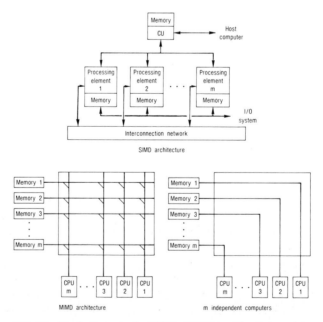

**FIG. 4.9**   Block diagrams for SIMD, MIMD architectures and *m*-independent computers [17].

of a program the central control unit (CU) fetches and decodes the instructions and then broadcasts control to the processing elements. Each processor performs the same instruction sequences, but uses different data. These operations are usually referred to as *lockstep operations.*

3. *Multiple-Instruction-Stream, Single-Data-Stream (MISD) Machines.* There is some disagreement on the computers belonging to this class. The various pipeline (or vector) processors, which segment computations into consecutive stations, are possible candidates [18]. However, in many computer-science publications pipeline processors are classified as SIMD machines. In pipeline processors, the basic arithmetic operations are broken up into a set of elementary steps which, when performed in series, achieve the desired operation. Each elementary step is then implemented into hardware, and the resulting arithmetic unit operates as a production (or assemby) line called the *pipeline.*

4. *Multiple-Instruction-Stream, Multiple-Data-Stream (MIMD) Machines.* These are computers which contain a number of *interconnected processors,* each of which is programmable and can execute its own instructions. The instructions for each processor can be the same or different. The processors operate on a shared memory (or memories), generally in an asynchronous manner. The interconnection between processors distinguishes an MIMD machine from a set of independent computers (Fig. 4.9). The computers of the MIMD class are the most general of all new computers and include all forms of multiprocessor configurations, from linked, mainframe computers to large arrays of microprocessors. However, the increased flexibility is at the cost of increased synchronization, overhead, and programming complexity.

Examples of computing systems which belong to each of the four classes are given in Fig. 4.8.

In this section, the major features of some of the new computing systems which can have a strong impact on finite-element computations are reviewed. For convenience, the computing systems considered are divided into five groups:

1. Supersystems

2. Highly parallel systems

3. Finite-element machines

4. Small systems

5. Attached processors

The first group consists of the general-purpose machines with very high throughput performance. The machines of the second group achieve high performance through extensive use of LSI, VLSI, and ULSI memory-chip technology. Finite-element machines are a subclass of the highly parallel systems and are discussed separately because of their high potential for cost-effective, large-scale finite-element computations. The small systems considered include the various minicomputers, engineering workstations, and microcomputers (e.g., desktop and handheld personal computers). The attached processors are fast back-end computers which, when combined with the minis (or the micros), can extend the range of the finite-element problems that are solved effectively on these small systems. Some of the computing systems considered herein are commercially available; others are still research tools aimed at achieving high-performance and/or low-cost computations.

***Supersystems*** Supersystems are a class of general-purpose computers designed for extremely high-performance throughout. The three major characteristics of supersystems are [19]: (1) high computational speeds (maximum speeds of the order of 50 MFLOPS or more); (2) large main (or central) memory (with a capacity of 8 Mbytes or more); and (3) fast and large secondary memory with a sophisticated memory management system.

The development of supersystems now spans two generations. The first generation included the array of processors ILLIAC IV (SIMD machine); and the pipeline (or vector) computers CDC STAR-100 and Texas Instruments Advanced Scientific Computer (ASC). The second-generation supersystems used a hybrid combination of pipeline and array processors to achieve peak computational speeds in excess of 100 MFLOPS. Examples of these supersystems are the CRAY X-MP and the CDC CYBER 205. As of 1986, 61 CRAY-1, 33 CRAY X-MP, 4 CRAY-2, and 35 CYBER 205 computers had been installed. The top sustained speed of the fastest machines at that time was in the neighborhood of 100 MFLOPS, with bursts to 500 MFLOPS. The next generation of supersystems, under design as this book went to press, include CRAY-3, CRAY Y-MP, ETA-10 (formerly CDC CYBER 2XX) (1986), and CDC multiparallel processors CYBERPLUS. The Japanese Super Speed Computer Project aimed at developing a machine with peak performance of 10 GFLOPS (1989); the Japanese fifth-generation project which appears to be aimed at establishing an artificial intelligence industry by the mid-1990s [20]; and the NASA numerical aerodynamic simulation (NAS) capability. The latter is designed to perform most of the calculations required to design a new aircraft, thereby eliminating the need for wind-tunnel and flight testing. The NAS capability in 1986 was based on a CRAY-2 with a peak performance of 1.6 GFLOPS and a memory of 256 million words.

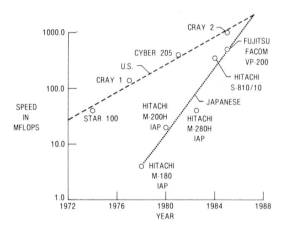

**FIG. 4.10** Trends in computing speeds for U.S. and Japanese supercomputers.

Figure 4.10 shows the trend in the computational speeds provided by the United States and Japanese supercomputers. Indications are that computational speeds will continue to increase, and will exceed 20 GFLOPS before the end of the present decade. Speeds in excess of 1 GFLOP are expected to be achieved by MIMD architectures.

In spite of a number of successful finite-element applications on the first-generation supersystems, these supersystems did not live up to their expectations in large-scale finite-element computations. This is because a system such as the ILLIAC IV operates efficiently *only* when performing an identical operation over an entire array, and one such as the STAR-100 operates efficiently *only on long vectors.*

On the other hand, the second-generation supersystems achieve reasonable performance with scalar and short-vector computations. Nonetheless, the efficient use of these supersystems in large-scale finite-element calculations requires new ways of structuring the finite-element procedure, new algorithms, and new software tools. Direct conversion of finite-element programs from sequential computers does not realize the full potential of these supersystems [21]. A number of large-scale finite-element programs have already been installed on the CRAY-1 computer. These include ANSYS, ASAS, ASKA, EISI-EAL, MARC, MSC/NAS-TRAN, PAFEC 75, and STAGS.

**Highly Parallel Systems**   The insatiable demand for increased computer performance over what can be provided by circuit speed alone, coupled with the advances made in the design and fabrication of VLSI circuits, has led to the introduction of parallelism in a number of new computing systems. *Parallelism* refers to the ability to overlap or to perform simultaneously many of the tasks performed by the computer (e.g., memory fetch or store, arithmetic or logical operation, and I/O operation). There are three principal ways of introducing parallelism into the architecture of computers [11]:

*Pipelining.*   Applying assembly-line techniques to improve the performance of an arithmetic or control unit.

*Functional Replication.*   Providing several independent units performing different operations such as logic, addition, or multiplication, and allowing these units to operate simultaneously on different data.

*Array Replication.*   Using several processors to perform the computations. The processors can form either an SIMD or an MIMD machine. In the first case, identical processors are used under common control, all performing the same operation simultaneously on different data. In the second case, several asynchronous processors are used, each obeying its own instructions, with some mechanisms for interprocessor communication, and local and global control.

Highly parallel systems composed of a large number of computing elements can be classified into the following groups [22]:

- Multiple special-purpose functional units
- Associative processors
- Array of processors
- Data-flow computers
- Multiple processors (with multiple CPUs)

For their specific tasks, multiple special-purpose functional units are the fastest, but they are the least general. They can be designed for almost 100% hardware efficiency (in the sense that a large percentage of the hardware is in use at any given time) and require little or no software to perform their unique tasks. In comparison with the multiple special-purpose functional units, the other machines are more general. However, the more general the machine is, the lower the hardware efficiency (in the sense described above), and the more complicated the software needed is likely to get.

Examples of the aforementioned machine types are given subsequently. There is not yet a truly general-purpose, parallel architecture to which all algorithms can be effectively mapped.

**Multiple Special-Purpose Functional Units**   Multiple special-purpose functional units are useful for performing computationally intensive basic mathematical operations such as matrix multiplication and solution of linear algebraic equations. An example of these machines is provided by *systolic arrays* in which high-level computations are directly mapped into hardware structures. Systolic arrays are based on the principle of replacing a single processing element (cell) by an array of processing elements (cells) in order to achieve a high computational throughput without having to increase the memory bandwidth [23]. This is depicted in Fig. 4.11.

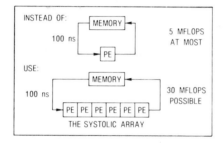

**FIG. 4.11**  Basic principle of a systolic system [23].

In a systolic system, data flow from the computer memory in a regular fashion, passing through many processing elements with built-in hardware instructions before returning to memory. Currently available systolic arrays have four basic characteristics:

- They involve only few types of simple cells.
- Data and control flows are simple and regular.
- Algorithms used support high degrees of pipelining and parallelism.
- Each input data item is used in a multiplicative and effective manner.

A list of prototype realizations of systolic arrays for various algorithms is given in Ref. [24]. Potential applications of systolic arrays for finite-element computations are discussed in Refs. [25, 26].

**Associative Processors**   In associative processors parallelism is introduced in the memory organization by using the bit-slice scheme. This is depicted in Fig. 4.12 for a $w$ word memory with word width $b$. In conventional computers, access is restricted to sets of $b$ bits which form a word; no other set of $b$ bits can usually be accessed in parallel. On the other hand,

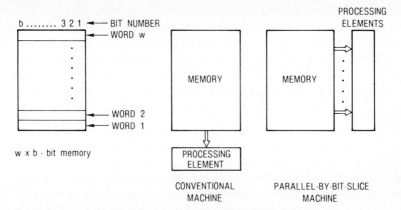

**FIG. 4.12**  Conventional and parallel-by-bit-slice machines.

in the bit-slice parallel computers, the memory slice accessed consists of $s$ bits, with only one bit from each word [11]. This structure is orthogonal to that of the conventional machines, or would be if $s$ were equal to $w$. In general, $s$ will be very large, measured in thousands. Since one bit of any memory word is available on one access, it is possible to search the whole memory simultaneously for specified contents by iteration on bit slices. This processor-memory organization is used to select memory words by their contents, or by some attribute of a subfield of their contents, rather than by address. The parallel-by-bit-slice memory is usually referred to as an *associative memory.*

Many machines have been designed around the concept of an associative memory, except that in addition to data-searching circuitry, each memory word or group of words has a simple arithmetic unit. This element can perform numerical comparisons as well as arithmetic operations. An example of associative machines is provided by the Goodyear Aerospace Staran, which is an SIMD machine which can accommodate up to 8192 simple processing elements. It has an integrated memory which may be accessed in different modes by the processing elements through a multistage switching network.

*Array of Processors*  An array of processors consists of SIMD machines with multiple arithmetic units operating in lockstep and performing the same operation on different data. The control unit broadcasts an instruction to be executed on local data by all processing elements. Each processing element can make minor modifications to the broadcast instruction (usually operand address modification) or be programmed to ignore the instruction. To achieve the potential parallelism of an array of processors, special attention must be paid to the data placement and algorithm design.

Machines built of processor arrays can be distinguished by the following characteristics:

- Number of processors
- Number of memory banks
- Form of communication network
- Form of local and global control

Examples of machines built of an array of processors are ILLIAC IV, ICL Distributed Array Processor (DAP) at Queen Mary College in London, and Goodyear Aerospace Massively Parallel Processor (MPP). The latter contains 16,384 single-bit serial-processing elements connected in a square array ($128 \times 128$) with strictly nearest-neighbor connections. It has a speed of 430 MFLOPS for 32-bit floating-point addition and 216 MFLOPS for multiplication. The input/output operations can be done simultaneously with processing.

***Data-Flow Computers***  Data-flow computers represent a radical departure from the classical von Neumann architecture (control-flow computers). In a data-flow computer, an instruction is ready for execution when its operands arrive. There is no concept of a control unit or a program counter. Rather, the data-flow concept is based on the dependency graph of a computation. The algorithm for performing a given computation is first written in a special programming language designed for data-flow applications. The program, which has the appearance of a directed graph, is then implemented directly by a network of hardware units corresponding to the graph. Operands flow to the functional units and operate whenever all the operands are present and the result can be accommodated. The output with new instruction packets is then forwarded to the next functional unit. Hence, data need not have any permanent residence. Since the dependency graph depicts all the parallelism of a computation whether or not the parallelism is regular, the data-flow architecture offers a high potential for capturing parallelism.

Two major problems arise for data-flow machines. The first problem is that conventional programming languages, which evolved basically from a von Neumann concept, are not well matched to data-flow architectures. The second problem, common to all highly parallel machines, is that concurrency is limited by the communication network which routes results from processing elements. In an attempt to overcome the first problem, the programming language VAL was developed at the Massachusetts Institute of Technology to provide simple expression of all levels of concurrency. As for the remedy to the second problem, all the viable possibilities for the data-flow interconnection network are identical to those of conventional multiprocessor structures.

Despite the aforementioned problems, data-flow structures have high potential for use as attached processors to general-purpose computers.

***Multiple Processors***  Multiple processors are MIMD machines in which each processor is fully programmable and can execute its own program. Various classifications exist for these machines according to interprocessor communication (including the data-transfer mode and the interconnection topology) and control [8]. Multiprocessor systems can provide, at most, a linear speedup factor over single processors. That is, $n$ processors, at best, can perform the same task as a single processor in $1/n^{th}$ the time. In practical applications, the actual speedup ranges from $0.3n$, for simple problems, to a lower bound of $\log_2 n$. The factors that prevent the realization of linear speedup include the following:

- *Synchronization.*  Performance can be lost if the algorithm requires the processors to be periodically coordinated.

- *Algorithm.*  An algorithm designed for a serial computer might not expose all the parallelism present in the problem. Also, a parallel algorithm might require more computations than its serial counterpart to solve the same problem.

- *Contention.* Multiple processors vying for the same resource (e.g., shared variable) can slow down the execution of individual processors.

- *Input/Output Operations.* Traditional I/O structures cannot feed a high-performance processor fast enough to avoid processor idle time.

Early examples of multiple-processor machines are the NASA Langley Finite Element Machine (FEM) and the CM* machine designed and built at Carnegie-Mellon University. The first will be discussed in the next section. The basic building block of the CM* machine is a processor-memory pair called a *computer module,* or CM. The memory local to a processor is also the shared memory in the system. Up to 14 CMs are connected to a cluster. The cluster processors share a single bus and memory-mapping processor. Clusters are connected via intercluster buses.

***Other Highly Parallel Architectures*** Several highly parallel architectures which do not fall into the previous categories have been designed and/or built. Most of these machines are research tools for advanced parallel architectures; a partial list of these machines follows [14].

The Blue CHiP (Configurable Highly Parallel Computer), designed and built at Purdue University in West Lafayette, Indiana, consists of a collection of homogeneous processing elements (PEs) placed at regular intervals in a lattice of programmable switches. Each PE is a computer with its own local memory. This architecture is targeted at wafer-scale implementation.

The Ultracomputer is a project at New York University which has, as yet, not been built. The highly parallel MIMD machine aims to combine hundreds of thousands of small, relatively conventional processing elements, all using a large shared memory. Processors communicate with memory through a very high-bandwidth switching network which executes a few operations vital to very highly parallel interprocess synchronization, in addition to its basic data-routing function.

***Potential of Highly Parallel Architectures for Finite-Element Computations*** In evaluating the impact of highly parallel machines on finite-element computations, it is useful to define two classes of problems and two distinct approaches to bringing the power of highly parallel machines to bear on these problems. The two classes of problems are:

- *Large-Scale Complicated Problems.* These are problems that are much too large to fit on any commercially available standard computer (e.g., number of unknowns in excess of 1 billion). Examples of these problems are large, three-dimensional turbulent-eddy simulations of aerodynamic flows and large nonlinear interaction problems.

- *Medium-Scale Problems.* These are problems that can be solved on current supersystems (e.g., nonlinear problems with tens of thousands of unknowns). However, the cost of running them can be fairly high and, therefore, parametric studies cannot be made. Examples are provided by aerodynamic simulations of compressor- or turbine-blade flow fields and large, nonlinear structural-dynamic problems.

The most suitable approach for the first class of problems is based on using multiple processors. The interconnection between the processors must reflect both the geometry of the problem and the nature of the algorithms employed. A square grid of processors with only nearest-neighbor connections is the most obvious first choice.

The spatial allocation of processors involves mapping the different activities to be performed onto the processors of the system. With static mapping, the spatial allocation is fixed before the program execution begins. A variety of mapping schemes can be used such as one zone and/or one node per processor, or one row of nodes per processor. Adjacent-zone computations can be mapped onto adjacent processors. As long as the size of the problem matches the size of the system, and the amount of computation per processor can be reasonably well equalized, this approach is quite attractive.

If, on the other hand, the program size and structure do not match the system size and structure, complete locality cannot be maintained. If resources are allocated dynamically, the assignment function must map operations which are likely to communicate only with nearby processors. This would greatly complicate the resource allocation problem. The practical application of multiprocessor machines to large-scale problems requires the development of semiautomatic procedures to program a large amount of processors to perform similar but different tasks.

For the second class of problems, high throughput performance can be obtained by attaching multiple special-purpose functional units to a mainframe (or a superminicomputer) through the use of a fast bus (or buses). These special-purpose functional units can be thought of as replacing many of the subroutines in a scientific software library. They could include linear-algebra systolic-array modules, a sparse-matrix processor, and an inner-product chip.

The major problem in the effective use of this approach is communication between the different devices. Much numerical analysis must be rethought in this architectural context. For example, higher-order temporal integration schemes and higher-order techniques for solution of nonlinear equations, requiring less data to drive them (at a cost of increased arithmetic), might be more attractive than lower-order methods.

**Finite-Element Machines**   Before parallel computers were manufactured, the Finite Element Machine (FEM), an MIMD computer was developed at NASA Langley Research Center as an experimental research tool with the goal of demonstrating the potential of using highly parallel architectures for high-speed yet low-cost solutions of finite-element problems. Many aspects of finite-element calculations are well suited to parallel computation (e.g., generation of elemental arrays and iterative solution of global equations).

The NASA Langley Finite Element Machine, shown in Fig. 4.13, is designed to have 36 processors operating either asynchronously or synchronously, in parallel, and communicating via a local and a global bus. In 1986, sixteen of the processors on the machine were operational. Each of the processors contains a 16-bit CPU, a special floating-point unit, 32 Kbytes of local RAM and 32 Kbytes of ROM. The ROM contains a special parallel operating system, termed NODAL EXEC, together with a library of frequently used PASCAL-callable routines, termed PASLIB. Figure 4.13 shows the cabinet that will house the 36 processors and a typical 16-bit CPU board (one of 108 boards). The controller of the array of processors is a minicomputer with 116 Mbytes of disk storage, tape drive, and printer. The controller is accessed via terminals (both text and graphics) and can transfer data to and from a DEC VAX 11/780 superminicomputer. Two strategies for exploiting parallelism are currently being explored using the first sixteen processors of FEM [27], performing all the computations in parallel on the array of processors, and distributing the computations between the array of processors

**FIG. 4.13**   Prototype NASA Langley FEM hardware.

and the controller. In Ref. [28] the application of iterative algorithms to the solution of large, sparse finite-element equations on the FEM is examined.

The architecture of the FEM provides for nearest-neighbor connection as well as global connection, which appears to have high potential for large-scale finite-element applications, including steady-state and transient response problems.

Recently other studies based on the FEM concept have been made [29–31]. In Ref. [29] the Japanese PAX-128 parallel computer is described. It is an MIMD microprocessor array with 128 (8-bit) processing elements arranged in a two-dimensional network with end-around and nearest-neighbor mesh connection, and data-broadcasting bus line. The system has three basic components—host computer, control unit, and processing unit—and has been used for solution of linear algebraic equations and partial differential equations. In Ref. [30] the application of an FEM concept to the generation and assembly of finite-element stiffness matrices is described. The hardware used consisted of an IEEE-696 S-100 bus microcomputer with a 16-bit CPU and a master processor which controls and coordinates the activities of 8086/8087 VLSI chip set processors working in parallel. In Ref. [31] several parallel algorithms for the solution of the finite-element equations are examined. On the basis of the results shown in Ref. [31], it appears that for computers with an unlimited number of processors, the direct-cyclic-reduction algorithm is best suited, and for machines with a limited number of parallel processors, both the direct Gauss factorization and the Jacobi-like iterative methods rank favorably.

***Small Systems***   A broad spectrum of low-cost small systems exist now, including handheld computers (the micro micros [32]), desktop computers, engineering workstations, minis, and superminis. Several classifications have been attempted for these systems based on wordlength (8-bit, 16-bit, and 32-bit machines), cost, amount of directly addressable memory, and computing speed (see, for example, Ref. [33]). However, the dramatic increase in hardware capabilities of small systems coupled with the rapid reduction in cost makes these classifications of questionable value. Herein, a brief discussion is given of the impact of minicomputers and microcomputers on finite-element computations.

***Engineering Workstations***    Minicomputers were introduced in the late 1960s as a new concept in decentralized computing. At first minicomputers were used only for pre- and postprocessing of finite-element calculations. However, as minicomputers with larger address spaces and faster arithmetic operations appeared, a migration of finite-element software to minicomputers started to take place, and with the emergence of the superminis having 32-bit wordlength, very large address spaces, and fast hardware or firmware for floating-point operations (e.g., the DEC VAX 11/780, the PRIME 750, ECLIPSE MV/10000 and Norske Data 570), many of the large-scale finite-element programs [e.g., ASKA, ANSYS, MARC, MSC/NASTRAN, and SPAR (predecessor of EISI-EAL)], were installed on the minicomputer (see, for example, Ref. [34]).

Recently, a new generation of high-performance superminis has been developed which outspeeds conventional superminis by a factor of 2. Examples of the new computers are provided by the PYRAMID 90X and the RIDGE 32 computers. The high performance of these machines is attributed to the use of reduced-instruction-set computer (RISC) architecture with large register stacks organized as overlapping register sets. In the RISC design all operations except memory loads and stores are register to register. Overlapped register sets minimize data movement in procedure calls and allow parameter passing through "windows" in the overlapping register sets.

Minicomputers provide user-friendly operational characteristics including interactive operating systems, local control over resources and turnaround, and high-speed graphics. However, currently available minicomputers (including the superminis) are considerably slower than mainframes, and, therefore, their effectiveness is limited in solving large-scale finite-element problems such as those encountered in crash dynamics and three-dimensional fluid-flow simulations [35, 36].

***Microcomputers***    There now exists a large number of microcomputers and desktop computers, both portable and stationary. A partial list of the desktop computers and some of their characteristics are given in Ref. [37]. The first generation of microcomputers had 8-bit processor chips and 64K RAM (a few 8-bit designs have increased the addressable RAM to 256K). The second-generation machines are 16-bit machines with up to 1 Mbyte of RAM. They generally use one of three CPU chips [38]: the Intel 8088, Intel 8086, or the Motorola 68000. The Intel 8088 uses 16-bit architecture internally but handles data on an 8-bit bus. By contrast, the 8086 is a 16-bit processor, and, therefore, it is more powerful and faster because it transfers more data at one time. The Motorola 68000, which is the most powerful of the three, takes data on either a 16-bit or 32-bit bus but does its processing internally, 32 bits at a time. The third-generation microcomputers, termed *engineering workstations*, have 32-bit processor chips and over 16 Mbytes (or more) of addressable memory, and are likely to replace current superminis. Examples of such systems are the HP 9000, the Apollo, and the IBM-9000 computers.

A number of large-scale finite-element programs (e.g., ANSYS, EISI-EAL, and MSC/NAS-TRAN) have been installed on the Apollo computer. Also, several small finite-element programs have been developed for the microcomputers [39–43]. If the program is segmented in order to reduce high-speed memory requirements, fairly large finite-element problems can be solved on the microcomputer [39]. However, since many large problems require 64-bit accuracy, it could be slow to run them on microcomputers with 8-bit or even 16-bit processors. The availability of 32-bit microcomputers such as the HP 9000 and Apollo computers is likely to extend the range of finite-element problems that can be solved by the microcomputer.

**Attached Processors**   For cost-effective computing a fast back-end computer can be attached to a slower host minicomputer to achieve computational speeds comparable to those of large mainframes at a fraction of the cost of the mainframes. The fast computer is referred to as the *attached processor*. The dual-processor system consisting of the minicomputer and the attached processor can be used to extend the range of problems that can be solved effectively on the minicomputer. The dual-processor arrangement is particularly useful for a small user community. Examples of attached processors include the floating-point systems FPS AP-120B, AP-190L, and FPS-164; the CSPI MAP-300 and MAP-6400 series; and the recently announced ST-100 attached processor of Star Technologies, Inc. While the FPS and ST-100 processors have synchronous architecture, the CSPI processors have asynchronous multiple-bus architecture. Each of the FPS attached processors has the following features [11]:

- It is designed and accessed as a peripheral (i.e., like a tape drive) for a conventional host minicomputer, and it is intended to enhance the performance of the host in specific numerical computing tasks.
- It achieves high performance through both parallelism and pipelining.
- It includes an arithmetic section containing one adder and one multiplier capable of operating in parallel.
- It is not hard-wired. Rather, it can be programmed by the user in FORTRAN or assembler language to perform a variety of computational tasks.

   Parallelism is a major feature of the FPS attached processors that allows high-speed vector and matrix processing. In addition, the parallel structure of the attached processors allows the overhead of loop indexing, array indexing, and data fetching to be performed in parallel with floating-point computations. Parallel operations include integer indexing, branch instructions, memory fetches, memory storage, I/O with the host, and floating-point arithmetic. These features make the FPS systems much faster processors than most general-purpose, sequential computers. The peak processing rate of the FPS attached processors is 12 MFLOPS and a concurrent 6 million integer and addressing operations per second. However, such performance is difficult to realize in practical applications.

   The ST-100 attached processor is advertised to have a peak performance of 100 MFLOPS. It has the following characteristics:

- Multiple programming internal processors and multiple arithmetic units
- High-speed logic circuitry
- Main memory of 32-bit words which can be expanded to 8 million words
- 48K data-cache RAM
- Multiple host interfaces

Software for attached processors can be developed on three different levels:

- FORTRAN high-level language with many specialized functions
- Assembly-language macros using a library of routines provided by the manufacturer
- Pure micro-assembly language at the machine level.

Recently, the software support capabilities of the attached processors have considerably improved. Such support software includes an ANSI FORTRAN-77 compiler, assembler, loader, object-code linker, and simulator—all running on the host computer.

Recent studies [44–46] have shown that the combination of a minicomputer and an attached processor in a dual-processor system can extend the range of finite-element problems that can be solved effectively by the minicomputer. This capability is accomplished through efficient implementation of both the numerical algorithms used in the finite-element solution and the communication protocol between the host minicomputer and the array processor. The question of synchronization between the different parts of the system to ensure correct and efficient function of the minicomputer and attached-processor system is of paramount importance.

## 4.2 ALGORITHMS AND SOFTWARE DEVELOPMENT

The advent of new high-performance computing systems has resulted in (1) numerical algorithms that execute efficiently on these systems, and (2) software with which these algorithms can be expressed. A number of survey papers have been written on these subjects [47–49]. These studies have demonstrated that severalfold increases in speed over conventional sequential machines can be obtained if the calculations are arranged to take advantage of the specific hardware.

In this section a brief review is given of the recent progress made in special numerical algorithms and programming languages that are influencing finite-element technology.

### 4.2A Parallel Numerical Algorithms

In parallel algorithms, independent computations are performed in parallel (i.e., executed simultaneously). To achieve this parallelism, the algorithm is divided into a collection of independent tasks (or task modules) which can be executed in parallel and which communicate with each other during the execution of the algorithms. Parallel algorithms can be characterized by the following three factors [23]:

1. Maximum amount of computation performed by a typical task module before communication with other modules

2. Intermodule communication topology, which is the geometric layout of the network of task modules

3. Executive control to schedule, enforce the interactions among the different task modules, and ensure the correctness of the parallel algorithm

The three aforementioned factors have been used in Ref. [21] as a basis for classifying parallel algorithms on the conceptual level, and to relate each parallel algorithm to the parallel (or pipeline) architecture to which it naturally corresponds.

The design of a parallel algorithm must deal with a host of complex problems, including data manipulation, storage allocation, memory interference, and, in the case of parallel processors, interprocessor communication.

## 4.2B Matching Numerical Algorithms with Computer Architectures

To obtain the optimum performance from any computing system, it is necessary either to tailor the numerical algorithm to suit the architecture of the computer, or to select the architecture which will effectively execute the numerical algorithm. The numerical algorithms developed for synchronous and for asynchronous parallel computers and systolic machines are discussed subsequently.

*Algorithms for Synchronous Parallel Computers (MISD and SIMD Machines)*  The introduction of parallelism in the numerical algorithm used on synchronous parallel computers is usually referred to as *vectorization*. The vectorization of any mathematical operation is dependent on the particular hardware. For example, for a task to be vectorizable on pipeline computers, it should contain three characteristics: (1) repeated operations, (2) independence of each result from the others, and (3) arrangement of the members of each operand either in contiguous memory locations or at fixed intervals from each other (with some restrictions in certain hardware configurations). Efficiency and effectiveness of vectorized numerical algorithms on pipeline computers are affected by both the startup time and the average vector length.

Vectorized algorithms have been widely studied for a variety of applications and a variety of hardware configurations. Examples of successful vectorized algorithms that have been developed for synchronous computers include matrix operations, direct and iterative methods of solution of algebraic equations, eigenvalue extraction techniques, multigrid finite-difference methods for solution of partial differential equations, and evaluation of elemental matrices for higher-order finite elements [50–53]. Also, the development of parallel algorithms for the solution of partial differential equations on associative processors has been discussed in Ref. [54].

*Algorithms for Asynchronous Parallel Computers (MIMD Machines)*  In comparison with the parallel algorithms for synchronous computers, only a few studies have been made on parallel algorithms for asynchronous computers. Of particular interest are the asynchronous parallel iterative methods in which processors are not synchronized at all. In a truly asynchronous iterative algorithm, a process keeps computing iterates by using whatever information is currently available and releases immediately its computed results to other processes. Thus, the actual iterates generated by the method depend on the relative speed of the processes. The philosophy of "not waiting for other processes to complete their tasks" has been found to be a useful criterion for developing efficient numerical algorithms for asynchronous multiprocessors [24]. A typical way to achieve this goal is to use copies. After a process completes its current task, it immediately starts working on a copy of the most recent global data.

**Algorithms for Systolic Machines**   Algorithms for systolic machines are designed for direct hardware implementation, and, therefore, their task modules are simple and the interactions among them are frequent.

## 4.2c Performance Evaluation of Parallel Algorithms

It is important to make a distinction between two means of evaluating the performance of new computing systems.

**Comparative Performance**   The ultimate judgment about cost-effectiveness that must be made in comparing new machines on a code can be a complicated function of architecture-related considerations. Moreover, the performance is so dependent on idiosyncrasies of the code and the compiler that such comparisons have a temporary value at best.

**Single-Machine Performance**   The comparison of different algorithms and codings on a parallel machine is difficult to make when both parallel-algorithm development (a general mathematical concept) and the control of data flow between parallel functional units and hierarchically organized memories (a machine-dependent coding concept) are involved.

A number of measures have been proposed to quantify the performance of a computer program. One of the simplest, though inadequate, measures is based on the CPU time consumed during the execution of the program [11]. The two most commonly used measures for the performance of parallel algorithms on multiple processors and array-of-processor machines are based on the ratio of the speedup over a single processor and the ratio of the theoretical number of computation steps to the actual number of parallel steps. The first measure is suitable for machines with few processors. The second measure is used for machines with many processors and is strongly dependent on the complexity of the algorithm.

## 4.2d Software for Parallel Processing

The necessary software for supporting parallel processing includes special programming languages, data-management systems, and operating systems. Parallel programming is significantly more complicated than sequential programming because:

- It is difficult to keep track of several simultaneously occurring events.
- The potentially complex (time-dependent) interactions of the systems' components may result in elusive and nonrepeatable bugs.

There is a wide spectrum of language possibilities for improving the performance through parallel execution. Examples of the parallel-processing languages are ADA [55] and PASCAL [56]. However, the suitability of these languages for multiple-processor machines has not been investigated. Data management in highly parallel systems can be a serious problem. The tasks performed by the data-management system include supplying input to and analyzing output from the processors, and following a trace of the execution.

The operating systems for highly parallel machines must be considerably more sophisticated than those for conventional machines. In addition to the usual issues encountered with conventional machines, a number of new issues have to be addressed, including physical distribution of tasks among different processors, resource sharing, and interprocessor communication.

## 4.3 INTERACTIVE COMPUTER GRAPHICS FOR CAD/CAM

*Computer-aided design* and *computer-aided manufacturing* (CAD/CAM) are terms that have gained prominence in the late 1970s and early 1980s to describe a vision of the modern engineering process in which virtually all stages of the process are unified through a computerized information repository and data flow. Among the stages of engineering usually included under the CAD/CAM rubric are conceptual design of overall systems, technical analysis and design of various subsystems, resolution of subsystem-integration difficulties, production of manufacturing or construction drawings and documents, programming of production, and generation of manufacturing control information. The unified computer-assisted process encompasses the development and evaluation of alternative designs and the capability to redesign the subsystems or the overall system. The intent is to maximize both engineering creativity and productivity by providing the engineer all the necessary information and tools for decisions and judgments to be made efficiently.

CAD/CAM systems are widely utilized in both research and industrial settings, although not as extensively as might be expected within some segments of engineering and industry. It is clear that further advances will occur as several developments in hardware and software are increasingly combined to create an appropriate environment. Three chief developments are *networking*, which enables the sharing and rapid transfer of large volumes of data; engineering *workstations*, which provide individual designers access to data and computing tools; and integral *interactive-graphics* capabilities, which present the opportunity for efficient control and manipulation of the complex engineering process. The obvious common thread which ties together all CAD/CAM developments is the focus on data bases and data flow.

The finite-element method has been used in engineering analysis for many years. However, its use throughout the entire engineering design process has been limited by the cost of both the computing resources and the workforce to synthesize and manage the data needed for the multiple analyses required by design modifications. The drastically reduced expense of computing resources and the development of more integrated design software are increasing the cost-effectiveness of finite-element methods to the point that they can become an integral part of the design process, not just a check on the final design or a tool for postfailure analysis.

The process of extracting the geometry of a design from a computer-aided design (CAD) data base, generating a finite-element model, shipping that model to an analysis program, and retrieving the results for interpretation requires the transmittal of vast amounts of information. Thus, data communication procedures between the various segments of the process are paramount for the effective integration of the process. The two conflicting requirements placed on this data transfer are that it be as general, complete, and foolproof as possible and that it be as rapid as possible. Since there are no methods currently available to address both of these requirements, two different approaches are currently being taken.

The more general approach places all the information generated into standardized formats for exchange between various systems. This approach has proved difficult to carry out and tends to be slow and inefficient. The other approach is the development of special-purpose systems that combine all the design and analysis functions for one area into a single package. The advantage of this approach is the speed and clarity of operation, but the price is lack of generality.

The purpose of this section is to discuss the integration of the finite-element method into computer-aided design techniques.

Although it is clear from the foregoing introductory comments that the data base and hardware are key ingredients of this integration, the limited scope of this section permits only a brief, specialized treatment of these complex topics. This treatment is restricted to aspects specifically related to finite elements. The first emphasis is on effective interfaces by which the engineer-designer manipulates finite-element tools and on the role that these interfaces play in the generation and modification of those portions of the data needed for finite-element analysis in design. In particular, the theme of this section is *interactive computer graphics* because this is the primary medium of computer-aided design. Within the finite-element context, emphasis is placed on the procedures that are used to generate a finite-element model from a geometric model, on the methods to control or intervene in analysis itself, and on the techniques used to extract the desired analysis results for use in modification of a design.

## 4.3A The Role of Interactive Computer Graphics

Because a designer can obtain and interpret information fastest visually, it is appropriate that the large quantities of data characteristic of engineering design be created and managed graphically. This is particularly important since nearly all design information is itself geometric or associated with geometric entities.

Basically, computer graphics is the use of computers to draw pictures. However, much of computer graphics is *passive*; that is, the desired drawings are specified before computing is done and are executed some time after the information is produced or recorded. For truly effective worker-machine communication, a more dynamic mode is necessary, interactive computer graphics. Interactivity has two distinguishing features. First, the responses by the computer should be rapid, that is, within a matter of seconds or fractions of seconds. This implies a rather large amount of computational power devoted to driving the graphical display devices. Second, in addition to visual output from the computer, as much input from the person as possible should be graphical or analog as this too is a more natural and reliable mode of communication. This second feature implies that graphical input devices, such as *pens* and *digitizing tablets*, or *lightpens*, are necessary.

The use of interactive graphics in CAD/CAM is vital in achieving the two fundamental goals of computer-assisted engineering—productivity and control. The concern with productivity is self-evident. For example, in structural and mechanical design a large proportion of the engineer's time is spent on the tedious and error-prone tasks of preparing detailed computer input and interpreting voluminous output. These are tasks that are significantly speeded by interactive graphics, and thus the engineer can perform analysis more quickly or can perform many more analyses in a given time to optimize a system. The second goal is sufficient control of computing so that it remains in its proper role as a means or tool in the larger creative design and production process. It is the engineer who is indispensable in the decision-making cycle, and interactive graphics can provide the opportunity not only for real-time choices but also for effective utilization of computers as unobtrusive but vital tools in this process.

Although the generation of a finite-element model is a relatively straightforward process, it has historically been the most time-consuming step. Initially finite-element meshes were manually generated on paper, and the various nodal coordinates and element connectivities were typed into the computer on the basis of the hand layout. In an attempt to reduce the number of input errors and to save time in the generation of problem input, many code developers built simple node and element generators into their programs. Although these procedures provided some savings in time and effort, the model-generation process was still too time-consuming. Thus, emphasis shifted to the development of stand-alone programs, referred to as *preprocessors*, that have a number of user-oriented features for the efficient generation of finite-element models. The more powerful packages make extensive use of the techniques of interactive computer graphics to improve the user-computer interface.

Although finite-element analysis or processing itself has traditionally been a batch procedure, the continued increase of cheap computational capability and the growing demands of designers and analysts indicate that in the near future some interactive processing will be effective and desirable. This notion has given rise to *interactive-adaptive analysis* [57], which is defined as analysis during which the user can continuously monitor what is happening, and can choose to intervene at any time to change system characteristics, models, analysis parameters, and algorithms. It is most suited to nonlinear and time-varying analyses. The engineer is able to move backward and forward in the analysis at will and to invoke a variety of parallel analyses at any stage. Moreover, different types of analyses can be strung together in a sequence. This analysis-control capability clearly must rely on interactive computer graphics for its success.

The generation of a finite-element model and the running of a finite-element analysis do not ensure that the results will be properly used. The reduction of the analysis output is also an important part of integrating finite-element techniques into the design process. The raw results of a finite-element analysis of a complex model are difficult to interpret without the aid of an additional program called a *postprocessor*. The function of the postprocessor is to take the vast amounts of output of a finite-element analysis and to give the user the ability to extract easily the information that will indicate how a design functions and how to improve the design. Again, interactive graphics are indispensable in the sifting and interpretation of analysis results during postprocessing.

Each of the three phases of finite-element analysis—preprocessing, processing, and postprocessing—are discussed in subsequent sections of this chapter with regard to their integration into a CAD/CAM through interactive computer graphics. In each case, examples provide glimpses of the dynamic interactive graphical dialogue between the engineer and the computer. Because the effectiveness of interactive graphics in CAD/CAM depends heavily upon the ergonomics of the software systems, human-factor characteristics must be taken into account in designing or selecting interactive systems. A discussion of such features is beyond the scope of this chapter, but ideal interactive systems are described in general terms in various texts and papers [58–62].

## 4.3ʙ Finite-Element Model Generation

In Sec. 3.4 of Part 4, some of the specific aspects of finite-element model generation are discussed along with the various mesh-generating approaches that are available. This section will focus on the integration of those finite-element modeling capabilities into interactive preprocessing packages that can be linked to geometric modeling systems and finite-element analysis programs.

The generation of a finite-element model ready for input to the desired analysis program can be considered a four-step process [63]:

1. The definition of the problem geometry.
2. The discretization of that geometry (i.e., dividing the domain of interest into a set of finite elements).
3. The application of problem attributes (i.e., the specification of material properties, loads, and boundary conditions).
4. The specification of the control parameters required by the analysis program and the linking of the model information to the analysis.

The first two steps are the most general since the definition and discretization of geometry are independent of the particular class of problem to be solved or the analysis program to be used. The type of element geometries and the way a mesh is graded are dependent on the problem to be solved, the type of elements to be selected, and the level of accuracy desired. However, the procedures used to define and discretize a geometry are unconstrained as long as all required features are available. The specification of problem attributes is only dependent on the class of problem to be solved; for example, the specification of loads, material properties, and boundary conditions is the same for all stress-analysis problems. The only step that is entirely dependent on the selected analysis program is the last, the specification of analysis-program attributes and the linking of data.

Today much of the emphasis on the development of methods to improve the generation of finite-element models is on the development of interactive graphics preprocessors. These programs combine a number of mesh-generating capabilities into one package that allows the user to generate quickly the type of desired element meshes. Interactive-graphics techniques are ideally suited to aid in the mesh-generation task because they afford the analyst a rapid means to generate and to verify user-defined meshes. This ability is particularly important with the current finite-element analysis capabilities since the analyst must use insight into the problem behavior and knowledge of finite-element methods to develop the graded meshes that are required for reasonable solution accuracy.

Many of the current finite-element preprocessors allow or require the user to create the geometric model. Such geometries may be independent of any mesh or may be defined only in terms of the nodes and elements themselves. However, there is an increasing emphasis on making direct use of the geometry provided by a geometric modeling system as input to the mesh-generating process.

***Mesh Generation***   Although there are a number of mesh-generating approaches available, the vast majority of them generate a mesh of elements in a user-specified patch which has node points placed along its boundary. Thus the finite-element preprocessor must have the ability to discretize boundary curves by placing nodes along them and to select the desired mesh patches. Because of the limitations of most mesh generators and the desire to exercise control over the mesh layout and mesh gradations, the mesh patches normally used represent only a portion of the entire geometry. Therefore, the patch-specification process must also allow for the definition of artificial geometric boundaries with nodes placed along them. The steps normally carried out to generate a mesh patch are as follows:

1. Selection of the discretized boundary curves that make up each of the sides of a mesh patch
2. Indication of the desired element type
3. Invocation of the desired mesh generator

This entire process is not as simple as indicated because the user must carefully monitor and control the procedure to ensure that the resulting mesh has the desired mesh gradations, that the elements generated are not overly distorted, and that the element edges along neighboring patches properly match. In some cases the user must also be concerned with the sequencing of node-point or element labels to ensure that the solution of the global matrices is efficient. However, this task should be delegated to the computer, which, with the aid of resequencing algorithms (see Sec. 3.2 of Part 4), can handle it efficiently.

The class of mesh generators best suited for use in an automated-batch mode is different from that for use in an interactive-graphic environment where the engineer wishes to exercise strong control on the resulting mesh. In this section emphasis is placed on the latter, while those procedures oriented to an automated-batch type of operation are discussed in Sec. 3.4 of Part 4. Although some mesh-generating techniques are generally better than others, preprocessors that combine a number of alternative techniques greatly increase the user's flexibility in the mesh-generating process. The selection of a mesh generator to be used today is strongly biased by the fact that for several classes of problems the most efficient element types available in the general-purpose finite-element codes are quadrilaterals in two dimensions and hexahedra in three dimensions. Because of their ability to generate meshes of well-shaped quadrilateral and hexahedral elements in general patches, the blending-function mesh generators (Sec. 3.4 of Part 4) are ideally suited to an interactive environment. A number of mesh-generating approaches are able to generate elements in large patches or even in the entire domain; however, they either are restricted to triangular elements or produce poorly shaped quadrilateral elements. Therefore, they tend not to be as widely used as the blending-function methods. (The problem of the degradation of accuracy with element distortion for quadrilateral and triangular elements does require active user consideration [64].)

*Attribute Specification*    The problem attributes of loads, material properties, and boundary conditions must also be specified before an analysis can be performed [65, 66]. The type of attributes specified depends on the type of analysis to be carried out. For example, the boundary conditions for a stiffness analysis of a structure are in terms of displacement components, while for a thermal analysis they are in terms of temperatures. However, the technique by which attributes are applied is not dependent on the type of analysis to be carried out. For example, the interactive specification of a linearly varying edge load is accomplished in much the same way as is a linearly varying heat flux along an edge.

At the lowest level, an attribute editor for the specification of loads, material properties, and boundary conditions must allow for a node-by-node and element-by-element assignment of information. At a higher level, an attribute editor should also allow for more general specification of attribute information, including designation of properties for entire regions, on faces of regions, and along edges of regions.

In addition to the specification of the attributes discussed above, analysis attributes including element formulations, numerical-integration rules, time-marching algorithms, and nonlinear solution schemes must be set. Much of this information consists of simple control flags that can be quickly set. Others are associated with the finite-element mesh and can be effectively specified in the same manner as the material properties or other attributes.

**Interactive Computer Graphics for Model Generation**  A finite-element preprocessor must allow the user to define a graded finite-element mesh and apply the required attributes to that model. The most effective means for doing this is a screen-menu-driven, interactive-graphic preprocessor, where the user communicates with the computer by pointing and the computer communicates with the user by pictures. Both essential features of interactivity are inherent in this type of implementation. The speed of response permits the pace of modeling to be set solely by the user. If the menus are displayed graphically so that the commands are activated by pointing, the user must neither be a skillful typist nor memorize a complicated command language.

A number of features of ideal, highly interactive graphic preprocessors are given in Refs. [61, 62, 65]. Some typical capabilities are described by the following examples taken from stand-alone preprocessors, i.e., those which do not obtain geometric information from geometric modeling systems. (The linking between geometric modelers and finite-element preprocessors is explored in the following subsection of this chapter.)

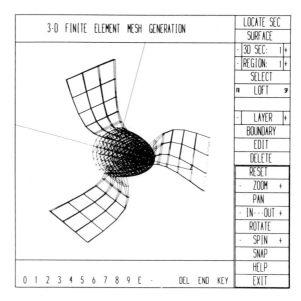

**FIG. 4.14**  Solid three-dimensional mesh defined by lofting.

In the stand-alone mode the user must first generate the basic geometric boundaries required for mesh generation. A number of possible interactive-graphic procedures can be used to carry out this process. The most basic of these is the ability to define cross-sectional curves either in a plane or directly in three dimensions by activating the desired curve types and interactively defining sets of key points that uniquely define that curve [63, 65, 67–69]. This input can be accomplished using a number of standard graphical input techniques such as hit-testing on reference grid intersections.

In addition to defining the various bounding curves one must also define the surfaces and solids they bound. This may be done as part of the meshing process or as a separate specification. The possible advantage of a separate specification is a strict separation of geometry definition from mesh generation. Again, interactive-graphics techniques are ideally suited for this process. Figure 4.14 shows a three-dimensional mesh generated by lofting a blending-function generated mesh between sets of cross-sectional curves [69]. Figure 4.15 shows a solid object to be meshed that was generated by extrusion techniques [70]. Surface meshes such as that shown in Fig. 4.16 can be generated by extrusion of lofting techniques and can be used to analyze surface structures with finite elements or solids with boundary elements.

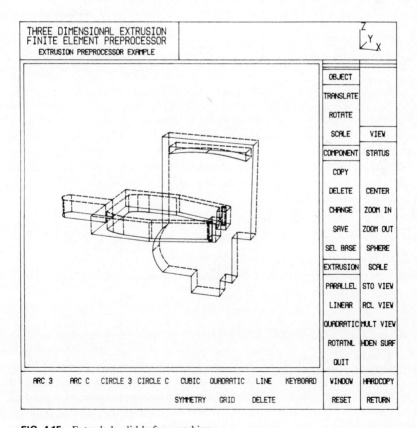

**FIG. 4.15**   Extruded solid before meshing.

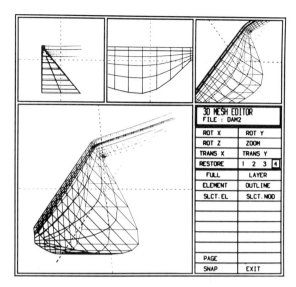

**FIG. 4.16** Surface mesh on a three-dimensional concrete gravity dam.

The actual discretization of a geometry is greatly facilitated by an interactive-computer-graphics environment that allows the user to gain immediate feedback of the meshes that are being generated. Such an environment allows for the effective use of a number of mesh-generating capabilities and invites the user to try a number of alternatives in arriving at the mesh to be analyzed. Blending-function mesh generators fit well into an interactive-graphic environment [63, 65, 67–69]. They have the basic advantage of generating meshes of well-conditioned elements in regions having complex shapes (see, for example, the mesh patches given in Sec. 3.4 of Part 4), while they have the disadvantage that it is possible to overspill the boundaries of the region. This overspill happens infrequently and can be quickly detected on a graphics display. In those few cases when overspill occurs or when the generated mesh patch is not entirely satisfactory, it is an easy matter to delete that patch and mesh it differently by one of the following methods:

1. Rearranging the nodes on the region boundary
2. Reordering or reselecting the sides of the mesh patch
3. Using a different mesh generator such as a higher-order blending function with constraints [67] or a triangulation algorithm
4. Subdividing the patch into two or more patches

In addition to blending-function mesh generators for surface mesh patches with two, three, or four sides, it is useful to have specific mesh-transitioning capabilities for use in creating mesh gradations, and automatic or interactive mesh-smoothing capabilities to improve the shape of the elements in the final mesh. Mesh-transitioning capabilities can be built into the blending-function mesh generators [71] or carried out by using triangulation algorithms (Sect. 3.4 of Part 4) or special transition generators [63]. As an indication of the possible combinations of mesh generators that can be effectively combined into an interactive-graphics preprocessor, one such program combines the three blending-function mesh generators [65] with an automatic triangulation algorithm [72], a one-element-deep transition mesh generator [63] and a mesh-smoothing algorithm [73].

The assignment of required problem attributes is also greatly facilitated by interactive computer graphics [65, 66, 69]. An interactive-graphics attribute editor lets the user define the loads, material properties, and boundary conditions in a more natural form than an element-by-element or node-by-node specification. For example, material properties can be interactively applied on a regional basis where the region boundaries directly correspond to material interfaces [66]. This specification can be accomplished by pointing first at the appropriate command and then at a single point in the material region. The boundary of the region is automatically determined, and the material properties of that material type are automatically associated with all the elements in that region.

Loads and boundary conditions can be applied quickly to single points, along segments of curves, on surface patches, and over entire volumes. This information, interactively specified in a general geometric manner, can also be automatically associated with the finite-element mesh. Figure 4.17 shows the application of a quadratically varying edge load to a two-dimensional structure, while Fig. 4.18 shows the assignment of a pressure load on a shell surface.

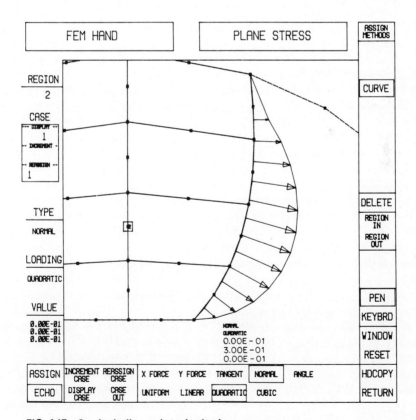

**FIG. 4.17**  Quadratically varying edge load.

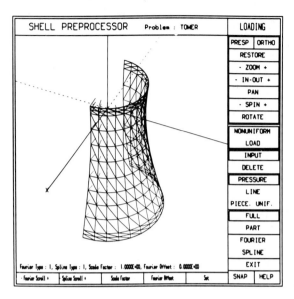

**FIG. 4.18**  Wind-pressure loading applied to a finite-element model of one-half of a hyperbolic cooling-tower shell.

*Linking Geometric Modeling and Finite-Element Meshing*  As geometric modeling techniques have evolved, so has an interest in directly linking them to finite-element preprocessing capabilities to avoid the need to redefine the geometry during the generation of the finite-element mesh. The level of sophistication possible in a link between a geometric modeler and a finite-element preprocessor is a function of the type of geometric modeler. For example, the direct link to a computer-aided drafting system allows only for the transfer of construction lines. In this case it is still necessary for the user to interpret the drawings and to reconstruct any surface and solid information within the preprocessor. Linking directly to a surface modeler improves this situation because information on the mathematical definition of the surfaces is available for use by the preprocessor. However, the user is still required to interpret the geometric model to determine which volumes are to be meshed. A solid modeling program [74] employs a complete and unique geometric representation that a preprocessor can use to determine properly not only the surfaces of an object but also the portions of the solid to be meshed. With a complete geometric representation it is possible to consider the use of a fully automatic mesh generator that generates the entire mesh when the geometry is known and the geometrically specified mesh-gradation information is given. The solid-model geometry information can also be used with blending-function mesh generators to carry out automatically validity checks of the mesh patches generated and to reduce the number of operations the user must perform to generate a mesh.

The majority of links from geometric modelers to finite-element preprocessor do not make the fullest use of the available geometric information [75, 76]. Typically, the information passed to the preprocessor consists of a list of the regional boundary curves in either parametric or discretized form.

Currently, efforts are under way to improve the links from solid modelers to finite-element preprocessors that make more effective use of the additional geometric information available. Since the input to the majority of mesh generators is edge and face information, boundary representations [75] of the solid models are preferred for preprocessing. This does not preclude the linking of these preprocessors to solid modelers based on constructive solid geometry, since the edge and face information can be, and in most cases already is, created for the model. The two approaches to the effective interface between a finite-element preprocessor and a solid modeler are either to build the preprocessor around the data structures of the solid model or to use a mesh-generating approach that interfaces to a solid model with a specific set of predefined operations. The first approach is ideally suited for an interactive-graphic environment, while the second is tractable only for use with a fully automatic mesh-generation algorithm.

An example of the first approach is a finite-element preprocessor [77–79] being developed to interface to a specific solid modeler [80]. This program employs a dual data structure: the first is the faceted boundary representation of the solid model, and the second is a finite-element mesh data base containing the mesh information and pointers back to the original geometry. This dual data base helps increase user interactivity and allows for a large number of automatic validity checking functions. The program operates by reading in the solid-model data base and allowing the user to manipulate the object graphically. Features are available that allow the user to add interior boundary curves (i.e., to create subvolumes for use in mesh generation), discretize the various boundaries, select mesh-patch boundaries, invoke the desired mesh generator, and manipulate the mesh on the screen (Fig. 4.19).

## 4.3c Interactive-Adaptive Processes

Interactive-adaptive analysis [57] has been defined in the introduction to this section as continuous graphical monitoring of the progress of analysis by the engineer with the opportunity to interrupt and to change either the design or the analysis. Obviously if analysis results are to be monitored in real time, the computation must be very rapid or the user will be wasting time sitting before a very slowly changing graphic display. Currently, this limits the use of interactive-adaptive techniques to relatively small problems, to efficient special-purpose design systems, to teaching applications, and to research. However, the trends toward increasingly cost-effective computing and memory and increasingly rapid data transfer indicate that these constraints will be alleviated.

In addition to the direct monitoring of analysis progress, the implementation of interactive-adaptive procedures presents two other possible computing strategies that are particularly significant for nonlinear analysis. The first of these is parallel analysis, in which an alternative analysis type is invoked to diagnose system behavior. Examples include buckling and free-vibration tests on nonlinear structures at an arbitrary stage of loading. The second is sequential analysis, where different analyses are performed to infer the effect of the order of application of influences. For example, a static preloading may precede a nonlinear structural-dynamic analysis.

The analysis and design opportunities presented by interactive-adaptive analysis are several. First, the high degree of interactivity of the combined preprocessing, processing, and postprocessing inherent to this approach encourages the designer to undertake preliminary

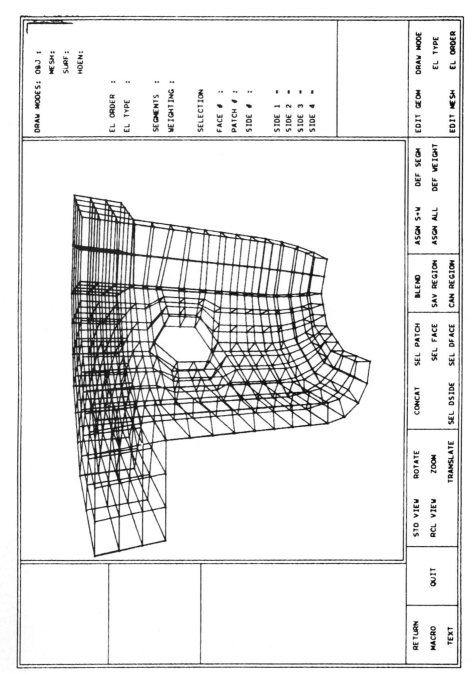

**FIG. 4.19** Mesh generated for object produced by a solid modeler.

4.244

studies of simplified versions of the system. Second, in the design itself, a completed analysis may not be necessary to indicate inadequacies of the trial design; intervention is then appropriate to make immediate changes. Third, the monitoring of time- or load-dependent behavior as it unfolds from analysis is a useful way to enhance one's understanding of system behavior [62]. The fourth opportunity is the ability to perform analyses which aid in establishing analysis parameters; for example, the ability to perform rapid natural period calculations assists in determining appropriate time increments that must be specified for marching algorithms. Finally, a growing number of self-adaptive algorithms are becoming available for such aspects as fracture propagation, substructuring, marching schemes, and mesh improvements (see Sec. 3.4 in Part 4). Although many of these self-adaptive algorithms are stable, some have heuristic bases and are best monitored to ensure the continued validity of computations. For example, the finite-element mesh changes that are necessary to trace an arbitrarily propagating crack may lead to meshes with excessively distorted elements; such distortions can be corrected by the user under an interactive-adaptive approach.

An example of a practical special-purpose program with partial interactive-adaptive capabilities is a CAD system for cable-reinforced membrane structures [67, 81]. These prestressed or air-supported structures are inherently unstable in that they must change shape to resist applied loadings. Therefore, one cannot begin design analysis with an arbitrary configuration; instead one must seek a combination of external loads, internal stresses, and overall shape which satisfies equilibrium. One method of doing this is by "shape finding," which is a nonlinear analysis to calculate the shape for a given loading and a desired internal

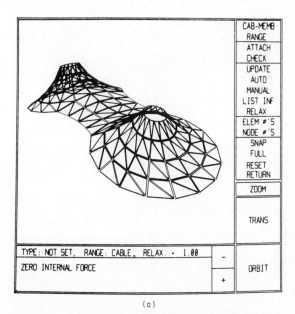

(a)

**FIG. 4.20** A prestressed, cable-reinforced membrane structure shown during interactive-adaptive shape-finding analysis. (a) Central saddle portion becoming too flat. (b) Increase in tension of crown-to-crown cable. (c) Equilibrium shape with more acceptable curvature in the saddle.

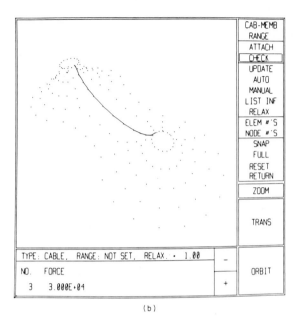

(b)

(c)

**FIG. 4.20**   (Continued)

stress distribution [82]. Figure 4.20 shows a prestressed cable-reinforced membrane at one
stage of the iterative shape finding. This view indicates that the central, "saddle" portion of
the structure is becoming too flat. When this becomes apparent to the engineer, he or she
halts the iterative shape finding before it even converges and interactively increases the

prestress force in the cable running between the two open crowns. This modification yields a more acceptable trial design with greater curvature in the saddle region [81, 82].

Finally, one of the features of interactive-adaptive analysis software is that the graphical-monitoring provisions are essentially the same as the provisions to "play back" the result of an analysis after it has been completed. This is a form of animated postprocessing as described in the next section. Because this playback capability is appropriate for analyses that currently run too slowly to be suitable for interactive monitoring, it may be considered an intermediate stage between pure interactive postprocessing and true interactive-adaptive analysis.

## 4.3D Interpretation of Finite-Element Results

The reduction of finite-element results to a manageable level of useful information is the function of a postprocessor. In general, postprocessing is concerned with the two separate questions of reducing and presenting results in an understandable fashion, and of ensuring that the results used are the most accurate results the given model can produce.

To enhance the engineer's capabilities to interpret the results of a finite-element analysis there are a number of ways to distill and present graphically the information obtained. Among these are:

1. Displaced shapes
2. Contour maps
3. Vector-display maps
4. Animation
5. Thresholding of results
6. Automatic checks against design codes
7. Automatic generation of result reports

*Displaced shapes* are typical of composite vector displays in that all components of a vector response are shown by an exaggerated, deformed mesh. *Contour maps* can be used to display scalars such as temperatures and concentrations of pollutants, or one component of vectors or tensors such as maximum principal stress or horizontal flow. *Vector-display maps* are an alternative depiction of vector fields such as displacements or velocities by means of arrows of appropriate length and direction displayed at each key point. The understanding of time-dependent or harmonic results can be greatly enhanced with *animation*. For example, the dynamic display of natural-vibration modes gives an improved understanding of vibrational tendencies of a structure, and the time-history display of displaced shapes or temperature contours greatly improves the understanding of the time-dependent results. *Automatic thresholding* quickly draws the analyst's attention to critical regions of a problem, while *automatic design checks* indicate the adequacy of the design. *Report generators* are likely to use many of these features in conjunction with specific formatting procedures to reduce greatly the effort of putting the results into a final form for presentation.

Since the major function of postprocessing is to give the user an understanding of the results, which is done best in a pictorial manner, and to allow the user to interpret the results as desired, interactive computer graphics is the ideal medium for postprocessing. An

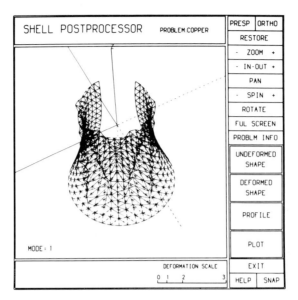

**FIG. 4.21**  Buckling-mode shape of a hyperbolic cooling tower.

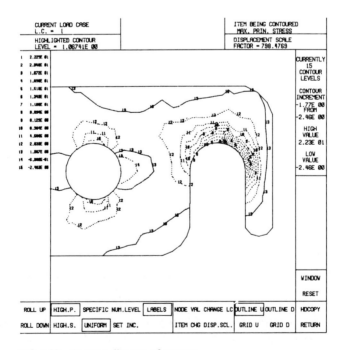

**FIG. 4.22**  Contour diagram of stresses.

interactive-graphic postprocessor allows the user to obtain quickly plots of deformed shapes (Fig. 4.21), stress contours (Fig. 4.22), and other desired parameters. Instead of scanning columns of numbers, the user can use overall displays to determine the basic trends and then can concentrate on the critical areas to determine the desired values (Fig. 4.23). The user also can exercise real-time control over all the factors that affect perception of the results, including viewing directions, magnifications, parameters displayed, scale factors, contour intervals, and color maps.

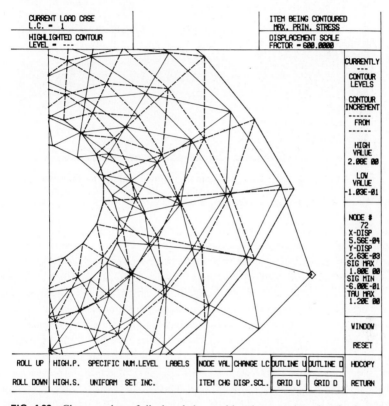

**FIG. 4.23** Close-up view of displaced shape with values at selected node shown.

   Color not only adds impact to the display of results but can also be used as an added dimension to transmit additional information. The most widely used application of color postprocessing is the display of color stress contours. In addition to the impact of color, the continuous color displays available on a raster display device can be used to highlight specific regions of interest. For example, the black band in the stress-contour plot shown in Fig. 4.24 indicates clearly the portion of the structure which experiences a chosen range of stress [83]. Color is also an effective method to increase the informational content of a display. For example, the color contours on the object shown in Fig. 4.25a give an indication of the surface stresses present, but the actual shape of the object is hard to discern. However, the addition of a shading model to that display (Fig. 4.25b) allows the user to determine clearly both the shape and surface stresses [84].

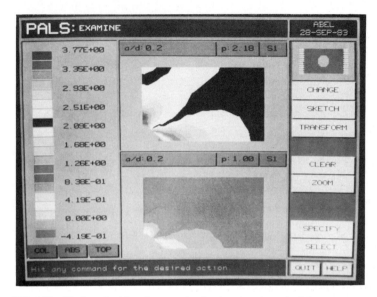

**FIG. 4.24**  Black-and-white photograph of colored major principle-stress contours at two different load levels for the inelastic analysis of a stretched plate with a circular hole. A selected stress range has been blackened to emphasize its extent.

In addition to the reduction of standard results, finite-element postprocessing includes the interpretation of additional quantities in the form of sensitivity parameters for use in making design decisions. Sensitivity parameters give an indication of the expected change in model behavior as a function of the change in design parameters. These parameters are commonly used in various optimization algorithms. Some of the general-purpose finite-element programs have features built in to calculate and output such parameters.

The determination and presentation of results corresponding to the derivatives of the primary variables must receive special consideration. An example of derivative values are the stresses derived from displacement-based finite-element models. The reason that care must be exercised in the determination of these values is that the accuracy of such quantities is a strong function of where and how they are determined [85]. For example, most finite-element contouring algorithms generate the contour displays based on nodal values; however, it is well known that the directly evaluated nodal stresses can be quite inaccurate. Therefore, care must be exercised in the determination of such quantities. A number of approaches have been developed to determine the most accurate values. These techniques range from the use of optimal sampling points and smoothing procedures [86, 87] to highly accurate special-purpose procedures for measuring values at specific locations [88].

## 4.3E Integrating Finite Elements into the CAD/CAM Environment

An integrated CAD/CAM system must have direct ties from geometric design through engineering analysis to the manufacturing floor that are capable of transferring large amounts

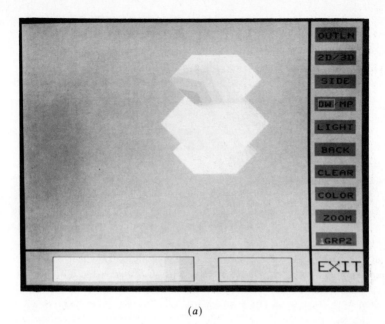

(a)

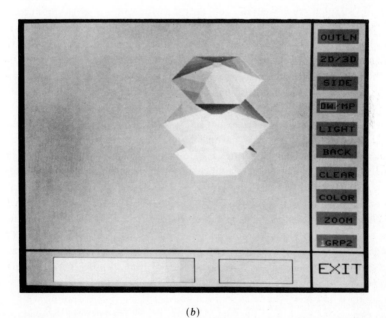

(b)

**FIG. 4.25** Black-and-white photographs of color contours on the surfaces of a three-dimensional object. (a) Without a shading model. (b) With colors modified to represent orientation of each surface with respect to the illumination direction.

of data quickly. Therefore, in addition to the development of more automated modeling techniques, there is a need to improve the data communications between geometric modeling systems, preprocessors, finite-element analysis programs, and postprocessors. It is also necessary for these communications to be carried out through two-way links. There are two approaches currently being used to address this problem. One is the development of general procedures that make use of advanced data-base management systems and, in some cases, specialized hardware to carry out standardized data communications between different systems. The other approach is to develop specific-purpose integrated systems that combine all aspects of the design process into a single package.

Specific-purpose integrated systems are by far the most efficient means to carry out a particular task. They have the advantage of streamlined data communications, and because they carry out a specific set of design operations, they allow for the development of a superior user interface. In essence, such a package is the direct combination of a geometric modeling system, analysis-model preprocessor, analysis program, and postprocessor into a single highly integrated package. The lack of generality for easy interfacing of such packages is often well outweighed by the effectiveness of the system. This is particularly true for specific types of designs for which it is difficult to carry out one portion of the design process without results from the others. A good example of this is the interactive-adaptive analysis and design of cable-reinforced prestressed or inflatable membrane structures, where the design of the basic shape depends on the results of an analysis. This type of design, as described earlier, has been effectively addressed [67, 81] by the integration of geometric design, attribute specification, shape-finding analysis, and postprocessing into a single interactive-graphics package. A disadvantage of special-purpose systems is the effort required to develop them. This disadvantage can be partially overcome by using modularized program structures so that those features from one design program common to the next can be used with little modification. For example, the membrane-structure design program uses geometric definition, attribute specification, and postprocessing features that could be directly transferred to a shell-design program.

The single most important aspect of a generalized approach to effective use of finite elements in a CAD/CAM environment is data-base management, which is concerned with the storage, manipulation, and shipping of large amounts of data. The objective of a data-base management system is to have a single scheme to store and retrieve efficiently large amounts of data shared by a number of diverse applications programs. A key feature of a data-base management system is the overall logical data-base description, referred to as the *data-base schema* [89]. An appropriate schema is important because the data-base management system must not only hold large amounts of information, but must be able to retrieve data selectively on the basis of various associations which must also be stored. There have been a number of effective data-base systems developed for business applications, such as hierarchical and CODASYL systems. However, recently, substantial efforts have gone into the development of engineering data bases. The relational data-base schema [90] is gaining wide acceptance for engineering data bases where the data to be stored are varied and the associations between the data are complex.

In addition to a central data base there is also the need for standard procedures to transmit data between the various application programs and/or the data base. To accomplish this, IGES (Initial Graphics Exchange Specification) [91] has been developed. This exchange specification is being used to transmit geometric data effectively. There are efforts currently under way to improve and expand the capabilities of IGES for the exchange of both geometry and applications data. In particular, an IGES committee is currently drafting an exchange specification for finite-element information.

Other efforts that are currently addressing the engineering data-base problem include the NASA IPAD project, which is designing and implementing at least portions of an integrated engineering data-exchange and manipulation system. One product of this effort is the relational information manager (RIM) [92]. In addition, consideration is being given to the development of specialized hardware for data-base manipulation. An example of such a piece of hardware is the Britton–Lee IDM 500, which is a multimicroprocessor data-base machine based on a relational data structure.

In connection with the storage and retrieval of finite-element data, a decision on exactly which data should be stored must be made. Since the storage of the vast amount of data associated with a finite-element analysis is expensive in terms of disk or tape storage and computing resources, it may not be desirable to keep it all. In addition, data-transfer rates are still sufficiently slow that there are situations where data can be recomputed faster than it can be saved and retrieved. Obviously in such cases it is better to recompute the data. The proper balance between storing or recomputing data is a function of the computing environment, which must be carefully considered to gain the most effective balance.

The importance of data-base management will continue to increase as engineering workstations become common. Although not uniquely defined, an engineering workstation consists of dedicated computing hardware with enough capabilities to carry out the majority of an engineer's tasks. Such a system includes interactive computer graphics, applications software, and enough computing power for the required computations. Many feel that most linear finite-element analysis problems will be carried out on such devices. These workstations are networked to mainframes, large mass-storage devices, various peripheral devices, and each other. The function of the mainframes is to carry out the massive-analysis runs and to transfer data between various segments of the system.

Workstations effective for CAD/CAM and finite-element capabilities have 32-bit, virtual-memory processors, several megabytes of core memory, and tens or hundreds of megabytes of disk space. In many cases, the graphics capabilities are integral; i.e., portions of the core memory are reserved for (or are available for) the buffering of graphical information, and graphical processors and *firmware* are built into the station.

The type of interactive-graphics hardware available strongly influences the level of user interactivity that can be obtained. For the effective use of a screen-menu-driven graphic system, the hardware needed includes a high-resolution display with a reasonable image-update rate and an interactive input device. Finite-element models of realistic objects tend to produce complex images that require a high-resolution display to be discernible. A reasonable image-update rate is needed to ensure an acceptable level of response for good interactive operation. An interactive input device is needed to allow easy and efficient communication from the user to the computer. Three-dimensional models tend to be difficult to work on any device. However, a highly interactive device with enough local graphical capabilities to allow for the real-time geometric manipulations of scaling, rotation, translation, clipping, and depth queuing assist the visualization immensely. Moreover, the user should have options to simplify the display by, for example, isolating selected portions or deleting certain details. The capability to do real-time hidden-line removal and real-time generation of shaded hidden-surface displays at the graphics display is a capability currently used in flight simulators and should soon be available in affordable graphics devices and workstations.

## 4.4 REFERENCES

1. Schrem, E., "Finite Element Software in the Next Decade," *Proceedings of the World Congress on Finite Element Methods in Structural Mechanics*, Bournemouth, Oct. 12–17, 1975.

2. Fenves, S. J., "Future Directions of Structural Engineering Applications," *Computers and Structures*, **10**(1/2):3–5 (April 1979).

3. MacNeal, R. H., "One Man's View of Trends in Finite Element Analysis," in J. F. Gloudeman and R. E. Rosanoff (eds.), *Computational Aspects of the Finite Element Method*, Bundesanstalt für Materialprufung, Berlin, 1979, pp. 1–19.

4. Swanson, J. A., "Present Trends in Computerized Structural Analysis," *Comput. Struct.*, **10**(1/2):33–37 (1979).

5. Stevenson, D., "New Computing Systems and Their Impact on Computation," suppl. to NASA CP-2147, National Aeronautics and Space Administration, Washington, D.C., 1981, pp. 1–6.

6. Swanson, J. A., "Opportunities Provided by Large Computers," in J. Robinson (ed.), *New and Future Developments in Commercial Finite Element Methods*, Robinson and Associates, Dorset, England, 1981, pp. 436–450.

7. MacNeal, R. H., "Trends in Finite Element Structural Analysis," presented at the *AIAA/ASME/ASCE/AHS 23d Structures, Structural Dynamics and Materials Conference*, New Orleans, May 10–12, 1982.

8. Lykos, P., and J. White, "An Assessment of Future Computer System Needs for Large-Scale Computation," NASA TM-78613, National Aeronautics and Space Administration, Washington, D.C., 1980.

9. Bloch, E., and D. J. Galage, "Component Progress: Its Effect on High Speed Computer Architecture and Machine Organization," in D. J. Kuck, D. H. Lawrie, and A. H. Sameh (eds.), *High Speed Computer and Algorithm Organization*, Academic Press, New York, 1977, pp. 13–39.

10. Chapman, D. R., "Computational Aerodynamics—Development and Outlook," *AIAA J.*, **17**(12):1293–1313 (December 1979).

11. Hockney, R. W., and C. R. Jesshope, *Parallel Computing*, Adam Hilger, Bristol, 1981.

12. Reisman, A., "Device, Circuit and Technology Scaling to Micron and Submicron Dimensions," *Proc. IEEE*, **71**(5) (May 1983).

13. Swartzlander, E. E., and B. K. Gilbert, "Supersystems: Technology and Architecture," *IEEE Trans. Comput.*, **C-31**(5):399–409 (May 1982).

14. Manuel, T., "Parallel Processing," *Electronics*, June 16, 1983, pp. 105–114.

15. Groves, B., "Getting VHSIC Into Real-World Systems," *Defense Electronics*, **15**(1):102–111 (January 1983).

16. Flynn, M. J., "Some Computer Organizations and Their Effectiveness," *IEEE Trans. Comput.*, **C-21**:948–960 (1972).

17. Ostlund, N. S., P. G. Hibbard, and R. A. Whiteside, "A Case Study in the Application of a Tightly Coupled Multiprocessor to Scientific Computations," in G. Rodrigue (ed.), *Parallel Computations*, Academic Press, New York, 1982, pp. 315–364.

18. Fathi, E. T., and M. Krieger, "Multiple Microprocessor Systems: What, Why and When," *Computer*, **16**(3):23–32 (March 1983).

19. "Supercomputers," Infotech State-of-the-Art Rep., Infotech International, Maidenhead, Berkshire, England, 1979, vols. 1, 2.

20. Feigenbaum, E. A., and P. McCorduck, *The Fifth Generation: Artificial Intelligence and Japan's Computer Challenge*, Addison-Wesley, Reading, Mass., 1983.

21. Oakes, W. R., and R. V. Browning, "Experiences Running ADINA on CRAY-1," Rep. 82448-9, *Proceedings of the ADINA Conference*, Massachusetts Institute of Technology, Cambridge, Mass., August 1979, pp. 27–42.

22. Haynes, L. S., R. L. Lau, D. P. Siewiorek, and D. W. Mizell, "A Survey of Highly-Parallel Computing," *Computer*, January 1982, pp. 9–24.

23. Kung, H. T., "Why Systolic Architectures," *Computer*, January 1982, pp. 37–46.

24. Kung, H. T., "The Structure of Parallel Algorithms," *Advances in Computers*, Academic Press, New York, 1980, vol. 19, pp. 65–112.

25. Law, K. H., "Systolic Schemes for Finite Element Methods," Rep. R-82-139, Department of Civil Engineering, Carnegie-Mellon University, Pittsburgh, Pennsylvania, July 29, 1982.

26. Melhem, R., "Formal Verification of a Systolic System for Finite Element Stiffness Matrices," Tech. Rep. ICMA-83-56, Institute for Computational Mathematics and Applications, University of Pittsburgh, Pittsburgh, Pennsylvania, 1983.

27. Storaasli, O. O., S. W. Peebles, T. W. Crockett, J. D. Knott, and L. Adams, "The Finite Element Machine: An Experiment in Parallel Processing," NASA TM-84514, NASA Langley Research Center, Hampton, Va., July 1982.

28. Adams, L. M., "Iterative Algorithms for Large Sparse Linear Systems on Parallel Computers," NASA CR-166027, NASA Langley Research Center, Hampton, Va., November 1982.

29. Hoshino, T., et al., "Highly Parallel Processor Array 'PAX' for Wide Scientific Applications," *Proceedings of the 1983 International Conference on Parallel Processing*, Columbus, Ohio, Aug. 23–26, 1983, published by IEEE Computer Society Press, Silver Spring, Md., 1983, pp. 95–105.

30. Salama, M., S. Utku, and R. Melosh, "Parallel Solution of Finite Element Equations," *Proceedings of the Eighth ASCE Conference on Electronic Computation*, University of Houston, Houston, Tex., Feb. 21–23, 1983, pp. 526–539.

31. McGregor, J., and M. Salama, "Finite Element Computation with Parallel VLSI," *Proceedings of the Eighth ASCE Conference on Electronic Computation*, University of Houston, Houston, Tex., Feb. 21–23, 1983, pp. 540–553.

32. Tyler, M., "The Micro Micros," *Datamation*, **28**(13):34–42 (December 1982).

33. Conaway, J. H., "Structural Engineering Software on Small Computers," Pap. 80-C2/Aero-7, American Society of Mechanical Engineers, New York, August 1980.

34. Foster, E. P., and O. O. Storaasli, "Structural Analysis on a Minicomputer," in R. A. Adey (ed.), *Engineering Software*, Pentech Press, London, 1979, pp. 43–54.

35. Storaasli, O. O., and R. C. Murphy, "Finite Element Analysis in a Minicomputer/Mainframe Environment," NASA CP-2059, in *Research in Computerized Structural Analysis and Design*, National Aeronautics and Space Administration, Washington, D.C., 1978, pp. 77–83.

36. Wilson, E. L., "The Use of Minicomputers in Structural Analysis," Rep. 82448-9, *Proceedings of the ADINA Conference*, Massachusetts Institute of Technology, Cambridge, Mass., August 1979, pp. 293–303.

37. Edwards, J., "The Desktop Buyer's Guide to Small Computers," *Desktop Computing*, April 1983, pp. 52–69.

38. Lu, C., "Microcomputers: The Second Wave," *High Technology*, September/October 1982, pp. 36–52.

39. Beckx, E., J. P. Rammant, and O. Schymkowitz, "Case Study on Desk Computer: Finite Element Analysis in BASIC," in J. Robinson (ed.), *Finite Element Methods in the Commercial Environment*, Robinson and Associates, Dorset, England, 1978, vol. 2, pp. 670–780.

40. Firmin, A., "FESDEC—A Finite Element System for Desktop Computers," *Finite Element News*, January 1980, pp. 22–23.

41. Wilson, E. L., "SAP-80—Structural Analysis Programs for Small or Large Computer Systems," *CEPA 1980 Fall Conference and Annual Meeting*, Newport Beach, Calif., Oct. 13–15, 1980.

42. Kelly, P., and A. S. Watson, "Structural Analysis Using Desktop Computers," in *Engineering Software II: Proceedings of the Second International Conference on Engineering Software*, Imperial College of Science and Technology, London, March 1981, CML Publications, Southampton, 1981, pp. 346–359.

43. Griffen, O. H., and C. R. Wilson, "Finite Element Analysis on a Microprocessor-Based Personal Workstation," Tech. Note, *Comput. Struct.*, **17**(4):617–619 (1983).

44. Strohkorb, G. A., and A. K. Noor, "Potential of Minicomputer/Array Processor System for Nonlinear Finite Element Analysis," *Computers and Structures*, **18**(4):703–718 (1984).

45. Swanson, J. A., G. R. Cameron, and J. C. Haberland, "Adapting the ANSYS Finite Element Analysis Program to an Attached Processor," *Computer*, **16**(6):85–91 (June 1983).

46. Thompkins, W. T., Jr., and R. Haimes, "A Minicomputer/Array Processor/Memory System for Large-Scale Fluid Dynamic Calculations," in *Impact of New Computing Systems on Computational Mechanics*, American Society of Mechanical Engineers, New York, 1983, pp. 117–126.

47. Miranker, W. L., "A Survey of Parallelism in Numerical Analysis," *SIAM Rev.*, **13**(4):524–547 (October 1971).

48. Sameh, A. H., "Numerical Parallel Algorithms—A Survey," in *High-Speed Computer and Algorithm Organization*, Academic Press, New York, 1977, pp. 217–228.

49. Heller, D., "A Survey of Parallel Algorithms in Numerical Linear Algebra," *SIAM Rev.*, **20**(4):740–777 (October 1978).

50. Voigt, R. G., "The Influence of Vector Computer Architecture on Numerical Algorithms," in *High-Speed Computer and Algorithm Organization*, Academic Press, New York, 1977, pp. 229–244.

51. Ortega, J. M., and R. G. Voigt, "Solution of Partial Differential Equations on Vector Computers," *SIAM Review*, **27**(2):149–240 (June 1985).

52. Rodrigue, G. (ed.), *Parallel Computations*, Academic Press, New York, 1982.

53. Noor, A. K., and S. J. Hartley, "Evaluation of Element Stiffness Matrices on CDC STAR-100 Computer," *Comput. Struct.*, **9**(2):151–161 (1978).

54. Gilmore, P. A., "Numerical Solution of Partial Differential Equations by Associative Processing," *Proceedings of the 1971 Fall Joint Computer Conference*, AFIPS, vol. 39, pp. 411–418.

55. Brender, R. F., and I. R. Massi, "What is Ada?," *Computer*, **14**(6):17–22, 24 (June 1981).

56. Coleman, D., R. M. Gallimore, J. W. Hughes, and M. S. Powell, "An Assessment of Concurrent Pascal," *Software—Practice and Experiment*, **9**(10):827–837 (October 1979).

57. Gattass, M., and J. F. Abel, "Interactive-Adaptive Large Displacement Analysis with Real-Time Computer Graphics," *Comput. Struct.*, **16**(1–4):141–152 (1983).

58. Newman, W. M., and R. F. Sproull, *Principles of Interactive Computer Graphics*, 2d ed., McGraw-Hill, New York, 1979.

59. Foley, J. D., and A. Van Dam, *Fundamentals of Interactive Computer Graphics*, Addison Wesley, Reading, Mass., 1982.

60. Kamel, H. A., "Design and Implementation of Interactive Engineering Software," in J. F. Abel et al. (eds.), *Interdisciplinary Finite Element Analysis*, College of Engineering, Cornell University, Ithaca, N.Y., 1981, pp. 773–803.

61. Pesquera, C. I., W. McGuire, and J. F. Abel, "Interactive Graphical Preprocessing of Three-Dimensional Framed Structures," *Comput. Struct.*, **17**(1):97–104 (1983).

62. Abel, J. F., "Interactive Computer Graphics for Applied Mechanics," *Proc. 9th U.S. Nat. Congr. Appl. Mech.*, American Society of Mechanical Engineers, New York, 1982, pp. 3–27.

63. Shephard, M. S., and L. J. Feeser, "RPIFEP—An Interactive Finite Element Package," in J. H. Conaway (ed.), *First Chautaugua on Finite Element Modeling*, Wallace Press, Milford, New Hampshire, 1980, pp. 99-117.

64. Stricklin, J. A., W. S. Ho, E. Q. Richardson, and W. E. Haisler, "On Isoparametric vs. Linear Strain Triangular Elements," *Int. J. Numer. Meth. Eng.*, 11:1041-1043 (1977).

65. Haber, R. B., M. S. Shephard, J. F. Abel, R. H. Gallagher, and D. P. Greenberg, "A General Two-Dimensional Finite Element Preprocessor Utilizing Discrete Transfinite Mappings," *Int. J. Numer. Meth. Eng.*, 17:1015-1044 (1981).

66. Shephard, M. S., C. N. Tonias, and T. J. Weidner, "Attribute Specification for Finite Element Models," *Comput. Graphics*, 6(2):83-91 (1982).

67. Haber, R. B., and J. F. Abel, "Discrete Transfinite Mappings for the Description and Meshing of Three-Dimensional Surfaces Using Interactive Computers Graphics," *Int. J. Numer. Meth. Eng.*, 18:41-66 (1982).

68. Wu, S. C., and J. F. Abel, "Representation and Discretization of Arbitrary Surfaces for Finite Element Shell Analysis," *Int. J. Numer. Meth. Eng.*, 14(7):813-836 (July 1979).

69. Perucchio, R., A. R. Ingraffea, and J. F. Abel, "Interactive Computer Graphic Preprocessing for Three-Dimensional Finite Element Analyses," *Int. J. Numer. Meth. Eng.*, 18:909-926 (1982).

70. Kanellopoulou, M., "Generation and Finite Element Modeling of Sweep-Based Solids," TR-82010, Masters thesis, Center for Interactive Computer Graphics, Rensselaer Polytechnic Institute, Troy, N.Y., 1982.

71. Cook, W. A., and W. R. Oakes, "A Mapping Method for Generating Three-Dimensional Meshes: Past and Present," *Comput. Eng.*, 3:9-16 (1982).

72. Tracy, F. T., "Graphics Pre- and Post-Processor for Two-Dimensional Finite Element Programs," *Comput. Graphics*, SIGGRAPH '77, 11(2):8-12 (1977).

73. Lorensen, W., "Grid Generation Tools for the Finite Element Analyst," in J. H. Conaway (ed.), *First Chautaugua on Finite Element Modeling*, Wallace Press, Milford, New Hampshire, 1980, pp. 119-136.

74. Requicha, A. A. G., and H. B. Voelcker, "Solid Modeling: A Historical Summary and Contemporary Assessment," *IEEE Comput. Graphics Appl.*, 2:9-24 (March 1982).

75. Butlin, G., "The CAD/FEM Interface," in J. Robinson (ed.), *New and Future Developments in Commercial Finite Element Methods*, Robinson and Associates, Dorset, England, 1981, pp. 286-297.

76. Shephard, M. S., "Linking Finite Element Analysis and Solid Modeling," *CAMP '83*, AMK Berlin, 1983, pp. 786-799.

77. Shephard, M. S., "The Effective Use of Finite Element Methods in Engineering Design," in H. G. Schaeffer (ed.), *Second Chautaugua on Productivity in Engineering and Design: The CAD Revolution*, Wallace Press, Milford, New Hampshire, 1982, pp. 299-312.

78. Kotsianas, P., "Finite Element Mesh Generation in Solid Models," Masters thesis, TR82012, Center for Interactive Computer Graphics, Rensselaer Polytechnic Institute, Troy, N.Y., August 1982.

79. Shephard, M. S., "Finite Element Models from Geometric Models," *NCGA '82*, 2, 1982.

80. Fitzgerald, W., F. Gracer, and R. Wolfe, "GRIN: Interactive Graphics for Modeling Solids," *IBM J. Res. Devel.*, 25(4):281-294 (July 1981).

81. Haber, R. B., J. F. Abel, and D. P. Greenberg, "An Integrated Design System for Cable Reinforced Membranes Using Interactive Computer Graphics," *Comput. Struct.*, 14(3-4):261-280 (1981).

82. Haber, R., and J. F. Abel, "Initial Equilibrium Solution Methods for Cable-Reinforced Membranes," *Comput. Meth. Appl. Mech. Eng.*, 33(1-3):557-573 (1982).

83. Abel, J. F., W. McGuire, and A. R. Ingraffea, "Computer Graphics for 3D Structural Analysis," *Proc. 8th Conf. Electronic Computation*, American Society of Civil Engineers, New York, 1983, pp. 594-607.

84. Schulman, M. A., "The Interactive Display of Parameters on Two- and Three-Dimensional Surfaces," M.S. thesis, Department of Architecture, Cornell University, Ithaca, N.Y., August 1981.

85. Barlow, J., "Optimal Stress Locations in Finite Element Models," *Int. J. Numer. Meth. Eng.*, **10**:243–251 (1976).

86. Oden, J. T., and H. J. Brauchli, "On the Calculation of Consistent Stress Distributions in Finite Element Approximations," *Int. J. Numer. Meth. Eng.*, **3**:317–325 (1971).

87. Hinton, E., and J. S. Campbell, "Local and Global Smoothing of Discontinuous Finite Element Functions Using a Least Squares Method," *Int. J. Numer. Meth. Eng.*, **8**:461–480 (1974).

88. Babuska, I., and A. Miller, "The Post-Processing Approach in the Finite Element Method: 1. Calculation of Displacements, Stresses and Other Higher Derivatives," *Int. J. Numer. Meth. Eng.*, **20**:1085–1109 (1985).

89. Martin, J., *Computer Data-Base Organization*, 2d ed., Prentice-Hall, Englewood Cliffs, N.J., 1977.

90. Codd, E. F., "Relational Database: A Practical Foundation for Productivity," *Communication of the ACM*, **25**(2) (February 1982).

91. "Initial Graphics Exchange Specification (IGES), Version 20," Rep. NBSIR 82-2631 (AF), National Bureau of Standards, 1983.

92. Erikson, W. J., "Rim Users Manual," National Aeronautics and Space Administration, Washington, D.C., 1981.

# CHAPTER 5
# SURVEY OF SOME FINITE-ELEMENT SOFTWARE SYSTEMS

## 5.1 INTRODUCTION

The significant advances made in finite-element technology, coupled with the rapid develop-ments in computer hardware and software, provided the foundation from which general-purpose finite-element programs have evolved. After many years of development, a wide variety of finite-element programs are currently being used in government and industry for the solution of a wide variety of practical problems. By the mid-1980s, there were about 500 user-oriented and several thousand research-oriented finite-element program systems. The number of pre- and postprocessing packages was estimated to be over 200. There were over 20,000 finite-element users worldwide who were estimated to spend about $500 million annually on finite-element analysis. The potential user of a finite-element system is faced with the problems of (1) getting information about, and sorting out, existing finite-element programs; and (2) identifying the program that is best suited for his or her particular needs.

Since early 1970 several bibliographies, data sheets, and tables have been compiled about finite-element software, including pre- and postprocessors (see, for example, Refs. [1-10]). In addition, a number of attempts have subsequently been made to evaluate commercial finite-element codes and assess the adequacy of their elements (see, for example, Refs. [4, 10-15]). This chapter gives an overview of the current capabilities of some finite-element software systems. Because of space limitations, only 14 codes are included in this survey. Most of these programs are general-purpose codes with a broad spectrum of capabilities, rich variety of element types, large user community, and comprehensive user support. Two of the programs surveyed, TUJAP and FINITE/GP, do not belong to the category of large general-purpose software systems. TUJAP is a special-purpose code for elastoplastic and fracture analysis of tubular joints. FINITE/GP is a linear-analysis program, especially designed for the IBM PC and its lookalikes. The latter program is included herein as an example of finite-element codes for personal computers. The capabilities of the programs surveyed are listed in tabular form, followed by a summary of the major features of each program.

As with any survey of computer programs, the present one has the following limitations:

1. It is useful only in the initial selection of the programs which are most suitable for a particular application. The final selection of the program to be used should, however, be based on a detailed examination of the documentation and the literature about the program.

2. Since computer software continually changes, often at a rapid rate, some means must be found for updating this survey and maintaining some degree of currency.

Nevertheless, the present survey provides an overview of the capabilities of some of the most popular finite-element programs in the world.

The coming few years promise to be exciting for finite-element analysts. The trends in finite-element system development appear to be toward:

- More user-friendly features such as artificial-intelligence aids and more powerful interactive color-graphics devices for modeling and postprocessing.

- Use of finite-element firmware (low-cost microprocessors based on VLSI and ULSI technology).

- Integration of finite-element analysis packages into CAD/CAM systems.

Before listing the capabilities of the programs, some of the sources of information about computer programs and references on the background material needed for effectively using the programs are listed, and guidelines for selecting the code are discussed.

## 5.2 SOURCES OF INFORMATION ABOUT COMPUTER PROGRAMS

A partial list of users' groups and software dissemination services that provide information about finite-element programs is given below. A more complete list and a description of each group may be found in Ref. [16].

- ASIAC. Aerospace Structures Information and Analysis Center, AFFDL/FBR Wright-Patterson Air Force Base, Ohio 45433.

- CEPA. Society for Computer Application in Engineering, Planning and Architecture, Inc., 15713 Crabbs Branch Way, Rockville, Maryland 20855.

- COSMIC. NASA's Computer Software Management and Information Center, 112 Barrow Hall, University of Georgia, Athens, Georgia 30602.

- ICES. Integrated Civil Engineering System Users Group, Inc., P.O. Box 8243, Cranston, Rhode Island 02920.

- ICP.  International Computer Programs, Inc., 9000 Keystone Crossing, Indianapolis, Indiana 46240.

- NISEE.  National Information Service for Earthquake Engineering, Computer Applications, 379 Davis Hall, University of California, Berkeley, California 94720.

- NTIS.  National Technical Information Service, U.S. Department of Commerce, 5285 Port Royal Road, Springfield, Virginia 22161.

- NAFEMS.  National Agency for Finite Element Methods and Standards, Department of Trade and Industry, National Engineering Laboratory, East Kilbride, Glasgow G75 0QU, United Kingdom.

These organizations publish catalogs and newsletters describing finite-element programs.


## 5.3 BACKGROUND MATERIAL NEEDED FOR EFFECTIVE EVALUATION AND USE OF FINITE-ELEMENT COMPUTER PROGRAMS

The user of a finite-element program is dependent on the detailed knowledge about theories, algorithms, and assumptions behind the program for the proper selection of models and algorithms as well as for monitoring the solution process. There are also many practical problems whose solution may require modifying (slightly) the program. Therefore, the effective evaluation and use of finite-element programs require some knowledge of the following:

1. Basic finite-element theory. Several texts and monographs have been written on the subject. A comprehensive list of these publications is included in a state-of-the-art survey [17, 18].

2. Mathematical modeling and formulation of the engineering and applied science problems included within the scope of the program.

3. Numerical algorithms used in the program and their efficiency. These include solution of linear (and nonlinear) algebraic equations, extraction of eigenvalues, and temporal-integration techniques.

4. Software engineering tools such as data-base management techniques, programming languages, decomposition of the program into functional modules, and structured programming concepts.


## 5.4 GUIDELINES FOR SELECTION OF A COMPUTER PROGRAM

The analysis capabilities and user features vary considerably from one code to the other, and, therefore, it is often difficult to identify the proper code that meets a specific need. A number of factors which affect the selection of a code are enumerated in the succeeding paragraphs. The order in which these factors are listed does not necessarily reflect the priority which should be given each factor; this remains the responsibility of the user of the code. (For a detailed discussion of the technical, operational, and commercial criteria for selecting a code see Refs. [19, 20]).

## 5.4ᴀ Analysis Capabilities

Analysis capabilities include the range of applications and limitations of the code. The limitations include both those implied by the formulation aspects and numerical solution procedures adopted by the code as well as the element library available in the code.

## 5.4ʙ Adequacy of User-Oriented Features

For finite-element analysis the users' features such as automatic (or semiautomatic) mesh (or model) generation, error checks, and displays of original model and of various intermediate results are essential for the effective use of the analysts' time.

## 5.4ᴄ Maintainability

Because of the rapid advances in computational methods, computer software, and hardware technology, the maintenance of finite-element codes usually includes updating the computational modules, extending the capabilities of the code, and improving its performance. There exist well-established formal mechanisms for integration and quality assurance of software extensions. Maintenance of the code by personnel other than the developer (e.g., users' organization) can be quite expensive and time-consuming.

## 5.4ᴅ Adequacy of User-Support Facilities

In addition to the printed documentation (users' manuals, training manuals, programming manuals, sample problems, test cases, and simple handbooks), the following services are desirable: help interactive commands, training courses including videotapes, users' meetings, hotline consulting, assistance by data centers, and consulting organizations.

## 5.4ᴇ Portability

Although most of the finite-element codes are written in standard ANSI FORTRAN language, a code developed on one computer system may not be entirely compatible with another system owing to differences in I/O facilities, operating system, precision of the machine (e.g., UNIVAC versus CDC), etc.

Once a code is acquired and implemented on the users' computer system, it is important to establish its reliability by benchmark problem runs. For a discussion on verification and qualification procedures see Ref. [21].

## 5.5 PROGRAM SURVEYS AND DESCRIPTIONS

This section gives an overview of the capabilities of 14 computer programs for the solution of various engineering problems. The information presented is based on a questionnaire sent to the developers of each program.

## 5.5A Summaries of Individual Programs

In this section is a brief description of each of the programs listed in the tables in Sec. 5.5B. These descriptions were supplied by the program developers.

### ABAQUS

**Descriptive Program Title**   General-purpose finite-element system.

**Program Developer**   Hibbitt, Karlsson and Sorensen, Inc.
100 Medway Street
Providence, RI 02906
(401) 861-0820

**Approximate Number of Technical Staff Supporting the Program**   16.

**Date of First Release and Most Recent Update**   First release, 1978. Current release, 4.5; originally released, 1984. Release 4.6 scheduled for November 1986.

**General Information**   ABAQUS is a general-purpose finite-element program designed for production use in a wide range of applications. Its principal advantages are its large library of capabilities, including large element library and wide range of nonlinear features, ease of use (very simple, readable keyword-and-parameter input, automatic time stepping for non-linear application, extensive graphical output), efficiency, and high-level support.

**Program Capability**   ABAQUS is designed as a production tool of maximum generality. Its major capabilities are focused on reliability in practical cases. Since much of the program's use is in the nonlinear range, it has an extensive library of nonlinear features that will provide solutions for a wide range of problem parameters, with minimum guidance from the user. For example, a strong emphasis is placed on automatic incrementation schemes for static cases (including unstable postbuckling response), dynamics (including impact), fully coupled stress problems, pore-fluid-flow–porous-medium deformation cases, etc. The program has capabilities for modeling offshore structures, including wave loading; elastomer modeling; and concrete modeling including general rebar definition, separate material models for concrete and rebar, as well as cracking and crushing of concrete. The program is under active, continual development with major new releases every 12 to 18 months.

**User Interface and Modeling Capabilities**   Four principal ideas form the basis of the user interface in ABAQUS: simple input, careful documentation, extensive plotting capability, and automatic time stepping. Input is organized by keywords and "sets." Keywords introduce blocks of data; keyword cards often include parameters. The set concept is an effective data organizer for the user, especially in large models. It allows collections of nodes or elements to be addressed by a user-defined name. Sets can be assembled into other sets, to any level. Sets are used for most specifications—material properties, loadings and boundary conditions, output edits, etc.

**Notable Items and Limitations**   ABAQUS is designed for advanced applications, especially in the nonlinear range. Because of its capabilities in that context, its other assets are often taken for granted: It is one of the easiest large-scale finite-element programs to learn and use, and it is one of the most computationally efficient, even in simple, linear applications.

*Programming Language*   FORTRAN 77.

*Hardware and Operating System*   All standard systems used for engineering applications.

*Program Size*   Preprocessor, 50,000 lines; core program and postprocessors, 90,000 lines.

*Documentation*   User's Manual, Example Problems Manual, Theory Manual, and Systems Manual issued by Hibbitt, Karlsson, and Sorensen. Videotape tutorials on basic usage and advanced topics available from EPRI (Electric Power Research Institute, 3412 Hillview Avenue, Palo Alto, California 94303).

*Program Availability*   ABAQUS is supplied under monthly or fully paid-up licenses. Academic licenses are also provided at nominal cost. Contact Hibbitt, Karlsson, and Sorensen for details. EPRI member utilities should contact EPRI for license information.

## ADINA

*Descriptive Program Title*   Automatic Dynamic Incremental Nonlinear Analysis.

*Program Developer*   ADINA Engineering, Inc.
71 Elton Avenue
Watertown, MA 02172, U.S.A.
Tel. (617) 926-5199
Telex 951-772 adina us wtwn

*Release Dates*   First release, 1975. Current release, December 1984. The upcoming release is due November 1986.

*General Information*   The ADINA computer program system is available for effective finite-element analysis of structural and heat-transfer problems, and other field problems. The program has been developed to provide a tool for linear and nonlinear practical state-of-the-art analysis, so emphasis has been placed on the use of reliable and efficient finite-element techniques, and user conveniences for modeling and performing the analyses of complex industrial problems.

The ADINA system consists currently of the following major programs: ADINA, for displacement and stress analysis; ADINAT, for analysis of heat-transfer and field problems; ADINA-IN, for free-format command-language input, generation, and display of input data; ADINA-PLOT, for graphical and alphanumeric display of program input and output data.

The philosophy in the program development is to provide maximum capabilities for modeling structural and heat-transfer systems with few but effective finite elements, an extensive material model library, and effective and general numerical procedures.

The ADINA system is applicable to general three-dimensional analysis and can be employed in many different technologies, for example, civil, mechanical and aerospace; nuclear; offshore; automobile; geomechanics; and manufacturing technologies.

*User Interface and Modeling Capabilities*   See Table 5.2, use of ADINA-IN, ADINA-PLOT.

*Notable Items*   The program is based on efficient and reliable finite-element procedures for linear and nonlinear analyses. Although a program for nonlinear analysis, ADINA is also very efficient in linear analyses. The source code contains many comment statements and the theory used is well documented. The source code is available to industry users licensing the program. The user is able to understand the program operation and, if desired, adapt the program to specific needs.

*Programming Language*   FORTRAN.

*Hardware and Operating System*   CRAY, CDC, IBM, UNIVAC, VAX, PRIME, MASSCOMP, HP 9000, etc.

*Program Size*   150,000 lines for complete system.

*Documentation*   Includes User's Manuals, Theory and Verification Manuals, Book and Video Course, and four conference proceedings which provide documentation on usage.

*Availability*   The program can be licensed from ADINA Engineering, usually with a 2-year support agreement:

ADINA Engineering, Inc.
71 Elton Avenue
Watertown, MA 02172
Tel. (617) 926-5199
Telex 951-772 adina us wtwn

The program can also be employed at various data centers.

## ANSYS

*Descriptive Program Title*   General-purpose, finite-element program for structural, heat-transfer, and static-electromagnetic analyses.

*Program Developer*   Swanson Analysis Systems, Inc.
P.O. Box 65, Johnson Road
Houston, PA 15342

*Approximate Number of Technical Staff Supporting the Program*   There are over 50 people supporting ANSYS in development, customer support, quality assurance, and distribution.

*Date of First Release and Most Recent Update*   ANSYS was first commercially available in 1970 and was currently operating at Revision 4.2A when this book went to press.

*General Information*   ANSYS is a large-scale, general-purpose computer program used by design engineers for structural, thermal, fluid, electrical, and static-electromagnetic analyses. ANSYS has been used since 1970 in many industries, including the nuclear, aerospace, transportation, medical, steel, railroad, packaging, and civil construction industries. ANSYS is supported by a full-time customer-support staff in Pennsylvania and by a network of ANSYS technical-support distributors in North America, Europe, Israel, and the Far East.

*Program Capability*   ANSYS is used for finite-element static, dynamic, thermal, linear, or nonlinear analyses performed in two or three dimensions. ANSYS can handle thermal stress analysis by a direct link between the thermal output and the structural input. ANSYS includes submodeling for detailed regions of linear and nonlinear structures. In addition to many analysis capabilities, ANSYS includes pre- and postprocessing and supports a wide range of graphic display devices.

*User Interface and Modeling Capabilities*   Preprocessing for model and load creation and verification is included in ANSYS. Both meshes and loads may be generated using automatic procedures. Both can be verified graphically. On-line documentation is available for each command. ANSYS postprocessing supports many graphic options—hidden line, section, *xy*-plots, distorted shape, and contour maps of stresses or temperatures. ANSYS postprocessing also includes a data-base language so that results can be selectively examined. ANSYS interfaces with many CAD systems.

*Notable Items and Limitations*   ANSYS is able to handle up to 3000 degrees of freedom on the wavefront. By using single- or multi-level substructuring, the number of possible degrees of freedom in a model is limited only by computer and time resources.

*Programming Language*   FORTRAN 77.

*Hardware and Operating System*   Alliant, Apollo, Amdahl, CDC, Celebrity, Convex, Computervision, CRAY, Data General, DEC VAX, ELXSI, Floating Point Systems, Fujitsu, Harris, Hewlett-Packard, IBM, PRIME, RIDGE, SUN, and UNIVAC.

*Program Size*   150,000 source statements.

*Documentation*   Verification Manual, Theoretical Manual, ANSYS Techniques, Introductory Manual, and User's Manual.

*Program Availability*   ANSYS is available on all the above machines for a monthly royalty or lease cost. The cost varies with the type of machine. ANSYS is also available to universities for $200 per year.

## ASKA

*Descriptive Program Title*   General-purpose finite-element software system.

*Program Developer*   Institut für Statik und Dynamik, University of Stuttgart, West Germany.

*Approximate Number of Technical Staff Supporting the Program*   15.

*Date of First Release and Most Recent Update*   First release, April 1, 1969. Recent update, July 1, 1984.

*General Information*   ASKA is a proven general-purpose finite-element software system that is also capable of solving very large problems. The program is highly reliable.

*Program Capability*

- Elaborate substructure analysis.
- Own data-base management.
- Comprehensive element library.
- User-supplied subroutines for input of time-dependent prescribed displacements and forces and for nonlinear material behavior.

*User Interface and Modeling Capabilities*

- Interfaces to all leading pre- and postprocessors.

- Free-format input, interface to all internal data, special interface to graphics, interface to external files.

*Notable Items and Limitations*  Limitations of problem size (large page version): 20,000 unknowns per substructure; 1000 substructures; 2000 loading cases.

*Programming Language*  Standard FORTRAN IV.

*Hardware and Operating System*  Any FORTRAN system with at least 300 Kbyte central memory and the capability of linking more than 10,000 subroutines (total program size more than 4 Mbytes).

*Program Size*  600,000 FORTRAN statements.

*Documentation*  32 volumes, including User's Manuals, Lecture Notes, and Programmer's Manual.

*Program Availability*  The system is distributed in object code. Maintenance and user support is also provided. Universities pay only a nominal fee. Contact developers for details.


## EAL

*Program Title*  Engineering Analysis Language.

*Program Developer*  Engineering Information Systems, Inc. (EISI)
5120 West Campbell Avenue, Suite 240
San Jose, CA 95130

*Release Dates*  First release, 1976. Current level, EAL/210.

*General Information*  EAL is a large-scale, comprehensive software system used for structural and thermal finite-element analysis and design. The advanced language form and general-purpose data-base management capabilities of EAL give the user great flexibility and simplicity of use in solving complicated or unusual problems for which canned solutions are not available. The capabilities of EAL are continuously being extended, and new program levels are released periodically. Extremely general capability for sensitivity analysis is provided.

*Program Capabilities*  The following are typical of the types of analyses that may be performed using EAL:

- Linear and nonlinear static analysis
- Bifurcation buckling from any static-equilibrium state
- Vibrational modes with respect to any equilibrium state
- Direct (exact, not modal) complex frequency response
- Dynamic fluid-structure interaction
- Modal dynamic response: transient, shock spectra, power spectral density, steady state, etc.

- Multilevel substructuring and general Rayleigh-Ritz analysis for static, buckling, and dynamic analyses
- Linear and nonlinear steady-state and transient thermal analysis
- Fluid network analysis
- View-factor computations for radiation-exchange analyses
- General-array arithmetic, e.g., $Z = \text{SUM}(X, Y)$, $MV = \text{PROD}(M, V)$, etc.
- Numerical determination of sensitivity matrices and redesign

***User Interface and Modeling Capabilities*** EAL is configured as an array of processors that communicate with each other through a random-access data-base. As each processor is executed, all pertinent source data is extracted from the data base, and computed results are stored in the data base. Each processor can be executed in interactive or batch mode.

Restarting an analysis is completely automatic. The user simply reattaches the file or files containing the data base and resumes execution as if the previous execution had not been terminated.

All input is in free field. Extensive facilities such as mesh generation, data validation, and automation of many aspects of problem definition allow the user to construct finite-element models quickly and efficiently.

EAL contains an extensive array of graphic and tabular report generators that can be used to display data in a variety of formats.

***Notable Items*** EAL provides the user with the facility to construct command and/or data image sequences called *runstreams* that can be used to control all aspects of an analysis. Runstreams can contain free parameters stored in "registers" and control branching logic, thereby giving the user great flexibility in solving complicated and unusual problems. For routine production usage an extensive library of easy-to-use runstreams is provided with the program.

Through the use of registers and control branching logic, the user can create generic model runstreams in which key parameters are left as variables that need not be assigned until the runstream is placed in execution. The key parameters may be anything the user desires—typically dimensions, mesh density and shape parameters, material constants, etc.

Through EAL's automated execution control and data-base management facilities, a totally automated verification system was developed to ensure that the entire system continues to function properly as new capabilities are added and when the system is installed on a new host computer. The verification system is machine-independent.

***Programming Language*** ANSI FORTRAN 66, and assembler.

***Hardware and Operating System*** EAL is designed to be as machine-independent as possible. EAL is currently in production use on CRAY, FPS-164, CDC CYBER, VAX, Harris, UNIVAC, and PRIME computers. Conversion for operation on a new type of computer usually requires less than a month, including verification.

***Program Size*** EAL contains approximately 150,000 lines of source code.

*Documentation*

EISI-EAL Reference Manual: vol. 1, General Rules and Utility Processors; vol. 2, Structural Analysis—Primary Processors

EISI-EAL Verification Manual

EISI-EAL Thermal Analysis Reference Manual: vol. 1, Program Execution; vol. 2, Theory; vol. 3, Demonstration Problems

Monographs are also available that address specific applications, e.g., acoustic-structure interaction, macro elements, cyclic symmetry, etc.

*Program Availability*   EAL is available at selected data centers and directly from EISI on a fixed-fee lease basis. Contact:

W. D. Whetstone
Engineering Information Systems, Inc.
5120 West Campbell Avenue, Suite 240
San Jose, CA 95130
(408) 379-0732

## *FENRIS*

*Descriptive Program Title*   FENRIS (Finite-Element Nonlinear Integrated System)—general-purpose nonlinear structural-analysis system.

*Program Developer*   Pal G. Bergan and project group from the Norwegian Institute of Technology (NTH), the Foundation for Scientific and Industrial Research at the Norwegian Institute of Technology (SINTEF), and Det norske Veritas. From 1984 A.S VERITEC, a subsidiary of Det norske Veritas, has replaced Det norske Veritas in the project group.

*Approximate Number of Technical Staff*   6.

*Date of First Release and Most Recent Updates*   First release, 1982. Most recent update, April 1984.

*General Information*   FENRIS is a general-purpose nonlinear finite-element program with its main field of application in connection with the offshore industry. The program is a result of a joint project between NTH and SINTEF in Trondheim, Norway, where an extensive research within nonlinear-analysis methods has been done the last decade, and Det norske Veritas, who has extensive experience in developing, maintaining, and applying large finite-element programs. FENRIS is marketed and supported by A.S VERITEC in Oslo, a subsidiary of Det norske Veritas, and by regional offices in London, Rotterdam, Houston, Kobe, and Singapore.

*Program Capability*   FENRIS is divided into several application programs referred to as *satellites.* Each satellite contains different sets of elements and/or other user facilities. Presently FENRIS consists of four satellites:

- Satellite 1 for three-dimensional structures, including cable and bar, beam, three- and four-node membranes, spring, contact, and link element with friction.

- Satellite 2 for planar structures and axisymmetric solids.
- Satellite 3 for stiffened plates and shells.
- Satellite 4 for three-dimensional solid structures.

The program allows very large displacements and rotations, using a corotated reference coordinate system for the elements. In a flexible and efficient way the history of application of the loads, conservative or nonconservative, may be given to the program. An automatic wave-load generation module and a hydrostatic module are available, together with automatic calculation of drag forces and added mass. Both nonlinear static and nonlinear dynamic analysis may be performed. A library of different material properties is available, including linear-elastic, hyperelastic, and elastoplastic with combined kinematic and isotropic hardening. The solution algorithms range from linear static and dynamic to automatic calculation of time step for nonlinear dynamic analysis.

*User Interface and Modeling Capabilities*    The FENRIS program has its own batch-oriented pre- and postprocessors. However, through a coupling to the finite-element system SESAM'80, the use of sophisticated interactive and graphic pre- and postprocessors for generation of the finite-element model is enabled. See the entry for SESAM'80. The structural model can be divided into substructures. Different satellites, with their different facilities, may be used for the substructures. All elements may have eccentric attachment to the nodes.

*Notable Items and Limitations*    Distinguishing features:

- Method of handling large rotations
- Shell and plate elements included
- Load-handling philosophy
- Hydrostatic stability calculations and wave-loading modules
- Contact and friction elements
- Automatic incrementation of loads and time steps
- Coupling to the SESAM'80 system and its pre- and postprocessors

FENRIS imposes no limitations to the size of the problem to be solved. A dynamic allocation of working space implies that the only practical limitation is dictated by the computer resources available.

*Programming Language*    FORTRAN 77 (ANSI X3.9, 1978).

*Hardware and Operating System*    VAX (VMS), NORD (SINTRAN), IBM (OS/MVS), IBM (VM/SP), FPS.

*Program Size*    Total number of lines (including comments) = 160,000; total number of executable statements = 50,000.

*Documentation*    FENRIS: User's Manuals, April 1984. SESAM'80: Verification and Examples Manual, June 1984.

*Program Availability*    FENRIS is in executable form available for sale, leasing, and renting.

*FINITE/GP*

*Descriptive Program Title*   Finite-element analysis for the personal computer.

*Program Developer*   J. E. Akin
Department of Mechanical Engineering
Rice University
P.O. Box 1892
Houston, TX 77251
(and COADE, Inc., Houston, Texas)

*Approximate Number of Technical Staff Supporting the Program*   6.

*Date of First Release and Most Recent Update*   PC version, June 1984. Original, 1970. Update, June 1986.

*General Information*   A personal-computer (PC) analysis system designed to meet most of the needs of linear stress and thermal analyses. The program includes interactive graphics and free-field input which are designed to make the system user-friendly. Capability is limited mainly by PC memory size. Additional capabilities on mainframe versions supported by COADE, Inc., Houston, Texas.

*Program Capability*   Mesh generation, interactive graphics, potential flow, heat transfer, and stress analysis. Plate bending; thermal stresses; two-dimensional, axisymmetric, and three-dimensional elements. Employs curved isoparametric elements. Flexible boundary-condition options.

*User Interface and Modeling Capabilities*   Mesh generator. Interactive-graphics display of mesh, boundary, element numbers, node numbers, material codes, boundary conditions, etc. Interactive window, zoom, and rotations. Postprocessing includes interactive deformed mesh plot, contours, surfaces of temperatures, thermal gradients, von Mises stresses, etc. Interactive-stress file offered to search binary files.

*Notable Items and Limitations*   Current PC release is restricted to linear analysis. Linear and quadratic numerically integrated isoparametric elements are used. Problem size is limited by PC memory size. A 512K machine can treat about 2000 degrees of freedom.
Support via toll-free number.

*Programming Language*   FORTRAN.

*Hardware and Operating System*   IBM PC, IBM XT, and lookalikes. 512K memory and hard disk.

*Program Size*   14,000 statements.

*Documentation*   User's Manual, Verification Manual. Theory covered in detail in two texts (see J. E. Akin, *Application and Implementation of Finite Element Methods*, Academic Press, New York, 1983).

*Program Availability*　IBM PC Executable Version is $3500 from COADE, Inc., Houston, Texas; (713) 973-9060. Mainframe versions quoted on request. Academic PC version, $70 per year.

## LARSTRAN '80

*Descriptive Program Title*　Large-strain analysis.

*Program Developer*　Institut für Statik und Dynamik der Luft- und
　　　　　　　　　　　　Raumfahrtkonstruktionen
　　　　　　　　　　　　University of Stuttgart
　　　　　　　　　　　　West Germany

*Approximate Number of Technical Staff Supporting the Program*　6.

*Date of First Release and Most Recent Update*　First release, 1981. Current release is version 6.0, July 1986.

*General Information*　LARSTRAN 80 is a nonlinear finite-element system aimed at three levels of users: engineers in industry, development engineers who wish to compose their own algorithms for unforeseen capabilities, and scientists who want to develop and test new methods. The system therefore allows access on different levels:

- Library of standard computations
- Library of finite elements
- Pre- and postprocessors
- Standard out-of-core hypermatrix operations
- Data-base manager
- Standard in-core matrix operations

*Program Capability*　LARSTRAN 80 is a general-purpose finite-element system for nonlinear analysis of two- and three-dimensional structures coded in single- and double-precision. At present static, dynamic, buckling, eigenfrequencies and forms, and viscous-flow problems can be solved by standard tools. Both material and geometrical nonlinearities are included. Tools for symmetric and nonsymmetric matrices are available and automatic break and restart are supported. An extensive diagnostic system and a data-base management system are implemented.

*User Interface and Modeling Capabilities*　The user supplies the system with data in free format identified by keywords optionally by the use of automatic data generation. A control program set up by the user monitors input computation and output. Standardized user-written subroutines allow for an individual and easy introduction to, e.g., material laws. Several interactive-graphic systems can be connected for the case of data checking and representation of results. A postprocessor for plots is available.

*Notable Items and Limitations*　The system is designed as an "open system" allowing for easy extension of the element library (up to now some 80 elements) as well as for development of special processors using the tools available.

*Programming Language*   FORTRAN IV, FORTRAN 77.

*Hardware and Operating System*   CDC-CYBER NOS, NOS/BE; IBM 3033 MVS, CRAY-1M, UNIVAC 1100/60 OS 11 00 EXEC 38; VAX 11/780; PRIME.

*Program Size*   200,000 source statements.

*Documentation*   LAUM—LARSTRAN 80 User Manual, published as ISD Reports, University of Stuttgart; LAEL—LARSTRAN 80 Element Library; LAMO—LARSTRAN 80 Output Manual.

*Program Availability*   The system is distributed as relocatable code by LASSO, Nobel Str. 15, 7000 Stuttgart 80, West Germany. The price of the present version is dependent on desired range of facilities. For prices, contact distributors.


## MARC

*Descriptive Program Title*   General-purpose finite-element program.

*Program Developer*   MARC Analysis Research Corporation
260 Sheridan, Suite 200
Palo Alto, CA 94306
(415) 326-7511

*Approximate Number of Technical Staff*   20.

*Date of First Release and Most Recent Update*   First release, 1970. Latest revision: Revision K.2, August 1985.

*General Information*   MARC is a general-purpose finite-element system with strong emphasis on nonlinear problems. MARC is distributed and supported worldwide. Offices in the United States, Europe, and Japan are involved in development, quality assurance, and user support. The MARC program is used throughout the aerospace, automotive, manufacturing, energy, and construction industries.

Ease of use is provided through simple but powerful input, and automatic load or time incrementation is provided wherever possible. Output is user-controlled to different devices. Pre- and postprocessing are available inside MARC or through MENTAT in fully interactive mode. MENTAT directly reads MARC input and result files and writes MARC input. No translator programs are required.

*Program Capability*   Major features include elastoplastic, viscoelastic, incompressible, and anisotropic materials with temperature-dependent properties. Finite strains and rotations are handled without restrictions to small-load or displacement increments. Structural procedures are available for nonlinear static, dynamic, and diffusion problems with self-adaptive time- or load-step control. Fracture, nodal dynamics, postbuckling, coupled analyses, and substructuring capabilities are also available. Great flexibility is provided by user subroutines, restart, postprocessing file, output control, and result sorting and tabulation features. A strong element library with a wide variety of isoparametric and hybrid elements, including contact friction and pipe-bending elements, is available.

The nonlinear solution algorithms are robust and efficient for solving strongly nonlinear problems. Consistent input style with powerful set-naming capability for nodal and element referencing, permitting logical operations on multiple sets. Nonlinearities in material, geometry, and boundaries are handled simultaneously. Other features include low-tension and cracking behavior, arbitrary loading of axisymmetric solids and shells, automatic load stepping for quasi-static postbuckling, response-spectrum analysis, Joule heating, and hydrodynamic bearing capability.

*User Interface and Modeling Capabilities*   MARC offers mesh generation and incremental data generators as well as full pre- and postprocessing graphics capabilities built into the program. A full-feature interactive pre- and postprocessing program, MENTAT, is also offered. MENTAT supports interactive model building and loading, and material and boundary-condition specification. MENTAT reads and writes MARC input files and can accept MARC result files in binary or formatted form for deformed shape, contour, symbol, and variable-versus-variable plots.

*Notable Items and Limitations*   Recent emphasis has been placed on manufacturing problems such as metal forming. An updated lagrangian formulation that handles finite-element plasticity is implemented. A rezoning capability to remesh strongly distorted areas is also available.

Contact and friction along arbitrarily shaped, rigid boundaries can be modeled. Intermittent contact between different surfaces of the model is also possible.

Solution procedures include full Newton–Raphson, modified Newton–Raphson, and strain-correction algorithms. Convergence checking is done automatically. The user, however, may control the convergence measure and acceptable tolerances.

*Programming Language*   FORTRAN IV, compatible with FORTRAN 66 and FORTRAN 77.

*Hardware and Operating System*   CRAY: CTSS, COS; DEC/VAX: VMS; IBM: VS1, CMS; PRIME: PRIMOS; CYBER: NOS, NOS/BE; Data General: AOS/VS; UNIVAC: EXEC; HP 9000: HP-UX.

*Program Size*   20,000 lines, preprocessing; 55,000 lines, analysis; 15,000 lines, postprocessing; 10,000 lines, internal documentation.

*Documentation*   MARC User's Manual, vols. A to D; MARC Demonstration Manual; MARC Background Information Manual; MARC Systems Manual. All documentation is published by MARC Analysis Research Corporation, 260 Sheridan Avenue, Suite 200, Palo Alto, California 94306.

*Program Availability*   Monthly license: from $800 per month. Paid-up license: from $20,000; one-time fee. For details, contact developer.


## PAFEC

*Program Title*   Programs for Automatic Finite-Element Calculations.

*Program Developer*   PAFEC, Ltd.

*Approximate Number of Technical Staff Supporting the Program*   60.

*Date of First Release and Most Recent Update*   1970; new releases every 2 years.

*General Information*   PAFEC is a general-purpose finite-element system available in FORT-RAN source form. It offers free-format input using common engineering keywords. It was developed and is widely used in the United Kingdom. PAFEC is available for most main-frames, minis, and workstations. Worldwide support is offered; in the United States, consult PAFEC, Inc., Norcross, Georgia, (404) 441-9300. PAFEC interfaces to CAD system and offers interactive graphics with color.

*Program Capability*   Linear stress analysis, creep, plasticity, large deflections, vibrations, dynamics, frequency response, thermal analysis, substructuring, cyclic symmetry, mesh gener-ation, interactive graphics, interactive edit of data base, automatic resequencing of element order, large element family with more than 90 element types.

*User Interface and Modeling Capabilities*   Extensive interactive and batch-model generation modes are offered for two- and three-dimensional regions as well as surfaces. Manual input is via free-format system with numerous defaults. Digitizing input as well as CAD interface is included. Extensive postprocessing graphics options are offered in batch and interactive modes.

*Notable Items and Limitations*   The most notable feature of PAFEC is the user-friendliness (ease of use and quality documentation).

*Programming Language*   FORTRAN.

*Hardware and Operating System*   Almost all supercomputers, mainframes, superminis, and engineering workstations.

*Program Size*   400,000 source statements.

*Documentation*   Very high-quality manuals and pocket guides: System Manual, Data Prepa-ration Manual, Theory Manual, etc.

*Program Availability*   FORTRAN source, executable files, installation and training: PRIME, VAX, DG, etc., $38,500; IBM, CDC, DEC-20, etc., $44,100; CRAY, CDC-205, etc., $47,600. Contact PAFEC, Inc., Norcross, Georgia 30071, (404) 441-9300.


### SAMCEF

*Descriptive Program Title*   General system for linear and nonlinear static, dynamic, and thermal analyses.

*Program Developer*   L.T.A.S.
                       Aerospace Laboratory of the University of Liège
                       Belgium

*Approximate Number of Technical Staff Supporting the Program*   20.

*Date of First Release and Most Recent Update*   First release, 1965. Current release, September 1983.

*General Information*  SAMCEF is a general-purpose finite-element software system designed to meet the needs of researchers and design engineers. Development of SAMCEF began in 1965 and is constantly continuing in collaboration with industries. SAMCEF is being maintained in a highly reliable manner on all computers by a staff of 20 L.T.A.S. engineers. SAMCEF's users can expect rapid and effective service: new versions are released yearly, new features are introduced on demand, and analysts are assigned on request. New developments are directed at composite materials, fracture, and viscoplasticity.

*Program Capability*  SAMCEF is a general-purpose software system that uses the finite-element method to solve a wide variety of problems in structural static and dynamic analysis, heat transfer, and fluid mechanics. SAMCEF covers linear and nonlinear analyses. The modeling of composite materials is fairly sophisticated. The dynamic analysis of fluid-structure systems is possible with either incompressible or compressible fluids. Shape optimization and weight optimization are accessible for two-dimensional and axisymmetric structures. Both interactive and batch-processing modes are supported. Any size problem may be handled through the substructuring facilities, and the solution algorithms may be adapted to new computers.

*User Interface and Modeling Capabilities*  Geometry, temperature distribution, material properties, element connections, loads, and boundary conditions may be specified in very concise language interactively or in batch mode. Input-model plotting facilities are numerous: perspective, projection, blow-up, hidden-lines elimination, unfolding of skin structures. Most input errors are detected automatically. Output results may take the following forms: deformed structure, dynamic mode shape, contour plots, principal stresses.

*Notable Items and Limitations*  SAMCEF offers a very large range of applications. Several interfaces between SAMCEF and CAD systems are available. It is possible and easy to incorporate new element types. Several elements are particularly well adapted to model composite structures. In thermal analysis, explicit mesh deformation for modeling steep gradients and implicit mesh deformation for phase-change problems are included for one- and two-dimensional situations.

*Programming Language*  FORTRAN IV.

*Hardware and Operating System*  IBM (OS, DOS, VS, CMS), UNIVAC, CDC, VAX, SIEMENS, CRAY.

*Program Size*  300,000 statements.

*Documentation*  User's Manuals (13 volumes, in French).

*Program Availability*  Information may be obtained from:

L.T.A.S.
University of Liège
21, Rue E. Solvay
B-4000, Liège
Belgium

## SESAM'80

*Descriptive Program Title*  General-purpose structural-analysis system (superelement structural-analysis program modules).

*Program Developer*  Det norske Veritas in cooperation with the Norwegian Institute of Technology (NTH), the Foundation for Scientific and Industrial Research at the Norwegian Institute of Technology (SINTEF), and other Norwegian research institutes and companies. Since 1984 A.S VERITEC, a subsidiary of Det norske Veritas, has taken over the responsibilities of Det norske Veritas for SESAM'80.

*Approximate Number of Technical Staff Supporting the Program*  30.

*Date of First Release and Most Recent Update*  First release, 1980. Most recent update, April 1984.

*General Information*  SESAM'80 is a general-purpose structural-analysis program designed to meet the demands of today and the future. The development has been performed mainly with two goals in mind: to be a tool in the services offered by the classification society Det norske Veritas and its subsidiaries, and through sale, leasing, and renting to be available to structural analysts worldwide. SESAM'80 is marketed and supported by A.S VERITEC in Oslo, a subsidiary of Det norske Veritas, and by regional offices in London, Rotterdam, Houston, Kobe, and Singapore.

*Program Capability*  SESAM'80 performs linear analysis of two- and three-dimensional structures subjected to static or dynamic loading. For static analysis a multilevel superelement (substructuring) technique is available. For dynamic analysis alternative solution techniques are available: the Householder, subspace-iteration, and Lanczos methods for the free-vibration (eigenvalue) problem, and the modal-superposition, direct frequency-response, and direct time-integration methods for the harmonic or arbitrary time-dependent forced-response problem. The master-slave and component-mode synthesis reduction methods may be employed for reducing the size (number of degrees of freedom) of dynamic problems. An extensive element library contains all commonly used elements for trusses, beams, membranes, shells, solids, and axisymmetric solids. Spring and damper elements are available as well. In addition, a specially developed transition element is available for coupling the shell and solid elements. Environmental effects on marine structures may be accounted for, and the computed loads are automatically transferred to the analysis program. Included herein are wave forces on jackets, semisubmersibles, gravity platforms, ships, etc. Lastly, the effect of earthquake loading on frame structures may be calculated.

*User Interface and Modeling Capabilities*  The SESAM'80 preprocessors offer a highly automatic interactive and graphic generation of the finite-element model. A general-purpose preprocessor is available for beam, membrane, shell, and solid modeling. Special-purpose preprocessors deal with modeling of truss and frame structures, coupling of superelements, and modeling of complex tubular joints. For graphical and tabular presentation of the results a general-purpose postprocessor is available. Code checking of results for frame structures, e.g., jackets, is performed by a special-purpose postprocessor.

*Notable Items and Limitations*  SESAM'80 imposes no limitation on the size of the problems to be solved. Any number of degrees of freedom, elements, loading conditions, etc., may be employed. In fact, the only practical limitation in this respect is dictated by the computer resources available. Further, in SESAM'80 an unlimited number of superelements may be merged through an unlimited number of levels to form the complete model.

SESAM'80 is coupled to the general-purpose nonlinear program FENRIS. Together these systems offer a solution to practically any structural-analysis problem.

The modularity of SESAM'80 both facilitates debugging and makes the system prepared for modifications or incorporation of totally new capabilities. The modularity also enables an analyst to acquire just the facilities needed. SESAM'80 is thus a structural-analysis system for both the actual problems of today and the unknown tasks of tomorrow.

*Programming Language*   FORTRAN 77 (ANSI X3.9, 1978).

*Hardware and Operating System*   VAX (VMS), PRIME (PRIMOS), NORD (SINTRAN), IBM (OS/MVS), IBM (VM/SP), FPS, CRAY.

*Program Size*   Total number of lines (including comments) = 800,000; total number of executable statements = 400,000.

*Documentation*   General Description; Theoretical Manuals; User's Manuals; Verification and Examples Manual.

*Program Availability*   SESAM'80 is in executable form available for sale, leasing, and renting. Price is dependent on desired range of facilities.

## SMART

*Descriptive Program Title*   Thermomechanical analysis of massive structures.

*Program Developer*   SMART Group at ISD/ICA
University of Stuttgart
Stuttgart, West Germany

*Approximate Number of Technical Staff Supporting the Program*   3 to 4.

*Date of First Release and Most Recent Update*   First release, 1976. Current release, Version 5.0/1984.

*General Information*   Finite-element analysis of thick-walled structures; fully compatible coupled thermomechanical problems. SMART I: Static Package (inelastic behavior, creep, cracking, fracture); SMART II: Diffusion Package (nonlinear, transient heat conduction and moisture migration, coupled; radiation).

*Program Capability*   There is no size limitation with the substructuring technique. Integrated coupled thermal stress analysis is offered. A comprehensive element library includes 13 point, line, surface, and solid isoparametric elements for two-dimensional, axisymmetric, and three-dimensional comprehensive material models for thermoviscoelasticity and aging creep, triaxial strength and deformation behavior, coupled heat and moisture transport, and radiation interchange (release 1985).

*User Interface and Modeling Capabilities*   SMART includes sophisticated coordinate, topological, and incidence data generation that minimizes the need for preprocessors. Interactive-graphic system INGA is fully compatible with SMART for postprocessing, i.e., displacement, stress, principal stress, and temperature, and contours, isolines, and vector plotting.

*Notable Items and Limitations* SMART includes the finite-element displacement method, incremental linearization, iterative correction (predictor-correction scheme), initial load approach for inelastic behavior, unconditionally stable time operators for inelastic analysis and transient-diffusion analysis, restart capability.

*Programming Language* ANSI 66 FORTRAN IV; few Assembler routines.

*Hardware and Operating System* CDC 6600/CYBER 174, 170-835; UNIVAC 1108; IBM 370/168; VAX 750-780.

*Program Size* 200,000 FORTRAN statements.

*Documentation* Eight User's Manuals: (1) Statics, (2) Creep, (3) Ultimate Load, (4) Diffusion, (5) Instationary Diffusion, (6) Radiation Interchange, (7) Program Control Manual, and (8) Error Messages.

*Program Availability* SMART is available in three categories: for universities, research institutes, and commercial applications. For prices contact developers.

*References*

1. J. H. Argyris, G. Faust, J. R. Roy, J. Szimmat, E. P. Warnke, and K. J. William, "Finite Elemente zur Berechnung von Spannbetonreaktordruckbehältern," DafStB Heft 234, 1973; also ISD Rep. 137.
2. "SMART I—Lineare Elastostatik, Benutzerhandbuch," ISD-Bericht No. 186, Stuttgart, 1976.
3. J. Szimmat, "SMART II, 2—Instationäre Diffusion, Benutzerhandbuch," ISD-Bericht No. 192, Stuttgart, 1979.
4. J. Szimmat, "SMART II, 3—Strahlungsaustausch," ICA Bericht No. 15, Stuttgart, 1986.

## *TUJAP*

*Descriptive Program Title* Tubular joints analysis program for elastoplastics and fracture mechanics.

*Program Developer* Det norske Veritas in cooperation with the Foundation for Scientific and Industrial Research at the Norwegian Institute of Technology (SINTEF). Since 1984 A.S VERITEC, a subsidiary of Det norske Veritas, has taken over the responsibilities of Det norske Veritas for TUJAP.

*Approximate Number of Technical Staff Supporting the Program* 4.

*Date of First Release and Most Recent Update* First release, May 1984. Most recent update, August 1984.

*General Information* TUJAP (Tubular Joints Analysis Program) is a program for elastoplastic and fracture-mechanics analysis of tubular joints as they are used, e.g., in offshore jacket structures. TUJAP is marketed and supported by A.S VERITEC in Oslo, a subsidiary of Det norske Veritas, and by regional offices in London, Rotterdam, Houston, Kobe, and Singapore.

*Program Capability* TUJAP performs elastoplastic static analysis of tubular joints. Highly complex joints with or without concrete grout may be treated. The joint is modeled either by 20-node solid elements, 8-node shell elements, or a combination of both. In the latter case, a specially developed transition element is applied for coupling the shell and solid elements. The grout, if present, is modeled by solid elements and connected to the steel-tube elements by a specially developed gap element. The welds are modeled by solid elements with a geometry according to the rules of the American Welding Society. Arbitrarily shaped cracks may be inserted in the model. Elliptic cracks are inserted by an automatic generation of the refined element mesh of the crack tip and the transition to the coarser mesh of the global structure. The local stresses and stress-intensity factors of the crack tip are computed by the program. Elastoplastic material behavior may be specified both for the steel tube and concrete grout. A multilevel superelement technique is a basic feature of the program.

*User Interface and Modeling Capabilities* The TUJAP preprocessor offers a highly automatic interactive and graphic generation of the finite-element model of the tubular joint. With a minimum of user input, such as tube radii and thicknesses and their relative position in space, all intersection curves and a complete finite-element model is generated. For graphical and tabular presentation of the results a general-purpose postprocessor is available.

*Notable Items and Limitations* TUJAP imposes no limitation on the size of the problems to be solved. Any number of degrees of freedom, elements, loading conditions, etc., may be employed. In fact, the only practical limitation in this respect is dictated by the computer resources available.

The most distinguishing features of TUJAP are:

- Automatic generation of the model. Multiple plane joints may be generated and the tubes may overlap each other. The meshing procedure gives a smooth transition between a coarse and a refined mesh.

- Large range of strategies for solving the elastoplastic problem.

- Multilevel superelement technique employed.

TUJAP is coupled to the general-purpose structural-analysis system SESAM'80.

*Programming Language* FORTRAN 77 (ANSI X3.9, 1978).

*Hardware and Operating System* VAX (VMS), NORD (SINTRAN), IBM (OS/MVS), IBM (VM/SP), FPS, CRAY.

*Program Size* Total number of lines (including comments) = 200,000; total number of executable statements = 100,000.

*Documentation* General Description, Theoretical Manuals, User's Manuals, Verification and Examples Manual.

*Program Availability* TUJAP is in executable form available for sale, leasing, and renting.

## 5.5B Program Capabilities and Comparisons

The capabilities of the programs are shown in Tables 5.1 to 5.5.

**TABLE 5.1**  Finite-Element System Features

| | | ABAQUS | ADINA | ANSYS | ASKA | EAL | FENRIS | FINITE/GP | LARSTRAN '80 | MARC | PAFEC | SAMCEF | SESAM '80 | SMART | TUJAP |
|---|---|---|---|---|---|---|---|---|---|---|---|---|---|---|---|
| 1. | *Goal of program system* | | | | | | | | | | | | | | |
| | General purpose | • | • | • | • | • | • | | • | • | • | • | • | • | |
| | Commercial | • | • | • | • | • | • | • | • | • | • | • | • | • | • |
| | Research | | • | • | • | • | • | | • | | • | • | • | • | • |
| | Educational | | • | • | • | • | • | • | • | | • | | • | | • |
| | Other (see Sec. 5.5A) | | | | | | | | | | | | | | |
| 2. | *Program operational on:* | | | | | | | | | | | | | | |
| | a) Supercomputers | | | | | | | | | | | | | | |
| | CRAY | • | • | • | • | • | | | • | • | • | • | • | | • |
| | CDC CYBER 203, 205 | • | • | • | | | | | | • | • | | | | |
| | Denelcor HEP | | | | | | | | | | • | | | | |

4.281

**TABLE 5.1**  Finite-Element System Features (*Continued*)

2.

| | ABAQUS | ADINA | ANSYS | ASKA | EAL | FENRIS | FINITE/GP | LARSTRAN '80 | MARC | PAFEC | SAMCEF | SESAM '80 | SMART | TUJAP |
|---|---|---|---|---|---|---|---|---|---|---|---|---|---|---|
| *b) Mainframes* | | | | | | | | | | | | | | |
| CDC | • | • | • | • | • | | • | • | • | • | • | | • | |
| IBM | • | • | • | • | | • | • | • | • | • | • | • | • | • |
| UNIVAC | • | • | • | • | • | | | • | • | • | • | | • | |
| Honeywell | | • | • | • | | | | | | • | | | | |
| Burroughs | | • | | • | | | | | | • | | | | |
| ICL | • | • | | • | | | | | | • | | | | |
| DEC | • | • | | • | • | • | • | • | • | • | | • | | • |
| Amdahl | • | • | • | • | | | | | • | • | • | | | |
| Fujitsu | • | • | • | | | | | | • | | | | | |
| Others (see Sec. 5.5A) | • | • | • | | • | | | | • | | • | | | |
| *c) Minicomputers* | | | | | | | | | | | | | | |
| VAX | • | • | • | • | • | • | • | • | • | • | • | • | • | • |
| PRIME | • | • | • | • | • | | | • | • | • | | • | | |

The following is a checklist matrix (rotated on the page). Rows are the category labels; columns (unlabeled on this page, continued from preceding pages — representing individual software packages) carry bullet (•) marks.

| Category | 1 | 2 | 3 | 4 | 5 | 6 | 7 | 8 | 9 | 10 | 11 | 12 |
|---|---|---|---|---|---|---|---|---|---|---|---|---|
| PDP |  |  |  |  | • |  |  |  |  |  | • | • |
| HP |  |  |  |  | • | • |  |  |  |  | • | • |
| Others (see Sec. 5.5A) | • |  | • |  | • | • |  |  | • |  | • | • |
| *d) Workstations and desktop computers* |  |  |  |  |  |  |  |  |  |  |  |  |
| Apollo |  |  |  |  | • | • |  |  |  | • | • | • |
| IBM PC, XT, and AT |  |  |  |  |  |  |  | • |  |  |  |  |
| Radio Shack (Tandy) |  |  |  |  |  |  |  |  |  |  |  |  |
| Sun Microsystem |  |  |  |  | • | • |  |  |  |  | • | • |
| Apple |  |  |  |  |  |  |  |  |  |  |  |  |
| Commodore |  |  |  |  |  |  |  |  |  |  |  |  |
| Others (see Sec. 5.5A) |  |  |  |  |  |  |  |  |  |  | • |  |
| **3. Documentation** |  |  |  |  |  |  |  |  |  |  |  |  |
| Programmer's Manual | • |  | • |  | • | • | • |  | • | • | • | • |
| Theoretical Manual | • | • | • | • | • | • | • | • | • | • | • | • |
| Data Preparation—User's Manual | • | • | • | • | • | • | • | • | • | • | • | • |
| Example Problems Manual |  | • |  | • | • | • | • |  | • | • | • | • |
| Verification/Validation Manual | • | • | • | • | • | • | • | • | • | • | • | • |
| Pre- and Postprocessor Manual | • | • | • | • | • | • | • | • | • | • | • | • |

**TABLE 5.2** Structural and Solid-Mechanics Applications

| 1. Types of elements* | ABAQUS | ADINA | ANSYS | ASKA | EAL | FENRIS | FINITE/GP | LARSTRAN '80 | MARC | PAFEC | SAMCEF | SESAM '80 | SMART | TUJAP |
|---|---|---|---|---|---|---|---|---|---|---|---|---|---|---|
| Three-dimensional rod element | LGM | LGM | LGM | LM | LG | LGM | | LGM | LGM | LG | LGM | L | LM | |
| Three-dimensional beam element | LGM | LGM | LGM | LM | LG | LGM | L | LGM | LGM | LG | L | L | | |
| Plane stress | LGM | LGM | LGM | LM | LG | LGM | L | | LGM | LGM | LGM | L | LM | |
| Plane strain | LGM | LGM | LGM | LM | LG | LGM | L | LGM | LGM | LGM | LGM | L | LM | |
| Membranes in space | | LGM | LGM | LM | LG | LGM | | LGM | LGM | LGM | L | L | LM | |
| Shear panels | | LGM | LGM | LM | LG | LGM | | | LGM | | L | L | | |
| Plates | LGM | LGM | LGM | LM | LG | LGM | L | LGM | LGM | LGM | L | L | | |
| Thin shells | LGM | LGM | LGM | LM | LG | LGM | | LGM | LGM | LGM | L | L | | |
| Thick shells | LGM | LGM | LGM | LM | | LGM | | LGM | LGM | LGM | LGM | L | | M |
| Shells of revolution | LGM | LGM | LGM | LM | | LGM | | | LGM | LG | LGM | L | | |
| Axisymmetric solids | LGM | LGM | LGM | LM | LG | LGM | L | LGM | LGM | LGM | LGM | L | LM | |
| Three-dimensional solids | LGM | LGM | LGM | LM | LG | LGM | L | LGM | LGM | LGM | LGM | L | LM | M |

*L = linear analysis only; G = geometric nonlinearity only; GM = combined geometric and material nonlinearity; M = material nonlinearity only; LGM = L, G, M, GM.

| | | | | | | | | | | | | | | | | |
|---|---|---|---|---|---|---|---|---|---|---|---|---|---|---|---|---|
| | Discrete stiffeners (for plates and shells) | | LGM | LGM | LGM | LM | LG | LGM | | | LGM | LG | L | L | | |
| | Boundary element | | LGM | LGM | LGM | | | | | | LGM | L | | | | |
| | Gap element | | LGM | LGM | LGM | | LM | LGM | | | LGM | LGM | LG | | | M |
| | Others (see Sec. 5.5A) | | LGM | LGM | | | | | L | | LGM | | | L | LM | M |
| 2. | *Range of applications and phenomena* | | | | | | | | | | | | | | | |
| | Linear statics | | • | • | • | • | • | • | • | • | • | • | • | • | • | • |
| | Eigenvalue problems | Free vibrations | • | • | • | • | • | | | • | • | • | • | • | • | • |
| | | Bifurcation buckling | • | • | • | • | • | | | • | • | • | • | | | |
| | Nonlinear statics | Nonlinear response | • | • | • | | • | • | | • | • | • | • | | | • |
| | | Postbuckling and nonlinear collapse | • | • | • | | • | • | | • | • | • | • | | | |
| | | Nonlinear contact problems | • | • | • | • | • | • | | • | • | • | • | | | • |
| | Nonlinear Dynamics | Nonlinear vibrations | • | • | • | | • | • | | • | • | • | • | | | |
| | | Transient response | • | • | • | | • | • | | • | • | • | • | | | |
| | | Wave propagation | • | • | | | | • | | | | • | | | | |
| | Nonlinear interaction problems | Fluid-structure interaction | • | • | • | | • | • | | | • | • | • | | | |
| | | Thermal-mechanical coupling | • | • | • | | • | | | | • | • | | | • | |
| | | Combustion-mechanical coupling | | | | | | | | | | | | | | |

TABLE 5.2  Structural and Solid-Mechanics Applications (*Continued*)

| | | ABAQUS | ADINA | ANSYS | ASKA | EAL | FENRIS | FINITE/GP | LARSTRAN '80 | MARC | PAFEC | SAMCEF | SESAM '80 | SMART | TUJAP |
|---|---|---|---|---|---|---|---|---|---|---|---|---|---|---|---|
| 2. | | | | | | | | | | | | | | | |
| | Large strain plasticity (or viscoplasticity problems) — Static | • | • | | • | | • | | • | • | • | | | | |
| | Dynamic | • | • | | | | • | | • | • | | | | | |
| | Sensitivity calculations (derivatives of response quantities with respect to design variables) for: Linear static response | | | | | • | | | | | | • | | | |
| | Free vibrations | | | | | • | | | | | | | | | |
| | Bifurcation buckling | | | | | • | | | | | | | | | |
| | Linear dynamic response | | | | | • | | | | | | | | | |
| 3. | *Formulation* | | | | | | | | | | | | | | |
| | a) *Fundamental unknowns* | | | | | | | | | | | | | | |
| | Displacement method | • | • | • | • | • | • | • | • | • | • | • | • | • | • |
| | Force method | | | | | | | | | | | | | | |
| | Hybrid method | | | | | • | | | | | • | | | | |
| | Mixed method | • | • | | | | | • | | • | | | | | |
| | Others (see Sec. 5.5A) | | | | | | | | | | | | | | |

Comparison matrix (rotated table). Row labels and section structure:

| Category | Subcategory | Detail | Program columns (•) |
|---|---|---|---|
| **b) Reference frame** | | | |
| | Total lagrangian | | • • |
| | Updated lagrangian | | • • • • • • • • |
| | Eulerian | | • • • • |
| | Others (see Sec. 5.5A) | | • • |
| **4. Solution techniques** | | | |
| | Nonlinear statics | Incremental (noniterative) | • • • • • • • • • • • |
| | | Newton-type methods | • • • • • • • • • • |
| | | Others (see Sec. 5.5A) | • • • • |
| | Nonlinear dynamics | Modal superposition | • • • |
| | | Direct integration — Explicit schemes | • • • • • • |
| | | Direct integration — Implicit schemes | • • • • • • • |
| | | Direct integration — Combined explicit implicit | • • • |
| | | Others (see Sec. 5.5A) | • |
| **5. Types of loading** | | | |
| | Concentrated loads | | • • • • • • • • • • • • • |
| | Line loads | | • • • • • • • • • • • • • |

4.287

**TABLE 5.2** Structural and Solid-Mechanics Applications (*Continued*)

| 5. | ABAQUS | ADINA | ANSYS | ASKA | EAL | FENRIS | FINITE/GP | LARSTRAN '80 | MARC | PAFEC | SAMCEF | SESAM '80 | SMART | TUJAP |
|---|---|---|---|---|---|---|---|---|---|---|---|---|---|---|
| Axisymmetric loads | • | • | • | • | • | • | • | • | • | • | • | • | • | |
| Surface loads | • | • | • | • | • | • | • | • | • | • | • | • | • | • |
| Volume loads | • | • | • | • | • | • | • | • | • | • | • | • | • | • |
| Gravity loads | • | • | • | • | • | • | • | • | • | • | • | • | • | • |
| Initial stresses, strains, or velocities | • | • | • | • | • | • | | • | • | • | • | • | • | • |
| Thermal loading | • | • | • | • | • | • | • | • | • | • | • | • | • | • |
| Centrifugal loading | • | • | • | • | • | • | • | • | • | • | • | • | | |
| Deformation-dependent loading (e.g., live load) | • | • | • | | • | • | | • | • | • | • | | • | |
| Cyclic loading | • | • | • | • | • | • | | | • | | • | • | | |
| Random loading | | | • | • | • | | | | | • | | | | |
| Gyroscopic loading | • | • | | | • | | | | | • | | | | |
| Nonproportional loading | • | • | • | • | | • | | • | • | • | • | | • | |
| Contact loading | • | • | • | • | | • | | | • | • | • | | | |
| Others (see Sec. 5.5A) | • | • | | | | • | | | • | | | | | |

4.288

| 6. Support conditions and constraints | | | | | | | | | | | | |
|---|---|---|---|---|---|---|---|---|---|---|---|---|
| Axisymmetric | | • | • | • | • | • | • | • | • | • | • | • |
| At boundaries | • | • | • | • | • | • | • | • | • | • | • | • |
| At internal points | • | • | • | • | • | • | • | • | • | • | • | • |
| Prescribed displacements | • | • | • | • | • | • | • | • | • | • | • | • |
| Sliding interfaces | • | • | • | • | | • | | | • | • | • | • |
| Support at contact points | • | • | • | • | • | • | | | • | • | • | • |
| Elastic foundation | • | • | • | • | • | • | | • | | • | • | • |
| Frictional forces | • | • | | • | • | • | • | | • | • | • | • |
| Multipoint constraints | | • | | • | • | | • | • | | • | • | • |
| Cyclic symmetry | • | • | • | | • | | • | | • | • | • | |
| Others (see Sec. 5.5A) | | | | | | | | | | | | • |
| 7. Material properties, material models, and wall construction | | | | | | | | | | | | |
| Isotropic | • | • | • | • | • | • | • | • | • | • | • | • |
| Anisotropic | • | • | • | • | • | • | • | • | • | • | • | • |
| Multilayered | | • | | • | • | • | • | | • | • | • | • |
| Nonhomogeneous | | • | | | • | • | • | • | | • | • | • |

**TABLE 5.2  Structural and Solid-Mechanics Applications (Continued)**

| 7. | ABAQUS | ADINA | ANSYS | ASKA | EAL | FENRIS | FINITE/GP | LARSTRAN '80 | MARC | PAFEC | SAMCEF | SESAM '80 | SMART | TUJAP |
|---|---|---|---|---|---|---|---|---|---|---|---|---|---|---|
| Temperature-dependent elastic properties | • | • | • |  | • |  |  | • | • | • | • |  | • |  |
| Temperature-dependent plastic or viscoplastic properties | • | • | • |  |  |  |  | • | • | • | • |  | • |  |
| Linear elastic | • | • | • | • | • | • | • | • | • | • | • | • | • | • |
| Nonlinear elastic | • | • | • |  |  | • |  | • | • | • | • |  | • | • |
| Elastic-perfectly plastic | • | • | • | • |  | • |  | • | • | • | • |  | • | • |
| Elastic-strain hardening | • | • |  | • |  | • |  | • | • | • | • |  |  | • |
| Viscoelastic | • |  | • |  |  |  |  |  | • | • | • |  |  |  |
| Viscoplastic | • | • | • | • |  |  |  | • | • |  |  |  | • |  |
| High-temperature creep | • | • | • | • |  |  |  |  | • | • |  |  | • |  |
| Others (see Sec. 5.5A) | • | • |  |  |  |  |  |  | • |  |  |  |  |  |

**TABLE 5.3**  Heat-Transfer Applications

| | TUJAP | SMART | SESAM '80 | SAMCEF | PAFEC | MARC | LARSTRAN '80 | FINITE/GP | FENRIS | EAL | ASKA | ANSYS | ADINA | ABAQUS |
|---|---|---|---|---|---|---|---|---|---|---|---|---|---|---|
| **1. Space dimensionality** | | | | | | | | | | | | | | |
| Three-dimensional | | ● | | ● | ● | ● | | ● | | ● | ● | ● | ● | ● |
| Two-dimensional | | ● | | ● | ● | ● | | ● | | ● | ● | ● | ● | ● |
| Solids of revolution | | ● | | ● | ● | ● | | ● | | ● | ● | ● | ● | ● |
| Boundary elements | | ● | | ● | ● | | | ● | | ● | ● | ● | ● | ● |
| Scalar elements | | ● | | ● | | | | | | ● | ● | ● | ● | ● |
| Point-contact elements | | ● | | ● | ● | ● | | | | ● | | ● | ● | ● |
| Others (see Sec. 5.5A) | | | | ● | | | | | | | | | ● | ● |
| **2. Range of applications and phenomena** | | | | | | | | | | | | | | |
| Linear steady state | | ● | | ● | ● | ● | | ● | | ● | ● | ● | ● | ● |
| Nonlinear steady state | | ● | | ● | ● | ● | | | | ● | ● | ● | ● | ● |
| Thermal frequencies and mode shapes | | ● | | ● | | | | | | ● | | | ● | |
| Linear transient response | | ● | | ● | ● | ● | | ● | | ● | ● | ● | ● | ● |

4.291

**TABLE 5.3**  Heat-Transfer Applications (*Continued*)

| | | ABAQUS | ADINA | ANSYS | ASKA | EAL | FENRIS | FINITE/GP | LARSTRAN '80 | MARC | PAFEC | SAMCEF | SESAM '80 | SMART | TUJAP |
|---|---|---|---|---|---|---|---|---|---|---|---|---|---|---|---|
| 2. | Nonlinear transient response | • | • | • | • | • | | | | • | • | • | | • | |
| | Sensitivity calculations (derivatives of response quantities with respect to design variables) for: Linear steady-state response | | | | | • | | | | | | | | | |
| | Thermal frequencies and mode shapes | | | | | • | | | | | | | | | |
| | Linear transient response | | | | | • | | | | | | | | | |
| | Nonlinear transient response | | | | | • | | | | | | | | | |
| | Others (see Sec. 5.5A) | • | | | | | | | | | | • | | | |
| 3. | *Formulation* | | | | | | | | | | | | | | |
| | *a) Fundamental unknowns* | | | | | | | | | | | | | | |
| | Temperatures | • | • | • | • | • | | • | | • | • | • | | • | |
| | Temperatures and flux | | | | | | | | | | | | | | |
| | Enthalpy | | | | | | | | | | | | | | |
| | Others (see Sec. 5.5A) | | | | | | | | | | | | | • | |

**b) Elemental matrices**

| Feature | 1 | 2 | 3 | 4 | 5 | 6 | 7 | 8 | 9 | 10 | 11 |
|---|---|---|---|---|---|---|---|---|---|---|---|
| Conduction | • | • | • | • |  | • |  | • | • | • | • |
| Capacitance — 1) Consistent | • | • | • | • |  | • |  | • | • | • | • |
| 2) Lumped |  | • | • | • |  |  |  | • | • | • | • |
| Convection — 1) Free | • | • | • | • | • | • |  | • | • | • | • |
| 2) Forced |  | • |  | • |  | • |  | • | • | • | • |
| Radiation | • | • | • | • |  | • |  | • | • | • | • |
| Interelement convection and radiation | • | • |  |  |  | • |  | • |  |  | • |
| User-supplied elements (see Sec. 5.5A) | • |  | • |  |  | • |  |  | • |  |  |
| Others (see Sec. 5.5A) |  |  |  | • |  |  |  |  |  |  |  |

**4. Material properties and material models**

| Feature | 1 | 2 | 3 | 4 | 5 | 6 | 7 | 8 | 9 | 10 | 11 |
|---|---|---|---|---|---|---|---|---|---|---|---|
| Isotropic | • | • | • | • |  | • |  | • | • | • | • |
| Anisotropic | • | • | • | • |  | • |  | • | • | • | • |
| Multilayered |  |  | • | • |  |  |  | • | • | • | • |
| Temperature-dependent properties — Conductivity | • | • | • | • |  |  |  | • | • | • | • |
| Specific heat | • | • | • | • |  |  |  | • | • | • | • |
| Density | • | • | • |  |  |  |  | • |  | • | • |
| Absorptivity (emissivity factors) | • | • |  |  |  |  |  | • | • | • |  |
| Convection coefficients | • | • | • | • |  |  |  | • |  | • | • |

**TABLE 5.3** Heat-Transfer Applications (*Continued*)

| | ABAQUS | ADINA | ANSYS | ASKA | EAL | FENRIS | FINITE/GP | LARSTRAN '80 | MARC | PAFEC | SAMCEF | SESAM '80 | SMART | TUJAP |
|---|---|---|---|---|---|---|---|---|---|---|---|---|---|---|
| **4.** | | | | | | | | | | | | | | |
| Perfect conductors (via multipoint constraints) | • | | • | | • | | • | | • | • | • | | • | |
| Time-dependent thermal properties | • | • | • | | • | | | | • | • | • | | • | |
| Latent heat and phase change effects | • | • | • | | | | | | • | | • | | • | |
| Material added or removed during analysis | • | • | | | | | | | • | | • | | • | |
| User-supplied (see Sec. 5.5A) | • | | | | | | | | • | | | | • | |
| Others (see Sec. 5.5A) | | | | | | | | | | | | | | |
| **5.** *Initial conditions* | | | | | | | | | | | | | | |
| Homogeneous | • | • | • | • | • | | | | • | • | • | | • | |
| Varying throughout the region | • | • | • | • | • | | | | • | • | • | | • | |
| Initial enthalpy (for phase change) | | • | • | • | | | | | • | • | • | | • | |
| User-supplied | | | | | | | | | | | | | | |
| Others (see Sec. 5.5A) | | | | | | | | | | | | | | |

| 6. | Boundary conditions and thermal loads | | | | | | | | | | | | | | | |
|---|---|---|---|---|---|---|---|---|---|---|---|---|---|---|---|---|
| Prescribed Temperatures | a) Steady-state | • | • | • | • | • | • | • | • | • | • | • | • | • | • | • |
| | b) Time-dependent | • | • | • | • | • | • | • | • | • | • | • | • | • | • | • |
| Thermal flux input | a) Steady | • | • | • | • | • | • | • | • | | • | • | • | | • | • |
| | b) Temperature-dependent | • | • | • | | | | • | • | | • | • | | | • | |
| | c) Time-varying | • | • | • | • | • | | • | • | | • | • | • | | • | • |
| Convection from a surface to its surroundings | a) Steady-state | • | • | • | • | • | • | • | • | | • | • | • | • | • | • |
| | b) Time-dependent | • | • | • | • | • | | • | • | | • | • | | | • | • |
| Convection from surroundings to a surface | a) Steady-state | • | • | • | • | • | | • | • | | • | • | • | | • | • |
| | b) Time-dependent | • | • | • | • | • | | • | • | | • | • | | | • | • |
| Forced convection | | • | • | • | • | • | | • | • | | • | • | • | | • | • |
| Radiation from a surface to its surroundings | a) Steady-state | • | • | • | • | • | | • | • | | • | • | • | • | • | • |
| | b) Time-dependent | • | • | • | • | • | | • | • | | • | • | | | • | • |
| Radiation from surroundings to a surface | a) Steady-state | • | • | • | • | • | | • | • | | • | • | | • | • | • |
| | b) Time-dependent | • | • | • | • | • | | • | • | | • | • | | • | • | • |
| Radiation between narrow gaps | | • | • | • | • | • | | • | • | | • | • | | • | • | • |
| Radiation between n surfaces with: | a) User-supplied view factors | • | • | • | | | | • | | | • | • | | | • | • |
| | b) Internally calculated view factors | • | | | | | | • | | | | | | | | • |

**TABLE 5.3** Heat-Transfer Applications (*Continued*)

| | ABAQUS | ADINA | ANSYS | ASKA | EAL | FENRIS | FINITE/GP | LARSTRAN '80 | MARC | PAFEC | SAMCEF | SESAM '80 | SMART | TUJAP |
|---|---|---|---|---|---|---|---|---|---|---|---|---|---|---|
| **6.** | | | | | | | | | | | | | | |
| Prescribed fluid flow | | | • | | • | | | | | | | | | |
| Boundary-layer convection | | • | | | | | | | | | | | | |
| Volumetric heat generation   *a*) On element level | • | • | • | • | • | | • | | • | • | • | | • | |
|   *b*) On node level | • | | • | • | • | | | | | | | | | |
| Gap (thermal resistance) | • | | • | | | | | | • | | • | | • | |
| Boundary conditions and loads added or removed during analysis | • | • | • | • | • | | | | • | • | | | • | |
| Others (see Sec. 5.5A) | | | | | | | | | | | | | | |
| **7.** *Solution techniques* | | | | | | | | | | | | | | |
| Linear steady state   *a*) Direct | • | • | • | • | • | | • | | • | • | • | | • | |
|   *b*) Iterative | | | | | | | | | | • | • | | | |
|   *c*) Others (see Sec. 5.5A) | | | | | | | | | | | | | | |
| Nonlinear steady state   *a*) Incremental | • | • | | | | | | | • | | | | | |
|   *b*) Iterative | • | • | • | • | • | | | | • | • | • | | • | |
|   *c*) Others (see Sec. 5.5A) | | | | | | | | | | | | | | |

| | | | | P1 | P2 | P3 | P4 | P5 | P6 | P7 | P8 | P9 | P10 |
|---|---|---|---|---|---|---|---|---|---|---|---|---|---|
| Transient | a) Thermal mode superposition | | | | • | | | | | | | | |
| | b) Direct integration | 1) Explicit | | • | • | | | | • | • | | • | |
| | | 2) Implicit | User-specified time step | • | • | • | • | | • | | • | • | • |
| | | | Automatic time step selection | | | • | • | | • | | • | | • |
| | | 3) Combined explicit and implicit | | | | | | | • | | | | |
| | c) Finite elements in the time domain | | | | • | | | | | | | | |
| | d) Moving and deforming grids | | | | | | | | | | | | |
| | e) Others (see Sec. 5.5A) | | | | | | | | | | | | |
| **8.** | *Other capabilities* | | | | | | | | | | | | |
| | Thermal-stress analysis | a) Uncoupled | | • | • | • | • | • | • | • | • | • | • |
| | | b) Coupled | | • | | | • | | | | | | |
| | Transmission of temperature field data directly from heat transfer modules to thermal stress modules | | | • | • | • | • | • | • | • | • | • | • |
| | Enclosure radiation with view factor calculation | | | | | • | • | • | • | • | • | • | |
| | Heat input/output at constrained boundaries | | | • | | • | | | | | • | | |
| | Cyclic symmetry | | | | | • | | | | | | | |

**TABLE 5.3**  Heat-Transfer Applications (*Continued*)

| | | ABAQUS | ADINA | ANSYS | ASKA | EAL | FENRIS | FINITE/GP | LARSTRAN '80 | MARC | PAFEC | SAMCEF | SESAM '80 | SMART | TUJAP |
|---|---|---|---|---|---|---|---|---|---|---|---|---|---|---|---|
| 8. | Substructuring  *a*) Repeated use of identical substructures | • | | • | • | | | | | • | • | | | • | |
| | *b*) Mixing of linear and nonlinear substructures | • | | | • | | | | | • | • | • | | • | |
| | *c*) Mixing of substructures with different types of nonlinearities | • | | • | | | | | | • | | • | | • | |
| | Restart | • | • | • | • | • | | | | • | • | • | | • | |
| | Others (see Sec. 5.5A) | | | | | | | | | | | • | | | |

**TABLE 5.4**  Fatigue and Fracture-Mechanics Applications

| 1. | Types of elements* | ABAQUS | ADINA | ANSYS | ASKA | EAL | FENRIS | FINITE/GP | LARSTRAN '80 | MARC | PAFEC | SAMCEF | SESAM '80 | SMART | TUJAP |
|---|---|---|---|---|---|---|---|---|---|---|---|---|---|---|---|
| | Plane stress | • | S | S | S | | | | | | S | | | | |
| | Plane strain | • | S | S | • | | | | | • | S | | | | |
| | Plates | • | • | | • | | | | | • | | | | | |
| | Thin shells | • | • | | • | | | | | • | | | | | |
| | Thick shells | • | • | | • | | | | | • | | | | | |
| | Shells of revolution | • | • | | • | | | | | • | | | | | |
| | Axisymmetric solids | • | S | S | S | | | | | • | S | | | | |
| | Three-dimensional solids | • | S | S | • | | | | | • | S | | | | S |

* Add S for singular elements

**TABLE 5.4** Fatigue and Fracture-Mechanics Applications (*Continued*)

| | | ABAQUS | ADINA | ANSYS | ASKA | EAL | FENRIS | FINITE/GP | LARSTRAN '80 | MARC | PAFEC | SAMCEF | SESAM '80 | SMART | TUJAP |
|---|---|---|---|---|---|---|---|---|---|---|---|---|---|---|---|
| 2. | *Range of applications* | | | | | | | | | | | | | | |
| | Fracture mechanics — Linear statics | • | • | • | • | | | | | • | • | | | | • |
| | Nonlinear statics | • | • | • | • | | | | | • | • | | | | |
| | Linear dynamics | | • | • | | | | | | | | | | | |
| | Nonlinear dynamics | | • | • | | | | | | | | | | | |
| | Fatigue | | • | • | | | | | | | | | | | |
| 3. | *Formulation* | | | | | | | | | | | | | | |
| | Displacement | • | • | • | • | | | | | • | • | | | | • |
| | Stress (force) | | | | | | | | | | | | | | |
| | Hybrid | | | | | | | | | | | | | | |
| | Mixed | • | • | | | | | | | | | | | | |

| | | C1 | C2 | C3 | C4 | C5 | C6 | C7 | C8 | C9 | C10 | C11 | C12 | C13 |
|---|---|---|---|---|---|---|---|---|---|---|---|---|---|---|
| 4. | *Loading* | | | | | | | | | | | | | |
| | Static | • | | | | • | • | | | | • | • | • | • |
| | Function of time | | | | | • | • | | | | | • | • | • |
| | Mode I | | | | | • | • | | | | • | • | • | • |
| | Mode II | | | | | • | • | | | | • | | • | • |
| | Mode III | | | | | • | • | | | | • | | • | • |
| | Combined modes | • | | | | • | • | | | | | | • | • |
| | Initial stresses/strains | | | | | | • | | | | • | | • | • |
| 5. | *Surface-crack geometry* | | | | | | | | | | | | | |
| | Straight | • | | | | | • | | | | • | • | • | • |
| | Curved | • | | | | • | • | | | | • | | • | • |
| | Circular | • | | | | | • | | | | • | | • | • |
| | Elliptic | • | | | | | • | | | | • | | • | • |
| | Multiple | • | | | | • | • | | | | • | | • | • |

**TABLE 5.4** Fatigue and Fracture-Mechanics Applications (*Continued*)

| | | ABAQUS | ADINA | ANSYS | ASKA | EAL | FENRIS | FINITE/GP | LARSTRAN '80 | MARC | PAFEC | SAMCEF | SESAM '80 | SMART | TUJAP |
|---|---|---|---|---|---|---|---|---|---|---|---|---|---|---|---|
| 6. | *Internal-crack geometry* | | | | | | | | | | | | | | |
| | Straight | • | • | • | • | | | | | • | | | | | • |
| | Curved | • | • | | • | | | | | • | • | | | | • |
| | Circular | • | • | | • | | | | | • | | | | | • |
| | Elliptic | • | • | | • | | | | | • | | | | | • |
| | Multiple | • | • | | • | | | | | • | • | | | | • |
| 7. | *Crack closure branching* | | | | | | | | | | | | | | |
| | Closure, frictionless | • | • | | | | | | | • | | | | | • |
| | Closure with friction | • | • | | | | | | | • | | | | | |
| | Branching | | | | | | | | | | | | | | • |

TABLE 5.5  Modeling Capabilities of the Programs, User Interface, and User Support

| | | ABAQUS | ADINA | ANSYS | ASKA | EAL | FENRIS | FINITE/GP | LARSTRAN '80 | MARC | PAFEC | SAMCEF | SESAM '80 | SMART | TUJAP |
|---|---|---|---|---|---|---|---|---|---|---|---|---|---|---|---|
| 1. | Input form and sequence | | | | | | | | | | | | | | |
| | a) Input form | | | | | | | | | | | | | | |
| | Fixed format | • | • | | • | | | | | • | | | | | |
| | Freeform list-directed format | • | • | • | • | • | • | • | • | • | • | • | • | | • |
| | Problem-oriented language | • | • | | • | • | • | | • | • | | • | • | | • |
| | Others (see Sec. 5.5A) | | | | | • | | | | | | | | | |
| | b) Input sequence | | | | | | | | | | | | | | |
| | User-directed | • | • | • | • | • | • | | • | • | • | • | • | | • |
| | System-directed | | • | | | • | | • | | | | | | | |
| | User-supplied subroutines (see Sec. 5.5A) | • | • | | • | | | | • | • | • | | | | |

4.303

TABLE 5.5  Modeling Capabilities of the Programs, User Interface, and User Support (*Continued*)

| | ABAQUS | ADINA | ANSYS | ASKA | EAL | FENRIS | FEINITE/GP | LARSTRAN '80 | MARC | PAFEC | SAMCEF | SESAM '80 | SMART | TUJAP |
|---|---|---|---|---|---|---|---|---|---|---|---|---|---|---|
| **2. Model generation and checking** | | | | | | | | | | | | | | |
| *a) Automatic or semiautomatic generator for:* | | | | | | | | | | | | | | |
| Nodal-point coordinates | • | • | • | | • | • | • | • | • | • | • | • | | • |
| Element connectivities | • | • | • | • | • | • | • | • | • | • | • | • | | • |
| Constraints, symmetry, and boundary conditions | • | • | • | • | • | • | • | • | • | • | • | • | | • |
| Substructure connectivity | • | • | • | • | • | • | | | • | | • | • | | • |
| Repetition of identical segments | • | | • | • | • | • | | | • | • | • | • | | • |
| Loads | • | • | • | | • | • | • | • | • | • | • | • | | • |
| Others (see Sec. 5.5A) | | | | | | | | | • | | | | | |
| *b) Automatic or semiautomatic generator for:* | | | | | | | | | | | | | | |
| One-dimensional elements | • | • | • | • | • | • | | | • | • | • | • | | |
| Triangular elements | • | • | • | • | • | • | • | | • | • | • | • | | |
| Quadrilateral elements | • | • | • | • | • | • | • | | • | • | • | • | | |

| | C1 | C2 | C3 | C4 | C5 | C6 | C7 | C8 | C9 | C10 | C11 | C12 |
|---|---|---|---|---|---|---|---|---|---|---|---|---|
| Body or shell of revolution elements | | | ● | ● | ● | ● | | ● | ● | ● | ● | ● |
| Three-dimensional solid elements | ● | | ● | ● | ● | ● | | | ● | ● | ● | ● |
| Two-dimensional shell elements | ● | | ● | ● | ● | ● | | | ● | ● | ● | ● |
| Intersections | | | ● | | ● | ● | | | ● | ● | ● | ● |
| Special types of structures | | | ● | | ● | ● | | | ● | ● | ● | ● |
| Others (see Sec. 5.5A) | ● | | ● | | ● | ● | | | | | | |
| c) Data-checking facilities | | | | | | | | | | | | |
| Line printer | ● | | ● | ● | ● | ● | ● | ● | ● | ● | ● | ● |
| Plotter | ● | | ● | ● | ● | ● | ● | | ● | ● | ● | ● |
| Interactive graphics | ● | | ● | ● | ● | ● | ● | ● | ● | ● | ● | |
| Others (see Sec. 5.5A) | | | | | | | | | | | | |
| d) Plots and graphics display of model | | | | | | | | | | | | |
| Complete analysis region (e.g., undeformed structure) | ● | | ● | ● | ● | ● | ● | ● | ● | ● | ● | ● |
| Part of analysis region | ● | | ● | ● | ● | ● | ● | ● | ● | ● | ● | ● |
| "Blowup" option | ● | | ● | ● | ● | ● | ● | ● | ● | ● | | ● |
| Hidden lines or surfaces | ● | | ● | ● | ● | | | ● | ● | | ● | ● |
| Orthographic views | ● | | ● | ● | ● | ● | | | ● | ● | ● | ● |

**TABLE 5.5**  Modeling Capabilities of the Programs, User Interface, and User Support (*Continued*)

| | ABAQUS | ADINA | ANSYS | ASKA | EAL | FENRIS | FINITE/GP | LARSTRAN '80 | MARC | PAFEC | SAMCEF | SESAM '80 | SMART | TUJAP |
|---|---|---|---|---|---|---|---|---|---|---|---|---|---|---|
| 2. | | | | | | | | | | | | | | |
| Perspective and isometric views | | | • | | • | | | | • | | • | | | |
| Section view on arbitrary plane | | • | • | | | • | | | | | | • | | • |
| Others (see Sec. 5.5A) | • | | | | | | | | • | | | | | |
| e) *Other facilities* | | | | | | | | | | | | | | |
| Digitizer input | | | • | | | | | | • | • | • | | | |
| Automatic renumbering of nodes, elements, or equations | • | • | • | • | • | • | | • | • | • | • | • | | • |
| Table lookup of data | • | | • | • | • | • | | | • | • | | • | | • |
| Others (see Sec. 5.5A) | | | | | | | | | | | | | | |
| 3. *Results output form* | | | | | | | | | | | | | | |
| a) *Tabular output* | • | | | • | • | | | | | • | | | | |
| Fixed set | • | • | • | • | • | | • | • | • | • | • | | | |
| User-defined set and sequences | • | • | • | • | • | • | | • | • | • | • | • | | • |

4.306

| | C1 | C2 | C3 | C4 | C5 | C6 | C7 | C8 | C9 | C10 | C11 | C12 |
|---|---|---|---|---|---|---|---|---|---|---|---|---|
| Maximum and minimum quantities | • | • | • | • | • | | • | • | • | • | | • |
| Average and maxima for blocks of nodes | • | • | • | • | • | | • | • | • | • | | • |
| Stress, temperature, or flux exceedances | • | • | • | | • | • | • | • | • | | | • |
| Others (see Sec. 5.5A) | | | | | | | | | | | | |
| b) File output for user postprocessing and plotting | • | • | • | • | • | • | • | • | • | • | | • |
| c) Plots | | | | | | | | | | | | |
| Isotherm plots (contours) of temperature/flux | • | | • | | • | | • | • | • | | | • |
| Surface functions | | • | | | | | • | | | | | |
| Selective output (e.g., by elements or regions) | • | • | • | • | • | | • | • | • | | | • |
| Histories (e.g., time history) | • | • | • | • | • | • | • | | • | • | | • |
| Others (see Sec. 5.5A) | • | | | | | | | | | | | |
| **4. Interactive input and control** | | | | | | | | | | | | |
| Parameter specification (e.g., load, flux or time steps) | • | • | • | • | | | | | • | • | | |
| Singularity check | • | • | • | • | | | | | • | • | | |
| Error correction/recovery | | • | • | | • | | | | | • | | |
| User control of matrix decomposition | | • | • | • | | | | | • | | | |
| Others (see Sec. 5.5A) | | | | • | | | | | | | | |

**TABLE 5.5** Modeling Capabilities of the Programs, User Interface, and User Support (*Continued*)

| | ABAQUS | ADINA | ANSYS | ASKA | EAL | FENRIS | FINITE/GP | LARSTRAN '80 | MARC | PAFEC | SAMCEF | SESAM '80 | SMART | TUJAP |
|---|---|---|---|---|---|---|---|---|---|---|---|---|---|---|
| **5. *Available user services (including training)*** | | | | | | | | | | | | | | |
| Hotline telephone support | ● | ● | ● | ● | ● | ● | ● | ● | ● | ● | ● | ● | | ● |
| Consulting | ● | ● | ● | ● | ● | ● | ● | ● | ● | ● | ● | ● | | ● |
| Seminars on code usage | ● | ● | ● | ● | ● | ● | ● | | ● | ● | ● | ● | | ● |
| Videotapes for training | ● | ● | | | | | | | | ● | | | | |
| Newsletter | | ● | ● | ● | | ● | ● | | ● | ● | | ● | | ● |
| User conferences | | ● | ● | ● | ● | ● | | | ● | ● | | ● | | ● |

4.308

## 5.6 REFERENCES

1. Pilkey, W. D., K. J. Sacazlski, and H. G. Schaeffer (eds.), *Structural Mechanics Computer Programs*, University Press of Virginia, Charlottesville, 1974.

2. Fredriksson, B., and J. Mackerle, "Finite Element Review," Rep. AEC-L0033, Advanced Engineering Corp., Linkoping, Sweden, 1978.

3. Fredriksson, B., and J. Mackerle, "Overview and Evaluation of Some Versatile General Purpose Finite Element Computer Programs," in J. Robinson (ed.), *Finite Element Methods in the Commercial Environment*, Robinson and Associates, Dorset, England, 1978, vol. 2, pp. 390-419.

4. Fong, H. H., "An Evaluation of Eight U.S. General Purpose Finite Element Computer Programs," Pap. No. 82-0699-CP, *Proceedings of the 23d AIAA/ASME/ASCE/AHS Structures, Structural Dynamics and Materials Conference*, New Orleans, May 10-12, 1982, pt. 1, pp. 145-160.

5. *Finite Element Systems Handbook*, 2d ed., CML Publications, Computational Mechanics Center, Ashurst Lodge, Hampshire, England, 1983.

6. Fredriksson, B., and J. Mackerle, "Structural Mechanics: Finite Element Computer Programs—New Up-to-Date Fourth Edition," Advanced Engineering Corp., Linkoping, Sweden, 1984.

7. Fredriksson, B., and J. Mackerle, "Structural Mechanics: Pre- and Post-Processor Programs—Surveys and Availability," Advanced Engineering Corp., Linkoping, Sweden, 1977.

8. Mackerle, J., "Review of Pre- and Postprocessor Programs Included in the Major Commercial General Purpose Finite Element Packages," *Adv. Eng. Software*, 5(1):43-53 (1983).

9. Niku-Lari, A. (ed.), *Structural Analysis Systems—Software, Hardware, Capability, Compatibility, Applications*, International Guidebook Series, vols. 1-3, Pergamon Press, New York, 1985.

10. Pilkey, W., and N. Perrone (eds.), *Structural Mechanics Software Series*, University Press of Virginia, Charlottesville, 1984, vols. I-V.

11. Nickell, R. E., "The Interagency Software Evaluation Group: A Critical Evaluation of the ADINA, NASTRAN, and STAGS Structural Mechanics Computer Programs," Contract N00014-79-C-0620, Report to the Office of Naval Research, Arlington, Va., December 1981.

12. Padovan, J., and T. Y. Chang, "Evaluation of ADINA: I. Theory and Programming Descriptions: II. Operating Characteristics," University of Akron, Akron, Ohio, June 8, 1980.

13. Fong, H. H., and J. W. Jones, "An Evaluation of COSMIC/NASTRAN," *Third World Congress and Exhibition on Finite Element Methods*, Oct. 12-16, 1981, Beverly Hills, Calif. (proceedings published as *New and Future Developments in Commercial Finite Element Methods*, J. Robinson (ed.), Robinson and Associates, Dorset, England, 1981, pp. 324-338.

14. Robinson, J., and S. Blackham, "An Evaluation of Lower Order Membranes as Contained in the MSC/NASTRAN, ASAS, PAFEC FEM Systems," Robinson and Associates, Dorset, England, September 1979.

15. Robinson, J., and S. Blackham, "An Evaluation of Plate Bending Elements: MSC/NASTRAN, ASAS, PAFEC, ANSYS, and SAP4," Robinson and Associates, Dorset, England, August 1981.

16. Pilkey, B. F., "Computerized Sources of Abstracts of Engineering Literature," in *Structural Mechanics Software Series*, University Press of Virginia, Charlottesville, 1980, vol. 3, pp. 29-39.

17. Noor, A. K., and W. D. Pilkey (eds.) *State-of-the-Art Surveys on Finite Element Technology*, American Society of Mechanical Engineers, New York, 1983.

18. Noor, A. K., "Books on Finite Element Technology," *J. Finite Elements Anal. Design*, 1(1) (January 1985).

19. Taig, I. C., "Selection Criteria for Structural Analysis Programs," AGARD Rep. No. 670, NATO-AGARD, Neuilly Sur Seine, France, January 1979, pp. 11-20.

20. Sollogoob, P., L. Wahl, and F. Dreyer, "Main Computer Systems Programs Presentation, Criteria for Selection," SNEXO/CTICM, 1978 (may be obtained from: CNEXO, P. B. 337, F-29273, Brest, or CTICM, 20 Rue Jean Jaures, F-92807, Puteaux).

21. Berman, I. (ed.), *Engineering Computer Software: Verification, Qualification, and Certification,* American Society of Mechanical Engineers, New York, 1971.

# INDEX

## ABOUT THE EDITORS

HAYRETTIN KARDESTUNCER, *Editor in Chief*, is Professor of Structural Engineering at the University of Connecticut. Storrs. A graduate of the Naval Academy of Istanbul MIT, and the Sorbonne, he is founder of the International Invitational Symposia on Unification of Finite Element Methods, which he successfully conducted for 15 years. He is author or editor of more than three dozen books and conference proceedings on FEM, as well as author and coauthor of numerous papers in refereed journals. Well known as a lecturer throughout the world, he is a founding member of the American Academy of Mechanics. He is also a member of the Scientific Council of the International Center of Mechanical Societies in Italy and of the Tensor Societies of Great Britain and Japan.

DOUGLAS H. NORRIE, *Project Editor*, is Professor of Mechanical Engineering at the University of Calgary in Western Canada. Formerly head of the Department of Mechanical Engineering, he was also Director of Information Services, with administrative responsibility for the University's libraries, computing services, and communications media. Since 1967 he has been involved in research in finite elements, with a particular interest in fluid-flow applications. Among his publications are three coauthored books as well as numerous papers, reports, and conference proceedings in the finite element area. Others of his publications relate to ship propulsion, liquefied natural gas, computer-aided design and manufacturing, and special-purpose computers. He is a chartered mechanical engineer, naval architect, and aeronautical engineer.